NON-LEAGUE CLUB DIRECTORY 2020-21

(43rd Edition)

EDITORS
MIKE & TONY WILLIAMS

NON-LEAGUE CLUB DIRECTORY 2020-21
ISBN 978-1-869833-84-8

Editors
Mike Williams
(Tel: 01548 531 339)
mwpublishing@btconnect.com
Tony Williams
Email: t.williams320@btinternet.com

Published by MW Publishing
(Tel: 01548 531 339)
Email: mwpublishing@btconnect.com

Printed by
CPI William Clowes - Suffolk

Sales & Distribution
MWPublishing (01548 531 339)

Front Cover: FA Vase Fifth Round tie between Bitton AFC (red/black) and
Sutton Common Rovers (all yellow). Bitton AFC won the game 2-1. Photo Peter Barnes.

FOREWORD

Mike and Tony have asked me to pen a few words for this edition of the Non-League Directory.

I was humbled when the invitation arrived and accepted with pleasure.

Having devoted over 50 years to the Kent County League (KCL), initially as a young Referee --- finally for 35 years as Chairman, I trust readers will appreciate I have been an admirer of all those involved in these publications.

During this time I have seen numerous changes, led great teams, met some fantastic administrators at differing levels of the game --- to EUFA level.

1987 saw the KCL sponsored for the first time. Our vision - To seek excellence at everything we did.

Three years later our ethos - 'Fair Play We Lead The Way'.

In 2002 along with my good friend and Secretary, Barry Bundock, the FA selected us from other leagues to represent England in the 3rd EUFA REGIONS' CUP.

Together with Czech Republic, Estonia and San Marino we played the three other countries in Estonia in a 'mini qualifying group' similar to the World Cup finishing as runners-up to the Czech Republic - our Jamie Salvidge scoring the only hat trick from all the matches.

To be a 'Leader' you need to have been through as many aspects of the 'field' as possible.

National Leaders usually seek power - history proves very few are ready for the office!

Having overcome several life-threatening issues football has kept me going. My message to players, fans and administrators everywhere - follow your dream - it may prove a long dark tunnel at times - stay with it - in the difficult and challenging times ahead - above all - have courage.

Good Luck - Enjoy this unique 43rd Edition.

Cyril Windiate
Honorary Life Fellow
KENT COUNTY LEAGUE

CONTENTS

THE 2019-20 SEASON

THE 2020-21 NATIONAL LEAGUE SYSTEM CLUB DIRECTORY

'IT'S FOOTBALL - BUT NOT AS WE KNOW IT'

There can be no doubt that of all the Directories I have worked on, this one is the strangest!

Over half the book dedicated to a season, that for most non-League clubs, has been scratched from the record books. Teams with 100% records and looking forward to promotion to the next level, denied by a world wide crisis. On the other hand there will be clubs who will no doubt be pleased to have dodged the 'relegation bullet' and to be given another go at proving they belong to the level from which they were expecting to leave.

I'm sure the debate will go on for years as to whether null and voiding all non-League football below Step 2 was the correct thing to do. The fact that Points Per Game will be used if this situation were to happen again in the future tells you all you need to know. However, at the time, none of the decisions made by the powers running football, or indeed the government, were made lightly and I do believe they were made with all the right intentions.

This year's Directory will stand unique to the other 42 editions as it records the shortened National league campaign, as well as the null & void season below that level. The allocations for the National League System are also included but may well have changed by the time the season actually kick's off, and all FA competitions are listed up until they came to an abrupt holt.

It would have been nice to have held out a bit longer before publishing the book but, like so many across the country, this virus has impacted hard and the loss of the job that helped me keep this Directory alive has meant there could not be any major delay to the publication date. So as I write this there are still a few things 'up in the air', will Stevenage get a reprieve for one. I just hope we all get through this safely and that we get to return to supporting the sport we all love.

'NEVER SAY NEVER'

Last season was the first in a very long time that I haven't been involved with a football club. Since moving back down to the West Country I have been a player, manager and then general manager of the same club for 19 years. Sadly we had to fold the club last summer, ending over 40 years of membership of the Devon FA.

Have I missed it?
Yes, and no. I miss the build up to a new season, getting the pitch looking right, meeting the new additions to the squad and that feeling of anticipation before the first match of every new campaign. The changing room banter which carries over into the post-match analysis over a pint, whether you win, lose or draw, in my opinion, is unique to team sport. However, I don't miss the daily phone calls from players, managers or league officials which turn your association with a club into a 24/7 job - until the phone stopped ringing last season I hadn't really appreciated how much running a club takes over your life.

It's also been very enjoyable watching matches without the 'stress' of wanting/needing your club to win - but I think, maybe, it's time to get back involved with local football...

Mike Williams

TIME TO PULL TOGETHER

I was lucky to have been born with some basic talent which enabled me to play football at an enjoyable level and the fun I had with senior non-league clubs encouraged me to became involved with football magazines and books.

I realise that being able to spend all your life involved with a sport you love, must be a very special privilege and to have a son who enjoys the sport in the same way is even more gratifying.

Having reached the age of 80 and still enjoying a full life, I certainly appreciate the wonderful televised sports coverage on a daily basis.

However the tragic national news which has brought all sport to a standstill is a desperate situation that none of us could possibly have forecast. Hopefully, publications and television will keep us involved with the situation and the massive non-league world will be well supported.

Tony Williams

SPECIAL ACKNOWLEDGMENTS
'OUR TEAM' OF PHOTOGRAPHERS
Peter Barnes, Keith Clayton,
Alan Coomes and Bill Wheatcroft.

A special note to remember Gordon Whittington who sadly passed away this year. Gordon contributed his photographs to many of our publications over the years and was known for his 'behind the goal-mouth' shots that used to capture both the jubilation and disappointment of goals being scored. I would always look forward to his critique of each new edition too, which, I'm pleased to say, was mostly positive. I will miss seeing your letter arrive this year Gordon but I hope I've done you proud again with this unique edition. Thank you and may you RIP.

FAV2Q 2017-18 - Wellingborough Whitworths v Wisbech St Mary's. A Gordon Whittington signature action shot.

CONTRIBUTORS
Scott Bolton (FA Competitions Department), Craig Pottage,
Richard Rundle (Football Club History Database), and the many league and club officials that have been kind enough to supply the necessary information.

Thank you one and all

FOR THE NLS

2020-21

STEP 1
NATIONAL

STEP 2
NATIONAL NORTH   NATIONAL SOUTH

STEP 3
ISTHMIAN   NORTHERN PREMIER   SOUTHERN PREMIER
PREMIER   PREMIER   CENTRAL / SOUTH

STEP 4
ISTHMIAN   NORTHERN PREMIER   SOUTHERN
NORTH / SOUTH CENTRAL / SOUTH EAST   NORTH / SOUTH   CENTRAL / SOUTH

STEP 5/6

COMBINED COUNTIES	MIDLAND FOOTBALL LEAGUE	SOUTH WEST PENINSULAR	UNITED COUNTIES
EAST MIDLANDS COUNTIES	NORTH WEST COUNTIES	SOUTHERN COMBINATION	WESSEX
EASTERN COUNTIES	NORTHERN COUNTIES EAST	SOUTHERN COUNTIES EAST	WEST MIDLANDS
ESSEX SENIOR	NORTHERN LEAGUE	SPARTAN SOUTH MIDLANDS	WESTERN
HELLENIC			

NATIONAL LEAGUE

As at 15/03/2020	P	W	D	L	F	A	GD	Pts
1 Barrow	37	21	7	9	68	39	29	70
2 Harrogate Town	37	19	9	9	61	44	17	66
3 Notts County	38	17	12	9	61	38	23	63
4 Yeovil Town	37	17	9	11	61	44	17	60
5 Boreham Wood	37	16	12	9	55	40	15	60
6 FC Halifax Town	37	17	7	13	50	49	1	58
7 Stockport County	39	16	10	13	51	54	-3	58
8 Solihull Moors	38	15	10	13	48	37	11	55
9 Hartlepool United	39	14	13	12	56	50	6	55
10 Woking	38	15	10	13	50	55	-5	55
11 Barnet	35	14	12	9	52	42	10	54
12 Dover Athletic	38	15	9	14	49	49	0	54
13 Bromley	38	14	10	14	57	52	5	52
14 Sutton United	38	12	14	12	47	42	5	50
15 Torquay United	36	14	6	16	56	61	-5	48
16 Aldershot Town	39	12	10	17	43	55	-12	46
17 Eastleigh	37	11	13	13	43	55	-12	46
18 Dagenham & Redbridge	37	11	11	15	40	44	-4	44
19 Chesterfield	38	11	11	16	55	65	-10	44
20 Wrexham	37	11	10	16	46	49	-3	43
21 Ebbsfleet United	39	10	12	17	47	68	-21	42
22 Maidenhead United	38	12	5	21	44	58	-14	41
23 AFC Fylde	37	9	12	16	44	60	-16	39
24 Chorley	38	4	14	20	31	65	-34	26

After Points Per Game	P	W	D	L	F	A	GD	PPG
1 Barrow	37	21	7	9	68	39	29	87.0
2 Harrogate Town*	37	19	9	9	61	44	17	82.1
3 Notts County	38	17	12	9	61	38	23	76.3
4 Yeovil Town	37	17	9	11	61	44	17	74.6
5 Boreham Wood	37	16	12	9	55	40	15	74.6
6 FC Halifax Town	37	17	7	13	50	49	1	72.1
7 Barnet	35	14	12	9	52	42	10	71.0
8 Stockport County	39	16	10	13	51	54	-3	68.4
9 Solihull Moors	38	15	10	13	48	37	11	66.6
10 Woking	38	15	10	13	50	55	-5	66.6
11 Dover Athletic	38	15	9	14	49	49	0	65.4
12 Hartlepool United	39	14	13	12	56	50	6	64.9
13 Bromley	38	14	10	14	57	52	5	62.9
14 Torquay United	36	14	6	16	56	61	-5	61.3
15 Sutton United	38	12	14	12	47	42	5	60.5
16 Eastleigh	37	11	13	13	43	55	-12	57.2
17 Dagenham & Redbridge	37	11	11	15	40	44	-4	54.7
18 Aldershot Town	39	12	10	17	43	55	-12	54.3
19 Wrexham	37	11	10	16	46	49	-3	53.5
20 Chesterfield	38	11	11	16	55	65	-10	53.3
21 Maidenhead United	38	12	5	21	44	58	-14	49.6
22 Ebbsfleet United	39	10	12	17	47	68	-21	49.5
23 AFC Fylde	37	9	12	16	44	60	-16	48.5
24 Chorley	38	4	14	20	31	65	-34	31.5

		1	2	3	4	5	6	7	8	9	10	11	12	13	14	15	16	17	18	19	20	21	22	23	24
1	AFC Fylde		1-0	0-4	0-1	1-2		1-3	0-0	3-0	0-0	3-1	1-0		0-0			1-2	0-0	1-2	0-0	2-3	1-4	3-2	
2	Aldershot Town	1-2		0-0	1-2	3-2	0-1	2-2	3-3	0-1	4-0	3-1		1-1	1-1	0-3	2-0	2-1		2-1	1-1			1-0	1-3
3	Barnet	2-1	2-0			2-2	1-2	2-2	2-1		0-1		5-2	1-1		2-1	1-0		0-0	1-2		2-2	2-2		1-0
4	Barrow	1-1	1-0	2-1			3-1	2-0		2-2	2-1	1-0	2-0	7-0	1-2	0-3	0-1	2-0	0-2	3-0		1-0	2-1		1-0
5	Boreham Wood	0-2	0-0	0-0	1-1			2-2		3-1	2-2	1-2		2-1	1-1	2-1	1-2	1-0	4-0	0-1		1-0	2-2	1-0	
6	Bromley	2-2		1-2	1-2	1-0		2-1		3-0	2-3	3-1	5-0	3-3		2-1	2-2	2-2	0-1	3-3	1-0	0-2		1-1	
7	Chesterfield	1-1	2-1		2-2		1-2		2-3	1-1	1-2	1-2	4-0	2-3	3-4	1-5		1-0	2-2		1-0	1-0	1-2	3-2	1-2
8	Chorley		0-0	0-1	1-3	1-3	0-0	1-2			1-0	1-1	1-2	0-4	0-1	0-2	0-0		1-6	3-0		1-0	1-1	0-2	1-2
9	Dagenham & Redbridge	1-2	6-1	1-1	0-2	0-3	1-1		0-0				1-1		4-2	3-1	1-2	2-0	2-0	1-1	1-2	0-0	0-2	2-1	3-2
10	Dover Athletic	5-1	2-0		2-1	0-2	3-0	1-1	1-1	1-2		3-1	1-1	0-2		1-1	3-4	2-2	1-1	0-1		1-2	1-2	2-1	0-1
11	Eastleigh	2-2	0-0		1-2		2-0	1-1	0-0	1-1			1-1		4-2	1-1	2-1	1-0			1-1	3-2	2-0	0-0	
12	Ebbsfleet United		1-2	3-0	0-3			2-2	1-0	1-1	0-1	1-1			1-4	0-2	2-2	1-2	2-2		0-1	1-1	2-4	2-1	1-3
13	Halifax Town	4-1		4-2	0-2		2-1	1-0	0-0	1-0	4-2	1-1	0-1		0-1	5-2	2-4	2-1	0-0	1-0	2-4	0-2			0-2
14	Harrogate Town		1-0	2-1		0-0	1-1	3-1	2-0		0-2	3-0	2-0	2-2		4-1	1-0	0-2	2-2	2-1	2-0	2-1		0-2	3-0
15	Hartlepool United	2-2	2-0	2-0	2-2			2-3	3-1		1-0	0-2	2-1		0-1			2-0		2-0	1-3		1-1	4-2	2-1
16	Maidenhead United	1-1	1-2	1-4	0-4	0-1	1-2	1-1	4-1	0-1	1-2	2-0	1-1	0-1	1-1	0-1			0-0	1-1	1-2		2-3	2-0	
17	Notts County	2-0	3-1	3-2		2-2	2-1	3-0	5-1	2-0	4-0		1-0		2-2	3-0			0-0	1-1	1-1	1-1		1-1	
18	Solihull Moors	3-1	2-1	1-0	0-0	0-2	2-1	3-0		2-1	3-0	1-2	2-1		0-1	0-2	0-1			2-0	2-0	3-0		3-1	0-1
19	Stockport County	2-1	1-2	1-1	3-2	1-3	1-0	2-0	4-2	1-0	0-2	2-0	1-1	5-1		2-1	0-1		1-4		0-0	0-4	1-3		
20	Sutton United			1-1	2-2			0-2	4-0	2-2	0-2	1-2		2-3	0-1	3-1	1-1	0-3	1-1	0-0		2-0	6-2	3-1	3-2
21	Torquay United	2-1	2-0		4-2	2-1		0-3	2-0	0-0		2-3	0-0	1-1	0-0	4-2	1-2	2-0			1-5		1-2	4-1	1-0
22	Woking		0-1	1-3	3-2	1-2	2-1		1-0			1-1	1-2	0-0	1-0	2-1	2-0	0-4	2-0	1-1	2-1	1-1		1-1	1-0
23	Wrexham	0-1	1-2	1-1	2-1		1-0	0-1	3-1	0-0		0-0	1-0	1-0	1-1		2-2		2-0	1-2	1-1		3-0		3-3
24	Yeovil Town	3-2	2-2			1-1	3-1		1-1		0-1	1-0		2-0	1-2	2-2	1-2	3-1	0-1	1-1	1-0	6-2	3-1	3-0	

*Promoted to the Football League via the play-offs.

AFC FYLDE MATCH RESULTS 2019-20

Date	Comp	Opponens	H/A	Att:	Result	Goalscorers	Pos
Aug 3	NL	Aldershot Town	A	2003	W 2 - 1	Byrne 30 Rowe 62 (pen)	5
6	NL	Chorley	H	2443	D 0 - 0		8
10	NL	Ebbsfleet United	H	1153	W 1 - 0	Rowe 4 (pen)	
13	NL	Hartlepool United	A	3222	D 2 - 2	Croasdale 80 82	
17	NL	Woking	H	1172	L 1 - 4	Montrose 56	11
24	NL	Halifax Town	A	1913	L 1 - 4	Rowe 45	
26	NL	Harrogate Town	H	1317	D 0 - 0		
31	NL	Bromley	A	1541	D 2 - 2	Williams 7 40	14
Sep 3	NL	Stockport County	A	3912	L 1 - 2	Williams 60	18
14	NL	Yeovil Town	A	2395	L 2 - 3	Willoughby 59 86	21
21	NL	Eastleigh	H	1134	W 3 - 1	Bradley 32 Williams 57 Croasdale 76	19
24	NL	Wrexham	H	1289	W 3 - 2	Rowe 29 Bradley 59 Haughton 68	15
28	NL	Notts County	A	9090	L 0 - 2		18
Oct 1	NL	Barnet	H	997	L 0 - 4		18
5	NL	Torquay United	A	2440	L 1 - 2	Williams 52	19
8	NL	Chesterfield	H	1217	L 1 - 3	Hornby-Forbes 90+2	21
Dave Challinor is sacked as manager.							
19	FAC4Q	**Peterborough Spors**	H	657	W 6 - 1	Rowe 27 66 71 Kosylo 57 Haughton 82 Bradley 90+2	
26	NL	Boreham Wood	A	501	W 2 - 0	Taylor 19 Bradley 90+1	19
Jim Bentley resigns as Morecambe manager to take up the reigns at AFC Fylde.							
29	NL	Maidenhead United	A	1010	D 1 - 1	Byrne 73	19
Nov 2	NL	Dover Athletic	H	1185	D 0 - 0		20
9	FAC1	**Nantwich Town**	A	1544	W 1 - 0	**Croasdale 44**	
16	NL	Solihull Moors	A	1389	L 1 - 3	Croasdale 45	20
23	NL	Dagenham & Redbridge	H	1268	W 3 - 0	Yeates 16 Williams 44 Rowe 45+1	
26	NL	Wrexham	A	2941	W 1 - 0	Philliskirk 30	18
30	FAC2	**Kingstonian**	A	1460	W 2 - 0	**Williams 9 45+1**	
Dec 7	NL	Barnet	A	661	L 1 - 2	Rowe 60	18
10	NL	Sutton United	H	1054	D 0 - 0		18
14	FAT1	**Curzon Ashton**	H	483	W 1 - 0	**Rowe 25**	
21	NL	Yeovil Town	H	1427	D 2 - 2	Osho 36 (og) Bradley 72	20
26	NL	Barrow	A	3267	D 1 - 1	Croasdale 85	19
28	NL	Stockport County	H	2764	L 1 - 2	Croasdale 6	20
Jan 1	NL	Barrow	H	2409	L 0 - 1		21
5	FAC3	**Sheffield United**	A	11113	L 1 - 2	**Williams 78**	
11	FAT2	**Southport**	H	907	W 4 - 1	**Williams 7 Bradley 21 Haughton 43 55**	
18	NL	Torquay United	H	1504	L 2 - 3	Walker 13 Williams 77	22
25	NL	Chesterfield	A	3262	D 1 - 1	Haughton 76	22
Feb 1	NL	Boreham Wood	H	1258	L 1 - 2	Williams 32	22
8	FAT3	**Dorking Wanderers**	A	1594	W 4 - 2	**Haughton 35 83 Byrne 55 Williams 76**	
11	NL	Eastleigh	A	1509	D 2 - 2	Walker 32 Proctor 45+6	
22	NL	Dover Athletic	A	1027	L 1 - 5	Walker 6 (pen)	23
29	FAT4	**Harrogate Town**	H	803	L 2 - 3	**Williams 53 Burke 90+3 (aet)**	
Mar 3	NL	Notts County	H	1353	L 1 - 2	Williams 18	23
7	NL	Solihull Moors	H	1310	D 0 - 0		23
10	NL	Dagenham & Redbridge	A	1064	W 2 - 1	Walker 48 Whitmore 90+4	23
14	NL	Aldershot Town	H	1668	W 1 - 0	Philliskirk 19	23

GOALSCORERS	SG	CSG	Pens	Hat tricks	Total		SG	CSG	Pens	Hat tricks	Total
Williams	13	3			15	Hornby-Forbes	1	1			1
Rowe	8	1	2	1	10	Kosylo	1	1			1
Croasdale	6	2			7	Montrose	1	1			1
Haughton	5	1			7	Opponent	1	1			1
Bradley	6	2			6	Proctor	1	1			1
Walker*	4	2	1		4	Taylor	1	1			1
Byrne	3	1			3	Whitmore	1	1			1
Philliskirk	2	1			2	Yeates	1	1			1
Willoughby	1	1			2						
Burke	1	1			1						

Player appearance grid (columns = players, rows = match No.):

	Montgomery J	Byrne N	Duxberry S	Burke L	Whitmore A	Yeates M	Craigen J	Croasdale R	Bradley D	Rowe D	Willoughby K	Kosylo M	Haughton N	Phillskirk D	Williams J	Jameson K	Montrose L	N'Gwatala E	Lavercombe D (Gk)	Green S	Hornby-Forbes T	Hornby S (Gk) (L)	Taylor A	Kellett A	Walker T	Proctor J (L)	Miller T	Stanley J	French T (L)	Lillis J (Gk) (L)	Thompson L (L)	No.
	x	x	x	xs	x	xs	x	x	x	x	xs	xs	sx	sx	sx	s	s															1
	x	xs	x	xs	x	x	x	x	xs	x	x	s	sx	sx	s	sx																2
	x	x	x	x	x	xs	x	x	x	xs	sx	sx	xs	s	sx	s																3
	x	x	x	xs	x	x	x	xs	sx	x	sx	x	s	x	xs	s																4
	x	x	x	xs	x	sx		x	sx	x	x	x	xs	x	s	s	xs															5
	x	x	x		xs	x	x			x	xs	x	sx	x	sx	x	sx	s														6
	x	x	x		s	xs	x	x		x	sx	xs	xs		sx	x	x	sx	s													7
	x	x	x		sx	xs	x	x		x	sx	xs	sx	x	xs	x		s	s													8
	x	x	x		s	xs	xs	x		x	sx	x	sx	x	x	x		s	s													9
	x	x	x		sx	xs	xs	x		sx	x	sx	x	x				s	s													10
	s	x	xs			x	x	x	xs	x	sx	x	x	xs		sx	x	s														11
	s	x	x		xs	s		x	sx	x	xs		sx	x	x	x		s	x		x											12
	s	x	x		s	sx	sx	x	x	x		xs	x	x	x		s	x		xs												13
	s	x	x		sx	s	sx	x	x	x		xs	xs	x	x		sx	x		x												14
		x	xs	xs	x	xs	x	x	x			sx	s	s	sx	s			x		sx											15
		x		x	x	xs	x	xs	x	xs			sx	sx	s	s	x				sx	x	s									16
	x	x		x	x	sx	sx	x	sx	x		xs	x	xs	xs	s				s	s	s		x								17
	x	x		x	x	sx		x	sx	x		xs	xs	x	x			s				s	s	x								18
	x	x		x	x	s		x	sx	x		x	xs	x	x	s						s	s	x								19
	x	x		x	x	sx		xs	sx	x		x	xs	x	x	sx						s	s	xs								20
	x	s	s	x	x	sx	s	x	xs	x		xs	sx	x	xs	s				x	s	sx		x								21
	x			x	sx		x	sx	x			xs	x	x	sx	s				x		sx	x	xs								22
	x	x	x	x	x		xs	xs	xs			sx	sx	x	x	s	sx			s			x									23
	x	xs	x	x	xs		x	sx	x			sx	s	x	x	sx	sx			s			x									24
	x	x	x	x	xs	sx	x	xs	sx			sx	x	x	x	s	sx			s			x	s								25
	x	x	x	x		x	xs	xs				sx	sx	xs	x	x	s			s			x									26
	x		x	xs		x	x	x				sx	s	s	x	sx	x			s			x	xs								27
	x	s	s	x	x	sx	x			x		xs	x	x	x		x	xs		s			s	x		sx						28
	x		x	x	xs	sx	xs	x	x	x		xs	xs	x	x		sx			s			x	x								29
	x		x	x	sx	s	x	xs	x	sx		x	xs	x		xs				s			x	sx								30
	x		x	x	xs	xs	x	sx	x			sx	sx	xs	x	s				s			x	x								31
	x		x	x		s	x	xs	xs	sx		sx	sx	x	x	x	xs			s			x									32
	x		x	x	sx	sx	x	xs	sx	sx			xs	x	x	x	s						x	s	s							33
	x		x	x	xs	sx	x	xs				sx		x	s	x	x	xs					x	s	sx							34
	x		x	x		s	x	x		sx			sx	x	x	xs	s			s			x	sx		x						35
	x		x	x	sx		x	sx				xs	sx	x	s	x	s						x	x		xs	xs					36
	x		x	x		x	sx					sx	xs	sx	x	s	xs						x	x		xs	x					37
	x		x	x		x	xs					xs	x	x	x	xs	sx	s		s	sx		x	s					sx	s		38
	x		x	x		x	sx					sx	xs	s	s	x		x			x	xs		xs	x	sx						39
	x		x	x	sx		x				x	sx	xs	x	x	sx		s			x		x	x	x		xs					40
	x		x	x	xs		x			x	sx	xs	x	sx	sx	s				x	xs			sx			xs					41
	x		x	x	sx		xs			x	s	x	s				x	x			x	xs				sx						42
	x		x	x	s		x	s		x	s			x	x		sx			s			xs	xs		x	x	sx				43
	x		x	x	xs		x	xs		sx			x	x		s				s			xs	sx		x	x	sx				44
	x		x	x	xs		x	xs		sx			x	x		s					sx	xs	sx		x	x	s					45
x	14	44	16	30	37	4	9	38	10	26	4	6	6	27	32	12	4	0	6	0	2	22	8	0	3	4	1	0	3	3	0	x
xs	0	1	3	5	2	17	4	5	14	7	4	9	14	6	4	4	7	0	0	0	1	0	6	0	5	3	0	0	2	0	0	xs
sx	0	0	0	3	15	7	0	12	0	14	14	14	5	3	8	7	4	0	1	4	0	2	2	1	2	3	0	1	0	2		sx
s	4	0	2	0	3	4	0	1	0	1	3	3	6	3	15	6	6	27	3	5	6	5	1	0	0	0	1	0	0	1		s

GOALKEEPERS	CS	CCS
Hornby	5	3
Montgomery	5	2
Lillis*	2	1
Lavercombe	1	1

x - Played full 90 minutes
xs - Substituted off
sx - Substituted on
s - Non-playing Substitute

ALDERSHOT TOWN MATCH RESULTS 2019-20

Date	Comp	Opponents	H/A	Att:	Result	Goalscorers	Pos
Aug 3	NL	AFC Fylde	H	2003	L 1 - 2	Fowler 74	15
6	NL	Woking	A	3992	W 1 - 0	Berkeley-Agyepong 23	12
10	NL	Solihull Moors	A	1109	L 1 - 2	Chislett 87	
13	NL	Bromley	H	1774	L 0 - 1		
17	NL	Halifax Town	H	1539	D 1 - 1	Fowler 1	19
24	NL	Torquay United	A	2668	L 0 - 2		
26	NL	Sutton United	H	1662	D 1 - 1	Berkeley-Agyepong 90+4	
31	NL	Ebbsfleet United	A	1109	W 2 - 1	Eyoma 43 Chislett 59	19
Sep 7	NL	Barrow	H	1163	L 1 - 2	Chislett 81	20
14	NL	Stockport County	A	4279	W 2 - 1	Panayiotou 30 Santos 33	20
17	NL	Barnet	A	1069	L 0 - 2		20
21	NL	Wrexham	H	1673	W 1 - 0	Panayiotou 90	17
24	NL	Yeovil Town	H	1684	L 1 - 3	Hunt 19	20
28	NL	Chesterfield	A	3657	L 1 - 2	Chislett 11	21
Oct 5	NL	Chorley	A	1425	D 0 - 0		21
8	NL	Dover Athletic	H	1255	W 4 - 0	Mullings 25 Berkeley-Agyepong 32 Powell 53 Santos 58	18
12	NL	Hartlepool United	H	2768	L 0 - 3		18
19	**FAC4Q**	**Bromley**	**A**	**1408**	**L 3 - 4**	**Bettamer 22 Mullings 59 Tinkler 80**	
26	NL	Harrogate Town	A	1507	L 0 - 1		20
29	NL	Boreham Wood	A	619	D 0 - 0		20
Nov 2	NL	Maidenhead United	H	1602	W 2 - 0	Panayiotou 63 Whittingham 90+2	19
16	NL	Dagenham & Redbridge	A	1616	L 1 - 6	Tinkler 77	19
23	NL	Notts County	H	2211	W 2 - 1	Bettamer 27 Whittingham 43	
26	NL	Yeovil Town	A	2545	D 2 - 2	Chislett 27 (pen) Powell 56	19
30	NL	Chesterfield	H	1637	D 2 - 2	Chislett 45+2 (pen) Powell 70	19
Dec 7	NL	Barrow	A	2024	L 0 - 1		19
14	**FAT1**	**Torquay United**	**A**	**1068**	**L 1 - 5**	**Bettamer 60**	
21	NL	Stockport County	H	1891	W 2 - 1	Tanner 16 Bettamer 65	19
28	NL	Barnet	H	2107	D 0 - 0		19
Jan 1	NL	Eastleigh	H	1953	W 3 - 1	Chislett 32 59 Tanner 69	18
4	NL	Wrexham	A	4222	W 2 - 1	Chislett 63 Bettamer 69	16
18	NL	Chorley	H	1931	D 3 - 3	Tanner 16 Bettamer 30 Rance 82	16
25	NL	Dover Athletic	A	1113	L 0 - 2		17
28	NL	Eastleigh	A	2130	D 0 - 0		
Feb 1	NL	Harrogate Town	H	1704	D 1 - 1	Bettamer 44	18
8	NL	Hartlepool United	A	3442	L 0 - 2		
22	NL	Maidenhead United	A	1778	W 2 - 1	Rance 7 Panayiotou 21	16
25	NL	Boreham Wood	H	1274	W 3 - 2	Lyons-Foster 53 68 Berkeley-Agyepong 71	14
Mar 7	NL	Dagenham & Redbridge	H	2103	L 0 - 1		17
10	NL	Notts County	A	4287	L 1 - 3	Tanner 17	17
14	NL	AFC Fylde	A	1668	L 0 - 1		16

GOALSCORERS	SG	CSG	Pens	Hat tricks	Total		SG	CSG	Pens	Hat tricks	Total
Chislett	8	2	2		9	Santos	2	1			2
Bettamer	7	2			7	Tinkler	2	1			2
Berkeley-Agyepong	4	1			4	Whittingham	2	1			2
Panayiotou	4	1			4	Eyoma	1	1			1
Tanner	4	1			4	Hunt	1	1			1
Powell	3	2			3						
Fowler	2	1			2						
Lyons-Foster	1	1			2						
Mullings	2	1			2						
Rance	2	1			2						

Walker M	Kinsella L	Finney A	Tinkler R	O'Dwyer O	Rance D	Rowe J	Alefe Santos	Shields C	Panayiotou H	Mullings S	Fowler G	Berkeley-Agyepong J	Chislett E	Eyoma A	Whitingham A	Kudjiwa S	Hall R (Gk)	Lyons-Foster K	Woodward H	Montague L	Hunt M (L)	Fletcher A (L)	Wylie R	Powell J (L)	Bettamer M	Anderson M (L)	Walker L (L)	Tanner C	Taylor H	Koue Niate J	van Velzen G (L)	Miller R	Drais Y	Grant R (L)	No.
X	X	X	X	XS	X	X	XS	X	XS	X	SX	SX	S	S																					1
X	X	X	X		X	X	XS	X	SX	X	X	XS	XS	S	SX	S																			2
X	X	X	X		X	XS	S	XS	SX	X	X	XS	X	SX	SX	S																			3
X	X	X	X		X	S	XS	S	X	X	X		X	X	SX	S	S																		4
X	X	XS	X	S	X	X	S	XS	X	SX	X	X		SX	XS	XS			SX																5
X	X	XS	X	SX	X	X		XS	X	S	X	X		SX	X	XS		S	SX																6
X	X		X			X		SX	XS	X	X	X	SX	X	X	X		S	X	S	S														7
X	X		X			X		S	X	S	X	X		X	X	X	S	S	X																8
X	X		X			X		SX	XS		XS	X		X	XS	X	S		X			SX	SX	S											9
X	X		X			X	X	X	SX	SX		XS	S	XS	S	SX	S		XS			X	XS		X										10
X	X		X			XS	X	XS	SX	S		X	SX	SX	S			X			X	XS		X											11
X	X		X			X	XS	X	SX	X	S		X	SX	S	S		X			X	XS		X											12
X	X	S				XS	XS	X	SX	X	SX	X	XS	S				X			X	SX		X											13
X	X		X			X		S	X	X		XS	X	S	S	S		X			X	SX		X											14
X	X	S		SX		XS	XS	XS	SX			X	X		S			X			X			X	SX										15
X	X	S	X	SX		X	SX		XS			XS	XS	XS	S			X			X	X													16
X	X	S	X	SX		X	SX		XS	XS	XS	S			X			X			X	X													17
X	X	S	XS	SX		XS	SX	SX	X	S	SX	X	S	S				X			X			X	X										18
X	X	X		X			X	S	XS	S	X		SX		SX			X			X			X	X										19
X	X	X		X				S	SX	X		XS	SX	S	S			X			X			X	XS										20
X	X	X		XS			X			SX	X	X	SX	X	S			X			X			X	XS										21
X		X	X			X	SX	XS		XS	X		SX	X	S	X		S			X			X	XS										22
X	X	X	XS			X	S		XS	S	SX		SX	X		X		SX			X			X	XS										23
X	X	X				X	S	SX	XS	SX	X			SX				SX			X			X	XS	X									24
X	X	X				X	XS	SX	XS	S				XS				S			SX			X	X	X	SX								25
X	X	X				X	SX	X	SX	XS				SX	X			S			XS			X		X	XS								26
X	X	S	X			X	S	XS				SX			SX	XS		S	X					XS	X	X	SX	X							27
X	X	X	X			X	SX	S	SX					XS		SX			X			X	XS	XS	X										28
X	X	X				X	S	SX	S					X		SX			X			X	X	S	XS	XS									29
X	X	X				X	SX	SX		SX				X		S			X			X	XS	X	S		XS								30
X	X	X				X	SX	SX	X	SX				X		SX			X			XS	X	S			XS								31
X	X	X	X			X	X	SX	X	SX				XS		S			X				X			SX	XS	SX							32
X	X	X				X	X	XS	SX				X		X		S	X	S			X			XS		S								33
X	X	X				X	X	XS	S	SX			XS	X		SX			X					S	S		X								34
X	X	XS		X			X	S		S			XS	X		SX			SX			X			SX	XS		X							35
X	X		X			X	S		SX			S	X	X		SX			X					XS		SX	XS								36
X	XS	X			X	X			X		X	X	S		S			SX						XS	X		X	SX	S						37
X		X			X	X		S	X		X	XS	SX		SX			X						XS	X		X	S	S						38
X		X			XS	XS			XS		X	X	X		X			X					S		X	X		X	XS	S	SX				39
X		X				X				X		X	XS		X		S						S	XS			X	SX	SX	XS					40
X		X				X				X	X	XS		X		S						S			SX	X		X	SX	XS	XS				41
41	35	21	30	0	27	10	6	7	10	12	15	5	21	4	6	0	0	26	0	0	19	0	0	19	13	4	1	6	0	8	0	0	0	0	x
0	1	2	2	1	2	3	11	10	8	5	0	11	11	3	4	0	0	1	0	0	1	3	0	3	6	0	7	7	0	0	0	0	2	1	xs
0	0	0	0	1	4	3	10	5	12	8	2	6	6	7	16	0	0	6	0	0	2	3	0	2	0	6	0	1	0	4	1	1	0	0	sx
0	0	0	5	1	1	0	6	6	10	7	1	3	2	1	8	13	9	8	3	2	2	0	0	0	3	0	0	3	2	1	1	0	1	3	s

GOALKEEPERS	CS	CCS
Walker M	8	2

x - Played full 90 minutes
xs - Substituted off
sx - Substituted on
s - Non-playing Substitute

BARNET MATCH RESULTS 2019-20

Date	Comp	Opponents	H/A	Att:	Result	Goalscorers	Pos
Aug 3	NL	Yeovil Town	H	1666	W 1 - 0	Akinola 61 (pen)	8
6	NL	Sutton United	A	1761	D 1 - 1	Akinola 38 (pen)	7
10	NL	Notts County	A	4096	W 2 - 1	Reynolds 28 Akinola 75	
13	NL	Dover Athletic	H	1143	L 0 - 1		
17	NL	Chesterfield	H	1119	D 2 - 2	Taylor J 5 Akinola 63 (pen)	10
24	NL	Wrexham	A	4533	D 1 - 1	Sparkes 8	
26	NL	Torquay United	H	1621	D 2 - 2	Mason-Clark 49 Taylor J 89	
31	NL	Eastleigh	A	1922	W 2 - 1	Taylor J 16 Coulthirst 90+4	8
Sep 14	NL	Maidenhead United	H	1086	W 1 - 0	Walker 65	9
17	NL	Aldershot Town	H	1069	W 2 - 0	Mason-Clark 48 Fonguck 58	5
21	NL	Halifax Town	A	1941	L 2 - 4	Akinola 17 Adams 20	6
24	NL	Ebbsfleet United	A	805	L 0 - 3		8
28	NL	Solihull Moors	H	1052	D 0 - 0		9
Oct 1	NL	AFC Fylde	A	997	W 4 - 0	Ricardo 9 Akinola 49 Walker 56 Vilhete 67	5
5	NL	Dagenham & Redbridge	A	1556	D 1 - 1	Walker 43	6
8	NL	Bromley	H	1083	L 1 - 2	Walker 10	9
12	NL	Woking	H	1651	D 2 - 2	Vilhete 59 Mason-Clark 90+7	10
19	**FAC4Q**	**Potters Bar Town**	**A**	**2011**	**D 1 - 1**	**Walker 16**	
22	**FAC4Qr**	**Potters Bar Town**	**H**	**1466**	**W 3 - 1**	**Walker 39 Mason-Clark 54 Taylor J 61 (pen)**	
26	NL	Hartlepool United	A	3089	L 0 - 2		12
29	NL	Harrogate Town	A	1121	L 1 - 2	Tutonda 36	15
Nov 2	NL	Chorley	H	1040	W 2 - 1	Taylor J 62 (pen) Vilhete 79	10
10	**FAC1**	**Fleetwood Town**	**H**	**1100**	**L 0 - 2**		
16	NL	Stockport County	H	1536	L 1 - 2	Mason-Clark 70	15
23	NL	Barrow	A	2120	L 1 - 2	Taylor J 85	
26	NL	Ebbsfleet United	H	776	W 5 - 2	Taylor J 27 Akinola 42 57 72 (pen) Walker 67	15
Dec 7	NL	AFC Fylde	H	661	W 2 - 1	Taylor J 37 Akinola 90+3	10
14	**FAT1**	**Weymouth**	**H**	**624**	**W 2 - 1**	**Walker 7 12**	
21	NL	Maidenhead United	A	1625	W 4 - 1	Akinola 35 (pen) 90+3 Tutonda 43 Alexander 47	10
28	NL	Aldershot Town	A	2107	D 0 - 0		12
Jan 1	NL	Boreham Wood	A	1401	D 0 - 0		11
4	NL	Halifax Town	H	1333	D 1 - 1	Taylor J 57	11
11	**FAT2**	**Farsley Celtic**	**A**	**402**	**D 1 - 1**	**Akinola 10**	
25	NL	Bromley	A	2035	W 2 - 1	Walker 26 Akinola 54	13
28	**FAT2r**	**Farsley Celtic**	**H**	**333**	**W 2 - 0**	**Sparkes 52 Walker 87**	
Feb 1	NL	Hartlepool United	H	1321	W 2 - 1	McCallum 64 Akinola 80	11
8	**FAT3**	**Barrow**	**H**	**763**	**W 3 - 0**	**Alexander 61 Akinola 62 Walker 69**	
11	NL	Solihull Moors	A	501	L 0 - 1		
22	NL	Chorley	A	925	W 1 - 0	McCallum 2	12
29	**FAT4**	**Halesowen Town**	**H**	**1483**	**L 1 - 2**	**Walker 65**	
Mar 3	NL	Boreham Wood	H	1273	D 2 - 2	Reynolds 12 McCallum 79	13
7	NL	Stockport County	A	5011	D 1 - 1	Akinola 9 (pen)	13
10	NL	Woking	A	1486	W 3 - 1	McCallum 26 Walker 77 90+4	10
July 18	**PO Q**	**Yeovil Town**	**A**	**0**	**W 2 - 0**	**McCallum 53 Vilhete 86**	
25	**PO SF**	**Notts County**	**A**	**0**	**L 0 - 2**		

GOALSCORERS	SG	CSG	Pens	Hat tricks	Total		SG	CSG	Pens	Hat tricks	Total
Akinola	14	3	6	1	17	Adams	1	1			1
Walker	13	3			15	Coulthirst	1	1			1
Taylor J	9	3	1		9	Fonguck	1	1			1
Mason-Clark	5	1			5	Ricardo	1	1			1
McCallum*	5	2			5						
Vilhete	4	1			4						
Alexander	2	1			2						
Reynolds	2	1			2						
Sparkes	2	1			2						
Tutonda	2	1			2						

Loach S	Reynolds C	Ricardo	Alexander C	Taylor H	Tutonda D	Elito M	Sparkes D	Dunne J	Taylor J	Akinola S	Coulthirst S	Mason-Clark E	Adams C	Barham J	Matrevics R (gk)	Vasiliou A	Syla R	Johnson E	Boucard A	Rowan C (L)	Walker J	Hernandez L	Fonguck W	Pavey A	Vilhete M	Sweeney D	Azaze A (Gk)	Edwards R	Chime O	Box M	McCallum P (L)	McBurnie A	No.
x	x	x	x	x	x	xs	x	x	xs	sx	sx	sx	s	s	s																		1
x	x		x	x	x	x	xs	x	x	x	xs	x			s	s	s	s															2
x	x	x	x	x	x	xs	sx	x	x	xs	sx	xs			s		sx	s															3
x	x	x	x	x	xs	xs	sx	x	x	x	sx	xs	s		s			sx															4
x	x		x	x		x	x	x	x	x	s	x	s		s	s	s		xs														5
x		x	x	x	sx	x	x	xs	xs	x	sx	x	s		sx	xs	s																6
x		x	x	x		x	sx	x	xs	sx	x	s			xs	xs	x																7
x	x	x	x	xs		x		x	x	sx	x	xs	s	s		sx	s	x															8
x	x	x	x			x	x		xs	x	sx	s	sx	s		sx	xs	x	xs														9
x	x	x	x		x		x	xs		xs	x		s	sx		s	x	s	x	sx													10
x	x	x	x			x	xs		xs	x		s	sx		s	sx	x	xs	x	sx													11
x	x	x	x	s		x	x		x		s	sx		s	sx	x	xs	x	xs														12
x	x	x	x			x	x		s		s	s		s	sx		x	xs	x	x													13
x	x	x	x	x	sx		x	x		xs		s	xs		s	xs		sx	sx	xs	x												14
x	x	x	x	x	xs	s		x	xs		xs		xs		xs	x	x	sx	s														15
x	x	x	x	x	s		sx		sx	sx		xs		xs	x	x	x	xs	s														16
x	x	x	x	xs	xs		xs		sx	xs		x		s	sx	x	x	s															17
x	x	x	x	x		s			x	s		sx	xs		s			sx	sx		xs			x	xs	x		s					18
x	x	x	x	x	xs	x		sx	xs	sx		x			s			sx	x		xs			s		s	s						19
x		xs	x	x	x	xs		sx	x	s		sx			s			sx	xs		x			x	x								20
x	x		x	x	x	xs		x		x		s			s		s	x		sx			s		x	x							21
x	x			x	xs		x	sx	s		sx			s			x	xs		sx			x	xs	s								22
x	x		x	x	xs	s		xs	x	sx		sx	s					x	s		x			xs	x				sx				23
x	x		x	x	x	xs	x		xs	x		x						x			x	s	s			s		sx					24
x	x		x	x	s	x		xs	x	sx		xs						s			xs			sx	sx	x							25
x	x		x	x			x	x	xs			sx				s	sx		x	s		xs	xs		sx	x							26
x	x		x	x	xs		sx	x	x	x		sx					s		x			xs	xs		sx	s							27
x	x		x	x	xs		sx	x	xs	x		sx					s	s	s	x		xs	s	x		s							28
x	x		x	x	x		x	x	xs			sx						x			xs	xs		sx	s	sx	s						29
x	x		x	x	xs		sx	x	x	x		sx						x			xs	xs		sx	s	s							30
x	x		x	x		s	x	x	x			sx	s	xs				x			xs	xs		s									31
x	x	xs	x	x		s	x	x	x			sx	s	xs				x			xs	sx		s									32
x	x		x	s	x		x			x		x	x			s			x		s	xs	sx		s	s		s					33
x	x			x			x			x	xs			s	x			x			xs			sx	s								34
x		sx		s	x	x	x		xs			sx	x					x			xs			xs	x	x	s	sx		s			35
x	x			x			sx	x		xs								x			xs			s	x	x	s		sx	s			36
x	x	sx	x		x	sx	s		x			x						x			xs			s	x	xs	s	sx		xs			37
x	x	sx	x		xs	sx	sx	x		x			xs					x			x			s	xs	x	s		x				38
x	x	x	x		x	sx	s	x		xs			s					x			x			sx	s	xs	s		x			s	39
x	x	x	x	s	xs	sx	sx	x		xs			sx					x			x	sxs		xs	x				s			s	40
x	xs	x	x			x	sx	x		xs			sx					x			s			s	x			x					41
x		x	x	x	sx		xs	x		xs			sx					x			sx	xs		s	x			x					42
x		x	x	x		s	x		xs			sx	sx					x			sx	xs		s	x			xs					43
x		x		x	x	sx		x				xs	x			s	s	x			xs			sx	x		sx		xs	s			44
x		x		x	xs		x			sx	sx	x	x			s		x			xs			sx	x		s		x	s			45
45	36	25	40	31	17	7	8	27	24	18	1	8	12	0	0	0	0	25	1	0	10	3	4	4	12	18	0	0	0	0	4	0	x
0	1	1	1	1	12	6	2	2	3	17	0	9	5	2	0	0	0	0	4	2	17	0	14	1	7	3	0	0	0	0	2	1	xs
0	0	2	1	0	3	7	9	4	1	5	7	16	7	2	0	5	0	4	4	1	7	0	4	6	10	1	0	4	2	0	1	0	sx
0	0	0	0	2	2	4	5	0	0	4	1	3	8	5	26	6	4	0	3	6	2	4	8	0	3	1	16	4	1	2	0	4	s

GOALKEEPERS	CS	CCS
Loach	11	2

x - Played full 90 minutes
xs - Substituted off
sx - Substituted on
s - Non-playing Substitute

BARROW MATCH RESULTS 2019-20

Date	Comp	Opponents	H/A	Att:	Result	Goalscorers	Pos
Aug 3	NL	Wrexham	A	5941	L 1 - 2	Granite 13	16
6	NL	Harrogate Town	H	1602	L 0 - 3		22
10	NL	Eastleigh	H	1060	W 2 - 0	Stryjek 51 (og) Quigley 90+1	
13	NL	Stockport County	A	4183	L 2 - 3	Quigley 4 Rooney 68	
17	NL	Yeovil Town	H	1218	W 1 - 0	Quigley 46	14
24	NL	Chesterfield	A	3812	D 2 - 2	Barry 18 Quigley 25	
26	NL	Halifax Town	H	1451	L 1 - 2	Hardcastle 2	
31	NL	Woking	A	1787	L 2 - 3	Dyson 25 Kay 73	21
Sep 3	NL	Hartlepool United	H	1257	L 0 - 1		21
7	NL	Aldershot Town	A	1163	W 2 - 1	Rooney 45 Kay 69	19
14	NL	Soilhull Moors	H	1152	W 3 - 0	Rooney 7 45+4 Quigley 46	14
21	NL	Ebbsfleet United	A	878	W 3 - 0	Rooney 8 Quigley 46 70	10
24	NL	Chorley	A	1272	W 3 - 1	Rooney 29 67 (pens) Dyson 45+3	7
28	NL	Maidenhead United	H	1401	W 2 - 0	Rooney 36 (pen) Quigley 57	7
Oct 5	NL	Bromley	A	2043	W 2 - 1	Angus 36 Quigley 53	5
8	NL	Boreham Wood	H	1758	W 3 - 1	Quigley 13 82 Angus 18	4
19	FAC4Q	Soilhull Moors	H	1523	L 0 - 1		
26	NL	Torquay United	A	2280	L 2 - 4	Angus 10 Brown 56	5
29	NL	Dagenham & Redbridge	A	1122	W 2 - 0	Angus 13 Quigley 25	5
Nov 2	NL	Sutton United	H	1827	W 1 - 0	Kay 51	4
16	NL	Notts County	A	5287	W 3 - 0	Angus 11 Rooney 13 Hindle 87	1
23	NL	Barnet	H	2120	W 2 - 1	Kay 27 Rooney 30	1
26	NL	Chorley	H	2324	D 2 - 2	Kay 22 Rooney 30	1
30	NL	Maidenhead United	A		W 4 - 0	Quigley 12 Angus 54 Brough 64 Dyson 87	1
Dec 7	NL	Aldershot Town	H	2024	W 1 - 0	Rooney 23	1
17	FAT1	Atherton Collieries	A	468	D 2 - 2	Hindle 57 Penfold 77	
26	NL	AFC Fylde	H	3267	D 1 - 1	Quigley 66	1
28	NL	Hartlepool United	A	3790	D 2 - 2	Hardcastle 46 Angus 68	1
Jan 1	NL	AFC Fylde	A	2409	W 1 - 0	Quigley 51	1
4	NL	Ebbsfleet United	H	2303	W 7 - 0	White 15 Rooney 26 83 89 Quigley 44 76 Dyson 70	1
7	FAT1r	Atherton Collieries	H	861	W 2 - 0	Hardcastle 35 Hindle 73 (pen)	
11	FAT2	United of Manchester	H	1892	W 7 - 0	Barry 16 Kay 35 Rooney 43 63 (pen) Harrison 70 Angus 83 88	
18	NL	Bromley	H	3155	W 2 - 0	Angus 34 Rooney 73	1
25	NL	Boreham Wood	A	1099	D 1 - 1	Kay 34	1
28	NL	Solihull Moors	A	892	D 0 - 0		1
Feb 1	NL	Torquay United	H	2586	W 2 - 1	Rooney 71 Quigley 76	1
4	NL	Dover Athletic	A	972	L 1 - 2	Rooney 81 (pen)	1
8	FAT3	Barnet	A	763	L 0 - 3		
18	NL	Dover Athletic	H	2016	W 1 - 0	Angus 72	1
22	NL	Sutton United	A	1871	D 2 - 2	Quigley 29 40	1
29	NL	Dagenham & Redbridge	H	2353	W 2 - 1	White 6 Brough 28	1
Mar 7	NL	Notts County	H	3307	L 0 - 2		1

GOALSCORERS	SG	CSG	Pens	Hat tricks	Total		SG	CSG	Pens	Hat tricks	Total
Rooney	15	5	5	1	20	Brown	1	1			1
Quigley	16	4			20	Granite	1	1			1
Angus	10	2			11	Harrison	1	1			1
Kay	7	2			7	Opponent	1	1			1
Dyson	4	1			4	Penfold	1	1			1
Hardcastle	3	1			3						
Hindle	3	1	1		3						
Barry	2	1			2						
Brough	2	1			2						
White	2	1			2						

Dixon J	Hird S	Granite J	Rooney J	Taylor J	Brough P	Barry B	Hardcastle L	Kay J	Quigley S	Angus D	Greaves O (L)	Harrison B	Hindle J	Brown C	Dyson O	Waddington M	Elsdon M	Penfold M	Platt M (L)	Saltmer J (Gk)	White T (L)	Simpson L (Gk)	Hodgson J	Fawcett C	Fitch K	Dawson T	Spence T	Jones D (L)	Soule J (L)	No.
x	x	x	x	x	x	x	xs	xs	xs	x	sx	sx	sx	s	s															1
x	x	x	x	x	x	x	xs	x	sx	x	sx	xs	s	s	s															2
x	x	x	xs	x	x	x	sx	x	x	x	x	s	xs	s	s	sx														3
x	x	x	x	x	xs	x	sx	xs	x	x	x	s	xs	s	sx	sx														4
x	x	s	x	x	x		x	x		x	xs	xs		sx	x	x	sx	s	s											5
x	x	s	x	x	x	s	x	x	sx	xs	xs	x	sx	xs	x	xs														6
x	x	x	x	xs	x	x	xs	sx	x	xs	sx	x	sx	s	x															7
x	x	s	x	x	x	s	x	x	sx	xs	x	x	sx	x	xs	s														8
x	x	s	xs	x	x	x	xs	xs		sx	sx	x		s	x	sx			x											9
x	x	x	x	sx	x		x		xs			x	sx		xs	s			x											10
x	x	s	x	x	x	x	sx	x	xs	sx	sx	s	xs						x											11
x	x	s	x	x	x	x	sx	x	xs	sx	sx		xs						x											12
x	x	s	x			x	x	x	xs	xs	sx	sx	sx						x											13
x	x	s	x	x	x	x	sx	x	xs	xs		sx	sx	s					x											14
x	x	s	x			x	xs	x	xs	xs		sx	sx	s	sx				x											15
x	x	s	x	x	x	x	xs	x	xs	xs		sx	sx	s	s				x											16
x	x	s	x	x	x	x	xs	x	x	xs	s		sx	s	sx	s		s	x											17
x	x	s	x	x	x	x	xs	xs	x	xs			xs	sx	s			sx	x											18
x		x	x	x	x		sx	x	x	xs	s		xs	x	sx			sx	xs	s										19
x		x	x	x	x			x	xs		sx	sx	x	x	xs	s	s	sx	x											20
x			x		x	x	x	x	xs	xs		sx	sx	x	sx	s		s	x		xs									21
x	x		x	sx	x		x	x	xs	xs		sx	sx	x	s			s	x		xs									22
x	x		x	xs	x		x	x	xs	xs		sx	sx	s	s				x		sx									23
x	x		x	sx	x		xs	x	xs	x		sx	s	s	s	sx			x		xs									24
x	x		x		x	x	xs	x	xs	xs	s		sx	sx	s	sx			x		x									25
s				x			sx	x		s	xs	x	x	x	x	x	xs	xs	x	s		sx	x	sx						26
x	x		xs	sx	x		x	xs	x	xs			s	s	sx	sx			x		x									27
x	x		x	s	xs	x	x			xs	xs	s	sx	sx	x	sx			x		x									28
x	x		x	x			x	sx	x	xs	sx		sx	s	x	xs		s	x		xs									29
x	x		x	x			xs	x	xs	x		sx	sx	s	sx	x		s	x		x									30
s		xs			x					xs			x	x	x	x	x	x	xs	xs	x	x		x	xs	sx	sx	sx	s	31
x	x		xs	x	x		sx	x	xs	sx			x	s	s	sx		s	x		xs		s							32
x	x		xs	x	x		x	x	xs	xs			sx	s	s	sx			x		x		sx							33
x	x		x	x	x	x	xs	x	xs	xs			sx	s	s	sx			x		sx									34
x	x	s	x	x	x		sx	x	xs	xs			s	sx	x	sx			x		xs									35
x	x		x	sx	x		x	xs	x	xs			sx	s	sx	s			x		sx									36
x			x	x	x		xs	xs	x	x			sx	sx	s	sx			x	s										37
s		x		x	x		x	sx		sx			xs	xs	x	xs			s	x		x	x	s		s	sx			38
x	x		x	sx	x		xs	x	xs	xs			sx		s	s			x		x							x	sx	39
x	x		x	x	x		sx	xs	x	xs			s		sx	s			x		xs							x	sx	40
x	x		x	sx	x		x	xs	x	xs			s		sx	s			x		xs							x	s	41
x	x		x	s	x		x	xs	x	x			sx	sx				xs			x							x	s	42
39	35	8	34	27	33	30	13	25	15	7	2	5	2	13	5	1	1	2	29	0	10	3	0	0	0	0	0	4	0	x
0	0	1	5	2	2	2	13	10	21	29	2	4	4	0	11	1	1	0	2	0	8	0	1	0	0	0	0	0	0	xs
0	0	0	0	6	0	0	15	4	1	4	6	24	20	7	17	2	0	3	0	0	3	0	1	1	1	2	0	0	2	sx
3	0	14	0	2	2	0	0	0	0	1	7	5	10	20	9	5	2	9	1	1	0	1	0	2	0	1	0	2	2	s

GOALKEEPERS	CS	CCS
Dixon	16	3
Simpson	1	1

x - Played full 90 minutes
xs - Substituted off
sx - Substituted on
s - Non-playing Substitute

BOREHAM WOOD MATCH RESULTS 2019-20

Date	Comp	Opponents	H/A	Att:	Result	Goalscorers	Pos
Aug 3	NL	Torquay United	A	3138	L 1 - 2	Marsh 90	17
6	NL	Wrexham	H	845	D 2 - 2	Murtagh 82 Shaibu 90+3	18
10	NL	Chesterfield	H	715	D 2 - 2	Tshimanga 16 (pen) 55	
13	NL	Dagenham & Redbridge	A	1179	W 3 - 0	Tshimanga 18 86 (pen) Shaibu 88	
17	NL	Sutton United	H	407	L 0 - 1		16
24	NL	Bromley	A	1443	L 0 - 1		
26	NL	Ebbsfleet United	H	533	L 1 - 2	Marsh 76 (pen)	
31	NL	Chorley	A	1035	W 3 - 1	Marsh 31 Stephens 38 Challoner 46 (og)	17
Sep 3	NL	Eastleigh	A	1641	L 0 - 2		19
7	NL	Boreham Wood	H	493	W 3 - 1	Tshimanga 3 19 Marsh 62	15
14	NL	Harrogate Town	A	942	D 0 - 0		16
21	NL	Stockport County	H	744	W 4 - 0	Tshimanga 20 42 Thomas 27 Marsh 89	12
24	NL	Notts County	H	756	L 1 - 2	Marsh 84 (pen)	18
28	NL	Woking	A	2219	W 2 - 1	Tshimanga 39 48	12
Oct 5	NL	Solihull Moors	H	540	W 1 - 0	Marsh 90+3	11
8	NL	Barrow	A	1758	L 1 - 3	Marsh 31	14
12	NL	Halifax Town	A	2244	W 2 - 0	Champion 44 McDonnell 75	11
19	**FAC4Q**	**Torquay United**	**A**	**1952**	**L 2 - 3**	**Marsh 51 (pen) Cundy 90 (og)**	
26	NL	AFC Fylde	H	501	L 0 - 2		14
9	NL	Aldershot Town	H	619	D 0 - 0		13
Nov 2	NL	Yeovil Town	A	2879	D 1 - 1	Tshimanga 90+1	15
16	NL	Maidenhead United	H	624	W 2 - 1	Tshimanga 72 Shaibu 88	13
23	NL	Hartlepool United	A	3377	D 2 - 2	Thomas 27 (pen) Tshimanga 50	
26	NL	Notts County	A	3256	D 2 - 2	Shaibu 15 Thomas 90+1	14
30	NL	Woking	H	682	W 1 - 0	Marsh 15	9
Dec 7	NL	Dover Athletic	A	728	W 2 - 0	Thomas 33 (pen) Shaibu 59	9
14	**FAT1**	**Royston Town**	**A**	**478**	**L 0 - 2**		
21	NL	Harrogate Town	H	501	W 2 - 1	Marsh 14 Tshimanga 90+1	6
28	NL	Eastleigh	H	601	D 2 - 2	Mingoia 9 Fyfield 46	8
Jan 1	NL	Barnet	H	1401	D 0 - 0		8
4	NL	Stockport County	A	4074	W 3 - 1	Marsh 3 22 Tshimanga 44	7
18	NL	Solihull Moors	A	882	W 2 - 0	Thomas 32 Smith K 68	5
25	NL	Barrow	H	1099	D 1 - 1	Marsh 67	5
Feb 1	NL	AFC Fylde	A	1258	W 2 - 1	Tshimanga 19 Fyfield 73	5
22	NL	Yeovil Town	H	1040	W 1 - 0	Tshimanga 74	3
25	NL	Aldershot Town	A	1274	L 2 - 3	Smith K 13 May 86	3
29	NL	Hartlepool United	H	932	D 1 - 1	Tshimanga 1	4
Mar 3	NL	Barnet	A	1273	D 2 - 2	Smith K 60 Marsh 72	5
7	NL	Maidenhead United	A	1296	W 1 - 0	Tshimanga 22	4
July 17	**PO Q**	**Halifax Town**	**H**	**0**	**W 2 - 1**	**Smith K 54 Rhead 80**	
26	PO SF	Harrogate Town	A	0	L 0 - 1		

GOALSCORERS	SG	CSG	Pens	Hat tricks	Total		SG	CSG	Pens	Hat tricks	Total
Tshimanga	14	3	2		19	Mingoia	1	1			1
Marsh	14	2	3		15	Murtagh	1	1			1
Shaibu	5	2			5	Rhead	1	1			1
Thomas	5	1	2		5	Stephens	1	1			1
Smith K	4	1			4						
Fyfield	2	1			2						
Opponent	2	1			2						
Champion	1	1			1						
May	1	1			1						
McDonnell	1	1			1						

Gregory D	Fyfield J	Stephens D	Ilesanmi O	Smith K	Murtagh K	Champion T	Mingoia P	McDonnell A	Tshimanga K	Thomas S	Shaibu J (L)	Marsh T	Ricketts M	Woodards D	Thompson J (L)	Shakes R	Huddart R (Gk)	Whickham C	Ashmore N (Gk) (L)	Yussuf A (L)	Smith G (Gk) (L)	Rhead M	May A (L)	Charles-Cook R (Gk) (L)	No.
x	x	x	x	x	x	x	x	x	xs	xs	xs	sx	sx	sx	s	s									1
x		x	x	x	x	x	x	x	x	xs	sx	sx	xs	s	sx	x	s								2
x		x	x	x	x	x	x	x		sx	xs	s	s	x	s	s	s								3
x		x	x	xs	x	x	xs	x	s	sx	xs	sx	x	s	sx										4
x		x	x	xs	x	x	x	x	sx	sx	xs	sx	xs	s	s										5
x	x	x	s	x		x	xs	x	x	sx	xs	sx	x	xs	s	sx									6
x		x	x	x	x	xs		xs	xs	x	sx	xs	x	x	sx	s	s								7
x		x	x	x		s	xs	xs	x	sx	x	x	xs	x	sx	s	sx								8
x		x	xs	x	x	sx		sx	x	x	sx	xs	xs		x	x	s	s							9
x	x	x	x	x	x		s	xs	xs	sx	x	x		x	sx	s	s								10
x	x	x	x	x	x	x	s	s	x	x	sx	xs	x		s	s									11
x	x	x	x	xs	x	x	sx	s	xs	xs	sx	x	x		s	sx									12
x	x	x	x		x	x	sx	sx	sx	x	sx	x	xs		s	xs	s								13
x	x	x	x		x	x	xs	sx	sx	x	sx	x			s	sx	s								14
s	x		x	x	x	xs	x	sx	x	x	s		s	sx	s	x			x						15
s	x	x		xs		sx	x	xs	x	sx	x		x	xs	sx		s	x							16
s	x		x	x	x	xs	x	sx	x	sx	x		xs	sx	sx		s	x							17
s	x	x	x	x	x	s	xs	xs	x	sx	x	sx	s	s	s			x							18
	x	x	x	x	x	xs	sx	s	x	xs	sx	x	x	s	s	s		x							19
	x	x	x	x	x	x	s	sx	x	x	x	s	x	x	s	s		x							20
	x	x	x	x	x	x	s	x	x	sx	x	x	xs	s	s	s		x							21
	s	x	x	x	x	s		xs	x	x	x	s	s	sx		x									22
	s	x	x	x	x	x		x	xs	x	x	s	s		x										23
	s	x	x	x	x	x	sx	sx	x	x	s	s	s		x										24
	sx	xs	x	x		x	s	x	x	s	s	s	sx		x										25
	s	x	x	x	x	x	x	s	x	x	x	s		sx		x									26
s	sx	x	x	x	xs	x	s	sx	x	x	xs	x	x	s		s			x						27
s	xs	x	x	x	x	sx	x	x		xs	xs	x	sx		sx			x							28
s	x	x	x	x	x	x	x	x		xs	s	x	s		sx			x							29
s	x	xs	x	x	x	xs	x	x		x	sx	x	sx		s			x							30
s	x		x	x	x	x	s	s	x	xs	x	x	x		sx			x							31
	x	s	x	x	x	x	x	s	x	x		xs	s	s		s			x	sx					32
	x	s	x	x	x	xs	x	x		x	x	s		s		x	sx								33
	x	s	x	x	x	xs		x	x		x	x	s	sx		x	s	s							34
	x	sx	x	x		x	xs	xs	x		x	x			x	s	s	sx	s						35
	x	s	x	xs		x	xs	xs	x	x					x	sx	s	sx	sx						36
	x	s	x	x		x	s		xs	x	sx	x	x			x	s	s	x	x					37
	x	x	x	x		x	s		x	x		x	x	s		s		x	s	s	x				38
	x	sx	x	xs	x		s		xs	x	sx	xs	x			x	s	sx	x						39
x	s	x	x	x	x	s		x	x	sx	xs	x		s		s	x	x			s				40
x	s	x	xs	x	x	s		x	x	sx	xs	x		s		x	sx	s	x						41
14	26	28	38	32	31	34	8	7	26	28	3	25	29	3	5	1	0	0	26	0	1	5	1	0	x
0	1	2	1	4	4	2	8	8	15	5	8	11	3	5	1	1	0	0	0	0	0	0	0	0	xs
0	2	2	0	0	0	1	6	4	0	3	23	4	4	3	2	17	0	1	0	4	1	2	1	0	sx
9	4	7	1	0	0	0	16	14	0	1	1	1	2	18	17	14	7	4	0	6	6	0	1	1	s

GOALKEEPERS	CS	CCS
Ashmore*	9	2
Gregory	3	2

x - Played full 90 minutes
xs - Substituted off
sx - Substituted on
s - Non-playing Substitute

BROMLEY MATCH RESULTS 2019-20

Date	Comp	Opponents	H/A	Att:	Result	Goalscorers	Pos
Aug 3	NL	Chorley	A	1469	D	0 - 0	13
6	NL	Ebbsfleet United	H	1471	W	3 - 1 Cheek 18 Bingham 30 73	5
10	NL	Torquay United	H	1398	D	3 - 3 Holland 1 Kizzi 45 Raymond 71	
13	NL	Aldershot Town	A	1774	W	1 - 0 Holland 28	
17	NL	Hartlepool United	A	3171	W	3 - 2 Cheek 9 Hackett-Fairchild 27 75	3
24	NL	Boreham Wood	H	1443	W	1 - 0 Cheek 45+1	
26	NL	Maidenhead United	A	1511	W	2 - 1 Hackett-Fairchild 77 89	
31	NL	AFC Fylde	H	1541	D	2 - 2 Bingham 16 Raymond 63 (pen)	3
Sep 4	NL	Dagenham & Redbridge	A	1526	D	1 - 1 Hackett-Fairchild 90+5	3
7	NL	Chesterfield	H	2110	W	2 - 1 Cheek 26 73	3
14	NL	Eastleigh	A	1752	D	1 - 1 Coulson 63	2
21	NL	Notts County	H	3122	W	2 - 1 Doughty 2 McCoulsky 73	1
24	NL	Woking	H	2358	W	1 - 0 Cheek 38	1
28	NL	Yeovil Town	A	3960	L	1 - 3 Cheek 22	1
Oct 5	NL	Barrow	H	2043	L	1 - 2 Cheek 86	2
8	NL	Barnet	A	1083	W	2 - 1 Bush 25 Kizzi 57	2
12	NL	Solihull Moors	A	2120	L	1 - 2 Doughty 90+4	2
19	FAC4Q	**Aldershot Town**	H	1408	W	4 - 3 Kizzi 7 Cheek 12 67 Holland 36	
26	NL	Halifax Town	H	2215	W	5 - 0 Mekki 52 Hackett-Fairchild 59 Bush 64 Rees 74 Kizzi 90+2	1
29	NL	Stockport County	H	2205	D	2 - 2 Hackett-Fairchild 17 Minihan 37 (og)	1
Nov 2	NL	Wrexham	A	3469	L	0 - 1	1
10	FAC1	**Bristol Rovers**	A	3649	D	1 - 1 Bush 83	
16	NL	Harrogate Town	H	2177	D	3 - 3 Hackett-Fairchild 44 Bush 47 73	2
19	FAC1r	**Bristol Rovers**	H	4558	L	0 - 1	
23	NL	Sutton United	A	1762	W	2 - 0 Williamson 14 Cheek 78	
26	NL	Woking	A	1769	L	1 - 2 Coulson 15	3
30	NL	Yeovil Town	H	2261	D	1 - 1 Raymond 65 (pen)	2
Dec 7	NL	Chesterfield	A	3270	W	2 - 1 Williamson 78 Evans 82 (og)	2
14	FAT1	**Dorking Wanderers**	A	759	L	0 - 3	
21	NL	Eastleigh	H	1651	L	2 - 3 Cheek 20 Coker 90+4	3
26	NL	Dover Athletic	A	1210	L	0 - 3	3
28	NL	Dagenham & Redbridge	H	2312	W	3 - 0 Cheek 43 Coulson 84 Rees 88	3
Jan 1	NL	Dover Athletic	H	2011	W	3 - 0 Raymond 45+1 (pen) Rees 49 Cheek 88	3
4	NL	Notts County	A	5192	L	1 - 2 Cheek 50	4
18	NL	Barrow	A	3155	L	0 - 2	4
25	NL	Barnet	H	2035	L	1 - 2 Rees 43	4
Feb 1	NL	Halifax Town	A	2026	L	1 - 2 Kizzi 45+2	7
8	NL	Solihull Moors	H	1716	D	2 - 2 Raymond 78 Whitely 90+3	
15	NL	Stockport County	A	4611	L	0 - 1	
22	NL	Wrexham	H	1743	L	0 - 2	9
29	NL	Sutton United	H	1909	L	0 - 1	12
Mar 7	NL	Harrogate Town	A	1339	D	1 - 1 Bradley 87 (og)	12

GOALSCORERS	SG	CSG	Pens	Hat tricks	Total		SG	CSG	Pens	Hat tricks	Total
Cheek	13	3			15	Doughty	2	1			2
Hackett-Fairchild	6	2			8	Williamson*	2	1			2
Bush	4	2			5	Coker*	1	1			1
Kizzi	5	2			5	McCoulsky*	1	1			1
Raymond	5	1	3		5	Mekki	1	1			1
Rees	4	2			4	Whitely	1	1			1
Bingham	2	1			3						
Coulson	3	1			3						
Holland	3	2			3						
Opponent	3	1			3						

Cousins M	Bush C	Coulson L	Kizzi J	Bingham B	Holland J	Raymond F	Wood S	Higgs J	Cheek M	Hackett-Fairchild R	Porter G	Clifton A	Klass M	Dunne A	Mekki A	Okoye M	Rees J	Henry K	Tanner O	Doughty A (L)	McCoulsky S (L)	Huddart R (Gk)	Najia T (Gk)	Edmonds-Green R (L)	Williamson B	Onen J (L)	Winfield D	Coker A	Chambers M	Whitely C (L)	Rowe A (L)	No.
x	x	xs	x	x	x	x	x	xs	xs	x		sx	sx	sx	s	s																1
x	x	xs	x	x	x	x	x	s	xs	x		xs	sx	sx	s	s																2
x	x	xs	x	x	x	x	sx	x	xs	xs		sx	s		sx	s																3
x	x	xs	x	x	x	x	sx	x		xs		sx	s	s	xs	sx																4
x	x	xs	x	x	x	xs		x	x	xs		sx	s		s	sx	sx															5
x	x	xs	x	x	xs	x		x	x			sx	s	sx	sx	xs	s															6
x	x	sx	x	x		x	x		x	x		xs	s	xs	s	sx	s	s														7
x	x	xs	x	x		x	x		x	x		sx	s	s	sx	x	xs	s														8
x	x	xs	x	x		s	xs	x		x	x		sx	sx		sx	x	sx	s													9
x	x	x	x	x	sx	x		x		xs	xs		sx		s	x	xs	s		sx												10
x	x	x	x	sx	x	x			x		xs	s		s	x	sx	sx		xs													11
x	x	xs	x	x	s	x	x			xs	x		sx	sx		x	s		xs	sx												12
x	x	xs	x	x	s		x			x		sx	s		s	x	x		xs	sx												13
xs	x	xs	x	x	sx				x		sx	x		s		s	x	x		xs	sx											14
	x		x	x	x		x	xs	xs	xs	s	x	s	x			xs	sx	x													15
	x	xs	x	x	x	xs	x		xs	xs	s	s				xs		x														16
	x	xs	x	x	x	xs	x		x	x		xs	sx	s	sx			sx	s	x												17
x	**xs**	**x**		**x**	**x**	**x**	**sx**	**x**		**sx**		**s**	**xs**	**s**	**x**	**s**	**s**	**x**		**x**	**s**											18
	x	x	x		x		xs	x	sx	x	s	x	xs	xs		x	s	sx														19
	x	x		x	sx	x		x	x	sx	xs	xs		x	s	sx																20
	x	x	x		x	xs	x		x	xs	sx	xs	sx	s		x	s	sx														21
x	**xs**	**x**	**x**	**x**	**x**	**sx**		**x**	**x**	**sx**	**s**	**s**	**xs**		**sx**		**s**	**x**	**s**	**xs**												22
	x	sx	x	x	x	x		x	x		s	xs	x	s	x	s	x															23
x	**x**	**x**	**x**	**x**	**xs**	**x**		**x**	**xs**		**sx**	**s**	**sx**	**xs**	**s**	**x**	**s**	**sx**														24
	x	x	xs	x	x	sx		x		sx	xs	x	sx	x	s	xs	xs	s														25
	x	xs	x	x	sx		x		sx	xs	xs	sx	x	s	x	x	x															26
	x	x	xs	x	x	xs		sx	sx	s	x	sx	x	s	x	sx																27
	x	x	x	x	x	xs	s	x	s	s	x	s	x	s	x	sx																28
x	**x**	**sx**	**x**	**xs**	**x**		**x**	**xs**	**s**	**xs**	**x**	**sx**	**x**	**s**	**x**	**sx**																29
	x	x	x	x	x	xs	s	x	s	xs	sx	x	s	x	x	sx																30
	xs	x	x	x	xs	sx	x	s	xs	sx	x	s	x	x	sx																	31
	x	x	x	x	sx	xs	sx	s	s	xs	x	s	x	x	sx																	32
	x	xs	x	x	x	sx	s	sx	x	s	x	s	x	xs	xs	sx																33
	x	xs	x	x	x	xs	x	s	sx	xs	x	s	x	x	sx																	34
	x	x		x	xs	x	xs	sx	x	s	xs	x	s	x	x	s	x	sx														35
	x	x	x		xs	x	sx	x	sx	x	s	xs	x	s	x	sx	xs															36
s	sx	x	x		x	x		x	xs	sx	x	s	xs	x	s	x	xs	xs	s													37
x	x	x	x		x	x	x	x	sx	x	s	xs	x	s	s	sx	s															38
x	x	x	sx	s	x	x	xs	xs	sx	s	xs	x	x																			39
x	x	x	x	s	xs	x		xs	sx	sx	s	xs	x	x	sx																	40
x	x	xs	xs	x	sx		s	x	sx	s	xs	x	x	sx																		41
	x	x	xs	x	sx	s		x	sx	xs	x	s	sx	xs	x																	42
17	36	21	39	29	27	23	34	2	28	17	0	0	1	0	0	9	13	0	0	1	0	24	0	3	8	0	10	0	0	1	4	x
1	0	19	1	3	1	11	2	2	13	5	4	2	5	0	13	0	13	0	0	6	0	0	2	7	0	2	0	1	2	0		xs
0	1	2	0	2	3	5	1	8	0	3	1	24	13	1	9	3	8	3	3	2	4	0	0	4	3	1	1	5	1	2	2	sx
1	0	0	0	1	5	0	1	4	0	0	0	0	14	13	9	3	4	8	5	0	1	4	20	0	0	2	0	2	1	0	2	s

GOALKEEPERS	CS	CCS
Cousins	4	1
Huddart	4	2

x - Played full 90 minutes
xs - Substituted off
sx - Substituted on
s - Non-playing Substitute

CHESTERFIELD MATCH RESULTS 2019-20

Date	Comp	Opponents	H/A	Att:	Result	Goalscorers	Pos
Aug 3	NL	Dover Athletic	H	4332	L 1 - 2	Boden 72	18
6	NL	Maidenhead United	A	1471	D 1 - 1	Yarney 77	19
10	NL	Boreham Wood	A	715	D 2 - 2	Boden 26 Smith 44	
13	NL	Woking	H	3927	L 1 - 2	Boden 86	
17	NL	Barnet	A	1119	D 2 - 2	Fondop-Talum 2 49	22
24	NL	Barrow	H	3812	D 2 - 2	Boden 45_5 (pen) Fondop-Talum 80	
26	NL	Stockport County	A	5578	L 0 - 2		
31	NL	Dagenham & Redbridge	H	3708	D 1 - 1	Fondop-Talum 68	22
Sep 3	NL	Halifax Town	H	3844	L 2 - 3	Fondop-Talum 50 Rowley 89	22
7	NL	Bromley	A	2110	L 1 - 2	Mandeville 72	24
14	NL	Torquay United	H	3706	W 1 - 0	Boden 12	22
21	NL	Sutton United	A	1649	L 0 - 4		23
24	NL	Hartlepool United	A	2953	D 1 - 1	Denton 37	23
28	NL	Aldershot Town	H	3657	W 2 - 1	Boden 39 Mandeville 56	22
Oct 5	NL	Eastleigh	H	3632	L 1 - 2	Denton 16	22
8	NL	AFC Fylde	A	1217	W 3 - 1	Weston 55 Fondop-Talum 66 81	22
15	NL	Wrexham	A	3479	W 1 - 0	Chambers 32 (og)	18
19	**FAC4Q**	**Wrexham**	**H**	**2199**	**D 1 - 1**	**Fondop-Talum 10**	
22	**FAC4Qr**	**Wrexham**	**A**	**2023**	**L 0 - 1**		
26	NL	Notts County	H	5432	W 1 - 0	Nepomuceno 27	18
Nov 2	NL	Ebbsfleet United	A	1025	D 2 - 2	Boden 12 Hollis 56	18
16	NL	Chorley	H	4090	L 2 - 3	Weston 68 Boden 82	18
23	NL	Harrogate Town	A	1710	L 1 - 3	Fondop-Talum 10	
26	NL	Hartlepool United	H	3420	L 1 - 5	Kioso 45+2 (og)	21
30	NL	Aldershot Town	A	1637	D 2 - 2	Boden 50 Denton 90+4	21
Dec 7	NL	Bromley	H	3270	L 1 - 2	Fondop-Talum 15	23
10	NL	Yeovil Town	H	3161	L 1 - 2	Weston 60	23
14	**FAT1**	**Notts County**	**H**	**931**	**L 0 - 1**		
21	NL	Torquay United	A	2288	W 3 - 0	McKay 1 Weston 54 Hollis 68	22
26	NL	Solihull Moors	H	3203	D 2 - 2	Fondop-Talum 1 McKay 17	22
28	NL	Halifax Town	A	2420	L 0 - 1		22
Jan 1	NL	Solihull Moors	A	1200	L 0 - 3		22
John Sheridan is sacked as manager. John Pemberton named as caretaker.							
4	NL	Sutton United	H	3283	W 1 - 0	Smith 50	22
18	NL	Eastleigh	A	2073	W 2 - 0	Denton 55 Smith 80	21
25	NL	AFC Fylde	H	3262	D 1 - 1	Smith 32	21
Feb 1	NL	Notts County	A	6347	L 0 - 3		21
8	NL	Wrexham	H	3728	W 3 - 2	Denton 24 Mandeville 72 Weston 90+4	
22	NL	Ebbsfleet United	H	3346	W 4 - 0	Tyson 60 77 83 Weston 90	21
Mar 3	NL	Harrogate Town	H	2912	L 3 - 4	Denton 26 Mandeville 29 Boden 82	21
7	NL	Chorley	A	1256	W 2 - 1	Denton 40 Cropper 64	20
14	NL	Dover Athletic	A	1214	D 1 - 1	Denton 80 (pen)	19

GOALSCORERS	SG	CSG	Pens	Hat tricks	Total		SG	CSG	Pens	Hat tricks	Total
Fondop-Talum*	9	2			11	Cropper	1	1			1
Boden	10	2	1		10	Nepomuceno	1	1			1
Denton	8	3	1		8	Rowley	1	1			1
Weston	6	2			6	Yarney	1	1			1
Mandeville	4	1			4						
Smith	4	3			4						
Tyson	1	1		1	3						
Hollis	2	1			2						
McKay	2	2			2						
Opponent	2	1			2						

No.	Jalal S	Buchanan D	Evans W	Yarney J	Weir R	Smith J	Weston C	Rowley J	Boden S	McKay J	Mandeville L	Wakefield C	Sharman J	Sheridan J	Coddington L (Gk)	Wedgbury S	Hollis H	Maguire L	Gerrard A	McGlashan J (L)	Fondop-Talum M	Denton T	Nepomuceno G	Spyrou A (L)	Shaw L (L)	Tootle M (L)	Wharton D (Gk)	Cropper J	Fitzsimons R (GK) (L)	Tyson N (L)	England K (Gk)	Hutchinson R
1	x	x	x	x	xs	x	x	x	x	x	x	sx	s	s	s	s																
2	x	xs	x	x	sx	xs	s	x	x	sx	x					sx	s	xs	x	x												
3	x	x	x	x	sx	x	sx	xs	x	s	x					s	s	xs	x	x												
4	x	x	x	x	xs	xs	sx	x	x	sx	x	s				sx	s	xs	x													
5	x	x	xs	sx	sx	x	s	xs								sx	s		x	x	x											
6	x	x	x	sx	xs	sx		sx	x	s	x					xs	s	x	xs	x	x											
7	x	x	x	x	sx	x		x	xs	sx	sx					s		s	xs	x	xs											
8	s		x	xs	xs	x		s	x	x		sx				s	x	x	x	x	sx											
9	s		x	sx		x	sx	x	xs	sx	x					s	x		xs	x	x	xs	x									
10	s		x	x		x	sx	xs	sx	x						s	x		x	x	x											
11	s		x			x	x	x	xs		xs					s	x		x	x		sx	sx	x								
12	s		x	xs	xs	x	x	sx	sx	x							x		x	x		s	x	sx	x							
13	x		x	x			x	x	sx				sx	xs		s	s	x	x		s	xs	x	x								
14	x		x	x			x	x	xs			x	sx			s	xs	x		s	sx	xs	x	x	sx							
15	x		x	x			x	xs	xs			x	s			s	xs	x			sx	sx	x	x	sx							
16	x		x	x			x	x	xs	s		sx				x	x	x			sx	sx	xs		xs							
17	x		x	x			x	x	sx			s				x	x	x		s	s	xs	x	x								
18	x		x	xs			sx	x	x	s		sx				x	s	xs	x		s	s	xs	x	x	sx						
19		s	s	xs			x			xs	x	s	x	sx		x	x		x		x	sx	s	sx	x	xs						
20	x		x				x	x	x	xs		s				x			x		s	s	sx	xs	x	sx						
21	xs	xs	x		x	x		x	xs	s		s				x	sx		x		sx	x		x	sx							
22	x	xs	x		xs	x	x	x	x			sx				x	s		x	sx		s	sx	xs								
23	x	x	x		s	sx	xs	s	sx			xs				x	s			x		x	x		x		x					
24	s	s	x				x		x	x		sx				x	x	xs		x		sx	sx	x		x						
25	s	xs	x				x	s	x			sx				x	x		x	x	x		sx	x		xs	xs					
26	s	s	x				x		xs			sx				x	x		x	xs	x	s	sx	x		sx	x					
27	s	sx	x				x		xs			sx				x	x		x	x	x	x	sx	xs		s	xs					
28	x	x	s		x	s	x	x				sx	xs	xs		s			x	s	x		sx	xs	xs		sx					
29	x	x	sx		xs			x	sx	s	xs	s				x			x	x	x		xs	sx	x							
30	x	x	x	x			sx	x	sx	s	xs	s				x			x	xs			x	s	x							
31	x	x	x	xs			sx	x			x	x	sx	s	s	x			x					xs	sx	xs						
32	x	x	x	xs	sx		s	x	x	x	xs	x	s			x			x					x	sx							
33	x	x	x		xs	x	x		xs	sx	xs		sx	s		x	x				x	sx						s				
34	x	x	x	sx	s	x	x		xs	sx	sx		xs				xs	x				x						x	s			
35	x	x	x	sx	x	x			xs		sx			s			xs	x				x				s	xs		sx			
36	x	x	x	sx	x	x			xs	sx	sx			s			xs	x				x					xs			s		
37	x	x	x		s	x	x			sx		sx					x				x	xs					x	s	xs		s	
38	x	x	x	sx	x	x			sx		xs						x				xs	xs					x	s	sx		s	
39	x	x	xs	x	x	x			sx		xs						x				sx	x					x	s	xs		sx	
40	xs	x	x	sx	x	x			sx		xs	s					x				s	xs					x	sx	x			
41	x	x	x	s	x	x			s		x		x				x				sx	x					xs	s	xs		sx	
x	29	20	38	21	2	22	30	17	12	2	13	0	1	16	10	4	32	11	11	3	15	9	15	0	2	1	0	5	0	1	0	0
xs	2	5	0	7	8	3	1	4	16	3	7	2	1	1	0	10	2	3	1	3	6	10	3	2	1	2	0	3	0	3	0	0
sx	0	1	1	3	9	6	3	5	7	10	14	3	1	3	1	0	0	1	0	9	10	9	0	5	2	0	0	0	1	2	0	2
s	9	3	2	0	5	2	2	3	5	4	4	5	5	9	15	1	2	1	3	8	2	1	0	0	1	0	2	0	5	0	1	2

GOALKEEPERS	CS	CCS
Jalal	6	2
Coddington	1	1

x - Played full 90 minutes
xs - Substituted off
sx - Substituted on
s - Non-playing Substitute

Barnet v Chesterfield 2-2

Ebbsfleet United's Gozie Ugwo equalising to make it one a piece against Chesterfield 2-2.

Bromley v Chesterfield 2-1

Solihull Moors v Chesterfield 3-0

Chesterfield v Woking 1-2

Chesterfield v Yeovil Town 1-2

Chesterfield v Chorley 2-3

CHORLEY MATCH RESULTS 2019-20

Date	Comp	Opponens	H/A	Att:	Result	Goalscorers	Pos
Aug 3	NL	Bromley	H	1469	D 0 - 0		14
6	NL	AFC Fylde	A	2443	D 0 - 0		17
10	NL	Sutton United	A	1436	D 2 - 2	Meppen-Walters 7 Holroyd 10	
13	NL	Solihull Moors	H	1020	L 1 - 6	Newby A 53	
17	NL	Maidenhead United	A	1172	L 1 - 4	Carver 26	23
24	NL	Hartlepool United	H	1395	D 0 - 0		
26	NL	Nots County	A	5082	L 1 - 5	Baines 9	
31	NL	Boreham Wood	H	1035	L 1 - 3	Holroyd 77 (pen)	24
Sep 3	NL	Harrogate Town	A	792	L 0 - 2		24
7	NL	Stockport County	H	2693	W 3 - 0	Holroyd 6 27 Newby E 90+4	22
14	NL	Dover Athletic	A	1011	D 1 - 1	Holroyd 67	23
21	NL	Woking	H	1336	D 1 - 1	Holroyd 8	22
24	NL	Barrow	H	1272	L 1 - 3	Challoner 24	24
28	NL	Dagenham & Redbridge	A	1212	D 0 - 0		24
Oct 5	NL	Aldershot Town	H	1425	D 0 - 0		23
8	NL	Halifax Town	A	2117	D 0 - 0		23
12	NL	Eastleigh	A	2053	D 0 - 0		23
19	FAC4Q	Spennymoor Town	H	859	W 2 - 0	Holroyd 45+1 (pen) Newby A 58	
26	NL	Yeovil Town	H	1279	L 1 - 2	Massanka 71	24
29	NL	Ebbsfleet United	H	921	L 0 - 4		24
Nov 2	NL	Barnet	A	1040	L 1 - 2	Carver 30	24
9	FAC1	Mansfield Town	A	2418	L 0 - 1		
16	NL	Chesterfield	A	4090	W 3 - 2	Vernam 16 74 (pen) Meppen-Walters 19	24
23	NL	Torquay United	H	1281	W 1 - 0	Carver 24	24
26	NL	Barrow	A	2324	D 2 - 2	Vernam 9 Carver 17	23
30	NL	Dagenham & Redbridge	H	1262	W 1 - 0	Newby A 63	22
Dec 7	NL	Stockport County	A	4510	L 2 - 4	Newby A 7 Massanka 90+1	24
14	FAT1	Matlock Town	A	400	D 2 - 2	O'Keefe 69 Holroyd 85	
21	NL	Dover Athletic	H	1054	D 1 - 1	Newby A 72	23
26	NL	Wrexham	A	4784	L 1 - 3	Massanka 87	24
28	NL	Harrogate Town	H	1077	L 0 - 2		24
Jan 1	NL	Wrexham	H	1684	L 0 - 2		24
4	NL	Woking	A	1748	L 0 - 1		24
18	NL	Aldershot Town	A	1931	D 3 - 3	Newby A 9 90+2 (pen) Cardwell 25	24
25	NL	Halifax Town	H	1263	L 0 - 1		24
Feb 1	NL	Yeovil Town	A	2729	D 1 - 1	Hall 45+2	24
15	NL	Ebbsfleet United	A	712	L 0 - 1		24
22	NL	Barnet	H	925	L 0 - 1		24
29	NL	Torquay United	A	2126	L 0 - 2		24
Mar 3	NL	Eastleigh	H	495	L 1 - 2	Hall 2	24
7	NL	Chesterfield	H	1256	L 1 - 2	Hall 76	24

GOALSCORERS	SG	CSG	Pens	Hat tricks	Total		SG	CSG	Pens	Hat tricks	Total
Holroyd	7	3	2		8	Newby E	1	1			1
Newby A	6	2	1		7	O'Keefe	1	1			1
Carver	4	2			4						
Hall	3	2			3						
Massanka	3	1			3						
Vernam	2	2	1		3						
Meppen-Walters	2	1			2						
Baines	1	1			1						
Cardwell*	1	1			1						
Challoner	1	1			1						

Anyon J	Leather S	Blakeman A	Challoner M	Teague A	Baines L	O'Keefe J	Newby A	Holroyd C	Carver M	Newby E	Massanka N	Meppen-Walters C	Cottrell J	Dodds L	Ross M	Hooper J	Crellin B (Gk) (L)	Eccles D (Gk)	Brickell T	Nortey N	Urwin M (Gk)	Almond L	Smith M (L)	Vernam C (L)	Duxberry S (L)	Kay A	Cardwell H (L)	Adams K (L)	Hall C (L)	Kiwomya A (L)	No.
x	x	x	x	x	x	x	x	xs	x	x	sx	s	s	s	s																1
x		x	x	x	x	x	x	xs	x	xs	sx	xs	s	sx	sx	s															2
x		x	x	x	x	x	xs	x	x	xs	sx	x	s	sx	sx	s	s														3
x		x	x	x	xs	x	x	sx	x	s	xs	x	xs	sx	sx	s															4
	xs	xs	x	x	sx	x	x	sx	x	x	sx	x	xs			s		x	s												5
	x	x	x	x	sx	xs	sx	x	x	x	x	sx	xs	x			s		x	s											6
	x	x	sx	x	x	x	xs	x	x	x	sx		x		x		x	s	s												7
	x	x	x	x	x		x	sx	x	xs	xs	s	x	sx	s		x	s													8
	x	xs	x	s	x	x	xs	xs	sx	sx	x	x	x	sx	s		x														9
	x	s	x	xs	x	x	xs	xs	x	sx	s	x	sx	sx			x														10
	x	sx	x	x	xs	x	x	xs	x	sx	xs	x	x	s	s		x														11
	xs	sx	x	x	x	xs	x	xs	x	sx	s	x	sx	s			x														12
	xs	sx	x	x	xs	xs	x	x	x	sx	s	x			s		x				sx										13
	x	x	xs	x	s	s	s	sx	x	xs	x	x	xs	sx						x	x										14
	xs	x	xs	x	s	x	xs	x	xs	x	x	x	s	sx						x	x										15
	x	x		x	sx	sx	sx	s	x	x	x	sx	x							s	x										16
	x	x		x	sx	xs	xs	s	x	x	xs	x								s	x										17
	x	x		x	sx	x	sx	x	sx	x	sx	xs	x							s	s	x	x	s							18
	xs	x		x	s	x	x		sx	x	x	x	s	x						s	xs	x	sx								19
	x	xs	xs	sx	sx	s	xs		x	x	x	x	x							x	x	x									20
	x		x	sx	sx		xs	xs	x	x	xs	s								s	x	sx	x								21
	x	x		x	s	sx		sx	x	xs	x	x	s	xs						s	x	x	sx	x	xs						22
	xs	x		x	sx	xs		x	s	s	x	sx	x							x	x		x	xs							23
	x	x		x	sx	xs	s	x	s	x	sx	x								x	x		x	xs							24
	x	x		x	sx	xs	s	x	s	x	sx	x								x	x	xs	x								25
	x		x	x	sx	xs	sx	x	s	s	x	sx	x							xs	x		x	xs							26
	xs	x	xs	sx	s	x	xs	x	sx	sx	x	s		x						x	x		x								27
	xs	s	s	x	x		sx	x	sx	xs	x	x	x	sx	x				x		xs		x								28
	x	x	s	x	sx	x	xs	xs		sx	x		sx	x					s		xs	x		x							29
	x	x	s	xs	xs	x	x	xs	sx	sx	x		s	x						sx	x		x								30
	xs	x	x	x	s	x	xs	x	sx	sx	x		sx	s						xs	x		x								31
	x	x	xs	s	s	x	sx	x	x	sx	x	xs		x						s	x		x								32
	xs	x		xs	sx	x	sx	x	x		x	xs	s	x						s	sx	x		x							33
	s	x	xs		x	sx	x	sx		x	x	s			x	x					x	x					x	x	xs	sxs		34
	s	x	x		sx	x	sx		x	xs	s	s		x	x					x	x			x	x			xs			35
	s	x		sx	xs	x	s		s	x	x		x	x						s	x		x		x	x		x			36
	s	x		s	xs	x		x	sx		x	xs		x						sx	x		xs		x	xs			sx		37
	s	x		s	x	xs		sx	x		x	sx		x						sx	x		xs		x			x	xs		38
	xs	s		x	sx	xs		x			x	s		sx	x					x	x		x		x			x	xs		39
	sx			x	s	x			x		s	sx	x				s			x	x		x		x			xs	xs		40
s	sx			x		xs			x		xs	s	sx	x						x	x		x		x	s		x	x		41
4	7	18	35	13	26	11	19	5	21	12	5	34	19	1	23	0	9	1	0	17	27	0	17	1	8	3	0	4	1		x
0	3	11	0	8	5	6	12	12	6	5	7	4	6	3	1	0	0	0	0	5	0	0	2	4	0	1	1	0	2	3	xs
0	0	5	1	0	5	13	8	12	7	12	15	0	7	15	5	0	0	0	0	5	0	4	0	0	0	0	0	0	0	1	sx
0	1	6	2	4	3	8	1	4	0	11	5	2	6	10	11	3	0	13	2	0	1	0	0	0	1	0	0	0	0		s

GOALKEEPERS	CS	CCS
Urwin*	7	5
Anyon	2	2
Crellin	2	1

x - Played full 90 minutes
xs - Substituted off
sx - Substituted on
s - Non-playing Substitute

DAGENHAM & REDBRIDGE MATCH RESULTS 2019-20

Date	Comp	Opponents	H/A	Att:	Result	Goalscorers	Pos
Aug 3	NL	Woking	H	1549	L 0 - 2		23
6	NL	Dover Athletic	A	1520	W 2 - 1	Balanta 26 Brundle 54 (pen)	15
10	NL	Halifax Town	A	1895	L 0 - 1		
13	NL	Boreham Wood	H	1179	L 0 - 3		
17	NL	Harrogate Town	H	1043	W 4 - 2	Kandi 14 Brundle 29 Balanta 60 85	15
24	NL	Eastleigh	A	1631	D 1 - 1	Luque 16	
26	NL	Yeovil Town	H	1453	W 3 - 2	Quigley 64 90+5 Onariase 81	
31	NL	Chesterfield	A	3708	D 1 - 1	Luque 36	11
Sep 4	NL	Bromley	H	1526	D 1 - 1	Balanta 2	12
7	NL	Maidenhead United	A	1551	W 1 - 0	Dobson 48 (pen)	10
14	NL	Hartlepool United	H	1392	W 3 - 1	Quigley 24 82 Balanta 69	5
21	NL	Torquay United	A	2524	D 0 - 0		7
24	NL	Sutton United	A	1513	W 2 - 0	Grant 43 Dobson 45+1	6
28	NL	Chorley	H	1212	D 0 - 0		5
Oct 5	NL	Barnet	H	1556	D 1 - 1	Balanta 40	7
8	NL	Notts County	A	3670	L 0 - 2		10
19	FAC4Q	Carshalton Athletic	A	726	L 1 - 2	Grant 65	
26	NL	Wrexham	H	1254	W 2 - 1	Balanta 45+2 Kandi 57	10
29	NL	Barrow	H	1122	L 0 - 2		10
Nov 2	NL	Solihull Moors	A	1214	L 1 - 2	Grant 20	14
9	NL	Stockport County	A	3771	L 0 - 1		
16	NL	Aldershot Town	H	1616	W 6 - 1	House 6 15 Onariase 17 Luque 25 Wright W 69 Quigley 76	12
23	NL	AFC Fylde	A	1268	L 0 - 3		
26	NL	Sutton United	H	1070	L 1 - 2	Brundle 52	16
30	NL	Chorley	A	1262	L 0 - 1		16
Dec 7	NL	Maidenhead United	H	1083	L 1 - 2	McQueen 64	17
14	FAT1	Sutton United	A	429	D 1 - 1	Quigley 56	
17	FAT1r	Sutton United	H	417	W 3 - 2	Luque 52 107 Brundle 109 (aet)	
21	NL	Hartlepool United	A	3259	L 0 - 1		18
26	NL	Ebbsfleet United	H	1402	D 1 - 1	Kandi 85	17
28	NL	Bromley	A	2312	L 0 - 3		18
Peter Taylor is sacked as manager. Terry Harris & Jody Brown take temporary charge.							
Jan 1	NL	Ebbsfleet United	A	1015	D 1 - 1	Wright W 85	20
4	NL	Torquay United	H	1542	D 0 - 0		19
Former Ebbsfleet manager, Daryl McMahon, is named as the club's new manager.							
11	FAT2	Notts County	A	2385	L 1 - 2	Brundle 76	
25	NL	Notts County	H	1697	W 2 - 0	Reid 61 79	20
Feb 1	NL	Wrexham	A	4024	D 0 - 0		20
8	NL	Stockport County	H	1512	D 1 - 1	Kandi 90+3	
22	NL	Solihull Moors	H	2345	W 2 - 0	Brundle 10 Balanta 43	19
29	NL	Barrow	A	2353	L 1 - 2	Reid 10	19
Mar 7	NL	Aldershot Town	A	2103	W 1 - 0	Brundle 86	18
10	NL	AFC Fylde	H	1064	L 1 - 2	Brundle 80	18

GOALSCORERS	SG	CSG	Pens	Hat tricks	Total		SG	CSG	Pens	Hat tricks	Total
Balanta	7	1			8	McQueen	1	1			1
Brundle	8	2	1		8	Onariase	1	1			1
Quigley	4	1			6						
Luque	4	1			5						
Kandi	4	1			4						
Reid*	2	1			3						
Dobson	2	1	1		2						
Grant	2	1			2						
House*	1	1			2						
Wright W	2	1			2						

Justham E	Clark K	Brundle M	McQueen A	Onariase E	Croll L	Eleftheriou A	Odametey H	Balanta A	Graham B	Quigley J	Dobson J	Luque J	Grant R	Robinson M	Wright W	Phipps H	Wood W	Kandi C	Gordon L	Strizovic J	Stevenson T (L)	Deering S	House B (L)	Seaden H (Gk)	Wright D (L)	Zakuani G	Reid A (L)	Weston M	Johnson G (Gk)	No.
x	x	x	xs	x	x	x	xs	x	xs	x	sx	sx	sx	s	s															1
x	x	x	s		x	x		xs	x	x	xs	xs	sx	x	sx	sx	s													2
x	x	x	sx		x	xs		x	x	x	xs	xs	sx	x	sx	s	s													3
x	x	x	s		x	x		x	x	xs	xs	sx	x	sx	s		sx													4
x	x	x	x		x			x		sx	s	sx	sx	s	x	x	xs	x	sx											5
x	x	x	x	s	x			xs	sx	sx	s	x	sx	x	x	x		xs												6
x	x	x	x	x	xs			xs	x	xs	x	sx	x	sx	x		s		s											7
x	x	x		x	x	s		xs		xs	sx	x	sx	x	sx	x	s		xs											8
x	x	x			x	x	s		x	sx	x	xs	x	x	x	x	s			s										9
x	x			x	x			x	s	xs	x	x	x	x	x	s					s									10
x	x	sx	x	x	s			xs	xs	x	xs	xs	sx	x	x				s											11
x	x		s	x	x		sx		x	sx	xs	x	xs	sx	x	x	xs			s										12
x	x		x	x			sx	xs	xs	sx	x	sx	xs	sx	x				s	s										13
x	xs		x	x	x		sx	x	s	x	x	xs	xs	sx	x			sx	s											14
x			x	x		sx	x	x	xs	x	xs	s	x	x	x		s		x	x										15
x		xs	x	s	x	s	x	xs	xs	sx	sx	sx	x	x	x				s	x										16
x		**x**	**xs**	**xs**	**x**	**s**		**x**	**s**	**x**	**xs**	**sx**	**sx**	**x**	**x**			**s**	**sx**	**x**	**s**									17
x		sx	x	x	s		xs	sx	sx	x	x	x	s	x	x			xs	xs											18
x		s	x	x	s			x	sx	x	sx	x	x	s	x			xs	x	s										19
x	x	x	xs	x		s		x	sx	sx	x	x	xs		s	xs			s	x										20
x	x	x	x		x			sx	x	sx	xs	xs	x	s		sx			s	xs										21
x	x		xs		x			s	sx	s	x	sx	x	sx				x		xs	xs									22
x	x	xs	s		x			sx	x	sx	xs	x	x	x		sx	xs		x		s									23
x	x	x	x			xs			x	sx	x	sx	x		s	sx			x		s									24
x	x	x	ys		x				xs	sx	x	x	x		s	x			x		s									25
x	x	xs		x					xs	sx	x	x	x		s	x			x		s	s								26
	x	**x**	**s**	**x**	**s**	**x**			**sx**	**x**	**x**	**s**	**sx**		**x**			**s**	**xs**		**x**			**xs**	**x**	**s**				27
s	**x**	**x**	**x**	**sx**	**x**				**sx**	**xs**	**sx**	**x**	**sx**			**s**	**xs**		**xs**		**xs**	**x**	**x**							28
x	x	x	x	x	xs	xs			sx	x		xs	sx		s			x			s	sx								29
x	x	x	sx	x	x				sx	xs		xs	s	x	x			x			s		x	s						30
x	x		x	x	x	xs			sx	sx			x	x	x			s	x		xs			s	s					31
x	xs		x	x	x	s			sx			x	xs	sx	x	x			x			xs			x	s	sx			32
x	x		xs	x	x				s	xs			x	sx	x	x			x	x	s		sx							33
x	**x**	**x**	**sx**	**x**	**x**	**s**			**sx**	**x**		**s**	**sx**	**x**	**x**			**s**	**xs**	**xs**	**s**		**xs**							34
x	x	x	sx	sx	x	x			sx			s	x			x	xs	s	xs					xs	x					35
x	x	x		x	x	x			s			s	x	s		sx	x	s	x	xs			x							36
x	x	x		x	x	x	sx			x		s		sx	xs	s	x	x			xs	sxs								37
x	x	x		x	x	x	xs			x		s	sx	sx	x		x	xs					s			s				38
x	x	x		x	xs	x			xs			s	sx	x	s	x	x				xs	sx								39
x	x	x		x	xs	x			xs	s		sx	x	s	x	x					x	sx			xs	sxs	s			40
x	x	x		x	s	x			xs	sx		sx	x		x	xs					sx	xs	s							41
39	34	30	13	28	31	12	2	15	5	15	5	11	3	31	24	5	0	11	9	0	8	6	4	2	1	0	2	0	0	x
0	2	1	7	2	1	7	1	7	5	10	9	13	3	3	0	1	3	7	5	0	4	3	6	0	0	1	3	1	0	xs
0	0	0	6	2	1	1	3	1	14	9	11	6	24	1	6	3	1	9	2	0	0	1	1	0	2	0	1	1	0	sx
1	0	0	6	1	1	12	0	0	6	0	3	3	6	3	6	5	16	0	5	12	1	0	0	8	3	0	1	0	3	s

GOALKEEPERS	CS	CCS
Justham	9	3

x - Played full 90 minutes
xs - Substituted off
sx - Substituted on
s - Non-playing Substitute

DOVER ATHLETIC MATCH RESULTS 2019-20

Date	Comp	Opponents	H/A	Att:	Result	Goalscorers	Pos
Aug 3	NL	Chesterfield	A	4332	W 2 - 1	Pavey 77 85	4
6	NL	Dagenham & Redbridge	H	1520	L 1 - 2	Pavey 37	11
10	NL	Wrexham	H	1187	W 2 - 1	Modeste 72 Pearson 90+1 (og)	
13	NL	Barnet	A	1143	W 1 - 0	Effiong 90+3	
17	NL	Torquay United	H	1217	L 1 - 2	Effiong 88 (pen)	7
24	NL	Sutton United	A	1552	W 2 - 1	Modeste 10 Effiong 50	
26	NL	Woking	H	1358	L 1 - 2	Modeste 30	
31	NL	Harrogate Town	A	900	W 2 - 0	Effiong 68 89	5
Sep 3	NL	Ebbsfleet United	H	1247	D 1 - 1	De Havilland 53	6
7	NL	Boreham Wood	A	493	L 1 - 3	Effiong 22	7
14	NL	Chorley	H	1011	D 1 - 1	Modeste 19	7
21	NL	Hartlepool United	A	3329	W 2 - 0	Effiong 36 (pen) Rigg 84	5
24	NL	Maidenhead United	A	1015	W 2 - 1	Cumberbatch 19 L'Ghoul 76	5
28	NL	Halifax Town	H	1020	L 0 - 2		6
Oct 5	NL	Notts County	H	1463	D 2 - 2	Taylor 35 Lokko 57	8
8	NL	Aldershot Town	A	1255	L 0 - 4		11
19	**FAC4Q**	**Weymouth**	**A**	**1506**	**W 2 - 1**	**Reason 82 Jeffrey 87**	
26	NL	Stockport County	H	1154	L 0 - 1		16
29	NL	Eastleigh	H	726	W 3 - 1	Gobern 18 Effiong 29 72 (pen)	11
Nov 2	NL	AFC Fylde	A	1185	D 0 - 0		12
10	**FAC1**	**Southend United**	**H**	**1754**	**W 1 - 0**	**Sotiriou 84**	
16	NL	Yeovil Town	A	2986	W 1 - 0	Doe 62	10
23	NL	Solihull Moors	H	1027	D 1 - 1	Effiong 5	9
26	NL	Maidenhead United	H	687	L 3 - 4	Sotiriou 4 14 Rooney 67	12
Dec 1	**FAC2**	**Peterborough United**	**A**	**4239**	**L 0 - 3**		
7	NL	Boreham Wood	H	728	L 0 - 2		15
14	**FAT1**	**King's Lynn Town**	**A**	**776**	**D 2 - 2**	**Reason 73 Lokko 79 (Lost 2-4 on pens aet)**	
21	NL	Chorley	A	1054	D 1 - 1	Lokko 90	15
26	NL	Bromley	H	1210	W 3 - 0	Modeste 25 De Havilland 29 Effiong 75	12
28	NL	Ebbsfleet United	A	1222	W 1 - 0	Woods 15	11
Jan 1	NL	Bromley	A	2011	L 0 - 3		13
11	NL	Hartlepool United	H	1023	D 1 - 1	L'Ghoul 90+1	13
18	NL	Notts County	A	5157	D 0 - 0		12
25	NL	Aldershot Town	H	1113	W 2 - 0	Lokko 15 Ogie 52	12
28	NL	Halifax Town	A	1726	L 2 - 4	Binnom-Williams 21 (og) Woods 49	12
Feb 1	NL	Stockport County	A	4506	W 2 - 0	Effiong 49 80	9
4	NL	Barrow	H	972	W 2 - 1	De Havilland 18 Woods 88	8
18	NL	Barrow	A	2016	L 0 - 1		8
22	NL	AFC Fylde	H	1027	W 5 - 1	Poleon 36 Effiong 45 (pen) 74 77 Taylor 88	6
29	NL	Solihull Moors	A	773	L 0 - 3		8
Mar 7	NL	Yeovil Town	H	1180	L 0 - 1		11
14	NL	Chesterfield	H	1214	D 1 - 1	L'Ghoul 89	12

GOALSCORERS	SG	CSG	Pens	Hat tricks	Total		SG	CSG	Pens	Hat tricks	Total
Effiong	11	3	4	1	16	Cumberbatch	1	1			1
Modeste	5	2			5	Doe	1	1			1
Lokko	4	2			4	Gobern	1	1			1
De Havilland	3	1			3	Ogie	1	1			1
L'Ghoul	3	1			3	Poleon	1	1			1
Pavey	2	2			3	Reason	1	1			1
Sotiriou	2	1			3	Rigg	1	1			1
Woods	3	1			3	Rooney	1	1			1
Opponent	2	1			2						
Taylor	2	1			2						

Worgan L	Doe S	Passley J	Lokko K	Woods M	Gobern O	Munns J	Taylor B	Modeste R	Effiong I	Rigg S	Pavey A	Reason J	L'Ghoul N	De Havilland W	Mersin Y (Gk)	Simpson A	Cumberbatch K	Hinchiri B	Wratten M	Rooney P	Jeffrey A	Ratti R	Bedford J	Sotiriou R (L)	Yussuff A	Ogie S (L)	Maynard-Brewer A (GK)(L)	Poleon D (L)	No.
x	x	x	x	x	x	xs	x	xs	xs	x	sx	sx	sx	s	s														1
x	x	x	x	x	x	xs	x	sx	xs	sx	x	xs	sx	s	s														2
x		x	x	x	xs	xs		sx	x	x	x	x	s	sx	x	s	x	sx											3
x		x	x	x		x	xs	sx	x	xs	s	sx	x	s	s	x	x												4
x		x		x	x	xs	sx	x	s	x	xs	sx	x	s	x	sx	xs												5
x		x	x	x	sx	s		x	x	xs	sx	xs	sx	x	s	x	xs												6
x		x	x	x	x	x		xs	sx	sx	xs	sx	xs	x	s	x	s												7
x	s	x	x	x	x	x			x	x		x	x	x	x		s	s	s										8
x	s	x	xs					x	x	sx	x	xs	x		s		s												9
x	sx	x	x		xs	xs		x		x	x	x	sx	x		xs	s	s	sx										10
x	x	x		x	x	xs		x	xs	sx	sx	x	sx	x	xs		s												11
x	x	x	s	x		s		x	x	xs		x	s	x	x	x	x		sx										12
x	x		s	x		x	xs	x	x		xs	sx	x	s	x	x		x	sx	s									13
x	x		x		s	x	xs	x	x		x	sx	x	s	x	xs			sx	sx									14
x	x	x	x			x	x	sx	x	xs		x	xs	xs	s	s	sx			sx									15
x	x	x	x		x	x		sx	x	x		xs	sx	s	s	xs	xs	sx			xs								16
s	s	x	x			sx	x	xs	x			x	xs	x	x	s	s		xs	sx	sx	x							17
s		x	xs			xs	x	xs	x	sx		x		x	x	s	x		x	sx	sx								18
	x	xs		x	xs	x	sx		x	xs		x	s		x	x	sx		x	sx	s								19
s	x	x		x	x	xs			x	x		x			x	x	s		s	x	sx	s	s						20
s	x			x	xs	xs	x		x	xs		x	sx		x	x	sx		x	s	s	s	s	sx					21
s	x			x	x	xs	x		x	x		xs			x	x	x		s	x	sx	sx	s						22
	x			x	x	xs	xs	x	sx	x	x		xs	sx	x	x	x		x	s			sx						23
	x			x	xs	xs	x		sx	xs		x	sx	x	x	x		x	sx	s		x							24
x	x			s	x		x	x	xs		x		xs	sx	x		s		xs	s	x	sx	sx	s					25
x	x	x	x		x		x	x	x		xs	xs	s			xs		x	sx	sx									26
s		x	x	sx		sx			x			sx	xs	x	x	x		sx	xs	s	x	xs	xs						27
x		x	x	x		s	sx	xs	x	s		xs	xs	x		x			x	xs			sx						28
x		x	x	x	xs	xs	x	x	sx				xs	x		s			sx	sx		s							29
	x	x	x	sx	xs	x	x		x			xs	xs	x	x	s			sx			sx							30
	x	x	x	sx	xs	x	x	x				xs	xs	x	x	s			sx			sx							31
x	x	x	x	x	xs	x	xs	x	sx			s	sx	x		s			xs			sx							32
x	x	x	x	x	s	xs	xs	xs	x			sx	s	x					sx			sx	x						33
	x	x	x	x	sx	xs		xs	x			xs	sx	x	x	s			s			sx	x						34
	x	x	x	s	x	sx		x	xs			x	x	x	s	s			sx			sx	x						35
	x	x	x	xs	xs	sx		x	x			xs			x	sx			s			s		x	sx				36
	x	x	x		x	x	sx	x	x			xs			x	s			s			s	s	x	sx				37
	xs	x		x	x	sx	x	xs				xs	s		x	s			sx				x	x	sx				38
	x			x	sx	xs	x	sx				s	xs	x		x	s		x			sx	x	x	xs				39
x			x		x	xs	x	x	s			s	x	x		x	s	s	x			sx	x						40
x		x	x		x	x	xs	x	s			sx	xs	x		sx			s			sx			xs				41
x		x	xs		x	x	s	xs				s	sx	x				xs				sx	x		x				42
25	16	30	26	34	16	14	22	7	30	15	4	15	2	31	13	19	5	1	0	12	1	0	1	1	0	7	4	1	x
0	0	1	3	1	7	15	5	15	6	10	2	14	11	1	0	2	6	3	0	1	3	1	1	0	0	0	0	2	xs
0	1	0	0	1	2	4	4	8	2	8	4	5	20	0	0	1	7	2	0	8	13	5	0	2	11	0	0	3	sx
6	3	0	3	0	6	2	0	5	0	6	4	6	17	10	9	5	2	8	2	4	3	1	3	1	3	1	0	0	s

GOALKEEPERS	CS	CCS
Mersin	5	3
Worgan	5	1
Maynard-Brewer*	1	1

x - Played full 90 minutes
xs - Substituted off
sx - Substituted on
s - Non-playing Substitute

EASTLEIGH MATCH RESULTS 2019-20

Date	Comp	Opponents	H/A	Att	Result	Goalscorers	Pos
Aug 3	NL	Newport County	H	2668	W 1 - 0	Johnson 13	9
6	NL	Yeovil Town	A	2813	L 0 - 1		13
10	NL	Barrow	A	1060	L 0 - 2		
13	NL	Sutton United	H	1750	D 1 - 1	Atkinson 13	
17	NL	Stockport County	A	3869	L 0 - 2		21
24	NL	Dagenham & Redbridge	H	1631	D 1 - 1	Barnett 48	
26	NL	Solihull Moors	A	1779	W 2 - 1	Hollands 18 49	
31	NL	Barnet	H	1922	L 1 - 2	McKnight 69	20
Sep 3	NL	Boreham Wood	H	1641	W 2 - 0	Williamson 7 Hollands 54	14
7	NL	Ebbsfleet United	A	865	D 1 - 1	Barnett 63	13
14	NL	Bromley	H	1752	D 1 - 1	Miley 85	15
21	NL	AFC Fylde	A	1134	L 1 - 3	Hollands 47	20
24	NL	Torquay United	A	2005	W 3 - 2	Hollands 51 Barnes 78 Bearwish 90+2	16
28	NL	Hartlepool United	H	1838	D 1 - 1	Hollands 72	15
Oct 5	NL	Chesterfield	A	3632	W 2 - 1	Barnett 45 Barnes 55	14
8	NL	Maidenhead United	H	1548	W 2 - 1	Hollands 26 Barnett 64	13
12	NL	Chorley	H	2053	D 0 - 0		13
19	**FAC4Q**	**Welling United**	**A**	**511**	**D 0 - 0**		
22	**FAC4Qr**	**Welling United**	**H**	**803**	**W 4 - 2**	**Rendell 11 51 (pens) Williamson 29 Bearwish 55**	
26	NL	Woking	A	1910	D 1 - 1	Rendell 90+6	13
29	NL	Dover Athletic	A	726	L 1 - 3	Barnett 61	16
Nov 2	NL	Harrogate Town	H	1592	W 4 - 2	Rendell 36 (pen) 41 70 Bearwish 57	11
9	**FAC1**	**Stourbridge**	**A**	**1846**	**D 2 - 2**	**Barnett 35 Rendell 86**	
19	**FAC1r**	**Stourbridge**	**H**	**1509**	**W 3 - 0**	**Rendell 50 (pen) Smart 69 Johnson 78**	
23	NL	Halifax Town	A	1817	D 1 - 1	Johnson 55	
26	NL	Torquay United	H	1888	W 3 - 2	Rendell 25 (pen) Hollands 29 Partington 35	11
30	**FAC2**	**Crewe Alexandra**	**H**	**1806**	**L 0 - 2**	**Barnes 86**	
Dec 3	NL	Wrexham	H	1542	L 0 - 2		14
7	NL	Ebbsfleet United	H	1715	D 1 - 1	Rendell 39	13
10	**FAC2r**	**Crewe Alexandra**	**A**	**2184**	**L 1 - 3**	**Barnes 90**	
14	**FAT1**	**Yate Town**	**H**	**353**	**W 6 - 1**	**Bearwish 20 McKnight 22 Barnes 44 Rendell 52 Smart 63 Seaman 78**	
21	NL	Bromley	A	1651	W 3 - 2	Winfield 32 (og) Barnett 45+3 Boyce 51	12
28	NL	Boreham Wood	A	601	D 2 - 2	Hollands 45+1 Barnett 90+1	13
Jan 1	NL	Aldershot Town	A	1953	L 1 - 3	Barnett 67	14
7	NL	Hartlepool United	A	2478	L 1 - 2	Smart 52	16
11	**FAT2**	**Matlock Town**	**H**	**718**	**W 2 - 1**	**Miley 45+1 Beale 47**	
18	NL	Chesterfield	H	2073	L 0 - 2		17
25	NL	Maidenhead United	A	1176	L 0 - 2		19
28	NL	Aldershot Town	H	2130	D 0 - 0		
Feb 1	NL	Woking	H	1885	W 2 - 0	Payne 10 Barnett 19	16
8	**FAT3**	**Harrogate Town**	**A**	**947**	**L 0 - 2**		
11	NL	AFC Fylde	H	1509	D 2 - 2	Hollands 52 Alabi 76 (pen)	
22	NL	Harrogate Town	A	1249	L 0 - 3		18
Mar 3	NL	Chorley	A	495	W 2 - 1	Barnett 60 90+5	17
7	NL	Wrexham	A	3436	D 0 - 0		16
14	NL	Notts County	A	4942	L 0 - 4		17

GOALSCORERS	SG	CSG	Pens	Hat tricks	Total		SG	CSG	Pens	Hat tricks	Total
Barnett	11	3			12	Alabi	1	1	1		1
Rendell	8	4	5	1	11	Atkinson	1	1			1
Hollands	9	3			10	Beale	1	1			1
Barnes	5	2			5	Boyce	1	1			1
Bearwish	4	1			4	Opponents	1	1			1
Johnson	3	1			3	Partington	1	1			1
Smart	3	1			3	Payne	1	1			1
McKnight	2	1			2	Seaman	1	1			1
Miley	2	1			2						
Williamson	2	1			2						

Player appearance grid:

	Stryjek M	Johnson R	Boyce A	Green M	Wynter A	Hollands D	Partington J	Payne J	Williamson B	Miley C	Barnett T	Rendell S	McKnight J	Atkinson R	Smart S	Bearwish T	Flintney R (Gk)	Baughan C	Scorey B	Seaman C (L)	Barnes M (L)	Beale L	Waterfield L	Garraway J	Feltham H	Philpott C (Gk)	Robinson W	Godwin-Malife U (L)	Alabi J (L)	Scrimshaw J	Baldwin A (L)	Grubb D (L)	No.
	x	x	x	x	x	x	x	x	xs	x	xs	sx	sx	s	s	s																	1
	x	x	xs	x	x	xs	x	x	x	x	xs	sx	sx	s	sx	s																	2
	x	xs	x	x	x	xs	x	xs	x	x		x	sx	sx	sx	s	s																3
	x		x	x	x	x	x	x	xs	sx	xs	xs	xs	s	sx	sx																	4
	x	x	x	x	x	x	x	xs	xs	x	sx	sx	xs	s	sx	sx		s															5
	x	x	x	x	x	x	xs	xs	x	sx	sx	x	xs	s	s	sx																	6
	x	x	x	s	x	x	x	xs	x	xs	sx	x	x	sx	s	s																	7
	x	x	x		x	x	x	x	x	xs	xs	sx	x		x	sx	s		s	s													8
	x	x	x		x	x	x	x	xs		xs	sx	x			s	s	s		x	sx												9
	x	x	x		x	x	x	x	sx	x	sx	xs			s	s			s	xs	sx												10
	x		x		x	x	x	x	sx	xs	sx	x	x			s	s			xs	sx												11
	x		x		x	x	x	x	x	x	xs	xs			sx	x	x	sx	s		sx	xs											12
	x		x		x	x	x	x	xs	xs					sx	x	x	sx	s		s	sx	xs										13
	x				x	x	x	xs	x	sx	sx				x	x	sx	s		s	xs	xs											14
	x		x		x	x	x	sx	x	xs	sx				x	xs	s				sx	xs											15
	x		x		x	x	x	sx	x	xs	sx				x	x	s			s	xs												16
	x		x		x	x	x	sx	xs	x	x				x	x	s	s		sx	xs												17
	x		x	xs		x		x	sx	x	x	x			x	xs	sx	s		s	sx	xs	s	s									18
	x		x			xs	xs	x	x	s	x		x		x	s			sx	x		sx	sx										19
	x		x			x	x	xs	x	x	x	x		x	sx	xs		sx	xs		sx	s											20
	x		x			x	xs	x	sx	x	x	x	xs		x	sx	s		sx	s	x												21
	x		x			x		x	sx	x	xs	x			x	x	s		sx	x		s	s										22
	x	s	x			x	sx	x	sx	x	x				x	x	xs	s		sx	xs	sx	s										23
	x	xs	x			x	s	x	xs	x		xs			x	x	sx	s		sx	x	sx	sx	s									24
	x	x	x			x	x	x		x	sx				x	xs	s	s		sx	x												25
	x	xs				x	x	x		x	sx				x	x	s	s		sx	x												26
	x		x	sx		x		x			xs	x	x		x	xs	s	s		sx	x	sx	s										27
	x		x	sx		x		x			xs	x	x		x	x	s	s		sx	x												28
	x		x	xs		x		x			xs	xs	x		x	sx	sx	s		sx	s	sx											29
	x	x	x	xs		x		x			x	xs	xs	s	x	sx	sx	s		sx	x	sx	s										30
		xs		s			x				x	s	xs	xs	s	x	x	x		x	x	x		sx	sx	sx	s						31
	x	xs	x			x	x	x			x	xs	x	s	x	sx	sx	s		s	x												32
	x		x		s	x	x	x			xs	x	x	xs	x		sx	s		s	x	sx											33
	x		xs		sx	x	x	x			x	x	x	sx	x	xs	sx			s	x												34
	x				x	x	x	x			x	x	x		x	x	s					s	s										35
	s				x	sx	x	x			x	sx	xs	x		x	x	x		x			xs	s	s	s		s					36
	x		x	xs	x	x	x				xs	xs	sx	s		sx	s													x	x	sx	37
	x		x		x	xs	x	x			x	xs	sx		x	sx	s	s												xs	x	sx	38
	x		x		x	x	x	x			x	sx	xs		x	sx	sx	s												s	xs	xs	39
	x		x	sx		x	x	x			x	xs	xs		xs	s	s													x	sx	xs	40
	s		x	sx	xs	s	x	xs			x	s	x	sx		x	xs	x												x	x	x	41
	x		x	x		x	x	x			x	x	s			x	sx	sx	s											xs	sx	xs	42
	x		x	xs		x	x	xs			x	x	s			x	sx	sx	s											xs	sx	x	43
	x		x	x		x	x	x			x	x	sx			xs	s	s												sx	sx	xs	xs	44
	x		x	x		x	x	x			x	xs	sx			xs	sx	s	s											s	sx	x	xs	45
	x		x	x		xs	x	x			x	x	sx			xs	sx	s												s	sx	x	x	46
x	43	8	39	20	11	39	38	41	5	33	14	17	5	26	16	4	3	0	2	15	1	0	0	0	0	0	3	3	0	3	1		x
xs	0	5	2	5	1	4	1	4	11	9	18	7	7	3	10	5	0	0	0	4	9	1	0	0	0	0	2	2	3	1	2		xs
sx	0	0	0	4	1	1	1	0	8	2	7	19	8	1	12	18	0	1	1	6	10	2	2	1	1	0	0	0	3	7	0	0	sx
s	2	1	0	1	2	1	1	0	0	0	3	1	5	4	3	19	36	5	20	1	0	10	6	1	1	1	1	1	2	0	0	0	s

GOALKEEPERS	CS	CCS
Stryjek	8	2

x - Played full 90 minutes
xs - Substituted off
sx - Substituted on
s - Non-playing Substitute

EBBSFLEET UNITED MATCH RESULTS 2019-20

Date	Comp	Opponents	H/A	Att	Result	Goalscorers	Pos
Aug 3	NL	Halifax Town	H	1091	L 1 - 4	Goddard 39	24
6	NL	Bromley	A	1471	L 1 - 3	Thomas 89	24
10	NL	AFC Fylde	A	1153	L 0 - 1		24
13	NL	Yeovil Town	H	1057	L 1 - 3	Thomas 78	24
17	NL	Solihull Moors	A	955	L 1 - 2	Weston 9	24
24	NL	Notts County	H	1293	D 2 - 2	Umerah 45+2 O'Brien 61 (og)	
26	NL	Boreham Wood	A	533	W 2 - 1	Ball 12 Ugwu 15	
31	NL	Aldershot Town	H	1109	L 1 - 2	Ugwu 83	23
Sep 3	NL	Dover Athletic	A	1247	D 1 - 1	Obileye 12	23
7	NL	Eastleigh	H	865	D 1 - 1	Reid 39	23
14	NL	Woking	A	1942	D 2 - 2	Reid 83 Weston 90+2	24
21	NL	Barrow	H		L 0 - 3		24
24	NL	Barnet	H	805	W 3 - 0	Weston 33 Reid 36 Obileye 71	22
28	NL	Wrexham	A	3627	L 0 - 1		23
Oct 5	NL	Harrogate Town	A	742	L 0 - 2		24
8	NL	Torquay United	H	908	L 2 - 4	Umerah 35 Ugwu 81	24
Garry Hill is sacked as manager - assistant Kevin Watson takes interim charge.							
12	NL	Maidenhead United	H	1003	L 1 - 2	Umerah 19	24
19	**FAC4Q**	**Woking**	**H**	**750**	**D 1 - 1**	**Reid 29**	
22	**FAC4Qr**	**Woking**	**A**	**942**	**W 1 - 0**	**Reid 24**	
26	NL	Sutton United	A	1566	W 3 - 2	Butler 10 (og) Payne 61 Ugwu 90+11 (pen)	23
29	NL	Chorley	A	921	W 4 - 0	Ekpiteta 5 Ugwu 43 60 Morgan 86	23
Nov 2	NL	Chesterfield	H	1025	D 2 - 2	Ugwu 17 51 (pen)	22
Kevin Watson is given the managerial job on a permanent basis.							
9	**FAC1**	**Notts County**	**H**	**1206**	**L 2 - 3**	**Payne 7 Ugwu 89 (pen)**	
16	NL	Hartlepool United	H	1086	D 2 - 2	Weston 72 80	23
23	NL	Stockport County	A	4167	D 1 - 1	Adeloye 35	
26	NL	Barnet	A	776	L 2 - 5	Obileye 37 Ugwu 55	24
30	NL	Wrexham	H	1036	W 2 - 1	Jennings 10 (og) Weston 74	23
Dec 7	NL	Eastleigh	A	1715	D 1 - 1	Weston 5	22
14	**FAT1**	**Enfield Town**	**A**	**417**	**W 2 - 0**	**Reid 1 Ugwu 27**	
26	NL	Dagenham & Redbridge	A	1402	D 1 - 1	Reid 62	23
28	NL	Dover Athletic	H	1222	L 0 - 1		23
Jan 1	NL	Dagenham & Redbridge	H	1015	D 1 - 1	Reid 6	23
4	NL	Barrow	A	2303	L 0 - 7		23
11	**FAT2**	**King's Lynn Town**	**H**	**680**	**W 1 - 0**	**Obileye 67 (pen)**	
18	NL	Harrogate Town	H	822	L 0 - 2		23
25	NL	Torquay United	A	2300	D 0 - 0		23
28	NL	Woking	H	674	W 2 - 1	Adeloye 70 89	23
Feb 1	NL	Sutton United	H	979	D 1 - 1	Ekpiteta 7	23
8	**FAT3**	**Royston Town**	**H**	**900**	**L 0 - 2**	**(aet)**	
15	NL	Chorley	H	712	W 1 - 0	King 57	
22	NL	Chesterfield	A	3346	L 0 - 4		22
25	NL	Maidenhead United	A	973	W 3 - 1	Umerah 17 Ugwu 30 31	22
29	NL	Stockport County	H	1030	L 0 - 1		22
Mar 7	NL	Hartlepool United	A	3868	W 1 - 0	Ugwu 78 (pen)	22
14	NL	Halifax Town	A	2154	W 1 - 0	Ugwu 16	21

GOALSCORERS	SG	CSG	Pens	Hat tricks	Total		SG	CSG	Pens	Hat tricks	Total
Ugwu	12	3	4		15	Ball	1	1			1
Reid	8	2			8	Goddard	1	1			1
Weston	6	2			7	King	1	1			1
Obileye	4	1	1		4	Morgan	1	1			1
Umerah	4	1			4						
Adeloye	2	1			3						
Opponent	3	1			3						
Ekpiteta	2	1			2						
Payne	2	1			2						
Thomas	2	1			2						

Ashmore N	Wilson L	Thomas A	Grimes J	Ball J	Weston M	Lawless A	King J	Obileye A	Goddard J	Ugwu G	Umerah J	Shields S	Egan A	Palmer H (GK)	Achuba M	Regini-Moran E	Thomas-Asante B	N'Gala B	Holmes J (GK)	Sutherland F	Reid A (L)	Biabi B	Cordner T (L)	Dainkeh Z	Payne J (L)	Adeloye T	Blackman A	Ekpiteta M (L)	Morgan A (L)	Gregory D (Gk) (L)	McGlashan J	Mekki A (L)	Timlin M	No.
x	xs	x	x	x	xs	xs	x	x	x	x	sx	sx	sx	s	s																			1
x	x	x	x	x	x	xs		x	x	x	s	x	sx	s	s	s																		2
x	xs	x	x	sx	xs	x	x	x	x	xs	s	s					sx	sx																3
x	xs	x	x	x	x		x	x	xs	x	xs	sx	s				sx	s																4
x	s	x	x	x	x		x	xs	x	xs	sx	s					sx	x																5
x	x	x	x	xs	x	s		x	sx	xs	sx	s						xs	x	sx														6
x	sx	x	x	x	sx	x	x	xs	xs	xs	sx	s						s	x	x														7
x	s	x	x	x	xs	x	s	x	x	xs								xs	x	sx	sx	sx												8
x	x	sx	x	x		x	xs	sx	xs	s	s								x	x	x	s	x											9
x	x	x	x	x		x	x	sx	xs	x	x								x	x	xs	sx	x											10
x		s	xs	x	sx	x	sx	x	xs	sx	x								sx	x	x	x	x											11
xs	x	x	x		x	xs	x	sx		x	sx	sx							x	x	xs	sx	x	x	s									12
xs	x	x	xs	x		x		s	x	sx	s	sx							x	xs	x	sx	x											13
x		x	xs	x	xs	x		sx	x	sx	s	s							x	x	x	sx	x											14
x		x	x		x	sx	x			xs	s	s							x	xs	x	s	x			x	sx							15
x		x	x		xs	s		x	x		s	s							x	x	xs		x			x	sx	sx						16
																																		17
x		s		x		x	sx		x	sx									x	sx			x			x	sx	xs	xs	x				18
s		s		x	sx	x	sx		sx	x			x	s					x	x	x		x			sx	s	s	s	xs				19
		sx		x	sx	x	sx	x	s		x			sx					xs	xs	x		x			x	s	xs	x	x				20
		sx		x	s	x	xs		x	sx			x						x	xs			x			x	s	xs	x	x				21
		x		x	s		x	sx	x		sx	x							xs	xs			x			x	s	x	x	x				22
s	s	x		xs	x	s		x	sx	xs	s								x	sx	xs		x			x	sx	x	x					23
xs	x	x		s	x	sx	xs	x			x								xs	sx		s		x	sx		x	x						24
s	xs	x		x	x		x			x	sx	x						s	x	xs		sx			x	x	sx	xs						25
s		x		x	xs	x		s	s	xs								s	x	x			x			x	sx	x	x					26
s		x	x	x		s	x	xs	x									xs	x	x			x			x	x	x	x					27
s		x	x	x		s	xs	sx	x		s							x	x	x			x			x	sx	x						28
x	x		s		x	sx		xs	sx	x		s	s					x	x	x			x			x	xs	s						29
x	x		x		x	s	sx	xs	sx	xs								x	x	x			x			x	xs							30
	s		xs		x	x	sx	x	sx			s						x	xs	x			x			x	sx	x	x					31
	s		x		x	xs	x	s										x	xs	x			x			x	sx	x	x					32
	x		x	xs	x	s	x											x	xs				x			x	sx	x						33
x	x			sx	x		xs	xs	s	s								x				s	x	sx	x		x			x	x			34
x	x		x		x	xs	sx	x	xs									x				s	x	sx		x		x	x	sx				35
x	x		x		x	xs	x	sx	s	s								x				sx				x		x	xs	x				36
x	x		x	xs	x		s	x	s	s								x			s					sx	x	x	x					37
x	x		s	x	sx	x	s	s										x					x	sx			x	xs	x					38
x	x	s		x	xs	sx	x	xs	sx	s		s						s	x				xs	sx	x		x	x						39
x	sx			x	xs	xs	xs	s	s									s	x				x	sx	x		x	sx	x					40
xs	sx			x	xs	sx	sx											s	x				x	x	xs		x	sx	x	s				41
x	x			x		s	x	xs	sx									sx	xs				x	s	s		xs	x	x	x				42
x	x		sx	x		xs	x	x										x					xs	sx	s	s			x	x	x			43
x	x		x	sx	s	x	xs											x					xs	sx	x			x			x	M	44
xs	x		sx	x		x	x	x	s									x					x	sx	x		s	x			x		45
5	24	8	29	12	26	1	36	17	11	27	7	1	5	6	0	0	0	1	24	21	10	0	23	0	23	3	11	21	5	8	8	7	4	x
0	8	0	1	2	3	7	3	6	8	7	19	0	6	0	0	0	0	2	1	10	12	0	0	0	3	3	3	4	0	1	2	0	0	xs
0	0	1	5	0	1	6	0	9	4	9	10	5	14	0	1	0	3	1	1	5	3	5	1	0	0	20	4	0	0	0	2	1	0	sx
0	8	1	8	0	1	3	1	10	2	1	3	0	10	33	12	1	0	2	5	0	0	2	1	4	0	5	4	1	0	1	0	0	1	s

GOALKEEPERS	CS	CCS
Holmes	5	2
Gregory	3	1
Palmer	1	1

x - Played full 90 minutes
xs - Substituted off
sx - Substituted on
s - Non-playing Substitute

FC HALIFAX TOWN MATCH RESULTS 2019-20

Date	Comp	Opponents	H/A	Att:	Result	Goalscorers	Pos
Aug 3	NL	Ebbsfleet United	A	1091	W 4 - 1	King C 12 Maher 68 Earing 71 Clarke 90+5	1
6	NL	Hartlepool United	H	2632	W 2 - 0	Staunton 53 Sho-Silva 68	1
10	NL	Dagenham & Redbridge	H	1895	W 1 - 0	McAlinden 15	1
13	NL	Wrexham	A	5517	L 0 - 1		
17	NL	Aldershot Town	A	1539	D 1 - 1	Binnom-Williams 82	4
24	NL	AFC Fylde	H	1913	W 4 - 1	McAlinden 11 Sho-Silva 36 King C 52 Binnom-Williams 75	
26	NL	Barrow	A	1451	W 2 - 1	Nolan 50 McAlinden 64 (pen)	
31	NL	Solihull Moors	H	2053	W 2 - 1	McAlinden 14 49	2
Sep 3	NL	Chesterfield	A	3844	W 3 - 2	Allen 8 Clarke 33 King C 47	1
7	NL	Yeovil Town	H	2341	L 0 - 2		2
14	NL	Notts County	A	5188	L 0 - 1		3
21	NL	Barnet	H	1941	W 4 - 2	Sho-Silva 11 90+2 McAlinden 15 Nolan 70	2
24	NL	Harrogate Town	H	1918	L 0 - 1		2
28	NL	Dover Athletic	A	1020	W 2 - 0	King C 11 90+4	2
Oct 5	NL	Maidenhead United	A	1249	W 1 - 0	McAlinden 2	1
8	NL	Chorley	H	2117	D 0 - 0		1
12	NL	Boreham Wood	H	2244	L 0 - 2		1
19	FAC4Q	**Harrogate Town**	**H**	**1241**	**L 1 - 2**	**Maher 46**	
26	NL	Bromley	A	2215	L 0 - 5		3
29	NL	Sutton United	A	1326	W 1 - 0	Duckworth 53	2
Nov 2	NL	Torquay United	H	2065	L 2 - 4	McAlinden 80 Duckworth 90+4	3
16	NL	Woking	A	2242	D 0 - 0		4
23	NL	Eastleigh	H	1817	D 1 - 1	Sho-Silva 1	4
26	NL	Harrogate Town	A	1185	D 2 - 2	McAlinden 11 (pen) King C 76	5
Dec 7	NL	Yeovil Town	A	2975	L 0 - 2		7
14	FAT1	**Wrexham**	**H**	**752**	**W 4 - 0**	**Maher 9 Redshaw 47 56 Williams 88**	
21	NL	Notts County	H	2491	L 2 - 4	McCoulsky 45 Allen 57	8
26	NL	Stockport County	A	5536	L 1 - 5	McAlinden 65	10
28	NL	Chesterfield	H	2450	W 1 - 0	Redshaw 66 (pen)	10
Jan 1	NL	Stockport County	H	3460	D 0 - 0		9
4	NL	Barnet	A	1333	D 1 - 1	Redshaw 24	10
11	FAT2	**Torquay United**	**A**	**1309**	**W 2 - 1**	**Sho-Silva 54 Staunton 67**	
18	NL	Maidenhead United	H	1981	W 5 - 2	Cooper 31 Redshaw 62 Rodney 68 Allen 82 Duckworth 89	7
25	NL	Chorley	A	1263	W 1 - 0	King C 60	6
28	NL	Dover Athletic	H	1726	W 4 - 2	Rodney 14 78 Binnom-Williams 45+1 De Havilland 66 (og)	4
Feb 1	NL	Bromley	H	2026	W 2 - 1	Maher 32 Rodney 42	3
8	FAT3	**Halesowen Town**	**H**	**1483**	**L 0 - 1**		
22	NL	Torquay United	A	2053	L 0 - 1		4
Mar 3	NL	Sutton United	H	1637	W 1 - 0	Rodney 88 (pen)	3
7	NL	Woking	H	1995	L 0 - 2		5
14	NL	Ebbsfleet United	H	2154	L 0 - 1		6
July 17	PO Q	**Boreham Wood**	**A**	**0**	**L 1 - 2**	**Sho-Silva 19**	

GOALSCORERS	SG	CSG	Pens	Hat tricks	Total		SG	CSG	Pens	Hat tricks	Total
McAlinden	9	3	2		10	Nolan	2	1			2
King C	6	1			7	Staunton	2	1			2
Sho-Silva	6	1			7	Cooper	1	1			1
Redshaw	4	1	1		5	Earing	1	1			1
Rodney*	4	2	1		5	McCoulsky	1	1			1
Maher	4	1			4	Opponent	1	1			1
Allen	3	1			3	Williams	1	1			1
Binnom-Williams	3	2			3						
Duckworth	3	2			3						
Clarke	2	1			2						

Johnson S	Clarke N	Brown M	Binnom-Williams J	Staunton J	Maher N	Duckworth M	Williams D	King J	King C	Sho-Silva T	Allen J	Earing J	Odelusi S	Nolan L	Appleyard W (Gk)	McAlinden L	Hanson J	MacDonald J	Cooper C	Southwell D	Redshaw J	McCoulsky S (L)	Rodney D (L)	No.
x	x	x	x	x	x	x	xs	xs	x	xs	sx	sx	sx	s	s									1
x	x	x	x	x	x	x	xs	x	xs	xs	sx	s		sx	s	sx								2
x	x	x	x	x	xs	x		sx	xs	x	x	sx	s	sx	s	xs								3
x	x	x	x	x	x		x	xs	x	xs	s	s	sx	x	s	sx	s							4
x	x	x	x	x	x		x	xs	x	sx	x	s	s	xs	s	x	s							5
x	x	x	x	x	x			sx	xs	xs	xs	sx		s	x	s	sx							6
x	x	x	x	x	x			sx	xs	x	x	s		x	s	x	s	sx						7
x	x	xs	x	x	x			x	s	x	x	s	sx	x	s	x	s	s						8
x	x	x	x	x		s	x	sx	xs	x	x	x		x	s	x	s	sx						9
x	x	x	x		x	sx	xs	xs	x	x	xs		x	s	sx	s	sx							10
x	x	x	x		x	sx	xs	sx	x	x	s		x	s	xs	s		x						11
x	x	x	x		x	xs	x	sx	x		s		x	s	xs	s		x	sx					12
x	x	x	x		x	xs	xs	sx	x		s		x	s	x	s		x	sx					13
x	x	x	x		x	xs	sx	x	xs		sx		x	s	xs	s		x	sx					14
x	x	x	x	x	s	x	xs	xs	xs	xs	sx		x	s				x	sx					15
x	x	x	x	x	s	x	xs	xs	sx	sx	sx		xs	s				x	x					16
x	x	x	x	sx	x		sx	xs	x	xs	s		xs	s				x	sx					17
x	x	x	x	xs	x		sx		x	sx	sx		x	s	x	s		xs	xs					18
x	x	x	x	xs	x		xs		x	xs	s		x	s	xs	xs		x	xs					19
x	x		x	sx	x		xs		x	sx	xs		x	s	xs	x	xs	x	s					20
x	x	s	x	sx	x			x	sx	xs		xs	s	x	x	xs	x		sx					21
x	x	x	x	x	x	x	x	sx	xs	x			s	s			xs	xs	s					22
x		x	x	x	x	x	s	sx	xs	x	sx		s	s	x		xs	x						23
x		x	x	x	sx	x	sx	xs	sx	x	x		x	s	xs		s	xs						24
x		x		x	sx	xs	s	x	x		xs	s	xs	x		x		sx	sx					25
x	x	x	x	x	x	x	x		sx	xs	xs		s	s	s		xs	s	xs	sx				26
x	x	x		x	x	x	xs		sx	x	x		s	sx	xs	s	sx		xs					27
x		x		x	x	x	sx		xs	xs	x		xs	s	x		s	x	sx	sx				28
x	x	x	s	x	x		x	x	xs	sx	xs		s	sx		x		x	s					29
x	x	x	s	x		x	x	x	xs	sx	xs		s	sx		x		x	sx					30
x	x	x	s	x		x	x	xs	sx	xs		s	sx	x		x	xs	sx						31
x	x	x	s	x	x	sx	x	x	xs	x		s		s	x	sx	xs							32
x	x	x	s	x	x	sx	x	xs	x	sx	sx		s		x		xs		xs					33
x	x		x	x	x	sx	x	xs	xs	sx		s	s		x		xs		xs					34
x	x		x	x	x	sx	x	xs	x	s	sx		sx	s		xs		xs		x				35
x	x		x	x	x	x	x		xs	sx	sx		s	s	s		xs		sx	xs				36
x	x		x	x		xs	x	x	xs	sx	xs		s	s		sx	sx	x		x				37
x	x	x	s	x		x		x	x	xs	x	sx		s	s	x		x		sx	xs			38
x	x	x	s	xs	x		x	x	sx	xs	sx		sx	s		x		xs		x				39
x	x	x	s	xs	x		x	x	sx	sx	x		sx	s		xs		xs		x				40
x	x		x	x	x		x	xs		sx		s	xs	s		s	sx		x		x			41
x	x	x	s	x		x	x	xs	sx	xs	xs	x	sx		s	s		x		sx				42
42	38	23	28	40	20	30	15	11	6	20	15	1	0	14	0	13	4	0	24	1	4	0	4	x
0	0	1	0	2	3	1	9	13	21	10	8	2	0	7	0	8	2	4	5	2	8	1	4	xs
0	0	0	0	0	4	4	5	12	8	10	13	9	2	6	0	7	1	7	2	6	6	5	0	sx
0	0	0	9	0	2	0	2	0	2	2	0	9	2	8	42	1	14	6	1	2	0	1	0	s

GOALKEEPERS	CS	CCS
Johnson	12	3

x - Played full 90 minutes
xs - Substituted off
sx - Substituted on
s - Non-playing Substitute

NATIONAL LEAGUE

HARROGATE TOWN MATCH RESULTS 2019-20

Date	Comp	Opponents	H/A	Att:	Result	Goalscorers	Pos
Aug 3	NL	Solihull Moors	H	1045	D 2 - 2	Beck 55 Leesley 57	11
6	NL	Barrow	A	1602	W 3 - 0	Smith W 34 56 Hall 86	2
10	NL	Woking	H	1470	L 0 - 1		
13	NL	Notts County	H	1863	L 0 - 2		
17	NL	Dagenham & Redbridge	A	1043	L 2 - 4	Balanta 7 (og) Kiernan 24	18
24	NL	Stockport County	H	1326	W 2 - 1	Beck 54 Bradley 90+3	
26	NL	AFC Fylde	A	1317	D 0 - 0		
31	NL	Dover Athletic	H	900	L 0 - 2		18
Sep 3	NL	Chorley	H	792	W 2 - 0	Kiernan 4 Muldoon 47	13
7	NL	Torquay United	A	2527	L 2 - 4	Stead 33 (pen) 58	17
14	NL	Boreham Wood	H	942	D 0 - 0		18
21	NL	Maidenhead United	A	1127	D 1 - 1	Jones 9	18
24	NL	Halifax Town	A	1918	W 1 - 0	Beck 87	14
28	NL	Sutton United	H	769	W 2 - 0	Thomson 34 Muldoon 90+2	11
Oct 5	NL	Ebbsfleet United	H	742	W 2 - 0	Kiernan 40 59	10
8	NL	Wrexham	A	3435	D 1 - 1	Fallowfield 80	12
12	NL	Yeovil Town	A	3237	W 2 - 1	Kiernan 71 Muldoon 79	8
19	FAC4Q	Halifax Town	A	1241	W 2 - 1	Beck 8 54	
26	NL	Aldershot Town	H	1507	W 1 - 0	Emmett 90+1	4
29	NL	Barnet	H	1121	W 2 - 1	Muldoon 15 Smith G 19	4
Nov 2	NL	Eastleigh	A	1592	L 2 - 4	Kiernan 9 Muldoon 69	6
11	FAC1	Portsmouth	H	3048	L 1 - 3	Beck 7	
16	NL	Bromley	A	2177	D 3 - 3	Emmett 13 Kieran 37 Muldoon 41 (pen)	7
23	NL	Chesterfield	H	1710	W 3 - 1	Falkingham 37 Fallowfield 65 Muldoon 70	6
26	NL	Halifax Town	H	1185	D 2 - 2	Thomson 54 Staunton 90+2 (og)	7
30	NL	Sutton United	A	1490	L 1 - 3	Falkingham 68	7
Dec 7	NL	Torquay United	H	1348	W 2 - 1	Bradley 9 Stead 56	6
14	FAT1	Hartlepool United	H	803	W 3 - 2	Kioso 77 (og) Hall 86 Kiernan 90+3	
21	NL	Boreham Wood	A	501	L 1 - 2	Bradley 39	7
26	NL	Hartlepool United	H	2383	W 4 - 1	Kerry 54 Muldoon 58 (pen) 90+1 Falkingham 68	4
28	NL	Chorley	A	1077	W 2 - 0	Muldoon 27 Stead 67	4
Jan 1	NL	Hartlepool United	A	3481	W 1 - 0	Stead 57	4
4	NL	Maidenhead United	H	1281	W 1 - 0	Hall 60	3
11	FAT2	Darlington	A	1240	W 2 - 0	Diamond 32 Kerry 86	
18	NL	Ebbsfleet United	A	822	W 2 - 0	Hall 39 Muldoon 63	2
25	NL	Wrexham	H	2415	L 0 - 2		2
Feb 1	NL	Aldershot Town	A	1704	D 1 - 1	Kerry 70	2
8	FAT3	Eastleigh	H	947	W 2 - 0	Bradley 23 Emmett 86	
11	NL	Yeovil Town	H	801	W 3 - 0	Thomson 43 73 Diamond 52	2
22	NL	Eastleigh	H	1249	W 3 - 0	Falkingham 20 Diamond 43 Muldoon 68	2
29	FAT4	AFC Fylde	A	803	W 3 - 2	Kerry 73 Muldoon 74 103 (aet)	
Mar 3	NL	Chesterfield	A	2912	W 4 - 3	Stead 9 60 Thomson 34 Muldoon 90+2	2
7	NL	Bromley	H	1339	D 1 - 1	Diamond 47	2
July 25	PO SF	Boreham Wood	H	0	W 1 - 0	Muldoon 64	
Aug 2	PO F	Notts County	N	0	W 3 - 1	Thomson 5 Hall 28 Diamond 71 (Promoted to the Football League)	

GOALSCORERS	SG	CSG	Pens	Hat tricks	Total		SG	CSG	Pens	Hat tricks	Total
Muldoon	14	3	2		16	Emmett	3	1			3
Kiernan	7	1			8	Opponent	3	1			3
Stead	5	2	1		7	Fallowfield	2	1			2
Beck	5	1			6	Smith W	1	1			2
Thomson	5	1			6	Jones	1	1			1
Diamond	5	2			5	Leesley	1	1			1
Hall	5	1			5	Smith G	1	1			1
Bradley	4	1			4						
Falkingham	4	1			4						
Kerry	4	1			4						

Belshaw J	Hall C	Smith G	Smith W	Burrell W	Falkingham J	Kiernan B	Emmett J	Beck M	Leesley J	Muldoon J	Fallowfield R	Kerry L	Stead J	Cracknell J (Gk)	Brown S	Jones S	Thomson G	Bradley A (L)	Diamond J (L)	Taylor M	Hancox M (L)	Gallagher O (L)	Hartley D	Clark H	Harratt K (L)	Kouogun M	Martin A	No.
x	x	x	xs	x	x	x	xs	x	x	xs	sx	sx	s	s														1
x	x	x	x	x	x	x	sx	x	xs	xs	s	s	sx	s	s													2
x	x	x	x	x	x	x	sx	x	x	xs	s	xs	sx	s	s													3
x	x	x	x	x	x	xs	sx	xs	x	x	s			sx	s	xs	sx											4
x	x	xs	x	x	x	x	x	xs	x	x				s	s	sx	sx											5
x	sx	x	x	xs	x	x	x	xs	s	x	x			sx	s		x											6
x	x	s	x	x	x	x	x	x	x	x	x			sx	s	sx		xs										7
x	x	s	x	x	x	x	x	xs	sx	xs	x			sx	s	xs	sx											8
x	x	x	x	x	xs	x	sx	sx		xs	x			xs	s	x	s		sx									9
x	x	x	x	x		xs	xs	sx		x	x			x	s	sx	s	s		s								10
x	x	x	x	x		x	x	sx		xs	x			s	s	xs	s	x	x	sx								11
x	x	x	x	x		x		sx		sx	x			xs	s	s	xs	sx	x	xs								12
x	x	x	x	x		xs	s	x		x	x			s	s	sx		x	xs	sx								13
x	x	x	x	x		xs	sx	s		x	x			s	s	sx	xs	xs	s									14
x	x	x	x	x		xs	s	x		x	x			s	s	sx		x	sx									15
x	x	x	x	x		xs	sx	x		x	x			s	s	s		xs	sx									16
x	x	x	x	x		xs	sx			xs	x			sx	s		sx	s	xs									17
x	x	x	x	x	x	xs	s	s		xs	x			sx	s	s		sx	s	x	s							18
x		x	x	x	x	xs	sx	x		xs	x			sx	s			sx	x	xs	s							19
x		x	x	x	x	xs	sx	x		xs	x			sx	s			sx	x	xs	s							20
x		xs	x	x	x	xs	sx	x		x	x				s	s	sx	xs	x	sx								21
x	x	x	xs	x	x	xs	sx	x		x	x				s	s	s	sx	sx	xs	s							22
x	x	x	x	x	x	x	xs	x		x	x			s			sx	sx	sx	s								23
x	x	s	x	x	x	xs	s	x		x	x			s			sx	s	x		x							24
x	x		x	x	x	sx	s	x		x	x			sx	s		xs	s	xs		x							25
x	x	s	x		x	sx	x			x	x	s	x	s			x	s	xs		x							26
x	x	s	x		x	xs	sx			xs			x	x	s		x	x	xs		x							27
s	x	s	x		x	s	x	sx			sx	xs	x	x	x	x	sx	xs	x	xs		x						28
x	x		x	x	x	xs	sx			x		xs	s	s	sx	x	x	s		x								29
x	x	s	x	x	x	x	s	x		x	s	x	x	s			sx	x	x									30
x	x	s	x	x	x	s	xs			x	s	x	x	x			sx	x	x									31
x	x	s	x		x	sx	xs	sx		x		x	xs	s			s	x	x									32
x	x	sx	xs	x	x	sx	xs	sx		x		x	xs	s			s	x	x									33
s		s	x	x		xs	sx	x		sx	x	x	xs				x	x	x			x	s	s				34
x	x		x	x	x	sx	xs			xs		x	s				sx	x	xs			s			sx			35
x	x		x	x	x	sx	xs			xs		x	x	s			s	x	x			s			sx			36
x	x		x	x	x	x				x	sx	x	x	s			sx	xs	xs			s			s			37
s	s	xs	x	x		x	sx			sx	x	s	s	x			x	x	xs			sx			xs	x		38
x	x	sx	xs	x	x	sx				x	x	x	xs	s			x	s	x						sx			39
x	x	s	x	x	x	sx	sx			x	x	s	x	.			xs	sx	sx						sx			40
s	sx	x	x	x	x	s	xs	xs		sx		xs	sx	x			x	x	sx						xs	x		41
x	x	s	x	x	x	x	s			x	x	x	x	s			x	s	x						s			42
x		s	x	x	x	x	s			x	x	xs	x	s			x	sx	x						s	x		43
x	x		x	x	x		sx	sx	s	xs	x	x	sx	s			xs		x						s		xs	44
x	x		x	x	x		s	sx	s	xs	x	x	sx	s			x		x						s		xs	45
41	38	19	41	38	35	14	7	19	3	23	30	14	12	4	2	0	11	18	13	0	6	1	0	0	0	3	0	x
0	0	3	3	2	1	17	9	3	2	17	1	5	5	0	2	2	5	6	14	0	0	0	0	0	2	0	2	xs
0	1	3	0	0	0	8	17	8	1	5	2	1	15	0	5	4	14	4	8	1	0	1	0	0	4	0	0	sx
4	1	13	0	0	2	4	6	0	4	0	5	2	7	41	13	3	5	7	2	5	0	3	1	1	5	0	0	s

GOALKEEPERS	CS	CCS
Belshaw	14	3
Cracknell	2	1

x - Played full 90 minutes
xs - Substituted off
sx - Substituted on
s - Non-playing Substitute

HARTLEPOOL UNITED MATCH RESULTS 2019-20

Date	Comp	Opponents	H/A	Att:	Result	Goalscorers	Pos
Aug 3	NL	Sutton United	H	3812	L 1 - 3	Toure 45+2	22
6	NL	Halifax Town	A	2632	L 0 - 2		23
10	NL	Maidenhead United	A	1330	W 1 - 0	Muir 55	
13	NL	AFC Fylde	H	3222	D 2 - 2	Toure 3 58	
17	NL	Bromley	H	3171	L 2 - 3	Holohan 13 Mafuta 39	20
24	NL	Chorley	A	1395	D 0 - 0		
26	NL	Wrexham	H	3462	W 4 - 2	Toure 42 60 Noble 48 (pen) 52	
31	NL	Torquay United	A	2683	W 2 - 1	Kennedy 16 Kioso 80	9
Sep 3	NL	Barrow	A	1257	W 1 - 0	Donaldson 71	8
7	NL	Woking	H	3429	D 1 - 1	Noble 46 (pen)	9
14	NL	Dagenham & Redbridge	A	1392	L 1 - 3	Donaldson 81	11
21	NL	Dover Athletic	H	3329	L 0 - 2		14
24	NL	Chesterfield	H	2953	D 1 - 1	Kioso 9	17
28	NL	Eastleigh	A	1838	D 1 - 1	Toure 12	18
Oct 5	NL	Yeovil Town	H	3273	W 2 - 1	Toure 47 Kennedy 90+2	15
8	NL	Stockport County	A	3465	L 1 - 2	Kabamba 86	16
Craig Hignett is sacked as manager, Antony Sweeney takes over as caretaker.							
12	NL	Aldershot Town	A	2768	W 3 - 0	Hawkes 4 Holohan 80 Kabamba 90+2	15
19	FAC4Q	**Brackley Town**	H	2506	**W 1 - 0**	**Donaldson 61**	
26	NL	Barnet	H	3089	W 2 - 0	Kabamba 6 27	11
Nov 2	NL	Notts County	A	5258	D 2 - 2	Holohan 8 James 42	13
5	NL	Solihull Moors	H	2703	L 0 - 1		13
Former AFC Fylde manager, Dave Challinor, takes charge.							
12	FAC1	**Yeovil Town**	A	2361	**W 4 - 1**	**James 6 Holohan 20 Kabamba 59 Toure 86 (pen)**	
16	NL	Ebbsfleet United	A	1086	D 2 - 2	Holohan 31 42	14
23	NL	Boreham Wood	H	3377	D 2 - 2	Featherstone 70 Toure 84 (pen)	
26	NL	Chesterfield	A	3420	W 5 - 2	Mafuta 23 55 James 27 Toure 48 68	10
Dec 1	FAC2	**Exeter City**	A	3638	**D 2 - 2**	**Featherstone 73 Kabamba 79**	
7	NL	Woking	A	2127	L 1 - 2	Toure 25 (pen)	14
10	FAC2r	**Exeter City**	H	2398	**W 1 - 0**	**Hawkes 93 (aet)**	
14	FAT1	**Harrogate Town**	A	803	**L 2 - 3**	**Hamilton 10 Donaldson 45+2**	
21	NL	Dagenham & Redbridge	H	3259	W 1 - 0	Kitching 79	13
26	NL	Harrogate Town	A	2383	L 1 - 4	Kabamba 76	14
28	NL	Barrow	H	2790	D 2 - 2	Holohan 55 Donaldson 76	15
Jan 1	NL	Harrogate Town	H	3481	L 0 - 1		16
4	FAC3	**Oxford United**	A	6240	**L 1 - 4**	**Kitching 9**	
7	NL	Eastleigh	H	2478	W 2 - 1	Holohan 51 Shelton 67	13
11	NL	Dover Athletic	A	1023	D 1 - 1	Lokko 22 (og)	12
18	NL	Yeovil Town	A	2716	D 2 - 2	Kioso 28 Mafuta 71	11
25	NL	Stockport County	H	3766	W 2 - 0	Keena 31 Shelton 52	11
Feb 1	NL	Barnet	A	1321	L 1 - 2	Sweeney 75 (og)	13
8	NL	Aldershot Town	H	3442	W 2 - 0	Molyneux 6 Shelton 20	
22	NL	Notts County	H	3839	W 2 - 0	Featherstone 47 58	11
29	NL	Boreham Wood	A	932	D 1 - 1	Toure 47	11
Mar 3	NL	Solihull Moors	A	896	W 1 - 0	Keena 86	8
7	NL	Ebbsfleet United	H	3868	L 0 - 1		10
14	NL	Sutton United	A	2126	D 1 - 1	Holohan 53	9

GOALSCORERS	SG	CSG	Pens	Hat tricks	Total		SG	CSG	Pens	Hat tricks	Total
Toure	10	2	3		13	Hawkes	2	1			2
Holohan	8	2			9	Keena	2	1			2
Kabamba	6	1			7	Kennedy	2	1			2
Donaldson	5	1			5	Kitching	2	1			2
Featherstone	3	1			4	Opponent	2	1			2
Mafuta	3	1			4	Hamilton	1	1			1
James	3	1			3	Molyneux	1	1			1
Kioso	3	1			3	Muir	1	1			1
Noble	2	1	2		3						
Shelton	3	1			3						

Killip B	Raynes M	Kerr F	Crichlow-Noble R (L)	Kennedy J	Noble L	Richardson K	James L	Toure G	Mafuta G	Kabamba N	Featherstone N	Kitching M	Holohan G	Bale A	Cunningham A	Kioso P	Williams L	Donaldson R	Muir N	Anderson M	Hawkes J	Hemming Z (L)	Grey J	Hamilton T (L)	Shepherd C	Konstantopoulos D (Gk)	Beeney M (Gk)	Shelton M (L)	Liddle G (L)	Molyneux L	Keena A	Odusina O (L)	Southam-Hales M (L)	Harker R (L)	No.
x	x	x	xs	x	x	xs	x	xs	x	x	sx	sx	sx	s	s																				1
x	x	x	xs	xs	x		x	sx	x	x	x	xs	s	sx		s	x	sx																	2
x	x	x		sx	x		x	xs	xs	x	x		s	x	s	s	x	s	xs	sx															3
x	x	x	s	sx	xs		sx	x	x		x	x	sx	x	xs		x	xs	x																4
x	x	x	s	sx	sx		sx	x	x		xs	xs	x	s		x		xs	x																5
x	x	x		s	s		sx	xs	x	sx	x	x	x			sx		x	xs	xs															6
x	x		xs	xs		x	xs	x		sx	x	s	sx	x	x	x		s		sx															7
x	x	x		xs		xs	x	x		sx	x	s	s	s	x	x	x	sx		s															8
x	x	x		x	x		s	xs	x	sx	x	s	s	s	x	x		x																	9
x	x	x		xs	xs		s	x	s	x	x	sx	x	s	x	x		x																	10
x	x	xs		xs	x	s		x	x	x	x	x	x	x		x		x		sx															11
x	x			s	xs	xs	sx	x	x	x	x	x	sx	s		x	x	x		s															12
x	x		s	x	sx	x	sx	x	x	x		x	xs	s	s	x		xs																	13
x	x		s	x		x	sx	xs	x	xs		x	x	s	x	x		sx		s															14
x	x	x		x		x	xs	xs	x	sx	x		s	x		s	x	x		s															15
x	x	x				xs	xs	x	x	x	x	sx	s	s	xs		x	x		sx															16
x	x	x	sx		s	sx	xs	x		x	x	x		xs			x	x		xs															17
x	x	x	sx		s	sx	xs	xs	x	x	x	x	sx	s	s	x		x	s	xs															18
x	x	x	sx			xs	sx	x	x	x	x	xs		s		x		xs	s	sx															19
x	x	x	sx			xs		x	x	x	x	xs		s	x	sx	xs	sx		s															20
x	x	x	s			x		xs	xs	x	x	x	x		s	x	sx	xs	sx		sx														21
x	x	x	s		sx	x	sx	x	x	x	xs	xs			x	sx	x			s	s														22
x	x	x	sx			x	sx	x	x	x	x	xs			x	x	s		s																23
x	xs	x	s			x	sx	xs	x	x	x	xs			sx	x	x	s		sx															24
x	x	x	s		sx	xs	xs	x	x	x			s	x		x	sx			xs															25
x	xs	x	s	s		x	x	x	xs	sx	x	s		sx			x	s		x		s													26
x	x	x	s	s		x	x	x	x	x		x					x			xs		sx													27
x	x	x	s	s		x	xs	xs	x	x	x	sx				x	s			xs	s		s												28
	x	sx	sx		x			sx	x	xs	x	x				x		x			xs		xs		x	s	s								29
x	x	s			s		x	xs	sx	x	x	s				x		x			xs		sx					x	x						30
x	xs	s			s		x	xs	sx	xs	x	sx				x		x			x		x					sx	x						31
x	s	x			xs		x	s	x	s	sx	x				x		x			s		sx					x	x						32
	xs	s			x			xs	s	x	x	sx	x			x		x			sx		x	xs	x	sx									33
s	xs	x		s			xs	sx	x	x	x	x	x		s	x		x			s	sx	x				sx								34
	xs	sx		s				x	x	x	xs					x	sx			x		s				x	x	x	s						35
s			s			x	xs	x	x	xs						x		x	x			x	x	x	s										36
s			sx			x		xs	x	x		s	x			x	sx	xs				x	x	x	sx	xs									37
			xs	sx					x	s						x	s	s	s			x	x	x	sx	xs	x	x							38
						x	s			xs	x	x				x		s	sx			x	xs	x	sx	xs	x	x	xs						39
x			s			x	sx		x	x						x		s	sx			xs	x	xs	sx	x	x	xs							40
x						xs	sx		x	x	sx					x		s	s			x	x	xs	s	x	x	xs							41
x						x	s		x	x	sx					x		s	sx			xs	x	x	sx	xs	x	x	xs						42
x						sx	s		x	x	sx					x		s	sx			xs	x	x	sx	xs	x	x	xs						43
x			s			x	s		x	x	sx					x		sx				s	xs	x	x	x	x	sx							44
x			s			sx	xs		x	x						xs		x				s	x	xs	sx	x	x	xs							45
37	27	27	0	6	5	8	9	18	27	11	30	39	12	0	7	29	0	31	2	1	3	0	0	1	0	1	7	8	15	2	1	8	7	0	x
0	6	1	2	4	5	5	7	13	8	9	5	2	8	0	1	1	0	8	1	2	8	0	0	1	0	0	0	5	0	4	3	0	0	5	xs
0	0	1	1	10	2	8	9	4	11	6	3	13	1	3	1	4	1	6	1	11	0	6	0	0	0	1	0	5	4	0	0	0	0	2	sx
3	1	3	7	12	1	8	2	0	6	1	2	1	8	10	15	0	1	1	8	6	10	1	3	1	1	0	3	1	0	2	1	0	0	0	s

GOALKEEPERS	CS	CCS
Killip	10	3
Beeney	1	1

x - Played full 90 minutes
xs - Substituted off
sx - Substituted on
s - Non-playing Substitute

MAIDENHEAD UNITED MATCH RESULTS 2019-20

Date	Comp	Opponents	H/A	Att:	Result	Goalscorers	Pos
Aug 3	NL	Stockport County	A	4626	W 1 - 0	Cassidy 79	10
6	NL	Chesterfield	H	1471	D 1 - 1	Clerima 60	9
10	NL	Hartlepool United	H	1330	L 0 - 1		
13	NL	Torquay United	A	2946	W 2 - 0	Kelly 31 Fenelon 90+3	
17	NL	Chorley	H	1172	W 4 - 1	Kelly 23 Cassidy 35 (pen) Whitehall 90+1 90+4	5
24	NL	Yeovil Town	A	2179	W 2 - 1	Smile 57 Whitehall 85	
26	NL	Bromley	H	1511	L 1 - 2	Smile 65	
31	NL	Sutton United	A	1554	W 3 - 0	Fenelon 61 Cassidy 79 Whitehall 90+6 (pen)	4
Sep 3	NL	Wrexham	A	3667	D 2 - 2	Young 22 (og) Smile 66	4
7	NL	Dagenham & Redbridge	H	1551	L 0 - 1		4
14	NL	Barnet	A	1086	L 0 - 1		6
21	NL	Harrogate Town	H	1127	D 1 - 1	Fenelon 22	8
24	NL	Dover Athletic	H	1015	L 1 - 2	Whitehall 61	9
28	NL	Barrow	A	1401	L 0 - 2		14
Oct 5	NL	Halifax Town	H	1249	L 0 - 1		16
8	NL	Eastleigh	A	1548	L 1 - 2	Whitehall 28	17
12	NL	Ebbsfleet United	A	1003	W 2 - 1	Whitehall 21 Upward 76	16
19	FAC4Q	**Wealdstone**	H	891	D 1 - 1	**Upward 86**	
22	FAC4Qr	**Wealdstone**	A	835	W 2 - 0	**Kelly 14 56**	
26	NL	Solihull Moors	H	1152	W 1 - 0	Clerima 90+3	15
29	NL	AFC Fylde	H	1010	D 1 - 1	Kelly 47	14
Nov 2	NL	Aldershot Town	A	1602	L 0 - 2		16
9	FAC1	**Rotherham United**	H	1924	L 1 - 3	**Cassidy 25**	
16	NL	Boreham Wood	A	624	L 1 - 2	Sekajja 82 (pen)	
23	NL	Woking	H	1307	L 2 - 3	Whitehall 60 85	17
26	NL	Dover Athletic	A	687	W 4 - 3	Cassidy 10 44 Upward 36 Ellul 53	17
30	NL	Barrow	H		L 0 - 4		17
Dec 7	NL	Dagenham & Redbridge	A	1083	W 2 - 1	Kelly 26 Clerima 71	16
14	FAT1	**Hemel Hempstead Town**	H	387	W 4 - 2	**Whitehall 7 Kelly 36 Fenelon 72 74**	
21	NL	Barnet	H	1625	L 1 - 4	Kelly 27	16
26	NL	Notts County	A	5129	L 0 - 3		18
28	NL	Wrexham	H	1472	W 2 - 0	Whitehall 23 52	17
Jan 1	NL	Notts County	H	1657	D 0 - 0		17
4	NL	Harrogate Town	A	1281	L 0 - 1		18
11	FAT2	**Halesowen Town**	A	892	D 2 - 2	**Ellul 2 Smile 43**	
18	NL	Halifax Town	A	1981	L 2 - 5	Upward 45+1 Mensah 90+2	19
21	FAT2r	**Halesowen Town**	H	275	L 1 - 3	**Whitehall 16**	
25	NL	Eastleigh	H	1176	W 2 - 0	Whitehall 7 (pen) 33	18
Feb 1	NL	Solihull Moors	A	797	W 2 - 0	Akintunde 66 Alfa 85	17
22	NL	Aldershot Town	H	1778	L 1 - 2	Clerima 66	20
25	NL	Ebbsfleet United	H	973	L 1 - 3	Mundle-Smith 8	20
29	NL	Woking	A	2019	L 0 - 2		20
Mar 7	NL	Boreham Wood	H	1296	L 0 - 1		21
14	NL	Stockport County	H	1662	L 1 - 2	Alfa 27	22

GOALSCORERS	SG	CSG	Pens	Hat tricks	Total		SG	CSG	Pens	Hat tricks	Total
Whitehall	11	2	2		15	Mensah	1	1			1
Kelly	7	3			8	Mundle-Smith	1	1			1
Cassidy	5	1	1		6	Opponent	1	1			1
Fenelon	4	1			5	Sekajja	1	1	1		1
Clerima	4	1			4						
Smile	4	2			4						
Upward	4	2			4						
Ellul	2	1			2						
Akintunde	1	1			1						
Alfa	1	1			1						

Ashby-Hammond T (L)	Steer R	Ofori-Twumasi N	Massey A	Clerima R	Ellul J	Comley J	Upward R	Smile J	Cassidy J	Akintunde J	Mensah B (L)	Davies A	Whitehall D	Kelly J	Fenelon S	Keetch B	Sheckleford R	Landers H	Dunn C (Gk)	Grant F	Thompson-Bissett J (L)	Sekajia I	Smith R	Alfa O (L)	Chapman F (Gk)	Curtis B	Mundle-Smith J (L)	Asonganyi D (L)	Acauah E (L)	No.
x	x	x	x	x	x	x	xs	x	xs	x	xs	sx	sx	sx	s	s														1
x	x	x	x	xs	x	x	x	x	x	s	s	sx	xs	sx	s															2
x	x	x	x	x	x	x	x	xs	sx	sx	xs	xs	sx	s	s															3
x		x	x	x	x		x	xs	x		xs	x	sx	xs	sx	s	sx	s												4
x		x	x	sx	x	xs	x		xs	x	sx	xs	sx	s		x	s													5
x		x	x	sx	x	x		xs	xs	sx	sx	s	s																	6
x	x	x	x		x	xs	x	x		xs	sx		x	sx	xs	s	sx	s												7
x	x	x	x		x	x	x		xs	x	sx	xs	s	sx		xs		s	sx											8
x	x	x	x	xs	x	x		x	x	xs	sx	sx	sx	s	xs		s													9
x	x	x	x		x	x	x	sx	sx	xs	xs		xs	sx	s		s													10
x	x	x	x		x		xs	x	x	sx	sx	x	sx		xs		s	sx	s											11
x	x	x	x	sx	xs	x	x	x	x	sx	xs	sx	s		x		s													12
x		x	x	x		x	x	x	xs	x	xs	sx		sx	sx	s	s	xs												13
x	x	x	x		x	xs	x	xs	x	sx	x	xs	sx	sx	x		s		s											14
s	x		x	x	x	x	x	sx	sx	xs		sx		x	s			sx	x	s										15
s	sx		x		x		xs	sx	sx	x		x		x	xs			x	x	xs										16
x	x	x	x	x		x	xs	sx	sx	sx	x		x	xs		x	s													17
s	x	x	x		x	sx	x	x		sx	x		sx	xs		x		x	x											18
s	x	x	x	xs	x	xs	x	x		sx	sx		s	xs		x		x	sx											19
x	x	x	x		x	xs	x		s	s	sx	x		x		x	s	s												20
s	x	x	xs		x	x	x		sx	sx	x	xs		x		x		s												21
s	x	x		x	x	xs	xs		sx	s	x	xs		x		x		sx	sx											22
xs	x	x		x	x	x	xs	x		s	sx	sx	xs		s	x		x		sx	s									23
x	x		x	x	x	x	s		sx	x	xs	xs		xs		x		s	sx	sx										24
x		x		x	x	x	sx	x		sx	x	sx	xs		x		x		s	s	xs									25
x	s		x	x		x	x	xs	x		sx		x		x	sx		sx												26
x		x	x		x	x	xs	x		sx	x		x		x	s		s												27
x	sx	x	x		x	x	xs	x		sx		xs	sx		x		x	s												28
x		x	x	x	xs	s	s	sx	xs	sx	x	xs	sx		x		x	s												29
x	s	x	x	x	x	xs	xs	x		s	sx	sx	sx		x		x													30
x	x	x	x	x	x		sx	x	s	s	xs	sx	xs	sx		xs		x												31
sx	x	x	x	x	x	s	sx	xs	s		xs	sx	xs		x		x													32
x	x	x	x		x	s	sx	x	s	s	xs	x	s		x		x													33
x	x	x	x		x	xs	x	s	x	xs	s	xs	sx	x		x														34
x	x	x	x	x	x	x	xs	s	s	s	x		s		x		x		s											35
x	s	x	x		x		x	x		xs	sx	xs	x		sx	sx	x		s	xs										36
x	x	x	x	xs	x	sx	xs		x	sx	s	x		xs		sx		s		x	s									37
x	sx	x	x		x		x	xs		xs		s	x	xs	sx	x		sx												38
x	s	x	x		x	x	s		xs		x	xs	sx	x		s	sx		x											39
x	s		x	x		x	xs	xs	sx	sx		xs		x	x	s	x		sx		x									40
x	s		x	x		x	xs		sx		x	xs	xs	x		s		s	sx		x									41
x	xs		x	x		x	x	xs			s	x	xs	sx	x		sx		sx											42
x	x	x	x	xs	x	xs		sx		sx		s	x	xs	sx	x		x												43
x	s	xs	x	x	x		x		sx		x	sx		x		xs		x	xs	sx										44
22	24	33	41	25	33	23	33	19	28	2	1	7	16	5	1	0	25	0	21	1	0	0	0	1	1	0	4	0	0	x
	2	1	0	3	5	6	6	17	1	14	8	7	10	21	8	0	3	0	0	2	0	1	0	2	0	0	0	1	0	xs
3		1	0	1	0	3	2	3	13	20	9	15	7	12	3	5	2	0	2	3	3	0	5	0	0	1	0	1		sx
9	3		0	0	0	0	0	5	1	4	8	13	2	2	6	7	5	5	8	9	3	3	5	0	0	1	0	0	0	s

GOALKEEPERS	CS	CCS
Ashby-Hammond	5	2
Dunn	4	2

x - Played full 90 minutes
xs - Substituted off
sx - Substituted on
s - Non-playing Substitute

NOTTS COUNTY MATCH RESULTS 2019-20

Date	Comp	Opponents	H/A	Att:	Result		Goalscorers	Pos
Aug 3	NL	Eastleigh	A	2668	L	0 - 1		19
6	NL	Stockport County	H	5820	D	1 - 1	O'Brien 36	20
10	NL	Barnet	H	4096	L	1 - 2	Boldewijn 9	
13	NL	Harrogate Town	A	1863	W	2 - 0	Dennis 45+2 (pen) Boldewijn 86	
17	NL	Wrexham	H	6236	D	1 - 1	Booty 69	17
24	NL	Ebbsfleet United	A	1293	D	2 - 2	Turner 12 Booty 48	
26	NL	Chorley	H	5082	W	5 - 1	Tyson 30 Boldewijn 49 Dennis 53 Thomas 65 71	
31	NL	Yeovil Town	A	2424	L	1 - 3	Dennis 90+4 (pen)	15
Sep 3	NL	Solihull Moors	H	4152	D	0 - 0		15
7	NL	Sutton United	A	2059	D	1 - 1	Wootton 52	17
14	NL	Halifax Town	H	5188	W	1 - 0	Wootton 57	13
21	NL	Bromley	A	3122	L	1 - 2	Wootton 35	16
24	NL	Boreham Wood	A	756	W	2 - 1	Boldewijn 42 Osborne 66	11
28	NL	AFC Fylde	H	9090	W	2 - 0	Thomas 19 McCrory 80	8
Oct 5	NL	Dover Athletic	A	1463	D	2 - 2	Rose 41 (pen) Dennis 90	12
8	NL	Dagenham & Redbridge	H	3670	W	2 - 0	Booty 24 Dennis 87	7
12	NL	Torquay United	H	5265	W	2 - 0	Brindley 8 Dennis 48	5
19	FAC4Q	**Belper Town**	H	5729	W	2 - 1	**Boldewijn 29 Wootton 76**	
26	NL	Chesterfield	A	5432	L	0 - 1		8
29	NL	Woking	A	2175	W	4 - 0	Boldewijn 7 72 Wootton 18 Thomas 60	7
Nov 2	NL	Hartlepool United	H	5258	D	2 - 2	Thomas 44 61	7
9	FAC1	**Ebbsfleet United**	A	1206	W	3 - 1	**Wootton 34 58 Turner 90+3**	
16	NL	Barrow	H	5287	L	0 - 3		9
23	NL	Aldershot Town	A	2211	L	1 - 2	Wootton 36	
26	NL	Boreham Wood	H	3256	D	2 - 2	Wootton 30 41	9
30	FAC2	**Northampton Town**	A	4489	L	1 - 3	**Dennis 84**	
Dec 7	NL	Sutton United	H	5652	D	1 - 1	Thomas 14	12
14	FAT1	**Chesterfield**	A	931	W	1 - 0	**Dennis 72**	
21	NL	Halifax Town	A	2491	W	4 - 2	Wootton 48 90+8 Rose 60 81 (pen)	11
26	NL	Maidenhead United	H	5129	W	3 - 0	Wootton 19 Osborne 29 Dennis 44	9
28	NL	Solihull Moors	A	3212	W	1 - 0	Thomas 76	6
Jan 1	NL	Maidenhead United	A	1657	D	0 - 0		7
4	NL	Bromley	H	5192	W	2 - 1	Thomas 4 Rawlinson 70	5
11	FAT2	**Dagenham & Redbridge**	H	2385	W	2 - 1	**Dennis 53 Doyle 90+3**	
18	NL	Dover Athletic	H	5157	D	0 - 0		6
25	NL	Dagenham & Redbridge	A	1697	L	0 - 2		7
Feb 1	NL	Chesterfield	H	6347	W	3 - 0	Boldewijn 52 Wootton 59 76	6
8	FAT3	**Yeovil Town**	A	1946	W	2 - 1	**Rawlinson 7 Wootton 70**	
15	NL	Woking	H	5074	D	1 - 1	Dennis 70	
22	NL	Hartlepool United	A	3839	L	0 - 2		7
29	FAT4	**Aveley**	H	4893	W	5 - 0	**O'Brien 32 Crawford 38 Osborne 44 Wootton 60 Wilson 64**	
Mar 3	NL	AFC Fylde	A	1353	W	2 - 1	Boldewijn 13 Long 76	6
7	NL	Barrow	A	3307	W	2 - 0	Crawford 68 Roberts 71	6
10	NL	Aldershot Town	H	4287	W	3 - 1	Roberts 35 Dennis 59 67	3
14	NL	Eastleigh	H	4942	W	4 - 0	Wootton 15 61 Dennis 53 Roberts 68	3
July 25	PO SF	**Barnet**	H	0	W	2 - 0	**Dennis 37 Roberts 59**	
Aug 2	PO F	**Harrogate Town**	N	0	L	1 - 3	**Roberts 46**	

GOALSCORERS	SG	CSG	Pens	Hat tricks	Total		SG	CSG	Pens	Hat tricks	Total
Wootton	14	3			19	Rawlinson	2	1			2
Dennis	14	3	2		15	Turner	2	1			2
Boldewijn	8	2			9	Brindley	1	1			1
Thomas	7	2			9	Doyle	1	1			1
Roberts	5	5			5	Long	1	1			1
Booty	3	2			3	McCrory	1	1			1
Osborne	3	1			3	Tyson	1	1			1
Rose	2	1	2		3	Wilson*	1	1			1
Crawford	2	1			2						
O'Brien	2	1			2						

Player appearance grid. (Abbreviations: x = Played full 90 minutes; xs = Substituted off; sx = Substituted on; s = Non-playing Substitute; L = on loan)

Slocombe S	Bakayogo Z	McCory D	Bird P	O'Brien J	Doyle M	Rose M	Kelly-Evans D	Oxlade-Chamberlain C	Tyson N	Boldewijn E	Hemmings K	Turner B	Tootle M	Dunn D	Fitzsimons R (GK)	Rawlinson C	Graham S (L)	Campbell R	Dennis K	Booty R	Osborne S	Thomas W	Wootton K	Shields S (L)	Brindley R	Kean J (Gk)	Lacey A	Crawford T	Howes A	Roberts C	McDonnell J (GK)(L)	Betts O	Bagan J (L)	Long A (L)	Wilson S (L)	No.
x	x	x	xs	x	x	x	xs	xs	x	x	xs	sx	sx	s	s																					1
x	x		xs	x		x	x		xs	x	x	sx	s	sx	s	x	x	s																		2
x	x		s	xs		x	xs		x		xs	sx	x	s	x	x	sx	sx																		3
x	x				x	x			xs	x		x	sx	s	x	s	sx	x	xs	xs	sx	sx														4
x	s	x		sx	x	x			sx	x		x		s	x	x		xs	xs	xs	xs															5
x	s	x		sx	x	x			sx	x		x		s	xs	x		xs	x	s	x															6
x	x	x		x	x	x	xs		xs	x		x		s			sx	x	sx	x	sx	s														7
x	s	x		x	x		x		x	x		x		sx	xs	x	xs	s	x	sx																8
x	s	x		x	x	x	x		xs	x		x		s	s	x	sx	s	x	x																9
x	s	x		s	x	x	x		x	x		x		xs	xs	sx	x	sx	sx																	10
x	s	x		x	x		x		xs	x		x		s	sx	x	s	sx	xs	x	x															11
x	xs	x	sx	xs		x			x			s		x		x	sx	sx	x	x	s															12
x	x	x	sx		x				xs			s		x		s	x	xs	x	x	sx	x	s													13
x	x	x	sx		x				xs			s		x		sx	x	xs	xs	x	x	s														14
x	x		s		x				s	x		x		x		sx	x	xs	xs	x	x															15
x	x		xs		sx				s	x		x		x		sx	x	sx	x	xs	x															16
x	x			x	x	sx			sx			x		x		xs	sx	x	sx	x	x															17
x	s	x		x	s				sx	x		x		s	x		xs	x	x	sx	x	xs	s													18
x	xs	x		x	x	s			sx	x		x		x			xs	sx	x	sx	x	xs	x													19
x	s	x		x	x	x			x			x		x		s	x	xs	x	sx	x															20
x	s	x		x	x				sx	x		x		x		sx	x	xs	x	sx	x															21
x	sx	x		x	x	s			sx	x		x		x		s	xs	s	xs	x		x	s													22
x	s	x		x	x	s			sx	s		x		x		sx	x	sx	x		x															23
x	s	x		x	xs	s			sx	s		x		x		sx	x	xs	x		x															24
x	s	x		x	x	s			sx	x		x		x		s	sx	xs	x	sx	x															25
x	s	x		x	x	s			sx	x		x		x		sx	xs	s	xs	x	xs	xs	sx	x	s											26
x	s	x		x	x	s			x			x		x		sx	xs	s	xs	x	x															27
xs	x	s		xs	sx		x		xs			x			x	x	x	x	s		x		sx	x	sx											28
	x	s		x	xs	xs			xs			x	x		sx		x	x	xs	xs	s	x	sx													29
x	x	sx		x	xs	x			xs			s	x		x		x	x	xs	x			x	sx												30
x	x	s		x	x	x			xs	xs			s		x		s	sx	xs	x			x	xs												31
x	s	x	s		x	x	x		sx	x					x		xs		xs	sx	x		x	s												32
x	s	x	sx		x	x			s	x					x		xs		xs	xs	x		x	s												33
s	x	x			x	s	x		sx			x	s		xs		x	x	sx	xs	s		x	x	s											34
x	s	x	s		x	x			sx	x					x		xs	xs	xs	x			x	s												35
	x		s	sx	x	x			x						x		x	x	xs		x		x	s				xs								36
		sx	xs	x	x				x						x		x	x	xs	sx	x	s	x	xs				xs								37
	x		x		sx	x			s						x		xs	x	x	sx	xs	sx	x	x	x			x	s							38
		x	x	x	x				x						x		x	s		x	s	x	s		s		x	x		s						39
		s	sx	x	xs	x			x						x		xs	sx			x		sx	xs	x		s	x								40
		x	xs	s	x				s					xs		x		x		xs	xs	s	s		x		x	sx	x	x	xs					41
		s	sx	x	x	x			xs						x		s		xs	x		x		s			xs	x		x	sx					42
	x		x	sx	xs	x			x						x		s		xs	x		x	x	sx	x		xs	x		xs	xs	xs				43
	x		x	sx	xs	x			x						sx		x		s	x		x	sx	x			xs	x		xs	s	sx				44
		s	x	xs	x				x						x		xs		sx	x		x	sx	x			xs	x		x	s	sx				45
x		x	x	x	s				sx	x					s		xs		sx	x		x	x	s			xs	s		x						46
x		xs	x	x	sx				sx	x					s		xs		sx	x		xs	x	s			x	s		x						47
4	14	30	1	12	33	34	18	0	2	32	1	22	0	1	4	34	6	0	7	12	5	7	32	1	26	0	16	4	0	2	8	0	4	3	0	x
1	2	0	2	5	1	6	3	1	5	7	0	2	0	0	0	3	1	0	16	5	7	19	3	10	2	0	0	1	0	7	0	0	1	1	2	xs
0	1	0	8	5	3	1	3	0	10	4	1	2	2	0	3	3	1		14	7	4	13	4	9	1	0	7	0	1	0	1	0	1	2		sx
1	17	2	9	2	0	3	9	0	5	3	0	0	1	5	11	4	0	2	8	1	0	2	4	9	0	8	1	0	2	1	2	1	1			s

GOALKEEPERS	CS	CCS
Slocombe	12	3
McDonnell	2	1
Fitzsimons	1	1
Kean	1	1

x - Played full 90 minutes
xs - Substituted off
sx - Substituted on
s - Non-playing Substitute

SOLIHULL MOORS MATCH RESULTS 2019-20

Date	Comp	Opponents	H/A	Att:	Result	Goalscorers	Pos
Aug 3	NL	Harrogate Town	A	1045	D 2 - 2	Blissett 34 McCallum 66	12
6	NL	Torquay United	H	1613	W 3 - 0	Osborne 6 43 Hawkridge 9 (pen)	3
10	NL	Aldershot Town	H	1109	W 2 - 1	McCallum 40 (pen) Stenson 76	
13	NL	Chorley	A	1020	W 6 - 1	McCallum 14 65 (pen) Blissett 41 51 57 Wright 83	
17	NL	Ebbsfleet United	H	955	W 2 - 1	Osborne 35 King J 80 (og)	1
24	NL	Woking	A	1997	L 0 - 2		
26	NL	Eastleigh	H	1779	L 1 - 2	Hancox 69	
31	NL	Halifax Town	A	2053	L 1 - 2	Nicholls 57	7
Sep 3	NL	Notts County	A	4152	D 0 - 0		7
7	SCC 3	Kelty Hearts	A	1146	D 1 - 1	Stenson 72 (won 4-2 on pens)	
14	NL	Barrow	A	1152	L 0 - 3		12
21	NL	Yeovil Town	H	1525	L 0 - 1		15
24	NL	Stockport County	H	1339	W 2 - 0	Howe 52 Reckord 63	10
28	NL	Barnet	A	1052	D 0 - 0		13
Oct 1	NL	Wrexham	H	1425	W 3 - 1	Osborne 11 70 Reckord 25	9
5	NL	Boreham Wood	A	540	L 0 - 1		13
8	NL	Sutton United	A	3043	W 2 - 0	Beesley 20 Wright 73 (pen)	8
12	NL	Bromley	H	2120	W 2 - 1	Gunning 41 Wright 54	6
19	FAC4Q	Barrow	A	1523	W 1 - 0	Daly 52	
26	NL	Maidenhead United	A	1152	L 0 - 1		9
29	SCC 4	Rangers U21	H	1598	D 3 - 3	Howe 8 Yussuf 36 Carter 60 (lost 3-4 on pens)	
Nov 2	NL	Dagenham & Redbridge	H	1214	W 2 - 1	Ball 2 McCallum 63	9
5	NL	Hartlepool United	A	2703	W 1 - 0	Beesley 59	6
9	FAC1	Oxford City	A	667	W 5 - 1	McCallum 10 Ball 32 42 46 51	
16	NL	AFC Fylde	H	1389	W 3 - 1	Wright 15 McCallum 20 (pen) Howe 25	3
23	NL	Dover Athletic	A	1027	D 1 - 1	Osborne 28	3
26	NL	Stockport County	A	3142	W 4 - 1	Howe 52 Ball 58 McCallum 67 Osborne 81	2
Dec 2	FAC2	Rotherham United	H	2317	L 3 - 4	Osborne 6 Gudger 8 Ball 62	
7	NL	Wrexham	A	3113	L 0 - 2		5
14	FAT1	Darlington	H	500	D 2 - 2	Jones 39 Beesley 61	
26	NL	Chesterfield	A	3203	D 2 - 2	Ball 44 Wright 90+5	5
28	NL	Notts County	H	3212	L 0 - 1		7
Jan 1	NL	Chesterfield	H	1200	W 3 - 0	Beesley 29 70 McCallum 79	6
4	NL	Yeovil Town	A	2907	D 0 - 0		6
8	FAT1r	Darlington	A	812	L 0 - 1		
18	NL	Boreham Wood	H	882	L 0 - 2		9
25	NL	Sutton United	H	1618	D 0 - 0		9
Tim Flowers departs as manager by mutuel consent. Assistant manager Gary Whild and coach James Quinn are in interim charge.							
28	NL	Barrow	H	892	D 0 - 0		8
Feb 1	NL	Maidenhead United	H	797	L 0 - 2		8
8	NL	Bromley	A	1716	D 2 - 2	Bush 68 (og) Carline 77	
11	NL	Barnet	H	501	W 1 - 0	Hawkridge 19 (pen)	
Jimmy Shan is named as the new manager.							
22	NL	Dagenham & Redbridge	A	2345	L 0 - 2		8
29	NL	Dover Athletic	H	773	W 3 - 0	Simpson 36 (og) Howe 70 81	6
Mar 3	NL	Hartlepool United	H	896	L 0 - 1		7
7	NL	AFC Fylde	A	1310	D 0 - 0		7

GOALSCORERS	SG	CSG	Pens	Hat tricks	Total		SG	CSG	Pens	Hat tricks	Total
McCallum	8	3	3		9	Stenson	2	1			2
Ball	5	2			8	Carline	1	1			1
Osborne	6	3			8	Carter	1	1			1
Howe	5	2			6	Daly	1	1			1
Beesley*	4	1			5	Gudger	1	1			1
Wright	5	2	1		5	Gunning	1	1			1
Blissett	2	1		1	4	Hancox	1	1			1
Opponent	3	1			3	Jones	1	1			1
Hawkridge	2	1	1		2	Nicholls	1	1			1
Reckord	2	1			2	Yussuf	1	1			1

	Vaughan L	Daly L	Reckord J	Gudger A	Howe C	Storer K	Hawkridge T	Osborne J	McCallum P	Blissett N	Carter D	Wright D	Stenson M	Hancox M	Williams T	Carline G	Flowers H	Nicholls A	Rowley S (Gk)	Neuville J (L)	Nesbit R	Yussuf A (L)	Gunning G	Ball J	Beesley J (L)	Bigirimana G	Jones S (L)	Maxwell L	Drysdale D (L)	Cowley J (L)	Wycherley A (Gk)	Bushaj M	Bajrami G (L)	Clayton-Phillips N (L)	No.
x	x	x	x	x	x	x	x	xs	xs	xs	sx	sx	sx	s	s																				1
x	x	x	xs	x	x	x	x	xs	xs	x	sx	sx	s	sx	s																				2
x	x	x	x	x	x	x	xs	xs	x	xs	sx	sx	s	sx	s																				3
x	x	x	x	x	x	x	xs	xs	x	xs	sx	sx	s	sx	s																				4
x	x	x		x	x	xs	x	x	xs	x	xs	sx	s	sx	s																				5
x	s	x	xs	x	x	x	sx	xs	x	sx	x	xs	sx	x	s																				6
x	x	x	xs	x	x	x			x	x	xs	sx	s	s	sx	s																			7
x	x	x	x	x	x	xs	x		x	sx	sx	xs	sx	s																					8
x	s	s	x	x	x	x	xs	x		x	sx	sx	x	xs	s																				9
x	sx		x	x	x	x	sx	xs		xs	x	sx	s																						10
x	sx		x	x	x	x	xs			x	xs	sx	s	sx	s																				11
x	xs	x	x	x	x	xs	x			sx	x	s	xs	s	sx	x																			12
x	x	x	x	x	x	sx	xs	xs			xs	s	s	sx	xs	x																			13
x	xs	x	x	x	x	sx	xs	xs		x	s	s	sx	sx	x																				14
x	x	x	x	x	x	sx	xs	xs		xs	s	s	sx	sx	x																				15
x	xs	x	xs	x	x	x		x		s	sx	sx	x	sx																					16
x	x	x	x	x	xs	x			xs		sx	x	sx	xs	x																				17
x	x	x	x	x	x	sx	xs		xs	sx	xs	sx	x																						18
x	x	x	x	x	x	s	xs	sx		xs	s	s	s	s	x	sx	x																		19
x	x	x	x	x	x	sx	xs	sx		xs	s	s	xs	sx	x																				20
x		xs	x		x		x	xs	x	s	x	x	s	x	xs	xs	sx	sx																	21
x	x	x	x	x	sx		x	s	s	s	sx	x	xs	x																					22
x	x	x	x	xs	x	x	xs	s	s	sx	xs	sx	x																						23
x	x	x	x	x	sx	s	xs	sx	xs	s	s	s	sx	x	xs	x																			24
x	x	x	x	sx	x	xs	sx	xs	s	sx	s	xs	x	x																					25
x	x	x	sx	x	x	x	xs	xs	s	s	x	x	xs																						26
x	x	x	sx	xs	x	xs	x	s	sx	x	xs	sx																							27
x	x	x	x	x	s	xs	xs	sx	sx	s	s	x	x	xs	sx																				28
x	xs	x	x	xs	sx	xs	sx	xs	x	xs	s																								29
s	x	x	x	s	x	xs	xs	s	x	x	x	sx	sx	x	sx	xs	s																	30
x	x	x	x	x	sx	xs	xs	x	s	s	x	xs	sx																						31
x	xs	x	sx	xs	xs	s	x	x	sx	s	x	xs	sx																						32
s	sx	x	x	x	sx	x	xs	sx	x	x	sx	xs	sx																						33
x	xs	sx	x	x	x	s	sx	xs	s	sx	x	x	xs	x																					34
x	x	xs	x	x	x	x	sx	xs	sx	x	s	x																							35
x	sx	sx	x	x	x	s	x	s	xs	sx	x	xs	xs	x	x																				36
x	xs	x	x	x	s	s	sx	x	x	x	x		x	x	s	s																			37
x	xs	x	x	x	s	sx	sx	sx	x	x	xs	x	x	xs	s																				38
x	x	x	xs	x	s	sx	sx	sx	x	x	x	x	s	xs	xs																				39
x	x	x	x	xs	xs	x	x	x	sx	xs	sx	s	sx	s																					40
x	x	x	xs	x	x	xs	x	x	sx	x	xs	sx	s	sx	s																				41
x	x	x	xs	xs	sx	x	x	s	x	sx	s	xs	s	xs	x	x	sx																	42
x	sx	x	x	x	s	x	sx	xs	x	s	xs	xs	x	x																					43
x	sx	x	x	xs	s	sx	sx	xs	x	s	x	x	x	xs																					44
x		x	x	x	sx	xs	sx	s	xs	x	x	s	x	xs																					45
4	24	17	24	39	45	36	14	11	11	5	9	7	0	5	19	7	0	0	1	1	0	1	12	15	15	0	0	0	2	1	0	0	4	0	x
0	5	0	9	1	0	3	7	17	13	12	3	13	3	5	0	1	0	2	0	0	0	3	6	7	11	0	1	0	1	3	0	0	0	1	xs
0	3	0	5	0	0	1	14	1	3	8	9	16	5	11	2	4	0	4	0	10	0	8	1	6	3	1	4	2	0	2	0	0	0	3	sx
1	3	1	0	0	0	0	10	1	0	7	3	4	1	12	20	2	2	1	13	2	1	5	2	0	0	0	1	4	2	0	4	1	0	0	s

GOALKEEPERS	CS	CCS
Boot	13	2

x - Played full 90 minutes
xs - Substituted off
sx - Substituted on
s - Non-playing Substitute

STOCKPORT COUNTY MATCH RESULTS 2019-20

Date	Comp	Opponents	H/A	Att:	Result	Goalscorers	Pos
Aug 3	NL	Maidenhead United	H	4626	L 0 - 1		20
6	NL	Newport County	A	5820	D 1 - 1	Osborne 71	21
10	NL	Yeovil Town	A	2602	D 1 - 1	Thomas 87	
13	NL	Barrow	H	4183	W 3 - 2	Mulhern 48 Keane 51 Thomas 71	
17	NL	Eastleigh	H	3869	W 2 - 0	Thomas 59 Osborne 83	8
24	NL	Harrogate Town	A	1326	L 1 - 2	Bell 69	
26	NL	Chesterfield	H	5578	W 2 - 0	Osborne 46 Bell 79	
31	NL	Wrexham	A	5777	W 2 - 1	Palmer 20 Minihan 39	6
Sep 3	NL	AFC Fylde	H	3912	W 2 - 1	Jackson 19 Craigen 22 (og)	5
7	NL	Chorley	A	2693	L 0 - 3		5
14	NL	Aldershot Town	H	4279	L 1 - 2	Piggott 75	8
21	NL	Boreham Wood	A	744	L 0 - 4		9
24	NL	Solihull Moors	A	1339	L 0 - 2		12
28	NL	Torquay United	H	4275	L 0 - 4		17
Oct 5	NL	Sutton United	A	1808	D 0 - 0		17
8	NL	Hartlepool United	H	3465	W 2 - 1	Palmer 5 Walker T 21	15
19	**FAC4Q**	**York City**	**A**	**2870**	**L 0 - 2**		
26	NL	Dover Athletic	A	1154	W 1 - 0	Mulhern 29	17
29	NL	Bromley	A	2205	D 2 - 2	Osborne 24 Walker T 34	17
Nov 2	NL	Woking	H	3888	L 1 - 3	Mulhern 86	17
9	NL	Dagenham & Redbridge	H	3771	W 1 - 0	Bell 90+3	
16	NL	Barnet	A	1536	W 2 - 1	Osborne 76 Mulhern 90	11
23	NL	Ebbsfleet United	H	4167	D 1 - 1	Walker S 90+3	
26	NL	Solihull Moors	H	3142	L 1 - 4	Turnbull 45	13
30	NL	Torquay United	A	2659	W 5 - 1	Walker T 47 Bell 52 Osborne 63 Rodney 86 Mulhern 90+3	8
Dec 7	NL	Chorley	H	4510	W 4 - 2	Bell 28 66 Arthur 45+1 Walker T 81	8
14	**FAT1**	**Blyth Spartans**	**H**	**1436**	**W 4 - 2**	**Palmer 30 Thomas 66 Walker T 76 Minihan 90+4**	
21	NL	Aldershot Town	A	1891	L 1 - 2	Rodney 57	9
26	NL	Halifax Town	H	5536	W 5 - 1	Arthur 25 Osborne 43 53 73 Brown 61 (og)	7
28	NL	AFC Fylde	A	2764	W 2 - 1	Walker S 53 Cowan 61	5
Jan 1	NL	Halifax Town	A	3460	D 0 - 0		5
4	NL	Boreham Wood	H	4074	L 1 - 3	Rodney 51	8
11	**FAT2**	**Dorking Wanderers**	**A**	**1604**	**D 1 - 1**	**Thomas 64**	
14	**FAT2r**	**Dorking Wanderers**	**H**	**1121**	**L 0 - 4**		
18	NL	Sutton United	H	5079	D 0 - 0		8
25	NL	Hartlepool United	A	3766	L 0 - 2		10
Feb 1	NL	Dover Athletic	H	4506	L 0 - 2		12
8	NL	Dagenham & Redbridge	A	1512	D 1 - 1	McAlinden 89	
15	NL	Bromley	H	46111	W 1 - 0	Hogan 53	
22	NL	Woking	A	2189	D 1 - 1	Lloyd 6	10
29	NL	Ebbsfleet United	A	1030	W 1 - 0	Palmer 87	7
Mar 7	NL	Barnet	H	5011	D 1 - 1	Palmer 45	9
14	NL	Maidenhead United	A	1662	W 2 - 1	Palmer 57 McAlinden 76	7

GOALSCORERS	SG	CSG	Pens	Hat tricks	Total		SG	CSG	Pens	Hat tricks	Total
Osborne	7	1		1	9	Opponent	2	1			2
Bell	5	2			6	Walker S	2	1			2
Palmer	6	3			6	Cowan	1	1			1
Mulhern	5	1			5	Hogan*	1	1			1
Thomas	5	3			5	Jackson	1	1			1
Walker T*	5	3			5	Keane	1	1			1
Rodney	3	1			3	Lloyd	1	1			1
Arthur	2	1			2	Piggott	1	1			1
McAlinden	2	1			2	Turnbull	1	1			1
Minihan	2	1			2						

Hinchliffe B	Palmer A	Minihan S	Cowan D	Turnbull P	Kirby J	Dimaio C	Keane A	Walker S	Thomas A	Mulhern F	Osborne E	Bell N	Jackson B	Curran A	Ormson I (Gk)	Arthur F	Downing J	Piggott J (L)	Leesley J (L)	Gorst A (Gk)	Greenhalgh M	Hammill A (L)	Walker T (L)	Garratt T	Rodney D (L)	Hopkins J	Cooper J	Stanyer F	Rattle M	Czubik S	Clarke E (L)	McAlinden L	Archer J (L)	Lloyd D (L)	Maynard L	Hogan L	Bennett R	No.
x	x	x	x	x	xs	xs	x	x	xs	x	sx	sx	sx	s	s																							1
x	x	x	x	x	xs	s	x	x	xs	x	x	sx	sx	s	s																							2
x	x	xs	x	x	sx	sx	x	xs	sx	x	x	xs	x		s	s																						3
x	x	x	x	x	sx	xs	x		x	xs	x	sx	xs	s	s	sx																						4
x	x	x	x	x	sx	xs	x		xs	xs	x	sx	x	s	s	sx																						5
x	x	x	x	x	sx	xs	x	sx	xs	xs	x	sx	x	s	s																							6
x	x	x	x	x	x	sx	x	xs	x	x	xs	xs	x	s	s	s																						7
x	x	x	x	xs	xs	x	x	x	sx	x	s	sx	s	sx	s																							8
x	x	x	x	x			sx	x	x	sx	xs	xs	xs	s	s	x	sx																					9
x	x	xs	x	x		sx	x	x	x		xs	xs	xs	sx	s	s			x																			10
x	x	xs	x	xs		sx	x	x	x		x	x	sx		s	s		sx	xs																			11
	x	sx	s	x		sx	x	x	xs	xs	xs	x	xs		x	x			x	s																		12
x		x	x	x		xs	x	x	x	xs	sx	sx	sx		s	x			xs		s																	13
x		x	x	x		sx	x		x	xs	x	sx	sx		s	x			xs		s	xs																14
x	x	x	x	x			s	x	x	x	xs	x	sx		s	s			sx			xs																15
x	x	x	sx	x			x	x		sx	sx	xs			s	x			x			s	xs															16
x	x	x	s	xs			x	xs	sx	sx	s	sx	x		s	x			x			sx	x	s	xs													17
x	x	x		xs			sx	x	x	xs	sx	sx			s	x						s	x	x	xs													18
x	x	x	sx				x	x	x	xs	xs	sx	sx		s	x						s	xs	x														19
x	x	x		x			s	x	xs	sx	x		sx		s	x						sx	xs	xs	x													20
x	x	x		s		sx	x	s	xs	sx	x	sx	x		s	x							x	xs	x													21
x	x	x		s			x	x	sx	sx	x	xs	sx		s	x							xs	xs	x													22
x	x	x		s			x	sx	sx	x	x	sx	x		s	x							xs	xs	x													23
x	x		x	xs			s	x	x	sx	xs	xs	xs		s	x			x				sx	sx	x													24
x	x	x					x	x	xs	sx	x	xs	sx		s	x			s				xs	x	sx													25
x	x	x	s	x			x		sx	sx	x	xs			s	x			sx				xs	x	xs													26
x	x	sx	x	x			x			sx	xs	xs			s	x							x	x	xs	sx	sx	s	s	s								27
x	x	xs	s	x			x	sx	sx	x	xs	sx			s	x							x	x	x													28
x	x	x	sx	x			x	sx	x	sx	x	sx			s	x			s				xs	x														29
x	x	sx	x	sx			x	x	sx	s	x	x			s	x			x				xs		xs													30
x	x	s	x	x			x	s	xs	sx	x	x			s	x			x				xs		sx													31
x	x	xs	sx	x			x	x	xs	sx	x	x			s	x							x	xs	sx													32
x	x	x	x	x			x	sx	x	sx	xs	xs	x		s	x	s									s		s				s						33
x	x	x	x	x			xs	xs	x	sx	xs	xs	x		s	sx	s									s				s								34
x	x	s	x	x			x		xs	sx	xs	sx	sx		s	x																		x	x	xs		35
x	x	sx	x	x			x	s	x		x	sx			s	x																	xs	sx	xs	x		36
x	x	x	x	x			s	x		sx	sx	sx	x		s	x																	x	xs	xs	xs		37
x	x	sx	x		xs	x	s	x			xs	sx			s	x																	xs	sx		x	x	38
x	x	x	x		sx	x	x	xs			xs	sx			s	sx																	s	x		xs	x	39
x	x	x	xs		's	x	x	xs			x	sx	sx		s	sx																	xs		x		x	40
x	x	x	x	sx		sx	x	xs			xs	sx	x		s	s																	xs		x		x	41
x	x	x	x			xs		x			sx	xs	xs		s	sx																	s	sx		x	x	42
x	x	x	x		xs		x	x			sx	s			s	sx																	sx		xs	x	xs	43
42	41	29	28	26	1	0	37	21	19	4	19	6	7	0	1	26	0	1	6	0	0	0	6	8	4	0	0	0	0	2	2	0	5	1	5	0	0	x
0	0	5	1	6	3	8	1	5	13	12	14	13	5	0	0	0	0	3	0	0	2	10	4	7	0	0	0	0	2	3	3	3	0	0	1			xs
0	0	5	4	2	4	10	1	5	8	15	9	21	14	2	0	9	1	1	2	0	0	3	1	0	3	1	0	0	0	0	0	4	0	0	0	0	0	sx
0	0	2	4	3	0	3	2	6	0	2	0	1	2	5	41	6	2	0	2	1	2	3	0	2	0	2	1	1	1	2	2	0	0	0	0	0	0	s

GOALKEEPERS	CS	CCS
Hinchliffe	7	1

x - Played full 90 minutes
xs - Substituted off
sx - Substituted on
s - Non-playing Substitute

SUTTON UNITED MATCH RESULTS 2019-20

Date	Comp	Opponents	H/A	Att:	Result	Goalscorers	Pos
Aug 3	NL	Hartlepool United	A	3812	W 3 - 1	Beautyman 7 23 Randall 90+4	2
6	NL	Barnet	H	1761	D 1 - 1	Beautyman 57	4
10	NL	Chorley	H	1436	D 2 - 2	Jarvis 14 Milsom 54	
13	NL	Eastleigh	A	1750	D 1 - 1	Collins 14	
17	NL	Boreham Wood	A	407	W 1 - 0	Wright 83	6
24	NL	Dover Athletic	H	1552	L 1 - 2	Collins 45+1	
26	NL	Aldershot Town	A	1662	D 1 - 1	Collins 83 (pen)	
31	NL	Maidenhead United	H	1554	L 0 - 3		13
Sep 3	NL	Yeovil town	A	2279	L 0 - 1		17
7	NL	Notts County	H	2059	D 1 - 1	Beautyman 11	16
14	NL	Wrexham	A	3824	D 1 - 1	Beautyman 63	17
21	NL	Chesterfield	H	1649	W 4 - 0	Jarvis 24 76 Wright 34 Beautyman 90+6	13
24	NL	Dagenham & Redbridge	H	1513	L 0 - 2		19
28	NL	Harrogate Town	A	769	L 0 - 2		19
Oct 5	NL	Stockport County	H	1808	D 0 - 0		18
8	NL	Solihull Moors	A	3043	L 0 - 2		19
19	**FAC4Q**	**Billericay Town**	**H**	**789**	**D 1 - 1**	**Bugiel 8**	
22	**FAC4Qr**	**Billericay Town**	**A**	**1113**	**L 2 - 5**	**Beautyman 10 Wright 55**	
26	NL	Ebbsfleet United	H	1566	L 2 - 3	Ajiboye 23 Bugiel 74	21
29	NL	Halifax Town	H	1326	L 0 - 1		21
Nov 2	NL	Barrow	A	1827	L 0 - 1		23
16	NL	Torquay United	A	2770	W 2 - 1	Ajiboye 12 Beautyman 69	21
23	NL	Bromley	H	2261	L 0 - 2		
26	NL	Dagenham & Redbridge	A	1070	W 2 - 1	Eastmond 65 Wright 68	20
30	NL	Harrogate Town	H	1490	W 3 - 1	Beautyman 29 Wright 71 86	20
Dec 7	NL	Notts County	A	5652	D 1 - 1	Beautyman 76	21
10	NL	AFC Fylde	A	1054	D 0 - 0		19
14	**FAT1**	**Dagenham & Redbridge**	**H**	**429**	**D 1 - 1**	**Bugiel 76**	
17	**FAT1r**	**Dagenham & Redbridge**	**A**	**417**	**L 2 - 3**	**Beautyman 62 (pen) Bugiel 102 (aet)**	
21	NL	Wrexham	H	1637	W 3 - 1	Bugiel 12 36 66 (pen)	17
26	NL	Woking	A	2257	W 2 - 0	Bugiel 1 30	16
28	NL	Yeovil Town	H	2189	W 3 - 2	Beautyman 24 Goodliffe 42 Ajiboye 62	16
Jan 1	NL	Woking	H	1965	W 6 - 2	Beautyman 8 42 (pen) Goodliffe 17 Wright 27 Ajiboye 30 Dundas 90+2	12
4	NL	Chesterfield	A	3283	L 0 - 1		12
18	NL	Stockport County	A	5079	D 0 - 0		15
25	NL	Solihull Moors	H	1618	D 0 - 0		15
Feb 1	NL	Ebbsfleet United	A	979	D 1 - 1	Beautyman 50	14
22	NL	Barrow	H	1871	D 2 - 2	Beautyman 45+3 66 (pen)	15
29	NL	Bromley	A	1909	W 1 - 0	Bugiel 16	15
Mar 3	NL	Halifax Town	A	1637	L 0 - 1		15
7	NL	Torquay United	H	1842	W 2 - 0	Milsom 19 Randall 37	14
14	NL	Hartlepool United	H	2126	D 1 - 1	Olaofe 3	14

GOALSCORERS	SG	CSG	Pens	Hat tricks	Total		SG	CSG	Pens	Hat tricks	Total
Beautyman	14	3	2		17	Eastmond	1	1			1
Bugiel	7	4	1		10	Olaofe	1	1			1
Wright	6	2			7						
Ajiboye	4	2			4						
Collins	3	2	1		3						
Jarvis	2	1			3						
Goodliffe	2	2			2						
Milsom	2	1			2						
Randall	2	1			2						
Dundas	1	1			1						

Butler J	Bennett D	Collins J	Barden J	Goodliffe B	Milsom R	Davis K	Beauhyman H	Randall W	Bolarinwa T	Jarvis A	Ajiboye D	Bugiel Omar	Matsuzaka D	Dudzinski B (Gk)	Dundas C	Kearney D	Wright T	Eastmond C	Tuson-Firth	Wyatt B	Reid K	Brown W	Tzanev N (Gk) (L)	John L	Brown S (Gk)	Mbeta C	Rowe C	Kealy C	Olaofe I (L)	Pearce B	No.
x	x	x	x	x	xs	x	x	x		xs	xs	sx	sx	sx	s	s															1
x	x	x	x	x	x	xs	x	x	sx	xs	xs	sx	sx	s	sx																2
x	x	x	x	x	x	x	x	xs	xs	sx	xs	sx	s	s	sx	sx															3
x	x	x	x	x	x	x	xs	x	xs	xs	xs	sx	s		s	sx															4
x	x	x	x	x	x	x		x	xs	xs	s		s	s	sx	xs	sx														5
x	xs	x		x	x	x	x		x	sx	x	xs	s		s		sx	xs	sx												6
x		sx		x	x	x	x		x	x	xs	s	xs	s	sx		sx	x	xs												7
x	x	xs	s	s	x	x	xs	x		x	x	x	sx		sx	sx			x	s											8
x		x	x	x	x	x	x		xs	xs			s	sx	sx	sx	x	x	xs	x											9
x		x	x	x	x	x	x	sx	x	xs			s	s	sx	s	xs	x		s											10
x		x	x	xs	x	xs	x		x	xs	x	sx	sx	s			s	x		sx											11
x		x	x	x	s	x	xs	x	x	x	sx	s		sx	xs			sx													12
x		x	x	x	s	x	sx	x	x	xs	s			sx	xs			sx													13
x		x	x	x	x	x	x	xs	s			s	s	sx	x			sx													14
x	xs	xs	x	s	xs	x	x	s	x	x		sx	s		s	x	x		sx												15
x	xs		xs	x	x	x	x	s	x	x	xs	sx		s			sx	x	s		s	x									16
x		**sx**	**x**	**x**	**x**	**x**	**s**	**s**	**sx**	**x**	**xs**	**x**	**s**		**xs**	**x**		**s**	**x**												17
x	**x**	**x**	**x**	**x**		**x**	**sx**	**sx**	**xs**	**xs**	**sx**	**sx**	**s**	**s**			**x**	**xs**		**s**	**x**	**s**									18
x		x	xs	x	x	x	xs		sx	x	xs		s	sx	xs			s	sx												19
x		xs	x	x	x	x	sx		sx	xs	x	x		s	xs	sx		s	x												20
x		xs	x	x	x	x	xs		sx	sx	x	x		s	xs	x		s	x												21
	s	x	x		x	x	sx	s	s	xs	xs			sx	x			x	x		x	x									22
	x	xs		x	x	sx	s	sx	x			s		sx	x			x	xs		x	x									23
	xs	x		x	x	x	s		sx	xs				sx	xs			x	sx		x	x									24
	s	x	x		xs	x	s		s	sx	xs			sx				x	x		x	x									25
s		x	x	sx		x	sx		x	sx				sx				x	xs		x	x									26
	s	x	x	s	x	x	x		xs	xs	sx			sx				x	sx		x	x									27
	s	**x**	**x**	**x**	**xs**	**x**	**xs**	**sx**	**s**	**sx**	**x**			**sx**	**x**			**s**	**xs**		**x**	**x**	**s**								28
	sx		**x**	**x**		**xs**	**xs**	**x**		**x**	**sx**		**s**	**xs**		**sx**		**x**	**x**		**x**	**x**									29
		x	x	sx	x		s	s	sx	xs				sx	xs	x		x	x		x	x									30
		x	x	s	x	s	x		sx	xs				sx	xs	x		x	xs		x	x									31
		x	x	x	x	x	sx	s	xs	x		s	sx		sx	xs	x		s		x	x									32
		x	xs	s	x	xs	sx		xs	xs				sx				x	x	x	s		x	x							33
		x	x	x	x		s	s		x				sx	x	x	s	xs			x	x		s							34
		x	x	s	x	x		s	x	x				s		x		x	x		x	x	s							35
		x	x	s	x	x			x	x				s		x		x	x		x	x	s							36
		x	x	s	x		sx		xs	xs				sx				x	x		x	x	s	sx							37
		x	x	sx	xs	x	x		x	xs				sx				x	s		x	x	s	sx	xs						38
		x	x	x		x	x	s		xs	x			sx				x	s	sx	x		x	s	xs						39
		x	x	x		xs	x		sx	xs				sx				x	x		x	s		x	xs	sx	s				40
		x		x		xs	s	x	xs				sx		sx		x	s		x	x		x	s	x						41
		x	x	x		x	x		x	xs				sx			sx	x		s	x	x		s	s	xs				42
21	6	14	32	36	28	22	36	10	11	4	17	6	5	0	0	0	9	19	0	19	13	0	21	19	0	0	3	0	1	0	x
0	2	3	5	3	0	6	2	9	3	12	15	21	1	0	1	0	12	4	2	0	5	0	0	0	0	0	0	1	3	0	xs
0	0	2	1	0	4	1	0	7	5	11	9	7	5	0	27	3	11	3	2	1	7	1	0	0	0	0	2	1	0	0	sx
1	0	4	1	0	5	4	1	5	11	6	0	1	7	13	11	3	1	1	1	9	4	2	0	0	2	1	5	3	0	1	s

GOALKEEPERS	CS	CCS
Tzanev	6	2
Butler	3	1

x - Played full 90 minutes
xs - Substituted off
sx - Substituted on
s - Non-playing Substitute

TORQUAY UNITED MATCH RESULTS 2019-20

Date	Comp	Opponents	H/A	Att:	Result	Goalscorers	Pos
Aug 3	NL	Boreham Wood	H	3138	W 2 - 1	Edwards 61 Reid 63	6
6	NL	Solihull Borough	A	1613	L 0 - 3		16
10	NL	Bromley	A	1398	D 3 - 3	Reid 34 (pen) Lemonheigh-Evans 64 Andrews 69	
13	NL	Maidenhead United	H	2946	L 0 - 2		
17	NL	Dover Athletic	A	1217	W 2 - 1	Andrews 51 Reid 53	13
24	NL	Aldershot Town	H	2668	W 2 - 0	Reid 45+1 Edwards 51	
26	NL	Barnet	A	1621	D 2 - 2	Koue Niate 5 Little 30	
31	NL	Hartlepool United	H	2683	L 1 - 2	Reid 51	10
Sep 3	NL	Woking	A	2599	D 1 - 1	Whitfield 79	11
7	NL	Harrogate Town	H	2527	W 4 - 2	Andrews 51 Kalala 70 Reid 73 80	8
14	NL	Chesterfield	A	3706	L 0 - 1		10
21	NL	Dagenham & Redbridge	H	2524	D 0 - 0		11
24	NL	Eastleigh	H	2005	L 2 - 3	Whitfield 35 Andrews 55	13
28	NL	Stockport County	A	4275	W 4 - 0	Reid 19 (pen) 26 45 Keane 42 (og)	10
Oct 5	NL	AFC Fylde	H	2440	W 2 - 1	Kalala 8 Buse 90+3	9
8	NL	Ebbsfleet United	A	908	W 4 - 2	Andrews 9 Reid 25 Buse 47 Davis 54	6
12	NL	Notts County	A	5265	L 0 - 2		9
19	FAC4Q	Boreham Wood	H	1952	W 3 - 2	Andrews 25 Reid 29 Whitfield 63	
26	NL	Barrow	H	2280	W 4 - 2	Reid 31 43 (pen) Little 51 75	7
29	NL	Wrexham	H	2313	W 1 - 0	Davis 56	6
Nov 2	NL	Halifax Town	A	2065	W 4 - 2	Cameron 8 Reid 17 (pen) 64 Kalala 90	5
9	FAC1	Maidstone United	A	2330	L 0 - 1		
16	NL	Sutton United	H	2770	L 1 - 2	Wynter 32	6
23	NL	Chorley	A	1281	L 0 - 1		8
26	NL	Eastleigh	A	1888	L 2 - 3	Keating 46 Andrews 49	8
30	NL	Stockport County	H	2659	L 1 - 5	Whitfield 75	10
Dec 7	NL	Harrogate Town	A	1348	L 1 - 2	Reid 68 (pen)	11
14	FAT1	Aldershot Town	H	1068	W 5 - 1	Janneh 7 82 Reid 24 (pen) 68 Keating 73	
21	NL	Chesterfield	H	2288	L 0 - 3		14
26	NL	Yeovil Town	A	5056	L 2 - 6	Hall 30 Whitfield 90+2	15
28	NL	Woking	H	3078	W 4 - 1	Hall 25 Reid 37 Whitfield 71 Keating 90+5	14
Jan 1	NL	Yeovil Town	H	4165	L 0 - 2		15
4	NL	Dagenham & Redbridge	A	1542	D 0 - 0		14
11	FAT2	Halifax Town	H	1309	L 1 - 2	Lemonheigh-Evans 72	
18	NL	AFC Fylde	A	1504	W 3 - 2	Hall 15 Reid 29 Whitfield 60	13
25	NL	Ebbsfleet United	H	2300	D 0 - 0		14
Feb 1	NL	Barrow	A	2586	L 1 - 2	Cameron 64	15
22	NL	Halifax Town	H	2053	W 1 - 0	Azeez 68	14
29	NL	Chorley	H	2126	W 2 - 0	Cundy 45+1 Reid 80	14
Mar 7	NL	Sutton United	A	1842	L 0 - 2		15

GOALSCORERS	SG	CSG	Pens	Hat tricks	Total		SG	CSG	Pens	Hat tricks	Total
Reid	16	2	6	1	22	Edwards	2	1			2
Andrews	7	1			7	Janneh	1	1			2
Whitfield*	7	2			7	Lemonheigh-Evans	2	1			2
Hall	3	2			3	Azeez*	1	1			1
Kalala	3	1			3	Cundy	1	1			1
Keating	3	1			3	Koue Niate	1	1			1
Little	2	1			3	Opponent	1	1			1
Buse	2	2			2	Wynter	1	1			1
Cameron	2	1			2						
Davis	2	1			2						

	MacDonald S	Koue Niate J	Cameron K	Hall A	Wynter B	Little A	Andrews J	Kalala K	Vincent F (L)	Reid J	Duku I	Lemonheigh-Evans C (L)	Edwards O (L)	Keating R	Lewis Joe (L)	Lucas (Gk)	Touray M (L)	Davis L	Whitfield B	Cundy R (L)	Dickson R	Buse M	Slough L	Koszela O	Janneh S (L)	Medford-Smith R (L)	Bansal-McNulty A (L)	Lewington J	James L (L)	Nemane A	Collings A (Gk)	Warren G (L)	Longridge J (L)	Azeez A (L)	No.
	X	X	X	X	X	X	XS	XS	X	X	X	SX	SX	S	S																				1
	X	X	X	X	X	X	SX	SX	S	X	SX	X	XS	XS	XS	S																			2
	X	X	X	X	X	XS	XS	X	XS	X	S	X	SX	SX	SX	S																			3
	X	XS	X	XS	X	X	XS	X	X	X	SX	X	S	SX	SX	S																			4
	S	X	X	X	X	X		XS		XS		XS	SX	SX	S	X	SX																		5
	S	X		X	X	XS	XS	SX	SX	X	XS	SX	S	X				X																	6
	S	X	X	X	X	X	XS	XS	X	X	SX	X	S	X				XS																	7
	S	X	X	X	XS	X	XS	XS	X	SX	X		S	SX	X			X																	8
	S		X	X	X	XS	SX	SX	X	X	XS			X	X			SX	S																9
	S		X		X		XS	SX	X	X	XS			XS	X			X	X	X	SX	SX	S												10
	S		X		X			X	X	X	XS			S	X			X	X	X	XS	SX	S	SX											11
	S	S	X		X		SX	XS	X	X	S			SX	XS	X		X	X	X		X													12
	S		X		X		XS	SX	X	X	SX			X	S	X		X	XS	X		X		S											13
	S		X		X		XS	SX	X	X	SX			SX	SX	X			XS	X		X	S												14
	S	S	X		X		SX	X	XS	X	S			SX	X			X	X	X		X													15
	S	S	X		X		SX	X	X	X	XS	SX		S				X	X	X		X													16
	S	S	X	S	X		SX	XS	X	X	SX			X				X	X	X		X													17
	X	S	X	S	X	XS	X		XS	XS	SX			SX	SX	S		X	X	X		X	S												18
	S		X		X	X	XS	XS	X	X	S	SX		SX	X		X	XS	X		X														19
	X		X		X		XS	XS	X	X	S	SX		SX	S		X	X	X		X		SX												20
	S	SX	X		X		X	SX	XS	X				SX	X		X	XS	X		X		XS												21
	S	S	X		X			XS	X	X	S			SX	SX	X		XS	X	X		X		X											22
	S	XS	X		X		SX	XS	X	SX				S		X		XS	X		X		SX	X	X										23
	X	S	X		X		X	XS		SX				SX	XS	S		X	X		X		S	X	X										24
	S	XS	X		X		X	XS			S			X	SX	X		X	X		X		S	X	XS										25
	X		X	XS	X		SX		XS		SX			S		S		X	X		X		X	X	X	XS	SX								26
	S	SX	X		X		X	XS		X		X		SX	X			X	XS		S			XS	SX										27
	X	X	X		X			S		XS				SX	X	S		XS	S		X		SX	X		SX		X	XS						28
	X	X	X		X			SX			X			SX	X	S		X	S		XS					SX	XS	XS							29
	X		X	X	X		XS	SX			X			SX	S	S		X	X		XS					X	X	SX							30
		X	X	XS	X		SX			X				X	X	X		XS	X				S			SX	SX	XS	S						31
		X	X	XS	X		SX			X				X	XS	X		X	X				S			SX	SX	XS	S						32
	S		X	X			X	S		X				X	X	X		X	X				S	X				S	S						33
	S	S	XS	XS			SX			X			X		SX	X		X	X				S				X		X	X					34
	S	S		X			SX	SX	XS		XS			SX	X	X		X	X					XS				X	X						35
	S		S	XS			SX	SX	XS		X			X	X			X	X		SX			XS				X	X						36
	S		X	X			XS	SX	SX		X			X	X			XS			S			SX				X	X						37
	S		X	X	SX		XS	SX	SX		X			X	X			XS	X				S					S					X	X	38
	X		X	X	S		X	S		X			XS		X			X	X				S	X	S				SX	S			X	X	39
	X		XS	XS			X	SX		X			X		X			X	X					S				SX	S				XS	XS	40
	13	10	37	13	29	8	11	4	9	30	1	17	0	5	13	27	0	13	22	27	0	16	0	0	8	3	0	1	2	2	0	4	6	2	x
	0	3	1	7	1	5	13	15	9	6	3	4	2	1	5	0	0	2	9	1	1	2	0	0	1	1	2	0	1	6	0	0	1	1	xs
	0	2	0	0	2	5	10	14	3	0	12	2	5	17	11	0	1	0	1	0	1	2	0	3	1	0	1	7	2	3	0	0	0	0	sx
	25	9	1	2	1	0	0	3	1	0	7	0	1	4	7	11	0	0	0	3	0	1	4	8	0	0	0	2	1	2	4	0	0	0	s

GOALKEEPERS	CS	CCS
Lucas	6	1
MacDonald	2	1

x - Played full 90 minutes
xs - Substituted off
sx - Substituted on
s - Non-playing Substitute

WOKING MATCH RESULTS 2019-20

Date	Comp	Opponents	H/A	Att:	Result	Goalscorers	Pos
Aug 3	NL	Dagenham & Redbridge	A	1549	W 2 - 0	Ferdinand 7 Diarra 52	3
6	NL	Aldershot Town	H	3992	L 0 - 1		10
10	NL	Harrogate Town	H	1470	W 1 - 0	Donnellan 19	
13	NL	Chesterfield	A	3927	W 2 - 1	Meite 51 Tarpey 59	
17	NL	AFC Fylde	A	1172	W 4 - 1	Tarpey 18 Ferdinand 39 Hyde 83 86 (pen)	2
24	NL	Solihull Moors	H	1997	W 2 - 0	Hyde 12 Parry 16	1
26	NL	Dover Athletic	A	1358	W 2 - 1	Hyde 41 Edser 87	1
31	NL	Barrow	H	1787	W 3 - 2	Johnson 51 Hyde 67 (pen) 77	1
Sep 3	NL	Torquay United	H	2599	D 1 - 1	Tarpey 53	2
7	NL	Hartlepool United	A	3429	D 1 - 1	Hodges 78	1
14	NL	Ebbsfleet United	H	1942	D 2 - 2	Johnson 7 Hyde 77	1
21	NL	Chorley	A	1336	D 1 - 1	Tarpey 21	3
24	NL	Bromley	A	2358	L 0 - 1		3
28	NL	Boreham Wood	H	2219	L 1 - 2	Ferdinand 10	4
Oct 5	NL	Wrexham	H	2061	D 1 - 1	Ferdinand 75	4
8	NL	Yeovil Town	A	3397	L 1 - 3	Meite 68	5
12	NL	Barnet	A	1651	D 2 - 2	Gerring 14 Shleton 53	7
19	**FAC4Q**	**Ebbsfleet United**	**A**	**750**	**D 1 - 1**	**Kretzschmar 90+1**	
22	**FAC4Qr**	**Ebbsfleet United**	**H**	**942**	**L 0 - 1**		
26	NL	Eastleigh	H	1910	D 1 - 1	Loza 90+5	6
29	NL	Notts County	H	2175	L 0 - 4		8
Nov 2	NL	Stockport County	A	3888	W 3 - 1	Hyde 22 76 Tarpey 70	8
16	NL	Halifax Town	H	2242	D 0 - 0		8
23	NL	Maidenhead United	A	1307	W 3 - 2	Diarra 11 Loza 44 Hyde 75	7
26	NL	Bromley	H	1769	W 2 - 1	Tarpey 43 Hyde 74	4
30	NL	Boreham Wood	A	682	L 0 - 1		5
Dec 7	NL	Hartlepool United	H	2127	W 2 - 1	Hyde 66 Tarpey 78	4
14	**FAT1**	**Kingstonian**	**A**	**655**	**L 1 - 3**	**Kretzschmar 45+1 (pen)**	
26	NL	Sutton United	H	2257	L 0 - 2		6
28	NL	Torquay United	A	3078	L 1 - 4	Hyde 12	9
Jan 1	NL	Sutton United	A	1965	L 2 - 6	Meite 73 87	10
4	NL	Chorley	H	1748	W 1 - 0	Tarpey 51	9
18	NL	Wrexham	A	3671	L 0 - 3		10
25	NL	Yeovil Town	H	2642	W 1 - 0	Donnellan 22	8
28	NL	Ebbsfleet United	A	674	L 1 - 2	Hyde 53 (pen)	9
Feb 1	NL	Eastleigh	A	1885	L 0 - 2		10
15	NL	Notts County	A	5074	D 1 - 1	Kretzschmar 50	
22	NL	Stockport County	H	2189	D 1 - 1	Wall 11	13
29	NL	Maidenhead United	H	2019	W 2 - 0	Jarvis 62 Hyde 83	9
Mar 7	NL	Halifax Town	A	1995	W 2 - 0	Kretzschmar 15 (pen) Hyde 44	8
10	NL	Barnet	H	1486	L 1 - 3	Cook 85	9

GOALSCORERS	SG	CSG	Pens	Hat tricks	Total		SG	CSG	Pens	Hat tricks	Total	
Hyde	13	4	3		16	Edser	1	1			1	
Tarpey	8	2			8	Gerring	1	1			1	
Ferdinand	4	2			4	Hodges	1	1			1	
Kretzschmar	4	1	2		4	Jarvis*	1	1			1	
Meite	3	1			4	Parry	1	1			1	
Diarra	2	1			2	Shelton*	1	1			1	
Donnellan	2	1			2	Wall	1	1			1	
Johnson	2	1			2							
Loza	2	1			2							
Cook	1	1			1							

Player appearance grid (x – played full 90 minutes, xs – substituted off, sx – substituted on, s – non-playing substitute).

Hoss C	Casey J	Gerring B	Ferdinand K	Parry I	Diarra M	Donnellan S	Cook J	Kretzschmar M	Tarpey D	Hyde J	Poku G	Meite I (L)	Johnson T (L)	Collier N	Howes S (Gk)	Hodges P	Edser T (L)	Loza J (L)	Tiehi C	Skinner J	Shelton M (L)	Rea G (L)	Paulat-Brigg C (Gk)	Gray J	Mason S (Gk)	Wareham J	Wall A	Neufville J (L)	Harris J (L)	Dempsey B (L)	Jarvis M	Guest A (Gk)	No.
X	X	X	X	X	X	XS	X		XS	XS	XS	SX	SX	SX	S	S																	1
X	X	X	X	X	X	XS	X		XS	XS	XS	SX	SX	SX	S	S																	2
X	X	X	X	X	XS	X	X		XS	SX	X	XS	SX	SX	S	S																	3
X	X	X	X	X		X	X		XS	SX	XS	XS	X	S	S	SX	XS																4
X	X	X	X	X		X	X		XS	SX	XS	XS	X	S	S	SX	XS																5
X	X	X	X	X		XS	X		XS	X	SX	X	S	SX	S	XS																	6
X	X	X	X	X		XS	X		XS	XS	SX	SX	X	S	S	SX	X																7
X	XS	X	X	SX	X	X	X		XS	SX	SX	X		S	S	XS																	8
X	X	X		S	X	XS	X		X	XS	X	SX	X	SX	S	S	X																9
X	X	X	X	S	X		X		X	X	X	S	X	S	S	SX	XS																10
X	XS	X	SX	X		X	S		X	X	X	XS	SX	S	SX	XS																	11
X	X	X	X	SX	X		X		XS	X	XS	S	S	SX	XS	SX																	12
X	X		X	X	X	XS	X	XS		XS		X	S	SX	SX	X	SX	S															13
X	X		X	X	X	S	X	S	X	X	XS		S	S	SX	X	X																14
X	X		X	X	X	X	X	SX	SX	SX		SX		S	S	SX	SX	X															15
X	X	XS	X	X	X	X	X	SX	X		XS	SX	S	S	SX		XS																16
X	X	X	X	X		SX	SX	XS	X		X		X	S	S	SX	XS		XS														17
X	X	X	X	S		SX	X	X	SX	X	SX		X	S	XS	S	SX		XS														18
X	X	X	X	S		XS	X	XS	X	SX	X	SX		X	S	SX	X	SX		S													19
X	X	X	SX		X		S	XS	XS	X		SX		X	S	SX		X			X	XS											20
X	X		X	SX	X		X	X		S		S	S	S	X			X			X	XS											21
X	X		X	X	X		X	X		S	S		S	S		S	X				S	X											22
X	X	X	X		X	XS	X	SX	X	X	S		S		SX		X				XS	S											23
X	X	X		X	X	X	SX	XS	X	XS		S		S	X		X				X	S	SX										24
X	X	X		X	X	X	X	X		SX		S		XS		X					X	S	S										25
X	X	X		X	X	X	SX	X	X		S		S		SX	X					XS	S	SX										26
X	X	X	X	S		XS	X	X	X	X	X		X	S	SX						S	SX											27
X	X	X	X	S		X	XS	XS	X	X	SX	X		SX	X	S	S																28
X	X	X	X		X	XS	X	SX	X	X	XS		S	S	SX	X						S											29
S		X	SX	S	X	S	X	X	X	X		XS	X	SX	X							XS											30
S		X	XS	X	X	X	SX		X		X	X	XS	SX	XS														SX				31
X		X	X	X	X	S	X	X		SX	XS	XS	X	S	S	X																	32
X	X	X	X	S	X	XS	X		XS	XS	X		SX	S	X												SX	SX					33
X	X	S	X	X	X	X		SX	XS	X	XS		SX	S	X												SX	X	XS				34
X	X	S	X	X	X	X		SX	SX	X	X		S	S	X												XS	X	XS				35
X	X	S	X	X	X	X		SX	SX	XS	XS			X	S									S			SX	X	XS				36
X	X	X	X		X	SX	X	X	XS		S		S	S	X												XS	XS		X			37
X	X	X	X		X	S	X	X	XS		SX		S	S	X												X	SX		XS			38
X	X	X	X		X	SX	X	XS	XS	SX			S		X												XS	S		X	SX		39
X	X	X	X		X	SX	X	X	XS	XS			S		XS								S			SX		SX		X			40
X	X	X	X		X	S	X	XS	XS	X			X		SX								SX					XS	XS	SX	S		41
39	38	32	35	16	30	16	36	6	18	18	11	2	7	9	2	0	4	19	0	0	2	3	0	0	0	0	1	3	0	3	0	0	x
0	0	3	0	1	1	10	0	10	18	10	8	5	2	1	0	2	7	4	0	0	2	4	0	2	0	0	3	0	3	2	0	0	xs
0	0	0	2	2	1	6	1	11	3	7	8	11	3	7	0	18	3	4	1	0	0	0	0	3	0	3	3	5	0	0	2	0	sx
2	0	3	0	9	0	4	1	2	0	0	5	5	0	17	30	11	2	0	0	1	2	0	7	3	1	0	0	1	0	0	0	1	s

GOALKEEPERS	CS	CCS
Ross	8	2

x - Played full 90 minutes
xs - Substituted off
sx - Substituted on
s - Non-playing Substitute

WREXHAM MATCH RESULTS 2019-20

Date	Comp	Opponents	H/A	Att:	Result	Goalscorers	Pos
Aug 3	NL	Barrow	H	5941	W 2 - 1	Hooper 47 Grant 62	7
6	NL	Boreham Wood	A	845	D 2 - 2	Harris 14 Grant 69	6
10	NL	Dover Athletic	A	1187	L 1 - 2	Harris 35	
13	NL	Halifax Town	H	5517	W 1 - 0	Harris 78	
17	NL	Notts County	A	6236	D 1 - 1	Redmond 74	9
24	NL	Barnet	H	4533	D 1 - 1	Hooper 2	
26	NL	Hartlepool United	A	3462	L 2 - 4	Wright 38 Grant 56 (pen)	
31	NL	Stockport County	H	5777	L 1 - 2	McIntosh 84	16
Sep 3	NL	Maidenhead United	H	3667	D 2 - 2	Oswell 40 Young 64	16
7	SCC 3	Ayr United	H	1697	D 1 - 1	Bickerstaff 70 (won 6-5 on pens)	
14	NL	Sutton United	H	3824	D 1 - 1	Grant 86	19
21	NL	Aldershot Town	A	1673	L 0 - 1		21
24	NL	AFC Fylde	A	1289	L 2 - 3	Lawlor 7 Oswell 45+2	21
Bryan Hughes leaves his position as manager, Brian Flynn takes temporary charge.							
28	NL	Ebbsfleet United	H	3627	W 1 - 0	Rutherford 73	20
Oct 1	NL	Solihull Moors	A	1425	L 1 - 3	Grant 63	20
5	NL	Woking	A	2061	D 1 - 1	Jennings 47	20
Dean Keates returns to take over the vacant managers post.							
8	NL	Harrogate Town	H	3435	D 1 - 1	Grant 5	20
12	SCC 4	St Mirren U21	H	1468	W 4 - 1	Redmond 46 McIntosh 55 (pen) 73 Tollitt 89	
15	NL	Chesterfield	H	3479	L 0 - 1		21
19	FAC4Q	Chesterfield	H	2199	D 1 - 1	Grant 62	
22	FAC4Qr	Chesterfield	A	2023	W 1 - 0	Hooper 30	
26	NL	Dagenham & Redbridge	A	1254	L 1 - 2	Young 51	22
29	NL	Torquay United	A	2313	L 0 - 1		22
Nov 2	NL	Bromley	H	3469	W 1 - 0	Young 77	21
10	FAC1	Rochdale	H	3274	D 0 - 0		
16	SCC 5	Rangers U21	A		L 0 - 2		
19	FAC1r	Rochdale	A	1628	L 0 - 1		
23	NL	Yeovil Town	H	3583	D 3 - 3	Wright 23 Rutherford 44 Grant 47	
26	NL	AFC Fylde	H	2941	L 0 - 1		22
30	NL	Ebbsfleet United	A	1036	L 1 - 2	Kennedy 31	24
Dec 3	NL	Eastleigh	A	1542	W 2 - 0	Patrick 16 41	21
7	NL	Solihull Moors	H	3113	W 2 - 0	Patrick 21 Jennings 45	20
14	FAT1	Halifax Town	A	752	L 0 - 4		
21	NL	Sutton United	A	1637	L 1 - 3	Jennings 89	21
26	NL	Chorley	H	4784	W 3 - 1	Hooper 7 11 Patrick 85	21
28	NL	Maidenhead United	A	1472	L 0 - 2		21
Jan 1	NL	Chorley	A	1684	W 2 - 0	Redmond 72 Patrick 80	19
4	NL	Aldershot Town	H	4222	L 1 - 2	Hooper 90+3	20
18	NL	Woking	H	3671	W 3 - 0	Summerfield 15 80 (pen) Jarvis 47	18
25	NL	Harrogate Town	A	2415	W 2 - 0	Jennings 11 Hooper 73	16
Feb 1	NL	Dagenham & Redbridge	H	4024	D 0 - 0		19
8	NL	Chesterfield	A	3728	L 2 - 3	Evans 21 (og) Ponticelli 68	21
22	NL	Bromley	A	1743	W 2 - 0	Keillor-Dunn 11 Ponticelli 90	17
29	NL	Yeovil Town	A	3040	L 0 - 3		17
Mar 7	NL	Eastleigh	H	3436	D 0 - 0		19

GOALSCORERS	SG	CSG	Pens	Hat tricks	Total		SG	CSG	Pens	Hat tricks	Total
Grant	8	2	1		8	Rutherford	2	1			2
Hooper	6	1			7	Summerfield	1		1		2
Patrick	4	2			5	Wright	2	1			2
Jennings	4	1			4	Bickerstaff*	1	1			1
Harris	3	3			3	Jarvis*	1	1			1
McIntosh	2	1	1		3	Keillor-Dunn	1	1			1
Redmond	3	1			3	Kennedy	1	1			1
Young	3	1			3	Lawlor	1	1			1
Oswell	2	1			2	Opponents	1	1			1
Ponticelli	2	2			2	Tollitt	1	1			1

Player appearance grid (matches 1–45):

	Dibble C	Jennings J	Pearson S	Summerfield L	Carrington M	Young L	Lawlor J	Redmond D	Grant B	Hooper J	Harris M (L)	Rutherford P	McIntosh L	Oswell J	Szczepaniak D (Gk)	Chambers M	Barnum-Bobb J	Barton A	Wright A	Tollitt B (L)	Lainton R (Gk)	Bickerstaff J	Tharme D	Cleworth M	Williams C	Jones M	Beaumont B	Huxley C	Parry L	Robinson-Murray K	Williams S	Humphreys J	Nash J	Horsfield J (L)	Reid T (L)	Patrick O (L)	Kennedy K (L)	Jarvis D (L)	Keillor-Dunn D	Ponticelli J (L)	Thompson J (L)	Harris J	Garratt T (L)	Barker K (L)	No.
	x	x	x	x	x	x	x	xs	x	x	x	x	xs	xs	s	s	s																												1
	x	x	x	x	x	x	x	xs	x	xs	x	x	sx	s	s	s																													2
	x	x	x	x	x	x	x	xs	x	xs	xs	s	sx	s	sx																														3
	x	x	x	x	sx	x	x	xs		xs	x	sx	xs	sx	s		x	s																											4
	x	x	x	s	xs		xs		x	x	x	sx		s	x	x	s	sx																											5
	x	x	x	x		x	xs		x	x	xs	x		x	s	x	x	s																											6
	x		x		x	sx	x	xs	x	xs	sx	s	sx		x	x	x	xs	s																										7
	x	x	x	x	x		xs	x		x		sx	xs	s	x	x	s	s	sx																										8
	x	x	x	xs	x	x		sx	s		sx	sx	s	s	x	s	xs	xs																											9
	s				x	xs				x	xs		x		x	x	x		x	x	x	xs	x	sx	sx	sx	s	s	s																10
	x	x	x	x	x	x		sx	x		x	s	oswell	s	x	s	s	xs	xs																										11
	x	x	x	sx	x	x		s	x		xs	sx	x	s	xs	xs	sx																												12
	x	x	x	s	x	xs	xs	sx			sx	sx	s	x	s	x																													13
																																													14
	x	xs	x	x	x	x	xs	xs	xs	xs	xs		x	s		x		s																											15
	x	x	x	x	x	x		x	xs	sx	x		xs	s		xs	s	s																											16
	x	x		x	xs	x	x	s	x		sx		x	s		x	s	s																											17
																																													18 placeholder

YEOVIL TOWN MATCH RESULTS 2019-20

Date	Comp	Opponents	H/A	Att:	Result	Goalscorers	Pos
Aug 3	NL	Barnet	A	1666	L 0 - 1		21
6	NL	Eastleigh	H	2813	W 1 - 0	Duffus 2	14
10	NL	Stockport County	H	2602	D 1 - 1	Duffus 21	
13	NL	Ebbsfleet United	A	1057	W 3 - 1	Murphy 26 Hutton 48 Whelan 82	
17	NL	Barrow	A	1218	L 0 - 1		12
24	NL	Maidenhead United	H	2179	L 1 - 2	Duffus 86	
26	NL	Dagenham & Redbridge	A	1453	L 2 - 3	Murphy 46 Worthington 82	
31	NL	Notts County	H	2424	W 3 - 1	Duffus 41 Wilkinson 82 Hippolyte 85	12
Sep 3	NL	Sutton United	H	2279	W 1 - 0	Bradbury 68	9
7	NL	Halifax Town	A	2341	W 2 - 0	Omotayo 4 69	6
14	NL	AFC Fylde	H	2395	W 3 - 2	Murphy 5 Hippolyte 14 Smith J 77	4
21	NL	Solihull Moors	A	1525	W 1 - 0	Wilkinson 58	4
24	NL	Aldershot Town	A	1684	W 3 - 1	Hippolyte 8 Smith J 38 Murphy 59	4
28	NL	Bromely	H	3960	W 3 - 1	Smith J 45+2 Okoye 72 (og) Lee 77	3
Oct 5	NL	Hartlepool United	A	3273	L 1 - 2	Murphy 90+1	3
8	NL	Woking	H	3397	W 3 - 1	Murphy 13 42 Smith J 45	3
12	NL	Harrogate Town	H	3237	L 1 - 2	Murphy 90+1	3
26	NL	Chorley	A	1279	W 2 - 1	Worthington 7 Murphy 86	2
29	FAC4Q	Haringey Borough	A	857	W 3 - 0	Dagnall 31 60 Wilkinson 56	
Nov 2	NL	Boreham Wood	H	2879	D 1 - 1	Smith J 6	2
12	FAC1	Hartlepool United	H	2361	L 1 - 3	D'Ath 3	
16	NL	Dover Athletic	H	2986	L 0 - 1		5
23	NL	Wrexham	A	3583	D 3 - 3	Murphy 3 39 67	5
26	NL	Aldershot Town	H	2545	D 2 - 2	Skendi 36 Murphy 71 (pen)	6
30	NL	Bromely	A	2261	D 1 - 1	Murphy 90+7	4
Dec 7	NL	Halifax Town	H	2975	W 2 - 0	Duffus 35 90+3	3
10	NL	Chesterfield	A	3161	W 2 - 1	Hippolyte 2 Murphy 24 (pen)	2
14	FAT1	Welling United	H	1554	W 3 - 1	Duffus 31 53 Dagnull 48	
21	NL	AFC Fylde	A	1427	D 2 - 2	Duffus 78 80	2
26	NL	Torquay United	H	5056	W 6 - 2	Hippolyte 3 Skendi 7 Duffus 15 60 87 Dagnall 72	2
28	NL	Sutton United	A	2189	L 2 - 3	Murphy 26 Skendi 38	2
Jan 1	NL	TOrquay United	A	4165	W 2 - 0	Duffus 16 Murphy 90+4	2
4	NL	Solihull Moors	H	2907	D 0 - 0		2
11	FAT2	Hampton & Richmond B.	H	1689	W 4 - 0	Murphy 39 46 62 Bradbury 71	
18	NL	Hartlepool United	H	2716	D 2 - 2	Worthington 24 Lee 41	3
25	NL	Woking	A	2642	L 0 - 1		3
Feb 1	NL	Chorley	H	2729	D 1 - 1	Richards M 88	4
8	FAT3	Notts County	H	1946	L 1 - 2	Duffus 77	
11	NL	Harrogate Town	A	801	L 0 - 3		
22	NL	Boreham Wood	A	1040	L 0 - 1		5
29	NL	Wrexham	H	3040	W 3 - 0	Duffus 44 Wilkinson 56 Skendi 90+4	3
Mar 7	NL	Dover Athletic	A	1180	W 1 - 0	Richards M 47	3
July 18	PO Q	Barnet	H	0	L 0 - 2		

GOALSCORERS	SG	CSG	Pens	Hat tricks	Total		SG	CSG	Pens	Hat tricks	Total
Murphy	15	4	2	2	20	Omotayo	1	1			2
Duffus	11	3		1	16	Richards M	2	1			2
Hippolyte	5	1			5	D'Ath	1	1			1
Smith J*	5	2			5	Hutton	1	1			1
Dagnall	3	1			4	Opponent	1	1			1
Skendi	4	2			4	Whelan	1	1			1
Wilkinson	4	1			4						
Worthington	3	1			3						
Bradbury	2	1			2						
Lee	2	1			2						

Nelson S	Collins L	Alcock C	Bradbury T	D'Ath L	Skendi A	Worthington M	Hutton R (L)	Whelan T	Murphy R	Hippolyte M	Seager R	Shako N	Ojo D	Driscoll L (Gk) (L)	McCoy O (L)	Duffus C	Rogers G	Dickinson C	Lee C	Brzozowski M (Gk) (L)	Wilkinson L	Omotayo G	O'Brien L (Gk)	Tilley J (L)	Smith J (L)	Smith A (Gk)	Dagnall C	Arnold D	Jones L (Gk) (L)	Williams M (L)	Osho G (L)	Cann T (Gk) (L)	Rose D	Behcet D (Gk)	Richards M	Richards C (L)	Cooper B (L)	No.
x	x	x	x	x	x	x	x	x	x	xs	sx	sx	s	s																								1
x	x	x	x	xs	x	x	x	x	x		s				sx	s	s	s	x	s																		2
x	x	x	x	x	x	x	x	xs	x						s	s	s	s	sx	x																		3
x	xs	x	x	xs	x	x	sx	x	xs	x	s						x			sx	sx	s																4
x		x	xs	x	xs	xs	x		x		sx				sx	x	s	x	sx	s																		5
x		x	x	x	x	s	xs	sx	xs							x	sx	x	x	s	sx																	6
	xs	x	xs	x	x	sx	sx	x	sx		s					x	s	x	xs	x	x																	7
	x	xs	sx	xs	x	sx		s	s							x	sx	x	xs	x	x	x																8
		sx	x		sx	x	xs	s		xs						x	xs	x	x	x	x	x	sx															9
		sx	x		sx	x	xs	s		x					sx	xs	s	x	xs	x	x	x	sx															10
xs	s	sx	s	sx	x	x		x	xs	x							x	x	x	x	x	xs	sx															11
x	x	s	sx	sx	x	x			x	xs					s		x	x	x	x	sx	sx	xs															12
x	x	x	sx	x	xs	s		xs	x						sx		x		x	x	sx	xs	x															13
x	x	x	sx	sx	xs	s		xs	x								x		x	x	sx	xs	x															14
x		s	xs	sx	s	x		x	xs						sx		x		x	x	xs	sx	x	x														15
x		s	sx	x	x	x		x									xs		x	x	x	s	xs	sx	x	sx												16
x	s	x	s	sx	xs	x		x	x								xs			x	sx		x	x	sx													17
x	x		x	x	x	xs	x		x	x					s	xs				sx			sx	xs		sx	s											18
x	xs		sx	x	x	sx	x		s	x					sx				x		x	xs		xs	s		x	s										19
x	x		s	xs	x	sx	x		x	x									sx		x	s		sx	xs		xs											20
x	x		s	x	s	xs	x		x	x					s	sx	s		x		x	sx		sx	xs		xs											21
x	x		x	x	sx		xs	x		x									sx		x			sx	xs		sx		s									22
x	x		x	x	sx			xs		x									sx		x	xs	s		x	xs		sx	s									23
x	x		x	x	s	x	s		x	x									sx			s		xs	x		sx	s										24
x	x		x	x	sx	xs		x	x										xs		x			sx	s		sx	s										25
x			x	x	sx			x					s				xs	s	x		x			x		s		x		x	x							26
x		sx	xs	x	sx	s	s	xs	x								x			x		x		sx			xs			x	x							27
x		x	xs	x	xs	x		s	sx						sx	x	sx	s	s			x		sx			xs			x	x							28
x	sx		xs	x	xs	x		x	xs								x	x	xs	x			sx			x			s	x								29
x	xs		x	x	s	sx		xs	xs								x	x	x	x		s			sx			x							sx	x		30
x			x	x	x	sx		x	xs								x	x	x	x		s			sx			sx	xs									31
x	x	xs		s	x	sx	x			sx							xs	x	x		x			x			x			sx								32
x	x	x		xs	x	sx	x			x	sx						x	x	x		x	sx		xs							s							33
	x		x		x	x				xs	x						xs	sx	xs		x	sx		x						x	sx	s					34
	x		s	x	x	x		x	x								sx	s	x	xs	x			sx						x		s	xs				35
	x		s	x	sx	xs		x	xs								sx	x	x	x		s		x	sx					x		sx					36
	x	xs			sx	xs											sx	x	x	x			x	xs					s		x	s					37
s	xs	s			x	s	x				sx	sx					sx	x	x	x		x		x		x				x	xs	s					38
x		sx			x	s	xs										sx	x	x	x		s								sx			x					39
x	x	xs	s		x	xs	sx		xs								x	x	x		s			sx		x						sx			x			40
sx	x				x	x	x									x	s	x	xs				xs		x		sx						xs	s	sx			41
x	x		sx		x	xs	x									x	x	x	x				xs	s	sx								xs	s	sx			42
x	x	s			x	xs	x									xs	x	x	x				sx	s	sx								sx		s			43
26	26	10	18	11	31	14	19	4	21	23	0	0	0	0	17	0	28	25	2	29	9	5	4	6	5	6	0	0	3	5	3	0	0	2	0	1		x
0	5	4	0	13	0	13	9	2	10	10	0	0	0	0	0	0	11	1	1	9	0	1	2	2	5	13	0	4	0	0	0	1	0	0	3	1	0	xs
1	1	3	4	4	10	9	4	2	3	4	2	1	1	0	7	8	4	1	2	0	1	6	0	14	4	0	15	0	0	1	1	1	0	1	0	4	0	sx
1	0	4	10	3	2	6	7	3	2	0	4	3	3	3	5	0	8	1	1	4	0	6	3	2	1	2	0	2	4	1	1	1	0	2	0	3	2	s

GOALKEEPERS	CS	CCS
Nelson	7	2
O'Brien*	4	2
Cann	1	1

x - Played full 90 minutes
xs - Substituted off
sx - Substituted on
s - Non-playing Substitute

Hinchcliffe (Stockport) beaten by a shot from O'Brien (Notts County). Photo Keith Clayton.

Great defensive header from Patterson (Rangers) to deny McCallum (Solihull) in the Scottish Challenge Cup. Photo Keith Clayton.

NATIONAL LEAGUE NORTH

As at 15/03/2020	P	W	D	L	F	A	GD	Pts
1 York City	34	19	9	6	52	28	24	66
2 King's Lynn Town	32	19	7	6	63	39	24	64
3 Brackley Town	34	16	12	6	61	25	36	60
4 Boston United	32	17	7	8	46	32	14	58
5 Altrincham	33	16	9	8	62	40	22	57
6 Spennymoor Town	34	15	10	9	63	45	18	55
7 Chester	32	15	9	8	58	38	20	54
8 Gateshead	31	14	10	7	47	31	16	52
9 Guiseley	33	14	8	11	52	41	11	50
10 Farsley Celtic	34	14	6	14	50	45	5	48
11 Darlington	33	14	6	13	43	50	-7	48
12 Southport	32	12	7	13	40	41	-1	43
13 AFC Telford United	34	11	9	14	51	56	-5	42
14 Alfreton Town	32	12	4	16	48	55	-7	40
15 Hereford	35	9	12	14	39	56	-17	39
16 Kidderminster Harriers	33	10	8	15	39	43	-4	38
17 Leamington	32	9	8	15	39	51	-12	35
18 Curzon Ashton	33	8	10	15	34	42	-8	34
19 Gloucester City	30	9	6	15	39	57	-18	33
20 Kettering Town	31	7	11	13	36	46	-10	32
21 Blyth Spartans	33	6	5	22	32	78	-46	23
22 Bradford (Park Avenue)	33	5	5	23	25	80	-55	20

After Points Per Game	P	W	D	L	F	A	GD	PPG
1 Kings Lynn Town	32	19	7	6	63	39	24	84.0
2 York City	34	19	9	6	52	28	24	81.5
3 Boston United	32	17	7	8	46	32	14	76.1
4 Brackley Town	34	16	12	6	6	25	36	74.1
5 Altrincham *	33	16	9	8	62	40	22	72.5
6 Chester	32	15	9	8	58	38	20	70.9
7 Gateshead	31	14	10	7	47	31	16	70.5
8 Spennymoor Town	34	15	10	9	63	45	18	67.9
9 Guiseley	33	14	8	11	52	41	11	63.6
10 Darlington	33	14	6	13	43	50	-7	61.1
11 Farsley Celtic	34	14	6	14	50	45	5	59.3
12 Southport	32	12	7	13	40	41	-1	56.4
13 Alfreton Town	32	12	4	16	48	55	-7	52.5
14 AFC Telford United	34	11	9	14	51	56	-5	51.9
15 Kidderminster Harriers	33	10	8	15	39	43	-4	48.4
16 Hereford	35	9	12	14	39	56	-17	46.8
17 Gloucester City	30	9	6	15	39	57	-18	46.2
18 Leamington	32	9	8	15	39	51	-12	45.9
19 Kettering Town	31	7	11	13	36	46	-10	43.4
20 Curzon Ashton	33	8	10	15	34	42	-8	43.3
21 Blyth Spartans	33	6	5	22	32	78	-46	29.3
22 Bradford Park Avenue	33	5	5	23	25	80	-55	25.5

	1	2	3	4	5	6	7	8	9	10	11	12	13	14	15	16	17	18	19	20	21	22
1 AFC Telford United		3-0	2-2	4-2	1-3	0-1		1-3		1-2	0-2	0-0	4-3	4-1		3-1	2-0	1-3	1-3		2-2	1-1
2 Alfreton Town	1-1			3-0	1-1	2-4	4-0		3-2	1-2	2-4		6-1		2-0	0-2		2-2	1-0	2-0	0-2	1-3
3 Altrincham	5-2	3-2		3-1			2-0		2-1	1-1	3-1	3-0		1-1	5-1	1-1		5-0	3-0	4-1	1-3	
4 Blyth Spartans	3-1		0-3		0-1	0-6		2-2	2-1	0-2	2-0	3-3	1-2	1-4	0-1		1-1	0-3		1-4		0-3
5 Boston United	1-0		5-0	2-0		1-0	2-1	1-1	0-0			0-3		1-1		2-1	2-0	0-3	1-0	2-0		3-1
6 Brackley Town	1-1	1-0	1-0	5-2	0-0		8-0	1-1	3-0	5-1	0-1		3-0	0-0		1-1	2-0	1-1		1-1	0-0	
7 Bradford (Park Avenue)	2-3		2-0	0-0	1-2	1-2		2-1	0-2		0-3		1-2	0-5	3-2		0-3	2-3	0-3	0-3	1-1	0-2
8 Chester	0-0	3-0	1-1	2-1		2-3	2-1		0-1	3-0	2-1		4-0	3-1	4-1		3-2	3-3	4-0			0-1
9 Curzon Ashton	2-1	0-2	0-1	0-1	1-1	0-4	5-0	1-3		3-1	4-0	0-1			2-0	0-0	0-1				1-1	1-0
10 Darlington	2-3	3-0		2-1	2-1	1-1	0-1	2-0			2-4	1-1	2-1	0-3	0-0	3-0	1-0			2-0	2-1	0-2
11 Farsley Celtic	1-1	1-1		2-0	2-4	1-1	5-0		2-1	3-1			1-1	1-1	3-2	0-1	1-2	2-1	0-3	1-0		
12 Gateshead	3-1	2-0	2-3	3-0	2-0	1-1	2-0	3-0		0-3		1-0	2-3	2-0		0-0	1-2	4-2	0-0	1-0		
13 Gloucester City	0-1		1-1		3-0		1-0		2-2	2-1				3-1	0-2	2-2		2-1	0-1	1-2	2-3	
14 Guiseley	1-2	2-4	1-1			0-2		0-1	1-0	1-2	2-0	2-2	2-1		3-0	1-2	1-2	3-0	3-0		3-1	0-0
15 Hereford	1-0	1-2	0-2		0-0	1-1	1-1		1-1	2-2	1-1	2-1		0-0		1-0	2-1		1-2	2-2	2-2	2-2
16 Kettering Town	2-1	2-1	0-2	4-4	0-2		4-0	1-1	0-0		1-0	1-2	1-1		0-0		3-5			0-2	0-0	
17 Kidderminster Harriers	0-1	2-0	0-1	1-3	1-3		0-1		1-1	2-0	1-1	2-3		3-1		2-4	2-2	0-1	1-1	0-1		
18 King's Lynn Town	3-2	2-2	3-0	1-0		0-1	2-2	4-1	2-0		1-0	2-2	0-1	3-1	2-1	0-2		5-2		3-0	1-0	
19 Leamington	0-1	0-1	0-2		2-0		0-0	1-1	3-0	0-3	0-0	3-0	2-2	0-2	3-1		0-0		1-0	2-2		
20 Southport	0-1		2-1	2-0	1-3	1-0	3-3	1-3	0-0			1-0	3-0	3-2	1-1	1-2	1-2	4-1				0-2
21 Spennymoor Town	3-3	5-0	3-2	5-0	2-1	0-0	3-0	2-1		3-1		1-3	5-1		4-0	1-2	2-1	2-2	2-0	1-0		1-4
22 York City	2-0	1-0			2-1	1-0	2-1	4-2	1-1	0-1	0-0	1-1		1-2	1-4	1-0	1-1	3-0	2-0	1-1		

*Promoted to the National League via the play-offs.

AFC TELFORD UNITED MATCH RESULTS 2019-20

Date	Comp	Opponents	H/A	Att:	Result	Goalscorers	Pos
Aug 3	NLN	Kettering Town	A	959	L 1 - 2	Morley 44	
6	NLN	Kidderminster Harriers	H	1557	W 2 - 0	Knights 28 Williams 66	7
10	NLN	Gateshead	H	1045	D 0 - 0		
13	NLN	Hereford	A	2440	L 0 - 1		
17	NLN	King's Lynn Town	H	1003	L 1 - 3	McQuilkin 62	18
24	NLN	Southport	A	910	W 1 - 0	Brown 56 (pen)	
26	NLN	Leamington	H	1012	L 1 - 3	Williams 2	
31	NLN	Bradford (Park Avenue)	A	378	W 3 - 2	Daniels 36 78 Walker 45+1	13
Sep 3	NLN	Gloucester City	H	925	W 4 - 3	Daniels 29 Dinanga 60 Sutton 71 Williams 79	11
7	NLN	Brackley Town	A	545	D 1 - 1	Dinanga 41 (pen)	11
14	NLN	Chester	H	2085	L 1 - 3	Reilly 68	12
21	**FAC2Q**	**Nantwich Town**	**H**	**718**	**L 0 - 3**		
28	NLN	Blyth Spartans	A	711	L 1 - 3	Knights 74	16
Oct 12	NLN	York City	H	1305	D 1 - 1	McQuilkin 64	15
19	NLN	Guiseley	H	1007	W 4 - 1	Williams 21 (pen) 49 71 Stenson 65	13
Nov 2	NLN	Boston United	H	1084	L 1 - 3	Walker 33	16
9	NLN	Curzon Ashton	A	340	L 1 - 2	Ali 27 (og)	
16	NLN	Spennymoor Town	H	1190	D 2 - 2	Walker 39 Sass-Davies 47	16
23	**FAT3Q**	**Guiseley**	**A**	**345**	**W 4 - 0**	**Lilly 31 Williams 69 77 Dinanga 79**	
30	NLN	Darlington	A	1012	W 3 - 2	Dinanga 47 76 90+6	14
Dec 7	NLN	Farsley Celtic	H	1006	L 0 - 2		16
17	**FAT1**	**Leamington**	**H**	**352**	**L 0 - 5**		
21	NLN	Chester	A	1756	D 0 - 0		
26	NLN	Alfreton Town	H	1115	W 3 - 0	Qualter 17 (og) Barnett 42 Stenson 69	
28	NLN	Gloucester City	A	325	W 1 - 0	Stenson 43	
Jan 1	NLN	Alfreton Town	A	511	D 1 - 1	McQuilkin 4	13
4	NLN	Brackley Town	H	1103	L 0 - 1		14
11	NLN	York City	A	2299	L 0 - 2		14
25	NLN	Farsley Celtic	A	403	D 1 - 1	Stenson 2	13
28	NLN	Blyth Spartans	H	602	W 4 - 2	Williams 25 Barnett 32 Mullen 36 (og) Dinanga 69	13
Feb 1	NLN	Altrincham	H	1159	D 2 - 2	Daniels 5 75	14
4	NLN	Altrincham	A	810	L 2 - 5	Dinanga 52 Daniels 61 (pen)	14
8	NLN	Guiseley	A	597	W 2 - 1	Dinanga 60 86	
22	NLN	Boston United	A	1269	L 0 - 1		14
29	NLN	Spennymoor Town	A	1077	D 3 - 3	Dinanga 13 36 Daniels 39	14
Mar 7	NLN	Darlington	H	1116	L 1 - 2	Dinanga 35	14
14	NLN	Kettering Town	H	1206	W 3 - 1	Sears 31 Barnett 36 Williams 63	13

GOALSCORERS	SG	CSG	Pens	Hat tricks	Total		SG	CSG	Pens	Hat tricks	Total
Dinanga	9	2	1	1	13	Lilly	1	1			1
Williams	7	1	1	1	10	Morley	1	1			1
Daniels	5	2	1		7	Reilly	1	1			1
Stenson	4	2			4	Sass-Davies	1	1			1
Barnett	3	1			3	Sears*	1	1			1
McQuilkin	3	1			3	Sutton	1	1			1
Opponent	3	1			3						
Walker	3	1			3						
Knights	2	1			2						
Brown	1	1	1		1						

Addai C (L)	Streete T	Sutton S	Morley S	Deeney E	Walker A	White R	Lait C	Knights D	Williams A	Dinanga M	Brown A	McQuilkin J	Cowans H	Royle J	Tharme D (L)	Daniels B	Lilley Z	Reilly L (L)	Wycherley A (Gk)	Sass-Davies B (L)	Martinez S	Yates M (Gk) (L)	Birch A	Stenson M (L)	Barnes Homer M	Barnett R (L)	Calder R	Luyambula N (Gk) (L)	Jones E	Griffiths R (Gk) (L)	Sears R (L)	Storer J	No.
x	x	x	x	xs	x	x	x	xs	x	xs	sx	sx	sx	sx	s	s																	1
x	x	x	xs	x	x	x	x	x	x	sx	x	sx	s	s	s	sx																	2
x	x	x	x	xs	x	x	xs	x	sx	sx	xs	sx	s	s																			3
x	x	x	x	xs	xs	x	xs	x	x	x	sx	sx	sx	s	s																		4
x	x	x		x	xs	x	sx	x	x	sx	sx	xs	x	s		xs	s																5
x	sx	x		x		x	xs	x	x	sx	xs	x	sx	s		x	xs	s															6
x	x	x	x		s	x	xs	sx	xs	sx	xs	x	x	x		s		sx															7
	s	x	x	x	x	x	sx	x	x	xs	s		s		x	x	s	x															8
	s	x	x	xs	x	x	xs	x	x			sx				xs	x	sx	x														9
	s	x	x	x	x	x	s	x	x	x		s				x	x	s	x														10
	xs	x		x	xs	x	sx	x	xs	x		s	sx			x	x	sx	x														11
	s	x	x	x		x	xs		xs	x	sx	sx	sx		s		x	s	x	x	x	s											12
	x			x	xs	x		sx	sx	x	sx		x		x		x	x	x	x	s												13
	x			x	x	sx		x	xs	x	sx		s		x	x		x		x	xs	xs											14
	x		xs	x	s		x	xs	sx			sx			x	x		x	s	x	x	xs	sx										15
	x			x	x	sx	sx	xs	x		s		s		xs	xs		x		x	x	x											16
	x			x	x		x	x	sx			s		s		xs	s		x	s	sx	xs	s	x									17
	x			x	x	sx		s	xs	sx		x				x	s		x	x	x	x	s	x	xs								18
	x			x			x	x	xs		x					x	x			x	x	sx		x									19
	x			x	x	s		s	x	sx		x	s			sx	x			x	x	xs		xs	x								20
	x	s		x	x	s		s	xs	x		xs				sx	x			x	x	sx		x	x								21
	x	sx			x	s		xs	sx	xs		x				x	x			s	x	x	xs	s	sx	x							22
	x	x		x	x			s	sx	sx		xs				x	s			x	x	xs		x	s								23
	x	x		x	x			s	sx	sx		xs				xs	s			x	x	xs		x									24
	x	x		x	x			sx	sx	s		xs				x	sx			x	x	xs	s		xs								25
	x	x		x	x			s	x			x				x	sx			x	x	x		x	s								26
	x	x		xs	x			sx	sx			sx				xs	s			x	x	x		x	s								27
	x	x		x	x			sx	sx			xs				xs				s	x	x	x		x	s							28
	x	x		x	x			s	x	s						s	s	sx		x	x	x		x									29
	x			x	xs	x		s	x	sx			sx	s	sx		x	x			x	x	xs		xs								30
s	x			x	x	x		s	x	s			sx		s						x	xs		x		x							31
x				x	xs	x		x	s	x		sx	s	sx		x	x					xs	xs		sx	x							32
x				x	x	x		s	s	x		xs	s	sx		x	x				x		s	x		x							33
x				x	x	x		s	sx	xs		xs	sx	s		x	x					xs	sx		x		x						34
x				x	x	x		s	sx	x		xs	s	x		x	x				s			x		x	s						35
x	x			x	x	x		s	sx	x		xs		s		x	x				sx			xs		s	x						36
	x			x	xs	x		xs	x	xs		s				sx	x	s				sx		x					x	x	sx		37
7	27	23	8	30	25	28	3	12	18	9	0	10	2	3	0	22	18	2	6	7	0	17	17	4	0	14	4	5	0	2	1	0	x
0	1	0	1	4	9	1	3	6	6	7	2	13	0	0	0	7	2	0	0	0	0	3	13	0	3	2	0	0	0	0	0	0	xs
0	1	1	0	0	0	3	5	4	11	17	5	7	5	8	1	2	1	3	0	0	0	0	1	4	2	2	0	0	0	0	0	1	sx
0	5	1	0	0	1	4	2	14	2	4	6	3	7	15	3	1	9	3	0	0	8	0	0	1	5	0	4	0	2	0	0	0	s

GOALKEEPERS	CS	CCS
Yates	4	3
Addai	3	1

x - Played full 90 minutes
xs - Substituted off
sx - Substituted on
s - Non-playing Substitute

ALFRETON TOWN MATCH RESULTS 2019-20

Date	Comp	Opponents	H/A	Att	Result		Goalscorers	Pos
Aug 3	NLN	Brackley Town	A	485	L	0 - 1		
6	NLN	Boston United	H	633	D	1 - 1	Morgan-Smith 37 (pen)	17
10	NLN	Blyth Spartans	H	460	W	3 - 0	Thacker 44 Johnson 57 Qualter 65	
13	NLN	Altrincham	A	878	L	2 - 3	Clarke 34 East 47	
17	NLN	Bradford (Park Avenue)	H	378	W	4 - 0	Morgan-Smith 12 39 (pen) Clarke 59 Lund 74 (og)	8
24	NLN	Guiseley	A	663	W	4 - 2	Johnson 25 Thacker 35 Morgan-Smith 75 (pen) Clarke 84	
26	NLN	Southport	H	507	W	2 - 0	Morgan-Smith 51 56	
31	NLN	Kidderminster Harriers	A	1183	W	1 - 0	Smith 41	4
Sep 3	NLN	King's Lynn Town	A	1203	L	2 - 3	Tomlinson 80 Morgan-Smith 90+3	5
7	NLN	Curzon Ashton	H	473	W	3 - 2	Morgan-Smith 11 20 (pen) 70	4
14	NLN	Kettering Town	A	656	L	1 - 2	Morgan-Smith 45+1	5
21	FAC2Q	King's Lynn Town	H	335	D	1 - 1	Lynch 44	
24	FAC2Qr	King's Lynn Town	A	712	L	1 - 2	Killock 51	
28	NLN	Darlington	H	561	L	1 - 2	Branson 3	7
Oct 12	NLN	Leamington	A	521	W	1 - 0	Johnson 8	4
19	NLN	Farsley Celtic	H	483	L	2 - 4	Blake 1 Branson 52	5
Nov 2	NLN	Spennymoor Town	H	412	L	0 - 2		9
9	NLN	Chester	A	1687	L	0 - 3		9
12	NLN	Hereford	A	1821	W	2 - 1	East 4 Morgan-Smith 50	9
23	FAT3Q	Blyth Spartans	A	526	D	1 - 1	Grice 82	
30	NLN	York City	A	2306	L	0 - 1		10
Dec 3	FAT3Qr	Blyth Spartans	H	165	L	1 - 3	Morgan-Smith	
7	NLN	Gateshead	A	721	L	1 - 3	Whitham 57	11
21	NLN	Kettering Town	H	493	L	0 - 2		
26	NLN	AFC Telford United	A	1115	L	0 - 3		
28	NLN	King's Lynn Town	H	555	D	2 - 2	Morgan-Smith 4 Qualter 8	
Jan 1	NLN	AFC Telford United	H	511	D	1 - 1	Tomlinson 25	16
4	NLN	Curzon Ashton	A	160	W	2 - 0	Morgan-Smith 2 Johnson 51 (pen)	13
18	NLN	Darlington	A	1271	L	0 - 3		15
28	NLN	Gloucester City	H	296	W	6 - 1	Elliott 13 27 63 Morgan-Smith 16 Johnson 46 67	14
Feb 1	NLN	Hereford	H	518	W	2 - 0	Clackstone 31 Elliott 55	13
8	NLN	Farsley Celtic	A	457	D	1 - 1	Elliott 60	
18	NLN	Leamington	H	283	W	1 - 0	Branson 63	
22	NLN	Spennymoor Town	A	1000	L	0 - 5		13
Mar 7	NLN	York City	H	802	L	1 - 3	Clarke 88	13
14	NLN	Brackley Town	H	583	L	2 - 4	Johnson 90 (pen) Walker 90+2 (og)	14

GOALSCORERS	SG	CSG	Pens	Hat tricks	Total		SG	CSG	Pens	Hat tricks	Total
Morgan-Smith	12	3	4	1	16	Clackstone	1	1			1
Johnson	6	1	2		7	East	1	1			1
Elliott*	3	3		1	5	Grice	1	1			1
Clarke	4	3			4	Killock	1	1			1
Branson	3	1			3	Lynch	1	1			1
Opponent	2	1			2	Smith	1	1			1
Qualter	2	1			2	Whitham	1	1			1
Thacker	2	1			2						
Tomlinson	2	1			2						
Blake	1	1			1						

Appearance grid (x = Played full 90 minutes, xs = Substituted off, sx = Substituted on, s = Non-playing Substitute)

Atkinson J	Wilde J	East D	Smith D	Qualter R	Clackstone J	Thacker J	Lynch D	Clarke D	Whitham D	Morgan-Smith A	Johnson B	Tomlinson B	Blake N	Bacon D	Williams T	Killock S	Hinchley K	Branson C	Andrew C (Gk) (L)	Grice H	Marris T	Bennett-Rivera J (L)	Preston D (L)	Brough M	Wright J (Gk) (L)	Oyibo J	Freiter M	Elliott D (L)	Tuton S	Stewart E (L)	Kellett A	No.
x	x	xs	x	x	x	x	x	xs	xs	x		sx	sx		s	s																1
x	x	x	x	x	xs	x	x	x	xs	x		sx	s		sx	s		s														2
x	x	x	x	x	x	x	x	xs	s	x		sx	s	s		s																3
x	x	xs	x	x	x	x	x	xs	sx	x		xs	s		sx			s	sx													4
x	xs		x	x	x	x	xs	sx	sx	x		sx	s		sx	s	x															5
x	x	sx	x	x	x	x	x	x	s	xs	xs	sx	s		s	x																6
x	x	sx	x	x	x	x	xs	sx	x	x		sx	s		s	x																7
x	x	sx	x	x	x	xs	s	xs	xs	sx	sx			x	s																	8
x	x	sx	x	x	x	x	xs	sx	sx	sx		s	xs																			9
x	x	x	x	x	x	x	xs		sx	x	s	s		s																		10
x	x	x	x	x	xs	x		s	x	sx	xs	sx		s	sx		sx															11
s	sx	x	x	x	x	x	xs	x		x	x		sx			x	s	x	x	s												12
s	sx	s	x	x	x	xs	xs	x		x	x		sx			x	s	x	x	s												13
	xs	sx	x	x	x	x	x	x		x	x		sx	sx	s			x	x		s											14
s		x	x	x	x	xs	x		x	x		sx	s		x	x	s		s													15
s		x	x	x	x	x		x	x		x	s	x	sx		s	x	x	s		xs											16
	x	x	x	x	x	xs		x	xs	sx	sx	s		x	x		s	s														17
s	xs	x	x	x	x		x	sx	x	xs		xs	sx		x		x	sx		s												18
x		x	x	x	x	x		x	x		s	s		x		x	s	s		s												19
x	xs	x	x	x	x		x	x			sx	xs		x	s	x	s	s	sx		s											20
x		x	x	x	x		x	x			sx	s		x	s	x	s	sx		s												21
x		xs	x	x	x		x	x			x	xs			x	s	x		sx	s	sx											22
x		x	x	sx	x	s		x	x			xs			x		x		sx	s	xs	x	s									23
	s	xs	xs	xs	x	sx	x		x	x	sx			xs		x	s			x		x	x		x	x	x					24
	sx		x	x	sx	xs	xs		x	xs	x	s				x	s			x		x			x	x	x	sx				25
	sx		x	x	x	xs	x		x	x	xs	s				x	s			x		x			x	x	sx	xs				26
	sx		x	x	x	xs	x		x	x	xs	s				s	s	x		x		x			x	x	sx	xs				27
		x	x	x	x		x	s	x	x	xs	s				x	s			x		x			x	x	sx	s				28
s	x	x	x	x	x		xs	x	sx		x	xs	sx			xs	s			x		x			x	x	sx					29
	sx	x	x	x	x		x	sx	x	xs	sx				xs	x	s			x		x			x	x	s		xs			30
xs	sx	x	x	x		sx	x	sx	x	x	sx				xs		xs			s					x		x		x			31
x	s	x	x	x		sx	x	s	x	x	s				xs		x			s					x		x		x			32
xs	x	x	x		xs	x	sx	x	x	sx				x		s				x		x			x		s	xs	sx			33
x	xs	x	x		s	x	sx	x	x	sx				x		xs				x		x			x		s	x	s			34
x	xs	x	x		s	x	x	x	x	xs				s		s				x		x			x		sx			x	sx	35
x		x	x		s	x	xs	x	x	sx				xs		sx				x		x			x		sx		s	xs	x	36
16	14	11	31	35	29	24	11	24	4	31	18	1	2	0	0	14	0	19	7	0	0	0	8	0	13	2	0	3	0	1	1	x
0	4	6	2	0	2	2	9	10	3	3	8	6	2	2	0	7	0	3	0	1	0	2	0	0	0	0	2	2	0	1	0	xs
0	1	11	0	1	1	1	3	0	7	0	4	14	15	4	0	1	0	2	0	4	0	1	0	0	0	4	3	0	1	0	1	sx
5	1	3	0	0	0	0	4	0	10	0	0	4	9	7	9	3	9	1	10	5	7	6	0	1	0	1	3	0	2	0	0	s

GOALKEEPERS	CS	CCS
Atkinson	4	2
Wright	3	1
Andrew	1	1

x - Played full 90 minutes
xs - Substituted off
sx - Substituted on
s - Non-playing Substitute

Alfreton Town v Gloucester City 6-1

Kettering Town v Alfreton Town 2-1

Kings Lynn Town v Alfreton Town 2-3. Photos Bill Wheatcroft.

Weaver (Leamington) saved by the crossbar against Gateshead

Bremang (Leamington) beats James (Gateshead) to the ball. Photos Keith Clayton.

ALTRINCHAM MATCH RESULTS 2019-20

Date	Comp	Opponents	H/A	Att:	Result	Goalscorers	Pos
Aug 3	NLN	York City	H	1879	L 1 - 3	Jones 12	
6	NLN	Chester	A	2153	D 1 - 1	Livesey 11 (og)	18
10	NLN	Gloucester City	A	305	D 1 - 1	Jones 11	
13	NLN	Alfreton Town	H	878	W 3 - 2	Hampson 23 Jones 40 Johnston 85	
17	NLN	Brackley Town	A	465	L 0 - 1		17
24	NLN	Darlington	H	994	D 1 - 1	Hulme 65	
26	NLN	Boston United	A	1143	L 0 - 5		
31	NLN	Farsley Celtic	H	913	W 3 - 1	Hemmings 17 Hulme 61 67	17
Sep 3	NLN	Southport	A	904	L 1 - 2	Hulme 67	18
7	NLN	Leamington	H	1025	W 5 - 0	Hulme 15 Hancock 45+1 90+3 Gittings 59 (og) Peers 90+1	14
14	NLN	Kidderminster Harriers	A	1463	L 0 - 2		15
21	FAC2Q	Chester	A	1804	D 1 - 1	Hancock 75	
24	FAC2Qr	Chester	H	942	W 1 - 0	Jones 2	
Oct 5	FAC3Q	Halesowen Town	A	1235	W 2 - 0	Peers 73 Johnston 82	
12	NLN	Guiseley	A	1065	D 1 - 1	Hancock 60	
19	FAC4Q	Southport	A	1507	W 3 - 1	Hulme 42 61 Peers 51	
Nov 2	NLN	King's Lynn Town	A	888	D 2 - 2	Hancock 79 Moult 90+5	18
10	FAC1	York City	A	3222	W 1 - 0	Peers 82	
16	NLN	Hereford	H	1506	W 5 - 1	Hannigan 26 Hulme 28 57 65 Densmore 68	
19	NLN	Gateshead	H	789	W 3 - 0	Mullarkey 22 Hulme 39 Hancock 54 (pen)	15
23	FAT3Q	York City	A	974	W 1 - 0	Peers 22	
Dec 7	NLN	Bradford (Park Avenue)	A	423	L 0 - 2		17
14	FAT1	Farsley Celtic	A	253	D 2 - 2	Hulme 2 57	
17	FAT1r	Farsley Celtic	H	536	L 1 - 2	Hulme 46 (aet)	
21	NLN	Kidderminster Harriers	H	988	D 1 - 1	Moult 74	
26	NLN	Curzon Ashton	A	602	W 1 - 0	Peers 75	
28	NLN	Southport	H	1519	W 3 - 0	Johnston 49 75 Hancock 71	
Jan 1	NLN	Curzon Ashton	H	1184	W 2 - 1	Moult 56 Hancock 58	12
4	NLN	Leamington	A	615	W 1 - 0	Hancock 56	12
7	NLN	Blyth Spartans	H	614	W 3 - 1	Moult 34 Hancock 70 Peers 74	
11	NLN	Guiseley	H	1242	D 1 - 1	Peers 15	6
18	NLN	Gateshead	A	967	L 0 - 2		10
25	NLN	Bradford (Park Avenue)	H	1266	W 2 - 0	Hancock 1 Jones 41	8
28	NLN	Kettering Town	A	543	W 2 - 0	Hancock 34 Hulme 44	6
Feb 1	NLN	AFC Telford United	A	1159	D 2 - 2	Walters 68 Jones 84	7
4	NLN	AFC Telford United	H	810	W 5 - 2	Hulme 28 49 Hancock 41 46 Moult 67	6
8	NLN	Kettering Town	H	1357	D 1 - 1	Mullarkey 63	
11	NLN	Spennymoor Town	A	869	L 2 - 3	Hancock 32 Durrell 83 (pen)	
15	NLN	Blyth Spartans	A	684	W 3 - 0	Hancock 20 Durrell 57 Mooney 65	6
29	NLN	Hereford	A	1698	W 2 - 0	Durrell 45 Richman 84	5
Mar 7	NLN	Spennymoor Town	H	1255	W 4 - 1	Durrell 3 Hulme 39 90 Hannigan 67	5
July 19	PO Q	Chester	H	0	W 3 - 2	Hancock 33 Durrell 53 (pen) 60	
25	PO SF	York City	A	0	W 2 - 0	Hancock 8 Peers 77	
Aug 1	PO F	Boston United	A	0	W 1 - 0	Mooney 64 (Promoted to the National League)	

GOALSCORERS	SG	CSG	Pens	Hat tricks	Total		SG	CSG	Pens	Hat tricks	Total
Hulme	12	3		1	19	Opponent	2	1			2
Hancock	16	4	1		18	Densmore	1	1			1
Peers	9	1			9	Hampson	1	1			1
Durrell*	5	5	2		6	Hemmings	1	1			1
Jones	6	2			6	Richman	1	1			1
Moult	5	1			5	Walters	1	1			1
Johnston	3	1			4						
Hannigan	2				2						
Mooney	2	1			2						
Mullarkey	2	1			2						

Drench S	Branson C	White A	Jones J	Arnold N	Hanigan T	Harrop M	Williams S	Hampson C	Johnston J	Hulme J	Mullarkey T	Walters L	Peers T	Densmore S	Thompson T (Gk)	Richman S	Hancock J	Hemmings A (L)	Moult J	Ceesay Y (L)	Torrance J (Gk)	Archer L	Wall L	Walker E (L)	Blackburn L (Gk)	Lundstram J (L)	Miller C	Mahon C	Mooney D	Durrell E	Hooper J	Wynne E (Gk)	No.
x	x	xs	x	xs	x	x	x	xs	x	xs	x	xs	xs	s	s																		1
x	x	x	x		x	xs	x	x	x	x	sx	xs	sx	s	s	s																	2
x	x	x	x	sx	x	xs	x	x	x	s	xs	sx	sx	s	x																		3
x	sx	x	x	xs	x	sx	xs	x	x	x	xs	s		sx	s		x	x															4
x	xs	x	x	s	x	sx	x	x	x	x	s		sx			sx	xs	xs															5
x	sx	x	x		x	xs	x	x	x	xs	sx	s	sx	s	x		x		xs														6
	xs	s	x			xs	x	x	xs	x	x	sx	x	x	x	sx		x	sx														7
	sx	x	x				x	x	x	x	x	x		sx	s	x	xs			x	s	xs											8
	s	x	x			s	xs	xs	x	x	x			x	x	sx	x	x	sx		x												9
	s	x	x			s	x	xs	xs	x	x			x	x	sx	x	x				xs											10
	x	xs		x	xs	x	x	xs	xs	sx					xs		x	x			s												11
	x	x		x	s	sx	x	x	x	x				s	s	s	x	xs	x		s												12
	x	x		x	s	sx	sx	x	xs	s				sx	x	x	x	xs	xs	x		s											13
	x	x		x	s	sx	s	x	xs	sx				sx	x	x	x	xs	x	x		s											14
	x	x		x	sx	xs		xs	xs	s				x	x	x	sx	x	xs	xs			s										15
	x	x		x	s	sx	xs	s	xs	xs	sx			x	x	x	sx	x		x			s										16
	x	x		x	s	xs		x	xs	sx				x	xs	x	sx	x		x	sx		s										17
	x	x		x	s	xs	xs	xs	sx	s				x	s	x	sx	x		x	xs	s											18
	x	x		xs	sx	x	x	x	x	sx				x	x	sx	x		xs		s		xs										19
	x	s		x	sx	xs	x	x	x					s	x	xs	sx			x			xs										20
	x	x		x	s	x	sx	sx	x	x				xs	x	x	sx	xs			s		xs										21
	x	x		x	s	x	x	x	x					xs	x	x	x			xs			sx										22
	s	s		x	sx	xs	x		x	x				x	x	x	sx	x		x				s	xs	s							23
	x	s		x	sx	x	xs		x	x				xs	sx	x	sx	x		xs				sx	xs	s							24
	x	x		x	s	x	s		x	x				xs	x	x	sx	x		x				sx	xs								25
	x	x		x	sx	x	x		xs	sx				xs	x		xs	x		x				sx	s								26
	xs	x		x	xs	xs	sx		x	x		sx					s				s				s								27
	x			x	x			sx	x	xs	x			sx	x	x	x	x		x				s	s								28
	x			x	xs			sx	x	xs	x			sx	xs	x	x	x		x				sx	s								29
	x	sx		x	s			sx	x	xs	x				x	x	x	xs		xs				s	sx								30
	x	sx		xs				sx	x	x	x			xs	x	x	xs	x		x				sx	s								31
	x	s		x				x	s	x	x				xs	x		x		s				xs			x	sx					32
	xs	x		x			sx		x	sx	s	xs	x			x				s				xs				sx					33
		x		x	s			x	sx	sx	x	x	x			x				s				s			x		xs				34
		x		x	sx				x	s	sx	xs	x	x	sx	x				s				xs			xs						35
		x		x	sx				x	s	sx	x	x	s	sx	x				s				x			xs	xs					36
		x		x	sx			xs		x	sx	sx	x			x				s				x			xs	xs					37
		x		x	sx				x	sx	s	x	sx	x						x				x			xs	xs	sx				38
	s	x		x				x		x	sx	sx	sx	x			xs			x				x			xs	xs	sx				39
		x		x				x		x	s	s	sx	x		sx	sx			x				x			sx	xs	xs				40
	sx	x		x				xs		x			sx	x		sx	x			x				x			x	xs	xs				41
		x		x	sx			x				sx		x			sx	x						xs			sx	xs	xs	s	s		42
	xs			x	s	sx	x			x	x			sx			x	sx	xs					xs			sx	xs	xs				43
				x	s	sx	x			xs	x			sx			x	x	x		x			x			sx	xs	xs	s	s		44
6	3	29	32	0	37	2	14	20	19	29	16	0	8	23	38	10	23	7	32	0	0	0	0	0	0	11	0	0	0	0	0	0	x
0	2	4	1	2	2	6	9	5	8	13	0	2	7	5	0	3	14	4	4	3	0	0	5	3	0	2	0	6	9	5	0	0	xs
0	3	1	2	1	0	16	6	10	2	2	17	7	19	1	0	19	1	0	1	2	0	0	6	1	0	0	1	5	0	0	2	0	sx
0	2	3	4	1	1	14	1	7	0	0	11	4	5	9	3	3	0	0	1	0	15	1	8	5	2	0	0	1	0	0	2	3	s

GOALKEEPERS	CS	CCS
Thompson	15	2

x - Played full 90 minutes
xs - Substituted off
sx - Substituted on
s - Non-playing Substitute

BLYTH SPARTANS MATCH RESULTS 2019-20

Date	Comp	Opponents	H/A	Att	Result	Goalscorers	Pos
Aug 3	NLN	Gloucester City	H	834	L 1 - 2	Mullen 82	
10	NLN	Alfreton Town	A	460	L 0 - 3		
13	NLN	York City	H	1389	L 0 - 3		
17	NLN	Hereford	H	756	L 0 - 1		22
24	NLN	Bradford (Park Avenue)	A	328	D 0 - 0		22
26	NLN	Guiseley	H	891	L 1 - 4	Dale 70	22
31	NLN	Leamington	A	495	L 0 - 2		22
Sep 4	NLN	Darlington	A	1355	L 1 - 2	Roberts 11	22
7	NLN	Kidderminster Harriers	H	796	D 1 - 1	Dale 63	22
10	NLN	Spennymoor Town	A	1217	L 0 - 5		22
14	NLN	Southport	A	887	L 0 - 2		22
21	FAC2Q	Curzon Ashton	A	189	D 4 - 4	Roberts x3 Scott	
24	FAC2Qr	Curzon Ashton	H	491	W 1 - 0	Sweet 47	
28	NLN	AFC Telford United	H	711	W 3 - 1	Roberts 9 67 87	22
Oct 5	FAC3Q	Hednesford Town	A	616	L 2 - 4	Roberts 40 50	
12	NLN	Curzon Ashton	A	374	W 1 - 0	Amantchi 75	22
19	NLN	Chester	H	869	D 2 - 2	Sweet 6 Wrightson 22	20
Nov 2	NLN	Farsley Celtic	H	770	W 2 - 0	Dale 64 Roberts 81 (pen)	19
16	NLN	Kettering Town	A	810	D 4 - 4	Roberts 26 44 70 Hutchinson 37	
19	NLN	Boston United	A	1007	L 0 - 2		21
23	FAT3Q	Alfreton Town	H	526	D 1 - 1	Sweet	
30	NLN	Brackley Town	H	640	L 0 - 6		21
Dec 3	FAT3Qr	Alfreton Town	A	165	W 3 - 1	Sweet Roberts McGlade	
7	NLN	King's Lynn Town	A	1022	L 0 - 3		21
14	FAT1	Stockport County	A	1436	L 2 - 4	Hawkins 41 Hunter 78	
21	NLN	Southport	H	587	L 1 - 4	Evans 54	
26	NLN	Gateshead	A	1390	W 3 - 2	Roberts 16 Thackray 31 Dale 85	
28	NLN	Darlington	H	1481	L 0 - 2		
Jan 1	NLN	Gateshead	H	1028	D 3 - 3	Roberts 75 77 (pens) Amantchi 90+3	21
4	NLN	Kidderminster Harriers	A	1532	W 1 - 0	Hawkins 55	21
7	NLN	Altrincham	A	614	L 1 - 3	Thackray 90+2	21
11	NLN	Curzon Ashton	H	721	W 2 - 1	Dale 64 72	21
25	NLN	King's Lynn Town	H	686	L 0 - 3		21
28	NLN	AFC Telford United	A	602	L 2 - 4	Thackray 66 Williams 76 (og)	21
Feb 1	NLN	Boston United	H	576	L 0 - 1		21
8	NLN	Chester	A	1751	L 1 - 2	Scott 81	
15	NLN	Altrincham	H	684	L 0 - 3		
22	NLN	Farsley Celtic	A	369	L 0 - 2		21

Manager Lee Clark leaves the club by mutual consent. Michael Nelson takes over for the rest of the season.

| Mar 7 | NLN | Brackley Town | A | 390 | L 2 - 5 | McIntosh 29 Wrightson 58 | 21 |

GOALSCORERS	SG	CSG	Pens	Hat tricks	Total		SG	CSG	Pens	Hat tricks	Total
Roberts	9	2	3	3	17	Hutchinson	1	1			1
Dale	5	1			6	McGlade	1	1			1
Sweet	4	1			4	McIntosh	1	1			1
Thackray	3	1			3	Mullen	1	1			1
Amantchi	2	1			2	Opponent	1	1			1
Hawkins	2	1			2						
Scott	2	1			2						
Wrightson	2	1			2						
Evans	1	1			1						
Hunter	1	1			1						

Harker N (L)	Mullen D	Mason C (L)	Spooner C (L)	Callaghan A	Evans R	Devitt T	Fenwick S	Orrell J	Wrightson A	Pearson D	Mouanda U (L)	Sweet M	Dale R	Robson J	Scott O	Nearney J	Hutchinson R	Butler J	Horner L	Ritson L (L)	Foden M (Gk)	Roberts C	Hawkins L	Amantchi L (L)	Hunter J	Shanley L	Gray	McKeown C	McClade D	Hemming Z (Gk)	Thackray K	Sanders J (L)	Wilson S (L)	Waddington M (L)	Lambert J (L)	Harmison B	Summerly J	Blaney S (L)	Langstaff M (L)	Cunningham A (L)	McIntosh L (L)	No.
x	x	x	xs	x	x	x	x	xs	x	xs		sx	sx	sx	s	s																										1
x	x	xs	s	xs	x	x	sx	sx	x			xs	x	x	x	sx	s																									2
x		x	x	xs	xs	x	sx	x	x	x		s	sx	x	x	x	sx	x																								3
x	x	x	xs	xs	x	x	x	x				sx			x	xs		s	sx	s		x	x	s																		4
x	xs	xs			s	x	x	xs	xs			sx		x	x	x			x	x	s																					5
x				sx	x	x	sx	x		x			x	x	x	xs		xs	x	s																						6
s		x			x	x	sx	sx	xs			x	sx	xs	x	x			s	xs	x	x																				7
s				s	x	xs	x	x				sx		x	x	sx			xs	x	x	x	x																			8
s			x	x	x	sx	sx	sx		xs			x	x	sx				s	x	x	x	xs																			9
s			x	x	x	sx	s	sx		x			xs	x	sx				sx	x	x	x	xs																			10
x			x	x	sx		x					sx	x	xs	x	s		xs			s	x	x	sx	xs																	11
s	x		x	x	x			x				sx	x	x		x				x	x	xs																				12
s	x		x	xs	x		s	x				s	xs	x	sx	x				x	x	x		sx		s	s															13
s	x		x		x					xs		s	xs	sx	x	x				x	x	x	xs	xs	sx																	14
s	x		x	xs	x		x					s	x	xs	x	xs				xs	x	x		sx	sx																	15
s	x		x	x	x			sx				xs	sx	s	sx					x	x	x	xs	xs	x																	16
s			x	x	x	s		x				xs	sx	s	x					x	x	xs	x	sx	x																	17
s	s		x	x	x			s				xs	x	s	x					x	x	x	sx	x																		18
	sx		x	x	xs							xs	x		x	sx				x	x	xs	xs	x				s	s													19
x	sx		x	x				s	x				x	xs	xs	sx	x			x	s	x	xs	sx	x			sx	xs													20
	sx		x	x	x			x				x	x		xs		x			x	xs		x					sx	x													21
s	s		x	x	x			sx				xs	x	x		x				x	xs	sx	x					s	x													22
	x		x	x	x			sx				x	xs		xs					x	x	sx	x					xs	x													23
	x		x	x	x			x				sx	s		s					x	xs	sx	x					s	xs	x												24
	x		x	sx				x				x		x	sx	xs				x	x	x						s	xs	x	x											25
	x		x	s				sx	x			xs	sx	sx						x	x	xs	x					s	s	x	x	x										26
	x		xs	s		sx		xs	x			sx	sx	x	x		s		xs	x		x						sx	x	x	x											27
xs			x		sx			xs	x			x	x	x	xs		xs			sx	sx	x						s		x	x	x										28
xs			x	s	sx			xs	x			x	x	xs	sx					x	x	sx	x					s		x	x	x										29
xs			x	s	sx			xs	x			s			x	x				sx		x	x	x	sx																	30
x			x	s	sx			x	xs				s		x	x			xs		s	x	x	x	sx																	31
sx			x	s	sx			xs	xs	s			x		xs				s	x	x	x	x	x																	32
s			x	s	sx			sx	x				x	xs					x	x	x	xs	x	xs	x	sx																33
xs			xs	sx			s		s	x			sx	x					x	x	x	x	x	x	x	x	s															34
s			x	sx				sx				sx	x		sx				x	s	x	x	x	xs	x	xs	xs															35
			sx	x			s		sx	xs	x		s	x	xs	x		xs	x	x			sx	x	x																	36
xs			x	x	sx		s			sx	x		x	xs				x	x		s	s			x	x	x															37
s			x	sx			x			sx	x		x	xs		s		x	xs			sx			xs	x	x															38
																																										39
8	14	3	1	17	27	24	4	4	11	1	3	11	19	12	17	0	2	0	1	15	12	22	19	0	19	0	0	0	0	19	13	11	4	7	1	2	0	1	2	3	3	x
0	6	2	2	6	1	1	1	6	1	2	11	9	0	7	0	4	0	2	4	0	3	6	3	6	0	0	0	4	0	2	0	2	0	2	2	0	0	1	0	0	0	xs
0	4	0	2	2	5	6	5	10	0	6	7	6	1	7	1	5	1	0	1	0	0	4	13	2	0	3	2	0	0	0	0	2	1	0	0	0	0	0	0	0	0	sx
12	6	0	1	0	2	7	1	2	4	0	5	1	1	4	3	1	3	0	3	2	4	0	0	0	1	1	11	3	0	0	0	0	0	0	0	1	1	2	0	0	0	s

GOALKEEPERS	CS	CCS
Foden	3	1
Harker	1	1

x - Played full 90 minutes
xs - Substituted off
sx - Substituted on
s - Non-playing Substitute

BOSTON UNITED MATCH RESULTS 2019-20

Date	Comp	Opponents	H/A	Att:	Result	Goalscorers	Pos
Aug 3	NLN	Chester	H	1393	D 1 - 1	Thewlis 38	
6	NLN	Alfreton Town	A	633	D 1 - 1	Wright 62	12
13	NLN	Leamington	H	1083	W 1 - 0	Thewlis 50 (pen)	
17	NLN	Guiseley	H	1059	D 1 - 1	Thewlis 72 (pen)	15
24	NLN	Gloucester City	A	330	L 0 - 3		
26	NLN	Altrincham	H	1143	W 5 - 0	Platt 40 63 Knowles 45 82 Shiels 87	
31	NLN	Hereford	A	2498	D 0 - 0		10
Sep 3	NLN	Kettering Town	A	835	W 2 - 0	Rollins 48 Cartwright 62 (og)	9
7	NLN	Bradford (Park Avenue)	H	1110	W 2 - 1	Abbott 64 Thewlis 66	6
14	NLN	Gateshead	A	1134	L 0 - 3		10
21	FAC2Q	Stamford	A	671	W 4 - 0	Thewlis 6 75 Knowles 60 Rollins 86	
28	NLN	Southport	H	1021	W 2 - 0	Abbott 42 Thewlis 68	8
Oct 5	FAC3Q	Sutton Coldfield Town	A	497	W 1 - 0	Shiels 69	
12	NLN	Darlington	A	1573	L 1 - 2	Knowles 18	10
19	FAC4Q	Hednesford Town	A	891	W 1 - 0	Thanoj 38	
29	NLN	York City	A	2768	L 1 - 2	Rollins 54	
Nov 2	NLN	AFC Telford United	A	1084	W 3 - 1	Thewlis 52 56 (pen) 62	10
9	FAC1	Carshalton Athletic	A	1859	W 4 - 1	Thanoj 33 90+1 Shiels 37 Wright 90+3	
12	NLN	Spennymoor Town	A	930	L 1 - 2	Knowles 8	
16	NLN	Farsley Celtic	A	742	W 4 - 2	Thewlis 25 75 (pens) Knowles 54 Abbott 90+3	
19	NLN	Blyth Spartans	H	1007	W 2 - 0	Knowles 11 Thanoj 52	5
23	FAT3Q	Atherstone Collieries	A	303	L 0 - 1		
Dec 1	FAC2	Rochdale	A	2583	D 0 - 0		
7	NLN	Kidderminster Harriers	A	1102	W 3 - 1	Thewlis 9 (pen) Knowles 51 Wafula 89	7
16	FAC2r	Rochdale	H	4190	L 1 - 2	Thewlis 49	
26	NLN	King's Lynn Town	A	2246	L 0 - 1		
28	NLN	Kettering Town	H	1718	W 2 - 1	Wright 33 45+1	
Jan 1	NLN	King's Lynn Town	H	2360	L 0 - 3		9
4	NLN	Bradford (Park Avenue)	A	481	W 2 - 1	Knowles 1 Ainge 38	6
7	NLN	Curzon Ashton	H	894	D 0 - 0		
18	NLN	Southport	A	883	W 3 - 1	Thanoj 44 60 Shiels 88	5
21	NLN	Brackley Town	H	967	W 1 - 0	Knowles 86	5
25	NLN	Kidderminster Harriers	H	1278	W 2 - 0	Knowles 37 43	5
Feb 1	NLN	Blyth Spartans	A	576	W 1 - 0	Rollins 67	3
8	NLN	York City	H	2155	W 3 - 1	Mulhern 38 Abbott 52 Thanoj 79	
22	NLN	AFC Telford United	H	1269	W 1 - 0	Knowles 27 (pen)	3
25	NLN	Gateshead	H	1108	L 0 - 3		3
Mar 3	NLN	Brackley Town	A	403	D 0 - 0		3
7	NLN	Curzon Ashton	A	290	D 1 - 1	Thewlis 20 (pen)	3
July 25	PO SF	Gateshead	H	0	W 5 - 3	Thewlis 34 43 (pens) Rollins 62 Wright 70 79	
Aug 1	PO F	Altrincham	H	0	L 0 - 1		

GOALSCORERS	SG	CSG	Pens	Hat tricks	Total		SG	CSG	Pens	Hat tricks	Total	
Thewlis	12	2	9		17	Opponent	1	1			1	
Knowles	11	3	1		13	Wafula	1	1			1	
Thanoj	5	1			7							
Wright J	4	1			6							
Rollins	5	1			5							
Abbott	4	1			4							
Shiels	4	1			4							
Platt	1				2							
Ainge	1	1			1							
Mulhern	1	1			1							

	Crook P	Shiels L	Middleton B	Thanoj A	Platt T	Whittle A	Abbott B	Rollins J	Ainge S (L)	Thewlis J	Wright J (L)	Tuton S	Green G	Walker N	Jackson A	Willis G (Gk)	Byrne K	Knowles D	Clare T	Adebayo-Smith J (L)	Gibbens L (L)	Wafula J	Woolford M	Duhaney D (L)	Penny A	Bird P (L)	Southwell D (L)	Rowe A (L)	Garner S	Mulhern F (L)	Heslop S	Warren T (L)	Challoner M	Nicholson J	No.
	x	x	x	xs	x	x	x	x	x	x	xs	xs		sx	sx		sx	sx		s	s														1
	x	x	x	xs	x	x	x	x	x	x	xs	xs		sx	sx		sx	sx		s															2
	x	x		sx	x	x	xs	x	x	x	xs	sx			sx		s	x	x	xs	s														3
	x	x		sx	x	xs	x	x	x	x		xs			s		sx	s	x	sx															4
	x	x	x	x	xs	xs	sx		x					sx	x		x	s	s		x	xs	sx												5
	x	x		s	x	x	xs	x		x				sx	x		sx	s		x	xs	sx	xs												6
	x	x	s	x	x	x	x		x					sx	x		s	s		x	xs	sx	xs												7
	x	x		x	x	x	x	xs	x	sx					xs		sx	s	x	xs	sx	s													8
	x	x		xs	x	x	x	x	sx					sx	xs		s	s	x	sx					sx										9
	x	x		xs	x	xs	x	x						sx	s		s	xs	x		sx	sx													10
	x	xs	x	s	x	x	x	x	x	x				sx	s		xs	s	s		xs		sx	sx											11
	x	x	x	sx	x	x	xs	x	x					sx	s	xs				xs			sx	s											12
	x	x	x	s	x	x	x	s	xs	xs			sx		x	s		s	x		xs	sx	sx												13
	x	x	xs	sx	xs	x	x	x	x	x			s		xs	s			x		sx		sx												14
	x		sx	x	x	x	x	x	x	sx				s	x	s		xs		s	xs	sx	xs												15
	x	x		sx	x	x	xs	xs	x	x				sx			x	s			xs	x	sx												16
	x	x		x	x	xs	x		x	x				s	sx		s			xs		x	xs	sx											17
	x	x		x	x	x	x	sx	xs	xs	sx	s			s		s			xs			s	x	x	sx									18
	x	x		x	x	x	xs		x	sx	sx			s	s					xs			sx	xs	x	x									19
	x	x		xs	x	x	xs		x	s	s			sx						xs			sx	x	x	xs									20
	x	x	s		x	x	sx		xs	xs	sx			x						xs			s	xs	x										21
	x	x	x	s	s	sx	s			sx	xs	x	x	x	x			s		xs		x					sx								22
	x	x	xs	x	x	x	x	s	xs	sx	sx			s	s	s	xs			sx		x		x											23
	x	x		x	x	x	x	s	xs	xs				s						xs			sx		x	x	sx	sx							24
	x	x		x	x	sx	x	sx	s					sx	s	s	s			xs	xs				x	x									25
	x	x		x	x	x	x	x	xs					sx	s		s			xs			s	xs					xs						26
	x	x		x	x	x	x		xs					sx	s		s			sx	sx								xs	xs					27
	x	x		x	x	x	x	sx	x	sx	x			s	s		x			x															28
	x			x	xs	x	sx	x	xs	xs				sx	x		x			sx		x			s		x								29
	x	x		xs		x	x	s	x	xs	sx			sx	x		sx			xs			x												30
	x	x	xs	x	xs	x	sx	s	s	x				sx	s		x			sx			x												31
	x	x	xs	x	x	x	x	xs						s			sx	s		sx	xs		x												32
	x	x		x	x	x		x	x	xs	sx			sx						xs			sx	s		x			s	xs					33
	x	x		x	x	x		x	xs	sx				sx						xs			s	x		x			s	xs					34
	x	x		xs	x	xs	x	sx	x	s				sx						sx			s	x		x			x	x	sx				35
	x	x		x	x		x	x	sx	sx				s						xs			x	xs		sx			x	xs	sx	s			36
	x	x		x	x	xs	xs	x	x	sx	sx			sx						xs			x	x		s			s						37
	x		s	xs	x		sx	x	x	x	xs			x					s				sx			x		sx	xs	x					38
	x	sx		x	x	x	sx	x	x	sx				s						xs			x	xs	s										39
	x	x		xs	x	x	xs	xs	sx	xs	xs				s			sx					x	sx	sx				x	sx					40
	x	x		x	xs	x	x	x	s	xs	xs				s			sx					x	sx					s	x	sx				41
	41	36	10	13	35	30	30	21	28	16	1	1	1	5	6	0	5	10	0	0	0	1	5	6	9	3	0	0	10	2	0	2	2	0	x
	0	1	1	12	4	8	5	4	2	13	11	1	0	5	0	0	2	23	1	4	1	2	9	1	2	1	3	1	0	4	1	0	0	0	xs
	0	1	1	5	0	1	2	10	2	7	10	14	4	6	14	0	0	2	4	5	4	11	4	0	3	0	1	1	0	3	3	0	0	2	sx
	0	0	3	1	0	1	1	5	1	1	7	4	5	14	27	4	4	1	2	1	4	3	0	0	0	1	0	2	0	2	3	0	0	0	s

GOALKEEPERS	CS	CCS
Crook	14	3

x - Played full 90 minutes
xs - Substituted off
sx - Substituted on
s - Non-playing Substitute

BRACKLEY TOWN MATCH RESULTS 2019-20

Date	Comp	Opponents	H/A	Att:	Result	Goalscorers	Pos
Aug 3	NLN	Alfreton Town	H	485	W 1 - 0	Langmead 84	
6	NLN	Leamington	A	608	L 0 - 2		10
10	NLN	York City	A	2039	L 0 - 1		
13	NLN	King's Lynn Town	H	500	D 1 - 1	Ndlovu 58	
17	NLN	Altrincham	H	465	W 1 - 0	Byrne 30	13
24	NLN	Hereford	A	2585	D 1 - 1	Armson 37	
26	NLN	Gloucester City	H	570	W 3 - 0	Armson 8 22 (pen) 69	
31	NLN	Gateshead	A	769	L 0 - 2		8
Sep 3	NLN	Kidderminster Harriers	A	1069	W 3 - 1	Byrne 20 Audel 32 Armson 64	7
7	NLN	AFC Telford United	H	545	D 1 - 1	Lowe 16	8
14	NLN	Curzon Ashton	A	204	W 4 - 0	Armson 6 Audel 65 Byrne 67 Ndlovu 78	7
21	**FAC2Q**	**Cinderford Town**	**H**	**397**	**W 4 - 0**	**Walker 52 Rhodes 60 (og) Lowe 78 84**	
28	NLN	Bradford (Park Avenue)	H	490	W 8 - 0	Wood 19 (og) Lowe 30 Armson 42 Ndlovu 45 80 Byrne 54 Audel 67 Holman 84	5
Oct 5	**FAC3Q**	**Warrington Town**	**H**	**452**	**W 2 - 0**	**Audel 25 Myles 80**	
12	NLN	Southport	A	1047	L 0 - 1		6
19	**FAC4Q**	**Hartlepool United**	**A**	**2506**	**L 0 - 1**		
Nov 2	NLN	Chester	H	476	D 1 - 1	Audel 19	7
5	NLN	Spennymoor Town	H	330	D 0 - 0		7
16	NLN	Darlington	H	730	W 5 - 1	Ndlovu 11 30 Lowe 14 York 42 Byrne 45	7
23	**FAT3Q**	**Chester**	**H**	**334**	**L 0 - 1**		
30	NLN	Blyth Spartans	A	640	W 6 - 0	Dean 8 Ndlovu 26 43 66 York 55 81	6
Dec 3	NLN	Farsley Celtic	A	292	D 1 - 1	Ndlovu 90	5
7	NLN	Guiseley	A	526	W 2 - 0	Walker 59 Ndlovu 90+5	5
21	NLN	Curzon Ashton	H	475	W 3 - 0	Lowe 28 Audel 42 Ndlovu 73	
28	NLN	Kidderminster Harriers	H	775	W 2 - 0	Audel 52 Ndlovu 85	
Jan 1	NLN	Kettering Town	H	905	D 1 - 1	Armson 34	4
4	NLN	AFC Telford United	A	1103	W 1 - 0	Ndlovu 33	4
18	NLN	Bradford (Park Avenue)	A	256	W 2 - 1	Ndlovu 45 Armson 61	3
21	NLN	Boston United	A	967	L 0 - 1		3
25	NLN	Guiseley	H	590	D 0 - 0		4
Feb 1	NLN	Farsley Celtic	H	440	L 0 - 1		5
8	NLN	Spennymoor Town	A	1035	D 0 - 0		
18	NLN	Southport	H	350	D 1 - 1	Ndlovu 77	
22	NLN	Chester	A	1918	W 3 - 2	Ndlovu 34 Audel 71 Lowe 90	5
29	NLN	Darlington	A	1183	D 1 - 1	Maye 78	6
Mar 3	NLN	Boston United	H	403	D 0 - 0		4
7	NLN	Blyth Spartans	H	390	W 5 - 2	Ndlovu 49 77 Lowe 52 68 Byrne 79	4
14	NLN	Alfreton Town	A	583	W 4 - 2	York 15 Armson 30 (pen) Lowe 57 Ndlovu 66	3
July 19	**PO Q**	**Gateshead**	**H**	**0**	**D 1 - 1**	**Byrne 45+4 (Lost 5-6 on pens)**	

GOALSCORERS	SG	CSG	Pens	Hat tricks	Total		SG	CSG	Pens	Hat tricks	Total
Ndlovu	15	5		1	20	Langmead	1	1			1
Armson	8	2	2	1	10	Maye	1	1			1
Lowe	8	1			10	Myles	1	1			1
Audel	8	2			8						
Byrne	7	1			7						
York	3	1			4						
Opponent	2	2			2						
Walker	2	1			2						
Dean	1	1			1						
Holman	1	1			1						

Lewis D	Franklin C	Langmead K	Dean G	Myles E	Armson J	Baker C	Walker G	Lowe M	Murombedzi S	Ndlovu L	Fairlamb L	Daire T	Holman D	Audel T	Byrne S	Worby A (Gk)	Noon M	York W (L)	Smith L	Maye S	No.
x	x	x	x	x	xs	xs	xs	x	x	x	xs	sx	sx	s							1
x	x	xs	x	x	sx	xs	xs	x	x	x	sx	sx	s	s	x						2
x	s	xs	x	x	sx	xs	x	sx	x	x	sx	s	xs	x							3
x	x	sx	x	x	xs	s	x	xs	x	x	sx	sx	s	xs	x						4
x	x	sx	x	x	xs	sx	xs	xs	x	x	sx	sx	s	x							5
x	xs	x	x	x	xs	sx	x	x	x	sx	s	s	x								6
x	s	s	x	x	xs	xs	x	x	x	xs	sx	sx	sx	x	x						7
x	s	s	x	xs	x	xs	x	xs	x	x	sx	sx	sx	x	x						8
x	s	s	x	x	x	xs	x	xs	x	x	sx	sx	x	x							9
x	x	sx	x	x	x	sx		xs	x	x	xs	sx		x	xs	s	s				10
x	x	s	x	x	xs	sx	x	xs		xs	x	sx	sx	x	x	s					11
x	**x**	**s**	**x**	**x**	**xs**	**sx**	**x**	**x**	**s**	**xs**	**xs**	**sx**	**sx**	**x**	**x**	**s**					12
x	x	sx	xs	x	xs	sx	xs	x		x	x		sx	x	x	s					13
x	**x**	**s**	**x**	**x**	**sx**	**x**	**x**		**xs**	**xs**		**sx**	**x**	**x**	**s**	**s**					14
x	xs	s	x	x	sx	x	x		xs	xs	sx	s	x	x			sx				15
x	**x**	**s**	**x**	**xs**	**x**	**xs**	**x**	**x**	**s**	**xs**	**sx**	**sx**	**sx**	**x**	**x**	**s**	**s**				16
x	x	s	x	x	xs		x	x	sx	x	sx	s		x	x	s		xs			17
x	x		x	x	xs		x	s	x	sx	sx		x	x	s			xs			18
x	x		x	x	s		xs	x	x	xs	sx	sx	sx	x	x			s	xs		19
x	**x**	**s**	**x**	**x**	**sx**		**xs**	**x**	**xs**	**xs**	**sx**	**sx**		**x**	**x**			**s**	**x**		20
x	x	sx	x	x	s		xs	x	x	xs	sx	sx		x	x			s	xs		21
x	xs		x	x	sx		x	x	xs	x	s	sx		x	x			s	x		22
x	x	s	x	x	s	s	xs	x	x	sx	sx		x	x			xs				23
x	x	x	x	sx	s	x	x	x	x	sx	sx		x	xs				x			24
x	x	x		sx	s	xs	x	x	x	x	sx	xs		x	x		s		s		25
x	xs	x		x	xs	s	x	x	x	x	sx	s		x	x		s	sx			26
x	x	sx	x	x	xs	s	x	xs	x	x	sx		x	x			s				27
x	x	s	x	x	xs	sx	xs	x	x	x	sx	s		x	x				s		28
x	xs	s	x	x	xs	sx	x	x	x	x	sx	sx		xs	x				s		29
x	xs	sx	x	x	x	sx	x	xs	x	xs	s	sx		x	x				s		30
x	x	s	x	x	xs	sx	xs	x	x		sx	xs		x	x			sx	s		31
x	x		x	x	xs	x	x	x	x	x	s	s	sx	x				s	s		32
x	x	sx	x	x	sx	x	x	x	x		s	xs		x				s	s		33
x	x	sx	x	x	sx	xs	xs	x	x		s	xs	sx	x					s		34
x	x	s	x	x	sx	xs		x	x	x	s	xs	x	x			s			sx	35
x	x	s	x	x	sx		x	x	x	s	xs	x	x			sx	s			xs	36
x	x	s	x	x	sx		x	xs	x	sx	xs	x	x			xs	s			sx	37
x	x	s	x	x	x	s	x	x	x	xs		sx	sx		xs			xs		sx	38
x	**xs**	**s**	**x**	**x**	**x**	**xs**	**x**	**x**	**xs**	**xs**	**sx**	**sx**			**x**	**s**		**sx**	**sx**		39
39	28	5	36	37	8	3	24	29	26	24	3	0	0	28	35	0	0	2	1	0	x
0	7	2	1	2	16	9	11	9	5	14	4	2	6	2	3	0	0	7	0	1	xs
0	0	8	0	0	12	11	0	1	1	0	23	24	12	1	0	0	0	2	3	4	sx
0	4	20	0	0	3	8	0	0	3	0	3	11	5	4	0	9	10	0	7	7	s

GOALKEEPERS	CS	CCS
Lewis	16	4

x - Played full 90 minutes
xs - Substituted off
sx - Substituted on
s - Non-playing Substitute

BRADFORD (PARK AVENUE) MATCH RESULTS 2019-20

Date	Comp	Opponents	H/A	Att:	Result	Goalscorers	Pos
Aug 3	NLN	Curzon Ashton	A	309	L 0 - 5		22
6	NLN	Guiseley	H	674	L 0 - 5		22
Garry Thompson sacked as manager. Marcus Law is installed as the new manager.							
10	NLN	Kidderminster Harriers	H	379	L 0 - 3		22
13	NLN	Gateshead	A	1001	D 1 - 1	Knight 58	21
17	NLN	Alfreton Town	A	378	L 0 - 4		21
24	NLN	Blyth Spartans	H	328	D 0 - 0		21
26	NLN	Darlington	A	1491	W 1 - 0	Headley 61	
31	NLN	AFC Telford United	H	378	L 2 - 3	Knight 44 Calder 66	21
Sep 3	NLN	Farsley Celtic	H	508	L 0 - 3		21
7	NLN	Boston United	A	1110	L 1 - 2	Dockerty 84	21
14	NLN	Spennymoor Town	H	402	D 1 - 1	Dockerty 11	21
21	**FAC2Q**	**Morpeth Town**	**H**	**217**	**L 2 - 4**	**Calder 25 Dockerty 89**	
28	NLN	Brackley Town	A	490	L 0 - 8		21
Mark Bower returns as manager.							
Oct 12	NLN	Hereford	H	484	W 3 - 2	Nowakowski 9 Knight 22 Sweeney 51 (pen)	20
19	NLN	Gloucester City	A	295	L 0 - 1		21
26	NLN	Southport	H	418	L 0 - 3		21
Nov 2	NLN	Kettering Town	A	625	L 0 - 4		22
9	NLN	King's Lynn Town	H	416	L 2 - 3	Knight 17 Johnson O 71	22
16	NLN	Leamington	H	442	L 0 - 3		22
23	**FAT3Q**	**Gloucester City**	**A**	**251**	**W 2 - 0**	**Bazeley 16 Hurst 83**	
30	NLN	Chester	A	1875	L 1 - 2	Priestley 15	22
Dec 7	NLN	Altrincham	H	423	W 2 - 0	Clare 12 Johnson O 88	22
14	**FAT1**	**Halesowen Town**	**H**	**285**	**D 2 - 2**	**Knight 19 Lowe 83**	
17	**FAT1r**	**Halesowen Town**	**A**	**426**	**L 0 - 2**		
21	NLN	Spennymoor Town	A	1097	L 0 - 3		22
26	NLN	York City	H	1127	L 0 - 2		22
28	NLN	Farsley Celtic	A	784	L 0 - 5		22
Jan 1	NLN	York City	A	2477	L 1 - 2	Hughes 90+3	22
4	NLN	Boston United	H	481	L 1 - 2	Clee 39	22
11	NLN	Hereford	A	1586	D 1 - 1	Clee 18	22
18	NLN	Brackley Town	H	256	L 1 - 2	Clare 90+4	22
25	NLN	Altrincham	A	1266	L 0 - 2		22
Feb 1	NLN	Southport	A	809	D 3 - 3	Knight 14 Clare 48 Priestly 83	22
8	NLN	Gloucester City	H	296	L 1 - 2	Hughes 68	22
Mar 7	NLN	Chester	H	525	W 2 - 1	Clare 41 Johnson O 67	22
10	NLN	King's Lynn Town	A	1220	W 1 - 0	Clare 26	22
14	NLN	Curzon Ashton	H	685	L 0 - 2		22

GOALSCORERS	SG	CSG	Pens	Hat tricks	Total		SG	CSG	Pens	Hat tricks	Total
Knight	6	1			6	Hurst	1	1			1
Clare	5	2			5	Lowe	1	1			1
Dockerty	3	3			3	Nowakowski	1	1			1
Johnson O	3	1			3	Sweeney	1	1	1		1
Calder	2	1			2						
Clee	2	2			2						
Hughes	2	1			2						
Priestley	2	1			2						
Bazeley	1	1			1						
Headley*	1	1			1						

Player appearance grid. Legend: x = Played full 90 minutes; xs = Substituted off; sx = Substituted on; s = Non-playing Substitute.

	Andrew C (L)	Cresswell R	Lund M	Moran J	Hinds A (L)	Hedley B	Marriott I (L)	Holmes E	Hakeem Z	Hurst A	Knight L	Croft J	Dockerty B	Wright S	Clarke M	Rathbone L	Digbeu N	Bennett J (Gk)	Taylor R (Gk)	Calder R	Wood M	Gibbons M (L)	Headley J (L)	Bazeley I (L)	Heaton J	Johnson A	Sweeney D (L)	Lowe K	Agustein K	Green J (Gk)	Priestley B	Nowakowski A	Hughes L	Johnson O	Royle J (L)	Dickinson S (Gk)	Toulson R	Staunton R (L)	Clare T	Clee N	Lyons J	Nicholson T (Gk)	Hall R (L)	Hibbs J (L)	Demetriou S	No.
	x	x		x	xs	x	x	x	xs	x		x	xs	sx	sx	sx	s																													1
	x			x	x		x	x	s	sx	xs	x	x	xs	xs	x	sx																													2
	x		x	x	x	xs	x	sx	xs	x	x		s	sx	s	xs		x																												3
	s		x	x	x	x	xs	xs	x	xs	s			sx	sx		x	x																												4
		x	x	x	xs	x	x	x	xs	x	x				sx	s		s	x																											5
		s	x	x		x	xs	sx		x	x		sx				xs			x	x	x	xs																							6
			x	x	sx	x		xs		x	xs		xs							x	s	x	x	x	x	sx	x																			7
			xs	xs		x	sx		x		x									x	s	x	x	xs	sx	x	sx																			8
		x	x	s		xs	sx		x	x			sx							x	x		x	x	s	xs	x																			9
	xs	x			x	xs		x	xs		sx							x	x		x	x	sx	sx	x																				10
	sx	x			x	sx		x	xs								s	x	x		x	s	xs	x	x	sx																				11
	sx	x	s		xs	sx		x	xs		x					s	x	x	xs	s		x	x	sx	x																					12
	xs	x			x	sx		xs						s	x	x	x		sx		s	x	x	xs																						13
		x	s		sx			x	xs		s								sx	x	sx	xs	x	xs	x	x	x																		14
		x	s		s			x	x		sx								sx	xs	sx	x	x	xs	x	x	xs																		15
		x			s			x	xs		sx								s	x	sx	x	x	x	xs	x	xs																		16
		x			s			x	x		sx								sx	xs		x	x		x	x	xs	sx																	17
		xs			x				xs							s			x		sx	x		x	x	xs	x	s																		18
					x			x	xs							s			x	sx	sx	xs	x		x	xs	x	sx	x																	19
					x			x	x										x		s		x		x	x	x		x		s		x				s									20
					x			x	x										xs		s		x	x	xs	sx	xs	sx	sx	s	x	x	sx													21
					x			x	xs							s			sx		sx		x	x	x	xs	x	s	sx		xs	x	x	xs	x											22
		xs			x			x	xs							s			x		sx		x	x	x	x	x	x	sx											sx						23
		x			x			x							sx				x		x		x	xs	x	x	xs	sx	sx				xs								xs					24
		xs			x			x	sx										sx		x		x	xs	sx	xs	x	s					x	x	s	x				x					25
		sx		x	x			sx	x		x								sx		x		s	s	sx	xs	x		xs	x	x	xs	x	s	x										26
		s		x	xs			sx	x										xs		x		s	s	sx	sx	x		x	x	x	x	xs	sx	x										27
		s		sx	x			x											x		x	x	x	xs	sx	xs	x		x	xs	xs	s	x												28
		sx		x	xs			x	x	sx									x	x	x	x	sx		xs	x	xs		s					x	x	x										29
		x		s	x	sx													x	x	x	x	xs		x		sx	x					s	xs	x											30
		x		s	x	sx													x	x	x	x	x		xs		sx	x					s	xs	x											31
		sx		x	x														s	x	sx	x	x		xs		sx	x	x		xs	x	x													32
		sx		sx	x														s	x	sx	x	sx		x		x	x	x		xs	x	x													33
		x		sx	x														s	x	x	x	xs		x		sx	x	sx		xs	x														34
		x		x	xs														s	x	x	x	x		xs		x	sx	x		x	x	x													35
		x		x	sx														s	x	sx	x	sx		sx		x	x	x		x	x	x													36
		x		x	x														s	x	sx	x	xs		x		x	x	x		x	x	x													37
x	3	3	23	6	3	5	18	1	1	33	15	1	2	0	1	0	6	3	7	8	6	0	2	9	4	1	6	16	1	14	23	11	11	4	6	0	8	7	6	8	0	9	4	9	5	x
xs	0	2	4	2	1	1	3	3	3	1	14	0	3	1	1	0	1	0	0	0	2	1	2	2	0	2	0	3	1	1	8	3	7	0	0	4	0	4	5	1	0	5	0	0		xs
sx	0	2	3	0	0	1	3	7	1	2	5	1	9	2	2	2	0	6	0	0	0	3	1	8	1	9	0	0	0	0	2	5	9	1	1	2	0	4	1	4	0	1	0	0		sx
s	1	1	2	4	0	0	5	1	0	0	2	1	1	1	5	0	6	0	0	0	3	0	1	0	3	0	0	0	7	0	0	0	0	0	4	0	0	0	0							s

Also Played: Gardner S - 03/08 (s) 06/08 (xs); Thompson G - 06/08 (s); Kabeya A - 10/08 13/08 (sx); Orlando-Young R - 17/08 (sx) 24/08 26/08 31/08 (s); Chidyausiku J - 24/08 26/08 (sx); Laird A - 03/09 (s); Keane C - 26/10 (sx) 02/11 (xs); Boshell D - 23/11 17/11 18/01 08/02 10/03 (s) 14/03 (sx); Byrne K - 03/07 (s) 10/03 14/03 (xs); Ockerby J - 14/03 (s)

GOALKEEPERS	CS	CCS
Green	2	1
Taylor	2	2
Nicholson	1	1

x - Played full 90 minutes
xs - Substituted off
sx - Substituted on
s - Non-playing Substitute

CHESTER MATCH RESULTS 2019-20

Date	Comp	Opponents	H/A	Att:	Result	Goalscorers	Pos
Aug 3	NLN	Boston United	A	1393	D 1 - 1	Waring 40	
6	NLN	Altrincham	H	2153	D 1 - 1	Roberts G 90+3	13
10	NLN	Farsley Celtic	H	1601	W 2 - 1	Jackson 46 Waring 63	
13	NLN	Kettering Town	A	971	D 1 - 1	Asante 90+3 (pen)	
17	NLN	Gloucester City	H	1612	W 4 - 0	Livesey 1 Waring 5 Jackson 53 Asante 90+4 (pen)	5
24	NLN	Kidderminster Harriers	A	1710	W 1 - 0	Hughes 27	
26	NLN	Hereford	H	2573	W 4 - 1	Asante 20 52 Dudley 29 Elliott 78	
31	NLN	Spennymoor Town	A	1049	L 1 - 2	Asante 7	
Sep 2	NLN	Curzon Ashton	A	870	W 3 - 1	Hughes 5 Asante 46 Roberts K 51	3
7	NLN	Guiseley	H	1989	W 3 - 1	Asante 3 30 (pen) Dudley 72	3
14	NLN	AFC Telford United	A	2085	W 3 - 1	Asante 11 22 62	2
21	**FAC2Q**	**Altrincham**	**H**	**1804**	**D 1 - 1**	**Hughes 2**	
24	**FAC2Qr**	**Altrincham**	**A**	**952**	**L 0 - 1**		
28	NLN	Leamington	A	1853	D 3 - 3	Jones 18 Glendon 46 Waters 89	2
Oct 12	NLN	King's Lynn Town	H	1637	D 2 - 2	Grand 56 Asante 63	2
19	NLN	Blyth Spartans	A	869	D 2 - 2	Elliott 3 Hughes 40	2
26	NLN	York City	H	3653	L 0 - 1		2
Nov 2	NLN	Brackley Town	A	476	D 1 - 1	Jackson 9	2
9	NLN	Alfreton Town	H	1687	W 3 - 0	Livesey 35 47 Elliott 89	3
23	**FAT3Q**	**Brackley Town**	**A**	**334**	**W 1 - 0**	**Dudley 73**	
30	NLN	Bradford (Park Avenue)	H	1875	W 2 - 1	Dudley 49 Asante 53	3
Dec 7	NLN	Darlington	A	1210	L 0 - 2		3
14	**FAT1**	**Hednesford Town**	**A**	**565**	**D 0 - 0**		
17	**FAT1r**	**Hednesford Town**	**H**	**613**	**W 2 - 1**	**Jackson 16 Asante 34**	
21	NLN	AFC Telford United	H	1756	D 0 - 0		
26	NLN	Southport	A	1830	W 3 - 1	Waring 34 Asante 49 Roberts G 70	
28	NLN	Curzon Ashton	H	2095	L 0 - 1		
Jan 1	NLN	Southport	H	1928	W 4 - 0	Grand 36 Asante 47 71 Dudley 58	3
4	NLN	Guiseley	A	1029	W 1 - 0	Jones 11	3
11	**FAT2**	**Royston Town**	**A**	**818**	**L 0 - 3**		
18	NLN	Leamington	A	865	D 0 - 0		4
25	NLN	Darlington	H	2119	W 3 - 0	Jackson 12 Asante 57 Livesey 59	3
28	NLN	Gateshead	A	842	L 0 - 2		3
Feb 1	NLN	York City	A	3543	L 2 - 4	Morgan 15 Glendon 54	4
8	NLN	Blyth Spartans	H	1751	W 2 - 1	Asante 12 Jones 70	
18	NLN	King's Lynn Town	H	1736	W 3 - 2	McAuley 29 (og) Dudley 76 Grand 90+3	
22	NLN	Brackley Town	H	1918	L 2 - 3	Jones 60 Livesey 85	4
Mar 7	NLN	Bradford (Park Avenue)	A	525	L 1 - 2	Waters 51	6
July 19	**PO Q**	**Altrincham**	**A**	**0**	**L 2 - 3**	**Glendon 63 Hughes 79**	

GOALSCORERS	SG	CSG	Pens	Hat tricks	Total		SG	CSG	Pens	Hat tricks	Total
Asante	15	5	3	1	19	Roberts G	2	1			2
Dudley	6	2			6	Waters	2	1			2
Hughes	5	1			5	Morgan	1	1			1
Jackson	5	1			5	Opponent	1	1			1
Livesey	4	1			5	Roberts K	1	1			1
Jones	4	1			4						
Waring	4	1			4						
Elliott	3	1			3						
Glendon	3	1			3						
Grand	3	1			3						

	Griffiths R	Roberts K	Livesey D	Grand S	Taylor J	Roberts G	Stopforth G	Jackson B	Dudley A	Waring G	Elliott D	Mahon C	Hughes M	Burton S	Morgan J	Waters M	Roberts T (Gk)	Asante A	Jones J (L)	Murray I	Glendon G	Cottrell J	Thomson M	N'Gwatala E	Goodwin W	Johnston J	Gray L (Gk) (L)	Worsnop J (Gk)	No.
	x	x	x	x	x	x	x	xs	x	xs	xs	sx	sx	sx	s	s													1
	x	x	x	x	x	x	x	x	x	xs	x	xs			sx	s	s	s											2
	x	x	x	x	x	xs	x	x	x	x	sx	xs	sx	sx	s	s													3
	x	x	x	x	x	x	x	xs	xs	sx	xs	sx	s		s			sx											4
	x	x	x	x	x	x	x	xs	xs	sx	sx	xs	s		sx	s		sx	s										5
	x	x	x	x	x	x	xs	xs	xs	s	sx	xs	sx		s			sx											6
	x	x	x	x	x		xs	x	x	sx	sx	s	xs	x		s		xs	sx										7
	x	x	x	x	x		x	xs	sx	s	sx	xs	x	s				xs	sx	x									8
	x	x	x	x	x		x	xs	sx	x	s	sx	s		s			xs	sx	x									9
	x	xs		x	x	sx		x	x	sx	s	s	xs	x	sx			xs	x		x								10
	x		x	x	x		x	xs	sx	sx	s	xs	x		xs	s		x			x								11
	x		x	x	xs		x	x	sx	s	s	x	xs		x			xs	sx	xs	x	x	s	s					12
	x		xs	x	sx	x		x	s	x	xs	xs	sx	x		x		s	sx	s	x		s						13
	x			x	x	s		x	sx	x	sx	s	xs	x		x		x	x		x								14
	x	x	x	x		x	sx	xs	x	sx	sx		xs		s			xs	s		x								15
	x	x	x	x		x	s	x	sx	xs	xs	sx	x		s	s			x										16
	x	xs		x	x	xs		x	x	sx	x		xs	s	sx	s													17
	x	x	xs	x	x	x		x	xs	x		sx	s	sx	sx														18
	x	x	x		xs	sx	x	x	sx	x	x		xs	s	s		xs												19
	x	sx	x	x	x	s	x	x	sx	xs	s		s	x	x	x	xs		sx		s		xs						20
	x		x	x	x		x	x	xs	sx	sx	s	x	s		xs					x					xs			21
	x	x	x	x	s		x	x	s	sx	sx		x						x					xs					22
	x	x	x	x	x	s	x	x	sx	sx	xs		xs		s	s		xs	s		x			sx					23
	x	s	x	x	x	x	s	x	xs	sx	xs		sx		x	s		xs	s		x			sx					24
	x	x	x	xs	x	s	x	xs	sx	s		s		sx		x			x		x			x					25
	x	sx	xs	x	x	x	xs	sx	x	s		sx		x		xs			x		s								26
	x	sx	x	x	x	x		sx	x	s		x	sx		x	xs		xs			x			xs					27
	x	x		x	s	xs	x	x	x	sx	sx		xs		s	x		x	x		sx								28
	x	x		sx	x	x	x	xs	sx	x		xs		x		sx		s											29
	x	x	s	x	sx	x	xs	x	x		sx		xs	s	s	xs			x		x			s	sx				30
	x	x	x	x	x	x	x	x	x		s		s	s				sx	x		xs			s					31
	x	x	xs	x	x	xs	x	x			sx		s			xs	xs		s		x								32
	x	x	x	x	x	xs	x	x	xs		sx	s			xs	s		sx			s		x						33
	x	s	x	x	x	s	sx	x	sx			xs	x		x	sx			xs	xs									34
	x	x		x	x	s	sx	xs	sx		xs	x		sx	x	x			s	xs									35
	x	x		x	xs	s	sx	x			xs	x		sx	x	x			s	xs									36
	x	x	sx	x	xs	s	s	x	x			xs		sx	x	x			sx										37
		x		x		x	xs	x	xs	sx	xs			sx	s	x		sx	x		s			x	x				38
		x	x	xs	xs		sx	x		sx	xs	xs		sx	xs	sx	sx			x					x	x	s		39
	37	27	25	38	29	19	16	32	11	7	0	0	2	10	7	6	0	8	10	0	24	0	0	1	0	5	2	0	x
	0	2	4	1	5	5	4	6	17	7	9	3	17	4	0	3	0	15	1	0	3	0	0	4	0	3	0	0	xs
	0	3	1	0	3	2	6	0	10	16	14	6	12	5	5	6	0	6	4	4	3	0	0	5	1	0	0	0	sx
	0	2	1	0	1	7	6	0	1	1	10	6	4	9	14	11	1	1	6	3	0	1	2	8	0	0	0	1	s

GOALKEEPERS	CS	CCS
Griffiths	10	2

x - Played full 90 minutes
xs - Substituted off
sx - Substituted on
s - Non-playing Substitute

CURZON ASHTON MATCH RESULTS 2019-20

Date	Comp	Opponents	H/A	Att:	Result	Goalscorers	Pos
Aug 3	NLN	Bradford (Park Avenue)	H	309	W 5 - 0	Sinclair 24 Wall 32 Miller 58 Thornley 69 Merrill 88	1
6	NLN	Southport	A	1120	D 0 - 0		2
10	NLN	Leamington	A	385	D 1 - 1	Miller 86	
13	NLN	Darlington	H	571	W 3 - 1	Miller 42 45+2 Sinclair 57	
17	NLN	Kidderminster Harriers	H	307	L 0 - 1		6
24	NLN	King's Lynn Town	A	833	L 1 - 4	Saunders 12	
26	NLN	Spennymoor Town	H	276	D 1 - 1	Saunders 78	
31	NLN	Guiseley	A	645	L 0 - 1		
Sep 2	NLN	Chester	H	870	L 1 - 3	Regan 21	16
7	NLN	Alfreton Town	A	473	L 2 - 3	Wall 88 (pen) Regan 90+2	18
14	NLN	Brackley Town	H	204	L 0 - 4		19
21	FAC2Q	Blyth Spartans	H	189	D 4 - 4	Saunders Merrill x2 Trickett-Smith 90+2	
24	FAC2Qr	Blyth Spartans	A	491	L 0 - 1		
28	NLN	Farsley Celtic	A	342	L 0 - 2		19
Oct 12	NLN	Blyth Spartans	H	374	L 0 - 1		19
Nov 2	NLN	Gloucester City	A	238	D 2 - 2	Miller 5 Hamilton 29 (og)	21
5	NLN	Gateshead	A	707	L 0 - 3		21
9	NLN	AFC Telford United	H	340	W 2 - 1	Miller 38 (pen) Halls 90+4	
16	NLN	York City	H	809	W 1 - 0	Dimaio 32	19
23	FAT3Q	Kidderminster Harriers	H	266	W 3 - 0	Calveley 45 Jolley 75 Dimaio	
Dec 2	NLN	Kettering Town	H	210	D 0 - 0		20
7	NLN	Hereford	H	237	W 2 - 0	Miller 4 (pen) Jolley 27	18
14	FAT1	AFC Fylde	A	483	L 0 - 1		
21	NLN	Brackley Town	A	475	L 0 - 3		
26	NLN	Altrincham	H	602	L 0 - 1		
28	NLN	Chester	A	2095	W 1 - 0	Halls 49	
Jan 1	NLN	Altrincham	A	1184	L 1 - 2	Calveley 29	19
4	NLN	Alfreton Town	H	160	L 0 - 2		20
7	NLN	Boston United	A	894	D 0 - 0		
11	NLN	Blyth Spartans	A	721	L 1 - 2	Dimaio 60	20
18	NLN	Farsley Celtic	H	215	W 4 - 0	Calveley 34 Askew 44 Scott 76 Bayode 81	19
25	NLN	Hereford	A	1950	D 1 - 1	Ali 15	18
Feb 1	NLN	Kettering Town	A	684	D 0 - 0		19
8	NLN	Gateshead	H	334	L 0 - 1		19
29	NLN	York City	A	2354	D 1 - 1	Broadbent 72	19
Mar 7	NLN	Boston United	H	290	D 1 - 1	Halls 84 (pen)	20
14	NLN	Bradford (Park Avenue)	A	685	W 2 - 0	Calveley 45+2 Tavares 84	18

GOALSCORERS	SG	CSG	Pens	Hat tricks	Total		SG	CSG	Pens	Hat tricks	Total
Miller	6	2	2		7	Ali	1	1			1
Calverley	4	1			4	Askew	1	1			1
Dimaio*	3	2			3	Bayode	1	1			1
Halls	3	1	1		3	Broadbent	1	1			1
Merrill	2	1			3	Opponent	1	1			1
Saunders	3	2			3	Scott	1	1			1
Jolley	2	1			2	Tavares	1	1			1
Regan	2	2			2	Thornley	1	1			1
Sinclair	2	1			2	Trickett-Smith	1	1			1
Wall	2	1	1		2						

Mason C	Halls A	Askew J (L)	Thornley O	Wroe N	Evans R	Ali Mahamud	Sinclair I	Miller S	Elstone M	Wall L	Bannister J	Davies L	Merrill L	Saunders C	Shaw D	Cooke E	Regan M	McCoy M	Tricket-Smith D (L)	Caldebank-Park K (Gk) (L)	Calveley M	Baillie J	Allen H (Gk) (L)	Baningime D (L)	Neild J	Smith A	Dimaio C (L)	Jolley C (L)	Worrall J	Doyle L (L)	Beckford E	McCann C	Lovell L (Gk)	Scott A (L)	Sloan J	Bayode O (L)	Watkinson O (L)	Crawford J	Broadbent G (L)	Tavares F (L)	No.
x	x	xs	x	x	x	x	xs	xs	x	x	sx	sx	sx	s	s																										1
x	x	x	x	x	x	x	sx		xs	x	sx	xs	xs	sx	s	s																									2
x	x	x	xs	x	x		sx	sx	xs	xs	sx	x	x	x	s																										3
x	xs	x	x	x	x		xs	xs	s	x	sx	sx	xs	s																											4
x	x	x	x	xs	x	x	xs	x	sx	sx	xs	sx	x	s	s																										5
x	x	x	x	xs	x	x	s	x	sx	s	sx	sx	x	xs			xs																								6
x	x	x	x	x	x		xs	x	xs	xs	sx	s	s	sx	x	sx																									7
x	x	xs	x	x	xs		xs	x	s	s	sx	sx	sx	x	x		x																								8
x	x	x	x				xs	x	sx	sx	xs	xs	s	x	sx	x																									9
x	x	x	s		x			x		sx	sx	x	x	x	xs	xs	sx	x	s																						10
x	x	x	s		x		x	x		s	x	x	x	s	xs			x	s	sx																					11
x		x	x				x			x			x	x			x		x																						12
s	x	sx	x	x		x	sx			x	xs	x	xs	x		s			x	x																					13
	x	xs	x	x		x	x			s	sx	x	sx	xs		x		x	x	xs	s																				14
			x			x	sx			sx	x	sx	x	xs	s	x		xs	x	x	x	xs	s																		15
x	x	s		x			xs	x			x	s	sx	s		xs		xs	x	x		x	sx																		16
x	x	s		xs			x	x			x	sx	sx	s		x		xs	x	x		sx	sx																		17
x	x	s		x	xs	x	xs	xs			x	s	sx	x		sx		x	x	sx																					18
x	x	s		sx	x	x	sx	x			x	s	sx	x		xs	xs			x	xs																				19
x	x			x		x		x			x			x		x		x	x			x	x	sx																	20
x	sx	s		x	xs	x	xs	xs			x	s	x					x		x	x	sx	sx																		21
x	x	s		x	xs		x			x			x					xs	x		x	xs	sx	sx	s																22
x	x			x	xs		xs	x			x			x				xs	x		x	s	sx	sx	sx	s															23
x	x	s	s	xs	x		sx	x			x			x				x	x			x	sx		xs	xs															24
x	x	s		x	x	x	xs	x			x		sx	x				x	x		xs	sx	s		s																25
x	x	sx		xs	x	x		xs			x		x					x	x		sx	sx	s	xs	s																26
x	x	sx			x	x					x		x				xs	x		xs	sx	sx	s	xs	s																27
x	x	xs		x	sx	x		x			x	xs	x		xs	sx	sx																								28
x	x	x		x	x	x	s			s	x	x	x	s	xs	s	sx																								29
x		x		x	x	xs		sx	x	x	xs	s	sx	s	x	xs	sx																								30
x		sx	xs	x	x		sx		x	x	sx	s	sx	sx	x	xs																									31
x	sx		sx	x	x		s		x	x	xs	xs	sx	sx																											32
x	x	x	s	s	x	x	xs		s	x	x	x	sx	s	x																										33
x	x	sx	x	x	x		sx	xs	x	x	s																														34
x	x	x	x		x	x	xs	s	s	x	x																														35
x	x	x	x	s	x	x	s	s	x	xs																															36
x	x	x	x	x	x	s	s	sx	x	xs																															37
34	31	18	15	22	20	26	7	13	1	5	3	17	4	6	19	0	9	0	3	2	18	18	1	1	0	0	10	4	0	0	0	0	0	0	0	2	2	0	3	0	x
0	0	4	0	6	6	0	17	7	3	2	3	1	3	6	2	0	1	0	3	0	5	5	0	2	0	0	1	3	0	0	0	0	5	0	1	3	0	2	0		xs
0	2	3	1	3	0	0	7	2	5	3	8	6	8	6	2	3	0	0	2	0	0	0	1	0	2	0	2	2	7	2	2	0	2	4	1	2	0	3			sx
1	0	9	4	3	0	0	2	0	2	4	0	6	14	1	7	3	0	2	0	0	0	1	0	0	1	0	0	2	0	1	4	6	0	7	0	0	1	0	0		s

GOALKEEPERS	CS	CCS
Mason	11	4

x - Played full 90 minutes
xs - Substituted off
sx - Substituted on
s - Non-playing Substitute

NATIONAL LEAGUE NORTH

DARLINGTON MATCH RESULTS 2019-20

Date	Comp	Opponents	H/A	Att:	Result	Goalscorers	Pos
Aug 3	NLN	Farsley Celtic	A	1123	L 1 - 3	Campbell 65	
7	NLN	Gateshead	H	1983	D 1 - 1	Liddle 79	19
10	NLN	Kettering town	H	1344	W 3 - 0	Thompson 18 75 (pen) Rivers 46	
13	NLN	Curzon Ashton	A	571	L 1 - 3	O'Neill 44	
17	NLN	Southport	H	1331	W 2 - 0	O'Neill 3 Campbell 29 (pen)	9
24	NLN	Altrincham	A	994	D 1 - 1	Campbell 90+3	
26	NLN	Bradford (Park Avenue)	H	1491	L 0 - 1		
31	NLN	King's Lynn Town	A	1229	L 0 - 2		18
Sep 4	NLN	Blyth Spartans	H	1355	W 2 - 1	Campbell 13 Thompson 75	14
7	NLN	Gloucester City	A	437	L 1 - 2	Campbell 29	17
14	NLN	York City	H	2023	L 0 - 2		17
21	FAC2Q	Trafford	A	795	W 3 - 1	Thompson 38 Campbell 67 Donawa 88	
28	NLN	Alfreton Town	A	561	W 2 - 1	O'Neill 84 Donawa 86	15
Oct 5	FAC3Q	Leamington	A	605	W 2 - 0	O'Neill 64 Donawa 88	
12	NLN	Boston United	H	1573	W 2 - 1	O'Neill 6 Campbell 9	12
19	FAC4Q	Tamworth	A	1358	W 3 - 0	O'Neill 9 56 Holness 38	
30	NLN	Kidderminster Harriers	H	1254	W 1 - 0	Rivers 40	
Nov 2	NLN	Hereford	H	1388	D 0 - 0		12
9	FAC1	Walsall	A	2882	D 2 - 2	Holness 17 Wheatley 90+7	
16	NLN	Brackley Town	A	730	L 1 - 5	Thompson 65 (pen)	14
20	FAC1r	Walsall	H	3106	L 0 - 1		
23	FAT3Q	Gainsborough Trinity	H	770	W 2 - 1	Lambert 16 Donawa 69	
30	NLN	AFC Telford United	H	1012	L 2 - 3	Story 18 Donawa 30	15
Dec 3	NLN	Leamington	A	485	L 0 - 3		16
7	NLN	Chester	H	1210	W 2 - 0	Holness 28 Taylor 45+2 (og)	12
14	FAT1	Solihull Moors	A	500	D 2 - 2	Hatfield 21 Lambert 85	
21	NLN	York City	A	3187	W 1 - 0	Campbell 8	
26	NLN	Spennymoor Town	H	2204	W 2 - 1	Campbell 24 Thompson 72 (pen)	
28	NLN	Blyth Spartans	A	1481	W 2 - 0	Reid 12 Donawa 42	
Jan 1	NIN	Spennymoor Town	A	2260	L 1 - 3	Donawa 38	10
4	NLN	Gloucester City	H	1446	W 2 - 1	Reid 3 Campbell 25 (pen)	9
8	FAT1r	Solihull Moors	H	812	W 1 - 0	Holness 73	
11	FAT2	Harrogate Town	H	1240	L 0 - 2		
18	NLN	Alfreton Town	H	1271	W 3 - 0	Campbell 18 54 Donawa 90	7
21	NLN	Guiseley	A	859	W 2 - 1	Campbell 5 Hatfield 29	6
25	NLN	Chester	A	2119	L 0 - 3		6
Feb 1	NLN	Guiseley	H	1411	L 0 - 3		10
8	NLN	Kidderminster Harriers	A	1509	D 1 - 1	Hatfield 58	
22	NLN	Hereford	A	1643	D 2 - 2	Rivers 35 Holness 87	11
29	NLN	Brackley Town	H	1183	D 1 - 1	Campbell 41 (pen)	10
Mar 7	NLN	AFC Telford United	A	1116	W 2 - 1	Hatfield 13 Campbell 59	9
14	NLN	Farsley Celtic	H	1318	L 2 - 4	Holness 14 Campbell 48 (pen)	11

GOALSCORERS	SG	CSG	Pens	Hat tricks	Total		SG	CSG	Pens	Hat tricks	Total
Campbell	15	3	4		16	Opponent	1	1			1
Donawa	8	3			8	Storey	1	1			1
Holness	6	1			6	Wheatley	1	1			1
O'Neill	6	4			6						
Thompson	5	1	3		6						
Hatfield	4	1			4						
Rivers	3	1			3						
Lambert	2	1			2						
Reid	2	1			2						
Liddle	1	1			1						

Elliot C	Liddle M	Holness O	Laing L	Trotman L	Galbraith T	Hatfield W	Rivers J	Thompson S	Campbell A	Holmes J	O'Neill T (L)	Donawa J	Watson J	Bascome O	Bell L	Heaton J	Wheatley J	Atkinson D	Holliday C	Morrison B	Hedley B	Stansfield H	Storey A	Connell L (Gk) (L)	Armstrong R	Lambert J (L)	Hurworth M	Johnson S	Reid S	Hall C (Gk)	Martin G (L)	No.
X	X	X	X	X	X	X	X	X	XS	X	XS	XS	SX	S	S	S																1
X	X	XS	X	XS	X	X	X	X	XS	XS	XS	S	S		SX																	2
X	X	SX	X		XS	XS	X	X	X		XS	SX	X	X	S	SX	S															3
X	X	S	X		SX	X	XS	X	X		X	SX	X	X	S	XS	S															4
X	XS	SX	X		X	X	X		X		X	XS	X	XS	S	SX	SX	S														5
X		SX	X		X	X	X	XS	X		X	SX	X	XS	S	S	S	XS														6
X		SX	X		XS	X	X	X	X		SX	XS	X	XS	S	SX	S	X														7
X		S	X		S	X	X	X	X		SX	X	XS	S	X	SX	XS															8
X		SX	X		X	X	X	X	X		X			S	S	X	XS	S	S													9
X		X	X		X	X	X	X			XS		X		SX	S	XS		SX	SX	S											10
X	SX	XS	XS		X	X	X	X			SX	S	S		S		X		S		X											11
X	X	SX			X	X	XS	XS	X		X	SX	X	SX	S		XS		S	S	S	X	S									12
X	X	XS			X	SX	XS	XS	X		X	SX		SX	S		X		S		X			X								13
S	X	XS	SX		X	X	X		XS		X	SX	S	S	S		X		S		X	X										14
X	XS	XS	SX		X	X	X		X		XS		X		SX		X		S		X	X	S									15
S	X	X	SX		X	XS	X	S	XS		XS	SX	X	S	SX	S	X				X		X	X								16
	X	XS	SX		X	X	X	SX	XS		XS	SX	S		X				X		X	X										17
	X	XS	S		X	X	XS	SX	X		X	SX	S	S			X				X	X										18
S		XS	SX		X	X	X	XS	XS		SX	X	SX		X				X		X	X	S									19
S		XS	X		X	X	XS	X	X			X			X		X	X	SX	SX	SX	S										20
S	X	X	SX		X	X	X	X	X		S			XS			S	X	S	X	X	X	S									21
X	X	XS	SX		X	X	XS	X	X		SX	S	SX				X		X		S	XS	S									22
S	X	S	X		X	SX	X	XS		X		S		X		S	X		X	X	X	X										23
X		XS			X	XS	X	X		SX	X	SX		XS	S		X		X		SX											24
	X	X	X			X	SX	X	XS	SX	XS	S		S	X		X		X		X	XS										25
X	X	XS	X		X	SX	XS	X		S	X	SX	S	XS	S		X		X		SX											26
X	X	S	X		X	X	XS	XS		SX	SX	S		X			X		S			X										27
X	X	S	X		X	XS	XS	XS		SX	SX	S		X			X		SX			X										28
X	X	SX	X		X	X	XS	X		X	S	S		XS			X		X			X										29
X	X	SX	X		X	X	XS	X		X	S	S		XS			X		X			X										30
	X	SX	X		SX	X	X	SX		X	S	S	S				X		X	X	XS					XS						31
X	X	X	X		SX	X	X	X		X	S	S	S			S		X		X		S					S					32
X	XS	X	X		S	X	SX	X	XS		X	SX	S			S		XS		X	S	SX			XS			X			X	33
X		SX	X		XS	X	X	S	XS		X	X	S			XS			X		X				SX			X			SX	34
X		SX	XS		XS	X	S	XS			X	X	S			X	SX		X		X							X			SX	35
X		SX	X		SX	X	X	XS			X	X	S			X	XS		X		X		S					X			SX	36
		S	X		S	X	X	SX	SX		X	X				XS	S		XS		X	X						X			X	37
S		SX	X		X	X	X	XS	X		SX	X				X	S		X		S	X						XS				38
X	X	SX	X		X	XS	SX	X			X	S				XS	S		X			X						XS			SX	39
X	X	XS	X		X	XS	SX	X			X	S				X	S		X			X						SX			S	40
X	X	XS	X		X	X	XS	X			SX	SX				X	SX		XS				S					S			S	41
X	X	X	X		X	X	XS	SX	X		X	S				XS	S		XS									SX			SX	42
29	26	8	29	1	22	36	26	14	25	0	9	13	19	2	0	1	19	1	0	0	26	0	26	13	0	1	0	0	8	0	2	x
0	2	14	2	1	3	4	9	13	16	2	5	4	0	4	0	1	11	4	0	0	4	0	0	0	0	4	0	0	3	0	0	xs
0	1	14	7	0	3	0	7	9	1	0	3	20	5	8	2	5	2	2	0	1	1	0	0	0	1	6	1	0	2	0	5	sx
8	0	6	1	0	3	0	0	3	0	0	0	0	16	17	16	2	4	8	10	3	0	3	1	2	4	3	1	1	1	1	2	s

GOALKEEPERS	CS	CCS
Elliot	6	1
Connell	5	2

x - Played full 90 minutes
xs - Substituted off
sx - Substituted on
s - Non-playing Substitute

FARSLEY CELTIC MATCH RESULTS 2019-20

Date	Comp	Opponents	H/A	Att	Result	Goalscorers	Pos
Aug 3	NLN	Darlington	H	1123	W 3 - 1	Walton 10 Cartman 17 Spencer 35	
6	NLN	York City	A	2938	D 0 - 0		5
10	NLN	Chester	A	1601	L 1 - 2	Hayhurst 79 (pen)	
13	NLN	Southport	H	389	L 0 - 3		
17	NLN	Spennymoor Town	H	424	W 1 - 0	Atkinson B 88	12
24	NLN	Gateshead	A	778	W 3 - 0	Spencer 52 Parkin 69 Walton 90+5	
26	NLN	King's Lynn Town	H	556	L 1 - 2	Hayhurst 61 (pen)	
31	NLN	Altrincham	A	913	L 1 - 3	Syers 82	12
Sep 3	NLN	Bradford (Park Avenue)	A	508	W 3 - 0	Allan 51 Richards 86 Atkinson B 90+4	10
7	NLN	Kettering Town	H	525	W 3 - 2	Syers 16 Allan 64 Hayhurst 77	7
14	NLN	Leamington	A	465	W 3 - 0	Spencer 39 Clayton 54 Cartman 72	6
21	FAC2Q	Runcorn Town	A	168	W 3 - 1	Cartman 25 72 Walton 83	
28	NLN	Curzon Ashton	H	342	W 2 - 0	Francis 88 Hayhurst 90+5	4
Oct 5	FAC3Q	Southport	H	411	L 0 - 5		
19	NLN	Alfreton Town	A	483	W 4 - 2	Allan 18 Spencer 22 32 Syers 67	3
22	NLN	Kidderminster Harriers	A	1045	L 0 - 2		3
Nov 2	NLN	Blyth Spartans	A	770	L 0 - 2		5
9	NLN	Gloucester City	H	372	D 1 - 1	Syers 1	
16	NLN	Boston United	H	742	L 2 - 4	Spencer 28 Hayhurst 59 (pen)	8
23	FAT3Q	Workington	A	469	W 1 - 0	Higgins 49	
30	NLN	Hereford	A	2075	D 1 - 1	Higgins 90+3	8
Dec 3	NLN	Brackley Town	H	292	D 1 - 1	Spencer 19	8
7	NLN	AFC Telford United	A	1006	W 2 - 0	Francis 57 Streete 84 (og)	8
14	FAT1	Altrincham	H	253	D 2 - 2	Spencer 17 Syers 75	
17	FAT1r	Altrincham	A	536	W 2 - 1	Cartman 4 102 (aet)	
21	NLN	Leamington	H	378	W 2 - 1	Hayhurst 17 (pen) Parkin 63	
26	NLN	Guiseley	A	1048	L 0 - 2		
28	NLN	Bradford (Park Avenue)	H	784	W 5 - 0	Cartman 48 Hayhurst 51 90+1 (pens) Syers 63 Higgins 65	
Jan 1	NLN	Guiseley	H	1010	L 0 - 1		6
4	NLN	Kettering Town	A	667	L 0 - 1		7
11	FAT2	Barnet	H	402	D 1 - 1	Walton 53	
18	NLN	Curzon Ashton	A	215	L 0 - 4		11
25	NLN	AFC Telford United	H	403	D 1 - 1	Ellis 90+4	12
28	FAT2r	Barnet	A	333	L 0 - 2		
Feb 1	NLN	Brackley Town	A	440	W 1 - 0	Clayton 34	11
8	NLN	Alfreton Town	H	457	D 1 - 1	Clayton 63	
11	NLN	Kidderminster Harriers	H	180	L 0 - 1		
22	NLN	Blyth Spartans	H	369	W 2 - 0	Syers 39 Spencer 61	9
Mar 7	NLN	Hereford	H	412	L 1 - 2	Hayhurst 75	11
9	NLN	Gloucester City	A	161	L 1 - 2	Syers 19	11
14	NLN	Darlington	A	1318	W 4 - 2	Syers 18 71 Spencer 68 Clayton 83	10

GOALSCORERS	SG	CSG	Pens	Hat tricks	Total		SG	CSG	Pens	Hat tricks	Total
Spencer	9	1			10	Parkin	2	1			2
Syers	9	2			10	Ellis	1	1			1
Hayhurst	8	1	6		9	Opponent	1	1			1
Cartman	5	2			7	Richards	1	1			1
Clayton	4	2			4						
Walton	4	1			4						
Allan	3	2			3						
Higgins	3	2			3						
Atkinson B	2	1			2						
Francis*	2	1			2						

Wynne E	Ellis D	Higgins J	Richards J	Baldwin I	Atkinson C	Clayton A	Hayhurst W	Walton T	Spencer J	Cartman N	Parkin L	Atkinson B	Syers D	Trennery K (Gk)	Walker P	Boateng K	Allan T (L)	Maltby J	Bett M	Francis A	Cogill D	Milambo J	Bower M (Gk)	Regan M	Earing J (L)	Barnes J (Gk) (L)	Jones B (Gk) (L)	Hudson E	Nicell C	No.
X	X	X	X	X	X		X	XS	XS	XS	SX	SX	SX	S	S															1
X	X	X	X	XS	X		X	XS	X	XS	SX	SX	S	S	S															2
X	X	X	X	X	X		X	XS	X	XS	SX	XS	SX	S	SX	S														3
X	X	X	X	X	X		X	XS	X	S	SX	X	SX	S	XS	S														4
X	XS	X	X	S	X		X	X	XS	SX	SX	X	XS	S	SX			X												5
X		X	X	S	X		X	SX	XS	XS	XS	X	SX	S	SX			X												6
X		X	SX	X	X		XS	X	X	SX	XS	XS	S	S				X												7
X	SX	XS	X	X	X		XS	X	X	XS	X	SX	S					X												8
S	X		X	SX	X		S	XS	X	SX	X	XS	X					X	SX											9
S	X		X	S	X		SX	X	X	SX	XS	X	XS					X		S										10
S	X	XS	X	SX	X		SX	X	X	SX	XS	X		X				X		S										11
								X		X																				12
S	X	XS	S	X	X	X	X	SX	X	XS	XS	X	SX	X						SX										13
																														14
S	X	X		X	X	X	X	XS	XS	S	SX		X	X			XS						SX	SX						15
S	XS	X		X	X	X	XS	X	SX	SX		XS					X						SX	S						16
S	X	XS		X	X	X	XS	XS	SX	S	SX	X	SX				X						SX							17
S	X	S		X	X	X	X	SX	XS	SX	XS	X					X						SX							18
S	X	SX		X	X	X	X	XS	X	SX	S	X					X						SX							19
XS	X	X		X		X	XS	X	XS	SX	SX	X	SX				X		S	S		S	S							20
	X	X		X		X		X	XS	SX	X	SX	X				X		S	SX	S		S							21
	X	X		X		SX		X	SX	X	SX	X					X			XS			S	S	SX					22
XS	X	X		X		SX		X	S	SX	X	SX					X			XS				S	SX					23
X	X	X		X		S	XS	SX	X	XS	SX	XS	S	S			S			SX				X						24
X	X	X		X		SX		SX	XS	X	SX	XS	XS				SX			S			S	XS						25
X	X	X		X		X		X	SX	SX		S	S				S			SX				X						26
X	X	X		X		SX	XS	SX		XS	X	X					S			SX				X						27
S	S	X		X		X	X	XS		XS	SX	SX	X	X			X			X				S						28
S	X	X		X		S	X	SX	SX	XS	SX	X	X				X			XS										29
SX	X	X		X		SX	XS	X	XS	X	S	SX	X				X	S												30
X	X	X		X		X	X	XS	X	S	S	SX	XS										SX	S	X					31
X	SX	X		X		X	X	XS	X	XS	XS	XS											SX	S	X					32
X	X	XS		X		X	X	XS	X	SX	S	X	SX											S	XS	SX				33
X	X	X		X		X	X	X	X	SX	SX	XS	S				S						S	XS						34
S	X	X		X		X	X	XS	XS	SX		X							S				SX	X	X					35
	X	X		X		X	X	XS	X	X		X		SX					S	S			SX	S		XS				36
	X	X		X		X	X	XS	X	X		SX	XS						S	S			S	SX			X			37
	X	X		X		X	XS	XS	X	S		X	XS								SX			X	SX	X		SX	S	38
	X	X		X		X	X	X	SX	XS	XS	X							S	S			S	X		X				39
	X	X		X		X	X	X	SX	XS	XS	XS							SX	S			S	X		X				40
S		X		X		X	X	X	X	SX	XS	XS	X						SX	S		X		S		X				41
16	30	27	38	3	39	26	30	10	26	6	3	15	9	12	0	0	18	0	0	1	1	0	0	8	1	5	1	0	0	x
1	3	4	1	1	0	0	6	19	8	15	11	10	15	1	1	0	1	0	0	3	0	0	0	3	0	1	0	0	0	xs
1	2	1	0	3	0	5	2	8	2	14	15	12	10	2	3	0	1	3	0	12	2	0	1	4	2	0	0	1	0	sx
12	2	1	0	5	0	2	1	0	0	5	6	0	2	11	3	2	3	3	12	2	1	3	12	3	0	0	0	0	1	s

GOALKEEPERS	CS	CCS
Trennery	6	1
Wynne	4	2
Barnes*	2	1

x - Played full 90 minutes
xs - Substituted off
sx - Substituted on
s - Non-playing Substitute

GATESHEAD MATCH RESULTS 2019-20

Date	Comp	Opponents	H/A	Att	Result	Goalscorers	Pos
Aug 3	NLN	Southport	H	879	D 0 - 0		
7	NLN	Darlington	A	1983	D 1 - 1	O'Donnell 21	14
10	NLN	AFC Telford United	A	1045	D 0 - 0		
13	NLN	Bradford (Park Avenue)	H	1001	D 1 - 1	O'Donnell 32	
17	NLN	Kettering Town	A	701	W 2 - 1	Lees 65 Kayode 90+1	11
24	NLN	Farsley Celtic	H	778	L 0 - 3		
26	NLN	York City	A	3157	D 1 - 1	Oliver 45+2 (pen)	
31	NLN	Brackley Town	H	769	W 2 - 0	Nelson 9 Kayode 63	9
Sep 3	NLN	Spennymoor Town	H	1337	W 1 - 0	O'Donnell 3	8
14	NLN	Boston United	H	1134	W 3 - 0	Deverdics 53 O'Donnell 56 Tear 61	8
17	NLN	Hereford	A	1703	L 1 - 2	Hall 62 (og)	8
21	FAC2Q	Ramsbottom United	H	480	W 6 - 0	Olley 32 68 Preston 40 (pen) Agnew 64 Lees 66 Kayode 75	
Oct 5	FAC3Q	Kidsgrove Athletic	A	322	W 1 - 0	O'Donnell 61	
12	NLN	Gloucester City	H	1189	W 1 - 0	Kayode 17	9
19	FAC4Q	Colne	H	878	W 5 - 0	Kayode 26 O'Donnell 54 Olley 73 Blackett 86 Preston 90+4	
Nov 2	NLN	Guiseley	H	1004	L 2 - 3	Deverdics 74 Kayode 81	14
5	NLN	Curzon Ashton	H	707	W 3 - 0	O'Donnell 2 Tear 40 Oliver 85	9
10	FAC1	Oldham Athletic	H	2199	L 1 - 2	Agnew 53	
19	NLN	Altrincham	A	789	L 0 - 3		11
23	FAT3Q	Halesowen Town	A	546	L 0 - 1		
30	NLN	King's Lynn Town	A	1060	L 0 - 1		11
Dec 3	NLN	Kidderminster Harriers	A	948	D 1 - 1	Preston 18	11
7	NLN	Alfreton Town	H	721	W 3 - 1	Kayode 9 90+1 Preston 78	9
26	NLN	Blyth Spartans	H	1390	L 2 - 3	Olley 25 Oliver 47 (pen)	
28	NLN	Spennymoor Town	A	1504	W 3 - 1	Barrow 7 (pen) Tear 28 Olley 74	
Jan 1	NLN	Blyth Spartans	A	1028	D 3 - 3	Barrow 19 (pen) Preston 58 Olley 90	11
4	NLN	Hereford	H	937	W 2 - 0	Forbes 30 Tear 88	11
18	NLN	Altrincham	H	967	W 2 - 0	Thompson 43 (og) Curry 67	9
21	NLN	Leamington	A	310	D 0 - 0		8
28	NLN	Chester	H	842	W 2 - 0	Preston 65 Keating 75	8
Feb 1	NLN	Leamington	H	806	W 4 - 2	Williamson 20 Nicholson 40 Preston 45+1 Southern-Cooper 66	6
8	NLN	Curzon Ashton	A	334	W 1 - 0	Keating 69	
15	NLN	Kidderminster Harriers	H	1075	D 0 - 0		
22	NLN	Guiseley	A	693	D 2 - 2	Olley 85 Southern-Cooper 90	9
25	NLN	Boston United	A	1108	W 3 - 0	Deverdics 16 Tear 38 Preston 72	6
Mar 7	NLN	King's Lynn Town	H	1084	L 1 - 2	O'Donnell 51	7
July 19	PO Q	Brackley Town	A	0	D 1 - 1	Southern-Cooper 45+4 (Won 6-5 on pens)	
25	PO SF	Boston United	A	0	L 3 - 5	O'Donnell 19 Nicholson 51 (pen) Forbes 85	

GOALSCORERS	SG	CSG	Pens	Hat tricks	Total		SG	CSG	Pens	Hat tricks	Total
Kayode	7	3			8	Forbes	2	1			2
O'Donnell	8	2			8	Keating*	2	1			2
Preston	8	2	1		8	Lees	2	1			2
Olley	6	3			7	Nicholson	2	1	1		2
Tear	5	1			5	Opponent	2	1			2
Deverdics	3	1			3	Blackett	1	1			1
Oliver	3	1	2		3	Curry*	1	1			1
Southern-Cooper	3	1			3	Nelson	1	1			1
Agnew	2	1			2	Williamson	1	1			1
Barrow	2	2	2		2						

James B (L)	Williamson M	Nicholson A	Lees T (L)	Barrow S	Agnew L (L)	Oliver C	Olley G	Greenfield D	Thomson C	Blackett P	Kayode J (L)	O'Donnell J	Forbes E	Nelson M	Guthrie S (Gk)	Preston J	Deverdics N	Tear D	Sakellaropoulos A	Cranstan D	Southern-Cooper J (L)	Curry M (L)	Keating R	Pattison M	Symons O	Hindle J (L)	Hunter J	No.
x	x	x	x	x	x	x	x	xs	xs	xs	s	sx	sx	sx	s	s												1
x	x	x	x	x	x	x	x	sx	sx	s	x	xs	xs	s	s													2
x	sx	x	x	x	x	xs	x		s	x	x	xs	sx	xs			sx											3
x	xs	x	x	x	x	x	x	sx			x	x	s		s	sx	xs											4
x			x	x	x	sx	x			sx	x	xs	xs	x	s	xs	sx	s										5
x		x	x		x	x	x		s	sx	sx	xs	x	xs	x	s		xs	sx									6
x	xs	x	x	x	x	x	x		s	sx	sx	x	sx	s	x	s												7
x	x	x	x	x	xs	x	s		sx	sx	xs	x	x	s	x	sx												8
x	x	x	x	x	x		x	xs	sx	sx	sx	x	x	s	x	s	s											9
x		x	x	x	x		s	sx	sx	xs	sx	x	s	sx	x	xs												10
x	x	x	x	xs	xs	x		sx	x	x	sx	s	s	sx	x	xs												11
x	xs	x	x		x		x	s	sx	sx	xs	x	s	sx	s	xs	x	x										12
x	x	x	x	x	xs	sx	x		s	s	x	xs	s	s	s	sx	x	x										13
x	x	x	x	x	x	s	x		s	xs		s	s	sx	x	x												14
x	x	x	x	x	x	sx	x		sx	xs	xs	s	s	s	s	xs	x											15
x		x	x	x	xs	sx	x		sx	x	x	x	s	s	xs	x	xs											16
x		x	x	x	sx	xs	x		s	sx	xs	x	x	s	s	xs	x	x										17
x		x	x	x	xs	s	x		s	x	x	s	x	s	s	sx	x	x										18
x		x	x	x	xs	sx	x		sx	xs	xs	x	s	s	sx	x	x											19
s		x	x	xs	x	x		x	sx	s	x	x	x	xs	sx	x	s											20
x	xs	x	x	x	s	xs	x		x	x	sx	s	s	x	x													21
x	x	x	sx	x	x	x	x		sx	x	s	s	xs	xs		s				s								22
x	x	x		x	x	x	x		xs	sx	x	s	s	xs	s	sx						x						23
x	x	x	s	x	x	x			x	xs	x	s	s	x	sx	sx						x						24
x	s	x		x	sx	sx	x		x		x	x	s	x	xs		s	x										25
x	x	x		x	sx	s	x		x		x	s	s	x	xs		s	x										26
x	x	x		x	s	x		xs		x	s	s	x	sx		s	x											27
x	x	x		x	xs	sx	x		sx		x		s	xs	s	sx		s	x	xs								28
x	x	x		x	sx	xs	x		s	s		x	s	x	x	xs			x	sx								29
x	x	x		x	sx	xs	x		s		x	s	xs	s	sx		x	xs	sx									30
x	xs	x		x	sx	xs	x		s		x	s	x	x	sx		x	xs	sx									31
x	x	x		x	sx	xs	x			s	s	x	x	x	x		x	xs	sx									32
x	x	x	xs	x	s	x			sx	xs		x	x	sx		x	s	x										33
x	x	x		xs	s	x			x		x	x	x	x		s	x	sx	xs	sx								34
x	x	x			x	x	x		x		s	xs	x	x		s	x	sx		s	s							35
	x	x	s		xs	xs	x		x		x	x	x	x		x		sx	s		sx							36
x	x	x		xs		x	s		sx		x	x		s	x	x		x		xs	sx			s				37
x	x	x		xs		x	s		sx		x	x		s	x	x		x		sx	s				xs			38
36	21	37	21	29	18	9	38	0	1	1	13	14	13	11	2	11	27	13	0	0	16	0	1	0	0	0	0	x
0	5	0	0	2	11	10	0	2	1	1	11	11	4	4	1	0	10	3	7	0	0	0	4	2	0	0	1	xs
0	1	0	1	0	7	7	0	1	6	13	3	4	8	1	0	11	3	9	0	0	0	3	5	2	0	1	0	sx
1	1	0	1	1	1	6	0	11	3	6	0	2	9	12	35	0	1	3	1	7	0	1	0	1	0	3	1	s

GOALKEEPERS	CS	CCS
James	17	4

x - Played full 90 minutes
xs - Substituted off
sx - Substituted on
s - Non-playing Substitute

GLOUCESTER CITY MATCH RESULTS 2019-20

Date	Comp	Opponents	H/A	Att:	Result	Goalscorers	Pos
Aug 3	NLN	Blyth Spartans	A	834	W 2 - 1	Hanks 43 (pen) Jackson M 79	
6	NLN	Hereford	H	1570	L 0 - 2		9
10	NLN	Altrincham	H	305	D 1 - 1	Hanks 50	
13	NLN	Kidderminster Harriers	A	1434	W 3 - 2	Parker 32 Jackson M 34 Hanks 66 (pen)	
17	NLN	Chester	A	1612	L 0 - 4		14
24	NLN	Boston United	H	330	W 3 - 0	Parker 11 80 Hanks 23 (pen)	
26	NLN	Brackley Town	A	570	L 0 - 3		
31	NLN	York City	H	652	L 2 - 3	Hanks 32 Jackson J 37	13
Sep 3	NLN	AFC Telford United	A	925	L 3 - 4	Russe 2 Hanks 17 Parker 90+2 (pen)	16
7	NLN	Darlington	H	437	W 2 - 1	Hanks 23 70	13
14	NLN	King's Lynn Town	A	1044	D 2 - 2	Hanks 26 Parker 61	14
21	**FAC2Q**	**Kidlington**	**H**	**197**	**W 5 - 0**	**Avery Jackson M (3) Kotwica**	
28	NLN	Guiseley	H	284	W 3 - 1	Jackson M 37 85 Russe 59	11
Oct 5	**FAC3Q**	**Whitby Town**	**A**	**273**	**D 1 - 1**	**Hanks**	
7	**FAC3Qr**	**Whitby Town**	**H**	**273**	**L 1 - 3**	**Kowitca 72**	
12	NLN	Gateshead	A	1189	L 0 - 1		13
19	NLN	Bradford (Park Avenue)	H	295	W 1 - 0	Hanks 50	10
26	NLN	Spennymoor Town	A	928	L 1 - 5	Harper 76	11
Nov 2	NLN	Curzon Ashton	H	238	D 2 - 2	Hamilton 14 Jackson M 55	13
9	NLN	Farsley Celtic	A	372	D 1 - 1	Avery 18	13
Manager Mike Cook leaves the club. James Rowe is named as the new boss.							
24	**FAT3Q**	**Bradford (Park Avenue)**	**H**	**251**	**L 0 - 2**		
30	NLN	Kettering Town	H	325	D 2 - 2	Senior 12 Robert 86	12
Dec 7	NLN	Southport	A	815	L 0 - 1		15
26	NLN	Leamington	A	535	L 0 - 3		
28	NLN	AFC Telford United	H	325	L 0 - 1		
Jan 1	NLN	Leamington	H	370	W 2 - 1	James 22 Jackson M 37	18
4	NLN	Darlington	A	1446	L 1 - 2	Kotwica 62	18
18	NLN	Guiseley	A	653	L 1 - 2	Daly 5	20
25	NLN	Southport	H	334	L 0 - 1		20
28	NLN	Alfreton Town	A	296	L 1 - 6	McClure 16	20
Feb 1	NLN	Spennymoor Town	H	236	L 1 - 2	Brunt 54	20
8	NLN	Bradford (Park Avenue)	A	296	W 2 - 1	Mensah 24 Brunt 56	20
Mar 7	NLN	Kettering Town	A	642	D 1 - 1	Mensah 9	19
9	NLN	Farsley Celtic	H	161	W 2 - 1	McClure 68 Mensah 90+2	18

GOALSCORERS	SG	CSG	Pens	Hat tricks	Total		SG	CSG	Pens	Hat tricks	Total
Hanks	10	4	3		11	Hamilton	1	1			1
Jackson M	6	2		1	9	Harper	1	1			1
Parker	4	1	1		5	Jackson J	1	1			1
Kotwica	3	1			3	James	1	1			1
Mensah	3	3			3	Robert	1	1			1
Avery	2	1			2	Senior*	1	1			1
Brunt	2	1			2						
McClure	2	1			2						
Russe	2	1			2						
Daly	1	1			1						

Appearance grid (player columns across the top; match numbers in the "No." column on the right). Reading: x = played full 90 minutes, xs = substituted off, sx = substituted on, s = non-playing substitute.

Jeacock Z (L)	Avery S	Hamilton S	Hanks J	Knowles C	Thomas J	Robert F	Jackson M	Parker J	Harper V (L)	Jackson J	Kotwica Z	Hainault A	Smith K	Richards I	Bremner J	King T	Spruce L (L)	Russe L (L)	Unwin J	Johnstone R	Bradley-Hurst J (Gk)(L)	Harrison T (L)	Myrie-Williams J	Smith H (L)	Spark J	Hodges H (L)	Henry W (Gk)(L)	Daly L	Senior J	Sweeney D (L)	Maher N (Gk)	Ebbutt C	James J	Maxwell L (L)	Pennell L	McClure M	Mensah B	Allen T (L)	Brunt L (L)	Nabay F	Gunning G	Andre A (Gk)(L)	No.
x	x	x	x	x	x	x	xs	x	x	xs	sx	sx	s	s	s																												1
x	x	x	x	x	x	x	sx	x	x	xs	s	s	s				s																										2
x	sx	x	x	x	xs	x	x	x	x	xs	sx	s	sx	xs			s																										3
x	x	x	x	x	xs		xs	x	x		xs	sx	xs	sx		s	sx																										4
x	x	xs	x	x	x	x		x	x		xs	s	s	sx			sx	x																									5
x	x	x	x	xs	x	xs		xs	x		x	sx	sx	s		s	sx	x																									6
x	x		xs	sx	x	x	s	x	x	xs	x	sx	sx	xs			s	x																									7
x	x		xs	x	x			x	x	x		sx	sx	xs			s	s	s																								8
	x		xs	xs	x	x		x	x	xs	sx	sx	s				x	sx	x	x	s																						9
x	x		xs	x	xs	x		x	x	xs	sx	sx	s				x	s	x	x	sx																						10
x	x		xs	x	x		sx	xs	x	xs	x	sx	s				x	s			x	sx																					11
x	x	s	x	sx	x			x	x	x		x	sx	sx			x				x	x																					12
x	x	xs	x	x			x	x	x		xs	s	sx			s	x				sx																						13
x	x	x	x	x		sx	x	x	x		x	s	s				x			s	x	sx																					14
	x	sx	x		x	x	x	x	x		sx		s			sx	x			x	x	x																					15
	x	x	x			xs	x	x	x		x		sx				s		x		s	x	xs	sx																			16
	x	x	xs			xs					xs		x	x	x		x	xs	x																								17
	x	x	x			xs		x	x	x	sx						xs			sx	x		x	xs	sx																		18
	x	x	x	x			sx	xs	xs	s	sx			s	x				x			s	x																				19
	x	x	x				x	sx	xs	xs	s	sx			x				x			x				x	x																20
		x	x			x	x	x	x	x	sx				s	s				x		s				x						x	x										21
	x	x	x	s	x	x	x	x					sx	s	s					s										x	x	x	xs										22
	x	x	xs	s	x	x	x						sx	s	s					sx										x	x	x	xs										23
	x	x			x	xs	x	xs					x	s									sx							x	x	sx	x	s	s								24
	s	xs	x		x		x	sx					xs	s						xs			x							x	x	sx	x	sx	x								25
	sx	x	xs		x	sx	x	xs					x							s										x	x	s	x	x	x	x							26
	s	x	x		x	xs	x						x	s						s										x	x		x	sx	x	x							27
x		s	xs		x		x	sx					x	sx																x	x		s	s	x	xs	x	x					28
x		xs			x	sx	x					s								x	xs			s		sx	x	x	xs	x	x	sx							29
x					x	x	sx					x								s						s			xs	xs	x	xs	x	sx	sx	x	xs			30
					x	x	sx					xs	s							sx										x		x	s	x		x	x	x	sx	x			31
		xs			x	xs	x					sx	sx							s										x		x	s	x		x	x	xs	sx	x			32
		x			x	xs	sx					s	s							s										x		x		x		x	x	x	sx	xs		x	33
		sx			xs	xs	x					s	sx							x										x		x		x		x	x	sx	xs		x	s	34
15	22	17	20	11	24	15	19	18	19	4	11	0	2	0	0	0	16	0	0	7	6	6	1	0	2	4	14	7	0	8	0	8	3	7	5	5	1	3	0	2	0		x
0	0	4	10	2	4	9	3	6	0	6	6	0	2	2	0	0	0	1	0	1	0	1	1	1	0	0	0	1	2	0	0	1	1	0	2	1	1	2	1	0	0		xs
0	2	1	1	2	0	4	4	3	0	3	11	12	7	2	0	1	3	0	0	5	0	0	6	0	1	0	0	0	2	0	2	1	1	0	0	0	0	4	1	0	0		sx
0	2	2	0	2	0	0	1	0	1	0	3	14	11	3	1	6	2	0	1	12	1	0	1	0	1	0	0	0	1	3	5	1	0	0	0	0	0	0	0	0	1		s

GOALKEEPERS	CS	CCS
Jeacock	2	1
Bradley-Hurst	1	1

x - Played full 90 minutes
xs - Substituted off
sx - Substituted on
s - Non-playing Substitute

GUISELEY MATCH RESULTS 2019-20

Date	Comp	Opponents	H/A	Att:	Result	Goalscorers	Pos
Aug 3	NLN	King's Lynn Town	H	671	W 3 - 0	Martin 20 Spencer 60 68	
6	NLN	Bradford (Park Avenue)	A	674	W 5 - 0	Martin 7 36 53 Soleman 25 Spencer 87	1
10	NLN	Southport	A	937	L 0 - 3		
13	NLN	Spennymoor Town	H	774	W 3 - 1	Martin 31 47 Shaw 76	
17	NLN	Boston United	A	1059	D 1 - 1	Martin 53	2
24	NLN	Alfreton Town	H	663	L 2 - 4	Martin 19 Spencer 60	
26	NLN	Blyth Spartans	A	891	W 4 - 1	Shaw 38 Martin 58 74 (pen) Ritson 67 (og)	
31	NLN	Curzon Ashton	H	645	W 1 - 0	Felix 83	5
Sep 3	NLN	York City	H	1891	D 0 - 0		4
7	NLN	Chester	A	1989	L 1 - 3	Martin 80	5
14	NLN	Hereford	H	873	W 3 - 0	Martin 9 81 86	4
21	FAC2Q	**Stockton Town**	H	483	W 1 - 0	**Nicholson 47 (og)**	
28	NLN	Gloucester City	A	284	L 1 - 3	Johnson 6	6
Oct 5	FAC3Q	**Peterborough Sports**	A	435	L 0 - 1		
12	NLN	Altrincham	H	1065	D 1 - 1	Felix 5	7
19	NLN	AFC Telford United	A	1007	L 1 - 4	Bencherif 64	7
Nov 2	NLN	Gateshead	A	1004	W 3 - 2	Martin 18 Bencherif 67 Felix 71	6
9	NLN	Kettering Town	H	765	L 1 - 2	Martin 90+1	10
23	FAT3Q	**AFC Telford United**	H	345	L 0 - 4		
30	NLN	Leamington	A	522	D 2 - 2	Nicholson 67 88	9
Dec 7	NLN	Brackley Town	H	526	L 0 - 2		10
10	NLN	Kidderminster Harriers	H	267	L 1 - 2	Felix 40	10
21	NLN	Hereford	A	1863	D 0 - 0		
26	NLN	Farsley Celtic	H	1048	W 2 - 0	Sang 55 Shaw 82	
28	NLN	York City	A	3136	W 2 - 1	Bencherif 4 Felix 87	
31	NLN	Farsley Celtic	A	1010	W 1 - 0	Sang 67	
Jan 4	NLN	Chester	H	1029	L 0 - 1		10
11	NLN	Altrincham	A	1242	D 1 - 1	Felix 33	10
18	NLN	Gloucester City	H	653	W 2 - 1	Felix 64 Johnson 71	6
21	NLN	Darlington	H	859	L 1 - 2	Felix 12	7
25	NLN	Brackley Town	A	590	D 0 - 0		9
Feb 1	NLN	Darlington	A	1411	W 3 - 0	Bencherif 32 Soleman 54 (pen) 83	9
8	NLN	AFC Telford United	H	597	L 1 - 2	Digie 34	
22	NLN	Gateshead	H	693	D 2 - 2	Jones 4 Martin 21	10
Mar 7	NLN	Leamington	H	584	W 3 - 0	Jones 45+3 Felix 49 Spencer 90+1	10
14	NLN	King's Lynn Town	A	1432	W 1 - 0	Felix 33	9

GOALSCORERS	SG	CSG	Pens	Hat tricks	Total		SG	CSG	Pens	Hat tricks	Total
Martin	11	4	1	2	17	Sang	2	1			2
Felix	10	3			10	Digie	1	1			1
Spencer	4	2			5						
Bencherif	4	2			4						
Shaw	3	1			3						
Soleman	2	1	1		3						
Johnson	2	1			2						
Jones	2	2			2						
Nicholson	1	1			2						
Opponent	2	1			2						

Player appearance grid:

No.	Sykes-Kenworthy (L)	Garner S	Cantrill G	McNally R	Nicholson B	Bencherif H	Soleman A	Spencer J	Felix K	Martin A	Johnson G	Shaw L	Barkers D	Digie K	Allinson L (Gk)	Clayton P	Scrivens S	Starcenko A	Jones A	Dewhurst M (Gk) (L)	Newall N	Thornton W	Smith S	Sang C (L)	Sheppeard H (L)	Ekpolo P	Wade B (Gk) (L)	Zanos J
1	X	X	X	X	X	X	X	XS	XS	X	X	SX	SX	S	S	S												
2	X	X	XS	X	X	X	X	X	X	X	XS	SX	SX	S	S	S												
3	X	X	X	X	X	X	X	XS	X	XS	SX	SX	S	S			S											
4	X	X	X	X	X	X	X	S	X	X	X	S	S	S		S												
5	X	X	X	X	X	X	X		XS	X	XS		X	S	S	S	S		SX	SX								
6	X	X			X	X	XS	X		SX	X	XS	X	XS	S	S			SX	SX								
7	X	X		X	X	X	X	X			X	X	XS	X	S	S	S	S	SX	S								
8	X	X		X	X	X	X			SX	X	XS	XS	X	S	S		SX		S								
9	X	X	X	X	X	X	XS	SX	X	X	S	X	X	S	S		S											
10		X	XS	X	XS	X		XS	X	X	SX	X	X	X	X		S	SX	SX									
11		X	X	X	X	X	XS	XS	SX	X	SX	XS	XS	X		S		SX	X									
12	S	X	X	X	X	XS	X	XS	X	X	SX		X	S	S	S		SX	X									
13		X	XS	X	XS	XS	SX	X	X	X		X	S	SX		SX			X									
14		X	X	X	X	X	X	X		X	X		X		SX				SX	X								
15	X	X	X		X		X	X		X	XS	XS			S		SX	X	X	SX	S							
16	X	X	XS	X	X	XS		X		X		X			S		SX	X	X	S	S	SX						
17	X	X		X	X	X	X	X			S	S			SX	XS			X	X	S							
18	XS	X		X	X	X	XS	X		X	SX	SX	S	SX			XS		X	X	S							
19	X	X	X	X		X	SX	XS	X	XS	SX	XS	X	S		S	SX		S	X			S					
20	X	X	X	X		X		X		X	X	SX	X	XS		S	S		S	X			S					
21	X	X	X	X		X		X		S	X	SX	X			S			X	S								
22	X	X	X	XS	X		X			X	XS	XS	X		SX		X	S	SX									
23		X	X	X	X	X		X		X	S	S	S	X			X	X	S		S	X						
24		X	X	X	X	X		X		X	S	X	S	X			X	X	S		S	XS						
25		X	X	X	X	X		X		XS	SX	SX	X		S		X	X	S		S	XS						
26		X	X	X	X	X		XS		X	SX	S	X				X	X	S		S	X						
27		XS	X	X	X	X		XS		X	SX	SX	S	X			X	X	SX		SX	X						
28		X	X	X	X	XS		X		X	SX	X	S				X	X	S			XS	XS	S				
29		X	X	X	X	X		X	SX	X	X	SX	XS				X	X	S					S	S			
30		X	X	X	X	XS		X		X	SX	SX	XS				XS	X	S					S	SX			
31		X	X	X	X	XS		X		X	SX	S	X				X	X	S					S	SX			
32		X	X	X	X	X		X		SX	XS	SX	X				XS					S	XS	SX	SX	X		
33		X	X	X	X	X		X		SX	XS		XS		S		X				SX	X	S	S	X			
34		X	X	X	X	XS	S	S	X	X	XS		SX				X				SX	S	X	X	L			
35		X	X	X	X	XS	SX	X		X			S		S		X				SX	XS	S	X	X			
36		X	X	X	X	XS	X		X		SX		X		S		S				S	X	X	S				
x	9	18	30	32	33	35	23	13	19	19	21	7	9	12	1	0	0	0	15	21	0	0	0	4	0	3	5	0
xs	0	1	3	2	2	0	10	7	7	2	7	9	4	4	0	0	2	0	2	0	0	0	0	5	0	0	0	0
sx	0	0	0	0	0	0	1	1	5	1	6	15	6	2	0	4	5	6	4	0	3	0	5	1	1	3	0	0
s	0	1	0	0	0	0	1	3	0	1	1	10	16	11	17	8	1	4	0	12	2	8	0	8	3	0	0	1

GOALKEEPERS	CS	CCS
Dewhurst*	6	2
Sykes-Kenworthy	4	2
Wade*	3	2

x - Played full 90 minutes
xs - Substituted off
sx - Substituted on
s - Non-playing Substitute

HEREFORD MATCH RESULTS 2019-20

Date	Comp	Opponents	H/A	Att:	Result	Goalscorers	Pos
Aug 3	NLN	Spennymoor Town	H	2707	D 2 - 2	Nicholson 27 Owen-Evans 79	
6	NLN	Gloucester City	A	1570	W 2 - 0	Thomas 33 Owen-Evans 79 (pen)	3
10	NLN	King's Lynn Town	A	1148	L 1 - 3	Symons 75	
Marc Richards is sacked as manager, Tim Harris takes over as caretaker.							
13	NLN	AFC Telford United	H	2440	W 1 - 0	Liburd 57	
17	NLN	Blyth Spartans	A	756	W 1 - 0	Symons 23	4
24	NLN	Brackley Town	H	2585	D 1 - 1	Liburd 17	
26	NLN	Chester City	A	2573	L 1 - 4	Cullinane-Liburd 88	
Russell Slade is named as the new manager.							
31	NLN	Boston United	H	2498	D 0 - 0		7
Sep 14	NLN	Guiseley	A	873	L 0 - 3		16
17	NLN	Gateshead	H	1703	W 2 - 1	Nicholson 65 O'Sullivan 90+5	11
21	**FAC2Q**	**Truro City**	**H**	**1115**	**W 5 - 2**	**Styche 21 (pen) Nicholson 51 Liburd 68 Symons 84 Vincenti 87 (pen)**	
28	NLN	Kettering Town	H	2557	W 1 - 0	Nicholson 67	9
Oct 1	NLN	Leamington	A	607	W 2 - 0	Vincenti 52 Gowling 68	
5	**FAC3Q**	**Tamworth**	**A**	**1206**	**D 0 - 0**		
8	**FAC3Qr**	**Tamworth**	**H**	**1271**	**D 0 - 0**	**(AET - lost 1-3 on pens)**	
12	NLN	Bradford (Park Avenue)	A	484	L 2 - 3	Vincenti 35 (pen) O'Sullivan 55	8
22	NLN	Southport	A	604	L 2 - 3	Styche 45+6 (pen) Mooney 89	
Nov 2	NLN	Darlington	A	1388	D 0 - 0		11
12	NLN	Alfreton Town	H	1821	L 1 - 2	Sodeinde 13	
16	NLN	Altrincham	A	1506	L 1 - 5	Vincenti 61	13
23	**FAT3Q**	**King's Lynn Town**	**A**	**846**	**D 0 - 0**		
26	**FAT3Qr**	**King's Lynn Town**	**H**	**715**	**L 0 - 3**		
30	NLN	Farsley Celtic	H	2075	D 1 - 1	Allen 67	13
Dec 3	NLN	York City	H	1552	D 2 - 2	Vincenti 35 Styche 74 (pen)	12
7	NLN	Curzon Ashton	A	237	L 0 - 2		13
21	NLN	Guiseley	H	1863	D 0 - 0		
26	NLN	Kidderminster Harriers	A	2117	L 1 - 2	Styche 51	
28	NLN	Leamington	H	1930	L 1 - 2	Sodeinde 34	
Jan 1	NLN	Kidderminster Harriers	H	2508	W 2 - 1	Sodeinde 50 (pen) Moyo 80 (og)	
4	NLN	Gateshead	A	937	L 0 - 2		16
11	NLN	Bradford (Park Avenue)	H	1586	D 1 - 1	Pope 4	15
Manager Russell Slade leaves the club. Josh Gowling is made interim boss.							
25	NLN	Curzon Ashton	H	1950	D 1 - 1	Owens-Evans 90+4 (pen)	16
Feb 1	NLN	Alfreton Town	A	518	L 0 - 2		17
8	NLN	Southport	H	1712	D 2 - 2	Mooney 90 90+4	
22	NLN	Darlington	H	1643	D 2 - 2	John-Lewis 56 Hodgkiss 85	17
29	NLN	Altrincham	H	1698	L 0 - 2		17
Mar 3	NLN	York City	A	2343	W 4 - 1	Mooney 4 John-Lewis 14 65 Pope 50	17
7	NLN	Farsley Celtic	A	412	W 2 - 1	Owen-Evans 5 Mooney 66	16
10	NLN	Kettering Town	A	640	D 0 - 0		15
14	NLN	Spennymoor Town	A	1259	L 0 - 4		15

GOALSCORERS	SG	CSG	Pens	Hat tricks	Total		SG	CSG	Pens	Hat tricks	Total
Mooney	4	2			5	Pope	2	1			2
Vincenti	5	1	2		5	Allen	1	1			1
Nicholson	4	1			4	Cullinane-Liburd	1	1			1
Owen-Evans	4	2	1		4	Gowling	1	1			1
Styche	4	1	3		4	Hodgkiss	1	1			1
John-Lewis	2	1			3	Opponent	1	1			1
Liburd	3	1			3	Thomas	1	1			1
Sodeinde	3	2			3						
Symons	3	1			3						
O'Sullivan	2	1			2						

Hall B	Riley M	Hodgkiss J	Gowling J	Thomas K	Cullinane-Liburd J	Cane J	Hanley R	Nicholson J	Styche R	Liburd R	Ash B	Symons M	Owen-Evans T	Pope J	O'Sullivan T	Maye S	Bray A	Carey J (Gk)	Bishop L	Bodenham J (L)	Vincenti P (L)	Finn K	Pollock B	Burwood W (Gk) (L)	Davies R	Muirhead A	Mooney K	Dawson S	Allen T (L)	Sodeinde V (L)	Greenslade D	Powell B (Gk)	Whitlock R	Henry W (Gk) (L)	Anderson J (L)	John-Lewis L	Raison T	No.
X	X	X	X	X	X	X	X	XS	XS	XS	SX	SX	SX	S	S																							1
X	XS	X	X	X	X	X	X	XS	SX	XS	SX	S	X	SX	S																							2
X		X	X	X	X	XS	X	SX	X	SX	X	XS	S	S																								3
X		X	X	X	X		S		X	X	X	X	S	S	X	S																						4
X		X	X		X	X	X	SX	SX	XS	X	XS	XS	SX	S	X	S																					5
X	S	X	X		X		XS	X	SX	X	XS		X	SX	XS	X	S		SX																			6
X		X	X	X	X	SX	XS	SX	XS	X	XS	SX	S	S	X																							7
X	XS	X		X	X	XS	SX	S	X	SX	X		SX	X	XS	XS	S																					8
X		X	X	X	X	X	SX	X	X	S	S	XS	XS	SX	SX						X																	9
X		XS	X	X	X	X		XS	SX	X	S	XS	SX	SX	S	X					X																	10
X		X	X	X	S		XS	XS	SX	S	SX	X	SX	X	XS						X	X	S															11
X		X	X	X			X	XS	XS	SX	SX	X	SX	S	X						X	XS	S															12
X		X	X	X			X		X	S	SX	SX	XS	XS	X	SX					X	XS	S															13
X		X	X	X	XS		X			SX	SX	X	X	X	S						X	XS	S		S	S	S											14
X		X	X	X	XS		XS			SX	X	X	X	S	X						X	XS	SX		SX	S	S	S										15
X		X	X	XS	S		XS			SX	X	XS	SX	X	S						X	X			X	S		SX										16
X		X	X	X				XS	SX	X	SX	S	X	S							X	XS			XS			SX	X									17
X		X	X	X	X		SX	XS	SX	S		S	S	X							S	XS			X			SX	X	XS	SX							18
X	S		X	X	X		X			XS	XS	SX	XS			SX					X				S			SX	X		X							19
X	S		X	X	X		X			SX		SX	X	X		SX					X	XS			XS			S	X		XS							20
X	X	X	S		X		SX	XS	SX	S		X	X	X							S	XS			X	S		XS		SX								21
X	X	X			X		SX	X	SX	S			X	X	X						S	XS			XS	S		XS		S		SX						22
X	XS	X			X			X	X			S		SX	SX						SX	XS						S	X	X		X						23
X	X	X			X			X	XS				SX	XS							X	XS			S			SX	XS	X								24
X	X	X		S			X	X	XS			SX		XS	XS						X				S			SX		X			X					25
X	X		X	X			X	XS	XS				S								SX				S	X		SX	X	X	SX		X					26
X		X		X	X			X	XS				S	S							SX				X	S		SX	X	XS	SX		X					27
X		S	X	X				XS	XS				X	X							SX				XS	S		X	X	SX	XS		X					28
	X		X	X					S				X	S		XS						SX			X			XS	X	SX	X	X	X	S				29
	X	X	XS					SX					X	SX	X						S				X			XS	X	SX	X	XS	S		X			30
S		X	S		X				X				X	X		X						SX	X		S	S	XS		X	X		X			X			31
	X			X	SX			SX	X				X	X	XS		XS				S	X			SX		S			X	XS		X					32
S		X		SX	X	X		SX	X				X	X	XS		XS					XS			S		SX						X	X				33
X	S	X		S	X			SX	XS				X	X	XS		SX					XS					SX						X	X				34
X	X	X		SX				XS	SX				X	X	X										S		X					S	X	X	X	S		35
X	X		XS		X			XS	X				X	S	SX						SX	XS			S		X							X	XS			36
X	X	X		X				SX	S				X	X	SX						XS	X					X						S	X	XS			37
X	X	X	SX	SX	X				S		S		X	X	XS							XS			S		X						X	X				38
X	X	X	SX	S	X			SX	S				XS	X	X							SX	X					XS					XS	X				39
X	X	X		S	X		X					S	S		X	X	X					SX	XS		S			XS						X				40
35	11	29	19	21	33	18	3	12	5	7	7	4	18	20	11	4	2	0	0	13	3	0	9	0	0	0	5	12	2	5	8	1	0	4	6	6	0	x
0	3	1	0	2	1	3	2	8	11	7	3	4	4	5	8	2	4	0	0	0	14	3	6	0	0	0	7	3	2	2	0	0	0	1	1	0	0	xs
0	0	0	0	4	1	1	2	5	9	10	11	7	6	8	7	1	8	0	1	1	5	1	0	1	0	10	0	4	3	1	0	0	0	0	0	0	0	sx
2	4	1	3	3	1	2	0	2	2	2	7	4	4	7	11	2	4	1	0	5	1	5	4	5	9	2	3	0	1	0	0	1	3	0	0	1		s

GOALKEEPERS	CS	CCS
Hall	12	4

x - Played full 90 minutes
xs - Substituted off
sx - Substituted on
s - Non-playing Substitute

KETTERING TOWN MATCH RESULTS 2019-20

Date	Comp	Opponents	H/A	Att:	Result	Goalscorers	Pos
Aug 3	NLN	AFC Telford United	H	959	W 2 - 1	Carta 52 Nti 88	
6	NLN	King's Lynn Town	A	1114	L 1 - 2	Solkhon 86	8
10	NLN	Darlington	A	1344	L 0 - 3		
13	NLN	Chester	H	971	D 1 - 1	Roberts 70 (og)	
17	NLN	Gateshead	H	701	L 1 - 2	Kelly 6	19
24	NLN	Leamington	A	575	L 1 - 3	Nti 90+2	
26	NLN	Kidderminster Harriers	H	911	L 3 - 5	Cartwright 17 Skarz 56 Kennedy 72	
31	NLN	Southport	A	825	D 1 - 1	McGrath 27	20
Sep 3	NLN	Boston United	H	835	L 0 - 2		20
7	NLN	Farsley Celtic	A	525	L 2 - 3	Kelly 72 Solkhon 78	20
14	NLN	Alfreton Town	H	656	W 2 - 1	Nti 1 (pen) Kelly 3	20
21	**FAC2Q**	**Sutton Coldfield**	**H**	**421**	**D 1 - 1**	**Nti 29 (pen)**	
24	**FAC2Qr**	**Sutton Coldfield**	**A**	**222**	**L 1 - 2**	**Stohrer 11**	

Nicky Eaden is sacked as manager - Steve Kinniburgh and Luke Graham become joint caretaker managers.

Date	Comp	Opponents	H/A	Att:	Result	Goalscorers	Pos
28	NLN	Hereford	A	2557	L 0 - 1		20
Oct 12	NLN	Spennymoor Town	H	752	L 0 - 2		21

Paul Cox is named as the new manager.

Date	Comp	Opponents	H/A	Att:	Result	Goalscorers	Pos
Nov 2	NLN	Bradford (Park Avenue)	H	625	W 4 - 0	Meikle 14 Kennedy 57 Milnes 62 O'Connor A 79 (pen)	20
9	NLN	Guiseley	A	765	W 2 - 1	Carta 42 47	
16	NLN	Blyth Spartans	H	810	D 4 - 4	McGrath 59 Graham 67 Meikle 74 Mitford 90	20
23	**FAT3Q**	**Peterborough Sports**	**A**	**346**	**W 3 - 0**	**Meikle 27 O'Connor A 52 Nti 86**	
30	NLN	Gloucester City	A	325	D 2 - 2	O'Connor A 42 (pen) Taylor 78	19
Dec 2	NLN	Curzon Ashton	A	210	D 0 - 0		19
7	NLN	York City	H	859	D 0 - 0		20
14	**FAT1**	**FC United of Manchester**	**A**	**1218**	**L 1 - 2**	**Graham 90**	
21	NLN	Alfreton Town	A	493	W 2 - 0	Mitford 28 77	
28	NLN	Boston United	A	1718	L 1 - 2	Mitford 40	
Jan 1	NLN	Brackley Town	A	905	D 1 - 1	McGrath 32	
4	NLN	Farsley Celtic	H	667	W 1 - 0	Richens 20	19
11	NLN	Spennymoor Town	A	1072	W 2 - 1	Curtis 64 (og) Law 90+4	17
25	NLN	York City	A	2767	L 0 - 1		17
28	NLN	Altrincham	H	543	L 0 - 2		17
Feb 1	NLN	Curzon Ashton	H	684	D 0 - 0		18
8	NLN	Altrincham	A	1357	D 1 - 1	Nti 18	18
Mar 7	NLN	Gloucester City	H	642	D 1 - 1	Mitford 5	18
10	NLN	Hereford	H	640	D 0 - 0		19
14	NLN	AFC Telford United	A	1206	L 1 - 3	Sterling-James 67	21

GOALSCORERS	SG	CSG	Pens	Hat tricks	Total		SG	CSG	Pens	Hat tricks	Total
Nti	6	2	2		6	Solkhon	2	1			2
Mitford	4	2			5	Cartwright	1	1			1
Carta	2	1			3	Law	1	1			1
Kelly	3	2			3	Milnes	1	1			1
McGrath*	3	1			3	Richens	1	1			1
Meikle	3	1			3	Skarz	1	1			1
O'Connor A	3	1	2		3	Sterling-James	1	1			1
Graham	2	1			2	Stohrer	1	1			1
Kennedy	2	1			2	Taylor*	1	1			1
Opponent	2	1			2						

White P	Skarz J	Vidal J	Brighton J	Richens M	Kennedy C	Cartwright S (L)	Meikle L	Carta J	O'Connor A	Nti D	Stohrer G	Kelly M	Graham L	Solkhon B	Hodge E	Milnes B	Massaro J	Nimely A	McGrath M	Sebbeh M	Norman J	Williams J	Mitford T	Honour A (Gk)	O'Connor J	Taylor M (L)	Harding M (L)	Law J (L)	Sykes J (Gk)	Bennett J (Gk)	Smith A (L)	Aghatise J	Sterling-James O (L)	Herbert G	No.
X	X	X	X	X	X	X	X	X	XS	X	S	SX	SX	S	S	S																			1
X	X	X	XS	X	X	X	X	XS	XS	X	SX	SX	S	SX	S																				2
X	X		S	XS	XS		X	S	X	X	X	X	X	X	SX	SX	S																		3
X	X		S	X	X	X	S	S	X	X	X	X	S	X	S																				4
X	X		S	X	X	XS	S	S	S	X	X	X	SX	XS			SX																		5
X	X	SX	XS	X	XS	X	SX		X	X		X	S	XS	SX	S	X																		6
X	X	X	SX	X	X	X	X	S	XS	X	XS	S	SX		XS																				7
X	X	X		X	X	SX	XS	X	X	XS	S	SX	S	XS		SX	X																		8
X	X	SX	X		XS	X	XS	X	X	X	S	SX	S	X		S	X																		9
X	X	XS	XS		X	SX	X		X	X	SX	S	X	SX		X		XS																	10
X	X	S	S		X	X	XS		XS	X	X	X	SX	SX	X		X	S																	11
X	XS	S	SX		X	X	X	SX	X	X	X	XS	S	XS	SX	X						S	S												12
X	SX	X		X	X	X	SX	XS	X	X	XS	XS	SX	S	X					S		S													13
X		X		X	S	SX	XS	XS	X	X	X	X	S		SX			XS				X	SX												14
X		X		X		XS	SX		XS	X	X	X	SX					S			X	XS	S	S											15
X	X		S		X		X	S	XS	X	X	X	S		X			X	S			SX													16
X	X			X		X	XS	XS		X	X	X	S		X			X	SX	S		SX	S												17
X	XS		SX	X		X	XS	X	SX	X	X	X	S		XS			X	S			SX													18
X			X	X		X	S	X	X	X	X	X	SX		XS			X	S			S	S	S											19
X			X	X		X	SX	X	X	X	X	S		XS			X	S			S		S	X											20
X			X	X		X	S	XS	X	X	X	X		X			X	S			SX			X											21
X			X	X		X	S	X	X	S	X	X		X			X	S			S		S	X											22
X		XS	X		X	XS		X	X	X	X		SX			X	S			SX		S	X												23
X		SX	X			S		X	X	X	X	X		X			X	S			X			XS											24
X		XS	X			SX	S	X	XS	X	S		X			X		SX	X			X													25
X		SX	X			S	S	X	X	X	X		X			XS			S	XS		X	S												26
X		SX	X			S	SX	X	X	X	X		X			XS			X	S															27
X	S		X			SX	X		X	X	X		XS			X	XS			X	SX	S													28
X			SX	S	X	X	XS	XS		X		XS	SX				X		SX	S															29
X		SX		XS	SX	XS		X	X	X		S			X	SX			X	XS	S														30
X			X	X	XS		SX	X		X	X	S		X			XS			X	S		S	SX											31
X		S	X	X		X	SX	X		X	S	X		X			XS			X	S			X	S										32
X			X	X			X	X	X	S	X		X				X		S		S	XS	X	SX	S										33
X		S	X	X		X	X	X	S	X		X		SX			X		XS		S	S	S	SX	X										34
X		S	X	XS		X	X	X	X	S	X		SX			X		XS	SX	S		S	X												35
35	13	2	7	9	31	9	21	1	8	30	33	16	26	12	1	17	0	1	17	0	0	4	5	0	0	14	0	0	0	0	1	1	2	0	x
0	2	1	2	4	1	2	6	8	9	2	0	6	1	2	2	6	0	0	4	0	0	1	6	0	0	2	0	1	0	0	1	0	0	0	xs
0	0	2	2	6	0	1	3	8	3	1	2	3	0	8	5	4	0	3	1	1	0	1	8	0	0	0	0	3	0	0	1	0	1	0	sx
0	1	2	5	3	0	1	0	11	5	0	0	1	7	11	5	2	2	2	1	12	2	1	3	2	6	0	2	4	1	6	1	3	0	1	s

GOALKEEPERS	CS	CCS
White	8	2

x - Played full 90 minutes
xs - Substituted off
sx - Substituted on
s - Non-playing Substitute

KIDDERMINSTER HARRIERS MATCH RESULTS 2019-20

Date	Comp	Opponents	H/A	Att:	Result	Goalscorers	Pos
Aug 3	NLN	Leamington	H	1551	D 2 - 2	Chambers 58 Williams E 72	
6	NLN	AFC Telford United	A	1557	L 0 - 2		20
10	NLN	Bradford (Park Avenue)	A	379	W 3 - 0	Davidson 14 Williams R 39 Chambers 86	
13	NLN	Gloucester City	H	1434	L 2 - 3	Chambers 12 Weeks 15	
17	NLN	Curzon Ashton	A	307	W 1 - 0	Chambers 58	10
24	NLN	Chester	H	1710	L 0 - 1		
26	NLN	Kettering Town	A	911	W 5 - 3	Chambers 65 90+1 Moyo 70 Peniket 73 Butterfield 88	
31	NLN	Alfreton Town	H	1183	L 0 - 1		11
Sep 3	NLN	Brackley Town	H	1069	L 1 - 3	Davidson 45	15
7	NLN	Blyth Spartans	A	796	D 1 - 1	Prosser 47	16
14	NLN	Altrincham	H	1463	W 2 - 0	Chambers 11 65	11
21	**FAC2Q**	**Stafford Rangers**	**H**	**950**	**D 0 - 0**		
24	**FAC2Qr**	**Stafford Rangers**	**A**	**663**	**L 0 - 3**		
28	NLN	Spennymoor Town	A	1036	L 1 - 2	Chambers 25	14
Oct 22	NLN	Farsley Celtic	H	1045	W 2 - 0	Davidson 19 (pen) Williams E 76	
30	NLN	Darlington	A	1254	L 0 - 1		
Nov 2	NLN	York City	A	2586	D 1 - 1	Hemmings 81	15
5	NLN	King's Lynn Town	H	1082	L 2 - 4	Chambers 7 Peniket 23	15
23	**FAT3Q**	**Curzon Ashton**	**A**	**266**	**L 0 - 3**		

John Pemberton resigns as manager, assistant, Russ Penn, is put in temporary charge.

Date	Comp	Opponents	H/A	Att:	Result	Goalscorers	Pos
30	NLN	Southport	H	1206	L 0 - 1		18
Dec 3	NLN	Gateshead	H	948	D 1 - 1	Johnson 11	18

Jimmy Shan appointed interim manager.

Date	Comp	Opponents	H/A	Att:	Result	Goalscorers	Pos
7	NLN	Boston United	H	1102	L 1 - 3	Moyo 19	19
10	NLN	Guiseley	A	267	W 2 - 1	Chambers 55 Austin 62	16
21	NLN	Altrincham	A	988	D 1 - 1	Butterfield 19	
26	NLN	Hereford	H	2117	W 3 - 1	Shenton 22 29 Hemmings 68	
28	NLN	Brackley Town	A	775	L 0 - 2		
Jan 1	NLN	Hereford	A	2508	L 1 - 2	Hemmings 90+1	
4	NLN	Blyth Spartans	H	1532	L 0 - 1		17
18	NLN	Spennymoor Town	H	1259	D 1 - 1	Chambers 40	18
25	NLN	Boston United	A	1278	L 0 - 2		19
Feb 1	NLN	King's Lynn Town	A	1678	W 2 - 0	Prosser 14 Chambers 37	16
8	NLN	Darlington	H	1509	D 1 - 1	Prosser 62	

Jimmy Shan leaves the club to take up the vacant managerial post at Solihull Moors. Russ Penn takes over again.

Date	Comp	Opponents	H/A	Att:	Result	Goalscorers	Pos
11	NLN	Farsley Celtic	A	180	W 1 - 0	Shenton 76	
15	NLN	Gateshead	A	1075	D 0 - 0		
22	NLN	York City	H	1574	L 0 - 1		15
Mar 7	NLN	Southport	A	903	W 2 - 1	Lowe 23 Hemmings 67	15

GOALSCORERS	SG	CSG	Pens	Hat tricks	Total		SG	CSG	Pens	Hat tricks	Total
Chambers	11	3			13	Johnson	1	1			1
Hemmings	4	1			4	Lowe	1	1			1
Davidson	3	1			3	Weeks	1	1			1
Prosser	3	2			3	Williams R	1	1			1
Shenton	2	1			3						
Butterfield	2	1			2						
Moyo	2	1			2						
Peniket	2	1			2						
Williams E	2	1			2						
Austin	1	1			1						

	Gregory C (L)	Moyo C	Johnson R	Williams R (L)	Weeks D	Davidson C	Williams E	Austin S	Butterfield M	Prosser A	Chambers A	Peniket R	Higginson H	O'Connor J	Palmer T (Gk)	Scott K	Lowth D	Mountjoy E (Gk)	White J	Freemantle E	Sharman J (L)	Shenton O (L)	Lowth S	Digie D	Fuller B	Diau B	Neligwa D	Hemmings A	De Garis K	Mannion W (Gk)(L)	Taylor-Randle R	Lowe K	Samuels A (L)	Nabi S	Penny A	No.
	x	x	x	x	x	x	x	x	x	xs	x	sx	s	s	s	s																				1
	x	x	x	x	x	xs	x	x	x	xs	x	sx	s		s	sx	s																			2
	x	x	x	x	x	xs	x	xs	sx	xs	x	sx				sx	s	s																		3
	x	x	x	x	x	x	x	x	x	s	x	xs	s			s	s	s																		4
	x	x	x	x	x	x	x	x	x	s	x	xs	xs	s		s	sx	s																		5
	x	x	x	x	xs	xs	x	x	x	sx	x	x	s			sx	s	s																		6
	x	x	x	x		xs	xs	x	x	xs	x		sx			s		s		sx	sx															7
	x	x	x	x			xs	x	x	xs	x	x				s		s			sx	sx														8
	x	x	x			x	x	x	xs	x	x	s			x	s		s		sx	sx	x	xs													9
		x	x	x		x	sx	x		x	x	x		x		s		sx			xs	xs														10
	x	x	x	x		xs	xs	x	x	sx	xs	x	sx			x		s	s			sx														11
	x			x	x	x	x	x		x	sx	x		xs	xs	x			s	s	s			sx	s	s										12
	x		x	x	x	xs		x	x	xs	x		sx	x			s		s	sx	s		sx	xs		s										13
s	x	x	x	x	x		x	x	sx	x			s					x	s			xs	sx													14
	x	x	x	x	xs	sx	x		x	x		s						sx								xs										15
	x	x	x	xs		x		sx	x		s	xs	xs			s			sx					sx		x										16
	x	x	x			x	x	xs	x		sx	xs	x			s			sx					sx		xs										17
	x	x	x		xs	x	xs	x		sx	xs	xs	x			s			sx					sx		x										18
	x	sx	x	x		x	xs	x	xs	x	xs	s	x	xs			x						sx		s		sx	s	x	s						19
	x	x	x	x	x	x	x	xs	s	xs	sx			s					s			sx		s		x		x								20
	x	x	x	x	x	x			sx	x	xs			s					s		s	sx		s		x										21
	x	x	x	x	x	x		x	xs			s						sx		s		sx	s	xs		x										22
	x	x	x	xs		x	x	x	xs			s					x		sx	sx	s			x	s											23
	x	x	x		x		x	x	xs		s	s					xs		x		s	s		x		x										24
	x	x	x	xs	xs	x	x	x			sx	sx	s	s			xs		xs					x		x										25
	x	x	x		x	sx	x	x			sx	s	s				xs		xs					x		x										26
	x	x	x		x	sx	x	x			xs	s	s				sx		xs					x		x										27
	x					sx	xs	x	x	x	sx	sx	x				xs		x			s			x		x		x							28
	x	x		sx		x	x	x	x								sx		xs		s			x		x		x	xs	s						29
	x	x		s	sx	x	xs	x	x								s		xs					x		x		x	x	sx						30
	x	x			x	x	x	x	x								sx						xs		x		x		x	xs	sx					31
	x	x	x		sx	xs	x	x	x	x							sx		s		s			x		x		xs								32
	x		x		x	sx	x	x	x	xs		s		s					xs		x				sx		x		x	s						33
	x	x	x		sx	sx	xs	x	x	xs			s						s		xs				x		x		x	sx						34
x	sx	xs			sx	x	x	x	xs			s						s		xs				x		x		x	sx		x					35
x	s	x	sx		xs	x	x	xs	x			s						sx		s				xs		x		x	sx	sxs						36
13	36	30	27	17	19	9	35	29	15	20	10	1	0	6	0	0	0	0	1	3	0	0	0	0	15	0	17	0	8	1	0	2			x
0	0	0	2	3	8	10	1	4	7	12	6	1	0	0	0	0	0	1	5	1	10	1	0	0	1	0	5	0	0	0	1	2	0	0	xs
0	0	2	0	1	4	11	0	0	8	1	6	5	0	0	3	1	0	4	6	1	11	0	1	0	8	1	1	0	0	0	0	3	1	0	sx
1	0	1	0	0	2	0	0	0	6	0	0	15	1	25	7	10	7	1	5	0	5	1	8	1	3	0	1	0	1	0	1	1	0		s

GOALKEEPERS	CS	CCS
Gregory	3	1
Mannion	3	2
Palmer	2	2

x - Played full 90 minutes
xs - Substituted off
sx - Substituted on
s - Non-playing Substitute

KING'S LYNN TOWN MATCH RESULTS 2019-20

Date	Comp	Opponents	H/A	Att:	Result	Goalscorers	Pos
Aug 3	NLN	Guiseley	A	671	L 0 - 3		
6	NLN	Kettering Town	H	1114	W 2 - 1	Marriott 67 Carey 84	11
10	NLN	Hereford	H	1148	W 3 - 1	Gash 25 Henderson 45+1 Jones 52	
13	NLN	Brackley Town	A	500	D 1 - 1	Marriott 90+3 (pen)	
17	NLN	AFC Telford United	A	1003	W 3 - 1	Gash 19 Marriott 44 Payne 55	3
24	NLN	Curzon Ashton	H	833	W 4 - 1	Marriott 33 (pen) 62 Gash 39 60	
26	NLN	Farsley Celtic	A	556	W 2 - 1	Payne 30 Gash 35	
31	NLN	Darlington	H	1229	W 2 - 0	Henderson 51 59	2
Sep 3	NLN	Alfreton Town	H	1203	W 3 - 2	Clunan 2 Payne 27 Marriott 82	1
7	NLN	Spennymoor Town	A	1063	D 2 - 2	Marriott 53 McAuley 76	1
14	NLN	Gloucester City	H	1044	D 2 - 2	Marriott 3 (pen) 90+3	3
21	**FAC2Q**	**Alfreton Town**	**A**	**335**	**D 1 - 1**	**Marriott 17**	
24	**FAC2Qr**	**Alfreton Town**	**H**	**712**	**W 2 - 1**	**Marriott 57 Fox 77**	
28	NLN	York City	A	3082	L 0 - 3		3
Oct 5	**FAC3Q**	**Leek Town**	**A**	**790**	**W 2 - 0**	**Carey 48 Richards 59**	
12	NLN	Chester	H	1637	D 2 - 2	Marriott 2 76	3
19	**FAC4Q**	**Nantwich Town**	**A**	**742**	**L 0 - 1**		
Nov 2	NLN	Altrincham	H	888	D 2 - 2	Marriott 77 84	4
5	NLN	Kidderminster Harriers	A	1082	W 4 - 2	Henderson 11 McAuley 35 Marriott 51 Jarvis 66	2
9	NLN	Bradford (Park Avenue)	A	416	W 3 - 2	Marriott 57 82 Carey 86	
12	NLN	Leamington	H	871	W 5 - 2	Marriott 15 34 Carey 27 Richards 48 Gash 89	
16	NLN	Southport	A	1257	W 2 - 1	Marriott 26 Henderson 57	1
23	**FAT3Q**	**Hereford**	**H**	**846**	**D 0 - 0**		
26	**FAT3Qr**	**Hereford**	**A**	**715**	**W 3 - 0**	**McAuley 5 Barrows 8 Carey 86**	
30	NLN	Gateshead	H	1060	W 1 - 0	Marriott 73	1
Dec 7	NLN	Blyth Spartans	H	1021	W 3 - 0	Henderson 16 Gash 38 Marriott 89	1
14	**FAT1**	**Dover Athletic**	**H**	**776**	**D 2 - 2**	**Kelly 41 Jones 90+5 (Won 4-2 on pens aet)**	
26	NLN	Boston United	H	2246	W 1 - 0	Gash 84	1
28	NLN	Alfreton Town	A	555	D 2 - 2	Marriott 6 Gash 77	1
Jan 1	NLN	Boston United	A	2360	W 3 - 0	Marriott 28 Richards 45 Gash 80	1
4	NLN	Spennymoor Town	H	1439	W 3 - 0	Barrows 44 Marriott 63 74	1
11	**FAT2**	**Ebbsfleet United**	**A**	**680**	**L 0 - 1**		
18	NLN	York City	H	4019	W 1 - 0	Marriott 67	1
25	NLN	Blyth Spartans	A	686	W 3 - 0	Marriott 13 19 McAuley 61	1
Feb 1	NLN	Kidderminster Harriers	H	1678	L 0 - 2		1
18	NLN	Chester	A	1736	L 2 - 3	Barrows 25 Henderson 61	2
Mar 3	NLN	Leamington	A	365	D 0 - 0		2
7	NLN	Gateshead	A	1084	W 2 - 1	Power 15 81	2
10	NLN	Bradford (Park Avenue)	H	1220	L 0 - 1		2
14	NLN	Guiseley	H	1432	L 0 - 1		2

GOALSCORERS	SG	CSG	Pens	Hat tricks	Total		SG	CSG	Pens	Hat tricks	Total
Marriott	22	5	3		30	Clunan	1	1			1
Gash	9	3			10	Fox	1	1			1
Hednerson	6	1			7	Jarvis	1	1			1
Carey	5	2			5	Kelly	1	1			1
McAuley	4	1			4						
Barrows	3	1			3						
Payne	3	1			3						
Richards	3	1			3						
Jones	2	1			2						
Power	1	1			2						

Street A	McAuley R	Fryatt R	Jones A	Fox N	Hednerson C	Clunan M	Smith C	Jarvis R	Gash M	Marriott A	Richards J	Kelly S	Hawkins R	Carey S	Payne A (L)	Barrows R	Stewart N	Bastock P	Gilbert O	Taylor	Ward T	Limb H	Power S (L)	Southwell D	No.
x	xs	x	x	x	xs	x		x	xs	x	x	sx	sx	sx	s	s									1
x	xs	x	x	x	xs	x		x	xs	x	x	sx	sx	s	sx	s									2
x	x	x	x	x	xs	x		x	xs	x	xs	sx	sx	sx	s	s									3
x	xs	x	x	x	xs	x		sx	x	x	xs	sx	s		sx	s									4
x	x	sx	x	x	x		s	x	x	x	x	sx	xs	s		xs	s								5
x	x	x	x	x	xs	x		xs	x	x	sx	sx		sx	xs	s	s								6
x	x	x	x	x	sx	xs			x	x	x	sx	xs		sx	xs	s	s							7
x	x	x	x	x	x	xs			x	x		sx	xs		sx	xs	sx	s	s						8
x	x	x	x	x	xs	x			x	x	x	sx	s		s	xs	sx	s							9
x	x	x	x	x	xs	x		xs	x	x	sx	sx		sx	xs	s	s								10
x		x	x	xs	sx	x	x	xs	x	x	x	xs		sx	s	sx	s								11
x		x	s	x	xs	xs	x	s	x	x	x	sx		xs	sx	x	sx	s							12
x		x	x	sx	x		x	xs		x	sx	xs		x	x	x	s								13
x	x		x	x	xs	xs	x	xs	x	x	sx	s		sx	x	sx	s								14
x	x		sx	xs	s		x		x	x	x	x		xs	x	x	sx	s							15
x	x		x	x	x	x	xs		x	x	xs	sx		s	sx	x	x	s	s						16
x	x		x	xs	xs	x			x	x	sx	xs		sx	xs	sx	x	sx	s	s	s				17
x	x		x	x	xs	x		xs	x	x	x	sx	sx	s	s	x	s								18
x	x		x	x	xs	x		x	x	xs	x	sx	s	sx	s	x	s								19
x	x		x	xs	xs	x		xs	x	x	sx	sx	sx	s	s					x					20
x	x		s	x	xs	xs			x	x	x	sx	sx	xs	sx	x	s			x					21
x	x		sx	x	xs	x		s		x	xs	x	sx	x	s		s			x					22
x	x		x	x	s	s		x	x	x	x	x	s	x	s	x		s							23
x	x		x	x	xs	s		s	x	x	x	xs	sx	sx	s	x		s							24
x	x		sx	x	xs	x		xs	x	x	x	s		sx	x		xs								25
x	x		x	x	x	xs		s	x	x	x	sx	xs	sx	x		s								26
x	x		x	x		xs		sx	x	x	x	xs	xs	sx	sx	x		s							27
x	x		x	xs	x		x	x	x	x	xs	sx	sx	sx	s	xs	s			sx					28
x	x		x	x	sx		xs	x	x	x	sx	xs	xs	xs	s	s				x					29
x	x		x	x	x		x	x	x	x	xs	s	sx	s	s			s	s						30
x		x	xs	xs			x	xs	x		sx	x	x	x	sx	s		x	sx						31
x		x	x	x		x	x	sx	xs		s	xs	xs	x	x	sx			sx						32
x	x		x	s	x		x	x	x	x	xs	s	s	s	sx	x			x						33
x	x		x	x	xs		x	x	x	x	xs	sx	s	sx	s				xs	xs					34
x	x		x	xs	xs		x	xs	x	x	x	s	sx	sx	s			x	sx						35
x	x		x	sx	xs		x	x	x	x	xs	s	s	s	x				sx						36
x	x		x	s	x		x	s	sx	x	x	xs	sx		sx	x		xs	xs						37
x	x		x		xs		x	x	x	xs	s	sx	sx	x		s		xs	xs						38
x	x		x		sx		x	x	x	x	sx	xs	s	xs		s		xs	xs						39
x	x		s	x	xs			sx	x	x	s	sx		x	x		xs			sx	xs				40
40	32	12	34	27	9	16	19	14	35	34	23	2	1	3	6	22	0	0	0	5	0	2	0		x
0	3	0	0	7	23	7	1	12	0	5	4	13	3	7	8	2	0	0	0	3	0	3	2		xs
0	0	1	3	2	4	0	0	3	3	0	12	16	12	19	9	4	5	0	0	0	1	2	1	5	sx
0	0	0	3	2	3	2	0	5	0	0	0	7	10	7	17	7	14	11	1	1	3	1	0	0	s

GOALKEEPERS	CS	CCS
Street	12	4

x - Played full 90 minutes
xs - Substituted off
sx - Substituted on
s - Non-playing Substitute

LEAMINGTON MATCH RESULTS 2019-20

Date	Comp	Opponents	H/A	Att:	Result	Goalscorers	Pos
Aug 3	NLN	Kidderminster Harriers	A	1551	D 2 - 2	March 41 (pen) Anderson 86	
6	NLN	Brackley Town	H	608	W 2 - 0	Lane 17 Murphy 71	4
10	NLN	Curzon Ashton	H	385	D 1 - 1	March 35 (pen)	
13	NLN	Boston United	A	1083	L 0 - 1		
17	NLN	York City	A	2258	L 0 - 2		16
24	NLN	Kettering Town	H	575	W 3 - 1	Edwards 36 March 39 (pen) 48	
26	NLN	AFC Telford United	A	1012	W 3 - 1	March 42 Shamsi 66 90+2	
31	NLN	Blyth Spartans	H	495	W 2 - 0	March 63 (pen) 75	6
Sep 7	NLN	Altrincham	A	1025	L 0 - 5		10
14	NLN	Farsley Celtic	H	465	L 0 - 3		13
21	FAC2Q	Chasetown	H	395	D 2 - 2	March 16 (pen) 56	
24	FAC2Qr	Chasetown	A	339	W 2 - 1	March 90+3 Lane 117 (aet)	
28	NLN	Chester	A	1853	D 3 - 3	March 15 Edwards 49 Anderson 78	13
Oct 1	NLN	Hereford	H	607	L 0 - 2		
5	FAC3Q	Darlington	H	605	L 0 - 2		
12	NLN	Alfreton Town	H	521	L 0 - 1		16
Nov 2	NLN	Southport	A	947	L 1 - 4	March 48 (pen)	17
12	NLN	King's Lynn Town	A	871	L 2 - 5	English 40 Edwards 86	
16	NLN	Bradford (Park Avenue)	A	442	W 3 - 0	March 8 11 (pen) 50	18
23	FAT3Q	Spennymoor Town	H	275	W 2 - 1	Taylor 18 Edwards 83	
30	NLN	Guiseley	H	522	D 2 - 2	Clarke 6 March 28	17
Dec 3	NLN	Darlington	A	485	W 3 - 0	Edwards 16 Mace 57 Carline 77	15
7	NLN	Spennymoor Town	H	359	D 2 - 2	Anderson 1 March 76 (pen)	14
17	FAT1	AFC Telford United	A	352	W 5 - 0	Carline 10 79 March 57 (pen) 59 62	
21	NLN	Farsley Celtic	A	378	L 1 - 2	March 11	
26	NLN	Gloucester City	H	535	W 3 - 0	Edwards 23 March 29 Dunbar 89	
28	NLN	Hereford	A	1930	W 2 - 1	Hall 19 (og) Anderson 47	
Jan 1	NLN	Gloucester City	A	370	L 1 - 2	Edwards 62	
4	NLN	Altrincham	H	615	L 0 - 1		15
11	FAT2	Kingstonian	A	529	D 1 - 1	Saraiva 56 (og)	
14	FAT2r	Kingstonian	H	308	W 1 - 0	Edwards 31	
18	NLN	Chester	H	865	D 0 - 0		13
21	NLN	Gateshead	H	310	D 0 - 0		13
25	NLN	Spennymoor Town	A	1003	L 0 - 2		14
Feb 1	NLN	Gateshead	A	806	L 2 - 4	Edwards 11 Taylor 86	15
8	FAT3	Concord Rangers	A	417	D 2 - 2	Morley 60 Maycock 105 (Lost 3-4 on pens aet)	
18	NLN	Alfreton Town	A	283	L 0 - 1		
22	NLN	Southport	H	458	W 1 - 0	Parker 84	16
Mar 3	NLN	King's Lynn Town	H	365	D 0 - 0		16
7	NLN	Guiseley	A	584	L 0 - 3		17

GOALSCORERS	SG	CSG	Pens	Hat tricks	Total		SG	CSG	Pens	Hat tricks	Total
March	15	4	9		22	English	1	1			1
Edwards	9	1			9	Mace	1	1			1
Anderson	4	1			4	Maycock	1	1			1
Carline	2	1			3	Morley	1	1			1
Lane	2	1			2	Murphy	1	1			1
Opponent	2	1			2	Parker	1	1			1
Shamsi	1	1			2						
Taylor	2	1			2						
Clarke	1	1			1						
Dunbar	1	1			1						

Weaver J (L)	Mace J	Gudger C	Keane C	English J	Clarke J	Gittings C	Lane J	Edwards J	Murphy J (L)	March J	Anderson K	Mussa R	Shamsi R	Hood J	King R	Taylor C	Dunbar K	Carline G (L)	James T	Newey B (Gk)	Naylor M	Flanagan R	Morley S	Walters D (L)	Nicholson S	Maycock C (L)	Rawlings R	Martin J	Allen J (Gk)	McFarlane K	Bremang D (L)	Parker J	Storer J	Meredith D (L)	Gwilliams L (Gk)	No.
x	x	x	xs	x	x	xs	x	x	x	xs	sx	sx	sx	s	s																					1
x	x	x	sx	x	x	xs	x	x	xs	x	xs	sx	s	s	sx																					2
x	x	x	sx	x	x	x	x	x	xs	xs	sx	s	sx	sx	s																					3
x	x			x	x	xs	x	x	x	xs	xs	s	sx	x	sx	sx	s																			4
x	xs	x		xs	xs	x	x	x	x	x	sx	x	s	x	sx	sx	s																			5
x	sx	xs			x	s	x	x		x	x	xs	sx	x	sx	s	xs	x																		6
x	x		x		x	xs	x	x		x	x	s	sx	s	sx	sx	xs	x																		7
x	x	xs		x	x	x	x		xs	x	s	s	sx	sx		sx	xs	x																		8
x	x		x		xs	x	x	x	sx	x	xs	sx	x	s		s	xs	x	s																	9
x	x	sx		x	x	x	xs		x	xs	sx	sx	x		s	xs	x	s																		10
x	x		x	s	x	xs	x	x		x	xs	sx	sx	x		s	x		s	s	s															11
x	x		xs	sx	x		x	x		x	sx	sx	xs	x		sx	xs		sx	s																12
x	x		sx	x	x	s	xs	x		x	x			s	x	xs	sx	x					s													13
x	x		s	x		xs	sx	x		x	x			sx	x	sx	xs			s			xs	x												14
x	x		sx	x		x	x	x		x	xs	s	sx	x		xs	s			s			xs			sx	s									15
x	x			x	xs	s	sx	x			x			x		s	sx	x		s			xs	x												16
x	x			x	xs	xs	s			x	sx	s		x		s	sx	x					x	x		x										17
x	x			xs	xs	sx	x	x	s	x	sx					s	sx	x					x	xs		x										18
x	x			x	x	sx	x		xs	s	xs	xs				sx	sx	x					x	s		x										19
x	x			x	x	x	x		x					s		x	x	s	s	s			x					s								20
x	x			x	x	x	x			xs	xs	sx				sx	s	x					x	s		x	s									21
x	x			xs	x	sx	x		xs	xs	s	xs	xs			s	sx	x					x	x		x										22
x	x			x	x	sx	x	sx	x		x					sx	s	x					xs			xs		s								23
x	x			x		xs	x	x	sx	xs	xs					sx	sx	x					x	s		x			s							24
x	x			x	s	xs	x	x	x		x					sx	s	x					x	sx		xs										25
x	x			x	sx	x	x	x	sx	xs	s					sx	x						x	xs		xs		s								26
x	x			x	x		x	x	xs	s	x					sx	sx		s				x	xs		xs		sx								27
x	x			x	x	xs	x	x	xs							sx	sx						x	x		xs		s	s							28
x	x			x	x	xs	x	x	sx							sx	sx						x	xs		xs		s	s							29
x	x			x	x	sx	x	x	x	s						x	s	s					x	xs		xs	s		s	sx						30
x	x			x	x	sx	x	x	s			xs				x	sx						x			xs	s		s	sx	xs					31
x	x			x	xs	sx	x	x	s		x					xs	sx						x			x		s		s	x					32
x	x			x		x	x	x		xs						xs	sx	s					x			x		s		sx	xs	sx				33
x	x			x		xs	x	x		sx						sx	xs	s					x			x		s		sx	xs	x				34
x	x			x		x	x	xs		xs						sx	sx						x	s		x		sx		s	xs	x				35
x	x			x		x	x	x			x					x	xs	s	s				x			x		x	s		s	s	sx			36
x	x			s	x	x	x			xs						sx	sx						x			x		x	x	s		xs	xs	sx		37
x	x			sx	x	x	x			sx						sx	s						x	xs		xs		x			x	xs	s			38
	x			x	sx	x	x			sx						sx	s						x	xs		x		x			xs	xs	s	x		39
x	xs			s	xs	sx	x	x			x					sx							x	s		xs		x			x	x	sx			40
39	37	4	3	26	22	13	36	34	3	16	13	0	0	11	0	4	2	16	0	0	0	0	24	4	0	13	0	4	0	0	1	4	1	0	1	x
0	2	1	3	2	7	12	1	4	5	9	17	2	1	0	0	4	9	0	0	0	0	2	1	8	0	10	0	0	0	0	0	4	2	3	0	xs
0	1	0	5	1	2	10	2	0	6	0	9	6	11	2	5	20	16	0	1	0	0	0	2	0	0	0	2	0	4	0	1	1	2	0	0	sx
0	0	0	1	2	2	3	1	0	6	2	1	6	3	4	2	8	9	0	8	7	2	1	0	5	1	0	5	7	5	4	1	0	0	2	0	s

GOALKEEPERS	CS	CCS
Weaver	10	3
Gwilliams*	1	1

x - Played full 90 minutes
xs - Substituted off
sx - Substituted on
s - Non-playing Substitute

SOUTHPORT MATCH RESULTS 2019-20

Date	Comp	Opponents	H/A	Att:	Result	Goalscorers	Pos
Aug 3	NLN	Gateshead	A	879	D 0 - 0		
6	NLN	Curzon Ashton	H	1120	D 0 - 0		15
10	NLN	Guiseley	H	937	W 3 - 0	Sampson 1 Correia 15 Glynn 50	
13	NLN	Farsley Celtic	A	389	W 3 - 0	Morgan 7 Green 29 Correia 43	
17	NLN	Darlington	A	1331	L 0 - 2		7
24	NLN	AFC Telford United	H	910	L 0 - 1		
26	NLN	Alfreton Town	A	507	L 0 - 2		
31	NLN	Kettering Town	H	825	D 1 - 1	McGrath 20 (og)	15
Sep 3	NLN	Altrincham	H	904	W 2 - 1	Correia 32 Glynn 44	12
7	NLN	York City	A	2748	D 1 - 1	Morgan 9	12
14	NLN	Blyth Spartans	H	887	W 2 - 0	Mohammed 66 Morgan 71	9
21	FAC2Q	Scarborough Athletic	H	875	W 5 - 2	Sampson 13 54 58 Mohammed 39 Newell 67	
28	NLN	Boston United	A	1021	L 0 - 2		12
Oct 5	FAC3Q	Farsley Celtic	A	411	W 5 - 0	Atkinson 18 (og) Sampson 64 Benjamin 66 Green 72 Morgan 83	
12	NLN	Brackley Town	H	1047	W 1 - 0	Morgan 64 (pen)	11
19	FAC4Q	Altrincham	H	1507	L 1 - 3	Mohammed 88	
22	NLN	Hereford	H	604	W 3 - 2	Mohammed 10 Morgan 69 Green 81	
26	NLN	Bradford (Park Avenue)	A	418	W 3 - 0	Astles 29 Green 65 Morgan 75	4
Nov 2	NLN	Leamington	H	947	W 4 - 1	Morgan 1 86 90+2 (pen) Bauress 13	3
9	NLN	Spennymoor Town	A	1333	L 0 - 1		
16	NLN	King's Lynn Town	H	1257	L 1 - 2	Green 3	6
23	FAT3Q	Colne	A	312	W 3 - 2	Green 45 Bauress 71 Morgan 90+1	
30	NLN	Kidderminster Harriers	A	1206	W 1 - 0	Green 73	4
Dec 7	NLN	Gloucester City	H	815	W 1 - 0	Bauress 36	4
14	FAT1	South Shields	A	776	D 2 - 2	Sampson 14 Correia 81	
17	FAT1r	South Shields	H	372	W 3 - 1	Bauress 17 Astles 72 Sampson 86	
21	NLN	Blyth Spartans	A	587	W 4 - 1	Bauress 3 Morgan 37 Sampson 45+1 Astles 59	
26	NLN	Chester	H	1830	L 1 - 3	Astles 21	
28	NLN	Altrincham	A	1519	L 0 - 3		
Jan 1	NLN	Chester	A	1928	L 0 - 4		
4	NLN	York City	H	1144	L 0 - 2		8
11	FAT2	AFC Fylde	A	907	L 1 - 4	Sampson 39	
18	NLN	Boston United	H	883	L 1 - 3	Newell 79	12
25	NLN	Gloucester City	A	334	W 1 - 0	Green 57	10
Feb 1	NLN	Bradford (Park Avenue)	H	809	D 3 - 3	Newell 45 65 Bauress 51	12
8	NLN	Hereford	A	1712	D 2 - 2	Newell 43 Sampson 85	
18	NLN	Brackley Town	A	350	D 1 - 1	Doyle 90+5	
22	NLN	Leamington	A	458	L 0 - 1		12
Mar 7	NLN	Kidderminster Harriers	H	903	L 1 - 2	Morgan 18	12

GOALSCORERS	SG	CSG	Pens	Hat tricks	Total		SG	CSG	Pens	Hat tricks	Total
Morgan	11	3	2	1	13	Benjamin	1	1			1
Sampson	8	3	1		10	Doyle	1	1			1
Green	8	3			8						
Bauress	6	2			6						
Newell	4	2			5						
Astles	4	3			4						
Correia	4	2			4						
Mohammed	4	2			4						
Glynn	2	1			2						
Opponent	2	1			2						

Hanford D	Winnard D	Parry A	Astles R	Ogle R (L)	Mohammed Z (L)	Morgan D	Bauress B	Sampson J	Charles D	Green D	Correia R	Albinson C (Gk)	Glynn K (L)	Homson-Smith M	Benjamin R	Doyle J	Woods C	Lacey P	Newell G	Wood M	Richards E	Carden A	Oliver C	Servuts E	Dunn J (L)	Sanders J (L)	Anson A	No.
x	x	x	x	x	x	x	x	x	xs	x	sx	s	s	s														1
x	x		x	x	s	x	xs	xs	x		sx	s	xs	sx	x	x	sx											2
x	x		x	x	x	x		x		sx	xs	s	xs	x	s	s	sx	xs										3
x	x		x	s	x	xs	x	x		xs	xs	s		sx	x	x	sx	sx										4
x	x		x	x	xs	x	x	x		sx	x	s	xs		sx	sx	s	xs										5
x	xs	s	x	x	sx	x	x	x		x	xs	s		s	x	x	sx											6
x		x	x	x	x	s	x		sx	sx	s	x	xs	xs	sx	xs												7
x		s	x	x	x	x	x		xs	x	s	sx	x	x	s													8
x	x	sx	x	xs	sx	x	x	x		sx	xs	s	sx		x	x	s											9
x	x	sx	x		x	x	x	xs		sx	x	s	sx		x	x	s	s										10
s	xs	s	x	x	sx	x	x		xs	x	x	xs		x	x	sx	sx											11
		x	x	x	x		xs		xs	x	xs				sx	sx	sx											12
s		x	x	x	x	xs	x	x		s	xs	x	xs	x		sx	sx	sx										13
	x		x	x		x	x	x		x		x		x		sx												14
s	x	xs	x	x	s	x	x	x		x	xs	x		sx	x	sx	sx											15
s	xs	s	x	x	sx	x	x	x		xs	xs	x	sx	s	x	x	sx											16
s		sx	x	xs	x	x	x	x		sx		x	s	s	x	x	xs		x									17
s	x	s		x	x	x	xs		xs	sx	x	sx		x	x				x									18
s	x	s		x	xs	xs		xs	x	x	sx		x	x	sx			x	sx									19
s	x		x	x	x	sx		x	xs	x	xs		x	x	sx			s										20
s	x		x	x	xs	x		x	xs	x	sx	xs	x	sx		s			sx									21
s	x		x		x	x	sx	x		x	sx	x		x	x	xs		xs		s								22
s	x		x		x	x	x	x		xs	sx	x		x	x	xs		xs		sx								23
s	x		x		x	x				sx	x	x		x	x	xs		xs	s									24
s	x		x		xs	x	x	x		sx	sx	x	s		x	x	xs		xs		sx							25
s	x		x		s	x	xs	x		s	x	x	s		x	x	sx		x		x							26
s	x		x		x	xs	xs			xs	x	x		x	x	sx		xs		sx								27
s	x		x		x	xs	x			xs	sx	x		x	x	sx		xs		sx								28
s	xs		x	sx	s	x		xs		sx	x	x		xs	x	x	sx		x		x							29
	x		x	x	x	xs	x		x	x	x		sx	x	xs	s			xs		sx							30
s			x	x	x	x	xs	x		x	xs	x		s	x		s	sx	sx		x							31
s	x	s	x	x	x	x	x	x		xs	s	x		x		sx		xs		sx								32
	s	s	x	x	x	x	xs	x		xs		x		sx	x	sx	x		x									33
x	x		x	sx	x	x	x	x			s			x	x	s	s		x									34
x	s	x	x	x	s	x	x	x			s		x	xs	xs	x			sx	sx								35
x	x	sx	x	x	xs	x	s	x			s		x	x	sx	xs		x		sx								36
x	xs	xs	x	x		s	sx	x			s		s	x	x	x		x		sx	x							37
x	xs	s	x	x	sx	s	sx	x			s		x	x	xs		x			x								38
x	s	s	x	x	s	x		x			s		xs	x	sx	x			x		x	x						39
16	25	2	39	22	23	33	20	29	1	10	7	23	1	1	30	27	1	0	5	5	0	0	9	0	0	3	1	x
0	6	2	0	2	3	4	9	7	1	11	11	0	9	2	3	2	7	2	1	8	0	0	0	0	0	0	0	xs
0	0	4	0	2	5	0	3	1	0	8	11	0	6	4	3	2	22	4	4	1	1	0	9	0	3	0	0	sx
19	2	12	0	1	6	2	3	0	0	2	2	16	6	8	2	1	7	1	2	0	0	1	1	1	0	0	0	s

GOALKEEPERS	CS	CCS
Albinson*	6	2
Hanford	5	4

x - Played full 90 minutes
xs - Substituted off
sx - Substituted on
s - Non-playing Substitute

SPENNYMOOR TOWN MATCH RESULTS 2019-20

Date	Comp	Opponents	H/A	Att:	Result	Goalscorers	Pos
Aug 3	NLN	Hereford	A	2707	D 2 - 2	Johnson 61 Taylor 75	
13	NLN	Guiseley	A	774	L 1 - 3	Sykes-Kenworthy 34 (og)	
17	NLN	Farsley Celtic	A	424	L 0 - 1		20
24	NLN	York City	H	1563	L 1 - 4	McKenna 45	
26	NLN	Curzon Ashton	A	276	D 1 - 1	Taylor 71	
31	NLN	Chester	H	1049	W 2 - 1	Johnson 51 Taylor 90+2	19
Sep 3	NLN	Gatehead	A	1337	L 0 - 1		19
7	NLN	King's Lynn Town	H	1063	D 2 - 2	Boyes 26 Roberts 65	19
10	NLN	Blyth Spartans	H	1217	W 5 - 0	Brogan 14 Boyes 17 Johnson 51 82 Roberts 56	19
14	NLN	Bradford (Park Avenue)	A	402	D 1 - 1	Boyes A 90+5	18
21	**FAC2Q**	**Lancaster City**	**A**	**294**	**W 5 - 0**	**Johnson 15 Roberts 25 Taylor 61 71 Anderson 86**	
28	NLN	Kidderminster Harriers	H	1036	W 2 - 1	Ramshaw 54 Taylor 90	17
Oct 5	**FAC3Q**	**Ashton United**	**A**	**283**	**W 6 - 2**	**Taylor 4 47 64 76 Ramshaw 43 Anderson 84**	
12	NLN	Kettering Town	A	752	W 2 - 0	Taylor 5 47	14
19	**FAC4Q**	**Chorley**	**A**	**895**	**L 0 - 2**		
26	NLN	Gloucester City	H	928	W 5 - 1	Henry 2 Taylor 10 Roberts 61 Chandler 72 Hall 88	12
Nov 2	NLN	Alfreton Town	A	412	W 2 - 0	Ramshaw 25 61	8
5	NLN	Brackley Town	A	330	D 0 - 0		8
9	NLN	Southport	H	1333	W 1 - 0	Taylor 65	
12	NLN	Boston United	H	930	W 2 - 1	Roberts 25 Henry 65	
16	NLN	AFC Telford United	A	1190	D 2 - 2	Taylor 12 (pen) Roberts 24	4
23	**FAT3Q**	**Leamington**	**A**	**275**	**L 1 - 2**	**Taylor**	
Dec 7	NLN	Leamington	A	359	D 2 - 2	Ramshaw 22 Hall 29	6
21	NLN	Bradford (Park Avenue)	H	1097	W 3 - 0	Ramshaw 35 Anderson 71 86	
26	NLN	Darlington	A	2204	L 1 - 2	Taylor 29	
28	NLN	Gateshead	H	1504	L 1 - 3	Ramshaw 30	
Jan 1	NLN	Darlington	H	2260	W 3 - 1	Roberts 19 McKenna 85 Boyes 89	
4	NLN	King's Lynn Town	A	1439	L 0 - 3		5
11	NLN	Kettering Town	H	1072	L 1 - 2	Taylor 59	7
18	NLN	Kidderminster Harriers	A	1259	D 1 - 1	Ramshaw 36	8
25	NLN	Leamington	H	1003	W 2 - 0	McKenna 33 Taylor 80	7
Feb 1	NLN	Gloucester City	A	236	W 2 - 1	Taylor 29 Roberts 45	8
8	NLN	Brackley Town	H	1035	D 0 - 0		
11	NLN	Altrincham	H	869	W 3 - 2	Roberts 7 Ramshaw 54 Buddle 67	
22	NLN	Alfreton Town	H	1000	W 5 - 0	Taylor 4 (pen) Roberts 47 Buddle 78 Ramshaw 83 90	7
29	NLN	AFC Telford United	H	1077	D 3 - 3	Taylor 14 Roberts 49 Horby-Forbes 90+5	7
Mar 7	NLN	Altrincham	A	1255	L 1 - 4	Hornby-Forbes 51	8
14	NLN	Hereford	H	1259	W 4 - 0	Taylor 7 (pen) 88 Horby-Forbes 21 Anderson 54	6

GOALSCORERS	SG	CSG	Pens	Hat tricks	Total		SG	CSG	Pens	Hat tricks	Total
Taylor	18	4	3		24	Henry	2	1			2
Ramshaw	9	2			11	Brogan	1	1			1
Roberts	11	3			11	Chandler	1	1			1
Anderson	4	1			5	Opponents	1	1			1
Johnson	4	1			5						
Boyes	4	3			4						
Horby-Forbes	3	3			3						
McKenna	3	1			3						
Buddle	2	2			2						
Hall	2	1			2						

Gould M	Curtis J	Magnay C	Buddle N	Chandler J	McKenna B	Johnson A	Henry S	Ward D	Taylor G	Roberts J	Hall R	Boyes A	Williams C	Anderson M	Atkinson J (Gk)	Brogan S	Cogdon G	Ramshaw R	Greenwood R	Mason C	Hibbs J	Webb D	Earing J (L)	Butroid L (L)	Hornby-Forbes T	Kennedy J (L)	Whitehouse B (L)	Eve D (Gk)	Hindson C	No.
x	x	x	x	x	x	xs	x	x	x	x	sx	x	x	sx	s	s	s	s												1
x	x	x	x	x	xs	xs	x	x	x	xs	sx	sx	s	s	sx	s														2
x	x	x	x	x	xs	x		sx	x	xs			s	s	sx	s	x													3
x	x		x	x	x	xs	xs	sx	x	sx		s		x	xs	xs	s													4
x	x	x	x	x	x		s	x	x	sx			s	sx		x	xs	xs	s											5
x	x	x	xs	x	x	xs		sx	x	s		sx	sx	x		x	s	xs												6
x	x		x	x	x	xs	x	xs	xs	sx		sx	x			x	sx	x		s										7
x	x	x		x	x	sx	xs	xs		xs		x	x		s	sx	sx	x		s										8
x	xs	x	sx	x	xs	sx		xs		x		x	x		s		sx	x		s										9
x	x		x	x	x	x		xs		x	xs		x	xs		s	x	sx		s	sx	s								10
x	x	x	x	x	x	xs			sx	x		xs		sx		x	s	x						s						11
x	xs	x	x	x	x	x		sx	x	x	s	sx			xs		x				sx									12
x	x	x	x	xs	xs			x	xs	x		xs			sx		sx			sx	x		x							13
x	x	x	x	x	x			xs	x	x		s		s	sx		sx	x		x										14
x	x	x	x	x	xs		s	xs	x	xs			sx		sx		s	sx		x		x								15
x	x	x	x	xs	x		xs	sx	x	xs		sx	s			sx				x	s									16
x	x	x	x	x	xs		x		xs	xs	x	sx		sx	s		sx			x	s									17
x	x		x	x	xs			xs		x	x	sx	sx	s		s	sx	x			x									18
x	x		x	x				xs	s	x	x	sx	sx	sx		xs		s		sx	x	x								19
x	x		x	x	sx			x	s	x	x	sx		sx		xs		s		s	x	x								20
x	x		x	x	xs			x	sx	x	x	sx				s		s		s	x	x								21
x	x	x	x	x	xs	s		x	s	x	x	sx		sx				s		x	x									22
x	x	xs	x	x	x	s	xs			x	s	x	sx			s		sx		x										23
x	x	x	x	x	x		s			xs	sx	xs	xs	sx		sx	x			x		s			xs					24
x	x	x	x	x	x		xs			x	sx	xs	xs	sx		sx	xs			x		s			s					25
x	x		s	x	sx	sx	s			x	xs	sx		x		x				x	xs			xs						26
x	x	x	x	x	x		x	s	x			x	xs	sx		s		x			x			s						27
x	x	xs	x	x	xs		s	x				x	xs	sx		sx		x			s			sx						28
x	x		x	x	xs	xs			x	x		sx		xs				sx	x	x										29
x	x		x	x		xs	x			x		x	x	s		sx		x			s		s		x					30
x	x	x	x	x	x		s	x		x		x	x	sx				s		s			x		xs					31
x	x	x	x	x	xs		x			x		x	x	s		s		x					xs		sx					32
x	xs	x	xs	x		sx			x	x		sx				s	x	x								x	sx			33
x	x		x	xs	xs	x		x		x		s		s		x				s						x	x	s		34
x	x		x		xs	x		xs	xs	sx				s		x				s						x	x	sx	s	35
x	x	sx	x			s	x		x	x		s		xs		x	sx	x								x	xs		s	36
x		x	x		sx	x		x	xs	sx		sx		x	s	x	sx	x			s					x	x		s	37
s		x	x			x		x	xs	sx		sx		x	s	x	sx	s								x	xs	x	sx	38
37	34	24	32	29	17	3	17	4	29	8	1	3	4	2	0	16	0	32	0	11	5	0	0	3	7	4	0	1	0	x
0	2	2	2	3	14	7	7	5	5	23	2	1	1	7	0	2	1	2	0	0	1	0	2	0	1	2	0	0	0	xs
0	0	1	1	0	2	6	1	6	1	5	6	21	1	17	0	2	14	0	0	0	2	0	2	0	0	1	2	0	1	sx
1	0	0	1	0	0	7	4	3	0	2	1	12	5	8	9	6	8	0	1	16	2	2	3	0	0	0	1	3	0	s

GOALKEEPERS	CS	CCS
Gould	10	3
Eve*	1	1

x - Played full 90 minutes
xs - Substituted off
sx - Substituted on
s - Non-playing Substitute

YORK CITY MATCH RESULTS 2019-20

Date	Comp	Opponents	H/A	Att	Result	Goalscorers	Pos
Aug 3	NLN	Altrincham	A	1879	W 3 - 1	Jones J 43 (og) Tait 49 Burrow 60	
6	NLN	Farsley Celtic	H	2938	D 0 - 0		6
10	NLN	Brackley Town	H	2039	W 1 - 0	Bond 56	
13	NLN	Blyth Spartans	A	1389	W 3 - 0	Griffiths 18 Kempster 24 Green 52	
17	NLN	Leamington	H	2258	W 2 - 0	Kempster 21 Burrow 52	1
24	NLN	Spennymoor Town	A	1563	W 4 - 1	Newton 19 Curtis 24 (og) Griffiths 43 Moke 80	
26	NLN	Gateshead	H	3157	D 1 - 1	Burrow 4	
31	NLN	Gloucester City	A	652	W 3 - 2	Kempster 6 49 Burrow 39	1
Sep 3	NLN	Guiseley	A	1891	D 0 - 0		2
7	NLN	Southport	H	2748	D 1 - 1	Kempster 45	2
14	NLN	Darlington	A	2023	W 2 - 0	Kempster 58 McLaughlin 86	1
21	FAC2Q	Irlam	A	798	W 2 - 0	Kempster 33 McFarlane 77	
28	NLN	King's Lynn Town	H	3082	W 3 - 0	Bond 22 Ferguson 72 Tait 86	1
Oct 5	FAC3Q	Buxton	A	901	W 2 - 1	Caulcott 49 (og) Dyer 79	
12	NLN	AFC Telford United	A	1305	D 1 - 1	Burrow 56	1
19	FAC4Q	Stockport County	H	2870	W 2 - 0	Kempster 27 Newton 29	
26	NLN	Chester	A	3653	W 1 - 0	Maguire 57	1
29	NLN	Boston United	H	2768	W 2 - 1	Kempster 35 Burrow 50	1
Nov 2	NLN	Kidderminster Harriers	H	2586	D 1 - 1	Griffiths 38	1
10	FAC1	Altrincham	H	3222	L 0 - 1		
16	NLN	Curzon Ashton	A	809	L 0 - 1		2
23	FAT3Q	Altrincham	H	974	L 0 - 1		
30	NLN	Alfreton Town	H	2306	W 1 - 0	Burrow 13	2
Dec 3	NLN	Hereford	A	1552	D 2 - 2	Kempster 9 Burrow 90	2
7	NLN	Kettering Town	A	859	D 0 - 0		2
21	NLN	Darlington	H	3187	L 0 - 1		2
26	NLN	Bradford (Park Avenue)	A	1127	W 2 - 0	Green 25 Burrow 50	2
28	NLN	Guiseley	H	3136	L 1 - 2	Green 14	2
Jan 1	NLN	Bradford (Park Avenue)	H	2477	W 2 - 1	Langstaff 13 Burrow 80	2
4	NLN	Southport	A	1144	W 2 - 0	Burrow 34 49	2
11	NLN	AFC Telford United	H	2299	W 2 - 0	Durrell 81 Burrow 89	2
18	NLN	King's Lynn Town	A	4019	L 0 - 1		2
25	NLN	Kettering Town	H	2767	W 1 - 0	Burrow 63	2
Feb 1	NLN	Chester	H	3543	W 4 - 2	Newton 9 Green 22 Willoughby 40 60	2
8	NLN	Boston United	A	2155	L 1 - 3	Willoughby 7	2
22	NLN	Kidderminster Harriers	A	1574	W 1 - 0	Maguire 46	1
29	NLN	Curzon Ashton	H	2354	D 1 - 1	Burrow 90+3	1
Mar 3	NLN	Hereford	H	2343	L 1 - 4	Kempster 28	1
7	NLN	Alfreton Town	A	802	W 3 - 1	Newton 8 79 Kempster 13	1
July 25	PO SF	Altrincham	H	0	L 0 - 2		

GOALSCORERS	SG	CSG	Pens	Hat tricks	Total		SG	CSG	Pens	Hat tricks	Total
Burrow	14	3			15	Durrell	1	1			1
Kempster	11	3			12	Dyer	1	1			1
Newton	4	1			5	Ferguson	1	1			1
Green	4	2			4	Langstaff	1	1			1
Griffiths	3	1			3	McFarlane*	1	1			1
Opponent	3	1			3	McLaughlin	1	1			1
Willoughby	2	2			3	Moke	1	1			1
Bond	2	1			2						
Maguire	2	1			2						
Tait	2	1			2						

Jameson P	McNulty S	Newton S	Tait J	Ferguson D	Griffiths K	Bond A	Moke A	Burrow J	Maguire D	Kempster A	McLaughlin P	Green K	Langstaff M	Whitley R (Gk)	Spratt H	York W	Dyer N	King J	Jebson-King C	McFarlane K	Allan T	Durrell E	Willoughby K (L)	Jones S (L)	Buxton A (L)	Henderson E	No.
x	x	x	x	x	x	x	xs	x	xs	xs	sx	sx	sx	s	s												1
x	x	x	x	x	x	xs	x	xs		x	sx	xs	sx	s	s	sx											2
x	x	x	x	x	xs	x	xs	x	xs	x		sx	sx	s	s	sx											3
x	x	x	x	x	x	xs	x	x		xs		x	sx	s	s	s	sx										4
x	x	x	x	x	x	xs	x	x		x		xs	sx	s	s	s	sx										5
x	x	x	x	x	x	x	x	x		xs		xs	sx	s	s	s	sx										6
x	xs	x	x	x	x	x	x	x		x		xs	sx	s	sx	sx	s										7
x		x	x	x	x	x	x	x		x		x	s	s	s	s	s	x									8
x		x	x	x	xs	x	x			x		xs	sx	s	x	s	sx	s									9
x		x	x	x	xs	x	x			x		x	xs	s	x	sx	sx		s								10
x		x	x	x			x	x		x	xs	xs	sx	s	x	sx	xs	sx		s							11
s		x	x	xs		xs	x	sx		x	x		s	x	s	x	xs	s	sx	sx	x						12
x		x	x	x		xs	x	x		x	x	sx		s	x		x	s		s		s					13
s		x	x	x		s	x	x		sx	x	s		sx	x	s		s	x	s		xs	x	xs			14
x	x	x	x	x		xs	xs	x		x	xs	sx		s	s		s	x		sx		sx					15
x	x	x	x	x	x	x	x	x	xs	x	sx		s	s	s		s		s		s						16
x	x	x	x	x	x		x	x	x	xs	x		sx		s	s			s		s						17
x	x	x	x	x	x		x	x	xs	xs		sx		s			x	s		sx	s						18
x	x	x	x	x	x		x	x	xs	xs		sx		s			s	sx		s							19
x	x	x	x	x	xs	x	x	sx	xs	x		s	xs	sx	s	s		s		sx							20
x	x	x	xs	x	x	x		x		xs	sx	sx	sx	s	sx		s		xs								21
x		x		x	x	x	xs	sx	x		s	sx	xs	s	xs		s	x	s		sx						22
x	x	x	s	x	x	xs	x		xs	sx	sx	sx	s		x		xs										23
x	x	x	x	x	x	xs	x		x	s	x	s	s		x		sx										24
x	x	xs	x	x	x	s	s	x		x	x	x	s	s	sx		x										25
x	x	x	x	x	xs	xs	x		x	sx	sx	sx	s	s		x		xs									26
x	x	x	x	x	sx	x	x	s	xs	x	xs	xs	s		sx		sx										27
x	xs	x	x	x	x	s	x	x		sx	xs	x	x	sx	s		s										28
x	x	x	x	x	x	s	x	x		x	xs	x	s		s	s		sx									29
x	x	x	x	x	x	x	s	x		x	x	sx	s		s		s										30
x	x	x	x	x	x	xs	s	x		x	sx	x	sx	s		s		sx									31
x	x	x	x	x	xs	s	x	x	sx	xs	x	x	sx	s		s		s									32
x	xs	x	x	x	x	s	sx	x	xs	sx	x	sx		s		s	x										33
x	x	x	x	x	x	sx	x	x	sx	s	x	xs	s		s		xs										34
x	x	x	x	x	x	xs	xs	xs	sx	sx	xs	x		s		s		x									35
x	x	x	x	x	sx	x	x	sx	xs	sx	xs	x		s		s		xs									36
x	xs	x	x	x	x	xs	x	x	x	sx	s	sx		sx		s		xs									37
x		x	x	x	x	s	x	x	x	x	xs	xs		s		sx	sx	s									38
x	x	x	x	x	x	s	sx	x	xs	xs	x	x	s		s		sx	x									39
x	xs	x	x	x	x	sx	sx	sx	x	sx	xs	sx	sx	s	s		xs										40
38	24	40	35	39	27	16	29	33	2	22	12	12	1	2	4	1	4	4	0	0	2	1	2	0	1	0	x
0	5	0	0	0	1	6	9	7	3	10	12	7	12	3	0	1	0	2	0	0	1	0	4	2	1	0	xs
0	0	0	0	0	1	4	3	3	6	5	13	20	0	3	6	5	2	1	3	0	8	0	2	1	0	0	sx
2	0	0	2	0	0	10	0	0	0	1	1	5	1	7	31	14	8	6	15	2	5	0	8	0	0	1	s

GOALKEEPERS	CS	CCS
Jameson	16	4
Whitley	1	1

x - Played full 90 minutes
xs - Substituted off
sx - Substituted on
s - Non-playing Substitute

Alfreton Town v Gloucester City. Photos Bill Wheatcroft.

NATIONAL LEAGUE SOUTH

As at 15/03/2020	P	W	D	L	F	A	GD	Pts
1 Wealdstone	33	22	4	7	69	35	34	70
2 Havant & Waterlooville	34	19	10	5	64	37	27	67
3 Weymouth	35	17	12	6	60	35	25	63
4 Bath City	35	18	9	8	50	37	13	63
5 Slough Town	35	17	9	9	51	38	13	60
6 Dartford	34	16	8	10	60	46	14	56
7 Dorking Wanderers	35	14	8	13	58	56	2	50
8 Hampton & Richmond B	33	14	5	14	51	50	1	47
9 Maidstone United	33	12	9	12	48	44	4	45
10 Chelmsford City	34	11	11	12	55	56	-1	44
11 Hemel Hempstead T	34	12	8	14	36	43	-7	44
12 Chippenham Town	35	10	12	13	39	45	-6	42
13 Welling United	34	12	6	16	38	46	-8	42
14 Oxford City	34	11	9	14	47	60	-13	42
15 Eastbourne Borough	33	8	14	11	38	54	-16	38
16 Dulwich Hamlet	35	9	10	16	51	50	1	37
17 Concord Rangers	32	10	7	15	44	48	-4	37
18 Billericay Town	32	8	13	11	46	55	-9	37
19 St Albans City	35	9	10	16	41	54	-13	37
20 Tonbridge Angels	31	9	9	13	46	54	-8	36
21 Braintree Town	35	10	5	20	44	67	-23	35
22 Hungerford Town	33	8	4	21	38	64	-26	28

After Points Per Game	P	W	D	L	F	A	GD	PPG
1 Wealdstone	33	22	4	7	69	35	34	89.1
2 Havant & Waterlooville	34	19	10	5	64	37	27	82.8
3 Weymouth *	35	17	12	6	60	35	25	75.6
4 Bath City	35	18	9	8	50	37	13	75.6
5 Slough Town	35	17	9	9	51	38	13	72.0
6 Dartford	34	16	8	10	60	46	14	69.2
7 Dorking Wanderers	35	14	8	13	58	56	2	60.0
8 Hampton & Richmond B	33	14	5	14	51	50	1	59.8
9 Maidstone United	33	12	9	12	48	44	4	57.3
10 Chelmsford City	34	11	11	12	55	56	-1	54.4
11 Hemel Hempstead T	34	12	8	14	36	43	-7	54.4
12 Welling United	34	12	6	16	38	46	-8	51.9
13 Oxford City	34	11	9	14	47	60	-13	51.9
14 Chippenham Town	35	10	12	13	39	45	-6	50.4
15 Tonbridge Angels	31	9	9	13	46	54	-8	48.8
16 Concord Rangers	32	10	7	15	44	48	-4	48.6
17 Billericay Town	32	8	13	11	46	55	-9	48.6
18 Eastbourne Borough	33	8	14	11	38	54	-16	48.4
19 Dulwich Hamlet	35	9	10	16	51	50	1	44.4
20 St. Albans City	35	9	10	16	41	54	-13	44.4
21 Braintree Town	35	10	5	20	44	67	-23	42.0
22 Hungerford Town	33	8	4	21	38	64	-26	35.6

	1	2	3	4	5	6	7	8	9	10	11	12	13	14	15	16	17	18	19	20	21	22
1 Bath City		2-1	2-0		3-2	3-1	3-0	1-0	3-2	2-2	3-0		2-0	2-1	1-1	1-2		0-3	0-0	0-0		0-0
2 Billericay Town	1-1		2-1	1-1				2-2		1-0		0-1		3-0		1-1	2-2	3-2	3-3	3-1	2-1	1-1
3 Braintree Town	2-0	2-3		1-2		0-1		3-2	2-1	5-0	0-4	3-3	0-0	0-3	1-1	1-0	0-1	0-1	0-1	0-4		1-1
4 Chelmsford City	1-0	1-1	4-1		3-3	1-1	4-0	2-2	1-1	1-1	4-1		2-1	4-1		2-6	1-1			1-3	1-1	
5 Chippenham Town	1-3	2-0	1-2	2-1		3-0	1-5	0-2	2-2			0-0	2-2		1-0	1-1	0-3	2-1	2-1	1-1	0-0	1-0
6 Concord Rangers	0-1	4-1	2-2	2-1	0-1			0-2	3-3		5-0	0-2	0-0	3-1	0-2	0-1		2-1		3-3		3-0
7 Dartford		3-2	2-1	3-0	1-1	0-1		3-4	1-0	2-1	1-2	1-1	1-1		2-2	3-0	2-3	1-1	3-0	0-0	4-0	
8 Dorking Wanderers	0-0		4-4	2-0	1-0		2-3		0-0	4-0	0-1	1-2	3-1	1-0	3-1	0-2	3-5		3-1	2-2	2-0	1-0
9 Dulwich Hamlet	1-3	0-1	6-0	5-3	1-1	2-2	1-1				1-2	1-3	2-1	2-3	0-1		2-3	2-1	0-1	1-0	0-1	2-2
10 Eastbourne Borough	1-2	1-1		0-4	2-1	2-2	0-2	3-2	0-3		4-1		1-1		3-0	1-1	0-2	3-3	2-0		2-1	1-1
11 Hampton & Richmond Borough	0-0	1-1			1-0	2-3	1-2		0-3				3-4	1-2	7-1	2-1	1-1	1-2	2-1	2-0	1-1	2-3
12 Havant & Waterlooville	2-1		1-3	0-0	2-1	2-1		6-0	0-0	0-0	2-0		1-2	3-1	1-2		1-0	1-2		2-4	1-1	
13 Hemel Hempstead Town	2-1	3-0	0-3	2-0	0-1	1-0		1-0	1-0	1-1		1-2		4-1		1-1	1-0	1-1	0-3	0-2	0-1	
14 Hungerford Town	0-1		2-0	1-0	1-1		2-2	0-1	1-4	0-1	0-2	1-3			1-3	1-2	1-0	1-2	1-0		1-2	
15 Maidstone United	0-2	2-1	1-0	4-1	0-0			2-3	4-1	1-0	1-2	2-2	1-1			1-0	1-1	4-0	2-2		3-1	1-2
16 Oxford City	2-2	1-4		1-3	0-3	0-1	2-1	2-1		3-2	0-3	1-2	3-2	1-2			2-1	3-3	0-3	3-2		0-0
17 Slough Town	3-2	3-1	1-0	2-1			1-0	0-1		1-1	3-1	1-1	2-0	0-2		0-1		1-1	0-0	2-1	1-0	1-1
18 St Albans City	0-1		0-3	1-1	0-0	2-1	1-2	1-1		1-3	1-1	1-3	2-0	2-2	1-0	0-0			2-3	1-2	1-4	
19 Tonbridge Angels	3-2	5-1	1-2	3-2	1-0	3-2		1-2			1-3	0-2	1-1		4-4		2-1				1-1	
20 Wealdstone	7-0	3-0		0-1	1-0	3-0	4-1	3-1	2-1	2-0		1-4		3-1	2-1	1-0	2-1	1-0	3-1		1-0	
21 Welling United	0-3	2-0	6-2		1-0		0-3	2-1	0-0	0-0	0-1		2-0	3-2	1-0	3-1	1-2	0-1	4-2	1-2		1-3
22 Weymouth	1-1	0-0	3-0	4-1		3-0	3-1		1-1	2-2	2-1	0-1		2-1	5-1	2-1	2-0	0-1		3-4	1-0	

*Promoted to the National League via the play-offs.

BATH CITY MATCH RESULTS 2019-20

Date	Comp	Opponents	H/A	Att:	Result	Goalscorers	Pos
Aug 3	NLS	Braintree Town	H	784	W 2 - 0	Smith T 47 Stearn 50	
6	NLS	Weymouth	A	1615	D 1 - 1	Harvey 57 (pen)	5
10	NLS	Welling United	A	416	W 3 - 0	Hartridge 10 Harvey 23 (pen) Richards 43	
13	NLS	Hungerford Town	H	901	W 2 - 1	Smith H 38 Stearn 64	
17	NLS	Tonbridge Angels	H	832	D 0 - 0		3
24	NLS	Slough Town	A	734	L 2 - 3	Harvey 24 Richards 38	
26	NLS	Oxford City	H	1030	L 1 - 2	Richards 26	
31	NLS	Chelmsford City	A	595	L 0 - 1		10
Sep 3	NLS	Hampton & Richmond B.	H	707	W 3 - 0	Brunt 17 (pen) 71 Smith T 82	5
7	NLS	Billericay Town	A	949	D 1 - 1	Brunt 38 (pen)	9
14	NLS	Eastbourne Borough	H	1444	D 2 - 2	Stearn 25 Hamblin 85	10
21	FAC2Q	Swindon Supermarine	A	461	W 4 - 0	Brunt 35 Smith T 62 Watkins 68 Bower 87	
28	NLS	Hemel Hempstead Town	A	515	L 1 - 2	Brunt 33	11
Oct 5	FAC3Q	Billericay Town	A	678	L 2 - 4	Mann 11 Brunt 71	
12	NLS	Maidstone United	H	1387	D 1 - 1	Brunt 90+5	10
19	NLS	St Albans City	A	678	W 1 - 0	Smith T 26	8
26	NLS	Dorking Wanderers	H	760	W 1 - 0	Mann 54	7
Nov 2	NLS	Dulwich Hamlet	A	2816	W 3 - 1	Chilvers 30 Pearson 53 Smith T 90+1	6
9	NLS	Concord Rangers	H	820	W 3 - 1	Mann 6 Chilvers 40 Smith T 74	
16	NLS	Havant & Waterlooville	A	1460	L 1 - 2	Mann 14	5
23	FAT3Q	Gosport Borough	H	528	D 0 - 0		
27	FAT3Qr	Gosport Borough	A	306	W 3 - 2	Smith T 28 Watkins 31 Brunt 112 (aet)	
30	NLS	Dartford	H	794	W 3 - 0	Smith T 9 Watkins 27 35	5
Dec 7	NLS	Wealdstone	H	1203	D 0 - 0		5
17	FAT1	Sholing	H	401	W 2 - 0	Brunt 23 Watkins 59	
21	NLS	Eastbourne Borough	A	373	W 2 - 1	Smith T 88 Hartridge 90+2	
26	NLS	Chippenham Town	H	1397	W 3 - 1	Brunt 12 Mann 54 Raynes 79	
28	NLS	Hampton & Richmond B.	A	647	D 0 - 0		
Jan 1	NLS	Chippenham Town	A	1239	W 3 - 1	Brunt 45+1 Smith T 70 Britton 90	
4	NLS	Billericay Town	H	995	W 2 - 1	Artus 30 Stearn 90+1	2
11	FAT2	Concord Rangers	A	263	D 1 - 1	Smith T 79	
18	NLS	Hemel Hempstead Town	H	1095	W 2 - 0	Smith T 78 Stearn 84	2
25	NLS	Wealdstone	A	1343	L 0 - 7		4
28	FAT2r	Concord Rangers	H	437	L 1 - 2	Brunt 24 (pen)	
Feb 1	NLS	Dorking Wanderers	A	732	D 0 - 0		5
8	NLS	St Albans City	H	995	L 0 - 3		
15	NLS	Concord Rangers	A	212	W 1 - 0	Stearn 39	
18	NLS	Maidstone United	A	1450	W 2 - 0	Artus 16 Pearson 90+3	
22	NLS	Dulwich Hamlet	H	1047	W 3 - 2	Smith T 15 41 84	2
29	NLS	Braintree Town	A	410	L 0 - 2		4
Mar 7	NLS	Weymouth	H	1902	D 0 - 0		5
14	NLS	Hungerford Town	A	619	W 1 - 0	Mann 45	4
July 19	PO Q	Dorking Wanderers	H	0	L 1 - 2	Brunt 80 (pen)	

GOALSCORERS	SG	CSG	Pens	Hat tricks	Total		SG	CSG	Pens	Hat tricks	Total
Smith T	13	2		1	15	Pearson	2	1			2
Brunt	12	4	4		13	Bower	1	1			1
Mann	6	2			6	Britton	1	1			1
Stearn	6	1			6	Hamblin	1	1			1
Watkins	4	1			5	Raynes	1	1			1
Harvey	3	2	2		3	Smith H	1	1			1
Richards	3	2			3						
Artus	2	1			2						
Chilvers	2	2			2						
Hartridge	2	1			2						

Clarke R	Bower M	Hartridge A (L)	Smith H (L)	Smith T	Riley-Lowe C	Hamblin H (L)	Raynes J	Richards T	Watkins A	Harvey T	Steam R	Mann A	Simpson J	Harper A	Wiles-Richards H (Gk)	Pardington J (Gk)	Brunt R	Artus F	Rooney D	Edwards O (L)	Pearson S (L)	Eglin L	Ball D	Kensdale O (L)	Bowry D (L)	Chilvers N (L)	Britton L (L)	Smith Z (L)	Harper V (L)	Martin D (L)	James L	No.
x	x	x	x	xs	x	xs	x	x	xs	x	sx	sx	s	s	s																	1
	x	x	x	x	x	s	x	x	x	x	x	xs	sx	s	s	x																2
	s	x	x	x	x	x	x	x	xs	x		x	sx	s	s	x																3
	s	x	x	x	x	x	x	x	xs	xs	sx	xs	sx	s		x	sx															4
x	s	x	x	x	xs	x	x		sx	xs	xs	sx	s			sx																5
x	sx	x	x	x	x	xs	x	x	s		xs	xs	x			s	sx	sx														6
x	x	x		x	x	x	xs	xs	x		xs	s			sx		s															7
x	x	x		x	x	x	sx	xs			sx	xs	sx		x		xs															8
x	x	x		x	x	x	sx	sx			s		xs		x	xs	x															9
x	x	x	s	x	x	x	sx	sx			s		xs		xs	x																10
x	xs	x	sx	x	x	x	sx	sx			xs	s	s		x		xs	x														11
x	x	x		x	x	xs	x	sx	sx		xs	xs	sx	s		x		s	x													12
x	x	x		x	x		x	x	xs		x	x	s		x		s		sx	s												13
x	x	x		x	x		x	xs	sx		xs	x	sx	s		x	s			x		s										14
x	s	x		x	x	sx	x	x		x		xs	xs	x		x	s				s	x										15
x		xs	x		x		x	sx			s	sx			s		sx	x			x		s	x	x	x						16
x		xs	x		x		x	sx	xs		sx	x	s				sx	x			xs				x	x						17
x		xs	x		x		s	sx		sx	xs	s			x		sx	x			xs				x	x	x					18
x		xs	x		x		s	sx		s	xs	s			x		sx	x			x				x	x	x					19
x			x		x	s	xs	x		sx	x	x			s		x				x		x		x							20
x		xs	x		x		sx	x		sx	s	xs			s		sx	x			x				x	x	x					21
x		sx	x		xs	s	x	sx	xs		sx	xs	sx	xs		s	sx	x					x		x	x	xs	x				22
x		x	x		x			sx	xs	xs	sx	x			s		xs	xs					x		s	x	x	x	sx			23
x		x	x		s			x	x	xs	sx	x			s		xs						x		s	x	x	x	sx			24
x		xs	sx		x		sx	xs			s	x	sx	s		x		xs			s		x		s	x	x	x				25
x		x	xs		s		s	xs	x		sx	xs	sx				sx	xs		sx			x		x	x	x	sx				26
x		xs	x		x		sx	xs	s		x	x			xs		sx	xs		sx			x		x	x	sx					27
x		x	sx		x		s				xs	x	x				sx	x					x		x	x	sx					28
x		x	xs		x		sx				sx	xs	x				xs	x					x		x	x	sx					29
x			xs		x		x	x				sx		s			xs	xs			x				x	x	sx	sx				30
x		x	sx		x		s				sx	xs	s	s			x	x		x			xs		x	x		s				31
x		x	sx		x		s				sx	xs	s				x	xs		xs			x		x	x	sx					32
x		x	x								sx	xs	sx	s			xs	xs		x			x		x	x	sx					33
x		x	xs								sx	x	s	s			x	x		x	s	x		x	x							34
x		x	x		s						x	s	x	x			x	x		x	s	x		x	x			x				35
x		x	sx		x						sx	xs	s				x	xs		x			x		x	x	s		xs	sx		36
x		x	x		x						xs	x	s	s			s	x					x		x	x	s		sx			37
x		x	s		x						x	sx	s				s	x		xs			x		x	x				x		38
x		x	s		x						x	s	sx	xs			sx	xs		x	s		x		x	x				x		39
x		x	sx		xs						xs	s	sx	xs			x	x			x				x	x				x	sx	40
	sx	x	x		xs		sx				xs	s	sx	s			sx	s		x			x		x	xs				x	x	41
s		x	x		xs		x	s			sx	x	xs				sx	x		x		s	sx		x	x				x	x	42
x		x	xs				x	sx			sx	xs	s				sx	s		xs			x		x			sx			x	xs	43
37	7	38	8	34	26	7	36	13	2	4	3	18	0	0	4	2	12	18	0	4	13	0	22	7	26	24	0	0	1	6	2	x
0	1	0	0	9	5	4	2	3	12	3	8	18	0	0	0	0	9	10	4	0	6	0	1	0	1	2	0	0	0	0	1	xs
0	1	2	1	0	6	1	0	12	9	0	19	5	8	0	0	0	16	1	0	0	3	0	0	0	0	0	0	0	10	3	1	sx
1	4	0	1	0	4	3	0	6	3	0	6	1	22	3	36	3	3	4	2	0	0	5	4	3	0	1	1	1	0	0	0	s

GOALKEEPERS	CS	CCS
Clarke	15	3
Wiles-Richards	2	1
Pardington	1	1

x - Played full 90 minutes
xs - Substituted off
sx - Substituted on
s - Non-playing Substitute

BILLERICAY TOWN MATCH RESULTS 2019-20

Date	Comp	Opponents	H/A	Att:	Result	Goalscorers	Pos
Aug 3	NLS	Eastbourne Borough	H	824	W 1 - 0	Robinson 90+3	
6	NLS	Braintree Town	A	868	W 3 - 2	Rhead 15 (pen) Emmanuel 61 Wassmer 70	3
10	NLS	Chippenham Town	A	583	L 0 - 2		
13	NLS	Welling United	H	890	W 2 - 1	Parkes 19 Robinson 90 (pen)	
17	NLS	Hampton & Richmond B.	A	424	D 1 - 1	Emmanuel 51	6
24	NLS	St Albans City	H	806	W 3 - 2	Robinson 7 85 Diedhiou 34 (og)	
26	NLS	Hemel Hempstead	A	838	L 0 - 3		
31	NLS	Hungerford Town	H	716	W 3 - 0	Emmanuel 46 Parkes 55 (pen) Rhead 64	
Sep 2	NLS	Chelmsford City	A	1395	D 1 - 1	Emmanuel 70	2
7	NLS	Bath City	H	949	D 1 - 1	Deering 18	
14	NLS	Oxford City	A	309	D 2 - 2	Robinson 10 17	7
Harry Wheeler is sacked as manager, with Jamie O'Hara taking over.							
21	FAC2Q	**Basildon United**	H	1106	W 1 - 0	**Parkes 67**	
28	NLS	Dorking Wanderers	H	811	D 2 - 2	Emmanuel 65 Robinson 70	8
Oct 5	FAC3Q	**Bath City**	H	678	W 4 - 2	**(og) 16 Robinson 38 90+3 Parkes 46**	
12	NLS	Slough Town	A	1115	L 1 - 3	Alfa 76	8
19	FAC4Q	**Sutton United**	A	789	D 1 - 1	**Julian 90+2**	
22	FAC4Qr	**Sutton United**	H	1113	W 5 - 2	**Robinson 21 39 90+7 Deering 32 Alfa 49**	
26	NLS	Maidstone United	A	2031	L 1 - 2	Loft 4	11
N 9	FAC1	**Forest Green Rovers**	A	1419	L 0 - 4		
16	NLS	Dulwich Hamlet	A	3132	W 1 - 0	Robinson 50	
19	NLS	Weymouth	H	606	D 1 - 1	Robinson 72	10
26	FAT3Q	**Hampton & Richmond B.**	H	353	L 1 - 2	**Robinson 69**	
Dec 7	NLS	Tonbridge Angels	A	557	L 2 - 3	Akinwande 6 Alfa 17	13
14	NLS	Dartford	A	1042	L 2 - 3	Akinwande 56 Robinson 65 (pen)	14
26	NLS	Concord Rangers	A	584	L 1 - 4	Akinwande 35	
28	NLS	Chelmsford City	H	1334	D 1 - 1	Kefalas 7	
Jan 4	NLS	Bath City	A	995	L 1 - 2	Noel-Williams 24	17
7	NLS	Wealdstone	H	642	W 3 - 1	Alfa 24 Robinson 76 (pen) Akinwande 90+1	
11	NLS	Slough Town	H	849	D 2 - 2	Alfa 41 Henry 90+1	16
18	NLS	Dorking Wanderers	A	915	D 4 - 4	Paxman 16 Akinwande 19 Robinson 52 (pen) Loft 76	16
25	NLS	Tonbridge Angels	H	831	D 3 - 3	Robinson 51 (pen) Akinwande 55 Potter 56	15
Feb 8	NLS	Wealdstone	A	1356	L 0 - 3		
22	NLS	Weymouth	A	983	D 0 - 0		18
25	NLS	Oxford City	H	414	D 1 - 1	Robinson 64 (pen)	19
29	NLS	Eastbourne Borough	A	589	D 1 - 1	Paxman 47	20
Mar 3	NLS	Havant & Waterlooville	H	413	L 0 - 1		20
7	NLS	Braintree Town	H	946	W 2 - 1	Shields 15 Henry 90+4	15
14	NLS	Welling United	A	925	L 0 - 2		18

GOALSCORERS	SG	CSG	Pens	Hat tricks	Total		SG	CSG	Pens	Hat tricks	Total
Robinson	15	3	6	1	20	Rhead	2	1	1		2
Akinwande*	6	3			6	Julian	1	1			1
Alfa	5	1			5	Kefalas	1	1			1
Emmanuel	5	2			5	Noel-Williams*	1	1			1
Parkes	4	1	1		4	Potter	1	1			1
Deering	2	1			2	Shields*	1	1			1
Henry	2	1			2	Wassmer	1	1			1
Loft	2	1			2						
Opponent	2	1			2						
Paxman	2	1			2						

Appearances grid (x = Played full 90 minutes, xs = Substituted off, sx = Substituted on, s = Non-playing Substitute)

Julian A	Nunn B	Henry R	Kennedy C	Wassmer C	Parkes J	Waldren D	Emmanuel M	Robinson J	Potter A	Rhead M	Eyong T	Paxman J	Robson C	Ramsay L	Tamplin A	Loft D	Gunning G	Deering S	O'Hara J	Laurent A	Oldaker D	Krasniqi A	Alfa O (L)	Reynolds J	Egole S	Agboola E (Gk)	Kefalas T (L)	Phillips H	McLeod-Urquhart J	Moore D (L)	Bettache F (L)	Cook J	Osei-Bonsu A	Jackson O	Akinwande O	Hudson H (L)	Galach B (L)	Noel-Williams D	Harness N (Gk)(L)	Ashley O (L)	Collins R (L)	Gilella D (L)	Chambers M	Cole A	No.
x	xs	x	x	x	xs	xs	x	x	x	x		sx	sx	sx	s	s																													1
x	s	x	x	x	xs	xs	xs	x	x	x		sx	sx	sx	s	s																													2
x	s	x	x	x	x	s	x	xs	x	x	x	sx	sx	sx	s																														3
x	sx	x	x	x	x	sx	xs	sx	x	x	s		x	xs	s	xs																													4
x	sx	x	xs	s	x	sx	x	sx	x	x			x	xs	s	xs	x																												5
x	xs	x	x		x	sx	x	x		xs			x		sx	xs	x	sx	s	s																									6
x	xs	x			x	x	sx	x		xs		xs	x		sx		x	sx	s	s																									7
x	s	x		x	sx	x	sx		xs		sx	x	x	s	xs	x	xs																												8
x	s	x	s	x	xs	x	xs		x		sx	xs	x		sx	x	xs																												9
x	x	x		s	xs	s	x	x	sx	x		sx		s	x	x	x																												10
x	xs	x		x	sx	sx	x	x	xs	sx		x	x		s	s	x	xs																											11
x	x	xs			sx		sx	x			x	x	xs		x	x	sx	xs		x	s	s			x	s	s																		12
x	x	x			sx		x	xs			xs		sx		x		x			s	x	x	xs	sx																					13
x	x	x			x		x	sx			sx		sx		xs		xs			s	xs	x	x	s	s	s																			14
x	xs	x			x		x	x			sx		sx		x		x			s	x	x		s	sx																				15
x	xs	x			x		x	sx			sx		sx		x		x			s	xs	xs	s	s	s	x																			16
x	sx	x			sx	x	x				x		x		x		x			s	s	x	xs	xs	s	s	x																		17
x	s	x		sx	x	x	sx				xs		x		xs				sx	xs	x		s	x																					18
x	x	x			sx	x	x	x			xs		x		x		xs	s	s		s	xs	sx		s	x	sx																		19
x	sx	x			xs	xs			s		sx	x					s	x			x	x	x	xs	x	sx																			20
x	s	x	sx			x	x			sx		x	xs				x			xs	s	x	sx	sx	xs																				21
x	s	x	xs			x				x		x				sx	x			s	x	x	x	s	s																				22
x	s	x	xs			x	x			sx		x				s	x			sx	x	xs	x	x	sx	xs																			23
x	xs	x			x	x				sx	sx				sx		x			x	xs	xs	s	s	x																				24
x	sx	x			x	x				x	s	xs				x			xs	x	sx	x	x																						25
x	sx	x			x	x				x	s	s				x			x	xs	s	x	s	x																					26
x	x	x			sx	x				sx	x				s	xs		sx		x	xs	x	x	xs	x																				27
	x	x			x	x				xs	s	s				xs	x	sx	xs	x	sx	x																						28
	x	x			sx	xs				x	s	x				x	s	s	x	x	x	x																						29
	x	x	sx		xs	x				xs	s	x				x	s	sx	xs	x	sx	x	x	x																				30
	x	x			x	x				x	sx				s		x	sx	x	x	s		x	xs																				31
x	sx	x			x	x				x	sx				xs	s	x	x	xs			xs	s																					32
x					sx	x				x	sx					sx	x	x	s	xs	sx	x		xs	x																				33
x					x	x				s						s	xs	x	x	s	x	s	x	x	sx	s	x	x	sx																34
x					xs	x				x	xs				sx		s	xs	x	x	sx	s	x	x	sx	s	x	x	x																35
x					x	x				x	sx				s	xs	xs	xs	xs	x	x	xs	sx																						36
x	sx	x			xs	x				s	xs				x	sx	s	x	x	sx				x	xs																				37
x	xs	x			sx	x				xs	xs				sx		x	xs	s					x	x	sx																			38
34	10	37	8	5	10	1	12	24	25	7	1	14	7	8	0	14	7	6	0	0	1	3	11	1	0	0	11	0	7	3	2	4	0	2	13	10	0	4	4	0	0	1	6	1	x
0	8	1	3	0	3	3	2	6	3	3	0	6	2	5	0	10	0	6	0	2	1	3	6	0	0	0	3	0	0	1	2	4	0	2	3	2	2	2	0	1	1	1	0	2	xs
0	8	0	2	0	4	5	8	3	1	2	12	12	9	2	0	2	0	5	0	1	1	0	2	0	5	1	1	0	3	3	1	0	3	5	6	3	2	1	0	0	2	2	0	0	sx
0	8	0	0	3	0	2	0	0	0	0	1	3	0	4	8	1	0	0	6	12	1	3	0	5	6	3	2	1	0	3	4	8	1	0	0	0	0	0	4	1	0	0	2	2	0	s

Also Played: McLennan G - 07/09 (xs); Anderson T (L) - 28/09 (s); Ambrose K - 28/12 (s); Shields C (L) - 07/03 14/03 (x); Quigley J (L) - 14/03 (x).

GOALKEEPERS	CS	CCS
Julian	5	1

x - Played full 90 minutes
xs - Substituted off
sx - Substituted on
s - Non-playing Substitute

BRAINTREE TOWN MATCH RESULTS 2019-20

Date	Comp	Opponents	H/A	Att:	Result	Goalscorers	Pos
Aug 3	NLS	Bath City	A	784	L 0 - 2		
6	NLS	Billericay Town	H	868	L 2 - 3	Richardson 12 62	
10	NLS	Wealdstone	H	482	L 0 - 4		
13	NLS	St Albans City	A	396	W 3 - 0	Mills 32 Akinwande 33 Clark 89	
17	NLS	Eastbourne Borough	H	356	W 5 - 0	Mills 26 81 Richardson 32 Banton 65 Akinwande 90+1	12
24	NLS	Dartford	A	874	L 1 - 2	Akinwande 3	
26	NLS	Dorking Wanderers	H	444	W 3 - 2	Banton 36 Christian-Law 60 Akinwande 90+4	
31	NLS	Chippenham Town	A	468	W 2 - 1	Coker 60 Cerulli 87	
Sep 3	NLS	Concord Rangers	A	534	D 2 - 2	Banton 37 Cole 69	11
7	NLS	Dulwich Hamlet	H	537	W 2 - 1	Cole 47 Cerulli 77	8
14	NLS	Havant & Waterlooville	A	1351	W 3 - 1	Richardson 4 40 Akinwande 88	6
21	**FAC2Q**	**Enfield Town**	**A**	**523**	**L 0 - 2**		
28	NLS	Oxford City	H	481	W 1 - 0	Cole 35 (pen)	5
Oct 12	NLS	Tonbridge Angels	A	612	L 1 - 5	Mills 74	7
26	NLS	Weymouth	A	782	L 0 - 3		9
29	NLS	Maidstone United	H	458	D 1 - 1	Mcleod-Urquhart 90+4	
Nov 2	NLS	Hungerford Town	H	412	L 0 - 3		9

Manager Glen Driver resigns, club caption Jake Hutchings takes temporary charge. (Permanent position given to Hutchings after the Hemel result.)

Date	Comp	Opponents	H/A	Att:	Result	Goalscorers	Pos
9	NLS	Hemel Hempstead Town	A	481	W 3 - 0	Banton 28 Cole 55 James 63	
16	NLS	Welling United	A	538	L 2 - 6	Cole 43 Akinwande 71	
23	**FAT3Q**	**Yate Town**	**H**	**202**	**L 1 - 2**	**Banton**	
30	NLS	Hampton & Richmond B.	H	390	L 0 - 4		8

Jake Hutchings steps down as manager, George Borg takes charge.

Date	Comp	Opponents	H/A	Att:	Result	Goalscorers	Pos
Dec 7	NLS	Slough Town	A	739	L 0 - 1		10
21	NLS	Havant & Waterlooville	H	430	D 3 - 3	Cerulli 22 Murrell-Williamson 87 90+5	
26	NLS	Chelmsford City	A	919	L 1 - 4	Christian-Law 50	
28	NLS	Concord Rangers	H	789	L 0 - 1		
Jan 1	NLS	Chelmsford City	H	971	L 1 - 2	Murrell-Williamson 70	
4	NLS	Dulwich Hamlet	A	2730	L 0 - 6		16
11	NLS	Tonbridge Angels	H	468	L 0 - 1		18
18	NLS	Oxford City	A	601	W 4 - 1	Chiedozie 53 O'Keefe 64 Smyth 66 Oyinsan 90+2	17
25	NLS	Slough Town	H	494	L 0 - 1		17
Feb 1	NLS	Weymouth	H	405	D 1 - 1	Smyth 51	18
8	NLS	Maidstone United	A	1875	L 0 - 1		
15	NLS	Hemel Hempstead Town	H	391	D 0 - 0		
22	NLS	Hungerford Town	A	207	L 0 - 2		21
29	NLS	Bath City	H	410	W 2 - 0	Chiedozie 60 Smyth 90+2	18
Mar 7	NLS	Billericay Town	A	946	L 1 - 2	Smyth 67	19
14	NLS	St Albans City	H	545	L 0 - 1		21

GOALSCORERS	SG	CSG	Pens	Hat tricks	Total		SG	CSG	Pens	Hat tricks	Total
Akinwande	6	4			6	Clark	1	1			1
Banton	5	1			5	Coker*	1	1			1
Cole	5	2	1		5	James	1	1			1
Richardson	3	1			5	Mcleod-Urquhart	1	1			1
Mills	3	2			4	O'Keefe	1	1			1
Smyth	4	2			4	Oyinsan	1	1			1
Cerulli	3	1			3						
Murrell-Williamson	2	1			3						
Chiedozie	2	1			2						
Christian-Law	2	1			2						

Player appearance grid. Columns (left to right): Johnson M, McLeod-Urquhart J, Hutchings J, Clark M, Saunders O, Akinwande O, Bonnet-Johnson S, Manesio S, Cole A, Richardson T, Mills A, Cerulli A, Banton J, Clements K, Harvey R, Gibson J, Barker C, Christian-Law T, Osborne H, Coker T, Green C (L), Donovan H, Murrell-Williamson R, James J, Lawrence B (L), Skubich I, Kirkpatrick L, Akinyemi D, Frimpong C, Sade Y (L), Matsuzaka D, Stone F, Brzozowski M (Gk) (L), Sheehan S, Ocran B, Chiedozie J, Gardner-Smith J (L), Oyinsan J, Johnson W (Gk) (L), Smith J (L), O'Keefe C, Howard R (L), Smyth L (L), Russell D, Iontton A (L).

No.	Johnson M	McLeod-Urquhart J	Hutchings J	Clark M	Saunders O	Akinwande O	Bonnet-Johnson S	Manesio S	Cole A	Richardson T	Mills A	Cerulli A	Banton J	Clements K	Harvey R	Gibson J	Barker C	Christian-Law T	Osborne H	Coker T	Green C (L)	Donovan H	Murrell-Williamson R	James J	Lawrence B (L)	Skubich I	Kirkpatrick L	Akinyemi D	Frimpong C	Sade Y (L)	Matsuzaka D	Stone F	Brzozowski M (Gk)(L)	Sheehan S	Ocran B	Chiedozie J	Gardner-Smith J (L)	Oyinsan J	Johnson W (Gk)(L)	Smith J (L)	O'Keefe C	Howard R (L)	Smyth L (L)	Russell D	Iontton A (L)
1	x	x	x	x	x	xs	x		x	xs	sx	sx	sx	s	s																															
2	x		x	x	xs	x	xs		x	x	sx	sx	sx	s	x	x	sx																													
3	x	x	x	x	x		x	xs	xs	x	sx	sx			x	s	s																													
4	x	x	x	x	xs	sx	x	x	xs	x	sx				sx	s	xs																													
5	x	x	x	x	x	s	x	xs	x	xs		xs			sx	s	sx																													
6	x		x	x	x	xs	xs	x	x	x	sx	xs		sx	s	s		x																												
7	x	x	x	x		x	sx		x	xs	x	sx		s	s	sx	xs	x																												
8	x	x	x	x	x	sx	x	x	xs	x	sx		sx		sx		s	x		xs																										
9	x	x	x	x		x	s	sx	x	x	sx		sx			s	xs	sx	xs	x																										
10	x	x	x	x		x	sx		x	xs	sx		sx		sx		s	x	xs	x	s																									
11	x	x	xs	x		x		xs	x	sx	x	s		sx	x	sx	s	x	xs	x	sx																									
12	x	x	x	s	x			x	x	xs	sx	xs	s		s	sx	x	sx	x	xs																										
13	x	x	x		xs			x	xs	sx	xs				sx	x	x	x	s	x	sx																									
14	x	x	x		x			x	xs	sx	xs				s	xs		xs	x	x	x	s	s																							
15	x	x	x		x				sx	x	sx				s	xs		xs	x	x	s	sx																								
16	x	x	x		x			x		xs	sx	s			s	xs		xs	x	x	s	x																								
17	x	x	x		x			xs	sx	xs	sx	s			sx	x		s	xs	sx	x																									
18	x	x	x		xs			x	s	sx	xs				sx	x		sx	x		xs																									
19	x	x	x		x			x	s	sx	x				sx	x		xs	xs	s																										
20	x	x	x					xs	xs	sx	x				x			x	sx	x	s	x	x																							
21	x		x					xs		x	xs				sx			x	x	x	sx	xs	x	x	sx																					
22	x	s	x					s			x				x			x	x	s	x	x	xs	x	x	s																				
23	s							x			xs	x			x	x		s	x	x	s	x	x	x	xs																					
24	s							x			s	x			x	xs		s	x	xs	x	x	x	x	sx	x																				
25	s							x			s	x			xs	x		s	x	xs	x	x	x	x	sx																					
26	x							xs			sx	x			s	x		s	x	s	x	x	sx	x	x	x																				
27	x							sx			sx	x			s	x		s	x	sx	x	xs	x	xs	x	x																				
28								sx			s	x			x	s	xs	x	s	x	x	x	xs	x	x	x	x	x																		
29											s	s	x	x	s	x	x	x	x	x	x	x	x																						
30								sx			sx	s	xs	x	s	x	x	sx	x	x	xs	x	x	xs																						
31								sx			x	x	s	x	sx	x	x	sx	x	x	x																									
32								sx		x	x	sx	x	x	s	x	xs	x	x	x	x	xs	sx																							
33								sx		x	sx	s	x	s	x	x	xs	x	x	x	x	xs	x																							
34								sx		x	x	sx	s	xs	s	x	xs	x	xs	x	x	sx	xs	x																						
35								xs		x	x	s	x	s	x	x	x	sx	sx	x	x	s	s																							
36								xs		x	x	sx	xs	x	x	xs	x	x	s	s																										
37								xs		x	s	x	sx	x	xs	x	x	x	x	x	x																									
x	24	16	20	18	6	16	1	3	13	8	4	6	2	5	2	1	2	11	6	0	16	6	0	6	7	2	0	17	3	2	1	14	1	3	13	3	12	11	3	9	8	8	4	3	4
xs	0	0	0	1	1	3	2	2	7	7	5	11	0	0	0	2	4	0	4	1	1	3	2	0	3	0	3	0	0	1	0	0	4	0	2	2	0	0	0	0	3	2	0		
sx	0	0	0	0	0	0	5	1	0	1	5	23	1	0	4	12	3	1	1	0	2	1	5	0	0	2	3	0	1	1	1	1	1	0	1	4	3	0	0	0	1	0	4	1	0
s	3	0	1	1	0	0	2	1	1	2	0	0	1	4	3	4	13	3	0	1	0	2	1	0	0	9	1	0	0	2	1	11	1	0	4	0	0	0	0	1	1	0	0	0	0

Also Played: Folarin E - 03/08 (xs) 06/08 10/08 (s); Charles T - 13/08 (s) 17/08 (sx); West H - 30/11 (s); Cadette G - 21/12 26/12 28/12 01/01 04/01 (s); Papple J - 04/01 11/01 18/01 01/02 14/03 (s); Bassle A - 01/02 08/02 (xs); Ryan M - 01/02 08/02 15/02 22/02 (s); Guerfi Z - 29/02 07/03 (xs) 14/03 (x); Cooney T - 07/03 (x) 14/03 (xs).

GOALKEEPERS	CS	CCS
Johnson M	4	2
Johnson W	2	1

x - Played full 90 minutes
xs - Substituted off
sx - Substituted on
s - Non-playing Substitute

CHELMSFORD CITY MATCH RESULTS 2019-20

Date	Comp	Opponents	H/A	Att:	Result	Goalscorers	Pos
Aug 3	NLS	Hampton & Richmond B.	H	908	W 4 - 1	Jelley 2 (og) Wraight 9 55 Fennell 90+3	
6	NLS	Concord Rangers	A	1016	L 1 - 2	Muldoon 80	9
10	NLS	Weymouth	A	951	L 1 - 4	Jeffers 13 (pen)	
13	NLS	Dartford	H	948	W 4 - 0	Whelpdale 52 Higgins 75 Giles 81 Hill 90+2 (og)	
17	NLS	Havant & Waterlooville	A	1382	D 0 - 0		10
24	NLS	Welling United	H	747	D 1 - 1	Jeffers 90	
26	NLS	Maidstone United	A	1914	L 1 - 4	Simpson 45+3	
31	NLS	Bath City	H	595	W 1 - 0	Jeffers 64 (pen)	
Sep 2	NLS	Billericay Town	H	1395	D 1 - 1	Church 51	9
7	NLS	Hemel Hempstead	A	638	L 0 - 2		14
14	NLS	Chippenham Town	H	657	D 3 - 3	Church 66 Higgins 81 Jeffers 90	14
21	FAC2Q	Corinthian-Casuals	A	374	L 0 - 2		
28	NLS	Eastbourne Borough	A	569	W 4 - 0	Whelpdale 12 Higgins 15 59 Jeffers 51 (pen)	12
Oct 12	NLS	Wealdstone	H	1263	L 1 - 3	Winfield 87	13
19	NLS	Tonbridge Angels	A	590	W 2 - 1	Whelpdale 90+2 Jeffers 90+4	11
26	NLS	Dulwich Hamlet	H	817	D 1 - 1	Higgins 16	10
Nov 2	NLS	Slough Town	A	731	L 1 - 2	Higgins 47	10
9	NLS	Dorking Wanderers	H	1001	D 2 - 2	Higgins 39 Jeffers 86	
16	NLS	Oxford City	H	759	L 2 - 6	Higgins 8 Jeffers 45+2	12
23	FAT3Q	Hungerford Town	H		W 2 - 1	Knowles 5 Winfield 26	
30	NLS	St Albans City	A	603	D 1 - 1	Jeffers 40	13
Dec 7	NLS	Hungerford Town	H	686	W 4 - 1	Knowles 41 Jeffers 43 (pen) Whelpdale 65 Simpson 90+4	11
14	FAT1	Havant & Waterlooville	H	386	W 2 - 1	Knott 16 Simpson 90+2	
21	NLS	Chippenham Town	H	526	L 1 - 2	Simpson 40	
26	NLS	Braintree Town	H	919	W 4 - 1	Simpson 41 Whelpdale 45 81 Jeffers 85 (pen)	
28	NLS	Billericay Town	A	1334	D 1 - 1	Kyei 44	
Jan 1	NLS	Braintree Town	A	971	W 2 - 1	Knowles 46 Jeffers 79 (pen)	
4	NLS	Hemel Hempstead	H	796	W 2 - 1	Whelpdale 54 Higgins 74	9
11	FAT2	Salisbury	H	557	W 4 - 0	Jeffers 28 86 Giles 75 Whelpdale 90+5	
18	NLS	Eastbourne Borough	H	977	D 1 - 1	Jeffers 6	9
25	NLS	Hungerford Town	A	240	L 0 - 1		9
Manager Rod Stringer leaves the club. Robbie Simpson is put in interim charge.							
Feb 1	NLS	Dulwich Hamlet	A	2628	L 3 - 5	Whelpdale 15 Higgins 53 59	11
8	FAT3	Aveley	A	811	L 1 - 3	Whelpdale 79	
15	NLS	Dorking Wanderers	A	517	L 0 - 2		
17	NLS	Tonbridge Angels	H	611	W 3 - 1	Wraight 27 Lita 47 Knowles 90+4	
22	NLS	Slough Town	H	866	D 1 - 1	Chidyausiku 60	11
25	NLS	Wealdstone	A	873	W 1 - 0	Knowles 46	9
Mar 7	NLS	Concord Rangers	H	839	D 1 - 1	Wraight 41	10
14	NLS	Dartford	A	1486	L 0 - 3		10

GOALSCORERS	SG	CSG	Pens	Hat tricks	Total		SG	CSG	Pens	Hat tricks	Total
Jeffers	14	2	6		15	Chidyausiku	1	1			1
Higgins	9	4			11	Fennell	1	1			1
Whelpdale	9	2			10	Knott	1	1			1
Knowles	5	1			5	Kyei	1	1			1
Simpson	5	4			5	Lita	1	1			1
Wraight	3	1			4	Muldoon	1	1			1
Church	2	1			2						
Giles	2	1			2						
Opponent	2	1			2						
Winfield*	2	1			2						

Pentney C	Omozusi E	Spillane M	Cascaval A	Shaw F	Whelpdale C	Church A	Wriaght T	Muldoon O	Higgins S	Jeffers S	Loza J	Isaac C	Fennell A	Knott B	Gibbons J	Giles J	Edobar J (L)	Osborn A	Simpson R	Gardiner T	Cotter B (L)	Porter M	Winfield D	Knowles T (L)	Lita L	Gregan C	Howes S (Gk) (L)	Drewe A (L)	Worman B (L)	Chidyausiku J	Chambers M (L)	Stevenson B	Ndaba C (L)	Walker L (Gk) (L)	Kyei N	Jessup J (Gk)	Olomowewe T	West-Asturi J (Gk)	Imray D	Ward E	Brown T	No.
x	x	x	x	xs	xs	x	xs	x	x	xs	x	sx	sx	s	s	s																										1
x	x	x	x	xs	x	xs	x	x	x	xs	sx	sx	s	s	sx																											2
x	sx	x		x		x	x	x	s	x	xs	x	s		xs	sx	xs	sx																								3
x	x	x	x	sx	xs	x	xs	x	x	s	xs	s	sx			x		sx																								4
x	x		x	x	x	x		x	xs	sx	xs	x	sx			xs	s	s	sx																							5
x	x		x	x	x	x	s	sx	xs	sx	xs	x				sx			s	sx																						6
x	x		x	s	x	x	x	x	xs	sx	xs	s	xs	x			sx			sx	x																					7
x	x		x	xs	x	x	x	xs	sx	s	s		sx			sx			xs	x																						8
x	xs	x		x	x	x	xs	x	sx	sx	sx		x			s			xs	s																						9
x		x	x	x	x	x	x	sx	xs	sx	s		xs			x	s																									10
x	x	x		x	x	x	s	s	sx	sx	sx		xs	x		x			xs	xs																						11
fx	fx	fx		fx	fxs	fx	fx		fxs	fx			s		sx	fx		fxs		sx	sx	s																				12
x		x		x	x			xs	x		x	sx	x		sx	x		x	s																							13
x	x	x	s	xs	xs	xs		x	x		x	sx	x	sx	sx					x																						14
x	x	s	x	x	sx	x		x	sx	xs	s	x	x			sx					x	sx																				15
x	sx	x	sx	x	x		x	x	x	sx	xs	s		sx	xs				x	s																						16
x	xs	x	sx	x	x		x	x	x	sx	x	sx	s	s		x	xs																									17
x	x	x	xs	x		xs	x	xs	s	sx		x	sx	sx	s																											18
x	x	xs	x	xs	xs		x	x		x	s	x	sx	sx	s	x																										19
x		**x**	**x**		xs	xs		**x**		**x**		sx			**x**	xs	sx	x	s	sx	s																					20
x		x	x		xs	xs		x		sx		sx			x	xs	sx	s	s																							21
x		x	x		xs	x	s			sx		sx			xs	s	x			x	x	s																				22
x		**x**	**x**	**xs**	**x**		**xs**	**sx**	**x**		**sx**		**x**			**x**	s	x	s	s					**s**																	23
x		x	x	x	x		xs	sx		sx		xs			x	sx	s	x		x	xs	s	x																			24
		x	x	x	x		sx	sx	xs		sx		xs			s	sx	s	x	s																						25
		x	x	x	x	sx	x		xs	x		sx			x	sx	xs	s	xs	s																						26
		x	x	x	x		x	xs	x		sx			x	sx		x	s	s	xs	xs	sx																				27
x		sx	x	x	x		xs	x		s		xs	xs	s		xs	sx	x																								28
x		**x**	**x**	**x**	**x**		**sx**	**xs**	**x**	**x**		**xs**		**sx**		**xs**	s	s	**x**	**sx**																						29
x		x	x	x	x		s	xs	x		sx	xs	sx	s				x	sx	x																						30
x		x	x	x	x		xs	xs	x		s	sx	s				xs	sx	xs	sx	x																					31
	xs		x	x	x		sx	sx	x	xs		x	xs	sx	x			x	s														x	s								32
		sx	x	x		x	x	xs	xs	x		sx	sx	x			xs	s	s												x						s	x				33
		x	sx	s		x	x	xs		xs	x		xs	sx	s			sx		sx											x			x		x						34
		x		sx	xs	x	x	sx	xs	xs	s		sx			x		sx	s												x			x		x	x					35
		x		sx	x	x	sx	xs	xs	s		sx	x			xs			sx												x			x	x	s						36
		sx		x	x	x	x		xs			s				xs	s		sx												x			x	x	x						37
s				x	x	x	sx	xs		x		sx			s			xs													x			x	x	x						38
x		sx		x	x	xs	xs	x		s			s				xs														x			x	xs	x						39
18	24	10	26	26	24	30	13	15	7	17	0	19	0	9	0	9	0	0	6	1	0	8	6	1	0	5	0	0	1	6	1	0	12	0	1	7	2	6	5	2		x
0	2	1	0	5	7	3	3	3	17	11	4	6	1	7	1	7	1	1	5	1	1	0	0	10	3	0	0	0	1	0	4	0	1	3	0	0	0	1	0	0		xs
0	1	1	2	5	1	2	1	2	7	9	5	6	7	7	0	14	0	7	9	0	0	0	6	8	1	0	0	1	3	0	0	0	3	1	1	0	0	0	0	0		sx
0	1	1	1	1	1	1	0	2	2	1	2	2	6	4	2	1	8	1	4	4	3	0	1	0	1	5	9	0	2	2	4	0	1	6	0	1	1	0	1	0	1	s

GOALKEEPERS	CS	CCS
Pentney	4	2
Walker	2	1

x - Played full 90 minutes
xs - Substituted off
sx - Substituted on
s - Non-playing Substitute

CHIPPENHAM TOWN MATCH RESULTS 2019-20

Date	Comp	Opponents	H/A	Att:	Result	Goalscorers	Pos
Aug 3	NLS	St Albans City	A	549	D 0 - 0		
6	NLS	Oxford City	H	582	D 1 - 1	Tyler 16	13
10	NLS	Billerciay Town	H	583	W 2 - 0	Hopper 6 (pen) Jarvis 90+1	
13	NLS	Wealdstone	A	837	L 0 - 1		
17	NLS	Hungerford Town	A	377	D 1 - 1	Pratt 47	13
24	NLS	Weymouth	H	759	W 1 - 0	Zebroski 40	
26	NLS	Hampton & Richmond B.	A	465	L 0 - 1		
31	NLS	Braintree Town	H	468	L 1 - 2	McDonald 11	14
Sep 3	NLS	Dorking Wanderers	A	453	L 0 - 1		16
7	NLS	Tonbridge Angels	H	578	W 2 - 1	Ossai 44 Zebroski 69	13
14	NLS	Chelmsford City	A	657	D 3 - 3	Foulston 35 Chambers 37 Zebroski 69	13
21	FAC2Q	**Cirencester Town**	A	336	D 2 - 2	**Gunner 35 Hopper 83**	
24	FAC2Qr	**Cirencester Town**	H	340	W 4 - 3	**Haines 10 Chambers 52 Ossai 107 Clayton 115 (og)**	
28	NLS	Dulwich Hamlet	H	628	D 2 - 2	Haines 6 Chambers 90+5	15
Oct 5	FAC3Q	**Slough Town**	H	606	D 3 - 3	**Parselle 37 Foulstone 64 (fk) Chambers 75**	
8	FAC3Qr	**Slough Town**	H	631	W 3 - 2	**Jarvis 42 Haines 54 Chambers 84**	
12	NLS	Concord Rangers	A	254	W 1 - 0	Hopper 80 (pen)	11
19	FAC4Q	**Whyteleafe**	A	512	W 3 - 0	**Chambers 34 Parselle 40 Tyler 58**	
26	NLS	Dartford	A	882	D 1 - 1	Parselle 24	12
Nov 2	NLS	Welling United	H	484	D 0 - 0		13
10	FAC1	**Northampton Town**	H	2625	L 0 - 3		
16	NLS	Slough Town	H	627	L 0 - 3		17
23	FAT3Q	**Dulwich Hamlet**	A	972	D 2 - 2	**Pratt 6 Whelan 68**	
26	FAT3Qr	**Dulwich Hamlet**	H	245	L 1 - 2	**McDonald 23**	
30	NLS	Eastbourne Borough	A	486	L 1 - 2	Richards 61	18
Dec 7	NLS	Havant & Waterlooville	A	1189	L 1 - 2	Chambers 79	19
10	NLS	Maidstone United	A	1337	D 0 - 0		18
21	NLS	Chelmsford City	H	526	W 2 - 1	Pratt 13 McDonald 75	
26	NLS	Bath City	A	1397	L 2 - 3	Rigg 5 Owen-Evans 22	
28	NLS	Dorking Wanderers	H	567	L 0 - 2		
Jan 1	NLS	Bath City	H	1239	L 1 - 3	Zebroski 42	
4	NLS	Tonbridge Angels	A	596	L 2 - 3	Owen-Evans 32 Chambers 53	19
7	NLS	Hemel Hempstead Town	H	400	D 2 - 2	Jarvis 1 Tyler 43	18

Manager Mark Collier departs. Michael Cook is made interim boss until the end of the season.

Date	Comp	Opponents	H/A	Att:	Result	Goalscorers	Pos
18	NLS	Dulwich Hamlet	A	2901	D 1 - 1	Gunner 66	21
25	NLS	Havant & Waterlooville	H	527	D 0 - 0		21
Feb 1	NLS	Dartford	H	614	L 1 - 5	Gunner 23	21
8	NLS	Hemel Hempstead Town	A	411	W 1 - 0	Jarvis 82	
15	NLS	Maidstone United	H	497	W 1 - 0	Haines 73	
22	NLS	Welling United	A	502	L 0 - 1		
25	NLS	Concord Rangers	H	424	W 3 - 0	Rigg 21 Twine 47 53	15
29	NLS	St Albans City	H	650	W 2 - 1	Parselle 74 Twine 78	14
Mar 7	NLS	Oxford City	A	366	W 3 - 1	Twine 19 61 Parselle 32	12
14	NLS	Wealdstone	H	1062	D 1 - 1	Twine 15	12

GOALSCORERS	SG	CSG	Pens	Hat tricks	Total		SG	CSG	Pens	Hat tricks	Total
Chambers	8	4			8	Tyler	3	1			3
Twine	4	4			6	Foulston	2	1			2
Parselle	5	1			5	Ossai	2	1			2
Haines	4	2			4	Owen-Evans	2	1			2
Jarvis	4	1			4	Rigg	2	1			2
Zebroski	4	2			4	Opponent	1	1			1
Gunner	3	1			3	Richards	1	1			1
Hopper	3	1	2		3	Whelan	1	1			1
McDonald	3	1			3						
Pratt	3	1			3						

No.	Puddy W	Parselle K	Tyler R	Foulston J (L)	Richards W	Chambers K	Evans D	Gunner C	Haines L (L)	Pratt D	Hopper L	Klukowski Y	Jarvis N	Youssef E	Ossai T	George A	Zebroski C	McDonald C	Rigg G	Guthrie J	Rutty H	Henry W (Gk)(L)	Hallett A	Horgan G	Thompson C (Gk)	Whelan T (L)	Warre D	Wakefield J	Lea H	Owen-Evans T (L)	Horton G (L)	Case R	Bradbury C	Russe L (L)	Twine S (L)	Bray A	Self J	Smedley J
1	x	x	x	x	x	x	x	xs	x	xs	x	sx	sx	s	s	s																						
2	x	x	x	x	x	sx	xs	sx	x	x	xs	s	x	x	s	s																						
3	x	x	x	x	x	xs	sx	x	x	xs	xs	s	sx	x			s	sx																				
4	x	x	x	x		sx	xs	xs	x	x	s			xs	sx		s	x	x	sx																		
5	x	x	x	x		sx	s	xs	x	xs	s		x	s			x	sx	x	sx																		
6	x	x	x	xs		sx	sx	x	sx	s	xs		s	x			x	sx	x																			
7	x	x	x	sx	x		xs	x	x	xs	xs	s	s				sx	xs	x																			
8	x	x	xs	x	x			sx	x	xs	s	s	sx				x	x	xs																			
9	x	x		x		sx	s	x	sx	sx	s	xs	s				xs	x	x	xs																		
10	x	x			x	s		x	s	xs	s	x	xs				x		sx	x																		
11		x			x			s	xs		sx	x	xs	s			x		sx	x	x	x	s															
12		x		s		x		x	x	xs	sx	sx		xs			x	x	x	sx	xs	x		s	s													
13		x		x		x		x	x	s	sx	x	s	sx			xs	x	xs	xs	sx	x			s													
14	x	x		x		x		s	x		x		x	s	x		x	x	x		s	s		s														
15	x	x	s		xs			sx	x	x	xs		x	sx	x		s	x	x	x		s	s															
16	x	x	x	s		x		x	x	s	sx		xs	xs	s	s	x	x	x		sx																	
17	x	x	sx		x		sx	xs	s	xs			xs				sx	x	x								x											
18	x	x	x	sx		sx	x		s		xs	xs		sx	x	xs	s			s							x	s										
19	x	x	x	sx	xs		xs	x	sx	s		xs	s				x	x	sx								x											
20	x		x	x	x	x		s	x	s	sx		xs	s			s	x	x								x											
21	x		x	x	x	x		sx	xs	s	sx		xs	sx			s	x	x	xs							s	x	s									
22	x	sx		x	xs		x	xs	sx	x			s	sx			x	x	s								xs											
23	x	x	x	x	x	s		x	x	x	x			s			x	s									s	s	x									
24	x	x	x	x	x	s		x	xs	x	xs		sx	sx			s	x	s								s	x										
25	x	x	x	x		x	xs	xs	x				sx				sx	x	s								x			s								
26	x	x	x	s	x	sx		x	x				x				xs	x	x										s	s								
27	x	x	x	sx	xs		x	x	xs	s			x				s	x									s		x									
28	x	x	x	x		sx		x	xs	xs	s		sx				x	x	x										x	s	s							
29	x	x	x	x		sx		x	xs	xs	s		sx				x	x	x			s							xs		sx							
30	x	x	x	sx		x			sx	x		s					xs	x	x		s						s			x	s	xs						
31	x	x	x	s		x			sx	sx		xs					xs	x	x		s						s			x	x	s						
32	x	x	x		x		xs		sx	s	x		sx				xs	x	x		s						s			x	x	sx						
33	x	x	x		x		s	sx			xs		xs	sx	x		x		s								s			x	x	s	s					
34	x	x	x		s		x		x	sx			xs	x	x		s										s			x	s			x				
35	x	x	x		xs		x		sx		xs		x	xs			s										sx			sx	x							
36	x	x	x		sx		x	s	s	sx			xs	x			s										s			x	x							
37	x	x	x		sx		x		x	xs			xs	x	sx		s										s			x	x							
38	x	x	x		x	x		sx			xs		x	x	xs		s										s			sx		x	xs	sx				
39	x	x	x	s		x		sx		x	xs		x	x			s										s			x	x	x	s					
40	x	x	x		x		s		xs		xs		x	xs			s										sx			x	x	xs	sx					
41	x	x	x		x	sx		s			xs		x	x			s										s			x	x	xs						
42	x	x	x		x	xs		s			sx		x	xs			s										s			x	x	x	sx					
43	x	x	x		xs	sx		s			x		x	x			s										sx			x	x	xs			s			
x	40	39	32	36	10	17	2	24	24	9	6	0	6	10	2	1	20	33	21	1	4	3	1	0	0	8	0	0	0	7	3	0	0	10	7	2	0	0
xs	0	0	1	0	1	6	2	6	8	10	9	0	12	3	3	0	13	1	9	3	1	0	0	0	0	1	0	0	0	1	0	1	0	0	1	3	0	0
sx	0	1	2	2	9	3	7	1	8	13	2	9	6	1	2	6	1	5	3	2	0	0	0	0	0	0	0	0	0	1	7	0	0	0	1	3	0	
s	0	0	2	4	0	5	2	3	1	9	13	6	7	7	3	9	1	1	5	0	8	2	0	4	17	0	2	3	0	3	7	1	0	0	0	1	1	

GOALKEEPERS	CS	CCS
Puddy	11	2

x - Played full 90 minutes
xs - Substituted off
sx - Substituted on
s - Non-playing Substitute

CONCORD RANGERS MATCH RESULTS 2019-20

Date	Comp	Opponents	H/A	Att.	Result	Goalscorers	Pos
Aug 3	NLS	Oxford City	A	325	W 3 - 0	Nouble 45 Krasniqi 75 Gardner 82	
6	NLS	Chelmsford City	H	1016	W 2 - 1	Sheriff 37 47	1
10	NLS	Slough Town	H	253	W 2 - 1	Sheriff 3 58	
13	NLS	Tonbridge Angels	A	476	L 0 - 1		
17	NLS	Dulwich Hamlet	A	1521	D 2 - 2	Roast 7 Nouble 31	4
24	NLS	Maidstone United	H	387	L 0 - 1		
26	NLS	St Albans City	A	457	L 1 - 2	McGavin 90	
31	NLS	Welling United	H	284	W 3 - 0	Reynolds 23 Nouble 65 Krasniqi 73	6
Sep 3	NLS	Braintree Town	H	534	D 2 - 2	Sheriff 57 Pollock 87	6
7	NLS	Hampton & Richmond B.	A	485	W 3 - 2	Reynolds 22 Barrington 67 Pollock 90	5
14	NLS	Dartford	H	526	L 0 - 2		9
21	FAC2Q	Margate	A	360	L 1 - 3	Pollock	
28	NLS	Weymouth	A	921	L 0 - 3		10
Oct 12	NLS	Chippenham Town	H	254	L 0 - 1		12
19	NLS	Hungerford Town	H	304	L 0 - 2		13
26	NLS	Havant & Waterlooville	A	1367	L 1 - 2	Roast 70	14
Nov 2	NLS	Hemel Hempstead Town	H	305	W 3 - 1	Pollock 7 Sheriff 9 Nouble 90+4	11
9	NLS	Bath City	A	820	L 1 - 3	Clifford 30	
16	NLS	Dorking Wanderers	H	412	D 3 - 3	Green 17 (pen) Cawley 77 Nouble 90 (pen)	13
23	FAT3Q	Slough Town	H	201	D 0 - 0		
26	FAT3Qr	Slough Town	A	295	W 3 - 2	Krasniqi 9 90+2 Green 73 (pen)	
30	NLS	Wealdstone	A	832	L 0 - 3		15
Dec 7	NLS	Eastbourne Borough	H	243	W 5 - 0	Krasniqi 3 27 Nouble 33 Elliott 40 Pollock 84	12
14	FAT1	Maidstone United	A	881	W 3 - 2	Elliott 35 Reynolds 82 Green 86	
21	NLS	Dartford	A	971	W 1 - 0	Nouble 63 (pen)	
26	NLS	Billericay Town	H	584	W 4 - 1	Kefalas 3 (og) Pollock 48 Blanchfield 63 Nouble 73	
28	NLS	Braintree Town	A	789	W 1 - 0	Blanchfield 76	
Jan 4	NLS	Hampton & Richmond B.	H	412	L 0 - 2		11
11	FAT2	Bath City	H	263	D 1 - 1	Pollock 77	
18	NLS	Weymouth	H	314	L 1 - 2	Williams 54 (og)	11
25	NLS	Eastbourne Borough	A	489	D 2 - 2	Olufemi 8 Sheriff 56	12
28	FAT2r	Bath City	A	437	W 2 - 1	Roast 15 Nouble 88	
Feb 1	NLS	Havant & Waterlooville	H	300	D 0 - 0		13
8	FAT3	Leamington	H	417	D 2 - 2	Reynolds 5 Blanchfield 95 (Won 4-3 on pens aet)	
15	NLS	Bath City	H	212	L 0 - 1		
22	NLS	Hemel Hempstead Town	A	361	L 0 - 1		
25	NLS	Chippenham Town	A	424	L 0 - 3		14
Mar 3	FAT4	Royston Town	H	852	W 2 - 1	Nouble 35 Sheriff 93 (aet)	
7	NLS	Chelmsford City	A	839	D 1 - 1	Sheriff 19 (pen)	16
14	NLS	Tonbridge Angels	H	703	D 3 - 3	Babalola 17 Sheriff 22 Blanchfield 45	17

GOALSCORERS	SG	CSG	Pens	Hat tricks	Total		SG	CSG	Pens	Hat tricks	Total
Nouble	10	2	2		10	Babalola	1	1			1
Sheriff	8	3	1		10	Barrington*	1	1			1
Pollock	7	2			7	Cawley	1	1			1
Krasniqi	4	1			6	Clifford	1	1			1
Blanchfield	4	2			4	Gardner	1	1			1
Reynolds	4	1			4	McGavin	1	1			1
Green	3	1	2		3	Olufemi	1	1			1
Roast	3	1			3						
Elliott	2	2			2						
Opponent	2	1			2						

Appearance grid — columns are players (read vertically), rows are match numbers (No.). Legend: x = Played full 90 minutes, xs = Substituted off, sx = Substituted on, s = Non-playing Substitute.

Haigh C	Roast B	Pollock A	Cawley J	Claridge J	Green D	Olufemi T	Krasniqi K	Blanchfield J	Sheriff D	Nouble J	Gardner J	Moncur F	Sanusi H	O'Donoghue M	Okojie S	Reynolds L	McGavin B (L)	Kiangebeni P	Barrington M	Hernandez A	Essuman G	McFadden A	Howett D (Gk)	Search B	Minshull L	Clifford T (L)	Woods H (L)	Gondoh R	High S (L)	Elliott K (L)	Wells B (L)	Armstrong T	Carlyle N (L)	Maloney T (L)	Babalola T	Laurent A	Marsh G (Gk)	Scott R	No.
x	x	x	x	x	xs	x	x	xs	xs	x	sx	sx	sx	s	s																								1
x	x	x	x	s	sx	x	x	xs	xs	x	sx	sx	sx	s	x	xs																							2
x	x	x	x	x	xs	x	x	xs	xs	x	sx	sx			s	sx	s																						3
x	x	xs	x	x	sx	x	x		xs	x	s	s	x		x	xs	sx	sx																					4
x	x	x	x	x	xs	x	x		xs	x	sx	s	s		s	sx	s	x																					5
x	x	s	x	x	x	x	x	xs	xs	x	s	sx		xs	sx	xs																							6
x	xs	x	x	x	sx	x	sx	xs	x	x	xs	s			s	x	sx																						7
x	sx	x	x	x	sx	x	x	x	xs	s	s	sx			x	sx																							8
x	sx	x	x	x	xs	xs	x	x	s	s	s				x	sx																							9
x	s	x	x	xs	x	x		xs	xs	x		sx		x		sx	sx	s																					10
x	x	x		x	sx	x		xs	x	xs			xs				x	x	sx	sx	s	s																	11
x	x	x		x	sx	x	x	x	x	s			sx				x		x	x	s	s	s																12
x	x	x		x	xs	x	x		sx				s				x		x	xs		x		s	sx	s													13
x	x	s	x	s		x	xs	x	x	sx				x			xs							s	sx	x	x												14
x	xs	x	x		x	sx	x	sx	x				xs				xs							s	s	x	x	x	sx										15
x	x	xs	x	s	sx	x	x	sx	x	x				sx	s										xs	x	xs												16
x	x	x		sx	x	x	sx	xs	xs				sx				s			s		x	x	xs															17
x	xs	x		s	x	x	xs	x	x				s				sx						xs	x		sx	sx												18
x	xs	x		xs	x	s	xs	x					sx				sx	s					x		x	sx													19
x	x	x		s	x	x	x	x	x				x				sx	sx	s	s	s			x	s														20
x	x	x		sx	x	x	x	sx	x				x				sx	s	s		s			x	x														21
x	xs	x		s	x	x	xs	xs	x				sx				sx	s		s			x		x	x													22
x	x	x		sx	x	xs	xs		xs				sx				s	s	x	x	sx																		23
x	xs	x		sx	x		xs		x				sx				s	s	x	xs	sx		x	s	s														24
x	x	x		sx	x	s	s	x					xs				s		x	x	sx	xs	s																25
x	x	x		s	xs	x	x						sx				s		x	x	sx	xs	x		sx														26
x	x	x		xs		xs	x	sx					x				s		x	sx	xs	sx	x	x															27
x	x	x		sx	xs	x							x				s	s	xs	x	sx		xs	sx															28
x	x	x		sx	x	x	xs	sx	x				xs				s	s	s	x	sx	xs	x	s															29
x	x	x			x	x		sx	x			xs		xs			sx		s	s	xs	x	x	sx															30
x	x	x		x	x	x	s	xs	x			xs		xs			s	xs	x	x	sx																		31
x	x	x		sx	x	xs	xs	sx	s	s		xs					s	sx	x	x	x																		32
x	xs	x		sx	x	sx	xs	s	s			s					x	x	xs	sx	x																		33
x	x	x	sx	sx	x		xs	sx	x			sx		s	s	s	xs	xs	x	x																			34
x	x	sx	x		x	x	xs	s	xs			x				x	sx	xs	s	x	sx																		35
x	x	x		sx	x	xs	x		x			sx	sx	xs	s	s	x	xs																					36
x	xs	sx		xs	x	xs		x				s	s	x	x	sx	sx																						37
x	x	x	s	xs	xs	sx	x	sx	sx	s	x	xs	x	x	s	s																							38
x	s	sx	xs	sx	xs	x	x	x	xs	s	x	x	x	sx	x	r																							39
x	x	x		s	x	xs	xs	sx	x	x	s	s	x	x	sx	r																							40
40	27	33	27	11	3	35	22	8	11	26	0	1	0	6	0	13	1	3	2	0	1	0	0	0	3	13	7	0	6	9	0	6	6	2	0	0	2		x
0	9	2	1	0	10	3	6	21	13	5	1	0	1	2	3	7	1	0	3	0	0	0	0	3	1	5	1	0	6	3	0	0	0	1	0	0	0		xs
0	2	3	1	0	18	0	3	3	8	2	4	4	5	3	2	9	4	1	8	2	1	0	0	1	3	0	2	7	1	7	1	0	4	0	2	3	0		sx
0	2	2	0	4	6	0	1	3	2	1	4	4	2	4	2	3	0	0	0	10	1	12	6	13	6	0	0	0	0	1	1	1	3	0	0	2	1	0	s

GOALKEEPERS	CS	CCS
Haigh	7	1

x - Played full 90 minutes
xs - Substituted off
sx - Substituted on
s - Non-playing Substitute

DARTFORD MATCH RESULTS 2019-20

Date	Comp	Opponents	H/A	Att:	Result	Goalscorers	Pos
Aug 3	NLS	Wealdstone	A	930	L 1 - 4	Cunnington 45	
6	NLS	St Albans City	H	919	D 1 - 1	Wanadio 62	
10	NLS	Havant & Waterlooville	H	873	D 1 - 1	Cunnington 40	
12	NLS	Chelmsford City	A	948	L 0 - 4		
17	NLS	Weymouth	A	1010	L 1 - 3	Wabo 90	21
24	NLS	Braintree Town	H	874	W 2 - 1	Allen 43 Wabo 87	
26	NLS	Hungerford Town	A	383	D 2 - 2	McQueen 19 Wanadio 32	
31	NLS	Hemel Hempstead Town	H	961	D 1 - 1	Wabo 84	
Sep 3	NLS	Tonbridge Angels	A	816	L 2 - 3	Hill 43 Sheringham 75	20
Adam Flanagan and Jamie Coyle leave their role as joint-managers.							
7	NLS	Dorking Wanderers	H	897	L 3 - 4	Greenhalgh 23 27 Sheringham 59	20
14	NLS	Concord Rangers	A	526	W 2 - 0	Sheringham 4 Flisher 27	18
21	**FAC2Q**	**Horsham**	**A**	**902**	**W 2 - 0**	**McQueen Allen**	
28	NLS	Slough Town	H	1085	L 2 - 3	McQueen 34 Hill 36	17
Oct 5	**FAC3Q**	**Blackfield & Langley**	**A**	**360**	**W 4 - 1**	**Sheringham 10 67 (pen) Allen 44 Cunnington 80**	
Steve King is named as the new manager.							
12	NLS	Oxford City	A	307	W 1 - 0	Greenhalgh 35	17
19	**FAC4Q**	**Kingstonian**	**H**	**850**	**L 2 - 3**	**Pugh 42 McQueen 71**	
26	NLS	Chippenham Town	H	882	D 1 - 1	Hill 88	18
Nov 2	NLS	Eastbourne Borough	A	444	W 2 - 0	Wabo 31 Romain 70	16
5	NLS	Hampton & Richmond B.	A	451	W 2 - 1	Marsh-Brown 25 Romain 35 (pen)	13
16	NLS	Maidstone United	H	2148	D 2 - 2	Bonner 86 McQueen 89	14
23	**FAT3Q**	**Maidstone United**	**A**	**1255**	**D 2 - 2**	**Romain 65 73**	
26	**FAT3Qr**	**Maidstone United**	**H**	**701**	**L 0 - 1**		
30	NLS	Bath City	A	794	L 0 - 3		16
Dec 7	NLS	Dulwich Hamlet	A	2365	D 1 - 1	Romain 74 (pen)	16
14	NLS	Billericay Town	H	1042	W 3 - 2	McQueen 10 Romain 22 60	12
21	NLS	Concord Rangers	H	971	L 0 - 1		
26	NLS	Welling United	A	1459	W 3 - 0	McQueen 13 (pen) 49 Romain 64	
28	NLS	Tonbridge Angels	H	1239	W 3 - 0	McQueen 27 Romain 68 Sheringham 90+4	
Jan 1	NLS	Welling United	H	1534	W 4 - 0	Berkeley-Agyepong 10 Romain 25 51 McQueen 71 (pen)	
4	NLS	Dorking Wanderers	A	827	W 3 - 2	McQueen 2 90+7 (pens) Romain 72	5
11	NLS	Oxford City	H	1116	W 3 - 0	McQueen 45+2 (pen) Berkeley-Agyepong 45+10 Wanadio 58	7
18	NLS	Slough Town	A	854	L 0 - 1		7
25	NLS	Dulwich Hamlet	H	1501	W 1 - 0	McQueen 23	7
Feb 1	NLS	Chippenham Town	A	614	W 5 - 1	McQueen 17 39 (pens) Nash 21 Bansal-McNulty 26 Puddy 32 (og)	6
8	NLS	Hampton & Richmond B.	H	1263	L 1 - 2	Wanadio 6	
22	NLS	Eastbourne Borough	H	1086	W 2 - 1	Jebb 24 McQueen 54 (pen)	7
29	NLS	Wealdstone	H	1403	D 0 - 0		6
Mar 7	NLS	St Albans City	A	712	W 2 - 1	Nash 29 McQueen 50 (pen)	6
14	NLS	Chelmsford City	H	1486	W 3 - 0	Hill 39 Romain 45+1 Husin 52	6
July 19	**PO Q**	**Slough Town**	**A**	**0**	**W 3 - 0**	**Sheringham 47 55 Wanadio 85**	
25	**PO SF**	**Havant & Waterlooville**	**A**	**0**	**W 2 - 1**	**McQueen 59 69 (pen)**	
Aug 1	**PO F**	**Weymouth**	**A**	**0**	**D 0 - 0**	**(Lost 0-3 on pens)**	

GOALSCORERS	SG	CSG	Pens	Hat tricks	Total		SG	CSG	Pens	Hat tricks	Total
McQueen	16	5	10		20	Nash	2	1			2
Romain	10	4	2		13	Bansal-McNulty*	1	1			1
Sheringham	6	3	1		8	Bonner	1	1			1
Wanadio	5	1			5	Flisher	1	1			1
Hill	4	1			4	Husin	1	1			1
Wabo	4	2			4	Jebb*	1	1			1
Allen	3	1			3	Marsh-Brown	1	1			1
Cunnington	3	1			3	Opponent	1	1			1
Greenhalgh	2	1			3	Pugh	1	1			1
Berkeley-Agyepong	2	1			2						

Appearance grid (player names across top; match numbers 1–42 down the right):

#	Smith M	Bonner T	Hill J	Warner-Eley L	Greenhalgh B	Hayes R	Allen L	Wynter J	Wanadio L	Nasha A	Cunnington A	Wabo N	Pugh A	Vint R	Brodie C	Odaudu S	Sheringham C	Flisher A	Noble L	McQueen D	Howard R (L)	Bacon J	Evans A	Onyemah M	Town J (Gk)	Crook B	Gibbons J	Romain E	Gordon L (L)	Marsh-Brown K	Mendy L	Sesay A (Gk)	Hyde T (L)	Liburd R (L)	Djouaher M	Ming S	Barrington M	Berkeley-Agyepong J (L)	Arnold N	Nash L	Braham-Barrett C	Bansai-McNulty A (L)	McGregor G (L)	Jebb J	Husin N
1	x	x	x	x	x	x	xs	x	x	x	xs	sx	sx	s	s																														
2	x	x	x	x	x	s	x	x	x	x	xs	x	sx	s	s	s																													
3	x	x	x	x	x	s	x	x	x	x	xs	xs	sx	s	s		sx																												
4	x	x	x	x	sx		x	xs	x	xs	xs	xs	s	x			sx	s																											
5	x	x	x	xs			xs	x	sx	x	sx	s	sx		s	sx	x																												
6	x	x	x	s	sx	x		x		xs	sx		x	s		sx	xs	x	xs	x																									
7	x	xs	x	sx	s	x		xs		x	sx	x		s			x	s	x	x	xs	x																							
8	x	xs	x		sx	sx	x		xs		x	sx		x	s		sx	xs	x	xs	x																								
9	x		x		xs	x	x	sx			xs	x		x			sx	xs	x	sx	x	s																							
10		x		xs	x	x	x			xs	sx		x	sx			x	xs	x	xs	s	s																							
11	x	x		xs	x	x	x	sx			sx		x		s	x	x		xs	x	s	s																							
12	x	s	x		x	x	x	x	s		s	s		x	x	s	x	x		x		s																							
13	x	sx	x		x	xs			x		sx	sx		x	x	s	sx	xs		xs	s		s																						
14	x	x	x		x	s	x			x	s			x	x		x	s	s	s																									
15	x	x			x	s	x			xs			sx	x	x	sx				xs	xs	x			sx	s																			
16	x	sx	x		xs	s	x		x			sx	x	x	s			x							xs	s	x	x																	
17	x	x	sx		s	sx	x		sx			s	x	x	xs			x							xs		x	x	xs																
18	x	x	x		s	x		sx			xs	s	sx	x				xs									x	x	x	x	s														
19	x	x	x		s	xs		sx			xs	sx	sx	x				sx									x	x	x	x	xs														
20	x	x	x		sx	x		xs			sx	xs	s	s				sx									x	x	x	x	xs														
21	x	x	x		xs	x		x			x	x						x						s			x		x	sx	s														
22	x	x	x		sx	xs		x			xs	x	sx					x						s			x		xs	x	s														
23	x	x	x		sx			xs			sx	xs	x					sx									x	x	x	x	xs	s													
24	x	s	x		s			s			x	s						x									x	x	x	x			x												
25		s	x		s			sx			x	s						xs									x	x	sx	x	xs	x	xs	sx										
26		s	x		sx		x	xs			xs							x									s	x	x	sx	x	x	xs	x	sx										
27		x	s		sx		x	sx			x		sx				sx	xs									x	xs	x	xs	x	x	s	x	sx										
28		x	x		sx		x	sx			s		sx				x										x	xs	x	xs	x	xs	s		x										
29		x	xs		s		x	sx			sx						s										x	xs	x	xs		sx		x											
30		x	x		s			x			s	s						x									x		x		x	x		x	x										
31		x	x		sx			x			s						sx	x									x		xs	x	x	x		x	xs	x	sx	s						
32		x	x		sx			x			s						sx	x									x		xs	x	x	x		x	xs	x	sx	s						
33		x	x		xs			x			s						sx	xs							xs		x		x	sx	x	x		x		s	sx	xs	xs	x					
34		x	x		s			x			s						sx	xs	xs								x		x		x	x		x		x	sx	xs	xs	x					
35		x	x		x			x			s						sx	s	x								x		x		x	x		x		s	sx	xs		xs					
36		x	x		sx	x		s			s						xs	x							sx		x		x			x		xs	x	xs	s	sx	x	x		xs			
37	x	x	x		x	sx		s			s						x										sx	x			x		x		xs	xs	s		x	xs			x	xs	
38	x	x	x		x	sx		sx			s						xs										sx	x			s		x		s	xs	x	xs		x			x	x	
39	x	x	x		x			s			s						xs										xs	x	sx		s		sx			x	x		x	xs					
40		x	x		x	sx		s			x						sx	xs									xs	sx	x	x					s		x		xs	x	xs				
41		x	x		x	sx		sx			sx						sx	xs									xs	sx	x	sx			xs		s		x		xs	x	xs				
42		x	x		x	s					xs						sx	x									x		sx	x	xs		s			x		x	x					

Totals:

	Smith M	Bonner T	Hill J	Warner-Eley L	Greenhalgh B	Hayes R	Allen L	Wynter J	Wanadio L	Nasha A	Cunnington A	Wabo N	Pugh A	Vint R	Brodie C	Odaudu S	Sheringham C	Flisher A	Noble L	McQueen D	Howard R (L)	Bacon J	Evans A	Onyemah M	Town J (Gk)	Crook B	Gibbons J	Romain E	Gordon L (L)	Marsh-Brown K	Mendy L	Sesay A (Gk)	Hyde T (L)	Liburd R (L)	Djouaher M	Ming S	Barrington M	Berkeley-Agyepong J (L)	Arnold N	Nash L	Braham-Barrett C	Bansai-McNulty A (L)	McGregor G (L)	Jebb J	Husin N
x	27	32	39	6	9	5	16	20	15	4	4	2	4	16	7	0	6	3	7	14	7	0	0	0	15	7	17	10	3	1	15	11	0	0	10	0	5	4	1	8	1	0	5	3
xs	0	1	1	0	4	3	3	0	9	1	7	4	3	2	1	0	1	5	2	17	0	0	0	2	0	2	0	8	0	6	1	0	2	2	0	1	0	1	0	3	2	2	1	1	4
sx	0	2	1	0	2	10	0	2	10	1	1	2	6	4	4	0	11	1	5	5	0	0	0	1	0	3	0	0	0	9	1	1	1	1	1	3	0	2	0	0	3	1	2	0	2	0	0
s	0	4	1	0	2	12	0	0	4	0	13	1	17	12	5	4	1	1	1	5	5	0	2	1	0	0	0	4	1	3	0	2	0	0	3	1	2	0	2	0	0	s

Also Played: Walsh M - 21/09 19/10 23/11 26/11 (s); Lashley - 05/10 (s); Calvert J - 19/10 (s); Edmondson C - 23/11 26/11 (sx); Hawkes T - 23/11 (s); Blackman S - 30/11 07/12 (s); Briggs M - 14/03 01/08 (s) 25/07 (xs). Edwards P (Gk) - 19/07 25/07 01/08 (s)

GOALKEEPERS	CS	CCS
Sesay	7	3
Smith	6	1

x - Played full 90 minutes
xs - Substituted off
sx - Substituted on
s - Non-playing Substitute

DORKING WANDERERS MATCH RESULTS 2019-20

Date	Comp	Opponents	H/A	Att:	Result	Goalscorers	Pos
Aug 3	NLS	Slough Town	A	874	W 1 - 0	Briggs 90+5	
6	NLS	Hemel Hempstead Town	H	694	W 3 - 1	Prior 16 58 McShane 63	2
10	NLS	Tonbridge Angels	H	535	W 3 - 1	McShane 18 Prior 39 Buchanan 62	
14	NLS	Havant & Waterlooville	A	1374	L 0 - 6		
17	NLS	St Albans City	A	442	D 1 - 1	Richards 55	7
24	NLS	Hampton & Richmond B	H	562	L 0 - 1		
26	NLS	Briartree Town	A	444	L 2 - 3	Buchanan 41 Richards 47	
31	NLS	Dulwich Hamlet	H	707	D 0 - 0		
Sep 3	NLS	Chippenham Town	H	453	W 1 - 0	Briggs 58	9
7	NLS	Dartford	A	897	W 4 - 3	McManus 12 Prior 45+3 (pen) Sole 84 McShane 87	6
14	NLS	Maidstone United	H	895	W 3 - 1	Prior 20 (pen) Gallagher 32 Buchanan 77	4
21	FAC2Q	Tooting & Mitcham United	A	326	L 0 - 1		
28	NLS	Billericay Town	A	811	D 2 - 2	Ray 85 Prior 90+4	7
Oct 12	NLS	Hungerford Town	H	662	W 1 - 0	McShane 36	4
26	NLS	Bath City	A	760	L 0 - 1		6
29	NLS	Oxford City	H	511	L 0 - 2		
Nov 2	NLS	Wealdstone	H	817	D 2 - 2	Barham 52 McShane 73	7
9	NLS	Chelmsford City	A	1001	D 2 - 2	Beard 53 Richards 59	
16	NLS	Concord Rangers	A	412	D 3 - 3	Barham 24 McShane 25 Richards 50	7
23	FAT3Q	Leatherhead	A	734	W 3 - 0	Barham x3	
30	NLS	Welling United	A	765	W 2 - 0	Muitt 25 Barham 59	6
Dec 7	NLS	Weymouth	H	619	W 1 - 0	Muitt 7	6
14	FAT1	Bromley	H	759	W 3 - 0	Barham 33 Richards 52 Prior 73	
21	NLS	Maidstone United	A	1730	W 3 - 2	Barham 35 Muitt 63 Prior 77	
26	NLS	Eastbourne Borough	H	514	W 4 - 0	Prior 2 62 Barham 42 Philpott 90+3	
28	NLS	Chippenham Town	A	567	W 2 - 0	Harris 11 Richards 68	
Jan 1	NLS	Eastbourne Borough	A	531	L 2 - 3	Briggs 26 Prior 89	
4	NLS	Dartford	H	827	L 2 - 3	Muitt 76 Moore 81	5
11	FAT2	Stockport County	H	1604	D 1 - 1	Prior 71	
14	FAT2r	Stockport County	A	1121	W 4 - 0	McShane 5 McManus 22 Briggs 68 73	
18	NLS	Billericay Town	H	915	D 4 - 4	McManus 11 Buchanan 58 Prior 73 Briggs 90+4	6
25	NLS	Weymouth	A	872	L 1 - 2	Buchanan 42	6
Feb 1	NLS	Bath City	H	732	D 0 - 0		7
4	NLS	Hungerford Town	A	185	W 1 - 0	Barham 37	6
8	FAT3	AFC Fylde	H	1594	L 2 - 4	McShane 22 Briggs 60	
15	NLS	Chelmsford City	H	517	W 2 - 0	Gallagher J 4 Buchanan 47	
18	NLS	Oxford City	A	223	L 1 - 2	McShane 40	
22	NLS	Wealdstone	A	1131	L 1 - 3	Sole 73	6
29	NLS	Slough Town	H	778	L 3 - 5	Barham 12 Muitt 27 Prior 71	7
Mar 7	NLS	Hemel Hempstead Town	A	401	L 0 - 1		7
14	NLS	Havant & Waterlooville	H	1022	L 1 - 2	Prior 37	7
July 19	PO Q	Bath City	A	0	W 2 - 1	McShane 6 Prior 41	
25	PO SF	Weymouth	A	0	L 2 - 3	McShane 72 Buchanan 84	

GOALSCORERS	SG	CSG	Pens	Hat tricks	Total		SG	CSG	Pens	Hat tricks	Total
Prior	14	3	2		16	Beard	1	1			1
Barham	9	3		1	11	Harris	1	1			1
McShane	11	2			11	Moore	1	1			1
Briggs	6	2			7	Philpott	1	1			1
Buchanan*	7	2			7	Ray	1	1			1
Richards	6	2			6						
Muitt	5	2			5						
McManus	3	2			3						
Gallagher J	2	1			2						
Sole	2	1			2						

Huk S	El-Abd S	Harris E	Ray D	Gallagher J	McManus N	Richards T	Briggs M	Moore L	Prior J	McShane J	Sole G	Beard S	Philpott I	Dyett B	O'Sullivan J	Buchanan E	Taylor L	Sandford R (GK)(L)	Beckles J	Gallagher D	Dixon J	Barham J (LP)	Muitt J	Membrillera G	Wheeler N	Barnett J (Gk)	Howes S (Gk)(L)	No.
X	X	XS	X	XS	X	X	X	X	X	XS	SX	SX	SX	S	S													1
X	X	XS	X	SX	X	XS	X	X	X	X	S	SX	XS	SX	S													2
X	X	XS	S	XS	X	X	X	X	XS	X	SX	S	X	SX			SX											3
X	X	X	XS	SX	X	X	X	X	X	XS	S	SX	SX			S	XS											4
X	X	XS	S	SX	XS	X	SX	X	X	X	S	SX	X			X	XS											5
	X	X	S	SX	X			X	X	SX		SX	X	S	XS	SX	X	X										6
	XS	X	SX	XS	X			X	X	SX		SX	X	X	X	S												7
		X	X	X	XS	XS		X	X	X	SX	X	X	XS			XS	SX	SX	S								8
		X	X	SX	X	X		XS	X	S	X	XS	X	SX	X		X	SX	X									9
S		SX	X	X	X	SX	X		X	X	SX	XS	X		S	XS	X		XS									10
X		X	X	X	X	SX	X		X	XS	XS	SX	X		S	SX			XS									11
X		X	X	XS	X	X			X	X	XS	SX	X		S	S	SX	SX			XS							12
X		X	X	X	X	SX	X		X	XS	SX	XS	X		S	SX	XS		S	X	XS							13
X		S	X	X	X	SX	XS		X	XS	SX	X	X		SX				S	X	XS							14
X		XS	X	X		SX	X		SX	X	SX	X				S	XS		XS									15
X		X	X	XS	X	SX	X		SX	X	X	S	SX	XS		S	X		XS									16
X		X		X	X	XS	S	X	XS	X	S	X				S	S	X	XS		X	SX						17
X		X		XS	X	SX		X	XS	XS	X	X				S	S	SX			X	SX						18
X				X	X	SX	X	SX	XS	SX	X	X	SX			S	S	X			X	XS						19
X		X		SX	X	S	SX	X	XS	X	SX	X	X	S			S	S	X		XS	XS						20
X		X		X	X	S	X	SX	X	SX	SX	S	X	SX		XS		SX	X		X	XS						21
X		X		X	X	SX	X	XS	SX	SX	X	X				XS		S	X		XS	XS						22
X		X		X	X	SX		X	XS	SX	SX	X	X			S		S	X		XS	XS						23
X				X	XS	X		X	X	X	X	S	X		SX		S		X	S	XS	SX						24
X		X		X	X	S	SX	X	X	XS	SX	X				SX		S		X	XS	XS						25
X		X		XS	S	X	X	S	X		SX	X	X			SX		XS		X	SX	XS						26
X	XS			X	XS	SX	X	X		XS	X	X				SX		S	SX	S								27
X	XS			XS	S	X	X	X	X	X	X	S	X			SX		S	X		SX							28
X			S	X	X	X	X	XS	X	X	X	SX	X	X				S		S		S						29
X			S	XS	XS	X	X	X		X	XS	X	X	SX				S	X	SX			SX					30
X			XS	XS	XS	X	X	X			S	SX	SX					X						SX				31
X			X	SX	X	XS	XS	X			X		X	X			S	X			S	SX	XS		SX			32
X		S		X	X	S	X	XS	X	SX		X				S		X		SX	SX	X						33
X		X		X	X	XS	SX		S	X	SX		X	X	S			SX		XS	S	X						34
X		X		XS	X	S	X	SX		X	SX	X	X	S				XS		X	X	S		S				35
X		X		X	XS	XS	X	X		X	S	SX	SX	XS				SX		X	X							36
X		X		X	SX	XS	X	X		X	SX	X	X			XS	S			XS	X							37
X		X		X	S	X	SX	SX	X		X	SX	S							XS	X							38
X		X		X	S	X		SX	XS	SX	X					SX	XS			XS	S	X	X					39
	X	X	SX	XS	XS	X	X	X	X	XS	SX	SX	X				S			S	X						X	40
	X	X	XS	X		X	X	X	X	S	XS	X				S				S	SX			SX			X	41
S	X		SX	X	SX	SX		X	X		XS	S	X	SX		XS	XS			SX		XS	XS		SX		X	42
S	X		SX	X	SX	X		X	X		X	XS	S	SX	XS		SX			SX		XS	XS		XS		X	43
34	6	23	18	16	29	15	27	25	26	28	0	23	30	3	1	3	2	5	0	15	0	9	5	0	1	0	4	X
0	0	8	1	14	8	8	5	1	6	11	5	4	3	3	0	7	9	0	0	8	0	11	9	0	2	0	0	XS
0	0	1	0	9	3	12	6	3	3	2	22	11	5	5	6	7	5	0	3	7	2	3	6	1	3	0	0	SX
3	0	2	5	1	2	7	1	1	1	0	13	1	0	5	15	2	7	1	14	4	5	0	0	1	0	1	0	S

GOALKEEPERS	CS	CCS
Huk	12	4
Sandford	2	2

x - Played full 90 minutes
xs - Substituted off
sx - Substituted on
s - Non-playing Substitute

DULWICH HAMLET MATCH RESULTS 2019-20

Date	Comp	Opponents	H/A	Att:	Result	Goalscorers	Pos
Aug 3	NLS	Tonbridge Angels	A	954	W 2 - 1	Ijaha 22 Monakana 62 (pen)	
6	NLS	Wealdstone	H	1484	W 1 - 0	Orlu 21	4
10	NLS	St Albans City	H	1401	W 2 - 1	Clunis 66 Merson 87 (og)	
13	NLS	Hemel Hempstead	A	367	L 0 - 1		
17	NLS	Concord Rangers	H	1521	D 2 - 2	Mills 45 66	7
24	NLS	Eastbourne Borough	A	650	W 3 - 0	Mills 28 36 Allassani 90	
26	NLS	Slough Town	H	2086	L 2 - 3	Allassani 6 28	
31	NLS	Dorking Wanderers	A	707	D 0 - 0		
Sep 3	NLS	Maidstone United	H	1565	L 0 - 1		8
7	NLS	Braintree Town	A	537	L 1 - 2	Mills 19	12
14	NLS	Hungerford Town	H	2071	L 2 - 3	Mills 14 Ijaha 41	12
21	FAC2Q	**Bognor Regis Town**	H	1689	W 6 - 1	**Taylor 2 Clunis 7 90 Mills 53 73**	
28	NLS	Chippenham Town	A	628	D 2 - 2	Taylor 24 Ijaha 90	13
Oct 5	FAC3Q	**Eastbourne Borough**	H	1834	W 3 - 0	**Orlu 8 Yusuff 68 90 (pens)**	
12	NLS	Weymouth	H	2906	D 2 - 2	Hunte 21 Smith C 56	14
19	FAC4Q	**Havant & Waterlooville**	A	826	W 2 - 1	**Smith C 11 Barnes 18**	
26	NLS	Chelmsford City	A	817	D 1 - 1	Smith C 49	13
Nov 2	NLS	Bath City	H	2816	L 1 - 3	Yussuff 48	15
8	FAC1	**Carlisle United**	H	3336	L 1 - 4	**Smith C 49**	
12	NLS	Welling United	A	469	D 0 - 0		
16	NLS	Billericay Town	H	3132	L 0 - 1		19
23	FAT3Q	**Chippenham Town**	H	972	D 2 - 2	**Mills 20 29**	
26	FAT3Qr	**Chippenham Town**	A	245	W 2 - 1	**Mills 2 Ijaha 75**	
30	NLS	Oxford City	A	323	L 1 - 2	Vose 36	19
Dec 7	NLS	Dartford	H	2365	D 1 - 1	Smith C 48	18
14	FAT1	**AFC Horchurch**	A	454	L 0 - 1		
21	NLS	Hungerford Town	A	310	W 4 - 1	Kearney 49 Chapman 58 Connors 73 (pen) Mills 75	
26	NLS	Hampton & Richmond B.	H	2089	L 1 - 2	Kearney 77	
28	NLS	Maidstone United	A	2309	L 1 - 4	Kearney 45	
Jan 1	NIS	Hampton & Richmond B.	A	773	W 3 - 0	Ainsworth 34 Kearney 37 Clunis 76	
4	NLS	Braintree Town	H	2770	W 6 - 0	Taylor 6 Mullings 20 28 Monakana 45 (pen) 82 Mills 80	15
11	NLS	Weymouth	A	912	D 1 - 1	Ainsworth 16	15
18	NLS	Chippenham Town	H	2901	D 1 - 1	Mullings 90	15
21	NLS	Havant & Waterlooville	H	844	L 1 - 3	Mills 51	15
25	NLS	Dartford	A	1501	L 0 - 1		16
Feb 1	NLS	Chelmsford City	H	2628	W 5 - 3	Monlouis 31 Mills 36 78 90 Smith 51	14
8	NLS	Havant & Waterlooville	A	1431	D 0 - 0		
15	NLS	Welling United	H	1710	L 0 - 1		
22	NLS	Bath City	A	1047	L 2 - 3	Mullings 39 Mills 79	16
29	NLS	Tonbridge Angels	H	2663	L 0 - 1		19
Mar 7	NLS	Wealdstone	A	1310	L 1 - 2	Monakana 32	20
14	NLS	Hemel Hempstead	H	2376	W 2 - 1	Ainsworth 66 Barnes 83	16

GOALSCORERS	SG	CSG	Pens	Hat tricks	Total		SG	CSG	Pens	Hat tricks	Total
Mills	12	3		1	18	Yussuff	2	1	2		3
Smith C	6	3			6	Barnes	2	1			2
Clunis	3	1			4	Orlu	2	1			2
Ijaha	4	1			4	Chapman	1	1			1
Kearney	4	4			4	Connors	1	1	1		1
Monakana	3	1	2		4	Hunte	1	1			1
Mullings	3	1			4	Monlouis	1	1			1
Ainsworth	3	1			3	Opponent	1	1			1
Allassani*	2	2			3	Vose	1	1			1
Taylor	3	2			3						

Player Appearance Grid

Maynard-Brewer A (L)	Orfu R	Taylor Q	Connors J	Barnes A	Smith C	Ijaha D	Monakana J	Clunis N	Monlouis K	Mills D	Ambroisine Y	Yusuff A	White L	Akinyemi D	Case R	Vose D	Morris M	Chapman B	Allassani R (L)	Hunte C	Splatt J	McCoy M	Grainger C (Gk)	Edwards P (Gk)	Smith N	Dempsey B (L)	Ainsworth L	Kearney D	Mullings S (L)	Debrah J (L)	Bedford J (L)	Barbosa D	Kuagica	No.
x	x	x	x	x	x	x	xs	xs	xs	x	sx	sx	sx	s	s																			1
x	x	x		x	x	xs	xs	x	x	sx	sx	sx	xs	x	s	s																		2
x	x		x	x	x	xs	sx	x	x	xs	s	sx	xs	sx	x	s																		3
x	x	x	x	x	x	sx	xs	x	xs	x	s		xs	sx	s	sx																		4
x	x	x	x	x	s	xs	x	sx	x	x	x	s	sx	xs		s	x																	5
x	x	x	xs	x		x		x	xs	xs	sx		x	s	sx		x	sx	s															6
x		xs	x	sx	x	xs	sx	x	x	xs		sx		s		x	x	s																7
x	x		sx	x	x	x	sx	x		x		xs		sx	xs	s	x	xs		s														8
x	x	s	x	x	xs	x	sx	xs	sx	x	x		s		xs		sx	x																9
x		x	x	xs	xs		sx	x	xs	s		sx		sx		s	x	x		x														10
x	xs	x	x	x	x	x		sx	x		xs		s		sx		xs																	11
x	x	x	x	sx	s	xs	xs	x	x	sx	x		sx		sx		s	s	x															12
x	x	x	x	sx	x	x	xs	x	s	x		sx		sx		s		xs																13
	x	x	x	sx	x	xs	s	xs	s	sx	xs		x	sx		s		sx		x	s	x	x											14
	x	x	x	x	sx		sx	x	s	x		x	s		xs		x		xs	s	x	x												15
	x	x	x	x	s	s	sx	sx	x	x		xs	s		x		x		xs	s	x	x	s											16
s	x	x	x	x	x	sx		sx	x	xs		xs	sx		x		x		xs		x	x												17
s	x	x	x	x	x	sx		s		xs		x	sx	sx	x		xs		xs		x	x												18
xs	s	s		x	s	xs	sx		x			xs		sx	x		x		sx		x	x	s	x	x									19
x		s	s	x	s	xs	sx		x			xs	sx		x		x				x	x		x	x									20
x		s		x	xs	sx	xs		x			xs			x		s		sx		x	x			x	x	sx							21
x	x	sx		x	s		sx		x			sx	xs		x		xs		s			x			x	x	xs							22
x	x	s		x	x	s	x		x			s	sx		x		s		s			xs	sx	x	x	xs								23
xs	x	s		x	x	sx	x		x			sx			xs		s		sx			x	x	x	xs									24
s	x	sx		x	x		xs	x				s			xs		sx				x	x	x	xs	x	sx								25
s	x	x	x	x	x	s	sx		sx			xs			sx		s				x	s	x	xs		x	xs							26
x	x	x	sx	x	xs	s	sx		xs			x		x							x	sx		s	x									27
x	x	x	xs	xs	xs	sx	x		x			s		x							x	s		sx	x									28
xs	x	xs	x		x	x		s				xs		x		sx					x	sx		s	x	x								29
	x		x	x	sx	xs	x					x		x		s					x	s		s	xs	x								30
	x		xs	x		x	sx	x		sx			x		x		s	s				x		sx		x	xs	xs	x					31
	x		xs	x		x	x	sx		sx			x		x		s	s				x		sx		x	xs	xs	x					32
	x		x	x	s	x	sx			sx			x		x		s					x		s		x	xs	xs	x	x				33
	xs	s	x	x	x	x	s		x						sx		x					sx		x		xs	s	x	x					34
		s	x	x	x	x	xs		sx						x		x					sx		s	x		xs	xs	xs	x				35
		s	x	x	x	xs	x	x	xs						s		x					sx		x				sx	sx		xs			36
	s	xs	x	x	xs	xs	sx	x	x						sx		x					s		x				sx		x	x			37
	x	sx	xs	x	x	x	x								s		x					s		x				s	sx	x	xs			38
x	x	x	s		s	xs	sx	x							x		x					sx	sx	xs	x		x	xs						39
x	x	x		s		xs		x	x						s		x					sx	sx	xs	x		xs	x	xs	sx				40
x	x			xs		xs		sx	xs						s		x		x			x		x		sx	sx	s			x	x		41
x	x	sx	sx			xs	xs	s							xs		x					xs	x		x		x	x		s		x	x	42
13	21	32	19	24	29	16	9	9	8	25	2	3	1	0	1	17	0	21	3	2	0	16	22	6	9	6	5	5	3	10	1	2	2	x
0	4	1	4	3	4	8	15	8	4	8	2	4	7	2	0	8	0	2	1	5	0	3	1	0	1	1	7	5	6	0	4	0	0	xs
0	0	0	5	5	2	6	5	21	4	5	3	7	10	3	3	6	0	5	1	7	0	1	0	1	3	0	5	5	4	0	0	1	0	sx
0	4	3	8	2	3	6	5	2	5	3	2	6	2	4	7	3	5	0	9	6	3	1	2	4	0	2	2	0	2	0	0	0	0	s

GOALKEEPERS	CS	CCS
Grainger	5	2
Maynard-Brewer	3	1

x - Played full 90 minutes
xs - Substituted off
sx - Substituted on
s - Non-playing Substitute

EASTBOURNE BOROUGH MATCH RESULTS 2019-20

Date	Comp	Opponents	H/A	Att:	Result	Goalscorers	Pos
Aug 3	NLS	Billericay Town	A	824	L 0 - 1		
6	NLS	Tonbridge Angels	H	656	W 2 - 0	Wheeler 14 Luer 45	12
10	NLS	Oxford City	H	454	D 1 - 1	Campbell 38	
13	NLS	Maidstone United	A	1713	D 0 - 0		
17	NLS	Braintree Town	A	356	L 0 - 5		16
24	NLS	Dulwich Hamlet	H	650	L 0 - 3		
26	NLS	Havant & Waterlooville	A	1584	D 0 - 0		
31	NLS	Hampton & Richmond B.	H	511	W 4 - 1	Luer 8 Romain 36 45+2 53 (pen)	
Sep 3	NLS	Welling United	A	412	D 0 - 0		15
7	NLS	Eastbourne Borough	H	677	L 0 - 2		17
14	NLS	Bath City	A	1444	D 2 - 2	Luer 76 Romain 79	16
21	FAC2Q	Tonbridge Angels	A	538	W 2 - 1	Wheeler 60 Romain 81	
28	NLS	Chelmsford City	H	569	L 0 - 4		16
Oct 5	FAC3Q	Dulwich Hamlet	A	606	L 0 - 3		
12	NLS	St Albans City	A	835	W 3 - 1	Ferry 17 Romain 42 West 69	16
Manager Lee Bradbury leaves the club, Sergio Torres takes over as interim player-manager.							
26	NLS	Hemel Hempstead Town	A	387	D 1 - 1	Luer 61	17
29	NLS	Weymouth	H	439	D 1 - 1	Walker 24	
Nov 2	NLS	Dartford	H	444	L 0 - 2		19
Danny Bloor is named as the new manager, with Torres becoming player-assistant manager.							
16	NLS	Hungerford Town	A	306	W 1 - 0	Cox 65	18
23	FAT3Q	Hartley Wintney	H	278	W 3 - 1	Wheeler 2 Cox 62 Walker 68	
30	NLS	Chippenham Town	H	486	W 2 - 1	Campbell 43 Walker 89 (pen)	14
Dec 7	NLS	Concord Rangers	A	243	L 0 - 5		17
10	NLS	Wealdstone	A	676	L 0 - 2		17
14	FAT1	Salisbury	H	371	D 2 - 2	Cox 7 Walker 20	
21	NLS	Bath City	H	373	L 1 - 2	Luer 41	
26	NLS	Dorking Wanderers	H	514	L 0 - 4		
28	NLS	Welling United	H	486	W 2 - 1	Walker 24 Bombelenga 38	
Jan 1	NLS	Dorking Wanderers	A	531	W 3 - 2	Cox 48 Walker 60 Gayle 80	
4	NLS	Slough Town	A	712	D 1 - 1	Wills 57	14
7	FAT1r	Salisbury	A	354	L 0 - 1		
11	NLS	St Albans City	H	431	D 3 - 3	Wheeler 21 Luer 78 Bombelenga 90+1	14
18	NLS	Chelmsford City	A	977	D 1 - 1	Walker 8	14
25	NLS	Concord Rangers	H	489	D 2 - 2	Luer 22 Gbolahan 65	14
Feb 1	NLS	Hemel Hempstead Town	H	474	D 1 - 1	Domi 17	15
8	NLS	Weymouth	A	960	D 2 - 2	Luer 29 Walker 90+4	
22	NLS	Dartford	A	1086	L 1 - 2	Luer 29	18
29	NLS	Billericay Town	H	589	D 1 - 1	Walker 2	17
Mar 14	NLS	Maidstone United	H	817	W 3 - 0	Lewington 42 (og) Skinner 48 Ferry 58	15

GOALSCORERS	SG	CSG	Pens	Hat tricks	Total		SG	CSG	Pens	Hat tricks	Total
Luer	9	2			9	Gbolahan*	1	1			1
Walker	9	2	1		9	Opponent	1	1			1
Romain	4	2	1	1	6	Skinner	1	1			1
Cox	4	1			4	West	1	1			1
Wheeler	4	1			4	Wills	1	1			1
Bombelenga	2	1			2						
Campbell	2	1			2						
Ferry	2	1			2						
Domi*	1	1			1						
Gayle	1	1			1						

Hadler T	Gayle I	Campbell K	Khinda-John K	Adebayo-Rowling T	Adebowale M	Torres S	Wills K	Ferry J	Luer G	Romain E	Cox D	Wheeler N	Walker C	West M	Gharbaoui A	Chalmers-Stevens S (Gk)	Nditi R (L)	Rose J	Debrah J (L)	Jennah A	Hanson J	Bray J	Overton B	Ebuzoeme E	James S	Blackmore D	Mendy S	Bombelenga S	Ravizzoli F (Gk)	Astle M	Skinner J (L)	Gbolahan A	Gravata L	Domi F (L)	Earl J (Gk)	Olosemu D	Kay J	Allen B (L)	No.
X	X	X	X	X	X	X	XS	XS	XS	SX	SX	SX	SX	S	S																								1
X	X	X	XS	X	X	XS	X	SX	X	X	S	XS	SX	SX	S																								2
X	X	X	XS	X	X	SX	XS	X	X	X	SX	XS	S	SX	S																								3
X	X	X	X	X	X	X	X	X	XS	S	S	SX	SX	S																									4
X	X	XS	X	X	X	XS	X	XS	X	X	SX	S	SX	SX	S																								5
X		XS	X	X	X	SX	XS	X	SX	X	X	XS	X	X	SX	S																							6
X	X	X	XS	X	X	XS	SX	X	X	X	S	XS	SX	S	SX																								7
X	X	X		X	XS	X	XS	X	XS	X	X	SX	SX	SX	S																								8
X	XS	X		X	X	X	X	X	XS	X	XS	SX	SX	S	S		SX																						9
X		X	XS	X	X	X	S	X	X	XS	SX	SX	SX	S		X	XS																						10
X		X		X	X	X	XS	X	X	SX	S	XS	X	S	S		X	SX																					11
X	SX	XS		X			X	X	X	XS	SX					X	X																						12
X	X	X	S		XS	XS	SX	X	X	X	S	XS		SX	SX		X	X																					13
X	X			X			X		X		X		X				X																						14
X	XS	X	SX			XS	X	X	SX	X	S	XS	SX	X	S		X	X																					15
X	X	X	S		X		X	X	X			SX	SX	X	XS	S	S	SX		X																			16
X	XS	X	SX	SX	X		X	X	X			SX	XS	X	X	S	S		XS																				17
X		X	X	X	X	S	X	XS	X			SX	XS	X	X	SX	S				S																		18
X	X	X	S	X	X		X	X	X			XS	X	XS	SX		S				SX	S																	19
X	X	X	S	X	X		X	XS	X			XS	X	X	SX	S	S				S	S	SX																20
X	XS	X	SX	X	X		X	X	X			X	X	XS							S		SX	S															21
X	X	X	X	X	X		X	X	X			SX	XS	XS	X						S		SX	S															22
X	X	X	XS	X	X			X	X		X					XS	SX	X			XS				S	SX	SX												23
X	X	X	SX	X	X			X	X			X	XS	XS	X	S	S				S	S	SX				S												24
X	X	X	S	X	X			X	X	XS		XS	X	SX	X	S	S				XS																		25
X	X	X	XS	X	X			X	X			XS		XS	X	SX	S				XS		S				SX												26
	X	X	X	X	S		X	X				XS	XS	X	SX	SX	X				XS			S		XS													27
	X	X	XS	X	SX		X	X				XS	X	XS	SX	S					X		S			SX				X									28
	X	X		X	X			X	SX			XS	X	XS	SX	SX	S				XS											X	S						29
	S	X	X	X			X	X	XS			X	XS	X	SX	X	X				S					SX						S							30
	X	X	XS	X	SX			X	X	XS			X	X	XS	XS	S				S						SX	X											31
	X	X		X	SX		X	X	X					XS	XS	XS	S				X					X	S			X		XS							32
	X		XS	X			X	X	X					X		SX	S				X					X	S			X		XS	XS	S					33
	X			XS			X	X	X					X			SX				XS					X	S	SX	X			X	S		X	S			34
S	X						X	X	X		X			X			S				XS					X				X		XS	SX		X	SX	S		35
S	X			S	X			X	X	X				X			SX				XS					X				X		XS	SX	SX	XS				36
S			X	X			X	XS	X				XS		XS	S					SX					X	SX		SX	X			X			X			37
S	X		X	X			X	X						X	XS	S					S					X		SX	X		XS				SX			SX	38
26	27	28	9	27	25	7	30	28	25	11	8	8	12	10	1	2	4	0	6	0	3	0	0	0	7	0	0	0	10	0	2	0	0	3	0	0	0	0	x
0	4	2	8	3	2	4	4	7	5	3	11	13	10	4	0	0	0	1	1	0	5	0	0	0	0	0	1	0	0	5	0	0	1	0	0	0	0	0	xs
0	1	0	4	0	1	3	2	1	2	3	0	8	4	10	16	12	0	2	0	0	1	5	0	4	0	0	4	1	5	0	0	0	3	1	0	0	1	1	sx
4	0	1	6	0	1	1	0	1	0	1	5	4	1	4	18	17	0	0	0	1	7	3	2	1	2	5	0	0	0	2	0	1	1	0	1	0	1	0	s

GOALKEEPERS	CS	CCS
Hadler	5	1
Ravizzoli	1	1

x - Played full 90 minutes
xs - Substituted off
sx - Substituted on
s - Non-playing Substitute

HAMPTON & RICHMOND BOROUGH MATCH RESULTS 2019-20

Date	Comp	Opponents	H/A	Att:	Result		Goalscorers	Pos
Aug 3	NLS	Chelsmford City	A	908	L	1 - 4	Lewthwaite 65	
6	NLS	Havant & Waterlooville	H	477	L	3 - 4	Lewthwaite 7 Orsi-Dadamo 30 47	
10	NLS	Hemel Hempstead Town	H	384	L	1 - 2	Lewthwaite 24	
13	NLS	Oxford City	A	301	L	2 - 3	Soares 69 (pen) Lewthwaite 78	
17	NLS	Billericay Town	H	424	D	1 - 1	Brown 38 (pen)	22
24	NLS	Dorking Wanderers	A	562	W	1 - 0	Deadfield 59	
26	NLS	Chippenham Town	H	465	W	1 - 0	Orsi-Dadamo 18	
31	NLS	Eastbourne Borough	A	511	L	1 - 4	Hill 71	
Sep 3	NLS	Bath City	A	707	L	0 - 3		21
7	NLS	Concord Rangers	H	485	L	2 - 3	Orsi-Dadamo 30 48	21
14	NLS	Slough Town	A	807	L	1 - 3	Deadfield 16	22
21	FAC2Q	Chesham United	A	413	W	2 - 1	Deadfield 31 Orsi-Dadomo 58 (pen)	
28	NLS	Tonbridge Angels	H	708	W	1 - 0	Deadfield 90+2	20
Oct 5	FAC3Q	Oxford City	A	347	L	0 - 2		
12	NLS	Welling United	A	541	W	1 - 0	Ruddick 75	18
26	NLS	Hungerford Town	A	268	W	2 - 0	Wassmer 19 Orsi-Dadamo 83	15
Nov 2	NLS	Maidstone United	H	619	W	2 - 1	Farrell 8 Lewthwaite 90	14
5	NLS	Dartford	H	451	L	1 - 2	Gray 26	15
9	NLS	Weymouth	A	954	L	1 - 2	Louis 59	
16	NLS	Wealdstone	H	927	W	2 - 0	Orsi-Dadamo 56 Gray 81	11
26	FAT3Q	Billericay Town	A	353	W	2 - 1	Inman 57 Lewthwaite 84	
30	NLS	Braintree Town	A	390	W	4 - 0	Donaldson 3 Soares 17 Hill 60 (pen) Wassmer 90	9
Dec 7	NLS	St Albans City	A	445	D	1 - 1	Young 54	9
14	FAT1	Tonbridge Angels	A	412	D	2 - 2	Orsi-Dadamo 5 Ahmidi 36	
17	FAT1r	Tonbridge Angels	H	238	W	2 - 0	Orsi-Dadamo 8 Donaldson 62	
26	NLS	Dulwich Hamlet	A	2089	W	2 - 1	Hill 35 Farrell 53	
28	NLS	Bath City	H	647	D	0 - 0		
Jan 1	NLS	Dulwich Hamlet	H	773	L	0 - 3		
4	NLS	Concord Rangers	A	412	W	2 - 0	Hill 14 Orsi-Dadamo 55	13
11	FAT2	Yeovil Town	A	1689	L	0 - 4		
25	NLS	St Albans City	H	603	W	2 - 1	Ruddick 23 Hill 31	10
28	NLS	Slough Town	H	415	L	1 - 2	Ruddick 16	9
Feb 1	NLS	Hungerford Town	H	449	W	7 - 1	Orsi-Dadamo 4 36 Hill 10 80 Inman 68 Muir 73 Deadfield 87	9
8	NLS	Dartford	A	1263	W	2 - 1	Orsi-Dadamo 25 Hill 42	
11	NLS	Welling United	H	313	D	1 - 1	Muir 42	
15	NLS	Weymouth	H	458	L	2 - 3	Inman 17 Muir 27	
22	NLS	Maidstone United	A	1769	W	2 - 1	Gray 14 Orsi-Dadamo 90+2	8
Mar 7	NLS	Havant & Waterlooville	A	1347	L	0 - 2		8
14	NLS	Oxford City	H	892	D	1 - 1	Gray 40	8

GOALSCORERS	SG	CSG	Pens	Hat tricks	Total		SG	CSG	Pens	Hat tricks	Total
Orsi-Dadamo	12	2			15	Soares	2	1	1		2
Hill	7	2	1		8	Wassmer	2	1			2
Lewthwaite	6	4			6	Ahmidi	1	1			1
Deadfield	5	3			5	Brown	1	1	1		1
Gray	4	1			4	Louis	1	1			1
Inman	3	1			3	Young	1	1			1
Muir	3	2			3						
Ruddick	3	2			3						
Donaldson	2	1			2						
Farrell	2	1			2						

	Walker L (L)	Inman D	Jelley T	Donaldson R	Fox C	Cook E	Miller-Rodney T	Deadfield S	Stead L	Lewthwaite T	Ewington J	Orsi-Dadamo D	Soares L	Hill R	Brown C	Mason J (L)	Pearce B (L)	McAuley S	Joseph Z	Ruddick L	Flannigan J	Paul C (L)	Mills B (L)	Coulson C (Gk)	Young M	Louis J	Cox S	Gray J	Al Hussaini Z	Lincoln D (Gk)	Wassmer C	Farrell K	Laarbi M (Gk)	Skinner J (L)	Ahmidi W	Wotton J	Hope J	Henry D (Gk) (L)	Muir N (L)	Coleman R	No.
	x	x	x	xs	x	x	x	xs	x	x	xs	sx	sx	sx	s	s																									1
	x	x	xs	s	x		x	xs	x	x	s		x	sx	sx	sx	xs	x																							2
	x	x	xs	s	x		x	s	x	x			x	sx	sx	sx	xs	xs	x																						3
	x	x	x	x	x		x	s	xs	x			xs	x	sx	sx		xs	sx	s																					4
	x	x	sx	x	x		x	x	sx	x			s	sx	xs	x		x	xs	s	xs																				5
	x	x	x	x	sx	x	x	x	s				x	sx	sx	xs		xs	s		sx																				6
	x	x	x	x	x		x	xs	xs	s			x	sx	sx	xs		sx	s		sx																				7
	x	x	x	x	x	xs	x	s		x			x		x	xs		s	xs	sx	s																				8
	x	x	x	x	x	s	xs		xs				x		x			x		sx				sx	xs	sx	s														9
	x	x		x	sx		s	x	sx	x			xs		x			x			s			xs	xs	sx		x													10
	x	x		x	x		x	xs	sx				x		x			s			sx			xs	s	sx		x	xs												11
		x		x			x	x	s	s			x		x					s	s			s	s	x		x	x	x	s	x	x								12
	x	x		x				x	sx	sx			x	sx	x						x			s		xs	xs	xs	x	s											13
		x		x				x	sx	xs			x	sx	x					s				sx		xs		x	x	x	s	x	x	s	s						14
	s	x		xs				x		xs			xs	sx	s			sx							x	xs		x		x	x	x									15
		x		x				x		sx			xs	xs	sx			s							x	xs	sx	x		x	x	x		s							16
		x		x				x		sx			xs	xs	sx	s		sx							x	xs	x	x		x	x	x									17
	xs		x					xs		x			x	x	sx			sx							x	s	x	x		xs	x		sx								18
			xs					x		sx			sx	xs	x			s			x				x	xs	s	x		x	x	x		sx							19
	x		x					x		sx			xs	s	xs	xs		sx			x				sx	s		x		x	x	x									20
		x		x				sx	x				sx	xs	sx	xs	s			s		x			x	s	x			x		x	s		xs					21
		x		x					xs				sx	xs	sx	sx				sx		s			x	s	x			x	x	x		xs							22
		x		x									sx	xs	sx	sx		sx				s			x	s	x			x	x	x		xs							23
		x		x				s	s				sx	xs	sx	sx	s			s					x	s	x			x		x	s	s	x						24
		x		x				s					sx	xs	sx	s	s		xs	s					x	sx	x			x	x	x		x	s						25
		x		x				sx		sx			xs	s	x	sx	s	s							x		x			x	xs	x		xs							26
		x		x				s	xs				xs	sx	sx	x	x								x	s				x	x	x		xs							27
	xs		x					s					sx	x	x	x		x			xs				s	xs				x	x	sx		xs							28
		x		x				s	xs				s	xs	sx	sx		sx			x				xs					x	x	x		x							29
		x		x				s	x				x		x	sx		sx	s						xs		xs	sx		x	x	x		xs	s						30
		x		x				sx	xs				sx	xs				sx	x						x	xs		x	s	x		x	s								31
		x		x				sx	x				sx	xs				s	x						xs	x		x	s	x		x	s		x						32
		x		x				sx	x		s		xs	xs				sx	xs						x	x			x		xs		s	x	sx						33
		x		sx				sx	x				xs	xs				sx	x						x	x		x	x		xs	x	x								34
		x		sx				sx	xs				xs	x				sx	x						x	xs		s	x		xs	x	x		x						35
		x		sx				xs	xs				sx					xs	s						x	xs		x	x		x	s	x		x						36
		x		sx				sx	x				x		x			s	x						sx	xs		x	x		xs	x	x		x	xs	s				37
		x		sx				sx	x				x		x			s	x						xs	x		s			xs	x	x		x	x	sx				38
		x		sx				x	x		s		xs		x			sx	x						xs	x					xs	x	x		x	xs	s				39
x	12	35	6	29	8	3	10	19	4	6	0	18	2	19	3	0	4	2	0	15	0	0	0	15	0	18	13	0	20	16	23	0	0	6	0	0	7	4	0		x
xs	0	2	2	3	0	1	3	10	2	2	1	16	4	11	4	2	1	6	0	3	2	2	0	4	6	5	5	0	0	2	0	0	10	0	0	0	1	0			xs
sx	0	0	1	4	2	0	8	3	4	14	0	4	16	8	7	0	0	16	4	0	4	1	4	0	1	1	2	1	0	0	1	0	2	3	0	0	2	1			sx
s	1	0	0	2	0	2	6	3	4	5	1	1	2	1	6	1	2	6	5	9	0	1	2	2	1	6	1	0	3	0	2	1	6	2	0	1	6	0	0	2	s

GOALKEEPERS	CS	CCS
Lincoln	7	2
Walker	3	2

x - Played full 90 minutes
xs - Substituted off
sx - Substituted on
s - Non-playing Substitute

HAVANT & WATERLOOVILLE MATCH RESULTS 2019-20

Date	Comp	Opponents	H/A	Att:	Result		Goalscorers	Pos
Aug 3	NLS	Welling United	H	1378	D	1 - 1	Deacon 12	
6	NLS	Hampton & Richmond B.	A	477	W	4 - 3	Deacon 2 Fogden 64 Ayunga 72 74	6
10	NLS	Dartford	A	873	D	1 - 1	Ayunga 67	
14	NLS	Dorking Wanderers	H	1374	W	6 - 0	Ayunga 29 78 Deacon 41 Taylor 42 Drury 58 Tarbuck 88	
17	NLS	Chelmsford City	A	1382	D	0 - 0		8
24	NLS	Tonbridge Angels	A	640	W	3 - 1	Ayunga 8 Bailey 18 Drury 45	
26	NLS	Eastbourne Borough	H	1584	D	0 - 0		
31	NLS	Oxford City	A	357	W	3 - 0	Rutherford 4 Deacon 32 Fogden 49	
Sep 4	NLS	Hungerford Town	H	1356	W	3 - 1	Taylor 7 Ayunga 22 55	2
7	NLS	Maidstone United	A	1903	D	2 - 2	Straker 66 (pen) Kedwell 82	2
14	NLS	Braintree Town	H	1351	L	1 - 3	Tarbuck 17	3
21	FAC2Q	**Taunton Town**	H	473	W	2 - 1	Addlesbury 69 (og) Drury 83	
28	NLS	Wealdstone	A	1140	W	4 - 1	Ayunga 15 Drury 35 Rutherford 50 Kedwell 68 (pen)	3
Oct 5	FAC3Q	**Hadley**	H	515	W	3 - 0	Ayunga 49 Rutherford Seager 85	
12	NLS	Hemel Hempstead Town	H	1327	L	1 - 2	Kedwell 80	5
19	FAC4Q	**Dulwich Hamlet**	H	826	L	1 - 2	Rutherford 28	
26	NLS	Concord Rangers	H	1367	W	2 - 1	Kedwell 21 Magri 81	3
Nov 2	NLS	St Albans City	A	409	W	3 - 1	Ayunga 19 69 Kedwell 45 (pen)	3
16	NLS	Bath City	H	1460	W	2 - 1	Rutherford 56 Kedwell 73 (pen)	3
23	FAT3Q	**Cinderford Town**	H	385	W	3 - 1	Robson 23 Rutherford 83 90	
Dec 7	NLS	Chippenham Town	H	1189	W	2 - 1	Kedwell 64 (pen) Paul 86	3
14	FAT1	**Chelmsford City**	A	386	L	1 - 2	Kedwell 54	
21	NLS	Braintree Town	A	430	D	3 - 3	Ayunga 35 Taylor 63 Rutherford 89	
28	NLS	Hungerford Town	A	383	W	3 - 1	Rutherford 23 Kedwell 38 Fogden 45	
Jan 1	NLS	Weymouth	A	1305	W	1 - 0	Walton 45	
4	NLS	Maidstone United	H	1451	L	1 - 2	Read 77	3
11	NLS	Hemel Hempstead Town	A	470	W	2 - 1	Magri 3 Kedwell 53 (pen)	3
18	NLS	Wealdstone	H	1749	L	2 - 4	Beckwith 4 Kedwell 48	4
21	NLS	Dulwich Hamlet	A	844	W	3 - 1	Magri 77 (pen) Tarbuck 82 Rutherford 90	3
25	NLS	Chippenham Town	A	527	D	0 - 0		3
Feb 1	NLS	Concord Rangers	A	300	D	0 - 0		4
5	NLS	Weymouth	H	1483	W	3 - 2	Kedwell 14 Taylor 44 Ayunga 58	2
8	NLS	Dulwich Hamlet	H	1431	D	0 - 0		
15	NLS	Slough Town	A	1028	D	1 - 1	Ayunga 65	
22	NLS	St Albans City	H	1226	L	1 - 2	Ayunga 18	
26	NLS	Slough Town	H	1175	W	1 - 0	Fogden 30	3
Mar 3	NLS	Billericay Town	A	413	W	1 - 0	Ayunga 25	2
7	NLS	Hampton & Richmond B.	H	1347	W	2 - 0	Fogden 77 Ayunga 86	2
14	NLS	Dorking Wanderers	A	1022	W	2 - 1	Bailey 60 Beckwith 90+6	2
July 25	PO SF	**Dartford**	H	0	L	1 - 2	Ayunga 13	

GOALSCORERS	SG	CSG	Pens	Hat tricks	Total		SG	CSG	Pens	Hat tricks	Total
Ayunga	15	3			19	Beckwith	2	1			2
Kedwell	12	3	5		12	Opponent	1	1			1
Rutherford	9	2			10	Paul	1	1			1
Fogden	5	1			5	Read	1	1			1
Deacon	4	2			4	Robson	1	1			1
Drury	4	2			4	Seager	1	1			1
Taylor	4	1			4	Straker	1	1	1		1
Magri	3	1	1		3	Walton	1	1			1
Tarbuck	3	1			3						
Bailey	2	1			2						

Worner R	Beckwith D	Magri S	Read B	Drury A	Bailey N	Straker A	Fogden W	Deacon R	Ayunga J	Taylor J	Rutherford A	Tarbuck B	Paul C	Cook J	Walton S	Dennett O	Kedwell D	Latham K (Gk) (L)	Seager R (L)	Casey M (L)	Flannigan J	Robson O	Eyres O (Gk)	Gomis B	Tiensia J (L)	Tupper J (Gk)	No.
x	x	x	x	xs	x	x	x	xs	x	xs	sx	sx	sx	s	s												1
x	x	x	xs	x	sx	x	x	x	x	xs		sx	s	s	xs	sx											2
x	x	x	xs	x	x	x	x	x	x	xs	sx	sx	s	s	s												3
x	s	x	sx	x	xs	x	x	xs	x	x	xs	sx	sx	s	x												4
x	s	x	sx	x	x	x	xs	x	x	x	xs	xs	sx	sx	x												5
x	s	x	x	x	x	x	x	sx	xs	xs	xs	sx		s		sx											6
x	s	x	x	x	x	x	x	x	x	xs		sx	s	s	xs	sx											7
x	sx	x	sx	xs	x	x	x	xs	x	x	xs	sx		s	x		s										8
x	x	x	x		x	x	x		x	x	xs	xs		sx	s		sx	s	sx								9
x	xs	x	x		x	x	x	xs	x		xs		sx	s		sx	s	sx									10
x		x	x		x	xs	xs	x		x	xs	sx		x	s		sx	s	sx								11
x		x	x	x			xs		xs	x						sx		sx	x	sx							12
x	sx	x	x	x	x	x		xs	x	x	sx		sx			xs		s	xs	s							13
x	s	x	x	x	x	x			x	x	xs		sx		x		xs	s	sx		sx						14
x	s	x	x	x	x	x			x	xs	x		xs		s		x		s		sx	x					15
x	s	x	xs	x	x		x		x	xs	x	sx	s		x		xs	s	sx		sx						16
x	x	x		x	x	x		xs	sx	xs	xs	s		s		s		x		sx		sx	x				17
x	x	x		x	xs	x		xs	x	xs	xs	sx		s		s		x		s		sx	x				18
x	x	x		x	xs	x		x	x	sx	xs	s	s		s		x	s				sx	x				19
s	s	x		x	sx	x			x	x	x	x		x		x		x	x			sx	x				20
x	x	x	sx		x	x		x	x	xs	xs	sx		x	s		s	x				s	x				21
x	x	x	s	x	x	x	xs	xs	x	sx	sx	s		s		s		x	s			s	x				22
x	x	x	sx	x	x	x	xs	xs	x	sx	x	sx	s		x		s					xs					23
x	s	s	x	xs	x	x	xs		x	xs	sx	sx	x	x		s		sx									24
x	sx	xs	sx	x	sx	x	x	xs		xs	x	xs	s	x		x		x									25
x	s	x	sx	x	sx	x	xs		x	x	xs	sx	s	xs	x		x										26
x	sx	xs	x	x	xs	x	x		xs	x	xs	s	s	sx		x											27
x	x	x	x	xs	sx	x	xs		xs	x	sx	x	s	s	s	x											28
x	s	x	x	sx	x	x	xs		x	x	x	x	s	s	x	s	x										29
x	s	x	xs	sx	x	x	xs		x	x	x	sx		x		x						s					30
x	s	x	x	sx	x	x		sx	x	xs	xs	sx		x		x					s		xs				31
x		x	x	xs	x	x		xs	x	sx	sx	x		x	s	xs				sx			x				32
x	s		x	xs	x	x	sx		x	x	sx	s	s		x		xs				x		x				33
x	x		x	sx	x	x	x		sx	x	sx	xs	s		x						x	s					34
x	x		x	s	x		x		xs	x	sx	xs	s		s		x				x		xs	x			35
x	x		x	xs	x			x	sx	s	s	sx		s	s	x					x		xs	x			36
x	x	x	x	s	x	sx	x		xs	x	sx	s	sx			x					x		xs	xs			37
x	x	x	x	s	sx		x		x	x	sx	sx	xs		s						xs		xs	x			38
x	x	x	xs	sx	x	x	x		xs	x	x	s									xs		s	sx			39
x	x	x	xs	sx	x	xs	xs	x	x			sx	sx			xs					s		sx			s	40
39	18	33	22	20	30	34	18	4	20	30	5	5	1	3	15	0	19	1	0	1	0	12	0	2	3	0	x
0	1	2	6	7	4	0	10	7	13	8	14	7	2	1	2	0	6	0	0	1	0	3	0	5	1	0	xs
0	4	0	7	6	6	1	1	1	2	1	17	19	14	3	0	1	6	0	7	0	9	1	0	1	1	0	sx
1	14	1	1	3	0	0	0	0	0	0	6	17	10	15	3	0	9	3	0	3	2	2	1	0	0	1	s

GOALKEEPERS	CS	CCS
Worner	12	3

x - Played full 90 minutes
xs - Substituted off
sx - Substituted on
s - Non-playing Substitute

HEMEL HEMPSTEAD TOWN MATCH RESULTS 2019-20

Date	Comp	Opponents	H/A	Att:	Result	Goalscorers	Pos
Aug 3	NLS	Hungerford Town	H	416	W 4 - 1	Nash 24 85 German 33 Galliford 48	
6	NLS	Dorking Wanderers	A	694	L 1 - 3	Nash 50	11
10	NLS	Hampton & Richmond B.	A	384	W 2 - 1	Essam 35 Ashford 49	
13	NLS	Dulwich Hamlet	H	367	W 1 - 0	Ashford 17	
17	NLS	Wealdstone	H	762	L 0 - 3		9
24	NLS	Oxford City	A	314	W 2 - 1	Phillips 5 German 82	
26	NLS	Billericay Town	H	838	W 3 - 0	Nash 81 German 87 90+2	
31	NLS	Dartford	A	961	D 1 - 1	Ashford 9	
Sep 3	NLS	Slough Town	A	713	L 0 - 2		4
7	NLS	Chelmsford City	H	638	W 2 - 0	Ashford 74 Midson 80 (pen)	3
14	NLS	Tonbridge Angels	A	576	W 2 - 0	Nash 48 52	2
21	FAC2Q	Beaconsfield Town	A	211	L 0 - 1		
28	NLS	Bath City	H	515	W 2 - 1	Nash 45 Midson 87	2
Oct 12	NLS	Havant & Waterlooville	A	1327	W 2 - 1	Ashford 83 90+3	2
26	NLS	Eastbourne Borough	H	387	D 1 - 1	Nash 48	2
Nov 2	NLS	Concord Rangers	A	305	L 1 - 3	Popo 72	4
9	NLS	Braintree Town	H	481	L 0 - 3		6
23	FAT3Q	Haringey Borough	A	234	W 4 - 1	Ashford 22 50 Krohomouh 62 Nash 83	
Dec 7	NLS	Welling United	A	517	L 0 - 2		7
14	FAT1	Maidenhead United	A	387	L 2 - 4	Essam 24 Wall 59	
21	NLS	Tonbridge Angels	H	424	D 1 - 1	Muir 90+3	
26	NLS	St Albans City	A	1078	L 0 - 2		
28	NLS	Slough Town	H	589	D 1 - 1	Ashford 31	
Jan 1	NLS	St Albans City	H	788	W 1 - 0	Essam 48	
4	NLS	Chelmsford City	A	796	L 1 - 2	Ashford 72	
7	NLS	Chippenham Town	A	400	D 2 - 2	Midson 24 Ashford 75	10
11	NLS	Havant & Waterlooville	H	470	L 1 - 2	Midson 62	10
14	NLS	Maidstone United	A	1278	D 1 - 1	Ashford 39	9
18	NLS	Bath City	A	1095	L 0 - 2		10
25	NLS	Welling United	H	467	L 0 - 2		11
28	NLS	Weymouth	H	294	L 0 - 1		11
Feb 1	NLS	Eastbourne Borough	A	474	D 1 - 1	Galliford 6	10
8	NLS	Chippenham Town	H	411	L 0 - 1		11
15	NLS	Braintree Town	A	391	D 0 - 0		
22	NLS	Concord Rangers	H	361	W 1 - 0	Dobson 45+3	11
Mar 7	NLS	Dorking Wanderers	H	401	W 1 - 0	Dobson 87	11
14	NLS	Dulwich Hamlet	A	2376	L 1 - 2	Jarvis 55	11

GOALSCORERS	SG	CSG	Pens	Hat tricks	Total		SG	CSG	Pens	Hat tricks	Total
Ashford	10	2			12	Phillips*	1	1			1
Nash	7	2			9	Popo	1	1			1
German	3	3			4	Wall	1	1			1
Midson	4	2	1		4						
Essam	3	1			3						
Dobson	2	2			2						
Galliford	2	1			2						
Jarvis	1	1			1						
Krohomouh	1	1			1						
Muir	1	1			1						

Football club player appearances table.

	Beasant S	Howells J	Essam C	Braham-Barrett C	Howell L	Sterling T	Midson J	Popo T	German R (L)	Nash L	Ashford S	Galliford I	Kpohomouh J	Dickinson M	Boness D (Gk)	Sundire M	Ibie S	Wallen J	Lacey J	Magagada A	Bettamer Mo (L)	Phillips D (L)	Wall A	Paulin G	Cunnington A	Sinclair R	Ndaba C (L)	Clements B (L)	Whittingham R	Muir N (L)	Grant F (L)	Hanson J	Moore D	Halliday K	Nketia J	Collins L	Dobson J (L)	Grimshaw D (GK)(L)	Davies A (L)	Evans J (L)	Jarvis A (L)	Cawley S	Widdrington T (L)	No.
	x	x	x	x	x	x	x	xs	x		x	xs	xs	sx	sx	s	s																											1
	x	xs	x	x	x	x	sx	x		x	x	xs	sx	xs	s	sx	s																											2
	x		x	x	x	x	x	xs		x	x	xs	x		s	sx	s	sx																										3
	x	x	x		x	x		xs	x	x	x		s	xs	sx	s	sx	s																										4
	x	x	x		x	xs		x	x	sx	x		s	x	s		s	x																										5
	x	xs	x		x	x		sx	xs	xs	sx	sx	s	x	s		x	x																										6
	x	x	x	x		x	x		sx	sx	x	xs	x	s	sx	s		x	x																									7
	x	x	x	xs		x	x	x		sx	xs	xs	x	x	s					s	x	sx																						8
		x	x	x	x		sx	s	xs	sx	x	xs	x		x	s									xs	x	sx																	9
		x	x		x		x	xs	sx	x	x	sx	s	x	x	sx									xs	xs																		10
	xs	x	x	sx		sx	x	x		sx	x	xs	xs	x	s	x	x	x																										11
																																												12
		x	x	xs		x	x	x		sx	xs	xs	sx	sx	x	x	s								s																			13
		x	x		x	xs	x		s	x	x		s	x	xs	x	sx								sx		xs	sx																14
	s	x	x	xs		x	xs	x		sx	x	x		s	x	x	sx								sx		xs																	15
	s	x	x	x		x	s	x		sx	x	xs	sx		x	x	xs								xs		sx																	16
	x	xs	x	x		x	sx	x		sx	x	x				sx	s								sx		x		xs	s														17
									x	x			x																															18
	x	xs			x	x		x	xs	sx	sx	x			x	x									x		sx		sx															19
	x	x	x	sx	x		x	xs	s	sx		xs	xs	x	s										x		sx		s	x														20
	x	x	x	xs	xs	x	sx	x	sx			xs			s										x		sx		s	x	x													21
	x	xs	x		x	sx	x	xs			x	s		s											sx		x		sx	xs	x													22
	x	x	x	sx		x	sx	x		xs	xs			x	s										sx		xs		s	x	x													23
	x	x	x	sx	x		sx	x	s		x	xs	s		x	s													xs	s														24
	x	xs	x	xs	x		sx	x			x	x	sx	x	s										s					x														25
	x	sx	x		x	x	x				sx	x	x	x	s										s				x		xs	xs	s										26
	x	s	x		xs	x	x	sx			x	xs	x	x	s										sx				x		xs	xs												27
	x	x	x		x	x	x			x	xs	x	x	s							sx				sx						xs	s	s											28
	x	x	x		x	x	x			xs	x	x	x	s											x					xs		xs	xs	s										29
	s	sx	x		xs	x	x	x			x	xs	sx	x											x					xs		sx	x			x								30
		xs	x			x	sx				sx	x	x	s							xs				s					s					x	x	x	x	x					31
		s	x			x				sx			x	sx											sx					xs					x	x	x	x	x					32
	s	xs	x			x	sx	x			x	sx	x	x											s											xs	x	sx	x	xs				33
	s			x	s	xs	x		x	s	x														x									sx		sx	x	x	xs	x				34
	s	x		xs	x	x	x				x	s	x	sx											s											xs	x	x	x	sx				35
		x		x	x	x	x				xs		x	sx	sx										xs											xs	x	x	s	sx	sx			36
			x	xs	x	sx					s	x	x	s																				sx		x	x	x	x	xs	sx	xs		37
x	20	16	34	12	17	30	15	20	0	11	19	6	19	18	8	3	0	0	0	3	4	3	0	1	4	0	0	6	4	0	0	0	0	4	7	4	6	3	0	0	0	0	0	x
xs	0	9	0	5	4	1	7	2	4	5	9	12	3	2	0	2	0	0	1	0	1	1	2	0	2	3	1	0	0	2	2	1	3	0	0	0	3	0	0	1	2	0	1	xs
sx	0	2	0	4	0	1	10	3	11	2	2	9	5	5	0	6	1	1	2	0	0	7	0	1	6	0	0	2	0	0	5	2	0	0	1	0	1	0	1	0	1	2	1	sx
s	6	3	0	0	0	1	1	3	2	0	0	4	5	0	24	3	5	1	0	2	1	0	0	1	0	5	0	1	3	0	0	0	1	3	1	1	0	0	0	0	1	0	0	s

GOALKEEPERS	CS	CCS
Beasant	3	1
Grimshaw	3	3
Boness	2	2

x - Played full 90 minutes
xs - Substituted off
sx - Substituted on
s - Non-playing Substitute

HUNGERFORD TOWN MATCH RESULTS 2019-20

Date	Comp	Opponents	H/A	Att:	Result	Goalscorers	Pos
Aug 3	NLS	Hemel Hempstead	A	416	L 1 - 4	Rusby 30	
6	NLS	Slough Town	H	451	W 1 - 0	Constable 4	13
10	NLS	Maidstone United	H	436	L 1 - 3	Constable 26	
13	NLS	Bath City	A	901	L 1 - 2	Halliday 90	
17	NLS	Chippenham Town	H	377	D 1 - 1	Rusby 6	18
24	NLS	Wealdstone	A	771	L 1 - 3	Martin 57	
26	NLS	Dartford	H	383	D 2 - 2	Akers 7 Lynch 90	
31	NLS	Billericay Town	A	716	L 0 - 3		
Sep 4	NLS	Havant & Waterlooville	A	1356	L 1 - 3	Constable 33	22
7	NLS	St Albans City	H	331	L 1 - 2	Lynch 8	22
14	NLS	Dulwich Hamlet	A	2071	W 3 - 2	Ferdinand 48 Tomlinson 50 Jones Matt 68	21
21	FAC2Q	Poole Town	A		L 1 - 2	Ferdinand	
28	NLS	Welling United	H	284	L 1 - 2	Lynch 90+1	22
Oct 12	NLS	Dorking Wanderers	A	662	L 0 - 1		22
19	NLS	Concord Rangers	A	304	W 2 - 0	Olomowewe 49 Ferdinand 90+4	20
26	NLS	Hampton & Richmond B.	H	268	L 0 - 2		22
Nov 2	NLS	Braintree Town	A	412	W 3 - 0	McGlip 19 78 Ferdinand 51	20
16	NLS	Eastbourne Borough	H	306	L 0 - 1		21
23	FAT3Q	Chelmsford City	A	427	L 1 - 2	Halliday 47	
30	NLS	Weymouth	A	862	L 1 - 2	Maturino 17	21
Dec 3	NLS	Tonbridge Angels	H	191	W 1 - 0	Johson-Schuster 61	20
7	NLS	Chelmsford City	A	686	L 1 - 4	Maturino 49	21
21	NLS	Dulwich Hamlet	H	310	L 1 - 4	Klukowski 88	22
26	NLS	Oxford City	A	328	L 2 - 3	Ferdinand 15 Rusby 70	22
28	NLS	Havant & Waterlooville	H	383	L 1 - 3	Lynch 90	22
Jan 1	NLS	Oxford City	H	283	L 1 - 2	Graham 45+2	22
4	NLS	St Albans City	A	571	D 2 - 2	Graham 57 Tomlinson 90	22
18	NLS	Welling United	A	564	L 2 - 3	Ferdinand 17 Jones Matt 77	22
25	NLS	Chelmsford City	H	240	W 1 - 0	Tomlinson 37	22
Feb 1	NLS	Hampton & Richmond B.	A	449	L 1 - 7	Akers 5	22
4	NLS	Dorking Wanderers	H	185	L 0 - 1		22
15	NLS	Tonbridge Angels	A	383	D 1 - 1	Jones Matt 50	22
22	NLS	Braintree Town	H	207	W 2 - 0	Tomlinson 6 Jones Matt 49	22
Mar 7	NLS	Slough Town	A	885	W 2 - 0	Artwell 8 Rusby 47	22
14	NLS	Bath City	H	619	L 0 - 1		22

GOALSCORERS	SG	CSG	Pens	Hat tricks	Total		SG	CSG	Pens	Hat tricks	Total
Ferdinand	6	2			6	McGlip	1	1			2
Jones Matt	4	2			4	Artwell	1	1			1
Lynch	4	1			4	Johnson-Schuster	1	1			1
Rusby	4	1			4	Klukowski	1	1			1
Tomlinson	4	1			4	Martin	1	1			1
Constable	3	2			3	Olomowewe	1	1			1
Akers	2	1			2						
Graham	2	2			2						
Halliday	2	1			2						
Maturino	2	1			2						

Siviter A (L)	Jones Matt	Johnson-Schuster M	Berry-Hargreaves M	Rusby J	Tomlinson J	Constable J	Jones Mike	McGory L	Akers Z	Ferdinand L	Bailey D	Halliday K	Lynch C	Thorp A	Dunstan J	Smith G	Martin J	Odimayo A (L)	Olomowewe T	Klukowski Y	McGlip C (L)	Maturino J	Rees T (Gk)	Bradley-Hurst J (Gk) (L)	Webb B (L)	Jarra B	Graham R (L)	Ohman P (Gk)	Artwell O (L)	Henry W (Gk) (L)	No.
x	xs	x	x	x	x	x	x	xs	xs	x	sx	sx	sx	s	s																1
x	s	x	s	x	x	x	x	x	s	x	x	x	s	s	x																2
x	sx	x	s	x	x	xs	x	xs	sx	x	x	xs	sx		x	s															3
x	s	xs	sx	x	x	x	xs	sx	x	x	x	sx	s		x	x															4
x	s		x	x	x	x	x	s	xs	xs	sx	x	x		x	xs	sx														5
x	s		xs	x	x	x	xs	sx	xs	sx	x	s	x	sx		x	x	x													6
x	xs	x		x	sx	x	sx	xs	x	s	x	sx				x	s	x													7
x		x	s	x	x	xs	xs	sx	x	sx	x	s				x	xs	x													8
x	x	x	sx		x	x	x	s	sx	sx	x	xs	xs			xs	s	x													9
x	xs	x	x		x	x	x	sx	xs	xs	s	s	x			xs	x														10
x	xs	x	x	x	x	x	x	sx	x	sx	s	x				s	s														11
x	x	x	x	xs	x	x	x	x	sx	x								x													12
x	xs		x	sx	x	xs		x	x	x	s	sx	sx		s				x	x	xs										13
x	s	x	s	x	x	sx		x	x	xs	xs	sx			sx				x	x	xs										14
x	sx	x	sx		x	x		x	x	sx	s	s			xs				x	x	xs	xs									15
x	sx	xs	s	xs	x	xs		x	x	s	sx	sx			x				x	x		x									16
x	xs	x	s	x	x	sx		x	x	sx	s				xs	x	xs	x	sx												17
x	x	x	x	x	sx	sx		x	x	sx								xs		x		s									18
xs	x	s	s	x	x		x	x	s	sx	xs			s	x			x			sx	x									19
	x	x		x	xs		xs		x	s	sx		s	sx	x	x	x	s		x		x									20
	s	x	x	x		sx		x	sx	xs	s			x	x	x	s		xs		x	x									21
	sx	xs		x	x		sx		x	sx	xs			xs	x	x	s			x	x	s									22
x	s	x		x	x		xs		x	x	sx			s		x	sx					xs	xs	x							23
x	x		sx	x		s		x	x	sx			s			x			x	xs		sx		xs	x	xs					24
x	x			sx	x			sx	x	xs	x			sx		x				x				xs	s		x	s			25
x	x	s			sx			xs	x		sx			sx		x				x				xs	s	sx	x	x			26
x	x	s			sx			sx	x		sx			sx		x				x				xs	s	sx	xs	xs			27
x	xs	s	s	x	x		x	sx	sx	x	xs					x										x	x	xs			28
x	xs		sx	x	x		x		xs	xs	sx					x			s		s					x	x	x			29
xs	x		sx	x	x		x	s	x	x	s					xs			sx							xs	x	x			30
	sx		x	x	x		xs		x	x	s					sx			xs			s				x	s	x	x		31
	x		x	x	x		s	sx	x	s						xs			xs			s				x	xs	x	sx		32
	x		xs	x	x		x		xs	xs	sx					sx			x		s	s				x	x	x	sx		33
	x		xs	x	x		x		sx	xs	sx					x			x		sx	s				xs	s	x	x	x	34
	x			x	x		xs	sx	x	sx	s					x			xs	x	s	s				x		x	x		35
25	13	17	8	28	33	11	16	4	18	21	5	5	1	0	7	13	5	8	15	2	4	2	1	3	5	8	7	3	2	2	x
1	9	3	2	3	1	4	7	3	8	5	6	3	5	0	1	8	0	1	0	8	1	4	0	0	3	2	5	0	0	0	xs
0	5	0	5	2	1	3	6	7	8	6	12	6	19	0	0	0	2	1	0	0	2	0	4	0	0	2	0	0	2	0	sx
0	7	3	10	0	0	0	1	4	1	1	9	3	6	2	4	6	0	0	0	4	0	4	8	0	0	2	1	1	0	0	s

GOALKEEPERS	CS	CCS
Siviter	4	1
Bradley-Hurst	1	1
Henry*	1	1
Ohman	1	1

x - Played full 90 minutes
xs - Substituted off
sx - Substituted on
s - Non-playing Substitute

MAIDSTONE UNITED MATCH RESULTS 2019-20

Date	Comp	Opponents	H/A	Att:	Result	Goalscorers	Pos
Aug 3	NLS	Weymouth	H	2015	L 1 - 2	Amaluzor 54	
6	NLS	Welling United	A	1015	L 0 - 1		
10	NLS	Hungerford Town	A	436	W 3 - 1	Wishart 39 Kyei 66 (pen) Kamdjo 72	
13	NLS	Eastbourne Borough	H	1713	D 0 - 0		
17	NLS	Slough Town	H	1815	D 1 - 1	McClure 37	14
24	NLS	Concord Rangers	A	387	W 1 - 0	McClure 26	
26	NLS	Chelmsford City	H	1914	W 4 - 1	Wishart 4 85 Amaluzor 61 Akanbi 68	
31	NLS	Wealdstone	A	1066	L 1 - 2	Wishart 86	
Sep 3	NLS	Dulwich Hamlet	A	1565	W 1 - 0	Akanbi 85	7
7	NLS	Havant & Waterlooville	H	1903	D 2 - 2	Edwards 25 Wishart 90+2	10
14	NLS	Dorking Wanderers	A	895	L 1 - 3	McClure 8	11
21	FAC2Q	Cheshunt	H	1129	W 4 - 1	McClure 5 Akanbi 12 Allen 58 Chesmain 65	
28	NLS	St Albans City	H	1806	W 4 - 0	McClure 22 45 63 Corne 74	9
Oct 5	FAC3Q	Hitchin Town	H	1253	W 2 - 1	Chesmain 12 Akanbi 14	
12	NLS	Bath City	A	1387	D 1 - 1	Johnson 76	9
19	FAC4Q	Kings Langney	H	1441	W 4 - 1	Johnson 53 Khan 58 Chesmain 77 Edwards 89 (pen)	
26	NLS	Billericay Town	H	2031	W 2 - 1	Akanbi 24 Amaluzor 28	8
29	NLS	Braintree Town	A	458	D 1 - 1	Allen 30	8
Nov 2	NLS	Hampton & Richmond B.	A	619	L 1 - 2	Kyei 50	8
9	FAC1	Torquay United	H	2330	W 1 - 0	Wishart 19	
16	NLS	Dartford	A	2148	D 2 - 2	Wishart 59 Akanbi 63	9
23	FAT3Q	Dartford	H	1255	D 2 - 2	Wishart 38 Amaluzor 70	
26	FAT3Qr	Dartford	A	701	W 1 - 0	Allen 59	
Dec 1	FAC2	Blackpool	A	3977	L 1 - 3	Khan 29	
7	NLS	Oxford City	A	344	W 4 - 1	Wishart 11 McClure 53 60 Amaluzor 81	8
10	NLS	Chippenham Town	H	1337	D 0 - 0		8
14	FAT1	Concord Rangers	H	881	L 2 - 3	Temelci 14 McClure 19	
21	NLS	Dorking Wanderers	H	1730	L 2 - 3	Akanbi 36 41	
28	NLS	Dulwich Hamlet	H	2309	W 4 - 1	Akanbi 17 Marshall 21 Hoyte 52 Allen 71	
Jan 1	NLS	Tonbridge Angels	H	2520	D 2 - 2	Hoyte 3 Allen 27	
4	NLS	Havant & Waterlooville	A	1451	W 2 - 1	Akanbi 32 45	8
14	NLS	Hemel Hempstead Town	H	1278	D 1 - 1	Elokobi 57	8
18	NLS	St Albans City	A	683	L 0 - 1		8
25	NLS	Oxford City	H	1739	W 1 - 0	Amaluzor 59	8
Feb 8	NLS	Braintree Town	H	1875	W 1 - 0	Amaluzor 17	
15	NLS	Chippenham Town	A	497	L 0 - 1		
18	NLS	Bath City	H	1450	L 0 - 2		
22	NLS	Hampton & Richmond B.	H	1769	L 1 - 2		10
29	NLS	Weymouth	A	956	L 1 - 5	Corne 75	10
Mar 7	NLS	Welling United	H	1943	W 3 - 1	Allen 52 Temelci 70 Ayuk 90+3	9
14	NLS	Eastbourne Borough	A	817	L 0 - 3		9

GOALSCORERS	SG	CSG	Pens	Hat tricks	Total		SG	CSG	Pens	Hat tricks	Total
Akanbi	9	2			11	Khan	2	1			2
McClure*	7	3		1	10	Kyei	2	1	1		2
Wishart	8	3			9	Temelci	2	1			2
Amaluzor	7	2			7	Ayuk	1	1			1
Allen	6	2			6	Elokobi	1	1			1
Chesmain	3	1			3	Kamdjo*	1	1			1
Corne	2	1			2	Marshall	1	1			1
Edwards	2	1	1		2						
Hoyte	2	2			2						
Johnson	2	2			2						

Cole J	Elokobi G	Hoyte G	Khan S	Pennell L	Johnson R	Allen I	Corne S	Edwards J	Kyei N	Amaluzor J	Chesmain N	Akanbi I	Olutade I	Lewington C (Gk)	Knight L	Wishart D	Kamdjo C	Divine D	Gilbert J	McClure M	Ayuk A	Embery J	Marshall R	James C (L)	Temelci Z	Tingley J	Wilkins L	Ribbens S (Gk)	Boucaud A	Freeman O	Watters M (L)	Felix J	Williams C	Seaman C (L)	No.
X	X	X	XS	X	X	XS	X	XS	X	X		SX	SX	S	S																				1
X	X	X	X	XS	X	XS	X	XS	X	X		SX	SX		S	S	SX																		2
X	X	X	X		X	XS	X		X		X	XS	SX	S		XS	SX	S	S																3
X	X	X	X		X	SX	XS		X		X	XS	SX	S		X	X	S	S																4
X	X	X	XS		X	SX	X		XS	XS	X	X		S	S	SX	X		X																5
X	X	X	X		S	X	SX		X	X	X	SX		S	S	X	SX		XS																6
X	XS	X	X		S	X	SX	XS	SX	X	X	SX		S	SX	X			XS																7
X		X	X		S	X	XS	XS	SX	XS	X	SX		S	X	X			X	SX															8
X	X	X	S			X	XS	SX	XS	X	X		S	X	X	X			X	S															9
X	X	X	S		SX	X	XS	XS		X	SX		S	X	X	X			XS	SX															10
X	X	X	X	SX		XS	XS		X	SX	X	X		S	SX	X	X		S	X		SX													11
X	X	XS	X	XS	X	XS	SX	S	SX		X	XS	S	S	X	X		S	X	SX															12
X	X	X	X	XS	SX		XS	SX	SX		X	XS		X	X	X			X	S															13
X	X	X	X	S	X	S		SX	XS	SX	X	XS		X	X	X			S																14
X	X	X		X	XS		SX	SX	SX	X	XS				XS	S			X			S	X												15
X	X	X	X	S	X	SX		SX	S	XS	X	XS		X	SX		S	XS		X															16
X	X	X	X	S	X	XS		SX		X	X	XS		X	S				SX	X															17
X	X	X	X	S	X	XS		SX		X	XS	X		X	S				S	X															18
X	X	X	X	S	X	X		SX	XS	X	X	XS		S			S			SX	X														19
X	X	X	X	X	X	S		SX	XS	SX	X	XS		S		X			S	S		S		X											20
X	X	X	XS	X	S		X			X	X	XS		S		X			SX		S	SX	XS												21
X	X	X	X	S	SX	SX		S	S	XS	X	XS		S		X			X		SX	X	XS												22
X	X	X	XS	S	X	X		SX	S	S	X		S		X	X	SX		X		XS	XS	SX												23
X	X	X	X	S	X	XS		S	SX	X	XS	S		X		X			SX		S	X	XS	SX											24
X	X	X	X	S	X	S		S	X	X	S			X	S	X					X		X												25
X	X	X		XS	X	SX		S	X	X	S		S	X	S	X					X		X												26
X	X	X		X		S		S	S	X	X	X		S	S	X	S				X		S	X		X									27
S	X	X		X		XS		X		S	X	X		X		X	S	S			SX		X		X										28
S	X	X		X	XS		SX			X	XS		X	S	X		SX	XS		SX	X		X		X										29
X	X		X	XS		X			X	X	X	S	X				SX	X		X	S														30
X	X		S	X	S			X	X	S	X	X	X		X		X		X		X		S	S											31
X	X	X		XS			SX	X	XS	S	X	X	X	S		SX		X	X		S														32
X	X	X		XS		X		X	SX	X	X	X	S		SX		X	X		S	SX	S													33
S	X	X	X		S			X	X	XS	SX	X	S	X	S		X		X		X														34
S	X	X	X	S	SX	SX		X	XS	XS	SX	X		X		X	XS		X																35
SX	X	X	X	SX	S	XS		XS	X	X	X	S	XS	SX	X	X		X																	36
X	X	X	X	XS		X		X	X	XS	S		SX		S		X	XS		S	X														37
S	X	X	X	SX	SX	X		X		X	X	S	X	X	XS	XS		X	X	S															38
S	X	X	X	XS	X	X		X	XS	X	S	X	SX	SX	X	S																			39
S	X	X	X	XS	X	X		X	S	X	S	SX	X	X	S																				40
S	X	X	X	S	XS	X	XS	X	SX	X	XS	SX	X	SX																				SX	41
27	36	40	31	5	27	3	8	2	5	18	33	8	0	13	6	33	8	0	0	14	0	0	23	1	12	0	0	0	4	0	4	0	0	0	X
0	1	0	4	4	0	15	5	8	6	6	2	18	0	1	2	2	0	0	0	5	0	1	2	3	4	0	0	0	1	0	0	0	0	0	XS
1	0	0	0	1	3	9	3	10	6	5	2	9	6	0	3	2	5	0	1	3	4	8	1	1	2	1	0	0	2	0	0	0	0	1	SX
8	0	0	0	12	2	10	0	4	7	2	0	0	4	26	11	0	10	2	13	1	1	8	0	0	0	2	1	4	0	1	0	1	1	0	S

GOALKEEPERS	CS	CCS
Cole	7	1
Lewington	2	2

x - Played full 90 minutes
xs - Substituted off
sx - Substituted on
s - Non-playing Substitute

OXFORD CITY MATCH RESULTS 2019-20

Date	Comp	Opponents	H/A	Att:	Result	Goalscorers	Pos
Aug 3	NLS	Concord Rangers	H	325	L 0 - 3		
6	NLS	Chippenham Town	A	582	D 1 - 1	Brown 78	
10	NLS	Eastbourne Borough	A	454	D 1 - 1	McEachran 69	
13	NLS	Hampton & Richmond B.	H	301	W 3 - 2	Owusu 6 Moore-Azille 48 64	
17	NLS	Welling United	A	424	L 1 - 3	Wiltshire 75	15
24	NLS	Hemel Hempstead Town	H	314	L 1 - 2	Wiltshire 52	
26	NLS	Bath City	A	1030	W 2 - 1	Moore-Azille 50 Brown 75 (pen)	
31	NLS	Havant & Waterlooville	H	357	L 0 - 3		
Sep 3	NLS	Weymouth	H	1102	D 0 - 0		17
7	NLS	Wealdstone	A	1102	L 0 - 1		18
14	NLS	Billericay Town	H	309	D 2 - 2	McEachran 20 Self 53	19
21	FAC2Q	North Leigh	H	334	W 7 - 0	Self 2 Learoyd 15 (og) Jefford 33 Ashby 72 Wiltshire 75 Wright 77 King R	
28	NLS	Braintree Town	A	481	L 0 - 1		18
Oct 5	FAC3Q	Hampton & Richmond B.	H	347	W 2 - 0	Owusu 52 McEachran 56	
12	NLS	Dartford	H	307	L 0 - 1		20
19	FAC4Q	Margate	H	442	W 2 - 1	Owusu 11 Wiltshire 15	

Manager Mark Jones leaves the club by mutual consent, Justin Merritt and Andy Ballard are put in temporary charge.

Date	Comp	Opponents	H/A	Att:	Result	Goalscorers	Pos
26	NLS	Slough Town	H	416	W 2 - 1	McEachran 46 Jones 71	19
29	NLS	Dorking Wanderers	A	511	W 2 - 0	Owusu 49 (pen) 56	
Nov 2	NLS	Tonbridge Angels	A	473	D 4 - 4	McEachran 31 Fleet 39 Brown 87 90	17
9	FAC1	Solihull Moors	H	667	L 1 - 5	Wiltshire 80	
16	NLS	Chelmsford City	A	759	W 6 - 2	Rowe 22 28 33 (pen) Ashby 58 (pen) Lofthouse 60 McEachran 63 16	
23	FAT3Q	AFC Hornchurch	H	228	D 1 - 1	Owusu 14	
26	FAT3Qr	AFC Hornchurch	A	139	D 4 - 4	Benyon 43 65 Ashby 95 Brown 108 (Lost 1-4 on pens aet)	
30	NLS	Dulwich Hamlet	H	323	W 2 - 1	Owusu 17 54 (pens)	12
Dec 7	NLS	Maidstone United	A	344	L 1 - 4	Lofthouse 50	15
17	NLS	St Albans City	H	205	D 3 - 3	Gordon 6 McEachran 57 Berkoe 80	15
26	NLS	Hungerford Town	H	328	W 3 - 2	McEachran 41 63 Benyon 47	
28	NLS	Weymouth	A	1131	L 1 - 2	Fleet 90+2	
Jan 1	NLS	Hungerford Town	A	283	W 2 - 1	Ashby 40 Lofthouse 76	
4	NLS	Wealdstone	H	449	W 3 - 2	Oastler 42 Benyon 47 Tapp 77	12
11	NLS	Dartford	A	1116	L 0 - 3		13
18	NLS	Braintree Town	H	601	L 1 - 4	Gordon 87	13
25	NLS	Maidstone United	A	1739	L 0 - 1		13
Feb 1	NLS	Slough Town	A	884	W 1 - 0	Bird 42 (og)	12
15	NLS	St Albans City	A	566	D 0 - 0		
18	NLS	Dorking Wanderers	H	223	W 2 - 1	McEachran 4 Owusu 73	
22	NLS	Tonbridge Angels	H	729	L 0 - 3		
25	NLS	Billericay Town	A	414	D 1 - 1	Berkoe 50	12

David Oldfield is named as the new manager.

Date	Comp	Opponents	H/A	Att:	Result	Goalscorers	Pos
Mar 7	NLS	Chippenham Town	H	366	L 1 - 3	Ashby 28 (pen)	13
14	NLS	Hampton & Richmond B.	A	892	D 1 - 1	Owusu 15	14

GOALSCORERS	SG	CSG	Pens	Hat tricks	Total		SG	CSG	Pens	Hat tricks	Total
McEachran	9	2			10	Fleet	2	1			2
Owusu	8	1	3		10	Gordon	2	1			2
Ashby	5	1	2		5	Opponent	2	1			2
Brown	4	1	1		5	Self	2	2			2
Wiltshire	5	2			5	Jefford	1	1			1
Benyon	3	1			4	Jones	1	1			1
Lofthouse*	3	1			3	King R	1	1			1
Moore-Azille	2	1			3	Oastler	1	1			1
Rowe	1	1	1	1	3	Tapp	1	1			1
Berkoe	2	1			2	Wright	1	1			1

King C	Oastler J	Jefford B	Tapp F	Fleet R	Ashby J	Self J	Wiltshire K	Jones E	Brown S	Rowe D	Owusu N	McEachran Z	Moore-Azille T	Fasanmade C	Caro S	Wright J	Isted H (Gk) (L)	King R	Barrett B	Hakwins T	Beckles R (L)	Paul-Jones T	Gough E (Gk)	Benyon E	Nyammey K	Lofthouse K (L)	Berkoe K (L)	Foster A (Gk)	Gordon J	George A	Harris M (Gk) (L)	Jones N (L)		No.
x	x	x	x	x	xs	xs	x	x	x	sx	sx	sx	s	s																				1
x	x	x	x	x	xs	x	xs	x	x	xs	sx	sx	sx	s	s																			2
x	x	s	x	x	x	x	xs	x	x	s	x	sx	x	s	s																			3
x	x	x	s	x	x	x	sx	x	xs	sx	xs	xs	x	sx	s																			4
x	x	xs	sx	xs	x	x	sx	x	s	sx	xs	x	x	x	s																			5
x	x	s	x	x	x	sx	x	x	x		xs	xs	x	sx	s	s																		6
x	x	x	xs	x	x	x	xs	x	x		s	sx	x	sx		s																		7
xs	x	x	s	x	x	xs	xs	x	x		sx	x	x	sx	sx	s																		8
	x	x	sx	x	x	x	x	xs			sx	x	xs	xs	s	s	x																	9
	x	x	x		x	x		x	x			x	s	x		x	x	s	s	s														10
	x	xs			x	xs	xs	sx			s	xs	s	x		x	x			s	x													11
x	x	x	x	x	x	xs	x				sx			xs		sx	sx		x	x	s													12
	x	x	x	xs	x	x	x				x			sx		xs	x	s		x	s	sx												13
x	x	x	x	x	x	x	sx	sx			xs	xs	s	s		sx							xs	s	s									14
x	x	x	x	x	x	x	xs	sx			xs	x	s	sx		s							xs			sx								15
x	x	x	x	x	x	x	xs	x			xs	sx	sx	sx		s							s	xs	s	s								16
x	x	x	x	x	x	sx	xs	x			sx	xs	xs	s		s						sx			x									17
x	x	x	x	x	x	sx	x	x			s	x	xs	s		s						s			x									18
x	x	x	x	x	x	sx	xs	x		sx	sx			xs	s		s									xs								19
x	x	x	x	x	x	s	x	xs	xs	sx	x	xs	sx	sx	s		s									s		sx						20
x	x	x		x	x	x	sx			s	xs	s	sx	x		sx			s							x		x						21
x	x	x	s	x	x	x	x	s	s	sx	sx	x					xs									xs		x	x	s				22
x	x	x	sx	x	x	x	xs	sx	sx	sx	xs	x		s	s	xs										x		xs	x					23
x		x	x	sx	x	x	x	x	x	s	s	x														xs		x	x		sx			24
x		x	x	xs	x	x	x		s	s	x	s		xs												x		x	x		sx			25
x	x		x	x	x		x			s	xs	sx	xs	s												sx		x	x		xs	sx		26
x	x	sx		x	x		x			s	s	sx	x	xs												x		xs	x		x	s		27
x	x	s	s	x	x		x				xs	sx	xs	x												xs		sx	x		x	sx		28
x	x	x	x	x	x		s	sx	sx		s	x														x		x	xs		xs	s		29
	x	x		x	x		s	sx	x		s	s	sx													xs		x	x		xs	xs	x	30
	x	x	xs	x	x		s	s	sx		sx	x	sx													xs		x	x		xs	x	x	31
	x	s		x	x		sx	x	sx		sx	x														xs		xs	x		xs	x	x	32
s	x	x		x	x		s	xs			sx	x														x		x	xs		sx	x	x	33
x	x	x		x	x		xs	x			s	xs	sx													xs		sx	x	s	sx	sx		34
x	x	x		x	x		xs	x			sx	xs	x							s						xs		x	s	sx	sx			35
x	x	x		x	x		xs	x			sx	x	x			s			s							xs		xs		sx	sx			36
x		x		x	x		xs	x			s		x	s		s			s							x		x	s		xs		x	37
x	x	xs		x	x		x	x			sx		x	sx						s						xs		x	xs		s		sx	38
x	x	xs		x	x		xs	x			sx	sx	s	sx												xs		x	x		s		x	39
x	x			x	x		sx	xs			xs	x	x	sx		s										x		xs	x		sx	s		40
31	37	30	20	35	36	15	10	23	7	0	6	13	16	3	0	2	4	0	0	0	3	1	0	10	0	11	15	0	2	1	4	2		x
1	0	3	2	2	1	5	14	4	3	6	10	16	2	2	0	2	0	0	0	0	3	0	0	12	0	4	4	0	4	2	0	0		xs
0	0	1	3	2	0	4	9	5	9	6	15	6	5	10	1	3	0	1	0	0	1	1	0	2	1	2	0	0	8	5	0	1		sx
1	0	4	4	0	0	1	6	2	6	5	7	0	10	6	7	14	0	2	5	5	1	2	4	0	0	0	0	4	0	7	0	0		s

GOALKEEPERS	CS	CCS
King C	5	2
Isted*	1	1

x - Played full 90 minutes
xs - Substituted off
sx - Substituted on
s - Non-playing Substitute

SLOUGH TOWN MATCH RESULTS 2019-20

Date	Comp	Opponents	H/A	Att:	Result		Goalscorers	Pos
Aug 3	NLS	Dorking Wanderers	H	874	L	0 - 1		
6	NLS	Hungerford Town	A	451	L	0 - 1		
10	NLS	Concord Rangers	A	253	L	1 - 2	Harris B 49	
13	NLS	Weymouth	H	776	D	1 - 1	Harris B 25 (pen)	
17	NLS	Maidstone United	A	1815	D	1 - 1	Lench 20	20
24	NLS	Bath City	H	734	W	3 - 2	Roberts 13 Williams 87 Harris W 90+4	
26	NLS	Dulwich Hamlet	A	2086	W	3 - 2	Harris W 5 Wells 78 Lench 86 (pen)	
31	NLS	St Albans City	H	744	D	1 - 1	Lench 39	
Sep 3	NLS	Hemel Hempstead	H	713	W	2 - 0	Harris W 25 Worsfold 41	13
7	NLS	Eastbourne Borough	A	677	W	2 - 0	Harris W 38 Roberts 66	11
14	NLS	Hampton & Richmond B.	H	807	W	3 - 1	Togwell S 6 Roberts 44 Jackman 46	8
21	FAC2Q	Flackwell Heath	A	484	W	3 - 0	Harris B 36 64 Williams 81	
28	NLS	Dartford	A	1085	W	3 - 2	Roberts 38 Lench 63 Harris B 79	6
Oct 5	FAC3Q	Chippenham Town	A	606	D	3 - 3	Togwell S 40 Harris B 45 Bird 90+2	
8	FAC3Qr	Chippenham Town	H	631	L	2 - 3	Togwell S 50 Lench 74	
12	NLS	Billericay Town	H	1115	W	3 - 1	Togwell S 27 Lench 45 Roberts 59	3
26	NLS	Oxford City	A	416	L	1 - 2	Wells 45+1	5
29	NLS	Welling United	H	630	W	1 - 0	Harris B 74	
Nov 2	NLS	Chelmsford City	H	731	W	2 - 1	Harris B 7 40 (pen)	2
16	NLS	Chippenham Town	A	627	W	3 - 0	Harris W 45+1 Worsfold 47 Lench 76	2
23	FAT3Q	Concord Rangers	A	201	D	0 - 0		
26	FAT3Qr	Concord Rangers	H	295	L	2 - 3	Harris W 38 54	
30	NLS	Tonbridge Angels	H	771	D	0 - 0		3
Dec 7	NLS	Braintree Town	H	739	W	1 - 0	Lench 83	2
26	NLS	Wealdstone	H	1307	W	2 - 1	Harris B 26 (pen) Worsfold 88	
28	NLS	Hemel Hempstead	A	589	D	1 - 1	Roberts 44	
Jan 1	NLS	Wealdstone	A	1289	L	1 - 2	Bird 81	
4	NLS	Eastbourne Borough	H	712	D	1 - 1	Davies 26	4
11	NLS	Billericay Town	A	849	D	2 - 2	Lench 14 Wells 73	4
18	NLS	Dartford	H	854	W	1 - 0	Roberts 34	3
25	NLS	Braintree Town	A	494	W	1 - 0	Harris W 42	3
28	NLS	Hampton & Richmond B.	A	415	W	2 - 1	Harris B 52 Wells 55	2
Feb 1	NLS	Oxford City	H	884	L	0 - 1		2
8	NLS	Welling United	A	615	W	2 - 1	Roberts 27 74 (pen)	
15	NLS	Havant & Waterlooville	H	1028	D	1 - 1	Lench 45+2	
22	NLS	Chelmsford City	A	866	D	1 - 1	Bird 66	
26	NLS	Havant & Waterlooville	A	1175	L	0 - 1		4
29	NLS	Dorking Wanderers	A	778	W	5 - 3	Roberts 16 49 66 Harris W 78 Harris B 83	2
Mar 7	NLS	Hungerford Town	H	885	L	0 - 2		4
14	NLS	Weymouth	A	1578	L	0 - 2		5
July 19	PO Q	Dartford	H	0	L	0 - 3		

GOALSCORERS	SG	CSG	Pens	Hat tricks	Total		SG	CSG	Pens	Hat tricks	Total
Harris B	10	2	3		12	Jackman	1	1			1
Roberts	9	2	1	1	12						
Lench	10	2	1		10						
Harris W	8	2			9						
Togwell S	4	3			4						
Wells	4	1			4						
Bird	3	1			3						
Worsfold	3	1			3						
Williams	2	1			2						
Davies	1	1			1						

Turner J	Hollis G	Fraser S	Togwell S	Harris W	Worsfold M	Dunn S	Lench M	Togwell L	Bird R	Harris B	Amartey F	Davies S	Williams M	Trinovas N (Gk)	Armsworth S	Wells G	Grant J	Roberts D	Jackman J	Nisbet M	Schwarzer J	Kuhl A	Soares L	Hodges P	No.
x	x	x	x	xs	xs	x	x	x	xs	sx	sx	sx	sx	s	s										1
x	xs	xs	x	x	x	xs	x	x	x	sx	x	sx	s	s	sx										2
x	x	s		x	x		x	x	sx	xs	x	x	xs	s	s	x	sx								3
x	x	x	x	x	s		x	x	sx	xs	sx	x		s		x	s	xs							4
x	x	x	x	x	sx		xs	x	sx	xs	sx	x				x	s	xs	s						5
x	xs	xs	x	x	x		x	x	sx			sx	s		x	sx	x	xs	s						6
x			x	x	xs	sx	x	x	sx		x	s			x	xs	xs	x	sx	s					7
x		x	xs	x	xs	x	x	s	sx		x	sx			x	sx	xs	x	s						8
x		x	x	x	sx	x	x		sx	s	x	s			x	s	xs	x	xs						9
x		x	x	x	xs	x	x	s	s	sx	x	s			x	sx	xs	x							10
x		s	x		x	xs	x	x	s	sx		x	sx			x	xs	xs	x	sx					11
x	sx	x	x	x	x	s	s	x	sx	xs		s	sx	s		x	s	xs	xs	x					12
x		s	x	x	x	x	xs	x	s	sx		sx		s		x		xs	x	x					13
x	s	sx	x	x	sx	s	x	x	sx	xs		x	s	s		x		x	xs	x					14
x	s	xs	x	x	x	sx	x	x	sx	xs		xs	s	s		x		sx							15
x	s	s	x	x	xs	x	x	sx	x			x	sx			x		xs	x						16
x	s	s	x	x	xs	x	x	sx	sx			xs	sx			x		xs	x						17
x	x	sx	x	x	x		xs	xs	x	sx			x	s		x		x	x						18
x		x	x	x	x		sx		x	xs	sx		s	s		x	s	xs	x						19
x		sx	x	x	x		sx		x	xs	xs	s	s			x		sx	x	x		xs			20
x	s	x	x	x	x				x	xs		s	sx			x		x	x	x					21
x	s	s	x	x	x		xs		x	sx		x	s	s		x		x	x	x					22
x		x	x	x	x		x	sx		sx	x	sx				xs		xs	x	xs					23
x	x	sx	x	xs	x		x	s	s	sx	sx	x				x		sx	x	xs					24
x	sx	xs	x	x	x		xs	x	x	sx	sx	s				x		s		x					25
x		s	x	x	x		xs	x	x	s	s	sx	sx			x		x	x	xs					26
x		x	x	xs	x		x	x	x	sx	sx	xs	sx	s		s		xs	x						27
x	sx	x	x	x	s		x	x	x		xs	x	xs			x	sx		x						28
x		x	x	x	x		xs	x	x		sx	sx	s			x	s	xs	x						29
x	x	s	x	x	x		x	x	x	sx	s	s	s			x		xs	x						30
x	x	s	x	x	xs		x	x	x	sx		s	sx			x		xs	x				s		31
x	x	sx	x	x	x		x	xs	x	xs		s	s			x		sx	x				s		32
x	x	sx	x	x	x		x	xs	x	xs		sx	s			xs		sx	x				s		33
x	x	s	x	x	x		x	x	x	xs		x	x			x		x	x	s		sx			34
x	x	s	x	x	x		x	x	x	sx		s	s			x		xs	x				s		35
x	x	s	x		x		xs	x	x	sx		x	x			x		x	x	s				x	36
x	x	x	x	x	x		x	xs		xs		sx	sx			x		s	xs					sx	37
x	x	s	x	x	sx		xs	x	xs	sx		s				x		xs	x	sx				x	38
x	x	s	x	x	x		x	xs		sx		sx	sx			xs		x	x	xs					39
x	x	xs	x	x	x		x	x	sx	xs		sx	s			sx		x	x	xs			s		40
x	x	s	xs	x	xs		xs	x	x	x		sx	s			x		sx	x		sx		sx		41
41	18	9	39	35	30	5	27	29	19	1	2	15	0	0	0	33	0	10	30	7	0	0	0	2	x
0	2	5	1	4	6	4	10	6	1	17	2	3	2	0	0	3	2	19	3	7	0	1	0	0	xs
0	1	8	0	0	3	3	2	1	8	18	10	11	14	0	1	0	5	7	0	3	0	1	1	2	sx
0	6	15	0	0	2	1	1	1	7	2	3	10	19	12	2	1	6	1	2	4	1	0	4	1	s

GOALKEEPERS	CS	CCS
Turner	10	2

x - Played full 90 minutes
xs - Substituted off
sx - Substituted on
s - Non-playing Substitute

ST ALBANS CITY MATCH RESULTS 2019-20

Date	Comp	Opponents	H/A	Att:	Result		Goalscorers	Pos
Aug 3	NLS	Chippenham Town	H	549	D	0 - 0		
6	NLS	Dartford	A	919	D	1 - 1	Iaciofano 12	
10	NLS	Dulwich Hamlet	A	1401	L	1 - 2	Iaciofano 70	
13	NLS	Braintree Town	H	396	L	0 - 3		
17	NLS	Dorking Wanderers	H	442	D	1 - 1	Longe-King 65	19
24	NLS	Billericay Town	A	806	L	2 - 3	Murrell-Williamson 30 Iaciofano 37	
26	NLS	Concord Rangers	H	457	W	2 - 1	Iaciofano 15 Foxley 87	
31	NLS	Slough Town	A	744	D	1 - 1	Foxley 56	18
Sep 3	NLS	Wealdstone	H	805	L	2 - 3	Adu 40 Murrell-Williamson 88	19
7	NLS	Hungerford Town	A	331	W	2 - 1	Iaciofano 50 Kaloczi 52	16
14	NLS	Weymouth	H	642	L	1 - 4	Iaciofano 40	17
21	FAC2Q	**Worthing**	H	473	D	2 - 2	**Iaciofano 29 Georgiou 58**	
24	FAC2Qr	**Worthing**	A	637	W	3 - 1	**Noble 27 Iaciofano 39 Nwabuokei 41**	
28	NLS	Maidstone United	A	1806	L	0 - 4		19
Oct 5	FAC3Q	**Weymouth**	A	974	L	1 - 4	**Banton 67**	
12	NLS	Eastbourne Borough	H	835	L	1 - 3	Iaciofano 5	21
19	NLS	Bath City	H	678	L	0 - 1		22
26	NLS	Welling United	A	406	W	1 - 0	Adu 42	20
Nov 2	NLS	Havant & Waterlooville	H	409	L	1 - 3	Shulton 58	21
16	NLS	Tonbridge Angels	A	592	L	1 - 2	Banton 89	22
23	FAT3Q	**Welling United**	A	337	L	1 - 3	**Banton 20**	
30	NLS	Chelmsford City	H	603	D	1 - 1	Sundrie 69	22
Dec 7	NLS	Hampton & Richmond B.	H	445	D	1 - 1	Bender 41 (pen)	22
17	NLS	Oxford City	A	205	D	3 - 3	Iaciofano 33 90 Musonda 71	22
21	NLS	Weymouth	A	833	W	1 - 0	Iaciofano 45	21
26	NLS	Hemel Hempstead Town	H	1078	W	2 - 0	Iaciofano 42 Banton 62	21
28	NLS	Wealdstone	A	1068	L	0 - 1		21
Jan 1	NLS	Hemel Hempstead Town	A	788	L	0 - 1		21
4	NLS	Hungerford Town	H	571	D	2 - 2	Louis 22 39	21
11	NLS	Eastbourne Borough	A	431	D	3 - 3	Iaciofano 11 Merson 83 Kaloczi 90+2	20
18	NLS	Maidstone United	H	683	W	1 - 0	Marshall 61 (og)	19
25	NLS	Hampton & Richmond B.	A	603	L	1 - 2	Banton 8	20
Feb 1	NLS	Welling United	H	754	L	1 - 2	Iaciofano 69	20
8	NLS	Bath City	A	995	W	3 - 0	Nwabuokei 20 Iaciofano 34 Banton 70	
15	NLS	Oxford City	H	566	D	0 - 0		
22	NLS	Havant & Waterlooville	A	1266	W	2 - 1	Merson 66 Banton 78	17
29	NLS	Chippenham Town	A	650	L	1 - 2	Bender 40	21
Mar 7	NLS	Dartford	H	712	L	1 - 2	Iaciofano 22	21
14	NLS	Braintree Town	A	545	W	1 - 0	Iontton 16 (og)	19

GOALSCORERS	SG	CSG	Pens	Hat tricks	Total		SG	CSG	Pens	Hat tricks	Total
Iaciofano	16	4			17	Opponent	2	1			2
Banton	7	2			7	Georgiou	1	1			1
Adu	2	1			2	Longe-King	1	1			1
Bender	2	1	1		2	Musonda	1	1			1
Foxley	2	2			2	Noble	1	1			1
Kaloczi	2	1			2	Shulton	1	1			1
Louis	1	1			2	Sundrie	1	1			1
Merson	2	1			2						
Murrell-Willimason	2	1			2						
Nwabuokei	2	1			2						

Snedker D	Diedhiou D	Kaloczi J	Longe-King D	Miles T	Bawling B	Sprague O	Nwabuokei S	Merson S	Iaciofano J	Foxley D	Adu A	Noble D	Bonfield A (Gk)	Murrell-Williamson R	Shutton S	Howe J	Bender T	Banton Z	Georgiou A (L)	Knight L (L)	Musonda F (L)	Brewer T	Oyinsan J	Fielding J (L)	Sundrie M	Clark M	Louis J	Gordon R	Vasiliou A (L)	Gordon L (L)	Forster H (L)	Tokarczyk A (Gk)	No.
x	x	x	x	x	x	x	x	x	xs	xs	x	sx	sx	s	s	s																	1
x	x	x	x	x	x	x	x	sx	xs	xs	x	sx	s	sx			sx																2
x	x	x	x	x	xs	xs	xs	sx	x	x	s	xs		sx			sx	s															3
x	s	x	x	x	xs	x		x	xs	xs	sx	sx	sx	s	sx		x	x															4
x	x	x	x	x	x	xs		sx	xs	x	sx	xs	x	s	s		x	sx															5
x	x	x	x	s	x	sx		sx	xs	xs	xs	sx	x	s	xs		x	x															6
x	x	x	x	x	xs	sx		s	x	sx	x		s	xs			x	xs	sx														7
x	x	x	x	x	x	s		s	xs	xs	sx	s		xs			x	x	sx														8
x	sx	x	x		xs	xs	x	sx	x	s	x	x		sx			xs	x	s														9
x	x	x	x	sx	sx	x	xs	sx	xs	xs	x	x		s			x	s															10
x		x	x	x	x	s	x	sx	x	x	xs	xs		xs	sx		x	sx															11
x	s	x	x	x	x	sx	x	s	x	s	sx	s		x	x	xs		xs															12
x	x	x	x	sx	s	xs	x	s	x	x	x	s	sx	s			x	s	sx	x													13
x	x	xs	x	s		x	sx	x	x	s	xs						x	sx	x	xs	sx												14
x	x	x	sx		xs	x	sx	xs	sx	s	s	s		x			x	s	x	x	xs												15
x	s	x	x	xs		s	x	x	xs	sx		sx		xs			x	x	x	x	sx												16
x	xs	s	s	sx		x	x		sx	xs		sx		x	x	x	xs	x	x														17
x	sx	x	x		xs	xs		s	x	sx	x		sx	s			x	xs	sx	x	x												18
x	xs	x	xs		x			s	x	sx		xs	s		x	sx	x	x	x	sx													19
x				x	x		sx		x	s		x	xs	xs	sx		x	x	sx	s													20
x	s	sx	x		xs	xs	xs	sx		sx	x		s		x	x		s	s	s	s												21
x	s	sx	x		sx	x	xs	xs		x		s		x	x		x		sx	xs	x												22
x	s	sx	x		s	xs	s	xs		x		sx		x	x		x		sx	x	x												23
x	s	sx	x		sx	xs	s	x		x		sx		x	xs		x		sx	xs	x												24
x	sx	sx	x	sx	xs	x		xs		xs	s			x	x		x		x	x	s												25
x	s	sx	x	xs		x		xs			x			x	x		x		s	xs	x	sx	sx										26
x	s	s	x	xs		x	xs			sx			x	x		x		x	x	s	sx												27
x	s	x	x		xs	s		x		s			x	x		x		s	x	x	sx												28
x	s	x	sx		sx	x	s	xs		xs			x	x		x	xs	x	x														29
x	s	x	xs		s	xs	sx	x		sx			x	x		x		x	xs														30
x	sx	x	x			sx	s	xs		x			x	x		xs	xs		x	sx	s												31
x	s	x	x		s	sx	xs		x			x	xs	xs		x	sx	x	x	sx													32
x	s	x			sx	xs	x		x		xs		x		x	xs	x	sx	sx	x	x												33
x	x		x		x	s	xs		x			x	xs		x		s	sx	xs	sx	x	x	sx										34
x	x		x		xs	sx	x		x			x	x		x		s	s	xs		x	sx	s										35
x	x		x		x	sx	xs		x			x	x		xs	sx	s	sx	s		x	xs											36
x	x		x		xs	sx	x		x			x	xs		x	sx	sx	xs		s	s												37
x	xs		x		sx	sx		xs			x	xs		x		x	s	sx	s		x	x											38
x	s	sx		x		x	sx	xs		x			x	x		x		x	s	s	x		xs										39
9	15	22	36	9	7	9	17	4	15	5	6	14	0	0	12	8	27	20	0	3	13	2	0	9	10	4	3	2	0	5	1	0	x
0	3	1	1	4	4	8	10	5	19	5	1	10	0	4	3	3	4	5	3	0	0	0	5	3	0	1	3	0	0	2	0		xs
0	4	8	0	6	1	6	3	16	2	3	8	7	0	4	3	3	3	4	3	0	0	0	5	0	1	3	8	2	2	0	2	0	sx
0	15	3	1	2	1	4	3	7	0	5	5	5	10	3	4	3	1	2	0	0	0	1	2	3	1	7	2	2	2	0	1	2	s

GOALKEEPERS	CS	CCS
Snedker	8	2

x - Played full 90 minutes
xs - Substituted off
sx - Substituted on
s - Non-playing Substitute

TONBRIDGE ANGELS MATCH RESULTS 2019-20

Date	Comp	Opponents	H/A	Att:	Result	Goalscorers	Pos
Aug 3	NLS	Dulwich Hamlet	H	954	L 1 - 2	Turner 67 (pen)	
6	NLS	Eastbourne Borough	A	656	L 0 - 2		
10	NLS	Dorking Wanderers	A	535	L 1 - 3	Hession-Harris 61	
13	NLS	Concord Rangers	H	476	W 1 - 0	Parter 89	
17	NLS	Bath City	A	832	D 0 - 0		17
24	NLS	Havant & Waterlooville	H	640	L 1 - 3	Hession-Harris 3	
26	NLS	Welling United	A	669	L 2 - 4	Yussuff 43 Theobalds 82	
31	NLS	Weymouth	H	629	D 1 - 1	Yussuff 84 (pen)	
Sep 3	NLS	Dartford	H	816	W 3 - 2	Turner 27 (pen) 45 Derry 85	18
7	NLS	Chippenham Town	A	578	L 1 - 2	Derry 89 (pen)	19
14	NLS	Hemel Hempstead Town	H	576	L 0 - 2		20
21	FAC2Q	Eastbourne Borough	H		L 1 - 2		
28	NLS	Hampton & Richmond B.	A	708	L 0 - 1		21
Oct 12	NLS	Braintree Town	H	612	W 5 - 1	Derry 21 Theobalds 26 (pen) Hession-Harris 28 62 Bray 80	19
19	NLS	Chelmsford City	H	590	L 1 - 2	Da Costa 16	19
26	NLS	Wealdstone	A	866	L 1 - 3	Theobalds 59 (pen)	21
Nov 2	NLS	Oxford City	H	473	D 4 - 4	Derry 48 Theobalds 56 Turner 85 90+2	22
16	NLS	St Albans City	H	592	W 2 - 1	Greenhalgh 29 Da Costa 77	20
23	FAT3Q	Bognor Regis Town	H	457	W 2 - 1	Turner 44 Derry 62	
30	NLS	Slough Town	A	771	D 0 - 0		20
Dec 3	NLS	Hungerford Town	A	191	L 0 - 1		21
7	NLS	Billericay Town	H	557	W 3 - 2	Da Costa 49 67 Derry 51	20
14	FAT1	Hampton & Richmond B.	H	412	D 2 - 2	Theobalds 90 Bentley 90+4	
17	FAT1r	Hampton & Richmond B.	A	238	L 0 - 2		
21	NLS	Hemel Hempstead Town	A	424	D 1 - 1	Turner 69	
28	NLS	Dartford	A	1239	L 0 - 3		
Jan 1	NLS	Maidstone United	A	2520	D 2 - 2	Williams 19 Donovan 77	
4	NLS	Chippenham Town	H	596	W 3 - 2	Williams 1 Theobalds 45 Turner 60	19
11	NLS	Braintree Town	A	468	W 1 - 0	Johnson 46 (og)	17
25	NLS	Billericay Town	A	831	D 3 - 3	Williams 48 78 Tiehi 74	19
Feb 15	NLS	Hungerford Town	H	383	D 1 - 1	Turner 5	
17	NLS	Chelmsford City	A	611	L 1 - 3	Turner 17	
22	NLS	Oxford City	A	729	W 3 - 0	Wood 15 84 Turner 89 (pen)	20
29	NLS	Dulwich Hamlet	A	2663	W 1 - 0	Turner 86	16
Mar 14	NLS	Concord Rangers	A	703	D 3 - 3	Greenhalgh 14 Wood 44 Bray 90	20

GOALSCORERS	SG	CSG	Pens	Hat tricks	Total		SG	CSG	Pens	Hat tricks	Total
Turner	10	4	2		12	Bentley	1	1			1
Theobalds	7	2	3		7	Donovan	1	1			1
Derry	6	2	1		6	Opponent	1	1			1
Da Costa	3	1			4	Parter	1	1			1
Hession-Harris	3	1			4	Tiehi	1	1			1
Williams	3	2			4						
Wood*	2	1			3						
Bray	2	1			2						
Greenhalgh*	2	1			2						
Yussuff	2	2	1		2						

No.	Henly J	Bentley A	Parter J	Bray R	Folkes J	Da Costa K	Theobalds D	Hession-Harris T	Turner J	Derry T	Brewer T	Small J	McKenzie C	Read A	Ovenden R	Stirman J	Roberts M (Gk)(L)	McDonnell T (Gk)	Miles S	Yusuff A (L)	Oseyemi J	Rudoni J (L)	Smith L	Tiehi C (L)	Martin C	Williams J	Greenhalgh B	Donovan H	Akinde S	Antwi J	Hudson H	Ratti R	Ajayi J (L)	Hinchiri B (L)	Burnett H (L)	Wood T (L)	Beere T
1	x	x	x	x	x	xs		xs	x	xs	x		sx	sx	sx	s	s																				
2		x	x	x	x	xs	x	s	x	x	x		sx	xs	sx	s		x	s																		
3		x	x	x	x	sx	x	xs	x	xs	s		xs	sx	sx	x	s	x																			
4		x	x	x	s	sx	x	xs	x	xs	x		xs	sx	s	sx		x				x															
5		s	x	x	x	sx	x	xs	x	xs	x		xs	sx	sx			x				x															
6		x	x	x				sx	x	xs	x	xs	x	xs		sx		x				x	sx	s													
7	x	sx	x	x	xs	xs	x	x	x	x		sx	xs	sx	s		s		x	x																	
8	x	x	x	x	x	x	x	xs	x	sx	s	xs	sx		sx				x	xs																	
9	x	x	x	x	x	x		x	sx	x	xs	sx		s	s				x	xs																	
10	x	s	x	x	x	x	x	sx		sx	x	xs	sx		xs				x	xs																	
11	x	xs	x	x	x	xs	x		x	sx		xs	sx		sx				x	x	s																
12	x	x	x	x	x	xs	x		x	sx		sx	xs		sx				s	x		s	xs	s	s												
13	x	x	x	x		x	x		sx	sx	x	xs	xs	s	s				x				x	s													
14	x	x	x	x	s	xs	x	xs	x	xs		sx	sx		x				x				x	s	sx												
15	x	xs	x	x	sx	xs	x	x	x	x		sx	s		x				x				xs		sx	s											
16	x	s	x	x	x		x	sx	x	x		x			x				x				x	s	xs												
17	x	x	x	x	s	sx	x	x	x	xs		xs	sx		x				x				s	xs		sx											
18	x		x	x	x	x	x	sx	sx	xs		x			s				x				x			sx	xs	s									
19	x		x	x	x	x	x	sx	x	xs					s				s	x			xs	x			sx	sx									
20	x	s	x	x	x		x	s	x	xs		x			s				x				x	sx	x	s											
21	x	s	x	x	x	x	sx		xs	xs	sx	xs			x				x				x	x	sx												
22	x	sx	x	x	xs	x		s	x	sx		sx			s				x				x	sx	xs	x											
23	x	x	s	s	x	x	sx		x	x		sx			s				s	x			x			xs	xs										
24	x	x	s	x	xs	x	x		x	x		sx			sx				s	x			xs			sx	sx										
25	x	x	x	x	x	x	s	x		xs		x			s				x				xs	x	sx	sx											
26	x	x	x	x	xs	sx	x		x		x				s				s	x			sx		x	xs		s									
27	x	x		x	x	s	x		x		sx				s				s	x			s	x	x	x		xs									
28	x	xs	sx	x	x		x		x		sx				s				x	sx	xs	x	x			x	s										
29	x		x	x	sx		x		sx		s				x	xs	sx	x					xs	x		sx	xs	x									
30	x	x		x		x		sx		s		x			x	x		x	xs					sx	xs	x	s										
31	x	x		x		x		sx		s		x			s			x	sx	x			sx	xs		x											
32	x	x		x	sx	xs		x		sx		s			s			xs	x			x	x	xs	sx		s										
33	x	x		x	x	sx		x		sx		s			x			s	x			xs	xs	sx		xs	x										
34	x	x		x	x	sx		x	s		s				x			s	x			xs	xs	sx		sx		xs	x								
35	x	x	s	x	x	xs		x		sx					x			s	x			xs	x	x	sx		x	s									
x	30	20	24	35	23	9	25	3	30	5	8	5	0	0	1	0	5	0	32	2	0	3	2	11	0	5	9	4	0	0	0	1	0	2	1	3	0
xs	0	3	0	0	4	9	0	8	2	11	1	11	3	0	1	0	0	0	0	3	0	2	2	4	0	7	6	4	0	0	0	1	3	0	2	0	0
sx	0	2	1	0	2	11	1	4	2	9	0	16	10	5	4	1	0	0	0	1	0	0	2	2	0	4	1	5	1	2	0	3	2	0	0	0	0
s	0	7	3	0	3	2	0	3	0	1	2	2	2	2	4	7	1	16	0	0	3	0	9	1	1	0	0	2	0	0	1	0	1	0	2	0	1

GOALKEEPERS	CS	CCS
Henley	4	2
Roberts	2	2

x - Played full 90 minutes
xs - Substituted off
sx - Substituted on
s - Non-playing Substitute

WEALDSTONE MATCH RESULTS 2019-20

Date	Comp	Opponents	H/A	Att:	Result	Goalscorers	Pos
Aug 3	NLS	Dartford	H	930	W 4 - 1	Lafayette 8 (pen) 85 Lewis 76 Stevens 80	
6	NLS	Dulwich Hamlet	A	1484	L 0 - 1		10
10	NLS	Braintree Town	A	482	W 4 - 0	Saunders 20 (og) Green 72 Mendy 83 Clifford 84	
13	NLS	Chippenham Town	H	837	W 1 - 0	Clifford 4	
17	NLS	Hemel Hempstead	A	762	W 3 - 0	Phillips 15 Lewis 43 Mendy 77	1
24	NLS	Hungerford Town	H	771	W 3 - 1	Mendy 36 Lewis 58 Lafayette 74	1
26	NLS	Weymouth	A	1522	W 4 - 3	Lewis 18 Lafayette 40 53 89	1
31	NLS	Maidstone United	H	1066	W 2 - 1	Clifford 22 Mendy 44	1
Sep 3	NLS	St Albans City	A	805	W 3 - 2	Mendy 26 Green 51 Lafayette 68 (pen)	1
7	NLS	Oxford City	H	1102	W 1 - 0	Efete 82	1
14	NLS	Welling United	A	594	W 2 - 1	Phillips 68 Lewis 77	1
21	FAC2Q	Farnborough	A	404	W 5 - 0	Lafayette 29 46 Lewis 39 Mendy 61 Watt 88	
28	NLS	Havant & Waterlooville	H	1140	L 1 - 4	Lafayette 10	1
Oct 5	FAC3Q	Bristol Manor Farm	A	422	D 0 - 0		
8	FAC3Qr	Bristol Manor Farm	H	524	W 4 - 0	Mendy 43 Efete 51 Clifford 67 Lewis 76	
12	NLS	Chelmsford City	A	1263	W 3 - 1	Green 16 Clifford 48 Okimo 54	1
19	FAC4Q	Maidenhead United	A	871	L 1 - 1	Lafayette 51	
22	FAC4Qr	Maidstone United	H	835	L 0 - 2		
26	NLS	Tonbridge Angels	H	866	W 3 - 1	Tiehi 15 (og) Clifford 52 Noel-Williams 90	1
Nov 2	NLS	Dorking Wanderers	A	817	D 2 - 2	Noel-Williams 9 45	1
16	NLS	Hampton & Richmond B.	A	927	L 0 - 2		1
23	FAT3Q	Royston Town	H	396	L 2 - 3	Lewis 60 Lafayette	
30	NLS	Concord Rangers	H	832	W 3 - 0	Mendy 49 Lafayette 68 Phillips 90	1
Dec 7	NLS	Bath City	A	1203	D 0 - 0		1
10	NLS	Eastbourne Borough	H	676	W 2 - 0	Lewis 15 Okimo 38	1
26	NLS	Slough Town	A	1307	L 1 - 2	Efete 90+2	1
28	NLS	St Albans City	H	1068	W 1 - 0	Lewis 45	1
Jan 1	NLS	Slough Town	H	1289	W 2 - 1	Efete 2 Lafayette 29	1
4	NLS	Oxford City	A	449	L 2 - 3	Mendy 60 Coombes 68	1
7	NLS	Billericay Town	A	643	L 1 - 3	Okimo 87	1
11	NLS	Welling United	H	932	W 1 - 0	Efete 27	1
18	NLS	Havant & Waterlooville	A	1749	W 4 - 2	Efete 25 Emmanuel 57 74 Green 81	1
25	NLS	Bath City	H	1343	W 7 - 0	Clifford 14 Stevens 42 Lewis 52 60 Green 69 Phillips 80	1
Feb 8	NLS	Billericay Town	H	1356	W 3 - 0	Emmanuel 33 Lafayette 62 76	1
22	NLS	Dorking Wanderers	H	1131	W 3 - 1	Emmanuel 39 Lewis 44 86 (pen)	1
25	NLS	Chelmsford City	H	873	L 0 - 1		1
29	NLS	Dartford	A	1403	D 0 - 0		1
Mar 7	NLS	Dulwich Hamlet	H	1310	W 2 - 1	Efete 67 Watt 68	1
14	NLS	Chippenham Town	A	1262	D 1 - 1	Efete 52	1

GOALSCORERS	SG	CSG	Pens	Hat tricks	Total		SG	CSG	Pens	Hat tricks	Total
Lafayette	10	2	2	1	15	Opponent	2	1			2
Lewis	11	3	1		13	Stevens	2	1			2
Mendy	9	2			9	Watt	2	1			2
Efete	8	2			8	Coombes	1	1			1
Clifford	7	2			7						
Green	5	2			5						
Emmanuel	3	2			4						
Phillips	4	1			4						
Noel-Williams	2	2			3						
Okimo	3	1			3						

Oxborough A (L)	Arnold N	Okimo J	Efete M	Phillips M	Stevens C	Green D	Watt S	Clifford B	Smith C	Lafayette R	Lewis D	Sheppard J	Ringer J (Gk)	Beckles R	Roberts P	North J (Gk)	Saunders A	Coker A	McLennan G	Charles A	Crotty	Noel-Williams D	Everett L (Gk)	Jebb J	Shomotun F	Isted H (Gk) (L)	Edjenguele W	Coombes A (L)	Emmanuel M	Cadogan K	McCoy O (L)	Krashiqi K	Sellers R	No.
X	X	X	X	X	X	X	XS	XS	XS	X	SX	SX	SX	S	S																			1
X	X	X	X	X	X	X	XS	XS	XS	X	SX	S	SX	S	SX																			2
X	X	X	X	X	X	XS		X	X	XS	XS	SX	SX	S	S	SX																		3
X	X	X	X	X	X	XS		X	X	XS	XS	SX	SX	S	S	SX																		4
X	X	X	X	X	SX	XS	XS	X	XS	SX	SX						S	S																5
X	X	X	X	X	X	SX	XS		X	XS	XS	SX					S	SX	S															6
XS	X	X	X	X	X	XS	SX	X		X	X	XS	SX				S		SX	S														7
X	X	X	X	X	X	XS	SX	XS	X	X	XS	SX					S		S		S													8
X	X	X	X	X	X	S	X	XS	XS	XS	SX	S					S		SX															9
X	X	X	X	X	X	S	XS	SX	X	X	XS	SX					S		SX															10
X	X	X	X	X	X	X	SX	SX	X	X	XS	SX					S	S																11
X	XS	X	X	X	X	SX	XS	X	XS	X	SX						S	S	S	SX														12
X	X	X	XS	X	X	X	SX	XS	XS	X	X	SX					S		S	SX														13
X	X	X	XS	X	X	SX	X	SX	X	SX	X	XS					S			S		S												14
X	XS	X	X	XS	X	S	SX	X	X	XS	X	X					S		S	SX		SX	S											15
X	X	X	X	X	XS	XS	X	XS	X			S					S		SX	SX		SX												16
X	S	X	X	X	XS	X	SX	X	SX	X	X						S	S				S	S											17
X	X	X	X	XS	X	XS	XS	SX	XS	X	X	SX					S		S	S														18
X	X	X	XS	X	X	SX	X		X	XS	SX	S							SX	SX														19
X	X	X	X		X	X	XS		X		X		XS		SX			S	SX		SX	XS	S											20
	X	X	X	X	X	XS		XS	X	SX	X	SX					X					S	XS	S	SX									21
XS	X	X	X	X	XS		X	XS	X	SX							X	S			S		SX	S	SX	S								22
	SX	X		X	X	SX		SX		X	XS	XS									XS		S	S	X		X	X						23
	SX	X		X		SX		X	S	XS	XS	X									X		SX		XS	S	X	X						24
	X	X		X	X	SX		XS	S	XS	X	XS									X		SX		SX	X	X	X						25
		XS	X	X	X	SX		XS		X	X	X									XS		S	S	SX		X	X	XS					26
	S		X	X	X	X		S	SX	SX	XS	X									XS			X	SX	X	X	XS						27
	X	X	X		X	SX		XS	S	X	X	X					S				SX			X		X	X	S						28
	X	XS	X		X	SX		X	S	X	XS	X					S				SX		XS		X	X	SX							29
	X		X	X		SX	XS	SX	X	X	XS	X					S				S		SX		X	X	X							30
	X	X	X		XS	S	XS			X	SX	XS									SX			SX		X		X	S					31
	X	X			X	X	SX	XS	X	SX	XS	X	SX	S							X				X		S	XS						32
X		X	X	SX	X	X	SX	X	X	SX	XS	XS									X				S		S	XS						33
X		X	X	SX	X	XS		X	X	SX	X	X									XS		S	S			XS		SX					34
X		X	XS	X	X	SX	X	X	SX	X	X	SX												S			XS	S	S					35
X		XS	XS	X	X	XS	X	XS	SX	X	X												S				X		S	SX				36
X		X	X	X	XS	SX		X	X	X	SX										X			S			XS		S					37
X		X	X		X	SX	XS		X	X		XS	S							X						XS		S	SX	SX				38
X		X	X	X		X	X	S			X		SX	S					S	X						XS		S	SX	XS				39
26	18	37	33	30	36	22	1	14	12	18	24	13	1	0	0	0	2	0	0	0	6	0	0	0	3	0	10	8	1	3	0	0	0	x
1	3	1	3	5	0	9	6	22	6	9	13	12	3	0	0	0	0	0	0	0	5	0	2	0	2	0	0	0	0	1	6	0	1	xs
0	2	0	0	2	0	6	15	1	7	8	2	9	17	0	2	6	1	0	4	2	7	0	5	0	6	1	0	0	2	0	0	1	3	sx
0	3	0	0	0	0	1	5	1	4	0	0	1	1	14	5	2	10	9	5	1	5	1	2	8	1	3	1	0	3	0	2	5	0	s

GOALKEEPERS	CS	CCS
Oxborough	10	3
Isted	5	3

x - Played full 90 minutes
xs - Substituted off
sx - Substituted on
s - Non-playing Substitute

WELLING UNITED MATCH RESULTS 2019-20

Date	Comp	Opponents	H/A	Att:	Result	Goalscorers	Pos
Aug 3	NLS	Havant & Waterlooville	A	1378	D 1 - 1	Coombes 39	
6	NLS	Maidstone United	H	1015	W 1 - 0	Cosgrove 55	8
10	NLS	Bath City	H	416	L 0 - 3		
13	NLS	Billericay Town	A	890	L 1 - 2	McCallum 38	
17	NLS	Oxford City	H	424	W 3 - 1	Dymond 62 Coombes 76 (pen) 85	11
24	NLS	Chelmsford City	A	747	D 1 - 1	Goldberg 84	
26	NLS	Tonbridge Angels	H	669	W 4 - 2	Coobes 27 35 McCallum 45+3 Cook 63	
31	NLS	Concord Rangers	A	284	L 0 - 3		
Sep 3	NLS	Eastbourne Borough	H	412	D 0 - 0		14
7	NLS	Weymouth	A	1034	L 0 - 1		15
14	NLS	Wealdstone	H	594	L 1 - 2	Coombes 85	15
21	FAC2Q	Chipstead	H	388	W 7 - 0	Coombes 5 30 Waldren 18 Cook 47 Goldberg 70 (pen) 74 Jebb 78	
28	NLS	Hungerford Town	A	284	W 2 - 1	Waldren 45+3 Cook 79	14
Oct 5	FAC3Q	Tavistock Town	H	491	W 4 - 1	Goldberg x3 Oyinsan	
12	NLS	Hampton & Richmond B.		541	L 0 - 1		15
19	FAC4Q	Eastleigh	H	511	D 0 - 0		
22	FAC4Qr	Eastleigh	A	803	L 2 - 4	Coombes 21 Cook 86	
26	NLS	St Albans City	H	406	L 0 - 1		16
29	NLS	Slough Town	A	630	L 0 - 1		
Nov 2	NLS	Chippenham Town	A	484	D 0 - 0		18
12	NLS	Dulwich Hamlet	H	469	D 0 - 0		
16	NLS	Braintree Town	H	538	W 6 - 2	Widdrington 8 Henry 20 29 51 (pen) 90 Cook 27	15
23	FAT3Q	St Albans City	H	337	W 3 - 1	Waldren 60 Emmanuel 62 Cook 86	
30	NLS	Dorking Wanderers	A	765	L 0 - 2		17
Dec 7	NLS	Hemel Hempstead	H	517	W 2 - 0	Agyemang 39 Green 86	14
14	FAT1	Yeovil Town	A	1554	L 1 - 3	Swaine 87	
26	NLS	Dartford	H	1459	L 0 - 3		
28	NLS	Eastbourne Borough	A	486	L 1 - 2	Emmanuel 90+5	
Jan 1	NLS	Dartford	A	1534	L 0 - 4		
4	NLS	Weymouth	H	541	L 1 - 3	Cook 65	20

Owner, Mark Goldberg, hands the managerial job over to Bradley Quinton.

Date	Comp	Opponents	H/A	Att:	Result	Goalscorers	Pos
11	NLS	Wealdstone	A	932	L 0 - 1		21
18	NLS	Hungerford Town	H	564	W 3 - 2	Cook 9 James 28 Wright 86	20
25	NLS	Hemel Hempstead	A	467	W 2 - 0	Akinyemi 11 Henry 77	18
Feb 1	NLS	St Albans City	A	754	W 2 - 1	Akinyemi 28 66	16
8	NLS	Slough Town	H	615	L 1 - 2	James 40	
11	NLS	Hampton & Richmond B.	A	313	D 1 - 1	Cook 72 (pen)	
15	NLS	Dulwich Hamlet	A	1710	W 1 - 0	Crichlow-Noble 8	
22	NLS	Chippenham Town	H	502	W 1 - 0	Akinyemi 43	13
Mar 7	NLS	Maidstone United	A	1943	L 1 - 3	Cook 89 (pen)	14
14	NLS	Billericay Town	H	925	W 2 - 0	Coombes 59 Cook 85 (pen)	13

GOALSCORERS	SG	CSG	Pens	Hat tricks	Total		SG	CSG	Pens	Hat tricks	Total
Cook	11	2	3		11	Cosgrave	1	1			1
Coombes	7	2	1		10	Crichlow-Noble	1	1			1
Goldberg	3	1	1	1	6	Dymond	1	1			1
Henry	2	1	1	1	5	Green	1	1			1
Akinyemi	3	2			4	Jebb	1	1			1
Waldren*	3	2			3	Oyinsan	1	1			1
Emmanuel	2	1			2	Swaine	1	1			1
James	2	1			2	Widdrington	1	1			1
McCallum	2	1			2	Wright	1	1			1
Agyemang	1	1			1						

Player appearance grid (matches 1–40). Legend: x = Played full 90 minutes; xs = Substituted off; sx = Substituted on; s = Non-playing Substitute.

Wilks D	Swaine R	Anderson J	Green N	Rich-Baghuelo J	Rooney L	Dymond C	Ming S	Coombes A	Goldberg B	Cosgrave A	Jebb J	Anau J	Agyemang M	Copeland D	Okosieme E	Platt R	Oyinsan J	McCallum G	Cook A	Prestedge R	Widdrington T (L)	Waldren D	Ryan B	Nwachuku N	Henry K (L)	Johnson C	Emmanuel M	Prall A (Gk)	Burstow M	Atkins L	Akinyemi D	Joseph H	James C (L)	Wright D (L)	Roberts P	Crichlow-Noble R (L)	Rolt B (L)	Krabbendam C	No.
x	x	x	x	x	xs	x	x	xs	xs	x	sx	sx	sx	s	s																								1
x	x	x	x	x	x	x	x	xs	x	x			sx	s	s	s	s																						2
x	x	x	x	x	x		x	xs	xs	x		xs	s	sx	s		sx	sx																					3
x	x	x	sx	x	x		x	xs	xs	sx		s	x	s			sx	xs	x																				4
x	x	x	sx	x	x	x	x	x	xs	sx		s	s				sx	xs	xs																				5
x	x	x	sx	x		xs	x	x	x	x		x		s			s	xs	xs	sx																			6
x	x	x	sx	x	s		x	xs	x	x		x		s			sx	xs	xs	x																			7
x	x	x	sx	x	sx		x	x	x	sx			xs	s			s	xs	xs	x																			8
x	x	x	xs	x	x	x		sx		xs	sx	s					xs	sx	x	s																			9
x	x	x	s	x	xs	x		xs		sx	sx	sx		sx			xs	x	x	s																			10
x	x	x	sx	x	s		x	xs	xs	sx		x		x			s	xs	x		xs																		11
x	x						x	x		x						x		x		x																			12
x	x	x	sx		s	x		x	xs	s	sx					xs	x		x	x																			13
x	x	x	xs	s		x		xs	x	sx	sx		s	s	s		sx			xs	x																		14
x	x	x	x	s		xs		xs	x		sx		x	sx			sx		x	xs	x																		15
x	x	xs	sx	s		x	x	x	x		xs		s	s	s		s		x		sx	x	s																16
x	x	x	sx		x	x	x	xs	xs	xs		sx	s	s		s	s	x		s	xs																		17
x	x	x	s	s	xs	x	x	xs	sx	x			x				sx	x		sx	xs																		18
x	x	x	x	x	s		sx			xs	s		sx	s			sx	x		xs	xs	xs																	19
x	x	xs	x	x	xs		sx			s			sx	x			sx	x		s	xs																		20
x	x	x	s	s		x		xs		s	x		x				x		sx	x		x																	21
x	x	xs	sx		x	x		s	sx		s	xs	xs				x		sx	x	sx		x																22
x	xs	x	sx		x			x	xs		x		sx			sx		x	x			s	sx	s	s	s													23
x	xs	x	x	sx		xs	sx	sx	x	x		x		x			s	x		x	xs																		24
x	x	sx	x	x		xs	xs	xs	sx	x	sx	x	s	x		s	x		x	xs																			25
x	x	x	sx		x	sx	s	x	xs	s		x	s	x	x	s	xs	sx		x	xs	x																	26
x	x	x	sx	x		xs	sx		x			x	x	sx	x	xs	s																						27
x	x	s	x	x		sx	xs		x			s	x	x	x		sx	xs	sx		xs																		28
x	x	x	xs	sx	xs	x		xs		s			sx	sx		x		s	x	x		x																	29
x	x	s	x	x	s		s	sx		x		x	xs	x	x			xs	sx	x																			30
x	xs		x	x		sx		xs	sx		s		x	x			xs								s	x	x	x	sx										31
x		x		x		xs	xs		s	x			s	x			sx	s						xs	x	x	x	sx	x	sx									32
x		x		x		s	sx	s	x					xs	sx			xs	x	x	x	xs	x	x															33
x		x		sx	xs	xs			s	x					sx	x	xs	x	x	x	sx	x		s															34
x		x			s	sx	sx	s		x					sx	x	x	xs	x	xs	x		xs																35
x		x		xs	s	xs		s		x					sx	x	x	x	xs	x	s																		36
x		x	sx		s	xs	sx		x						s	x	xs	x	x	xs	xs	sx																	37
x	x	x	sx		s	xs	sx		x					sx	x	xs	x	x	s	x																		38
x	x		s	sx	xs	s		x	x					sx	xs	x	x	x	xs	sx																		39
x	x		x	xs	sx	x			xs	x				sx	sx	x	x	xs	s	s																		40
6	5	4	0	1	0	5	2	3	4	0	1	0	2	0	4	0	1	0	4	0	1	4	0	0	1	0	1	0	0	0	0	0	0	0	0	0	0	0	x
14	26	23	17	17	5	16	13	7	7	4	3	0	10	2	9	0	0	3	27	2	6	8	0	0	3	9	2	0	0	7	9	8	10	0	5	2	0		xs
0	2	0	7	0	3	4	1	11	17	8	1	1	4	0	3	0	3	9	5	0	5	1	0	1	3	2	3	0	0	5	0	2	0	5	1	0	1		sx
0	0	0	8	6	1	3	0	5	3	19	6	3	7	5	0	0	7	8	1	1	4	3	1	0	9	3	2	1	1	1	0	0	0	0	4	0	3	0	s

GOALKEEPERS	CS	CCS
Wilks	11	2

x - Played full 90 minutes
xs - Substituted off
sx - Substituted on
s - Non-playing Substitute

WEYMOUTH MATCH RESULTS 2019-20

Date	Comp	Opponents	H/A	Att:	Result	Goalscorers	Pos
Aug 3	NLS	Maidstone United	A	2015	W 2 - 1	Thomson 74 89	
6	NLS	Bath City	H	1615	D 1 - 1	Hartridge 5 (og)	7
10	NLS	Chelmsford City	H	951	W 4 - 1	McQuoid 41 52 (pens) 55 Thomson 80	
13	NLS	Slough Town	A	776	D 1 - 1	Baggie 5	
17	NLS	Dartford	H	1010	W 3 - 1	Baggie 41 Williams 48 79	2
24	NLS	Chippenham Town	A	759	L 0 - 1		
26	NLS	Wealdstone	H	1522	L 3 - 4	Odubade 7 Baggie 62 Williams 66 (pen)	
31	NLS	Tonbridge Angels	A	629	D 1 - 1	Williams 49	
Sep 3	NLS	Oxford City	A	362	D 0 - 0		10
7	NLS	Welling United	H	1034	W 1 - 0	Williams 76	7
14	NLS	St Albans City	A	642	W 4 - 1	Odubade 33 Zubar 44 Hobson 70 McCarthy 90+1	5
21	FAC2Q	**Sholing**	**A**	**515**	**W 3 - 0**	**Robinson 15 Thomson 24 Williams 90+4**	
28	NLS	Concord Rangers	H	921	W 3 - 0	Thomson 13 Odubade 63 Murray 68	4
Oct 5	FAC3Q	**St Albans City**	**H**	**974**	**W 4 - 1**	**McCarthy 11 Wakefield 37 Odubade 65 87**	
12	NLS	Dulwich Hamlet	A	2906	D 2 - 2	Odubade 40 Ainsworth 49 (pen)	6
19	FAC4Q	**Dover Athletic**	**H**	**1506**	**L 1 - 2**	**McCarthy 78**	
26	NLS	Braintree Town	H	782	W 3 - 0	McCarthy 25 72 Thomson 85	4
29	NLS	Eastbourne Borough	A	439	D 1 - 1	McCarthy 81 (pen)	
Nov 9	NLS	Hampton & Richmond B.	H	954	W 2 - 1	McQuoid 52 Thomson 54	
19	NLS	Billericay Town	A	606	D 1 - 1	Baggie 61	4
23	FAT3Q	**Hastings Town**	**H**	**734**	**W 1 - 0**	**Baggie 59**	
30	NLS	Hungerford Town	H	862	W 2 - 1	Baggie 30 McQuoid 87	2
Dec 7	NLS	Dorking Wanderers	A	619	L 0 - 1		4
14	FAT1	**Barnet**	**A**	**624**	**L 1 - 2**	**McCarthy 20**	
21	NLS	St Albans City	H	833	L 0 - 1		
28	NLS	Oxford City	H	1131	W 2 - 1	Odubade 70 Baggie 84	
Jan 1	NLS	Havant & Waterlooville	H	1305	L 0 - 1		
4	NLS	Welling United	A	541	W 3 - 1	Baggie 44 McQuoid 73 (pen) McCarthy 90+6	
11	NLS	Dulwich Hamlet	H	912	D 1 - 1	McCarthy 43	6
18	NLS	Concord Rangers	A	314	W 2 - 1	Baggie 40 Odubade 56	5
25	NLS	Dorking Wanderers	H	872	W 2 - 1	Williams 16 Baggie 90+4	5
28	NLS	Hemel Hempstead Town	A	294	W 1 - 0	Midson 87 (og)	2
Feb 1	NLS	Braintree Town	A	405	D 1 - 1	Odubade 83	3
5	NLS	Havant & Waterlooville	A	1483	L 2 - 3	Hobson 18 McQuoid 41	4
8	NLS	Eastbourne Borough	H	960	D 2 - 2	Baggie 55 McCarthy 83	
15	NLS	Hampton & Richmond B.	A	458	W 3 - 2	Williams 47 Brooks 65 74	
22	NLS	Billericay Town	H	983	D 0 - 0		5
29	NLS	Maidstone United	H	956	W 5 - 1	Brooks 3 Thomson 22 Johnson 43 (og) Whelan 54 (pen) Hoey 843	
Mar 7	NLS	Bath City	A	1902	D 0 - 0		3
14	NLS	Slough Town	H	1578	W 2 - 0	McQuoid 51 (pen) Robinson 89	3
July 25	PO SF	**Dorking Wanderers**	**H**	**0**	**W 3 - 2**	**McQuoid 3 (pen) Anthony 11 Odubade 90+5**	
Aug 1	PO F	**Dartford**	**H**	**0**	**D 0 - 0**	**(Won 3-0 on pens and promoted to the National League)**	

GOALSCORERS	SG	CSG	Pens	Hat tricks	Total		SG	CSG	Pens	Hat tricks	Total
Baggie	11	3			11	Ainsworth	1	1			1
McCarthy	9	3	1		10	Anthony	1	1			1
Odubade	9	2			10	Hoey	1	1			1
McQuoid	7	1	5	1	9	Murray	1	1			1
Thomson	7	2			8	Wakefield	1	1			1
Williams	7	2	1		8	Whelan	1	1	1		1
Brooks	2	1			3	Zubar	1	1			1
Opponent	3	1			3						
Hobson	2	1			2						
Robinson	2	1			2						

Ward C (L)	Zubar S	Buckley C	Harfield O	Thomson B	Brooks C	Robinson A	McCarthy J	Ngalo J	Williams B	Baggie A	Odubade Y	Murray C	Wakefield J	Rose J	Childs M (Gk)	McQuoid J	Sherring S (L)	Hoey J	Wells A	Ainsworth L	Hobson S (L)	Rees T (Gk)	Olumuyiwa A	Prodomo J (Gk)	Molesley M	Camp B (L)	Suraci P	Randall J (L)	Medway C	Burns H	Whelan T (L)	Anthony J (L)	No.
x	x	x	x	x	xs	x	x	x	xs	xs	x	sx	sx	sx	s	s																	1
x	x	x	x	x	x	x	x	xs	sx	xs	sx	s			s	xs																	2
x		sx	x	x	x	x	x	xs			xs	sx	sx	x	s	xs	x	s															3
x	xs	s	x	x	x	sx	x	sx			x	s	x	x		s	sx	x															4
x	x	s	x		sx	xs	x	x		sx	sx	x	xs	sx	x		s		x														5
x	x	s	x			sx	x	xs	xs	x	x		x	sx			x	sx	xs														6
x		xs	x		x	x	x	x	sx	x	x	xs	sx	x	sx	s		xs	s														7
x	x		x	s	x	x	x		x	xs	x	sx	xs	xs	s	s		x			sx												8
x	s		x	xs	x	x	x		sx	x	sx	x	sx		s		xs				xs	x											9
x	x		x	x	x	xs	x			sx	x	x	s	sx				s	xs	x	s												10
x	x		x	x	x	x	x		s	xs	xs	sx	sx					sx	xs		s												11
x	x		xs	xs	x	x	sx		sx	x	x	x	s	xs		s			sx	x	x	s	s										12
x	xs		x	x	x	x	x		sx	x	xs	sx	s		sx					xs	x			s									13
x	sx		xs	xs	x	xs	x		sx	sx	x	x	x	x		s					s	s	s										14
x	xs	sx	x	x					x	s	x	sx	sx		sx					x	sx												15
x	x			x	x		x	x	sx	xs	xs	sx	sx	x		xs			s	sx	x	x	s		s								16
x			x	xs		x	x	x	sx	sx	x	x			xs				sx	x	s		s	x									17
x	s		x	x		x	x	x	sx	x	xs	x	x			s			s	x	s				x								18
x	sx		x	x	x		x	x		xs	s	sx	x			s	xs			s		x			x								19
x	s		x	xs	x		x	xs		x	sx	sx	xs		s	x			sx						x								20
x	s		x		x		x	x			xs	xs	sx			x			sx		x				s		x						21
x	s		x		x		x	xs	x	x	sx					xs			sx		x	s			x	s							22
x	s	xs	x	xs	x		x			sx	x					x				x	s	s			x		sx						23
x	x	s	x	x			x	sx	x	xs	sx					xs	s			x	s				x			s	s				24
x			x	x			x	sx	sx	sx	x		x			xs	x			x	s	s			xs	xs							25
x			x	sx			x	sx	xs	x	sx	sx	s			x				x	s	xs			x					x			26
	xs		x	x			x	s	sx	x	sx		sx			x	xs	x		x	s				x						xs		27
	x		x	x			x	xs	s	x	sx		xs			x	xs	x		xs	s	sx			x						sx		28
	x		x	x			x	xs	s	x	sx		xs			x	x			x	s	s			x						sx		29
x	s		x	sx			x	s	x	sx	x		x			s	xs			x		x			x						x		30
x	sx		x	s			x	x	x	x		x				s		sx		x		xs			x						x		31
x	x		x				x	sx	x	xs	x		x			s		xs		x		s			x						xs		32
x	s		x				sx	x	x	x	x		x			s	xs			x		s			s	xs							33
x	xs		x	xs			x	xs	x	x	x		xs			sx				x		xs			s						x		34
x	sx		x	x		x	x	xs	x	x	xs		sx			s	s			x		xs			x						x		35
x	x		x	x		x	x			x	xs		s			s			sx	x		s			s	x							36
x	x		x	x	xs	s	x		xs	x	sx		sx			s	xs			x		sx			x						x		37
x			x	xs	x	sx	x			sx	xs					xs	s	x		sx		x			s						x	x	38
x			x	x	x	sx	x			s	x	s				sx	s	xs		x					s						xs	x	39
x			x	x	x	sx	x	xs	s	sx	s					s	xs			x					s						x	x	40
x	sx		x	sx	xs	xs	x	xs			sx	sx	xs			s	xs			x					s						sx	x	41
x	s		x	sx	x	xs	x	xs			sx	sx	xs			s	xs			x					s						sx	x	42
39	15	2	37	22	25	11	39	9	9	29	5	5	18	1	3	5	9	0	0	1	31	0	2	0	0	18	0	0	0	0	9	5	x
0	5	2	2	8	5	4	1	11	4	7	15	1	8	0	0	0	19	2	1	1	5	1	0	3	0	0	1	0	1	0	4	0	xs
0	5	2	0	4	4	4	1	8	17	3	14	16	11	1	0	2	0	3	7	2	0	0	2	0	0	0	0	1	0	0	4	0	sx
0	9	4	0	2	0	1	0	3	5	0	5	2	4	2	24	4	1	2	4	1	1	15	8	2	2	0	1	0	1	3	0	0	s

GOALKEEPERS	CS	CCS
Ward	11	2

x - Played full 90 minutes
xs - Substituted off
sx - Substituted on
s - Non-playing Substitute

Wootton (Notts County) outjumps Smith and Hall (Harrogate).

Thomson (Harrogate) celebrates his opening goal

Martin (Harrogate) Turner (Notts County)

Lacey (Notts County) tackles Muldoon (Harrogate).

Brindley (Notts County) takes on Falkingham (Harrogate) down the wing.

NATIONAL LEAGUE,
NORTH AND SOUTH PLAYERS 2019-20

If a player featured on a team sheet during the 2019-20 season, in the starting 11 or as an unused substitute, then they should be contained within the following pages. Over 2,100 players laced up their boots to play for their respective clubs during the shortened 2019-20 season.

Appearance details, for National League (Step 1 & 2) games, FA Cup and FA Trophy are all included in the players' totals as well as any goals scored or clean sheets registered.
The key for appearances is as follows: X = starting 11 SX = sub on S = unused sub.
Note, there are a few missing line-ups, mainly in the early rounds of the FA Trophy so some players/ clubs totals will be out by one or two.

Also included is the position of the player, their age and club history. Within this section (L) denotes 'On Loan', (Lx2) denotes two loan periods within the same season and (LP) is a loan move that turned into a permanent one. The word dual denotes the player was signed for two clubs for the same period of time.

Mike Fondop (Chesterfield) runs at Harry Taylor (Barnet). Photo Bill Wheatcroft.

SURNAME	FIRSTNAME	AGE	POSITION	CLUB PLAYED FOR	X	SX	S	Ap	G/Cs
Abbott	Bradley	25	Midfielder	Boston United	35	2	1	37	4
Barnsley (Y), Harrogate (L), Chester (L), Barrow (L), Buxton, Boston U									
Acauah	Emile	19	Forward	Maidenhead United (L)		1		1	
Southend (Y), Maidenhead (L)									
Achuba	Mathew		Defender	Ebbsfleet United		1	12	1	
Ebbsfleet (Y)									
Adams	Charlee	25	Midfielder	Barnet	17	7	8	24	1
Birmingham, Lincoln (L), Lincoln (L), Kilmarnock (L), Dagenham & R, Barnet									
Adams	Kielen	19	Forward	Chorley (L)	1			1	
Oldham (Y), Chorley (L)									
Addai	Cory	22	Goalkeeper	AFC Telford United (L)	7			7	1
Coventry (Y), Hendon (L), Telford (L)									
Adebayo-Rowling	Tobi	23	Defender	Eastbourne Borough	30	1		31	
Brighton, Eastbourne B, Peterborough, Sligo Rovers, Cork City, Bromley, Eastbourne B (L), Eastbourne B									
Adebayo-Smith	Jordan	19	Forward	Boston United (L)	4	5	2	9	
Lincoln C, Boston U (L)									
Adebowale	Emmanuel (Manny)	22	Defender	Eastbourne Borough	27	3	1	30	
West Ham, Sheffield United, Goole AFC (L), Sheffield FC (L), Dover, Bognor Regis (L), Eastbourne B (L), Eastbourne B									
Adeloye	Tomi	24	Forward	Ebbsfleet United	6	20	5	26	3
Stoke, Macclesfield (L), Chelmsford, Dover, Welling, Altrincham, FC Utd, Hartlepool, Whitehawk, Dagenham & R, Ebbsfleet									
Adu	Albert	31	Forward	St Albans City	7	8	5	15	2
TB (F Isle), KI, Eloois-Winkel (Bel), St Albans									
Agboola	Manny	21	Goalkeeper	Billericay Town			6		
Reading (Y), Oxford U (Y), Hampton & R (L), Leatherhead (L), Solihull (L), Billericay, Romford									
Aghatise	Jordan		Defender	Kettering Town	1		3	1	
Barnstaple, Kettering									
Agnew	Liam	25	Midfielder	Gateshead (L)	27	7	1	34	2
Sunderland (Y), Boston (L), Boston, Harrogate, Boston (L), York (L), Spennymoor (L), Gateshead (L)									
Agustien	Kemy	33	Midfielder	Bradford Park Avenue	4			4	
Willem II (Y), AZ Alkmaar, Roda JC (L), Birmingham (L), RKC Waalwijk (L), Swansea, Crystal P (L), Brighton, Vendsyssel FF, Hamilton, FC Dordrecht, Global Cebu, SV TEC, Nuneaton, Barrow, Wrexham, Bradford PA									
Agyemang	Montel	23	Midfielder	Welling United	15	6	13	21	1
Leyton O, Grays (L), Malden & T, East Thurrock, Wealdstone, Welling									
Ahmidi	Wadah		Midfielder	Hampton & Richmond Borough	16	3		19	1
Maidenhead, Staines, Wealdstone, Hampton & R									
Ainge	Simon	32	Forward	Boston United (L)	30	2	5	32	1
Bradford, Halifax (L), Cambridge U (L), Guiseley, Luton (L), Halifax, Bradford PA, Harrogate T, Wrexham (L), Darlington, Boston U (L)									
Ainsworth	Lionel	32	Midfielder	Weymouth	6	2	1	8	1
				Dulwich Hamlet	12	5	2	17	3
Watford (Y), Huddersfield, Brentford (L), Shrewsbury, Burton (L), Rotherham, Aldershot (L), Motherwell (L), Motherwell, Plymouth, Bradford (L), Weymouth, Dulwich H									
Ajayi	Joshua	18	Forward	Tonbridge Angels (L)	3	2	1	5	
Crystal P (Y), Tonbridge A (L)									
Ajiboye	David	21	Forward	Sutton United	32	9		41	4
Brighton, Worthing, Sutton U									
Akanbi	Ibrahim	22	Forward	Maidstone United	26	9		35	11
Crystal P (Y), Guildford, Whyteleafe, Whitehawk, Maidstone									
Akers	Zidan	21	Forward	Hungerford Town	26	8	1	34	2
Maidenhead, Binfield, Basingstoke, Thatcham, Hungerford									
Akinde	Sam	27	Forward	Tonbridge Angels		1		1	
Ebbsfleet (Y), Alfreton, Dover, Welling, Basingstoke, St Albans, Barnet, Hemel H, Margate, Tonbridge A									
Akinola	Simeon	27	Forward	Barnet	35	5	4	40	17
Boreham W, Harrow, Braintree, Barnet									
Akintunde	James	24	Forward	Maidenhead United	16	13	4	29	1
Cambridge U (Y), Histon (L), Brackley (L), Needham (L), Chester, Maidenhead									
Akinwande	Olufemi	24	Midfielder	Braintree Town	19			19	6
				Billericay Town	16			16	6
Dartford, Colchester, Bishop's S (L), East Thurrock (L), East Thurrock, Concord, Braintree, Billericay									

Key: X - Started; SX - Sub on; S - Non-playing Sub; Ap - Total Appearances; G/Cs - Total goals/clean sheets.

SURNAME	FIRSTNAME	AGE	POSITION	CLUB	X	SX	S	Ap	G/Cs
Akinyemi	Dipo	23	Forward	Dulwich Hamlet	2	2	2	4	
				Braintree Town	3			3	
				Welling United	12		2	12	4
Stevenage (Y), Aldershot (L), St Albans (L), Dulwich H (L), Dulwich H, Braintree, Welling									
Al Hussaini	Zaid	20	Midfielder	Hampton & Richmond Borough (L)			3		
Derby, Gloucester (L), Hampton & R, Staines									
Alabi	James	25	Forward	Eastleigh (L)	5	3	2	8	1
Stoke, Scunthorpe (L), Mansfield (L), Forest Green (L), Scunthorpe (L), Accrington (L), Ipwsich, Grimsby (L), Chester, Tranmere, Dover (L) Leyton Orient, Eastleigh (L)									
Albinson	Charlie	23	Goalkeeper	Southport	23		16	23	5
Blackburn (Y), Southport									
Alcock	Craig	32	Defender	Yeovil Town	14	3	4	17	
Yeovil, Peterborough, Sheff Utd, Doncaster (L), Doncaster, Cheltenham, Yeovil									
Alexander	Cheye	25	Defender	Barnet	41	1		42	2
Port Vale, Concord R, Bishop's St., Aldershot, Barnet									
Alfa	Oddyseus	21	Forward	Billericay Town (L)	17			17	5
				Maidenhead United (L)	3	5		8	1
QPR (Y), Atletico Baleares (L), Billericay (L), Maidenhead (L)									
Ali	Mahamud	25	Midfielder	Curzon Ashton	26			26	1
Curzon A									
Allan	Tom	25	Defender	Farsley Celtic (L)	19	1	3	20	3
				York City	2			2	
York (Y), Hucknall (L), Harrogate T (L), Tadcaster A (L), Gateshead, Alfreton, York, Alfreton (L), Farsley C (Lx2)									
Allassani	Reise	24	Forward	Dulwich Hamlet (L)	4	1		5	3
Crystal Pal (Y), Bromley (L), Dulwich H, Coventry, Ebbsfleet (L), Woking (L), Dulwich H (L)									
Allen	Ben	19	Midfield	Eastbourne Borough (L)			1	1	
Phoenix Sports (Y), Gillingham (Y), Eastbourne B (L)									
Allen	Harry		Goalkeeper	Curzon Ashton (L)	1			1	
Man Utd (Y), Burnley (Y), Curzon A (L)									
Allen	Ifeanyi (Iffy)	26	Midfielder	Maidstone United	18	9	10	27	6
Barnet, Yeovil, Torquay (L), Aldershot, Wrexham, Bromley, Wealdstone (L) Dulwich H, Braintree, Maidstone									
Allen	Jamie	25	Forward	FC Halifax Town	23	13		36	3
Fleetwood, AFC Fylde (L), Stalybridge (L), Southport, Dover, Halifax									
Allen	Josh		Goalkeeper	Leamington			5		
Leamington (Y)									
Allen	Luke	27	Midfielder	Dartford	19			19	3
Tottenham (Y), Cambridge U (Y), Cambridge C (L), Hemel (L), Hemel, St Albans, Tonbridge A, Braintree, Dartford									
Allen	Taylor	20	Forward	Hereford (L)	5	4	1	9	1
				Gloucester City (L)	2	4		6	
Leicester (Y), Nuneaton (L), Forest GR, Hereford (L), Gloucester (L)									
Allinson	Lloyd	26	Goalkeeper	Guiseley	1		11	1	
Huddersfield (Y), Chesterfield, FC United, Guiseley									
Almeida Santos (Ricardo)	Ricardo Alexandre	25	Defender	Barnet	26	2		28	1
Dag & Red, Billericay (L), Thurrock, Peterborough, Barnet									
Almond	Louis	28	Forward	Chorley		4	1	4	
Blackpool (Y), Cheltenham (L), Barrow (L), Barrow (L), Barrow (L), Hyde U (L), Hyde U (L), Hyde U, Southport, Tranmere, Southport (L), York, Chorley									
Amaluzor (Formerly Nwogu)	Justin	23	Forward	Maidstone United	24	5	2	29	7
Dartford (Y), Barnet, Hayes & Y (L), Hemel (L), Hemel (L), Hampton & R (L), Bognor (L), Braintree, Maidstone									
Amantchi	Levi	19	Forward	Blyth Spartans (L)	3	13		16	2
Chesterfield (Y), Blyth S (L)									
Amartey	Francis	21	Forward	Slough Town	4	10	3	14	
Slough (Y)									
Ambroisine	Yannis	29	Defender	Dulwich Hamlet	4	3	3	7	
Leatherhead, Whitehawk, Welling, Dulwich H									
Ambrose	Kobie		Midfielder	Billericay Town			1		
Billericay (Y)									
Anau	Julien	25	Forward	Welling United	1	3	3	4	
Larne, Carrick Rangers, Welling									

SURNAME	FIRSTNAME	AGE	POSITION	CLUB PLAYED FOR	X	SX	S	Ap	G/Cs
Anderson	Jevan	20	Defender	Hereford FC (L)	7			7	
Formartine Utd, Burton, Hereford (L)									
Anderson	Joe	30	Defender	Welling United	27		2	27	
Fulham, Woking (L), Lincoln (L), Lincoln, Cambridge U, Bromley, Maidstone, Chelmsford, Welling									
Anderson	Kaiman	23	Forward	Leamington	30	9	1	39	4
Shrewsbury (Y), Telford (L), Halesowen (L), Oxford C (L), Southport, Stourbridge, Leamington									
Anderson	Mark	31	Midfielder	Spennymoor Town	9	17	8	26	5
Fort Lauderdale, North Carolina, Spennymoor									
Anderson	Myles	30	Defender	Hartlepool United	3	1	6	4	
				Aldershot Town (L)	4		3	4	
Leyton Orient Aberdeen, Blackburn R, Aldershot (L), Exeter, Monza, Chievo, Barrow, Torquay, Chester (L), Chester, Hartlepool, Aldershot (L)									
Anderson	Tommy	20	Midfielder	Billericay Town (L)			1		
Birmingham (Y), Hungerford (L), Billericay (L)									
Andre	Alexis	23	Goalkeeper	Gloucester City (L)			1		
Schiltigheim (Fra), Bristol R, Truro (L), Gloucester (L)									
Andrew	Charlie	20	Goalkeeper	Bradford Park Avenue (L)	3		1	3	
				Alfreton Town (L)	7		10	7	1
Hull (Y), Bradford PA (L), Alfreton (L)									
Andrews	Jake	22	Midfielder	Torquay United	24	10		34	7
Bristol C (Y), Chippenham (L), Cheltenham (L), Torquay (L), Torquay									
Angus	Dior	26	Forward	Barrow	36	4	1	40	11
Solihull, Kidderminster, Worcester (L), Solihull, Stratford, Redditch U, Port Vale, Tamworth (L), Nuneaton (L), Barrow (L), Barrow									
Anson	Adam	23	Defender	Southport	1			1	
Wigan Athletic, Macclesfield Town, Wigan Athletic Chorley, Witton, Southport, Witton (L)									
Anthony	Jaidon	20	Forward	Weymouth (L)	5			5	1
Arsenal (Y), Bournemouth, Weymouth (L)									
Antwi	Jayden	21	Midfielder	Tonbridge Angels		2		2	
Wimbledon (Y), Cheshunt, Tonbridge A									
Anyon	Joe	33	Goalkeeper	Chorley	4			4	2
Port Vale (Y), Lincoln C, Morecambe (L), Shrewsbury, Macclesfield (L), Unattached, Crewe, Scunthorpe, Chesterfield, Chorley									
Appleyard	William	20	Goalkeeper	FC Halifax Town			42		
Stevenage (Y), FC Halifax									
Archer	Jordan	26	Forward	Stockport County (L)	3			3	
Bedworth United, Stourbridge, Chester, Bury, Maidenhead (L), Southport (L), Port Vale, Stockport (L)									
Archer	Lewis	21	Forward	Altrincham			1		
Guiseley, Altrincham									
Armson	James	30	Midfielder	Brackley Town	24	12	3	36	10
Nuneaton, Solihull, Brackley									
Armstrong	Rhys	18	Forward	Darlington		1	4	1	
Blyth S (Y), Darlington									
Armstrong	Taylor		Defender	Concord Rangers			1		
Concord R									
Armsworth	Sam	19	Midfielder	Slough Town		1	2	1	
Fulham (Y), Slough, Basingstoke (L)									
Arnold	Devon	18	Forward	Yeovil Town			2		
Yeovil (Y)									
Arnold	Nathan	32	Midfielder	Altrincham	2	1	1	3	
Mansfield (Y), Hyde U, Alfreton, Cambridge U, Grimsby (L), Grimsby, Lincoln, Salford (L), Boston U, Altrincham									
Arnold	Nick	29	Defender	Wealdstone	21	2	3	23	
				Dartford	4	1	3	5	
Reading, Wycombe (L), Woking, Whitehawk, Aldershot, Wealdstone, Dartford									
Arthur	Festus	19	Defender	Stockport County	26	9	6	35	2
Stockport (Y)									
Artus	Frankie	31	Midfielder	Bath City	28	1	4	29	2
Exeter, Brentford, Kettering, Cheltenham, Grimsby, Hereford, Bath									
Artwell	Oliver		Midfielder	Hungerford Town (L)	2	2		4	1
Forest GR (Y), Hungerford (L)									

Key: X - Started; SX - Sub on; S - Non-playing Sub; Ap - Total Appearances; G/Cs - Total goals/clean sheets.

SURNAME	FIRSTNAME	AGE	POSITION	CLUB	X	SX	S	Ap	G/Cs
Asante	Akwasi	27	Forward	Chester	23	6	1	29	19
Birmingham, Northampton (L), Shrewsbury (L), Shrewsbury (L), Kidderminster, Solihull M, Grimsby, Solihull M (L), Tamworth, Chester (L), Chester									
Ash	Bradley	24	Forward	Hereford	10	11	7	21	
Weston-s-Mare, Barnsley, Weston-s-Mare (L), Boreham W (L), Boreham W, Weston-s-Mare (L), Hereford									
Ashby	Josh	24	Midfielder	Oxford City	36			36	5
Oxford U (Y), Telford (L), Brackley (L), Oxford C (L), Oxford C									
Ashby-Hammond	Taye	21	Goalkeeper	Maidenhead United (L)	22		3	22	5
Fulham (Y), Maidenhead (L)									
Ashford	Sam		Forward	Hemel Hempstead Town	28	2		30	12
Witham, East Thurrock, Concord R, Hemel H									
Ashley	Ossama	19	Midfielder	Billericay Town (L)	1			1	
Wimbledon (Y), Billericay (L)									
Ashmore	Nathan	30	Goalkeeper	Ebbsfleet United	5			5	
				Boreham Wood (L)	26			26	9
Havant & W, Gosport B, Ebbsfleet, Boreham W (L)									
Askew	Josh	22	Defender	Curzon Ashton (L)	22	3	9	25	1
Blackburn (Y), Ramsbottom (L), Salford, Stockport (L), Ashton U (L), Curzon A (L)									
Asonganyi	Dylan	19	Forward	Maidenhead United (L)	1			1	
MK Dons (Y), Maidenhead (L)									
Astle	Matthew		Forward	Eastbourne Borough			2		
Eastbourne B (Y)									
Astles	Ryan	25	Defender	Southport	39			39	4
Rhyl, Northwich V, Chester, Southport									
Atkins	Lucus		Defender	Welling United			1		
Welling (Y)									
Atkinson	Ben	24	Midfielder	Farsley Celtic	25	12		37	2
Huddersfield (Y), Curzon A, Brighouse (L), Farsley C									
Atkinson	Chris	28	Midfielder	Farsley Celtic	39			39	
Huddersfield (Y), Darlington (L), Chesterfield (L), Tranmere (L), Bradford (L), Crewe, Crawley (L), Salford, Farsley C (L), Farsley C									
Atkinson	David	27	Defender	Darlington	5	2	8	7	
Middlesbrough (Y), Hartlepool (L), Carlisle (L), Carlisle, Blyth S, ÍBV (Icel), Blyth S, ÍBV, Blyth S (L), Darlington									
Atkinson	Jack		Goalkeeper	Alfreton Town	16		5	16	2
Halifax (Y), Bradford PA, Alfreton									
Atkinson	Joe		Goalkeeper	Spennymoor Town			9		
Spennymoor, Ryhope CW (dual)									
Atkinson	Robert	21	Defender	Eastleigh	25	1	4	26	1
				Eastleigh (L)	4			4	
Basingstoke, Fulham, Braintree (L), Eastleigh, Oxford U, Eastleigh (L)									
Audel	Thierry	33	Defender	Brackley Town	30	1	4	31	8
Triestina, Pisa, Macclesfield, Crewe, Lincoln (L), Lincoln (L), Macclesfield, Notts Co, Barrow, Welling, Brackley									
Austin	Sam	23	Midfielder	Kidderminster Harriers	36			36	1
Burton, Telford (L), Leamington (L), Kidderminster									
Avery	Sam	31	Defender	Gloucester City	22	2	2	24	2
Shortwood, Gloucester									
Ayunga	Jonah	23	Forward	Havant & Waterlooville	33	2		35	19
Dorchester, Brighton, Burgess Hill (L), Sligo Rovers (L), Galway (L), Sutton, Havant & W (L), Havant & W									
Azaze	Aymen	18	Goalkeeper	Barnet			16		
Barnet (Y)									
Azeez	Ade	26	Forward	Torquay United (L)	3			3	1
Charlton, Wycombe (L), Leyton O (L), Torquay (L), Dagenham & R (L), AFC Wimbledon, Partick, Cambridge U, Dover (L), Newport C, Torquay (L)									
Babalola	Temi	19	Forward	Concord Rangers	3	2		5	1
Woodford T, Romford, Brentwood T, Concord R (Dual)									
Bacon	Declan		Forward	Alfreton Town	2	4	7	6	
Bottesford, Alfreton									
Bacon	Jay		Defender	Dartford			5		
Dartford (Y), Romford									

2019-20 NATIONAL, NORTH & SOUTH PLAYERS

SURNAME	FIRSTNAME	AGE	POSITION	CLUB PLAYED FOR	X	SX	S	Ap	G/Cs
Bagan	Joel	18	Defender	Notts County (L)	3			3	
Cardiff (Y), Notts Co (L)									
Baggie	Abdulai	28	Forward	Weymouth	36	3		39	11
Rotherham, Port V, Yeovil, Hayes & Y, Salisbury, Tranmere, Bristol R, Stockport, Poole, Weymouth									
Bailey	Dan		Midfielder	Hungerford Town	11	12	9	23	
Hungerford									
Bailey	Nicky	36	Midfielder	Havant & Waterlooville	34	6		40	2
Sutton U, Barnet, Southend, Charlton, Middlesbrough, Millwall, Barnet, Sutton U, Havant & W									
Baillie	James	24	Defender	Curzon Ashton	23		1	23	
Crewe (Y), Nantwich (L), Curzon A									
Baines	Lewis	21	Defender	Chorley	31	5	3	36	1
Fleetwood (Y), Bamber B (L), Ashton U (L), Ashton U (L), Chorley (L), Stockport (L), Chorley									
Bajrami	Geraldo	20	Defender	Solihull Moors (L)	4			4	
Birmingham (Y), Solihull M (L)									
Bakayogo	Zoumana	33	Defender	Notts County	16	1	17	17	
Millwall, Tranmere, Leicester, Yeovil (L), Crewe, Tranmere, Notts Co									
Baker	Carl	37	Midfielder	Brackley Town	12	11	8	23	
Prescot C, Southport, Morecambe, Stockport, Coventry, MK Dons, Portsmouth, Nuneaton, Brackley									
Balanta	Angelo	30	Midfielder	Dagenham & Redbridge	22	1		23	8
QPR, Wycombe (L), MK Dons (L), MK Dons (L), MK Dons (L), Yeovil (L), Bristol R, Carlisle, Boreham W, Dagenham & R									
Baldwin	Aiden	23	Defender	Eastleigh (L)	4			4	
Forest GR (Y), Bath (L), Bristol C, Weston SM (L), Weston SM (L), Cheltenham (L), Eastleigh (L)									
Baldwin	Isaac	23	Defender	Farsley Celtic	4	3	5	7	
Halifax, Ossett A, Brighouse, Spennymoor, Farsley C									
Bale	Adam	21	Midfielder	Hartlepool United		1	10	1	
Sunderland (Y), Hartlepool									
Ball	Danny	28	Defender	Bath City	23		4	23	
Bristol C (Y), Bath									
Ball	Jimmy	24	Defender	Ebbsfleet United	14			14	1
				Solihull Moors	22	6		28	8
Bolton (Y), Hyde U (L), Northwich V, Stalybridge, Stockport, Stevenage, Ebbsfleet, Solihull M									
Baningime	Divin	19	Forward	Curzon Ashton (L)	3	1		4	
Wigan (Y), Curzon A (L)									
Bannister	Jack		Midfielder	Curzon Ashton	6	8		14	
Widnes, FC United, Curzon A									
Bansal-McNulty	Amrit	20	Midfielder	Torquay United (L)	2	1		3	
				Dartford (L)	3	1		4	1
QPR (Y), Torquay (L), Dartford (L)									
Banton	Jason	27	Midfielder	Braintree Town	13	1	2	14	5
Arsenal, Blackburn, Liverpool, Leicester, Burton (L), Crystal Palace, Plymouth (L), MK Dons (L), Plymouth, Wycombe,									
Hartlepool (L), Notts Co (L), Crawley, Partick (L), Woking, Torquay, St Albans (L), Dulwich H (L), Truro (L), Braintree									
Banton	Zane	24	Forward	St Albans City	25	4	2	29	7
Luton (Y), Concord R (L), Hemel H (L), Boreham W (L), Hemel H (L), St Albans (L), St Albans									
Barbosa	Diogo	24	Midfielder	Dulwich Hamlet	2	1		3	
Torrense (Por), Vilafranquense, Dulwich H									
Barden	Jonathan	27	Defender	Sutton United	37	1	1	38	
ÍBV, Ottawa Fury, St Louis, Sutton U									
Barham	Jack	24	Forward	Barnet	2	2	5	4	
				Dorking Wanderers (LP)	20	3		23	
Heybridge Swifts, Tilbury, Thurrock, Greenwich, Barnet, Bromley (L), Welling (L), Dorking W (LP)									
Barker	Charley	21	Midfielder	Braintree Town	4	12	13	16	
Leyton Orient, Wingate (L), Northwood (L), Haringey B (L), Braintree									
Barker	Kyle	19	Midfielder	Wrexham (L)		1	2	1	
Peterborough (Y), Wrexham (L)									
Barkers	Dylan	20	Midfielder	Guiseley	13	6	10	19	
Solihull (Y), Guiseley									
Barnes	Aaron	23	Defender	Dulwich Hamlet	27	5	2	32	2
Charlton, Torquay (L), Colchester, Torquay (L), Dulwich H									

Key: X - Started; SX - Sub on; S - Non-playing Sub; Ap - Total Appearances; G/Cs - Total goals/clean sheets.

SURNAME	FIRSTNAME	AGE	POSITION	CLUB	X	SX	S	Ap	G/Cs
Barnes	Joshua	22	Goalkeeper	Farsley Celtic (L)	6			6	2
Derby (Y), Eastleigh (L), Farsley C (L)									
Barnes	Marcus	23	Forward	Eastleigh (L)	10	10		20	5
Southampton (Y), Yeovil (L), Eastleigh (L)									
Barnes-Homer	Matthew	34	Forward	AFC Telford United		2	5	2	
Aldershot (Y), Hednesford, Bromsgrove, Willenhall, Wycombe, Kidderminster, Luton (L), Luton, Rochdale (L), Nuneaton, Ostersund (Swe), Macclesfield, Forest GR, Cambridge U, Tamworth (L), Whitehawk, Macclesfield (L), Aldershot, Wilmington (US), Brackley, Telford, Halesowen (Dual)									
Barnett	Josh		Goalkeeper	Dorking Wanderers			1		
Dorking W (Y)									
Barnett	Ryan	20	Midfielder	AFC Telford United (L)	17	2		19	3
Shrewsbury (Y), Telford (L), Telford (L)									
Barnett	Tyrone	34	Forward	Eastleigh	32	7	3	39	12
Macclesfield, Crawley, Peterborough, Ipswich (L), Bristol C (L), Oxford U (L), Shrewsbury, Southend (L), Wimbledon, Port Vale, Cheltenham (L), Cheltenham, Eastleigh									
Barnum-Bobb	Jazzi	24	Defender	Wrexham	13		3	13	
Cardiff, Newport Co (L), Newport Co, Torquay (L), Chelmsford, Wrexham									
Barrett	Ben		Midfielder	Oxford City			5		
Oxford C									
Barrington	Marcel	24	Forward	Concord Rangers	5	8		13	1
				Dartford		1		1	
Stoke (Y), Harrow B (L), Leicester, Nuneaton (L), Bishop's S (L), Walton C, Tooting & M, Margate, Grays, Tooting & M, Hendon, Braintree, Hampton & R, Concord R, Dartford									
Barrow	Scott	31	Defender	Gateshead	29		1	29	2
Tamworth, Macclesfield, Newport, Gateshead									
Barrows	Ross		Defender	King's Lynn Town	24	4	7	28	3
Halifax (Y), North Ferriby (L), King's Lynn									
Barry	Bradley	25	Defender	Barrow	32			32	2
Brighton (Y), Swindon, Chesterfield, Dover (L), Barrow									
Barton	Adam	29	Midfielder	Wrexham	10	1	7	11	
Preston (Y), Crawley (L), Coventry, Fleetwood (L), Portsmouth, Partick, Dundee U, Connah's Q (L), Wrexham									
Bascome	Osagi	21	Forward	Darlington	6	8	17	14	
Darlington									
Bassele	Aristede	26	Forward	Braintree Town	2			2	
Bournemouth, Hayes & Y (L), Lincoln C (L), Dorchester (L), Welling (L), Havant & W (L), Welling, Maldon/Tiptree, Chelmsford, Hampton & R, Concord R, Margate, Hythe T, Braintree									
Bastock	Paul	50	Goalkeeper	King's Lynn Town			11		
Cambridge U, Bath (L), Cheltenham, Fisher A, Kettering, Aylesbury U (L), Boston U, Scarborough, Dagenham & R, St Albans, Rushden & D, St Albans, Boston U, Worksop, St Albans, Royston T, St Neots, Dunstable, Stamford, Corby, Wisbech (dual), Wisbech, Kettering (dual), Grantham, Pinchbeck, King's Lynn (Asst Man)									
Baughan	Callum		Defender	Eastleigh		1	5	1	
Eastleigh (Y)									
Bauress	Bradley	24	Midfielder	Southport	29	3	3	32	6
Blackburn, Colwyn Bay, Witton, Barrow, Southport									
Bawling	Alfred Bobson	24	Midfielder	St Albans City	11	1	1	12	
Watford, Crawley, Woking, Torquay, Oxford C (L), Oxford C, St Albans, Enfield T									
Bayode	Tunde	21	Forward	Curzon Ashton (L)	3	4		7	1
Burnley (Y), Curzon A (L)									
Bazeley	Isaiah	20	Defender	Bradford Park Avenue (L)	11	8	1	19	1
Aston Villa (Y), Bradford PA (L)									
Beale	Lewis		Forward	Eastleigh	1	2	10	3	1
Eastleigh (Y)									
Beard	Sam		Midfielder	Dorking Wanderers	27	11	1	38	1
Loxwood, Dorking W									
Bearwish	Tom	20	Forward	Eastleigh	9	18	19	27	4
Eastleigh (Y)									
Beasant	Sam	32	Goalkeeper	Hemel Hempstead Town	20		6	20	3
Maidenhead, Woking, Billericay, Woking, Stevenage, Cambridge U, Braintree, Chelmsford, Concord R, Hemel H									
Beaumont	Bobby		Defender	Wrexham	3	1		4	
Wrexham (Y)									

2019-20 NATIONAL, NORTH & SOUTH PLAYERS — APPEARANCES

SURNAME	FIRSTNAME	AGE	POSITION	CLUB PLAYED FOR	X	SX	S	Ap	G/Cs
Beautyman	Harry	28	Midfielder	Sutton United	38		1	38	17
Leyton O, Sutton U, Welling, Peterborough, Northampton, Stevenage, Sutton U									
Beck	Mark	26	Forward	Harrogate Town	22	8		30	6
Carlisle (Y), Falkirk (L), Yeovil, Wrexham (L), Darlington, Harrogate									
Beckford	Ethan	21	Forward	Curzon Ashton		2	1	2	
Toronto II, Penn State Uni, Curzon A									
Beckles	Jerome		Midfielder	Dorking Wanderers		3	14	3	
Dorking W									
Beckles	Reece	24	Forward	Wealdstone		2	5	2	
				Oxford City (L)	6	1	1	7	
Woking (Y), Farnborough (L), Wingate & F, Wealdstone, Oxford C (L)									
Beckwith	Dean	36	Defender	Havant & Waterlooville	19	4	14	23	2
Gillingham, Margate (L), Hereford U, Northampton, Luton, Eastleigh, Sutton U, Maidstone (L), Havant & W									
Bedford	Joe	22	Midfielder	Dover Athletic	2		3	2	
				Dulwich Hamlet (L)	5			5	
Southend, East Thurrock (L), Dover, Dulwich H (L)									
Beeney	Mitchell	24	Goalkeeper	Hartlepool United	7		3	7	1
Chelsea (Y), Newport C (L), Crawley (L), Sligo Rovers, Hartlepool									
Beere	Tom	25	Midfielder	Tonbridge Angels			1		
Wimbledon (Y), Bishop's S (L), Gateshead (L), Hampton RB, Leatherhead, Tonbridge A									
Beesley	Jake	23	Forward	Solihull Moors (L)	26	3		29	5
Chesterfield (Y), Salford, Boston U (L), Bradford PA, Salford, Solihull M (L)									
Behcet	Darren	33	Gk Coach	Yeovil Town			2		
West Ham (Y), Cambridge U (L), Yeovil, Dorchester (L), Sutton U, Tooting & M, Cray W, Maldon/Tip, Ware, Heybridge, Yeovil									
Bell	Lucas	18	Midfielder	Darlington		2	16	2	
Sunderland (Y), Darlington									
Bell	Nyal	23	Forward	Stockport County	19	21	1	40	6
Rochdale (Y), Chester (L), Gateshead (L), Chester (L), Alfreton (L), Stockport									
Belshaw	James	29	Goalkeeper	Harrogate Town	41		4	41	15
Walsall (Y), Blue Devils (US), Chicago Fire, Nuneaton, Tamworth, Harrogate									
Bencherif	Hamza	32	Defender	Guiseley	35			35	4
Lincoln C, Macclesfield, Notts Co, Plymouth, JS Kabylie (Alg) Lincoln C, Halifax, Wrexham, York, Guiseley									
Bender	Thomas	27	Defender	St Albans City	31	3	1	34	2
Colchester, Accrington (L), Chelmsford (L), Millwall, Welling (L), Dartford, Forest GR, St Albans (L), St Albans									
Benjamin	Russell	28	Midfielder	Southport	33	3	2	36	1
Southport, Colwyn B (L), Telford, Stockport, Warrington, Southport									
Bennett	Dale	30	Defender	Sutton United	8			8	
Watford (Y), Wealdstone (L), Kettering (L), Brentford (L), AFC Wimbledon (L), Yeovil (L), Forest GR, Sutton U									
Bennett	Jack	22	Goalkeeper	Bradford Park Avenue	3		6	3	
				Kettering Town			6		
Bradford PA, Stratford T, Kettering (Dual)									
Bennett	Richie	29	Forward	Stockport County	1			1	
Northwich V, Barrow, Carlisle, Morecambe (L), Port Vale, Stockport									
Bennett-Rivera	Jake	24	Midfielder	Alfreton Town (L)	2	1	6	3	
Telford, Sheff Utd, Alfreton (L)									
Bentley	Alex	30	Defender	Tonbridge Angels	23	2	7	25	1
Fisher A, Hornchurch, Tonbridge A									
Benyon	Elliot	32	Forward	Oxford City	21	2		23	4
Torquay (Y), Swindon, Wycombe (L), Southend, Torquay (L), Torquay, Hayes & Y (L), Hayes & Y, Wealdstone, Whitehawk, Leatherhead, Oxford C									
Berkeley-Agyepong	Jacob Kwame	23	Midfielder	Aldershot Town	16	6	2	22	
				Dartford (L)	6			6	2
Crystal Palace (Yth), Aldershot, Dartford (L)									
Berkoe	Kevin	18	Defender	Oxford City (L)	18			18	2
Wolves (Y), Sunderland (U23), Oxford U, Oxford C (L)									
Berry-Hargreaves	Matt		Defender	Hungerford Town	10	5	10	15	
Wickham W, Hungerford (Y), Oxford U, AFC Rushden & D (L), Banbury (L), Hungerford									
Bett	Mark	38	Midfielder	Farsley Celtic			12		
Farsley C, Guiseley, Bradford PA, Ossett T, Curzon A, Farsley C (Asst Man)									

Key: X - Started; SX - Sub on; S - Non-playing Sub; Ap - Total Appearances; G/Cs - Total goals/clean sheets.

SURNAME	FIRSTNAME	AGE	POSITION	CLUB	X	SX	S	Ap	G/Ca
Bettache	Faysal	19	Midfielder	Billericay Town (L)	4	1		5	
QPR (Y), Billericay (L)									
Bettamer	Mohamed	27	Forward	Hemel Hempstead Town (L)	4		1	4	
				Aldershot Town	19	2		21	7
Watford (Y), London Tigers, Hayes & Y, Hampton & R, Al-Ahli Ben (Libya), Staines, Braintree, Barnet, Welling (L), Hemel H (L), Aldershot									
Betts	Owen	19	Defender	Notts County		1	1	1	
Notts Co (Y)									
Biabi	Botti	24	Forward	Ebbsfleet United		5	2	5	
Falkirk (Y), Swansea, Hamilton (L), Macclesfield (L), Ebbsfleet									
Bickerstaff	Jake		Defender	Wrexham	2	1	2	3	1
Wrexham (Y)									
Bigirimana	Gael	26	Midfielder	Solihull Moors (L)		1		1	
Coventry (Y), Newcastle U, Rangers (L), Coventry (L), Coventry, Motherwell, Hibernian, Solihull M									
Bingham	Billy	29	Midfielder	Bromley	32	2	1	34	3
Dagenham & R, Grays (L), Crewe, Gillingham, Bromley									
Binnom-Williams	Jerome	25	Defender	FC Halifax Town	28		9	28	3
Crystal P (Y), Forest Green (L), Southend (L), Burton (L), Leyton O (L), Peterborough, Chesterfield, Halifax									
Birch	Arlen	23	Defender	AFC Telford United	20	1		21	
Everton (Yth), Burnley (Yth), AFC Fylde, Telford									
Bird	Pierce	21	Defender	Notts County	3	8	9	11	
				Boston United (L)	4			4	
Notts Co (Y), Alfreton (L), Boston U (L)									
Bird	Ryan	32	Forward	Slough Town	20	8	7	28	3
Burnham, Portsmouth, Cambridge U (L), Cambridge U, Hartlepool (L), Yeovil, Eastleigh, Newport Co, Dover, Maidenhead, Slough									
Bishop	Liam	19	Forward	Hereford		1		1	
Hereford (Y), Mangotsfield (L)									
Blackburn	Liam		Goalkeeper	Altrincham			2		
Altrincham (Y)									
Blackett	Paul	22	Forward	Gateshead	1	13	5	14	1
Newcastle (Y), Sheffield U (Y), Heaton S, Newcastle B, Gateshead									
Blackman	Andre	29	Defender	Ebbsfleet United	14	4	4	18	
Wimbledon, Celtic, Inverness (L), Plymouth, Dover, Maidenhead, Blackpool, Crawley, Barnet, Southend, Ebbsfleet									
Blackman	Sam		Midfielder	Dartford			2		
Leatherhead, Margate, Concord R, Dartford									
Blackmore	Daniel		Defender	Eastbourne Borough		4	5	4	
Eastbourne B									
Blake	Nyle	21	Forward	Alfreton Town	4	15	9	19	1
Mansfield (Y), Alfreton (L), Alfreton									
Blakeman	Adam	28	Midfielder	Chorley	29	5	6	34	
Bolton Wanderers, Hyde United, Ayr United, Southport, Chorley									
Blanchfield	James	22	Midfielder	Concord Rangers	29	3	3	32	4
Arsenal (Y), Ipswich (Y), Aldershot (L), Dagenham & R, Concord R									
Blaney	Shane	21	Defender	Blyth Spartans (L)	1			1	
Finn Harps, Doncaster, Blyth S (L)									
Blissett	Nathan	29	Forward	Solihull Moors	17	8	7	25	4
Romulus, Kidderminster, Cambridge U (L), Hednesford (L), Bristol R (L), Bristol R, Tranmere (L), Lincoln (L), Torquay,									
Plymouth, Macclesfield (L), Macclesfield, Solihull									
Boateng	Kwame	21	Defender	Farsley Celtic			2		
Bradford (Y), Guiseley, Farsley C									
Boden	Scott	30	Forward	Chesterfield	28	7	5	35	10
Chesterfield, Macclesfield (L), Macclesfield, Halifax, Newport Co, Inverness CT, Wrexham, Gateshead, Chesterfield									
Bodenham	Jack	20	Defender	Hereford (L)	13	1	5	14	
Cardiff (Y), TNS (L), Hereford (L)									
Bolarinwa	Tom	30	Midfielder	Sutton United	14	5	11	19	
Sutton U, Grimsby, Sutton U (L), Sutton U									
Boldewijn	Enzio	27	Forward	Notts County	39	4	3	43	9
Utrecht, Den Bosch (L), Almere, Crawley, Notts Co									
Bombelenga	Stephane		Forward	Eastbourne Borough	1	5		6	2
Eastbourne B									

SURNAME	FIRSTNAME	AGE	POSITION	CLUB PLAYED FOR	X	SX	S	Ap	G/Cs
Bond	Andy	34	Midfielder	York City	25	4	10	29	2
Crewe, Barrow, Colchester, Crewe (L), Bristol R (L), Chester, Stevenage, Chorley, Crawley, AFC Fylde, York									
Boness	Danny	22	Goalkeeper	Hemel Hempstead Town	8		24	8	2
Hemel H									
Bonfield	Alfie	19	Goalkeeper	St Albans City			10		
Wealdstone, St Albans									
Bonner	Thomas	32	Defender	Dartford	33	2	4	35	1
Hinckley U, Ilkeston, Dartford, Cambridge U, Dover (L), Ebbsfleet, Dartford									
Bonnett-Johnson	Sean	30	Midfielder	Braintree Town	3	5	2	8	
Kettering, Broxbourne, Billericay, Dundee, Billericay, Kingstonian, Merstham, Hendon, Potters B, Braintree, East Thurrock									
Boot	Ryan	25	Goalkeeper	Solihull Moors	44		1	44	13
Port Vale (Y), Worcester (L), Norton U (L), Newcastle T (L), Worcester (L), Worcester (L), Macclesfield (L), Solihull									
Booty	Regan	22	Midfielder	Notts County	17	7	1	24	3
Huddersfield (Y), Aldershot (L), Notts Co									
Boshell	Danny	39	Midfielder	Bradford Park Avenue		1	5	1	
Oldham (Y), Bury (L), Stockport, Grimsby, Chesterfield, Guiseley, Altrincham (L), Altrincham, Guiseley, Bradford PA									
Boucaud	Andre	35	Midfielder	Barnet	5	4	3	9	
				Maidstone United	5	2		7	
QPR, Reading, Peterborough (L), Peterborough (L), Peterborough, Aldershot (L), Kettering, York (L), York, Luton, Notts Co (L), Notts Co, Dagenham & R, Barnet, Maidstone									
Bower	Mark	40	Goalkeeper	Farsley Celtic		1	12	1	
Notts F (Y), Thackley, Yorkshire Am, Eccleshill U, Farsley C									
Bower	Matthew	21	Defender	Bath City	8	1	4	9	1
Cheltenham (Y), Weston (Lx2), Bath									
Bowry	Daniel	22	Defender	Bath City (L)	27			27	
Charlton (Y), Hampton & R (L), Cheltenham, Bath (L)									
Box	Martyn	18	Defender	Barnet			2		
Barnet (Y)									
Boyce	Andrew	30	Defender	Eastleigh	41			41	1
Gainsborough, Lincoln, Scunthorpe, Scunthorpe (L), Grimsby (L), Grimsby (L), Hartlepool (L), Notts Co (L), Grimsby, Eastleigh									
Boyes	Adam	29	Forward	Spennymoor Town	4	21	12	25	4
York, Kidderminster (L), Scunthorpe, Boston U, Barrow, Gateshead, Guiseley (L), Guiseley, Bradford PA, Spennymoor									
Bradbury	Caine		Midfielder	Chippenham Town			1		
Chippenham (Y)									
Bradbury	Thomas	22	Defender	Yeovil Town	18	4	10	22	2
Dundee, York (L), Yeovil									
Bradley	Alex	21	Midfielder	Harrogate Town (L)	24	4	7	28	4
WBA (Y), Havant & W (L), Burton (L), Lincoln C, Harrogate (L)									
Bradley	Daniel	29	Midfielder	AFC Fylde	24	12	1	36	6
Aston Villa (Y), Tamworth, Kidderminster, Alfreton, Barnet, Alfreton, AFC Fylde, Kidderminster, AFC Fylde									
Bradley-Hurst	Josh	18	Goalkeeper	Gloucester City (L)	7		1	7	1
				Hungerford Town (L)	3			3	1
Celtic (Y), Birmingham (Y), Gloucester (L), Hungerford (L)									
Braham-Barrett	Craig	31	Defender	Hemel Hempstead Town	17	4		21	
				Dartford	10		2	10	
Welling, Grays, Farnborough, Havant & W, Sutton U, Macclesfield, Cheltenham (L), Cheltenham, Ebbsfleet, Woking (L), Whitehawk (L), Dover, Braintree, Welling (L), Chelmsford, Welling, Hemel H, Dartford									
Branson	Connor	28	Defender	Altrincham	5	3	2	8	
				Alfreton Town	22	2	1	24	3
Barnsley (Y), Guiseley, Golden Eagles (US), Pittsburgh, Bradford PA, Altrincham, Alfreton									
Bray	Alexander	24	Midfielder	Hereford	7	8	4	15	
				Chippenham Town	5	1		6	
Swansea (Y), Plymouth (L), Rotherham (L), Rotherham, Forest GR (L), York (L), Weston-s-Mare (L) Hereford, Chippenham									
Bray	Josh		Midfielder	Eastbourne Borough			3		
Isthmian Lge, Eastbourne B									
Bray	Rian	21	Defender	Tonbridge Angels	34			34	2
Millwall (Y), Welling (L), Bishop's S (L), Hendon, Hampton & R, Tonbridge A									
Bremang	David	20	Forward	Leamington (L)	5		1	5	
Coventry (Y), Leamington (L)									

Key: X - Started; SX - Sub on; S - Non-playing Sub; Ap - Total Appearances; G/Cs - Total goals/clean sheets.

SURNAME	FIRSTNAME	AGE	POSITION	CLUB	X	SX	S	Ap	G/Cs
Bremner	Jamie		Defender	Gloucester City			1		
Bristol R (Y), Gloucester									
Brewer	Tommy	28	Forward	Tonbridge Angels	9		2	9	
				St Albans City	2		1	2	
Hampton & R, Staines, Tonbridge A, St Albans									
Brickell	Taylor		Midfielder	Chorley			2		
Chorley (Y)									
Briggs	Matt		Midfielder	Dorking Wanderers	32	6	1	38	7
Blackburn (Y), Dorking W									
Briggs	Matt	29	Defender	Dartford	1		2	1	
Fulham (Y), Leyton O (L), Peterborough (L), Bristol C (L), Watford (L), Millwall, Colchester (L), Colchester, Chesterfield, Barnet, Maldon, HB Koge (Den), Dartford									
Brighton	James	27	Defender	Kettering Town	9	2	5	11	
Cambridge U (Y), Cambridge C (L), Cambridge C, Hemel H, Kettering,									
Brindley	Richard	27	Defender	Notts County	28	1	4	29	1
Norwich (Y), Chelmsford, Chesterfield, Rotherham, Scunthorpe (L), Oxford U (L), Colchester (L), Colchester, Barnet, Bromley, Notts Co									
Britton	Louis	19	Forward	Bath City (L)		10	1	10	1
Bristol C (Y), Yate (L), Bath (L)									
Broadbent	George	19	Midfielder	Curzon Ashton (L)	5			5	1
Man Utd (Y), Sheff Utd, Curzon A (L)									
Brodie	Cameron		Midfielder	Dartford	8	4	12	12	
Dartford (Y)									
Brogan	Stephen	32	Defender	Spennymoor Town	18	2	6	20	1
Rotherham (Y), Stalybridge (L), Alfreton, Stalybridge, Guiseley, Forest GR, Southport, Stalybridge, Gainsborough, North Ferriby, Boston U, Spennymoor									
Brooks	Calvin	26	Midfielder	Weymouth	30	4		34	3
Dorchester, Yeovil, Weymouth (L), Weymouth									
Brough	Morgan	20	Forward	Alfreton Town			1		
Alfreton (Y), North F (L)									
Brough	Patrick	24	Midfielder	Barrow	35		2	35	2
Carlisle, Lincoln C (L), Salford (L), Morecambe, Falkirk, Barrow									
Brown	Andre	24	Forward	AFC Telford United	2	5	6	7	1
Crewe (Y), Worcester (L), Rushall (L), Kidderminster, Telford, Hednesford (L)									
Brown	Cole	22	Forward	Hampton & Richmond Borough	7	7	6	14	1
Hayes & Y, Hendon, Walton C, Hampton & R									
Brown	Connor	27	Defender	Barrow	13	7	20	20	1
Sheffield U, Oldham, Carlisle (L), Guiseley, York, Barrow									
Brown	Matt	30	Defender	FC Halifax Town	24			24	
Manchester C, Chesterfield, Southport (L), Chester (L), Chester, Halifax									
Brown	Scott	35	Midfielder	Harrogate Town	4	5	13	9	
Port Vale (Y), Cheltenham, Morecambe, Fleetwood, York, Macclesfield, Chester, Southport, Grimsby, Accrington, Harrogate									
Brown	Sebastian	30	Goalkeeper	Sutton United			2		
AFC Wimbledon, Woking (L), Bromley, Whitehawk (L), Hampton & R, Whitehawk, Hampton & R, Sutton U									
Brown	Stefan	30	Forward	Oxford City	10	8	6	18	5
Totton, Basingstoke, Hungerford, Maidenhead, Hungerford, Wealdstone, Oxford C									
Brown	Troy	29	Defender	Chelmsford City	2		1	2	
Ipswich (Y), Rotherham, Aldershot (L), Aldershot, Cheltenham, Exeter, Dundee U, Chelmsford									
Brown	Wayne	31	Midfielder	Sutton United		1	2	1	
Fulham (Y), Brentford, TPS (Fin) (L), Bristol R (L), Bristol R, TPS, SLK Seinajoki, Newcastle (Aus), Sutton U									
Brundle	Mitch	25	Midfielder	Dagenham & Redbridge	31			31	8
Yeovil, Bristol C, Cheltenham, Braintree, Hemel H (L), Gateshead, Dover, Dagenham & R									
Brunt	Lewis	19	Midfielder	Gloucester City (L)	5	1		6	2
Aston Villa (Y), Gloucester (L)									
Brunt	Ryan	27	Forward	Bath City	21	16	3	37	13
Stoke (Y), Nantwich (L), Luton (L), Tranmere (L), Leyton O (L), Bristol R (L), Bristol R, York (L), Stevenage (L), Plymouth (L), Plymouth, Exeter, Bath									
Brzozowski	Marcin	21	Goalkeeper	Yeovil Town (L)	2		4	2	
				Braintree Town (L)	3		1	3	
QPR, Yeovil (L), Braintree (L)									

2019-20 NATIONAL. NORTH & SOUTH PLAYERS — APPEARANCES

SURNAME	FIRSTNAME	AGE	POSITION	CLUB PLAYED FOR	X	SX	S	Ap	G/Cs
Buchanan	David	37	Defender	Chesterfield	25	1	3	26	
Bury, Hamilton, Tranmere, PNE, Northampton, Chesterfield									
Buchanan	Elliott	30	Forward	Dorking Wanderers	10	7	2	17	7
Hayes & Y, Newport Co, Boreham W, Bromley, St Albans, Staines, Bishop's S, Margate, Chelmsford, Kingstonian, Dorking W, Hayes & Y (L)									
Buckley	Callum	24	Defender	Weymouth	4	2	4	6	
Bournemouth (Y), Concord R (L), Basingstoke (L), Eastbourne B (L), Aldershot (L), Weymouth, Hayes & Y (L),									
Buddle	Nathan	26	Defender	Spennymoor Town	34	1	1	35	2
Hartlepool (Y), Blyth S, Carlisle, Gateshead, Blyth S, Spennymoor									
Bugiel	Omar	25	Forward	Sutton United	27	7	1	34	10
Forest Green Rovers, Bromley (L), Bromley, Sutton U									
Burke	Luke	22	Defender	AFC Fylde	35			35	1
Wigan Athletic, Barrow, AFC Fylde (L), AFC Fylde									
Burnett	Henry		Midfielder	Tonbridge Angels (L)	3		2	3	
Southend (U23), Tonbridge A (L)									
Burns	Harry		Midfielder	Weymouth			3		
Weymouth (Y)									
Burrell	Warren	30	Midfielder	Harrogate Town	40			40	
Mansfield (Y), Harrogate, Sheffield FC, Leek, Buxton, Harrogate									
Burrow	Jordan	27	Forward	York City	36	3		39	15
Chesterfield, Morecambe, Stevenage, Lincoln, Halifax, Gateshead, York									
Burstow	Mason		Forward	Welling United			1		
Welling (Y)									
Burton	Scott	32	Midfielder	Chester	14	5	9	19	
Salford, Chester									
Burwood	Warren	20	Goalkeeper	Hereford (L)			5	5	
Cardiff (Y), Hereford (L)									
Buse	Matt	22	Midfielder	Torquay United	18	2	1	20	2
Taunton, Torquay									
Bush	Chris	28	Defender	Bromley	36	1		37	5
Brentford, Wimbledon (L), Wimbledon, Gateshead, Hereford, Welling, Lincoln, Chelmsford, Ebbsfleet, Bromley									
Bushaj	Melis		Defender	Solihull Moors			1		
Solihull M (Y)									
Butler	Jack	19	Midfielder	Blyth Spartans		1		1	
Blyth S (Y),									
Butler	Jamie	28	Goalkeeper	Sutton United	21		1	21	3
Met Police, Concord R, Hemel H, Braintree (L), Sutton U									
Butroid	Lewis	21	Defender	Spennymoor Town (L)	3			3	
Scunthorpe (Y), Spennymoor (L)									
Butterfield	Milan	22	Midfielder	Kidderminster Harriers	33			33	2
Walsall (Y), Leamington (L), Kidderminster									
Buxton	Adam	28	Defender	York City (L)	2	1		2	
Wigan, Burton (L), Accrington (L), Accrington, Portsmouth, Tranmere, Morecambe, York (L)									
Byrne	Karl	23	Midfielder	Boston United	7		4	7	
				Bradford Park Avenue	2		1	2	
Cabinteely, Boston U, Bradford PA									
Byrne	Neill	27	Defender	AFC Fylde	45			45	3
Nottingham Forest, Rochdale, Barrow (L), Southport (L), Telford, Macclesfield, Gateshead, AFC Fylde									
Byrne	Shane	27	Midfielder	Brackley Town	38			38	7
Leicester (Y), Bury (L), Bury, Bray W, Corby, Nuneaton, Brackley									
Cadogan	Kieron	29	Midfielder	Wealdstone			2		
Crystal Palace, Burton (L), Rotherham (L), Aldershot (L), Barnet (L), Sutton U, Billericay, Woking (L), Wealdstone									
Calder	Riccardo	24	Midfielder	Bradford Park Avenue	8			8	1
				AFC Telford United	6		4	6	
Aston Villa (Y), Dundee (L), Doncaster (L), Doncaster (L), Lincoln C (L), Inverness, Bradford PA, Telford									
Calderbank-Park	Kai	19	Goalkeeper	Curzon Ashton (L)	2			2	
Burnley (Y), Curzon A (L)									
Callaghan	Anthony	26	Defender	Blyth Spartans	19	2		21	
South Shields, Blyth S									

Key: X - Started; SX - Sub on; S - Non-playing Sub; Ap - Total Appearances; G/Cs - Total goals/clean sheets.

SURNAME	FIRSTNAME	AGE	POSITION	CLUB	X	SX	S	Ap	G/Cs
Calveley	Mike	21	Midfielder	Curzon Ashton	23			23	4
Port Vale (Y), Nuneaton (L), Curzon A									
Calvert	Jack		Midfielder	Dartford			1		
Dartford (Y)									
Cameron	Kyle	23	Defender	Torquay United	38		1	38	2
Newcastle (Y), York (L), Newport Co (L), Queen OTS (L), Torquay									
Camp	Brennan	19	Defender	Weymouth (L)	19			19	
Bournemouth (Y), Weymouth (L)									
Campbell	Adam	25	Forward	Darlington	41	1		42	16
Newcastle (Y), Carlisle (L), St Mirren (L), Fleetwood (L), Hartlepool (L), Gateshead (L), Notts Co, Morecambe, Carlisle (L), Darlington									
Campbell	Kristian		Defender	Eastbourne Borough	30		1	30	2
Merstham, Bromley, Bognor R (Lx2), Eastbourne B									
Campbell	Remaye	19	Forward	Notts County		1	2	1	
Notts Co (Y)									
Cane	Jacob	26	Midfielder	Hereford	21	1	2	22	
Exeter (Y), Weston, Hereford									
Cann	Ted	19	Goalkeeper	Yeovil Town (L)	3		1	3	1
Liverpool (Y), WBA, Worcester (L), Yeovil (L)									
Cantrill	George	20	Defender	Guiseley	33			33	
Sheff Utd (Y), Guiseley (L), Guiseley									
Carden	Adam	34	Midfielder	Southport			1		
Southport, AFC Fylde, Nantwich, Stalybridge, Warrington, Southport									
Cardwell	Harry	23	Forward	Chorley (L)	1			1	1
Reading (Y), Woking (L), Braintree (L), Brighton (L), Grimsby, Chorley (L)									
Carey	James	20	Goalkeeper	Hereford			1		
Hereford (Y)									
Carey	Sonny	19	Midfielder	King's Lynn Town	10	19	7	29	4
Norwich (Y), Wroxham, King's Lynn									
Carline	George	27	Midfielder	Solihull Moors	8	4	2	12	1
				Leamington (L)	16			16	3
Solihull M, Leamington (Lx2)									
Carlyle	Nathan	19	Defender	Concord Rangers (L)	6	4	3	10	
QPR (Y), Concord R (L)									
Caro	Steven		Goalkeeper	Oxford City		1	7	1	
Oxford C									
Carrington	Mark	33	Defender	Wrexham	23	3	9	26	
Crewe, MK Dons, Hamilton, Bury, Wrexham									
Carta	Joel	21	Midfielder	Kettering Town	9	8	11	17	3
Coventry (Y), Shrewsbury (Y), Mansfield (Y), Harrowby, Corby, Kettering									
Carter	Darren	36	Midfielder	Solihull Moors	12	9	3	21	1
Birmingham, Sunderland (L), West Brom, Preston, Millwall (L), Cheltenham, Northampton, Forest Green, Solihull M									
Cartman	Nathan	30	Forward	Farsley Celtic	21	14	5	35	7
Leeds (Y), Harrogate RA, Darlington, Farsley C (L), Farsley C									
Cartwright	Samuel	19	Defender	Kettering Town (L)	11	1	1	12	1
Peterborough (Y), Kettering (L)									
Carver	Marcus	26	Forward	Chorley	27	7		34	4
Accrington Stanley, Marine, FC Halifax Town, Barrow, AFC Fylde, Chorley (L), Chorley									
Cascaval	Adrian	33	Defender	Chelmsford City	26	2	1	28	
Academia (Mol), Kaisar (L) (Kaz), Veris (Mol), Costuleni, AGMK (Uzb), Neftchi, Dinamo-Auto (Mol), Luch Vlad (Rus),									
Naxxar Lions (Malta), Vikingur (F Isle), Chelmsford									
Case	Ryan	26	Defender	Dulwich Hamlet	1	3	4	4	
				Chippenham Town	1	7	7	8	
Havant & W, Dorchester, Braintree, Basingstoke, Wealdstone, Basingstoke, Poole, Eastbourne B, Bath, Gosport B, Oxford C,									
Dulwich, Chippenham									
Casey	Josh	28	Defender	Woking	38			38	
Salisbury, Hampton & R, Woking									
Casey	Matthew	20	Defender	Havant & Waterlooville (L)	2			2	
Portsmouth (Y), Havant & W (L)									
Cassidy	Jake	27	Forward	Maidenhead United	29	3	1	32	6
llandudno J, Airbus, Wolves, Tranmere (Lx3), Notts Co (L), Southend (L), Oldham, Guiseley, Hartlepool Maidstone (Lx2), Maidenhead									

SURNAME	FIRSTNAME	AGE	POSITION	CLUB PLAYED FOR	X	SX	S	Ap	G/Cs
Cawley	Jack	27	Defender	Concord Rangers	28	1		29	1
Ann Arbor (US), Heybridge S, Malden/Tiptree, Concord R									
Cawley	Steve	28	Midfielder	Hemel Hempstead Town		2		2	
Bishop's S, Concord R, Hemel H									
Ceesay	Yusifu	25	Forward	Altrincham (L)	3	2		5	
Alvechurch, Blackpool, Boston (L), Telford (L), Nuneaton (L), Alvechurch, Altrincham (L), Altrincham (L)									
Cerulli	Alfie		Forward	Braintree Town	11	23		34	3
Braintree (Y)									
Challoner	Matt	26	Defender	Chorley	35	1	2	36	1
				Boston United	2			2	
Blackpool, Northwich Victoria, Southport, Chorley, Boston U									
Chalmers-Stevens	Scott	34	Goalkeeper	Eastbourne Borough	2		17	2	
Tonbridge A, Folkestone, Eastbourne B									
Chambers	Ashley	30	Forward	Kidderminster Harriers	32	1		33	13
Leicester (Y), Wycombe (L), Grimsby (L), York (L), York, Cambridge U, Dagenham & R (L), Dagenham & R, Grimsby,									
Nuneaton (L), Nuneaton, Kidderminster									
Chambers	Karnell	22	Midfielder	Chippenham Town	23	9	5	32	8
Cheltenham, Gloucester, Chippenham									
Chambers	Michael	25	Defender	Wrexham	14	1	4	15	
				Chelmsford City (L)	6			6	
				Bromley	2	1	1	3	
				Billericay Town	6			6	
Crystal P (Y), Welling (L), Welling, Dulwich H, Wrexham, Chelmsford (L), Bromley, Billericay									
Champion	Tom	34	Midfielder	Boreham Wood	36	1		37	1
Dartford, Cambridge U, Barnet, Lincoln (L), Boreham W									
Chandler	Jamie	31	Midfielder	Spennymoor Town	32			32	1
Darlington, Gateshead, Spennymoor									
Chapman	Ben	21	Midfielder	Dulwich Hamlet	23	5	5	28	1
Crystal P (Y), Bearsted, Gillingham, Dulwich H									
Chapman	Fred		Goalkeeper	Maidenhead United	1			1	
Maidenhead (Y)									
Charles	Ashley	21	Midfielder	Wealdstone	11	7	5	18	
Watford (Y), Barnet (L), Wealdstone									
Charles	Dion	24	Forward	Southport	2			2	
Blackpool, Fylde (L), Fylde, Fleetwood, Halifax (L), Southport									
Charles	Tre	26	Midfielder	Braintree Town		1	1	1	
Hitchin, Braintree, Biggleswade									
Charles-Cook	Reice	26	Goalkeeper	Boreham Wood			1		
Arsenal (Y), Chelmsford (L), Bury, Coventry, Nuneaton (L), Swindon, Sonderjyske (Den), Shrewsbury, Macclesfield, Boreham W									
Cheek	Michael	32	Forward	Bromley	41			41	15
Heybridge S, Stanway R, Chelmsford, Braintree, Dagenham & R, Ebbsfleet, Bromley									
Chesmain	Noah	22	Defender	Maidstone United	35	2		37	3
Millwall, Welling (L), Boreham W (L), Colchester, Hitchin (L), Hungerford (L), Maidstone									
Chidyausiku	Joseph	22	Forward	Bradford Park Avenue		2		2	
				Chelmsford City	2	3	4	5	1
Havant & W, Bradford PA, Chelmsford									
Chiedozie	Jordan	30	Forward	Braintree Town	12	3		15	2
Bournemouth, Dorchester (L), Poole (Lx2), Concord R, Cambridge U, Dartford (L), Braintree (L), Boreham W, Concord R,									
Margate, Chelmsford, Braintree									
Childs	Mark		Goalkeeper	Weymouth	3		24	3	
Eastleigh, Gosport B (L), Weymouth									
Chilvers	Noah	19	Midfielder	Bath City (L)	26		1	26	2
Colchester (Y), Bath (L)									
Chime	Oken	18	Forward	Barnet		2	1	2	
Barnet (Y)									
Chislett	Ethan		Midfielder	Aldershot Town	32	6	1	38	9
Met Police, Aldershot									
Christian-Law	Tyler	27	Midfielder	Braintree Town	15	3	3	18	2
Enfield (Y), Margate, Wealdstone, Burnham, Ware, Hanwell, E & Belvedere (L), Romford, Wingate & F (L), Braintree									

Key: X - Started; SX - Sub on; S - Non-playing Sub; Ap - Total Appearances; G/Cs - Total goals/clean sheets.

APPEARANCES

SURNAME	FIRSTNAME	AGE	POSITION	CLUB	X	SX	S	Ap	G/Cs
Church	Anthony	33	Midfielder	Chelmsford City	33	2		35	2
Boston U, Grimsby, Alfreton (L), Chelmsford, Bishop's S, Chelmsford									
Clackstone	Josh	23	Midfielder	Alfreton Town	31	1		32	1
Hull, Notts Co (L), Halifax (L), Alfreton									
Clare	Tom	20	Forward	Boston United	1	4	1	5	
				Bradford Park Avenue	10	4		14	5
Boston U, Bradford PA									
Claridge	Joe	25	Defender	Concord Rangers	11		4	11	
West Ham (Y), Chelsea (Y), Maldon, Sudbury, Heybridge S, Concord R									
Clark	Harry		Defender	Harrogate Town			1		
Harrogate T									
Clark	Kenny	31	Defender	Dagenham & Redbridge	36			36	
Dagenham & R, Thurrock, Chelmsford, Dartford, Ebbsfleet, Dagenham & R									
Clark	Michael	22	Defender	Braintree Town	19		1	19	1
				St Albans	4	3	7	7	
Leyton Orient, East Thurrock (L), Braintree, Concord R, St Albans, Braintree, St Albans									
Clarke	Danny	35	Midfielder	Alfreton Town	34			34	4
Hull United, Frickley, Hall Road R, Winterton R, North Ferriby, Halifax, Alfreton									
Clarke	Eddie	21	Defender	Stockport County (L)	4		2	4	
Tranmere (Y), Fleetwood, Macclesfield (L), Stockport (L)									
Clarke	Joe	31	Midfielder	Leamington	29	2	2	31	1
Redditch, Darlington, Solihull, Wrexham, Kidderminster, Brackley (L), Brackley, Tamworth, Leamington									
Clarke	Matty	21	Midfielder	Bradford Park Avenue	2	2	1	4	
Penrith, Bradford PA									
Clarke	Nathan	36	Defender	FC Halifax Town	38			38	2
Huddersfield, Colchester (L), Oldham (L), Bury (L), Leyton O, Bradford, Coventry, Grimsby, FC Halifax									
Clarke	Ryan	38	Goalkeeper	Bath City	37		1	37	14
Bristol R, Southend (L), Kidderminster (L), Forest Green (L), Salisbury, Northwich, Oxford U, Northampton, AFC Wimbledon, Eastleigh, Torquay, Bath									
Clayton	Adam	33	Defender	Farsley Celtic	26	5	2	31	4
Bradford (PA), Farsley C									
Clayton	Paul	35	Forward	Guiseley		4	17	4	
Gainsborough, Alfreton, Harrogate (L), Harrogate, Alfreton, Shaw Lane, Guiseley									
Clayton-Phillips	Nick	20	Forward	Solihull Moors (L)	1	3		4	
WBA (Y), Braintree (L), Kidderminster (L), Solihull M (L)									
Clee	Nicky	36	Midfielder	Bradford Park Avenue	13	1		14	2
Hyde U, Altrincham, Guiseley, Harrogate, Altrincham, Bradford PA									
Clements	Bailey	19	Defender	Hemel Hempstead Town (L)			1		
Ipswich (Y), Hemel H (L)									
Clements	Kyran	23	Defender	Braintree Town	5		4	5	
AFC Sudbury, Bury T, Braintree, Leiston (L)									
Clerima	Remy	30	Defender	Maidenhead United	28	1		29	4
Histon, Braintree, Maidenhead									
Cleworth	Max		Midfielder	Wrexham	4		2	4	
Wrexham (Y)									
Clifford	Billy	27	Midfielder	Wealdstone	36	1	1	37	7
Chelsea (Y), Colchester (L), Yeovil (L), Royal Antwerp (L), Walsall, Boreham W, Crawley, Boreham W, Hemel H, Billericay, Slough (L), Wealdstone									
Clifford	Tom	20	Defender	Concord Rangers (L)	14			14	1
Southend (Y), Concord R (L)									
Clifton	Adrian	31	Midfielder	Bromley	2	24		26	
Maidenhead, Havant & W, Maidenhead, Bromley									
Clunan	Michael	26	Midfielder	King's Lynn Town	23		2	23	1
Norwich (Y), Boston U, Histon, Lowestoft, Dereham, King's Lynn									
Clunis	Nyren		Midfielder	Dulwich Hamlet	17	21	2	38	4
Dulwich H (Y)									
Coddington	Luke	25	Goalkeeper	Chesterfield	10	1	15	11	
Middlesbrough, Huddersfield, Northampton, Wrexham (L), Guiseley (L), Chesterfield									
Cogdon	Gavin	37	Forward	Spennymoor Town	1	14	8	15	
Spennymoor, Sth Shields, Spennymoor									

SURNAME	FIRSTNAME	AGE	POSITION	CLUB PLAYED FOR	X	SX	S	Ap	G/Cs
Coghill	Dylan	22	Defender	Farsley Celtic	1	2	1	3	
Huddersfield (Y), Clyde, Farsley C									
Coker	Afolabi	24	Defender	Wealdstone		4	5	4	
Leeds U (Y), Norwich, Lewes, Staines, Sutton U, Ashford U, Wealdstone									
Coker	Andre	22	Forward	Bromley		5	2	5	1
Crystal Palace, Maidstone (L), Maidstone, Dartford (L), Bromley, Kingstonian (L)									
Coker	Tobi	21	Midfielder	Braintree Town	4	1	1	5	1
Barnet, Hornchurch (L), Hornchurch, Braintree									
Cole	Adeyinka	25	Midfielder	Braintree Town	20		1	20	5
				Billericay Town	3	3		6	
Blackpool (Y), Enfield T, Romford, Grays, Braintree, Billericay									
Cole	Jake	34	Goalkeeper	Maidstone United	27	1	8	28	6
QPR, Hayes (L), Farnborough, Plymouth, Woking, Aldershot, Maidstone									
Coleman De-Graft	Razzaq		Forward	Hampton & Richmond Borough		1	2	1	
Tooting & M (Y), Hampton & RB									
Collier	Nathan	34	Midfielder	Woking	10	7	17	17	
Hampton & R, Dartford, Eastbourne B, Hampton & R, Dartford, Woking									
Collings	Andy		Goalkeeper	Torquay United			4		
Torquay (Y)									
Collins	Jamie	35	Midfielder	Sutton United	17	2	4	19	3
Watford, Newport Co, Aldershot, Forest Green, Eastleigh, Sutton U									
Collins	Lee	31	Defender	Yeovil Town	31	1		32	
Port Vale, Barnsley (L), Barnsley, Shrewsbury (L), Northampton, Mansfield, Forest GR, Yeovil									
Collins	Lewis	19	Forward	Hemel Hempstead Town			1		
Hemel H (Y), Leverstock (L)									
Collins	Reuben	19	Defender	Billericay Town (L)	1		2	1	
Wimbledon (Y), Billericay (L)									
Comley	James	29	Midfielder	Maidenhead United	29	3		32	
Crystal Palace, St Albans, Maidenhead									
Connell	Liam	34	Goalkeeper	Darlington (L)	13		2	13	5
South Shields, Darlington (L)									
Connors	Jack	25	Defender	Dulwich Hamlet	23	5	8	28	1
Fulham, Dagenham & R, Hendon (L), Boreham W (L), Ebbsfleet, Dover, Hampton & R (Lx2), Dulwich H									
Constable	James	35	Forward	Hungerford Town	15	3		18	3
Chippenham, Walsall, Kidderminster (L), Kidderminster, Shrewsbury, Oxford U (L), Oxford U, Eastleigh, Poole (L), Hungerford									
Cook	Anthony	30	Midfielder	Welling United	35	2		37	11
Dagenham & R, Chelmsford, Bromley, Ebbsfleet, Woking (L), Dulwich H, Welling									
Cook	Ed	20	Defender	Hampton & Richmond Borough	4		2	4	
Bradfield College, Burnley, Hampton & R									
Cook	Jack	26	Defender	Woking	36	1	1	37	1
Worthing, Hampton & R, Woking									
Cook	Jacob		Midfielder	Billericay Town	8	3	4	11	
Kings Langley, Wealdstone, Hayes & Y (L), Billericay									
Cook	Joe		Defender	Havant & Waterlooville	4	3	10	7	
Havant & W, Bognor R (L)									
Cooke	Elliot	19	Midfielder	Curzon Ashton		3	3	3	
Curzon A (Y)									
Coombes	Adam	29	Midfielder	Welling United	21	4	5	25	10
				Wealdstone (L)	2	2	3	4	1
Chelsea, Yeovil (L), Notts Co, Bromley, Welling, Sutton U, Hampton & R (L), Welling, Billericay, Welling (L), Welling, Wealdstone (L)									
Cooney	Tommy		Defender	Braintree Town	2			2	
Boston U, Cefn Druids, Margate, Bognor R, Hungerford, Leatherhead, Glenavon, Skellefta (Swe), VPS (Fin), Braintree									
Cooper	Brandon	20	Defender	Yeovil Town (L)	1	2	2	3	
Swansea (Y), Yeovil (L)									
Cooper	Charlie	23	Midfielder	FC Halifax Town	29	2	1	31	1
Birmingham (Y), Forest GR (L), York (L), Forest GR (L), Forest GR, Newport Co (L), Boreham W (L), FC Halifax									
Cooper	Jack		Forward	Stockport County			1		
Stockport (Y)									
Copeland	Dquame	22	Defender	Welling United	2	1	11	3	
Ytterhogdals IK (Swe), Greenwich B, Bedfont S, Welling, Lewes (L)									

Key: X - Started; SX - Sub on; S - Non-playing Sub; Ap - Total Appearances; G/Cs - Total goals/clean sheets.

SURNAME	FIRSTNAME	AGE	POSITION	CLUB	X	SX	S	Ap	G/Cs
Cordner	Tyler	21	Defender	Ebbsfleet United (L)	23	1	1	24	
Bournemouth (Y), Havant & W (L), Ebbsfleet (L)									
Corne	Sam	23	Midfielder	Maidstone United	13	3		16	2
Welling, Braintree, Greenwich B, Ashford U, Maidstone									
Correia	Raul	27	Forward	Southport	18	11	2	29	4
Chorley, Blackpool, Guiseley (L), York (L), Barrow, Southport									
Cosgrave	Aaron	20	Forward	Welling United	11	18	2	29	1
West Ham (Y), Colchester (Y), Coggeshall, Havant & W, Chelmsford, Welling									
Cotter	Barry	21	Defender	Chelmsford City (L)	2			2	
Limerick, Ipswich, Chelmsford (L)									
Cottrell	Jake	32	Midfielder	Chorley	25	7	6	32	
FC United, Chorley									
Cottrell	James		Midfielder	Chester			1		
Stoke (Y), Chester (Y)									
Coulson	Connor	22	Goalkeeper	Hampton & Richmond Borough			2		
Dunstable T, Hampton & R, Barton R (L), Bedford T (L)									
Coulson	Luke	26	Midfielder	Bromley	40	2		42	3
Cardiff, Oxford C, Eastleigh, Barnet, Ebbsfleet, Bromley									
Coulthirst	Shaq	25	Forward	Barnet	1	7	1	8	1
Tottenham (Yth), Leyton O (L), Torquay (L), Southend (L), York (L), Wigan (L), Peterborough, Mansfield (L), Barnet									
Cousins	Mark	33	Goalkeeper	Bromley	18		1	18	4
Fulham, Colchester U, Dagenham & R, Barnet, Bromley									
Covolan Cavagnari	Lucas	29	Goalkeeper	Torquay United	27		11	27	6
Esportivo (Bra), Rio Branco, Whitehawk, Worthing, Torquay									
Cowan	Dan	28	Defender	Stockport County	29	4	4	33	1
Macclesfield, Chorley (L), Stockport									
Cowans	Henry	24	Midfielder	AFC Telford United	2	5	7	7	
Aston Villa (Y), Stevenage (L), Telford									
Cowley	Jason	24	Forward	Solihull Moors (L)	4	2		6	
Stevenage, Solihull M (L)									
Cox	Dean	32	Midfielder	Eastbourne Borough	19	8	5	27	4
Brighton, Leyton O, Crawley, Eastbourne B									
Cox	Sam	29	Midfielder	Hampton & Richmond Borough	23	2	1	25	
Cheltenham, Histon (L), Torquay (L), Barnet, Boreham W (L), Hayes & Y, Boreham W, Wealdstone, Hampton & R (L), Hampton & R									
Cracknell	Joe	26	Goalkeeper	Harrogate Town	4		41	4	2
Hull (Y), Scarborough Ath (L), Bradford, Bradford PA (L), Harrogate									
Craigen	James	29	Midfielder	AFC Fylde	13	7	4	20	
Partick Thistle, Forfar (L), Raith Rovers, Falkirk, Dunfermline, AFC Fylde									
Cranston	Dan		Midfielder	Gateshead			7		
Gateshead (Y)									
Crawford	Jamal	22	Midfielder	Curzon Ashton		2	1	2	
Llandudno, FC United, Chester, Curzon A									
Crawford	Tom	21	Midfielder	Notts County	5	7	8	12	2
Stoke City, Chester, Notts Co, AFC Fylde (L)									
Crellin	Billy	19	Goalkeeper	Chorley (L)	9			9	2
Fleetwood (Y), FC United (L), Chorley (L)									
Cresswell	Ryan	32	Defender	Bradford Park Avenue	5	2	1	7	
Sheffield U, Halifax (L), Rotherham (L), Morecambe (L), Macclesfield (L), Bury, Rotherham, Southend, Fleetwood,									
Northampton, Eastleigh, Boston U, Bradford PA									
Crichlow-Noble	Romoney	21	Defender	Hartlepool United (L)	2	1	7	3	
				Welling United (L)	6			6	1
Huddersfield (Y), Bradford PA (L), Hartlepool (L), Welling (L)									
Croasdale	Ryan	25	Midfielder	AFC Fylde	43			43	7
PNE, Tamworth (L), Sheffield Wed, Kidderminster, AFC Fylde									
Croft	Jake	21	Defender	Bradford Park Avenue	1	1	2	2	
Leeds (Y), Ytterhogdal IK (Swe), Bradford PA									
Croll	Luke	25	Defender	Dagenham & Redbridge	32	1	1	33	
Crystal P (Y), Plymouth (L), Exeter (L), Exeter, Dagenham & R									
Crook	Billy	29	Midfielder	Dartford	17	3	1	20	
Peterborough (Y), Weymouth (L), Histon (L), Tooting & M, Carshalton, Met Police, Enfield T, Braintree, Dartford									

SURNAME	FIRSTNAME	AGE	POSITION	CLUB PLAYED FOR	X	SX	S	Ap	G/Cs
Crook	Peter	26	Goalkeeper	Boston United	41			41	14
Harrogate T, Hyde U, Boston U									
Cropper	Jordan	20	Forward	Chesterfield	8			8	1
Chesterfield (Y)									
Crotty	Jayde		Midfielder	Wealdstone			1		
Wealdstone (Y)									
Cullinane-Liburd	Jordan	25	Defender	Hereford	34	1	1	35	1
Redditch, Solihull M, Rushall, Hereford									
Cumberbatch	Kurtis	24	Forward	Dover Athletic	11	7	9	18	1
Tottenham (Y), Watford (Y), Charlton (Y), Hadley Town, Welling, Harrow B, Farnborough, Dover									
Cundy	Robbie	24	Defender	Torquay United (L)	28		3	28	1
Oxford U, Gloucester (L), Oxford C (L), Southport (L), Gloucester, Bath, Bristol C, Exeter (L), Torquay (L)									
Cunningham	Aaron	22	Defender	Hartlepool United	8	3	15	11	
				Blyth Spartans (L)	3			3	
Hartlepool (Y), Blyth S (L), Blyth S (L)									
Cunnington	Adam	32	Forward	Dartford	11	1	1	12	3
				Hemel Hempstead Town	3	1		4	
Solihull, Kettering, Dag & Red (L), Dag & Red, Alfreton (L), Tamworth, Cambridge U, Bristol R (L), Ebbsfleet, Woking (L), Bromley, Billericay, Dartford, Hemel H									
Curran	Alex	21	Midfielder	Stockport County		2	5	2	
Blackburn (Y), Colne, Stockport									
Curry	Mitchell	20	Forward	Gateshead (L)	4	3	1	7	1
Middlesbrough (Y), Harrogate T (L), Gateshead (L)									
Curtis	Brandon		Midfielder	Maidenhead United			1		
Maidenhead (Y)									
Curtis	James	38	Defender	Spennymoor Town	36			36	
Gateshead, Spennymoor									
Czubik	Szymon	21	Forward	Stockport County			2		
Stockport Co (Y)									
D'Ath	Lawson	27	Midfielder	Yeovil Town	24	4	3	28	1
Reading, Yeovil (L), Cheltenham (L), Exeter (L), Dagenham & R, Northampton, Luton, MK Dons, Yeovil									
Da Costa	Khale	26	Midfielder	Tonbridge Angels	18	11	2	29	4
Harlow, Concord R, St Albans, Tonbridge A									
Dagnall	Chris	34	Forward	Yeovil Town	10	15		25	4
Rochdale, Scunthorpe, Barnsley, Bradford (L), Coventry (L), Leyton O, Kerala Blasters (Ind), Hibernian, Crewe, Bury, Tranmere, Yeovil									
Dainkeh	Zach		Midfielder	Ebbsfleet United			4		
Ebbsfleet (Y)									
Daire	Tendai	24	Forward	Brackley Town	2	24	11	26	
Lutterworth, Brackley									
Dale	Robert	36	Forward	Blyth Spartans	28	6	1	34	6
West Alloment, Blyth S, Whitley B, Blyth S									
Daly	Liam	32	Defender	Solihull Moors	17		1	17	1
				Gloucester City	14			14	1
Evesham, Corby, Redditch, Solihull M, Halesowen, Leamington, Barwell, Leamington, Solihull M, Kidderminster, Solihull M, Gloucester									
Daniels	Brendon	26	Forward	AFC Telford United	29	2	1	31	7
Crewe (Y), Leicester, Blackburn, Chester, Tamworth, Harrogate, AFC Fylde, Alfreton, Port Vale, Altrincham (L), Telford (L), Telford									
Davidson	Correy	27	Midfielder	Kidderminster Harriers	27	4	2	31	3
Bohemians, Carrick, Ards, AFC Sudbury, Walthamstow, Bishop's S, Concord R, Kidderminster									
Davies	Aron	22	Defender	Maidenhead United	14	9	13	23	
				Hemel Hempstead Town (L)	4	1		5	
Bristol C (Y), Fulham (Y), Maidstone (L), Maidenhead, Hemel H (L)									
Davies	Liam	23	Midfielder	Curzon Ashton	18	6	6	24	
Tranmere, Chester, Southport, Marine (L), Curzon A									
Davies	Rhys	19	Defender	Hereford			2		
Shrewsbury (Y), Nuneaton (L), Chippenham (L), Hereford									
Davies	Scott	32	Midfielder	Slough Town	18	11	10	29	1
Reading (Y), Wycombe (L), Yeovil (L), Wycombe (L), Bristol R (L), Crawley, Aldershot (L), Oxford U, Wealdstone, Oxford C, Chelmsford, Slough									
Davis	Kenny	32	Midfielder	Sutton United	28	1	4	29	
Grays, Braintree, Boreham W, Sutton U									

Key: X - Started; SX - Sub on; S - Non-playing Sub; Ap - Total Appearances; G/Cs - Total goals/clean sheets.

SURNAME	FIRSTNAME	AGE	POSITION	CLUB	X	SX	S	Ap	G/Cs
Davis	Liam	33	Defender	Torquay United	15			15	2
Coventry, Peterborough (L), Northampton, Oxford U, Yeovil, Cleethorpes T, Cheltenham, Torquay									
Dawson	Stephen	34	Midfielder	Hereford	12			12	
Bury, Leyton O, Barnsley, Rochdale, Scunthorpe, Bury, Hereford									
Dawson	Tom		Forward	Barrow		2		2	
Barrow (Y)									
De Garis	Kyle		Goalkeeper	Kidderminster Harriers			1		
FCV International, Kidderminster									
De Havilland	Will	25	Defender	Dover Athletic	32		6	32	3
Millwall, Sheffield W, Wycombe, Aldershot (L), Maidstone (L) Maidstone, Dover									
Deacon	Roarie	28	Midfielder	Havant & Waterlooville	11	1		12	4
Arsenal (Y), Sunderland, Stevenage, Crawley, Sutton U, Dundee, Sutton U, Havant & W									
Deadfield	Sam	23	Midfielder	Hampton & Richmond Borough	29	3	3	32	5
Reading (Y), Birmingham (Y), Basingstoke, Beaconsfield, Hungerford, Basingstoke, Hampton & R									
Dean	Gareth	30	Defender	Brackley Town	37			37	
Nuneaton, Solihull, Brackley									
Debrah	Jesse		Defender	Eastbourne Borough (L)	7			7	
				Dulwich Hamlet (L)	10		2	10	
Millwall (Y), Billericay (L), Eastbourne B (L), Dulwich H (L)									
Deeney	Ellis	28	Defender	AFC Telford United	34			34	
Aston Villa (Y), Kettering, Worcester, Tamworth, Telford									
Deering	Sam	29	Midfielder	Billericay Town	12	2		14	2
				Dagenham & Redbridge	9	1		10	
Newport, Oxford U, Barnet (L), Whitehawk, Ebbsfleet, Billericay, Dagenham & R									
Demetriou	Stelios	29	Defender	Bradford Park Avenue	5			5	
Apollon (Cyp), Lok Plovdiv (Bul), Ermis (Cyp), Akropolis (Gre), Doxa (Cyp), St Mlrren, Ross Co, Macclesfield, Haringey B, Bradford PA									
Dempsey	Ben	20	Defender	Dulwich Hamlet (L)	7			7	
				Woking (L)	5			5	
Charlton (Y), Dulwich H (L), Woking (L)									
Dennett	Ollie		Forward	Havant & Waterlooville		1	3	1	
Eastleigh (Y), Bashley (L) Brockenhurst (Dual), Gosport (Dual), Havant & W, Poole (L)									
Dennis	Kristian	30	Forward	Notts County	22	14	8	36	14
Macclesfield, Curzon A, Stockport, Macclesfield (L), Chesterfield, Notts Co, Grimsby (L),									
Densmore	Shaun	31	Defender	Altrincham	28	1	9	29	1
Everton (Y), Altrincham									
Denton	Tom	30	Forward	Chesterfield	19	9	1	28	8
Wakefield, Huddersfield, Woking (L), Cheltenham (L), Wakefield, Alfreton, North Ferriby, Halifax, Alfreton, Chesterfield									
Derry	Tom	25	Forward	Tonbridge Angels	16	9	1	25	6
Gillingham (Y), Chelmsford (L), Eastbourne B (L), Eastbourne B, Aldershot, Hayes & Y, East Thurrock, Tonbridge A									
Deverdics	Nicky	32	Midfielder	Gateshead	29	2	1	31	3
Gretna, Barnet, Alfreton, Dover, Hartlepool, Dover (L), Wrexham, Gateshead									
Devitt	Tom	24	Defender	Blyth Spartans	25	5	7	30	
Lionsbridge (US), Gateshead, Blyth S									
Dewhurst	Marcus	19	Goalkeeper	Guiseley (L)	21			21	5
Sheff Utd (Y), Guiseley (L), Guiseley (L)									
Diamond	Jack	20	Forward	Harrogate Town (L)	27	8	2	35	5
Sunderland (Y), Spennymoor (L), Harrogate (L)									
Diarra	Moussa	30	Defender	Woking	31	1		32	2
St Albans, Hemel H, Hampton & R (L), Hampton & R, Barrow, Dover, Woking (L), Woking									
Diau	Brandan	27	Forward	Kidderminster Harriers	1	8	1	9	
Bayer L (Ger) (Y), SF Troisdorf (Y), Hamburg (Y), Hilal Bergheim, TSC Euskirchen, Hapoel A, SVN Zweibracken, Billericay T,									
Burgess H, Met Police, Westfield, Tunbridge, Truro, G Wakering, Kidderminster, Redditch (L)									
Dibble	Christian	26	Goalkeeper	Wrexham	18		26	18	2
Bury, Barnsley, Nuneaton (L), Chelmsford (L), Boston Utd, Nuneaton, Chorley (L), Wrexham									
Dickinson	Carl	33	Defender	Yeovil Town	29	1	1	30	
Stoke (Y), Blackpool (L), Leeds (L), Barnsley (L), Portsmouth (L), Watford, Portsmouth (L), Coventry (L), Port Vale, Notts Co, Yeovil									
Dickinson	Mitchell	23	Defender	Hemel Hempstead Town	20	5		25	
Gillingham (Y), Hythe, Hemel H, Hornchurch (L)									

SURNAME	FIRSTNAME	AGE	POSITION	CLUB PLAYED FOR	X	SX	S	Ap	G/Cs
Dickinson	Steve	47	Goalkeeper	Bradford Park Avenue		1	7	1	
Southport, Bradford PA, Southport, Kendal T (L), Ossett T, Guiseley, Bradford PA									
Dickson	Ryan	33	Midfielder	Torquay United	1	1		2	
Brentford (Y), Southampton, Yeovil (L), Leyton O (L), Bradford (L), Colchester, Crawley, Yeovil, Torquay									
Diedhiou	Dave	31	Defender	St Albans City	18	4	15	22	
Hendon, St Albans									
Digbeu	Nelson		Midfielder	Bradford Park Avenue	7			7	
Chauvigny (Fra), Bradford PA									
Digie	Dennis		Defender	Kidderminster Harriers			2		
Kidderminster (Y)									
Digie	Kennedy	23	Forward	Guiseley	16	2	16	18	1
Kidderminster, Hednesford (L), Worcester (L), Nuneaton (L), York (L), Guiseley									
Dimaio	Connor	24	Midfielder	Stockport County	8	10	3	18	
				Curzon Ashton (L)	11			11	3
Sheff Utd (Y), Chesterfield, Stockport, Ashton U (L), Curzon A (L)									
Dinanga	Marcus	22	Forward	AFC Telford United	16	17	4	33	13
Burton (Y), Mickleover (L), Matlock (L), Telford (L), Hartlepool (L), Telford									
Divine	Danny	20	Defender	Maidstone United			2		
Gillingham (Y), Maidstone, Hythe T (L)									
Dixon	James	32	Forward	Dorking Wanderers		2	5	2	
Penybont, Dorking W									
Dixon	Joel	26	Goalkeeper	Barrow	39		3	39	16
Sunderland, Workington (L), Hartlepool (L), Boston (L), Gateshead (L), Barrow									
Djouaher	Miloud	25	Midfielder	Dartford		1		1	
Chateauroux (Fra), Dartford									
Dobson	James	28	Midfielder	Dagenham & Redbridge	14	11	3	25	2
				Hemel Hempstead Town (L)	7	1		8	2
Oxford U (Y), North Leigh, Slough, Sutton U, Dagenham & R, Hemel H (L)									
Dockerty	Brad		Midfielder	Bradford Park Avenue	5	9	1	14	3
Hemsworth MW, Bradford PA									
Dodds	Louis	33	Forward	Chorley	4	15	10	19	
Port Vale, Shrewsbury, Chesterfield, Port Vale (L), Chorley									
Doe	Scott	31	Defender	Dover Athletic	16	1	3	17	1
Weymouth, Dagenham & Redbridge, Boreham Wood, Dagenham & Redbridge, Whitehawk (L), Boreham W, Billericay, Dover, Romford									
Domi	Franklin	19	Defender	Eastbourne Borough (L)	4			4	1
Enfield Boro, QPR, Eastbourne B (L)									
Donaldson	Ruaridh	26	Defender	Hampton & Richmond Borough	32	4	2	36	2
Bonnyrigg, Stenhousemuir, Hampton & R									
Donaldson	Ryan	29	Midfielder	Hartlepool United	39	1	1	40	5
Newcastle, Hartlepool (L), Tranmere (L), Gateshead, Cambridge U, Plymouth, Hartlepool									
Donawa	Justin	23	Forward	Darlington	17	20		37	8
Somerset Trojans (Y) (Ber), Black Rock, Darlington									
Donnellan	Shaun	23	Defender	Woking	26	6	4	32	
WBA (Y), Worcester (L), Stevenage (L), Dagenham & R (L), Walsall (L), Yeovil, Maidstone, Woking									
Donovan	Harry	22	Midfielder	Braintree Town	1	1	2	2	
				Tonbridge Angels	8	5	2	13	1
Arsenal (Y), Millwall (Y), Dagenham & R (L), Havant & W (L), Braintree, Tonbridge A									
Doughty	Alfie	20	Midfielder	Bromley (L)	7	2		9	2
Charlton (Y), Bromley (L)									
Downing	Jordan	22	Defender	Stockport County		1	2	1	
Stockport									
Doyle	Jack	23	Defender	Southport	29	2	1	31	1
Blackburn (Y), Derry (L), Maidstone (L), Southport									
Doyle	Lewis	19	Midfielder	Curzon Ashton (L)		7		7	
PNE (Y), Witton (L), Southport, Accrington, Curzon A (L)									
Doyle	Michael	38	Midfielder	Notts County	34	3		37	1
Coventry, Leeds (L), Sheff Utd, Portsmouth, Coventry, Notts Co									
Drais	Yannis	26	Defender	Aldershot Town	2	1		3	
Avoine OCC, Besancon, Aldershot									

Key: X - Started; SX - Sub on; S - Non-playing Sub; Ap - Total Appearances; G/Cs - Total goals/clean sheets.

SURNAME	FIRSTNAME	AGE	POSITION	CLUB	X	SX	S	Ap	G/Cs
Drench	Steven	34	Goalkeeper	Altrincham	6			6	
Blackburn (Y), Morecambe, Southport, Cambridge U (L), Leigh Genesis, Guiseley, Halifax, Bradford PA, Altrincham									
Drewe	Aaron	19	Defender	Chelmsford City (L)			2		
QPR (Y), Chelmsford (L)									
Driscoll	Liam	21	Goalkeeper	Yeovil Town (L)			3		
Reading (Y), Hungerford (L), Yeovil (L)									
Drury	Andy	36	Midfielder	Havant & Waterlooville	27	6	3	33	4
Sittingbourne, Ebbsfleet, Lewes, Stevenage, Luton, Ipswich, Crawley (L), Crawley, Luton, Eastleigh, Ebbsfleet, Havant & W									
Drysdale	Declan		Defender	Solihull Moors (L)	3		2	3	
Tranmere (Y), Coventry, Solihull M (L)									
Duckworth	Michael	28	Defender	FC Halifax Town	31	4		35	3
York, Harrogate Railway, Bradford PA, Hartlepool, Fleetwood, Morecambe (L), Halifax									
Dudley	Anthony	24	Forward	Chester	28	10	1	38	6
Bury (Y), Guiseley (Lx2), Macclesfield (L), Salford, Chester (L), Chester									
Dudzinski	Ben	24	Goalkeeper	Sutton United			13		
Durham City, Hartlepool, Darlington (L), Lowestoft, Havant & W, Sutton U									
Duffus	Courtney	24	Forward	Yeovil Town	28	8		36	
16 Everton (Y), Bury (L), Oldham, Waterford (L), Yeovil									
Duhaney	Demeaco	21	Defender	Boston United (L)	7			7	
Man City (Y), Huddersfield, Boston U (L)									
Duku	Manny	27	Forward	Torquay United	4	12	7	16	
Legmeervogels, FC Abcoude, FC Breukelen, VV Eemdijk, Chesham, Hemel H, King's Langley, Banbury, Hayes & Y, Cheltenham, Barnet (L), FC Halifax (L), Torquay									
Dunbar	Kieran	23	Midfielder	Leamington	11	16	9	27	1
Fleetwood, Stalybridge, Telford, Leamington (L), Leamington									
Dundas	Craig	39	Forward	Sutton United	1	27	11	28	
Sutton U, Hampton & R (L), Hampton & R, Sutton U									
Dunn	Chris	32	Goalkeeper	Maidenhead United	21		8	21	4
Northampton, Coventry, Yeovil, Cambridge U, Wrexham, Walsall, Maidenhead									
Dunn	Declan	19	Defender	Notts County	1	2	5	3	
Notts Co (Y)									
Dunn	Jack	25	Forward	Southport (L)			3	3	
Liverpool, Cheltenham (L), Burton (L), Morecambe (L), Tranmere (L), Tranmere, Warrington, Southport (L)									
Dunn	Simon	27	Midfielder	Slough Town	9	3	1	12	
Basingstoke, Slough									
Dunne	Alan	37	Defender	Bromley		1	13	1	
Millwall, Leyton O, Bromley,									
Dunne	James	30	Midfielder	Barnet	29	4		33	
Exeter (Y), Stevenage, St Johnstone (L), Portsmouth, Dagenham & R, Cambridge U, Swindon, Barnet									
Dunstan	Josiah		Midfielder	Hungerford Town	8		4	8	
Hartbury Acad, Hungerford, Taunton (Dual)									
Durrell	Elliott	30	Midfielder	York City	5	8	8	13	1
				Altrincham	4	2		6	6
Hednesford, Wrexham, Tamworth, Chester, Macclesfield, York, Altrincham									
Duxberry	Scott	25	Defender	AFC Fylde	19		2	19	
				Chorley (L)	8			8	
Blackburn (Y), Burnley (Y), PNE (Y), Stockport, Northwich V, Stockport, AFC Fylde, Chorley (L)									
Dyer	Nathan	19	Defender	York City	6	5	6	11	1
York (Y)									
Dyett	Ben	30	Midfielder	Dorking Wanderers	6	5	5	11	
KaPa (Fin), Hayes, Chipstead, Dorking W									
Dymond	Connor	25	Midfielder	Welling United	25	3	2	28	1
Crystal P (Y), Barnet (L), Newport Co (L), Bromley, Welling, Hemel H, Welling									
Dyson	Olly	20	Midfielder	Barrow	16	17	9	33	4
Barrow (Y)									
Earing	Jack	21	Midfielder	FC Halifax Town	3	9	9	12	1
				Spennymoor Town (L)	2	2	3	4	
				Farsley Celtic (L)	1	2		3	
Bolton (Y), Curzon A (L), FC Halifax, Spennymoor (L), Farsley C (L)									

SURNAME	FIRSTNAME	AGE	POSITION	CLUB PLAYED FOR	X	SX	S	Ap	G/Cs
Earl	James		Goalkeeper	Eastbourne Borough			1		
Eastbourne B (Y)									
East	Danny	28	Defender	Alfreton Town	17	11	3	28	1
Hull City, Northampton (L), Gillingham (L), Portsmouth, Aldershot (L), Grimsby, Guiseley, Bradford PA, Alfreton									
Eastmond	Craig	29	Midfielder	Sutton United	23	3	1	26	1
Arsenal, Millwall (L), Wycombe (L), Colchester (L), Colchester, Yeovil, Sutton U									
Ebbutt	Cameron		Forward	Gloucester City		2	5	2	
Birmingham (Y), Bristol R, Evesham (L), Dorchester (L), Yate (L), Hereford, Gloucester									
Ebuzoeme	Eze		Midfielder	Eastbourne Borough			1		
Hayes & Y, Eastbourne B									
Eccles	Danny	23	Goalkeeper	Chorley	1		13	1	
Carlisle (Y), Barrow, Bradford PA, Kendal, Congleton, Chorley									
Edjenguele	William	33	Defender	Wealdstone	8			8	
Neuchatel (Swiz), Panaitolikos (Gr), Coventry, Bury, Panaitolikos, Veria, Dundee U, Falkirk, Wealdstone									
Edmonds-Green	Rarmani	26	Defender	Bromley (L)	5	4		9	
Huddersfield (Y), Bromley (L)									
Edmundson	Charlie		Forward	Dartford		1	1	1	
Dartford (Y)									
Edobor	Jarvis	21	Defender	Chelmsford City (L)	1		1	1	
Chalfont St. P, Brentford (Y), Maidstone, Chelmsford									
Edser	Toby	21	Midfielder	Woking (L)	11	3	2	14	1
Nottm Forest, Woking (L), Port Vale (L), Woking (L)									
Edwards	Jack	28	Midfielder	Leamington	38			38	9
Leamington, Solihull M, Leamington									
Edwards	Jonathan	23	Forward	Maidstone United	10	10	4	20	2
Peterborough, Ilkeston (L), Scarborough (L), St Albans (L), Hull, Accrington (L), Woking (L), FC Halifax, Maidstone									
Edwards	Opanin	21	Midfielder	Torquay United (L)	2	5	1	7	2
Bristol C, Bath (L), Solihull M (L), Bath (L), Torquay (L), Torquay (L)									
Edwards	Owura		Forward	Bath City (L)	4			4	
Bristol C (Y), Bath (L)									
Edwards	Preston	33	Goalkeeper	Dulwich Hamlet	6	1	2	7	
				Dartford			3		
Liverpool (Y), Millwall, Dover (L), Grays, Ebbsfleet, Boreham W (L), Dulwich H, Dartford									
Edwards	Ronnie	17	Midfielder	Barnet		4	4	4	
Barnet (Y)									
Efete	Michee	23	Defender	Wealdstone	36			36	8
Norwich, Torquay (L) Maidstone, Bath (L), Billericay (L), Wealdstone									
Effiong	Inih	29	Forward	Dover Athletic	36	2		38	16
Boreham W, Barrow, Woking, Ross Co, Dover									
Egan	Alfie	22	Midfielder	Ebbsfleet United	11	14	10	25	
AFC Wimbledon, Sutton U (L), East Thurrock (L), Ebbsfleet									
Eglin	Leo		Midfielder	Bath City			5		
Bath (Y)									
Egole	Samuel		Midfielder	Billericay Town			5		
Billericay									
Ekpiteta	Marvel	24	Defender	Ebbsfleet United (L)	25		1	25	2
Chelmsford, Bishop's S, East Thurrock, Hungerford, Newport Co, Ebbsfleet (L)									
Ekpolo	Prince	26	Midfielder	Guiseley	3	3	3	6	
Glossop NE, Guiseley									
El-Abd	Sami	33	Defender	Dorking Wanderers	6			6	
Team Bath, Hayes & Y, Chelmsford, Whitehawk, Bognor R, Dorking W									
Eleftheriou	Andrew	22	Defender	Dagenham & Redbridge	19	1	12	20	
Watford (Y), Sandefjord (Nor) (L), Braintree (L), Dagenham & R									
Elito	Medy	29	Midfielder	Barnet	13	7	4	20	
Colchester (Yth), Cheltenham (L), Dagenham & R (L), Cheltenham (L), Dagenham & R, VVV-Venlo, Newport Co, Cambridge U, Barnet									
Elliot	Chris	27	Goalkeeper	Darlington	29		8	29	6
Bradford C (Y), Harrogate (L), Harrogate, Alfreton, Spennymoor, Darlington									

Key: X - Started; SX - Sub on; S - Non-playing Sub; Ap - Total Appearances; G/Cs - Total goals/clean sheets.

SURNAME	FIRSTNAME	AGE	POSITION	CLUB	X	SX	S	Ap	G/Cs
Elliott	Daniel	24	Forward	Chester	9	14	10	23	3
				Alfreton Town (L)	5			5	5
NC Fusion (US), San Cristobel (L), Port Vale, Chester, Alfreton (L)									
Elliott	Kit		Forward	Concord Rangers (L)	12	7	1	19	2
Huddersfield (Y), Concord R (L)									
Ellis	Daniel	31	Defender	Farsley Celtic	33	2	2	35	1
Guiseley, Harrogate T, Farsley									
Ellul	Joe	31	Defender	Maidenhead United	38			38	2
East Thurrock, Billericay, Braintree, Tasman Utd (NZ), Maidenhead									
Elokobi	George	34	Defender	Maidstone United	37			37	1
Dulwich H, Colchester, Chester (L), Wolves, Nottingham F (L), Bristol C, Oldham, Colchester, Braintree (L), Leyton Orient, Aldershot, Maidstone									
Elsdon	Matty	22	Defender	Barrow	2		2	2	
Sunderland (Y), Middlesbrough (Y), Inverness C (L), Barrow									
Elstone	Michael	21	Forward	Curzon Ashton	4	5	2	9	
Bangor, Fulham (Y), Marine, Glossop NE, Curzon A, Hyde U									
Embery	Jake	20	Forward	Maidstone United	1	8	8	9	
Herne Bay, Maidstone									
Emmanuel	Moses	30	Forward	Billericay Town	14	5		19	5
				Welling United	5	3		8	2
				Wealdstone	9			9	4
Brentford, Woking (L), Woking, Bromley, Dover, Sutton, Maidenhead (L), Billericay, Welling, Wealdstone									
Emmett	Jack	26	Midfielder	Harrogate Town	16	17	6	33	3
Harrogate									
England	Kurtis		Goalkeeper	Chesterfield			1		
Chesterfield (Y)									
English	Junior	34	Midfielder	Leamington	28	1	2	29	1
Solihull, Brackley (L), Worcester, Leamington									
Essam	Connor	27	Defender	Hemel Hempstead Town	34			34	3
Gillingham, Luton (L), Crawley, Dartford (L), Dover, Leyton O, Dover (L), Eastleigh, Woking (L), Dover (L), Dover, Concord R (L), Hemel H									
Essuman	George	23	Defender	Concord Rangers	1	1	1	2	
Hemel H, Aveley Leverstock Green, London Colney, Waltham F, Ware, Maldon & Tiptree, Grays, VCD Ath, Dover, Oxford C (L),									
Whitehawk (L), Margate (L), Torquay, Dulwich H (L), Concord R									
Evans	Alfie		Forward	Dartford			5		
Dartford (Y)									
Evans	Dean		Midfielder	Chippenham Town	4	3	2	7	
Weymouth, Chippenham									
Evans	Jake	22	Midfielder	Hemel Hempstead Town (L)	7			7	
Swindon (Y), Farnborough (L), Waterford (L), Cardiff, Hemel H (L)									
Evans	Rhys	23	Defender	Blyth Spartans	32	2	2	34	1
South Shields, Blyth S									
Evans	Rob	24	Midfielder	Curzon Ashton	26			26	
Wrexham (Y), Billericay, Warrington, Curzon A									
Evans	Will	28	Defender	Chesterfield	38	1	2	39	
Swindon, Hereford (L), Hereford, Newport Co (L), Eastleigh, Aldershot, Chesterfield									
Eve	Dale	25	Goalkeeper	Spennymoor Town	1		3	1	1
Derby (Y), Stoke, Nuneaton (L), Newcastle T (L), Congleton (L), Forest GR (L), Forest GR, Spennymoor									
Everett	Lewis		Goalkeeper	Wealdstone			8		
West Virginia Uni, Hanwell T, Harrow B, Rayners L, Wealdstone									
Ewington	James		Forward	Hampton & Richmond Borough	1		1	1	
Potters Bar, London C, Hertford T, Welwyn GC, Colney H, Harpendon T, Northwood, St Albans, Walton C, Hampton & R,									
Walton C, Beaconsfield T									
Eyoma	Aaron	22	Midfielder	Aldershot Town	7	7	8	14	1
Arsenal (Y), Derby, Woking (L), Braintree (L), Aldershot									
Eyong	Tambeson	30	Midfielder	Billericay Town	1	2	1	3	
Hornchurch, Canvey Is, Dover, Canvey Is, Bishop's St, Billericay, Romford									
Eyres	Oliver		Goalkeeper	Havant & Waterlooville			2		
Havant & W (Y)									
Fairlamb	Luke	26	Midfielder	Brackley Town	7	23	3	30	
Corby, Brackley									

SURNAME	FIRSTNAME	AGE	POSITION	CLUB PLAYED FOR	X	SX	S	Ap	G/Cs
Falkingham	Josh	29	Midfielder	Harrogate Town	39			39	4
Leeds (Y), St Johnstone, Arbroath, Dunfermline, Darlington, Harrogate									
Fallowfield	Ryan	24	Midfielder	Harrogate Town	31	2	5	33	2
Hull (Y), Harrogate (L), Harrogate, Matlock (L), North Ferriby, Harrogate									
Farrell	Kyron	24	Midfielder	Hampton & Richmond Borough	23	1	1	24	2
Millwall (Y), Braintree (L), Concord R, Cray W, Hampton & R									
Fasanmade	Craig	20	Midfielder	Oxford City	5	10	6	15	
Reading (Y), Oxford C									
Fawcett	Callum			Barrow		1		1	
Barrow (Y), Kendal (L)									
Featherstone	Nicky	31	Midfielder	Hartlepool United	35	6	2	41	4
Hull, Grimsby (L), Hereford, Walsall, Scunthorpe, Hartlepool									
Felix	Joe	20	Defender	Maidstone United			1		
Fulham (Y), QPR (U23), Burgess H (L), Woking, Farnborough (L), Hampton & RB, Hendon, Maidstone									
Felix	Kaine	24	Forward	Guiseley	26	5	3	31	10
St Neots, Boston U, York, Stockport (L), Leamington, Brackley, Guiseley									
Feltham	Harris		Midfielder	Eastleigh		1	1	1	
Eastleigh (Y)									
Fenelon	Shamir	25	Forward	Maidenhead United	9	12	6	21	5
Brighton, Torquay (L), Rochdale (L), Tranmere (L), Dagenham & R (L), Crawley, Whitehawk (L), Aldershot, Maidenhead									
Fennell	Andy	21	Forward	Chelmsford City	1	7	4	8	1
Chelmsford (Y), Heybridge S, Coggeshall U, Chelmsford, Leiston (L)									
Fenwick	Scott	30	Forward	Blyth Spartans	5	6	1	11	
Hartlepool, Tranmere (L), York, Darlington, Naxxar Lions (Malta), Chelmsford, Blyth S									
Ferdinand	Kane	27	Midfielder	Woking	35	2		37	4
Southend, Peterborough, Northampton (L), Luton (L), Cheltenham (L), Dagenham & R, East Thurrock, Woking									
Ferdinand	Liam		Forward	Hungerford Town	26	6	1	32	6
Thatcham, Bracknell, Hungerford									
Ferguson	David	26	Defender	York City	40			40	1
Darlington, Sunderland, Boston U (L), Blackpool, Shildon, Darlington, York									
Ferry	James	23	Midfielder	Eastbourne Borough	35	2	1	37	2
Brentford (Y), Wycombe (L), Welling (L), Stevenage, Nuneaton (L), FC Halifax (L), Woking, Eastbourne B									
Fielding	Jamie	20	Defender	St Albans City (L)	14		3	14	
Stevenage (Y), St Albans (L)									
Finn	Kyle	21	Midfielder	Hereford	3	5	5	8	
Coventry (Y), Hereford (L), Hereford, Rushall O (L)									
Finney	Alex	24	Defender	Aldershot Town	23		5	23	
Leyton Orient, Bolton, QPR, Maidstone (L) Maidstone, Aldershot									
Fisher	Taylor		Midfielder	Dartford					
Dartford									
Fitch	Kane		Defender	Barrow		1	1	1	
Barrow (Y)									
Fitzsimons	Ross	26	Goalkeeper	Notts County	4		11	4	1
				Chesterfield (L)		1	5	1	
Crystal P (Y), Havant & W (L), Farnborough (L), Bolton, Bishop's S (L), Braintree, Chelmsford, Notts Co, Chesterfield (L)									
Flanagan	Reece	25	Midfielder	Leamington	2		1	2	
Walsall (Y), Leamington (L), Leamington									
Flannigan	Jake	24	Midfielder	Hampton & Richmond Borough	2	4		6	
				Havant & Waterlooville		9	3	9	
Southampton (Y), Burton (L), Hampton & R, Havant & W									
Fleet	Reece	28	Midfielder	Oxford City	36	2		38	2
Oxford C, Solihull, Oxford C									
Fletcher	Alex	21	Forward	Aldershot Town (L)	3	3		6	
Plymouth, Torquay (L), Aldershot (L)									
Flintney	Ross	36	Goalkeeper	Eastleigh	3		36	3	
Fulham, Brighton (L), Brighton (L), Doncaster (L), Barnet, Grays, Dover, Gillingham, Eastleigh, Whitehawk, Bromley, Eastleigh									
Flisher	Alex	28	Midfielder	Dartford	8	1	1	9	1
Maidstone, Margate, Dartford									

Key: X - Started; SX - Sub on; S - Non-playing Sub; Ap - Total Appearances; G/Cs - Total goals/clean sheets.

SURNAME	FIRSTNAME	AGE	POSITION	CLUB	X	SX	S	Ap	G/Cs
Flowers	Harry	24	Defender	Solihull Moors			2		
Brocton, Burnley (Y), Guiseley, Solihull, Kidderminster (L)									
Foden	Mark	24	Goalkeeper	Blyth Spartans	12		4	12	3
Hartlepool (Y), St Mirren (Y), Ross Co (Y), Stirling (L), Stenhousemuir (L), Gateshead, Blyth S (L), Blyth S									
Fogden	Wes	32	Midfielder	Havant & Waterlooville	28	1		29	5
Brighton (Y), Bognor (L), Dorchester (L), Dorchester, Havant & W, Bournemouth, Portsmouth, Yeovil, Havant & W									
Folarin	Emmanuel	28	Defender	Braintree Town	1		2	1	
Coggeshall T, Braintree									
Folkes	James	30	Midfielder	Tonbridge Angels	27	2	3	29	
Hayes & Y, Ebbsfleet, Sutton U, Tonbridge A									
Fondop-Talom	Mike	26	Forward	Chesterfield	21	10	2	31	11
Whitehawk, Billericay, Oxford C, Guiseley, Halifax (L) Wrexham, Maidenhead (L), Chesterfield									
Fonguck	Wesley	22	Midfielder	Barnet	18	4	8	22	1
Barnet (Y), Hendon (L), Hampton & R (L), Barnet									
Forbes	Elliot	21	Midfielder	Gateshead	16	8	8	24	2
Gateshead (Y), Benfield (L)									
Forster	Harry	20	Defender	St Albans City (L)	3	2	1	5	
Watford (Y), St Albans (L)									
Foster	Alan		Gk Coach	Oxford City			4		
Oxford C, Thame, Oxford CN, Witney, Oxford C									
Foulston	Jay	19	Defender	Chippenham Town (L)	36	2	4	38	2
Newport Co (Y), Norwich U18, Brighton U18, Chippenham (L)									
Fowler	George	22	Defender	Aldershot Town	15	2	3	17	2
Ipswich, Aldershot (L), Aldershot									
Fox	Charlie	21	Defender	Hampton & Richmond Borough	8	2		10	
QPR (Y), Wycombe (L), Basingstoke (L), Hampton & R									
Fox	Nathan	27	Defender	King's Lynn Town	34	2	2	36	1
Notts Co (Y), Corby, Kettering (L), Rugby T (L), Rugby T, Stamford, Slough, Mickleover, Rushall O, Rugby T, Coalville,									
Sutton C, Redditch U, Hednesford, King's Lynn Town									
Foxley	Darren	23	Forward	St Albans City	10	3	5	13	2
Hungerford, St Albans									
Francis	Akeel	21	Forward	Farsley Celtic	4	12	2	16	2
Rotherham (Y), North Ferriby (L), Accrington, Guiseley, Farsley C									
Franklin	Connor	32	Defender	Brackley Town	35		4	35	
Leicester (Y), Nuneaton, Hinckley U, Alfreton, Nuneaton, Solihull, Brackley									
Fraser	Sean	39	Defender	Slough Town	14	8	15	22	
Slough									
Freeman	Ollie		Forward	Maidstone United			1		
Maidstone (U23)									
Freemantle	Ethan		Forward	Kidderminster Harriers	5	6	5	11	
Walsall (Y), Kidderminster									
Freiter	Michael	24	Midfielder	Alfreton Town	2	3	3	5	
Gillingham (Y), Staines (L), East Thurrock, Faversham T, Alfreton									
French	Tyler	21	Defender	AFC Fylde (L)	5	1		6	
AFC Sudbury, Bradford C, AFC Fylde (L)									
Frimpong	Christian	21	Defender	Braintree Town	5	1		6	
Swindon (Y), Braintree									
Fryatt	Ryan	26	Defender	King's Lynn Town	12	1		13	
Norwich (Y), Cambridge U (Y), Dereham, King's Lynn, Dereham (Dual), Wisbech (Dual), Dereham (Dual)									
Fuller	Bailey		Midfielder	Kidderminster Harriers			1		
Kidderminster (U23)									
Fyfield	Jamal	31	Defender	Boreham Wood	27	2	4	29	2
York, Grimsby, Welling, Wrexham, Gateshead, Boreham W									
Galach	Brian	19	Forward	Billericay Town (L)	2	3	4	5	
Crawley (Y), Billericay (L)									
Galbraith	Terry	30	Defender	Darlington	25	3	3	28	
Darlington									
Gallagher	Daniel	23	Midfielder	Dorking Wanderers	23	7	4	30	
Wimbledon, Leatherhead, Dorking W									

SURNAME	FIRSTNAME	AGE	POSITION	CLUB PLAYED FOR	X	SX	S	Ap	G/Cs
Gallagher	Jake	27	Midfielder	Dorking Wanderers	30	9	1	39	2
Millwall, Welling, Aldershot, Dorking W									
Gallagher	Owen	21	Midfielder	Harrogate Town (L)	1	1	3	2	
Newcastle U (Y), Notts F, Harrogate T (L)									
Galliford	Isaac	23	Midfielder	Hemel Hempstead Town	18	9	4	27	2
Luton, Hitchin, Hemel H									
Gardiner	Tom	25	Defender	Chelmsford City	2		3	2	
Dartford, St Albans, Wealdstone, Eastbourne B, Chelmsford, Enfield T									
Gardiner-Smith	Jacob	22	Midfielder	Braintree Town (L)	13			13	
St Albans, Wycombe, Braintree (L)									
Gardner	Joe	29	Forward	Concord Rangers	1	4	4	5	1
Concord R, Braintree, East Thurrock, Heybridge, Concord R									
Gardner	Shaun		Forward	Bradford Park Avenue	1		1	1	
Penrith, Bradford PA (player-assistant manager)									
Garner	Scott	30	Defender	Guiseley	19		1	19	
				Boston United	10		2	10	
Leicester, Mansfield, Grimsby, Cambridge U, Lincoln (L), Boston, Halifax, Guiseley, Boston U									
Garratt	Tyler	23	Defender	Stockport County	12		2	12	
				Wrexham (L)	3		1	3	
Bolton (Y), Doncaster, Eastleigh (L), Wimbledon (L), Stockport, Wrexham (L)									
Garraway	Joshua		Defender	Eastleigh		1	1	1	
Eastleigh (Y)									
Gash	Michael	33	Forward	King's Lynn Town	35	3		38	10
Peterborough (Y), Cambridge U (Y), Cambridge C (Y), Cambridge U, Cambridge C, Ebbsfleet, York, Rushden & D (L),									
Cambridge U, Braintree (L), Kidderminster (L), Kidderminster, Nuneaton (L), Barnet, King's Lynn									
Gayle	Ian	27	Defender	Eastbourne Borough	31	1		32	1
Dag & Red, Histon (L), Whitehawk (L), St Albans (L), St Albans (L), Bishop's S (L), Welling (L), Braintree, Welling, Wealdstone,									
Woking, Eastbourne B									
Gbolahan	Ade		Forward	Eastbourne Borough		3	1	3	1
Eastbourne B									
George	Adriel	23	Midfielder	Chippenham Town	1	2	9	3	
				Oxford City	3	5	7	8	
Oxford U (Y), Banbury (L), Mansfield, Mickleover (L), Hednesford (L), North Ferriby (L), Chippenham, Oxford C									
Georgiou	Andronicos	20	Forward	St Albans City (L)	3	3		6	1
Stevenage (Y), St Albans (L)									
German	Ricky	21	Forward	Hemel Hempstead Town (L)	4	11	2	15	4
Chesterfield (Y), Alfreton (L), Hendon, Crawley, Hemel H (L)									
Gerrard	Anthony	34	Defender	Chesterfield	12		3	12	
Everton (Y), Accrington (L), Walsall, Cardiff, Hull (L), Huddersfield, Oldham, Carlisle, Chesterfield									
Gerring	Ben	29	Defender	Woking	35		3	35	1
Cambridge U, Taunton, Truro, Bideford, Hayes & Y, Gosport, Hayes & Y, Truro, Margate, Hayes & Y, Bideford, Torquay,									
Weston-s-Mare (L), Truro (L), Billericay, Truro (L), Woking									
Gharbaoui	Ayman	20	Midfielder	Eastbourne Borough	1	12	18	13	
Eastbourne B									
Gibbens	Lewis		Defender	Boston United (L)	1	4	1	5	
Mansfield (Y), Boston U (L), Boston U (L)									
Gibbons	Jordan	26	Midfielder	Chelmsford City	1		1	1	
				Dartford	7			7	
QPR, Inverness (L), Yeovil, Phoenix Rising, Whitehawk, Welling, Chelmsford, Dartford									
Gibbons	Myron	19	Forward	Bradford Park Avenue (L)	1	3	3	4	
Doncaster (Y), Bradford PA									
Gibson	Jayden		Midfielder	Braintree Town	1	1	4	2	
Braintree (Y)									
Gilbert	Jacob	18	Midfielder	Maidstone United		1	13	1	
Maidstone (Y)									
Gilbert	Owen		Defender	King's Lynn Town			1		
Peterborough (Y), King's Lynn									
Gilella	Dinesh	20	Defender	Billericay Town (L)	2	2	2	4	
Watford (Y), Bournemouth (Y), Billericay (L)									

Key: X - Started; SX - Sub on; S - Non-playing Sub; Ap - Total Appearances; G/Cs - Total goals/clean sheets.

SURNAME	FIRSTNAME	AGE	POSITION	CLUB	X	SX	S	Ap	G/Cs
Giles	Jonny	26	Midfielder	Chelmsford City	16	14	8	30	2
Oxford U, Southport (L), Oxford C (L), Aldershot (L), Chelmsford									
Gittings	Callum	34	Midfielder	Leamington	25	10	3	35	
Kidderminster, Solihull, Telford, Leamington									
Glendon	George	25	Midfielder	Chester	27	3		30	3
Man City (Y), Fleetwood (L), Fleetwood, Carlisle, Chester									
Glynn	Kieran	22	Midfielder	Southport (L)	10	6	6	16	2
FC United, Salford, Chorley (L), Woking (L), Southport (L)									
Gobern	Oscar	29	Midfielder	Dover Athletic	23	2		25	1
Southampton (Y), MK Dons (L), Huddersfield, Chesterfield (L), QPR, Doncaster (L), Mansfield, Ross Co, Yeovil, Eastleigh, Dover									
Goddard	John	27	Forward	Ebbsfleet United	19	4	2	23	1
Reading (Y), Hayes & Y, Woking, Swindon, Stevenage, Bromley (L), Aldershot, Ebbsfleet									
Godwin-Malife	Udoka	20	Defender	Eastleigh (L)	5		1	5	
Oxford C, Forest GR, Eastleigh (L)									
Goldberg	Bradley	26	Forward	Welling United	28	3	4	31	6
Charlton (Y), Bromley (L), Hastings, Bromley, Hastings, Dag & Red, Bromley (L), Bristol R (L), Bromley (L), Bromley, Welling									
Gomis	Bedsente	32	Midfielder	Havant & Waterlooville	7	1	1	8	
FC Lens, Puertollano, Almeria, Southend, Sutton, Barrow, Dover, Havant & W									
Gondoh	Ryan	23	Defender	Concord Rangers	1	7		8	
Barnet, Maldon, Colchester, FC Halifax (L), Concord R									
Goodliffe	Ben	21	Defender	Sutton United	39			39	2
Boreham Wood (Y), Wolves, Dagenham & R (L), Sutton U									
Goodwin	Will		Forward	Chester		1		1	
Chester (Y), Sandbach U (L)									
Gordon	Jaanai	24	Forward	Oxford City	6	8		14	2
Peterborough (Y), West Ham, Chelmsford (L), Nuneaton (L), Sligo (L), Newport (L), Cheltenham, Oxford C									
Gordon	Lewis	19	Defender	St Albans City (L)	5			5	
Watford (Y), St Albans (L)									
Gordon	Liam	21	Defender	Dagenham & Redbridge	14	2	5	16	
				Dartford (L)	10			10	
Dagenham & R, Whitehawk (L), Dartford (L)									
Gordon	Rohdell	24	Midfielder	St Albans City	5	2	2	7	
Arlesey, Bishop's S, Stevenage, Chelmsford (L), Bromley (L), Braintree, Bishop's S, Walton C, St Albans									
Gorst	Alex		Goalkeeper	Stockport County			1		
Stockport (Y)									
Gough	Ethan		Goalkeeper	Oxford City			4		
Oxford C (Y)									
Gould	Matt	26	Goalkeeper	Spennymoor Town	37		1	37	10
Hawkes Bay (NZ), Cheltenham, Livingston, Stenhousemuir (L), Stourbridge, Spennymoor									
Gowling	Josh	36	Defender	Hereford	19		3	19	1
West Brom, Herfolge, Bournemouth, Carlisle, Hereford (L), Gillingham (L), Gillingham, Lincoln (L), Lincoln, Kidderminster (L),									
Kidderminster, Grimsby (L), Grimsby, Torquay, Alfreton (L), Hereford									
Graham	Bagasan	27	Midfielder	Dagenham & Redbridge	10	14	6	24	
Cheltenham, Telford (L), Chelmsford, Ebbsfleet, Chelmsford (L), Dagenham & R									
Graham	Luke	34	Defender	Kettering Town	27		7	27	2
Northampton (Y), Billericay (L), Aylesbury U (L), Kettering (L), Forest GR (L), Kettering, King's Lynn (L), Mansfield, York (L),									
York, Kettering, Luton (L), Forest GR, Hereford U, Alfreton, Brackley, Kettering									
Graham	Ralph		Midfielder	Hungerford Town (L)	12		1	12	2
Swindon (Y), Highworth T (L), Hungerford (L)									
Graham	Sam	19	Defender	Notts County (L)	7	3		10	
Sheffield U, Halifax (L), C Coast (Aus) (L), Notts Co (L)									
Grainger	Charlie	23	Goalkeeper	Dulwich Hamlet	23		1	23	5
Leyton Orient, Farnborough (L), Hampton & R (L), Dulwich H									
Grand	Simon	36	Defender	Chester	39			39	3
Rochdale, Carlisle, Grimsby, Morecambe, Northwich, Fleetwood, Mansfield, Aldershot (L), Southport, AFC Telford,									
Barrow, Salford, AFC Fylde, Chester									
Granite	Josh	28	Defender	Barrow	9		14	9	1
Stockport Sports, Mossley, Trafford, Ashton Utd, Barrow									

SURNAME	FIRSTNAME	AGE	POSITION	CLUB PLAYED FOR	X	SX	S	Ap	G/Cs
Grant	Freddie	23	Defender	Maidenhead United	3	2	9	5	
				Hemel Hempstead Town (L)	6			6	
Oxford U (Y), Farnborough (L), Oxford C, Wealdstone, Maidenhead, Hemel H (L)									
Grant	Joe	23	Forward	Slough Town	2	5	6	7	
Ascot, Slough (Dual), Molesey, Bracknell, Slough, Hayes & Y (L), Hartley W (Dual)									
Grant	Reece	25	Forward	Dagenham & Redbridge	6	24	6	30	2
				Aldershot Town (L)	1			1	
Wealdstone, Northwood (L), Heybridge, Braintree, Kingstonian (L), Aldershot, Dagenham & R, Aldershot (L)									
Grant	Robert (Bobby)	29		Wrexham	28	2	1	30	8
Accrington (Y), Scunthorpe, Rochdale (L), Accrington (L), Rochdale, Blackpool, Fleetwood (L), Shrewsbury (L), Fleetwood, Wrexham (L), Wrexham									
Gravata	Leone	19	Midfielder	Eastbourne Borough		1	1	1	
Brighton (Y), Eastbourne B									
Gray	Jake	24	Midfielder	Hampton & Richmond Borough	9			9	4
				Woking	2	3	3	5	
				Hampton & Richmond Borough (L)	9	1		10	
Crystal P (Y), Cheltenham (L), Hartlepool (L), Luton, Yeovil, Woking, Hampton & R, Woking, Hampton & R (L)									
Gray	Louis	24	Goalkeeper	Chester (L)	2			2	
Wrexham (Y), Rhyl (L), Cefn Druids (L), Everton, Carlisle (L), Nuneaton, Carlisle, Chester (L)									
Gray	Daniel		Midfielder	Blyth Spartans			1		
Blyth S (Y)									
Greaves	Oliver		Midfielder	Barrow (L)	4	6	7	10	
Sheff U (Y), Barrow (L)									
Green	Cameron	21	Defender	Braintree Town (L)	17			17	
Met Police, Reading (Y), Watford U23, Braintree (L)									
Green	Danny	31	Midfielder	Concord Rangers	13	18	6	31	3
Dag & Red, Charlton, MK Dons (L), MK Dons, Luton, Chelmsford, Concord R									
Green	Danny	29	Midfielder	Wealdstone	31	6	1	37	5
Bishop's S, St Albans, Braintree, Boreham W, Dag & Red, Bishop's S, Maidenhead, Margate, Wealdstone									
Green	Devarn	23	Forward	Southport	21	8	2	29	8
Blackburn, Tranmere, Warrington (L), Southport									
Green	George	24	Forward	Boston United	1	4	4	5	
Everton (Y), Tranmere (L), Oldham, Burnley, Kilmarnock (L), Salford (L), Viking, Nuneaton, Chester, Boston U									
Green	Joe	24	Goalkeeper	Bradford Park Avenue	15		7	15	2
Mustangs (US) Newport Co, Handsworth P, Scarborough Ath, Guiseley, Bradford PA									
Green	Kieran	22	Midfielder	York City	24	13	1	37	4
Hartlepool, Gateshead (L), Gateshead, Blyth S (Lx2), Blyth S, York									
Green	Mike	31	Defender	Eastleigh	25	4	1	29	
Bristol R, Port Vale, Eastleigh									
Green	Nathan	28	Defender	Welling United	21	11	4	32	1
Lewes, Billericay, Tonbridge A, Dag & Red, St Albans (L), Dartford, Margate, Dulwich H, Welling									
Green	Sheldon	18	Forward	AFC Fylde		1	3	1	
AFC Fylde (Y)									
Greenfield	Danny	19	Midfielder	Gateshead	2	1	11	3	
Gateshead, West Auckland (L)									
Greenhalgh	Ben	28	Midfielder	Dartford	13	2	2	15	3
				Tonbridge Angels	15	1		16	2
Welling, Ebbsfleet, Inverness, Maidstone, Concord R, Maidstone, Hemel H (L), Concord R, Dartford, Tonbridge A (L), Tonbridge A									
Greenhalgh	Ben		Midfielder	Stockport County			2		
Stockport (Y)									
Greenslade	Danny	26	Defender	Hereford	10	1		11	
Bristol R (Y), Bath (L), Gloucester (L), Weston (L), Weston, Hereford FC									
Greenwood	Rees	23	Midfielder	Spennymoor Town			1		
Sunderland, Gateshead, Falkirk, Spennymoor									
Gregan	Chris		Defender	Chelmsford City		1	9	1	
Chelmsford									
Gregory	Cameron	20	Goalkeeper	Kidderminster Harriers (L)	13		1	13	3
Shrewsbury (Y), Kidderminster (L)									

Key: X - Started; SX - Sub on; S - Non-playing Sub; Ap - Total Appearances; G/Cs - Total goals/clean sheets.

SURNAME	FIRSTNAME	AGE	POSITION	CLUB	X	SX	S	Ap	G/Cs
Gregory	David	25	Goalkeeper	Boreham Wood	14		9	14	3
				Ebbsfleet United (L)	9		1	9	3
Crystal Palace, Eastbourne (L), Leyton O (L), Cambridge U, Bromley, Boreham W, Ebbsfleet (L)									
Grey	Joe	-	Forward	Hartlepool United			3		
Hartlepool (Y)									
Grice	Harvey		Midfielder	Alfreton Town	1	4	5	5	1
Alfreton (Y)									
Griffiths	Kallum	30	Defender	York City	33	1		34	3
Spennymoor, York									
Griffiths	Russell	24	Goalkeeper	Chester	37			37	8
				AFC Telford United (L)	2			2	
Everton (Yth), Northwich Vic (L), Colwyn (L), Halifax (L), Cheltenham (L), Motherwell (L), Motherwell, AFC Fylde, Chester, Telford (L)									
Grimes	Jamie	29	Defender	Ebbsfleet United	30	5	8	35	
Haverfordwest, Forest GR, Brackley, Kidderminster, Worcester (L), Dover, Cheltenham, Macclesfield, Ebbsfleet									
Grimshaw	Daniel	22	Goalkeeper	Hemel Hempstead Town (L)	7			7	3
Man City (Y), Hemel H (L)									
Grubb	Dayle	28	Midfielder	Eastleigh (L)	3			3	
Weston SM, Forest GR, Eastleigh (L)									
Gudger	Alex	27	Defender	Solihull Moors	40			40	1
Brackley, Solihull M									
Gudger	Connor	27	Defender	Leamington	5			5	
Hinckley U, Tamworth, Hinckley U (L), Barwell, Worcester, Barwell (L), Leamington									
Guerfi	Zak	21	Midfielder	Braintree Town	3			3	
Stevenage (Y), Boden (Swe), Monastir (Tunisa), Braintree									
Guest	Adam		Goalkeeper	Woking			1		
Woking (Y)									
Gunner	Callum	21	Midfielder	Chippenham Town	30	7	3	37	3
Swindon (Y), Bradford, Chippenham (L), Chippenham									
Gunning	Gavin	29	Defender	Billericay Town	7			7	
				Solihull Moors	18	1	2	19	1
				Gloucester City	2			2	
Blackburn (Y), Tranmere (L), Rotherham (L), Bury (L), Motherwell (L), Dundee U, Birmingham, Oldham, Dundee U, Morton, Grimsby, Port Vale, Forest GR, Billericay, Solihull M, Gloucester									
Guthrie	James		Midfielder	Chippenham Town	4	3		7	
Highworth, Chippenham									
Guthrie	Sam	24	Goalkeeper	Gateshead	1		34	1	
Huddersfield (Y), Salford (L), Clitheroe, Consett, Gateshead									
Gwilliams	Lewis		Goalkeeper	Leamington	1			1	1
Sutton Coldfield, Alvechurch, Leamington (Dual) Worcester, Leamington									
Hackett-Fairchild	Recco	21	Forward	Bromley	22	3		25	8
Dagenham & R (Y), Dulwich (L), Charlton (Y), Boreham W (L), Bromley (L), Bromley									
Hadler	Tom	23	Goalkeeper	Eastbourne Borough	26		4	26	5
Gillingham (Y), Gloucester (L), Gloucester (L), Eastbourne B									
Haigh	Chris	23	Goalkeeper	Concord Rangers	40			40	7
Northwood, Braintree, Merstham, East Grinstead (L), Maldon/Tiptree (L), Heybridge S, Concord R									
Hainault	Alex		Defender	Gloucester City			12	14	12
St Francis Uni (US), Ytterhogdal IK (Swe), Gimo IF FK, Westfields, Gloucester, Lydney T (Dual)									
Haines	Luke	19	Midfielder	Chippenham Town (L)	32	1	1	33	4
Swindon (Y), Chippenham (L)									
Hakeem	Zayn	21	Forward	Bradford Park Avenue	4	1		5	
Mansfield (Y), Bradford PA,									
Hall	Asa	33	Midfielder	Torquay United	20		2	20	3
Birmingham , Boston (L), Shrewsbury (L), Luton, Oxford U, Shrewsbury, Aldershot (L), Oxford U (L), Cheltenham, York (L), Barrow, Torquay									
Hall	Brandon	26	Goalkeeper	Hereford	35		2	35	8
Charlton (Y), Nike Acad, St Mirren, Hayes & Y, Ebbsfleet, Lewes (L), Woking, Kidderminster, Hereford									
Hall	Cameron	18	Goalkeeper	Darlington			1		
Darlington (Y)									
Hall	Connor	27	Defender	Harrogate Town	38	1	1	39	4
Biggleswade, Brackley, Harrogate									

SURNAME	FIRSTNAME	AGE	POSITION	CLUB PLAYED FOR	X	SX	S	Ap	G/Cs
Hall	Connor	22	Forward	Chorley (L)	6			6	3
Sheff Utd (Y), Woking (L), Bolton, Accrington (L), Chorley (L)									
Hall	Ryan	26	Forward	Spennymoor Town	3	6	1	9	2
				Bradford Park Avenue (L)	9	1		10	
Workington, Curzon Ashton, Spennymoor, Bradford PA (L)									
Hall	Ryan		Goalkeeper	Aldershot Town			8		
Aldershot (Y)									
Hallett	Alex		Defender	Chippenham Town	1			1	
Chippenham (Y)									
Halliday	Kofu	24	Forward	Hungerford Town	8	6	3	14	2
				Hemel Hempstead Town		2	3	2	
Aldershot (Y), Godalming, Fleet, Hungerford, Hemel H									
Halls	Andy	28	Defender	Curzon Ashton	31	2		33	3
Stockport, Macclesfield, Chester, Guiseley, Curzon A									
Hamblin	Harry	20	Midfielder	Bath City (L)	10	1	3	11	1
Southampton (Y), Bath (L)									
Hamilton	Spencer		Defender	Gloucester City	21	1	2	22	1
Gloucester									
Hamilton	Tyler	21	Midfielder	Hartlepool United (L)	2	6	1	8	1
Hull (Y), Hartlepool (L)									
Hammill	Adam	32	Midfielder	Stockport County (L)	2	3	3	5	
Dunfermline, Southampton, Blackpool, Barnsley, Wolves, Middlesbrough (L), Huddersfield (L), Huddersfield, Rotherham (L), Barnsley, St Mirren, Scunthorpe, Stockport (L)									
Hampson	Connor	27	Midfielder	Altrincham	24	10	7	34	1
Curzon Ashton, Stockport, Altrincham									
Hancock	Josh	29	Midfielder	Altrincham	36	1		37	17
Witton, Telford, Witton (L), Witton, Salford, Nantwich, Altrincham									
Hancox	Mitch	26	Defender	Solihull Moors	10	11	12	21	1
				Harrogate Town (L)	6			6	
Birmingham, Crawley (L), Macclesfield, MK Dons, Solihull M, Harrogate T (L)									
Hanford	Dan	29	Goalkeeper	Southport	16		19	16	4
Hereford, Floriana, Carlisle, Gateshead, Southport									
Hanks	Joe	25	Midfielder	Gloucester City	30	1		31	11
Cheltenham, Gloucester (L), Gloucester (L), Gloucester									
Hanley	Raheem	26	Defender	Hereford	5	2		7	
Man Utd (Y), Blackburn (Y), Swansea, Northampton, Halifax (L), Connah's QN, Chorley, Hereford									
Hannigan	Tom	31	Midfielder	Altrincham	38		1	38	2
Vauxhall M (Y), AFC Fylde, Altrincham									
Hanson	Jack		Midfielder	Hemel Hempstead Town	1			1	
Hemel H									
Hanson	Jacob	22	Defender	FC Halifax Town	6	1	14	7	
Huddersfield, Bradford, Halifax (L), Halifax (L), Halifax									
Hanson	Jethro	20	Midfielder	Eastbourne Borough	8	5	7	13	
Millwall (Y), Eastbourne B									
Hardcastle	Lewis	21	Midfielder	Barrow	26	15		41	3
Blackburn (Y), Salford (L), Port Vale (L), Barrow (L), Barrow									
Harding	Michael	18	Midfielder	Kettering Town (L)			2		
Northampton (Y), Kettering (L)									
Harfield	Ollie	22	Defender	Weymouth	39			39	
Bournemouth, Poole (L), Boreham W (L), Dagenham & R, Weymouth									
Harker	Nathan	21	Goalkeeper	Blyth Spartans (L)	8		12	8	1
Newcastle U (Y), Blyth S (L)									
Harker	Rob	20	Forward	Hartlepool United (L)	5	2		7	
Bury (Y), Hartlepool (L)									
Harmison	Ben	34	Forward	Blyth Spartans	4	2	1	6	
Ashington, North Shields, South Shields, Morpeth T, Blyth S									
Harness	Nathan	20	Goalkeeper	Billericay Town (L)	4			4	
West Ham (Y), Charlton, Billericay (L)									

Key: X - Started; SX - Sub on; S - Non-playing Sub; Ap - Total Appearances; G/Cs - Total goals/clean sheets.

SURNAME	FIRSTNAME	AGE	POSITION	CLUB	X	SX	S	Ap	G/Cs
Harper	Ashley	22	Defender	Bath City			3		
Bristol C (Y), Weston (L), Bristol R, Weston,									
Harper	Vincent	19	Midfielder	Gloucester City (L)	19		1	19	1
				Bath City (L)	1	1		2	
Bristol C (Y), Gloucester (L), Bath (L)									
Harratt	Kian	18	Forward	Harrogate Town (L)	2	4	5	6	
Huddersfield (Y), Harrogate T (L)									
Harris	Ben	29	Forward	Slough Town	19	18	2	37	12
Team Wellington (NZ), Slough									
Harris	Ed	29	Defender	Dorking Wanderers	30	1	2	31	1
QPR (Y), Hayes & Y (L), AFC Wimbledon, Dover, Havant & W, Dorking W									
Harris	Jay	33	Midfielder	Wrexham	4	1		5	
Everton, Accrington, Chester, Wrexham, Tranmere, Macclesfield, Wrexham									
Harris	Jayden	20	Forward	Woking (L)	3			3	
Fulham (Y), Woking (L)									
Harris	Mark	21	Forward	Wrexham (L)	13	14	4	27	3
Cardiff (Y), Newport Co (L), Port Vale (L), Wrexham (L)									
Harris	Max	20	Goalkeeper	Oxford City (L)	4			4	
Oxford U (Y), Oxford C (L)									
Harris	Warren	29	Midfielder	Slough Town	39			39	9
Staines, Slough									
Harrison	Byron	33	Forward	Barrow	9	24	5	33	1
Havant & W, Worthing, Boreham Wd, Harrow B, Ashford (Mx), Carshalton, Stevenage, AFC Wimbledon, Cheltenham,									
Chesterfield, Stevenage (L), Barrow, Sutton U (L), Barnet, Barrow									
Harrison	Tom		Defender	Gloucester City (L)	7			7	
Yate (Y), Paulton, Bristol C, Hereford (L), Weston (L), Gloucester (L)									
Harrop	Max	26	Midfielder	Altrincham	8	16	13	24	
Bury (Y), Blyth S (L), Hinckley U (L), Tamworth (L), Nantwich, Altrincham									
Hartley	Dan		Defender	Harrogate Town			1		
Harrogate T									
Hartridge	Alex	21	Defender	Bath City (L)	38	2		40	2
Exeter (Y), Truro (L), Truro (Lx2), Truro (Lx2), Bath (Lx2)									
Harvey	Robert	21	Midfielder	Braintree Town	2	4	3	6	
West Bergholt, Brightlingsea R, Millwall, Braintree									
Harvey	Tyler	24	Forward	Bath City	7			7	3
Plymouth (Y), Salisbury (L), Bath (L), Wrexham, Bath (L), Truro, Bath									
Hatfield	Will	28	Midfielder	Darlington	40			40	4
Leeds, York (L), Accrington (L), Accrington, Halifax (L), Guiseley, Darlington									
Haughton	Nick	25	Midfielder	AFC Fylde	20	14	3	34	7
Bolton (Y), Runcorn Town, Fleetwood, Nantwich (L), Salford (L), Chorley (L), Salford, AFC Fylde									
Hawkes	Josh	21	Midfielder	Hartlepool United	11	11	10	22	2
Hartlepool									
Hawkes	Taylor			Dartford			1		
Dartford (Y)									
Hawkins	Lewis	27	Defender	Blyth Spartans	25	4		29	2
Horden CW, Hartlepool, York (L), Spennymoor (L), Blyth S									
Hawkins	Ryan	25	Forward	King's Lynn Town	4	12	10	16	
Norwich (Y), Dereham, St Neots, King's Lynn, Dereham (L)									
Hawkins	Tyan		Midfielder	Oxford City			5		
Oxford C (Y)									
Hawkridge	Terry	30	Midfielder	Solihull Moors	21	14	10	35	2
Tranmere (Y), Carlton, Hucknall, Carlton, Gainsborough, Scunthorpe, Mansfield (L), Lincoln C (L), Lincoln C, Notts Co, Solihull									
Hayes	Ryan	34	Midfielder	Dartford	8	10	12	18	
Dartford Concord R, Dartford									
Hayhurst	Will	26	Midfielder	Farsley Celtic	36	2	1	38	9
PNE (Y), York (L), Notts Co, Warrington, Farsley C									
Headley	Jaheim	18	Midfielder	Bradford Park Avenue (L)	4	1		5	1
Huddersfield (Y), Bradford PA (L)									

SURNAME	FIRSTNAME	AGE	POSITION	CLUB PLAYED FOR	X	SX	S	Ap	G/Cs
Heaton	Josh	23	Defender	Darlington	2	5	2	7	
				Bradford Park Avenue	6	1		7	
PNE (Y), Tamworth (L), Colne (L), Droylsden, Stalybridge, Bamber B, Ramsbottom, Darlington, St Mirren, Kidderminster (L), Darlington, Bradford PA									
Hedley	Ben	21	Midfielder	Bradford Park Avenue	6	1		7	
				Darlington	30	1		31	
Morecambe (Y), Bradford PA, Darlington									
Hemming	Zac	20	Goalkeeper	Hartlepool United (L)			1		
				Blyth Spartans (L)	19			19	
Middlesbrough (Y), Darlington (L), Hartlepool (L), Blyth S (L)									
Hemmings	Ashley	29	Midfielder	Altrincham (L)	11			11	1
				Kidderminster Harriers	20	1		21	4
Wolves (Yth), Cheltenham (L), Torquay (L), Plymouth (L), Walsall, Burton (L), Dagenham & R, Mansfield, Boston U, Salford, AFC Fylde, Altrincham (L), Altrincham (L), Kidderminster									
Hemmings	Kane	29	Forward	Notts County	1	1		2	
Rangers (Y), Cowdenbeath, Barnsley, Dundee, Oxford U, Mansfield (L), Notts Co, Dundee									
Henderson	Chris	30	Midfielder	King's Lynn Town	32	4	3	36	7
Bury T (Y), Gorleston, Kirkley & P, Lowestoft, Leiston, King's Lynn									
Henderson	Ethan	18	Forward	York City			1		16
Hartlepool (Y), Carlisle (Y), Tennessee FC (Y), York (Y)									
Henly	Jonathan	26	Goalkeeper	Tonbridge Angels	30			30	4
Reading (Y), Bromley (L), Aldershot (L), Oxford U (L), Welling (L), Ipswich, Hemel H, Margate (L), Tonbridge A (L), Tonbridge A									
Henry	Dion	22	Goalkeeper	Hampton & Richmond Borough (L)	7			7	
Peterborough (Y), Soham R (L), Boston U (L), Crystal P, Maidstone (L), Hampton & RB (L)									
Henry	Korrey	20	Forward	Bromley		3	8	3	
				Welling United (L)	7	9	2	16	5
West Ham (Y), Yeovil, Braintree, Bromley, Welling (L)									
Henry	Ronnie	36	Defender	Billericay Town	38			38	2
Tottenham (Y), Southend (L), Dublin City, Stevenage, Luton, Stevenage, Billericay T									
Henry	Shane		Midfielder	Spennymoor Town	24	1	4	25	2
Spennymoor									
Henry	Will	21	Goalkeeper	Chippenham Town (L)	3		2	3	
				Gloucester City (L)	3			3	
				Hereford (L)	4			4	
				Hungerford Town (L)	2			2	1
Swindon (Y), Hampton & R (L), Chippenham (L), Gloucester (L), Chippenham (L), Gloucester (L), Hereford (L), Hungerford (L)									
Herbert	George			Kettering Town			1		
Kettering									
Hernandez	Alex	17	Forward	Concord Rangers		2	10	2	
Concord R (Y)									
Hernandez	Loic	20	Defender	Barnet	3		4	3	
Barnet (Y), Wingate & F (L)									
Heslop	Simon	33	Midfielder	Boston United	1	3	2	4	
Barnsley, Kidderminster (L), Tamworth (L), Northwich (L), Halifax (L), Grimsby (L), Kettering (L), Luton (L), Oxford U, Stevenage, Mansfield, Torquay, Wrexham, York, Eastleigh (L), Boston U									
Hession-Harris	Tommie	24	Midfielder	Tonbridge Angels	11	4	3	15	4
USA, Maldon & T, Tonbridge A									
Hibbs	Jake	24	Midfielder	Spennymoor Town	6	2	2	8	
				Bradford Park Avenue (L)	9			9	
Halifax, Droylsden (L), Hyde (L), Telford (L), Bradford PA (L), Spennymoor, Bradford PA (L)									
Higgins	Jack	28	Defender	Farsley Celtic	31	1	1	32	3
Ashton U, Stalybridge C, Clitheroe, Warrington, York, Southport, Warrington, Farsley C									
Higgins	Sam	30	Forward	Chelmsford City	24	7	1	31	11
Fisher, Bishop's S, Chelmsford, East Thurrock, Dartford, East Thurrock, Concord R, Bromley, East Thurrock, Chelmsford									
Higginson	Harry	19	Defender	Kidderminster Harriers	2	5	15	7	
Kidderminster (Y)									
Higgs	Jordan	23	Midfielder	Bromley	4	8	4	12	
Bromley, Carshalton, Bromley									

Key: X - Started; SX - Sub on; S - Non-playing Sub; Ap - Total Appearances; G/Cs - Total goals/clean sheets.

Haydn Hollis (Chesterfield)
Photo Bill Wheatcroft.

SURNAME	FIRSTNAME	AGE	POSITION	CLUB PLAYED FOR	X	SX	S	Ap	G/Cs
High	Scott	19	Midfielder	Concord Rangers (L)	6	1		7	
Huddersfield (Y), Concord R (L)									
Hill	Josh	28	Defender	Dartford	40	1	1	41	4
Ilkeston T, Coalville T, Worksop, Dartford, Boreham W, Hemel (L), Havant & W (L), St Albans, Wealdstone, Braintree, Welling, Dartford									
HIll	Ryan	22	Midfielder	Hampton & Richmond Borough	30	8	1	38	8
Stoke (Y), Hampton & R									
Hinchiri	Bilel	24	Midfielder	Dover Athletic	4	2	5	6	
				Tonbridge Angels (L)	2			2	
Charitoise (Fra), Dover, Tonbridge A (L)									
Hinchley	Kieron		Defender	Alfreton Town			9		
Alfreton (Y)									
Hinchliffe	Ben	31	Goalkeeper	Stockport County	42			42	7
PNE (Y), Kendal (L), Tranmere (L), Derby, Oxford U, Worcester, Kendal, Bamber B, Northwich V, AFC Fylde, Stockport									
Hindle	Jack	26	Forward	Barrow	6	20	10	26	3
				Gateshead (L)		1		1	
Radcliffe B, Colwyn, Barrow, Gateshead (L)									
Hinds	Akeem	21	Defender	Bradford Park Avenue (L)	4			4	
Rotherham (Y), Bradford PA (L)									
Hinds-Cadette	Gavin	26	Defender	Braintree Town			5		
Hoddesdon, Aylesbury U, Berkhamsted, Braintree Town									
Hindson	Charlie		Midfielder	Spennymoor Town		1		1	
Middlesbrough (Y), Spennymoor									
Hippolyte	Myles	25	Forward	Yeovil Town	33	4		37	5
Tamworth, Hayes & Y, Livingston, Falkirk, St Mirren, Dunfermline, Yeovil									
Hird	Adrian (Sam)	32	Defender	Barrow	35			35	
Leeds (Y), Doncaster (L), Doncaster, Grimsby (L), Chesterfield, Alfreton, Barrow									
Hobson	Shaun	21	Defender	Weymouth (L)	32		1	32	2
Burnley, Bournemouth, Eastbourne B (L), Chester (L), Eastleigh (L), Weymouth (L)									
Hodge	Elliot	24	Midfielder	Kettering Town	3	5	5	8	
Notts Co (Y), Lincoln, Stamford (L), Gainsborough (L), Stafford R (L), Telford (L), Notts Co, Alfreton (L), Burton, Leamington,									
Kettering, Hednesford									
Hodges	Harry	20	Defender	Gloucester City (L)	2			2	
Plymouth (Y), Gloucester (L), Bristol R, Gloucester (L)									
Hodges	Paul	27	Forward	Woking	2	18	11	20	1
				Slough Town	2	2	1	4	
Hartley, Woking, Slough									
Hodgkiss	Jared	33	Defender	Hereford	30		1	30	1
West Brom, Aberdeen (L), Northampton (L), Forest Green, Kidderminster, Torquay (L), Macclesfield, Hereford									
Hodgson	Jamie		Midfielder	Barrow	1	1	2	2	
Barrow (Y)									
Hoey	Jack		Midfielder	Weymouth	1	3	2	4	1
Bournemouth (Y), AFC Totton, Greenville (US), Gardner Webb Uni, Weymouth									
Hogan	Liam	31	Defender	Stockport County	5			5	1
Stockport Sports, Halifax, Fleetwood, Macclesfield (L), Tranmere, Gateshead, Salford, Stockport									
Holland	Jack	28	Defender	Bromley	28	3	5	31	3
Bromley, Crystal Palace, Eastbourne (L), Bromley,									
Hollands	Danny	34	Midfielder	Eastleigh	43	1	1	44	10
Chelsea, Torquay (L), Bournemouth, Charlton, Swindon (L), Gillingham (L), Portsmouth (L), Portsmouth, Crewe, Eastleigh									
Holliday	Cameron	20	Defender	Darlington			10		
Darlington (Y)									
Hollis	Guy	29	Defender	Slough Town	20	1	6	21	
Carshalton, Godalming, Slough									
Hollis	Haydn	27	Defender	Chesterfield	34		2	34	2
Notts Co (Y), Barrow (L), Darlington (L), Forest Green, Chesterfield (L), Chesterfield									
Holman	Dan	30	Forward	Brackley Town	6	12	5	18	1
Braintree, Colchester, Wrexham (L), Aldershot (L), Dover (L), Woking (L), Cheltenham (L), Cheltenham, Boreham W (L),									
Leyton O (L), Aldershot, Kettering, Brackley									
Holmes	Elliot		Midfielder	Bradford Park Avenue	4	7	1	11	
Hull (Y), Bradford PA									

Key: X - Started; SX - Sub on; S - Non-playing Sub; Ap - Total Appearances; G/Cs - Total goals/clean sheets.

2019-20 NATIONAL. NORTH & SOUTH PLAYERS — APPEARANCES

SURNAME	FIRSTNAME	AGE	POSITION	CLUB	X	SX	S	Ap	G/Cs
Holmes	Jamie	22	Forward	Darlington	2			2	
Newcastle (Y), South Shields, Blyth S, Darlington									
Holmes	Jordan	23	Goalkeeper	Ebbsfleet United	25	1	5	26	5
Bournemouth (Y), Eastbourne B (L), St Mirren (L), Ebbsfleet									
Holness	Omar	26	Defender	Darlington	22	14	6	36	6
Real Salt Lake, Real Monarchs (L), Bethlehem Steel, Darlington									
Holohan	Gavan	28	Midfielder	Hartlepool United	20	13	8	33	9
Hull, Alfreton, Drogheda, Cork, Galway Utd, Waterford, Hartlepool									
Holroyd	Chris	33	Forward	Chorley	17	12	4	29	8
Chester, Cambridge U, Brighton (L), Brighton, Stevenage (L), Bury (L), Rotherham, Preston, Macclesfield (L), Morecambe, Macclesfield, Wrexham, Chorley									
Homson-Smith	Morgan		Midfielder	Southport	3	4	8	7	
Southport									
Honour	Adam	19	Goalkeeper	Kettering Town			2		
Kettering (Y)									
Hood	Jamie	36	Defender	Leamington	11	2	4	13	
Barwell, Leamington									
Hooper	James	23	Midfielder	Chorley			3		
				Altrincham			2		
Rochdale (Y), FC United (L), Stockport (L), Carlisle, FC United, Radcliffe B, Salford, Chorley, Radcliffe, Altrincham									
Hooper	Jonathan	26	Forward	Wrexham	18	4	1	22	7
Newcastle (Y), Workington (L), Northampton, Alfreton (L), Farnborough (L), Havant & W, Port Vale, Northampton (L), Grimsby, Bromley (L), Wrexham									
Hope	Jamie	18	Midfielder	Hampton & Richmond Borough			6		
Hampton & R (Y)									
Hopkins	Jack		Midfielder	Stockport County		1	2	1	
Stockport (Y)									
Hopper	Luke	31	Forward	Chippenham Town	15	13	13	28	3
Swindon Sup, Gloucester, Hungerford, Salisbury, Chippenham									
Horgan	Gary	43	Defender	Chippenham Town			4		
Swindon Sup, Hungerford, Chippenham									
Hornby	Sam	25	Goalkeeper	AFC Fylde (L)	22		6	22	5
Burton, Brackley (L), Kidderminster (L), Port Vale, Chester (L), Bradford C, AFC Fylde (L)									
Hornby-Forbes	Tyler	24	Midfielder	AFC Fylde	3	4	5	7	1
				Spennymoor Town	8			8	3
Fleetwood (Y), Brighton U23, Accrington (L), Newport, AFC Fylde, Spennymoor									
Horner	Lewis	28	Midfielder	Blyth Spartans	3		3	3	
Hibernian, East Stirling (L), Inverness, Blyth S									
Horsfield	James	24	Defender	Wrexham (L)	5			5	
Man City (Y), Doncaster (L), NAC Breda (Hol), NAC Breda, Scunthorpe, Dundee (L), Wrexham (L)									
Horton	Grant		Defender	Chippenham Town (L)	3	1	3	4	
Cheltenham (Y), Yate (L), Chippenham (L)									
House	Ben	20	Forward	Dagenham & Redbridge (L)	10	1		11	2
Reading (Y), Swindon (L), Dagenham & R (L)									
Howard	Rob	21	Midfielder	Dartford (L)	7		1	7	
				Braintree Town (L)	4			4	
Southend (Y), Dartford (L), Braintree (L)									
Howe	Callum	26	Defender	Solihull Moors	45			45	6
Scunthorpe, Gateshead (L), Alfreton (L), Lincoln, Southport (L), Eastleigh (L), Port Vale, Harrogate, Solihull M									
Howe	Joe	32	Midfielder	St Albans City	11	3	3	14	
Ebbsfleet, Bromley, Leatherhead, Hemel H, St Albans									
Howell	Luke	33	Midfielder	Hemel Hempstead Town	21			21	
Gillingham, MK Dons, Lincoln (L), Lincoln, Dagenham & R, Boreham W, Dagenham & R, Aldershot, Hemel H									
Howells	Jake	29	Midfielder	Hemel Hempstead Town	25	2	3	27	
Luton, Yeovil (L), Eastleigh Dagenham & R, Ebbsfleet (L), Billericay, Hemel H									
Howes	Alex	20	Midfielder	Notts County			1		
Notts Co (Y)									

SURNAME	FIRSTNAME	AGE	POSITION	CLUB PLAYED FOR	X	SX	S	Ap	G/Cs
Howes	Sam	22	Goalkeeper	Woking	2		30	2	
				Chelmsford City (L)	5			5	
				Dorking Wanderers (L)	4			4	
West Ham (Y), Wealdstone (L), Hampton & R (L), Watford, Hampton & R (L), Eastbourne B (L), Woking, Chelmsford (L), Dorking W (L)									
Howett	Daniel		Goalkeeper	Concord Rangers			6		
Grays, Concord R (Goalkeeper coach)									
Hoyte	Gavin	30	Defender	Maidstone United	40			40	2
Arsenal, Watford (L), Brighton (L), Lincoln (L), AFC Wimbledon (L), Dagenham & R, Gillingham, Barnet, Eastleigh, Dagenham & R, Maidstone									
Huddart	Ryan	23	Goalkeeper	Boreham Wood			7		
				Bromley	24		4	24	4
Charlton (Y), Arsenal (Y), Eastleigh (L), Boreham, Bromley									
Hudson	Ellis	21	Midfielder	Farsley Celtic		1		1	
Bradford C (Y), Harrogate T (L), Guiseley (L), Florida Tech Panthers, Farsley C									
Hudson	Harry		Forward	Tonbridge Angels			1		
Tonbridge A (Y)									
Hudson	Harry	19	Defender	Billericay Town (L)	12			12	
West Ham (Y), Leicester (Y), Watford (Y), Billericay (L)									
Hughes	Liam	27	Midfielder	Bradford Park Avenue	14	5		19	2
Cambridge U, Inverness CT, Barrow, Guiseley, Billericay, Darlington, Bradford PA									
Hughes	Matty	27	Forward	Chester	19	12	4	31	5
Skelmersdale, Fleetwood, Chester (L), AFC Fylde, Chorley, Chester									
Huk	Slavomir	27	Goalkeeper	Dorking Wanderers	34		3	34	12
Kosice (Slovakia), Dorking W									
Hulme	Jordan	29	Midfielder	Altrincham	41	2		43	19
Padiham, Ramsbottom, Salford, Altrincham									
Humphreys	Jac		Midfielder	Wrexham			2		
Wrexham (Y)									
Hunt	Max	21	Defender	Aldershot Town (L)	20	2		22	1
WBA (Y), Derby U23, Aldershot (L)									
Hunte	Connor	23	Midfielder	Dulwich Hamlet	7	7	9	14	1
Chelsea (Y), Wolves, Stevenage (L), Billericay, Dulwich (L), Dulwich H									
Hunter	Jack	22	Midfielder	Blyth Spartans	25	2		27	1
				Gateshead	1		1	1	
Newcastle (Y), Gateshead, Blyth S, Gateshead									
Hurst	Alex	20	Forward	Bradford Park Avenue	34	2		36	1
Bradford PA									
Hurworth	Mason	18	Midfielder	Darlington	1		2	1	
Darlington (Y)									
Husin	Noor	23	Midfielder	Dartford	7			7	1
Reading (Y), Hemel H (L), Crystal P, Accrington (L), Notts Co, Stevenage, Dartford									
Hutchings	Jake	24	Defender	Braintree Town	20		1	20	
Torquay (Y), Enfield T, Grays, Leiston, Braintree									
Hutchinson	Regan	18	Defender	Chesterfield		2	2	2	
Rotherham (Y), Chesterfield (Y), Sheffield FC (L)									
Hutchinson	Ryan	27	Midfielder	Blyth Spartans	6	5	3	11	1
St Johnstone, Blyth S									
Hutton	Remeao	21	Midfielder	Yeovil Town (L)	28	4	7	32	1
Walsall (Y), Sutton Coldfield, Hednesford, Birmingham, Yeovil (L)									
Huxley	Callum		Defender	Wrexham		2	2	2	
Wrexham (Y)									
Hyde	Jake	29	Forward	Woking	28	7		35	16
Swindon, Weymouth (L), Weymouth (L), Barnet, Hayes & Yeading, Dundee, Dunfermline, Dundee, Barnet, York, Stevenage,									
Maidenhead (L), Maidenhead, Woking									
Hyde	Tyrique	21	Midfielder	Dartford (L)	13	1	1	14	
Dagenham & Redbridge, Whitehawk (L), Ware (L), Colchester, Maldon/T (L), Dartford (L)									
Iaciofano	Joe	21	Forward	St Albans City	34	2		36	17
Northampton (Y), Chesham (L), Brackley (L), St Albans									
Ibie	Sydney	23	Forward	Hemel Hempstead Town		1	5	1	
Hemel H									

Key: X - Started; SX - Sub on; S - Non-playing Sub; Ap - Total Appearances; G/Cs - Total goals/clean sheets.

SURNAME	FIRSTNAME	AGE	POSITION	CLUB	X	SX	S	Ap	G/Cs
Ijaha	David	30	Midfielder	Dulwich Hamlet	24	6	6	30	4
Harrow, Tonbridge A, Hayes & Y, Whitehawk, Plymouth, Wealdstone, Whitehawk, Welling, Dulwich H									
Ilesanmi	Femi	29	Defender	Boreham Wood	39		1	39	
AFC Wimbledon, QPR, Ashford T (Kent), Dagenham & R, Histon (L), York, Boreham W, Dover, Boreham W,									
Imray	Danny		Midfielder	Chelmsford City	7		1	7	
Chelmsford (Y)									
Inman	Dean	29	Defender	Hampton & Richmond Borough	37			37	3
Hampton & R, Hayes & Yeading, Maidenhead, Billericay, Hampton & R									
Iontton	Arthur	19	Midfielder	Braintree Town (L)	4			4	
Stevenage (Y), Braintree (L)									
Isaac	Chez	27	Midfielder	Chelmsford City	25	6	6	31	
Watford, Tamworth (L), Boreham W, Braintree, Woking, Dartford, Chelmsford									
Isted	Harvey	23	Goalkeeper	Oxford City (L)	4			4	1
				Wealdstone (L)	10		1	10	4
Stoke (Y), Luton, Oxford C (L), Wealdstone (L)									
Jackman	Josh		Defender	Slough Town	33		2	33	1
Slough									
Jackson	Ashley		Defender	Boston United	6	14	14	20	
Leek Town, Ossett T, Boston U									
Jackson	Ben	19	Midfielder	Stockport County	12	14	2	26	1
Darlington, Stockport									
Jackson	Bradley	23	Forward	Chester	38			38	5
Burnley (Y), Bangor (L), Southport (L), Ashton U, Chester									
Jackson	Jake		Forward	Gloucester City	10	3		13	1
Chippenham, Gloucester									
Jackson	Marlon	29	Forward	Gloucester City	22	4	1	26	9
Bristol C (Y), Hereford (L), Aldershot (L), Aldershot (L), Northampton (L), Cheltenham (L), Telford (L), Hereford, Bury,									
Lincoln (L), Halifax, Oxford C, Tranmere, Oxford C, Newport Co, Hereford, Weston, Gloucester									
Jackson	Oran	21	Defender	Billericay Town	4	1	6	5	
MK Dons (Y), Hemel H (L), Brackley (L), IBV, Billericay									
Jalal	Shawn	36	Goalkeeper	Chesterfield	31		9	31	6
Tottenham, Woking (L), Woking, Sheff Wed (L), Peterborough, Morecambe (L), Bounemouth, Oxford U (L), Leyton Orient (L),									
Bury, Northampton, Macclesfield, Wrexham, Macclesfield, Chesterfield									
James	Bradley	20	Goalkeeper	Gateshead (L)	35			35	15
Middlesbrough (Y), Gateshead (L)									
James	Cameron	22	Defender	Maidstone United (L)	4	1		5	
				Welling United (L)	10			10	2
Colchester (Y), Chelmsford (L), Braintree (L), Maidstone (L), Welling (L)									
James	Jack	20	Defender	Braintree Town	9			9	1
				Gloucester City	9	1	1	10	1
Luton (Y), Hitchin (L), Havant & W (L), Braintree, Gloucester									
James	Lloyd	32	Midfielder	Torquay United (L)	3	2	1	5	
				Bath City	3	1		4	
Southampton (Y), Colchester, Leyton O, Exeter, Forest GR, Torquay (L), Bath									
James	Luke	25	Forward	Hartlepool United	16	8	2	24	3
Hartlepool, Peterborough (L), Bradford (L), Hartlepool (L), Bristol (L), Forest Green, Barrow (L), Hartlepool									
James	Steven		Defender	Eastbourne Borough	7		2	7	
Lewes (Y), US Colleges, Eastbourne B									
James	Tom	31	Defender	Leamington		1	8	1	
Watford (Y), Nuneaton, Daventry, Tamworth, Hednesford, Leamington									
Jameson	Kyle	21	Defender	AFC Fylde	16	8	15	24	
Southport (Y), Chelsea (Y), West Brom (Y), Barrow (L), AFC Fylde									
Jameson	Pete	27	Goalkeeper	York City	38		2	38	
South Shields, Darlington, Blyth S, York									
Janneh	Saikou		Forward	Torquay United (L)	9	1		10	2
Bristol C (Y), Torquay (L), Torquay (L)									
Jarra	Baboucarr		Defender	Hungerford Town	10		2	10	
Thatcham, Flackwell H, Windsor, AFC Hayes, Chalfont St P, Swindon S, Hungerford									

SURNAME	FIRSTNAME	AGE	POSITION	CLUB PLAYED FOR	X	SX	S	Ap	G/Cs
Jarvis	Aaron	22	Forward	Sutton United	16	11	6	27	3
				Hemel Hempstead Town (L)	5	1	1	6	1
Basingstoke, Luton, Boreham W (L), Falkirk (L), Sutton U, Hemel H (L)									
Jarvis	Daniel	22	Midfielder	Wrexham (L)	6		1	6	1
Stoke (Y), Wrexham (L)									
Jarvis	Matt	34	Midfielder	Woking		2		2	1
Gillingham (Y), Wolves, West Ham, Norwich (L), Norwich, Woking									
Jarvis	Nathaniel	28	Forward	Chippenham Town	18	9	7	27	4
Cardiff (Y), Southend (L), Newport Co (L), Forest GR (L), Kidderminster (L), Brackley, Bath, Gloucester, Hungerford, Bath, Chippenham									
Jarvis	Ryan	33	Forward	King's Lynn Town	26	3	5	29	1
Norwich (Y), Colchester (L), Leyton O (L), Kilmarnock (L), Notts Co (L), Leyton O, Northampton (L), Walsall, Torquay (L),									
Torquay, York, Aldershot (L), Lowestoft, King's Lynn									
Jeacock	Zach	19	Goalkeeper	Gloucester City (L)	15			15	1
Birmingham (Y), Gloucester (L)									
Jebb	Jack	24	Midfielder	Welling United	4	7		11	1
				Wealdstone	5	6	1	11	
				Dartford	6			6	1
Arsenal (Y), Stevenage (L), Newport Co, Sutton U, Welling, Wealdstone, Dartford									
Jebson-King	Charlie	18	Defender	York City		1	2	1	
Leeds (Y), York									
Jeffers	Shaun	28	Forward	Chelmsford City	28	9	2	37	15
Coventry, Cheltenham (L), Cambridge U (L), Tamworth (L), Peterborough, Newport Co, Yeovil, Woking (L), Chelmsford,									
Boreham W, Hampton & R (L) Brackley, Chelmsford									
Jefford	Ben	25	Defender	Oxford City	32	1	4	33	1
Reading (Y), Boreham W (L), Basingstoke (L), Port Vale, Southport (L), Welling, Ebbsfleet (L), Forest GR, Woking (L),									
Sutton U, Welling, Oxford C									
Jeffrey	Anthony	25	Midfielder	Dover Athletic	4	13	2	17	
Arsenal, Stevenage (L), Boreham W (L), Wycombe (L), Boreham W, Welling, Concord R, Boreham W (L), Boreham W,									
Forest Green, Boreham W (L), Boreham W (L), Sutton, Dover (L), Dover									
Jelley	Tom	33	Defender	Hampton & Richmond Borough	8	1		9	
Hampton & R, Hayes & Y, Hampton & R									
Jennah	Ansu		Midfielder	Eastbourne Borough		1	1	1	
Eastbourne B (Y)									
Jennings	James	32	Defender	Wrexham	34			34	4
Macclesfield, Altrincham (L), Kettering, Cambridge U, Mansfield (L), Mansfield, Forest Green, Cheltenham (L), Morecambe (L),									
Wrexham (L), Wrexham									
Jessup	Jake		Goalkeeper	Chelmsford City	1	1	1	2	
Lowestoft, Chelmsford, AFC Sudbury (L), Needham M, Leiston, Chelmsford									
John	Louis	26	Defender	Sutton United	19			19	
Sutton U, Hemel H (L), Hampton & R (L), Ebbsfleet (L), Cambridge U, Sutton U (L), Sutton U									
John-Lewis	Lenell	31	Forward	Hereford FC	7			7	3
Lincoln C, Bury, Grimsby, Newport, Shrewsbury, Hereford									
Johnson	Andre		Forward	Bradford Park Avenue	1	9	3	10	
Worksop, Heanor, Corby, Alfreton, Boston U Hednesford (dual), Bradford PA									
Johnson	Andrew		Midfielder	Spennymoor Town	10	6	7	16	5
Ashington, Spennymoor									
Johnson	Bobby		Midfielder	Alfreton Town	26	4		30	7
AFC Goole, North Ferriby, Alfreton									
Johnson	Chiori	22	Defender	Welling United	11	2	2	13	
Arsenal (Y), Blackburn (L), Bolton, Welling									
Johnson	Elliott	25	Midfielder	Barnet	25	4		29	
Barnet (Yth)									
Johnson	Gabriel	23	Forward	Guiseley	28	6	1	34	2
Brighouse, Guiseley									
Johnson	Glen	34	Goalkeeper	Dagenham & Redbridge			3		
Dagenham & R (Gk Coach)									
Johnson	Michael	26	Goalkeeper	Braintree Town	24		3	24	4
Hitchin, Braintree									

Key: X - Started; SX - Sub on; S - Non-playing Sub; Ap - Total Appearances; G/Cs - Total goals/clean sheets.

SURNAME	FIRSTNAME	AGE	POSITION	CLUB	X	SX	S	Ap	G/Cs
Johnson	Oli	32	Forward	Bradford Park Avenue	11	9		20	3
Nostell Miners, Stockport, Norwich, Yeovil (L), Yeovil (L), Oxford U, York, Guiseley, Bradford PA (L), Bradford PA									
Johnson	Reda	32	Defender	Eastleigh	13		1	13	3
Amiens, Plymouth, Sheffield Wed, Coventry, Eastleigh									
Johnson	Ryan	23	Defender	Kidderminster Harriers	30	2	1	32	1
Stevenage Borough, St Albans City (L), Boreham Wood (L), Nuneaton Town (L), Kidderminster (L), Kidderminster									
Johnson	Ryan	33	Defender	Maidstone United	27	3	2	30	2
Welling, Maidenhead, Dartford, Margate, E Grinstead, Maidstone									
Johnson	Sam	27	Goalkeeper	FC Halifax Town	42			42	12
Stoke, Port Vale, Stafford (L), Alfreton (L), Halifax (L), Gateshead (L), Halifax (L), Halifax									
Johnson	Steven	17	Forward	Darlington			1		
Darlington (Y)									
Johnson	Tyreke	21	Defender	Woking (L)	9	3		12	
Southampton (Y), Woking (L)									
Johnson	William	20	Goalkeeper	Braintree Town (L)	9			9	2
Norwich (Y), Braintree (L)									
Johnson-Schuster	Marcus		Defender	Hungerford Town	20		3	20	1
Basingstoke, Wealdstone, Hungerford									
Johnston	John	25	Midfielder	Altrincham	27	2		29	4
				Chester	8			8	
Kidsgrove, Leek, Crewe, Leek (L), Alfreton (L), Alfreton, Salford (L), Salford, Nantwich (L), Altrincham, Chester									
Johnstone	Ross		Midfielder	Gloucester City	1	5	12	6	
Gloucester									
Jolley	Charlie	19	Forward	Curzon Ashton (L)	7	2		9	2
Wigan (Y), Curzon A (L)									
Jones	Andrai Ricardo	28	Defender	Guiseley	17	4	4	21	2
Bury (Y), Altrincham (L), Barnsley, Tranmere (L), Alfreton (L), Gateshead, Southport, Bala, Guiseley									
Jones	Aron	26	Defender	King's Lynn Town	34	3	3	37	2
Ipswich (Y), College Football (US), Philadelphia Union, Bethlehem Steel (L), Harlow, King's Lynn									
Jones	Bobby	18	Goalkeeper	Farsley Celtic (L)	1			1	
Middlsbrough (Y), Wigan (Y), Farsley C (L)									
Jones	Dan	25	Defender	Barrow (L)	4			4	
Hartlepool, Grimsby, Gateshead (L), AFC Fylde (L), Barrow, Salford, Barrow (L)									
Jones	Eddie	29	Midfielder	Oxford City	27	4	2	31	1
Solihull, Telford, Oxford C									
Jones	Emem		Defender	AFC Telford United			2		
Telford (Y)									
Jones	James	21	Defender	Chester (L)	11	4	6	15	4
Chester, Salford, Boston U (L) Ashton U (L), Chester (L)									
Jones	James	23	Defender	Altrincham	33	2	4	35	6
New Saints, Gresford (L), Altrincham									
Jones	Louis	21	Goalkeeper	Yeovil Town (L)			4		
Doncaster (Y), Gainsborough (L), Yeovil (L)									
Jones	Mathew		Defender	Wrexham	2	2		4	
Wrexham (Y)									
Jones	Matthew	24	Defender	Hungerford Town	22	5	7	27	4
Swindon (Y), Farnborough (L), Chippenham, Hungerford									
Jones	Mike	25	Midfielder	Hungerford Town	23	6	1	29	
Fisher FC, Greenwich, Bromley, Canvey Isle, Hungerford, Chippenham, Hungerford									
Jones	Nico	18	Defender	Oxford City (L)	2	1		3	
Oxford U (Y), Oxford C (L)									
Jones	Sam	28	Midfielder	Harrogate Town	2	4	3	6	1
				Solihull Moors (L)	1	4	1	5	1
				York City (L)	1	2		3	
Heanor, Alfreton, Gateshead, Grimsby, Shrewsbury, Cheltenham (L), Harrogate, Solihull M (L), York (L)									
Joseph	Harold	24	Defender	Welling United	9			9	
Stevenage, Kings Langley, Tamworth, Enfield T, Oxford C, Hayes & Y, Enfield T, St Albans, Royston, Welling									
Joseph	Zak	27	Forward	Hampton & Richmond Borough			4	5	4
Egham, Hendon, Hampton & R									

2019-20 NATIONAL. NORTH & SOUTH PLAYERS · APPEARANCES

SURNAME	FIRSTNAME	AGE	POSITION	CLUB PLAYED FOR	X	SX	S	Ap	G/Cs
Julian	Alan	37	Goalkeeper	Billericay Town	34			34	5
Gillingham, Stevenage, Newport, Dartford, Sutton U, Bromley, Billericay									
Justham	Elliot	29	Goalkeeper	Dagenham & Redbridge	39		1	39	9
Waltham F, Leyton, Redbridge, Brentwood, East Thurrock, Luton, Dagenham & R									
Kabamba	Nicke	27	Forward	Hartlepool United	20	11	1	31	7
Hayes, Uxbridge, AFC Hayes, Burnham, Hemel H (L), Hampton & R (L), Hampton & R, Portsmouth, Colchester (L), Aldershot (L) Havant & W, Hartlepool (L), Hartlepool									
Kabeya	Amos	27	Midfielder	Bradford Park Avenue		2		2	
Hinckley U, KA (Ice), Torquay, Braintree, Bishop's S, Qormi (Malta), Bradford PA									
Kalala	Kalvin	22	Midfielder	Torquay United	19	14	3	33	3
Cheltenham, Torquay									
Kaloczi	James	25	Defender	St Albans City	23	8	3	31	2
St Albans, Hemel H, St Albans									
Kamdjo	Clovis	29	Defender	Maidstone United	8	5	10	13	1
Barnet, Salisbury, Forest GR, Boreham W (L), York, St Albans, Maidstone									
Kandi	Chike	24	Forward	Dagenham & Redbridge	18	9		27	4
Birmingham, Chelsea, West Brom, Brighton, Bognor Regis (Lx2), Woking, Leatherhead, Dagenham & R									
Kay	Antony	37	Midfielder	Chorley	4		1	4	
Tranmere, Huddersfield, MK Dons, Bury, Port Vale, Chorley									
Kay	Joseph		Defender	Eastbourne Borough			1		
Eastbourne B (Y)									
Kay	Josh	23	Midfielder	Barrow	35	4		39	7
AFC Fylde, Barnsley, AFC Fylde (L), Tranmere (L), Chesterfield (L), Chesterfield, Barrow									
Kayode	Joshua	20	Forward	Gateshead (L)	23	2		25	8
Rotherham (Y), Chesterfield (L), Gateshead (L)									
Kealy	Callum	21	Forward	Sutton United	1	2	3	3	
Worthing, Sutton U (Dual)									
Kean	Jake	29	Goalkeeper	Notts County		1	9	1	1
Blackburn (Y), Hartlepool (L), Rochdale (L), Yeovil (L), Oldham (L), Norwich, Colchester (L), Swindon (L), Sheff Wed, Mansfield (L), Grimsby (L), Mansfield, Notts Co									
Keane	Cieron	23	Defender	Leamington	6	5	1	11	
				Bradford Park Avenue	1	1		2	
Wolves (Y), Notts Co, Nuneaton, Worcester, Kidderminster, Alfreton, Boston U & Basford (Dual), Leamington, Bradford PA									
Keane	Jordan	26	Midfielder	Stockport County	38	1	2	39	1
Stoke (Y), Tamworth (L), Alfreton (L), Lincoln (L), Nuneaton, Worcester, Boston U, Stockport									
Kearney	Dylan	22	Forward	Sutton United		3	3	3	
				Dulwich Hamlet	10	5	2	15	4
Hayes & Y, Wealdstone, Uxbridge (L), Harrow B, Sutton U, Dulwich H									
Keating	Ruairi	24	Forward	Torquay United	6	17	4	23	3
				Gateshead	3	5		8	2
Sligo Rovers, Galway, Finn Harps, Torquay, Gateshead									
Kedwell	Danny	36	Forward	Havant & Waterlooville	25	6		31	12
Herne Bay, Welling, Grays, Wimbledon, Gillingham, Ebbsfleet, Havant & W									
Keena	Aidan	21	Forward	Hartlepool United	4	4	1	8	2
St Patrick's A, Hearts, Queen's Park (L), Dunfermline (L), Hartlepool									
Keetch	Bradley	19	Midfielder	Maidenhead United		3	7	3	
Maidenhead (Y)									
Kefalas	Themis	20	Defender	Billericay Town (L)	14	4	3	18	1
QPR, Billericay (L)									
Keillor-Dunn	Davis	22	Midfielder	Wrexham	3	3	1	6	1
Middlesbrough (Y), Sunderland (Y), Chesterfield, Ross Co, Falkirk (L), Wrexham									
Kellett	Andy	26	Defender	AFC Fylde		2	1	2	
				Alfreton Town	1	1		2	
Bolton (Y), Plymouth (L), Man U (L), Wigan, Chesterfield (L), Notts Co, AFC Fylde, Alfreton									
Kelly	Josh	21	Forward	Maidenhead United	26	7	2	33	8
Maidenhead (Y)									
Kelly	Marcus	34	Midfielder	Kettering Town	22	3	1	25	3
Rushden, Oxford U, Kettering, Mansfield (L), Tamworth, Forest Green, Wrexham, Kettering									
Kelly	Sam	26	Midfielder	King's Lynn Town	15	16	7	31	1
Norwich (Y), Everton, Cambridge C, Norwich, Port Vale, Grimsby, Hamilton, Braintree, Billericay, King's Lynn									

Key: X - Started; SX - Sub on; S - Non-playing Sub; Ap - Total Appearances; G/Cs - Total goals/clean sheets.

SURNAME	FIRSTNAME	AGE	POSITION	CLUB	X	SX	S	Ap	G/Cs
Kelly-Evans	Dion	23	Midfielder	Notts County	21	3	9	24	
Coventry (Y), Kettering, Notts Co									
Kempster	Alex	24	Forward	York City	34	5	1	39	12
York, Spennymoor (L)									
Kennedy	Callum	31	Defender	Billericay Town	11	2		13	
Swindon (Y), Gillingham (L), Rotherham (L), Scunthorpe, Wimbledon, Leyton O, Wimbledon, Billericay									
Kennedy	Connor	23	Defender	Kettering Town	32			32	2
Corby, Kettering									
Kennedy	Jason	33	Midfielder	Hartlepool United	10	10	12	20	2
				Spennymoor Town (L)	6	1		7	
Middlesbrough (Y), Darlington, Rochdale, Bradford, Rochdale (L), Carlisle (L), Carlisle, Hartlepool, Spennymoor (L)									
Kennedy	Kieran	26	Defender	Wrexham (L)	15	1	1	16	1
Man City (Y), Leicester, Motherwell, AFC Fylde, Macclesfield, Shrewsbury, Wrexham, Port Vale, Wrexham (L)									
Kensdale	Ollie	20	Defender	Bath City (L)	7		3	7	
Colchester (Y), Bath (L)									
Kerr	Fraser	27	Defender	Hartlepool United	28	1	3	29	
Birmingham, Motherwell, Cowdenbeath, Stenhousemuir, Gateshead, Hartlepool									
Kerry	Lloyd	31	Midfielder	Harrogate Town	19	1	2	20	4
Sheffield U (Y), Torquay (L), Chesterfield, Alfreton (L), Kidderminster (L), Hinckley U, Tamworth, Harrogate									
Khan	Saido	24	Defender	Maidstone United	35			35	2
Tooting & M, Maidstone									
Khinda	Kiran	24	Defender	Eastbourne Borough	17	4	6	21	
Eastbourne B, Woking, Chelmsford, Eastbourne B									
Kiangebeni	Percy	23	Defender	Concord Rangers	3	1		4	
St Albans, Concord R									
Kiernan	Brendan	27	Midfielder	Harrogate Town	31	8	4	39	8
Wimbledon, Braintree (L), Bromley, Staines, Ebbsfleet, Hayes & Y, Bromley, Hampton & R, Welling, Harrogate									
Killip	Ben	24	Goalkeeper	Hartlepool United	37		3	37	10
Chelsea (Y), Norwich, Lowestoft (L), Grimsby, Braintree, Hartlepool									
Killock	Shane	31	Defender	Alfreton Town	21	1	3	22	1
Huddersfield (Y), Hyde U (L), Harrogate T (L), Oxford U (L), Telford, Harrogate T, Guiseley (L), Hyde U, Scarborough,									
Bradford PA, Boston U (L), Alfreton									
King	Cameron	24	Midfielder	FC Halifax Town	27	8	2	35	7
Norwich (Y), Thetford, Shamrock, King's Lynn, FC Halifax									
King	Craig	23	Goalkeeper	Oxford City	31		1	31	5
Luton (Y), Bishop's S (L), Southport (L), Oxford C									
King	Jack		Defender	Ebbsfleet United	39		1	39	1
Stevenage, Ebbsfleet									
King	Jeff	24	Midfielder	FC Halifax Town	24	12		36	
Altrincham, Prescot C (L), Nantwich, Kendal, Trafford, Witton, Droylsden, Bolton, FC United (L), St Mirren, FC Halifax									
King	Josh		Defender	York City	4	2	15	6	
Chester-le-Street, Carlisle U Acad, York									
King	Reece		Midfielder	Leamington		5	2	5	
Malvern, Gloucester, Hednesford, Leamington, Hednesford									
King	Rhys		Defender	Oxford City		1	2	1	1
Oxford C (Y)									
King	Tom		Goalkeeper	Gloucester City		1	6	1	
Shortwood, Gloucester									
Kinsella	Lewis	25	Defender	Aldershot Town	36			36	
Arsenal, Aston Villa, Luton (L), Kidderminster (L), Colchester, Aldershot									
Kioso	Peter	21	Defender	Hartlepool United	30	1		31	3
MK Dons (Y), Dunstable, Hartlepool, Luton									
Kirby	Jake	26	Midfielder	Stockport County	4	4		8	
Tranmere, Stockport (L), Stockport, Warrington (L)									
Kirkpatrick	Lucas		Midfielder	Braintree Town	20	3	1	23	
Hitchin, Biggleswade, Braintree									
Kitching	Mark	24	Defender	Hartlepool United	41	3	1	44	2
Middlesbrough (Y), York (L), Rochdale, Hartlepool									

SURNAME	FIRSTNAME	AGE	POSITION	CLUB PLAYED FOR	X	SX	S	Ap	G/Cs
Kiwomya	Alex	24	Forward	Chorley (L)	4	1		5	
Chelsea (Y), Barnsley (L), Fleetwood (L), Crewe (L), Doncaster, Chesterfield (L), Chorley (L)									
Kizzi	Joseph	26	Defender	Bromley	40			40	5
Billericay, Bromley									
Klass	Michael	21	Midfielder	Bromley	6	13	14	19	
Southend (Y), Bromley									
Klukowski	Yan	33	Midfielder	Chippenham Town		2	6	2	
				Hungerford Town	10	2	4	12	1
Forest Green, Newport Co, York, Torquay, Kidderminster (L), Chippenham, Hungerford									
Knight	Lewis		Forward	Bradford Park Avenue	29	5		34	6
Bradford PA									
Knight	Lewis	27	Defender	Maidstone United	8	3	11	11	
				St Albans City (L)	3			3	
Concord R, East Thurrock, St Albans, Maidstone, St Albans (L)									
Knights	Darryl	32	Forward	AFC Telford United	18	4	14	22	2
Ipswich (Y), Yeovil, Cambridge U (L), Kidderminster, Newport Co, Solihull, Kidderminster, Tamworth, Telford									
Knott	Billy	27	Midfielder	Chelmsford City	16	7	2	23	1
Sunderland (Y), Wimbledon (L), Wycombe (L), Bradford, Gillingham, Lincoln C (L), Lincoln, Rochdale (L), Concord R, Chelmsford									
Knowles	Chris		Midfielder	Gloucester City	13	2	2	15	
Gloucester									
Knowles	Dominic	28	Forward	Boston United	33	2	4	35	13
Burnley (Y), Gainsborough, Harrogate, Burton, Kidderminster (L), Harrogate, Boston U									
Knowles	Tom		Forward	Chelmsford City (L)	12	6	1	18	5
Cambridge U (Y), Dartford (L), Hemel H (L), Chelmsford (L)									
Konstantopoulous	Dimitrios	41	Goalkeeper	Hartlepool United	1			1	
Hartlepool, Coventry, Cardiff (L), Swansea (L), Kerkyra (Gre), AEK, Middlesbrough, Hartlepool									
Kosylo	Matt	27	Midfielder	AFC Fylde	15	14	3	29	1
Stockport, Ashton, Hyde, Nantwich, Halifax, AFC Fylde									
Koszela	Olaf		Forward	Torquay United		3	8	3	
Torquay (Y)									
Kotwica	Zack	25	Midfielder	Gloucester City	17	11	3	28	2
Cheltenham (Y), Gloucester (L), Cirencester, Gloucester, Tamworth, Salisbury, Gloucester									
Koue Niate	Jean-Yves	27	Defender	Torquay United	13	2	9	15	1
				Aldershot Town	8			8	
Solihull M, Oxford C, Guiseley, Torquay, Aldershot									
Kouogun	Maxim	23	Defender	Harrogate Town	3			3	
Uni College Dublin, Warrenpoint, Waterford, Harrogate T									
Kpohomouh	Jacques	23	Midfielder	Hemel Hempstead Town	22	5	5	27	1
Bangor, Radcliffe B, Southport, Droylsden, Hemel H									
Krabbendam	Che	20	Midfielder	Welling United	1		3	1	
Staines, Welling									
Krasniqi	Arjanit	20	Midfielder	Billericay Town	6	1	3	7	
Waltham Forest, Colchester, Billericay									
Krasniqi	Kreshnic	25	Midfielder	Concord Rangers	28	3	1	31	6
				Wealdstone		3		3	
Ethnikos Achna (Cyp) Concord R, Wealdstone									
Kretzschmar	Max	26	Midfielder	Woking	16	11	2	27	4
Wycombe, Woking, Hampton & R, Woking									
Kuagica		29	Defender	Dulwich Hamlet	2			2	
Recreativo (Angola), Stumbras (Lith), Ermis (Cyp), Dulwich H									
Kudyiwa	Simba		Forward	Aldershot Town			9		
Aldershot (Y)									
Kuhl	Aaron	24	Midfielder	Slough Town	1	1		2	
Reading (Y), Dundee U (L), Boreham W (L), Slough									
Kyei	Nana	22	Midfielder	Maidstone United	11	6	7	17	2
				Chelmsford City	3	3	1	6	1
Barnet (Y), Concord R (L), Hampton & R (L), Potters B (L), Maidstone, Chelmsford									
L'Ghoul	Nassim	22	Midfielder	Dover Athletic	13	20	4	33	3
St Neots, Whitehawk (L), Welling, Dover									

Key: X - Started; SX - Sub on; S - Non-playing Sub; Ap - Total Appearances; G/Cs - Total goals/clean sheets.

2019-20 NATIONAL. NORTH & SOUTH PLAYERS — APPEARANCES

SURNAME	FIRSTNAME	AGE	POSITION	CLUB	X	SX	S	Ap	G/Cs
Laarbi	Mohamed Oulad		Goalkeeper	Hampton & Richmond Borough			6		
Hampton & R									
Lacey	Alex	27	Defender	Notts County	16			16	
Luton, Cambridge C (L), Thurrock (L), Eastbourne B (L), Eastleigh (L), Yeovil, Gillingham, Notts Co									
Lacey	Jonathan		Forward	Hemel Hempstead Town	1	2		3	
Berkhamsted, Hemel H (Dual)									
Lacey	Patrick	27	Midfielder	Southport	2	4	1	6	
Bradford (Y), Vauxhall M (L), Droylsden (L), Altrincham, Barrow, Accrington, Southport									
Lafayette	Ross	34	Forward	Wealdstone	27	8		35	15
Wealdstone, Welling, Luton, Woking (L), Welling (L), Eastleigh, Aldershot (L), Dover, Sutton U, Maidstone (L), Billericay, Wealdstone									
Laing	Louis	27	Defender	Darlington	31	7	1	38	
Sunderland, Wycombe (L), Nottingham F, Notts Co (L), Motherwell (L), Motherwell, Notts Co (L), Inverness CT, Hartlepool, Blyth S, Darlington									
Lainton	Rob	30	Goalkeeper	Wrexham	26		2	26	11
Bolton (Y), Bury, Burton (L), Cheltenham (L), Port Vale, Wrexham (L), Wrexham									
Laird	Alex	21	Defender	Bradford Park Avenue				1	
Bradford C (Y), Bradford PA									
Lait	Chris	27	Midfielder	AFC Telford United	6	5	2	11	
Solihull (Y), Stratford T, Banbury, Stratford T, Halesowen, Wulfrunians (L), Rushall, Stourbridge, Solihull M, Rushall Olympic, Stourbridge, Tamworth, Telford									
Lambert	Jack	21	Midfielder	Darlington (L)	5	6	3	11	2
				Blyth Spartans (L)	3		1	3	
Middlesbrough (Y), Dundee, Scunthorpe, Darlington (L), Blyth S (L)									
Landers	Henry	20	Forward	Maidenhead United		2	5	2	
Maidenhead (Y)									
Lane	Jack	27	Defender	Leamington	37	2	1	39	2
Macclesfield (Y), Newcastle T (L), Stockport S (L), Hinckley U, Ventura County (US), Sacramento, Ilkeston, Nuneaton, Tamworth, Alfreton, Leamington									
Langmead	Kelvin	35	Defender	Brackley Town	7	8	20	15	1
Preston (Y), Tamworth (L), Carlisle (L), Kidderminster (L), Shrewsbury, Peterborough, Northampton, Ebbsfleet, Kidderminster (L), Nuneaton, Harrogate, Brackley									
Langstaff	Macaulay	23	Forward	York City	4	20	7	24	1
				Blyth Spartans (L)	3			3	
Gateshead, Blyth (L), York, Bradford PA (L), Blyth S (L)									
Lashley	Harry		Midfielder	Dartford				1	
Dartford (Y)									
Latham	Kingsley	21	Goalkeeper	Havant & Waterlooville (L)	1		9	1	
Southampton (Y), Dorchester (L), Havant & W (L)									
Laurent	Acea		Midfielder	Billericay Town	2		12	2	
				Concord Rangers		3	2	3	
Senrab, Tilbury, Kingstonian, Ware, Billericay T, Concord R									
Lavercombe	Dan	23	Goalkeeper	AFC Fylde	6		27	6	1
Torquay, Wigan, Torquay (L), Torquay (L), Rhyl (L), Torquay (L), AFC Fylde									
Law	Jason	21	Forward	Kettering Town (L)	1	3	4	4	1
Mansfield (Y), Kettering (L)									
Lawless	Alex	35	Midfielder	Ebbsfleet United	8	6	3	14	
Fulham, Torquay, Forest Green, York, Luton (L), Luton, Yeovil, Leyton Orient, Ebbsfleet									
Lawlor	Jake	29	Midfielder	Wrexham	36			36	1
Guiseley, AFC Fylde (L), Salford, Wrexham									
Lawrence	Byron	24	Midfielder	Braintree Town (L)	2			2	
Ipswich (Y), Colchester, Bishop's S, Leiston, Billericay (L), Dulwich H (L), Braintree (L)									
Lea	Harrison		Midfielder	Chippenham Town				1	
Chippenham									
Leather	Scott	27	Defender	Chorley	10		1	10	
PNE (Y), Altrincham, Chorley									
Lee	Charlie	33	Midfielder	Yeovil Town	34	2	1	36	2
Tottenham, Millwall (L), Peterborough, Gillingham (L), Gillingham, Stevenage, Leyton Orient, Yeovil									
Lees	Toby	23	Defender	Gateshead (L)	19	1	1	20	2
Harrogate Harrogate RW (L), Boston (L), Whitby (L), Gateshead (L)									

SURNAME	FIRSTNAME	AGE	POSITION	CLUB PLAYED FOR	X	SX	S	Ap	G/Cs
Leesley	Joe	26	Midfielder	Harrogate Town	5	1	4	6	1
				Stockport County (L)	9	2	2	11	
Matlock, Alfreton, Harrogate, Stockport (L), Stevenage (L)									
Lemonheigh-Evans	Connor	23	Midfielder	Torquay United (L)	21	2		23	2
Bristol C, Bath (L), Torquay (L), Torquay (L), Torquay (L)									
Lench	Matt		Midfielder	Slough Town	37	2	1	39	
Hitchin, Slough, Wealdstone, Slough									
Lewington	Chris	31	Goalkeeper	Maidstone United	14		26	14	2
Charlton, Dulwich, Fisher Ath, Sittingbourne, Leatherhead, Dagenham & R, Colchester, Margate, Welling, Dover, Maidstone									
Lewington	Jared	25	Forward	Torquay United	1	7	2	8	
Buckland, Tiverton, Truro, Torquay									
Lewis	Danny	38	Goalkeeper	Brackley Town	39			39	16
Alvechurch, Studley, Kidderminster, Moor Green, Redditch, Kidderminster, Solihull, Brackley									
Lewis	Dennon	23	Forward	Wealdstone	37	2		39	13
Watford (Y), Woking (L), Crawley (L), Falkirk, Bromley, Weladstone									
Lewis	Joe	20	Defender	Torquay United (L)	18	11	7	29	
Swansea (Y), Torquay (L)									
Lewthwaite	Tyrone	19	Forward	Hampton & Richmond Borough	8	14	5	22	6
Watford (Y), Rotherham, Hampton & R									
Liburd	Rowan	27	Forward	Hereford	14	10	2	24	3
				Dartford (L)	2	1	3	3	
Billericay, Reading, Wycombe (L), Stevenage, Leyton Orient (L), Hemel H (L), Guiseley (L), Guiseley, Hereford, Dartford (L)									
Liddle	Gary	34	Midfielder	Hartlepool United (L)	15			15	
Hartlepool, Notts Co, Bradford C, Chesterfield, Carlisle, Walsall, Hartlepool (L)									
Liddle	Michael	30	Defender	Darlington	28	1		29	1
Sunderland (Y), Carlisle (L), Leyton O (L), Gateshead (L), Accrington (L), Accrington, Dunston UTS, Blyth S, Darlington									
Lillis	Josh	32	Goalkeeper	AFC Fylde (L)	3			3	2
Scunthorpe (Y), Notts Co (L), Grimsby (L), Rochdale (L), Rochdale, AFC Fylde (L)									
Lilly	Zak		Defender	AFC Telford United	20	1	9	21	1
Telford (Y), Tamworth (L)									
Limb	Harry	20	Forward	King's Lynn Town		2	1	2	
Boston U, Burnley, King's Lynn									
Lincoln	Dan	25	Goalkeeper	Hampton & Richmond Borough	20			20	7
Farnborough, Reading, Nuneaton (L), Hayes & Y, Basingstoke, Bognor R, Braintree, Bognor R, Hampton & R									
Lita	Leroy	35	Forward	Chelmsford City	4	8	5	12	1
Bristol C (Y), Reading, Charlton (L), Norwich (L), Middlesbrough, Swansea, Birmingham (L), Sheff Wed (L), Brighton (L), Barnsley, Notts Co (L), Chania (Gre), Yeovil, Sisaket (Thl'd), Chelmsford									
Little	Armani	23	Midfielder	Torquay United	13	5	.	18	3
Southampton (Y), Oxford U, Woking (Lx3), Torquay									
Livesey	Danny	35	Defender	Chester	29	1	1	30	5
Carlisle, Wrexham (L), Barrow, Salford, Chester (L), Chester									
Lloyd-McGoldrick	Danny	28	Midfielder	Stockport County (L)	8			8	1
Southport (Y), Chorley (L), Skelmersdale (L), Colwyn, Lincoln C, Colwyn, Tamworth, AFC Fylde, Stockport, Peterborough, Salford, Stockport (L)									
Loach	Scott	32	Goalkeeper	Barnet	45			45	11
Ipswich, Lincoln C, Watford, Stafford (L), Morecambe (L), Bradford (L), Ipswich, Rotherham, Bury (L), Peterborough (L), Yeovil (L), Notts Co, York (L), Hartlepool, Barnet									
Loft	Doug	33	Midfielder	Billericay Town	24	2	1	26	2
Brighton, Dag & Red (L), Port Vale, Gillingham, Colchester, Shrewsbury, Dag & Red (L), Billericay									
Lofthouse	Kyran	19	Forward	Oxford City (L)	14	2		16	3
Oxford U (Y), Oxford C (L)									
Lokko	Kevin	24	Defender	Dover Athletic	29		3	29	4
Colchester, Welling, Maidstone, Stevenage, Dagenham & R (L), Dover (L), Dover									
Long	Adam	19	Defender	Notts County (L)	1			1	1
Wigan (Y), Notts Co (L)									
Longe-King	David	25	Defender	St Albans City	37		1	37	1
St Albans, Biggleswade, St Albans									
Longridge	Jackson	25	Defender	Torquay United (L)	7			7	
Ayr Utd, Stranraer, Livingston, Dunfermline, Bradford C, Torquay (L)									

Key: X - Started; SX - Sub on; S - Non-playing Sub; Ap - Total Appearances; G/Cs - Total goals/clean sheets.

SURNAME	FIRSTNAME	AGE	POSITION	CLUB	X	SX	S	Ap	G/Cs
Louis	Jefferson	41	Forward	Hampton & Richmond Borough	6	1	6	7	1
				St Albans City	4	8	2	12	2
Maidenhead, Brackley, Lincoln C, Newport, Brackley, Hendon, Margate, Lowestoft, Wealdstone, Staines, Oxford C, Hampton & R, St Albans									
Lovell	Liam	18	Goalkeeper	Curzon Ashton			6		
Curzon A (Y)									
Lowe	Keith	34	Defender	Bradford Park Avenue	16			16	1
				Kidderminster Harriers	9			9	1
Wolves, Burnley (L), QPR (L), Swansea (L), Brighton (L), Cheltenham (Lx2) Port Vale (L), Kidderminster, Hereford, Cheltenham, York (L), York, Kidderminster, Macclesfield, Bradford PA, Kidderminster									
Lowe	Matt	24	Midfielder	Brackley Town	38	1		39	10
Cambridge U (Y), Wealdstone (Lx2), Brackley (L), Brackley									
Lowth	Darragh		Midfielder	Kidderminster Harriers		1	10	1	
Tralee Dynamos, Limerick, Cobh Ramblers, Tralee D, Kidderminster									
Lowth	Shane	22	Forward	Kidderminster Harriers	1		1	1	
Traylee Dynamos, Limerick, Cobh Ramblers, Traylee D, Kidderminster									
Loza	Jamar	26	Forward	Chelmsford City	4	5	2	9	
				Woking	23	4		27	2
Norwich, Coventry (L), Leyton Orient (L), Southend (L), Yeovil (L), Stevenage (L), Southend (L), Maidstone, Woking (L), Billericay, Chelmsford, Woking (L)									
Luer	Greg	25	Forward	Eastbourne Borough	30	3		33	9
Hull, Port Vale (L), Scunthorpe (L), Stevenage (L), Maidstone (L), Woking, Eastbourne B									
Lund	Mitchell	23	Defender	Bradford Park Avenue	27	3	2	30	
Doncaster (Y), Wrexham (L), Morecombe (L), Bradford PA									
Lundstram	Josh	21	Midfielder	Altrincham (L)	12			12	
Crewe (Y), Nuneaton (L), Altrincham (L)									
Luque	Joan	28	Forward	Dagenham & Redbridge	24	6	3	30	5
Cornella (Y), Gramenet B, Montanesa, Vilassar de Mar, FC Santboia, CE Sabadell B, San Rafael, CD Llosetense, Heybridge S, Lincoln C, Bromley (L), Concord R, Dagenham & R									
Luyambula	Ngemba	21	Goalkeeper	AFC Telford United (L)	5			5	
Borussia Dort (Y), Birmingham (Y), Hungerford (L), Crawley (L), Telford (L)									
Lynch	Conor		Forward	Hungerford Town	6	19	6	25	4
Hungerford									
Lynch	David	27	Midfielder	Alfreton Town	20	3	4	23	1
Burnley (Y), Droylsden (L), Stalybridge (L), Nantwich (L), Burscough, Workington, Clitheroe, Altrincham, Halifax, Southport, Alfreton									
Lyons	Jamie		Forward	Bradford Park Avenue	1	4	3	5	
Bradford PA (Y)									
Lyons-Foster	Kodi	23	Defender	Aldershot Town	27	6	3	33	2
Aldershot, Whitehawk (L), Whitehawk, Braintree, Aldershot									
MacDonald	Josh	25	Midfielder	FC Halifax Town	4	7	6	11	
Middlesbrough, Marske Utd, Halifax									
MacDonald	Shaun	23	Goalkeeper	Torquay United	13		25	13	2
Gateshead, Blyth, Torquay									
Mace	James	35	Defender	Leamington	39	1		40	1
Hinckley U, Leamington									
Mafuta	Gus	25	Midfielder	Hartlepool United	35	4	6	39	4
Colchester (Y), Bristol C (Y), Weston (L), Nuneaton (L), Gateshead, Salford, Hartlepool									
Magagada	Alvin		Forward	Hemel Hempstead Town			2		
Hemel H (Y)									
Magnay	Carl	31	Defender	Spennymoor Town	26	1		27	
Leeds, Chelsea, MK Dons (L), Northampton (L), Gateshead, Grimsby, Hartlepool, Spennymoor									
Magri	Sam	26	Defender	Havant & Waterlooville	35		1	35	3
Portsmouth, QPR, Nuneaton (L), Dover (L), Dover, Ebbsfleet, Havant & W									
Maguire	Dan	27	Forward	York City	12	6	1	18	2
Blyth S, Halifax, Blyth S, York									
Maguire	Laurence	23	Defender	Chesterfield	14	1	1	15	
Chesterfield (Y), AFC Fylde (L)									
Maher	Niall	24	Defender	FC Halifax Town	23	4	2	27	4
Bolton, Blackpool (L), Bury, Galway, Telford, Halifax									

SURNAME	FIRSTNAME	AGE	POSITION	CLUB PLAYED FOR	X	SX	S	Ap	G/Cs
Maher	Niall	21	Goalkeeper	Gloucester City	8		3	8	
Wolves (Y), Morecambe Halesowen (L), Stourbridge, Weston SM, Gloucester									
Mahon	Craig	31	Midfielder	Chester	3	6	6	9	
				Altrincham	6	4	1	10	
Wigan, Accrington (L), Salford, Vauxhall M, Chester, Altrincham									
Maloney	Taylor	21	Midfielder	Concord Rangers (L)	6			6	
Charlton (Y), Concord R (L), Newport Co (L), Concord R (L)									
Maltby	Jake	20	Midfielder	Farsley Celtic		3	3	3	
Bradford C (Y), Farsley C									
Mandeville	Liam	23	Forward	Chesterfield	20	14	4	34	4
Doncaster, Colchester (L), Morecambe (L), Chesterfield									
Manesio	Sergio	25	Midfielder	Braintree Town	5	1	1	6	
Ottawa Fury, Hampton & R, Braintree									
Mann	Adam	28	Forward	Bath City	36	5	1	41	6
Gloucester, Shortwood, Gloucester, Evesham, Bath									
Mannion	Will	22	Goalkeeper	Kidderminster Harriers (L)	17			17	3
Wimbledon (Yth), Hull (Yth), Plymouth (L), Aldershot (L), Kidderminster (L)									
March	Josh	23	Forward	Leamington	25		2	25	22
Alvechurch, Leamington, Forest GR									
Marriott	Adam	29	Forward	King's Lynn Town	39			39	30
Cambridge U (Y), Cambridge C (L), Bishop's S (L), Cambridge C (L), Stevenage, Lincoln C, Royston T, Boston U, King's Lynn									
Marriott	Isaac	20	Midfielder	Bradford Park Avenue (L)	21	3	5	24	
Huddersfield (Y), Larne (L), Bradford PA (L)									
Marris	Teddy		Goalkeeper	Alfreton Town			7		
Chesterfield (Y), Alfreton									
Marsh	George		Goalkeeper	Concord Rangers			1		
Concord R									
Marsh	Tyrone	26	Forward	Boreham Wood	36	4	1	40	15
Oxford U, Welling (L), Torquay, Dover, Macclesfield, Boreham W									
Marsh-Brown	Kyjoun	23	Midfielder	Dartford	11	7	1	18	1
Whitehawk, Welling, Dartford									
Marshall	Ross	20	Defender	Maidstone United	25	1		26	1
Broxbourne B, Ipswich (Y), Lowestoft (L), Braintree (L), Maidstone									
Martin	Aaron	28	Forward	Guiseley	21	1		22	17
				Harrogate Town (L)	2			2	
Brighouse, Guiseley, Harroagte T									
Martin	Charlie		Goalkeeper	Tonbridge Angels			1		
Tonbridge A (Y)									
Martin	Dan	20	Midfielder	Bath City (L)	6			6	
Fulham (Y), Cardiff, Bath (L)									
Martin	Gary	29	Forward	Darlington (L)	2	5	2	7	
Middlesbrough (Y), Ujpest D (Hun) (L), IA Akranes (Ice), K Reykjavik, V Reykjavik, Lillestrom (Nor) (L), Lokeren (Bel),									
York Lillestrom, Valur (Ice), IBV, Darlington (L)									
Martin	Josh	21	Defender	Hungerford Town	5	1		6	1
				Leamington	4	2	7	6	
Hungerford, Leamington									
Martinez	Sheridan	27	Goalkeeper	AFC Telford United			8		
Khalsa, Telford, Solihull, Telford									
Mason	Cameron	24	Goalkeeper	Curzon Ashton	34		1	34	11
Chesterfield (Y), Southport (L), Curzon A									
Mason	Chris	33	Defender	Blyth Spartans (L)	5			5	
				Spennymoor Town	11		16	11	
Darlington, Bishop A, Harrogate T, Gateshead, Ostavalls (Swe), Spennymoor, Blyth S (L)									
Mason	Jude	19	Defender	Hampton & Richmond Borough (L)	2		1	2	
Sutton U (Y), Hamptn & R (L)									
Mason	Sam	20	Goalkeeper	Woking			1		
Woking									
Mason-Clarke	Ephron	20	Forward	Barnet	17	16	3	33	5
Barnet (Yth), Met Police (L)									

Key: X - Started; SX - Sub on; S - Non-playing Sub; Ap - Total Appearances; G/Cs - Total goals/clean sheets.

SURNAME	FIRSTNAME	AGE	POSITION	CLUB	X	SX	S	Ap	G/Cs
Massanka	Ntumba	23	Midfielder	Chorley	12	15	5	27	3
Burnley (Y), York (L), Morecambe (L), Wrexham (L), Wrexham (L), Dover (L), RWDM (Bel), Chorley									
Massaro	Joe	19	Forward	Kettering Town			2		
Kettering (Y), St Neots (L)									
Massey	Alan	31	Defender	Maidenhead United	41			41	
Wealdstone, Braintree (L), Braintree, Maidenhead									
Matrevics	Rihards	21	Goalkeeper	Barnet			26		
West Ham (Yth), Barnet									
Matsuzaka	Daniel	21	Defender	Sutton United	6	5	7	11	
				Braintree Town	14	1	1	15	
Southend (Y), Harlow (L), Kataller Toyama (Jap), Braintree, Sutton U, Braintree									
Maturino Da Silva	Jose Manuel		Forward	Hungerford Town	6	4	4	10	2
Hungerford									
Maxwell	Luke	22	Midfielder	Gloucester City (L)	4	1		5	
				Solihull Moors		2	4	2	
Kidderminster, Birmingham, Kidderminster (L), Grimsby (L), Gateshead (L) Solihull (L), Solihull, Gloucester (L)									
May	Adam	22	Midfielder	Boreham Wood (L)	1	1	1	2	1
Portsmouth (Yth), Sutton (L), Aldershot (L), Swindon (L), Boreham W (L)									
Maycock	Callum	22	Defender	Leamington (L)	23			23	1
Coventry (Y), Macclesfield (L), Leamington (L)									
Maye	Simeon	25	Midfielder	Hereford	6	1	2	7	
				Brackley Town	1	4	7	5	1
Redditch, Hednesford, Solihull, Rushall O, Hereford, Brackley									
Maynard	Lois	31	Midfielder	Stockport County	1			1	
Winsford, Halifax, Tranmere, Salford, Stockport									
Maynard-Brewer	Ashley	20	Goalkeeper	Dulwich Hamlet (L)	13			13	3
				Dover Athletic (L)	4			4	1
Charlton (Y), Chelmsford (L), Hampton & R (L), Dulwich H (L), Dover (L)									
Mbeta	Christian		Goalkeeper	Sutton United			1		
Sutton U (Y)									
McAlinden	Liam	26	Forward	FC Halifax Town	21	7	1	28	10
				Stockport County	5	4		9	2
Wolves (Y), Shrewsbury (L), Fleetwood (Lx2), Shrewsbury (L), Crawley (L), Exeter, Cheltenham, Brackley (L), Kidderminster (L)									
FC Halifax, Stockport									
McAuley	Rory	30	Defender	King's Lynn Town	35			35	
Norwich (Y), Cambridge C (Y), Cambridge U (Y), Chelmsford (L), Dartford (L), Dartford, Chelmsford, Lowestoft, King's Lynn									
McAuley	Shaun	33	Midfielder	Hampton & Richmond Borough	8	16	6	24	
Eastleigh, Basingstoke, Oxford C, Hampton & R									
McBurnie	Alexander	22	Forward	Barnet	1		4	1	
Ytterhogdal (Swe), Barnet									
McCallum	Gavin	32	Defender	Welling United	12	6	7	18	2
Hereford, Lincoln C, Barnet (L), Woking, Sutton U, Tonbridge A (L), Eastbourne B, Welling									
McCallum	Paul	26	Forward	Solihull Moors	24	3		27	9
				Barnet (L)	6	1		7	5
Dulwich H, West Ham, Rochdale (L), AFC Wimbledon (L), Aldershot (L), Torquay (L), Hearts (L), Portsmouth (L), Leyton Orient									
Eastleigh, Solihull M, Barnet (L)									
McCann	Cody	17	Defender	Curzon Ashton		2	4	2	
Curzon A (Y)									
McCarthy	Jake	24	Midfielder	Weymouth	40	1		41	10
Bournemouth (Y), Dorchester (L), Havant & W (L), Maidstone, Weymouth									
McClure	Matt	28	Forward	Maidstone United	19	3	1	22	10
				Gloucester City	7			7	2
Wycombe, Hayes & Y Utd (L), Dagenham & R, Aldershot, Maidstone, Gloucester									
McCory	Damien	30	Defender	Notts County	30		2	30	1
Plymouth, Port Vale (L), Grimsby (L), Dagenham & R, Burton, Portsmouth (L), Notts Co									
McCoulsky	Shawn	23	Forward	Bromley (L)		4	1	4	1
				FC Halifax (L)	1	5	1	6	1
Bristol C (Y), Weston (L), Torquay (L), Newport (L), Southend (L), Forest GR, Bromley (L), FC Halifax (L)									

SURNAME	FIRSTNAME	AGE	POSITION	CLUB PLAYED FOR	X	SX	S	Ap	G/Cs
McCoy	Mark		Goalkeeper	Curzon Ashton			2		
Curzon A									
McCoy	Marvin	31	Defender	Dulwich Hamlet	19	1	3	20	
Arsenal, Watford, Wealdstone, Wycombe, York, Ebbsfleet, Aldershot, Dulwich H									
McCoy	Ollie	22	Forward	Yeovil Town (L)		7	5	7	
				Wealdstone (L)		1	5	1	
Birmingham (Y), Yeovil (L), Wealdstone (L)									
McDonald	Curtis	32	Midfielder	Chippenham Town	34	1	1	35	3
Newport Co, Forest GR, Brackley, Chippenham									
McDonnell	Adam	23	Midfielder	Boreham Wood	15	4	14	19	1
Ipswich, Aldershot (L), Aldershot, Boreham W									
McDonnell	Edward (Ted)		Goalkeeper	Tonbridge Angels			16		
Tonbridge A									
McDonnell	Joe	26	Goalkeeper	Notts County (L)	8		2	8	2
Basingstoke, Wimbledon, Notts Co (L)									
McEachran	Zac		Forward	Oxford City	28	6		34	10
Oxford C Banbury, Oxford C									
McFadden	Archie		Defender	Concord Rangers			12		
Concord R (Y)									
McFarlane	Kyle	23	Forward	York City	1	3	5	4	1
				Leamington		4	4	4	
Birmingham (Y), Nuneaton (L), Nuneaton (L), Barrow (L), York, Stratford T (L), Leamington									
McGavin	Brett	20	Midfielder	Concord Rangers (L)	2	4		6	1
Ipswich (Y), Concord R (L)									
McGlade	Dylan	25	Midfielder	Blyth Spartans	4	2	3	6	1
Shelbourne, St Patricks, Longford, Blyth S, Longford, Bray, Blyth S, Cork									
McGlashan	Jermaine	32	Midfielder	Chesterfield (L)	6	9	8	15	
				Ebbsfleet United	10	2		12	
Tooting & M, Staines, Bracknell (L), Kingstonian, Merstham, Ashford T, Aldershot, Cheltenham, Gillingham, Southend,									
Swindon, Wrexham (L), Chesterfield (L), Ebbsfleet									
McGlip	Cameron	22	Midfielder	Hungerford Town (L)	5			5	2
Swindon (Y), Hungerford (L)									
McGory	Louis	23	Forward	Hungerford Town	7	7	4	14	
Forest GR (Y), Aldershot (L), Hungerford (L), Gloucester (L), Telford, Weston, Hungerford									
McGrath	Michael	34	Midfielder	Kettering Town	21	1	1	22	3
Redditch, Kidderminster, Worcester (L), Galway Utd, Sligo R, Rushall, Stratford T, Hednesford, Hereford, Bromsgrove Sp,									
Redditch, Kettering									
McGregor	Giovanni		Midfielder	Dartford (L)	1		2	1	
Crystal P (Y), Dartford (L)									
McIntosh	Leighton	27	Forward	Wrexham	5	8	5	13	3
				Blyth Spartans (L)	3			3	1
Dundee (Y), Montrose (L), Arbroath, Montrose, Peterhead, Selfoss (Ice), Arbroath, Airdrieonians, Wrexham, Blyth S (L)									
McKay	John	23	Forward	Chesterfield	5	10	4	15	2
Doncaster (Y), Ilkeston (L), Leeds, Airdrieonians (L), Cardiff, Chesterfield (L), Chesterfield									
McKenna	Ben	27	Midfielder	Spennymoor Town	31	2		33	3
Burnley (Y), Carlisle (Y), Annan Ath (L), Workington, Stalybridge, Bradford PA, Southport, Stockport, Curzon A, Bradford PA,									
Chester, Spennymoor									
McKenzie	Chinedu	25	Forward	Tonbridge Angels	3	10	2	13	
Maidenhead, Bognor R (L) Greenwich, Haringey, Tonbridge A									
McKeown	Corey	17	Forward	Blyth Spartans		3	11	3	
Gateshead (Y), Blyth S									
McKnight	Jack		Midfielder	Eastleigh	12	8	5	20	2
Beaconsfield, Eastleigh									
McLaughlin	Patrick	29	Midfielder	York City	19	5	5	24	1
Newcastle, York, Grimsby, Harrogate T (L), Gateshead, Hartlepool, York (L), York									
McLennan	George	24	Defender	Billericay Town	1			1	
				Wealdstone		2	1	2	
Reading (Y), Hayes & Y (L), Cheltenham, Sutton U, Ashford U, Maidstone, Billericay, Wealdstone									

Key: X - Started; SX - Sub on; S - Non-playing Sub; Ap - Total Appearances; G/Cs - Total goals/clean sheets.

SURNAME	FIRSTNAME	AGE	POSITION	CLUB	X	SX	S	Ap	G/Cs
McLeod-Urquhart	Josh	29	Defender	Braintree Town	16			16	1
				Billericay Town	7	2	1	9	
St Albans, Harlow, Wealdstone, Billericay, Hampton & R, Biggleswade, East Thurrock, St Albans, Braintree, Billericay T									
McManus	Niall	25	Midfielder	Dorking Wanderers	37	3	2	40	3
Millwall (Y), Hayes & Y (L), Leatherhead, Dorking W									
McNally	Reiss	19	Defender	Guiseley	34			34	
Guiseley									
McNulty	Steve	36	Defender	York City	29			29	
Fleetwood, Luton, Tranmere, York									
McQueen	Alex	25	Defender	Dagenham & Redbridge	20	6	6	26	1
Tottenham (Y), Carlisle, VPS, Dagenham & R									
McQueen	Darren	25	Forward	Dartford	31	5	1	36	20
Tottenham, Ipswich, Maldon & Tiptree, Ebbsfleet, Sutton U, Dartford (L), Dartford									
McQuilkin	James	31	Midfielder	AFC Telford United	23	7	3	30	3
FC Zlin (Czech), Tescoma Zlin, Hereford, Walsall, Hednesford, Torquay, Kidderminster, Telford									
McQuoid	Josh	30	Midfielder	Weymouth	24	2	4	26	9
Bournemouth, Millwall (L), Millwall, Burnley (L), Bournemouth, Peterborough (L), Coventry (L), Luton, Stevenage (L), Torquay (L), Aldershot, Weymouth									
McShane	James		Forward	Dorking Wanderers	39	2		41	11
Dorking W									
Medford-Smith	Ramarni	21	Defender	Torquay United (L)	4			4	
Reading (Y), Wealdstone (L), Torquay (L)									
Medway	Charles		Midfielder	Weymouth			1		
Weymouth (Y)									
Meikle	Lindon	32	Midfielder	Kettering Town	27	3		30	3
Eastwood, Mansfield, York, Macclesfield, Alfreton, Barrow, Southport (L), Kettering									
Meite	Ibrahim	24	Forward	Woking (L)	7	11	5	18	4
Harrow, Cardiff, Crawley (L), Crawley, Woking (L)									
Mekki	Adam	28	Midfielder	Bromley	13	9	9	22	1
				Ebbsfleet United (L)	7	1		8	
Aldershot Town, Barnet, Dover Athletic, Tranmere Rovers, Bromley, Ebbsfleet (L)									
Membrillera	George		Forward	Dorking Wanderers		1	1	1	
Dorking W (Y)									
Mendy	Jacob	23	Forward	Wealdstone	25	9	1	34	9
Carshalton, Wealdstone									
Mendy	Laurent		Midfielder	Dartford	2	1		3	
Dartford (Y)									
Mendy	Santana	20	Forward	Eastbourne Borough		1		1	
Marseille (Y), St Julia, Eastbourne B									
Mensah	Bernard	25	Forward	Maidenhead United (L)	9	20	8	29	1
				Gloucester City	6			6	3
Watford, Braintree (L), V Guimaraes (L), V Guimaraes (L), Barnet (L), Braintree (L), Aldershot, Bristol R, Lincoln C (L), Aldershot (L), Maidenhead (L), Gloucester									
Meppen-Walters	Courtney	25	Defender	Chorley	38		2	38	2
Man City (Y), Carlisle, Ashton U, Chorley, Stockport, Glossop, Chorley, AFC Telford									
Meredith	Dan	20	Defender	Leamington (L)		2	2	2	
WBA (Y), Maidstone (L), Leamington (L)									
Merrill	Luke	19	Midfielder	Curzon Ashton	7	8	14	15	1
Blackburn (Y), Curzon A									
Mersin	Yusuf	25	Goalkeeper	Dover Athletic	13		17	13	5
Kasimpasa (Tur), Crawley, Dover									
Merson	Sam	25	Forward	St Albans City	9	16	7	25	2
Redditch, St Albans									
Middleton	Ben	25	Defender	Boston United	11	1	3	12	
Scarborough A, North Ferriby, Harrogate, Boston U (Lx2), Boston U									
Midson	Jack	36	Forward	Hemel Hempstead Town	22	10	1	32	4
Histon, Oxford U, Wimbledon, Eastleigh, Braintree, Leatherhead, Concord R, Hemel H									
Milambo	Mukanya	19	Defender	Farsley Celtic			3		
Wolves (Y), Bradford C (Y), Farsley C, Ossett U (Dual)									

SURNAME	FIRSTNAME	AGE	POSITION	CLUB PLAYED FOR	X	SX	S	Ap	G/Cs
Miles	Sonny	30	Defender	Tonbridge Angels	32			32	
Tonbridge A (Y), Maidstone, Tonbridge A									
Miles	Taylor	24	Midfielder	St Albans City	13	6	2	19	
West Ham (Y), Concord R (L), Concord R, Braintree, Lincoln C, Boston U (L), Concord R (L), Hemel H, Chelmsford, St Albans									
Miley	Cavanagh	25	Midfielder	Eastleigh	42	2		44	2
Jersey, Eastleigh									
Miller	Curtis		Forward	Altrincham		1		1	
Altrincham (Y)									
Miller	Reece	19	Forward	Aldershot Town		1	3	1	
Watford (U18), Aldershot (Y)									
Miller	Sean	25	Forward	Curzon Ashton	20	2		22	7
Chester (Y), Connah's Q, Altrincham, Chester, Droylsden (Dual), Curzon A									
Miller	Tom	29	Defender	AFC Fylde	1	3		4	
Dundalk, Newport C, Lincoln C, Carlisle, Bury, AFC Fylde									
Miller-Rodney	Tyrell	26	Midfielder	Hampton & Richmond Borough	13	8	6	21	
Brentford (Y), Maidenhead (L), Boreham W (L), Maidenhead (L), Hayes & Y, Hampton & R									
Mills	Adam		Midfielder	Braintree Town	9	5		14	4
Needham M (Y), Braintree, Needham M									
Mills	Bobby	19	Midfielder	Hampton & Richmond Borough (L)		4	2	4	
Bromley (Y), Hampton & R (L)									
Mills	Danny	28	Forward	Dulwich Hamlet	33	5	3	38	18
Crawley, Peterborough, Torquay (L), Rushden (L), Histon (L), Kettering (L), Tamworth (L), Kettering (L), Carshalton, Whitehawk, Ebbsfleet, Dartford (L), Welling (L), Dulwich H									
Milnes	Ben	28	Midfielder	Kettering Town	23	4	2	27	1
Boston U, Corby, Kettering									
Milsom	Robert	33	Midfielder	Sutton United	28	4	5	32	2
Brentford, Fulham, Southend (L), TPS (Fin) (L), Aberdeen, Rotherham, Bury (L), Notts Co, Crawley, Notts Co (L), Notts Co, Sutton U									
Ming	Sanchez	30	Forward	Welling United	15	1		16	
				Dartford	11	1	2	12	
Fisher, Welling, Bishop's S, Bromley, Staines, Dulwich H, Welling, Dartford									
Mingoia	Piero	28	Midfielder	Boreham Wood	16	6	16	22	1
Watford (Y) Hayes & Y (L), Accrington, Boreham W (L), Cambridge U, Accrington, Morecambe (L), Boreham W									
Minihan	Sam	26	Defender	Stockport County	34	5	2	39	2
Rochdale, Droylsden U, Loughborough U, Worcester, Stockport									
Minshull	Lee	34	Midfielder	Concord Rangers	6	3	6	9	
Wimbledon, Newport Co (L), Newport Co, Bromley, Leatherhead, Concord R									
Mitford	Tre	25	Forward	Kettering Town	11	8	3	19	5
Leatherhead, Kettering									
Modeste	Ricky	32	Forward	Dover Athletic	22	8		30	5
Chelmsford, Dover, Billericay, Dover									
Mohammed	Zehn	22	Defender	Southport (L)	26	5	6	31	4
Accrington, Southport (L), FC United (L), Southport (L)									
Moke	Adriano	30	Midfielder	York City	36	3		39	1
York (Y), Cambridge U, Tamworth (L), Halifax, Stockport, Macclesfield, Wrexham, Boreham, York									
Molesley	Mark	39	Midfielder	Weymouth			2		
Weymouth (Manager)									
Molyneux	Luke	22	Midfielder	Hartlepool United	6	5	2	11	1
Sunderland (Y), Gateshead (L), Hartlepool (L), Hartlepool									
Monakana	Jeffrey	26	Midfielder	Dulwich Hamlet	24	5	5	29	4
Arsenal, PNE, Colchester (L), Brighton, Crawley (L), Aberdeen (L), Mansfield (L), Carlisle (L), Bristol R (L), Voluntari (Rom),									
Sutton U, Margate (L), Welling (L), Wealdstone (L), Welling, Wealdstone, Dulwich H									
Moncur	Freddy	23	Midfielder	Concord Rangers	1	4	4	5	
Leyton Orient, Bishop's St. (L), Wingate, Kingstonian, East Thurrock, Ebbsfleet, Concord R, Romford									
Monlouis	Kieran	24	Midfielder	Dulwich Hamlet	12	4	5	16	1
AFC Sudbury, St Albans, Hamilton, Hemel H, Dulwich H									
Montague	Liam		Forward	Aldershot Town			2		
Aldershot (Y)									
Montgomery	James	26	Goalkeeper	AFC Fylde	14		4	14	5
Telford, Gateshead, Forest GR, AFC Fylde									

Key: X - Started; SX - Sub on; S - Non-playing Sub; Ap - Total Appearances; G/Cs - Total goals/clean sheets.

SURNAME	FIRSTNAME	AGE	POSITION	CLUB	X	SX	S	Ap	G/Cs
Montrose	Lewis	31	Midfielder	AFC Fylde	11	7	6	18	1

Man City, Wigan, Rochdale (L), Cheltenham (L), Cheltenham (L), Chesterfield (L), Wycombe, Gillingham, Oxford U (L), York , Stockport, AFC Fylde

					X	SX	S	Ap	G/Cs
Mooney	Daniel	20	Forward	Altrincham	9			9	2

Fleetwood (Y), Chorley (L), Chester (L), Altrincham

Mooney	Kelsey	21	Forward	Hereford	12	10	3	22	5

Aston Villa (Y), Cheltenham (L), Hereford

Moore	Deon	21	Defender	Billericay Town (L)	4			4	
				Hemel Hempstead Town	3	5	1	8	

Peterborough (Y), Bristol R, Bath (L), Billericay (L), Hemel H

Moore	Luke	32	Forward	Dorking Wanderers	26	3	1	29	1

Ebbsfleet, Wimbledon, Margate, Dorking W

Moore-Azille	Tarik	24	Defender	Oxford City	18	5	10	23	3

Bishop's S, Margate, St Albans, Hungerford, Oxford C

Moran	Jon	23	Defender	Bradford Park Avenue	8		4	8	

Nantwich, Forest GR, Altrincham (L), Weston (L), Chester, Bradford PA

Morgan	Albie	20	Midfielder	Ebbsfleet United (L)	5			5	1

Charlton (Y), Ebbsfleet (L)

Morgan	David	25	Midfielder	Southport	37		2	37	13

Nottm Forest (Y), Lincoln C (L), Dundee (L), Tamworth (L), Ilkeston, Nuneaton, AFC Fylde, Harrogate, Southport

Morgan	Jamie	22	Defender	Chester	7	5	14	12	1

Nantwich, Chester

Morgan-Smith	Amari	31	Forward	Alfreton Town	34			34	16

Crewe (Y), Stockport, Ilkeston T, Luton, Macclesfield, Kidderminster (L), Kidderminster, Oldham, Cheltenham, York (L), York, Telford, Alfreton

Morley	Stephan	33	Defender	AFC Telford United	9			9	1
				Leamington	25			25	1

Hinckley U, Leamington, Corby, Brackley, Tamworth, Telford, Leamington

Morris	Maliq	19	Forward	Dulwich Hamlet			3		

Dulwich H (Y)

Morrison	Brandon		Midfielder	Darlington		1	3	1	

Darlington

Mouanda	Ursene	21	Midfielder	Blyth Spartans (L)	5	6	5	11	

Monkseaton Acad, Rangers (Y), Kilmarnock, South Shields, Blyth S (L)

Moult	Jake	31	Midfielder	Altrincham	35	1	1	36	5

Plymouth (Y), Kidderminster, Leek, Stafford R, Alfreton, Altrincham

Mountjoy	Ewan		Goalkeeper	Kidderminster Harriers			7		

Kidderminster (Y)

Moyo	Cliff	27	Defender	Kidderminster Harriers	36			36	2

Alfreton, Barrow, Northwich, Drolsden, Trafford, Halifax, Guiseley, Kidderminster

Muir	Niko	27	Forward	Hartlepool United	3	6	8	9	1
				Hemel Hempstead Town (L)	8			8	1
				Hampton & Richmond Borough (L)	5	2		7	3

Grays, Northwood, Hendon, Northwood, Wingate, Northwood, VCD Ath, Northwood, Hendon, Leiston, Hendon, Hartlepool, Hemel H (L), Hampton & RB (L)

Muirhead	Archie		Forward	Hereford			1		

Hereford (Y)

Muitt	Jimmy		Forward	Dorking Wanderers	14	6		20	5

Brighton & HA (Y), Bognor R, Dorking W

Muldoon	Jack	31	Forward	Harrogate Town	40	5		45	16

Worksop, Rochdale, FC Halifax, Lincoln, AFC Fylde, Harrogate

Muldoon	Oliver	25	Midfielder	Chelmsford City	18	2	2	20	1

Charlton, Gillingham (L), Dagenham & R (L), Braintree (L), Gillingham, Maidstone, Chelmsford

Mulhern	Euan (Frank)	23	Forward	Stockport County	16	15	2	31	5
				Boston United (L)	6	3		9	1

Leeds, Southport (L), Huddersfield, Guiseley, Stockport, Boston U (L)

Mullarkey	Toby	24	Defender	Altrincham	15	17	11	32	2

Crewe (Y), Nantwich, Altrincham

Mullen	Damen	31	Defender	Blyth Spartans	20	4	6	24	1

Ashington, Blyth S

Amari Morgan-Smith (Alfreton Town). Photo Bill Wheatcroft.

Perfect tackle from Ashley Palmer (Stockport) on Zumana Bakayogo (Notts County). Photo Keith Clayton.

2019-20 NATIONAL. NORTH & SOUTH PLAYERS   APPEARANCES

SURNAME	FIRSTNAME	AGE	POSITION	CLUB	X	SX	S	Ap	G/Cs
Mullings	Shamir	26	Forward	Aldershot Town	17	8	1	25	2
				Dulwich Hamlet (L)	9	4		13	4

Southend (Y), Thurrock (L), Tilbury (L), Harlow (L), Bromley, Thamesmead (L), Havant & W, Chelmsford, Forest Green, Macclesfield, Maidstone, Dagenham & R (L), Macclesfield, Aldershot, Dulwich H (L)

SURNAME	FIRSTNAME	AGE	POSITION	CLUB	X	SX	S	Ap	G/Cs
Mundle-Smith	Jayden	20	Defender	Maidenhead United (L)	4	1		5	1

Fulham (Y), Maidenhead (L)

SURNAME	FIRSTNAME	AGE	POSITION	CLUB	X	SX	S	Ap	G/Cs
Munns	Jack	26	Midfielder	Dover Athletic	29	4	6	33	

Leyton O, Tottenham, Aldershot, Charlton, Cheltenham, Hartlepool, Dagenham & R, Dover

SURNAME	FIRSTNAME	AGE	POSITION	CLUB	X	SX	S	Ap	G/Cs
Murombedzi	Shepherd	25	Midfielder	Brackley Town	31	1	3	32	

Reading, Torquay, Nuneaton, Hayes & Y, Solihull M, Chester, Brackley

SURNAME	FIRSTNAME	AGE	POSITION	CLUB	X	SX	S	Ap	G/Cs
Murphy	Jordan	24	Forward	Leamington (L)	8	6	6	14	1

Stourbridge, Walsall, Worcester (L), Kidderminster (L), Worcester (L), Worcester (L), Telford U, Solihull, Leamington (L), Leamington (L)

SURNAME	FIRSTNAME	AGE	POSITION	CLUB	X	SX	S	Ap	G/Cs
Murphy	Rhys	29	Forward	Yeovil Town	31	3	2	34	20

Arsenal, Brentford (L), Preston (L), Dagenham & R, Oldham, Crawley (L), AFC Wimbledon (L), Forest Green, York (L), Crawley (L), Torquay (L), Gillingham, Chelmsford, Yeovil

SURNAME	FIRSTNAME	AGE	POSITION	CLUB	X	SX	S	Ap	G/Cs
Murray	Cameron	25	Midfielder	Weymouth	6	16	2	22	1

York (Y), Scarborough, FC United, Stalybridge, Dorchester, Weymouth

SURNAME	FIRSTNAME	AGE	POSITION	CLUB	X	SX	S	Ap	G/Cs
Murray	Iwan	19	Forward	Chester			4	3	4

Rhyl, Chester, Warrington (L)

SURNAME	FIRSTNAME	AGE	POSITION	CLUB	X	SX	S	Ap	G/Cs
Murrell-Williamson	Rhys	26	Midfielder	St Albans City	4	4	3	8	2
				Braintree Town	9	5	1	14	3

Sutton U, Harrow, Hayes & Y, Dulwich, Boreham W, Dulwich, Welling (L), St Albans, Hampton & R, Billericay, Woking, St Albans, Braintree

SURNAME	FIRSTNAME	AGE	POSITION	CLUB	X	SX	S	Ap	G/Cs
Murtagh	Keiran	31	Midfielder	Boreham Wood	35			35	1

Charlton, Fisher, Yeovil, Wycombe, Cambridge U, Macclesfield, Mansfield, Woking (L), Woking, Boreham W

SURNAME	FIRSTNAME	AGE	POSITION	CLUB	X	SX	S	Ap	G/Cs
Musonda	Frankie	22	Midfielder	St Albans City (L)	13			13	1

Luton (Y), Braintree (L), Oxford C (L), Oxford C (L) Hemel H (L), St Albans (L)

SURNAME	FIRSTNAME	AGE	POSITION	CLUB	X	SX	S	Ap	G/Cs
Mussa	Gift		Midfielder	Leamington	2	6	6	8	

Coventry U, Leamington, Bromsgrove S

SURNAME	FIRSTNAME	AGE	POSITION	CLUB	X	SX	S	Ap	G/Cs
Myles	Ellis	27	Defender	Brackley Town	39			39	1

Brackley, Rugby T, Stamford, Corby, Brackley

SURNAME	FIRSTNAME	AGE	POSITION	CLUB	X	SX	S	Ap	G/Cs
Myrie-Williams	Jennison	32	Midfielder	Gloucester City	7	6	1	13	

Bristol C, Cheltenham (L), Tranmere (L), Cheltenham (L), Carlisle (L), Hereford (L), Dundee Utd, St Johnstone, Stevenage, Port Vale (L), Port Vale, Scunthorpe, Tranmere (L), Sligo Rovers, Newport Co, Torquay, Hereford, Weston, Gloucester

SURNAME	FIRSTNAME	AGE	POSITION	CLUB	X	SX	S	Ap	G/Cs
N'Gala	Bondz	30	Defender	Ebbsfleet United	3	1	2	4	

West Ham, Weymouth (L), MK Dons (L), Scunthorpe (L), Plymouth (L), Plymouth, Yeovil, Stevenage, Barnet (L), Portsmouth, Barnet, Eastleigh, Dover, Dagenham & R, Leyton O (L), Crawley, Ebbsfleet,

SURNAME	FIRSTNAME	AGE	POSITION	CLUB	X	SX	S	Ap	G/Cs
N'Gwatala	Elton	27	Midfielder	AFC Fylde		4	6	4	
				Chester	5	5	8	10	

Beauvais (Y) (Fra), Chambly, Kidderminster, Dundee, AFC Fylde, Chester

SURNAME	FIRSTNAME	AGE	POSITION	CLUB	X	SX	S	Ap	G/Cs
Nabay	Foday	21	Midfielder	Gloucester City	1			1	

Birmingham (Y), Fulham (Y), Nuneaton, Stratford T, Gloucester

SURNAME	FIRSTNAME	AGE	POSITION	CLUB	X	SX	S	Ap	G/Cs
Nabi	Samir	23	Midfielder	Kidderminster Harriers		1	1	1	

WBA (Y), Delhi Dynamos, Carlisle, Torquay, Halesowen (L), Kidderminster

SURNAME	FIRSTNAME	AGE	POSITION	CLUB	X	SX	S	Ap	G/Cs
Najia	Tarek	18	Goalkeeper	Bromley				20	

Dagenham & R (Y), Bromley (L), Bromley

SURNAME	FIRSTNAME	AGE	POSITION	CLUB	X	SX	S	Ap	G/Cs
Nash	Jamie		Forward	Wrexham				2	

Wrexham (Y)

SURNAME	FIRSTNAME	AGE	POSITION	CLUB	X	SX	S	Ap	G/Cs
Nash	Liam	24	Forward	Hemel Hempstead Town	16	2		18	9
				Dartford	4	4	1	8	2

Gillingham, Leatherhead (L), Dulwich (L), Concord R (L), Cork, Hemel H, Dartford

SURNAME	FIRSTNAME	AGE	POSITION	CLUB	X	SX	S	Ap	G/Cs
Nasha	Amos	24	Midfielder	Dartford	5	1		6	

West Ham (Y), Dover, Concord R, Chelmsford, East Thurrock, Dartford

SURNAME	FIRSTNAME	AGE	POSITION	CLUB	X	SX	S	Ap	G/Cs
Naylor	Martyn	42	Defender	Leamington				2	

TNS, Telford, Rhyl, Telford, Stafford R, Worcester, Rushall, Leamington

SURNAME	FIRSTNAME	AGE	POSITION	CLUB	X	SX	S	Ap	G/Cs
Ndaba	Corrie	20	Midfielder	Hemel Hempstead Town (L)	1			1	
				Chelmsford City (L)			6		

Ipswich (Y), Hemel H (L), Chelmsford (L)

SURNAME	FIRSTNAME	AGE	POSITION	CLUB	X	SX	S	Ap	G/Cs
Nditi	Roberto	19	Midfielder	Eastbourne Borough (L)	4	2		6	

Reading (Y), Eastbourne B (L)

APPEARANCES

SURNAME	FIRSTNAME	AGE	POSITION	CLUB PLAYED FOR	X	SX	S	Ap	G/Cs
Ndlovu	Lee		Forward	Brackley Town	38			38	20
Holbeach U, Grantham, Ilkeston, Brackley									
Nearney	Josh	24	Defender	Blyth Spartans		1	1	1	
Middlesbrough (Y), Hartlepool, Darlington (L), Whitby T (L), Whitley B (L), Whitley B, Whitby T, Whitley B, North Shields, Blyth S									
Neild	James	18	Defender	Curzon Ashton			1		
Rochdale (Y), Curzon A									
Neligwa	David		Forward	Kidderminster Harriers		1	3	1	
Nantwich, Eccleshall, Kidderminster									
Nelson	Michael	40	Defender	Gateshead	11	1	11	12	1
Leek, Spennymoor, Bishop A, Bury, Hartlepool, Norwich, Scunthorpe, Kilmarnock, Bradford, Hibernian, Cambridge U, Barnet, Chesterfield, Gateshead									
Nelson	Stuart	38	Goalkeeper	Yeovil Town	26	1	1	27	7
Brentford, Leyton O, Norwich, Aberdeen, Notts Co, Gillingham, Yeovil									
Nemane	Aaron	22	Midfielder	Torquay United	8	3	2	11	
Man City (Y), Rangers (L), Go Ahead Eagles (Hol), Tubize (Ger), Torquay									
Nepomuceno	Gevaro	27	Forward	Chesterfield	18			18	1
Den Bosch (Hol), Fortuna, Petrolul (Rom), Maritimo (Por), Famalicao (L), Oldham, Chesterfield									
Nesbitt	Ryan		Forward	Solihull Moors			1		
Solihull M (Y)									
Neufville	Josh	20	Midfielder	Solihull Moors (L)	1	10	2	11	
				Woking (L)	3	5	1	8	
Luton (Y), Solihull M (L), Woking (L)									
Newall	Nathan	18	Defender	Guiseley		3	12	3	
Guiseley (Y)									
Newby	Alex	24	Forward	Chorley	31	8	1	39	7
Barrow (Y), Kendal (L), Clitheroe, Chorley									
Newby	Elliott	24	Midfielder	Chorley	17	12	11	29	1
Bolton (Y), Barrow, Burscough (L), Altrincham (L), Telford, Chorley									
Newell	George	23	Forward	Southport	6	4	2	10	5
Bolton (Y), AFC Fylde (L), Motherwell, Albion R (L), Southport									
Newey	Ben		Goalkeeper	Leamington			7		
Leamington (Y)									
Newton	Sean	31	Defender	York City	40			40	5
Droylsden, Barrow, Telford, Stockport (L), Stockport, Lincoln C, Notts Co (L), Wrexham, York (L), York									
Ngalo	Jordan	21	Midfielder	Weymouth	20	8	3	28	
Poole, Blackfield & L, Weymouth, Blackfield & L (L)									
Nicell	Callum	20	Midfielder	Farsley Celtic			1		
Leeds (Y), Farsley C									
Nicholls	Alex	32	Forward	Solihull Moors	2	4	1	6	1
Walsall, Northampton, Exeter (Lx2), Exeter, Barnet, Dundee U (L), Crewe, Solihull M									
Nicholson	Alex	26	Defender	Gateshead	36			36	2
PNE (Y), Chorley (L), Blyth S, South Shields, Blyth S, Gateshead									
Nicholson	Brad	21	Defender	Guiseley	35			35	2
Guiseley									
Nicholson	Jodan	26	Midfielder	Hereford	20	5	2	25	4
				Boston United		2		2	
Histon, Peterborough, Nuneaton (L), Nuneaton (L), Barnet, Brackley (L), Darlington, Hereford, Boston U									
Nicholson	Shay		Forward	Leamington			1		
Leamington (Y)									
Nicholson	Tom	32	Goalkeeper	Bradford Park Avenue	9		4	9	1
Scarborough, Garforth, Hull City, North Ferriby, Halifax, Alfreton, Bradford PA									
Nisbet	Mark	33	Defender	Slough Town	14	3	4	17	
Maidenhead, Slough									
Nketia	Joel		Defender	Hemel Hempstead Town			1		
Hemel H (Y)									
Noble	David	38	Midfielder	St Albans City	24	7	5	31	1
Bristol C, Yeovil (L), Exeter, Rotherham, Cheltenham (L), Oldham, Exeter (L), Exeter, St Albans									
Noble	Lee	31	Midfielder	Dartford	11	3	1	14	
Dartford									

Key: X - Started; SX - Sub on; S - Non-playing Sub; Ap - Total Appearances; G/Cs - Total goals/clean sheets.

SURNAME	FIRSTNAME	AGE	POSITION	CLUB	X	SX	S	Ap	G/Cs
Noble	Liam	29	Midfielder	Hartlepool United	10	2	1	12	3
				Sunderland (Y), Carlisle (L), Carlisle (L), Carlisle, Notts Co, Forest GR, Notts Co, Hartlepool					
Noel-Williams	Dejon	21	Forward	Wealdstone	2	5	2	7	3
				Billericay Town	6	2	1	8	1
				Oxford U (Y), Aylesbury U (L), North Leigh (L), Abingdon U (L), Chesham (L), Slough (L), Gloucester (L), Wealdstone, Hayes & Y (L), Billericay					
Nolan	Liam	25	Midfielder	FC Halifax Town	21	6	8	27	2
				Crewe (Y), Southport, Accrington, Salford (L), FC Halifax					
Noon	Mark	36	Midfielder	Brackley Town			10		
				Coventry (Y), Tamworth, Nuneaton, Brackley					
Norman	Jack		Midfielder	Kettering Town			2		
				Kettering (Y)					
Nortey	Nortei	25	Midfielder	Chorley	22	5	2	27	
				Chelsea, Welling, Wrexham, Solihull M, Dover, Chorley					
North	Jonathan	29	Goalkeeper	Wealdstone	2	1	10	3	
				Wealdstone, Chesham (L)					
Nouble	Joel	24	Forward	Concord Rangers	31	2	1	33	10
				Chelsea (Y), Millwall (Y), Dagenham & R (Y), Thurrock (L), Grays (L), Welling (L), St Albans (L), Bishop's S, Haringey B, Concord R					
Nowakowski	Adam	32	Midfielder	Bradford Park Avenue	19	2		21	1
				Harrogate T, Darlington, Bradford PA (L), Bradford PA					
Nti	Daniel	26	Forward	Kettering Town	32	1		33	6
				Worcester, York, Halifax (L), Kidderminster, Nuneaton, Brackley, Kettering					
Nunn	Ben	30	Defender	Billericay Town	18	8	8	26	
				Boston, Chelmsford, Boreham W (L), Boreham W, St Albans (L), Dagenham & R, Billericay					
Nwabuokei	Solomon	24	Midfielder	St Albans City	27	3	3	30	2
				Biggleswade, St Albans					
Nwachuku	Nnamdi	25	Forward	Welling United	1		1	1	
				Reading (Y), Colchester (Y), Bishop's S (L), Coggeshall, Welling					
Nyammey	Kingston		Midfielder	Oxford City		1		1	
				Oxford C (Y)					
O'Brien	Jim	32	Midfielder	Notts County	17	5	2	22	2
				Motherwell, Barnsley, Coventry, Scunthorpe, Shrewsbury, Ross Co (L), Ross Co, Bradford C, Notts Co					
O'Brien	Liam	28	Goalkeeper	Yeovil Town	7		3	7	4
				Portsmouth, Eastbourne B, Barnet, Hastings U (L), Brentford, Dagenham & R, Portsmouth, Coventry, Yeovil					
O'Connor	Aaron	36	Forward	Kettering Town	17	3	5	20	3
				Ilkeston T, Scunthorpe, Nuneaton B, Ilkeston T, Gresley, Grays, Mansfield, Rushden & D, Luton, Newport, Forest GR, Stevenage (L), Stevenage, Kettering					
O'Connor	Jack	20	Defender	Kettering Town			6		
				Kettering (Y)					
O'Connor	James	35	Defender	Kidderminster Harriers			1		
				Aston Villa (Y), Port Vale (L), Bournemouth, Doncaster, Derby, Bristol C (L), Walsall, Kidderminster					
O'Donnell	Jonathan	28	Midfielder	Gateshead	24	4	1	28	8
				Luton, Hyde (L), Gateshead (L), Gateshead					
O'Donoghue	Michael	24	Defender	Concord Rangers	8	3	4	11	
				Reading (Y), Leyton O (Y), Colchester (Y), Haringey B, Concord R					
O'Dwyer	Oliver	23	Defender	Aldershot Town	1	1	1	2	
				Crystal Palace (Y), Aldershot					
O'Hara	Jamie	33	Midfielder	Billericay Town		5	6	5	
				Tottenham (Y), Chesterfield (L), Millwall (L), Portsmouth (L), Wolves (L), Wolves, Blackpool, Fulham, Gillingham, Billericay					
O'Keefe	Charley	20	Defender	Braintree Town	8	1	1	9	1
				Stevenage, Wingate & F, Braintree					
O'Keefe	Josh	31	Midfielder	Chorley	17	13	8	30	1
				Walsall, Lincoln C, Southport, Hereford, Kidderminster, Telford (L), Chester (L), Altrincham, Chorley					
O'Neill	Tyrone	20	Forward	Darlington (L)	14	3		17	
				Middlesbrough (Y), Hartlepool (L), Darlington (L)					
O'Sullivan	Jerry		Defender	Dorking Wanderers	1	7	17	8	
				South Park, Dorking W					
O'Sullivan	Tommy	25	Midfielder	Hereford	19	7	11	26	2
				Cardiff, Port Vale (L), Newport Co (Lx2), Colchester, Torquay (L), Hereford					

SURNAME	FIRSTNAME	AGE	POSITION	CLUB PLAYED FOR	X	SX	S	Ap	G/Cs
Oastler	Joe	29	Defender	Oxford City	36			36	1
QPR (Y), Torquay (L), Torquay, Aldershot, Gosport B, Oxford C									
Obileye	Ayo	25	Defender	Ebbsfleet United	23	9	10	32	4
Sheffield Wed, Dagenham & Red (L), Dagenham & Red (L), Eastleigh, Dover (L), Maidenhead, Ebbsfleet									
Ockerby	Joe		Defender	Bradford Park Avenue			1		
Bradford PA (Y)									
Ocran	Brandan	22	Forward	Braintree Town	7	4	4	11	
Barnet (Y), Colchester (Y), Billericay T, Northwood, Needham M, Merstham, Braintree									
Odametey	Harold	27	Midfielder	Dagenham & Redbridge	3	3		6	
Hampton & R, Maidenhead, Dagenham & R									
Odaudu	Samuel		Defender	Dartford			5		
Dartford (Y)									
Odelusi	Sanmi	27	Forward	FC Halifax Town		2	2	2	
Bolton (Y), MK Dons (L), Coventry (L), Wigan, Rochdale (L), Blackpool (L), Colchester, Cheltenham, FC Halifax									
Odimayo	Akinwale Joseph	20	Defender	Hungerford Town (L)	9			9	
Reading (Y), Hungerford (L)									
Odubade	Yemi	32	Forward	Weymouth	20	14	5	34	10
Oxford U, Stevenage, Newport Co, Gateshead, Forest GR (L), Eastleigh, Woking (L), Maidstone, Eastbourne B, Weymouth									
Odusina	Oluwarotimi Mark	20	Defender	Hartlepool United (L)	8			8	
Norwich (Y), AFC Fylde (L), Hartlepool (L)									
Ofori-Twumasi	Nathan	30	Defender	Maidenhead United	34	1	3	35	
Chelsea, Dagenham & R (L), Peterborough, Northampton (L), Northampton, Yeovil, Newport Co, Maidstone, Maidenhead									
Ogie	Shadrach	18	Defender	Dover Athletic (L)	7		1	7	1
Leyton Orient (Y), Dover (L)									
Ogle	Reagan	21	Defender	Southport (L)	24	2	1	26	
Accrington (Y), Stoke U23 (L), Wealdstone (L), Southport (L), Southport (L)									
Ohman	Patrik		Goalkeeper	Hungerford Town	3		1	3	1
Upsala (Swe), Egham, Chelmsford, Carshalton, Hendon, Walton C, Hungerford									
Ojo	Daniel	19	Defender	Yeovil Town		1	3	1	
Yeovil (Y)									
Okimo	Jerome	32	Defender	Wealdstone	38			38	3
Stevenage, Braintree, Wealdstone									
Okojie	Shaun		Forward	Concord Rangers	3	2	2	5	
Aldershot, Wealdstone (L), Eastbourne (L), Eastbourne, Leatherhead, Concord R									
Okosieme	Ejiro	27	Defender	Welling United	15	1	7	16	
Bishop's St, Macclesfield, Dover, Braintree, Welling									
Okoye	Marc-Anthony		Defender	Bromley	9	3	3	12	
Bromley, Merstham, Dulwich, Erith & Bel, Braintree, Bromley									
Olaofe	Isaac		Midfielder	Sutton United (L)	4	1		5	1
Millwall (Y), Sutton U (L)									
Oldaker	Darren	21	Midfielder	Billericay Town	2	1	1	3	
QPR (Y), Gillingham, Billericay T									
Oliver	Charlie	22	Defender	Southport	9	9	1	18	
Man City (Y), Fleetwood (L), Brentford B (L), Southport									
Oliver	Connor	26	Midfielder	Gateshead	18	6	6	24	3
Sunderland (Y), Hartlepool (L), Blackpool (L), Morecambe (L), North Ferriby, Halifax, Blyth S, Gateshead									
Olley	Greg	24	Midfielder	Gateshead	36			36	7
Newcastle (Y), Hull (Y), Gateshead									
Olomowewe	Taofiq	23	Defender	Hungerford Town	15			15	1
				Chelmsford City	7	1		8	
Wealdstone, Hungerford, Chelmsford									
Olosemu	Daniel			Eastbourne Borough		1		1	
Royston, Eastbourne B									
Olufemi	Tosin	26	Midfielder	Concord Rangers	38			38	1
Colchester (Y), Hayes & Y, Haringey B, Concord R									
Olumuyiwa	Adeoye		Defender	Weymouth	5	2	8	7	
New Orleans Jesters, Team Solent, Blackfield & L, Weymouth									
Olutade	Ibrahim	21	Forward	Maidstone United		6	4	6	
Hanwell, Leatherhead, Maidstone, Leatherhead (L)									

Key: X - Started; SX - Sub on; S - Non-playing Sub; Ap - Total Appearances; G/Cs - Total goals/clean sheets.

SURNAME	FIRSTNAME	AGE	POSITION	CLUB	X	SX	S	Ap	G/Cs
Omotayo	Gold	26	Forward	Yeovil Town	11	6	6	17	2

FC Zurich (Y), FC Schlieren, FC Wettswil, Whitehawk, Bury, Maidstone (L), Yeovil

| Omozusi | Elliot Junior | 31 | Defender | Chelmsford City | 26 | 1 | 1 | 27 | |

Fulham (Y), Norwich (L), Charlton (L), Leyton O, Cambridge U, Whitehawk, Chelmsford

| Onariase | Emmanuel | 23 | Defender | Dagenham & Redbridge | 30 | 2 | 1 | 32 | 1 |

West Ham (Y), Brentford, Cheltenham (L), Rotherham, Cheltenham (L), Dagenham & R (L), Dagenham & R

| Onen | Jayden | 19 | Midfielder | Bromley (L) | | 1 | 2 | 1 | |

Arsenal (Y), Brighton (Y), Brentford (Y), Bromley (L)

| Onyemah | Mark | 24 | Defender | Dartford | 2 | 1 | | 3 | |

Luton, Dartford (L), Concord R, Dartford

| Orlando-Young | Rod | 25 | Midfielder | Bradford Park Avenue | | 1 | 3 | 1 | |

Norwich (Y), Bishop's S (L), Welling, Bishop's S (L), Havant & W, Shaw Lane, Bradford PA

| Orlu | Richard | 31 | Defender | Dulwich Hamlet | 25 | | 4 | 25 | 2 |

Staines, Farnborough, Canvey I, Dover, Woking, Welling, Hampton & R (L), Dulwich H

| Ormson | Ian | 26 | Goalkeeper | Stockport County | 1 | | 41 | 1 | |

Stockport (Y)

| Orrell | Jake | 22 | Forward | Blyth Spartans | 5 | 5 | 2 | 10 | |

Sunderland (Y), Gateshead, Chesterfield, Hartlepool, Spennymoor, Newcastle Benfield, Blyth S

| Orsi-Dadamo | Danilo | | Forward | Hampton & Richmond Borough | 34 | 4 | 1 | 38 | 15 |

East Thurrock, Hungerford, Hampton & R

| Osborn | Alex | 26 | Forward | Chelmsford City | 1 | 7 | 4 | 8 | |

Grays, Dag & Red, Thurrock (L), Chelmsford (L), Billericay, Ebbsfleet, Hayes & Y (L), Maidstone (L), Concord R (L), Whitehawk (L), Margate, Whitehawk, Hemel H, East Thurrock, Chelmsford

| Osborne | Elliot | 24 | Midfielder | Stockport County | 33 | 9 | | 42 | 9 |

Nantwich, Fleetwood, Tranmere (L), Stockport (L), Southport, Stockport (L), Stockport

| Osborne | Harry | 26 | Defender | Braintree Town | 6 | 1 | | 7 | |

Charlton (Y), Sutton U (L), Sutton U (L), Welling (L), Welling, Hemel H, Bishop's S, Assyriska (Swe), Braintree, Kingstonian

| Osborne | Jamey | 28 | Midfielder | Solihull Moors | 28 | 1 | 1 | 29 | |

Hednesford, Ringmer (L), Redditch, Solihull M, Grimsby, Solihull M (L), Solihull M

| Osborne | Samuel | 20 | Midfielder | Notts County | 12 | 4 | 15 | 16 | 3 |

Notts Co (Y)

| Osei-Bonsu | Andrew | 21 | Midfielder | Billericay Town | | 3 | 3 | 3 | |

MK Dons (Y), Corby (L), Wealdstone, Larne (NI), Billericay

| Oseyemi | Joseph | | Defender | Tonbridge Angels | | | 3 | | |

Banbury U, Tonbridge A

| Osho | Gabriel | 21 | Defender | Yeovil Town (L) | 6 | 1 | 1 | 7 | |

Reading (Yth), Maidenhead (L), Aldershot (L), Yeovil (L)

| Ossai | Tariq | 20 | Defender | Chippenham Town | 5 | 1 | 3 | 6 | 2 |

Chippenham

| Oswell | Jason | 27 | Forward | Wrexham | 8 | 12 | 8 | 20 | 2 |

Crewe (Y), Rhyl (L), Inverness, Nantwich, APIA Leichhardt (Aus), Rhyl, Airbus, Newtown, Stockport, Morecambe, Wrexham

| Ovenden | Rhyle | 21 | Midfielder | Tonbridge Angels | 2 | 4 | 4 | 6 | |

Watford (Y), Hemel H, Whitehawk, Worthing, Tonbridge A

| Overton | Ben | | Midfielder | Eastbourne Borough | | 4 | 2 | 4 | |

Eastbourne B (Y)

| Owen-Evans | Tom | 23 | Midfielder | Hereford | 22 | 6 | 4 | 28 | 4 |
| | | | | Chippenham Town (L) | 8 | | | 8 | 2 |

Newport Co (Y), Gloucester (L), Truro (L), Falkirk, Hereford, Chippenham (L)

| Owusu | Nana | 24 | Defender | Oxford City | 16 | 15 | 6 | 31 | 10 |

Tranmere, Maidenhead, Oxford C

| Oxborough | Aston | 22 | Goalkeeper | Wealdstone (L) | 27 | | | 27 | 10 |

Norwich (Y), Wealdstone (L)

| Oxlade-Chamberlain | Christian | 21 | Midfielder | Notts County | 1 | | | 1 | |

Portsmouth (Y), Eastbourne B (L), Oxford C (Lx2), Notts Co

| Oyibo | Jude | | Forward | Alfreton Town | 2 | 4 | 1 | 6 | |

Glossop NE, Buxton, Alfreton

APPEARANCES

SURNAME	FIRSTNAME	AGE	POSITION	CLUB PLAYED FOR	X	SX	S	Ap	G/Cs
Oyinsan	Josh	25	Forward	Welling United	3	6	5	9	1
				St Albans City		5	2	5	
				Braintree Town	5			5	1
Bromley, Cambridge C, Welling, St Albans, Braintree, Royston									
Palmer	Ashley	27	Defender	Stockport County	41			41	6
Scunthorpe, Southport (L), Droylsden, Buxton, North Ferriby, Guiseley, Stockport									
Palmer	Harry	25	Goalkeeper	Ebbsfleet United	6		33	6	1
Braintree, Lewes, Haringey B, Dorking W, Brightlingsea R, AFC Hornchurch, Canvey I, Ebbsfleet									
Palmer	Tom	20	Goalkeeper	Kidderminster Harriers	6		25	6	1
Kidderminster (Y)									
Panayiotou	Harrison (Harry)	25	Forward	Aldershot Town	18	12	7	30	4
Leicester, Port Vale (L), Raith (L), Barrow, Salford City (L), Nuneaton, Aittitos (Gre), Aldershot									
Papple	Jordi			Braintree Town			5		
Braintree (Y)									
Pardington	James	19	Goalkeeper	Bath City (L)	2		3	2	1
Wolves (Y), Bath (L)									
Parker	Joe	25	Forward	Gloucester City	24	3		27	5
				Leamington	6	1		7	1
Gloucester, Newport Co, Gloucester (L), Gloucester (Lx2), Gloucester, Leamington									
Parkes	Jordan	30	Midfielder	Billericay Town	13	4		17	4
Watford (Y), Brentford, Barnet, Farnborough (L), Chelmsford, Hemel H, Ebbsfleet, Hemel H, Billericay T, King's L									
Parkin	Luke	24	Forward	Farsley Celtic	14	15	6	29	2
Leeds (Y), Guiseley (L), Gainsborough, Brighouse, Farsley C									
Parry	Andrew	28	Defender	Southport	5	4	12	9	
Kettering, Radcliffe, Southport, Luton, Telford (L), Southport (L), Altrincham (L), Barrow (L), Barrow, Southport									
Parry	Immanuel (Manny)	26	Defender	Woking	17	2	9	19	1
Millwall, Stoke, Maidenhead (L), Nuneaton T (L), Weston-S-M (L), Worcester (L), Grays Ath, Maidstone, Margate, Braintree,									
Dover, Boreham W, Woking									
Parry	Lewis		Midfielder	Wrexham			3		
Wrexham (Y)									
Parselle	Kieran	23	Defender	Chippenham Town	39	1		40	5
Newport Co, Salisbury (L), Gloucester, Chippenham									
Parter	Jack	26	Defender	Tonbridge Angels	24	1	3	25	1
Gillingham (Y), Ramsgate (L), Whitstable, Tonbridge A, Kingstonian (L),									
Partington	Joe	30	Midfielder	Eastleigh	39	1	1	40	1
Bournemouth (Y), Aldershot (L), Eastleigh (L), Eastleigh, Bristol R, Eastleigh									
Passley	Josh	25	Defender	Dover Athletic	31			31	
Fulham, Shrewsbury (L), Portsmouth (L), Dagenham & R, Whitehawk, Dover									
Patrick	Omari	24	Midfielder	Wrexham (L)	7	3	1	10	5
Kidderminster, Barnsley, Bradford C, Yeovil (L), Wrexham (L)									
Pattison	Matthew	33	Midfielder	Gateshead		2	3	2	
Newcastle U (Y), Norwich (L), Norwich, Mamelodi S (SA), Santos, Bidvest Wits, Gateshead, South Shields, Gateshead									
Paul	Christopher	22	Midfielder	Havant & Waterlooville	3	14	17	17	1
				Hampton & Richmond Borough (L)	2	1	1	3	
Tottenham (Y), QPR (Y), Havant & W, Hampton & R (L)									
Paul-Jones	Ty-Rhys		Midfielder	Oxford City	1	1	2	2	
Oxford C (Y)									
Paulat-Brigg	Christian	26	Goalkeeper	Woking			7		
Leeds (Y), Silsden, Albion Sp, Eccleshill, Clitheroe, Molesey, Woking, Hampton & R (L)									
Paulin	George		Goalkeeper	Hemel Hempstead Town			1		
Hemel H (Y)									
Pavey	Alfie	24	Forward	Dover Athletic	6	4		10	3
				Barnet	5	6		11	
Maidstone, Millwall (Y), Barnet (L), Aldershot (L), Bromley (L), Hampton & R (L), Dartford (L), Welling, Dartford, Havant & W,									
Dover, Barnet									
Paxman	Jack	26	Midfielder	Billericay Town	20	12	3	32	2
Maidstone, East Thurrock (L), Billericay									
Payne	Alfie	20	Midfielder	King's Lynn Town (L)	14	9	17	23	3
Norwich (Y), King's Lynn (L)									

Key: X - Started; SX - Sub on; S - Non-playing Sub; Ap - Total Appearances; G/Cs - Total goals/clean sheets.

SURNAME	FIRSTNAME	AGE	POSITION	CLUB	X	SX	S	Ap	G/Cs
Payne	Jack	28	Midfielder	Eastleigh	45			45	1
Gillingham, Peterborough (L), Peterborough, Leyton Orient (L), Blackpool, Ebbsfleet, Eastleigh (L), Eastleigh									
Payne	Josh	29	Midfielder	Ebbsfleet United (L)	26			26	2
Portsmouth (Y), Southampton (Y), West Ham (Y), Cheltenham (L), Colchester (L), Wycombe (L), Doncaster, Oxford U (L), Oxford U, Aldershot (L), Aldershot, Woking, Eastleigh, Crawley, Ebbsfleet (L)									
Pearce	Bradley	21	Defender	Hampton & Richmond Borough (L)	5		2	5	
				Sutton United			1		
Sutton U (Y), Hampton & R (L)									
Pearson	Dale	25	Forward	Blyth Spartans	2			2	
North Shields, Blyth S									
Pearson	Sam	18	Midfielder	Bath City (L)	19	3		22	2
Bristol C (Y), Bath (L), Bath (L)									
Pearson	Shaun	31	Defender	Wrexham	34			34	
Grimsby, Wrexham									
Peers	Tom	24	Forward	Altrincham	15	18	5	33	8
Chester (Y), Salford (L), Hednesford (L), Hednesford, Telford, Nantwich, Altrincham, FC United, Altrincham									
Penfold	Morgan	21	Midfielder	Barrow	2	3	9	5	1
Peterborough (Y), Boston U (L), Barrow									
Peniket	Richard	27	Forward	Kidderminster Harriers	16	6		22	2
Fulham, Hereford (L), Kidderminster (L), Telford (L), Tamworth, Halifax, Telford (L), Gateshead, Alfreton, Kidderminster									
Pennell	Luke	24	Defender	Maidstone United	9	1	12	10	
				Gloucester City	7			7	
MK Dons, Rushden, Banbury United, Wolverton, Dunstable, Dagenham & R, Maidstone, Gloucester									
Penny	Alex	23	Defender	Boston United	11	3		14	
				Kidderminster Harriers	2			2	
Stourbridge, Hinckley, Nuneaton, Peterborough, Hamilton, Boston U, Kidderminster									
Pentney	Carl	30	Goalkeeper	Chelmsford City	18			18	3
Leicester, York (Lx2) Ilkeston (L), Woking (L), Colchester, Bath (L), Hayes & Yeading (L), Chelmsford, Braintree, Maidenhead, Chelmsford									
Phillips	Daniel	19	Midfielder	Hemel Hempstead Town (L)	5			5	1
Watford (Y), Hemel H (L)									
Phillips	Harry	22	Midfielder	Billericay Town		1	2	1	
Southend, Billericay									
Phillips	Michael	22	Midfielder	Wealdstone	35	2		37	4
Crystal Palace, Maidstone, Wealdstone									
Philliskirk	Danny	29	Midfielder	AFC Fylde	33	5	6	38	2
Chelsea, Oxford U (L), Sheffield U (L), Sheffield U, Oxford U (L), Coventry, Oldham, Blackpool, AFC Fylde									
Philpott	Charlie		Goalkeeper	Eastleigh			1		
Eastleigh (Y)									
Philpott	Isaac	25	Defender	Dorking Wanderers	33	5		38	1
Sutton U, Cardiff M Uni, Dorking W									
Phipps	Harry	21	Midfielder	Dagenham & Redbridge	6	3	5	9	
Margate, Maidstone, Welling (L), East Thurrock (L), Dagenham & R									
Piggott	Joe	20	Forward	Stockport County (L)	1	1		2	1
Rochdale (Y), Dundee Utd, Warrington, Wigan, Morecambe (L), Altrincham (L), Stockport (L)									
Platt	Matthew	22	Defender	Barrow (L)	31		1	31	
Blackburn (Y), Barrow (L), Accrington, Southport (L), Barrow (L)									
Platt	Richard		Defender	Welling United			1		
Anderlecht (Y), AFC Rushden & D, Banbury U, North L, Kings Langley, Bedford T, Redditch U, Gloucester, Hednesford, Chesham U, Bedworth T, Welling, Stratford									
Platt	Tom	26	Midfielder	Boston United	39		1	39	2
York (Y), Halifax (L), Harrogate, Alfreton, Boston U									
Poku	Godfrey	29	Midfielder	Woking	19	8	5	27	
Luton (Y), St Albans (L), Southport (L), Mansfield, Southport (L), Alfreton (L), Telford (L), Woking, Havant & W (L), Oxford C, Wealdstone, Woking									
Poleon	Dominic	26	Forward	Dover Athletic (L)	3	3		6	1
Leeds (Y), Bury (L), Sheff Utd (L), Oldham, Wimbledon, Bradford C, Crawley, Newport C, Dover (L)									
Pollock	Aron	22	Defender	Concord Rangers	35	3	2	38	7
Leyton Orient, Wingate (L), Wealdstone (L), Leatherhead (L), Leatherhead, Concord R									

SURNAME	FIRSTNAME	AGE	POSITION	CLUB PLAYED FOR	X	SX	S	Ap	G/Cs
Pollock	Ben	22	Midfielder	Hereford	15	1	4	16	
Middlesbrough (Y), Leeds (Y), Newcastle U (Y), Hartlepool, Dunston, Billingham S, Hereford									
Ponticelli	Jordan	21	Forward	Wrexham (L)	4	1	1	5	2
Coventry (Y), Macclesfield (L), Tranmere (L), Wrexham (L)									
Pope	Jason	24	Midfielder	Hereford	25	8	7	33	2
Exeter (Y), Weston (L), Weston, Hereford									
Popo Ebigbeyi	Tosan	27	Forward	Hemel Hempstead Town	22	3	3	25	1
Charlton, Chelmsford (L), San Roque Lepe (Sp), San Roque Lepe, Concord R, Hemel H									
Porter	George	27	Forward	Bromley	4	1		5	
Leyton O, Burnley, Colchester (L), AFC Wimbledon (L), Rochdale, Dagenham & R, Welling, Bromley									
Porter	Max	32	Midfielder	Chelmsford City			1		
Barnet, Rushden & D, Wimbledon, Newport Co (L), Newport Co, Bromley, Chelmsford									
Potter	Alfie	31	Forward	Billericay Town	28	3		31	1
Peterborough, Kettering (L), Oxford U, Wimbledon, Northampton, Mansfield, Billericay									
Powell	Brandon		Goalkeeper	Hereford FC	1		1	1	
Hereford (Y), Hereford Pegasus (L)									
Powell	Jack	26	Midfielder	Aldershot Town (L)	21			21	3
West Ham, Millwall, Concord R (L), Braintree (L), Ebbsfleet, Maidstone, Crawley, Aldershot (L)									
Power	Simon	22	Midfielder	King's Lynn Town (L)	5	1		6	2
Cabinteely, Uni College Dublin, Norwich, Dordrecht (L), Ross (L), King's Lynn (L)									
Prall	Aiden		Goalkeeper	Welling United			1		
Welling (Y)									
Pratt	David	32	Forward	Chippenham Town	19	8	9	27	3
Basingstoke, Maidenhead, Bath, Chippenham, Wealdstone, Chippenham									
Prestedge	Reece	34	Midfielder	Welling United	2	1	2	3	
Bishop's St, Bromley, Chelmsford (L), Maidstone Hemel H, East Thurrock, Welling, Margate									
Preston	Danny	19	Defender	Alfreton Town (L)	8			8	
Nottm F (Y), Alfreton (L)									
Preston	Jordan	24	Forward	Gateshead	20	10		30	8
Blackburn, Ayr (L), Ayr, Guiseley, Gateshead, FC Halifax, Gateshead									
Priestley	Billy	31	Defender	Bradford Park Avenue	24			24	2
Bradford PA, Salford, Alfreton, Southport, FC United (L), Bradford PA									
Prior	Jason	31	Forward	Dorking Wanderers	31	3	1	34	16
Wimbledon, Dartford (L), Dartford, Gosport (L), Margate, Bognor R, Havant & W, Dorking W									
Proctor	Jamie	28	Forward	AFC Fylde (L)	7	2		9	1
PNE (Y), Stockport (L), Swansea, Shrewsbury (L), Crawley, Fleetwood, Bradford (L), Bradford, Bolton, Carlisle (L), Rotherham, Scunthorpe (L), AFC Fylde (L)									
Prodomo	Joe	28	Goalkeeper	Weymouth			2		
Christchurch, Bashley, Weymouth, Bournemouth (Coach), Weymouth (Coach)									
Prosser	Alexander	21	Midfielder	Kidderminster Harriers	22	8	6	30	3
Aston Villa (Y), Brackley (L), Kidderminster									
Puddy	Willem	32	Goalkeeper	Chippenham Town	40			40	11
Swindon Sup, Chippenham, Salisbury, Bristol R, Braintree (L), Sutton U (L), Hereford, Chippenham									
Pugh	Andy	31	Forward	Dartford	7	6	1	13	1
Gillingham (Y), Welling (L), Maidstone (L), Folkestone I (L), Grays (L), Dover (L), Welling (L), Histon (L), Welling, Cambridge U, Ebbsfleet (L), Dartford (L), Dartford									
Qualter	Ryan	28	Defender	Alfreton Town	35	1		36	2
Ossett T, Bradford PA, Scarborough A (L), Shaw Lane, Boston U, Alfreton									
Quigley	Joe	23	Forward	Dagenham & Redbridge	25	9		34	6
				Billericay Town (L)	1			1	
Bournemouth, Torquay (L), Wrexham (L), Woking (L), Woking (L), Gillingham (L), Gillingham (L), Newport Co (L), Boreham W (L) Maidstone, Bromley, Eastbourne B (L) Havant & W (L), Dagenham & R, Billericay T (L)									
Quigley	Scott	27	Forward	Barrow	36	1		37	20
The New Saints, Blackpool, Wrexham (L), Port Vale (L), FC Halifax (L), Barrow									
Raison	Toby		Defender	Hereford FC			1		
Hereford (Y)									
Ramsay	Louis	22	Defender	Billericay Town	13	9	4	22	
Tottenham (Y), Norwich U23, Woking (L), Leicester U23, Billericay T									
Ramshaw	Rob	26	Midfielder	Spennymoor Town	34			34	11
Darlington, Gateshead, Spennymoor									

Key: X - Started; SX - Sub on; S - Non-playing Sub; Ap - Total Appearances; G/Cs - Total goals/clean sheets.

SURNAME	FIRSTNAME	AGE	POSITION	CLUB	X	SX	S	Ap	G/Cs
Rance	Dean	29	Midfielder	Aldershot Town	29	4		33	2
				Gillingham, Maidstone (L), Bishop's S (L), Dover (L), Dover, Ebbsfleet, Aldershot					
Randall	Joel	20	Midfielder	Weymouth (L)	1	1		2	
				Exeter (Y), Weymouth (L)					
Randall	Will	23	Midfielder	Sutton United	19	7	5	26	2
				Swindon (Y), Wolves, Walsall (L), Forest GR (L), FC Jumilla (Spa) (L), Newport Co, Sutton U					
Rathbone	Lewis	25	Midfielder	Bradford Park Avenue		2	5	2	
				Man City (Y), University (US), Bradford PA, Pickering (L)					
Ratti	Roberto	21	Forward	Dover Athletic	1	5	4	6	
				Tonbridge Angels	2	3		5	
				Lugano FC (Swiss), Dover, Tonbridge A					
Rattle	Michael		Midfielder	Stockport County			1		
				Stockport (Y)					
Ravizzoli	Franco	22	Goalkeeper	Eastbourne Borough	10			10	2
				Merlo (Arg), Moron, Eastbourne B					
Rawlings	Reece		Midfielder	Leamington			5		
				Leamington (Y)					
Rawlinson	Connell	28	Defender	Notts County	37	3	4	40	2
				Chester, TNS, Newtown (L), Port Vale, Notts Co					
Ray	David	35	Defender	Dorking Wanderers	19		5	19	1
				Basingstoke, Dorking W					
Raymond	Frankie	27	Midfielder	Bromley	34	5		39	5
				Reading, Dagenham & R, Bromley					
Raynes	Joe	25	Midfielder	Bath City	38			38	1
				Bath (Y), Odd Down, Larkhall Ath, Frome, Bath					
Raynes	Michael	32	Defender	Hartlepool United	33		1	33	
				Stockport (Y), Scunthorpe, Rotherham, Oxford U, Mansfield, Carlisle, Crewe, Hartlepool (L), Hartlepool					
Rea	Glen	25	Defender	Woking (L)	7			7	
				Brighton (Y), Southend (L), Luton (L), Luton, Woking (L)					
Read	Alex	32	Forward	Tonbridge Angels		5	2	5	
				Bishop's S, Harlow, Tonbridge A					
Read	Benny	22	Defender	Havant & Waterlooville	28	7	1	35	1
				Horndean, Havant & W					
Reason	Jai	30	Midfielder	Dover Athletic	29	5	6	34	1
				Ipswich, Cambridge U (L), Cambridge U, Crawley, Braintree, Eastleigh, Boreham W, Maidstone Chelmsford, Dover					
Reckord	Jamie	28	Defender	Solihull Moors	33	5		38	2
				Wolves, Northampton (L), Scunthorpe (L), Coventry (L), Plymouth (L), Swindon (L), Ross Co, Oldham, Solihull M					
Redmond	Devonte	23	Midfielder	Wrexham	20	7	10	27	3
				Man United (Y), Scunthorpe (L), Salford, Wrexham					
Redshaw	Jack	29	Forward	FC Halifax Town	12	6		18	5
				Rochdale (Y), Altrincham, Morecambe, Altrincham (L), Blackpool, Rochdale, Salford, Halifax					
Rees	Josh	20	Midfielder	Bromley	26	8	4	34	4
				Nottingham F, Nuneaton (L), Torquay (L), Torquay, Chelmsford, Bromley, Gillingham, Bromley					
Rees	Tom		Goalkeeper	Weymouth			15		
				Poole, Weymouth					
Rees	Tommy		Goalkeeper	Hungerford Town	1		8	1	
				Hungerford					
Regan	Matt	26	Defender	Curzon Ashton	10			10	2
				Farsley Celtic	11	4	3	15	
				Wrexham (Y), Liverpool (Y), Notts F, Tamworth (L), Hednesford (L), Worcester (L), Stalybridge, New Mills, Colwyn B, Ashton U, Curzon A, Farsley					
Regini-Moran	Emilio		Midfielder	Ebbsfleet United			1		
				Ebbsfleet					
Reid	Alex	24	Forward	Ebbsfleet United (L)	22	3		25	9
				Dagenham & Redbridge (L)	5	1	1	6	3
				Fleetwood, Wrexham (L), Solihull M (L), Stevenage, AFC Fylde (L), Ebbsfleet (L), Dagenham & R (L)					
Reid	Jamie	25	Forward	Torquay United	36			36	22
				Exeter (Y), Dorchester (L), Torquay (L), Truro (L), Torquay (L), Torquay					

SURNAME	FIRSTNAME	AGE	POSITION	CLUB PLAYED FOR	X	SX	S	Ap	G/Cs
Reid	Kyel	32	Midfielder	Sutton United	18	7	4	25	
West Ham (Y), Barnsley (L), Crystal P (L), Blackpool (L), Wolves (L), Sheffield U, Charlton, Bradford, PNE, Bradford (L), Coventry, Colchester (L), Chesterfield, Sutton U									
Reid	Sean	28	Midfielder	Darlington	11	2	1	13	2
Ryton & Crawcrook A, West Allotment C, Ryton, Newcastle Benfield, Blyth S, Morpeth, Darlington									
Reid	Tyler	22	Defender	Wrexham (L)	5	2	1	7	
Swansea (Y), Newport Co (L), Swindon, Wrexham (L)									
Reilly	Lewis	20	Forward	AFC Telford United (L)	2	3	3	5	1
Crewe (Y), Curzon A (L), Telford (L)									
Rendell	Scott	33	Forward	Eastleigh	24	19	1	43	11
Aldershot, Forest Green, Crawley, Cambridge U, Peterborough (L), Peterborough, Yeovil (L), Cambridge U (L), Torquay (L), Wycombe, Bristol R (L), Oxford U (L), Luton, Woking, Aldershot, Eastleigh									
Reynolds	Callum	30	Defender	Barnet	37			37	2
Rushden, Portsmouth, Luton (L), Tamworth, Corby (L), Boreham W, Aldershot, Barnet									
Reynolds	Jamie	20	Defender	Billericay Town	1	2	3	3	
Tottenham (Y), Billericay,									
Reynolds	Lamar	24	Midfielder	Concord Rangers	20	9	3	29	4
Newport Co, Leyton Orient (L), Dag & Red, Chelmsford (L), Concord R									
Rhead	Matthew	36	Forward	Billericay Town	10	1		11	2
				Boreham Wood	5	2		7	1
Eastwood, Corby, Mansfield, Lincoln C, Billericay T, Boreham W									
Ribbens	Sam	21	Goalkeeper	Maidstone United			4		
Chatham T, Snodland T, Maidstone (U23)									
Rich-Baguelou	Jay	20	Defender	Welling United	18	4	5	22	
Fulham (Y), Dulwich H, Welling, Crystal P									
Richards	Caleb	21	Defender	Yeovil Town (L)	1		3	1	
Marine, Blackpool, Southport (L), Norwich, FC United (L), Tampa Bay (L), Yeovil (L)									
Richards	Elliot	18	Midfielder	Southport		1		1	
Everton (Y), Southport									
Richards	Ioan		Defender	Gloucester City	2	2	3	4	
Cheltenham (Y), Gloucester, Slimbridge (Dual)									
Richards	Jordan	27	Defender	Farsley Celtic	39			39	1
Hartlepool, Alfreton (L), Darlington, AFC Fylde, Southport, Farsley C									
Richards	Jordan	22	Defender	King's Lynn Town	27	12		39	3
Notts Co (Y), Boston U (L), Sligo Rovers, Gainsborough, King's Lynn									
Richards	Marc	37	Forward	Yeovil Town	5	4		9	2
Port Vale, Chesterfield, Northampton, Swindon, Cambridge U, Yeovil									
Richards	Tom	21	Midfielder	Bath City	16	12	6	28	3
Bristol C, Truro (L), Bath									
Richards	Tom	25	Midfielder	Dorking Wanderers	23	12	7	35	6
Wimbledon, Fulham, Wimbledon (L), Aldershot (L), Aldershot, Kitzbuhel (Austria), Walton C, Welling, Leatherhead, Dorking W									
Richards	Will	28	Midfielder	Chippenham Town	11	2		13	1
Stourbridge, Redditch, Solihull, Stourbridge, Redditch, Chippenham									
Richardson	Kenton	20	Defender	Hartlepool United	13	2	8	15	
Hartlepool									
Richardson	Tom	26	Forward	Braintree Town	15	1	2	16	5
Brentwood, Brightlingsea, East Thurrock, Aveley, Braintree									
Richens	Michael	25	Defender	Kettering Town	13	6	3	19	1
Peterborough (Y), Histon (L), Nuneaton (L), Whitehawk (L), Bishop's S (L), Stevenage (L), Farnborough (L), Stevenage, Farnborough (L), Hemel H, Bishop's S, Kettering									
Richman	Simon	30	Midfielder	Altrincham	13	18	3	31	1
Port Vale (Y), Worcester, Altrincham									
Ricketts	Mark	35	Midfielder	Boreham Wood	32	4	2	36	
Charlton, MK Dons (L), Ebbsfleet, Woking, Boreham W									
Rigg	George	26	Midfielder	Chippenham Town	30	5	5	35	2
Weymouth, Bath, Chippenham									
Rigg	Steven	27	Forward	Dover Athletic	25	8	5	33	1
Penrith (Y), Carlisle, Queen OTS, Carlisle, Chorley, Workington (L), Gateshead, Dover									

Key: X - Started; SX - Sub on; S - Non-playing Sub; Ap - Total Appearances; G/Cs - Total goals/clean sheets.

SURNAME	FIRSTNAME	AGE	POSITION	CLUB	X	SX	S	Ap	G/Cs
Riley	Martin	33	Defender	Hereford FC	14		4	14	
Wolves, Shrewsbury (L), Kidderminster, Cheltenham, Mansfield, Wrexham, Mansfield, Tranmere, Wrexham, Halifax, Alfreton, Hereford									
Riley-Lowe	Connor	24	Midfielder	Bath City	31	6	4	37	
Exeter (Y), Truro (L), Truro (L), Truro, Bath									
Ringer	Joe	19	Goalkeeper	Wealdstone			14		
Wealdstone (Y), Northwood (Dual)									
Ritson	Lewis	21	Defender	Blyth Spartans (L)	19	1	2	20	
Hull C, Blyth S (L)									
Rivers	Jarrett	26	Midfielder	Darlington	35	7		42	3
Middlesbrough (Y), Sunderland RCA (L), Whitley B, Blyth S, Blackpool, Blyth S, Darlington									
Roast	Billy	25	Defender	Concord Rangers	36	2	2	38	3
Colchester, Maldon, Concord R, Dartford, Concord R									
Robert	Fabien	31	Midfielder	Gloucester City	24	4		28	1
Lorient, Boulogne (L), Doncaster (L), Swindon, Forest Green, Aldershot (L) Gloucester (Lx2), Gloucester									
Roberts	Callum	23	Forward	Blyth Spartans	25			25	17
				Notts County	9	1		10	5
Newcastle U (Y), Gateshead (L), Kilmarnock (L), Colchester (L), Middlesbrough U23, Blyth S, Notts Co									
Roberts	Dan		Forward	Slough Town	29	7	1	36	12
Slough									
Roberts	Gary	33	Midfielder	Chester	24	2	7	26	2
Crewe, Yeovil, Rotherham, Port Vale, Mansfield, Connah's Q, Bangor, Southport, Chester									
Roberts	James	24	Forward	Spennymoor Town	31	5	2	36	11
Wycombe (Y), Oxford U (Y), Chester (L), Oxford C (L), Barnet (L), Oxford C (L), Chelmsford (L), Guiseley (L) Hereford, Spennymoor									
Roberts	Kevin	30	Defender	Chester	29	3	2	32	1
Chester, Cambridge U, Halifax, Wrexham, Chester									
Roberts	Myles	18	Goalkeeper	Tonbridge Angels (L)	5		1	5	2
Reading (Y), Wealdstone (L), Tonbridge A (L)									
Roberts	Phil	26	Forward	Wealdstone		6	2	6	
				Welling United	5	4	1	9	
Arsenal (Y), Inverness (L), Falkirk, Dundee, Alloa (L), Sligo, Chelmsford, Braintree, Chelmsford, Hemel H, Dartford, Wealdstone, Hayes & Y, Welling									
Roberts	Theo	21	Goalkeeper	Chester			1		
Wigan (Y), Chester									
Robinson	Andy	27	Midfielder	Weymouth	15	4	1	19	2
Southampton (Y), Bolton (L), Bolton, Dorchester, Gosport, Havant & W, Weymouth									
Robinson	Jake	33	Forward	Billericay Town	30	8		38	20
Brighton, Aldershot, Shrewsbury (L), Northampton, Luton (L), Whitehawk, Hempstead, Billericay, Maidstone, Billericay									
Robinson	Matt	26	Midfielder	Dagenham & Redbridge	34	1	3	35	
Leicester, Luton, Kidderminster (L), Grimsby (L), Woking (L), Dagenham & R									
Robinson	Wayne		Forward	Eastleigh			1		
Eastleigh (Y)									
Robinson-Murray	Kyle			Wrexham	1	1	2	2	
Wrexham (Y)									
Robson	Craig	28	Defender	Billericay Town	9	2		11	
				Havant & Waterlooville	15	1	2	16	1
Havant & W, Sorrento FC (W.Aus), Bognor Regis, Dagenham & R, Barnet, Billericay, Havant & W									
Robson	Joe	22	Midfielder	Blyth Spartans	12	1	4	13	
Gateshead, North Shields, Newcastle Benfield, Blyth S									
Rodney	Devante	22	Forward	Stockport County (L)	11	3		14	3
				FC Halifax (L)	8			8	5
Man City (Y), Sheff Wed (Y), Hartlepool, Salford, FC Halifax (L), Stockport (L), FC Halifax (L)									
Rogers	Gabriel	20	Midfielder	Yeovil Town	1	4	8	5	
Yeovil (Y)									
Rollins	Jay		Midfielder	Boston United	25	10	1	35	5
Armthorpe, Boston U									
Rolt	Bradley		Forward	Welling United (L)	2	3	1	5	
Peterborough (Y), Welling (L)									

SURNAME	FIRSTNAME	AGE	POSITION	CLUB PLAYED FOR	X	SX	S	Ap	G/Cs
Romain	Elliott	28	Forward	Eastbourne Borough	14			1	14	6
				Dartford	25				25	13

Brighton, Millwall, Three Bridges, Lewes, Horsham YMCA (L), Eastbourne B, Dagenham & R, Welling (L), Torquay (L), Maidstone, Eastbourne B, Dartford

SURNAME	FIRSTNAME	AGE	POSITION	CLUB PLAYED FOR	X	SX	S	Ap	G/Cs
Rooney	Daniel	21	Midfielder	Bath City	4		2		4	

Plymouth (Y), Truro (L), Bath

SURNAME	FIRSTNAME	AGE	POSITION	CLUB PLAYED FOR	X	SX	S	Ap	G/Cs
Rooney	John	29	Midfielder	Barrow	39				39	20

Macclesfield, Barnsley, Bury, Chester, Wrexham, Guiseley, Barrow

SURNAME	FIRSTNAME	AGE	POSITION	CLUB PLAYED FOR	X	SX	S	Ap	G/Cs
Rooney	Luke	29	Midfielder	Welling United	8	1	4		9	

Gillingham, Swindon, Burton (L), Rotherham (L), Crawley (L), Maidstone, Luton, Ebbsfleet, Crawley, Phoenix Rising, Billericay, Welling

SURNAME	FIRSTNAME	AGE	POSITION	CLUB PLAYED FOR	X	SX	S	Ap	G/Cs
Rooney	Paul	23	Defender	Dover Athletic	13	8	8		21	1

St Pats, Bohemians, Millwall, Torquay (L), Colchester, Bromley (L), Billericay (L), Dover

SURNAME	FIRSTNAME	AGE	POSITION	CLUB PLAYED FOR	X	SX	S	Ap	G/Cs
Rose	Declan	18	Defender	Yeovil Town		1		1	

Yeovil (Y)

SURNAME	FIRSTNAME	AGE	POSITION	CLUB PLAYED FOR	X	SX	S	Ap	G/Cs
Rose	Jordan	30	Defender	Weymouth	1	1	2		2	
				Eastbourne Borough	1				1	

SM Caen (F) (Y) Bournemouth (Y), Bashley, Weymouth, Paulton, Stockport, Eastleigh, Hereford Utd, Hayes & Y, Stockport, Telford, Alfreton, Tamworth, Whitehawk, Havant & W, Weymouth (L), Weymouth, Eastbourne B

SURNAME	FIRSTNAME	AGE	POSITION	CLUB PLAYED FOR	X	SX	S	Ap	G/Cs
Rose	Mitchell	25	Midfielder	Notts County	39	1	3		40	3

Rotherham (Y), Crawley (L), Ilkeston (L), Mansfield, Newport, Grimsby, Notts Co

SURNAME	FIRSTNAME	AGE	POSITION	CLUB PLAYED FOR	X	SX	S	Ap	G/Cs
Ross	Craig	30	Goalkeeper	Woking	39		2		39	8

Hampton & R, Cambridge U, Eastbourne B (L), Eastbourne B, Farnborough, Whitehawk, Macclesfield, Barnet, Boreham W, Woking

SURNAME	FIRSTNAME	AGE	POSITION	CLUB PLAYED FOR	X	SX	S	Ap	G/Cs
Ross	Mark	30	Defender	Chorley	24	5	11		29	

Leigh Gen, Chorley, Stockport, Bradford PA, Chorley

SURNAME	FIRSTNAME	AGE	POSITION	CLUB PLAYED FOR	X	SX	S	Ap	G/Cs
Rowan	Charlie	22	Defender	Barnet (L)	2	1	6		3	

Watford (Y), Accrington (L), QPR, Barnet (L)

SURNAME	FIRSTNAME	AGE	POSITION	CLUB PLAYED FOR	X	SX	S	Ap	G/Cs
Rowe	Aaron	19	Forward	Boston United (L)	1	1			2	
				Bromley (L)		2	2		2	

Huddersfield (Y), Boston U (L), Bromley (L)

SURNAME	FIRSTNAME	AGE	POSITION	CLUB PLAYED FOR	X	SX	S	Ap	G/Cs
Rowe	Coby	24	Defender	Sutton United	3		5		3	

Haringey B, Sutton U

SURNAME	FIRSTNAME	AGE	POSITION	CLUB PLAYED FOR	X	SX	S	Ap	G/Cs
Rowe	Danny	23	Forward	Oxford City	5	6	5		11	3

Leicester (Y), QPR (Y), Braintree, Boston U, Hemel H, Oxford C

SURNAME	FIRSTNAME	AGE	POSITION	CLUB PLAYED FOR	X	SX	S	Ap	G/Cs
Rowe	Danny M	30	Forward	AFC Fylde	33				33	10

Man Utd (Y), Fleetwood, Droylsden (L), Stockport, Barrow, Macclesfield, AFC Fylde, Oldham

SURNAME	FIRSTNAME	AGE	POSITION	CLUB PLAYED FOR	X	SX	S	Ap	G/Cs
Rowe	James	28	Midfielder	Aldershot Town	13	3	6		16	

Forest Green, Tranmere, Cheltenham, Aldershot

SURNAME	FIRSTNAME	AGE	POSITION	CLUB PLAYED FOR	X	SX	S	Ap	G/Cs
Rowley	Joe	21	Midfielder	Chesterfield	21	5	3		26	1

Chesterfield (Y)

SURNAME	FIRSTNAME	AGE	POSITION	CLUB PLAYED FOR	X	SX	S	Ap	G/Cs
Rowley	Shaun	23	Goalkeeper	Solihull Moors	1		13		1	

Shrewsbury (Y), Watford (Y) (L), Halesowen (L), Chorley (L), Tamworth (L), FC Halifax, Solihull M

SURNAME	FIRSTNAME	AGE	POSITION	CLUB PLAYED FOR	X	SX	S	Ap	G/Cs
Royle	Jonathan	25	Midfielder	AFC Telford United	3	8	15		11	
				Bradford Park Avenue (L)	6	1			7	

Wrexham (Y), Colwyn (L), Hednesford (L), Southport, Telford (L), Telford, Bradford PA (L)

SURNAME	FIRSTNAME	AGE	POSITION	CLUB PLAYED FOR	X	SX	S	Ap	G/Cs
Ruddick	Luke	30	Defender	Hampton & Richmond Borough	18		9		18	3

Salisbury, Bath, Salisbury, Sutton U, Oxford C, Hampton & R

SURNAME	FIRSTNAME	AGE	POSITION	CLUB PLAYED FOR	X	SX	S	Ap	G/Cs
Rudoni	Jack	19	Midfielder	Tonbridge Angels (L)	5				5	

Wimbledon (Y), Tonbridge A (L)

SURNAME	FIRSTNAME	AGE	POSITION	CLUB PLAYED FOR	X	SX	S	Ap	G/Cs
Rusby	James		Defender	Hungerford Town	31	2			33	4

Hungerford

SURNAME	FIRSTNAME	AGE	POSITION	CLUB PLAYED FOR	X	SX	S	Ap	G/Cs
Russe	Luke	20	Midfielder	Gloucester City (L)	17				17	2
				Chippenham Town (L)	10				10	

Bristol R, Gloucester (L), Gloucester (L), Chippenham (L)

SURNAME	FIRSTNAME	AGE	POSITION	CLUB PLAYED FOR	X	SX	S	Ap	G/Cs
Russell	Darrelle	30	Forward	Braintree Town	5	1			6	

Antigua Barracuda, Haringey B, Hayes, Arlesey, Billericay, Harrow B, Cheshunt, Barking, Waltham Abbey, Braintree

SURNAME	FIRSTNAME	AGE	POSITION	CLUB PLAYED FOR	X	SX	S	Ap	G/Cs
Rutherford	Alfie		Forward	Havant & Waterlooville	19	17			36	10

Moneyfields, Bognor, Havant & W, Eastbourne B (L)

SURNAME	FIRSTNAME	AGE	POSITION	CLUB PLAYED FOR	X	SX	S	Ap	G/Cs
Rutherford	Paul	32	Midfielder	Wrexham	24	14	3		38	2

Chester, Barrow, Southport, Wrexham

Key: X - Started; SX - Sub on; S - Non-playing Sub; Ap - Total Appearances; G/Cs - Total goals/clean sheets.

SURNAME	FIRSTNAME	AGE	POSITION	CLUB	X	SX	S	Ap	G/Cs
Rutty	Harry	20	Defender	Chippenham Town	5	2	8	7	
Chippenham, Melksham (L)									
Ryan	Bradley			Welling United			1		
Welling (Y)									
Ryan	Max	21	Defender	Braintree Town			4		
Watford (Y), Kings Langley, Biggleswade, Hitchin, Braintree									
Sade	Yoav	19	Defender	Braintree Town (L)	1	1	2	2	
Oxford U (Y), Braintree (L)									
Sakellaropoulos	Alexandros		Defender	Gateshead			1		
Panegialios (Gre), Carlisle, Gateshead									
Saltmer	Jonathan	21	Goalkeeper	Barrow			1		
Barrow (Y)									
Sampson	Jack	27	Forward	Southport	36	1		37	10
Bolton (Y), Southend (L), Accrington (L), Morecambe, Macclesfield (L), Macclesfield, Chorley (L), Southport									
Samuels	Austin	19	Forward	Kidderminster Harriers (L)	3	3	1	6	
Wolves (Y), Kidderminster (L)									
Sanders	Jack		Defender	Blyth Spartans (L)	11			11	
				Southport (L)	3			3	
Wigan (Y), Blyth S (L), Southport (L)									
Sandford	Ryan	21	Goalkeeper	Dorking Wanderers (L)	5		1	5	2
Millwall (Y), Welling (L), Dorking W (L)									
Sang	Chris	20	Forward	Guiseley (L)	9	1		10	2
Wigan (Y), Bury, Southport (L), Marine (L), Altrincham (L), Barnsley, Guiseley (L)									
Santos	Alefe	25	Midfielder	Aldershot Town	17	10	6	27	2
Bristol R, Derby, Notts Co (L), Eastleigh (L), Yeovil, Aldershot									
Sanusi	Hafeez	25	Defender	Concord Rangers	1	5	2	6	
Solihull (Y), Whitehawk, Concord R									
Sass-Davies	Billy	20	Defender	AFC Telford United (L)	7			7	1
Crewe (Y), Colwyn B (L), Leek (L), FC United (L), Altrincham (L), Telford (L)									
Saunders	Callum	24	Forward	Curzon Ashton	12	6	1	18	2
Crewe (Y), Notts Co, Nantwich, Curzon A									
Saunders	Matthew	30	Midfielder	Wealdstone			9		
Lincoln C, Dagenham & R, Whitehawk, Dover, Hemel H, Aldershot, Hemel H (L), Hemel H, Wealdstone									
Saunders	Ollie	19	Defender	Braintree Town	7			7	
Norwich (Y), Grimsby (Y), Braintree (Y), Leiston (L), Lowestoft									
Schwarzer	Julian	20	Goalkeeper	Slough Town			1		
Fulham (Y), Pipinsried (Ger), Harlow, Slough									
Scory	Ben		Midfielder	Eastleigh	2	1	20	3	
Eastleigh (Y)									
Scott	Andrew	20	Forward	Curzon Ashton (L)	5	2		7	1
Accrington, Curzon A (L)									
Scott	Knory	21	Forward	Kidderminster Harriers		3	7	3	
Kidderminster (U23)									
Scott	Oliver	19	Midfielder	Blyth Spartans	24	7	3	31	2
Blyth S (Y)									
Scott	Ryan	26	Defender	Concord Rangers	2			2	
East Thurrock, Concord R									
Scrimshaw	Jake	19	Forward	Eastleigh	3	7		10	
Eastleigh (Y)									
Scrivens	Sam	23	Forward	Guiseley	2	5	8	7	
Penistone Church, Guiseley									
Seaden	Harry	19	Goalkeeper	Dagenham & Redbridge	2		8	2	
Dagenham & R (Y)									
Seager	Ryan	24	Forward	Yeovil Town		2	4	2	
				Havant & Waterlooville (L)		7	3	7	1
Southampton (Y), Crewe (L), MK Dons (L), Yeovil (L), Yeovil, Havant & W (L)									
Seaman	Charlie	20	Defender	Eastleigh (L)	19	6	1	25	
				Maidstone United (L)		1		1	
Bournemouth (Y), Dundee U (L), Eastleigh (L), Maidstone (L)									

SURNAME	FIRSTNAME	AGE	POSITION	CLUB PLAYED FOR	X	SX	S	Ap	G/Cs
Search	Ben			Concord Rangers		1	13	1	
Concord R (Y)									
Sears	Ryan	21	Defender	AFC Telford United (L)	1			1	1
Shrewsbury (Y), Newtown (L), Telford (L), Telford (L)									
Sebbeh-Njie	Mo	22	Midfielder	Kettering Town		1	12	1	
CF Damm, VA Horta, Redditch, Stratford T, Kettering									
Sekajja	Ibra	27	Forward	Maidenhead United	1	3	3	4	1
Crystal P (Y), Kettering (L), MK Dons (L), Barnet (L), Inverness C, Livingston, Braintree, Hemel, Dulwich, Bognor, Havant & W, Maidenhead									
Self	Jack		Midfielder	Oxford City	19	4	1	23	2
				Chippenham Town		3	1	3	
Didcot, Oxford C, Chippenham									
Sellers	Ryan	25	Defender	Wealdstone	1	1		2	
Bolton, Wycombe, Wingate, Wealdstone, FC Halifax, Wealdstone									
Senior	Jack	23	Defender	Gloucester City	8			8	1
Huddersfield (Y), Luton, Harrogate (L), Gloucester									
Servuts	Edvards		Midfielder	Southport			1		
Southport (Y)									
Sesay	Alhaji	21	Goalkeeper	Dartford	15		4	15	6
Bristol C (Y), Gloucester (L), Dartford									
Shaibu	Justin	22	Forward	Boreham Wood (L)	11	23	1	34	5
HB Koge (Y), Brentford, Walsall (L), Boreham W (L), Boreham W (L)									
Shakes	Ricky	35	Midfielder	Boreham Wood	2	17	14	19	
Bolton, Bristol R (L), Bury (L), Swindon, Brentford, Ebbsfleet, Kidderminster, Boreham W									
Shako	Nestor	19	Midfielder	Yeovil Town		1	3	1	
Yeovil (Y)									
Shamsi	Ravi	22	Midfielder	Leamington	1	11	3	12	2
Oxford U (Y), Fulham (Y), Banbury, Chesham, Maidenhead, Banbury (L), Leamington									
Shanley	Liam		Forward	Blyth Spartans			1		
Blyth S									
Sharman	Jamie		Defender	Chesterfield	2	1	5	3	
				Kidderminster Harriers (L)	2	1		3	
Chesterfield (Y), Kidderminster (L)									
Shaw	Danny	35	Defender	Curzon Ashton	21	2	7	23	
Curzon A									
Shaw	Frazer	25	Defender	Chelmsford City	31	5	1	36	
Dulwich H, Leyton Orient, Accrington, Woking, Eastleigh, Leatherhead, Concord R, Chelmsford									
Shaw	Lee	26	Forward	Guiseley (L)	16	15	1	31	3
Grantham, Chesterfield, Guiseley (L)									
Shaw	Liam	19	Midfielder	Chesterfield (L)	3	2	1	5	
Sheff Wed (Y), Chesterfield (L)									
Sheckleford	Ryheem	23	Defender	Maidenhead United	28	5	5	33	
Fulham (Y), Wealdstone (L), Maidenhead									
Sheehan	Steve		Defender	Braintree Town	13	1		14	
East Thurrock, Billericay, Canvey I, East Thurrock, Braintree									
Shelton	Mark	23	Midfielder	Woking (L)	4		2	4	1
				Hartlepool United (L)	13	1	1	14	3
Burton (Y), Ilkeston, Alfreton, Salford, Woking (L), Hartlepool (L)									
Shenton	Oliver	22	Midfielder	Kidderminster Harriers (L)	13	11	5	24	3
Stoke (Y), Wrexham (L), Kidderminster (L)									
Shepherd	Coleby		Midfielder	Hartlepool United			1		
Hartlepool (Y)									
Sheppard	Jake	23	Defender	Wealdstone	4	17	1	21	
Reading (Y), Hayes & Y (L), Eastbourne B (L), Dag & Red (L), Guiseley (L), Wealdstone (L), Wealdstone									
Sheppeard	Harrison		Defender	Guiseley (L)		1	8	1	
Sheff Utd (Y), Guiseley (L)									
Sheridan	Jay	20	Defender	Chesterfield	17	3	9	20	
Oldham (Y), Chesterfield									
Sheriff	Decarrey	22	Midfielder	Concord Rangers	24	8	2	32	10
Dulwich H, Concord R									

Key: X - Started; SX - Sub on; S - Non-playing Sub; Ap - Total Appearances; G/Cs - Total goals/clean sheets.

SURNAME	FIRSTNAME	AGE	POSITION	CLUB	X	SX	S	Ap	G/Cs
Sheringham	Charlie	32	Forward	Dartford	7	11	4	18	8
Bishop's S, Histon, Dartford, Bournemouth, Dartford (L), Wimbledon, Salisbury (L), Ebbsfleet, Bishop's S (L), Hemel H, Hemel H, Saif (Bangl), Hemel H, Dartford									
Sherring	Sam	20	Defender	Weymouth (L)	11		1	11	
Bournemouth (Y), Weymouth (L), Weymouth (L)									
Shields	Connor	22	Midfielder	Aldershot Town	17	5	10	22	
				Billericay Town (L)	2			2	1
Albion Rovers, Sunderland U23, Alloa (L), Aldershot, Billericay T (L)									
Shields	Sean	28	Midfielder	Ebbsfleet United	1	5		6	
				Notts County (L)	11	9	2	20	
Tottenham, Potters Bar, St Albans, Dagenham & R, St Albans (L), Ebbsfleet (L), Ebbsfleet, Chelmsford (L), Margate (L), Hemel (L) Maidstone (L), Boreham W (L), Notts Co (L)									
Shiels	Luke	30	Defender	Boston United	37	1		38	4
Worksop, Harrogate, Alfreton, Boston U									
Sho-Silva	Tobi	25	Forward	FC Halifax Town	30	10	2	40	7
Charlton Welling (L), Welling (L), Inverness CT (L), Bromley, Dover, Chelmsford (L), Halifax									
Shomotun	Fumnaya	23	Midfielder	Wealdstone		1	3	1	
Brentford (Y), Barnet (Y), Staines (L), Margate (L), Wealdstone (L), Wealdstone									
Shulton	Scott	30	Midfielder	St Albans City	15	3	4	18	1
Ebbsfleet, Bishop's S, Braintree, Bishop's S, Enfield T, Braintree, Hemel H, St Albans									
Simpson	Aaron	23	Defender	Dover Athletic	21	1	10	22	
Wolves (Y), AFC Telford (L), Kilmarnock (L), FC Jumilla (L) (Spa), Waterford, Dover									
Simpson	Jordan	21	Midfielder	Bath City		8	22	8	
Swindon (Y), Forest GR, Havant & W (L), Hampton & R (L), Bath									
Simpson	Luke	25	Goalkeeper	Barrow	3		1	3	1
Oldham (Y), Workington (L), Leicester (L), Accrington, Watford, York, Macclesfield, Tamworth, Wrexham, Barrow									
Simpson	Robbie	35	Forward	Chelmsford City	11	9	4	20	5
Cambridge C, Coventry, Huddersfield, Brentford (L), Oldham (L), Oldham, Leyton O, Cambridge U, Exeter, MK Dons, Chelmsford									
Sinclair	Isaac	18	Midfielder	Curzon Ashton	24	7	2	31	2
Curzon A									
Sinclair	Robert	30	Forward	Hemel Hempstead Town	7	6	5	13	
Salisbury, Stevenage, Aldershot (L), Salisbury, Forest GR, Oxford C, Hemel H									
Siviter	Adam	20	Goalkeeper	Hungerford Town (L)	26			26	4
Birmingham (Y), Hungerford (L)									
Skarz	Joe	30	Defender	Kettering Town	15		1	15	1
Huddersfield (Y), Shrewsbury (L), Bury, Rotherham (L), Rotherham, Oxford U, Bury, FC Halifax (L), Kettering									
Skendi	Albi	26	Midfielder	Yeovil Town	31	10	2	41	4
Oxford C, Stratford, Yeovil									
Skinner	Jack	20	Midfielder	Woking			1		
				Hampton & Richmond Borough (L)		2	2	2	
				Eastbourne Borough (L)	7			7	1
Woking (Y), Hampton & R (L), Eastbourne B (L)									
Skubich	Isaac		Midfielder	Braintree Town		2	9	2	
Ipswich (Y), AFC Sudbury, Braintree, Felixstowe & W (Dual), Leiston									
Sloan	Jack	17	Defender	Curzon Ashton		2	7	2	
Curzon A (Y)									
Slocombe	Sam	32	Goalkeeper	Notts County	35		1	35	13
Scunthorpe, Oxford U, Blackpool, Bristol R, Lincoln C (L), Notts Co									
Slough	Louie		Defender	Torquay United			4		
Torquay (Y)									
Small	Jared	29	Forward	Tonbridge Angels	16	16	2	32	
Billericay T, Enfield T, Harlow, Tonbridge A									
Smart	Sam	21	Midfielder	Eastleigh	26	12	3	38	3
Basingstoke (Y), Eastleigh									
Smedley	Joel		Midfielder	Chippenham Town			1		
Chippenham (Y)									
Smile	Josh	23	Midfielder	Maidenhead United	36	3	5	39	4
Fulham (Y), Chippenham, Maidenhead									

SURNAME	FIRSTNAME	AGE	POSITION	CLUB PLAYED FOR	X	SX	S	Ap	G/Cs
Smith	Aaron	22	Midfielder	Curzon Ashton		2		2	
Hamilton, Ashton U, Curzon A									
Smith	Adam	27	Goalkeeper	Yeovil Town (L)	5		2	5	
Leicester (Y), Chesterfield (L), Lincoln (L), Nuneaton (L), Stevenage (L), Cambridge U (L), Mansfield (L), Northampton, Bristol R, Forest GR, Yeovil (L)									
Smith	Alistair	21	Midfielder	Kettering Town (L)	2	1	1	3	
Mansfield (Y), Kettering (L)									
Smith	Chris	22	Defender	King's Lynn Town	20			20	
Ipswich (Y), Chelmsford (L), Aldershot (L), King's Lynn									
Smith	Christian	32	Midfielder	Dulwich Hamlet	33	2	3	35	6
Port Vale, Cambridge U (L), Northwich (L), Clyde, Wrexham, York, Wrexham, Newport Co (L), Barrow (L), Tamworth (L), Telford, Chelmsford, Hayes & Yeading, Bishop's St, Maidenhead, Wealdstone, Dulwich H									
Smith	Connor	27	Midfielder	Wealdstone	18	7	4	25	
Watford (Y), Wealdstone (L), Gillingham (L), Stevenage (L), AFC Wimbledon, Plymouth, Yeovil, Boreham W, Billericay, Wealdstone									
Smith	Dominic	24	Defender	Alfreton Town	33			33	1
Shrewsbury (Y), Tamworth (L), Barrow (L), Southport (L), Telford, Alfreton (L), Alfreton									
Smith	George	23	Defender	Harrogate Town	22	3	13	25	1
Barnsley (Y), Crawley (L), Gateshead, Northampton, Chesterfield, Dover (L) Boston U (L), Harrogate									
Smith	George		Midfielder	Hungerford Town	21	2	6	23	
Kintbury R, Hungerford									
Smith	Grant	26	Goalkeeper	Boreham Wood (L)	1	1	6	2	
Fulham, Brighton, Hayes & Y (L), Bognor (L), Bognor, Boreham W Lincoln C, Maidstone (L), Boreham W (L)									
Smith	Harvey	21	Defender	Bath City (L)	8	1	1	9	1
				Gloucester City (L)	2			2	
Bristol C (Y), Weston (L), Hereford (L), Bath (L), Gloucester (L)									
Smith	Jack	18	Defender	Braintree Town (L)	8	1	1	9	
Dover (Y), Stevenage, Braintree (L)									
Smith	Jimmy	33	Midfielder	Yeovil Town (L)	19	4	1	23	5
Chelsea (Y), Sheff Wed (L), Leyton O (L), Leyton O, Stevenage, Crawley, Yeovil (L)									
Smith	Jonathan	33	Midfielder	Chesterfield	25	6	2	31	4
Morecambe (Y), Fleetwood (L), Forest Green, York, Swindon, York, Luton (L), Luton, Stevenage, Chesterfield (L), Chesterfield									
Smith	Kane	24	Defender	Boreham Wood	36			36	4
Hitchin, Boreham W									
Smith	Kieran		Defender	Gloucester City	4	7	11	11	
Bristol C (Y), Gloucester, Clevedon (L)									
Smith	Liam	20	Defender	Tonbridge Angels	4	2	9	6	
Tonbridge A, Sevenoaks T (Dual)									
Smith	Lorrell	24	Forward	Brackley Town	1	3	7	4	
Biggleswade U, Brackley (Dual)									
Smith	Mark	24	Goalkeeper	Dartford	27			27	6
Brentford (Y), Lowestoft (L), Aldershot, Eastbourne B (L), Eastbourne B, Billericay, Eastbourne B (L), Dartford									
Smith	Martin	24	Midfielder	Chorley (L)	19			19	
Sunderland (Y), Gateshead (L), Carlisle (L), Kilmarnock, Coleraine, Swindon, Salford, Chorley (L)									
Smith	Nathan	33	Defender	Dulwich Hamlet	10	3	4	13	
Enfield T, Waltham F, Potters Bar, Yeovil, Chesterfield, Yeovil, Dagenham & R, Dulwich H									
Smith	Reece		Midfielder	Maidenhead United			5		
Maidenhead (Y)									
Smith	Scott	21	Midfielder	Guiseley		5	8	5	
Guiseley									
Smith	Tom	22	Midfielder	Bath City	43			43	15
Swindon (Y), Waterford (L), Bath (Lx3), Cheltenham, Bath (L), Bath									
Smith	William	21	Defender	Harrogate Town	44			44	2
Barnsley (Y), Darlington (L), Harrogate									
Smith	Zac	19	Midfielder	Bath City (L)		3	1	3	
Bristol C (Y), Bath (L)									
Smyth	Liam	18	Forward	Braintree Town (L)	6	4		10	4
Stevenage (Y), Braintree (L)									
Snedker	Dean	25	Goalkeeper	St Albans City	39			39	8
Northampton, Brackley (Lx2), Brackley, Kidderminster, Nuneaton, Hempstead, Kettering, Cambridge C, St Albans									

Key: X - Started; SX - Sub on; S - Non-playing Sub; Ap - Total Appearances; G/Cs - Total goals/clean sheets.

SURNAME	FIRSTNAME	AGE	POSITION	CLUB	X	SX	S	Ap	G/Cs
Soares	Louie	35	Midfielder	Hampton & Richmond Borough	6	16	2	22	2
				Slough Town		1	4	1	

Aldershot, Southend, Hayes & Y, Grimsby, Ebbsfleet (L), Alfreton (L), Hayes & Y, Basingstoke, Oxford C, Hungerford, Slough, Hampton & R, Slough

SURNAME	FIRSTNAME	AGE	POSITION	CLUB	X	SX	S	Ap	G/Cs
Sodeinde	Victor		Forward	Hereford (L)	7	3		10	3

Maidstone (Y), Nottingham F, Hereford (L)

SURNAME	FIRSTNAME	AGE	POSITION	CLUB	X	SX	S	Ap	G/Cs
Sole	Giuseppe	32	Forward	Dorking Wanderers	5	22	13	27	2

Havant & W, Woking, Basingstoke (L), Basingstoke (L), Hampton & R, Dorking W

SURNAME	FIRSTNAME	AGE	POSITION	CLUB	X	SX	S	Ap	G/Cs
Soleman	Aram	20	Midfielder	Guiseley	33	1		34	3

WBA (Y), Guiseley

SURNAME	FIRSTNAME	AGE	POSITION	CLUB	X	SX	S	Ap	G/Cs
Solkhon	Brett	37	Midfielder	Kettering Town	14	8	11	22	2

Kettering, Rushden & D, Corby, Brackley, Kettering

SURNAME	FIRSTNAME	AGE	POSITION	CLUB	X	SX	S	Ap	G/Cs
Sotiriou	Ruel	18	Forward	Dover Athletic (L)	1	2	1	3	3

Leyton O, Chelmsford (L), Hampton & R (L), Dover (L)

SURNAME	FIRSTNAME	AGE	POSITION	CLUB	X	SX	S	Ap	G/Cs
Soule	Jamie	19	Forward	Barrow (L)			2	2	2

WBA (Y), Barrow (L)

SURNAME	FIRSTNAME	AGE	POSITION	CLUB	X	SX	S	Ap	G/Cs
Southam-Hales	Macauley	24	Defender	Hartlepool United (L)	7			7	

Barry Town, Fleetwood, Hartlepool (L)

SURNAME	FIRSTNAME	AGE	POSITION	CLUB	X	SX	S	Ap	G/Cs
Southern-Cooper	Jake	20		Gateshead (L)	16			16	3

Rotherham (Y), Gateshead (L)

SURNAME	FIRSTNAME	AGE	POSITION	CLUB	X	SX	S	Ap	G/Cs
Southwell	Dayle	26	Forward	FC Halifax Town	3	6	2	9	
				Boston United (L)	3	1	1	4	
				King's Lynn Town	2	5		7	

Grimsby, Harrogate (L), Boston U, Wycombe, Guiseley, FC Halifax, Boston U (L), King's Lynn

SURNAME	FIRSTNAME	AGE	POSITION	CLUB	X	SX	S	Ap	G/Cs
Spark	Jack	19	Defender	Gloucester City		1	1	1	

Gloucester (Y)

SURNAME	FIRSTNAME	AGE	POSITION	CLUB	X	SX	S	Ap	G/Cs
Sparkes	Daniel	28	Midfielder	Barnet	10	9	5	19	2

Histon, Braintree, Torquay, Dagenham & R, Barnet

SURNAME	FIRSTNAME	AGE	POSITION	CLUB	X	SX	S	Ap	G/Cs
Spence	Tyler		Midfielder	Barrow			1		

Barrow (Y)

SURNAME	FIRSTNAME	AGE	POSITION	CLUB	X	SX	S	Ap	G/Cs
Spencer	James (Jimmy)	28	Forward	Farsley Celtic	34	2		36	10

Huddersfield (Y), Northwich V (L), Morecambe (L), Cheltenham (L), Brentford (L), Crawley (L), Scunthorpe (L), Notts Co, Plymouth, Mansfield, Farsley C

SURNAME	FIRSTNAME	AGE	POSITION	CLUB	X	SX	S	Ap	G/Cs
Spencer	Jamie	22	Midfielder	Guiseley	20	1	1	21	5

Bradford PA, Guiseley

SURNAME	FIRSTNAME	AGE	POSITION	CLUB	X	SX	S	Ap	G/Cs
Spillane	Michael	31		Chelmsford City	11	1	1	12	

Norwich, Luton (L), Brentford, Dag & Red (L), Dag & Red, Southend, Cambridge U, Sutton U, Lowestoft, Chelmsford

SURNAME	FIRSTNAME	AGE	POSITION	CLUB	X	SX	S	Ap	G/Cs
Splatt	Jamie		Defender	Dulwich Hamlet			6		

Dulwich H

SURNAME	FIRSTNAME	AGE	POSITION	CLUB	X	SX	S	Ap	G/Cs
Spooner	Craig	21	Defender	Blyth Spartans (L)	3		1	3	

Newcastle U (Y), Newcastle Benfield, Blyth S,

SURNAME	FIRSTNAME	AGE	POSITION	CLUB	X	SX	S	Ap	G/Cs
Sprague	Oliver	25	Midfielder	St Albans City	17	6	4	23	

Hendon, Welling, Billericay, Hampton & R, St Albans

SURNAME	FIRSTNAME	AGE	POSITION	CLUB	X	SX	S	Ap	G/Cs
Spratt	Harry	20	Defender	York City	5	3	14	8	

Man Utd (Y), Huddersfield U23, York

SURNAME	FIRSTNAME	AGE	POSITION	CLUB	X	SX	S	Ap	G/Cs
Spruce	James	20	Forward	Gloucester City		3	2	3	

Bristol R (Y), Gloucester, Lydney T (Dual)

SURNAME	FIRSTNAME	AGE	POSITION	CLUB	X	SX	S	Ap	G/Cs
Spyrou	Anthony	20	Midfielder	Chesterfield (L)	2	5		7	

Norwich (Y), Wrexham (L), Chesterfield (L)

SURNAME	FIRSTNAME	AGE	POSITION	CLUB	X	SX	S	Ap	G/Cs
Stanley	James		Midfielder	AFC Fylde			1		

AFC Fylde (Y)

SURNAME	FIRSTNAME	AGE	POSITION	CLUB	X	SX	S	Ap	G/Cs
Stansfield	Harry		Midfielder	Darlington			3		

Darlington

SURNAME	FIRSTNAME	AGE	POSITION	CLUB	X	SX	S	Ap	G/Cs
Stanyer	Finley		Defender	Stockport County			1		

Stockport (Y)

SURNAME	FIRSTNAME	AGE	POSITION	CLUB	X	SX	S	Ap	G/Cs
Starcenko	Aleksandrs	19	Midfielder	Guiseley		6	1	6	

Frickley Ath (Y), Guiseley

SURNAME	FIRSTNAME	AGE	POSITION	CLUB	X	SX	S	Ap	G/Cs
Staunton	Joshua	24	Defender	FC Halifax Town	42			42	2

Gillingham, St Albans (L), Dagenham & R, Woking, FC Halifax

SURNAME	FIRSTNAME	AGE	POSITION	CLUB PLAYED FOR	X	SX	S	Ap	G/Cs
Staunton	Reece	18	Defender	Bradford Park Avenue (L)	7			7	
Bradford C (Y), Bradford PA									
Stead	Jon	37	Forward	Harrogate Town	17	15	7	32	7
Huddersfield (Y), Blackburn, Sunderland, Derby (L), Sheff Utd, Ipswich, Coventry (L), Bristol C, Huddersfield, Oldham (L), Bradford (L), Bradford (Lx2), Notts Co, Harrogate									
Stead	Louis	28	Midfielder	Hampton & Richmond Borough	6	4	4	10	
Egham T, Northwood, Greenford U, Chalfont St P, Beaconsfield T, Hampton & R									
Stearn	Ross	29	Midfielder	Bath City	11	19	6	30	6
Forest Green, Sutton U, Eastleigh, Sutton U, Bath (L), Bath									
Steer	Rene	30	Defender	Maidenhead United	26	3	9	29	
Arsenal, Gillingham (L), Oldham, Boston Utd, Maidenhead									
Stenson	Matty		Forward	Solihull Moors	3	5	1	8	2
				AFC Telford United (L)	17	4	1	21	4
Barwell, Leamington, Solihull, Telford (L)									
Stephens	Dave	28	Defender	Boreham Wood	30	2	7	32	1
Norwich , Lincoln (L), Hibernian, Barnet, Boreham W									
Sterling	Tyrone	32	Defender	Hemel Hempstead Town	31	1	1	32	
Cray W, Dartford, Dover, Bromley, Concord R, Hemel H									
Sterling-James	Omari	26	Forward	Kettering Town (L)	2	1		3	1
Birmingham (Y), Cheltenham, Oxford C (L), Gloucester (L), Solihull M, Mansfield, Solihull M (L), Brackley (L), Kettering (L)									
Stevens	Connor	22	Defender	Wealdstone	36			36	2
Watford (Y), Oxford C (L), Wealdstone									
Stevenson	Bradley	21	Midfielder	Chelmsford City	5		1	5	
Gillingham (Y), Chelmsford									
Stevenson	Toby	20	Defender	Dagenham & Redbridge (L)	12		1	12	
Charlton (Y), Dagenham (L)									
Stewart	Ethan	20	Defender	Alfreton Town (L)	2			2	
Nottm Forest (Y), Billericay (L), Alfreton (L)									
Stewart	Nathan	21	Midfielder	King's Lynn Town		5	14	5	
Wroxham, Norwich U, King's Lynn, Wroxham (L), Leiston (L)									
Stirman	Josh	19	Midfielder	Tonbridge Angels		1	7	1	
Tonbridge A (Y), Leicester (U18)									
Stohrer	Gary	27	Defender	Kettering Town	33	2		35	1
Irchester, Long Buckby, Garforth, Ossett T, Shaw Lane, Frickley, Kettering									
Stone	Frankie		Defender	Braintree Town	2	1	11	3	
Braintree (Y)									
Stopforth	Gary	33	Midfielder	Chester	20	6	6	26	
Ramsbottom, Salford, Stockport, Colne, Chester									
Storer	Jack	22	Defender	Leamington	4	1		5	
				AFC Telford United		1		1	
Stevenage, Birmingham, Yeovil (L), Gloucester (L), Solihull M (L), Partick, Leamington, Telford									
Storer	Kyle	33	Midfielder	Solihull Moors	39	1		40	
Leicester (Y), Bedworth U, Tamworth, Hinckley U, Atherstone, Nuneaton, Kidderminster, Wrexham, Cheltenham, Solihull									
Storey	Alex	21	Defender	Darlington	26		1	26	1
Sunderland (Y), Sunderland RCA, Darlington (Dual)									
Straker	Anthony	31	Midfielder	Havant & Waterlooville	34	1		35	1
Aldershot (Y), Southend, York, Motherwell (L), Grimsby, Aldershot, Bath, Havant & W									
Street	Alex	28	Goalkeeper	King's Lynn Town	40			40	12
Wisbech, King's Lynn, Wisbech (Dual), Deeping R (Dual), Spalding (Dual), Leiston (L)									
Streete	Theo	32	Defender	AFC Telford United	28	1	5	29	
Derby (Y), Doncaster (L), Rotherham, Solihull, Alfreton, Nuneaton, Solihull, Brackley, Telford									
Strizovic	Josh	20	Goalkeeper	Dagenham & Redbridge			12		
Braintree (Y), Waltham F (L), Burnham R, Billericay, Maidstone, Dagenham & R									
Stryjek	Max	23	Goalkeeper	Eastleigh	43		2	43	8
Polonia (Y), Sunderland (Y), Boston U (L), Accrington (L), Eastleigh (L), Eastleigh									
Styche	Reece	31	Forward	Hereford FC	16	9	2	25	4
Hednesford, Bromsgrove (L), Grantham, Coalville T, Shepshed D, Chasetown, Forest GR, Wycombe (L), Kidderminster, Tamworth (Lx2), Macclesfield (L), Macclesfield, Gateshead, Nuneaton (L), Tamworth, Darlington, Alfreton, Hereford									

Key: X - Started; SX - Sub on; S - Non-playing Sub; Ap - Total Appearances; G/Cs - Total goals/clean sheets.

2019-20 NATIONAL. NORTH & SOUTH PLAYERS — APPEARANCES

SURNAME	FIRSTNAME	AGE	POSITION	CLUB	X	SX	S	Ap	G/Cs
Summerfield	Luke	32	Midfielder	Wrexham	29	5		34	2
Plymouth (Y), Bournemouth (L), Leyton O (L), Cheltenham, Shrewsbury, York, Grimsby, Macclesfield (L), Wrexham									
Summerly	Jordan	23	Defender	Blyth Spartans		1	2	1	
North Shields, Blyth S									
Sundrie	Munashe	23	Defender	Hemel Hempstead Town	5	6	3	11	
				St Albans City	13	1	1	14	1
Kettering, Hemel H, St Albans									
Suraci	Patrick		Forward	Weymouth			1		
Portsmouth (Y), Eastleigh (L), Lommel U (Bel), Gosport B, Bognor R, Weymouth (L), Gosport B, Weymouth, Blackfield & L									
Sutherland	Frankie	26	Forward	Ebbsfleet United	31	5		36	
QPR, Portsmouth (L), Leyton O (L), AFC Wimbledon (L), Dagenham & R (L), Crawley Town (L), Woking, Whitehawk, Bromley, Ebbsfleet									
Sutton	Shane	31	Defender	AFC Telford United	23	1	1	24	1
Newtown, Telford									
Swaine	Rob	32	Defender	Welling United	33			33	1
Chelmsford, Billericay, Bromley, Billericay, Chelmsford, Maidstone, Welling									
Sweeney	Dan	26	Midfielder	Barnet	21	1	1	22	
Wimbledon (Yth), Kingstonian, Dulwich Hamlet, Maidstone, Barnet, Hampton & R (L)									
Sweeney	Dan	22	Midfielder	Bradford Park Avenue (L)	8			8	1
				Gloucester City (L)	2	2	1	4	
Kidderminster (Y), Halesowen (L), Stourport (L), Rushall (L), Sutton C (L), Stourport (L), Stourport, Solihull, Hednesford (L),									
Leamington (L), Bradford PA (L), Gloucester (L)									
Sweet	Michael	26	Forward	Blyth Spartans	22	7	1	29	4
Gateshead (Y), Darlington (L), Billingham Syth, Consett, Blyth S									
Syers	David	32	Midfielder	Farsley Celtic	24	10	2	34	10
Farsley C, Harrogate T, Guiseley, Bradford, Doncaster, Scunthorpe (L), Scunthorpe, Rochdale, Guiseley, Darlington, Farsley C									
Sykes	Jamie		Goalkeeper	Kettering Town			1		
Kettering (Y)									
Sykes-Kenworthy	George	20	Goalkeeper	Guiseley (L)	9			9	4
Bradford C (Y), Guiseley (L)									
Syla	Roy	20	Midfielder	Barnet			4		
Barnet (Y), Hampton & R (L)									
Symons	Michael	33	Forward	Hereford	8	7	4	15	3
Gloucester, Worcester, Oxford C, Worcester, Gloucester, Hereford									
Symons	Oliver		Forward	Gateshead			1		
Gateshead (Y)									
Szczepaniak	Dawid	20	Goalkeeper	Wrexham	1		17	1	
Airbus, Morecambe, Wrexham									
Tait	Joe	30	Defender	York City	37		2	37	2
Dayton Dutch Lions (US), Philadelphia Union, Gateshead, Spennymoor, York									
Tamplin	Archie	17	Midfielder	Billericay Town		2	8	2	
Billericay T									
Tanner	Craig	25	Forward	Aldershot Town	13		1	13	4
Plymouth (Y), Reading, Wimbledon (L), Plymouth (L), Plymouth (L), Motherwell, Aldershot									
Tanner	Ollie		Forward	Bromley		3	5	3	
Bromley (Y)									
Tapp	Finn	20	Defender	Oxford City	22	2	4	24	1
MK Dons (Y), Oxford C									
Tarbuck	Bradley	24	Forward	Havant & Waterlooville	12	19	6	31	3
Portsmouth (Y), Dartford (L), Dorchester (L), Dorchester, Havant & W									
Tarh	Ayuk	27	Midfielder	Maidstone United		4	1	4	1
DAC (Slov), Roye Noyon (Fra), Maidstone									
Tarpey	Dave	31	Forward	Woking	36	3		39	8
Henley Town, Basingstoke, Hampton & R, Walton & H (L), Chertsey (L), Farnborough, Hampton & R, Maidenhead, Barnet,									
Maidenhead (L), Woking (L), Woking									
Tavares	Fabio	19	Forward	Curzon Ashton (L)		3		3	1
Rochdale (Y), Curzon A (L)									
Taylor	Andy	34	Defender	AFC Fylde	14	2	5	16	1
Blackburn (Y), QPR (L), Blackpool (L), Crewe (L), Huddersfield (L), Tranmere, Sheff Utd, Walsall, Blackpool, Oldham, AFC Fylde									
Taylor	Bobby-Joe	25	Midfielder	Dover Athletic	27	4	2	31	2
Chelsea (Y), Cambridge, Bishop's St (L), Maidstone, Aldershot, Bromley, Dover (L), Dover									

SURNAME	FIRSTNAME	AGE	POSITION	CLUB PLAYED FOR	X	SX	S	Ap	G/Cs
Taylor	Connor	27	Forward	Leamington	8	20	8	28	2
Aston Villa (Y), Tamworth (L), Walsall, Nuneaton (L), Nuneaton, Tamworth, Leamington									
Taylor	Glen	30	Forward	Spennymoor Town	34	1		35	24
Blyth Spartans, Spennymoor									
Taylor	Harry	23	Defender	Barnet	32		2	32	
Chelsea (Y), Barnet (Y), Woking (L)									
Taylor	Harry		Midfielder	Aldershot Town		1	1	1	
Aldershot (Y)									
Taylor	Jack	21	Midfielder	Barnet	27	1		28	9
Cheslea (Y), Barnet (Y), Hampton & R (L)									
Taylor	Jason	33	Midfielder	Barrow	29	6	2	35	
Oldham , Stockport (L), Stockport, Rotherham, Rochdale (L), Cheltenham, Northampton, Eastleigh AFC Fylde, Barrow									
Taylor	Joe			King's Lynn Town			1		
King's Lynn									
Taylor	Joel	24	Defender	Chester	34	3	1	37	
Stoke (Y), Rochdale (L), Kidderminster, Chester									
Taylor	Josh	25	Forward	Havant & Waterlooville	38	1		39	4
Halifax, Sutton U, Hampton & R (L), Maidstone (L), Havant & W									
Taylor	Lewis	33	Midfielder	Dorking Wanderers	11	5	7	16	
Fulham (Y), Wimbledon, Tonbridge A, Bromley, Carshalton, Kingstonian, Whitehawk, Margate, Dorking W									
Taylor	Matthew	20	Defender	Harrogate Town		1	5	1	
				Kettering Town (L)	16			16	1
Wigan (Y), Derby (Y), Gainsborough T (L), Oxford U, Banbury (L), Harrogate (NC), Kettering (L)									
Taylor	Quade	26	Defender	Dulwich Hamlet	33		3	33	3
Dulwich H, Crystal P (U23), Welling (L), Bolton, Dag & Red (L), Braintree, Dulwich H									
Taylor	Rhys	30	Goalkeeper	Bradford Park Avenue	7			7	2
Chelsea, QPR (L), Crewe (L), Crewe (L), Rotherham (L), Southend, PNE, Macclesfield, Newport Co, Wrexham (L),									
AFC Fylde, Tranmere (L), Macclesfield, Bradford PA									
Taylor-Randle	Reiss		Midfielder	Kidderminster Harriers			1		
Bromsgrove SP (Y), Kidderminster (Y) Stourport S (L) Lye (L)									
Tchuimeni-Nimely	Alex	28	Forward	Kettering Town	1	3	2	4	
Man City (Y), Middlesbrough (L), Coventry (L), C Palace (L), Port Vale, Poli Timisoara (Rom), Viitorul, Stabaek (Nor),									
Honka (Fin), Kettering									
Teague	Andrew	34	Defender	Chorley	21		4	21	
Macclesfield, Hyde U (L), Leigh Gen, Lancaster C, Chorley									
Tear	Dominic	20	Midfielder	Gateshead	18	9	3	27	5
Huddersfield (Y), Larne (NI) (L), Gateshead									
Temelci	Zihni	21	Midfielder	Maidstone United	16	2		18	2
Goztepe (Y) (Tur), Maidstone									
Thacker	Josh	20	Defender	Alfreton Town	26	1		27	2
Hull C (Y), Alfreton									
Thackray	Kris	32	Defender	Blyth Spartans	15			15	3
Reggina, Monopoli (L), Ancona (L), Andria, Cosenza, QFC (Malta), Alem Aachen (Ger), KFC Uerduingen, Gzira Utd (Malta),									
Spennymoor, Blyth S									
Thanoj	Andi	27	Midfielder	Boston United	25	5	3	30	7
Grimsby (Y), Alfreton, Harrogate, Redditch, Boston U									
Tharme	Douglas		Defender	AFC Telford United (L)		1	3	1	
				Wrexham	3		1	3	
Wrexham (Y), Telford (L)									
Theobalds	D'Sean		Midfielder	Tonbridge Angels	25	1		26	6
Leatherhead, Concord R, Leatherhead, Tonbridge A									
Thewlis	Jordan	27	Forward	Boston United	29	7	1	36	17
Scunthorpe (Y), Gainsborough, Harrogate, Boston U (L), Boston U									
Thomas	Adam	26	Midfielder	Stockport County	32	8		40	5
Stoke (Y), Macclesfield (L), Hednesford (L), Hednesford, Stockport									
Thomas	Aswad	30	Defender	Ebbsfleet United	8	1	1	9	2
Charlton, Accrington (L), Barnet (L), Woking, Braintree, Grimsby, Woking, Dover (L), Dover, Sutton U, Ebbsfleet									
Thomas	Josh	21	Midfielder	Gloucester City	28			28	
Cheltenham (Y), Gloucester									

Key: X - Started; SX - Sub on; S - Non-playing Sub; Ap - Total Appearances; G/Cs - Total goals/clean sheets.

SURNAME	FIRSTNAME	AGE	POSITION	CLUB	X	SX	S	Ap	G/Cs
Thomas	Kieran		Defender	Hereford	23	4	3	27	1
Cinderford, Gloucester, Hereford									
Thomas	Sorba	20	Midfielder	Boreham Wood	33	3	1	36	5
Boreham W (Y)									
Thomas	Wes	33	Forward	Notts County	26	13	2	39	9
Fisher, Dagenham & R, Grays (L), Cheltenham, Crawley, Bournemouth, Portsmouth (L), Blackpool (L), Birmingham (L),									
Rotherham, Birmingham, Swindon (L), Bradford (L), Oxford U, Grimsby, Notts Co									
Thomas-Asante	Brandon	21	Forward	Ebbsfleet United		3		3	
MK Dons (Y), Sutton U (L), Oxford C (L), Ebbsfleet, Salford									
Thompson	Conor	25	Goalkeeper	Chippenham Town			17		
Swindon (Y), Gloucester, Chippenham, Torquay, Newport Co, Gloucester, Chippenham									
Thompson	Gary	39	Midfielder	Bradford Park Rangers			1		
Morecambe, Scunthorpe, Bradford C, Notts Co, Wycombe, Morecambe, Bradford PA (Manager),									
Thompson	Jordan	21	Defender	Boreham Wood (L)	6	2	17	8	
				Wrexham (L)	5			5	
Coventry, Barrow (L), Boreham W (L), Wrexham (L)									
Thompson	Lewis	20	Defender	AFC Fylde (L)	2	1		3	
Blackburn (Y), FC United (L), AFC Fylde (L)									
Thompson	Stephen	31	Forward	Darlington	27	9	3	36	6
Middlesbrough (Y), Port Vale, Stafford R (L), Telford, Durham C, Darlington									
Thompson	Tony	25	Goalkeeper	Altrincham	37		3	37	15
Rotherham (Y), Southport (L), Morecambe, Chester, AFC Fylde, Altrincham									
Thompson-Brissett	Jaden	19	Midfielder	Maidenhead United (L)		3	3	3	
Norwich (Y), Brentford, Maidenhead (L)									
Thomson	Ben	31	Midfielder	Weymouth	30	4	2	34	8
Team Bath, Weymouth									
Thomson	Connor	24	Defender	Gateshead	2	6	2	8	
Carlisle (Y), Blackburn (Y), Barrow (L), FC Halifax, Gateshead, Scarborough (L)									
Thomson	George	28	Midfielder	Harrogate Town	16	14	5	30	5
Histon, King's Lynn (L), King's Lynn, Chester, FC United (L), FC United, Harrogate									
Thomson	Matthew	20	Defender	Chester			2		
Chester									
Thornley	Oliver	21	Defender	Curzon Ashton	15	1	4	16	1
Curzon A									
Thornton	William	22	Defender	Guiseley			2		
Guiseley									
Thorp	Ali		Forward	Hungerford Town			2		
Hungerford (Y)									
Tiehi	Christ Junior	22	Midfielder	Woking		1		1	
				Tonbridge Angels (L)	15	2	1	17	1
Le Harve (Y), Woking, Tonbridge A (L)									
Tiensia	Junior	19	Defender	Havant & Waterlooville (L)	4	1		5	
Millwall (Y), Havant & W (L)									
Tilley	James	22	Forward	Yeovil Town (L)	9	14	2	23	
Brighton (Y), Cork (L), Yeovil (L)									
Timlin	Michael	35	Midfielder	Ebbsfleet United	4		1	4	
Swindon (Y), Southend (L), Southend (L), Southend, Stevenage, Ebbsfleet									
Tingley	James		Midfielder	Maidstone United		1	2	1	
Maidstone (Y)									
Tinkler	Robbie	23	Defender	Aldershot Town	32		1	32	2
Middlesbrough (Y), North Ferriby (L), Gateshead (L), Gateshead, Aldershot									
Togwell	Lee		Midfielder	Slough Town	35	1	1	36	
Slough									
Togwell	Sam	35	Midfielder	Slough Town	40			40	4
Crystal Palace, Oxford U (L), Northampton (L), Port Vale (L), Barnsley, Scunthorpe, Chesterfield, Wycombe (L), Barnet, Eastleigh, Slough									
Tokarczyk	Alex	28	Goalkeeper	St Albans City			2		
Farnborough, Maidenhead, Hemel H, Falkirk, Montrose (L), Basingstoke, Whitehawk, St Albans									
Tollitt	Ben	25	Midfielder	Wrexham (L)	10	7	6	17	1
Skelmersdale, Portsmouth, Tranmere, Wrexham (L), Blackpool, Wrexham (L)									

2019-20 NATIONAL. NORTH & SOUTH PLAYERS — APPEARANCES

SURNAME	FIRSTNAME	AGE	POSITION	CLUB PLAYED FOR	X	SX	S	Ap	G/Cs
Tomlinson	Ben	30	Forward	Alfreton Town	7	14	4	21	2
				Worksop, Macclesfield, Alfreton, Lincoln, Barnet, Grimsby (L), Tranmere (L), Barrow (L), Carlisle, Halifax, Alfreton					
Tomlinson	Joe	20	Defender	Hungerford Town	34	1		35	4
				Yeovil (Y), Brighton, Bognor R (L), Hungerford					
Tootle	Matt	29	Defender	Notts County		2	1	2	
				Chesterfield (L)	3			3	
				Crewe (Y), Shrewsbury, Notts Co, Chesterfield (L)					
Torrance	Joel		Goalkeeper	Altrincham			15		
				Altrincham (Y)					
Torres	Sergio	36	Midfielder	Eastbourne Borough	11	2	1	13	
				Wycombe, Peterborough, Lincoln, Crawley, Whitehawk, Eastbourne B					
Toulson	Ryan	34	Defender	Bradford Park Avenue	12	2		14	
				Halifax, Harrogate T, Guiseley, Halifax, Guiseley, Bradford PA					
Touray	Momodou	20	Forward	Torquay United (L)		1		1	
				Newport Co, Leicester U23, Barry Town (L), Torquay (L), Barry Town (L)					
Toure	Gime	26	Forward	Hartlepool United	31	9		40	13
				Brest Viry-Chatillon, West Brom, La Roche Vendee, Fontenay-Foot-Vendee, Macclesfield, Unattached, AFC Fylde, Sutton U, Hartlepool					
Town	Jim		Goalkeeper	Dartford			2		
				Dartford (Y)					
Trennery	Kyle	20	Goalkeeper	Farsley Celtic	13	2	11	15	6
				Halifax (Y), Albion Sports (L), Farsley C, Clitheroe (L)					
Trickett-Smith	Daniel	24	Midfielder	Curzon Ashton (L)	6	2		8	
				Sacramento R (US), Port Vale, Curzon A (L)					
Trinovas	Nojus		Goalkeeper	Slough Town			12		
				Slough (Y)					
Trotman	Luke	23	Defender	Darlington	2			2	
				Luton (Y), Nuneaton, Darlington					
Tshimanga	Kabongo	24	Forward	Boreham Wood	41			41	19
				MK Dons, Aldershot (L), Chelmsford (L), Corby (L), Nuneaton (L), Throttur Reykjavik, MK Dons, Yeovil (L), Boston U, Oxford C, Boreham W					
Tupper	Joe	22	Goalkeeper	Havant & Waterlooville			1		
				Reading (Y), Margate (L), Crystal P (U23), Margate, Havant & W					
Turnbull	Paul	31	Midfielder	Stockport County	32	2	3	34	1
				Stockport, Altrincham (L), Northampton, Stockport (L), Stockport (L), Lincoln (L), Macclesfield, Barrow, Chester, Stockport					
Turner	Ben	31	Defender	Notts County	24	2		26	2
				Coventry, Peterborough (L), Oldham (L), Cardiff, Coventry (L), Burton, Mansfield, Notts Co					
Turner	Jack	27	Goalkeeper	Slough Town	41			41	8
				Wimbledon, Staines, Slough					
Turner	Joe	26	Forward	Tonbridge Angels	32	2		34	12
				Hampton & R, Wealdstone, Tonbridge A					
Tuson-Firth	George	22	Midfielder	Sutton United	2	2	1	4	
				Aldershot (Y), Sutton U					
Tuton	Shaun	28	Forward	Boston United	2	14	7	16	
				Alfreton Town		1	2	1	
				Halifax, Barnsley, Grimsby (L), Barrow (L), Halifax (L), Chester (NC), Spennymoor, Chorley (L), Boston U, Alfreton					
Tutonda	David	24	Defender	Barnet	29	3	2	32	2
				Cardiff (Yth), Newport Co (L), York (L), Barnet					
Twine	Scott	20	Forward	Chippenham Town (L)	8			8	6
				Swindon (Y), Chippenham (Lx2), Waterford (L), Chippenham (L)					
Tyler	Rhys	28	Defender	Chippenham Town	33	1	2	34	3
				Hungerford, Wealdstone, Chippenham					
Tyson	Nathan	38	Forward	Notts County	7	10	5	17	1
				Chesterfield (L)	4	2		6	3
				Wycombe, Notts F, Derby, Millwall (L), Blackpool, Fleetwood (L), Notts Co (L), Doncaster, Kilmarnock, Wycombe, Notts Co, Chesterfield (L)					
Tzanev	Nik	23	Goalkeeper	Sutton United (L)	21			21	6
				Wimbledon, Sutton U (L)					
Ugwu	Gozie	27	Forward	Ebbsfleet United	34	9	1	43	15
				Reading (Y), Ebbsfleet (L), Yeovil (L), Plymouth (L), Shrewsbury (L), Dunfermline, Yeovil, Wycombe, Woking, Chesterfield, Boreham W (L), Ebbsfleet (L), Ebbsfleet					

Key: X - Started; SX - Sub on; S - Non-playing Sub; Ap - Total Appearances; G/Cs - Total goals/clean sheets.

APPEARANCES

SURNAME	FIRSTNAME	AGE	POSITION	CLUB	X	SX	S	Ap	G/Cs
Umerah	Josh	22	Forward	Ebbsfleet United	26	10	3	36	4
Charlton (Y), Kilmarnock (L), Wycombe (L), Boreham W (L), Ebbsfleet									
Unwin	James		Defender	Gloucester City			1		
Gloucester									
Upward	Ryan	28	Midfielder	Maidenhead United	39	2		41	4
Maidenhead									
Urwin	Matthew	26	Goalkeeper	Chorley	27			27	7
Blackburn (Y), Stalybridge (L), Bradford, AFC Fylde, Fleetwood, Telford (L), Chorley (L), Chorley (L), Chorley									
van Velzen	Gyliano	26	Forward	Aldershot Town (L)		4	1	4	
Man Utd (Y), Antwerp (L), Utrecht, Volendam, Roda, Crawley, Aldershot (L)									
Vasiliou	Antonis	19	Midfielder	Barnet		5	6	5	
				St Albans City (L)		2	2	2	
Barnet (Y), St Albans (L)									
Vaughan	Lee	33	Defender	Solihull Moors	29	3	3	32	
Walsall (Y), Telford U, Kidderminster, Cheltenham, Tranmere, Kidderminster, Solihull									
Vernam	Charles	23	Midfielder	Chorley (L)	5			5	3
Derby (Y), IBV (L), Coventry (L), Grimsby (L), Grimsby, Chorley (L)									
Vidal	Javan	31	Defender	Kettering Town	3	2	2	5	
Man City (Y), Derby (L), Chesterfield (L), Stockport, Rochdale, Tamworth, Wrexham, Guiseley, Bradford PA, Hednesford, Kettering									
Vilhete	Mauro	27	Midfielder	Barnet	19	10	3	29	4
Barnet, Hendon (L), Boreham W (L), Boreham W (L), Boreham W (L)									
Vincent	Frank		Midfielder	Torquay United (L)	18	3	1	21	
Bournemouth (Y), Torquay (L), Torquay (L)									
Vincenti	Peter	33	Midfielder	Hereford (L)	17	1	1	18	5
Stevenage, Mansfield (L), Aldershot, Rochdale, Coventry, Macclesfield, Hereford (L)									
Vint	Ronnie	23	Defender	Dartford	18	4	17	22	
Dartford									
Vose	Dominic	26	Midfielder	Dulwich Hamlet	25	6	7	31	1
Braintree, Barnet, Colchester, Welling, Wrexham, Scunthorpe, Grimsby (L), Whitehawk, Bromley, Chester, Dulwich H									
Wabo	Norman	22	Forward	Dartford	6	12	3	18	4
Southend, Cambridge C (L), Ebbsfleet (L), Maidstone (L), Braintree (L), Dartford									
Waddington	Mark	23	Midfielder	Barrow	2	2	5	4	
				Blyth Spartans (L)	7	2		9	
Blackpool (Y), Stoke, Kilmarnock (L), Falkirk (L), Barrow, Blyth S (L)									
Wade	Bradley	19	Goalkeeper	Guiseley (L)	5			5	3
Rochdale (Y), Barrow (L), Guiseley (L)									
Wafula	Jonathan	26	Midfielder	Boston United	3	11	4	14	1
Chesterfield, Worksop, Gainsborough, Boston U									
Wakefield	Charlie	20	Midfielder	Chesterfield	2	3	5	5	
Chesterfield (Y)									
Wakefield	Jack	20	Midfielder	Chippenham Town			3		
Chippenham (Y), Mangotsfield (L)									
Wakefield	Josh	26	Defender	Weymouth	26	11	4	37	1
Bournemouth (Y), Dagenham & R (L), Dorchester (L), Welling (L), Torquay (L), Bristol R (L), Yeovil (L), Walsall (L), Aldershot, Poole, Weymouth									
Waldren	Darren	31	Midfielder	Billericay Town	4	5	2	9	
				Welling United	13	3		16	3
Bromley, Dulwich H, Welling, Billericay, Welling									
Walker	Adam	29	Midfielder	AFC Telford United	34		1	34	3
Coventry (Y), Nuneaton (L), Nuneaton, Solihull, Brackley, Telford									
Walker	Charlie	30	Forward	Eastbourne Borough	22	10	1	32	9
Luton, Boreham W (L), Aldershot, St Albans, Eastbourne B									
Walker	Ethan	17	Midfielder	Altrincham (L)	3	1	5	4	
PNE (Y), Altrincham (L)									
Walker	Glenn	33	Midfielder	Brackley Town	35			35	2
Banbury, Corby, Brackley, Hednesford, Brackley									
Walker	Josh	22	Forward	Barnet	27	7	2	34	15
Tottenham (Yth), Fulham (Yth), Hendon, Barnet									

SURNAME	FIRSTNAME	AGE	POSITION	CLUB PLAYED FOR	X	SX	S	Ap	G/Cs
Walker	Laurie	30	Goalkeeper	Hampton & Richmond Borough (L)	12		1	12	3
				Chelmsford City (L)	13			13	2
Cambridge U, Morecambe, Kettering, Brackley, Leamington, Hemel H, Oxford C, Brackley, Hemel H, MK Dons, Hampton & R (L), Chelmsford (L)									
Walker	Lewis	22	Forward	Aldershot Town (L)	8	6	2	14	
Derby (Y), Darlington (L), QPR, Aldershot (L)									
Walker	Mitch	28	Goalkeeper	Aldershot Town	41			41	8
Brighton, Eastbourne B (L), Dover, Aldershot									
Walker	Nicky	25	Midfielder	Boston United	10	6	5	16	
Rotherham (Y), Barrow (L), Wycombe (L), Boston U, Bradford PA, Boston U, Clipstone (L), Buxton, Shaw Lane, Gainsborough, Boston U									
Walker	Paul	33	Forward	Farsley Celtic	1	3	3	4	
Liversedge, Garforth T, Buxton, Bradford PA, Farsley C (L), Farsley C									
Walker	Sam	33	Midfielder	Stockport County	26	5	6	31	2
Curzon Ashton, Halifax, Salford, Stockport, Curzon Ashton (L)									
Walker	Tom	24	Midfielder	Stockport County (L)	16	1		17	5
				AFC Fylde	8	1		9	
Bolton (Y), Bury (L), FC United, Salford City, Stockport (L), AFC Fylde									
Wall	Alex	29	Forward	Hemel Hempstead Town	5	7		12	1
				Woking	4	3		7	1
Maidenhead, Luton (L), Luton, Dartford (L), Bristol R (L), Bromley, Hungerford, Concord R, Hemel H, Woking									
Wall	Luke	23	Forward	Curzon Ashton	7	3	4	10	2
				Altrincham	5	6	8	11	
Blackburn (Y), Skelmersdale (L), Accrington, Bangor, Curzon A, Witton (NC), Altrincham									
Wallen	Joshua	23	Midfielder	Hemel Hempstead Town		1	1	1	
QPR, Chelmsford (L), FC United, Hemel H, Buxton									
Walsh	Max		Defender	Dartford			4		
Dartford (Y)									
Walters	Dexter	21	Midfielder	Leamington (L)	12	2	5	14	
Tamworth, Coventry, Leamington (L)									
Walters	Lewis	25	Forward	Altrincham	2	7	4	9	1
Leeds (Y), Nottingham F, Barrow (L) Guiseley, AFC Fylde, Altrincham									
Walton	Simon	32	Midfielder	Havant & Waterlooville	17		15	17	1
Leeds, Charlton, Ipswich (L), Cardiff (L), QPR, Hull (L), Plymouth, Blackpool (L), Crewe (L), Sheff U (L), Hartlepool, Stevenage, Crawley, Guiseley, Sutton U, Billericay, Maidstone (L), Maidstone, Havant & W									
Walton	Tyler	21	Midfielder	Farsley Celtic	29	8		37	4
Man City (Y), Leeds (Y), Barnsley, York, Frickley, Farsley C									
Wanadio	Luke	27	Midfielder	Dartford	26	8	4	34	4
Staines, Welling, Dartford, Bromley, Aldershot, Dulwich H (L), Dartford									
Ward	Calum	19	Goalkeeper	Weymouth (L)	39			39	11
Bournemouth (Y), Weymouth (L)									
Ward	Dan	22	Midfielder	Spennymoor Town	9	6	3	15	
Newcastle (Y), Middlesbrough U23, Spennymoor									
Ward	Elliott	35	Defender	Chelmsford City	5			5	
West Ham (Y), Peterborough (L), Bristol R (L), Plymouth (L), Coventry, Doncaster (L), PNE (L), Norwich, Notts F (L), Bournemouth, Huddersfield (L), Blackburn, MK Dons (L), Notts Co, Cambridge U, Chelmsford									
Ward	Tom	29	Defender	King's Lynn Town	8	1	3	9	
Sleaford, Boston U, Gainsborough T, St Albans (L), St Albans, St Neots, King's Lynn, Grantham, King's Lynn									
Wareham	Jayden		Forward	Woking			3	3	
Woking (Y)									
Waring	George	25	Forward	Chester	14	16	1	30	4
Stoke (Y), Barnsley (L), Oxford U (L), Shrewsbury (L), Carlisle (L), Tranmere, Halifax (L), Kidderminster (L), Kidderminster (L), Chester									
Warner-Eley	Luke		Defender	Dartford	6			6	
Uxbridge, St Ives, Barton R, Chesham, Dartford, Harrow B, Royston									
Warre	Dan		Forward	Chippenham Town			2		
Chippenham (Y)									
Warren	Gary	35	Defender	Torquay United (L)	4			4	
Team Bath, Newport Co, Inverness, Yeovil, Exeter, Torquay (L)									
Warren	Tyrell	21	Defender	Boston United (L)	2		3	2	
Man Utd (Y), Boston U (L)									

Key: X - Started; SX - Sub on; S - Non-playing Sub; Ap - Total Appearances; G/Cs - Total goals/clean sheets.

SURNAME	FIRSTNAME	AGE	POSITION	CLUB	X	SX	S	Ap	G/Cs
Wassmer	Charlie	29	Defender	Billericay Town	5		3	5	1
				Hampton & Richmond Borough	18		2	18	2

Hayes (Y), Harrow B (L), Crawley, Fleetwood (L), Dagenham & R (L), Cambridge U, Hayes & Y, Margate, Maidenhead, Hampton & R, Woking, Met Police (L), Leatherhead (L), Maidstone (L), Billericay, Hampton & R (L), Hampton & R

					X	SX	S	Ap	G/Cs
Waterfield	Lewis		Midfielder	Eastleigh		2	6	2	

Eastleigh (Y)

| Waters | Matty | 22 | Midfielder | Chester | 9 | 6 | 11 | 15 | 2 |

Chester

| Watkins | Andy | 35 | Forward | Bath City | 14 | 9 | 3 | 23 | 5 |

Truro, Bath

| Watkinson | Owen | 19 | Forward | Curzon Ashton (L) | 5 | 1 | | 6 | |

Blackpool (Y), Curzon A (L)

| Watson | Jordan | 27 | Defender | Darlington | 19 | 5 | 16 | 24 | |

Sunderland (Y), Blyth S, Darlington, Blyth S, Darlington

| Watt | Sanchez | | Midfielder | Wealdstone | 7 | 15 | 5 | 22 | 2 |

Arsenal (Y), Southend (L), Leeds (L), Sheff Wed (L), Crawley (L), Colchester (L), Colchester, Kerala Blasters (India), Crawley, Billericay, Hemel H (L), Hemel H, Wealdstone

| Watters | Max | 21 | Forward | Maidstone United (L) | 4 | | | 4 | |

Doncaster (Y), Maidstone (L)

| Weaver | Jake | 23 | Goalkeeper | Leamington (L) | 39 | | | 39 | 9 |

Birmingham (Y), Hungerford (L), Kidderminster (L), Leamington (L)

| Webb | Bradley | 19 | Midfielder | Hungerford Town (L) | 8 | 2 | | 10 | |

Fulham (Y), Bristol C, Yate (L), Taunton (L), Hungerford (L)

| Webb | David | | Midfielder | Spennymoor Town | | | 2 | | |

Spennymoor

| Wedgbury | Samuel | 31 | Midfielder | Chesterfield | 14 | | 1 | 14 | |

Sheff Utd, Mansfield (L), Macclesfield, Altrincham (L), Stevenage, Forest Green, Wrexham, Chesterfield

| Weeks | Declan | 24 | Midfielder | Kidderminster Harriers | 20 | 1 | | 21 | 1 |

Southport, Kidderminster

| Weir | Robbie | 31 | Midfielder | Chesterfield | 10 | 9 | 5 | 19 | |

Aye United (Y), Larne, Sunderland, York (L), Tranmere (L), Tranmere, Burton, Leyton O, Chesterfield

| Wells | Ashley | 28 | Defender | Weymouth | 1 | 7 | 4 | 8 | |

Weymouth, Dorchester (Dual)

| Wells | Ben | 20 | Midfielder | Concord Rangers (L) | 12 | 1 | 1 | 13 | |

West Ham (Y), QPR (Y), Concord R (L)

| Wells | George | 24 | Midfielder | Slough Town | 36 | | 1 | 36 | 4 |

Slough

| West | Hayden | | Goalkeeper | Braintree Town | | | 1 | | |

Braintree (Y)

| West | Michael | 29 | Midfielder | Eastbourne Borough | 14 | 16 | 4 | 30 | 1 |

Ebbsfleet, Crewe, Hereford (L), Ebbsfleet, Whitehawk (L), Whitehawk, Chelmsford, Eastbourne B

| West-Astuti | Jack | 21 | Goalkeeper | Chelmsford City | 2 | | 1 | 2 | |

Moreland (Aus), Chelmsford

| Weston | Curtis | 33 | Midfielder | Chesterfield | 31 | 3 | 2 | 34 | 6 |

Millwall (Y), Swindon, Leeds, Scunthorpe (L), Gillingham, Barnet, Chesterfield

| Weston | Myles | 32 | Midfielder | Ebbsfleet United | 29 | 1 | 1 | 30 | 7 |
| | | | | Dagenham & Redbridge | 1 | 1 | | 2 | |

Charlton, Notts Co (L), Notts Co, Brentford, Gillingham, Southend, Wycombe, Ebbsfleet, Dagenham & R

| Wharton | Dylan | | Goalkeeper | Chesterfield | | | 2 | | |

Chesterfield (Y)

| Wheatley | Josef | 23 | Midfielder | Darlington | 30 | 2 | 4 | 32 | 1 |

Middlesbrough (Y), Darlington

| Wheeler | Nick | 29 | Midfielder | Eastbourne Borough | 21 | 4 | 4 | 25 | 4 |
| | | | | Dorking Wanderers | 3 | 3 | | 6 | |

Charlton, Lewis, Burgess Hill, Lewes, Tonbridge A, Dagenham & R, Billericay, Woking, Eastbourne B, Dorking W

Whelan	Tom	24	Midfielder	Yeovil Town	6	2	3	8	1
				Chippenham Town (L)	9			9	1
				Weymouth (L)	13	4		17	1

Bury, Salisbury, Yeovil, Chippenham (L), Weymouth (L)

2019-20 NATIONAL, NORTH & SOUTH PLAYERS — APPEARANCES

SURNAME	FIRSTNAME	AGE	POSITION	CLUB PLAYED FOR	X	SX	S	Ap	G/Cs
Whelpdale	Chris	31	Midfielder	Chelmsford City	31	1	1	32	10
Peterborough, Gillingham (L), Gillingham, Stevenage, Wimbledon, Stevenage, Chelmsford									
Whickham	Charlie	20	Defender	Boreham Wood		1	4	1	
Boreham W (Y)									
White	Andy	27	Defender	Altrincham	32	1	3	33	
Crewe (Y), Nantwich, Southport, Altrincham									
White	Jaiden		Forward	Kidderminster Harriers	1	4	1	5	
Kidderminster (Y), Stafford R (L)									
White	Lewis	21	Midfielder	Dulwich Hamlet	8	10	6	18	
Millwall (Y), Concord R (L), Dulwich H									
White	Nicholas (Ross)	23	Defender	AFC Telford United	29	3	4	32	
Wrexham (Y), Southport, Telford									
White	Paul	25	Goalkeeper	Kettering Town	35			35	8
Cork, Forest GR, Gloucester (Lx2), Boreham W, Accrington, Kettering									
White	Tom	23	Midfielder	Barrow (L)	18	3		21	2
Gateshead (Y), Spennymoor (L), West Auckland (L), Ashington (L), Scarborough (L), Blackburn, Barrow (L)									
Whitehall	Danny	24	Forward	Maidenhead United	26	15	2	41	15
Liverpool (Y), Rochdale (L), Southport, Marine, Chattanooga FC (US), Maidenhead									
Whitehouse	Billy	24	Midfielder	Spennymoor Town (L)		2	1	2	
Doncaster (Y), Halifax (L), Leeds, Guiseley (L), Alfreton, Shaw Lane, TNS, Spennymoor (L)									
Whitely	Corey	28	Forward	Bromley (L)	6	2		8	1
Tottenham, Waltham F, Cheshunt, Enfield T, Dagenham & R, Ebbsfleet, Newport, Bromley (L)									
Whitfield	Ben	24	Midfielder	Torquay United	31	1		32	7
Guiseley, Bournemouth, Kidderminster (L), Yeovil (L), Port Vale (L), Port Vale, Torquay									
Whitham	Dale	24	Midfielder	Alfreton Town	7	7	10	14	1
Maine Road, Leigh Gen, Chorley, FC United (L), Alfreton									
Whitley	Ryan	20	Goalkeeper	York City	2		31	2	1
York Whitby T (L)									
Whitlock	Rob		Midfielder	Hereford FC			3		
Hereford (Y)									
Whitmore	Alex	24	Defender	AFC Fylde	39	3	3	42	1
Burnley (Y), Chester (L), Gateshead (L), Morecambe (L), Bury (L), Chesterfield, Grimsby, AFC Fylde									
Whittingham	Alfy		Midfielder	Aldershot Town	10	16	13	26	2
Havant & W (Y), Hungerford, Aldershot									
Whittingham	Richard	29	Midfielder	Hemel Hempstead Town		2	3	2	
Gosport B, Whitehawk, Hungerford (L), Hungerford, Hemel H									
Whittle	Alex	27	Midfielder	Boston United	38	1		39	
Dunfermline, AFC Fylde, Southport, York, Forest GR, Southport (L), Warrington, Boston U									
Widdrington	Theo	21	Midfielder	Welling United (L)	10	5	1	15	1
				Hemel Hempstead Town (L)	1	1		2	
Portsmouth (Y), Havant & W (L), Bristol R, Welling (L), Hemel H (L)									
Wilde	Josh	28	Defender	Alfreton Town	18	1	1	19	
Sheffield U, Buxton, Gainsborough, North Ferriby, Halifax, Alfreton									
Wiles-Richards	Harvey	18	Goalkeeper	Bath City	4		36	4	2
Bath (Y)									
Wilkins	Liam		Midfielder	Maidstone United			1		
Maidstone (U23)									
Wilkinson	Luke	28	Defender	Yeovil Town	30	1		31	4
Eastleigh, Dagenham & R, Boreham W (L), Dartford (L), Luton, Stevenage, Yeovil									
Wilks	Daniel	24	Goalkeeper	Welling United	40			40	10
Watford (Y), St Mirren, Maldon, Whitehawk (L), Whitehawk, Welling									
Williams	Aaron	26	Forward	AFC Telford United	24	11	2	35	10
Walsall (Y), Redditch (L), Romulus (L), Telford (L), Worcester, Rushall, Nuneaton, Peterborough, Nuneaton (L), Newport C,									
Brackley (L), Brackley, Harrogate, AFC Telford									
Williams	Brett	32	Forward	Weymouth	13	17	5	30	8
Reading, Rotherham (L), Northampton, Woking (L), Aldershot, Stevenage, Forest Green, Torquay, Bromley, Torquay,									
Sutton U (L), Sutton U, Weymouth									
Williams	Callum	23	Defender	Spennymoor Town	5	1	5	6	
Newcastle, Gateshead (L), Spennymoor									

Key: X - Started; SX - Sub on; S - Non-playing Sub; Ap - Total Appearances; G/Cs - Total goals/clean sheets.

SURNAME	FIRSTNAME	AGE	POSITION	CLUB	X	SX	S	Ap	G/Cs
Williams	Cameron	18	Midfielder	Maidstone United			1		
				Maidstone (Y)					
Williams	Cian		Midfielder	Wrexham		2		2	
				Bangor, Wrexham					
Williams	Danny	32	Midfielder	FC Halifax Town	24	5	2	29	1
				Daisy Hill, FC United, Clitheroe, Kendal, Chester (L), Inverness, Dundee, Unattached, Accrington, AFC Fylde (L), FC Halifax					
Williams	Ed	24	Midfielder	Kidderminster Harriers	19	11		30	2
				Cheltenham (Y), Gloucester (L), Gloucester, Kidderminster					
Williams	Jason	24	Forward	Tonbridge Angels	12	4		16	4
				Southend, Chelmsford (L), Welling (L), Chelmsford (L), Boreham W (L), Concord R, Hemel H, Tonbridge A					
Williams	Jay	19	Defender	Kettering Town	5	1	1	6	
				Northampton (Y), Kettering (L)					
Williams	Jordan	27	Midfielder	AFC Fylde	36	3	3	39	15
				Northwich Victoria, Barrow, Rochdale, Lincoln C (L), AFC Fylde					
Williams	Luke	27	Forward	Hartlepool United		4	1	4	
				Middlesbrough (Y), Hartlepool (L), Scunthorpe (L), Coventry (L), Peterborough (L), Scunthorpe, Northampton (L), Hartlepool					
Williams	Manny	38	Forward	Slough Town	2	14	19	16	2
				Weston-s-Mare, Havant & W, Maidenhead, Hayes & Y, Basingstoke, Hampton & R, Hungerford, Slough					
Williams	Morgan	20	Defender	Yeovil Town (L)	3	1	1	4	
				Coventry (Y), Yeovil (L)					
Williams	Rhys	19	Defender	Kidderminster Harriers (L)	29			29	1
				Liverpool (Y), Kidderminster (L)					
Williams	Sam		Forward	Wrexham			1		
				Wrexham (Y)					
Williams	Sean	28	Midfielder	Altrincham	23	5	1	28	
				Stockport, Vauxhall M, Hyde, Vauxhall M, Colwyn, Halifax, Colwyn, Altrincham, Hinckley U, Hednesford, Telford, Warrington, Altrincham					
Williams	Tyler		Midfielder	Alfreton Town				9	
				Brighouse, Alfreton,					
Williams	Tyrone	25	Defender	Solihull Moors	19	2	20	21	
				Kidderminster, Hednesford (L), Solihull M					
Williamson	Ben	31	Forward	Eastleigh	16	8		24	2
				Bromley	15	3		18	2
				Worthing, Jerez Ind., Bournemouth, Hyde, Port Vale (L), Port Vale, Gillingham, Cambridge U (L), Cambridge U, Eastleigh, Bromley					
Williamson	Mike	36	Defender	Gateshead	25	1	1	26	1
				Torquay (Y), Southampton, Torquay (L), Doncaster (L), Wycombe, Watford, Portsmouth, Newcastle, Wolves (L), Wolves, Oxford U, Gateshead					
Willis	George	24	Goalkeeper	Boston United				27	
				Sheff Utd (Y), Bradford PA (L), Alfreton (L), Matlock (L), Stalybridge, Gainsborough, Boston U					
Willoughby	Kurt	22	Forward	AFC Fylde	8	14	1	22	2
				York City (L)	4			4	3
				Fleetwood (Y), Clitheroe, FC United, AFC Fylde, York (L)					
Wills	Kane	30	Midfielder	Eastbourne Borough	34	1		35	1
				Ebbsfleet, Eastbourne B (L), Lewes (L), Margate, Worthing, Eastbourne B					
Wilson	Lawrie		Defender	Ebbsfleet United	32		8	32	
				Charlton, Colchester, Stevenage, Charlton, Rotherham (L), Bolton, Peterborough (L), Port Vale, Ebbsfleet					
Wilson	Scott	20	Defender	Blyth Spartans (L)	6			6	
				Burnley (Y), Blyth S (L)					
Wilson	Scott	27	Forward	Notts County (L)	1			1	1
				Bristol C (Y), Gloucester, Bath, Gloucester, Paulton, Weston SM, Eastleigh, Macclesfield, Oldham (L), Notts Co (L)					
Wiltshire	Kyran		Midfielder	Oxford City	24	8	6	32	5
				Maidenhead, Bishop's S (L), Oxford C					
Winfield	Dave	32	Defender	Chelmsford City	8			8	2
				Bromley	12	1		13	
				Aldershot, Salisbury (L), Wycombe, Shrewsbury, York, Wimbledon (L), Ebbsfleet, Chelmsford, Bromley					
Winnard	Dean	30	Defender	Southport	31		2	31	
				Accrington (Y), Morecambe, Southport					
Wishart	Dan	28	Defender	Maidstone United	35	2		37	9
				Hayes & Y, Alfreton, Hayes & Y (L), Margate (L), Eastleigh (L), Hayes & Y, Sutton U, Forest GR, Sutton U, Maidstone					

SURNAME	FIRSTNAME	AGE	POSITION	CLUB PLAYED FOR	X	SX	S	Ap	G/Cs
Wood	Marcus	22	Midfielder	Bradford Park Avenue	8			8	
				Southport	13	1		14	
Man City (Y), Bolton, Southport (L), Bradford PA, Southport									
Wood	Sam	33	Midfielder	Bromley	36	1	1	37	
Brentford, Rotherham (L), Wycombe, Eastleigh, Bromley									
Wood	Tommy	21	Forward	Tonbridge Angels (L)	3			3	3
Wimbledon, Slough (L), Tonbridge A (L)									
Wood	William	23	Defender	Dagenham & Redbridge	3	1	16	4	
Southampton (Y), Accrington, Havant & W (L), Dagenham & R									
Woodards	Danny	36	Defender	Boreham Wood	8	3	18	11	
Exeter, Crewe, MK Dons, Bristol R, Tranmere, Boreham W									
Woods	Connor		Midfielder	Southport	8	22	7	30	
St Helens T, Southport									
Woods	Henry	20	Midfielder	Concord Rangers (L)	12	2		14	
Gillingham (Y), Concord R (Lx2)									
Woods	Michael	30	Midfielder	Dover Athletic	35	1		36	3
Leeds, Chelsea, Notts Co (L), Yeovil, Doncaster, Harrogate T, Hartlepool, Harrogate, Dover									
Woodward	Harry		Defender	Aldershot Town			2		
Aldershot (Y)									
Woolford	Martyn	34	Midfielder	Boston United	14	4	3	18	
York, Scunthorpe, Bristol C, Millwall, Sheff Utd, Fleetwood, Grimsby, Hyde U, Boston U									
Wootton	Kyle	23	Forward	Notts County	35	4		39	19
Scunthorpe (Y), North Ferriby (L), Cheltenham (L), Stevenage (L), FC Halifax (L), Notts Co									
Worby	Alastair	27	Goalkeeper	Brackley Town			9		
Reading (Y), Coventry, St Johnstone, Nike Academy, Loughborough Uni, Brackley									
Worgan	Lee	36	Goalkeeper	Dover Athletic	25		6	25	5
MK Dons, Wycombe (L), Rushden, Cardiff, Merthyr T (L), Eastbourne, Hastings, Tonbridge A, Maidstone, Dover									
Worman	Ben	18	Midfielder	Chelmsford City (L)		1	2	1	
Cambridge U (Y), Chelmsford (L)									
Worner	Ross	30	Goalkeeper	Havant & Waterlooville	39		1	39	12
Woking (Y), Charlton, Aldershot, Eastbourne B (L), AFC Wimbledon, Woking (L), Sutton U, Chelmsford (L), Maidstone (L), Havant & W									
Worrall	Jack	18	Defender	Curzon Ashton		2	2	2	
Curzon A (Y)									
Worsfold	Max	27	Midfielder	Slough Town	36	3	2	39	3
Aldershot (Y), Maidenhead (L), Dorchester (L), Staines, Hayes & Y, Staines, Maidenhead, Slough									
Worsnop	John	37	Goalkeeper	Chester			1		
Droylsden, Worksop, FC United, Guiseley, Alfreton, Chester, Bradford PA, York, Southport, Guiseley, Chester									
Worthington	Matt	22	Midfielder	Yeovil Town	26	9	6	35	3
Bournemouth, Eastbourne B (L), Yeovil (L), Forest GR (L), Yeovil									
Wotton	Joe		Midfielder	Hampton & Richmond Borough			1		
Hampton & R (Y)									
Wraight	Tom	25	Forward	Chelmsford City	16	1	2	17	4
East Thurrock, Maidstone, Chelmsford									
Wratten	Marshall		Forward	Dover Athletic			2		
Dover (Y)									
Wright	Akil	24	Defender	Wrexham	16	4	6	20	2
Fleetwood, AFC Fylde (L), Barrow (L), Wrexham									
Wright	Danny	35	Forward	Solihull Moors	20	16	4	36	5
Dereham, Histon, Cambridge U, Wrexham, Forest GR, Gateshead, Kidderminster, Cheltenham, Solihull									
Wright	Diaz	22	Midfielder	Dagenham & Redbridge (L)	1	2	3	3	
				Welling United (L)	10			10	1
Colchester (Y), Braintree (L), Dagenham & R (L), Welling (L)									
Wright	Jake	23	Forward	Boston United (L)	12	10	1	22	6
Sheff Utd (Y), York (L), Southport (L), Gateshead (L), Harrogate (L), Harrogate, York, Boston U (L), Boston U (L)									
Wright	Jenson	19	Midfielder	Oxford City	4	3	13	7	1
MK Dons (Y), Oxford C, Banbury U (Dual)									
Wright	Jordan		Goalkeeper	Alfreton Town (L)	13			13	1
Nottm F (Y), Alfreton (L), Kettering (L), Alfreton (L)									

Key: X - Started; SX - Sub on; S - Non-playing Sub; Ap - Total Appearances; G/Cs - Total goals/clean sheets.

SURNAME	FIRSTNAME	AGE	POSITION	CLUB	X	SX	S	Ap	G/Cs
Wright	Sam	23	Midfielder	Bradford Park Avenue	1	2	1	3	
Bradford C (Y), Ossett T, Bradford PA, Belper									
Wright	Tommy	23	Forward	Sutton United	21	11	1	32	7
Sutton U, Salisbury (L)									
Wright	Will	23	Defender	Dagenham & Redbridge	24	6	6	30	2
Hitchen, Colchester, Dagenham & R (L), Dagenham & R									
Wrightson	Adam	23	Forward	Blyth Spartans	17	10	4	27	2
Gateshead (Y), South Shields (L), Blyth S (L), Blyth S									
Wroe	Nicky	34	Midfielder	Curzon Ashton	28	3	3	31	
Barnsley (Y), Bury (L), Hamilton, York, Torquay, Shrewsbury, PNE, Shrewsbury (L), Oxford U (L), Notts Co, Halifax (L), Halifax, Bradford PA, Boston U, Curzon A									
Wyatt	Ben	24	Defender	Sutton United	19	1	9	20	
Ipswich (Y), Colchester, Concord R (L), Braintree, St Albans, Sutton U									
Wycherley	Andrew	22	Goalkeeper	AFC Telford United	6			6	
				Solihull Moors			4		
Shrewsbury (Y), New Saints (Y), Telford, Hednesford (L), Solihull M									
Wylie	Reece	18	Midfielder	Aldershot Town			3		
Aldershot (Y)									
Wynne	Elliot	22	Goalkeeper	Farsley Celtic	17	1	12	18	4
				Altrincham			3		
Oldham (Y), Rochdale, AFC Fylde, Fleetwood, Lancaster (L), Glossop NE (L), Abbey Hey, Altrincham, Trafford (L) Trafford (L), Farsley C, Altrincham									
Wynter	Alex	26	Defender	Eastleigh	12	1	2	13	
Crystal Palace, Colchester (L), Portsmouth (L), Colchester, Maidstone, Eastleigh									
Wynter	Ben	22	Defender	Torquay United	30	2	1	32	1
Crystal Palace, Bromley Hampton & R (L), Hampton & R, Torquay									
Wynter	Jordan	26	Midfielder	Dartford	20	2		22	
Arsenal, Bristol C, Cheltenham (L), Cheltenham, Telford (Lx2), Bromley, Woking, Maidstone, Dartford (L), Dartford									
Yarney	Josef	22	Defender	Chesterfield	28	3		31	1
Everton (Y), Newcastle (Y), Morecambe (L), Chesterfield (L), Chesterfield									
Yates	Matthew	21	Goalkeeper	AFC Telford United (L)	17			17	4
Derby (Y), Gloucester (L), Hereford (L), Telford (L)									
Yeates	Mark	35	Midfielder	AFC Fylde	21	15	4	36	1
Tottenham, Brighton (L), Swindon (L), Colchester (L), Hull (L), Leicester (L), Colchester, Middlesbrough, Sheffield U, Watford, Bradford, Oldham, Blackpool, Notts Co, Eastleigh, AFC Fylde									
York	Wesley	27	Forward	York City	1	6	8	7	
				Brackley Town (L)	8	2		10	4
Nuneaton, Wrexham, Gateshead, York, Brackley (L)									
Young	Luke	27	Midfielder	Wrexham	40	1		41	3
Plymouth, Torquay, Wrexham									
Young	Matt	26	Defender	Hampton & Richmond Borough	19	1	1	20	1
Sheff Wed, Carlisle (L), Dover, Kidderminster, Chelmsford, Welling, Woking, Chelmsford, Hampton & R									
Yousseff	Elias	20	Midfielder	Chippenham Town	13	6	7	19	
Chippenham (Y)									
Yussuf	Adi	28	Forward	Solihull Moors (L)	4	8	5	12	1
				Boreham Wood (L)		4	6	4	
Tamworth, Burton Albion, Lincoln City, Oxford City, Mansfield Town, Crawley Town (L), Grimsby Town (L), Barrow, Solihull Moors, Blackpool, Solihull Moors (L), Boreham W (L)									
Yusuff	Ade	26	Forward	Dulwich Hamlet	7	7	2	14	3
				Tonbridge Angels (L)	5	1		6	2
				Dover Athletic			11	3	11
Chatham, Dagenham & R, St Albans (L), East Thurrock (L), Welling (L), Chatham, Heybridge S, Folkestone I, Dulwich H, Tonbridge A (L), Dover									
Zakuani	Gabriel	34	Defender	Dagenham & Redbridge	1			1	
Leyton O (Y), Fulham, Stoke (L), Peterborough, Kalloni (Gre), Peterborough, Northampton, Gillingham, Swindon, Dagenham & R									
Zanos	Jed		Midfielder	Guiseley			1		
Beerwah Glasshouse (Aus), Buderim W, Sunshine Coast F, Ripon C, Guiseley									
Zebroski	Chris	33	Forward	Chippenham Town	33	6	1	39	4
Cirencester, Plymouth, Millwall, Oxford U (L), Torquay (L), Wycombe, Torquay (L), Torquay, Bristol R Cheltenham, Eastleigh,									

ISTHMIAN LEAGUE

PREMIER DIVISION 2019-20

		P	W	D	L	F	A	GD	Pts
1	Worthing	34	21	8	5	72	41	31	71
2	Cray Wanderers	33	18	10	5	63	45	18	64
3	Hornchurch	33	17	11	5	62	28	34	62
4	Folkestone Invicta	32	18	8	6	60	34	26	62
5	Carshalton Athletic	34	18	8	8	59	38	21	62
6	Horsham	33	17	6	10	51	35	16	57
7	Enfield Town	32	16	8	8	61	51	10	56
8	Bognor Regis Town	32	16	5	11	58	46	12	53
9	Leatherhead	31	15	7	9	48	42	6	52
10	Kingstonian	31	11	14	6	42	36	6	47
11	East Thurrock United	30	14	4	12	47	40	7	46
12	Margate	33	11	10	12	47	54	-7	43
13	Potters Bar Town	32	11	8	13	47	56	-9	41
14	Bowers & Pitsea	33	11	7	15	49	42	7	40
15	Haringey Borough	30	11	6	13	44	47	-3	39
16	Lewes	34	8	7	19	35	55	-20	31
17	Bishop's Stortford	32	8	4	20	37	63	-26	28
18	Cheshunt	31	8	3	20	39	59	-20	27
19	Corinthian-Casuals	31	6	8	17	33	44	-11	26
20	Wingate & Finchley	33	5	10	18	34	58	-24	25

		1	2	3	4	5	6	7	8	9	10	11	12	13	14	15	16	17	18	19	20	21	22
1	Bishop's Stortford		3-1	2-2			3-2	1-3	1-5	1-0	0-1		1-2	0-2	2-0	1-2	0-1	0-2	2-2		1-4	0-1	0-1
2	Bognor Regis Town				3-2	0-2	1-2		7-2		4-1	4-3	2-0		1-1	1-1	5-1		1-2	2-1	0-4		0-3
3	Bowers & Pitsea	2-0	1-2		7-0	0-1		0-2	1-2	1-2	0-1	3-1	3-2	0-1			3-0		0-1	1-1		1-1	1-2
4	Brightlingsea Regent	1-0		2-4			1-1	2-1	0-2		0-2	0-0		1-0	0-4	0-2		2-3	1-1	0-0	0-0	1-1	0-3
5	Carshalton Athletic	4-2	1-0		2-0		2-0		4-0	1-2	2-0	1-1		1-4	4-0	2-2	1-0	1-1	1-0	1-1	5-1	3-2	1-2
6	Cheshunt	0-1		1-1		0-1		1-1		2-3		0-1		0-1	3-1	1-3	0-2	1-2	3-0	2-0	1-0		1-2
7	Corinthian-Casuals		1-1	0-1		0-1	2-3		3-1		2-1		0-1	1-1	1-2		3-0	1-0	1-2	0-1	0-0	3-3	
8	Cray Wanderers			3-1	1-0		6-1	0-0		1-1	3-5	2-3	1-1	1-1	2-1	0-0	0-1	2-1	3-2	3-1	4-0	0-0	2-2
9	East Thurrock United		3-0	3-1	2-1	2-0	4-1		0-1		1-3	4-2			3-3	3-0	1-0	1-2		1-3	3-1		0-0
10	Enfield Town	5-0	2-0	0-4	2-2	2-1	2-1	3-1	2-3			1-3	5-3	1-1	1-4		1-1		2-0	2-2	2-2		
11	Folkestone Invicta	1-0	1-2		3-2	1-3	4-2	3-1		4-1	1-1		1-1	2-1	2-1	1-1	1-1		4-0	3-1		0-1	2-0
12	Haringey Borough	2-1	2-1	1-1	5-1	2-2		1-0		2-0			1-1	1-2	0-1		0-1	1-0		3-2	2-1		2-2
13	Hornchurch	4-0	0-0	2-1	3-0		3-0	1-1		4-0	1-0	2-1		2-1	3-0	1-1		2-2	2-2	3-1	2-0		
14	Horsham	3-3	0-2	4-0		2-2	2-0	1-0	1-1	1-0		0-1	2-0	1-0		1-1	3-0	0-3	4-0	2-0	2-1		
15	Kingstonian	0-3	0-1	1-0		2-1	3-1	2-4	3-1	0-0	0-0	0-0			1-1		3-1	3-3	4-0				0-0
16	Leatherhead	3-1	1-2	1-0	2-1	2-0		2-1	3-0		1-1				1-4					0-0	4-0		
17	Lewes		0-1	0-2	0-1		0-1	1-6	1-0	2-3	0-3	1-1	0-0	2-1	0-0	0-2	1-2		0-1		3-3	1-2	1-3
18	Margate	3-4	1-6	1-0	0-0	1-1		2-2	3-4	0-1	0-3		4-2	2-2		0-0	2-0			2-1	2-2	1-0	0-2
19	Merstham	2-2	2-2	1-3				1-2	2-1	1-4	0-4	1-0	1-2	1-0	0-1	1-4	2-4	1-0			2-3		1-3
20	Potters Bar Town	1-0	0-1	0-2	4-2	2-0		3-1	1-1		1-2	1-4		2-1	0-2	1-2			2-1				1-1
21	Wingate & Finchley	1-2	0-5	2-2	0-0	0-2	1-2		0-1	2-1		1-1	1-0	2-3		1-1	1-2	1-1		0-4	1-2		2-3
22	Worthing		3-0		3-0	1-1	2-0	2-0	1-2	2-3	3-2	0-1		0-6	3-0	2-1	5-5	3-1	2-1	6-1	1-1	4-2	

www.nonleagueclubdirectory.co.uk   237

NORTH DIVISION 2019-20

		P	W	D	L	F	A	GD	Pts
1	Maldon & Tiptree	26	22	2	2	65	20	45	65*
2	Aveley	26	14	9	3	66	31	35	51
3	Tilbury	27	15	5	7	49	30	19	50
4	Heybridge Swifts	29	15	5	9	54	43	11	50
5	Bury Town	29	15	5	9	49	41	8	50
6	Coggeshall Town	26	12	10	4	40	24	16	46
7	Great Wakering Rovers	28	13	4	11	45	36	9	43
8	Dereham Town	29	11	8	10	52	43	9	41
9	Cambridge City	28	12	3	13	42	39	3	39
10	Canvey Island	27	11	5	11	49	54	-5	38
11	AFC Sudbury	26	11	4	11	42	42	0	37
12	Histon	28	10	6	12	40	53	-13	36
13	Soham Town Rangers	28	10	4	14	41	47	-6	34
14	Grays Athletic	29	9	4	16	41	47	-6	31
15	Witham Town	28	8	5	15	36	63	-27	29
16	Hullbridge Sports	27	7	7	13	33	53	-20	28
17	Brentwood Town	28	7	5	16	41	54	-13	26
18	Felixstowe & Walton United	29	6	7	16	40	62	-22	25
19	Romford	25	7	3	15	41	66	-25	24
20	Basildon United	25	6	5	14	29	47	-18	23

		1	2	3	4	5	6	7	8	9	10	11	12	13	14	15	16	17	18	19	20
1	AFC Sudbury		3-3	3-0	1-0	3-0	0-2	2-1			0-1			2-1	5-0			4-3	2-4	0-2	3-3
2	Aveley			4-0	0-0	3-1			1-2		4-3			5-0	3-2	0-0	0-2	6-0	5-1		4-2
3	Basildon United				3-2				0-0	0-3		4-2	1-1	1-1	0-1			6-0		1-3	1-3
4	Brentwood Town	3-1	1-3				0-2		0-1	1-3	0-2		2-2	0-1	1-1	3-4	1-2		2-1	4-3	2-0
5	Bury Town	3-0		3-1	1-1		3-1	0-1	1-1	2-1	4-1	2-1	0-3		2-1	2-2	1-2	3-1	2-1	1-2	
6	Cambridge City	2-0	1-4	3-2	2-3	1-2			3-2	1-1		1-1	2-4	1-2		0-1		1-0	1-2		
7	Canvey Island	2-2	1-1	2-1	3-2	0-2	2-1			1-2	3-1	2-1	0-2	4-4	0-3	0-3	1-3		0-1		
8	Coggeshall Town	3-1			0-1		2-1	3-1		0-2	0-0	1-0	2-0		5-1	3-0			1-1	1-1	4-0
9	Dereham Town	1-1	2-2		5-2	2-3			4-1				1-4	1-1	0-0	1-1	1-2	3-1	1-2	1-3	5-1
10	Felixstowe & Walton United			2-0	3-3	1-2	3-1	3-3	2-2	2-3		1-0	1-4	1-2		1-1	0-2	1-2	2-2		
11	Grays Athletic	1-2	1-6	3-1	4-1	1-2	0-1		0-0	2-2	1-2		1-0	2-3		2-0	1-2	0-0	3-2	3-1	
12	Great Wakering Rovers	2-0	0-1	0-1		0-2	0-4	1-1	0-0	1-2		3-1			1-3		0-1			2-0	2-0
13	Heybridge Swifts	0-1	1-1	0-1		1-0	0-1	2-3	1-1		3-1	1-2	4-2			3-2		5-1	3-2		4-1
14	Histon	1-4	1-1	3-3		3-0	1-0		1-1	4-1	1-0	0-1	4-1	1-3		2-1	0-1			0-2	1-4
15	Hullbridge Sports	2-0			1-1		3-3	0-5	1-3	0-1	0-2	3-1		1-4	1-3			0-1			0-3
16	Maldon & Tiptree		3-1	3-0			0-0	5-0		2-1	6-2	3-1		2-1	1-1	5-0		1-3	3-1	1-2	5-1
17	Romford	1-2	1-4		3-2			1-2	2-3		3-1	1-6	1-4		5-1	1-2			3-3	1-0	2-4
18	Soham Town Rangers	1-0	1-1	3-0	2-1		2-0	1-3		1-0	3-0		0-1	0-2	2-3	0-1		1-4		0-1	1-2
19	Tilbury		1-1	0-1	1-0	2-1	1-2	5-3		1-0	1-1	2-0		3-0	5-0	3-3	1-2				1-1
20	Witham Town		1-2	1-0	0-3	1-1	1-2	1-7		1-1	3-1	1-0	0-1	0-2			0-5	1-1		0-2	

SOUTH CENTRAL DIVISION 2019-20

		P	W	D	L	F	A	GD	Pts
1	Ware	30	19	7	4	81	44	37	64
2	Hanwell Town	28	17	7	4	72	32	40	58
3	Uxbridge	29	16	7	6	59	35	24	55
4	Chertsey Town	28	15	7	6	74	40	34	52
5	Westfield	28	15	7	6	65	32	33	52
6	Bracknell Town	26	15	5	6	63	33	30	50
7	Waltham Abbey	29	15	5	9	68	52	16	50
8	Tooting & Mitcham United	27	14	5	8	53	29	24	47
9	Barking	29	14	4	11	51	45	6	46
10	Chipstead	28	13	6	9	53	40	13	45
11	Marlow	28	11	10	7	39	30	9	43
12	Bedfont Sports	29	10	9	10	42	44	-2	39
13	Chalfont St Peter	30	10	7	13	45	59	-14	37
14	Harlow Town	29	10	4	15	42	57	-15	34
15	South Park	26	6	9	11	37	52	-15	27
16	Hertford Town	29	6	4	19	39	81	-42	22
17	Ashford Town (Middx)	29	5	5	19	30	70	-40	20
18	Northwood	29	6	2	21	34	81	-47	20
19	FC Romania	28	4	4	20	35	84	-49	16
20	Staines Town	29	2	8	19	39	81	-42	14

		1	2	3	4	5	6	7	8	9	10	11	12	13	14	15	16	17	18	19	20
1	Ashford Town		1-1	0-1	2-4	0-4	1-2	0-2			1-2			1-3	3-0	2-0		0-5	0-1	0-3	0-4
2	Barking			0-0	4-3	2-2	4-2		0-1	0-1		4-1		1-0	3-1	2-1	1-2	3-4			2-0
3	Bedfont Sports	0-0	0-0		0-2		1-0	1-1	3-2	0-4	1-0	1-0	1-2	4-1	2-2		2-0	1-3		1-3	1-2
4	Bracknell Town	4-0				1-0	0-0		4-2	1-1	5-1	2-0		2-0	4-0	7-1		2-0	1-1	1-6	1-2
5	Chalfont St Peter		2-1	2-1	2-2		2-1	3-2		1-2	2-3	1-1	1-3		1-2	3-2	1-4	0-2	0-0		1-1
6	Chertsey Town	4-0		3-3	2-1			7-0	1-1	3-0	6-1		8-2	3-0	6-3	0-5			1-1	2-2
7	Chipstead	0-2	1-2	1-0	2-0	1-1			2-1		4-2	6-0	1-1		0-0		1-2	0-2	3-2		
8	FC Romania	3-2	1-2		0-2	1-2	1-1	0-3		1-2			1-4	4-2	4-1	2-2	1-1		1-4	1-3	1-5
9	Hanwell Town	0-1	5-0			3-0		3-3	6-0		1-0	4-1	3-2		1-2	6-0	2-5		6-1	1-0	3-4
10	Harlow Town	1-1	2-3		0-3	0-1		3-2	4-3			2-1		1-2	1-1	1-0	1-1	0-1	4-3	3-4	2-0
11	Hertford Town	3-5	2-1	1-4		1-5	2-3	2-0	2-1	0-3	0-2		0-0		0-0	4-1	0-1	1-5		1-3	1-9
12	Marlow	1-1	3-1	1-1		1-1	2-4	1-2	2-1		1-1	1-0		1-0	2-1		0-2	0-0	2-3	3-0
13	Northwood	2-1		2-5	2-2	0-2	1-4	0-3		1-3		1-6	1-0		0-1	3-1	0-1	3-2	1-6	1-2	0-3
14	South Park	3-3	0-5		4-2			1-4		4-4			4-0			3-0		0-1	2-2	2-3	0-2
15	Staines Town			0-0	1-5	6-1	0-4	0-2		2-2	1-2	2-3	2-2	1-1			1-1	3-3	0-2		
16	Tooting & Mitcham United	3-1	2-1	4-0		1-2	1-4	6-0	0-1		0-0	2-1		1-2			1-2	3-0	2-1	
17	Uxbridge	3-2	2-1	3-3		3-0	2-2	2-2	6-0	0-0	2-1		0-2		2-1			0-1	0-2	2-2
18	Waltham Abbey		1-2	2-3		7-3	2-0		5-1	0-2	3-1	5-2	0-2	5-2		4-3	0-3	2-0		
19	Ware	6-0	4-2	3-2		2-1	2-0	6-1	1-1		4-1	3-3	0-0	4-1	3-3	3-3	2-1	2-2	2-3	
20	Westfield	5-0	0-1		0-2	4-0	0-3	2-0		2-2	3-1		2-0		1-1	3-0	1-1		2-2	4-0	

SOUTH EAST DIVISION 2019-20

		P	W	D	L	F	A	GD	Pts
1	Hastings United	28	18	8	2	53	21	32	62
2	Ashford United	30	19	2	9	75	41	34	59
3	Cray Valley PM	28	17	6	5	53	29	24	57
4	Whitehawk	28	16	8	4	61	33	28	56
5	Herne Bay	28	15	6	7	53	40	13	51
6	Chichester City	25	13	6	6	46	34	12	45
7	Whyteleafe	28	13	6	9	47	40	7	45
8	VCD Athletic	30	12	6	12	48	53	-5	42
9	Phoenix Sports	27	13	2	12	46	40	6	41
10	Sevenoaks Town	29	11	8	10	43	37	6	41
11	Hythe Town	29	11	7	11	34	37	-3	40
12	Haywards Heath Town	27	10	9	8	37	33	4	39
13	Guernsey	28	9	9	10	39	47	-8	36
14	Whitstable Town	28	9	8	11	38	41	-3	35
15	Burgess Hill Town	27	9	4	14	47	60	-13	31
16	Sittingbourne	29	8	4	17	31	42	-11	28
17	Faversham Town	30	7	7	16	30	51	-21	28
18	Ramsgate	30	4	8	18	35	68	-33	20
19	Three Bridges	29	5	3	21	35	68	-33	18
20	East Grinstead Town	26	1	7	18	25	61	-36	10

		1	2	3	4	5	6	7	8	9	10	11	12	13	14	15	16	17	18	19	20
1	Ashford United		2-0	2-3	1-2	5-0	2-0	1-3	1-0	1-1				4-2	4-1	2-1	3-0	1-4	2-3		
2	Burgess Hill Town	0-7		1-2	2-3		3-1	3-0	1-3			7-2	0-3	2-2	2-3	2-1	4-2			3-2	
3	Chichester City	2-3	2-2		3-0	2-1	0-0			2-1		3-1	1-1	0-1	2-0			1-1	2-3
4	Cray Valley Paper Mills	3-1	1-0	0-2		3-1	2-0	1-1	0-0		1-2	1-1	2-0	5-3	1-0		1-0	5-0		4-3	3-2
5	East Grinstead Town	1-3	1-1				0-1	3-3	0-0	1-2				2-3		1-2	2-2	1-2	1-1	0-3	
6	Faversham Town		1-2	2-1	0-0	2-0		3-3			3-3	1-0	2-2	0-0	0-2	1-0	1-0	1-2	2-1	0-2	0-0
7	Guernsey	0-6		0-3					2-2	2-2	2-3	0-0	1-2		1-0	3-1		3-1	1-2	0-2	0-0
8	Hastings United	0-3		5-1		5-1	2-0			1-0	0-0	2-0	3-1	3-0	3-1	4-0		3-2	2-0	2-1	1-0
9	Haywards Heath Town	1-0	5-1		3-1		5-1	1-1	1-1		0-2	0-3	0-1	2-1	1-0	2-1	0-2		2-2		
10	Herne Bay	2-2	0-1	2-0	0-3	3-1		3-1		0-0		0-2	3-1	4-0	3-2	2-1	2-1	0-1		3-0	
11	Hythe Town	1-4		0-0		2-1	2-1	2-1		2-0	1-1			0-1	1-0		3-0	0-1	2-0	2-2
12	Phoenix Sports	1-2	3-2	2-3	2-0	6-3	2-1	1-2		1-0		2-0			3-0	0-3	1-2	0-2			
13	Ramsgate		2-4	1-2	0-2	2-0	3-0	1-4			0-3	0-2	1-1		1-2	0-2	0-1	2-2	1-1	3-1
14	Sevenoaks Town	3-0		2-2	1-1		3-1		2-2	1-2		0-0	1-0	3-1		1-2		2-1	1-1	4-0	0-2
15	Sittingbourne	0-1			1-3	2-2		0-1	0-1		2-0	1-0		7-0	0-3		1-0	2-1	1-1		0-1
16	Three Bridges	0-5	0-0	3-4		1-2		0-2	1-2	1-3	3-5	4-1	0-4	0-0	0-1			3-5	1-3	
17	VCD Athletic	3-1	4-0	0-3			2-1	0-1	0-0	2-2	2-4	2-2	2-3	2-2	2-2		4-3			1-0	2-1
18	Whitehawk		2-0		2-0	1-0	2-2		2-2	1-1	5-1	3-0	1-2	3-1		1-0	8-1	3-2		3-0	1-0
19	Whitstable Town	1-2	2-1		1-1	3-1		1-3	1-1	3-0		2-1	1-1	1-1	1-1	2-0	1-1				0-2
20	Whyteleafe	3-4	4-3		0-4	0-0	3-1	4-1	0-1	2-0	2-2	0-2	2-1	3-2	1-1	2-1	3-1		4-2		

ALAN TURVEY TROPHY 2019-20

HOLDERS: ENFIELD TOWN

GROUP STAGE

GROUP 1	P	W	D	L	F	A	GD	Pts
1 Maldon & Tiptree	5	4	0	1	23	6	17	12
2 Bury Town	5	3	0	2	14	10	4	9
3 Coggeshall Town	5	3	0	2	10	10	0	9
4 Heybridge Swifts	5	3	0	2	7	15	-8	9
5 AFC Sudbury	5	2	0	3	9	12	-3	6
6 Felixstowe & Walton Utd	5	0	0	5	6	16	-10	0

GROUP 2	P	W	D	L	F	A	GD	Pts
1 Barking	5	4	0	1	11	1	10	12
2 Aveley	5	3	0	2	10	8	2	9
3 Brentwood Town	5	3	0	2	9	9	0	9
4 Romford	5	3	0	2	6	7	-1	9
5 Grays Athletic	5	2	0	3	9	12	-3	6
6 Waltham Abbey	5	0	0	5	4	12	-8	0

GROUP 3	P	W	D	L	F	A	GD	Pts
1 Histon	5	4	0	1	13	6	7	12
2 Ware	5	3	0	2	19	9	10	9
3 Cambridge City	5	3	0	2	12	12	0	9
4 Soham Town Rangers	5	2	0	3	9	13	-4	6
5 Harlow Town	5	2	0	3	9	14	-5	6
6 Hertford Town	5	1	0	4	5	13	-8	3

GROUP 4	P	W	D	L	F	A	GD	Pts
1 Burgess Hill Town	5	5	0	0	12	4	8	15
2 Hastings United	5	4	0	1	21	7	14	12
3 Haywards Heath	5	2	0	3	5	4	1	6
4 Three Bridges	5	2	0	3	8	14	-6	6
5 Chichester City	5	1	0	4	6	14	-8	3
6 East Grinstead	5	1	0	4	10	19	-9	3

GROUP 5	P	W	D	L	F	A	GD	Pts
1 Bracknell Town	5	5	0	0	13	3	10	15
2 Westfield	5	4	0	1	18	8	10	12
3 Hanwell Town	5	2	0	3	8	6	2	6
4 Chalfont St Peter	5	2	0	3	11	13	-2	6
5 Marlow	5	2	0	3	6	11	-5	6
6 FC Romania	5	0	0	5	3	18	-15	0

GROUP 6	P	W	D	L	F	A	GD	Pts
1 Basildon United	5	4	0	1	16	11	5	12
2 Tilbury	5	3	0	2	13	9	4	9
3 Great Wakering	5	3	0	2	7	6	1	9
4 Hullbridge Sports	5	3	0	2	7	7	0	9
5 Canvey Island	5	2	0	3	12	8	4	6
6 Witham Town	5	0	0	5	5	19	-14	0

GROUP 7	P	W	D	L	F	A	GD	Pts
1 Ramsgate	5	5	0	0	6	2	4	15
2 Ashford United	5	3	0	2	10	7	3	9
3 Herne Bay	5	2	0	3	7	7	0	6
4 Whitstable Town	5	2	0	3	6	9	-3	6
5 Hythe Town	5	2	0	3	6	13	-7	6
6 Faversham Town	5	1	0	4	11	8	3	3

GROUP 8	P	W	D	L	F	A	GD	Pts
1 Staines Town	4	3	0	1	9	3	6	9
2 Northwood	4	3	0	1	7	5	2	9
3 Uxbridge	4	2	0	2	2	5	-3	6
4 Ashford Town (Mx)	4	1	0	3	3	5	-2	3
5 Bedfont Sports	4	1	0	3	6	9	-3	3

GROUP 9	P	W	D	L	F	A	GD	Pts
1 Sevenoaks Town	4	4	0	0	8	4	4	12
2 Sittingbourne	4	3	0	1	13	10	3	9
3 Phoenix Sports	4	2	0	2	5	9	-4	6
4 Cray Valley PM	4	1	0	3	5	8	-3	3
5 VCD Athletic	4	0	0	4	9	9	0	0

GROUP 10	P	W	D	L	F	A	GD	Pts
1 Whyteleafe	4	3	0	1	5	4	1	9
2 Chertsey Town	4	2	0	2	8	6	2	6
3 Chipstead	4	2	0	2	7	7	0	6
4 South Park	4	2	0	2	7	8	-1	6
5 Tooting & Mitcham United	4	1	0	3	5	7	-2	3

ROUND ONE

Wingate & Finchley	v	Bowers & Pitsea	2-0
Ramsgate	v	Leatherhead	2-3
East Thurrock United	v	Bishop's Stortford	3-0
Brightlingsea Regent	v	Histon	1-0
Kingstonian	v	Merstham	2-3
Potters Bar Town	v	Basildon United	2-4
Lewes	v	Sevenoaks Town	2-0
Horsham	v	Whyteleafe	1-0
Bracknell Town	v	AFC Hornchurch	2-0
Worthing	v	Cray Wanderers	3-2
Haringey Borough	v	Maldon & Tiptree	2-3
Margate	v	Carshalton Athletic	5-1
Barking	v	Cheshunt	1-2
Enfield Town	v	Staines Town	5-1
Folkestone Invicta	v	Bognor Regis Town	4-3
Corinthian-Casuals	v	Burgess Hill Town	1-2

ROUND TWO

Bracknell Town	v	Lewes	2-1
Worthing	v	Leatherhead	2-0
Wingate & Finchley	v	Margate	1-3
East Thurrock United	v	Cheshunt	2-2, 3-4p
Enfield Town	v	Brightlingsea Regent	1-2
Maldon & Tiptree	v	Merstham	0-0, 5-4
Horsham	v	Burgess Hill Town	5-0
Basildon United	v	Folkestone Invicta	2-2, 4-5p

QUARTER-FINALS

Worthing	v	Cheshunt	1-3
Bracknell Town	v	Maldon & Tiptree	0-0, 4-1p
Horsham	v	Margate	1-0
Folkestone Invicta	v	Brightlingsea Regent	2-2, 4-3p

SEMI-FINALS

Horsham	v	Cheshunt	
Folkestone Invicta	v	Bracknell Town	

BISHOP'S STORTFORD MATCH RESULTS 2019-20

Date	Comp	H/A	Opponents	Att:	Result	Goalscorers	Pos	No.
Aug 10	Isth P	H	Bognor Regis Town	307	W 3 - 1	Callender 9 Cureton 32 Charles 38		1
13	Isth P	A	Enfield Town	372	L 0 - 5			2
17	Isth P	A	Carshalton Athletic	345	L 2 - 4	Callender 16 Cureton 64	15	3
26	Isth P	A	Kingstonian	302	W 3 - 0	Barnwell 42 Renee 56 Worman 79	11	4
31	Isth P	H	Cheshunt	325	W 3 - 2	Cureton 4 30 Charles 33	7	5
Sep 7	FAC1Q	A	Dunstable Town	221	W 5 - 3	Shomari Barnwell Cureton Charles (2)	12	6
14	Isth P	A	Folkestone Invicta	533	L 0 - 1		12	7
17	Isth P	H	Cray Wanderers	320	L 1 - 5	Thomas 29	13	8
21	FAC2Q	H	Peterborough Sports	296	L 1 - 2	Barnwell 67 (pen)		9
28	Isth P	A	Hornchurch	315	L 0 - 4		13	10
Oct 1	Isth P	H	Potters Bar Town	157	L 1 - 4	Barnwell 73	18	11
12	Isth P	H	Horsham	302	W 2 - 0	Chiedozie 73 Mycroft-Edwards 35	14	12
22	Isth P	H	Wingate-Finchley	96	W 2 - 1	Henshaw 11 Barnwell 13	14	13
26	FAT1Q	H	Enfield Town	317	D 1 - 1	Barnwell 25		14
29	FAT1Qr	A	Enfield Town	204	L 2 - 4	Chiedozie 26 Barnwell 99 (aet)		15
Nov 2	Isth P	H	Leatherhead	248	L 0 - 1		15	16
9	Isth P	H	Corinthian-Casuals	189	L 1 - 3	Miles 90	15	17
12	Isth P	A	Bowers + Pitsea	105	L 0 - 2		16	18
16	Isth P	A	Haringey Borough	402	L 1 - 2	Cureton 66	16	19
19	Isth P	A	Margate	171	W 4 - 3	Manu 23 Cureton 45 90 Barnwell 63	16	20
23	Isth P	H	Lewes	219	L 0 - 2		16	21
30	Isth P	A	Merstham	161	D 2 - 2	Cureton 21 Sweeney 61	15	22
Dec 3	Isth P	H	East Thurrock United	179	W 1 - 0	Cureton 90 (pen)	13	23
7	Isth P	A	Cheshunt	208	W 1 - 0	Cureton 9	11	24
Jan 1	Isth P	H	Kingstonian	355	L 1 - 2	Cureton 89 (pen)	14	25
4	Isth P	H	Bowers & Pitsea	338	D 2 - 2	Cureton 66 85	15	26
11	Isth P	A	Potters Bar Town	189	L 0 - 1		16	27
18	Isth P	H	Margate	277	D 2 - 2	Haines 80 Barnwell 87	15	28
25	Isth P	A	Horsham	593	D 3 - 3	CURETON 45 53 (pen) 67 (pen))	15	29
28	Isth P	A	Brighlingsea Regent	102	L 0 - 1		16	30
Feb 1	Isth P	H	Wingate & Finchley	240	L 0 - 1		16	31
4	Isth P	H	Worthing	181	L 0 - 1		16	32
8	Isth P	A	Leatherhead	361	L 1 - 3	Calver 56	16	33
22	Isth P	H	Hornchurch	327	L 0 - 2		16	34
Mar 7	Isth P	H	Haringey Borough	236	L 1 - 2	Baker 7	17	35
10	Isth P	H	Enfield Town	206	L 0 - 1		18	36

GOALSCORERS	SG	CSG	Pens	Hat tricks	Total		SG	CSG	Pens	Hat tricks	Total
Cureton	12	5	4	1	17	Miles	1				1
Barnwell	9	2	1		9	Mycroft-Edar	1				1
Charles	2				4	Renee	1				1
Callender	2				2	Shomari	1				1
Chiedozie	2				2	Sweeney	1				1
Baker	1				1	Thomas	1				1
Calver	1				1	Worman	1				1
Haines	1				1						
Henshaw	1				1						
Manu	1				1						

BOGNOR REGIS TOWN MATCH RESULTS 2019-20

Date	Comp	H/A	Opponents	Att:	Result		Goalscorers	Pos	No.
Aug 10	Isth P	A	Bishops Stortford	307	L	1 - 3	Smith 74 (pen)		1
13	Isth P	H	Horsham	545	D	1 - 1	Mitford 78		2
17	Isth P	A	Wingate & Finchley	127	W	5 - 0	Leigh 49 Smith 51 69 Miltord 58 Muitt 87	13	3
26	Isth P	A	Worthing	1684	L	0 - 3			4
31	Isth P	H	Carshalton Athletic	618	L	0 - 2		18	5
Sept 7	FAC1Q	H	Sittingbourne	339	W	3 - 0	Muitt 11 13 Lethbridge 31		6
14	Isth P	A	East Thurrock United	205	L	0 - 3		20	7
17	Isth P	H	Cheshunt	312	L	1 - 2	Leigh 61	20	8
21	FAC2Q	A	Dulwich Hamlet	1689	L	1 - 6	Crane 62 (pen)		9
28	Isth P	H	Haringey Borough	408	W	2 - 0	Leigh 31 Muitt 78	17	10
Oct 1	Isth P	H	Leatherhead	386	W	5 - 1	Smith 11 39 73 80 Muitt 90	12	11
12	Isth P	H	Potters Bar Town	530	L	0 - 4		15	12
19	Isth P	A	Folkestone Invicta	538	W	2 - 1	Crane 41 Smith 89	11	13
23	Isth P	A	Kingstonian	261	W	1 - 0	Hammond 87	10	14
26	FAT1Q	A	Uxbridge	136	W	3 - 1	Crane 20 Tuck 43 62		15
29	Isth P	A	Bowers & Pitsea	99	W	2 - 1	Smith 24 Leigh 74	10	16
Nov 9	FAT2Q	H	East Thurrock United	302	W	3 - 1	Lethbridge 9 54 Tuck 33	9	17
12	Isth P	A	Margate	212	W	6 - 1	Smith 9 Crane 11 57 90 Leigh 54 Tuck 83		18
16	Isth P	H	Merstham	577	W	`2 - 1	Leigh 34 Smith 89	8	19
23	FAT3Q	A	Tonbridge Angels	457	L	1 - 2	Crane 83 (pen)		20
30	Isth P	A	Hornchurch	320	D	0 - 0		9	21
Dec 3	Isth P	H	Enfield Town	425	W	4 - 1	Smith 17 53 63 Cook 83	8	22
7	Isth P	A	Carshalton Athletic	411	L	0 - 1		9	23
14	Isth P	H	Cray Wanderers	527	W	7 - 2	Leigh 21 74 Smith 32 87 Tuck 50 76 Nelson 30 (og)	7	24
Jan 1	Isth P	H	Worthing	1236	L	0 - 3		9	25
4	Isth P	H	Margate	535	L	1 - 2	Whyte 51	10	26
11	Isth P	A	Leatherhead	437	W	2 - 1	Lethbridge 11 Leigh 89	10	27
18	Isth P	H	Folkestone Invicta	497	W	4 - 3	Walsh 44 Tuck 67 Casey 82 Lethbridge 90	9	28
25	Isth P	A	Potters Bsr Town	190	W	1 - 0	Lethbridge 15	9	29
28	Isth P	A	Corinthian-Casuals	22	D	1 - 1	Crane 71	9	30
Feb 1	Isth P	H	Kingstonian	623	D	1 - 1	Smith 76	8	31
4	Isth P	H	Brightlingsea	342	W	3 - 2	Smith 5 17 Walsh 18	7	32
8	Isth P	A	Enfield Town	412	L	0 - 2		8	33
22	Isth P	A	Haringey Borough	422	L	1 - 2	Whyte 61	9	34
26	Isth P	A	Lewes	278	W	1 - 0	Leigh 2	8	35
Mar 7	Isth P	A	Merstham	222	D	2 - 2	Smith 45 Leigh 68	9	36
10	Isth P	A	Horsham	576	W	2 - 0	Leigth 22 Whyte 54	7	37

GOALSCORERS	SG	CSG	Pens	Hat tricks	Total		SG	CSG	Pens	Hat tricks	Total
Smith	12	2	1	2	20	Cook	1				1
Leigh	12	2			12	Hammond	1				1
Crane	5		2	1	8	Opponents	1				1
Tuck	5	2			7						
Lethbridge	5				6						
Muitt	4	2			5						
Whyte	3				3						
Mitford	2				2						
Walsh	2				2						
Casey	1				1						

BOWERS & PITSEA MATCH RESULTS 2019-20

Date	Comp	H/A	Opponents	Att:	Result	Goalscorers	Pos	No.
Aug 10	Isth P	H	Wingate & Finchley	130	D 1 - 1	Knight 69		1
13	Isth P	A	Brighlingsea Regent	172	W 4 - 2	Knght 25 (pen) Sartain 57 Manor 72 Warner 83 (pen)		2
17	Isth P	A	Lewes	410	W 2 - 0	Warner 36 Manor 86	3	3
24	FACP	H	Barkingside	156	W 4 - 2	Manor 6 33 Knight 79 Monville 84		4
26	Isth P	A	East Thurrock United	398	L 1 - 3	Knight 89	8	5
31	Isth P	H	Enfield Town	161	L 0 - 1		12	6
Sept 7	FAC1Q	H	Brentwood Town	158	W 2 - 1	Monville 52 Cornhill 62		7
14	Isth P	A	Kingstonian	241	D 0 - 0		13	8
21	FAC2Q	A	Lewes	479	W 2 - 1	Thomas 71 Warner 76		9
28	Isth P	A	Leatherhead	328	L 0 - 1		14	10
Oct 2	Isth P	A	Cray Wanderers	135	L 1 - 3	Warner 64 (pen)	14	11
5	FAC3Q	A	Canvey Island	387	D 1 - 1	Warner 48		12
8	FAC3Qr	H	Canvey Island	452	W 1 - 1	Warner (Won 5-3 on pens)		13
12	Isth P	A	Hornchurch	435	L 1 - 2	Cornhill 45	20	14
19	FAC4Q	H	Chichester City	531	L 1 - 2	Cornhill 90		15
26	FAT1Q	A	Aveley	127	L 0 - 3			16
29	Isth P	H	Bognor Regis Town	99	L 1 - 2	Manor 63	20	17
Nov 9	Isth P	A	Horsham	497	L 0 - 4		21	18
12	Isth P	H	Bishop's Stortford	105	W 2 - 0	Leahy 32 Warner 52	17	19
16	Isth P	H	Margate	181	L 0 - 1		17	20
19	Isth P	H	Worthing	111	L 1 - 2	Warner 90 (pen)	17	21
30	Isth P	A	Potters Bar Town	168	W 2 - 0	Warner 20 54	17	22
Dec 7	Isth P	A	Enfield Town	307	W 4 - 0	Manor 13 61 Monville 27 Warner 66	13	23
14	Isth P	H	Folkestone Invicta	159	W 3 - 1	Manor 24 73	15	24
Jan 1	Isth P	H	East Thurrock United	254	L 1 - 2	Monville 90 Sartain 90	17	25
4	Isth P	A	Bishops Stortford	338	D 2 - 2	Warner 44 Cornhill 72	17	26
7	Isth P	A	Merstham	103	W 3 - 1	Sartain 53 Richmond 73 (og) Gardner 79	17	27
11	Isth P	H	Cray Wanderers	154	L 1 - 2	Warner 32 (pen)	17	28
18	Isth P	A	Corinthian-Casuals	286	W 1 - 0	Warner 45	17	29
21	Isth P	H	Corinthian Casuals	92	L 0 - 2		17	30
25	Isth P	H	Hornchurch	196	L 0 - 1		16	31
28	Isth P	A	Cheshunt	133	D 1 - 1	Warner 28 (pen)	15	32
Feb 1	Isth P	A	Haringey Borough	428	D 1 - 1	Norton 47	15	33
4	Isth P	H	Carshalton Athletic	104	L 0 - 1		15	34
8	Isth P	H	Merstham	154	D 1 - 1	Leahy 10	15	35
11	Isth P	H	Haringey Borough	98	W 3 - 2	Warner 8 (pen) 53 Richards 62 (og)	15	36
15	Isth P	A	Wingate & Finchley	119	D 2 - 2	Warner 24 (pen) Dicks 72	14	37
18	Isth P	H	Brightlingsea Regent	135	W 7 - 0	Sartain 9 Monville 11 62 MANOR 3 (35 54 71) Leahy 42	13	38
22	Isth P	H	Leatherhead	181	W 3 - 0	Monville 5 Manor 44 Warner 87	12	39
Mar 7	Isth P	A	Margate	296	L 0 - 1		13	40

GOALSCORERS	SG	CSG	Pens	Hat tricks	Total		SG	CSG	Pens	Hat tricks	Total
Warner	17	3	7		19	Norton	1				1
Manor	8	3		1	13	Thomas	1				1
Monville	7	2			7						
Cornhill	5	2			4						
Knight	5	2	1		4						
Sartain	4				4						
Leahy	3				3						
Opponents	2				2						
Dicks	1				1						
Gardner	1				1						

BRIGHTLINGSEA REGENT MATCH RESULTS 2019-20

Date	Comp	H/A	Opponents	Att:	Result	Goalscorers	Pos	No.
Aug 10	Isth P	A	Margate	418	D 0 - 0			1
13	Isth P	H	Bowers & Pitsea	172	L 2 - 4	Bennett 45 Dunne 85		2
17	Isth P	H	Merstham	150	D 0 - 0		19	3
24	Isth P	A	Haringey Borough	319	L 1 - 5	Lindoe 82	20	4
26	Isth P	H	Hornchurch	247	W 1 - 0	Hunt 82	14	5
31	Isth P	A	Corinthian-Cauals	203	W 1 - 0	Howell 76	11	6
Sept 7	FAC1Q	A	Cheshunt	144	L 0 - 1			7
14	Isth P	H	Horsham	166	L 0 - 4		14	8
21	Isth P	A	East Thurrock United	215	L 1 - 2	Turner 80		9
28	Isth P	H	Lewes	148	L 2 - 3	Cripps 14 Griggs 35	15	10
Oct 1	Isth P	H	Enfield Town	154	L 0 - 2		16	11
5	Isth P	A	Folkestone Invicta	477	L 2 - 3	Dunne 27 Hunt 65 (pen)		12
12	Isth P	H	Wingate & Finchley	182	D 1 - 1	Hunt 85	19	13
19	Isth P	A	Worthing	867	L 0 - 3		19	14
22	FAT1Q	H	Royston	121	L 1 - 2	Turner 90 (pen)	19	15
Nov 2	Isth P	H	Kingstonian	178	L 0 - 2		19	16
16	Isth P	H	Cray Wanderers	157	L 0 - 2		21	17
18	Isth P	A	Carshalton Athletic	224	L 0 - 2		21	18
30	Isth P	H	Cheshunt	131	D 1 - 1	Bugg 7	21	19
Dec 3	Isth P	A	Potters Bar Town	128	L 2 - 4	Bugg 63 85	21	20
7	Isth P	H	Corinthian-Casuals	139	W 2 - 1	Hewitt 35 Boyland 70	19	21
14	Isth P	A	Leatherhead	299	L 0 - 1		19	22
28	Isth P	A	Hiornchurch	354	L 0 - 3		20	23
Jan 4	Isth P	H	Folkestone Invicta	164	D 0 - 0		21	24
11	Isth P	A	Enfield Town	344	D 2 - 2	Turner 11 (pen) Dunne 83	20	25
18	Isth P	H	Worthing	152	L 0 - 3		20	26
25	Isth P	A	Wingate & Finchley	102	D 0 - 0		21	27
28	Isth P	H	Bishops Stortford	110	W 1 - 0	Clowsley 61	20	28
Feb 1	Isth P	A	Potters Bar Town	140	D 0 - 0		21	29
4	Isth P	A	Bognor Regis Town	342	L 2 - 3	Kamanzi 8 Hewitt 87	21	30
8	Isth P	A	Kingstonian	261	L 1 - 2	Dunne 90	22	31
15	Isth P	H	Margate	189	D 1 - 1	Clowsley 84	22	32
18	Isth P	A	Bowers & Pitsea	135	L 0 - 7		22	33
22	Isth P	A	Lewes	402	W 1 - 0	Thompson 45	21	34
Mar 7	Isth P	A	Cray Wanderers	187	L 0 - 1		22	35

GOALSCORERS	SG	CSG	Pens	Hat tricks	Total		SG	CSG	Pens	Hat tricks	Total
Dunne	4				4	Howell	1				1
Bugg	2	2			3	Kamanzi	1				1
Hunt	3		1		3	Lindoe	1				1
Turner	3		2		3	Thompson	1				1
Clowsley	2				2						
Hewitt	2				2						
Bennett	1				1						
Boyland	1				1						
Cripps	1				1						
Griggs	1				1						

CARSHALTON ATHLETIC MATCH RESULTS 2019-20

Date	Comp	H/A	Opponents	Att:	Result	Goalscorers	Pos	No.
Aug 10	Isth P	A	Potters Bar Town	165	L 0 - 2			1
12	Isth P	H	East Thurrock United	414	L 1 - 2	Koroma 83		2
17	Isth P	H	Bishops Stortford	345	W 4 - 2	Koroma 3 71 Amoo 32 Pappoe 51	13	3
24	Isth P	A	Corinthian-Casuals	271	W 3 - 2	Haxhiu 2 Korboa 6 Amoo 48 (pen)	9	4
26	Isth P	H	Leatherhead	460	W 1 - 0	Hamilton-Downes 68	6	5
31	Isth P	A	Bognor Regis Town	618	W 2 - 0	Pattisson 6 Amoo 21	4	6
Sept 7	FAC1Q	A	**Bracknell Town**	294	W 2 - 0	Pattisson 36 Koroma 72		7
14	Isth P	H	Hornchurch	450	L 1 - 4	Amoo 31	6	8
21	FAC2Q	A	**Harrow Borough**	157	W 1 - 0	Pattisson 25		9
28	Isth P	H	Margate	378	W 1 - 0	Korboa 79	7	10
30	Isth P	H	Lewes	297	D 1 - 1	Korboa 24	9	11
Oct 5	FAC3Q	A	**Lowestoft**	500	W 2 - 1	Korboa 35 67		12
8	Isth P	A	Horsham	556	D 2 - 2	Koroma 36 (pen) Price 77	8	13
12	Isth P	H	Kingstonian	709	D 2 - 2	Dudley 69 Korboa 76	8	14
19	FAC4Q	H	**Dagenham**	726	W 2 - 1	Price 51 Korboa 85		15
22	Isth P	A	Worthing	470	D 1 - 1	Bradford 63	9	16
26	FAT1Q	H	**Merstham**	286	W 3 - 1	Pattisson 18 Haxhiu 75 Koroma 87	8	17
Nov 2	Isth P	H	Folkestone Invicta	502	D 1 - 1	Bradford 39	8	18
9	FAC1P	H	**Boston United**	1815	L 1 - 4	Pattisson 72	9	19
12	FAT2Q	H	**Frome Town**	197	W 5 - 3	Korboa 9 Patisson 16 70 Bradford 34 51		20
16	Isth P	A	Cheshunt	178	W 1 - 0	Koroma 41	9	21
18	Isth P	H	Brightlingsea Regent	224	W 2 - 0	Amoo 31 Korboa 82	8	22
23	FAT3Q	H	**Tooting & Mitcham U**	466	W 2 - 1	Bradford 50 Amoo 56		23
26	Isth P	A	Enfield	261	L 1 - 2	Hamilton-Downes 54	8	24
30	Isth P	H	Cray Wanderers	332	W 4 - 0	Pattisson 5 Korboa 21 Price 61 (pen) Hamilton-Downes 677		25
Dec 3	Isth P	A	Wingate & Finchley	78	W 2 - 0	Amoo 21 51	5	26
7	Isth P	H	Bognor Regis Town	411	W 1 - 0	Samuels 24	4	27
10	FAT1P	H	**Aveley**	349	D 3 - 3	Ottaway 56 Pattisson 81 Hamilton-Downes 90 (pen)		28
16	FAT1Pr	A	**Aveley**	186	L 0 - 2		5	29
21	Isth P	H	Merstham	401	D 1 - 1	Hsamilton-Downes 35	5	30
Jan 1	Isth P	A	Leatherhead	489	L 1 - 2	Hamilton-Downes 24	5	31
4	Isth P	H	Enfield Town	494	W 2 - 1	Ottaway 74 White 78	5	32
11	Isth P	A	Lewes	576	W 1 - 0	Pattisson 45	4	33
18	Isth P	H	Wingate & Finchley	448	W 3 - 2	Hamilton-Downes 48 (pen) Adeniyi 58 Korboa 65	4	34
25	Isth P	A	Kingstonian	356	L 1 3	White 77	6	35
27	Isth P	A	Haringey Borough	245	D 2 - 2	Salmon 18 Walker 37	6	36
Feb 1	Isth P	H	Worthing	550	L 1 - 2	White 9	6	37
4	Isth P	A	Bowers & Pitsea	104	W 1 - 0	Cheadle 84	5	38
8	Isth P	A	Folkestone Invicta	619	W 3 - 1	Hamilton-Downes (pen) 32 Pappoe 38 Sogbanmu 47	3	39
15	Isth P	H	Potters Bar Town	355	W 5 - 1	Read 11 52 Korboa 32 Pattisson 48 Koroma 63	3	40
18	Isth P	A	East Thurrock United	165	L 0 - 2		3	41
22	Isth P	A	Margate	311	D 1 - 1	Korboa 90	5	42
29	Isth P	H	Horsham	461	W 4 - 0	Pattisson 2 Haxhiu 32 Samuels 73 Korboa 86	4	43
Mar 7	Isth P	H	Cheshunt	376	W 2 - 0	White 40 Pattisson 80	5	44
21	Isth P	H	Merstham	401	D 1 - 1	Hsamilton-Downes 35	5	45

GOALSCORERS	SG	CSG	Pens	Hat tricks	Total		SG	CSG	Pens	Hat tricks	Total
Korboa	15	3			14	Pappoe	2				2
Pattisson	10	2			13	Read	1				2
Hamilton-Downes	7	2	3		9	Samuels	2				2
Amoo	7	2	1		8	Adeniyi	1				1
Koroma	6	2	1		8	Cheadle	1				1
Bradford	4				5	Dudley	1				1
White	4				4	Salmon	1				1
Haxhiu	3				3	Sogbanmu	1				1
Price	3		1		3	Walker	1				1
Ottaway	2				2						

CHESHUNT MATCH RESULTS 2019-20

Date	Comp	H/A	Opponents	Att:	Result	Goalscorers	Pos	No.
Aug 10	Isth P	A	East Thurrock United	217	L 1 - 4	Moses 14		1
13	Isth P	H	Potters Bar Town	262	W 2 - 0	Moses 23 Hitchcock 45		2
17	Isth P	H	Haringey Borough	249	L 0 - 1		14	3
24	**FACP**	H	**Stowmarket Town**	187	W 1 - 0	**Hitchcock 58 (pen)**	14	4
26	Isth P	H	Corinthian-Casuals	185	D 1 - 1	Hitchcock 34 (pen)	16	5
30	Isth P	A	Bishops Stortford	325	L 2 - 3	Hitchcock 25 (pen) McKenna 87	19	6
Sept 7	**FAC1Q**	H	**Brightlingsea Regent**	144	W 1 - 0	**Camara 90**		7
14	Isth P	H	Margate	450	L 1 - 2	Amoc 31	19	8
17	Isth P	A	Bognor Regis Town	312	W 2 - 1	Akinyemi 35 51	17	9
21	**FAC2Q**	A	**Maidstone United**	1129	L 1 - 4	**Camara 51**		10
28	Isth P	H	Horsham	197	L 0 - 1		18	11
Oct 1	Isth P	H	Wingate & Finchley	115	W 1 - 0	Akinyemi 54	16	12
5	Isth P	A	Leatherhead	311	L 0 - 3		17	13
12	Isth P	H	Worthing	295	L 1 - 2	Akinyemi 23	17	14
15	Isth P	A	Folkestone Invicta	396	L 2 - 4	Moncur 32 Camara 38	17	15
19	Isth P	A	Enfield Town	431	L 1 - 2	Weatherstone 47 (og)	17	16
26	**FAT1Q**	H	**East Thurrock United**	396	L 1 - 2	**Cronin 90**	18	17
Nov 2	Isth P	H	Lewes	175	L 0 - 2		18	18
9	Isth P	A	Cray Wanderers	162	L 1 - 6	Moss 17 (pen)	19	19
16	Isth P	H	Carshalton Athletic	176	L 0 - 1		20	20
23	Isth P	H	Merstham	158	W 3 - 0	Moss 34 Newton 60 Diallo 75	18	21
30	Isth P	A	Brightlingsea Regent	131	D 1 - 1	Moss 54	18	22
Dec 7	Isth P	H	Bishops Stortford	208	L 0 - 1		18	23
28	Isth P	A	Corinthian-Casuals	301	L 1 - 3	Beccles-Richards 36	18	24
Jan 4	Isth P	H	Kingstonian	202	W 3 - 1	Moss 6 Kassarate 19 Beccles-Richards 62	18	25
11	Isth P	A	Wingate & Finchley	97	W 2 - 1	Beccles-Richards 39 Moss 67 (pen)	18	26
18	Isth P	H	Enfield Town	556	L 2 - 3	Camara 7 Moss 36	18	27
25	Isth P	A	Worthing	1128	L 0 - 2		18	28
28	Isth P	H	Bowers & Pitsea	133	D 1 - 1	Newton 24	18	29
Feb 1	Isth P	H	Leatherhead	191	L 1 - 3	Newton 90	20	30
4	Isth P	A	Hornchurch	311	L 0 - 3		20	31
8	Isth P	A	Lewes	505	W 6 - 1	Beccles-Richards 19 75 Moss 48 Kassarate 57 Newton 85 Camara 90	18	32
22	Isth P	A	Horsham	604	L 0 - 2		18	33
Mar 7	Isth P	A	Carshalton Athletic	376	L 0 - 2		21	34
11	Isth P	A	Kingstonian	222	W 4 - 2	Abrahams 38 Reynolds 53 Beccles-Richards 65 Moss 70	17	35

GOALSCORERS	SG	CSG	Pens	Hat tricks	Total		SG	CSG	Pens	Hat tricks	Total
Moss	7	3	2		8	Cronin	1				1
Beccles-Richards	5	3			6	Diallo	1				1
Camara	4				5	McKenna	1				1
Akinyemi	3				4	Moncur	1				1
Hitchcock	4	3	3		4	Opponents	1				1
Newton	4				4	Reynolds	1				1
Kassarate	2				2						
Moses	2				2						
Abrahams	1				1						
Amoc	1				1						

CORINTHIAN-CASUALS MATCH RESULTS 2019-20

Date	Comp	H/A	Opponents	Att:	Result	Goalscorers	Pos	No.
Aug 10	Isth P	A	Haringey Borough	424	L 0 - 1			1
13	Isth P	H	Merstham	286	L 0 - 1			2
17	Isth P	A	Cray Wanderers	207	D 0 - 0		21	3
24	Isth P	H	Carshalton Athletic	271	L 2 - 3	Pinney 44 (pen) Dell 79	21	4
26	Isth P	A	Cheshunt	185	D 1 - 1	Maan 90	21	5
31	Isth P	H	Brighlingsea Regent	203	L 0 - 1		21	6
Sept 7	FAC1Q	H	**Sevenoaks Town**	**234**	**W 4 - 0**	**Ekim 29 Pinney 44 53 (pen) Dillon 90**		7
14	Isth P	A	Enfield Town	310	L 1 - 3	Okojie 32	22	8
21	FAC2Q	H	**Chelmsford City**	**374**	**W 2 - 0**	**Pinney 35 (pen) Okojie 64**		9
28	Isth P	H	Potters Bar Town	273	D 0 - 0		22	10
Oct 1	Isth P	H	Horsham	177	L 1 - 2	Ekim 2	22	11
5	FAC3Q	A	**Kings Langley**	**362**	**L 0 - 3**			12
12	Isth P	H	Folkestone Invicta	277	L 0 - 1		22	13
23	Isth P	A	Lewes	357	L 0 - 1		22	14
26	FAT1Q	A	**Kingstonian**	**417**	**L 2 - 4**	**Okojie (pen) Pinney (pen)**	**22**	15
Nov 2	Isth P	H	Margate	252	L 1 - 2	Wilson 80	22	16
9	Isth P	A	Bishop's Stortford	189	W 3 - 1	Pinney 25 28 (pen) Strange 36	22	17
12	Isth P	A	Leatherhead	368	L 1 - 2	Wilson 42	22	18
16	Isth P	A	Hornchurch	309	D 1 - 1	Pinney 58 (pen)	22	19
23	Isth P	A	Worthing	662	L 0 - 2		22	20
Dec 7	Isth P	A	Brightlingsea Regent	139	L 1 - 2	Pinney 65	22	21
14	Isth P	H	Wingate & Finchley	213	D 3 - 3	Cheklit 11 Sitch 63 Jamison 90	22	22
28	Isth P	H	Cheshunt	301	W 3 - 1	Serbponij 37 Ekim 32 Okojie 90	22	23
Jan 4	Isth P	H	Leatherhead	515	W 3 - 0	Okojie 2 Checklit 73 Sitch 82	20	24
11	Isth P	A	Horsham	557	L 0 - 1		20	25
18	Isth P	H	Bowers & Pitsea	286	L 0 - 1		20	26
21	Isth P	A	Bowers & Pitsea	92	W 2 - 0	Cheklit 8 Odunaike 53	19	27
25	Isth P	A	Folkestone Invicta	499	L 1 - 3	Okojie 49	20	28
28	Isth P	H	Bognor Regis Town	242	D 1 - 1	Wilson 44	20	29
Feb 1	Isth P	H	Lewes	278	W 1 - 0	Cheklit 81	19	30
8	Isth P	A	Margate	358	D 2 - 2	Bakare 26 Checklit 83	20	31
22	Isth P	A	Potters Bar Town	164	L 1 - 3	Pinney 90	22	32
26	Isth P	A	Kingstonian	397	L 1 - 3	Cheklit 31	22	33
Mar 3	Isth P	H	East Thurrock United	160	W 2 - 1	Odunaike 2 Checklit 29	20	34
7	Isth P	H	Hornchurch	277	D 1 - 1	Pinney 20 (pen)	18	35

GOALSCORERS	SG	CSG	Pens	Hat tricks	Total		SG	CSG	Pens	Hat tricks	Total
Pinney	5		7		11	Jamison	1				1
Cheklit	7				7	Maan	1				1
Okojie	5	2	1		6	Serbponij	1				1
Ekim	3				3	Strange	1				1
Wilson	3				3						
Odunaike	2				2						
Sitch	2				2						
Bakare	1				1						
Dell	1				1						
Dillon	1				1						

CRAY WANDERERS MATCH RESULTS 2019-20

Date	Comp	H/A	Opponents	Att:	Result	Goalscorers	Pos	No.
Aug 10	Isth P	A	Kingstonian	277	D	0 - 0		1
14	Isth P	H	Folkestone Invicta	240	L	2 - 3	Coker 41 50		2
17	Isth P	H	Corinthian-Casuals	207	D	0 - 0		18	3
21	Isth P	H	Margate	242	W	3 - 2	Parker 30 73 Taylor 35	8	4
24	FACP	H	Hythe Town	230	W	5 - 0	Murphy 5 39 Taylor 45 90 Pritchard 63		5
31	Isth P	A	Potters Bar Town	181	D	1 - 1	Taylor 90	14	6
Sept 8	FAC1Q	H	Bedfont Sports	225	W	2 - 1	Lewis 6 Taylor 26		7
14	Isth P	H	Haringay Borough	162	D	1 - 1	Taylor 73	15	8
17	Isth P	A	Bishops Stortford	340	W	5 - 1	Taylor 25 55 Murphy 38 68 Dent 43	12	9
22	FAC2Q	H	Soham Town Rangers	184	W	5 - 2	Taylor 18 38 75 Hudson 49 Murphy 66		10
28	Isth P	H	East Thurrock United	174	D	1 - 1	Murphy 75	9	11
Oct 2	Isth P	H	Bowers & Pitsea	135	W	3 - 1	Coker 20 Taylor 28 Carlse 31	9	12
5	FAC3Q	A	Haringey Borough	344	L	0 - 1		9	13
12	Isth P	H	Enfield Town	621	L	3 - 5	Taylor 73 Murphy 73 Leader 85	10	14
15	Isth P	H	Merstham	147	W	2 - 1	Taylor 18 Pritchard 58	10	15
19	Isth P	A	Lewes	648	W	3 - 2	Taylor 33 Nelson 45 Coker 50		16
22	Isth P	A	Horsham	481	D	1 - 1	Leader 37	7	17
26	FAT1Q	A	Malden & Tiptree	145	L	0 - 3		7	18
Nov 2	Isth P	H	Worthing	172	D	2 - 2	Taylor 30 Agulor 90 (og)	7	19
9	Isth P	H	Cheshunt	162	W	6 - 1	Rollinson 1 Lewis 40 54 Taylor 59 65 67	6	20
12	Isth P	A	Wingate & Finchley	102	W	1 - 0	Rollinson 3	6	21
16	Isth P	A	Brightlingsea Regent	157	W	2 - 0	Taylor 24 26 (pen)	6	22
30	Isth P	A	Carshalton Athletic	332	L	0 - 4		6	23
Dec 7	Isth P	H	Potters Bar Town	163	W	4 - 0	Coker 22 Lewis 40 Taylor 54 Dent 56	6	24
14	Isth P	A	Bognor Regis Town	527	L	2 - 7	Taylor 71 82	6	25
26	Isth P	H	Leatherhead	188	L	0 - 1		7	26
Jan 1	Isth P	A	Margate	367	W	4 - 3	Taylor 31 48 Lewis 70 Mundele 80	6	27
4	Isth P	A	Wingate & Finchley	144	D	0 - 0		6	28
11	Isth P	A	Bowers & Pitsea	154	W	2 - 1	Taylor 64 Murrell-Williamson 88	6	29
15	Isth P	H	Hornchurch	210	D	1 - 1	Mundele 69	6	30
18	Isth P	H	Lewes	198	W	2 - 1	Dent 11 Leader 30	5	31
25	Isth P	A	Enfield Town	303	W	3 - 2	Allen 38 82 Leader 90	3	32
Feb 1	Isth P	H	Horsham	193	W	2 - 1	Taylor 24 (pen) Murrell-Williamson 28	3	33
8	Isth P	A	Worthing	932	W	2 - 1	Taylor 69 Robinson 90	3	34
15	Isth P	H	Kingstonian	239	D	0 - 0		4	35
22	Isth P	A	East Thurrock United	185	W	1 - 0	Murrell-Williamson 52	4	36
Mar 1	Isth P	H	Merstham	329	W	3 - 1	Taylor 6 44 (pen) Pritchard 40	4	37
7	Isth P	H	Brightlingsea Regent	187	W	1 - 0	Taylor 9	2	38

GOALSCORERS	SG	CSG	Pens	Hat tricks	Total		SG	CSG	Pens	Hat tricks	Total
Taylor	22	7	3	2	32	Mundele	2				2
Murphy	5				7	Parker	1				2
Coker	5				5	Carlse	1				1
Lewis	4				5	Hudson	1				1
Leader	4	2			4	Nelson	1				1
Dent	3				3	Opponents	1				1
M-Williamson	3				3						
Pritchard	3				3						
Rollinson	3	2			3						
Allen	1				2						

EAST THURROCK UNITED MATCH RESULTS 2019-20

Date	Comp	H/A	Opponents	Att:	Result		Goalscorers	Pos	No.
Aug 10	Isth P	H	Cheshunt	217	W	4 - 1	Clark 11 Merrifield 50 76 Marlow 63		1
12	Isth P	A	Carshalton Athletic	414	W	2 - 1	Clark 20 Gilbey 43		2
17	Isth P	H	Potters Bar Town	220	L	1 - 3	Gilbey 89	5	3
24	Isth P	A	Merstham	151	L	1 - 2	Merrifield 14 (pen)	8	4
26	Isth P	H	Bowers & Pitsea	398	W	3 - 1	Pugh 27 69 Smith 90	6	5
31	Isth P	A	Haringey Borough	420	L	0 - 2		6	6
Sept 7	FAC1Q	H	**Peterborough Sports**	?	D	1 - 1	**Smith 36**		7
10	FAC1Qr	A	**Peterborough Sports**	162	L	2 - 3	**Merrifield 34 Olukoga 90**		8
14	Isth P	H	Bognor Regis Town	205	W	3 - 0	Harris 30 Olukoga 39 Clark 56	5	9
21	Isth P	H	Brightlingsea Regent	215	W	2 - 1	Merrifield 36 (pen) 90	4	10
28	Isth P	A	Cray Wanderers	174	D	1 - 1	Pugh 48	4	11
Oct 1	Isth P	H	Margate	185	L	1 - 2	Pugh 45	5	12
5	Isth P	A	Worthing	661	W	3 - 2	Merrifield 38 58 Marlow 84	5	13
12	Isth P	H	Lewes	272	W	1 - 0	Gilbey 35	5	14
22	Isth P	A	Folkestone Invicta	404	L	1 - 4	Sheehan 52	6	15
26	FAT1Q	A	**Cheshunt**	115	W	2 - 1	**Girling 2 Merrifield 12**	6	16
Nov 2	Isth P	H	Wingate & Finchley	154	W	3 - 1	Gilbey 84 Marsh 87 Bonnet-Johnson 90	6	17
9	FAT2Q	A	**Bognor Regis Town**	302	L	1 - 3	**Clark 31**	6	18
16	Isth P	H	Leatherhead	183	W	3 - 0	Merrifield 25 90 Foxley 88	5	19
Dec 3	Isth P	A	Bishop's Stortford	179	L	0 - 1		8	20
7	Isth P	H	Haringey Borough	257	W	4 - 2	Foxley 33 Nasha 41 Merrifield 45 Gilbey 61	8	21
14	Isth P	A	Horsham	539	L	0 - 1		9	22
Jan 1	Isth P	A	Bowers & Pitsea	254	W	2 - 1	Foxley 27 Merrifield 70	8	23
4	Isth P	H	Worthing	254	D	0 - 0		8	24
11	Isth P	A	Margate	325	W	1 - 0	Merrifield 37	8	25
18	Isth P	H	Kingstonian	208	D	3 - 3	Gilbey 14 Marlow 35 Price 87	8	26
25	Isth P	A	Lewes	506	W	3 - 0	Merrifield 15 Gilbey 84 Harris 88	7	27
29	Isth P	A	Kingstonian	238	D	0 - 0		7	28
Feb 1	Isth P	H	Folkestone Invicta	252	L	1 - 3	Merrified 82	9	29
8	Isth P	A	Wingate & Finchley	95	L	1 - 2	Foxley 4	10	30
18	Isth P	H	Carshalton Athletic	165	W	2 - 0	Junior 23 Foxley 38 (pen)	9	31
22	Isth P	H	Cray Wanderers	185	L	0 - 1		8	32
Mar 3	Isth P	A	Corinthian-Casuals	160	L	1 - 2	Cossington 57	8	33
7	Isth P	A	Leatherhead	325	L	0 - 3		11	34

GOALSCORERS	SG	CSG	Pens	Hat tricks	Total		SG	CSG	Pens	Hat tricks	Total
Merrifield	13		2		16	Cossington	1				1
Gilbey	7	2			7	Girling	1				1
Foxley	5		1		5	Junior	1				1
Clark	3	2			4	Marsh	1				1
Pugh	4	2			4	Nasha	1				1
Marlow	3				3	Price	1				1
Harris	2				2	Sheehan	1				1
Olukoga	2	2			2						
Smith	2				2						
Bonnet-Johnson	1				1						

ENFIELD TOWN MATCH RESULTS 2019-20

Date	Comp	H/A	Opponents	Att:	Result	Goalscorers	Pos	No.
Aug 10	Isth P	A	Lewes	420	D 1 - 1	Charles 38		1
13	Isth P	H	Bishops Stortford	372	W 5 - 0	Charles 4 36 Youngs 4 Bricknell 14 Mubiayi 86		2
17	Isth P	H	Horsham	333	L 1 - 4	Chsrles 54	9	3
24	Isth P	A	Leatherhead	361	W 2 - 1	Weatherstone 8 Faal 79	5	4
26	Isth P	H	Potters Bar Town	476	D 2 - 2	Charles 39 Faal 42	5	5
31	Isth P	A	Bowers & Pitsea	161	W 1 - 0	Bricknell 23 (pen)	5	6
Sept 7	FAC1Q	H	AFC Rushden & Diamonds	501	W 1 - 0	Faal 60		7
14	Isth P	H	Corinthian-Casuals	310	W 3 - 1	Bricknell 18 Faal 25 61	4	8
21	FAC2Q	H	Braintree Town	523	W 2 - 0	Faal 26 86		9
28	Isth P	H	Merstham	332	W 2 - 0	Blackman 25 Faal 77	4	10
Oct 1	Isth P	A	Brightlingsea Regent	154	W 2 - 0	Youngs 50 Taaffe 74	4	11
5	FAC3Q	A	Chichester Town	515	L 0 - 1			12
12	Isth P	A	Cray Wanderers	621	W 5 - 3	Faal 7 38 Charles 52 64 Payne 70	4	13
19	Isth P	H	Cheshunt	431	W 2 - 1	Faal 29 48	4	14
22	Isth P	H	Hornchurch	396	D 1 - 1	Youngs 6	4	15
26	FAT1Q	A	Bishop's Stortford	317	D 1 - 1	Bricknell 80		16
29	FAT1Qr	H	Bishop's Stortford	204	W 4 - 2	Blackman 78 Weatherstone 105 Charles 107 Faal 119		17
Nov 9	FAT2Q	H	Thatcham Town	248	W 5 - 0	Bricknell 38 43 70 Faal 70 85		18
16	Isth P	H	Folkestone Invicta	468	L 1 - 3	Faal 56	7	19
20	Isth P	A	Kingstonian	271	D 0 - 0		7	20
23	FAT3Q	H	Maldon & Tiptree	275	W 4 - 3	Faal 1 Weatherstone 59 Bricknell 71 75		21
26	Isth P	H	Carshalton Athletic	261	W 2 - 1	Faal 1 Bricknell 28	6	22
30	Isth P	H	Wingate & Finchley	356	D 2 - 2	Faal 56 Payne 90	5	23
Dec 3	Isth P	A	Bognor Regis Town	425	L 1 - 4	Faal 48	6	24
7	Isth P	H	Bowers & Pitsea	307	L 0 - 4		7	25
14	FAT1P	H	Ebbsfleet United	417	L 0 - 2		8	26
17	Isth P	A	Worthing	480	L 2 - 3	Faal 25 (pen) 57	8	27
21	Isth P	H	Haringey Borough	411	W 5 - 3	Blackman 16 Faal 43 67 Della-Verde 55 Bricknell 90	7	28
Jan 1	Isth P	A	Potters Bar Town	445	W 2 - 1	Pudden 17 (og) Bricknell 58	7	29
4	Isth P	A	Carshalton Athletic	494	L 0 - 2		7	30
11	Isth P	H	Brightlingsea Regent	344	D 2 - 2	Youngs 27 Della-Verde 78	7	31
18	Isth P	A	Cheshunt	556	W 3 - 2	Bricknell 1 61 Youngs 23	7	32
25	Isth P	H	Cray Wanderers	303	L 2 - 3	Blackman 56 Bricknell 69 (pen)	8	33
28	Isth P	A	Margate	215	W 3 - 0	Della-Verde 58 Bricknell 72 Blackman 90	7	34
Feb 1	Isth P	A	Hornchurch	365	L 0 - 4		7	35
8	Isth P	H	Bognor Regis Town	412	W 2 - 0	Taaffe 48 Charles 88	7	36
22	Isth P	A	Merstham	203	W 4 - 1	Charles 10 Youngs 22 Della-Verde 51 Bricknell 85	7	37
Mar 3	Isth P	H	Lewes	307	D 1 - 1	Weatherstone 72	7	38
7	Isth P	A	Folkestone Invicta	587	D 1 - 1	Bricknel 6	7	39
10	Isth P	A	Bishops Stortford	206	W 1 - 0	Okojie 24	7	40

GOALSCORERS	SG	CSG	Pens	Hat tricks	Total		SG	CSG	Pens	Hat tricks	Total
Faal	16	4	1		24	Opponents	1				1
Bricknell	15		1	1	19						
Charles	7	3			10						
Blackman	5				5						
Youngs	5				5						
Della-Verde	4				4						
Weatherstone	4				4						
Payne	2				2						
Taaffe	2				2						
Mubiayi	1				1						
Okojie	1				1						

FOLKSTONE INVICTA MATCH RESULTS 2019-20

Date	Comp	H/A	Opponents	Att:	Result	Goalscorers	Pos	No.
Aug 10	Isth P	H	Worthing	516	W 2 - 0	Dos Santos 63 Jackson 86		1
14	Isth P	A	Cray Wanderers	240	W 3 - 2	Dos Santos 3 81 Ter Horst 90		2
17	Isth P	H	Leatherhead	504	D 1 - 1	Jackson 86	4	3
24	Isth P	A	Potters Bar Town	190	W 4 - 1	Heard 36 61 Jackson 76 90	3	4
26	Isth P	H	Merstham	484	W 3 - 1	Dos Santos 18 McCann 22 Jackson 54	3	5
31	Isth P	A	Horsham	622	W 1 - 0	Ter Horst 79	1	6
Sept 7	FAC1Q	A	Whitstable Town	503	W 4 - 0	Jackson 25 53 Ter Horst 54 Hasler 81		7
14	Isth P	H	Bishops Stortford	533	W 1 - 0	Vincent 77	1	8
21	FAC2Q	H	Kings Langley	335	L 0 - 4			9
28	Isth P	A	Wingate & Finchley	124	D 1 - 1	Vincent 73	1	10
Oct 1	Isth P	A	Hornchurch	247	L 0 - 1		2	11
5	Isth P	H	Brightlingsea Regent	477	W 3 - 2	McCann 20 54 Dos Santos 43	2	12
12	Isth P	A	Corinthian-Casuals	277	W 1 - 0	McCann 34	1	13
15	Isth P	H	Cheshunt	396	W 4 - 2	Jackson 23 Dos Santos 58 Vincent 68 Paxman 74	1	14
19	Isth P	H	Bognor Regis Town	538	L 1 - 2	Jackson 47		15
22	Isth P	H	East Thurrock United	404	W 4 - 1	Dolan 15 Dos Santos 61 Jackson 77 O'Mara 85	1	16
26	FAT1Q	H	Lewes	332	W 2 - 0	Paxman 51 Hasler 76	1	17
Nov 2	Isth P	A	Carshalton Athletic	502	D 1 - 1	Dos Santos 49	1	18
16	Isth P	A	Enfield	468	W 3 - 1	Jackson 26 Heard 32 90	1	19
30	Isth P	A	Lewes	565	D 0 - 0		2	20
Dec 3	Isth P	H	Kingstonian	389	D 1 - 1	Jackson 45	1	21
7	Isth P	H	Horsham	536	W 2 - 1	Jackson 66 (pen) Shelley 78 (og)	1	22
14	Isth P	A	Bowers & Pitsea	159	L 1 - 3	Heard 5	1	23
26	Isth P	H	Margate	769	W 4 - 0	Jackson 55 90 Ter Horst 57 McKenzie 90	1	24
Jan 1	Isth P	A	Merstham	201	W 4 - 0	Ter-Horst 19 Paxman 45 McKenzie 76 Jackson 80 (pen)	1	25
4	Isth P	A	Brightlingsea Regent	164	D 0 - 0		1	26
11	Isth P	H	Haringey Borough	536	D 1 - 1	Vincent 80	2	27
18	Isth P	A	Bognor Regis Town	497	L 3 - 4	JACKSON 3 (8 17 (pen) 60 pen)	2	28
25	Isth P	H	Corinthian-Casuals	499	W 3 - 1	Bracken (og) 39 Vincent 60 Jackson 75	2	29
26	Isth P	H	Hornchurch	404	W 2 - 1	Dolan 33 Paxman 50	2	30
Feb 1	Isth P	A	East Thurrock United	252	W 3 - 1	Jackson 42 Heard 49 Dos Santos 71	2	31
8	Isth P	H	Carshallton Athletic	619	L 1 - 3	Sterling 81	2	32
15	Isth P	A	Worthing	1410	W 1 - 0	Jackson 87	2	33
22	Isth P	H	Wingate & Finchley	554	L 0 - 1		2	34
Mar 7	Isth P	H	Enfield Town	587	D 1 - 1	Jackson 86	4	35

GOALSCORERS	SG	CSG	Pens	Hat tricks	Total		SG	CSG	Pens	Hat tricks	Total
Jackson	16	3	4	1	23	Opponents	2				2
Dos Santos	7	2			9	O'Mara	1				1
Heard	5				6	Sterling	1				1
Ter Horst	5	2			5						
Vincent	5				5						
McCann	3	2			4						
Paxman	4				4						
Dolan	2				2						
Hasler	2				2						
McKenzie	2	2			2						

HARINGEY BOROUGH MATCH RESULTS 2019-20

Date	Comp	H/A	Opponents	Att:	Result	Goalscorers	Pos	No.
Aug 10	Isth P	H	Corinthian-Casuals	424	W 1 - 0	Onokwai 50		1
13	Isth P	A	Leathhead	335	W 3 - 2	Onokwai 16 (pen) Akinola 51 Sambu 67	1	2
17	Isth P	A	Cheshunt	249	W 1 - 0	Onokwai 67	1	3
24	Isth P	H	Brightlingsea Regent	319	W 5 - 1	Solomou 30 49 67 Rowe 44 Aresti 90	1	4
26	Isth P	A	Wingate & Finchley	231	L 0 - 1		2	5
31	Isth P	H	East Thurrock United	420	W 2 - 0	Solomou 9 Aresti 43	2	6
Sept 7	FAC1Q	H	Herne Bay	325	W 3 - 0	Stone 44 Aresti 71 McDonald 85		7
14	Isth P	A	Cray Wanderers	162	D 1 - 1	Froxylias 34	3	8
21	FAC2Q	H	Staines Town	343	W 5 - 0	Richards 36 Froxylias 70 (pen) Onokwai 75 (pen) 78 85		9
28	Isth P	A	Bognor Regis Town	406	L 0 - 2		5	10
30	Isth P	H	Kingstonian	294	L 0 - 1		6	11
Oct 5	FAC3Q	H	Cray Wanderers	344	W 1 - 0	Froxylias 56 (pen)		12
12	Isth P	H	Margate	452	W 1 - 0	Akinola 45	6	13
26	FAT1Q	H	Horsham	285	W 3 - 0	Ademiluyi 23 Onokwai 45 Sambu 55		14
29	FAC4Q	H	Yeovil Town	857	L 0 - 3			15
Nov 2	Isth P	H	Horsham	386	L 1 - 2	Aresti 32	8	16
9	FAT2Q	H	Canvey Island	323	W 2 - 1	Solomou 43 Froxylias 62	9	17
16	Isth P	H	Bishops Stortford	402	W 2 - 1	Akinola 36 Onokwai 90 (pen)	10	18
18	Isth P	H	Hornchurch	362	D 1 - 1	Froxylias 79	10	19
23	FAT3Q	H	Hemel Hempstead Town	234	L 1 - 4	Staunton 90		20
30	Isth P	H	Worthing	389	D 2 - 2	Mitchell 41 Froxylies 69	11	21
Dec 7	Isth P	A	East Thurrock United	257	L 2 - 4	Solomou 24 Onokwai 80	12	22
17	Isth P	A	Merstham	123	L 0 - 1		13	23
26	Isth P	A	Enfield Town	411	L 3 - 5	Onokwai 21(pen) 63 Akindayini 51	15	24
Jan 1	Isth P	H	Wingate & Finchley	403	W 2 - 1	Onokwai 50 Aresti 64	14	25
4	Isth P	H	Lewes	435	L 0 - 1		14	26
11	Isth P	A	Folkestone Invicta	536	D 1 - 1	Akinola 89	13	27
18	Isth P	H	Pottersw Bar town	433	W 3 - 2	Michael-Percil 61 (pen) Akinola 65 Richards 83	12	28
25	Isth P	A	Margate	354	L 2 - 4	Solomou 59 Michael-Percil 74 (pen)	14	29
27	Isth P	H	Carshalton Athletic	245	D 2 - 2	Akinola 24 Michael-Percil 49	13	30
Feb 1	Isth P	H	Bowers & Pitsea	428	D 1 - 1	McDonald 87	13	31
8	Isth P	H	Horsham	564	L 0 - 2		14	32
11	Isth P	A	Bowers & Pitsea	98	L 2 - 3	Akindayini 20 (pen) 87	15	33
22	Isth P	H	Bognor Regis Town	422	W 2 - 1	Aresti 47 McDonald 82	15	34
29	Isth P	A	Hornchurch	318	L 1 - 2	Michael-Percil 88	15	35
Mar 7	Isth P	A	Bishop's Stortford	236	W 2 - 1	Aderniluyi 59 Onokwai 89 (pen)	15	36
11	Isth P	A	Lewes	228	L 1 - 2	Onokwai 71 (pen)	15	37

GOALSCORERS	SG	CSG	Pens	Hat tricks	Total		SG	CSG	Pens	Hat tricks	Total
Onokwai	10	3	5	1	14	Sambu	2				2
Solomou	5		1		7	Mitchell	1				1
Akinola	6				6	Rowe	1				1
Aresti	6	2			6	Staunton	1				1
Froxylias	6	2	2		6	Stone	1				1
Michael-Percil	4	3	2		4						
Akindayini	2		1		3						
McDonald	3				3						
Ademiluyi	2				2						
Richards	2				2						

HORNCHURCH MATCH RESULTS 2019-20

Date	Comp	H/A	Opponents	Att:	Result	Goalscorers	Pos	No.
Aug 10	Isth P	A	Merstham	164	W 2 - 1	Spence 56 Christou 81		1
13	Isth P	H	Margate	254	D 2 - 2	Dickson 33 Spence 82		2
17	Isth P	A	Worthing	701	W 6 - 0	Dickson 56 71 72 Winn 71 82 Stimson 89	2	3
24	Isth P	H	Kingstonian	238	W 3 - 0	Dickson 8 Christou 16 Winn 68	2	4
26	Isth P	A	Brightlingsea Regent	247	L 0 - 1		3	5
31	Isth P	H	Wingate & Finchley	258	W 2 - 0	Dickson 45 Christou 67	3	6
Sept 7	FAC1Q	H	**Kempston Rovers**	**240**	**W 6 - 0**	**Spence (2) Christou Parcell Dickson Johnson**		7
14	Isth P	A	Carshalton Athletic	450	W 4 - 1	Saunders 15 Spence 29 Dickson 51 Uchechi 75	2	8
21	FAC2Q	A	**Potters Bar Town**	**184**	**L 0 - 2**			9
28	Isth P	H	Bishops Stortford	315	W 4 - 0	Johnson 29 88 Dickson 42 52	2	10
Oct 1	Isth P	H	Folkestone Invicta	247	W 1 - 0	Spence 61	2	11
5	Isth P	A	Horsham	619	L 0 - 1		3	12
12	Isth P	H	Bowers & Pitsea	435	W 2 - 1	Dickson 69 Johnson 90	2	13
19	Isth P	A	Leatherhead	356	L 1 - 2	Stimson 49	4	14
22	Isth P	A	Enfield Town	396	D 1 - 1	Muleba 46 (og)	4	15
26	FAT1Q	H	**Berkhamsted**	**133**	**W 3 - 1**	**Stimson 33 43 Morgan 90**		16
Nov 2	Isth P	H	Potters Bar Town	219	W 3 - 1	Stimson 25 Morgan 63 Uchechi 71	3	17
9	FAT2Q	A	**Basildon United**	**163**	**W 6 - 1**	**Stimson 38 67 88 Morgan 14 Uchechi 48 Spence 90**	3	18
16	Isth P	H	Corinthian Casuals	309	D 1 - 1	Dickson 68	4	19
18	Isth P	A	Haringey Borough	362	D 1 - 1	Stimson 75	3	20
23	FAT3Q	A	**Oxford City**	**228**	**D 1 - 1**	**Hayles 30**		21
26	FAT3Qr	H	**Oxford City**	**139**	**W 4 - 4**	**Dickson 47 Spence 89 Saunders 93 Morgan 97 (Won 4-1 on pens)**		22
30	Isth P	H	Bognor Regis Town	320	D 0 - 0		4	23
Dec 7	Isth P	A	Wingate & Finchley	118	W 3 - 2	Dickson 6 16 50	4	24
14	FAT1P	H	**Dulwich Hamlet**	**454**	**W 1 - 0**	**Cooper 53**		25
28	Isth P	H	Brightlingsea Regent	354	W 3 - 0	Hayles 30 Dickson 45 (pen) Cooper 8	4	26
Jan 4	Isth P	H	Horsham	380	W 2 - 1	Hayles 27 Dickson 65	4	27
11	FAT2P	H	**Aveley**	**589**	**L 1 - 2**	**Dickson 45 (pen)**	**6**	28
15	Isth P	A	Cray Wandeerers	210	D 1 - 1	Roninson 44 (og)	6	29
18	Isth P	H	Leatherhead	323	D 1 - 1	Clark 67	6	30
25	Isth P	A	Bowers & Pitsea	196	W 1 - 0	Spence 2	5	31
28	Isth P	A	Folkestone invicta	404	L 1 - 2	Cunnington 3	5	32
Feb 1	Isth P	H	Enfield Town	365	W 4 - 0	Dickson 15 Cunnington 26 Parcell 31 Clark 34	4	33
4	Isth P	H	Cheshunt	211	W 3 - 0	Dickson 15 Cunnington 28 51	3	34
8	Isth P	A	Potters Bar Town	229	L 1 - 2	Cureton 17	4	35
11	Isth P	A	Cray Wanderers	269	D 0 - 0		4	36
15	Isth P	H	Merstham	297	D 2 - 2	Saunders 12 Lee 90	5	37
18	Isth P	A	Margate	218	D 2 - 2	Cureton 77 Saunders 90	4	38
22	Isth P	A	Bishop's Stortford	327	W 2 - 0	Dickson 37 Johnson 78	3	39
29	Isth P	H	Haringey Borough	318	W 2 - 1	Dickson 59 81	2	40
Mar 7	Isth P	A	Corinthian-Casuals	277	D 1 - 1	Clark 33	3	41

GOALSCORERS	SG	CSG	Pens	Hat tricks	Total		SG	CSG	Pens	Hat tricks	Total
Dickson	18	4	2	2	24	Hayles	3	2			3
Stimson	6	3		1	9	Uchechi	3	2			3
Spence	8	2			9	Parcell	2				2
Johnson	4				5	Cureton	2				2
Christou	4	2			4	Cooper	2	2			2
Cunnington	3	3			4	Opponents	2				2
Morgan	4	3			4	Lee	1				1
Saunders	4				4						
Clark	3				3						
Winn	2	2			3						

HORSHAM MATCH RESULTS 2019-20

Date	Comp	H/A	Opponents	Att:	Result	Goalscorers	Pos	No.
Aug 10	Isth P	H	Leatherhead	711	D 1 - 1	O'Toole 39		1
13	Isth P	A	Bognor Regis Town	545	D 1 - 1	O'Toole 45		2
17	Isth P	A	Enfield Town	333	W 4 - 1	Smith 45 71 Harris 67 Newton 82	12	3
24	**FACP**	A	**Tower Hamlets**	**89**	**W 6 - 1**	**Miles 15 Smith 26 45 Newton 74 Zuqolli (og) 84 Rance 87**		4
26	Isth P	A	Lewes	600	W 2 - 0	Hayward 46 Shelley 57	8	5
31	Isth P	H	Folkestone Invicta	258	L 0 - 1		9	6
Sept 7	**FAC1Q**	A	**Metropolitan Police**	**143**	**D 1 - 1**	**Smith 40**		7
10	**FAC1Qr**	A	**Metropolitan Police**	**445**	**W 3 - 2**	**Sparks 41 Smith 48 90**		8
14	Isth P	A	Brighlingsea Rgent	166	W 4 - 0	SMITH 7 9 66 Harris 36	7	9
17	Isth P	H	Wingate & Finchley	412	W 2 - 1	Harris 3 Smith 27	5	10
21	**FAC2Q**	H	**Dartford**	**902**	**L 0 - 2**			11
28	Isth P	A	Cheshunt	197	W 1 - 0	Diallo 61 (og)	3	12
Oct 2	Isth P	A	Corinthian-Casuals	177	W 2 - 1	Brivio 87 Lavery 90	1	13
5	Isth P	H	Hornchurch	619	W 1 - 0	Harris 80	1	14
8	Isth P	H	Carshalton Athletic	556	D 2 - 2	Smith 41 Harris 43	1	15
12	Isth P	A	Bishops Stortford	302	L 0 - 2		2	16
19	Isth P	H	Merstham	602	W 4 - 0	Harris 24 O'Toole 31 Smith 65 Dawson 77	2	17
22	Isth P	H	Cray Wanderers	481	D 1 - 1	Dawson 35	2	18
26	**FAT1Q**	A	**Haringey Borough**	**285**	**L 0 - 3**			19
Nov 2	Isth P	A	Haringey Borough	386	W 2 - 1	O'Toole 9 Pamment 90	2	20
9	Isth P	H	Bowers & Pitsea	497	W 4 - 0	Smith 12 74 90 Merchant-Simmonds 24	1	21
16	Isth P	A	Potters Bar Town	229	W 2 - 0	Dawson 86 Harding 89	1	22
30	Isth P	H	Margate	747	L 0 - 3		2	23
Dec 7	Isth P	A	Folkestone Invicta	536	L 1 - 2	Charman 79	3	24
14	Isth P	H	East Thurrock United	539	W 1 - 0	Charman 34	2	25
26	Isth P	A	Worthing	937	L 0 - 3		3	26
Jan 1	Isth P	H	Lewes	913	W 3 - 0	Shelley 12 O'Toole 41 Brivio 52	3	27
4	Isth P	A	Hornchurch	380	L 1 - 2	Cundle 22L	3	28
11	Isth P	H	Corinthian-Casals	557	W 1 - 0	Mills 75 (pen)	3	29
18	Isth P	A	Merstham	240	L 0 - 1		3	30
25	Isth P	H	Bishops Stortford	593	D 3 - 3	O'Toole 27 90 (pen) Smith 82	4	31
Feb 1	Isth P	A	Cray Wanderers	193	L 1 - 2	Harding 29	5	32
5	Isth P	A	Kingstonian	255	D 1 - 1	Charman 90	6	33
8	Isth P	H	Haringey Borough	564	W 2 - 0	Harding 14 Cundle 76	6	34
22	Isth P	H	Chester	604	W 2 - 0	Harding 27 Brivic 52	6	35
29	Isth P	A	Carshalton Athletic	461	L 0 - 4		6	36
Mar 7	Isth P	H	Potters Bar Town	540	W 2 - 0	Shelley 72 Cundle 89	6	37
10	Isth P	H	Bognor Regis Town	576	L 0 - 2		6	38

GOALSCORERS	SG	CSG	Pens	Hat tricks	Total		SG	CSG	Pens	Hat tricks	Total
Smith	9	4		2	17	Opponents	2				2
O'Toole	6	2	1		7	Hayward	1				1
Harris	6	2			6	Lavery	1				1
Harding	4	2			4	M-Simmonds	1				1
Brivio	3				3	Mlles	1				1
Charman	3	2			3	Mills	1		1		1
Cundle	3				3	Pamment	1				1
Dawson	3				3	Rance	1				1
Shelley	3				3	Sparks	1				1
Newton	2	2			2						

KINGSTONIAN MATCH RESULTS 2019-20

Date	Comp	H/A	Opponents	Att:	Result	Goalscorers	Pos	No.
Aug 10	Isth P	H	Cray Wanderers	277	D	0 - 0		1
13	Isth P	A	Wingate & Finchley	131	D	1 - 1	Cronin 1 (og)		2
17	Isth P	H	Margate	297	D	3 - 3	Theophanous 41 45 66	12	3
24	Isth P	A	Hornchurch	238	L	0 - 3		15	4
26	Isth P	H	Bishops Stortford	302	L	0 - 3		16	5
31	Isth P	A	Merstham	256	W	1 - 0	Kavanagh 47	16	6
Sept 8	FAC1Q	H	**Walton Casuals**	**376**	W	2 - 0	Cook 67 Theophanous 75		7
14	Isth P	H	Bowers & Pitsea	241	D	0 - 0		16	8
25	FAC2Q	H	**March Town United**	**227**	W	3 - 0	Bennett 39 67 Bamba 91		9
28	Isth P	A	Worthing	797	L	1 - 2	Theophanous 50	19	10
30	Isth P	A	Haringey Borough	294	W	1 - 0	Puemo 35	16	11
Oct 5	FAC3Q	H	**Weston-s-Mare**	**358**	D	1 - 1	Hall 56		12
8	FAC3Qr	A	**Weston-s-Mare**	**272**	W	4 - 1	Saraiva 18 Puemo 24 Hall 64 Theophanous 88		13
12	Isth P	A	Carshalton Athletic	709	D	2 - 2	Theophanous 21 Hall 58	14	14
19	FAC4Q	A	**Dartford**	**850**	W	3 - 2	Hall 9 Theophanous 22 Kavansgh (pen) 40	14	15
23	Isth P	H	Bognor Regis Town	261	L	0 - 1		16	16
26	FAT1Q	H	**Corinthian-Casuals**	**417**	W	4 - 2	Theophanous 4 Osborne 9 Kavanagh 24 79 (pen)	16	17
Nov 2	Isth P	A	Brightlingsea Regent	178	W	2 - 0	Bennett 44 89	16	18
10	FAC1	A	**Macclesfield Town**	**995**	W	4 - 0	Hector 7 Theophanous 11 69 Bennett 47		19
13	FAT2Q	A	**Blackfield & Langley**	**85**	W	3 - 0	Kavanagh 56 66 (pen) Theophanous 89		20
16	Isth P	H	Lewes	387	W	3 - 1	Kavanagh 32 Theophanous 60 Hector 66	14	21
20	Isth P	H	Enfield Town	271	D	0 - 0		13	22
23	FAT3Q	H	**AFC Sudbury**	**294**	W	2 - 1	Davies 53 Bennett 87		23
30	FAC2P	A	**AFC Fylde**	**1460**	L	0 - 2			24
Dec 3	Isth P	A	Folkesto0n Invicta	389	D	1 - 1	Theophanous 33	15	25
7	Isth P	H	Merstham	285	W	4 - 0	Cook 6 Theophanous 15 71 Bennett 57	9	26
15	FAT1P	H	**Woking**	**665**	W	3 - 1	Saraiva 25 Bennett 66 70		27
28	Isth P	A	Potters Bar Town	214	W	2 - 1	Theophanous 36 Bennett 41	13	28
Jan 1	Isth P	A	Bishops Stortford	355	W	2 - 1	Hall 35 Clohessy 47	13	29
11	FAT2P	H	**Leamington**	**529**	D	1 - 1	Hector 90		30
14	FAT2Pr	A	**Leamington**	**308**	L	0 - 1			31
18	Isth P	A	East Thurrock United	208	D	3 - 3	Clohessey 40 60 Hector 75	14	32
25	Isth P	H	Carshalton Athletic	356	W	3 - 1	Bennett 16 Sow 30 Cooper 70	13	33
29	Isth P	H	East Thurrock United	236	D	0 - 0		11	34
Feb 1	Isth P	H	Bognor Regis Town	623	D	1 - 1	Kavanagh 78	11	35
5	Isth P	H	Horsham	255	D	1 - 1	Hector 55	11	36
8	Isth P	H	Brightlingsea Regent	261	W	2 - 1	Bennett 4 D'Sane 56	11	37
11	Isth P	A	Leatherhead	357	D	1 - 1	Sow 37	11	38
15	Isth P	A	Cray Wanderers	239	D	0 - 0		11	39
22	Isth P	H	Worthing	384	D	0 - 0		11	40
26	Isth P	H	Corinthian-Casuals	397	W	3 - 1	Dsane 39 Kavanagh 85 (pen) Bennett 90	11	41
Mar 7	Isth P	A	Lewes	604	W	2 - 1	Bennett 27 Sow 36	10	42
11	Isth P	H	Cheshunt	222	L	2 - 4	Lawson 57 Dsane 90	10	43

GOALSCORERS	SG	CSG	Pens	Hat tricks	Total		SG	CSG	Pens	Hat tricks	Total
Theophanous	9	3		1	17	Saraiva	2				2
Bennett	11	3			14	Bamba	1				1
Kavanagh	7	4	4		9	Cooper	1				1
Hall	4	4			5	D'Sane	1				1
Hector	5				5	Davies	1				1
Clohessey	2				3	Lawson	1				1
Sow	3				3	Opponents	1				1
Cook	2				2	Osborne	1				1
Dsane	2				2						
Puemo	2				2						

LEATHERHEAD MATCH RESULTS 2019-20

Date	Comp	H/A	Opponents	Att:	Result	Goalscorers	Pos	No.
Aug 10	Isth P	A	Horsham	711	D 1 - 1	D'Sane 8 (pen)		1
13	Isth P	H	Haringey Borough	335	L 2 - 3	D'Sane 45 (pen) Gallagher 86		2
17	Isth P	A	Folkestone Invicta	504	D 1 - 1	Nnamani 40	16	3
24	Isth P	H	Enfield Town	361	L 1 - 2	Salmon	18	4
26	Isth P	A	Carshalton Athletic	460	L 0 - 1		20	5
30	Isth P	H	Lewes	392	L 1 - 4	D'Sane 79	22	6
Sept 7	FAC1Q	H	Lewes	305	D 2 - 2	Nnamani 16 36		7
11	FAC1Qr	A	Lewes	395	L 2 - 2	D'Sane 18 (pen) Wood 23 (Lost 1-3 on pens)		8
14	Isth P	A	Worthing	739	D 5 - 5	Gregory 17 Hester-Cook 24 Wood 61 64 Olutade 65	21	9
28	Isth P	H	Bowers & Pitsea	328	W 1 - 0	Olutade 13	20	10
Oct 1	Isth P	A	Bognor Regis Town	386	L 1 - 5	Wood 24	20	11
5	Isth P	H	Cheshunt	311	W 3 - 0	Olutade 10 Gregory 43 Wood 60	17	12
12	Isth P	A	Merstham	351	W 4 - 1	Olutade 15 Wood 34 Gregory 41 Mensah 57	13	13
19	Isth P	H	Hornchurch	356	W 2 - 1	Wood 31 Olutade 45	13	14
26	FAT1Q	H	Ware	225	W 3 - 0	Wood 2 81 Olutade 18	13	15
Nov 2	Isth P	A	Bishop Stortford	28	W 1 - 0	Gregory 40	12	16
9	FAT2Q	A	Needham Market	203	W 2 - 1	Olutade 55 Gregory 67		17
12	Isth P	H	Corinthian-Casuals	368	W 2 - 1	Dsane 1 Olutade 30	11	18
16	Isth P	A	East Thurrock United	183	L 0 - 3		12	19
23	FAT3Q	H	Dorking Wanderers	734	L 0 - 3			20
Dec 7	Isth P	A	Lewes	524	W 1 - 0	Mensah 4	14	21
14	Isth P	H	Brightlingsea Town	299	W 1 - 0	Salmon 10	10	22
21	Isth P	A	Margate	457	D 0 - 0		10	23
26	Isth P	A	Cray Wanderers	188	W 1 - 0	Driver 49	10	24
Jan 1	Isth P	H	Carshalton Athletic	489	W 2 - 1	Gregory 27 Olutade 49	9	25
4	Isth P	A	Corinthian-Casuals	515	L 0 - 3		9	26
7	Isth P	A	Wingate & Finchley	109	W 2 - 1	Embury 56 71	8	27
11	Isth P	H	Bognor Regis Town	437	L 1 - 2	Hester-Cook 41	10	28
18	Isth P	A	Hornchurch	323	D 1 - 1	Gregory 30	10	29
25	Isth P	H	Merstham	386	D 0 - 0		10	30
Feb 1	Isth P	A	Leatherhead	191	W 3 - 1	Robinson 61 82 Hester-Cook 62	10	31
8	Isth P	H	Bishop's Stortford	361	W 3 - 1	Robinson 22 Rowe 53 Brown 75	9	32
11	Isth P	H	Kingstonian	357	D 1 - 1	Nnamani 40	9	33
22	Isth P	A	Bowers & Pitsea	181	L 0 - 3		10	34
Mar 3	Isth P	H	Potters Bar Town	247	W 4 - 0	Brown 45 Robinson 77 (pen) 79 Olutade 86	9	35
7	Isth P	H	East Thurrock United	325	W 3 - 0	Olutade 6 Robinson 24 Ikebuasi 30	9	36

GOALSCORERS	SG	CSG	Pens	Hat tricks	Total		SG	CSG	Pens	Hat tricks	Total
Olutade	8	4			11	Salmon	2				2
Wood	9	5			9	Deane	1				1
Gregory	7				7	Driver	1				1
Robinson	4	2	1		6	Gallagher	1				1
D'Sane	4	2	3		4	Ikebussi	1				1
Nnamani	3				4	Rowe	1				1
Hester-Cook	3				3						
Brown	2				2						
Embury	1				2						
Mensah	2				2						

LEWES MATCH RESULTS 2019-20

Date	Comp	H/A	Opponents	Att:	Result	Goalscorers	Pos	No.
Aug 10	Isth P	H	Enfield	420	D 1 - 1	Ilic 86		1
13	Isth P	A	Worthing	1150	L 1 - 3	Mongoy 51	21	2
17	Isth P	H	Bowers & Pitsea	410	L 0 - 2		22	3
24	Isth P	A	Margate	509	L 0 - 2		22	4
26	Isth P	H	Horsham	600	L 0 - 2		22	5
31	Isth P	A	Leatherhead	392	W 4 - 1	Coppola 9 Mongoy 26 Box 60 Diedrick-Roberts 82	20	6
Sept 7	**FAC1Q**	**A**	**Leatherhead**	**395**	**D 2 - 2**	**Diedrick-Roberts 47 Golding 75**		7
14	Isth P	H	Potters Bar Town	386	D 3 - 3	Hammond 41 Adeyemo 65 78	17	8
21	**FAC2Q**	**H**	**Bowers & Pitsea**	**479**	**L 1 - 2**	**Diedrick-Roberts 53 (pen)**		9
28	Isth P	A	Brightlingsea Regent	146	W 3 - 1	Golding 57 Diedrick-Roberts 82 (pen) Adeyemo 90	15	10
30	Isth P	A	Carshalton Athletic	297	D 1 - 1	Hammond 45	14	11
Oct 12	Isth P	A	East Thurrock United	272	L 0 - 1		18	12
19	Isth P	H	Cray Wanderers	648	L 2 - 3	Golding 23 Ilic 85	18	13
23	Isth P	H	Corinthian-Casuals	357	W 1 - 0	Hammond 87	15	14
26	**FAT1Q**	**A**	**Folkestone Invicta**	**332**	**L 0 - 2**		15	15
Nov 2	Isth P	A	Cheshunt	175	W 2 - 0	Hammond 36 Redwood 45	14	16
9	Isth P	H	Wingate & Finchley	392	L 1 - 2	Coppolar 62	14	17
16	Isth P	A	Kingstonian	387	L 1 - 3	Coppola 11	15	18
23	Isth P	A	Bishops Stortford	219	W 2 - 0	Dome-Bernwin 7 Ilic 72	14	19
30	Isth P	H	Folkestone Invicta	565	D 0 - 0		14	20
Dec 7	Isth P	H	Leatherhead	524	L 0 - 1		16	21
14	Isth P	A	Merstham	189	W 4 - 2	Medlock 5 (pen) 48 Ilic 15 Golding 36	16	22
Jan 1	Isth P	A	Horsham	913	L 0 - 3		16	23
4	Isth P	A	Haringey Borough	436	W 1 - 0	Coppola 69	16	24
11	Isth P	H	Carshalton Athletic	576	L 0 - 1		17	25
18	Isth P	A	Cray Wanderers	198	L 1 - 2	Coppola 38	17	26
25	Isth P	H	East Thurrock United	506	L 0 - 3		17	27
Feb 1	Isth P	A	Corinthian-Casuals	278	L 0 - 1		17	28
8	Isth P	H	Cheshunt	505	L 1 - 6	Golding 23 Ilic 85	17	29
12	Isth P	H	Hornchurch	269	D 0 - 0		17	30
19	Isth P	H	Worthing	732	L 1 - 3	Golding 41	17	31
22	Isth P	H	Brightlingsea Regent	402	L 0 - 1		17	32
26	Isth P	H	Bognor Regis Town	278	L 0 - 1		17	33
29	Isth P	A	Wingate & Finchley	102	D 1 - 1	Conlon 7	17	34
Mar 3	Isth P	A	Enfield	307	D 1 - 1	Cosgrave 39	16	35
7	Isth P	H	Kingstonian	604	L 1 - 2	Hammond 64	16	36
11	Isth P	H	Haringey Borough	228	W 2 - 1	Hammond 15 Hatzimouratis 45	16	37

GOALSCORERS	SG	CSG	Pens	Hat tricks	Total		SG	CSG	Pens	Hat tricks	Total
Golding	6				6	Cosgrave	1				1
Hammond	5				6	D-Berwin	1				1
Compola	4				5	Hatzimouratis	1				1
D-Roberts	4	2	1		4	Redwood	1				1
Ilic	4				4						
Adeyemo	2				3						
Medlock	1				2						
Mongoy	2				2						
Box	1				1						
Conlon	1				1						

MARGATE MATCH RESULTS 2019-20

Date	Comp	H/A	Opponents	Att:	Result	Goalscorers	Pos	No.
Aug 10	Isth P	H	Brightlingsea Regent	418	D 0 - 0			1
13	Isth P	A	Hornchurch	254	D 2 - 2	Daniel 27 71		2
17	Isth P	A	Kingstonian	297	D 3 - 3	Oyenuga 19 44 71 pen		3
21	Isth P	A	Cray Wanderers	242	L 2 - 3	Leighton 52 Johnson 90	13	4
24	Isth P	H	Lewes	509	W 2 - 0	Oyenuga 32 Daniel 85	9	5
31	Isth P	H	Worthing	420	L 0 - 2		15	6
Sept 7	FAC1Q	A	**Horsham YMCA**	**172**	**W 2 - 1**	**Richards 68 Reeves 87**		7
14	Isth P	A	Cheshunt	220	W 2 - 1	Daniel 65 90 (pen)	11	8
21	FAC2Q	H	**Concord Rangers**	**362**	**W 3 - 1**	**Leighton 3 Ramadan 35 Reeves 88**		9
28	Isth P	A	Carshalton Athletic	378	L 0 - 1		12	10
Oct 2	Isth P	A	East Thurrock United	185	W 2 - 1	Leighton 73 Oyenuga 83	11	11
5	FAC3Q	H	**Salisbury**	**743**	**W 4 - 2**	**Daniel 23 Oseni (og) 50 Leighton 55 64**		12
12	Isth P	A	Haringey Borough	457	L 0 - 1		11	13
19	FAC4Q	A	**Oxford City**	**442**	**L 1 - 2**	**Stewart 58**		14
22	Isth P	H	Merstham	158	W 2 - 1	Ramadan 23 87	12	15
Nov 2	Isth P	A	Corinthian-Casuals	252	W 2 - 1	Reeves 1 Sanusi 59	11	16
9	FAT2Q	H	**Tooting & Mitcham United**	**312**	**L 0 - 4**		12	17
16	Isth P	A	Bowers & Pitsea	181	W 1 - 0	Prestige 47	12	18
19	Isth P	H	Bishop Stortford	171	L 3 - 4	Reeves 52 Leighton 64 72	12	19
23	Isth P	H	Potters Bar Town	266	D 2 - 2	Reeves 20 25	11	20
30	Isth P	A	Horsham	747	W 3 - 0	Leighton 35 Moniouis 61 Ramadan 65	10	21
Dec 7	Isth P	A	Worthing	727	L 1 - 2	Leighton 69	10	22
21	Isth P	H	Leatherhead	457	D 0 - 0		10	23
26	Isth P	A	Folkestone Invicta	769	L 0 - 4		12	24
Jan 1	Isth P	H	Cray Wanderers	367	L 3 - 4	Daniel 49 82 (pen) Leighton 53	12	25
4	Isth P	A	Bognor Regis Town	535	W 2 - 1	Campbell 49 Monlouis 90	12	26
11	Isth P	H	East Thurrock United	325	L 0 - 1		12	27
18	Isth P	A	Bishop Stortford	277	D 2 - 2	Monlouis 14 Ramadan 86	13	28
25	Isth P	H	Haringey Borough	354	W 4 - 2	Swift 22 Daniel 29 Reeves 39 Moniouis 90	12	29
28	Isth P	H	Enfield Town	215	L 0 - 3		12	30
Feb 1	Isth P	A	Merstham	187	L 0 - 1		14	31
8	Isth P	H	Corinthian-Casuals	358	D 2 - 2	Leighton 52 Johnson 90	14	32
15	Isth P	A	Brightlingsea Regent	189	D 1 - 1	Prestege 63	13	33
18	Isth P	H	Hornchurch	218	D 2 - 2	Ramadan 40 Swift 81	13	34
22	Isth P	H	Carshalton Athletic	311	D 1 - 1	Reeves 42	14	35
29	Isth P	H	Bognor Regis Town	212	L 1 - 6	Ramadan 47	14	36
Mar 7	Isth P	H	Bowers Sports	296	W 1 - 0	Reeves 88	14	37
10	Isth P	H	Wingate & Finchley	206	W 1 - 0	Daniel 24	12	38

GOALSCORERS	SG	CSG	Pens	Hat tricks	Total		SG	CSG	Pens	Hat tricks	Total
Leighton	9	2			12	Opponents	1				1
Daniel	7				10	Richards	1				1
Reeves	8	2			9	Sanusi	1				1
Ramadan	5				7	Stewart	1				1
Oyenuga	3		1		5						
Monlouis	4	2			4						
Prestige	2				2						
Swift	2				2						
Campbell	1				1						
Johnson	1				1						

MERSTHAM MATCH RESULTS 2019-20

Date	Comp	H/A	Opponents	Att:	Result	Goalscorers	Pos	No.
Aug 10	Isth P	H	Hornchurch	164	L 1 - 2	Brown 19		1
13	Isth P	A	Corinthian-Casuals	286	W 1 - 0	Folkes 7		2
17	Isth P	A	Brighlingsea Regent	150	D 0 - 0		8	3
24	Isth P	H	East Thurrock United	151	W 2 - 1	Sam-Yorke 47 Folkes 59	6	4
26	Isth P	A	Folkestone Invicta	484	L 1 - 3	Sam-Yorke 73	9	5
31	Isth P	H	Kingstonian	256	L 0 - 1		13	6
Sept 7	**FAC1Q**	**A**	**Whyteleafe**	**233**	**L 0 - 1**			7
14	Isth P	A	Wingate & Finchley	94	W 4 - 0	Sam-Yorke 38 Folkes 7 73 (Pen) Brown 68	8	8
28	Isth P	A	Enfield Town	332	L 0 - 2		10	9
Oct 1	Isth P	H	Worthing	221	L 1 - 3	Folkes 26	13	10
12	Isth P	H	Leatherhead	351	L 1 - 4	Folkes 39 (pen)	16	11
15	Isth P	H	Cray Wanderers	147	L 1 - 2	Monga 4	17	12
19	Isth P	A	Horsham	602	L 0 - 4		18	13
22	Isth P	A	Margate	158	L 1 - 2	Ebwa 60	18	14
26	**FAT1Q**	**A**	**Carshalton Athletic**	**286**	**L 1 - 2**	**Hayles 89**		15
Nov 16	Isth P	A	Bognor Regis Town	577	L 1 - 2	Hayles 81	18	16
19	Isth P	A	Potters Bar Town	171	L 1 - 2	Brown 67	18	17
23	Isth P	A	Cheshunt	158	L 0 - 3		18	18
30	Isth P	H	Bishops Stortford	161	D 2 - 2	O'Halloran 23 Jacquart 82	20	19
Dec 7	Isth P	A	Kingstonian	285	L 0 - 4		21	20
14	Isth P	H	Lewes	189	L 2 - 4	Folkes 7 Jacquart 89	21	21
17	Isth P	H	Haringey Borough	123	W 1 - 0	Ayoola 79	18	22
21	Isth P	A	Carshalton Athletic	401	D 1 - 1	Hamilton-Downes 29 (og)	18	23
Jan 1	Isth P	H	Folkestone Invicta	201	L 0 - 4		19	24
4	Isth P	H	Potters Bar Town	144	L 2 - 3	Ayoola 79 Mensah 78	19	25
7	Isth P	H	Bowers & Pitsea	103	L 1 - 3	Ekpiteta 81	20	26
11	Isth P	A	Worthing	905	L 1 - 6	Ayoola 25	20	27
18	Isth P	H	Horsham	240	W 1 - 0	Ekpiteta 31	19	28
25	Isth P	A	Leatherhead	386	D 0 - 0		19	29
Feb 1	Isth P	H	Margate	187	W 1 - 0	Ekpiteta 21 (pen)	18	30
8	Isth P	A	Bowers & Pitsea	154	D 1 - 1	Ekpiteta 21 (pen)	18	31
15	Isth P	A	Hornchurch	297	D 2 - 2	Ekpiteta 67 Purcell 90 (og)	19	32
22	Isth P	H	Enfield Town	203	L 1 - 4	Ayoola 41	20	33
Mar 1	Isth P	A	Cray Wanderers	329	L 1 - 3	Ayoola 90	20	34
7	Isth P	H	Bognor Regis Town	222	D 2 - 2	Mills 17 Gough 38	20	35

GOALSCORERS	SG	CSG	Pens	Hat tricks	Total		SG	CSG	Pens	Hat tricks	Total
Folkes	6	2	2		7	Mensah	1				1
Ayoola	5				5	Mills	1				1
Ekpiteta	5	3	2		5	Monga	1				1
Brown	3				3	O'Halloran	1				1
Sam-Yorke	3	2			3						
Hayles	2				2						
Jacquart	2				2						
Opponents	2				2						
Ebwa	1				1						
Gough	1				1						

POTTERS BAR TOWN MATCH RESULTS 2019-20

Date	Comp	H/A	Opponents	Att:	Result	Goalscorers	Pos	No.
Aug 10	Isth P	H	Carshalton Athletic	165	W 2 - 0	Sach 51 Hutchinson 65		1
13	Isth P	A	Cheshunt	262	L 0 - 2			2
17	Isth P	A	Esst Thurrock United	220	W 3 - 1	Hutchinson 21 59 Young 37	8	3
24	Isth P	H	Folkestone Invicta	190	L 1 - 4	Hutchinson 55	10	4
26	Isth P	A	Enfield Town	476	D 2 - 2	Hutchinson 10 Sach 56	10	5
31	Isth P	H	Cray Wanderers	181	D 1 - 1	Sach 85	10	6
Sept 7	FAC1Q	A	Takeley	160	L 0 - 1			7
14	Isth P	A	Lewes	386	D 3 - 3	Sach 32 Hutchinson 78 Gogo 90	11	8
21	FAC2Q	H	Hornchurch	184	W 2 - 0	Budden 35 Hutchinson 39		9
28	Isth P	A	Corinthian-Casuals	273	D 0 - 0		11	10
Oct 1	Isth P	A	Bishop Stortford	157	W 4 - 1	Hutchinson 37 Sach 51 Craddock 71 Ward-Cochrane 75	10	11
5	FAC3Q	A	Ware	387	W 2 - 1	Budden 15 Hutchinson 90 (pen)		12
12	Isth P	A	Bognor Regis Town	530	W 4 - 0	Ward-Cochrane 54 71 76 Gogo 82	9	13
19	FAC4Q	H	Barnet	2011	L 0 - 1			14
22	FAC4Qr	A	Barnet	1407	L 1 - 3	Ward-Cochrane 26		15
29	Isth P	H	Worthing	210	D 1 - 1	Craddock 17	10	16
Nov 2	Isth P	A	Hornchurch	219	L 1 - 3	Hutchinson 19 (pen)	13	17
9	FAT2Q	A	Cinderford Town	103	L 0 - 1			18
16	Isth P	H	Horsham	229	L 0 - 2		13	19
19	Isth P	H	Merstham	171	W 2 - 1	Hutchinson 3 Sach 60	12	20
23	Isth P	A	Margate	266	D 2 - 2	Michael-Percil 35 Nicholas 90 (pen)	12	21
30	Isth P	H	Bowers & Pitsea	168	L 0 - 2		12	22
Dec 3	Isth P	H	Brightlingsea Regent	128	W 4 - 2	Hutchinson 4 29 78 Ward-Cochrane 57	12	23
7	Isth P	A	Cray Wanderers	163	L 0 - 4		13	24
21	Isth P	A	Wingate & Finchley	171	W 2 - 1	Cole 18 Sach 87	11	25
28	Isth P	H	Kingstonian	214	L 1 - 2	Hutchinson 90	11	26
Jan 1	Isth P	H	Enfield Town	445	L 1 - 2	Sach 27	11	27
4	Isth P	A	Merstham	144	W 3 - 2	Hutchinson 2 24 Ward-Cochrane 53	11	28
11	Isth P	H	Bishops Stortford	189	W 1 - 0	Nicholas 11	11	29
18	Isth P	A	Haringey Borough	433	L 2 - 3	Ward-Cochrane 18 Young 80	11	30
25	Isth P	H	Bognor Regis Town	190	L 0 - 2		11	31
Feb 1	Isth P	A	Brightlingsea Regent	140	D 0 - 0		12	32
8	Isth P	H	Hornchurch	229	W 2 - 1	Ward-Cochrane 7 (pen) 13	12	33
15	Isth P	A	Carshalton Athletic	355	L 1 - 5	Barker 72	13	34
22	Isth P	H	Corinthian-Casuals	184	W 3 - 1	Ward-Cochrane 18 22 52	12	35
29	Isth P	A	Worthing	854	D 1 - 1	Morgan 33	11	36
Mar 3	Isth P	A	Leatherhead	247	L 0 - 4		12	37
7	Isth P	A	Horsham	540	L 0 - 2		12	38

GOALSCORERS	SG	CSG	Pens	Hat tricks	Total		SG	CSG	Pens	Hat tricks	Total
Hutchinson	11	3	2	1	17	Michael-Percil	1				1
Ward-Cochrane	8		1	2	13	Morgan	1				1
Sach	7				8						
Budden	2				2						
Craddock	2				2						
Gogo	1				2						
Nicholas	2		1		2						
Young	2				2						
Barker	1				1						
Cole	1				1						

ISTHMIAN LEAGUE

WINGATE & FINCHLEY MATCH RESULTS 2019-20

Date	Comp	H/A	Opponents	Att:	Result	Goalscorers	Pos	No.
Aug 10	Isth P	A	Bowers & Pitsea	130	D 1 - 1	Oluwatimilehin 36		1
13	Isth P	H	Kingstonian	131	D 1 - 1	Tejan-Sie 3		2
17	Isth P	H	Bognor Regis Town	127	L 0 - 5		20	3
24	FAC P	H	Welwyn Garden City	121	W 2 - 0	Oluwatimilehin 49 87	19	4
26	Isth P	H	Haringey Borough	231	W 1 - 0	Kennedy 74	15	5
31	Isth P	A	Hornchurch	258	L 0 - 2		17	6
Sept 7	FAC1Q	H	London Colney	111	W 4 - 1	Fleming 34 82 Abrahams 61 Kennedy 78		7
14	Isth P	H	Merstham	94	L 0 - 4		18	8
17	Isth P	A	Horsham	412	L 1 - 2	Kennedy 69	20	9
21	FAC2Q	A	Malden & Tiptree	149	L 2 - 4	Rifat 40 Morgan 60		10
28	Isth P	H	Folkestone Invicta	124	D 1 - 1	Oluwatimilehin 62	21	11
Oct 1	Isth P	A	Cheshunt	115	L 0 - 1			12
12	Isth P	A	Brightlingsea Rgent	182	D 1 - 1	Fleming 13	21	13
22	Isth P	H	Bishops Stortford	96	L 1 - 2	Tejan-Se 32	21	14
26	FAT1Q	H	Hayes & Yeading United	126	D 1 - 1	Michael-Percil 40		15
29	FAT1Qr	A	Hayes & Yeading United	137	L 1 - 2	Rifat		16
Nov 2	Isth P	A	East Thurrock United	154	L 1 - 3	Ruff 24	21	17
9	Isth P	A	Lewes	392	W 2 - 1	Ruff 3 Ochieng 32	19	18
12	Isth P	H	Cray Wanderers	102	L 0 - 1		20	19
16	Isth P	H	Worthing	202	L 2 - 3	Ruff 15 Akinsanya 27	20	20
30	Isth P	A	Enfield Town	150	D 2 - 2	Akinsanya 37 51	20	21
Dec 3	Isth P	H	Carshalton Athletic	78	L 0 - 2		20	22
7	Isth P	H	Hornchurch	118	L 2 - 3	Ruff 22 Kennedy 37	20	23
14	Isth P	A	Corinthian-Casuals	213	D 3 - 3	Akinsanya 39 74 87	20	24
21	Isth P	H	Potters Bar Town	171	L 1 - 2	Sayoud 3	20	25
Jan 1	Isth P	A	Haringey Borough	403	L 1 - 2	Read 39	22	26
4	Isth P	A	Cray Wanderers	144	D 0 - 0		22	27
7	Isth P	H	Leatherhead	109	L 1 - 2	Ifil 20	22	28
13	Isth P	H	Cheshunt	97	L 1 - 2	Nicholas 11	22	29
18	Isth P	A	Carshalton Athletic	448	L 2 - 3	Forino-Joseph 18 Akinsanya 90 (pen)	22	30
25	Isth P	H	Brightlingsea Regent	102	D 0 - 0		22	31
Feb 1	Isth P	A	Bishop's Stortford	240	W 1 - 0	Sayoud 90	22	32
8	Isth P	H	East Thurrock United	95	W 2 - 1	Kennedy 79 Ruff 84	21	33
15	Isth P	H	Bowers & Pitsea	119	D 2 - 2	Farrell 57 Ifil 90	21	34
23	Isth P	A	Folkestone Invicta	554	W 1 - 0	Antwi-Nyame 54	19	35
29	Isth P	H	Lewes	102	D 1 - 1	Evans 25	18	36
Mar 7	Isth P	A	Worthing	951	L 2 - 4	Bancroft 12 Evans 89	19	37
10	Isth P	A	Margate	206	L 0 - 1		19	38

GOALSCORERS	SG	CSG	Pens	Hat tricks	Total		SG	CSG	Pens	Hat tricks	Total
Akinsanya	3	2	1	1	7	Abrahams	1				1
Kennedy	4				5	Antwi-Nyame	1				1
Ruff	5	2			5	Bancroft	1				1
Oluwatimilehin	3				4	Farrell	1				1
Fleming	2				3	Forino-Joseph	1				1
Evans	2				2	Morgan	1				1
Ifil	2				2	Michael-Percil	1				1
Rifat	2				2	Nicholas	1				1
Sayoud	2				2	Ochieng	1				1
Tejan-Sie	2				2	Read	1				1

WORTHING MATCH RESULTS 2019-20

Date	Comp	H/A	Opponents	Att:	Result	Goalscorers	Pos	No.
Aug 10	Isth P	A	Folkestone Invicta	516	L	0 - 2		1
13	Isth P	H	Lewes	1150	W	3 - 1	Budd 48 Parsons 15 40	14	2
17	Isth P	H	Hornchurch	701	L	0 - 6		17	3
26	Isth P	H	Bognor Regis Town	1684	W	3 - 0	Armstrong 32 Pearce 56 64	12	4
31	Isth P	A	Margate	420	W	2 - 0	Aguiar 74 Barker 84	8	5
Sept 7	FAC1Q	A	Hastings United	541	D	3 - 3	Myles-Meekuns 10 Barker 22 Ayoola 90		6
10	FAC 1Qr	H	Hastings United	510	W	3 - 2	Dawes 76 Pearce 82 Armstrong 118 (aet)		7
14	Isth P	H	Leatherhead	739	D	5 - 5	Pearce 3 Myles-Meekuns 44 51 Dawes 67 (pen) Doughty 86	9	8
21	FAC2Q	A	St Albans City	473	D	2 - 2	Colbran 54 Myles-Meekum 89		9
24	FAC2Qr	H	St Albans City	637	L	1 - 3	Jones 90		10
28	Isth P	H	Kingstonian	73	W	2 - 1	Kealy 7 Aguiar 47	8	11
Oct 1	Isth P	A	Merstham	221	W	3 - 1	Pearce 24 Starkey 76 Dawes 84	7	12
5	Isth P	H	East Thurrock United	661	L	2 - 3	Myles-Meekums 10 Barker 22 Ayoola 90	7	13
12	Isth P	A	Cheshunt	295	W	2 - 1	Dawes 58 (pen) Starkey 79	5	14
19	Isth P	H	Brightlingsea Regent	867	W	3 - 0	Armstrong 16 46 Kealy 87	5	15
22	Isth P	H	Carshalton Athletic	470	D	1 - 1	Cowes 26	6	16
26	FAT1Q	H	Walton Casuals	356	W	2 - 1	Aguiar 53 Dawes 90		17
29	Isth P	A	Potters Bar Town	210	D	1 - 1	Myles-Meekuns 8	5	18
Nov 2	Isth P	A	Cray Wanderers	172	D	2 - 2	Aguiar 64 Ayoola 90	6	19
9	FAT2Q	H	AFC Sudbury	521	L	1 - 4	Colbran 79		20
16	Isth P	A	Wingate & Finchley	202	W	3 - 2	Colbran 37 Aguiar 48 Kealy 55	6	21
19	Isth P	H	Bowers & Pitsea	111	W	2 - 1	Chalaye 80 Pearce 89	5	22
23	Isth P	H	Corinthian Casuals	662	W	2 - 0	Aguiar 39 Myles-Meekums 41	4	23
30	Isth P	A	Haringey Borough	389	D	2 - 2	Starkey 4 Jelley 47	3	24
Dec 7	Isth P	H	Margate	727	W	2 - 1	Kealy 14 Parsons 44	2	25
17	Isth P	H	Enfield Town	486	W	3 - 2	Myles-Mekums 5 Pearce 10 Colbran 83	2	26
25	Isth P	H	Horsham	937	W	3 - 0	Parsons 49 Pearce 85 90	2	27
Jan 1	Isth P	A	Bognor Regis Town	1236	W	3 - 0	Parsons 10 Colbran 52 Starkey70	2	28
4	Isth P	A	East Thurrock United	254	D	0 - 0		2	29
11	Isth P	H	Merstham	905	W	6 - 1	Aguiar 9 81 Pattenden 13 Parsons 32 Pearce 67 Marshal-Mirands 84	1	30
18	Isth P	A	Brightlingsea Regent	152	W	3 - 0	Parsons 14 Pearce (45 (pen) 65	1	31
25	Isth P	H	Cheshunt	1128	W	2 - 0	Aguiar 74 Dawes 86	1	32
Feb 1	Isth P	A	Carshalton Athletic	550	W	2 - 1	Stevens 33 Dawes 90 (pen)	1	33
4	Isth P	A	Bishops Stortford	181	W	1 - 0	Aguiar 45	1	34
8	Isth P	H	Cray Wanderers	932	L	1 - 2	Myles-Meekuns 23	1	35
15	Isth P	H	Folkeston Invicta	1410	L	0 - 1		1	36
19	Isth P	A	Lewes	732	W	3 - 1	Hunte 21 Aguiar 57 Pattenden 58	1	37
22	Isth P	A	Kingstonian	384	D	0 - 0		1	38
29	Isth P	H	Potters Bar Town	854	D	1 - 1	Pearce 69	1	39
Mar 7	Isth P	H	Wingate & Finchley	951	W	4 - 2	Racine 17 Golding 29 Pearce 48 (pen) Pamment 84	1	40

GOALSCORERS	SG	CSG	Pens	Hat tricks	Total		SG	CSG	Pens	Hat tricks	Total
Pearce	11	2	2		14	Budd	2				2
Aguiar	10				10	Jelley	2				2
Dawes	8	2	2		8	Pattendon	2				2
M-Meekums	7				8	Chalaye	1				1
Parsons	6	2			7	Doughty	1				1
Colbran	5				5	Golding	1				1
Armstrong	4				4	Hunte	1				1
Kealy	4				4	Jones	1				1
Starkey	4				4	Pearce	1		1		1
Ayoola	3				3	Racine	1				1
Barker	3				3	Stevens	1				1

IsthN - Matty Allan (Soham) turns to celebrate his penalty against Cambridge City.

IsthP - Close call for Corinthians v Carshalton.

IsthP - Hamilton-Downes scores the winner for
Carshalton against Leatherhead.
Photos Keith Clayton.

NORTHERN PREMIER LEAGUE
PREMIER DIVISION 2019-20

		P	W	D	L	F	A	GD	Pts
1	South Shields	33	21	6	6	64	34	30	69
2	FC United of Manchester	32	16	9	7	73	51	22	57
3	Warrington Town	32	14	13	5	57	44	13	55
4	Basford United	32	16	7	9	49	39	10	55
5	Lancaster City	34	15	8	11	58	46	12	53
6	Nantwich Town	31	15	7	9	55	39	16	52
7	Whitby Town	31	14	8	9	54	42	12	50
8	Scarborough Athletic	35	14	8	13	44	47	-3	50
9	Morpeth Town	27	14	6	7	48	37	11	48
10	Hyde United	33	12	7	14	55	55	0	43
11	Gainsborough Trinity	32	11	9	12	53	50	3	42
12	Stalybridge Celtic	33	12	6	15	42	50	-8	42
13	Bamber Bridge	33	12	4	17	53	64	-11	40
14	Witton Albion	31	10	9	12	40	43	-3	39
15	Mickleover Sports	29	11	5	13	42	52	-10	38
16	Radcliffe	32	11	5	16	34	50	-16	38
17	Ashton United	29	10	7	12	40	45	-5	36*
18	Buxton	32	8	11	13	56	52	4	35
19	Grantham Town	32	7	9	16	38	71	-33	30
20	Matlock Town	28	8	5	15	36	43	-7	29
21	Atherton Collieries	26	8	4	14	36	49	-13	28
22	Stafford Rangers	33	4	11	18	29	53	-24	23

		1	2	3	4	5	6	7	8	9	10	11	12	13	14	15	16	17	18	19	20	21	22
1	Ashton United		2-2				1-2	3-1			1-0	1-1	3-1		0-4	0-3	2-0	0-2	2-1	0-2	1-1	0-1	3-1
2	Atherton Collieries			4-1	1-3	1-1	2-3	1-3	2-0	2-1	2-1		1-3	1-5	3-1					3-0	2-4		
3	Bamber Bridge	3-2	3-0		1-3	2-1	3-0		2-1			1-2	3-2	3-0	2-2	2-1	1-2	1-2	2-0	2-3	3-3		1-1
4	Basford United	3-2	2-1	3-0		0-2	1-1	4-3	0-0	1-4	4-1	0-1		1-0	0-2	1-0	0-1		3-1	3-0		3-3	1-0
5	Buxton	1-2		1-1			2-2	3-3	7-0	1-2	1-1		0-1	2-3	1-2		5-0	1-2	5-1	0-0		3-4	2-0
6	FC United of Manchester			1-0	1-3	7-0		2-2	4-0	1-2	3-2	5-2	3-3	4-2		3-2	0-1	0-2	2-1		4-4		
7	Gainsborough Trinity		0-2	4-1	1-0	0-0					2-4	2-1	2-2	0-1	0-0	4-1	2-3	1-4		1-3	0-0	2-0	3-1
8	Grantham Town	0-4		1-0	1-0	1-3	3-2	1-5		2-2	0-3		1-1	1-2		4-0	2-1	1-3	2-0	2-0		0-4	
9	Hyde United	3-3		4-1	2-3	3-1	1-5	1-1	3-0		5-2	3-1	2-3	1-1	2-0		0-1		4-0	1-2		0-2	0-0
10	Lancaster City	3-0	1-0	2-3			0-0	0-1	3-3	2-2		1-0		4-1	0-0	1-0		1-2	2-1	0-0	2-1	1-3	1-1
11	Matlock Town		1-1	1-0	0-1	2-4		2-1	2-2	1-1			3-1	1-1		3-1	4-1	1-2	1-2		0-1	1-2	0-2
12	Mickleover Sports	0-1				4-2	0-4		4-1		1-3			1-1	2-1	0-1	1-0		1-0	1-0		1-3	1-4
13	Morpeth Town	1-4	3-0		1-1	2-1			2-1	3-2				1-0	3-1		1-1	1-1		4-0			3-2
14	Nantwich Town			3-2		2-2	0-1	2-1	2-0	4-0	3-2	3-1				0-1	3-2	0-1	2-1		1-3		3-0
15	Radcliffe	1-1	1-0	0-4	3-0			1-1	0-2		3-0	0-3	1-0		2-2		3-1	0-1		1-0	1-1	2-2	1-0
16	Scarborough Athletic	3-1		5-0	1-1	1-1			1-0	0-1	2-1	4-1	1-0	1-1	3-1			0-0	1-1	1-1	1-1	2-1	0-0
17	South Shields	3-0	3-0	4-1	2-0	1-1	5-3	2-0	1-1	0-1	0-1		5-2		1-4	3-0	2-1			2-1	1-1		1-2
18	Stafford Rangers			0-0	0-0	0-0	2-1		1-1	1-3	0-3	0-1	0-1	0-2		2-0	1-0	1-2		1-1	2-2	2-1	1-1
19	Stalybridge Celtic	0-0	1-2	1-2	2-3	2-3	2-0	2-3	1-2	3-2			1-3		0-2	1-3	5-1	2-2	0-3		2-1	0-2	2-1
20	Warrington Town		1-1	3-1	1-1	L	0-1		3-3	4-1	2-2	3-2	1-0	1-3	3-1	1-0	2-0		2-1	1-2		2-1	1-1
21	Whitby Town	1-1	3-1	0-1			1-2	2-2	1-1	2-0		0-3	1-1	2-1	3-3		2-0	2-1	2-1		0-1		1-1
22	Witton Albion	1-0	2-1			0-2	3-3	1-0	3-1	2-0	1-3		1-0		1-2		3-1	3-1	2-2	0-1		2-3	

NORTH WEST DIVISION 2019-20

		P	W	D	L	F	A	GD	Pts
1	Workington AFC	31	22	5	4	77	25	52	71
2	Ramsbottom United	28	19	4	5	71	36	35	61
3	Marine	30	17	7	6	66	34	32	58
4	Pontefract Collieries	25	16	4	5	47	24	23	52
5	Marske United	26	15	6	5	50	25	25	51
6	Clitheroe	30	12	8	10	46	39	7	44
7	Mossley	30	12	6	12	37	49	-12	41*
8	Tadcaster Albion	27	11	7	9	40	30	10	40
9	Trafford	29	10	8	11	46	39	7	38
10	Runcorn Linnets	27	10	8	9	41	40	1	38
11	Brighouse Town	29	13	3	13	38	41	-3	38*
12	Widnes	31	9	10	12	47	49	-2	37
13	Dunston FC	28	9	8	11	41	45	-4	35
14	Prescot Cables	30	8	9	13	32	41	-9	33
15	Colne	25	7	9	9	31	31	0	30
16	Droylsden	30	7	6	17	28	75	-47	27
17	City of Liverpool FC	27	9	5	13	32	45	-13	26*
18	Ossett United	28	5	7	16	38	57	-19	22
19	Kendal Town	29	5	6	18	29	72	-43	21
20	Pickering Town	30	4	4	22	37	77	-40	16

		1	2	3	4	5	6	7	8	9	10	11	12	13	14	15	16	17	18	19	20
1	Brighouse Town		2-1	3-1	2-1	0-1	4-3		0-1	0-1	4-0	0-4	3-2	0-2	2-0	2-3	2-0		2-1	0-2	
2	City of Liverpool			3-0	1-0	0-1		4-1		0-1	1-0	1-0			3-0	2-5	0-2	1-5		2-2	0-1
3	Clitheroe	0-0			0-2	4-0	0-0	2-0	1-1		1-3	6-1	2-2	1-2	1-2	2-1	4-4	1-2		1-0	2-0
4	Colne		1-1	0-1		1-0	0-1		1-3	0-0		4-0	2-0						1-2	2-3	0-3
5	Droylsden		1-1	0-4	3-3			1-4	2-2	0-7	2-1	2-1		3-1	1-4	1-1	0-3		2-0	0-1	0-4
6	Dunston UTS		3-0	0-0	2-2			2-0	0-0		1-1	1-0		0-1		3-2	3-3	1-0	3-4	2-2	
7	Kendal Town	4-2	0-1	1-2	0-1	1-1				3-1	2-3	0-1	1-2	0-1	2-2	2-7	0-0	0-6
8	Marine	2-2	4-0		3-3	3-1	1-1	4-1		3-1	6-0	3-0	2-1	1-1	2-1	0-1		1-0	1-2	5-2	
9	Marske United	3-1	1-0	0-0		6-0	2-1	4-0	4-1		3-0			3-0	2-1		6-1			1-1	2-2
10	Mossley		2-1	0-1	2-1	0-2	5-0	2-0	1-0		3-2	1-0	3-1	1-1		2-1	0-4	1-1	2-2	2-0
11	Ossett United	1-2	2-3		3-3	2-1	2-3	0-1	2-2	0-0		1-0	0-2	3-2	1-1	2-2			4-2	2-4
12	Pickering Town	0-1	0-3	2-3	3-2		4-1	1-1		3-2	3-2		2-4	1-1	1-2		0-3		1-1	1-4
13	Pontefract Collieries	0-1			4-0	3-0		0-1		4-1		1-0	3-0	2-0	1-0	1-0	2-2		2-1
14	Prescot Cables	2-1	2-0	2-2	0-0	4-0	1-0	1-1	1-2		0-1		1-0		1-2		1-1	0-0	3-0	0-2
15	Ramsbottom United	2-0	5-0	2-0		5-0			3-4	5-1	7-1	3-2				1-1	3-0	1-0	3-2	2-0
16	Runcorn Linnets	1-0	4-2	0-1	1-1	0-1		4-0		1-2	2-1	2-1	2-1	1-1	2-2			2-1		1-1
17	Tadcaster Albion	0-0	0-0			2-0	2-3	1-2	2-1	0-2		1-1	5-0	0-0		2-2	1-0		2-1		2-4
18	Trafford		2-2	0-2	0-0		3-2	1-2	2-0	1-1		1-0	8-1		1-0	1-2	2-1	1-2		0-2	0-1
19	Widnes	0-1			1-2	3-1	3-0	4-0	1-4		0-0	2-2	3-2	2-3	3-1	2-2	1-2	0-1	0-0	
20	Workington	3-1		4-1	1-1		4-1	5-0	0-0	2-0	2-0	2-0	4-1	2-1	4-0	5-1		2-0	2-2	2-0	

SOUTH EAST DIVISION 2019-20

		P	W	D	L	F	A	GD	Pts
1	Leek Town	28	23	3	2	64	19	45	72
2	Stamford	29	22	4	3	74	27	47	70
3	Cleethorpes Town	29	17	6	6	67	40	27	57
4	Belper Town	26	14	7	5	44	29	15	49
5	Carlton Town	26	14	6	6	52	33	19	48
6	Stocksbridge Park Steels	30	13	8	9	49	45	4	47
7	Sutton Coldfield Town	28	13	5	10	45	34	11	44
8	Frickley Athletic	31	14	4	13	49	44	5	43*
9	Ilkeston Town	32	12	7	13	52	50	2	43
10	Kidsgrove Athletic	27	11	6	10	42	31	11	39
11	Loughborough Dynamo	29	11	6	12	43	45	-2	39
12	Worksop Town	32	12	2	18	41	55	-14	38
13	Sheffield FC	27	10	7	10	49	47	2	37
14	Glossop North End	30	8	9	13	36	45	-9	33
15	Chasetown	30	9	5	16	38	52	-14	32
16	Spalding United	30	8	8	14	33	53	-20	32
17	Newcastle Town	30	8	4	18	42	55	-13	28
18	Lincoln United	29	8	3	18	30	60	-30	27
19	Market Drayton Town	30	6	2	22	34	85	-51	20
20	Wisbech Town	29	4	6	19	29	64	-35	18

		1	2	3	4	5	6	7	8	9	10	11	12	13	14	15	16	17	18	19	20
1	Belper Town		2-1	0-1	1-2	3-1	2-0	1-1		0-2			5-2	2-2		2-2		1-0	1-0		1-2
2	Carlton Town			2-2		3-2	4-0		0-1	0-4		2-3	4-0	3-1	2-2	1-1		1-0	6-4		1-3
3	Chasetwon		0-2		1-1	0-3		0-2	0-1	0-1	2-2	0-1	2-1	1-2	2-1	2-2	1-2	0-2		1-1	0-2
4	Cleethorpes Town	2-1	1-1				3-1	2-1	2-0	2-1	5-0	5-4		2-3	2-0	5-0	1-2	3-1	2-2	2-1	
5	Frickley Athletic	1-2		0-3	1-1		1-0	1-3	0-0	0-1		3-0	4-1	0-1	0-1	2-1	1-0	4-1		1-1	1-2
6	Glossop North End		1-1	4-3	1-2	1-3		3-2		0-3	0-1	1-1	0-1	1-1		6-1	0-1	2-2	0-1		1-1
7	Ilkeston Town	0-0	2-4		0-0	2-2	0-1			2-0		5-0	3-0	3-1	1-1	0-0	2-4	2-5	2-0	1-2	2-1
8	Kidsgrove Athletic	2-2	0-1	4-0		1-3	0-0	4-1		2-3		1-1	1-0	3-3	3-1	0-1	0-4		5-0		
9	Leek Town		3-2			2-0		2-1	2-1		2-0		4-1		4-0		2-2	2-0		4-0	3-0
10	Lincoln Town	0-2	0-2		0-3	0-5	1-3	2-2	0-5	0-2		4-1	1-1	1-2	5-1	1-0	1-3		1-2	1-2	1-2
11	Loughborough Dynamo	1-2		3-1		1-0	1-1	3-1	2-0		1-0		7-0	1-0	1-4	0-1	1-1	0-0	4-4	2-0	3-2
12	Market Drayton Town	3-4		0-1	2-9	0-2		0-1	0-2	1-2	2-3			2-5			0-3	0-1	0-6	2-1	1-4
13	Newcastle Town	0-2		2-4	1-2	0-1	0-2	1-2		2-2	0-1	2-1	2-3		3-0	1-2			1-3	1-2	2-2
14	Sheffield	1-1	0-3		3-1	6-0	1-0	2-3		2-3			3-4	2-1			1-1				3-1
15	Spalding United	1-3		0-3	2-1			1-0	2-2	0-2	0-1	2-0	0-1		0-0		2-2	0-1	2-2		0-2
16	Stamford		0-3	2-0	4-1	5-1	5-1	4-2	2-0	3-0			3-1	1-3	5-1			3-0	2-1	4-0	2-1
17	Stocksbridge Park Steels	0-0		2-3	1-1		1-2			0-3	1-1	2-1	2-1	4-2	3-2	1-3	1-1		2-1	3-1	2-2
18	Sutton Coldfield Town		1-1	2-1	1-3	2-3	1-1	3-1	1-0		3-1		2-0			0-1	0-2	3-0		2-0	2-0
19	Wisbech Town	1-2	0-1	2-3			1-1	0-2		0-2	4-1	0-0	0-4		2-2	3-0	0-2	1-3			0-1
20	Worksop Town	1-2	0-1	3-1	4-1	0-3	0-2		0-1	0-4		1-0	3-1	0-2	0-4	1-4	0-5		0-1	4-0	

NPLP - Mitchley (Witton) De Girolamo (Buxton). Photo Keith Clayton.

NPLNW - Ramsbottom United v Tadcaster Albion 3-0.

NPLNW - Ramsbottom United v Tadcaster Albion 3-0. Ramsbottom score. Photos Bill Wheatcroft.

LEAGUE CUP 2019-20

HOLDERS: TRAFFORD

ROUND ONE

Basford United	v	Carlton Town	3-0
Atherton Collieries	v	Prescot Cables	0-0, 4-3p
City of Liverpool	v	Mossley	0-1
Cleethorpes Town	v	Grantham Town	1-4
Radcliffe	v	Droylsden	4-0
Spalding United	v	Gainsborough Trinity	0-0, 5-6p
Tadcaster Albion	v	South Shields	0-4
Workington	v	Kendal Town	6-1
Worksop Town	v	Wisbech Town	4-1
Frickley Athletic	v	Sheffield	1-1, 3-4p
Brighouse Town	v	Stocksbridge Celtic	1-2
Kidsgrove Athletic	v	Warrington Town	2-2, 4-2p
Ashton United	v	Stalybridge Celtic	1-2
Buxton	v	Ilkeston Town	3-0
Marine	v	Clitheroe	1-1, 3-2p
Newcastle Town	v	Witton Albion	1-0
Stafford Rangers	v	Chasetown	0-2
Stamford	v	Lincoln United	0-0, 4-5p
Scarborough Athletic	v	Dunston UTS	1-5
United of Manchester	v	Glossop North End	2-2, 6-5p
Lancaster City	v	Colne	2-1
Mickleover Sports	v	Loughborough Dynamo	3-2
Nantwich Town	v	Widnes	5-6
Belper Town	v	Matlock Town	2-2, 5-6p
Pickering Town	v	Whitby Town	2-1
Runcorn Linnest	v	Leek Town	0-1
Market Drayton Town	v	Sutton Coldfield Town	2-0
Pontefract Collieries	v	Ossett United	0-2
Morpeth Town	v	Marske United	5-2
Ramsbottom United	v	Bamber Bridge	2-1

ROUND TWO

Kidsgrove Athletic	v	Market Drayton Town	2-1
Grantham Town	v	Worksop Town	0-0, 0-3p
Hyde United	v	Lancaster City	0-0, 5-4p
Marine	v	Radcliffe	3-0
Workington	v	Mossley	2-0
Gainsborough Trinity	v	Lincoln United	1-1, 0-3p
Mickleover Sports	v	Buxton	2-3
Leek Town	v	Widnes	2-2, 4-5p
Ossett United	v	Brighouse Town	3-0
Newcastle Town	v	Chasetown	2-1
Basford United	v	Matlock Town	0-5
Trafford	v	Ramsbottom United	5-2
United of Manchester	v	Sheffield	1-2
Dunston UTS	v	South Shields	1-1, 5-6p
Morpeth Town	v	Pickering Town	3-1
Atherton Collieries	v	Stalybridge Celtic	4-1

ROUND THREE

Newcastle Town	v	Buston	3-1
Widnes	v	Hyde United	1-2
Worksop Town	v	Matlock Town	1-2
South Shields	v	Morpeth Town	2-5
Atherton Collieries	v	Marine	
Gainsborough Trinity	v	Kidsgrove Atheltic	1-1, 9-10p
Sheffield	v	Trafford	3-3, 4-3p
Workington	v	Ossett United	2-0

QUARTER-FINALS

Kidsgrove Athletic	v	Hyde United	1-2
Newcastle Town	v	Matlock Town	
Workington	v	Sheffield	
Atherton or Marine	v	Morpeth Town	

ASHTON UNITED MATCH RESULTS 2019-20

Date	Comp	H/A	Opponents	Att:	Result		Goalscorers	Pos	No.
Aug 17	NPL P	H	Atherton Colleries	202	D	2 - 2	Sheridan 46 71		1
20	NPL P	A	South Shields	1283	L	0 - 3			2
24	NPL P	A	Bamber Bridge	238	L	2 - 3	Wilson 38 Chalmers 71	20	3
26	NPL P	H	Stalybridge Celtic	382	L	0 - 2		22	4
31	NPL P	H	Matlock Town	202	D	1 - 1	Wilson 41 (pen)	20	5
Sept 7	FAC1Q	A	Tadcaster Albion	361	D	2 - 2	Havern 63 Hughes 73		6
10	FAC1Qr	H	Tadcaster Albion	197	W	4 - 2	Smith 45 53 Wilson 68 Tames 90		7
14	NPL P	A	Micleover Sports	227	W	1 - 0	Smith 6	18	8
21	FAC2Q	H	Pontefract Colleries	192	W	1 - 0	Tames 5		9
24	NPL P	H	Whitby Town	144	L	0 - 1		18	10
28	NPL P	A	Hyde United	552	D	3 - 3	Tames 7 Rowney 26 Wilson 70	18	11
Oct 1	NPL P	A	Grantham Town	206	W	4 - 0	Clee 3 Hughes 12 Sheridan 56 Slew 84	15	12
5	FAC3Q	H	Spennymoor Town	284	L	2 - 6	Anghel 9 Tames 15	15	13
12	NPL P	A	Lancaster City	317	L	0 - 3		18	14
15	NPL P	A	Witton Albion	299	L	0 - 1		19	15
19	NPL P	H	Gainsborough Trinity	204	W	3 - 1	Havern 44 Wilson 47 Slew 52	16	16
26	FAT1Q	A	Warrington Town	327	W	1 - 0	Sheridan 67		17
Nov 2	NPL P	A	Buxton	402	W	2 - 1	Wilson 9 (pen) 20 (pen)	17	18
9	FAT2Q	A	Matlock Town	284	L	0 - 1		17	19
23	NPL P	H	Nantwich Town	144	L	0 - 4		17	20
30	NPL P	H	Radcliffe	254	L	0 - 3		19	21
Dec 7	NPL P	A	Basford United	204	L	2 - 3	Wilson 69 (pen) Havern 90	19	22
28	NPL P	H	FC United of Manchester	1502	L	1 - 2	Smith 87	21	23
Jan 1	NPL P	A	Stalybridge Celtic	435	D	0 - 0		22	24
4	NPL P	H	South Shields	277	L	0 - 2		22	25
11	NPL P	H	Stafford Rangers	220	W	2 - 1	Wilson 62 Brewster 85	21	26
18	NPL P	A	Morpeth	652	W	4 - 1	Sheridan 36 Hardcastle 64 Wilson 71(pen) Almond 76	21	27
21	NPL P	A	Radcliffe	255	D	1 - 1	Tomsett 11	21	28
25	NPL P	H	Lancaster City	228	W	1 - 0	Almond 33	18	29
Feb 1	NPL P	A	Scarborough Athletic	900	L	1 - 3	Wilson 12 (pen)	19	30
8	NPL P	H	Witton Albion	215	W	3 - 1	Tames 45 Brewster 60 Wilson 67 (pen)	19	31
29	NPL P	A	Whitby Town	394	D	1 - 1	Davies 81	19	32
Mar 3	NPL P	H	Warrington Town	202	D	1 - 1	Almond 17	19	33
7	NPL P	H	Scarborough Athletic	278	W	2 - 0	Wilson 11 83 (pen)	19	34
10	NPL P	H	Mickleover Sports	160	W	3 - 1	WILSON 3 (63 72 pen 84 pen)	17	35

GOALSCORERS	SG	CSG	Pens	Hat tricks	Total		SG	CSG	Pens	Hat tricks	Total
Wilson	9	2	10	1	17	Chalmers	1				1
Sheridan	4				5	Clee	1				1
Tames	6				5	Davies	1				1
Smith	3	2			4	Hardcastle	1				1
Almond	3				3	Rowney	1				1
Havern	3				3	Tomsett	1				1
Brewster	2				2						
Hughes	2				2						
Slew	2				2						
Anghel	1				1						

ATHERTON COLLERIES MATCH RESULTS 2019-20

Date	Comp	H/A	Opponents	Att:	Result	Goalscorers	Pos	No.
Aug 17	NPL P	A	Ashton United	202	D 2 - 2	Lynch 64 Roberts 76		1
20	NPL P	H	Warrington Town	645	L 2 - 4	Lafferty 64 Peet 67 (pen)		2
24	**FACP**	**H**	**Runcorn Linnets**	**252**	**W 2 - 1**	**Hardcastle 68 Peet 90**	18	3
26	NPL P	A	Lancaster City	330	L 0 - 1		18	4
31	NPL P	H	Nantwich Town	324	W 3 - 1	Bailey 21 27 Roberts 90	16	5
Sept 3	NPL P	A	Bamber Bridge	297	L 0 - 3		16	6
7	**FAC1Q**	**A**	**FC United of Manchester**	**1216**	**D 2 - 2**	**Lynch 57 Smith 77**		7
10	**FAC1Qr**	**H**	**FC United of Manchester**	**947**	**L 0 - 1**			8
14	NPL P	A	Stalybridge	269	W 2 - 1	Bentham 4 Lynch 39	14	9
21	NPL P	H	Mickleover Sports	255	L 1 - 3	Bentham 79	14	10
24	NPL P	A	Matlock Town	276	D 1 - 1	Bentham 24 (pen)	15	11
Oct 5	NPL P	A	South Shields	1752	L 0 - 3		16	12
12	NPL P	A	Gainsborough Trinity	408	W 2 - 0	Bentham 3 (pen) Cover 78	17	13
15	NPL P	A	Morpeth Town	502	L 0 - 3		17	14
19	NPL P	H	FC United of Manchester	1019	L 2 - 3	Bentham 5 Cover 43	18	15
29	**FATQ1**	**H**	**Scarborough**	**212**	**W 3 - 2**	**Cover 47 Bentham 74 (pen) Hardcastle 84**		16
Nov 2	NPL P	H	Basford United	201	L 1 - 3	Cover 90	18	17
9	**FATQ2**	**H**	**Morpeth Town**	**216**	**W 2 - 1**	**Thompson 32 Bentham 52**		18
16	NPL P	H	Buxton	332	D 1 - 1	Bentham 90 (pen)	18	19
23	**FATQ3**	**H**	**Boston United**	**303**	**W 1 - 0**	**Brewster 87**	17	20
30	NPL P	H	Bamber Bridge	374	W 4 - 1	Bentham 26 (pen) 36 Conway 45 Hardcastle 56	17	21
Dec 7	NPL P	H	Hyde United	357	W 2 - 1	O'Brien 30 Lafferty 50	17	22
17	**FAT1P**	**H**	**Barrow**	**468**	**D 2 - 2**	**Conway 2 Bailey 64**		23
26	NPL P	A	Radcliffe	571	L 0 - 1		18	24
Jan 1	NPL P	H	Lancaster City	401	W 2 - 1	Peet 51 Bentham 60	18	25
4	NPL P	A	Warrington Town	507	D 1 - 1	Lafferty 82	19	26
7	**FAT1Pr**	**A**	**Barrow**	**861**	**L 0 - 2**		19	27
11	NPL P	H	Stalybridge Celtic	371	W 3 - 0	Myers 22 Lafferty 44 Bentham 81 (pen)	18	28
18	NPL P	A	Witton Albion	348	L 1 - 2	Myers 17	17	29
25	NPL P	H	Gainsborough Trinity	329	L 1 - 3	Peet 85	17	30
Feb 1	NPL P	A	Whitby Town	330	L 1 - 3	Glass 83	18	31
8	NPL P	H	Morpeth Town	260	L 1 - 5	Cover 64	20	32
22	NPL P	A	Basford United	270	L 1 - 2	Noble 31	21	33
Mar 7	NPL P	H	Grantham Town	276	W 2 - 0	Myers 2 Conway 51	21	34

GOALSCORERS	SG	CSG	Pens	Hat tricks	Total		SG	CSG	Pens	Hat tricks	Total
Bentham	11	4	6		11	Brewster	1				1
Cover	4	3			5	Glass	1				1
Lafferty	4	2			4	Hardcastle	1				1
Peet	4		1		4	Noble	1				1
Bailey	3				3	O'Brien	1				1
Conway	3				3	Smith	1				1
Hardcastle	3				3	Thompson	1				1
Lynch	2				3						
Myers	3				3						
Roberts	2				2						

BAMBER BRIDGE MATCH RESULTS 2019-20

Date	Comp	H/A	Opponents	Att:	Result	Goalscorers	Pos	No.
Aug 17	NPL P	A	Matlock Town	402	L 0 - 1			1
24	NPL P	H	Ashton United	238	D 3 - 3	Forbes 58 Pett 87 Marlow 90	14	2
26	NPL P	A	Warrington	402	L 1 - 3	Charnock 66	16	3
31	NPL P	A	South Shields	1231	L 1 - 4	Waddecar 61 (pen)	18	4
Sept 3	NPL P	H	Atherton Colleries	297	W 3 - 0	Forbes 39 Waddecar 48 Wisdom 61	14	5
7	FAC1Q	A	Trafford	298	L 0 - 3			6
10	NPL P	A	Buxton	235	D 1 - 1	Marlow 89	14	7
14	NPL P	H	Basford United	281	L 1 - 3	Fowler 33	15	8
21	NPL P	A	Grantham Town	201	L 0 - 1		16	9
28	NPL P	A	FC United of Manchester	1543	L 0 - 1		16	10
Oct 1	NPL P	A	Gainsborough Trinity	303	L 1 - 4	Charnock 48	19	11
5	NPL P	H	Witton Albion	278	D 1 - 1	Charnock 90	20	12
8	NPL P	H	Nantwich Town	180	D 2 - 2	Waddecar 42 78 (pen)		13
12	NPL P	A	Stalybridge Celtic	322	L 2 - 3	Waddecar 29 38 (pen)	19	14
19	NPL P	H	Scarborough Athletic	430	L 1 - 2	Waddecar 42 (pen)	22	15
29	FAT1Q	A	Nantwich Town	234	L 1 - 2	Pett 15		16
Nov 2	NPL P	H	Stafford Rangers	364	W 2 - 0	Waddecar 60 (pen) 90	18	17
9	NPL P	H	Stalybridge Celtic	241	L 2 - 3	Dean 13 22	18	18
16	NPL P	A	Hyde United	392	L 1 - 4	Dean 22	19	19
23	NPL P	H	Morpeth	285	W 3 - 0	Dudley 13 57 Dean 83	18	20
30	NPL P	A	Atherton Colleries	374	L 1 - 4	Pett 78	18	21
Dec7	NPL P	H	Mickleover Sports	291	W 3 - 2	Booth 6 Waddecar 45 61	17	22
14	NPL P	A	Whitby Town	364	W 1 - 0	Marlow 42	15	23
21	NPL P	H	Matlock Tiown	326	L 1 - 2	Waddecar 44	16	24
28	NPL P	A	Lancaster City	325	W 3 - 2	Allen 40 Thomson 88 Roache 90	16	25
Jan 1	NPL P	H	Warrington Town	386	D 3 - 3	Roache 45 (pen) Charnock 82 Allen 90	15	26
4	NPL P	A	Radcliffe	432	W 4 - 0	Grant 38 Allen 56 Dudley 60 Booth 62	15	27
11	NPL P	A	Basfoerd UNited	251	L 0 - 3		15	28
18	NPL P	H	Buxton	362	W 2 - 1	Allen 5 Green 82	15	29
25	NPL P	H	Radcliffe	414	W 2 - 1	Allen 89 Dudley 90	13	30
Feb 1	NPL P	A	Nantwich Town	455	L 2 - 3	Wisdom 49 Allen 85	14	31
8	NPL P	A	Grantham Town	291	W 2 - 1	Dudley 3 51	14	32
15	NPL P	A	Scarborough Athletic	859	L 0 - 5		14	33
22	NPL P	H	FC United of Manchester	1014	W 3 - 0	Waddecar 8 Green73 Shaw 88	11	34
Mar 7	NPL P	H	South Shields	453	L 1 - 2	Waddecar 44	13	35

GOALSCORERS	SG	CSG	Pens	Hat tricks	Total		SG	CSG	Pens	Hat tricks	Total
Waddecar	10	3	5		14	Roach	2		1		2
Allen	6				6	Wisdom	2				2
Dudley	5				6	Fowler	1				1
Charnock	4	2			4	Grant	1				1
Dean	3	3			4	Shaw	1				1
Marlow	3				3	Thomson	1				1
Pett	2				3						
Booth	2				2						
Forbes	2				2						
Green	2				2						

BASFORD UNITED MATCH RESULTS 2019-20

Date	Comp	H/A	Opponents	Att:	Result	Goalscorers	Pos	No.
Aug 17	NPL P	A	Hyde United	384	W 3 - 2	Reid 19 Richards 59 Grantham 74		1
19	NPL P	H	Matlock Town	501	L 0 - 1			2
24	NPL P	H	Lancaster City	225	W 4 - 1	Thomas 11 Watson 42 (pen) Cavell 82 Grantham 84	2	3
26	NPL P	A	Grantham Town	330	L 0 - 1		9	4
31	NPL P	H	Radcliffe	259	W 1 - 0	Thornhill 73	6	5
Sept 3	NPL P	A	Stafford Rangers	481	D 0 - 0			6
7	FAC1Q	A	Matlock Town	431	L 1 - 2	Hearn 79 (pen)		7
9	NPL P	H	Stalybridge Celtic	266	W 3 - 0	Watson 56 67 Thornhill 85	4	8
14	NPL P	A	Bamber Bridge	281	W 3 - 1	Hearn 54 Watson 74 Grantham 90	2	9
21	NPL P	A	South Shields	1634	L 0 - 2		3	10
Oct 1	NPL P	A	Scarborough Athletic	735	D 1 - 1	Watson 71	5	11
7	NPL P	H	Gainsborough Trinity	293	W 4 - 3	Gascoigne 20 Richards 29 59 Grantham 72	2	12
12	NPL P	A	Morpeth Town	625	D 1 - 1	Reid 55 (pen)	2	13
15	NPL P	A	FC United of Manchester	1402	W 3 - 1	Richards 27 Gainski 52 Grantham 90	2	14
19	NPL P	H	Stafford Rangers	289	W 3 - 1	Richards 6 Reid 39 Hearn 83	2	15
26	FAT1Q	H	Mickleover Sports	352	W 3 - 0	Hearn 12 89 Law 38		16
Nov 2	NPL P	A	Atherton Collieries	201	W 3 - 1	Watson 13 Reid 64 Richards 76	2	17
9	FAT2Q	A	FC United of Manchester	907	L 1 - 3	Gascoigne 26		18
16	NPL P	H	Whitby Town	382	D 3 - 3	Reid 36 (pen) Worsfold 76 (pen) Watson 89	3	19
23	NPL P	A	Radcliffe	315	L 0 - 3		4	20
Dec 7	NPL P	H	Ashton United	204	W 3 - 2	Thomas 54 66 Grantham 77	3	21
14	NPL P	A	Warrington	336	D 1 - 1	Grantham 79	3	22
21	NPL P	H	Hyde United	259	L 1 - 4	Galinski 73	3	23
Jan 1	NPL P	H	Grantham Town	322	D 0 - 0		4	24
4	NPL P	A	Matlock Town	424	W 1 - 0	Thornhill 39	4	25
11	NPL P	H	Bamber Bridge	251	W 3 - 0	Watson 32 88 Worsfold 38	3	26
18	NPL P	A	Stalybridge Celtic	343	W 3 - 2	Richards 60 66 O'Halloran 70 (og)	3	27
25	NPL P	H	Morpeth Town	255	W 1 - 0	Reid 32	2	28
27	NPL P	H	Witton Albion	260	W 1 - 0	Richards 62	2	29
Feb 1	NPL P	A	Gainsborough Trinity	521	L 0 - 1		2	30
8	NPL P	H	FC United of Manchester	901	D 1 - 1	Richards 60	2	31
23	NPL P	H	Atherton Collieries	270	W 2 - 1	Thornhill 43 Watson 86	2	32
Mar 2	NPL P	H	Nantwich Town	263	L 0 - 2		2	33
7	NPL P	H	Buxton	351	L 0 - 2		4	34
14	NPL P	H	Scarborough Athletic	501	L 0 - 1		4	35

GOALSCORERS	SG	CSG	Pens	Hat tricks	Total		SG	CSG	Pens	Hat tricks	Total
Richards	8	2			10	Cavell	1				1
Watson	8	2	1		9	Law	1				1
Grantham	7				7	Opponents	1				1
Read	6		2		6						
Hearn	4		1		5						
Thornhill	4				5						
Thomas	2				3						
Gainski	2				2						
Gascoigne	2				2						
Worsfold	2		1		2						

BUXTON MATCH RESULTS 2019-20

Date	Comp	H/A	Opponents	Att	Result	Goalscorers	Pos	No.
Aug 17	NPL P	A	Scarborough Athletic	1157	D 1 - 1	Pilkington 81		1
20	NPL P	H	Northwich Town	353	L 1 - 2	Chippendale 80		2
24	NPL P	H	Whitby Town	335	L 3 - 4	Hardy 8 Roscoe 27 Young 70	17	3
26	NPL P	A	Hyde United	494	L 1 - 3	De Girolamo 17	21	4
31	NPL P	H	Stalybridge Celtic	400	D 0 - 0		19	5
Sept 3	NPL P	A	Mickleover Sports	222	L 2 - 4	Young 35 Hardy 87 (pen)	19	6
7	FAC1Q	A	Romulus	131	W 2 - 0	Jennings 2 Grayson 16 (pen)		7
10	NPL P	H	Bamber Bridge	235	D 1 - 1	Hardy 34	19	8
14	NPL P	A	Morpeth Town	635	L 1 - 2	Grayson 90 (pen)	20	9
21	FAC2Q	H	Corby Town	264	W 5 - 0	Hardy 21 24 Oyibo 54 Clarke 70 Pilkington 86		10
28	NPL P	H	South Shields	515	L 1 - 2	Hardy 38	22	11
Oct 5	FAC3Q	H	York City	901	L 1 - 2	De Girolamo 11		12
8	NPL P	H	Grantham Town	180	W 7 - 0	De Girolamo 4 39 64 Hardy 8 (pen) Oyibo 47 58 O'Grady 77	19	13
12	NPL P	A	FC United of Manchester	1888	L 0 - 7		22	14
15	NPL P	A	Gainsborough Trinity	347	D 0 - 0		22	15
19	NPL P	H	Witton Albion	417	W 2 - 0	De Girolamo 62 73	19	16
26	FAT1Q	H	Hyde United	360	W 3 - 2	De Girolamo 18 45 Hardy 90	19	17
Nov 2	NPL P	H	Ashton United	402	L 1 - 2	De Girolamo 4	19	18
9	FAT2Q	A	Colne	191	L 1 - 3	De Girolamo 45		19
16	NPL P	A	Atherton Colleries	332	D 1 - 1	De Girolamo 26	20	20
23	NPL P	A	Stalybridge Celtic	423	L 0 - 2		20	21
30	NPL P	H	Mickleover Sports	335	L 0 - 1		20	22
Dec 7	NPL P	H	Lancaster City	326	D 1 - 1	Hardy 47 (pen)	20	23
14	NPL P	A	Nantwich Town	331	D 2 - 2	Hardy 8 De Girolamo 33	20	24
21	NPL P	H	Scarborough Athletic	401	W 5 - 0	Hardy 40 (pen) 52 (pen) De Girolamo 61 72 Elliott 81	19	25
26	NPL P	A	Matlock Town	922	W 4 - 2	Byrne 38 Hardy 47 De Girolamo 55 88	18	26
Jan 1	NPL P	H	Hyde United	600	L 1 - 2	De Girolamo 54	19	27
4	NPL P	A	Witton Albion	313	W 2 - 0	Elliott 66 Hardy 90	18	28
11	NPL P	H	Morpeth Town	376	L 2 - 3	De Girolamo 15 20	20	29
18	NPL P	A	Bamber Bridge	362	L 1 - 2	De Girolamo 45	20	30
23	NPL P	H	FC United of Manchester	1206	D 2 - 2	De Girolamo 26 47 (pen)	21	31
Feb 1	NPL P	A	Grantham Town	202	W 3 - 1	De Girolamo 77 (pen) 89 Barai 90	17	32
4	NPL P	A	Stafford Rangers	403	D 0 - 0		17	33
8	NPL P	H	Gainsborough Trinity	537	D 3 - 3	Clarke 4 Curley 46 De Girolamo 52	17	34
22	NPL P	A	South Shields	1508	D 1 - 1	Clarke 6	17	35
29	NPL P	H	Stafford Rangers	463	W 5 - 1	Chippendale 24 87 De Girolamo 29 O'Grady 72 Hardy 77	17	36
Mar 7	NPL P	A	Basford United	351	W 2 - 0	Clsrke 19 De Girolamo 33	18	37

GOALSCORERS	SG	CSG	Pens	Hat tricks	Total		SG	CSG	Pens	Hat tricks	Total
De Girolamo	18	5	2	1	28	Bari	1				1
Hardy	12	2	5		15	Byrne	1				1
Carke	4				4	Curley	1				1
Chippendale	2				3	Jennings	1				1
Oyibo	2				3	Roscoe	1				1
Elliott	2				2						
Grayson	2		2		2						
O'Grady	2				2						
Pilkington	2				2						
Young	2				2						

FC UNITED OF MANCHESTER MATCH RESULTS 2019-20

Date	Comp	H/A	Opponents	Att:	Result	Goalscorers	Pos	No.
Aug 17	NPL P	A	Grantham Town	821	L 2 - 3	Rodney 18 Linney 26		1
20	NPL P	H	Hyde United	1809	L 1 - 2	Linney 70		2
24	NPL P	H	Scarborough Athletic	1532	L 0 - 1		22	3
26	NPL P	A	Radcliffe	1228	D 1 - 1	Linney 26	19	4
31	NPL P	H	Morpeth Town	1434	W 4 - 2	Owolabi 5 31 Ennis 24 71 (pen)	15	5
Sept 3	NPL P	A	Lancaster City	522	D 0 - 0		15	6
7	FAC1Q	H	Atherton Colleries	1216	D 2 - 2	Dean 33 59		7
10	FAC1Qr	A	Atherton Colleries	947	W 1 - 0	Morris 79		8
14	NPL P	A	Stafford Rangers	936	D 0 - 0		16	9
21	FAC2Q	H	Warrington Town	1253	L 1 - 2	Linney 26 (pen)		10
24	NPL P	A	Warrington Town	702	W 1 - 0	Buckley 65	13	11
18	NPL P	H	Bamber Bridge	1543	W 1 - 0	Owolabi 57	11	12
Oct 1	NPL P	H	South Shields	1349	L 0 - 2		12	13
5	NPL P	A	Stalybridge Celtic	1188	W 3 - 2	Owolabi 56 Ennis 65 90	11	14
12	NPL P	H	Buxton	1888	W 7 - 0	Buckley 13 Owalabi 17 20 26 73 Curran 31 Ennis 48	9	15
15	NPL P	H	Basford United	1402	L 1 - 3	Owolabi 8	9	16
19	NPL P	A	Atherton Colliers	1019	W 3 - 2	Owolabi 31 Potts 39 Linney 53	5	17
29	FAT1Q	A	Radcliffe	523	W 2 - 0	Owalabi 25 (pen) Leniehen 86		18
Nov 2	NPL P	H	Gainsborough Trinity	1614	D 2 - 2	Buckley 30 Owolabi 74	5	19
9	FAT2Q	H	Basford United	907	W 3 - 1	Donohue 21 Ennis 32 Owolabi 43		20
16	NPL P	A	Witton Albion	933	D 3 - 3	Potts 50 Dodd 58 88	6	21
23	FAT3Q	A	Runcorn Linnets	962	W 3 - 0	Owolabi 2 68 Dodd 82		22
30	NPL P	H	Lancaster City	1873	W 3 - 2	Ennis 6 (pen) 7 Doyle 90	8	23
Dec 7	NPL P	H	Matlock Town	1574	W 5 - 2	Doyle 10 Owolabi 27 64 84 Linney 30	8	24
14	FAT1P	H	Kettering Town	1218	W 2 - 1	Owolabi 23 84	7	25
21	NPL P	H	Grantham Town	1701	W 4 - 0	Owolabi 7 14 Potts 16 Morris 90	5	26
28	NPL P	A	Ashton United	1502	W 2 - 1	Linney 77 (pen) Owolabi 90	3	27
Jan 1	NPL P	H	Radcliffe	2124	W 3 - 2	Potts 64 Owolabi 68 90	3	28
4	NPL P	A	Hyde United	1293	W 5 - 1	Linney 30 65 Owolabi 41 45 Jones 77	3	29
11	FAT2P	A	Barrow	1892	L 0 - 7			30
18	NPL P	A	Whitby Town	963	W 2 - 1	Curran 52 Hawley 86	4	31
25	NPL P	A	Buxton	1206	D 2 - 2	Linney 45 (pen) Ennis 90	3	32
Feb 1	NPL P	H	Mickleover Sports	1747	D 3 - 3	Hornson-Smith 42 Owolabi 55 Sinclair-Smith 79	3	33
8	NPL P	A	Basford United	901	D 1 - 1	Ennis 17	4	34
18	NPL P	H	Stafford Rangers	1336	W 2 - 1	Griffiths 11 Homson-Smith 79	4	35
22	NPL P	A	Bamber Bridge	1014	L 0 - 3		4	36
25	NPL P	A	Nantwich Town	580	W 1 - 0	Morris 43	3	37
29	NPL P	H	Warrington Town	2088	D 4 - 4	Homson-Smith 9 Owolabi 30 Ennis 69 (pen) Jones 90	3	38
Mar 5	NPL P	A	Mickleover Sports	804	W 4 - 0	Owolabi 2 45 80 Dodd 88	2	39
14	NPL P	A	South Shields	3274	L 3 - 5	Owolabi 50 69 90	2	40

GOALSCORERS	SG	CSG	Pens	Hat tricks	Total		SG	CSG	Pens	Hat tricks	Total
Owolabi	20	7		4	36	Doyle	2				2
Ennis	8		3		10	Jones	2				2
Linney	8	2	3		10	Donohue	1				1
Dodd	3				4	Griffiths	1				1
Potts	4				4	Hawley	1				1
Buckley	3				3	Lenehan	1				1
Hornson-Smith	3				3	Rodney	1				1
Morris	3				3	Sinclair-Smith	1				1
Curran	2				2						
Dean	1				2						

GAINSBOROUGH TRINITY MATCH RESULTS 2019-20

Date	Comp	H/A	Opponents	Att:	Result	Goalscorers	Pos	No.
Aug 17	NPL P	A	Nantwich Town	315	L 1 - 2	Allot 54		1
20	NPL P	H	Whitby Town	415	W 2 - 0	Worsfold 27 42		2
24	NPL P	H	Warrington Town	508	D 0 - 0			3
26	NPL P	A	Matlock Town	540	L 1 - 2	Worsfold 83 (pen)	14	4
31	NPL P	H	Lancaster City	483	L 2 - 4	Horton 55 Morrison 68	17	5
Sept 7	FAC1Q	A	Banbury United	473	D 2 - 2	Worsfold 30 (pen) James 85		6
10	FAC1Qr	H	Banbury United	321	W 1 - 0	James 48		7
14	NPL P	A	Witton Albion	288	L 0 - 1		19	8
21	FAC2Q	A	Rushall Olympic	249	L 0 - 2			9
24	NPL P	A	South Shields	205	L 0 - 2		19	10
28	NPL P	H	Mickleover Sports	347	D 2 - 2	Worsfold 37 Russell 89		11
Oct 1	NPL P	H	Bamber Bridge	303	W 4 - 1	Allot 9 Hannah 23 Middleton 31 Russell 90	16	12
5	NPL P	A	Basford United	293	L 3 - 4	Hannah 58 Gibbons 75 Russell 82	17	13
12	NPL P	H	Atherton Colleries	408	L 0 - 2		20	14
15	NPL P	H	Buxton	347	D 0 - 0		20	15
19	NPL P	A	Ashton United	204	L 1 - 3	Worsfold 74 (pen)	21	16
29	FATQ1	A	Dunston	216	W 4 - 0	ALLOT 3 (8 41 64) James 19		17
Nov 2	NPL P	A	FC United of Manchester	1614	D 2 - 2	Allot 21 Hannah 43	21	18
9	FAT2Q	A	Tamworth	515	W 5 - 3	Litchfield 7 Morrison 9 35 Hannah 71 Russell 76		19
16	NPL P	H	Morpeth	512	L 0 - 1		21	20
23	FAT1P	A	Darlington	770	L 1 - 2	James 24	21	21
Dec 7	NPL P	H	Scarborough Athletic	774	L 2 - 3	Maguire 37 Bacon 53	22	22
14	NPL P	A	Hyde United	323	D 1 - 1	Dunne 75	22	23
21	NPL P	H	Nantwich Town	444	D 0 - 0		22	24
26	NPL P	A	Grantham Town	259	W 5 - 1	Thornton 18 Russell 20 (pen) 60 Morrison 25 50	22	25
Jan 1	NPL P	H	Matlock Town	613	W 2 - 1	Smith 25 Dunne 82	20	26
4	NPL P	A	Whitby Town4	462	D 2 - 2	Russell 2 Smith 56	20	27
11	NPL P	H	Wtton Albion	473	W 3 - 1	Wiles 21 66 Thornton 73	19	28
18	NPL P	H	Radcliffe	332	W 2 - 0	Smith 3 10	19	29
25	NPL P	A	Atherton Colleries	329	W 3 - 1	Walker 3 (18 39 90)	16	30
Feb 1	NPL P	H	Basford United	521	W 1 - 0	Wiles 78	18	31
4	NPL P	A	Stalybridge Celtic	245	W 2 - 1	Smith 49 Adebayo-Smith 52	18	32
8	NPL P	A	Buxton	537	D 3 - 3	Adebayo-Smith 19 Smith 14 (pen) 28	16	33
15	NPL P	H	Stalybridge Celtic	457	L 1 - 3	Smith 70	16	34
22	NPL P	H	South Shields	712	L 1 - 4	Smith 85 (pen)	16	35
Mar 3	NPL P	H	Radcliffe	272	W 4 - 1	Adebayo-Smith 26 Smith 68 (pen) 76 Russell 81	15	36
7	NPL P	A	Lancaster City	197	W 1 - 0	Walker 7	13	37
10	NPL P	A	Stafford Rangers	323	D 2 - 2	Moran 52 (og) Bacon 73	11	38

GOALSCORERS	SG	CSG	Pens	Hat tricks	Total		SG	CSG	Pens	Hat tricks	Total
Smith	8	5	3		11	Bacon	2				2
Russell	7	3	1		8	Dunne	2				2
Allot	4			1	6	Thornton	2				2
Worsfold	5	3			6	Gibbons	1				1
Morrison	3				5	Horton	1				1
Hannah	4				4	Litchfield	1				1
James	4				4	Maguire	1				1
Walker	2			1	4	Middleton	1				1
Adebayo-Smith	3				3	Opponents	1				1
Wiles	2				3						

GRANTHAM TOWN MATCH RESULTS 2019-20

Date	Comp	H/A	Opponents	Att:	Result	Goalscorers	Pos	No.
Aug 17	NPL P	H	FC United of Manchester	821	W 3 - 2	Westcarr 7 77 (pen) Ward 88		1
21	NPL P	A	Stafford Rangers	564	D 1 - 1	Adelekan 76	7	2
24	FACP	A	Barton Town	207	W 3 - 1	Smith 37 Westcarr 48 Baldwin 88		3
26	NPL P	H	Basford United	330	W 1 - 0	Smith 50	6	4
31	NPL P	H	Whitby Town	281	L 0 - 4		10	5
Sept 3	NPL P	A	Matlock Town	372	D 2 - 2	Chilaka 18 Hall 56	10	6
7	FAC1Q	A	Nantwich Town	359	L 1 - 3	Westcarr 38		7
10	NPL P	H	Mickleover Sports	189	D 1 - 1	Chilaka 15	10	8
14	NPL P	A	Lancaster City	201	D 3 - 3	Westcarr 8 56 Goncalves 80	11	9
21	NPL P	H	Bamber Bridge	201	W 1 - 0	Rigby 17 (og)	8	10
24	NPL P	A	Stalybridge Celtic	146	L 2 - 3	Berrett 39 Broadhesd 68	8	11
28	NPL P	H	Radcliffe	199	W 4 - 0	Hughes 24 (og) Ward 35 Wright 59 Zoko 65	6	12
Oct 1	NPL P	H	Ashton United	206	L 0 - 4		8	13
8	NPL P	A	Buxton	180	L 0 - 7		10	14
12	NPL P	H	Hyde United	305	D 2 - 2	Westcarr 15 89	11	15
19	NPL P	A	South Shields	2014	D 1 - 1	Westcarr 73	14	16
26	FAT1Q	H	Rushall Olympic	215	W 5 - 3	Atkinson 28 Smith 29 Campbell 61 Westcarr 69 89 (pen)		17
Nov 2	NPL P	H	Scarborough	345	W 2 - 1	Berrett 19 Campbell 33	13	18
9	FAT2Q	A	Halesowen Town	493	L 1 - 2	Zoko 90	13	19
16	NPL P	A	Nantwich Town	462	L 0 - 2		15	20
Dec 7	NPL P	A	Witton Albion	263	L 1 - 3	McGowan 12	16	21
14	NPL P	H	Morpeth Town	145	L 1 - 2	Westcarr 19	16	22
21	NPL P	A	FC United of Manchester	1701	L 0 - 4		17	23
26	NPL P	H	Gainsborough Trinity	259	L 1 - 5	Atkinson 30	17	24
Jan 1	NPL P	A	Basford United	322	D 0 - 0		17	25
4	NPL P	H	Stafford Rangers	233	W 2 - 0	Green 72 Westcarr 89	16	26
11	NPL P	H	Lancaster City	202	L 0 - 3		16	27
18	NPL P	A	Mickleover Sports	272	L 1 - 4	Westcarr 29	17	28
25	NPL P	A	Hyde United	351	L 0 - 3		19	29
Feb 1	NPL P	H	Buxton	202	L 1 - 3	Morrison 29	20	30
8	NPL P	A	Bamber Bridge	291	L 1 - 2	Willock 60	21	31
15	NPL P	H	South Shields	401	L 1 - 3	Hughes 45	21	32
18	NPL P	A	Warrington Town	263	D 3 - 3	Francis 20 45 Carta 28	20	33
28	NPL P	H	Stalybridge Celtic	269	W 2 - 0	Dunn 70 Westcarr 84	19	34
Mar 7	NPL P	A	Atherton Colleries	276	L 0 - 2		19	35
10	NPL P	A	Grantham Town	288	D 1 - 1	Robertson 31	19	36

GOALSCORERS	SG	CSG	Pens	Hat tricks	Total		SG	CSG	Pens	Hat tricks	Total
Westcarr	11	3	2		15	Broadhead	1				1
Smith	3	2			3	Carta	1				1
Atkinson	2				2	Dunn	1				1
Berrett	2				2	Gonvalves	1				1
Campbell	2				2	Green	1				1
Chilaka	2				2	Hall	1				1
Francis	1				2	Hughes	1				1
Opponents	2				2	McGowan	1				1
Ward	2				2	Morrison	1				1
Zoko	2				2	Robertson	1				1
Adelekan	1				1	Willock	1				1
Baldwin	1				1	Wright	1				1

HYDE UNITED MATCH RESULTS 2019-20

Date	Comp	H/A	Opponents	Att:	Result		Goalscorers	Pos	No.
Aug 17	NPL P	H	Basford United	384	L	2 - 3	O'Brien 4 White 77		1
21	NPL P	A	FC United of Manchester	1809	W	2 - 1	O'Brien 12 Tongue 36 (pen)		2
24	NPL P	A	South Shields	1287	W	1 - 0	Tongue 70		3
26	NPL P	H	Buxton	494	W	3 - 1	Pratt 33 Dyche 44 Turner 75 (pen)	3	4
31	NPL P	H	Stafford Rangers	455	W	4 - 0	Tongue 61 O'Brien 79 Dyche 81 Pratt 90	2	5
Sept 3	NPL P	A	Witton Albion	336	L	0 - 2		2	6
7	FAC1Q	A	**Morpeth Town**	551	L	1 - 3	**Gooda 75**		7
10	NPL P	H	Nantwich Town	329	W	2 - 0	Thompson 45 Dyche 65	1	8
14	NPL P	A	Whitby Town	462	L	0 - 2		3	9
28	NPL P	H	Ashton United	552	D	3 - 3	Turner 14 18 Tongue 53	5	10
Oct 1	NPL P	H	Mickleover Sports	247	L	2 - 3	Turner 57 Pratt 74	7	11
5	NPL P	A	Radcliffe	494	L	0 - 3		8	12
12	NPL P	A	Grantham Town	305	D	2 - 2	Morrison 75 Lane 79 (pen)	10	13
15	NPL P	A	Scarborough Athletic	885	L	0 - 1		11	14
19	NPL P	H	Morpeth Town	413	D	1 - 1	Pratt 90	12	15
26	FAT1Q	A	**Buxton**	360	L	2 - 3	**Pratt 11 Lee 41 (pen)**		16
Nov 2	NPL P	A	Warrington Town	385	L	1`- 4	Sharp 26	13	17
9	NPL P	A	Lancaster City	226	D	2 - 2	Turner 65 Tongue 90	13	18
16	NPL P	H	Bamber Bridge	392	W	4 - 1	Sharp 41 57 Tongue 68 Crawford 83	10	19
23	NPL P	A	Stafford Rangers	493	W	3 - 1	Sharp 13 Lane 53 Tongue 79	9	20
30	NPL P	H	Witton Albion	432	D	0 - 0		10	21
Dec 7	NPL P	A	Atherton Colleries	357	L	1 - 2	Roscoe 57	10	22
14	NPL P	H	Gainsborough Trinity	323	D	1 - 1	Dyche 50	10	23
21	NPL P	A	Basford United	259	W	4 - 1	Lane 7 Turner 17 36 Hughes 25	9	24
26	NPL P	H	Stalybridge Celtic	900	L	1 - 2	Starcenko 56	10	25
Jan 1	NPL P	A	Buxton	500	W	2 - 1	Fagbola 37 Hughes 45	9	26
4	NPL P	H	FC United of Manchester	1293	L	1 - 5	Turner 90 (pen)	9	27
11	NPL P	H	Whitby Town	291	L	0 - 2		9	28
18	NPL P	A	Nantwich Town	405	L	0 - 4		10	29
25	NPL P	H	Grantham Town	351	W	3 - 1	Pratt 13 Tongue 52 Sharp 83	11	30
Feb 1	NPL P	A	Matlock Town	543	D	1 - 1	Pratt 90	11	31
8	NPL P	H	Scarborough Athletic	585	L	0 - 1		12	32
29	NPL P	H	Lancaster City	452	W	5 - 2	PRATT 3 (2 49 59) Tongue 19 McCombe 48	11	33
Apr 5	NPL P	H	Matlock Town	351	W	3 - 1	Lane 22 Harris 65 (og) Ndiaye 86	10	34
10	NPL P	A	Morpeth Town	420	L	1 - 2	Pratt 61	10	35

GOALSCORERS	SG	CSG	Pens	Hat tricks	Total		SG	CSG	Pens	Hat tricks	Total
Pratt	10	2			11	Gooda	1				1
Tongue	9	3	1		9	Lee	1		1		1
Turner	5	2	2		8	McCombe	1				1
Sharp	4				5	Morrison	1				1
Dyche	4	2			4	Ndiaye	1				1
Lane	4		1		4	Opponents	1				1
O'Brien	3	2			3	Roscoe	1				1
Hughes	2				2	Starcenko	1				1
Crawford	1				1	Thompson	1				1
Fagbola	1				1	White	1				1

LANCASTER CITY MATCH RESULTS 2019-20

Date	Comp	H/A	Opponents	Att:	Result	Goalscorers	Pos	No.
Aug 17	NPL P	H	Stafford Rangers	362	W 2 - 1	Wilson 3 Armer 32		1
20	NPL P	A	Morpeth Town	775	L 2 - 3	Norris 9 Lowson 84 (og)		2
24	NPL P	A	Basford United	22	L 1 - 4	Bailey 42		3
27	NPL P	H	Atherton Collieries	330	W 1 - 0	Norris 90	12	4
31	NPL P	A	Gainsborough Trinity	483	W 4 - 2	NORRIS 3 (18 30 42) Walker 57	8	5
Sept 3	NPL P	H	FC United of Manchester	522	D 0 - 0		8	6
7	FAC1Q	H	Northwich Victoria	261	D 0 - 0			7
11	FAC1Qr	A	Northwich Victoria	310	W 2 - 1	Norris 49 87		8
14	NPL P	H	Grantham Town	201	D 3 - 3	Dawson 44 72 Blinkhorn 54	9	9
21	FAC2Q	A	Spennymoor United	294	L 0 - 5			10
28	NPL P	A	Nantwich Town	343	L 2 - 3	Carsley 8 Dawson 85	13	11
Oct 1	NPL P	A	Witton Albion	203	W 3 - 1	Wilson 42 Bailey 45 Roache 52	10	12
5	NPL P	H	Matlock Town	234	W 1 - 0	Dawson 18	7	13
8	NPL P	A	Warrington Town	338	D 2 - 2	Dawson 13 Wilson 88	5	14
12	NPL P	H	Ashton United	317	W 3 - 0	Norris 18 59 Wilson 26 (pen)	3	15
15	NPL P	H	Radcliffe	257	W 1 - 0	Raven 42 (og)	3	16
19	NPL P	A	Mickleover Sports	238	W 3 - 1	Blinkhorn 26 Norris 38 Bailey 61	3	17
26	FAT1Q	H	Witton Albion	288	W 1 - 0	Wilson 34 (pen)		18
Nov 2	NPL P	A	South Shields	1570	W 1 - 0	Norris 66	3	19
9	NPL P	H	Hyde United	226	D 2 - 2	Norris 32 Fensome 83	3	20
12	FAT2Q	A	Stourbridge	315	D 2 - 2	Wilson 41 Armer 45		21
16	NPL P	A	Scarborough Athletic	1057	W 1 - 0	Norris 59	2	22
23	FAT2Qr	H	Stourbridge	241	L 1 - 2	Wilson 68 (pen)		23
30	NPL P	A	FC United of Manchester	1873	L 2 - 3	Wilson 84 Rodney 86	2	24
Dec 7	NPL P	A	Buxton	326	D 1 - 1	Wilson 44 (pen)	2	25
14	NPL P	H	Stalybridge Celtic	208	D 0 - 0		1	26
21	NPL P	A	Stafford Rangers	454	W 3 - 0	Steel 16 Blinkhorn 35 Carsley 63	1	27
28	NPL P	H	Bamber Bridge	325	L 2 - 3	Carsley 24 Dawson 64	2	28
Jan 1	NPL P	A	Atherton Collieries	401	L 1 - 2	Norris 16	2	29
4	NPL P	H	Morpeth Town	224	W 4 - 1	DAWSON 3 (37 48 71) Bailey 64	2	30
11	NPL P	A	Grantham Town	202	W 3 - 0	Blinkhorn 30 Carsley 63 86	2	31
18	NPL P	H	South Shields	688	L 1 - 2	Wilson 34 (pen)	2	32
25	NPL P	A	Ashton United	228	L 0 - 1		4	33
Feb 1	NPL P	H	Warrington Town	264	W 2 - 1	Bailey 31 44	4	34
8	NPL P	A	Radcliffe	367	W 3 - 0	Bailey 9 Carsley 39 Norris 55	3	35
22	NPL P	H	Nantwich Town	293	D 0 - 0		3	36
25	NPL P	H	Whitby Town	305	L 1 - 3	Rydel 81	4	37
29	NPL P	A	Hyde United	452	L 2 - 5	Steel 30 Bailey 56	4	38
Mar 7	NPL P	H	Gainsborough Trinity	197	L 0 - 1		6	39
14	NPL P	H	Witton Albion	398	D 1 - 1	Dawson 45	5	40

GOALSCORERS	SG	CSG	Pens	Hat tricks	Total		SG	CSG	Pens	Hat tricks	Total
Norris	13	2		1	16	Rodney	1				1
Dawson	7	3		1	10	Rydel	1				1
Wilson	9	3	4		10	Steel	1				1
Bailey	7	2			8	Walker	1				1
Carsley	5				6						
Blinkhorn	4				4						
Armer	2				2						
Opponents	2				2						
Fensome	1				1						
Roache	1				1						

MATLOCK TOWN MATCH RESULTS 2019-20

Date	Comp	H/A	Opponents	Att:	Result	Goalscorers	Pos	No.
Aug 17	NPL P	H	Bamber Bridge	402	W 1 - 0	Marshall 34		1
19	NPL P	A	Basford United	501	W 1 - 0	Crouz 84		2
24	NPL P	A	Stafford Rangers	486	W 1 - 0	Marshall 81	1	3
26	NPL P	H	Gainsborough Trinity	540	W 2 - 1	Hotte 10 (og) Green 90 (og)	1	4
31	NPL P	A	Ashton United	202	D 1 - 1	Marshall 65	1	5
Sept 3	NPL P	H	Grantham Town	372	D 2 - 2	Bennett 86 (og) Hinsley 90	1	6
7	FAC1Q	H	Basford United	431	W 2 - 1	Harris 2 (pen) Sinnott 61		7
14	NPL P	H	South Shields	614	L 1 - 2	Marshall 75	5	8
21	FAC2Q	H	Kidsgrove Athletic	377	L 1 - 2	Williamson 45		9
24	NPL P	H	Atherton Colleries	276	D 1 - 1	Marshall 5	5	10
28	NPL P	A	Whitby Town	464	W 3 - 0	Bramall 45 Hinsley 49 Marshall 88	3	11
Oct 1	NPL P	A	Nantwich Town	255	L 1 - 3	Sinnott 39	3	12
5	NPL P	A	Lancaster City	234	L 0 - 1		6	13
8	NPL P	H	Scarborough	419	L 1 - 2	Hinsley 60	6	14
12	NPL P	H	Mickleover Sports	729	W 3 - 1	Bramall 4 Hinsley 44 Scrivens 52	4	15
15	NPL P	H	Warrington Town	380	L 1 - 2	Raven 42 (og)	5	16
19	NPL P	A	Radcliffe	327	L 0 - 1		6	17
30	FATQ1	A	Carlton Town	142	W 2 - 1	Sinnott 25 (pen) Hinsley 27		18
Nov 9	FAT2Q	H	Ashton United	284	W 1 - 0	Harris 33 (pen)		19
16	NPL P	H	Stalybridge Celtic	463	L 0 - 1		12	20
23	FAT3Q	H	Redditch United	259	W 2 - 0	Marshall 54 Sinnott 74	12	21
Dec 7	NPL P	A	FC United of Manchester	1574	L 2 - 5	Poole 7 Marshall 12	14	22
14	FAT1P	H	Chorley	400	D 2 - 2	Harris 47 Hinsley 66		23
17	FAT1Pr	A	Chorley	229	W 2 - 2	Chilaka 16 Marshall 110 (Won 4-3 on pens)		24
21	NPL P	A	Bamber Bridge	326	W 2 - 1	Marshall 20 Bramall 70	14	25
26	NPL P	H	Buxton	922	L 2 - 4	Hinsley 3 Poole 5	15	26
Jan 1	NPL P	A	Gainsborough Trinity	613	L 1 - 2	Bramall 80	16	27
4	NPL P	H	Basford United	424	L 0 - 1		17	28
11	FAT2P	A	Eastleigh	718	L 1 - 2	Marshall 69	18	29
18	NPL P	A	Scarborough Athletic	1083	L 1 - 2	Valentine 53	18	30
Feb 1	NPL P	H	Hyde United	543	D 1 - 1	Crouz 52	20	31
4	NPL P	H	Radcliffe	297	W 4 - 0	Valentine 7 Crouz 43 Tague 87 Wilson 90	18	32
22	NPL P	H	Whitby Town	460	L 0 - 2		18	33
Mar 3	NPL P	H	Morpeth Town	249	D 1 - 1	Marshall 54	18	34
7	NPL P	A	Hyde United	354	L 1 - 3	Chilaka 90	18	35
10	NPL P	A	Warrington Town	308	L 2 - 3	Oyibo 49 Turner 74	20	36

GOALSCORERS	SG	CSG	Pens	Hat tricks	Total		SG	CSG	Pens	Hat tricks	Total
Marshall	11	2			12	Oyibo	1				1
Hinsley	7				7	Scrivens	1				1
Bramall	3				4	Tague	1				1
Opponents	4				4	Turner	1				1
Sinnott	4		1		4	Williamson	1				1
Crouz	3				3	Wilson	1				1
Harris	3		2		3						
Chilaka	2				2						
Poole	2				2						
Valentine	2				2						

MICKLEOVER SPORTS MATCH RESULTS 2019-20

Date	Comp	H/A	Opponents	Att:	Result	Goalscorers	Pos	No.
Aug 17	NPL P	H	Stalybridge Celtic	368	W 1 - 0	Storer 3 (pen)		1
20	NPL P	A	Witton Albion	284	L 0 - 1			2
23	**FACP**	**H**	**Coventry Sphinx**	**249**	**W 3 - 0**	**CADMAN 3 (22 40 60)**		3
26	NPL P	H	Stafford Rangers	355	W 1 - 0	Warren 85 (pen)	11	4
31	NPL P	A	Warrington Town	355	L 0 - 1		12	5
Sept 3	NPL P	H	Buxton	222	W 4 - 2	Bacon 45 77 Warren 64 (pen) 67 (pen)	12	6
7	**FAC1Q**	**A**	**Stafford Rangers**	**519**	**L 0 - 3**			7
10	NPL P	A	Grantham Town	189	D 1 - 1	Warren 82	7	8
14	NPL P	H	Ashton United	227	L 0 - 1		10	9
21	NPL P	A	Atherton Colleries	255	W 3 - 1	Beavon 1 Hughes 16 Warren 41	7	10
28	NPL P	A	Gainsborough Trinity	347	D 2 - 2	Hughes 15 Watters 50	9	11
Oct 1	NPL P	A	Hyde United	247	W 3 - 2	Hughes 7 Modest 47 Beavon 87	6	12
5	NPL P	H	Scarborough Athletic	261	W 1 - 0	Hughes 24	3	13
8	NPL P	H	Morpeth Town	216	D 1 - 1	Warren 73 (pen)		14
12	NPL P	A	Matlock Town	729	L 1 - 3	Hughes 33	5	15
19	NPL P	H	Lancaster City	238	L 1 - 3	Boula 90	7	16
26	**FAT1Q**	**A**	**Basford**	**352**	**L 0 - 3**		7	17
Nov 9	NPL P	H	Witton Albion	162	L 1 - 4	Warren 50	10	18
16	NPL P	A	Radcliffe	285	L 0 - 1		13	19
30	NPL P	A	Buxton	335	W 1 - 0	Beavon 8	11	20
Dec 7	NPL P	A	Bamber Bridge	291	L 2 - 3	Hughes 10 Young 26	11	21
14	NPL P	A	Scarborough Athletic	826	L 1 - 4	Beavon 57	12	22
21	NPL P	A	Stalybridge Celtic	323	W 3 - 1	Beavon 35 52 Aman 48	11	23
Jan 1	NPL P	A	Stafford Rangers	591	W 1 - 0	Patrick 72	11	24
4	NPL P	H	Nantwich Town	374	W 2 - 1	Beavon 18 62	9	25
11	NPL P	A	South Shields	1459	L 2 - 5	Patrick 68 Wright 73	10	26
18	NPL P	H	Grantham Town	272	W 4 - 1	Tvaroh 41 Wright 55 Nesbitt 67 Beavon 69	9	27
Feb 1	NPL P	A	FC United of Manchester	1747	D 3 - 3	Patrick 37 71 Beavon 50	9	28
8	NPL P	H	Whitby Town	304	L 1 - 3	Patrick 31	13	29
Mar 3	NPL P	A	Whitby Town	290	D 1 - 1	Aman 12	14	30
7	NPL P	H	FC United of Manchester	804	L 0 - 4		14	31
10	NPL P	A	Ashton United	160	L 1 - 3	Patrick 21	15	32

GOALSCORERS	SG	CSG	Pens	Hat tricks	Total		SG	CSG	Pens	Hat tricks	Total
Beavon	8		1		10	Nesbitt	1				1
Warren	6		3		7	Storer	1				1
Hughes	6	4			6	Tvaroh	1				1
Patrick	5				6	Watters	1				1
Cadman	1			1	3	Young	1				1
Aman	2				2						
Bacon	1				2						
Wright	2				2						
Boula	1				1						
Modest	1				1						

MORPETH TOWN MATCH RESULTS 2019-20

Date	Comp	H/A	Opponents	Att:	Result	Goalscorers	Pos	No.
Aug 17	NPL P	A	Warrington Town	447	W 3 - 1	Reid 45 Foalle 47 Harmison 88		1
20	NPL P	H	Lancaster City	775	W 3 - 2	Walton 34 (pen) 90 (pen) Henderson 89		2
24	FACP	A	Brighouse Town	127	D 2 - 2	Henderson 6 Foalle 21		3
26	NPL P	A	Whiby Town	458	L 1 - 2	Henderson 45	10	4
31	NPL P	A	FC United of Manchester	1434	L 2 - 4	Harmison 23 Walton 57 (pen)	11	5
Sept 3	FACPr	H	Brighouse Town	503	W 3 - 2	Taylor 37 54 Sayer 68		6
7	FAC1Q	H	Hyde United	551	W 3 - 1	Henderson 13 Taylor 54 59		7
14	NPL P	H	Buxton	635	W 2 - 1	Walton 75 82 (pen)	12	8
21	FAC2Q	A	Bradford PA	217	W 4 - 2	Walton 9 37 Reid 35 66		9
28	NPL P	H	Stafford Rangers	517	D 1 - 1	Phillips 40	14	10
Oct 5	FAC3Q	A	Nantwich Toswn	476	L 0 - 1			11
8	NPL P	A	Mickleover Sports	216	D 1 - 1	Henderson 20	14	12
12	NPL P	H	Basford United	625	D 1 - 1	Harmison 45	14	13
15	NPL P	H	Alfreton Colleries	502	W 3 - 0	Walton 9 Foalle 54 Potter 67	14	14
19	NPL P	A	Hyde United	413	D 1 - 1	Ramsey 89	15	15
26	FAT1Q	H	Cleethorps	502	W 6 - 1	Reid 32 50 Taylor 40 Henderson 43 Phillips 48 Noble 73		16
Nov 9	FAT2Q	A	Atherton Collieries	216	L 1 - 2	Henderson 83	15	17
16	NPL P	A	Gainsborough Trinity	512	W 1 - 0	Walton 34	15	18
23	NPL P	A	Bamber Bridge	285	L 0 - 3		16	19
Dec 7	NPL P	H	Nantwich Town	395	W 1 - 0	Harmison 77	14	20
14	NPL P	A	Grantham Town	145	W 2 - 1	Reid 45 Henderson 84	12	21
21	NPL P	H	Warrington Town	410	W 4 - 0	Noble 3 Finnigan 23 Henderson 30 37	10	22
26	NPL P	A	Scarborough	1207	L 0 - 1		12	23
Jan 4	NPL P	A	Lancaster City	224	L 1 - 4	Taylor 63	14	24
11	NPL P	A	Buxton	376	W 3 - 2	Foalle 41 50 81	13	25
18	NPL P	H	Ashton United	652	L 1 - 4	Henderson 4	14	26
25	NPL P	A	Basford United	255	L 0 - 1		15	27
Feb 1	NPL P	H	Radcliffe	510	W 3 - 1	Finnigan 7 Henderson 50 Foalle 90	14	28
4	NPL P	A	South Shields	1704	D 1 - 1	Finnigan 79	13	29
8	NPL P	A	Atherton Collieries	260	W 5 - 1	Noble 7 Sayer 14 Walton 54 69 Foalle 90	9	30
22	NPL P	A	Stafford Rangers	407	W 2 - 0	Henderson 15 Reid 56	10	31
Mar 3	NPL P	A	Matlock Town	249	D 1 - 1	Hutchinson 78	10	32
7	NPL P	H	Wittan Albion	571	W 3 - 2	Taylor 8 49 Forster 65	9	33
10	NPL P	H	Hyde United	420	W 2 - 1	Walton 13 Henderson 27	8	34

GOALSCORERS	SG	CSG	Pens	Hat tricks	Total		SG	CSG	Pens	Hat tricks	Total
Henderson	13	3			15	Forster	1				1
Walton	7		2		11	Hutchinson	1				1
Foalle	6		1		8	Potter	1				1
Taylor	5				8	Ramsey	1				1
Reid	5				7						
Harmison	4				4						
Finnigan	3				3						
Noble	3				3						
Phillips	2				2						
Sayer	2				2						

NANTWICH TOWN MATCH RESULTS 2019-20

Date	Comp	H/A	Opponents	Att:	Result	Goalscorers	Pos	No.
Aug 17	NPL P	H	Gainsborough Trinity	315	W 2 - 1	Malkin 68 71		1
20	NPL P	A	Buxton	353	W 2 - 1	Hughes 24 Cooke 52		2
26	NPL P	H	Witton Albion	505	W 3 - 0	Mwasile 10 63 Cooke 35	2	3
31	NPL P	A	Atherton Colliers	324	L 1 - 3	Lawrie 45	7	4
Sept 3	NPL P	H	Warrington Town	406	L 1 - 3	Malkin 68	7	5
7	FAC1Q	H	Grantham Town	359	W 3 - 1	Cooke 21 Harrison 61 Schousboe 73		6
10	NPL P	A	Hyde United	329	L 0 - 2		9	7
14	NPL P	H	Scarborough Athletic	329	W 3 - 2	Langley 76 Malkin 79 Hughes 81	7	8
21	FAC2Q	A	AFC Telford United	718	W 3 - 0	Malkin 17 Davis 23 Hughes 77		9
24	NPL P	H	Lancaster City	343	W 3 - 2	Malkin 5 Walsh 14 44	8	10
Oct 1	NPL P	H	Matlock Town	255	W 3 - 1	Malkin 51 72 Hughes 90	4	11
5	FAC3Q	H	Morpeth	476	W 1 - 0	Mwasile 90		12
8	NPL P	A	Bamber Bridge	287	D 2 - 2	Lawrie 6 (pen) 75 (pen)	6	13
12	NPL P	H	Radcliffe	609	L 0 - 1		8	14
19	FAC4Q	A	Kings Lynn Town	742	W 1 - 0	Bourne 39		15
29	FAT1Q	H	Bsmber Bridge	234	W 2 - 1	Stair 21 Bourne 29		16
Nov 2	NPL P	A	Whitby Town	407	D 3 - 3	Malkin 37 52 Cooke 74	9	17
9	FAC1P	H	AFC Fylde	1554	L 0 - 1			18
12	FAT2Q	H	Coalville Town	208	L 0 - 1			19
16	NPL P	H	Grantham Town	462	W 2 - 0	Mwasile 17 Cooke 64	7	20
23	NPL P	A	Ashton United	144	W 4 - 0	Lawrie 16 (pen) Saunders 50 71 Fuller 75	6	21
30	NPL P	A	Warrington Town	512	L 1 - 3	Cooke 10	9	22
Dec 7	NPL P	A	Morpeth Town	395	L 0 - 1		9	23
14	NPL P	H	Buxton	331	D 2 - 2	Davis 53 Malkin 67	9	24
21	NPL P	A	Gainsborough Trinity	444	D 0 - 0		10	25
28	NPL P	H	Stafford Rangers	508	W 2 - 1	Stair 90 Cooke 90	8	26
Jan 1	NPL P	A	Witton Albion	535	W 2 - 1	Cooke 62 Stair 58	8	27
4	NPL P	A	Mickleover Sports	374	L 1 - 2	Hughes 7	8	28
11	NPL P	A	Scarborough Atrhletic	948	D 1 - 1	Mwasile 58	7	29
18	NPL P	H	Hyde United	405	W 4 - 0	Varian 1 33 Bourne 23 Webb 37	7	30
25	NPL P	A	Stalybridge Celtic	314	W 2 - 0	Mwsaile 12 Lawrie 36	6	31
Feb 1	NPL P	H	Bamber Bridge	455	W 3 - 2	Webb 39 89 Stair 42	6	32
8	NPL P	A	South Shields	2017	W 4 - 0	Hughes 37 Cooke 80 Fuller 90 Walsh 90	5	33
22	NPL P	A	Lancaster City	293	D 0 - 0		5	34
25	NPL P	H	FC United of Manchester	580	L 0 - 1		6	35
Mar 2	NPL P	A	Basford United	263	W 2 - 0	Hayward 84 Malkin 90	5	36
7	NPL P	A	Radcliffe	377	D 2 - 2	Cooke 48 (pen) Fuller 62	5	37
10	NPL P	H	South Shields	498	L 0 - 1		5	38
								39
								40
								41
								42
								43
								44
								45
								46

GOALSCORERS	SG	CSG	Pens	Hat tricks	Total		SG	CSG	Pens	Hat tricks	Total
Malkin	9	4			12	Davis	2				2
Cooke	10	2	1		10	Saunders	1				2
Hughes	6	2			6	Varien	1				2
Mwasile	6				6	Harrison	1				1
Lawrie	3		2		5	Langley	1				1
Stair	4				4	Schousboe	1				1
Bourne	3	2			3	Shields	1				1
Fuller	3				3						
Walsh	2				3						
Webb	2				3						

RADCLIFFE MATCH RESULTS 2019-20

Date	Comp	H/A	Opponents	Att:	Result	Goalscorers	Pos	No.
Aug 17	NPL P	H	South Shields	604	L 0 - 1			1
24	**FACP**	H	**Runcorn Town**	**200**	D 0 - 0			2
26	NPL P	H	FC United of Manchester	1228	D 1 - 1	Wolfenden 13	17	3
31	NPL P	A	Basford United	259	L 0 - 1		21	4
Sept 4	**FACPr**	A	**Runcorn Town**	**188**	L 1 - 2	**Wharton 37 (pen)**		5
14	NPL P	H	Warrington Town	396	D 1 - 1	Sinclair 18	22	6
21	NPL P	A	Stalybridge Celtic	266	W 3 - 1	Winter 45 Crothers 75 Wolfenden 88	18	7
28	NPL P	A	Grantham Town	199	L 0 - 4		19	8
Oct 5	NPL P	H	Hyde United	494	W 3 - 0	Ellis 17 Sinclair 84 (pen) Smith 86	16	9
12	NPL P	A	Nantwich Town	609	W 1 - 0	Williams 80	16	10
15	NPL P	A	Lancaster City	257	L 0 - 1		16	11
19	NPL P	H	Matlock Town	327	W 1 - 0	Ellis 48	16	12
29	**FAT1Q**	H	**FC United of Manchester**	**523**	L 0 - 2			13
Nov 2	NPL P	A	Stalybridge Celtic	262	W 1 - 0	Wharton 25	16	14
8	NPL P	H	Scarborough	374	W 3 - 1	Ellis 4 Williams 52 Wharton 90 (pen)	12	15
16	NPL P	H	Mickleover Sports	285	W 1 - 0	Rokka 87	8	16
23	NPL P	H	Basford United	315	W 3 - 0	Wharton 2 Sinclair 72 Wolfenden 90	7	17
30	NPL P	A	Aston United	254	W 3 - 0	Ellis 44 Sinclair 46 55	5	18
Dec 7	NPL P	A	Stafford Rangers	125	L 0 - 2		7	19
14	NPL P	H	Witton Albion	263	W 1 - 0	Sinclair 68	7	20
21	NPL P	A	South Shields	1405	L 0 - 3		8	21
26	NPL P	H	Atherton Collieries	571	W 1 - 0	Forrester 68	5	22
Jan 1	NPL P	A	FC United of Manchester	2124	L 2 - 3	Sinclair 37 Forrester 90	7	23
4	NPL P	H	Bamber Bridge	432	L 0 - 4		7	24
11	NPL P	A	Warrington Town	449	L 0 - 1		8	25
18	NPL P	H	Gainsborough Trinity	332	L 0 - 2		8	26
21	NPL P	H	Ashton United	255	D 1 - 1	McKnight 36	9	27
25	NPL P	A	Bamber Bridge	414	L 1 - 2	Hanley 69	10	28
Feb 1	NPL P	A	Morpeth Town	510	L 1 - 3	Hughes 73	11	29
4	NPL P	A	Matlock Town	297	L 0 - 4		11	30
8	NPL P	H	Lancaster City	357	L 0 - 3		15	31
29	NPL P	A	Scarborough Athletic	972	L 1 - 3	Mitchley 84	15	32
Mar 3	NPL P	A	Gainsborough Trinity	272	L 1 - 4	Akpro 72	16	33
7	NPL P	H	Nantwich Town	377	D 2 - 2	Langley 25 (og) McKnight 70	16	34
14	NPL P	H	Whitby Town	480	D 2 - 2	Hall 40 Cummings 42	16	35

GOALSCORERS	SG	CSG	Pens	Hat tricks	Total		SG	CSG	Pens	Hat tricks	Total
Sinclair	5	2	1		6	Hall	1				1
Ellis	5				5	Hanley	1				1
Wharton	4	2	1		4	Hughes	1				1
Wolfenden	3				3	Mitchley	1				1
Forrester	2				2	Opponents	1				1
McKnight	2				2	Rokka	1				1
Williams	2				2	Smith	1				1
Akpro	1				1	Winter	1				1
Crothers	1				1						
Cummings	1				1						

SCARBOROUGH ATHLETIC MATCH RESULTS 2019-20

Date	Comp	H/A	Opponents	Att:	Result	Goalscorers	Pos	No.
Aug 17	NPL P	H	Buxton	1157	D 1 - 1	Johnson 89		1
20	NPL P	A	Stalybridge Celtic	355	L 1 - 5	Dawson 45		2
24	NPL P	A	FC United of Manchester	1532	W 1 - 0	Deacey 28	12	3
26	NPL P	H	South Shields	1311	D 0 - 0		13	4
31	NPL P	H	Witton Albion	891	D 0 - 0		13	5
Sept 3	NPL P	A	Whitby Town	1038	L 0 - 2		13	6
7	FAC1Q	H	Marske United	698	D 1 - 1	Walshaw 26		7
10	FAC1Qr	A	Marske United	550	W 2 - 1	Walshaw 23 Assenso 81		8
14	NPL P	A	Nantwich Town	329	L 2 - 3	Lofts 15 Walshaw 16	17	9
21	FAC2Q	A	Southport	875	L 2 - 5	Walshaw 6 Coulson 88 (pen)		10
24	NPL P	H	Warrington Town	845	D 1 - 1	Dawson 22	17	11
Oct 1	NPL P	H	Basford United	735	D 1 - 1	Walshaw 27	18	12
5	NPL P	A	Mickleover Sports	261	L 0 - 1		18	13
8	NPL P	A	Matlock Town	419	W 2 - 1	Walker 19 Coulson 88		14
12	NPL P	H	Stafford Rangers	1027	D 1 - 1	Coulson 23	15	15
15	NPL P	H	Hyde United	885	W 1 - 0	Dawson 4	14	16
19	NPL P	A	Bamber Bridge	430	W 2 - 1	Coulson 4 (pen) Watson 90	13	17
29	FAT1Q	A	Atherton Collieries	212	L 2 - 3	Walshaw 52 Lofts 90		18
Nov 2	NPL P	A	Grantham Town	345	L 1 - 2	Thomson 6	14	19
9	NPL P	A	Radcliffe	374	L 1 - 3	Bignot 54		20
16	NPL P	H	Lancaster City	1057	L 0 - 1		16	21
23	NPL P	A	Witton Albion	333	L 1 - 3	Walshaw 72	16	22
30	NPL P	H	Whitby Town	1358	W 2 - 1	Walshaw 31 Thomson 48	14	23
Dec 7	NPL P	A	Gainsborough Trinity	772	W 3 - 2	Walshaw 45 Assenso 76 Thomson 90	12	24
14	NPL P	H	Mickleover Sports	826	W 4 - 1	Thomson 26 Walshaw 33 71 Coulson 90	10	25
21	NPL P	A	Buxton	401	L 0 - 5		11	26
26	NPL P	H	Morpeth Town	1207	W 1 - 0	Walshaw 57	11	27
Jan 1	NPL P	A	South Shields	1908	L 1 - 2	Coulson 12	12	28
4	NPL P	H	Stalybridge Celtic	963	D 1 - 1	Watson 73	12	29
11	NPL P	H	Nantwich Town	948	D 1 - 1	Watson 40	11	30
18	NPL P	H	Matlock Town	1083	W 2 - 1	Barrett 18 Walshaw 30	10	31
25	NPL P	A	Stafford Rangers	573	L 0 - 1		12	32
Feb 1	NPL P	H	Ashton United	900	W 3 - 1	Coulson 18 (pen) 65 Watson 90	10	33
8	NPL P	A	Hyde United	585	W 1 - 0	Glynn 35	7	34
15	NPL P	H	Bamber Bridge	859	W 5 - 0	Walshaw 16 55 62 Coulson 19 (pen) Watson 49	7	35
22	NPL P	A	Warington Town	522	L 0 - 2		7	36
29	NPL P	H	Radcliffe	972	W 3 - 1	Spratt 12 Walshaw 44 76	7	37
Mar 7	NPL P	A	Ashton United	278	L 0 - 2		9	38
14	NPL P	A	Basford United	501	W 1 - 0	Walshaw 24	8	39

GOALSCORERS	SG	CSG	Pens	Hat tricks	Total		SG	CSG	Pens	Hat tricks	Total
Walshaw	14	4		1	19	Glynn	1				1
Coulson	8	2	4		9	Johnson	1				1
Watson	5				5	Spratt	1				1
Thomson	4				4	Walker	1				1
Dawson	3				3						
Assenso	2				2						
Lofts	2				2						
Barrett	1				1						
Bignot	1				1						
Deacey	1				1						

SOUTH SHIELDS MATCH RESULTS 2019-20

Date	Comp	H/A	Opponents	Att:	Result	Goalscorers	Pos	No.
Aug 17	NPL P	A	Radcliffe	604	W 1 - 0	Briggs 51		1
20	NPL P	H	Ashton United	1283	W 3 - 0	Briggs 7 (pen) Brown 42 Gilchrist 80		2
24	NPL P	H	Hyde United	1287	L 0 - 1		4	3
26	NPL P	A	Scarborough Athletic	1311	D 0 - 0		4	4
31	NPL P	H	Bamber Bridge	1231	W 4 - 1	Brown 28 Thurston 32 Mason 35 Gillies 38 (pen)	3	5
Sept 7	FAC1Q	H	Colne	1157	D 0 - 0			6
10	FAC1Qr	A	Colne	231	L 0 - 1			7
14	NPL P	A	Matlock Town	614	W 2 - 1	Shaw 46 Briggs 58 (pen)	6	8
21	NPL P	H	Basford Town	1634	W 2 - 0	Hunter 15 Shaw 51	1	9
24	NPL P	H	Gainsborough Trinity	205	W 2 - 0	Gillies 42 Shaw 90	1	10
28	NPL P	A	Buxton	515	W 2 - 1	Shaw 45 Mason 88	1	11
Oct 1	NPL P	A	FC United of Manchester	1349	W 2 - 0	Mason 36 Gilchrist 82	1	12
5	NPL P	H	Alfreton Collieries	1752	W 3 - 0	Foley 28 51 Odelusi 38	1	13
8	NPL P	H	Stalybridge Celtic	1407	W 2 - 1	Foley 35 Briggs 90 (pen)	1	14
12	NPL P	A	Witton Albion	448	L 1 - 3	Briggs 62	1	15
19	NPL P	H	Grantham Town	2014	D 1 - 1	Lowe 16	1	16
29	FATQ1	A	Stalybridge Celtic	203	W 2 - 0	Gilchrist 10 Shaw 15		17
Nov 2	NPL P	H	Lancaster City	1570	L 0 - 1		1	18
9	FAT2Q	H	AFC Rushden & Diamonds	934	W 4 - 0	Gilchrist 21 66 Thurston 29 Mason 89		19
16	NPL P	A	Stafford Rangers	625	W 2 - 1	Baxter 30 Gilchrist 45	1	20
26	FAT3Q	A	Stourbridge	356	D 1 - 1	Gilchrist 17	1	21
Dec 3	FAT3Qr	H	Stourbridge	612	W 4 - 0	Shaw 4 Gilchrist 6 Adams 11 Briggs 36 (pen)		22
7	NPL P	H	Warrington	1589	D 1 - 1	Briggs 30	1	23
14	FAT1	H	Southport	776	D 2 - 2	Brown 66 Gilchrist 73		24
17	FAT1r	A	Southport	372	L 1 - 3	Gilchrist 3		25
21	NPL P	H	Radcliffe	1405	W 3 - 0	Jenkins 32 Briggs 52 (pen) 70	1	26
26	NPL P	A	Whitby Town	879	L 1 - 2	Morse 83	1	27
Jan 1	NPL P	H	Scarborough Athletic	1908	W 2 - 1	Lowe 50 90	1	28
4	NPL P	A	Ashton United	277	W 2 - 0	Gilchrist 4 19	1	29
11	NPL P	H	Mickleover Sports	1452	W 5 - 2	Turnbull 22 Lowe 32 Gonzales 75 88 Gilchrist 75	1	30
18	NPL P	A	Lancaster City	688	W 2 - 1	Gilchrist 11 70	1	31
25	NPL P	H	Witton Albion	1856	L 1 - 2	Gonzales 45	1	32
Feb 1	NPL P	A	Stalybridge Celtic	471	D 2 - 2	Verstraaten 12 Briggs 61 (pen)	1	33
4	NPL P	A	Morpeth	1704	D 1 - 1	Gilchrist 55	1	34
8	NPL P	H	Nantwich Town	2017	L 1 - 4	Gilchrist 72	1	35
15	NPL P	A	Grantham Town	401	W 3 - 1	Mason 12 McHale 74 Gillies 85	1	36
22	NPL P	H	Buxton	1508	D 1 - 1	Lowe 30	1	37
29	NPL P	A	Gainsborough Trinity	712	W 4 - 1	Osei 9 Lowe 34 Morse 70 Gillies 80	1	38
Mar 7	NPL P	A	Bamber Bridge	453	W 2 - 1	Gillies 61 Gilchrist 74	1	39
10	NPL P	A	Nantwich Town	498	W 1 - 0	Mumba 47	1	40
14	NPL P	H	FC United of Manchester	3274	W 5 - 3	Gilchrist 21 41 Gillies 41 Lowe 52 Mumba 89	1	41

GOALSCORERS	SG	CSG	Pens	Hat tricks	Total		SG	CSG	Pens	Hat tricks	Total
Gilchrist	14	4			20	Thurston	2				2
Briggs	8	3	6		10	Adams	1				1
Lowe	7				7	Baxter	1				1
Gillies	6				6	Gillies	1				1
Shaw	6	4			6	Hunter	1				1
Mason	5		1		5	Jenkins	1				1
Brown	3				3	McHale	1				1
Foley	2				3	Odelusi	1				1
Gonzales	2				3	Turnbull	1				1
Morse	2				2	Verstraten	1				1
Mumba	2				2						

STAFFORD RANGERS MATCH RESULTS 2019-20

Date	Comp	H/A	Opponents	Att:	Result	Goalscorers	Pos	No.
Aug 17	NPL P	A	Lancaster City	362	L 1 - 2	Garnett 85		1
20	NPL P	H	Grantham Town	564	D 1 - 1	Burns 25		2
24	NPL P	H	Matlock Town	486	L 0 - 1		19	3
26	NPL P	A	Mickleover Sports	355	L 0 - 1		20	4
31	NPL P	A	Hyde United	455	L 0 - 4		22	5
Sept 3	NPL P	H	Basford United	481	D 0 - 0		22	6
7	FAC1Q	H	Mickleover Sports	519	W 3 - 0	Briscoe 53 Jones 79 Garnett 90		7
14	NPL P	H	FC United of Manchester	936	D 0 - 0		21	8
21	FAC2Q	A	Kidderminster Harriers	950	D 0 - 0			9
28	FAC2Qr	H	Kidderminster Harriers	663	W 3 - 0	Burns 28 Green 41 Charles 87 (pen)		10
28	NPL P	A	Morpeth Town	517	D 1 - 1	Berks 10	21	11
Oct 5	FAC3Q	A	Stourbridge	1048	L 1 - 2	Charles 45		12
8	NPL P	H	Witton Albion	453	D 1 - 1	Charles 49 (pen)	21	13
12	NPL P	A	Scarborough Athletic	1027	D 1 - 1	Grayson 65	21	14
15	NPL P	A	Stalybridge Celtic	292	W 3 - 0	Dawes 7 Berks 43 Grayson 61	20	15
19	NPL P	A	Basford United	289	L 1 - 3	Grayson 9	20	16
26	FAT1Q	A	Sutton Coldfield Town	196	L 1 - 2	Grayson 51		17
Nov 2	NPL P	A	Bamber Bridge	364	L 0 - 2		20	18
9	NPL P	A	Warrington Town	374	L 1 - 2	Bignot 54	20	19
16	NPL P	H	South Shields	625	L 1 - 2	Sherratt 60	22	20
23	NPL P	H	Hyde United	493	L 1 - 3	Sherratt 22	22	21
Dec 7	NPL P	H	Radcliffe	425	W 2 - 0	Charles 3 75 (pen)	22	22
14	NPL P	H	Lancaster City	454	L 0 - 3		22	23
26	NPL P	A	Nantwich Town	508	L 1 - 2	Grayson 66	22	24
Jan 1	NPL P	H	Mickleover Sports	591	L 0 - 1		22	25
4	NPL P	A	Grantham Town	233	L 0 - 2		22	26
11	NPL P	A	Ashton United	220	L 1 - 2	Green 27	22	27
18	NPL P	H	Warrington Town	543	D 2 - 2	Charles 71 Grayson 73	22	28
25	NPL P	H	Scarborough Athletic	573	W 1 - 0	Charles 70	22	29
Feb 1	NPL P	A	Witton Albion	338	D 2 - 2	Diau 38 Moran 67	22	30
4	NPL P	H	Buxton	403	D 0 - 0		22	31
8	NPL P	H	Stalybridge Celtic	518	D 1 - 1	Fojticek 33 (og)	22	32
15	NPL P	A	Whitby Town	299	L 1 - 2	Diau 80	22	33
18	NPL P	A	FC United of Manchester	1336	L 1 - 2	Moran 55	22	34
21	NPL P	A	Morpeth Town	407	L 0 - 2		22	35
29	NPL P	A	Buxton	453	L 1 - 5	Hill 52	22	36
Mar 7	NPL P	H	Whitby Town	349	W 2 - 1	Harvey 16 Charles 86	22	37
10	NPL P	H	Gainsborough Trinty	323	D 2 - 2	Charles 12 90 (pen)	22	38

GOALSCORERS	SG	CSG	Pens	Hat tricks	Total		SG	CSG	Pens	Hat tricks	Total
Charles	8		4		10	Broscoe	1				1
Grayson	5	3			5	Dawes	1				1
Berks	2				2	Grayson	1				1
Burns	2				2	Harvey	1				1
Diau	2				2	Hill	1				1
Garnett	2				2	Jones	1				1
Green	2				2	Opponents	1				1
Moran	2				2						
Sherratt	2				2						
Bignot	1				1						

STALYBRIDGE CELTIC MATCH RESULTS 2019-20

Date	Comp	H/A	Opponents	Att:	Result	Goalscorers	Pos	No.
Aug 17	NPL P	A	Mickleover Sports	368	L 0 - 1			1
20	NPL P	H	Scarborough Athletic	355	W 5 - 1	Hobson 9 49 Mantack 29 Walker 69 McDevitt 90	13	2
24	FACP	H	West Didsbury & Chorlton	352	D 0 - 0		10	3
26	NPL P	A	Ashton United	382	W 2 - 0	Bakkor 13 (pen) Hobson 59	8	4
31	NPL P	A	Buxton	400	D 0 - 0		9	5
Sept 7	FAC1Q	H	Marine	294	L 0 - 2			6
9	NPL P	A	Basford United	266	L 0 - 3		12	7
14	NPL P	H	Atherton Colliers	269	L 1 - 2	Bakkor 56	13	8
21	NPL P	H	Radcliffe	266	L 1 - 3	Dent 41	13	9
24	NPL P	H	Grantham Town	146	W 3 - 2	Hobson 45 Osei 59 83	11	10
28	NPL P	A	Witton Albion	326	W 1 - 0	Hobson 56	10	11
Oct 5	NPL P	H	FC United of Manchester	1188	L 2 - 3	Osei 2 81	12	12
8	NPL P	A	South Shields	1407	L 1 - 2	Smalley 75	13	13
12	NPL P	H	Bamber Bridge	322	W 3 - 2	Osie 3 Valantine 61 Hobson 72	12	14
15	NPL P	H	Stafford Rangers	292	L 0 - 3		13	15
19	NPL P	A	Warrington Town	454	W 2 - 1	Ustabasi 10 Kengni 8	11	16
29	FAT1Q	H	South Shields	203	L 0 - 2			17
Nov 2	NPL P	H	Radcliffe	262	L 0 - 1		12	18
9	NPL P	A	Bamber Bridge	241	W 3 - 2	Osei 64 77 Hobson 79	7	19
16	NPL P	A	Matlock Town	463	W 1 - 0	Whitehead 54	5	20
23	NPL P	H	Buxton	423	W 2 - 0	Dent 10 Osei 48	5	21
Dec 7	NPL P	H	Whitby Town	290	W 2 - 1	Smalley 18 Osei 57	5	22
14	NPL P	A	Lancaster City	208	D 0 - 0		5	23
21	NPL P	H	Mickleover Sports	323	L 1 - 3	Osei 28	6	24
435	NPL P	A	Hyde United	900	W 2 - 1	Ustabasi 11 Bakkor 34	6	25
Jan 1	NPL P	H	Ashton United	435	D 0 - 0		5	26
4	NPL P	A	Scarborough Athletic	963	D 1 - 1	Osei 42	5	27
11	NPL P	A	Atherton Colleries	371	L 0 - 3		6	28
18	NPL P	H	Basford United	343	L 2 - 3	Ustabasi 38 Osei 45	6	29
25	NPL P	A	Nantwich Town	314	L 0 - 2		8	30
Feb 1	NPL P	H	South Shields	471	D 2 - 2	Osiei 22 (pen) 83	8	31
4	NPL P	H	Gainborough Trinity	245	L 1 - 2	O'Reilly 33	8	32
8	NPL P	A	Stafford Rangers	518	D 1 - 1	Hobson 58	8	33
15	NPL P	A	Gainsborough Trinity	457	W 3 - 1	Lacey 8 (pen) Ustabasi 56 Bakkor 90	6	34
29	NPL P	A	Grantham Town	269	L 0 - 2		9	35
Mar 7	NPL P	H	Warrington Town	385	L 0 - 2		12	36

GOALSCORERS	SG	CSG	Pens	Hat tricks	Total		SG	CSG	Pens	Hat tricks	Total
Osie	10		1		14	O'Reilly	1				1
Hobson	7				8	Valantine	1				1
Bakkor	4		1		4	Walker	1				1
Ustabasi	4				4	Whitehead	1				1
Dent	2				2						
Smalley	2				2						
Kengni	1				1						
Lacey	1				1						
Mantack	1				1						
McDevitt	1				1						

WARRINGTON TOWN MATCH RESULTS 2019-20

Date	Comp	H/A	Opponents	Att:	Result	Goalscorers	Pos	No.
Aug 17	NPL P	H	Morpeth Town	447	L 1 - 3	Roberts 66		1
20	NPL P	A	Atherton Collieries	645	W 4 - 2	Mackreth 27 (pen) Gray 30 Barnes 44 Chadwick 60		2
24	NPL P	A	Gainsborough Trinity	508	D 0 - 0			3
26	NPL P	H	Bamber Bridge	402	W 3 - 1	Garrity 9 54 Chadwick 39	4	4
31	NPL P	H	Mickleover Sports	355	D 1 - 1	Chadwick 27 (pen)	5	5
Sept 3	NPL P	A	Nantwich Town	406	W 3 - 1	Raven 36 Chadwick 65 (pen) Amis 89	5	6
7	FAC1Q	H	City of Liverpool	602	D 2 - 2	Dixon 44 Amis 90		7
10	FAC1Qr	A	City of Liverpool	1099	W 4 - 0	Byrne 1 Roberts 27 Garrity 45 Gray 71		8
14	NPL P	A	Radcliffe	396	D 1 - 1	Gray 60	4	9
21	FAC2Q	A	FC United of Manchester	1263	W 2 - 1	Duggan 28 Roberts 70		10
24	NPL P	H	FC United of Manchester	702	L 0 - 1		6	11
28	NPL P	A	Scarborough Athletic	845	D 1 - 1	Sephton 20	7	12
Oct 5	FAC3Q	A	Brackley Town	452	L 0 - 2			13
8	NPL P	H	Lancaster City	338	D 2 - 2	Raven 8 Garrity 25	7	14
12	NPL P	A	Whitby Town	532	W 1 - 0	Gray 78	6	15
15	NPL P	A	Matlock Town	380	W 2 - 1	Garrity 50 Mackreth 52 (pen)	5	16
19	NPL P	H	Stalybridge Celtic	454	L 1 - 2	Garrity 90	4	17
26	FAT1Q	H	Ashton United	127	L 0 - 1			18
Nov 2	NPL P	H	Hyde United	385	W 4 - 1	Gray 20 80 Dixon 40 Garrity 56	4	19
9	NPL P	H	Stafford Rangers	374	W 2 - 1	Garrity 71 Gray 88	4	20
30	NPL P	H	Nantwich Town	512	W 3 - 1	Roberts 4 Garrity 9 Dixon 564	3	21
Dec 7	NPL P	A	South Shields	1589	D 1 - 1	Garrity 21	3	22
14	NPL P	H	Basford United	336	D 1 - 1	Dunn 34	3	23
21	NPL P	A	Morpeth Town	410	L 0 - 4		4	24
26	NPL P	H	Witton Albion	501	D 1 - 1	Roberts 20	7	25
Jan 1	NPL P	A	Bamber Bridge	386	D 3 - 3	Dunn 30 Mackreth 33 Gray 90	6	26
4	NPL P	H	Atherton Collieries	507	D 1 - 1	Garrity 29	6	27
7	NPL P	H	Radcliffe	449	W 1 - 0	Buckley 29	5	28
14	NPL P	A	Stafford Rangers	543	D 2 - 2	Gray 55 Amis 90	5	29
21	NPL P	H	Whitby Town	504	W 2 - 1	Raven 49 Dixon 89	5	30
Feb 1	NPL P	A	Lancaster City	264	L 1 - 2	Mackreth 10	5	31
18	NPL P	H	Grantham Town	263	D 3 - 3	Brown 26 74 (pen) Amis 63	6	32
21	NPL P	H	Scarborough Athletic	511	W 2 - 0	Amis 15 Mackreth 90	6	33
29	NPL P	A	FC United of Manchester	2088	D 4 - 4	Buckley 41 45 Mackreth 54 Roberts 71	6	34
Mar 3	NPL P	A	Ashton United	202	D 1 - 1	Gray 84	6	35
7	NPL P	A	Stalybridge Celtic	385	W 2 - 0	Buckley 47 Amis 90	5	36
10	NPL P	H	Matlock Town	308	W 3 - 2	Buckley 76 Roberts 86 Warren 90	3	37

GOALSCORERS	SG	CSG	Pens	Hat tricks	Total		SG	CSG	Pens	Hat tricks	Total
Garrity	10	3			11	Dunn	2				2
Gray	9				10	Barnes	1				1
Roberts	7				7	Byrne	1				1
Amis	6				6	Duggan	1				1
Mackreth	6		2		6	Sephton	1				1
Buckley	4				5	Warren	1				1
Chadwick	4	3	2		4						
Dixon	4				4						
Raven	3				3						
Brown	1				2						

WHITBY TOWN MATCH RESULTS 2019-20

Date	Comp	H/A	Opponents	Att	Result	Goalscorers	Pos	No.
Aug 17	NPL P	H	Witton Albion	373	D 1 - 1	Tymon 47		1
20	NPL P	A	Gainsborough Trinity	415	L 0 - 2			2
24	NPL P	A	Buxton	335	W 4 - 3	Fewster 17 20 Tymon 49 Rowe 81	11	3
26	NPL P	H	Morpeth Town	458	W 2 - 1	Bythway 19 Fewster 78 (pen)	7	4
31	NPL P	A	Grantham Town	281	W 4 - 0	Wearmouth 5 Fewster 18 39 Rowe 57	4	5
Sept 3	NPL P	H	Scarborough Athletic	1038	W 2 - 0	Weledji 49 Fewster 79	4	6
7	FAC1Q	A	Widnes	153	W 4 - 0	Fewster 9 Rowe 56 Dixon 85 Hopson 88 (pen)		7
14	NPL P	H	Hyde United	462	W 2 - 0	Hopson 71 Fewster 75	8	8
21	FAC2Q	A	1874 Northwich	397	W 1 - 0	Fewster 19		9
24	NPL P	A	Ashton United	144	W 1 - 0	Hopson 27 (pen)	2	10
28	NPL P	H	Matlock Town	464	L 0 - 3		2	11
Oct 5	FAC3Q	H	Gloucester City	581	D 1 - 1	Jackson 90		12
7	FAC3Qr	A	Goucester City	273	W 3 - 1	Weledji 25 50 Gell 86		13
12	NPL P	H	Warrington Town	532	L 0 - 1		7	14
19	FAC4Q	H	Stourbridge	1171	D 1 - 1	Tymon 80		15
21	FAC4Qr	A	Stourbridge	1092	L 2 - 3	Tynon 12 Gell 38		16
29	FAT1Q	H	Worksop Town	443	W 4 - 1	Tymon 34 86 Hackett 41 (pen) Bell 74		17
Nov 2	NPL P	H	Nantwich Town	407	D 3 - 3	Wearmouth 73 Hackett 80 (pen) 87 (pen)	8	18
9	FAT2Q	A	Peterborough Sports	202	L 0 - 2			19
16	NPL P	A	Basford United	382	D 3 - 3	Tymon 7 Wearmouth 68 Rowe 90	11	20
30	NPL P	A	Scarborough Athletic	1358	L 1 - 2	Bell 75	12	21
Dec 7	NPL P	A	Stalybridge Celtic	290	L 1 - 2	White 85	13	22
14	NPL P	H	Bamber Bridge	364	L 0 - 1		13	23
21	NPL P	A	Witton Albion	348	W 3 - 2	Hackett 23 (pen) Blackett 35 Roper 38	12	24
26	NPL P	H	South Shields	879	W 2 - 1	Blackett 5 White 67	13	25
Jan 4	NPL P	H	Gainsborough Trinity	462	D 2 - 2	Blackett 45 Hackett 85 (pen)	13	26
11	NPL P	A	Hyde United	291	W 2 - 0	Rowe 32 Blackett 90	13	27
18	NPL P	H	F.C.United of Manchester	963	L 1 - 2	Blackett 68 (pen)	13	28
25	NPL P	A	Warrington Town	504	L 1 - 2	Blackett 46	13	29
Feb 1	NPL P	H	Atherton Colleries	330	W 3 - 1	Gell 5 Hopson 41 (pen) Patton 49	14	30
8	NPL P	A	Mickleover Sports	304	W 3 - 1	Patton 35 83 Blackett 52	11	31
15	NPL P	H	Stafford Rangers	299	W 2 - 1	Tymon 27 Blackett 40 (pen)	9	32
22	NPL P	A	Matlock Town	460	W 2 - 0	White 22 Fewster 82	8	33
25	NPL P	A	Lancaster City	305	W 3 - 1	Tymon 19 71 Patton 90	7	34
29	NPL P	H	Ashton United	394	D 1 - 1	Fewster 1	7	35
Mar 3	NPL P	H	Mickleover Sports	290	D 1 - 1	Lowe 59	7	36
7	NPL P	A	Stafford Rangers	349	L 1 - 2	Weledji 14	7	37
10	NPL P	H	Grantham Town	288	D 1 - 1	Gell 67	7	38
14	NPL P	A	Radcliffe	480	D 2 - 2	Sukar 48 Blackett 57 (pen)	7	39

GOALSCORERS	SG	CSG	Pens	Hat tricks	Total		SG	CSG	Pens	Hat tricks	Total
Fewster	9	7	1		11	White	3				3
Tymon	8	3			10	Bell	2				2
Blackett	9	5	2		9	Bythway	1				1
Hackett	5		5		5	Dixon	1				1
Rowe	5				5	Jackson	1				1
Gell	4				4	Lowe	1				1
Hopson	4		2		4	Roper	1				1
Patton	3				4	Sukar	1				1
Weledji	3				4						
Wearmouth	3				3						

WITTON ALBION MATCH RESULTS 2019-20

Date	Comp	H/A	Opponents	Att:	Result	Goalscorers	Pos	No.
Aug 17	NPL P	A	Whitby Town	373	D	1 - 1	McKenna 21 (pen)		1
20	NPL P	H	Mickleover Sports	284	W	1 - 0	McKenna 70	9	2
26	NPL P	A	Nantwich Town	505	L	0 - 3		15	3
31	NPL P	A	Scarborough Town	891	D	0 - 0		14	4
Sept 3	NPL P	H	Hyde United	336	W	2 - 0	Short 11 McKenna 84	14	5
7	FAC1Q	A	**Seaham Red Star**	272	L	0 - 1			6
14	NPL P	H	Gainsborough Trinity	288	W	1 - 0	Goulding 77	8	7
21	FAC2Q	A	**Belper Town**	503	D	0 - 0	(aet)		8
24	FAC2Qr	H	**Belper Town**	279	L	0 - 1			9
28	NPL P	H	Stalybridge	326	L	0 - 1		12	10
Oct 1	NPL P	H	Lancaster City	203	L	1 - 3	Goulding 48	13	11
5	NPL P	A	Bamber Bridge	278	D	1 - 1	Smart 27	13	12
8	NPL P	A	Stafford Rangers	453	D	1 - 1	Jones 64	13	13
12	NPL P	H	South Shields	448	W	3 - 1	McKenna 34 (pen) Jones 63 Heath 67	13	14
15	NPL P	H	Ashton United	299	W	1 - 0	Lingouba 90	11	15
19	NPL P	A	Buxton	417	L	0 - 2		10	16
26	FAT1Q	H	**Lancaster City**	288	L	0 - 1			17
Nov 9	NPL P	A	Mickleover Sports	162	W	4 - 1	Baldwin 4 McKenna 40 87 Jones 41	9	18
16	NPL P	H	FC United of Manchester	933	D	3 - 3	Sambor 69 84 Smart 90	9	19
23	NPL P	H	Scarborough Athletic	333	W	3 - 1	Smart 16 Jones 62 Anson 77 (pen)	7	20
30	NPL P	A	Hyde United	432	D	0 - 0		7	21
Dec 7	NPL P	H	Grantham Town	263	W	3 - 1	Sambor 19 McKenna 30 Owens 90	6	22
14	NPL P	A	Radcliffe	263	L	0 - 1		7	23
21	NPL P	H	Whitby Town	348	L	2 - 3	Jones 34 Goulding 90	8	24
26	NPL P	A	Warringrton Town	501	D	1 - 1	Foley 27 (pen)	9	25
Jan 1	NPL P	H	Nantwich Town	535	L	1 - 2	Mitchley 24	10	26
4	NPL P	H	Buxton	313	L	0 - 2		12	27
11	NPL P	A	Gainsborough Trinity	473	L	1 - 3	Owens 22	12	28
18	NPL P	H	Atherton Colleries	963	W	2 - 1	Mitchley 39 Jones 46	10	29
25	NPL P	A	South Shields	1856	W	2 - 1	Monaghan 90 Sambor 90	7	30
27	NPL P	A	Basford United	260	L	0 - 2		7	31
Feb 1	NPL P	H	Stafford Rangers	338	D	2 - 2	Smart 25 54	8	32
8	NPL P	A	Ashton United	215	L	1 - 3	Owens 8	10	33
Mar 8	NPL P	A	Morpeth Town	571	L	2 - 3	Baldwin 27 Hooper 56	14	34
11	NPL P	A	Lancaster City	398	D	1 - 1	Foley 72	14	35

GOALSCORERS	SG	CSG	Pens	Hat tricks	Total		SG	CSG	Pens	Hat tricks	Total
McKenna	6	2	2		7	Heath	1				1
Jones	6	2			6	Hooper	1				1
Smart	4	2			5	Lingouba	1				1
Sambor	3				4	Monaghan	1				1
Goulding	3				3	Short	1				1
Owens	3				3						
Baldwin	2				2						
Foley	2		1		2						
Mitchley	2				2						
Anson	1		1		1						

SOUTHERN LEAGUE LEAGUE
PREMIER DIVISION CENTRAL 2019-20

		P	W	D	L	F	A	GD	Pts
1	Peterborough Sports	33	19	8	6	90	46	44	65
2	Tamworth	30	21	2	7	63	27	36	65
3	Royston Town	30	19	6	5	62	28	34	63
4	Bromsgrove Sporting	32	17	6	9	80	43	37	57
5	Rushall Olympic	33	15	8	10	58	43	15	53
6	Stourbridge	32	16	5	11	53	52	1	53
7	Banbury United	32	14	10	8	48	31	17	52
8	Coalville Town	30	14	9	7	51	32	19	51
9	Nuneaton Borough	33	14	8	11	57	46	11	50
10	Kings Langley	30	15	5	10	51	41	10	50
11	AFC Rushden & Diamonds	30	14	7	9	50	45	5	49
12	Barwell	32	14	6	12	58	54	4	48
13	Needham Market	33	13	9	11	43	40	3	48
14	Hednesford Town	32	14	5	13	50	44	6	47
15	Biggleswade Town	30	13	4	13	45	46	-1	43
16	Lowestoft Town	33	13	2	18	48	62	-14	41
17	Hitchin Town	32	10	9	13	43	49	-6	39
18	Stratford Town	33	8	4	21	42	74	-32	28
19	Leiston	32	6	8	18	39	87	-48	26
20	St Ives Town	33	6	5	22	33	76	-43	23
21	Alvechurch	30	4	5	21	25	58	-33	17
22	Redditch United	33	3	3	27	24	89	-65	12

		1	2	3	4	5	6	7	8	9	10	11	12	13	14	15	16	17	18	19	20	21	22
1	Alvechurch			2-2	1-1	1-4		0-1	5-0	1-0		0-0		1-2	0-2	2-2	1-2	0-2	0-1		0-3		0-2
2	Banbury United	2-1		2-1	3-2	0-1	1-1		0-0	1-0	1-2			4-2	1-1	0-2	2-1	4-2	2-0		2-0	5-0	0-1
3	Barwell	2-1	2-1		3-1	1-3		4-4		1-0	3-1	5-0	0-3	1-0	0-1	2-0	0-2		3-2	0-0			1-2
4	Biggleswade Town					2-4		1-0	2-0	2-0			3-0		2-0	0-3	3-1	3-1	0-5		1-2	0-1	2-1
5	Bromsgrove Sporting		0-2	1-4	1-1		0-3	4-0	1-2	3-2	4-1		6-0	0-1	1-3		0-0	7-1	1-1	1-1	4-1		1-0
6	Coalville Town		1-1	4-1	2-0	2-2		2-1	1-2	1-2	3-0	1-1		0-1	5-3	1-2	1-0		1-4	2-0		1-1	
7	Hednesford Town	3-0	2-0			0-1			4-2		1-3		2-1	0-1	0-3	3-3	1-1	4-0	4-1		1-2	1-0	0-3
8	Hitchin Town	3-1	0-0	4-1		2-2	1-0			0-1		1-3	0-0	1-1	0-2	1-1			1-2	1-2	2-0	0-3
9	(St) Ives Town			0-3		1-2	1-1	0-3		2-1	1-0	2-5		2-0	0-3	3-4	2-1	0-4	2-4	0-2	2-2	1-1
10	Kings Langley			1-1	2-1	3-1		0-2	3-1			1-2		2-2	2-0	2-2	1-0		0-1	4-0	1-4	1-0
11	Leiston	1-2	1-5	1-1	0-4	0-8	1-1	0-3	3-1	4-4	0-4			2-1	1-1	2-4	2-3			2-2	0-1		1-2
12	Lowestoft Town	4-0	0-0	3-2	2-1	0-1	2-1	0-2		1-0	2-1	1-3		0-2	0-2		6-0	0-1	0-0	2-1	2-0	
13	Needham Market	1-1	0-1	2-3	0-1	0-3		4-3	1-1	1-1		3-0	1-0		1-3	2-1		2-2		1-1	3-3	1-0
14	Nuneaton Borough	3-2	2-2	3-1	2-2		0-0			4-0	0-3		4-1	1-0		0-3	0-1	3-0	2-2	1-3	4-0	2-0	
15	Peterborough Sports	3-0	1-3	5-4	1-1	3-2			0-4	5-0	2-2	8-1	3-1	0-0	2-1			7-0		1-1	2-2	6-0	4-2
16	Rushden & Diamonds		2-1	3-1		2-8	0-3	1-1		1-0		5-1	3-0	1-2	2-0			3-0	1-1		3-2	4-2	
17	Redditch United	2-3	0-0	0-1	0-2		2-3	0-1	0-2	0-1	0-2	0-6	5-3	0-3	3-2		1-1		0-3		0-2	0-2	
18	Royston Town	3-0	1-0		3-0		1-1	1-0	1-1	5-0		0-0	5-1	1-0		4-1		2-1		2-1	3-1	3-2	1-2
19	Rushall Olympic	2-0	1-1	0-1	3-2		0-2	1-0	4-2	4-3	0-1	6-0	4-1			0-2	1-1	3-1	1-3		2-0	4-1
20	Stourbridge	1-0	1-1	1-1		2-1	1-1	0-3	1-2	3-1	1-3	5-1	2-0		1-6		1-0		2-1		3-1
21	Stratford Town	2-0		1-5	1-2	1-2	1-4	4-1	3-3		3-3	3-1	0-3	2-1		3-1	2-0		1-2	1-2		1-3
22	Tamworth	2-0		4-0	1-3		0-1	1-0	3-0	2-0	1-2	4-1	1-2	3-3	3-1	3-0	3-0	2-0	2-1		4-1	

PREMIER DIVISION SOUTH 2019-20

		P	W	D	L	F	A	GD	Pts
1	Truro City	31	21	4	6	65	30	35	67
2	Chesham United	33	21	3	9	70	44	26	66
3	Hayes & Yeading United	32	17	6	9	65	42	23	57
4	Swindon Supermarine	32	17	6	9	50	41	9	57
5	Tiverton Town	29	16	7	6	69	41	28	55
6	Taunton Town	31	15	8	8	63	53	10	53
7	Salisbury	30	14	9	7	57	42	15	51
8	Gosport Borough	33	13	10	10	35	32	3	49
9	Poole Town	27	14	6	7	46	28	18	48
10	Weston-super-Mare	29	13	6	10	54	45	9	45
11	Metropolitan Police	30	13	4	13	46	48	-2	43
12	Farnborough	30	13	3	14	41	43	-2	42
13	Merthyr Town	31	9	11	11	37	37	0	38
14	Hendon	31	10	8	13	47	51	-4	38
15	Wimborne Town	33	10	7	16	39	52	-13	37
16	Hartley Wintney	27	10	6	11	38	39	-1	36
17	Harrow Borough	34	9	9	16	44	62	-18	36
18	Blackfield & Langley	31	8	9	14	33	50	-17	33
19	Yate Town	31	8	5	18	38	56	-18	29
20	Walton Casuals	33	7	6	20	40	71	-31	27
21	Beaconsfield Town	32	6	7	19	29	54	-25	25
22	Dorchester Town	32	4	6	22	36	81	-45	18

		1	2	3	4	5	6	7	8	9	10	11	12	13	14	15	16	17	18	19	20	21	22
1	Beaconsfield Town		2-0	1-3	3-1	1-3	0-1		1-2	2-3		1-2	0-0	2-1		0-0		4-0	0-1	0-4	1-2	2-2	1-1
2	Blackfield & Langley	0-1		0-2	2-1	2-0	0-0	2-0	0-0			2-2	3-4	0-0	1-1			0-1	0-2	1-0	2-2	2-1	2-0
3	Chesham United	3-0	2-1		6-3	2-0	3-0	1-1	1-2	3-2	2-1		2-0	2-1	2-0	1-2	1-1		2-1	1-0			4-2
4	Dorchester Town	1-0	2-2					1-2	2-3	2-3	0-3	0-3	0-0	0-1	0-5	1-1	2-2	1-5	2-3	1-0	2-2	1-2	2-0
5	Farnborough	2-0	1-1		3-1			0-1	1-1		0-1	4-0		1-0	1-4	0-0	0-1	4-0	0-7	0-2	2-1	2-1	4-0
6	Gosport Borough	0-0		2-1	4-4			1-0	0-1	1-1	1-0	2-1	2-2	0-2	0-0		3-0		1-0		2-1	1-0	1-1
7	Harrow Borough	1-2	3-1	2-2			0-2		1-4	3-2		1-2	1-0	0-0	2-2	2-3	1-1	1-5	1-2	0-1	2-0	0-4	
8	Hartley Wintney			1-2	2-0		0-0	1-1		1-5				3-0		1-2		1-4		2-2	1-0		
9	Hayes & Yeading United	1-1	6-0		5-0	2-0	2-1	2-3				3-2	0-2		1-2	1-0	1-0	2-2	0-0	0-1	3-1	1-2	2-1
10	Hendon	2-1		3-1	1-3		2-1	0-1	2-2			1-1	2-1	1-3	0-3		1-2	1-4	1-1	2-0	4-0	2-1	
11	Metropolitan Police	3-1	2-0	2-1		1-2	0-0	1-3	0-1		0-3		1-2		3-2	2-3	1-1		0-2	2-2	0-3	2-1	2-0
12	Merthyr Town	0-0	2-0	1-3		2-0	1-0	2-2	3-2	1-2		1-2			1-1	3-1	4-2		3-1	0-2	1-1	2-1	
13	Poole Town	3-1			3-1		3-1					1-1			2-0	0-1	1-2		3-1				3-0
14	Salisbury		1-1	3-2	4-1		1-0	3-1	2-0		2-0	1-3	2-1	2-1		0-2	2-1	2-2	0-3	3-1			3-2
15	Swindon Supermarine		3-0	2-1	1-0	3-2	1-0		3-2	1-1	2-0		2-2	0-1	2-2			1-2		1-3		3-2	3-2
16	Taunton Town	3-0	4-1	3-2		3-1	3-2	3-2		2-1	3-3	4-3			1-1			3-1	2-0	3-0		1-2	0-4
17	Tiverton Town	6-1			2-1		2-3		2-0	2-2		2-1	1-0	0-1	3-3	2-0	3-2				2-2	2-2	0-2
18	Truro City			0-1	3-0	2-1	1-0	4-1	3-4	3-0	2-1	4-0		3-3		1-0	1-1	3-3			5-1	0-2	
19	Wimborne Town	2-0	2-0	1-2	2-1		1-2		0-0		0-2		0-0	2-1	0-2	0-3	0-3	2-2			4-1	2-1	2-0
20	Walton Casuals		2-3	1-6		0-2	1-1	1-2	0-3	2-3	1-1		2-1	0-3	2-1	2-4	1-5	1-3		0-2		2-1	1-1
21	Weston-super-Mare	1-0		1-2	6-0	1-3		1-1	2-1	1-5	2-2			1-1	3-3		3-2	3-2	5-0	1-0			
22	Yate Town		1-4	4-1		0-1		2-1	2-1	0-2	2-2	1-0		1-1	2-4	2-0	4-1		0-3		0-2	1-2	

DIVISION ONE CENTRAL 2019-20

		P	W	D	L	F	A	GD	Pts
1	Berkhamsted	28	20	4	4	69	24	45	64
2	Halesowen Town	27	20	3	4	72	19	53	63
3	Corby Town	28	18	5	5	64	26	38	59
4	Welwyn Garden City	29	15	6	8	59	36	23	51
5	Aylesbury United	29	13	10	6	49	30	19	49
6	Biggleswade	27	13	5	9	44	33	11	44
7	Barton Rovers	29	13	5	11	65	55	10	44
8	Yaxley	29	13	5	11	55	52	3	44
9	Bedworth United	27	13	5	9	46	43	3	44
10	North Leigh	27	13	3	11	50	50	0	42
11	Thame United	27	12	4	11	51	35	16	40
12	Bedford Town FC	29	11	7	11	49	54	-5	40
13	Daventry Town	28	12	4	12	42	48	-6	40
14	Coleshill Town	28	10	6	12	50	47	3	36
15	AFC Dunstable	29	10	4	15	51	54	-3	34
16	Kidlington	28	9	6	13	32	48	-16	33
17	Didcot Town	27	7	4	16	20	44	-24	25
18	St Neots	28	6	3	19	33	59	-26	21
19	Kempston Rovers	28	5	2	21	29	68	-39	17
20	Wantage Town	28	1	1	26	16	121	-105	4

		1	2	3	4	5	6	7	8	9	10	11	12	13	14	15	16	17	18	19	20
1	AFC Dunstable		0-0	4-1	2-3	2-0	0-1	3-2			2-2	3-4	1-4		0-3	1-0	4-3		7-0	2-0	0-3
2	Aylesbury United	3-1		2-1	3-1	2-1	0-0		2-0	0-0		0-0			3-0		2-3	0-0	2-0	0-0	1-1
3	Bedford Town	1-3	2-1		3-3		2-2	3-2	2-3	2-3	2-1	2-1	1-2	2-1	2-0	0-0		4-0	2-0		
4	Bedford United		0-0	1-1		1-1	1-2		1-3	2-2	2-1		3-1	2-0	3-0	1-2	4-5	2-1	6-0		2-1
5	Biggleswade	3-0	2-1				0-5	4-2	2-0	2-0		2-1	0-1		2-1	0-0	3-0		3-1	1-3	3-0
6	Berkhamsted			3-1	4-0				1-0		3-0	4-0	1-0	0-1	4-0	3-1	3-2	3-2	6-0	1-4	
7	Barton Rovers	0-0	2-4	4-2	2-2		1-1		3-0	2-1	2-1	2-0	1-3		5-1	3-0		2-1	4-1		2-3
8	Coleshill Town	1-1	0-6			0-3	2-2			2-1	4-1	5-1	1-1	4-1	1-3		1-2	1-0	7-1	0-0	1-1
9	Corby Town	2-0	5-2		3-0	2-0	3-2	2-1	3-1		1-1		1-1	1-2	2-0			0-2	8-1	1-0	
10	Daventry Town		1-4		0-2	0-2		3-0	1-0	1-3		0-0	0-4	2-1		2-1	2-0	2-3	4-1	2-2	
11	Didcot Town	1-3	1-1		0-0	1-0	2-4	0-3		0-1	0-4			1-0		2-1		2-0		0-1	1-0
12	Halesowen Town	2-0	4-1	3-0	6-0			3-1		1-2	5-0			4-0	4-1	2-0		1-0		0-2	5-0
13	Kempston Rovers	3-2	2-4		1-2	2-4		1-4			0-2	1-0	0-5		1-1	0-2	2-4		4-0	0-3	0-3
14	Kidlington	2-1	1-1	0-1		1-1			0-0	0-1	1-0	1-1	0-0			1-0	3-0	3-0	3-2		3-2
15	(St) Neots Town	2-5	0-1	1-2		1-1	0-1	0-2	3-0	1-3	1-2	1-0		5-1			1-5		5-0		2-5
16	North Leigh		2-1		0-2		1-2	4-2	2-2	0-3		3-0	1-2	2-1				3-2	2-1	1-0	1-1
17	Thame United	2-1		1-2	3-0	2-1	1-2	2-2				1-0		2-1	3-0	6-0	2-2		9-0	2-2	
18	Wantage Town		0-2	1-3		1-4	0-7		0-6	0-8		1-2	0-5			1-0	1-2			1-5	1-1
19	Welwyn Garden City	3-1		1-1	4-2	1-0	1-1	4-1	0-3		2-4			4-2	4-1	7-1	0-1	1-2	2-1		3-2
20	Yaxley	3-2		0-1	3-1	2-2	1-0	4-6	3-2	0-3	1-2		1-2	3-1	4-2	3-2	3-1	1-0			

DIVISION ONE SOUTH 2019-20

		P	W	D	L	F	A	GD	Pts
1	Thatcham Town	27	18	4	5	66	28	38	58
2	Frome Town	28	17	7	4	57	27	30	58
3	Larkhall Athletic	27	14	7	6	45	37	8	49
4	Winchester City	27	14	6	7	53	37	16	48
5	Melksham Town	28	14	5	9	58	51	7	47
6	Cirencester Town	27	14	3	10	58	38	20	45
7	Paulton Rovers	27	13	6	8	61	43	18	45
8	Cinderford Town	26	13	4	9	59	45	14	43
9	Evesham United	28	11	8	9	52	50	2	41
10	Sholing	25	12	2	11	39	33	6	38
11	Bideford	28	10	7	11	49	50	-1	37
12	Slimbridge	26	11	2	13	54	53	1	35
13	Highworth Town	28	8	8	12	36	41	-5	32
14	Willand Rovers	24	10	2	12	32	37	-5	32
15	Bristol Manor Farm	27	8	6	13	31	44	-13	30
16	AFC Totton	27	7	8	12	39	53	-14	29
17	Mangotsfield United	29	8	4	17	46	65	-19	28
18	Moneyfields	25	7	6	12	37	50	-13	27
19	Basingstoke Town	27	5	4	18	34	76	-42	18*
20	Barnstaple Town	27	5	1	21	26	74	-48	16

		1	2	3	4	5	6	7	8	9	10	11	12	13	14	15	16	17	18	19	20
1	Basingstoke Town		3-2	1-3	3-4		1-2			3-2	1-2	2-1	4-2		0-1	1-6			0-2	1-1	1-1
2	Bideford			0-2	3-2	3-0		2-2	2-1	0-0		3-0	1-3	1-0	1-3		4-1	1-1	2-1	2-1	
3	Bristol Manor Farm		2-1		1-2		0-3		0-0	0-0	0-1	0-1	1-0			2-2	0-3	2-3	2-1	3-3	
4	Barnstaple Town	0-2		1-2			0-2	0-2		3-1	3-1	1-3	0-3	0-6	0-0	0-3		1-0		1-6	
5	Cirencester Town	3-2		3-0	2-1		5-3		1-2	0-0	4-0	5-0	5-0	4-1	2-4	2-1		2-1	6-0	3-4	
6	Cinderford Town		1-2	5-1	2-0	3-1		4-3	1-4	1-2		3-1	1-1		2-0		1-2		4-2		3-1
7	Evesham United	3-1	2-2	0-0		0-0	0-4			2-2	1-2	4-0	1-0		1-1		4-3	2-4		1-0	2-0
8	Frome Town	8-0	3-0		3-1	2-1	2-1	1-1		1-1		2-1			2-0	1-0	1-2	3-0	3-0	1-1	2-0
9	Highworth Town	4-2		2-5	2-1	0-1			0-1		1-3		0-3	5-1		1-0	2-0	0-1	1-2		1-3
10	Larkhall Athletic		2-2	3-1		2-1	2-2	3-2	2-2			2-1	2-2	2-0	1-3			2-0	0-0	3-1	3-1
11	Mangotsfield United	1-1	4-2		5-1		1-3	3-5		0-0	2-0				3-1	3-0	3-3	0-4	3-3	2-3	1-2
12	Melksham Town	3-1	2-3	0-0		3-2	3-1	0-1	4-1	1-0		2-1		4-6	2-4	1-4	6-3	1-1	2-2		
13	Moneyfields		0-0		5-2	0-0	1-1	3-1	2-2	1-0		1-0			1-1			1-1	0-3		0-2
14	Paulton United	4-2		4-2	4-0	0-1	3-1	5-3	2-2	3-1	2-2		1-3	3-2		3-4		1-2			
15	Sholing	2-0	3-2	1-0	3-1	3-1		1-2	0-0		1-2	2-4		2-1			3-1	0-2		1-0	1-2
16	Slimbridge	2-0	2-1		4-0	0-3		5-2	1-2	2-4	0-1	4-1	2-4		1-0				5-2	0-1	1-2
17	Thatcham Town	8-0	4-3	1-2	5-1	3-0	2-2			2-0	2-0	0-2	4-3		1-0	1-3			2-0	2-1	
18	Totton	0-0	2-2	1-0		3-4	3-1	2-3	2-2	1-3			1-4	1-1		0-6		1-0		0-0	
19	Willand Rovers	4-1	3-2		1-0		2-1		1-0	0-1	1-0	2-3		7-0		2-0		0-4			
20	Winchester City	5-1		2-0			0-3	1-1		2-2			3-0	3-1	1-1	0-1	3-2		2-1	3-0	

SthD1S - Dean Stamp (Willand) sets up the first goal with Rhodes (Cinderford) looking on. Photo Keith Clayton.

SthD1S - Evesham United v Bristol MF 0-0. Photo Bill Wheatcroft.

SthD1S - Evesham United v Bristol Manor Farm 0-0. Photo Bill Wheatcroft.

THE LEAGUE CUP 2019-20

HOLDERS: STRATFORD TOWN

PRELIMINARY ROUND

Barton Rovers	v	AFC Dunstable	1-2
Basingstoke Town	v	Moneyfields	1-1, 3-5p
Beasconsfield Town	v	Harrow Borough	3-2
Biggleswade	v	Kings Langley	0-1
Lowestoft Town	v	St Ives Town	0-1
Poole Town	v	Wimborne Town	2-4
Rushall Olympic	v	Stourbridge	3-2
Stratford Town	v	Halesowen Town	0-1
Swindon Supermarine	v	Larkhall Athletic	4-1
Tamworth	v	Barwell	3-0
Truro City	v	Tiverton Town	3-1
Welwyn Garden City	v	Hitchin Town	5-0
Kidlington	v	Didcot Town	1-2
Sholing	v	Gosport Borough	5-1
Evesham United	v	Daventry Town	1-1, 4-2p
Highworth Town	v	Mangotsfield United	1-0
Taunton Town	v	Willand Rovers	2-2, 5-4p
AFC Kempston Rovers	v	St Neots Town	0-1
Bedford Town	v	Peterborough Sports	4-4, 5-3p
Leiston	v	Needham Market	1-3

ROUND ONE

Coleshill Town	v	Hednesford Town	0-4
AFC Rushden & Dia	v	Corby Town	3-2
Aylesbury United	v	Chesham United	0-1
Barnstaple Town	v	Truro City	2-5
Bideford	v	Taunton	2-5
Blackfield & Langley	v	AFC Totton	2-1
Bromsgrove Sporting	v	Bedworth United	5-0
Cirencester Town	v	Wantage Town	1-1, 4-3p
Hartley Wintney	v	Thatcham Town	3-4
Kings Langley	v	AFC Dunstable	0-3
Merthyr Town	v	Cinderford Town	1-2
Paulton Rovers	v	Salisbury	4-0
Redditch United	v	Alvechurch	2-1
Sholing	v	Moneyfields	2-1
Tamworth	v	Coalville Town	1-3
Walton Casuals	v	Hendon	0-1
Weston-super-Mare	v	Bristol Manor Farm	1-1, 3-1
Wimborne Town	v	Dorchester Town	0-1
St Ives Town	v	Needham Market	1-2
Yaxley	v	St Neots Town	2-1
Highworth Town	v	Swindon Supermarine	0-4
Slimbridge	v	Yate Town	1-2
Melksham Town	v	Frome Town	1-3
Beaconsfield Town	v	Berkhamsted	2-2, 5-4p
Hayes & Yeading United	v	Metropolitan Police	6-0
North Leigh	v	Banbury United	3-4
Nuneaton Borough	v	Rushall Olympic	3-2
Thame United	v	Didcot Town	0-1
Welwyn Garden City	v	Royston Town	5-3
Winchester City	v	Farnborough	2-0
Biggleswade Town	v	Bedford Town	3-1
Daventry Town	v	Halesowen Town	2-0

ROUND TWO

Biggleswade Town	v	AFC Dunstable	1-3
Chesham United	v	Didcot Town	4-1
Coalville Town	v	Bromsgrove Sporting	2-1
Redditch United	v	Hednesford Town	2-0
Welwyn Garden City	v	Needham Market	1-2
Daventry Town	v	Nuneaton Borough	1-3
Beaconsfield Town	v	Banbury United	1-1, 3-4p
Cirencester Town	v	Yate Town	2-1
AFC Rushden & Dia	v	Yaxley	4-0
Blackfield & Langley	v	Sholing	1-1, 2-4p
Hendon	v	Hayes & Yeading United	2-2, 7-6p
Swindon Supermarine	v	Cinderford Town	6-0
Winchester City	v	Thatcham Town	4-0
Frome Town	v	Dorchester Town	1-1, 4-2p
Taunton Town	v	Truro City	2-2, 12-11p
Paulton Rovers	v	Weston-super-Mare	12-1

ROUND THREE

AFC Dunstable	v	Hendon	0-2
AFC Rushden & Dia	v	Needham Market	1-2
Chesham United	v	Banbury United	2-0
Nuneaton Borough	v	Coalville Town	0-3
Redditch United	v	Circenster Town	0-4
Paulton Rovers	v	Taunton Town	6-3
Swindon Supermarine	v	Frome Town	1-1, 5-6p
Winchester City	v	Sholing	4-0

QUARTER-FINALS

Chesham United	v	Coalville Town	3-0
Needham Market	v	Hendon	5-1
Paulton Rovers	v	Winchester City	0-3
Frome Town	v	Cirencester Town	0-0, 3-4p

SEMI-FINALS

Chesham United	v	Needham Market	1-0
Cirencester Toqn	v	Winchester City	2-1

FINAL (Over two legs)

Cirencester Town	v	Chesham United
Chesham United	v	Cirencester Town

AFC RUSHDEN & DIAMONDS MATCH RESULTS 2019-20

Date	Comp	H/A	Opponents	Att:	Result	Goalscorers	Pos	No.
Aug 10	Sth PC	A	Barwell	337	W 2 - 0	Dolman 52 Ashton 74		1
13	Sth PC	H	Leiston	446	W 5 - 1	Lorraine 44 59 Collard 40 Acquaye 68 Hicks 80		2
17	Sth PC	H	Nuneaton Borough	575	W 2 - 0	McDonald 90 Johnson 90	1	3
24	Sth PC	A	Stratford Town	325	L 1 - 3	Fishwick 90	3	4
26	Sth PC	H	St Ives Town	525	W 1 - 0	Collard 90		5
31	Sth PC	A	Redditch United	315	D 1 - 1	Dove 82	3	6
Sept 7	FAC1Q	A	**Enfield Town**	**501**	L 0 - 1			7
14	Sth PC	H	Royston Town	453	D 1 - 1	Collard 54	5	8
16	Sth PC	H	Hitchin Town	369	D 1 - 1	Ashton 68	6	9
28	Sth PC	A	Hednesford Town	412	D 1 - 1	Acquaye 6	6	10
Oct 5	Sth PC	H	Bromsgrove Town	523	L 2 - 8	Dove 21 Bowen 38	8	11
12	Sth PC	H	Coalville Town	558	L 0 - 3		9	12
15	Sth PC	A	Tamworth	496	D 0 - 0		9	13
19	Sth PC	A	Rushall Olympic	236	D 1 - 1	Dolman 19	9	14
22	Sth PC	H	Banbury United	382	W 2 - 1	Mcleod 5 Roberts 33	8	15
26	FAT1Q	H	**Banbury United**	**315**	D 0 - 0			16
29	FAT1Qr	A	**Banbury United**	**310**	W 2 - 1	**Lorraine Macleod**		17
Nov 2	Sth PC	A	Biggleswade Town	257	L 1 - 3	Hicks 87	10	18
9	FAT2Q	A	**South Shields**	**934**	L 0 - 4			19
16	Sth PC	A	Alvechurch	272	W 2 - 1	Shariff 78 Lorraine 87	10	20
23	Sth PC	H	Lowestoft Town	386	W 3 - 0	Shariff 60 Macleod 72 Slinn 77	7	21
30	Sth PC	H	Stourbridge	446	W 3 - 2	Lorraine 55 Acquaye 57 Ashton 87	7	22
Dec 7	Sth PC	A	Kings Langley	234	L 0 - 1		10	23
21	Sth PC	A	Bromsgrove Sporting	871	D 0 - 0		11	24
Jan 1	Sth PC	A	St Ives Town	377	W 4 - 3	Shariff 27 Kaziboni 50 Reynolds 68 Dolman 77	11	25
4	Sth PC	H	Barwell	496	W 3 - 1	Akubuine 18 Ashton 71 Lorraine 87	11	26
11	Sth PC	H	Leison	275	W 3 - 2	Hutchins 28 (og) Kaziboni 83 Dolman 90	8	27
18	Sth PC	H	Stratford Town	417	W 4 - 2	Akubuine 18 Acquaye 32 Dolman 63 Farrell 69	8	28
21	Sth PC	H	Hednesford Town	327	D 1 - 1	Dove 86	7	29
25	Sth PC	A	Nuneaton Borough	654	W 1 - 0	Farrell (pen) 88	7	30
28	Sth PC	H	Needham Market	318	L 1 - 2	Farrell 33	7	31
Feb 1	Sth PC	H	Redditch United	550	W 3 - 0	Loraine 8 Dolman 26 Shariff 32	5	32
22	Sth PC	A	Coalville Town	305	L 0 - 1		8	33
Mar 7	Sth PC	A	Banbury United	604	L 1 - 2	Gyasi 86	11	34

GOALSCORERS	SG	CSG	Pens	Hat tricks	Total		SG	CSG	Pens	Hat tricks	Total
Lorraine	6				7	Kaziboni	2				2
Dolman	6	2			6	Bowen	1				1
Acquaye	4				4	Fishwik	1				1
Ashton	4				4	Gyasi	1				1
Shariff	4	2			4	Johnson	1				1
Collard	3				3	McDonald	1				1
Dove	3				3	Opponents	1				1
Farrell	3	2	1		3	Reynolds	1				1
Macleod	3				3	Roberts	1				1
Akubuine	2				2	Slinn	1				1
Hicks	2				2						

ALVECHURCH MATCH RESULTS 2019-20

Date	Comp	H/A	Opponents	Att:	Result	Goalscorers	Pos	No.
Aug 10	Sth PC	A	Royston Town	253	L 0 - 3			1
13	Sth PC	H	Barwell	190	D 2 - 2	Rowley 3 Ezewele 43		2
17	Sth PC	H	Hitchin Town	195	W 5 - 0	Morrison 5 Atherton 23 Nesbitt 48 61 74 pen	11	3
24	Sth PC	A	Hednesford Town	440	L 0 - 3		14	4
26	Sth PC	H	Redditch United	403	L 0 - 2		14	5
31	Sth PC	A	Leiston	154	W 2 - 1	Ezewele 28 Knights 40	13	6
Sept 7	FAC1Q	A	Belper Town	329	L 0 - 1			7
14	Sth PC	H	Peterborough Sports	190	D 2 - 2	Monteiro 58 62	14	8
17	Sth PC	A	Stratford Town	201	L 0 - 2		15	9
21	Sth PC	A	Nuneaton Borough	429	L 2 - 3	Roberts 50 Richards 86	17	10
28	Sth PC	H	Biggleswade Town	160	D 1 - 1	Perry 90	18	11
Oct 12	Sth PC	A	Needham Market	302	D 1 - 1	Botfield 72	18	12
29	FAT1Q	A	Peterborough Sports	170	L 0 - 1			13
19	Sth PC	H	St Ives Town	183	W 1 - 0	Roberts 28	18	14
Nov 9	Sth PC	A	Rushall Olympic	304	L 0 - 2		18	15
12	Sth PC	H	Tamworth	447	L 0 - 2		18	16
16	Sth PC	H	AFC Rushden & Diamonds	272	L 1 - 2	Miller 7	19	17
23	Sth PC	A	Banbury United	406	L 1 - 2	Perry 68	19	18
Dec 7	Sth PC	A	Lowestoft	389	L 0 - 4		19	19
26	Sth PC	H	Bromsgrove Sporting	897	L 1 - 4	Perry 7	21	20
Jan 1	Sth PC	A	Redditch United	315	W 3 - 2	Birch 16 Morrison 31 Wright 50	20	21
4	Sth PC	H	Royston Town	178	L 0 - 1		20	22
11	Sth PC	A	Barwell	189	L 1 - 2	Wollacott 5	20	23
18	Sth PC	H	Hednesford Town	223	L 0 - 1		20	24
21	Sth PC	H	Stourbridge	274	L 0 - 3		20	25
25	Sth PC	A	Hitchin Town	324	L 1 - 3	Morrison 23	20	26
Feb 1	Sth PC	H	Leiston	151	D 0 - 0		21	27
4	Sth PC	H	Tamworth	252	L 0 - 2		21	28
8	Sth PC	A	Peterborough Sports	178	L 0 - 3		21	29
15	Sth PC	A	Stourbridge	481	L 0 - 1		21	30
22	Sth PC	H	Needham Market	170	L 1 - 2	Deards 87	21	31
Mar 7	Sth PC	H	Nuneaton Borough	271	L 0 - 2		21	32

GOALSCORERS	SG	CSG	Pens	Hat tricks	Total		SG	CSG	Pens	Hat tricks	Total
Morrison	3				3	Knights	1				1
Nesbitt	1			1	3	Miller	1				1
Perry	3				3	Richards	1				1
Ezewele	2				2	Rowley	1				1
Monteiro	1				2	Wollacott	1				1
Roberts	2				2	Wright	1				1
Atherton	1				1						
Birch	1				1						
Botfield	1				1						
Deards	1				1						

BANBURY UNITED MATCH RESULTS 2019-20

Date	Comp	H/A	Opponents	Att:	Result	Goalscorers	Pos	No.
Aug 10	Sth PC	A	Redditch United	261	D 0 - 0			1
13	Sth PC	H	Nuneaton Borough	457	D 1 - 1	Johnson 80		2
17	Sth PC	H	Royston Town	164	W 2 - 0	Mills 1 Johnson 90	10	3
24	Sth PC	H	Kings Langley	384	L 1 - 2	Gordon 78	12	4
26	Sth PC	H	Barwell	354	W 2 - 1	Rasulo 8 Gordon 90	8	5
31	Sth PC	A	Bromsgrove Sporting	870	W 2 - 9	Gordon 29 Bosio 32	4	6
Sept 3	Sth PC	A	Peterborough Sports	183	W 3 - 1	Dias 8 Mills 38 Gordon 72	1	7
7	FAC1Q	H	Gainsborough Trinity	473	D 2 - 2	Gordon 74 (pen) 90 (pen)		8
10	FAC1Qr	A	Gainsborough Trinity	321	L 0 - 1			9
14	Sth PC	H	Hitchin Town	405	D 0 - 0		4	10
17	Sth PC	A	Hednesford Town	388	L 0 - 2		6	11
28	Sth PC	H	Coalville Town	451	D 1 - 1	Rasulo 7	7	12
Oct 5	Sth PC	A	Needham Market	244	W 1 - 0	Mills 85	5	13
12	Sth PC	A	Stourbridge	1073	D 1 - 1	Mills 50	5	14
19	Sth PC	H	Biggleswade Town	419	W 3 - 1	Gordon 38 90 Rasulo 59	3	15
22	Sth PC	A	AFC Rushden & Diamonds	382	L 1 - 2	Gordon 29	4	16
26	FAT1Q	A	AFC Rushden & Diamonds	315	D 0 - 0			17
29	FAT1Qr	H	AFC Rushden & Diamonds	310	L 1 - 2			18
Nov 2	Sth PC	A	Lowestoft Town	305	D 0 - 0		3	19
9	Sth PC	H	St Ives Town	318	W 1 - 0	Gordon 41	2	20
16	Sth PC	A	Leiston	232	W 5 - 1	Gordon 14 62 66 71 Mills 58	2	21
23	Sth PC	H	Alvechurch	406	W 2 - 1	Rasulo 29 Gordon 87	2	22
30	Sth PC	A	Rushall Olympic	220	D 1 - 1	Fasanmade 66	2	23
Dec 7	Sth PC	H	Tamworth	561	L 0 - 1		2	24
14	Sth PC	A	Coalville Town	181	D 1 - 1	Westbrook 71	3	25
26	Sth PC	H	Stratford Town	411	W 5 - 0	Roberts 26 68 Shamsi 60 Mills 61 Rasulo 90	3	26
Jan 1	Sth PC	A	Barwell	226	L 1 - 2	Shamsi 15	4	27
4	Sth PC	H	Redditch United	446	W 4 - 2	Roberts 8 Shamsi 54 Mills 63 Awadh 75	4	28
11	Sth PC	A	Nuneaton Borough	523	D 2 - 2	Shamsi 14 66	7	29
18	Sth PC	H	Peterborough Sports	443	L 0 - 2		7	30
25	Sth PC	A	Royston Town	338	L 0 - 1		9	31
Feb 1	Sth PC	H	Bromsgrove Rovers	633	L 0 - 1		10	32
8	Sth PC	A	Hitchin Town	360	D 0 - 0		11	33
22	Sth PC	H	Stourbridge	542	W 2 - 0	Shamsi 33 Johnson 70	12	34
Mar 3	Sth PC	H	Needham Market	270	W 4 - 2	Kaziboni 3 Shamsi 33 54 Fairlamb 68	8	35
7	Sth PC	H	AFC Rushden & Diamonds	604	W 2 - 1	Johnson 32 Shamsi 41	7	36

GOALSCORERS	SG	CSG	Pens	Hat tricks	Total		SG	CSG	Pens	Hat tricks	Total
Gordon	10	5	2	1	15	Fasanmade	1				1
Shamsi	6	4			9	Kaziboni	1				1
Mills	7				7	Westbrook	1				1
Rasulo	5				5						
Johnson	4				4						
Roberts	2				3						
Awadh	1				1						
Bosio	1				1						
Diss	1				1						
Fairlamb	1				1						

BARWELL MATCH RESULTS 2019-20

Date	Comp	H/A	Opponents	Att:	Result	Goalscorers	Pos	No.
Aug 10	Sth PC	H	AFC Rushden & Diamonds	337	L 0 - 2			1
13	Sth PC	A	Alvechurch	190	D 2 - 2	Towers 7 Hickey 32		2
17	Sth PC	A	Lowestoft Town	413	L 2 - 3	Hickey 51 Omotola 61		3
24	Sth PC	H	BiggleswadeTown	202	W 3 - 1	Hickey 9 (pen) 83 Hollis 90	15	4
26	Sth PC	A	Banbury United	354	L 1 - 2	Omotola 51	15	5
31	Sth PC	H	Kings Langley	154	W 3 - 1	Brown-Hill 25 Hlckey 62 Omotola 90	12	6
Sept 7	FAC1Q	H	AFC Mansfield	149	W 4 - 1	Brown-Hill Omotola Dunkley Eze		7
14	Sth PC	A	Needham Maeket	190	W 3 - 2	Garnham 45 Omotola 60 78	13	8
17	Sth PC	H	Tamworth	324	L 1 - 2	Evans 69	13	9
21	FAC2Q	A	Hednesford Town	393	L 2 - 3	Omotola 7 Hickey 61		10
28	Sth PC	A	Nuneaton Borough	730	L 1 - 3	Towers 15	15	11
Oct 12	Sth PC	H	Leiston	173	W 5 - 0	Williams 5 Hickey 20 Dunkley 34 Omotola 55 Towers 63	15	12
15	Sth PC	A	Rushall Olympic	239	W 1 - 0	Hickey 41	12	13
19	Sth PC	A	Redditch United	210	W 1 - 0	Omotola 31	9	14
22	Sth PC	H	Bromsgrove Sporting	235	L 1 - 3	Hickey 63	12	15
29	FAT1Q	A	Bromsgrove Sporting	544	W 7 - 2	Dunkley 29 33 Hickey 37 Hollis 77 Evans 75 Towers 80 86	16
Nov 2	Sth PC	H	Hednesford Town	257	D 4 - 4	Hickey 52 Towers 85 Omotola 90 Hollis 90	12	17
12	FAT2Q	H	Redditch United	129	D 3 - 3	Hickey 64 (pen) McAteer 69 Dunkley 89		18
16	Sth PC	H	Royston Town	163	W 3 - 1	Hickey 25 76 (pen) Warner-Eley 64 (og)	8	19
19	FAT2Qr	A	Redditch United	111	L 2 - 3	Omotola 35 Hickey 53		20
30	Sth PC	A	Hitchin Town	348	L 1 - 4	Hollis 34	12	21
Dec 3	Sth PC	A	Stratford Town	121	W 5 - 1	OMOTOLA 3 (26 59 76) Dunkley 59 Williams 71	10	22
7	Sth PC	H	St Ives Town	149	W 1 - 0	Omotola 42	8	23
14	Sth PC	H	Nuneaton Borough	477	L 0 - 1		10	24
21	Sth PC	A	Peterborough Sports	214	L 4 - 5	Hickey 6 51 Williams 58 Hakeem 73	12	25
26	Sth PC	A	Coalville	240	L 1 - 4	Omotola 35	13	26
Jan 1	Sth PC	H	Banbury United	226	W 2 - 1	Omotola 36 Dunkley 61	12	27
4	Sth PC	A	AFC Rushden & Diamonds	496	L 1 - 3	Hakeem 82	12	28
7	Sth PC	H	Peterborough Sports	146	W 2 - 0	Hickey 46 54	12	29
11	Sth PC	H	Alvechurch	189	W 2 - 1	Towers 75 Wilıams 76	11	30
18	Sth PC	H	Lowestoft Town	182	L 0 - 3		13	31
Feb 1	Sth PC	A	Kings Langley	211	D 1 - 1	Minter (og) 30	13	32
3	Sth PC	A	Stourbridge	381	D 1 - 1	Redhead 24	12	33
8	Sth PC	H	Needham Maeket	183	W 1 - 0	Williams 88	12	34
15	Sth PC	H	Rushall Olympic	159	D 0 - 0		12	35
22	Sth PC	A	Leiston	217	D 1 - 1	Williams 34	13	36
Mar 7	Sth PC	A	Bromsgrove Sporting	846	W 4 - 1	Dunckley 26 Williams 53 Hlckey 76 Omotola 83	12	37

GOALSCORERS	SG	CSG	Pens	Hat tricks	Total		SG	CSG	Pens	Hat tricks	Total
Hickey	15	6	3		20	Eze	1				1
Omotola	14	4			18	Garnham	1				1
Williams	7				9	McAteer	1				1
Dunkley	7				8	Redhead	1				1
Towers	6	2			7						
Hollis	4	2			4						
Brown-Hill	2				2						
Evans	2				2						
Hakeem	2				2						
Opponents	2				2						

BIGGLESWADE TOWN MATCH RESULTS 2019-20

Date	Comp	H/A	Opponents	Att:	Result	Goalscorers	Pos	No.
Aug 10	Sth PC	A	Bromsgrove Sporting	837	D 1 - 1	Brooks 8		1
13	Sth PC	H	Royston Town	208	L 0 - 5			2
17	Sth PC	H	St Ives Town	160	W 2 - 0	Lucien 58 Brooks 71 (pen)	14	3
24	Sth PC	A	Barwell	202	L 1 - 3	White 50	17	4
26	Sth PC	H	Peterborough Sports	215	L 0 - 3		17	5
31	Sth PC	H	Stratford Town	192	W 2 - 1	White 45 Brooks 84	16	6
Sept 7	FAC1Q	A	St Neots Town	288	D 2 - 2			7
11	FAC1Qr	H	St Neots Town		W 2 - 0	Marsh 55 (pen) Inskip		8
14	Sth PC	H	Nuneaton Borough	181	W 2 - 8	Marsh-Brown 18 Ball 81	11	9
17	Sth PC	A	Leiston	166	W 4 - 0	Lucien 30 Ball 42 Brooks 68 White 85	9	10
21	FAC 2Q	H	Ware	253	L 1 - 2			11
28	Sth PC	A	Alvechurch	160	D 1 - 1	White 89	10	12
Oct 5	Sth PC	H	Redditch United	150	W 3 - 1	Lucien 38 White 68 Richardson 90	9	13
12	Sth PC	H	Tamworth	260	W 2 - 1	White 3 59	6	14
15	Sth PC	A	Coalville Town	230	L 0 - 2		7	15
19	Sth PC	A	Banbury United	419	L 2 - 3	Milenge 14 Richardson 84	8	16
26	FAT1Q	H	Bedworth United	126	W 2 - 1			17
Nov 2	Sth PC	H	AFC Rushden & Diamonds	257	W 3 - 1	White 24 Sambou 35 Lucien 43	11	18
9	FAT2Q	A	Met Police	123	D 2 - 2			19
19	FAT2Q	H	Met Police	92	W 1 - 0			20
23	FAT3Q	H	Aveley	156	L 1 - 4	Carey-Morrell 81		21
30	Sth PC	H	Hednesford Town	165	W 1 - 0	Charles 66	11	22
Dec 7	Sth PC	A	Needham Market	243	W 1 - 0	Williams 88	10	23
21	Sth PC	A	Redditch United	157	W 2 - 0	Charles 50 Perters 77	9	24
26	Sth PC	H	Hitchin Town	390	W 2 - 0	Richardson 52 Williams 84	8	25
28	Sth PC	H	Stourbridge	202	L 1 - 2	Williams 35	8	26
Jan 1	Sth PC	A	Perterborough Sports	230	D 1 - 1	Ball 17	9	27
4	Sth PC	H	Bromsgrove Sporting	239	L 2 - 4	Lucan 72 85	13	28
7	Sth PC	A	Rushall Olympic	153	L 2 - 3	Bush 16 79	13	29
25	Sth PC	A	St Ives Town	161	W 3 - 0	Edwards 46 61 72	12	30
Feb 1	Sth PC	H	Stratford Town	165	L 0 - 1		12	31
4	Sth PC	A	Kings Langley	153	L 1 - 2	Ball 17	12	32
8	Sth PC	A	Nuneaton Borough	499	D 2 - 2	Edwards 19 (pen) 62	14	33
18	Sth PC	A	Royston Town	293	L 0 - 3		15	34
22	Sth PC	A	Tamworth	601	L 0 - 4		15	35
25	Sth PC	H	Lowestoft Town	75	W 3 - 0	Charles 42 44 Peters 51	15	36
Mar 7	Sth PC	A	Lowestoft Town	370	L 1 - 2	Bell 90	15	37

GOALSCORERS	SG	CSG	Pens	Hat tricks	Total		SG	CSG	Pens	Hat tricks	Total
White	7	3			8	Peters	2				2
Ball	5				5	Carey-Morrell	1				1
Edwards	2		1	1	5	Inskip	1				1
Brooks	4		1		4	Marsh	1		1		1
Charles	3				4	Marsh-Brown	1				1
Lucien	4				4	Milenge	1				1
Richardson	2				3	Sambou	1				1
Williams	3	3			3						
Bush	1				2						
Lucan	1				2						

BROMSGROVE SPORTING MATCH RESULTS 2019-20

Date	Comp	H/A	Opponents	Att:	Result	Goalscorers	Pos	No.
Aug 10	Sth PC	H	Bridgewater Town	837	D 1 - 1	Gregory 45		1
13	Sth PC	A	Tamworth	707	W 3 - 1	Gregory 22 McDonald 38 Perry 90		2
17	Sth PC	A	Coalville Town	332	D 2 - 2	Perry 89 90	8	3
24	**FACP**	**H**	**Leicester Road**	**620**	**W 2 - 1**	**McDonald 1 Dowd 3**	11	4
26	Sth PC	A	Stourbridge	1158	L 1 - 2	McDonald 11	14	5
31	Sth PC	H	Banbury United	870	L 0 - 2		19	6
Sept 7	**FAC1Q**	**H**	**Stourbridge**	**1205**	**L 0 - 1**			7
14	Sth PC	A	Lowestoft Town	398	W 1 - 0	Gregory 71	12	8
17	Sth PC	H	Rushall Olympic	772	D 1 - 1	McDonald 83	16	9
28	Sth PC	H	Needham Market	936	L 0 - 1		16	10
Oct 5	Sth PC	A	AFC Rushden & Diamonds	523	W 8 - 2	Taylor 11 44 82 90 Wilson 34 Hayward 61 Dowd 88 90	12	11
12	Sth PC	A	Hitchin Town	633	D 2 - 2	Gregory 19 (pen) McDonald 80	14	12
15	Sth PC	H	Hednesford Town	845	W 4 - 0	Westwood 20 Hayward 55 Taylor 66 Gregory 84	12	13
19	Sth PC	H	Nuneaton Borough	1172	L 1 - 3	Taylor 13	12	14
22	Sth PC	A	Barwell	235	W 3 - 1	Mills 15 McDonald 53 Taylor 67	12	15
29	**FAT1Q**	**H**	**Barwell**	**544**	**L 2 - 7**			16
Nov 2	Sth PC	A	Leiston	148	W 8 - 0	Mills 3 14 78 Taylor 49 51 66 Shorrock 70 Gregory 71	8	17
16	Sth PC	A	Peterborough Sports	367	L 2 - 3	McDonald 37 Taylor 54	11	18
23	Sth PC	H	St Ives Town	737	W 3 - 2	Higginson 21 Taylor 4 83	8	19
30	Sth PC	H	Royston Town	706	D 1 - 1	Higginson 16	8	20
Dec 3	Sth PC	H	Kings Langley	417	W 4 1	Mills 3 (pen) 30 Taylor 41 McDonald 89 (pen)	4	21
7	Sth PC	A	Stratford Town	422	W 2 - 1	Taylor 13 Broadhurst 67	3	22
14	Sth PC	A	Needham Market	280	W 3 - 0	McDonald 18 41 Gregory 60	2	23
21	Sth PC	H	AFC Rushden & Diamonds	871	D 0 - 0		2	24
26	Sth PC	A	Alvechurch	897	W 4 - 1	Taylor 45 Gregory 48 81 (pen) Quaynor 75	2	25
Jan 1	Sth PC	H	Stourbridge	1730	W 4 - 1	Taylor 23 90 Shorrock 40 Mills 76	2	26
4	Sth PC	A	Biggleswade Town	239	W 4 - 2	Taylor 29 65 71 Gregory 46	2	27
11	Sth PC	H	Tamworth	1764	W 1 - 0	Broadhurst 58	1	28
18	Sth PC	A	Kings Langley	169	L 1 - 3	Gregory 29	1	29
21	Sth PC	H	Redditch United	944	W 7 - 1	Shorrock 2 86 Gregory 41 63 Mills 45 Taylor 64 McDonald 82	1	30
25	Sth PC	H	Coalville Town	1075	L 0 - 3		1	31
Feb 1	Sth PC	A	Banbury United	633	W 1 - 0	Taylor 39	1	32
8	Sth PC	H	Lowestoft Town	1110	W 6 - 0	Gregory 6 13 82 McDonald 34 37 52	2	33
22	Sth PC	H	Hitchiin Town	966	L 1 - 2	Shorrick 74	4	34
Mar	Sth PC	H	Barwell	846	L 1 - 4	Broadhurst 30	4	35

GOALSCORERS	SG	CSG	Pens	Hat tricks	Total		SG	CSG	Pens	Hat tricks	Total
Taylor	14	4		3	23	Quaynor	1				1
Gregory	12	2	2	1	16	Westwood	1				1
McDonald	11	2	1	1	14	Wilson	1				1
Mills	5		1		8						
Shorrock	4				5						
Broadhurst	3				4						
Dowd	2	2			3						
Perry	2				2						
Hayward	2				2						
Higginson	2				2						

COALVILLE TOWN MATCH RESULTS 2019-20

Date	Comp	H/A	Opponents	Att:	Result	Goalscorers	Pos	No.
Aug 10	Sth PC	A	Leiston	218	D 1 - 1	McGurk 79		1
13	Sth PC	H	Hednesford Town	290	W 2 - 1	Dean 15 Duggan 63		2
17	Sth PC	H	Bromsgrove Sporting	332	D 2 - 2	Mitchell 6 McGurk 78	9	3
24	Sth PC	A	Royston Town	245	D 1 - 1	Mitchell 58	9	4
26	Sth PC	H	Nuneaton Town	495	W 5 - 3	Mitchell 11 84 Berridge 13 McGurk Pierpoint 28	7	5
31	Sth PC	A	St Ives Town	154	W 2 - 1	Mitchell 55 McGlinchey 62	6	6
Sept 7	FAC1Q	A	**South Normanton**	129	W 1 - 0	**McGlinchey 85**		7
14	Sth PC	H	Stratford Town	175	D 1 - 1	Dean 83	8	8
17	Sth PC	A	Redditch United	154	W 3 - 2	McGlinchey 12 Dean 61 70	4	9
21	FAC2Q	H	**Stourbridge**	315	L 1 - 2	**Birch 28**		10
28	Sth PC	A	Banbury Uni9ted	451	D 1 - 1	Doyle -Charles 75	5	11
Oct 12	Sth PC	A	AFC Rushden & Diamonds	558	W 3 - 0	Dolman 60 (og) McGlinchey 65 Shaw 90	3	12
15	Sth PC	H	Biggleswade Town	230	W 2 - 0	Berridge 42 Shaw 62	1	13
21	Sth PC	A	Hitchin Town	282	L 0 - 1		4	14
26	FAT1Q	A	**Lowestoft Town**	264	W 4 - 2			15
Nov 9	Sth PC	H	Stratford Town	210	W 4 - 1	McGurk 53 58 (pen) 67 McGlinchey 71	4	16
12	FAT2Q	A	**Nantwich Town**	208	W 1 - 0	**Berridge 90**		17
16	Sth PC	A	Lowestoft Town	406	L 1 - 2	McGurk 45	4	18
23	FAT3Q	A	**Hednesford Town**	354	L 1 - 2			19
26	Sth PC	H	Kings Langley	172	W 3 - 0	McGlinchey 35 Thomas 70 Mitchell 84	4	20
Dac 7	Sth PC	A	Stourbridge	529	D 1 - 1	Shaw 33	5	21
14	Sth PC	H	Banbury United	181	D 1 - 1	McGlinchey 24	6	22
17	Sth PC	H	Peterborough	116	L 1 - 2	Mitchell 37	6	23
21	Sth PC	A	Rushall Olympic	231	W 2 - 0	Berridge 26 59	6	24
26	Sth PC	H	Barwell	240	W 4 - 1	Mitchell 12 50 McAteer (og) McGlinchey 78	5	25
Jan 1	Sth PC	A	Nuneaton Borough	695	D 0 - 0		5	26
4	Sth PC	H	Leiston	174	D 1 - 1	Berridge 34	5	27
11	Sth PC	A	Hednesford Town	365	W 1 - 0	Berridge 73	6	28
18	Sth PC	A	Royston Town	256	L 1 - 4	Bennett 87	6	29
21	Sth PC	H	Rushall Olympic	141	W 2 - 0	McGurk 65 O'Callaghan (og)	5	30
25	Sth PC	A	Bromsgrove sporting	1075	W 3 - 0	Shaw 10 McGlinchey 59 Mitchell 82	4	31
Feb 1	Sth PC	H	St Ives Town	195	L 1 - 2	McGlinchey 36	6	32
11	Sth PC	H	Needham Market	191	L 0 - 1		6	33
22	Sth PC	A	AFC Rushden & Diamonds	305	W 1 - 0	Mitchell 58	5	34
Mar 7	Sth PC	H	Hitchin Town	238	L 1 - 2	Kee 28	8	35

GOALSCORERS	SG	CSG	Pens	Hat tricks	Total		SG	CSG	Pens	Hat tricks	Total
Mitchell	9	4			11	Duggan	1				1
McGlinchey	10	2			10	Kee	1				1
McGurk	6		1		8	Pierpoint	1				1
Berridge	6				7	Thomas	1				1
Dean	3				4						
Shaw	4				4						
Opponents	3				3						
Bennett	1				1						
Birch	1				1						
Doyle-Charles	1				1						

HEDNESFORD TOWN MATCH RESULTS 2019-20

Date	Comp	H/A	Opponents	Att:	Result	Goalscorers	Pos	No.
Aug 10	Sth PC	H	Lowestoft Town	482	W 2 - 1	Hallahan 30 Glover 76		1
13	Sth PC	A	Coalville Town	290	L 1 - 2	Glover 79		2
17	Sth PC	A	Stourbridge	588	W 3 - 0	Wells 11 Glover 30 Abadaki 40		3
24	Sth PC	H	Alvechurch	440	W 3 - 0	Elliott 41 Glover 67 Morris 82	2	4
26	Sth PC	A	Tamworth	819	W 1 - 0	Truslove 78 (pen)	2	5
31	Sth PC	H	Needham Market	461	L 0 - 1		2	6
Sept 7	FAC1Q	A	Lutterworth Town	309	W 3 - 0	Wells 68 82 89		7
14	Sth PC	A	Kings Langley	268	W 2 - 0	Elliott 52 Wells 68	3	8
17	Sth PC	H	Banbury United	388	W 2 - 0	Hurst 45 (pen) Glover 84		9
21	FAC2Q	H	Barwell	393	W 3 - 2	Hurst 42 55 King 90		10
28	Sth PC	H	AFC Rushden & Diamonds	412	D 1 - 1	Griffiths 56	2	11
Oct 5	FAC3Q	A	Blyth Spartans	616	W 4 - 2	King 12 Morris 42 63 Glover 65		12
12	Sth PC	H	Royston Town	491	W 4 - 1	Elliott 8 Glover 16 78 (pen) Brown 88	1	13
15	Sth PC	A	Bromsgrove Sporting	845	L 0 - 4		4	14
19	FAC4Q	H	Boston United	891	L 0 - 1			15
22	Sth PC	H	Redditch United	310	W 4 - 0	Brown 4 58 King 10 Elliott 57	3	16
29	FAT1Q	A	Stratford Town	210	W 2 - 1	King 23 Elliott 56		17
Nov 2	Sth PC	A	Barwell	257	D 4 - 4	Hallahan 6 42 78 Glover 83	3	18
9	FAT2Q	A	Sutton Coldfield Town	296	W 5 - 1	Elliott 8 86 Glover 13 Bailey 32 Abadaki 36		19
12	Sth PC	A	Leiston	168	W 3 - 0	Brown 4 49 Scott 68	3	20
19	Sth PC	A	St Ives Town	171	L 1 - 4	Bailey 45	3	21
23	FAT3Q	H	Coalville Town	354	W 2 - 1	Hallahan 44 Bailey		22
30	Sth PC	A	Biggleswade Town	165	L 0 - 1		4	23
Dec 7	Sth PC	H	Hitchin Town	314	W 4 - 2	Abadaki 6 Glover 47 Morris 50 Brown 83	4	24
14	FAT1P	H	Chester	565	D 0 - 0			25
17	FAT1Pr	A	Chester	613	L 1 - 2	Glover 50		26
21	Sth PC	H	Stratford Town	269	W 1 - 0	Glover 70	4	27
26	Sth PC	A	Rushall Olympic	619	L 0 - 1		5	28
Jan 1	Sth PC	H	Tamworth	802	L 0 - 3		7	29
4	Sth PC	A	Lowestoft Town	387	W 2 - 0	Glover 15 Abadaki 25	7	30
11	Sth PC	H	Coalville Town	364	L 0 - 1		9	31
18	Sth PC	A	Alvechurch Town	223	W 1 - 0	Glover 53	9	32
21	Sth PC	A	AFC Rushden & Diamonds	327	D 1 - 1	Glover 44	9	33
25	Sth PC	H	Stourbridge	515	L 1 - 2	Bailey 46	10	34
Feb 1	Sth PC	H	Needeham Market	225	L 3 - 4	Bailey 9 King 74 Hodge 78	11	35
4	Sth PC	H	Nuneaton Borough	245	L 0 - 3		11	36
8	Sth PC	H	Kings Langley	291	L 1 - 3	King 45	13	37
22	Sth PC	A	Royston Town	385	L 0 - 1		14	38
25	Sth PC	H	Peterborough Sports	151	D 3 - 3	Glover 35 66 Sweeney 42	14	39
Mar 7	Sth PC	A	Redditch United	203	W 1 - 0	Thompson 86	13	40
10	Sth PC	A	St Ives Town	116	D 1 - 1	Glover 67	12	41

GOALSCORERS	SG	CSG	Pens	Hat tricks	Total		SG	CSG	Pens	Hat tricks	Total
Glover	17	4			19	Hurst	3				3
Elliott	6	2			7	Griffiths	1				1
Brown	5				6	Scott	1				1
King	6	2			6	Sweeney	1		1		1
Hallahan	3			1	5	Thompson	1				1
Wells	3			1	5	Truslove	1				1
Abadaki	4				4						
Morris	3				4						
Bailey	3	2			3						
Hodge	2		1		3						

HITCHIN TOWN MATCH RESULTS 2019-20

Date	Comp	H/A	Opponents	Att	Result	Goalscorers	Pos	No.
Aug 10	Sth PC	H	Stourbridge	322	L 1 - 2	Draper 77		1
13	Sth PC	A	Needham Market	313	D 1 - 1	Draper 4		2
17	Sth PC	A	Alvechurch	190	L 0 - 5		21	3
24	Sth PC	H	Rushall Olympic	303	L 1 - 2	Draper 61 (pen)	21	4
31	Sth PC	H	Tamworth	344	L 0 - 3		21	5
Sept 7	FAC 1Q	A	**Wisbech Town**	255	W 2 - 1	**Dowie 18 (pen) Verney 53**		6
14	Sth PC	A	Banbury United	405	D 0 - 0		20	7
16	Sth PC	H	AFC Rushden & Diamonds	360	D 1 - 1	Eadie 88 (pen)	20	8
21	FAC 2Q	A	**Barton Rovers**		W 1 - 0	**Barker 32**		9
24	Sth PC	A	Kings Langley	163	L 1 - 3	Gauge 61	21	10
28	Sth PC	H	Stratford Town	328	W 2 - 0	Cawley 3 (pen) Webb 75	21	11
Oct 5	FAC 3Q	A	**Maidstone United**	1258	L 1 - 2	**Verney 10**		12
12	Sth PC	H	Bromsgrove Sporting	633	D 2 - 2	Broadhurst 23 (og) Webb 90	21	13
15	Sth PC	A	Royston Town	324	D 1 - 1	Ferrell 29	21	14
19	Sth PC	A	Leiston	201	L 1 - 3	Cawley 33	22	15
21	Sth PC	H	Coalville Town	282	W 1 - 0	Webb 4	21	16
Nov 2	Sth PC	A	St Ives Town	169	W 3 - 0	Gauge 9 Marsh 31 Barker 66	16	17
9	FAT1Q	H	**Bedfont Sports**	218	D 1 - 1	**Dhillon 72**		18
12	FAT1Qr	A	**Bedfont Sports**	71	D 1 - 1	**Simms 60 (Lost 4-5 on pens aet)**		19
16	Sth PC	A	Redditch United	267	W 2 - 0	Marsh 3 9	16	20
23	Sth PC	H	Nuneaton Borough	404	D 1 - 1	Barker 87	16	21
30	Sth PC	H	Barwell	346	W 4 1	Chilton 18 44 Webb 36 Hutchinson 61	15	22
Dec 2	Sth PC	H	Lowestoft Town	214	L 1 - 3	Hutchinson 44	15	23
7	Sth PC	A	Hednesford Town	314	L 2 - 4	Barker 43 Jellis 90	15	24
26	Sth PC	A	Bigleswade Town	390	L 0 - 2		17	25
Jan 1	Sth PC	H	Kings Langley	327	L 0 - 1		17	26
4	Sth PC	A	Stourbridge	571	W 2 - 1	Webb 16 Gouveia 20	16	27
11	Sth PC	H	Needham Market	334	D 0 - 0		17	28
18	Sth PC	A	Rushall Olympic	241	L 2 - 4	Cawley 38 Hutchinson 81	17	29
21	Sth PC	A	Peterborough Sports	153	W 4 - 0	Gouveia 21 Cawley 64 69 79	17	30
25	Sth PC	H	Alvechurch	324	W 3 - 1	Hutchinson 13 Marsh 30 Gouveia	17	31
28	Sth PC	A	Startford Town	144	D 3 - 3	Marsh 67 Hutchinson 69 90	17	32
Feb 1	Sth PC	A	Tamworth	625	L 0 - 1		17	33
8	Sth PC	H	Banbury United	360	D 0 - 0		16	34
22	Sth PC	A	Bromsgrove Sporting	966	W 2 - 1	Eadie 50 Marsh 60	17	35
Mar 7	Sth PC	A	Coalville Town	238	W 2 - 1	Dhillon 32 Barker 62	16	36
9	Sth PC	H	Peterborough Sports	183	L 0 - 2		16	37

GOALSCORERS	SG	CSG	Pens	Hat tricks	Total		SG	CSG	Pens	Hat tricks	Total
Cawley	4	1		1	6	Gauge	2				2
Hutchinson	5				6	Verney	2				2
Marsh	5				6	Dowie	1		1		1
Barker	5				5	Ferrell	1				1
Webb	5				5	Jellis	1				1
Chiton	2				3	Opponents	1				1
Draper	3		1		3	Simms	1				1
Gouveia	3				3						
Dhillon	2				2						
Eadie	2		1		2						

KINGS LANGLEY MATCH RESULTS 2019-20

Date	Comp	H/A	Opponents	Att:	Result	Goalscorers	Pos	No.
Aug 10	Sth PC	A	Nuneaton Borough	554	W 3 - 0	Weiss 12 Azdebiyi 72 Crawford 86		1
13	Sth PC	H	Peterborough Sports	215	D 2 - 2	Farrell 27 McKeown 42		2
17	Sth PC	H	Stratford Town	255	D 3 - 3	Campbell-Mhlope 7 McKeown 19 61	7	3
24	Sth PC	A	Banbury United	384	W 2 - 1	Campbell-Mhlope 38 65	5	4
31	Sth PC	A	Barwell	154	L 1 - 3	Weiss 13	11	5
Sept 7	FAC1Q	H	Barking	281	W 3 - 1	Ruff 35 (pen) McKeown 60 Hercules 86		6
14	Sth PC	H	Hednesford Town	268	L 0 - 2		14	7
17	Sth PC	A	St Ives Town	120	L 1 - 2	Ruff 6	16	8
21	FAC2Q	H	Folkestone Invicta	335	W 4 - 0	Doyley 18 Weiss 55 Campbell-Mhlope 88 Ruff 90		9
24	Sth PC	H	Hitchin Town	163	W 3 - 1	Hercules 17 Crawford 51 Pattison 68	12	10
28	Sth PC	H	Stourbridge	312	L 1 - 4	Connelly 43	12	11
Oct 5	FAC3Q	H	Corinthian-Casuals	362	W 3 - 0	Weiss 15 60 Collins 62		12
12	Sth PC	H	Rushall Olympic	291	W 4 - 0	Connelly 6 Ward 33 Caldicott-Stevens 41 Collier 90	15	13
19	FAC4Q	A	Maidstone United	1449	L 1 - 4	Collins 90+5 (pen)		14
22	Sth PC	H	Leiston	153	L 1 - 2	Ward 26	17	15
26	FAT1Q	A	Phoenix Sports	90	W 5 - 3	Farrell 2 Weiss 17 39 Collier 14 Hercules 77		16
Nov 2	Sth PC	A	Redditch United	177	W 2 - 0	Weiss 76 Collier 90	15	17
9	FAT2Q	A	Salisbury	445	L 1 - 2	Weiss 37		18
12	Sth PC	A	Lowestoft Town	228	L 1 - 2	Ward 53	15	19
16	Sth PC	A	Tamworth	711	L 0 - 2		15	20
23	Sth PC	H	Needham Market	207	D 2 - 2	Parkes 7 90	15	21
26	Sth PC	A	Coalville	172	L 0 - 3		15	22
Dec 3	Sth PC	A	B romsgrove Sporting	417	L 1 - 4	Weiss 87	16	23
7	Sth PC	H	AFC Rushden & Diamonds	234	W 1 - 0	Parkes 78	15	24
14	Sth PC	A	Stourbridge	460	W 3 - 1	Williams 41 Ward 49 Linsell 64	15	25
26	Sth PC	H	Royston	216	L 0 1		15	26
Jan 1	Sth PC	A	Hitchin Town	327	W 1 - 0	Doyley 90	14	27
4	Sth PC	H	Nuneaton Borough	270	W 2 - 0	Ward 27 Williams 64	14	28
11	Sth PC	H	Peterborough Sports	254	D 2 - 2	Crawford 84 Parkes 90	14	29
18	Sth PC	H	Bromsgrove Sporting	369	W 3 - 1	Crawford 9 51 74	14	30
25	Sth PC	H	Stratford Town	245	W 1 - 0	Hoskins 37	14	31
Feb 1	Sth PC	H	Barwell	211	D 1 - 1	Ford 89 (og)	15	32
4	Sth PC	H	Biggleswade Town	153	W 2 - 1	Connelly 19 Parkes 79	12	33
8	Sth PC	A	Hednesford Town	291	W 3 - 1	Ward 24 39 Parkes 36	10	34
22	Sth PC	A	Rushall Olympic	192	W 1 - 0	Connelly 52	10	35
Mar 7	Sth PC	A	Leiston	162	W 4 - 0	Hoskins 17 Parkes 60 Whichelow 69 Ward 78	10	36

GOALSCORERS	SG	CSG	Pens	Hat tricks	Total		SG	CSG	Pens	Hat tricks	Total
Weiss	8	3			10	Doyley	2				2
Ward	7				8	Farrell	2				2
Parkes	6				7	Hoskins	2				2
Crawford	4		1		6	Williams	2				2
Campbell-Mhlope	3	2			4	Azdebiyi	1				1
Connolly	4				4	Caldiicott- Stevens	1				1
McKeown	3	2			4	Linsell	1				1
Collier	3				3	Opponents	1				1
Hercules	3				3	Pattison	1				1
Ruff	3		1		3	Whichelow	1				1
Collins	2		1		2						

LEISTON MATCH RESULTS 2019-20

Date	Comp	H/A	Opponents	Att:	Result	Goalscorers	Pos	No.
Aug 10	Sth PC	H	Coalville Town	218	D 1 - 1	Davies 38		1
13	Sth PC	A	AFC Rushden & Diamonds	446	L 1 - 5	Blake 22		2
17	Sth PC	A	Rushall Olympic	186	L 0 - 6		22	3
24	Sth PC	H	Tamworth	242	L 1 - 2	Henry 60	22	4
26	Sth PC	A	Needham Market	474	L 0 - 3		22	5
31	Sth PC	H	Alvechurch	154	L 1 - 2	Ransome (og) 53	22	6
Sept 7	FAC1Q	A	Ware	157	L 1 - 5	Blake 73		7
14	Sth PC	A	Stourbridge	615	L 1 - 5	Castro 9	22	8
17	Sth PC	H	Biggleswade Town	166	L 0 - 4		22	9
28	Sth PC	A	Peterborough Sports	270	L 1 - 8	Henry 60	22	10
Oct 5	Sth PC	A	Stratford	170	L 1 - 3	Hughes 5	22	11
12	Sth PC	A	Barwell	173	L 0 - 5		22	12
15	Sth PC	H	St Ives Town	139	D 4 - 4	Woerndl 25 Bloom 35 Cheetham 75 Aitkins 90	22	13
19	Sth PC	H	Hitchin Town	201	W 3 - 1	Davies 14 Odelusi 23 Hitter 42	21	14
22	Sth PC	A	Kings Langley	153	W 2 - 1	Knights 39 Davies 82	20	15
26	FAT1Q	A	Tamworth	385	L 0 - 4			16
Nov 2	Sth PC	H	Bromsgrove Sporting	148	L 0 - 8		20	17
12	Sth PC	H	Hednesford Town	168	L 0 - 3		21	18
16	Sth PC	H	Banbury United	232	L 1 - 5	Kamanzi 90	22	19
30	Sth PC	H	Nuneaton Borough	238	D 1 - 1	Fennell 18	21	20
Dec 3	Sth PC	A	Roystion Town	211	D 0 - 0		21	21
7	Sth PC	A	Redditch	175	W 6 - 0	Debenham 4 82 Sands 47 65 75 Lawrence 59	21	22
14	Sth PC	H	Peterborough Sports	165	L 2 - 4	Hammond 78 Henry 90	21	23
26	Sth PC	A	Lowestoft Town	428	W 3 - 1	Sands 32 Debenham 49 Henry 90	20	24
Jan 1	Sth PC	H	Needham Market	414	W 2 - 1	Lawrence 36 Odelusi 80	18	25
4	Sth PC	A	Coalville Town	174	D 1 - 1	Clements 86	18	26
11	Sth PC	H	Rushden & Diamonds	275	L 2 - 3	Aitkins 43 Eagle 43	18	27
18	Sth PC	A	Tamworth	251	W 2 - 1	Sands 15 69	18	28
25	Sth PC	H	Rushall Olympic	242	D 2 - 2	Eagle 61 Brown 83	18	29
Feb 1	Sth PC	A	Alvechurch	151	D 0 - 0		19	30
8	Sth PC	H	Stourbridge	255	L 0 - 1		19	31
22	Sth PC	H	Barwell	217	D 1 - 1	Harvey 38	19	32
Mar 3	Sth PC	H	St Ives Town	105	L 0 - 1		18	33
7	Sth PC	H	Kings Langley	162	L 0 - 4		18	34

GOALSCORERS	SG	CSG	Pens	Hat tricks	Total		SG	CSG	Pens	Hat tricks	Total
Sands	3			1	6	Cheetham	1				1
Henry	4				4	Clements	1				1
Debenham	2				3	Davies	1				1
Aitkins	2				2	Fennell	1				1
Blake	2				2	Hammond	1				1
Davies	2				2	Harvey	1				1
Eagle	2				2	Hitter	1				1
Lawrence	2				2	Hughes	1				1
Odelusi	2				2	Kamanzi	1				1
Bloom	1				1	Knights	1				1
Brown	1				1	Opponents	1				1
Castro	1				1	Woerndl	1				1

LOWESTOFT TOWN MATCH RESULTS 2019-20

Date	Comp	H/A	Opponents	Att:	Result	Goalscorers	Pos	No.
Aug 10	Sth PC	A	Hednesford Town	482	L 1 - 2	Deeks 36		1
13	Sth PC	H	St Ives Town	436	W 1 - 0	Reed 62		2
17	Sth PC	H	Barwell	413	W 3 - 2	Bammant 32 Reed 40 Williams 49	5	3
24	Sth PC	A	Redditch United	20	L 3 - 5	Stoddart 39 Fisk 42 Reed 51	10	4
26	Sth PC	H	Royston Town	474	L 0 - 1		12	5
31	Sth PC	A	Nuneaton Borough	485	L 1 - 4	Linton 58	15	6
Sept 7	FAC1Q	H	Leighton Town	388	W 2 - 0	Linton 51 Cole 75		7
14	Sth PC	H	Bromsgrove Sporting	396	L 0 - 1		19	8
21	FAC2Q	H	Needham Market	495	W 4 - 0	Bammant 44 Reed 57 75 Cole 70	19	9
28	Sth PC	A	Rushall Olympic	230	L 1 - 4	Bammant 10	20	10
Oct 5	FAC3Q	H	Carshalton Athletic	500	L 1 - 2	Linton 89		11
12	Sth PC	A	Stratford Town	254	W 3 - 0	Reed 7 Linton 70 90	19	12
19	Sth PC	H	Needham Market	416	L 0 - 2		20	13
26	FAT1Q	H	Coalville Town	264	L 2 - 4	Linton 61		14
Nov 2	Sth PC	H	Banbury United	305	D 0 - 0		20	15
5	Sth PC	A	Peterborough Sports	167	L 1 - 3	Reed 21	20	16
12	Sth PC	H	Kings Langley	228	W 2 - 1	Reed 70 Cole 77	20	17
16	Sth PC	H	Coalville Town	406	W 2 - 1	Reed 79 Richardson 85	18	18
19	Sth PC	A	AFC Rushden & Diamonds	386	L 0 - 3		18	19
30	Sth PC	A	Tamworth	593	L 1 - 4	Linton 45	18	20
Dec 2	Sth PC	A	Hitchin Town	214	W 3 - 1	Reed 39 Linton 48 Wilkinson 65	17	21
7	Sth PC	H	Alvechurch	389	W 4 - 0	McIntosh 50 Linton 54 66 Reed 63	16	22
14	Sth PC	H	Rushall Olympic	340	D 0 - 0		16	23
26	Sth PC	H	Leiston	428	L 1 - 3	Wilkinson 20	16	24
Jan 1	Sth PC	A	Royston Town	230	L 1 - 5	Reed 67	17	25
4	Sth PC	H	Hednesford Town	387	L 0 - 2		17	26
11	Sth PC	A	St Ives Town	183	W 5 - 2	Linton 12 Deeks 45 Lopez 53 Reed 54 83	16	27
18	Sth PC	H	Redditch United	363	W 6 - 0	Reed 14 17 29 Linton 41 Zielonka 49 71	16	28
25	Sth PC	A	Barwell	182	W 3 - 0	McIntosh 12 Zielonka 47 Linton 77	16	29
Jan 1	Sth PC	H	Nuneaton Borough	449	L 0 - 2		16	30
8	Sth PC	A	Bromsgrove Sporting	1110	L 0 - 6		17	31
15	Sth PC	A	Needham Market	346	L 0 - 1		17	32
18	Sth PC	H	Stourbridge	274	W 2 - 1	Deeks 9 McIntosh 68	16	33
22	Sth PC	H	Stratford Town	369	W 2 - 0	Linton 32 Lopez 90	16	34
25	Sth PC	A	Biggleswade Town	75	L 0 - 3		16	35
29	Sth PC	A	Stourbridge	569	L 0 - 2		16	36
Mar 6	Sth PC	H	Biggleswade Town	370	W 2 - 1	Linton 50 80	15	37

GOALSCORERS	SG	CSG	Pens	Hat tricks	Total		SG	CSG	Pens	Hat tricks	Total
Reed	13	3		1	17	Lopez	1				1
Linton	15	3			14	Richardson	1				1
Bammant	3				3	Stoddart	1				1
Cole	3				3	Williams	1				1
McIntosh	3				3						
Zielonka	2				3						
Deeks	2				2						
Wilkinson	2				2						
Zielonka	2				2						
Fisk	1				1						

NEEDHAM MARKET MATCH RESULTS 2019-20

Date	Comp	H/A	Opponents	Att:	Result	Goalscorers	Pos	No.
Aug 10	Sth PC	A	Stafford Town	221	L 1 - 2	Marsden 90		1
13	Sth PC	H	Hitchin Town	313	D 1 - 1	Sturgess 44		2
17	Sth PC	H	Redditch United	225	D 2 - 2	Parker 5 Marsden 41	14	3
24	Sth PC	A	Nuneaton Borough	471	L 0 - 1		18	4
26	Sth PC	H	Leiston	474	W 3 - 0	Ingram 47 80 Craig 52	15	5
31	Sth PC	A	Hednesford Town	461	W 1 - 0	Ingram 18	10	6
Sept 7	FAC1Q	A	Dereham Town	256	D 1 - 1	Ingram 85		7
10	FAC1Qr	H	Dereham Town	234	W 2 - 1	Heath 42 Neal 85		8
14	Sth PC	H	Barwell	190	L 2 - 3	Marsden 55 Heath 87	10	9
21	FAC2Q	A	Lowestoft Town	495	L 0 - 4			10
28	Sth PC	A	Bromsgrove Sporting	936	W 1 - 0	Marsden 65	11	11
Oct 5	Sth PC	H	Banbury United	244	L 0 - 1			12
12	Sth PC	H	Alvechurch	302	D 1 - 1	Marsden 52	16	13
15	Sth PC	A	Lowestoft Town	416	W 2 - 0	Marsden 41 Ingram 59	14	14
22	Sth PC	H	Peterborugh Sports	220	W 2 - 1	Neal 40 Parker 66	13	15
25	FAT1Q	A	Cambridge City	163	W 3 - 0	Marsden 48 Neal 68 79		16
29	Sth PC	A	Royston Town	248	L 0 1		13	17
Nov 2	Sth PC	H	Stourbridge	254	D 3 - 3	Morphew 20 Parker 3 82	14	18
9	FAT2Q	H	Leatherhead	203	L 1 - 2	Baker 90		19
16	Sth PC	H	Rushall Olympic	236	D 1 - 1	Ingram 78	14	20
23	Sth PC	A	Kings Langley	207	D 2 2	Parker 45 Ingram 63	14	21
Dec 7	Sth PC	H	Biggleswade Town	243	L 0 - 1		15	22
10	Sth PC	A	Tamworth	450	W 2 - 1	Ingram 39 Morphew 74	13	23
14	Sth PC	H	Bromsgrove Sporting	280	L 0 - 3		14	24
26	Sth PC	H	St Ives Town	214	D 1 - 1	Parker 6	14	25
Jan 1	Sth PC	A	Lwiston	414	L 1 - 2	Marsden 44	15	26
4	Sth PC	H	Stratford	243	W 1 - 0	Marsden 90 (pen)	15	27
11	Sth PC	A	Hitchin Town	334	D 0 - 0		15	28
18	Sth PC	H	Nuneaton Town	293	L 1 - 3	Hunt 41	15	29
25	Sth PC	H	Redditch United	126	W 3 - 0	Parker 27 Hunt 29 Page 31	15	30
28	Sth PC	A	AFC Rushden & Diamonds	318	W 2 - 1	Page 16 Marsden 57	15	31
Feb 1	Sth PC	H	Hednesford Town	223	W 4 - 3	Page 1 Mills 33 Hunt 36 Baker 84	14	32
8	Sth PC	A	Barwell	183	L 0 - 1		15	33
11	Sth PC	A	Coalville Town	191	W 1 - 0	Page 90	14	34
15	Sth PC	H	Lowestoft Town	346	W 1 - 0	Mills 52	11	35
22	Sth PC	A	Alvechurch	170	W 2 - 1	Page 41 Mills 90	11	36
Mar 3	Sth PC	A	Banbury United	270	L 2 - 4	Ingram 42 Parker 90	11	37
7	Sth PC	A	Peterborugh Sports	195	D 0 - 0		10	38

GOALSCORERS	SG	CSG	Pens	Hat tricks	Total		SG	CSG	Pens	Hat tricks	Total
Marsden	10			1	10	Craig	1				1
Ingram	8	3			9	Sturgess	1				1
Parker	7				8						
Page	5				5						
Neal	3	2			4						
Hunt	3				3						
Mills	3				3						
Baker	2				2						
Heath	2	2			2						
Morphew	2				2						

NUNEATON BOROUGH MATCH RESULTS 2019-20

Date	Comp	H/A	Opponents	Att:	Result	Goalscorers	Pos	No.
Aug 10	Sth PC	H	Kings Langley	554	L 0 - 3			1
13	Sth PC	A	Banbury United	457	D 1 - 1	Benbow 19		2
17	Sth PC	A	AFC Rushden & Diamonds	575	L 0 - 2		20	3
24	Sth PC	H	Needham Market	471	W 1 - 0	Benbow 2 (pen)	16	4
26	Sth PC	A	Coalville Town	495	L 3 - 5	Verma 3 Powell 41 Edmunds 66	16	5
31	Sth PC	H	Lowestoft Town	485	W 4 - 1	Benbow 19 23 Clifton 45 Powell 64	14	6
Sept 7	FAC1Q	A	Tamworth	1047	L 1 - 3	Clifton 65		7
14	Sth PC	A	Biggleswade Town	181	L 0 - 2		18	8
17	Sth PC	H	Stourbridge	385	W 4 - 0	Clifton 4 Benbow 10 54 Candlin 59	12	9
21	Sth PC	H	Alvechurch	429	W 3 - 2	Benbow 3 Candlin 44 Edmunds 83	9	10
28	Sth PC	H	Barwell	735	W 3 - 1	Benbow 23 Richens 40 Powell 45	9	11
Oct 5	Sth PC	A	St Ives Town	251	L 0 - 2		9	12
12	Sth PC	H	Redditch United	565	W 3 - 0	Benbow 60 90 Kettle 71	8	13
15	Sth PC	A	Peterborough Sports	234	L 1 - 2	Malone 5 (og)	8	14
19	Sth PC	A	Bromsgrove Sporting	1172	W 3 - 1	Kettle 26 Henshall 54 Powell 77	6	15
29	FAT1Q	A	Stourbridge	423	L 1 - 2	Benbow 72		16
Nov 2	Sth PC	H	Royston Town	515	D 2 - 2	Candlin 3 Powell 30	6	17
16	Sth PC	H	Stratford Town	425	W 2 - 0	Kettle 68 Powell 88 (pen)	5	18
23	Sth PC	A	Hitchin Town	404	D 1 - 1	Byrne 21	5	19
30	Sth PC	A	Leiston	238	D 1 - 1	Edmunds 89	7	20
Dec 7	Sth PC	H	Rushall Olympic	470	L 1 - 3	Clifton 67	8	21
14	Sth PC	A	Barwell	477	W 1 - 0	Bremang 32	7	22
21	Sth PC	H	St Ives Town	392	W 4 - 0	Edmunds 17 Bremang 50 86 Benbow 75 (pen)	7	23
26	Sth PC	A	Tamworth	1326	D 3 - 3	Benbow 27 Kettle 58 Bremang 88 (pen)	7	24
Jan 1	Sth PC	H	Coalville Town	695	D 0 - 0		8	25
4	Sth PC	A	Kings Langley	270	L 0 - 2		9	26
11	Sth PC	H	Banbury United	523	D 2 - 2	Edmunds 61 Powell 74 (0pen)	10	27
18	Sth PC	A	Needham Market	293	W 3 - 1	Sharpe 28 Towers 39 Goddard 90	10	28
25	Sth PC	A	AFC Rushden & Diamonds	654	L 0 - 1		11	29
Feb 1	Sth PC	A	Lowestoft Town	449	W 2 - 0	Edmunds 5 Addison 10	8	30
4	Sth PC	A	Hednesford Town	245	W 3 - 0	Kettle 7 Goddard 51 Benbow 85	8	31
8	Sth PC	H	Biggleswade Town	499	D 2 - 2	Kettle 70 90	8	32
15	Sth PC	H	Peterborough Sports	369	L 0 - 3		9	33
22	Sth PC	A	Redditch United	190	L 2 - 3	Osbourne 23 Addison 90	9	34
Mar 7	Sth PC	A	Alvechurch	271	W 2 - 0	Hood 57 Benbow 86 (pen)	9	35

GOALSCORERS	SG	CSG	Pens	Hat tricks	Total		SG	CSG	Pens	Hat tricks	Total
Benbow	12	3	3		15	Henshall	1				1
Kettle	6				7	Hood	1				1
Powell	7	3	2		7	Opponents	1				1
Edmunds	6				6	Osbourne	1				1
Bremang	3	3	1		4	Richens	1				1
Clifton	4				4	Sharpe	1				1
Candlin	3				3	Towers	1				1
Addison	2				2	Verma	1				1
Goddard	2				2						
Byrne	1				1						

PETERBOROUGH SPORTS MATCH RESULTS 2019-20

Date	Comp	H/A	Opponents	Att:	Result	Goalscorers	Pos	No.
Aug 10	Sth PC	H	Rushall Olympic	201	D 1 - 1	Lawlor 62		1
13	Sth PC	A	Kings Langley	215	D 2 - 2	M.Jones 1 Semble-Ferris 65		2
17	Sth PC	A	Tamworth	563	L 1 - 3	Toseland 88	16	3
24	FACP	H	Bugbrooke St M	175	W 7 - 0	Vieira 2 Johnson 2 Sembie-Ferris Sani Moreman		4
26	Sth PC	A	Biggleswade Town	215	W 3 - 0	Stevenson 30 McCammon 80 Mamadu 87	19	5
31	Sth PC	H	Stourbridge	182	D 2 - 2	Malone 58 Johnson 63	17	6
Sept 3	Sth PC	H	Banbury United	183	L 1 - 3	Johnson 89	17	7
7	FAC1Q	A	East Thurrock United	161	D 1 - 1	Smith 36		8
10	FAC1Qr	H	East Thurock United	162	W 3 - 2	Lawlor 6 (pen) Johnson 45 Sembie-Ferris 83		9
14	Sth PC	A	Alvechurch	190	D 2 - 2	R.Jones 67 Malone 90	17	10
21	FAC2Q	A	Bishops Stortford	296	W 2 - 1	Johnson 8 Sembie-Ferris 84		11
28	Sth PC	H	Leiston	270	W 8 - 1	R.Jones 6 33 M.Jones 11 21 Sembie-Ferris 24 74 89 Willock 66	14	12
Oct 5	FAC3Q	H	Guiseley	435	W 1 - 0	Sani 90		13
12	Sth PC	A	St Ives Town	285	W 3 - 0	Johnson 20 Sembie-Ferris 69 Stevenson 72	13	14
15	Sth PC	H	Nuneaton Borough	234	W 2 - 1	Macleod 11 M.Jones 74	11	15
19	FAC4Q	A	AFC Fylde	657	L 1 - 6	Sembie-Ferris 90		16
22	Sth PC	A	Needham Market	220	L 1 - 2	Sembie-Ferris 48	14	17
29	FAT1Q	H	Alvechurch	170	W 1 - 0	Johnson 90+4		18
Nov 2	Sth PC	H	Stratford Town	152	W 6 - 0	M.Jones 51 68 Moreman 13 70 Sembie-Feris 54 McCammon 90	10	19
5	Sth PC	H	Lowestoft Town	167	W 3 - 1	Lawlor 60 Curry 76 (og) Sani 90	7	20
9	FAT2Q	H	Whitby Town	202	W 2 - 0	Grifiths 21 Vieira 89		21
16	Sth PC	H	Bromsgrove Rovers	367	W 3 - 2	Moreman 21 Lawlor 27 M.Jones 36	6	22
23	FAT3Q	H	Kettering Town	436	L 0 - 3			23
30	Sth PC	H	Redditch United	178	W 7 - 0	Hall (og) 4 M.Jones 18 McCammon 49 65 Sani 57 77 81	6	24
Dec 7	Sth PC	A	Royston Town	226	L 1 - 4	Lawlor 90	11	25
14	Sth PC	A	Leiston Town	165	W 4 - 2	Lawlor 44 Sembie-Ferris 60 Moreman 76 McCammon 79	5	26
17	Sth PC	A	Coalvelle Town	116	W 2 - 1	Semble-Ferris 32 Lawlor 76	4	27
21	Sth PC	H	Barwell	214	W 5 - 4	Malone 27 Lawlor 30 80 Vieira 38 43	4	28
Jan 1	Sth PC	H	Coalville Town	230	D 1 - 1	Vieira 7	4	29
4	Sth PC	A	Rushall Olympic	251	W 2 - 0	Moreman 45 Stevenson 90	3	30
7	Sth PC	A	Barwell	146	L 0 - 2		4	31
11	Sth PC	A	Kings Langley	254	D 2 - 2	Adebiyi (og) 28 M.Jones 72	3	32
18	Sth PC	A	Banbury United	443	W 2 - 0	McCammon 18 Moreman 84	3	33
21	Sth PC	H	Hitchijn Town	153	L 0 - 4		3	34
25	Sth PC	H	Tamworth	320	W 4 - 2	Semble-Ferris 26 61 M.Jones 30 Sani 65	3	35
Feb 1	Sth PC	A	Stourbridge	582	W 6 - 1	Moreman 3 Semble-Ferris 27 59 82 McCammon 75 Johnson 76	3	36
8	Sth PC	H	Alvechurch	252	W 3 - 0	Semble-Ferris 30 51 Johnson 75	3	37
15	Sth PC	A	Nuneaton Borough	369	W 3 - 0	Moremsn 23 50 Johnson 90	3	38
22	Sth PC	H	St Ives Town	352	W 5 - 0	M.Jones 10 14 Malone 41 Moreman 67 Vieira 89	2	39
25	Sth PC	A	Hednesford Town	151	D 3 - 3	Moreman 26 Sani 56 Stevenson 77	2	40
Mar 7	Sth PC	H	Needham Market	195	D 0 - 0		3	41
9	Sth PC	A	Hitchin Town	183	W 2 - 0	Lawlor 11 Semble-Ferris 87	1	42

GOALSCORERS	SG	CSG	Pens	Hat tricks	Total		SG	CSG	Pens	Hat tricks	Total
Sembie-Ferris	15	2		2	21	Jones R	3				3
Jones M	7				12	Opponents	3				3
Johnson	10	2			11	Griffiths	1				1
Moreman	9				11	Macleod	1				1
Lawlor	8	4	1		10	Mamadu	1				1
Sani	6			1	8	Sani	1				1
McCammon	6				7	Smith	1				1
Vieira	5				7	Toseland	1				1
Malone	4				4	Willock	1				1
Stevenson	4				4						

REDDITCH UNITED MATCH RESULTS 2019-20

Date	Comp	H/A	Opponents	Att:	Result	Goalscorers	Pos	No.
Aug 10	Sth PC	H	Banbury United	261	D 0 - 0			1
13	Sth PC	A	Rushall Olympic	255	L 1 - 3	Moore 22		2
17	Sth PC	A	Needham Market	225	D 2 - 2	Coyle 34 Hilton 90	17	3
24	Sth PC	H	Lowestoft Town	200	W 5 - 3	Hickman 7 Deards 6 55 90 Sweeney 57	13	4
26	Sth PC	A	Alvechurch	403	W 2 - 0	Hilton 47 Coyle 52	11	5
31	Sth PC	H	AFC Rushden & Diamonds	315	D 1 - 1	Hilton 25	9	6
Sept 7	FAC1Q	A	**Sutton Coldfield Town**	218	D 1 - 1	**Marsella 70**		7
10	FAC1Qr	H	**Sutton Coldfield Town**	205	L 1 - 3	**Nelson 22**		8
14	Sth PC	A	Tamworth	591	L 0 - 3		10	9
17	Sth PC	H	Coalville Town	154	L 2 - 3	Newell 38 Monaghan 90	11	10
28	Sth PC	H	St Ives Town	184	L 0 - 1		17	11
Oct 5	Sth PC	A	Biggleswade Town	150	L 1 - 3	Truslove 53	19	12
12	Sth PC	A	Nuneaton Borough	565	L 0 - 3		20	13
19	Sth PC	H	Barwell	210	L 0 - 1		20	14
22	Sth PC	A	Hednesford Town	310	L 0 - 4		21	15
26	FAT1Q	H	**Corby Town**	200	W 4 - 2			16
Nov 2	Sth PC	H	Kings Langley	177	L 0 - 2		21	17
12	FAT2Q	A	**Barwell**	129	D 3 - 3	**Barlone 76 Staten 79 Martin 90+2**		18
19	FAT2Q	H	**Barwell**	111	W 3 - 2	**Martin 41 90+1 Truslove 60**		19
16	Sth PC	H	Hitchin Town	267	L 0 - 2		21	20
23	FAT3Q	A	**Margate Town**	259	L 0 - 2			21
30	Sth PC	A	Peterborough Sports	176	L 0 - 7		22	22
Dec 7	Sth PC	H	Leiston	175	L 0 - 6		22	23
14	Sth PC	A	St IvesTown	126	L 1 - 2	Lucas 10	22	24
21	Sth PC	H	Biggleswade Town	157	L 0 - 2		22	25
26	Sth PC	A	Stourbridge	823	L 0 - 1		22	26
Jan 1	Sth PC	H	Alvechurch	315	L 2 - 3	Endall 57 Diau 72	22	27
4	Sth PC	A	Banbury United	446	L 2 - 4	Endall 10 Diau 24	22	28
6	Sth PC	A	Royston	165	L 1 - 2	Diau 79	22	29
11	Sth PC	H	Rushall Olympic	192	L 0 - 3		22	30
14	Sth PC	H	Stratford	158	L 0 - 2		22	31
18	Sth PC	A	Lowestoft Town	362	L 0 - 6		22	32
21	Sth PC	A	Bromsgrove Sporting	944	L 1 - 8	Endall 50	22	33
25	Sth PC	H	Needham Market	126	L 0 - 3		22	34
Feb 1	Sth PC	A	AFC Rushden & Diamonds	550	L 0 - 3		22	35
8	Sth PC	H	Tamworth	361	L 0 - 2		22	36
15	Sth PC	A	Stratford Town	206	L 0 - 2		22	37
22	Sth PC	H	Nuneaton Borough	190	W 3 - 2	Martin 54 81 Traore 56	22	38
Mar 7	Sth PC	H	Hednesford Town	203	L 0 - 1		22	39

GOALSCORERS	SG	CSG	Pens	Hat tricks	Total		SG	CSG	Pens	Hat tricks	Total
Martin	3	2			5	Marsella	1				1
Deards	1		1		3	Monaghan	1				1
Diau	3	2			3	Moore	1				1
Endall	3	2			3	Nelson	1				1
Hilton	3				3	Newell	1				1
Coyle	2				2	Staten	1				1
Truslove	2				2	Sweeney	1				1
Barlone	1				1	Traore	1				1
Hickman	1				1						
Lucas	1				1						

ROYSTON TOWN MATCH RESULTS 2019-20

Date	Comp	H/A	Opponents	Att:	Result	Goalscorers	Pos	No.
Aug 10	Sth PC	H	Alvechurch	253	W 3 - 0	Bridges 31 Adams 43 Bateman 90		1
13	Sth PC	A	Biggleswdae Town	208	W 3 - 0	Murray 32 Ofuso 51 Adams 83		2
17	Sth PC	A	Banbury United	164	L 0 - 2		3	3
24	Sth PC	H	Coalville Town	245	D 1 - 1	Bateman 38	3	4
26	Sth PC	A	Lowestoft Town	474	W 1 - 0	Murray 74	2	5
31	Sth PC	H	Rushall Olympic	277	W 2 1	Scott-Morriss16 Bateman 46	2	6
Sept 7	FAC1Q	H	Rothwell Corinthians	262	W 7 - 2	Adams 18 59 62 (pen) Bateman 32 Ofosu 79 Newton 82 Murray 90		7
14	Sth PC	A	AFC Rushden & Diamonds	463	D 1 - 1	Bateman 45	5	8
21	FAC2Q	A	Balham	233	W 5 - 3	Bridges 14 Newton 39 Bateman 59 Murray 79 88		9
28	Sth PC	H	Tamworth	312	L 1 - 2	Bridges 34	9	10
Oct 5	FAC3Q	H	Beaconsfield Town	407	W 2 - 1	Castiglione 29 Bateman 79		11
12	Sth PC	A	Hednesford Town	491	L 1 - 4	Adams 28	10	12
15	Sth PC	H	Hitchin Town	324	D 1 - 1	Murray 83	13	13
19	FAC4Q	H	Maldon & Tiptree	1152	L 1 - 3	Martin 55	15	14
22	Sth PC	A	St Ives Town	143	W 4 - 0	Woodward (og) 47 Murray 57 Adams 80 Bateman 89	12	15
26	FAT1Q	A	Brightlingsea Regent	121	W 2 - 1	Watkins 33 Castiglione 81		16
29	Sth PC	H	Needham Market	248	W 1 - 0	Bateman 66 (pen)	7	17
Nov 2	Sth PC	A	Nuneaton Borough	515	D 2 - 2	Bateman 5 Bridges 90	10	18
9	FAT2Q	H	Haywards Heath	225	W 7 - 0	Castiglione 17 89 Murray 24 Bridges 40 Bateman 60 90 Ofosu 75		19
16	Sth PC	A	Barwell	163	L 1 - 3	Bateman 1	12	20
23	FAT3Q	A	Wealdstone	396	W 3 - 2	Adams 10 84 Castiglione 29		21
26	Sth PC	H	Stratford	160	W 3 - 2	Ofosu 37 Watkins 49 Adams 84	11	22
30	Sth PC	A	Bromsgrove Sporting	706	D 1 - 1	Ofusu 84	10	23
Dec 3	Sth PC	H	Leiston	211	D 0 - 0		9	24
7	Sth PC	H	Peterborough Sports	226	W 4 - 1	Murray 65 90 Ofosu 66 Bateman 77	6	25
13	FAT1P	H	Boreham Wood	478	W 2 - 0	Murray 21 87		26
26	Sth PC	H	Kings Langley	216	W 1 - 0	Watkins 10	9	27
Jan 1	Sth PC	H	Lowestoft Town	280	W 5 - 1	Watkins 55 62 Martin 31 Bateman 41 Ofuso 47	7	28
4	Sth PC	A	Alvechurch	178	W 1 - 0	Mentis 23	6	29
7	Sth PC	H	Redditch United	165	W 2 - 1	Bateman 10 Castiglione 73	5	30
11	FAT2P	H	Chester	818	W 3 - 0	Bateman 51 84 Castiglione 56	4	31
18	Sth PC	H	Coalville Town	256	L 1 - 4	Bennett 87	6	32
25	Sth PC	H	Banbury United	338	W 1 - 0	Bateman 88	3	33
28	Sth PC	A	Tamworth	424	L 0 - 2		4	34
Feb 1	Sth PC	A	Rushall Olympic	181	W 3 - 1	Castiglione 7 89 Bridges 30	4	35
8	FAT3P	A	Ebbsfleet United	900	W 2 - 0	Oyinsan 92 Bateman 115 (aet)		36
15	Sth PC	H	Biggleswade Town	293	W 3 - 0	Bateman 12 Adams 22 50	4	37
22	Sth PC	H	Hednesford Town	380	W 1 - 0	Warner-Eley 90	4	38
25	Sth PC	H	Stourbridge	293	W 3 - 1	Bateman 12 Adams 22 50	2	39
Mar 3	FAT4P	A	Concord Rangers	852	L 1 - 2	Warner-Eley 54		40
7	Sth PC	H	St Ives Town	415	W 5 - 0	Scott-Morriss 22 Martin 40 Oyinsan 65 Bateman 68 Parr 773		41

GOALSCORERS	SG	CSG	Pens	Hat tricks	Total		SG	CSG	Pens	Hat tricks	Total
Bateman	21	5	1		23	Scott-Moriss	2				2
Adams	9	2	1	1	14	Warner-Ely	2				2
Murray	9				12	Bennett	1				1
Castiglione	7				9	Mentis	1				1
Ofusu	7				7	Opponents	1				1
Bridges	6	2			6	Parr	1				1
Watkins	4				5						
Martin	2				2						
Newton	2				2						
Oyinsan	2				2						

RUSHALL OLYMPIC MATCH RESULTS 2019-20

Date	Comp	H/A	Opponents	Att:	Result	Goalscorers	Pos	No.
Aug 10	Sth PC	A	Peterborough Sports	201	D 1 - 1	Whittall 90		1
13	Sth PC	H	Redditch United	255	W 3 - 1	Letford 15 Waldron 68 Whittall 84		2
17	Sth PC	H	Leiston	186	W 6 - 0	Rowley 24 O'Callaghan 39 Whittall 54 Letford 75 85 Leachman-Whittingham 77	2	3
24	Sth PC	A	Hitchin Town	303	W 2 - 1	Rowley 67 Letford 68	1	4
26	Sth PC	H	Stafford Town	374	W 4 - 1	Smith 10 Letford 28 67 Leachman-Whittingham 90	1	5
31	Sth PC	A	Royston Town	277	L 1 - 2	Letford 8	1	6
Sept 7	FAC1Q	H	Sheffield	259	W 3 - 1	Letford 50 61 Moore 85	,	7
14	Sth PC	H	St Ives Town	223	W 4 - 3	Rowley 31 Letford 42 O'Callaghan 47 Charlton 90	1	8
17	Sth PC	A	Bromsgrove Rovers	772	D 1 - 1	Letford 44	1	9
21	FAC2Q	H	Gainsborough Trinity	249	W 2 - 0	Letford 18 Clarke 76		10
28	Sth PC	H	Lowestoft Town	230	W 4 - 1	Steele 7 60 Letford 28 59	1	11
Oct 5	FAC3Q	A	Belper Town	528	L 1 - 2	Letford 69		12
12	Sth PC	A	Kings Langley	291	L 0 - 4		2	13
15	Sth PC	H	Barwell	239	L 0 - 1			14
19	Sth PC	H	AFC Rushden & Diamonds	236	D 1 - 1	Whittall 44	6	15
26	FAT1Q	A	Grantham Town	215	L 3 - 5	Rowley 13 20 54		16
Nov 2	Sth PC	A	Tamworth	636	L 1 - 2	Letford 25	9	17
9	Sth PC	H	Alvechurch	304	W 2 - 0	Letford 45 Pendley 52	5	18
16	Sth PC	A	Needham Market	236	D 1 - 1	Whittall 87	9	19
30	Sth PC	H	Banbury United	220	D 1 - 1	Waldron 88	9	20
Dec 7	Sth PC	A	Nuneaton Borough	470	W 3 - 1	Letford 11 Waldron 52 Leachman-Whittingham 89	7	21
9	Sth PC	A	Stourbridge	408	L 1 - 2	Pendley 37	7	22
14	Sth PC	A	Lowestoft Town	340	D 0 - 0		8	23
21	Sth PC	H	Coalville Town	231	L 0 - 2		10	24
26	Sth PC	H	Hednesford Town	619	W 1 - 0	Whittall 47 (pen)	10	25
Jan 1	Sth PC	A	Stratford Town	193	W 2 - 1	Letford 50 Rowley 72	8	26
4	Sth PC	H	Peterborough Sports	251	L 0 - 2		8	27
7	Sth PC	H	Biggleswade Town	153	W 3 - 2	Whittall 18 Rowley 22 Boroughs 90	10	28
11	Sth PC	A	Redditch United	192	W 3 - 0	Clarke 6 Waldron 14 Wreh 37	8	29
18	Sth PC	H	Hitchin Town	241	W 4 - 2	Cook 1 Waldron 8 Whittall 8 Clarke 59	5	30
21	Sth PC	A	Coalville Town	141	L 0 - 2		6	31
25	Sth PC	A	Leiston	242	D 2 - 2	Whittall 29 32	6	32
Feb 1	Sth PC	H	Royston Town	181	L 1 - 3	Waldron 66	7	33
8	Sth PC	A	St Ives Town	133	W 4 - 2	Whitall 28 49 68 Smith 87	5	34
15	Sth PC	A	Barwell	159	D 0 - 0		5	35
22	Sth PC	H	Kings Langley	192	L 0 - 1		6	36
Mar 7	Sth PC	H	Stourbridge	433	W 2 - 0	Batchelor 42 Waldren 61	5	37

GOALSCORERS	SG	CSG	Pens	Hat tricks	Total		SG	CSG	Pens	Hat tricks	Total
Letford	15	11			19	Batchelor	1				1
Whittall	9		1	1	13	Boroughs	1				1
Rowley	6			1	9	Charlton	1				1
Waldron	7				6	Cook	1				1
Clarke	3				3	Moore	1				1
Leachman-Whittingham	3				3	Wreh	1				1
O'Callaghan	2				2						
Pendley	2				2						
Smith	2				2						
Steele	1				2						

SOUTHERN LEAGUE

ST IVES TOWN MATCH RESULTS 2019-20

Date	Comp	H/A	Opponents	Att:	Result	Goalscorers	Pos	No.
Aug 10	Sth PC	H	Tamworth	271	D 1 - 1	Kelly 31		1
13	Sth PC	A	Lowestoft Town	436	L 0 - 1			2
17	Sth PC	A	Biggleswade Town	160	L 0 - 2		19	3
24	Sth PC	H	Stourbridge	204	L 0 - 2		19	4
26	Sth PC	A	AFC Rushden & Diamonds	525	L 0 - 1		20	5
31	Sth PC	H	Coalville Town	154	L 1 - 2	Parker 50	20	6
Sept 7	FAC1Q	H	Berkhamstead	223	W 2 - 1	De'Ath 32 Seymore-Shove 55 (pen)	20	7
14	Sth PC	A	Rushall Olympic	120	L 3 - 4	Parker 25 (pen) 43 Foy 28	21	8
17	Sth PC	H	Kings Langley	120	W 2 - 1	Pattison (og) Snelus 60		9
21	FAC2Q	H	Canvey Island	187	D 0 - 0			10
24	FAC2Qr	A	Canvey Island	194	L 2 - 3	Johnson 24 Wilson 65 (aet)		11
28	Sth PC	A	Redditch United	184	W 1 - 0	Johnson 54	19	12
Oct 5	Sth PC	H	Nuneaton Bioorough	251	W 2 - 0	Wood 71 Seymore-Shove 84		13
12	Sth PC	H	Peterborough Sports	285	L 0 - 3		18	14
15	Sth PC	A	Leiston	139	D 4 - 4	Foy 45 48 78 Seymore-Shove 62	18	15
19	Sth PC	A	Alvechurch	183	L 0 - 1		18	16
22	Sth PC	H	Royston	143	L 0 - 4		18	17
26	FAT1Q	H	Soham Town Rangers	231	D 0 - 0			18
29	FAT1Qr	A	Soham Town Rangers	202	L 0 - 3			19
Nov 2	Sth PC	H	Hitchin Town	169	L 0 - 3		19	20
9	Sth PC	A	Banbury United	318	L 0 - 1		19	21
23	Sth PC	A	Bromsgrove Rovers	737	L 2 - 3	McWilliams 10 Parker 51	20	22
30	Sth PC	H	Stratford Town	118	D 2 - 2	Wilson 9 Foy 52	20	23
Dec 7	Sth PC	A	Barwell	149	L 0 - 1		20	24
14	Sth PC	H	Redditch Town	126	W 2 - 1	Seymore-Shove 3 Parker 78	19	25
21	Sth PC	A	Nuneaton Borough	392	L 0 - 4		19	26
26	Sth PC	A	Needham Market	214	D 1 - 1	Seymore-Shove 87	19	27
Jan 1	Sth PC	H	AFC Rushden & Diamonds	377	L 3 - 4	Curtis 9 Wilson 61 Toseland 88	21	28
4	Sth PC	A	Tamworth	638	L 0 - 3		21	29
11	Sth PC	H	Lowestoft Town	183	L 2 - 4	Wilson 57 64	21	30
18	Sth PC	A	Stourbridge	712	L 1 - 3	Wilson 67	21	31
25	Sth PC	H	Bggleswade Town	161	L 0 - 3		21	32
Feb 1	Sth PC	A	Coalville Town	195	W 2 - 1	Foy 67 82	20	33
8	Sth PC	A	Rushall Olympic	133	L 2 - 4	Parker 37 Wilson 88	20	34
22	Sth PC	A	Peterborough Sports	352	L 0 - 5		20	35
Mar 3	Sth PC	H	Leisron	105	W 1 - 0	Parker 12	19	36
6	Sth PC	A	Royston	415	L 0 - 5		20	37
10	Sth PC	H	Hednesford Town	116	D 1 - 1	Curtis 66	20	38

GOALSCORERS	SG	CSG	Pens	Hat tricks	Total		SG	CSG	Pens	Hat tricks	Total
Foy	4			1	7	Snekus	1				1
Parker	6				7	Toseland	1				1
Wilson	6	2	2		7	Wood	1				1
S-Shove	5		1		5						
Curtis	2				2						
Johnson	2	2			2						
De'Ath	1				1						
Kelly	1				1						
McWilliams	1				1						
Opponents	1				1						

STOURBRIDGE MATCH RESULTS 2019-20

Date	Comp	H/A	Opponents	Att:	Result	Goalscorers	Pos	No.
Aug 10	Sth PC	A	Hitchin Town	322	W 2 - 1	Brown 7 Finn 52		1
12	Sth PC	H	Stratford Town	719	W 3 - 1	Grocutt 26 Landell 49 Brown 63		2
17	Sth PC	H	Hednesford Town	588	L 0 - 3			3
24	Sth PC	A	St Ives Town	204	W 2 - 0	Johnson 15 Taylor 90		4
26	Sth PC	H	Bromsgrove Sporting	1158	W 2 - 1	Taylor 19 Brown 28		5
31	Sth PC	A	Peterborough Sports	182	D 2 - 2	Lloyd 88 Green 90		6
Sept 7	FAC1Q	A	**Bromsgrove Sporting**	**385**	**W 1 - 0**	**Mills 48**		7
14	Sth PC	H	Leiston	615	W 5 - 1	Williams 24 Taylor 28 53 Mills 60 Tonks 81		8
17	Sth PC	A	Nuneaton Borough	385	L 0 - 4			9
21	FAC2Q	A	**Coalville Town**	**315**	**W 2 - 1**	**Birch 35 Cook 79**		10
28	Sth PC	A	Kings Langley	312	W 4 - 1	Yurton 40 Williams 45 Till 71 Landell 79		11
Oct 5	FAC3Q	H	**Stafford Rangers**	**1048**	**W 2 - 1**	**Brown 10 Tilt 16**		12
12	Sth PC	H	Banbury United	1073	D 1 - 1	Tilt 77		13
19	FAC4Q	H	**Whitby Town**	**1171**	**D 1 - 1**	**Lloyd 72**		14
21	FAC4Qr	H	**Whitby Town**	**1092**	**W 3 - 2**	**Bellis 40 Nicholls 75 Green 82**		15
29	FAT1Q	H	**Nuneaton Borough**	**423**	**W 2 - 1**	**Carter Ezewele**		16
Nov 2	Sth PC	A	Needham Market	254	D 3 - 3	Tilt 38 60 Lloyd 68		17
9	FAC1P	H	**Eastleigh**	**1845**	**D 2 - 2**	**Lloyd 25 Grocott 52**		18
12	FAT2Q	H	**Lancaster City**	**315**	**D 2 - 2**			19
19	FAC1Pr	A	**Eastleigh**	**1509**	**L 0 - 3**			20
23	FAT2Qr	A	**Lancaster City**	**241**	**W 2 - 1**	**Dwyer 10 Birch 74**		21
26	FAT3Q	H	**South Shields**	**356**	**D 1 - 1**			22
30	Sth PC	A	AFC Rushden & Diamonds	446	L 2 - 3	Willetts 25 Lloyd 64		23
Dec 3	FAT3Qr	A	**South Shields**	**612**	**L 0 - 4**			24
7	Sth PC	A	Coalville Town	528	D 1 - 1	Dwyer 84		25
9	Sth PC	H	Rushall Olympic	408	W 2 - 1	Dwyer 53 Tilt 70		26
14	Sth PC	H	Kings Langley	460	L 1 - 3	Tilt 35		27
26	Sth PC	H	Redditch United	823	W 1 - 0	Tilt 54		28
28	Sth PC	A	Biggleswade Town	202	W 2 - 1	Williams 55 Landell 85		29
Jan 1	Sth PC	A	Bromsgrove Sporting	1730	L 1 - 4	Landell 11		30
4	Sth PC	H	Hitchin Town	571	L 1 - 2	Hayward 51		31
11	Sth PC	A	Stratford Town	353	W 2 - 1	Nicholls 33 Tonks 41		32
18	Sth PC	H	St Ives Town	712	W 3 - 1	Dwyer 6 Brown 20 Hayward 40		33
21	Sth PC	A	Alvechurch	274	W 3 - 0	Dwyer 12 (pen) Hayward 78 Nicholls 80		34
25	Sth PC	A	Hednesford Town	515	W 2 - 1	Tonks 17 Willets 69		35
Feb 1	Sth PC	H	Peterborough Sports	532	L 1 - 6	Dwyer 42		36
3	Sth PC	H	Barwell	381	D 1 - 1	Tilt 90		37
8	Sth PC	A	Leiston	255	W 1 - 0	Williams 19		38
15	Sth PC	H	Alvechurch	487	W 1 - 0	Tilt 8		39
18	Sth PC	A	Lowestoft Town	274	L 1 - 2	Green 59		40
22	Sth PC	A	Banbury United	542	L 0 - 2			41
25	Sth PC	A	Royston Town	223	L 1 - 3	Landell 39		42
29	Sth PC	H	Lowestoft Town	569	W 2 - 0	Dwyer 23 Landell 83		43
Mar 7	Sth PC	A	Rushall Olympic	433	L 0 - 2			44

GOALSCORERS	SG	CSG	Pens	Hat tricks	Total		SG	CSG	Pens	Hat tricks	Total
Tilt	9	3			10	Birch	2				2
Dwyer	7		1		7	Grocutt	2				2
Landell	6	2			6	Mills	2				2
Lloyd	5	2			5	Willetts	2				2
Brown	4	2			5	Bellis	1				1
Taylor	4	2			4	Carter	1				1
Williams	4				4	Cook	1				1
Green	3				3	Ezewele	1				1
Hayward	3				3	Finn	1				1
Nicholls	3				3	Johnson	1				1
Tonks	3				3	Yurton	1				1

STRATFORD TOWN MATCH RESULTS 2019-20

Date	Comp	H/A	Opponents	Att:	Result	Goalscorers	Pos	No.
Aug 10	Sth PC	H	Needham Market	221	W 2 - 1	Glover 70 Wreh 90		1
12	Sth PC	A	Stourbridge	719	L 1 - 3	Shariff 67 (pen)		2
17	Sth PC	A	Kings Langley	255	D 3 - 3	Ball 6 Wilson 26 Wren 90	13	3
24	Sth PC	H	AFC Rushden & Diamonds	325	W 3 - 1	Wreh 28 78 Ball 48	12	4
26	Sth PC	A	Rushall Olympic	374	L 1 - 4	Glover 19	14	5
31	Sth PC	H	Biggleswade Town	192	L 1 - 2	Shariff 44 (pen)	15	6
Sept 7	**FAC1Q**	**H**	**Boldmere St Michaels**	**180**	**W 6 - 1**	**Shariff 59 62 89 Lyng (og) Hughes 38 (pen) Ball 90**		7
14	Sth PC	A	Coalville Town	175	D 1 - 1	Shariff 17	14	8
17	Sth PC	H	Alvechurch	201	W 2 - 0	Curtis 3 Shariff 68	11	9
21	**FAC2Q**	**A**	**Halesowen Town**	**611**	**L 1 - 4**	**Morrison 30**	11	10
28	Sth PC	A	Hitchin Town	328	L 0 - 2		13	11
Oct 5	Sth PC	H	Leiston	170	W 3 - 1	Edwards-John 33 Wreh 53 Eze 84	12	12
12	Sth PC	H	Lowestoft Town	254	L 0 - 3		12	13
22	Sth PC	A	Tamworth	272	L 1 - 3	Wilson 6 (pen)	16	14
Nov 2	Sth PC	A	Peterborough Sports	152	L 0 - 6		17	15
9	Sth PC	H	Coalville Town	210	L 1 - 4	McFarlane 90	17	16
16	Sth PC	A	Nuneaton Borough	425	L 0 - 2		17	17
19	Sth PC	H	Hednesford Town	171	W 4 - 1	Shamsi 6 65 Wreh 12 McFarlane 85	16	18
26	Sth PC	A	Royston Town	160	L 2 - 3	Rowley 77 87	16	19
29	**FAT1Q**	**H**	**Hednesford Town**	**210**	**L 1 - 2**	**Shamsi 16**		20
30	Sth PC	A	St Ives Town	118	D 2 - 2	McFarlane 67 88	17	21
Dec 3	Sth PC	H	Barwell	121	L 1 - 5	Shamsi 45	17	22
7	Sth PC	H	Bromsgrove Sporting	422	L 1 - 2	Wreh 18	17	23
21	Sth PC	A	Hednesford Town	269	L 0 - 1		18	24
26	Sth PC	A	Banbury United	411	L 0 - 5		18	25
Jan 1	Sth PC	H	Rushall Olympic	193	L 1 - 2	McLean 90	19	26
4	Sth PC	A	Needham Market	243	L 0 - 1		19	27
11	Sth PC	H	Stourbridge	353	L 1 - 2	Flanagan 21	19	28
14	Sth PC	A	Redditch United	158	W 2 - 0	Sweeney 32 (Pen) 80	19	29
18	Sth PC	A	AFC Rushden & Diamonds	417	L 2 - 4	Sweeney 35 78	19	30
25	Sth PC	A	Kings Langley	245	L 0 - 1		19	31
28	Sth PC	H	Hitchin Town	144	D 3 - 3	Vann 2 Roberts 45 Howards 73	19	32
Feb 1	Sth PC	A	Biggleswade Town	165	W 1 - 0	Richards 81	18	33
15	Sth PC	H	Redditch United	206	W 2 - 0	Thompson-Brown 70 Perry 90	18	34
22	Sth PC	A	Lowestoft Town	369	L 0 - 2		18	35
Mar 7	Sth PC	A	Tamworth	688	L 1 - 4	Perry 49	17	36

GOALSCORERS	SG	CSG	Pens	Hat tricks	Total		SG	CSG	Pens	Hat tricks	Total
Shariff	5	3	2	1	7	Eze	1				1
Wreh	6				7	Flanagan	1				1
McFarlane	3				4	Harris	1		1		1
Shamsi	3				4	Howards	1				1
Sweeney	2		1		4	McLean	1				1
Ball	3				3	Morrison	1				1
Glover	2				2	Opponents	1				1
Perry	2				2	Richards	1				1
Rowley	1				2	Roberts	1				1
Wilson	2		2		2	Thompson-Brown	1				1
Curtis	1				1	Vann	1				1
Edwards-John	1				1						

TAMWORTH MATCH RESULTS 2019-20

Date	Comp	H/A	Opponents	Att:	Result	Goalscorers	Pos	No.
Aug 10	Sth PC	A	St Ives Town	271	D 1 - 1	Beswick 14		1
13	Sth PC	H	Lowestoft Town	707	L 1 - 3	Hoenes 4		2
17	Sth PC	H	Biggleswade Town	563	W 3 - 1	Clement 9 29 Creaney 15	12	3
24	Sth PC	A	Leiston	242	W 2 - 1	Clement 76 Creaney 90	8	4
26	Sth PC	H	Hednesford Town	819	L 0 - 1		9	5
31	Sth PC	A	Hitchin Town	344	W 3 - 0	Kaziboni 7 43 Creaney 55	8	6
Sept 7	FAC1Q	H	**Nuneaton Town**	1047	W 3 - 1	Beswick (pen) 22 Obeng 25 Yafai 53		7
14	Sth PC	H	Redditch United	591	W 3 - 0	Obeng 11 Waite 13 Kaziboni 34	7	8
17	Sth PC	A	Barwell	324	W 2 - 1	Obeng 21 Waite 38	7	9
21	FAC2Q	A	**Loughborough Dynamo**	416	W 3 - 0	Beswick 8 (pen) 47 (pen) Hoenes 75		10
28	Sth PC	A	Royston Town	313	W 2 - 1	Waite 16 Forde 54	7	11
Oct 5	FAC3Q	H	**Hereford**	1206	D 0 - 0			12
8	FAC3Qr	A	**Hereford**	1271	W 0 - 0	(Won 3-1 on pens)		13
12	Sth PC	A	Biggleswade Town	260	L 1 - 2	Yafai 29	7	14
15	Sth PC	H	AFC Rushden & Diamonds	496	W 3 - 0	Gough 34 Waite 43 Beswick 79 (pen)	5	15
19	FAC4Q	A	**Darlington**	1358	L 0 - 3			16
22	Sth PC	A	Stratford Town	272	W 3 - 0	Beswick 42 (pen) 66 (pen) Waite 73	3	17
26	FAT1Q	H	**Leiston**	385	W 4 - 0	Hoenes 30 Waite 40 Creaney 62 65		18
Nov 2	Sth PC	H	Rushall Olympic	636	W 2 - 1	Beswick 19 34 (pen)	1	19
9	FAT2Q	H	**Gainsworth Trinity**	515	L 3 - 5	Hoenes 17 (pen) Yafai 65 Creaney 78		20
12	Sth PC	H	Alvechurch	447	W 2 - 0	Creaney 6 Obeng 13	1	21
16	Sth PC	H	Kings Langley	711	W 2 - 0	Yafai 29 Waite 75	1	22
30	Sth PC	H	Lowestoft Town	593	W 4 - 1	Beswick 3 9 Waite 47 Hoenes 51	1	23
Dec 7	Sth PC	A	Banbury United	561	W 1 - 0	Lait 87	1	24
10	Sth PC	H	Needham Market	450	L 1 - 2	Creaney 76	1	25
26	Sth PC	H	Nuneaton Borough	1326	D 3 - 3	Beswick 36 (pen) 45 (pen) Waite 50	1	26
Jan 1	Sth PC	A	Hednesford Town	802	W 3 - 0	Yafai 13 Lait 68 87	1	27
4	Sth PC	H	St Ives Town	638	W 3 - 0	Creaney 21 Lait 71 Hoenes 74	1	28
11	Sth PC	A	Bromsgrove Sporting	1764	L 0 - 1		2	29
18	Sth PC	H	Leiston	651	L 1 - 2	Beswick 75	2	30
25	Sth PC	A	Peterborough Sports	320	L 2 - 4	Creaney 48 Obeng 85	5	31
28	Sth PC	H	Royston Town	424	W 2 - 0	Creaney 12 Beswick 60 (pen)	2	32
Feb 1	Sth PC	H	Hitchin Town	625	W 1 - 0	Creaney 71	2	33
4	Sth PC	A	Alvechurch	252	W 2 - 0	Lait 76 90	1	34
8	Sth PC	A	Redditch United	361	W 2 - 0	Hewarn 20 Little 47	1	35
22	Sth PC	H	Biggleswade Town	601	W 4 - 0	Beswick 27 74 Gough 61 Fry 63	1	36
Mar 7	Sth PC	H	Stratford Town	688	W 4 - 1	Waite 23 Obeng 47 Beswick 60 (pen) Carta 90	2	37

GOALSCORERS	SG	CSG	Pens	Hat tricks	Total		SG	CSG	Pens	Hat tricks	Total
Beswick	12	2	11		18	Carta	1				1
Creaney	11	3			12	Forde	1				1
Waite	9	2			10	Fry	1				1
Hoeness	6		1		6	Hearn	1				1
Lait	4				6	Little	1				1
Obeng	6	2			6						
Yafai	5				5						
Clement	2	2			3						
Kaziboni	2				3						
Gough	2				2						

BEACONSFIELD TOWN MATCH RESULTS 2019-20

Date	Comp	H/A	Opponents	Att:	Result	Goalscorers	Pos	No.
Aug 10	Sth PS	A	Dorchester Town	316	L 0 - 1			1
13	Sth PS	H	Chesham United	226	L 1 - 3	Yorke 19		2
17	Sth PS	H	Farnborough	103	L 1 - 3	Losasso 89	22	3
24	Sth PS	A	Tiverton Town	204	L 1 - 6	Brown 45	22	4
26	Sth PS	H	Metropolitan Police	104	L 1 - 2	Matthew 75	22	5
31	Sth PS	A	Weston-s-Mare	516	L 0 - 1		22	6
Sept 6	FAC1Q	A	Sutton Common Rovers	139	W 3 - 1	Yorke Morgan 83 McCluskey 90+2		7
14	Sth PS	H	Wimborne Town	77	L 0 - 4		22	8
17	Sth PS	A	Harrow Borough	150	W 2 - 1	Mitford 80 85	22	9
21	FAC2Q	H	Hemel Hempstead Town	211	W 1 - 0	Yorke 86		10
28	Sth PS	H	Blackfield & Langley	75	W 2 - 0	Matthew 12 Mitford 90	21	11
Oct 5	FAC3Q	A	Royston Town	407	L 1 - 2	Mitford 38		12
15	Sth PS	H	Hartley Witney	67	L 1 - 2	Matthew 78	22	13
19	Sth PS	H	Merthyr Tydfil	91	D 0 - 0		21	14
22	Sth PS	A	Gosport Borough	219	D 0 - 0		22	15
26	FAT1Q	A	Westfield	75	L 0 - 1			16
Nov 2	Sth PS	H	Walton Casuals	77	L 1 - 2	Stead 10	22	17
8	Sth PS	A	Hendon	187	L 1 - 2	Losasso 66	22	18
16	Sth PS	H	Yate Town	119	D 1 - 1	Taylor 45	22	19
23	Sth PS	H	Swindon Supermarine	80	D 0 - 0		22	20
30	Sth PS	H	Truro City	83	L 0 - 1		22	21
Dec 7	Sth PS	A	Taunton Town	499	L 0 - 3		22	22
14	Sth PS	A	Blackfield & Langley	69	W 1 - 0	Losasso 45	22	23
21	Sth PS	H	Hayes & Yeadiing United	324	L 2 - 3	Stead 13 Ewington 68	22	24
Jan 4	Sth PS	H	Dorchester Town	115	W 3 - 1	Ewington 16 38 Winspur 48 (og)	21	25
7	Sth PS	A	Hayes & Yeading	174	D 1 - 1	Ajanlekoko 25	21	26
11	Sth PS	A	Chesham United	505	L 0 - 3		21	27
24	Sth PS	A	Farnborough	275	L 0 - 2		21	28
Feb 1	Sth PS	H	Weston-s-Mare	71	D 2 - 2	Stead 32 Losasso 75	21	29
4	Sth PS	A	Metropolitan Police	90	L 1 - 3	Ewington 67	21	30
8	Sth PS	A	Wimborne Town	299	L 0 - 2		21	31
22	Sth PS	H	Poole Town	108	W 2 - 1	Ewington 64 72	21	32
29	Sth PS	A	Merthyr Town	368	D 0 - 0		21	33
Mar 3	Sth PS	H	Tiverton Town	65	W 4 - 0	Ewington 1 53 78 Minhas 60	21	34
7	Sth PS	H	Gosport Borough	76	L 0 - 1		21	35
10	Sth PS	A	Poole Town	188	L 1 - 3	Ewington 81	21	36

GOALSCORERS	SG	CSG	Pens	Hat tricks	Total		SG	CSG	Pens	Hat tricks	Total
Ewington	7	2		1	10	Morgan	1				1
Losasso	3				4	Opponents	1				1
Mitford	3	2			4	Taylor	1				1
Matthew	3				3						
Stead	3				3						
Yorke	3				3						
Ajanlekoko	1				1						
Brown	1				1						
McCluskey	1				1						
Minhas	1				1						

BLACKFIELD & LANGLEY MATCH RESULTS 2019-20

Date	Comp	H/A	Opponents	Att:	Result	Goalscorers	Pos	No.
Aug 10	Sth PS	A	Yate Town	205	W 4 - 1	Plummer 16 77 90 Griffin 45		1
13	Sth PS	H	Wimborne Town	147	W 1 - 0	Saadi 85		2
17	Sth PS	H	Metropolitan Police	64	L 3 - 4	Kasimu 11 Harfield 34 Arthur (og) 50	5	3
26	Sth PS	H	Dorchester Town	155	W 2 - 1	Bongou 1 Plummer 46	9	4
31	Sth PS	A	Chesham United	375	L 1 - 3	Plummer 45	10	5
Sept 7	FAC 1Q	A	**Mangotsfield United**	169	W 5 - 0	**Gwengwe 5 32 Gunson 26 Kasimu 42 (pen) Bongou 83**		6
14	Sth PS	H	Farnborough	123	W 2 - 0	Bongou 31 Makhloufi 90	6	7
21	FAC 2Q	H	**Dorchester Town**	161	W 1 - 0	**Gunson 79**		8
24	Sth PS	A	Harrow Borough	110	L 1 - 3	Makhloufi 66	7	9
28	Sth PS	A	Beaconsfield Town	75	L 0 - 2		10	10
Oct 5	FAC 3Q	A	**Dartford**	295	L 1 - 4	**Kasimu 65**	11	11
8	Sth PS	A	Swindon Supermarine	153	L 0 - 3		12	12
12	Sth PS	A	Merthyr Town	496	L 0 - 2		14	13
15	Sth PS	H	Weston-super-Mare	63	W 2 - 1	Plummer 54 90	11	14
19	Sth PS	H	Hartley Wintney	104	D 0 - 0		11	15
Nov 5	FAT1Q	A	**Truro City**	131	D 1 - 1			16
9	FAT1Qr	H	**Truro City**	57	W 3 - 1	**Kasimu 16 Plummer 56 Gwengwe 86**		17
13	FAT 2Q	H	**Kingstonian**	85	L 0 - 3			18
16	Sth PS	A	Taunton Town	538	L 1 - 4	Gunson 56	18	19
23	Sth PS	H	Truro City	91	L 0 - 2		18	20
26	Sth PS	H	Walton Casuals	60	D 2 - 2	Yobo 26 Griffin 33	17	21
30	Sth PS	H	Hendon	86	D 2 - 2	Kasimu 32 Makhloufi 45	18	22
Dec 7	Sth PS	A	Salisbury	486	D 1 - 1	Orvis 90	18	23
14	Sth PS	H	Beaconsfield Town	69	L 0 - 1		18	24
17	Sth PS	H	Tiverton Town	78	L 0 - 1		18	25
21	Sth PS	A	Walton Casuals	164	W 3 - 2	Kasimu 27 Speechley- Price 63 Rae 68	16	26
26	Sth PS	H	Gosport Boorough	133	D 0 - 0		15	27
Jan 1	Sth PS	A	Dorchester Town	306	D 2 - 2	Kasimu 28 66	15	28
4	Sth PS	H	Yate Town	103	W 2 - 0	Kasimu 25 48	14	29
11	Sth PS	A	Wimborne Town	317	L 0 - 2		16	30
18	Sth PS	H	Harrow Borough	106	W 2 - 0	Griffin 47 Speechley-Price 87	15	31
25	Sth PS	A	Metropolitan Police	105	L 0 - 2		15	32
Feb 1	Sth PS	H	Chesham United	96	L 0 - 2		17	33
8	Sth PS	A	Farnborough	389	D 1 - 1	Suraci 42	17	34
18	Sth PS	A	Hayes & Yeading	150	L 0 - 6		17	35
22	Sth PS	H	Merthyr Town	112	D 0 - 0		17	36
Mar 7	Sth PS	H	Poole Town	181	D 1 - 1	Spetch 31	17	37

GOALSCORERS	SG	CSG	Pens	Hat tricks	Total		SG	CSG	Pens	Hat tricks	Total
Kasimu	7		1		10	Orvis	1				1
Plummer	5	2		1	8	Rae	1				1
Bongou	3				3	Saadi	1				1
Griffin	2				3	Spetch	1				1
Gunson	3				3	Suraci	1				1
Gwengwe	3				3	Yobo	1				1
Makhloufi	3				3						
Speechley-Price	2				2						
Harfield	1				1						
Opponents	1				1						

CHESHAM UNITED MATCH RESULTS 2019-20

Date	Comp	H/A	Opponents	Att:	Result	Goalscorers	Pos	No.
Aug 10	Sth PS	H	Salisbury	452	W 2 - 0	Wynter 57 68		1
13	Sth PS	A	Beaconsfield Town	226	W 3 - 1	Wynter 11 Hart 31 Oliyide 82		2
17	Sth PS	A	Taunton Town	500	L 2 - 3	Casey 12 Price (og) 61	6	3
24	Sth PS	H	Truro City	401	W 2 - 1	Kirby 68 Oliyide 90	3	4
26	Sth PS	A	Hendon	319	L 1 - 3	Wynter 83	4	5
31	Sth PS	H	Blackfield & Langley	375	W 2 - 1	Brown 32 Pearce 88	4	6
Sept 7	FAC1Q	H	Fleet Town	289	W 4 - 2	Brown 50 Casey 57 O)lyide 75 Hart 88		7
14	Sth PS	A	Merthyr Town	493	W 3 - 1	Pearce 23 59 Hart 47	3	8
17	Sth PS	H	Hayes & Welling United	373	W 3 - 2	Oliyide 26 Pearce 73 80	3	9
21	FAC2Q	H	Hampton & Richmond B	430	L 1 - 2	Brown 35		10
28	Sth PS	H	Yate Town	369	W 4 - 2	Olyide 31 77 Pearce 27 Kirby 62	2	11
Oct 5	Sth PS	A	Swindon Supermarine	249	L 1 - 2	Olyide 90		12
12	Sth PS	A	Gosport Borough	487	L 1 - 2	Casey 38	4	13
15	Sth PS	H	Harrow Borough	359	D 1 - 1	Pearce 67	4	14
19	Sth PS	H	Wimborne Town	348	W 1 - 0	Clayton 84	3	15
22	Sth PS	A	Hartley Wintney	178	W 2 - 1	Casey 7 Martin 26 (pen)	3	16
26	FAT1Q	A	Basildon United	96	L 3 - 5	Casey 17 Clayton 69 Wynter 84		17
Nov 9	Sth PS	H	Farnborough	358	W 2 - 0	Casey 45 Kirby 68	1	18
16	Sth PS	A	Weston-s-Mare	599	W 2 - 1	Joseph 11 Prosper 52	1	19
23	Sth PS	H	Dorchester Town	367	W 6 - 3	Pearce 15 Doyle 24 Clayton 52 65 75 Martin 72	1	20
30	Sth PS	A	Metroploitan Police	150	L 1 - 2	Jenkins 85	2	21
Dec 7	Sth PS	H	Poole Town	435	W 2 - 1	Pearce 42 Oliyide 57	2	22
26	Sth PS	A	Walton Casuals	183	W 6 - 1	Oliyidi 2 45 Clayton 18 56 Fox 54 (og) Wynter 76	3	23
Jan 1	Sth PS	H	Hendon	558	W 2 - 1	Pearce 53 Casey 74	3	24
4	Sth PS	A	Salisbury	628	L 2 - 3	Casey 65 Oliyide 74	3	25
11	Sth PS	H	Beaconsfield Town	505	W 3 - 0	Pearce 33 Clayton 65 86	3	26
18	Sth PS	A	Truro City	620	W 1 - 0	Brown 41	1	27
21	Sth PS	A	Yate Town	146	L 1 - 4	Oliyidi 61	1	28
25	Sth PS	H	Taunton Town	551	D 1 - 1	Brown 13	1	29
Feb 1	Sth PS	A	Blackfield & Langley	96	W 2 - 0	Oliyidi 7 32	1	30
8	Sth PS	H	Merthyr Town	561	W 2 - 0	Brown 24 Casey 29	1	31
11	Sth PS	H	Swindon Supermarine	354	L 1 - 2	Pearce 36	1	32
15	Sth PS	A	Harrow Borough	252	D 2 - 2	Pearce 49 Clayton 68	1	33
22	Sth PS	A	Gosport Borough	516	W 3 - 0	Casey 39 84 Joseph 80	1	34
29	Sth PS	A	Wimborne Town	306	W 2 - 1	Casey 24 Joseph 33	1	35
Mar 7	Sth PS	H	Hartley Wintney	476	L 1 - 2	Pearce 14	2	36

GOALSCORERS	SG	CSG	Pens	Hat tricks	Total		SG	CSG	Pens	Hat tricks	Total
Oliyide	10	2			14	Opponents	2				2
Pearce	14				14	Doyle	1				1
Casey	8	3			12	Jenkins	1				1
Clayton	8	2		1	10	Prosper	1				1
Brown	5	2			6						
Wynter	5	2			6						
Hart	3				3						
Joseph	3				3						
Kirby	3				3						
Martin	2		1		2						

DORCHESTER TOWN MATCH RESULTS 2019-20

Date	Comp	H/A	Opponents	Att:	Result	Goalscorers	Pos	No.
Aug 10	Sth PS	H	Beaconsfield Town	316	W 1 - 0	Blair 10		1
13	Sth PS	A	Truro City	470	L 0 - 3			2
17	Sth PS	A	Salisbury	632	L 1 - 4	Bath 58 (pen)	16	3
26	Sth PS	A	Blackfield & Langley	155	L 1 - 2	Bath 50	19	4
31	Sth PS	H	Hartley Wintney	311	L 2 - 3	Blair 80 90	20	5
Sept 8	**FAC1Q**	**A**	**Evesham United**	**320**	**W 2 - 0**	**Bath x2**		6
14	Sth PS	A	Hendon	195	W 3 - 1	Hoey 49 56 87	19	7
17	Sth PS	H	Taunton Town	348	D 2 - 2	Davis 27 Bath 49		8
21	**FAC2Q**	**A**	**Blackfield & Langley**	**161**	**L 0 - 1**		20	9
24	Sth PS	H	Hayes & Yeading United	276	L 2 - 3	Bath 27 32	19	10
28	Sth PS	H	Swindon Supermarine	389	D 1 - 1	Wright 87	19	11
Oct 5	Sth PS	A	Tiverton Town	267	L 1 - 2	Bath 50	19	12
12	Sth PS	A	Weston-super-Mare	561	L 0 - 4		20	13
15	Sth PS	H	Merthyr Town	296	D 0 - 0		20	14
19	Sth PS	H	Yate Town	378	W 2 - 0	Martin 25 Blair 32	19	15
22	Sth PS	A	Wimborne Town	361	L 1 - 2	Blair 10	19	16
26	**FAT1Q**	**A**	**Salisbury**	**342**	**D 3 - 3**	**Bath x2 Blair**		17
29	**FAT1Qr**	**H**	**Salisbury**	**336**	**L 0 - 3**			18
Nov 2	Sth PS	H	Harrow Borough	326	L 1 - 2	Wells 83	20	19
16	Sth PS	H	Walton Casuals	338	D 2 - 2	Lolos 7 Martin 90	21	20
23	Sth PS	A	Chesham United	367	L 3 - 6	Lolos 32 Murphy 57 (og) Peck 86	21	21
30	Sth PS	A	Farnborough Town	306	L 1 - 3	Bath 87	21	22
Dec 7	Sth PS	H	Metropolitan Police	275	L 0 - 3		21	23
10	Sth PS	A	Gosport Borough	197	D 4 - 4	Martin 6 Bath 48 Morris 55 Bath 89	21	24
21	Sth PS	H	Tiverton Town	247	L 1 - 5	Lolos 65	21	25
26	Sth PS	H	Poole Town	377	L 0 - 1		21	26
Jan 1	Sth PS	H	Blackfield & Langley	306	D 2 - 2	Lolos 14 Blair 20	21	27
4	Sth PS	A	Beaconsfield Town	115	L 1 - 3	Bath 78	22	28
11	Sth PS	H	Truro City	334	L 2 - 3	Wright 70 Bath 85	22	29
18	Sth PS	A	Hayes & Yeading	230	L 0 - 5		22	30
21	Sth PS	A	Swindon Supermarine	217	L 0 - 1		22	31
25	Sth PS	H	Salisbury	469	L 0 - 5		22	32
Feb 1	Sth PS	A	Hartley Wintney	237	L 0 - 2		22	33
8	Sth PS	H	Hendon	309	L 0 - 3		22	34
22	Sth PS	H	Weston-s- Mare	282	L 1 - 2	Bath 18	22	35
Mar 7	Sth PS	H	Wimborne Town	406	W 1 - 0	Stokoe 12 (og)	22	36

GOALSCORERS	SG	CSG	Pens	Hat tricks	Total		SG	CSG	Pens	Hat tricks	Total
Bath	12	2	1		15	Peck	1				1
Blair	6	3			7	Wells	1				1
Lolos	4	2			4						
Hoey	1			1	3						
Martin	3				3						
Opponents	2				2						
Wright	2				2						
Bath	1				1						
Davis	1				1						
Morris	1				1						

SOUTHERN LEAGUE

FARNBOROUGH MATCH RESULTS 2019-20

Date	Comp	H/A	Opponents	Att:	Result	Goalscorers	Pos	No.
Aug 10	Sth PS	H	Poole Town	379	L 1 - 4	Cullen 19		1
13	Sth PS	A	Walton Casuals	211	W 2 - 0	Sealy-Harris 26 Cullen 61		2
17	Sth PS	A	Beaconsfield Town	103	W 3 - 1	Cullen 15 Coles 31 48	4	3
24	Sth PS	H	Merthyr Town	387	W 1 - 0	Cullen 39	4	4
26	Sth PS	A	Hayes & Yeading United	261	L 0 - 2		8	5
31	Sth PS	H	Truro City	329	L 0 - 2		10	6
Sept 7	FAC1Q	A	**Ashton United**	**358**	**W 3 - 0**	**Coles Cullen Musunga**		7
14	Sth PS	A	Blackfield & Langley	123	L 0 - 2		12	8
21	FAC2Q	H	**Wealdstone**	**404**	**L 0 - 5**		15	9
28	Sth PS	H	Tiverton Town	289	L 0 - 7		16	10
Oct 5	Sth PS	H	Salisbury	604	L 1 - 3	Flood 15	18	11
12	Sth PS	A	Swindon Supermarine	251	L 2 - 3	Sealy-Harris 7 Young 16	19	12
16	Sth PS	H	Wimborne Town	221	W 2 - 1	Sealy-Harris 6 36	16	13
19	Sth PS	H	Gosport Borough	261	L 0 - 1		16	14
22	Sth PS	A	Yate Town	170	W 1 - 0	Cullen 19	16	15
26	FAT1Q	A	**Gosport Borough**	**234**	**L 1 - 3**	**Cullen 1**		16
Nov 2	Sth PS	H	Salisbury City	473	D 0 0		15	17
6	Sth PS	H	Hendon	176	W 4 - 0	Leggett 5 Cullen 32 Sealy-Harris 59 Fearn 83	12	18
9	Sth PS	A	Chesham United	358	L 0 - 2		12	19
16	Sth PS	H	Harrow Borough	312	D 1 - 1	Sealy-Harris 38	12	20
23	Sth PS	A	Metropolitan Police	139	W 2 - 1	Sealy-Harris 37 Cullen 87	9	21
30	Sth PS	H	Dorchester Town	306	W 3 - 1	Owens 12 Young 37 Cullen 5l	9	22
Dec 7	Sth PS	A	Weston-s-Mare	493	W 3 - 1	Young 30 Owens 77 Sealy-Harris 90	7	23
Jan 1	Sth PS	H	Hayes & Yeading United	343	L 0 - 1		9	24
4	Sth PS	A	Poole Town	412	L 1 - 3	Young 67 (pen)	11	25
11	Sth PS	H	Walton Casuals	282	W 2 - 1	Sealy-Harris 15 Keetch 32	11	26
18	Sth PS	A	Merthyr Town	402	L 0 - 2		12	27
25	Sth PS	H	Beaconsfield Town	275	W 2 - 0	Sealy-Harris 50 89	11	28
Feb 1	Sth PS	A	Truro City	516	L 1 - 2	Cullen 30	11	29
8	Sth PS	H	Blackfield & Langley	389	D 1 - 1	Pearce 65	13	30
	Sth PS	H	Swindon Supermarine	328	L 0 - 1		14	31
Mar 7	Sth PS	H	Yate Town	193	W 4 - 0	Fitzpatrick 28 Lee 45 (og) Akongo78 Cullen 87	14	32
11	Sth PS	H	Taunton Town	143	W 4 - 0	Howe 3 Price 34 (og) Fitzpatrick 44 (pen) Tanner 61	12	33

GOALSCORERS	SG	CSG	Pens	Hat tricks	Total		SG	CSG	Pens	Hat tricks	Total
Cullen	12	4			12	Howe	1				1
Sealy-Harris	8	2			11	Keetch	1				1
Young	4	2	1		4	Lee	1				1
Coles	2				3	Leggett	1				1
Opponents	2	2			2	Musunga	1				1
Owens	2	2			2	Pearce	1				1
Akongo	1				1	Tanner	1				1
Fearn	1				1						
Fitzpatrick	1	2	1		1						
Flood	1				1						

GOSPORT BOROUGH MATCH RESULTS 2019-20

Date	Comp	H/A	Opponents	Att:	Result	Goalscorers	Pos	No.
Aug 10	Sth PS	H	Taunton Town	342	W 3 - 0	Lewis 3 Barker 64 Ridge 90		1
13	Sth PS	A	Salisbury	688	L 0 - 1			2
17	Sth PS	A	Merthyr Town	427	L 0 - 1		13	3
24	Sth PS	H	Hendon	372	W 1 - 0	Barker 56	10	4
26	Sth PS	A	Hartley Wintney	305	D 0 - 0		12	5
31	Sth PS	H	Hayes & Yeading United	374	D 1 - 1	Paterson 13	13	6
Sept 7	FAC1Q	A	Cirencester Town	138	L 0 - 1			7
14	Sth PS	A	Truro City	412	L 0 - 1		15	8
25	Sth PS	H	Poole Town	244	L 0 - 2		16	9
28	Sth PS	A	Harrow Borough	144	W 2 - 0	Lea 27 Paterson 39	12	10
Oct 5	Sth PS	H	Metropolitan Police	299	W 2 - 1	Paterson 80 Huggins 83	7	11
12	Sth PS	H	Chesham United	487	W 2 - 1	Robinson 7 Paterson 73	7	12
15	Sth PS	A	Walton Casuals	184	D 1 - 1	Paterson 68	7	13
19	Sth PS	A	Farnborough	261	W 1 - 0	Lewis 58	6	14
22	Sth PS	H	Beaconsfield Town	219	D 0 - 0		6	15
26	FAT1Q	H	Farnborough	332	W 3 - 1	Ridge 54 Lea 66 Warwick 90+6		16
Nov 2	Sth PS	A	Swindon Supermarine	161	L 0 1		8	17
9	FAT 2Q	H	Melksham Town	235	W 4 - 2	Paterson 3 68 Lewis 18 Flood 52		18
16	Sth PS	A	Wimborne Town	406	W 2 - 1	Paterson 85 Woodford 90	8	19
23	FAT3Q	A	Bath City	528	D 0 - 0			20
27	FAT3Qr	H	Bath City	306	L 2 - 3	Williams 57 Flood 65 (aet)		21
30	Sth PS	A	Tiverton Town	233	W 3 - 2	Kennedy 16 Williams 20 Argent 74	6	22
Dec 7	Sth PS	H	Yate Town	219	D 1 - 1	Williams 5	6	23
10	Sth PS	H	Dorchester Town	197	D 4 - 4	Paterson 15 73 Robinson 20 Woodford 90	6	24
14	Sth PS	H	Harrow Borough	219	W 1 - 0	Lewis 3 Barker 64 Ridge 90	6	25
21	Sth PS	A	Metropolitan Police	130	D 0 - 0		6	26
26	Sth PS	A	Blackfield & Langley	133	D 0 - 0		6	27
Jan 1	Sth PS	H	Hartley Wintney	411	L 0 - 1		7	28
4	Sth PS	A	Gosport Borough	552	L 2 - 3	Williams 11 Flood 14	9	29
18	Sth PS	A	Hendon	180	L 1 - 2	Paterson 87	10	30
25	Sth PS	H	Merthyr Town	296	D 2 - 2	Plummer 10 Paterson 90	9	31
28	Sth PS	H	Weston-s-Mare	172	W 1 - 0	Strugnell 72	7	32
Feb 1	Sth PS	A	Hayes & Yeading United	218	L 1 - 2	Paterson 45	9	33
8	Sth PS	H	Truro City	305	W 1 - 0	Lewis 49	9	34
15	Sth PS	H	Walton Casuals	178	W 2 - 1	Paterson 84 90	7	35
22	Sth PS	A	Chesham United	516	L 0 - 3		9	36
25	Sth PS	H	Salisbury	205	D 0 - 0		9	37
Mar 7	Sth PS	A	Beaconsfield Town	76	W 1 - 0	Woodford 51	9	38

GOALSCORERS	SG	CSG	Pens	Hat tricks	Total		SG	CSG	Pens	Hat tricks	Total
Paterson	11	4			15	Huggins	1				1
Lewis	5				5	Kennedy	1				1
Williams	3	3			4	Plummer	1				1
Barker	2				3	Strugnell	1				1
Flood	3				3	Warwick	1				1
Woodford	3				3						
Lea	2				2						
Ridge	2				2						
Robinson	2				2						
Argent	1				1						

HARROW BOROUGH MATCH RESULTS 2019-20

Date	Comp	H/A	Opponents	Att:	Result	Goalscorers	Pos	No.
Aug 10	Sth PS	H	Merthyr Town	173	W 1 - 0	Bryan 62		1
13	Sth PS	A	Hayes & Yeading	267	W 3 - 2	Bryan 29 Keita 45 O'Connor 81		2
17	Sth PS	A	Hartley Wintney	234	D 1 - 1	O'Connor 68	3	3
26	Sth PS	A	Walton Casuals	207	W 2 - 1	O'Connor 68 Otudeko 70	3	4
31	Sth PS	H	Taunton Town	155	D 1 - 1	Moore 49	6	5
Sept 7	**FAC1Q**	**H**	**Binfield**	**157**	**W 5 - 0**	**Bryan 10 (pen) Moore 42 85 O'Connor 77 90**		6
14	Sth PS	A	Poole Town	467	L 1 - 3	Muhemba 90	7	7
17	Sth PS	H	Beaconsfield Town	150	L 1 - 2	Moss 18	8	8
21	**FAC2Q**	**H**	**Carshalton Athletic**	**157**	**L 0 - 1**			9
24	Sth PS	H	Blackfield & Langley	110	W 3 - 1	Warner-Eley 20 Moss 30 Williams 74	9	10
28	Sth PS	H	Gosport Borough	144	L 0 - 2		8	11
Oct 12	Sth PS	H	Truro City	197	L 1 - 2	Keita 89	13	12
15	Sth PS	A	Chesham United	359	D 1 - 1	O'Connor 90	12	13
19	Sth PS	A	Salisbury	615	L 1 - 3	Keita 30	13	14
22	Sth PS	H	Metropolitan Police	96	L 1 - 2	Otudeko 5	15	15
26	**FAT1Q**	**A**	**AFC Sudbury**	**148**	**L 0 - 2**			16
Nov 2	Sth PS	A	Dorchester Town	326	W 2 - 1	Moore 26 Kearney 90	11	17
9	Sth PS	H	Swindon Supermarine	146	L 2 - 3	Moore 71 Kirby 68	11	18
16	Sth PS	H	Farmborough	312	D 1 - 1	Kearney 81	10	19
23	Sth PS	A	Wimborne	113	L 0 - 1		13	20
30	Sth PS	A	Yate Town	153	L 1 - 2	Kearney 25	16	21
Dec 7	Sth PS	H	Tiverton Town	150	L 1 - 5	Preddie 41	16	22
14	Sth PS	A	Gosport Borough	219	L 0 - 1		16	23
21	Sth PS	H	Weston-s-Mare	116	L 0 - 4		18	24
26	Sth PS	A	Hendon	305	W 1 - 0	Charles-Smith 70	16	25
Jan 1	Sth PS	H	Weston-s-Mare	118	L 0 - 4		16	26
4	Sth PS	A	Merthyr Town	392	D 2 - 2	Tricker 10 63	15	27
11	Sth PS	H	Hayes & Yeading	255	W 3 - 2	Bryan 35 Scott 49 Moore 65	12	28
18	Sth PS	A	Blackfield & Langley	106	L 0 - 2		13	29
25	Sth PS	H	Hartley Whitney	163	L 1 - 4	O'Connor 81	17	30
Feb 1	Sth PS	A	Taunton Town	602	L 2 - 3	Fenton 64 Chime 69	18	31
8	Sth PS	H	Poole Town	173	D 0 - 0		17	32
15	Sth PS	H	Chesham United	252	D 2 - 2	Bryan 35 Preddie 77	16	33
22	Sth PS	A	Truro City	347	L 1 - 4	Moore 23	18	34
Mar 7	Sth PS	A	Metropolitan Police	139	W 3 - 1	Matthew 55 Otudeko 83 Ive 90	16	35
10	Sth PS	H	Salisbury	171	D 2 - 2	Matthew 23 33	16	36

GOALSCORERS	SG	CSG	Pens	Hat tricks	Total		SG	CSG	Pens	Hat tricks	Total
O'Connor	7	3			8	Charles-Smith	1				1
Moore	7	2			7	Chime	1				1
Bryan	5	2	1		5	Fenton	1				1
Kearney	2				3	Ive	1				1
Keita	3				3	Kirby	1				1
Matthew	2	2			3	Muhemba	1				1
Otudeko	3				3	Scott	1				1
Moss	2				2	Warner-Eley	1				1
Preddie	2				2	Williams	1				1
Tricker	1				2						

HARTLEY WINTNEY MATCH RESULTS 2019-20

Date	Comp	H/A	Opponents	Att:	Result	Goalscorers	Pos	No.
Aug 10	Sth PS	A	Wimborne Town	286	D	0 - 0		1
13	Sth PS	H	Swindon Supermarine	228	L	1 - 2 Smith 80		2
17	Sth PS	H	Harrow Borough	234	D	1 - 1 Parker 4 (pen)	18	3
24	Sth PS	A	Metropolitan Police	111	W	1 - 0 Rule 73	13	4
26	Sth PS	H	Gosport Borough	305	D	0 - 0	12	5
31	Sth PS	A	Dorchester Town	311	W	3 - 2 Albert 44 Ball 48 Bird 70	11	6
Sept 7	FAC1Q	H	Spelthorne Sports	192	W	3 - 0 Platt 37 Rule 55 Bird 75		7
14	Sth PS	H	Tiverton Town	212	L	1 - 4 Rule 17	12	8
21	FAC2Q	H	Chichester City	205	D	0 - 0		9
25	FAC2Qr	A	Chichester City	210	L	0 - 1		10
28	Sth PS	A	Salisbury	599	L	0 - 2	17	11
Oct 8	Sth PS	A	Yate Town	167	L	1 - 2 Cornell 49	17	12
12	Sth PS	H	Walton Casuals	198	W	1 - 0 Albert 65	15	13
15	Sth PS	A	Beaconsfield Town	67	W	2 - 1 Albert 47 Bird 88	12	14
19	Sth PS	A	Blackfield & Langley	104	D	0 - 0	12	15
22	Sth PS	H	Chesham United	178	L	1 2 Cornell 61	16	16
29	FAT1Q	A	Poole Town	271	W	1 - 0		17
Nov 9	FAT2Q	A	Westfield	122	D	1 - 1 Webb 88		18
12	FAT2Qr	H	Westfield	153	W	2 - 1		19
16	Sth PS	A	Truro City	412	L	1 - 2 Hollamby 34	16	20
19	Sth PS	H	Poole Town	203	W	3 - 0 Duff 6 Smith 45 (pen) Cornell 56	12	21
23	FAT3Q	A	Eastbourne Borough	278	L	1 - 3		22
30	Sth PS	A	Merthyr Town	377	L	2 - 3 Smith 33 Ball 62	14	23
Dec 7	Sth PS	H	Hayes & Yeading United	246	L	1 - 5 Grant 55	16	24
21	Sth PS	A	Hendon	285	D	2 - 2 Bird 64 Webb 66	18	25
Jan 1	Sth PS	A	Gosport Borough	411	W	1 - 0 Grant 5	18	26
4	Sth PS	H	Wimborne Town	262	D	2 - 2 Rule 50 Miller 52	17	27
7	Sth PS	A	Weston-s-Mare	403	L	1 - 2 Cornell 51	17	28
11	Sth PS	A	Swindon Supermarine	309	L	2 - 3 Kuhl 58 Duff 90	18	29
15	Sth PS	A	Harrow Borough	163	W	4 - 1 Parker 20 49 86 88	18	30
Feb 1	Sth PS	H	Dotchester Town	237	W	2 - 0 Smith 45 (pen) Grant 52	16	31
8	Sth PS	A	Tiverton Town	248	L	0 - 2	18	32
22	Sth PS	A	Walton Casuals	175	W	3 - 0 Ridge 15 Argent 22 Smith 76 (pen)	16	33
Mar 7	Sth PS	A	Chesham United	476	W	2 - 1 Smith 10 (pen) Argent 75	15	34

GOALSCORERS	SG	CSG	Pens	Hat tricks	Total		SG	CSG	Pens	Hat tricks	Total
Smith	6	2	4		6	Webb	2				2
Parker	2		1		5	Hollamby	1				1
Bird	4	2			4	Kuhl	1				1
Cornell	4		1		4	Miller	1				1
Rule	4				4	Platt	1				1
Albert	3	2			3	Ridge	1				1
Duff	3				3						
Argent	2				2						
Ball	2				2						
Grant	2				2						

HAYES & YEADING UNITED MATCH RESULTS 2019-20

Date	Comp	H/A	Opponents	Att:	Result	Goalscorers	Pos	No.
Aug 10	Sth PS	A	Tiverton Town	232	D 2 - 2	Clark 53 Obi 70		1
13	Sth PS	H	Harrow Borough	267	L 2 - 3	Clark 32 Obi 39		2
17	Sth PS	H	Weston-s-Mare	171	L 1 - 2	Benyon 50	20	3
26	Sth PS	H	Farnborough	261	W 2 - 0	Donnelly 45 (pen) Della-Verdy 90	18	4
31	Sth PS	A	Gosport Borough	372	D 1 - 1	Switters 28	17	5
Sept 7	FAC1Q	A	Haywards Heath Town	167	W 1 - 0	Noel-Williams		6
14	Sth PS	H	Yate Town	200	W 2 - 1	Donnellan 30 Obi 82	16	7
17	Sth PS	A	Chesham United	373	L 2 - 3	Noel-Williams 34 Obi 43	16	8
21	FAC2Q	A	Bradshot Lea	189	W 4 - 0	Della-Verdy 8 Clark 43 Switters 69 Little 75		9
24	Sth PS	A	Dorchester Town	276	W 3 - 2	Cook 5 Clark 18 22	17	10
28	Sth PS	A	Truro City	340	L 0 - 3		17	11
Oct 5	FAC3Q	H	Hendon	289	W 5 - 4	Obi 31(pen) Grant 43 Jalloh 45 88 (pen) Rowe 66		12
12	Sth PS	A	Taunton Town	701	L 1 - 2	Jalloh 73 (pen)	17	13
15	Sth PS	H	Hendon	179	W 3 - 2	Rowe 36 Jalloh 48 Obi 60	14	14
19	FAC4Q	H	Poole Town	416	D 1 - 1	Clark 90		15
22	FAC4Qr	A	Poole Town	1066	W 3 - 2	Grant 31 Clark 45 Little 48		16
26	FAT1Q	A	Wingate & Finchley	126	D 1 - 1	Roberts 61		17
29	FAT1Qr	H	Wingate & Finchley	137	W 2 - 1	Grant 47 McDevitt 90		18
Nov 13	FAT2Q	H	Soham Town Rangers	144	W 4 - 2	Buchanan 23 87 Obi 51 Jalloh 90		19
16	Sth PS	H	Salisbury	284	W 1 - 0	Obi 61 (pen)	16	20
23	FAT3Q	A	Salisbury	454	L 3 - 4	Obi 68 Buchanan 73 78		21
30	Sth PS	H	Wimborne	201	W 3 - 1	Buchanan 35 McCreadie 49 Donnelly 76	15	22
Dec 7	Sth PS	A	Hartley Wintney	246	W 5 - 1	Rowe 5 Jailoh 12 44 Buchanan 24 35	15	23
14	Sth PS	H	Truro City	237	L 0 - 1		14	24
17	Sth PS	A	Walton Casuals	178	W 3 - 2	Clark 32 Donnelly 48 Rowe 50	12	25
21	Sth PS	A	Beaconsfield Town	324	W 3 - 2	Buchanan 48 69 Clark 55	8	26
28	Sth PS	H	Metropolitan Police	221	L 0 - 2		10	27
Jan 1	Sth PS	A	Farnborough	343	W 1 - 0	Obi 83	8	28
4	Sth PS	H	Tiverton Town	236	D 0 - 0		8	29
7	Sth PS	H	Beaconsfield Town	174	D 1 - 1	Donnelly 64	8	30
11	Sth PS	A	Harrow Borough	255	L 2 - 3	Jalloh 44 85	10	31
18	Sth PS	H	Dorchester Town	230	W 5 - 0	Duku 2 60 Little 29 43 Jalloh 45	8	32
21	Sth PS	H	Poole Town	125	L 1 - 2	Duku 45	8	33
25	Sth PS	A	Weston-s-Mare	540	W 5 - 1	Duku 37 Rowe 73 88 Amartey 79	7	34
28	Sth PS	A	Merthyr Town	318	W 2 - 1	Rowe 19 51	6	35
Feb 1	Sth PS	H	Gosport Borough	218	W 2 - 1	Sheppard 52 Robinson 90	6	36
8	Sth PS	A	Yate Town	236	W 2 - 0	Amartey 23 34	6	37
18	Sth PS	H	Blackfield & Langley	150	W 6 - 0	Rowe 4 Cunningham 49 Clark 52 Amartey 61 84 Jalloh 87	5	38
22	Sth PS	H	Taunton Town	223	D 2 - 2	Duku 10 Rowe 45	5	39
25	Sth PS	A	Swindon Supermarine	217	D 1 - 1	Amartey 3	5	40
Mat 7	Sth PS	H	Swindon Supermarine	211	W 1 - 0	Amartey 12	5	41

GOALSCORERS	SG	CSG	Pens	Hat tricks	Total		SG	CSG	Pens	Hat tricks	Total
Jalloh	8	2	2		11	Donnellan	2				2
Clark	8	2			10	Noel-Williams	1				2
Obi	10	3	2		10	Switters	2				2
Rowe	8				10	Benyon	1				1
Buchanan	6	3			9	Cook	1				1
Amartey	5				7	Cunningham	1				1
Duku	4	3			5	McCreadie	1				1
Donnelly	4		1		4	McDevitt	1				1
Little	3				4	Roberts	1				1
Grant	3				3	Robinson	1				1
Della-Verdy	2				2	Sheppard	1				1

HENDON MATCH RESULTS 2019-20

Date	Comp	H/A	Opponents	Att:	Result	Goalscorers	Pos	No.
Aug 10	Sth PS	A	Weston-super-Mare	518	D 2 - 2	Tingey 6 English 21		1
13	Sth PS	H	Metropolitan Police	176	D 1 - 1	Calcutt 80		2
17	Sth PS	H	Wimborne Town	189	D 1 - 1	Harriott 32	14	3
24	Sth PS	A	Gosport Borough	372	L 0 - 1		16	4
26	Sth PS	H	Chesham United	319	W 3 - 1	Anderson 37 Calcutt 72 Smith 90	14	5
31	Sth PS	A	Yate Town	247	D 2 - 2	Valantine 7 Calcutt 69	14	6
Sept 7	FAC1Q	A	Little Common	119	W 1 - 0	Jonas 80		7
14	Sth PS	H	Dorchester Town	195	L 1 - 3	Harriott 8	18	8
21	FAC2Q	H	Deeping Rangers	196	W 3 - 2	Jarvis (og) 47 English 64 Calcutt 70	19	9
28	Sth PS	H	Poole Town	172	L 1 - 3	Amartey 76 (pen)	20	10
Oct 5	FAC3Q	A	Hayes & Yeading United	289	L 4 - 5	English 62 Corcoran 68 Amartey 75 80		11
12	Sth PS	H	Salisbury	302	L 0 - 3		21	12
15	Sth PS	A	Hayes & Yeading	179	L 2 - 3	Amartey 18 88	21	13
19	Sth PS	A	Truro City	428	L 1 - 2	Amartey 87	21	14
22	Sth PS	H	Walton Casuals	154	W 2 - 0	Charles 4 Mitchell 18	21	15
26	FAT1Q	A	Whitehawk	207	L 1 - 4	Calcutt 71		16
Nov 6	Sth PS	A	Farnborough	175	L 0 - 4		21	17
9	Sth PS	H	Beaconsfield Town	197	W 2 - 1	Hamblin 68 Galliford 83	20	18
16	Sth PS	A	Swindon Supermarine	311	L 0 - 2		20	19
23	Sth PS	H	Tiverton Town	202	L 1 - 2	Galliford 64	20	20
30	Sth PS	A	Blackfield & Langley	86	D 2 - 2	Galliford 6 Brooks 82	20	21
Dec 7	Sth PS	H	Merthyr Town	234	W 2 - 1	Lucien 35 Brooks 44	20	22
21	Sth PS	H	Hartley Wintney	285	D 2 - 2	Eshun 1 Oshodi 86	19	23
26	Sth PS	H	Harrow Borough	305	L 0 - 1		20	24
Jan 1	Sth PS	A	Chesham United	558	L 1 - 2	Brooks 90	20	25
4	Sth PS	H	Weston-s--Mare	218	W 4 - 0	Tingey 29 Brooks 59 Felix 64 Purnell (og) 75	19	26
11	Sth PS	A	Metropolitan Police	135	W 3 - 0	White 9 48 Oshodi 36	17	27
18	Sth PS	H	Gosport Borough	280	W 2 - 1	Lucien 55 White 76	16	28
25	Sth PS	A	Wimborne Town	314	W 2 - 0	Brooks 2 White 45	14	29
Feb 1	Sth PS	H	Yate Town	234	W 2 - 1	White 31 75	13	30
8	Sth PS	A	Dorchester Town	309	W 3 - 0	Brewer 56 White 88 Olarerin 90	12	31
22	Sth PS	A	Salisbury	515	L 0 - 2		13	32
29	Sth PS	H	Truro City	304	L 1 - 4	Lucien 40	13	33
Mar 4	Sth PS	A	Taunton Town	378	D 3 - 3	Grimes (og) White 32 Olarerin 36	13	34
7	Sth PS	A	Walton Casuals	174	D 1 - 1	White 34	12	35

GOALSCORERS	SG	CSG	Pens	Hat tricks	Total		SG	CSG	Pens	Hat tricks	Total
White	7				9	Anderson	1				1
Amartey	4	2	1		6	Brewer	1				1
Brooks	5	2			5	Charles	1				1
Calcutt	5	2			5	Corcoran	1				1
English	3				3	Eshun	1				1
Galliford	3	2			3	Felix	1				1
Lucien	3				3	Hamblin	1				1
Opponents	3				3	Jonas	1				1
Harriott	2				2	Mitchell	1				1
Olarerin	2				2	Smith	1				1
Oshodi	2				2	Valantine	1				1
Tingey	2				2						

MERTHYR TOWN MATCH RESULTS 2019-20

Date	Comp	H/A	Opponents	Att:	Result	Goalscorers	Pos	No.
Aug 10	Sth PS	A	Harrow Borough	173	L 0 - 1			1
13	Sth PS	H	Weston super Mare	492	D 1 - 1	Traylor 70		2
17	Sth PS	H	Gosport Borough	427	W 1 - 0	Traylor 70	11	3
24	Sth PS	A	Farnborough	387	L 0 - 1		14	4
26	Sth PS	H	Swindon Supermarine	509	W 3 - 1	Lucas 18 Traylor 65 85		5
31	Sth PS	A	Metropolitan Police	158	W 2 - 1	Wright 27 Clarke 90	8	6
Sept 7	FAC1Q	A	**Plymouth Parkway**	201	W 1 - 0		8	7
14	Sth PS	H	Chesham United	493	L 1 - 3	Traylor 70	10	8
18	Sth PS	A	Tiverton Town	468	L 0 - 1		10	9
21	FAC2Q	A	**Weston-s-Mare**	355	L 1 - 2	**Prosser 86**		10
28	Sth PS	A	Walton Casuals	293	L 1 - 2	Traylor 51	15	11
Oct 5	Sth PS	H	Wimborne Town	434	W 3 - 1	Wright 2 Traylor 15 Prosser 90	10	12
12	Sth PS	H	Blackfield & Langley	496	W 2 - 0	Hill 1 Richards 7	9	13
15	Sth PS	A	Dorchester Town	296	D 0 - 0		10	14
19	Sth PS	A	Beaconsfield Town	91	D 0 - 0		9	15
22	Sth PS	H	Salisbury	372	D 1 - 1	Richards 3	9	16
29	FAT1Q	A	**Cinderford Town**	175	D 2 - 2			17
30	Sth PS	H	Hartley Wintney	377	W 3 - 2	Yakubu 36 Hill 38 Traylor 41	9	18
Nov 5	FAT1Qr	H	**Cinderford Town**	187	L 4 - 5			19
Dec 7	Sth PS	A	Hendon	234	L 1 - 2	Lewis 54	10	20
14	Sth PS	H	Walton Casuals	363	L 0 - 2		13	21
26	Sth PS	H	Yate Town	510	W 2 - 1	Jenkins 3 Traylor 15	13	22
Jan 1	Sth PS	A	Swindon Supermarine	333	D 2 - 2	Hill 2 Jones 89	14	23
4	Sth PS	H	Harrow Borough	392	D 2 - 2	Hill 80 Tricker 82 (og)	15	24
18	Sth PS	H	Farnborough	402	W 2 - 0	Hill 26 Jones 28	13	25
25	Sth PS	A	Gosport Borough	296	D 2 - 2	Lucas 56 Jones 62	12	26
28	Sth PS	H	Hayes & Yeading	318	L 1 - 2	Patten 17	12	27
Feb 1	Sth PS	H	Metropolitan Police	322	L 1 - 2	Jones 90	15	28
4	Sth PS	A	Poole Town	347	D 1 - 1	Traylor 42	14	29
8	Sth PS	A	Chesham United	561	L 0 - 2		14	30
11	Sth PS	H	Taunton Town	304	W 4 - 2	Richards 14 33 60 Traylor 49	13	31
22	Sth PS	A	Blackfield & Langley	112	D 0 - 0		13	32
25	Sth PS	A	Wimborne Town	188	D 0 - 0		13	33
29	Sth PS	H	Beaconsfield Town	368	D 0 - 0		13	34
Mar 7	Sth PS	A	Salisbury	547	L 1 - 2	Jones 15	13	35

GOALSCORERS	SG	CSG	Pens	Hat tricks	Total		SG	CSG	Pens	Hat tricks	Total
Traylor	11	2			11	Opponents	1				1
Hill	5	3			5	Pattern	1				1
Jones	5	2			5	Yakubu	1				1
Richards	3		1		5						
Lucas	2				2						
Prosser	2				2						
Wright	2				2						
Clarke	1				1						
Jenkins	1				1						
Lewis	1				1						

METROPOLITAN POLICE MATCH RESULTS 2019-20

Date	Comp	H/A	Opponents	Att:	Result	Goalscorers	Pos	No.
Aug 10	Sth PS	H	Truro City	159	L 0 - 2			1
13	Sth PS	A	Hendon	176	D 1 - 1	Arthur 86		2
17	Sth PS	A	Blackfield & Langley	64	W 4 - 3	Mazzone 29 (pen) Berchiche 61 Robinson75 Sayoud 90	12	3
24	Sth PS	H	Harley Witney	111	L 0 - 1		15	4
26	Sth PS	A	Beaconsfield Town	104	W 2 - 1	Mazzone 48 Murdoch 66	13	5
31	Sth PS	H	Merthyr Town	158	L 1 - 2	Robertson 2	15	6
Sept 7	FAC1Q	H	Horsham	143	D 1 - 1	Knight 75		7
10	FAC1Qr	A	Horsham	445	L 2 - 3	Sayoud 9 Robertson 81		8
14	Sth PS	A	Salisbury	737	W 3 - 1	Mazzone 16 44 Assai 47	11	9
17	Sth PS	H	Walton Casuals	150	L 0 - 3		14	10
28	Sth PS	H	Taunton Town	142	D 1 - 1	Sayoud 71	14	11
Oct 5	Sth PS	A	Gosport Borough	349	L 1 - 2	Robertson 12	16	12
12	Sth PS	A	Yate Town	192	L 0 - 1		17	13
15	Sth PS	H	Swindon	130	L 2 - 3	Murdoch 15 Robertson 27	17	14
19	Sth PS	H	Weston-super-Mare	122	W 2 - 1	Robertson 87 Ness 90	15	15
22	Sth PS	A	Harrow Borough	96	W 2 - 1	Assal 36 Mazzone 59	13	16
26	FAT1Q	H	Tilbury	104	W 4 - 3	Murdoch 16 48 Arthur 53 Mazzone 66		17
Nov 9	FAT2Q	H	Biggleswade Town	123	D 2 - 2	Knight 75 Brooks 80 (pen)		18
16	Sth PS	A	Tiverton Town	276	L 1 - 2	Robinson 90	15	19
19	FAT2Qr	A	Biggleswade Town	92	L 0 - 1			20
23	Sth PS	H	Farnborough	139	L 1 - 2	Murdoch 16	16	21
26	Sth PS	H	Wimborne	89	D 2 - 2	Mazzone 74 87 (pen)	15	22
30	Sth PS	H	Chesham United	150	W 2 - 1	Clarke 67 Knight 90	12	23
Dec 7	Sth PS	A	Dorchester Town	275	W 3 - 0	Mazzone 14 Beale 18 75	11	24
14	Sth PS	A	Taunton Town	540	L 3 - 4	Beale 19 Mazzone 45 84	12	25
21	Sth PS	H	Gosport Borough	130	D 0 - 0		12	26
28	Sth PS	A	Hayes & Yeaing Utd	221	W 2 - 0	Mazzone 6 17	11	27
Jan 4	Sth PS	A	Truro City	444	L 0 - 4		12	28
11	Sth PS	H	Hendon	255	L 0 - 3		14	29
16	Sth PS	H	Blackfield & Langley	105	W 2 - 0	Knight 45 Mazzone 85	13	30
Feb 1	Sth PS	A	Merthyr Town	322	W 2 - 1	Hamilton 53 Frith 73	12	31
4	Sth PS	H	Beaconsfield Town	90	W 3 - 1	Beale 18 Wilkin 21 Knight 33	10	32
8	Sth PS	H	Salsbury	197	W 3 - 2	Mazzone 11 Knight 74 Cursons 90	10	33
22	Sth PS	H	Yate Town	118	W 2 - 0	Mazzone 4 87	10	34
Mar 7	Sth PS	H	Harrow Borough	139	L 1 - 3	Birch 3	11	35

GOALSCORERS	SG	CSG	Pens	Hat tricks	Total		SG	CSG	Pens	Hat tricks	Total
Mazzone	12	2	2		17	Birch	1				1
Knight	7				7	Brooks	1				1
Murdoch	4				5	Clarke	1				1
Robertson	5	2			5	Cursons	1				1
Beale	3				4	Frith	1				1
Sayoud	3				3	Hamilton	1				1
Arthur	2				2	Ness	1				1
Assai	2				2						
Robinson	2				2						
Berchiche	1				1						

POOLE TOWN MATCH RESULTS 2019-20

Date	Comp	H/A	Opponents	Att:	Result	Goalscorers	Pos	No.
Aug 10	Sth PS	A	Farnborough	379	W 4 - 1	Dennett 27 47 53 Spetch 33		1
13	Sth PS	H	Tiverton Town	403	L 1 - 2	Whisken 45		2
17	Sth PS	H	Yate Town	424	W 3 - 0	Leslie-Smith 16 Baker 39 Spetch 67	4	3
24	Sth PS	A	Weston-s- Mare	579	D 1 - 1	Dennett 41	5	4
26	Sth PS	H	Wimborne Town	768	W 3 - 1	Baker 59 71 Dennett 86	2	5
31	Sth PS	A	Swindon Supermarine	271	W 1 - 0	Moore 75	1	6
Sept 7	FAC1Q	A	Didcot Town	257	W 1 - 0	Moore 86		7
14	Sth PS	H	Harrow Borough	467	W 3 - 1	Baker 4 Brooks 79 Holmes 87	1	8
21	FAC2Q	H	Hungerford Town	427	W 2 - 1	Baker 30 Cope 82		9
25	Sth PS	A	Gosport Borough	244	W 2 - 0	Baker 43 Holmes 51	3	10
28	Sth PS	A	Hendon	172	W 3 - 1	Dennett 26 Brooks 53 Bedford 65	1	11
Oct 5	FAC3Q	A	Tooting & Mitcham United	434	W 2 - 0	Brooks 13 Dennett 84		12
15	Sth PS	A	Truro City	370	D 3 - 3	Baker 16 31 Carmichael 47	3	13
19	FAC4Q	A	Hayes & Yeading United	416	D 1 - 1	Cope 67		14
22	FAC4Qr	H	Hayes & Yeading United	1066	L 2 - 3	Brooks 39 Cairney 90		15
29	FAT1Q	H	Hartley Wintney	271	L 0 - 1			16
Nov 19	Sth PS	A	Hartley Wintney	203	L 0 - 3		8	17
23	Sth PS	A	Walton Casuals	144	W 3 - 0	Baker 24 31 Spetch 55	8	18
30	Sth PS	H	Taunton Town	414	L 0 - 1		8	19
Dec 7	Sth PS	A	Chesham United	435	L 1 - 2	Baker 28	9	20
21	Sth PS	A	Salisbury	668	L 1 - 2	Brooks 46	10	21
26	Sth PS	A	Dorchester Town	277	W 1 - 0	Brooks 89	8	22
Jan 1	Sth PS	A	Wimborne Town	720	L 1 - 2	Spetch 90	9	23
4	Sth PS	H	Farnborough	412	W 3 1	Spetch 2 Brooks 13 52	9	24
11	Sth PS	A	Tiverton Town	270	W 1 - 0	Spetch 32	8	25
21	Sth PS	A	Hayes & Yeading U	125	W 2 - 1	McDevitt (og) Whisken 84	7	26
25	Sth PS	A	Yate Town	259	D 1 - 1	Spetch 45	8	27
Feb 1	Sth PS	H	Swindon Supermarine	334	W 2 - 0	Brooks 14 Spetch 20	8	28
4	Sth PS	H	Merthyr Town	347	D 1 - 1	Dickson 58	8	29
8	Sth PS	A	Harrow Borough	173	D 0 - 0		7	30
22	Sth PS	A	Beaconsfield Town	108	L 1 - 2	Baker 62	10	31
Mar 7	Sth PS	A	Blackfield & Langley	181	D 1 - 1	Spetch 31	10	32
10	Sth PS	H	Beaconsfield Town	188	W 3 - 1	Moore 17 Baker 23 Pardoe 82	10	33

GOALSCORERS	SG	CSG	Pens	Hat tricks	Total		SG	CSG	Pens	Hat tricks	Total
Baker	11			1	14	Dickson	1				1
Brooks	8				9	Leslie-Smith	1				1
Spetch	9	3			9	Opponents	1				1
Dennett	5				7	Pardoe	1				1
Moore	3				3	Whisken	1				1
Cope	2				2						
Holmes	2				2						
Bedford	1				1						
Cairney	1				1						
Carmichael	1				1						

SALISBURY MATCH RESULTS 2019-20

Date	Comp	H/A	Opponents	Att:	Result	Goalscorers	Pos	No.
Aug 10	Sth PS	A	Chesham United	452	L 0 - 2			1
13	Sth PS	H	Gosport Borough	688	W 1 - 0	Colson 90		2
17	Sth PS	H	Dorchester Town	632	W 4 - 1	Holmes 17 26 Colson 76 (pen) 80	7	3
24	Sth PS	A	Swindon Supermarine	389	D 2 - 2	Fitchett 39 Bentley 55	6	4
26	Sth PS	H	Yate Town	632	W 3 - 2	Holmes 22 42 49	6	5
31	Sth PS	A	Tiverton Town	327	D 3 - 3	Fitchett 44 Mullings 61Sommerton 70	7	6
Sept 7	FAC1Q	A	**Thatcham Town**	**661**	W 3 - 2	**Colson 7 Holmes 42 Amankwaah 76**		7
14	Sth PS	H	Metropolitan Police	737	L 1 - 3	Holmes 42	8	8
17	Sth PS	A	Weston-s-Mare	518	D 3 - 3	Fitchett 35 Amankwash 72 Hippolyte-Patrick 74	8	9
21	FAC2Q	A	**Portland United**	**574**	W 1 - 0	**Holmes 45**		10
28	Sth PS	H	Hartley Witney	599	W 2 - 0	Downing 7 Benson 43	5	11
Oct 5	FAC3Q	H	**Margate**	**743**	L 2 - 4	**Benson 59 Hippolyte-Patrick 87**		12
12	Sth PS	A	Hendon	302	W 3 - 0	Leak 33 Holmes 30 Lita 90	6	13
15	Sth PS	H	Taunton Town	584	W 2 - 1	Irish (og) 45 Wright 69 (og)	5	14
19	Sth PS	H	Harrow Borough	615	W 3 1	Hippolyte-Patrick 1 87 Oseni 56	4	15
22	Sth PS	A	Merthyr Town	372	D 1 - 1	Lita 90		16
26	FAT1Q	H	**Dorchester Town**	**342**	D 3 - 3	**Fichett Downing Holmes**		17
29	FAT1Qr	A	**Dorchester Town**	**336**	W 3 - 0	**Holmes Oseni Knowles**		18
Nov 2	Sth PS	A	Farnborough	473	D 0 - 0		4	19
9	FAT2Q	H	**Kings Langley**	**445**	W 2 - 1	**Holmes 27 61**		20
16	Sth PS	A	Hayes & Yeading United	284	L 0 - 1		5	21
Nov 23	FAT3Q	H	**Hayes & Yeading United**	**454**	W 4 - 3	**Mullings Downing Lafleur Bentley**		22
30	Sth PS	A	Walton Casuals	249	L 1 - 2	Bentley 87	8	23
Dec 7	Sth PS	H	Blackfield & Langley	486	D 1 - 1	Amankwaah 74	8	24
14	FAT1P	A	**Eastbourne Borough**	**668**	D 2 - 2	**Holmes 5 Adebowale 84**		25
21	Sth PS	H	Poole Town	668	W 2 - 1	Downing 23 (pen) Hippolyte-Patrick 84	7	26
26	Sth PS	H	Wimborne Town	536	W 3 - 1	Hippolyte-Patrick 51 Downing 78 (pen) Benson 84	7	27
Jan 1	Sth PS	A	Yate Town	340	W 4 - 2	Downing 42 (pen) Fitchett 53 Hippolyte-Patrick 56 Young 87	6	28
4	Sth PS	H	Chesham United	628	W 3 - 2	Knowles 22 Holmes 61 Downing 75 (pen)	6	29
Jan 7	FAT1Pr	H	**Eastbourne Borough**	**354**	W 1 - 0	**Fitchett**		30
11	FAT2P	A	**Chelmsford City**	**557**	L 0 - 4		6	31
18	Sth PS	H	Swindon Supermarine	650	L 0 - 2		6	32
25	Sth PS	A	Dorchester Town	469	W 5 - 0	Holmes 11 Knowles 64 Bentley 68 Jefferies 78 Fitchett 88	6	33
Feb 1	Sth PS	H	Tiverton Town	642	D 2 - 2	Fitchett 37 Knowles 82	7	34
8	Sth PS	A	Metropolitan Police	197	L 2 - 3	Downing 5 (pen) Howe 90	9	35
18	Sth PS	H	Truro City	414	L 0 - 3		9	36
22	Sth PS	H	Hendon	515	W 2 - 0	Wannell 42 Holmes 75	7	37
25	Sth PS	A	Gosport Borough	205	D 0 - 0		7	38
Mar 7	Sth PS	H	Merthyr Town	547	W 2 - 1	Jones (og) 57 Leak 79	7	39
10	Sth PS	A	Harrow Borough	171	D 2 - 2	Bentley 17 Benson 90	7	40

GOALSCORERS	SG	CSG	Pens	Hat tricks	Total		SG	CSG	Pens	Hat tricks	Total
Holmes	12	2		1	17	Lita	2				2
Fitchett	8				8	Mullings	2				2
Downing	7	4	5		7	Oseni	2				2
Hippolyte-Patrick	6	3			7	Adebowale	1				1
Benson	5				5	Benson	1				1
Bentley	4				4	Howe	1				1
Colson	3		1		4	Jefferies	1				1
Knowles	4				4	Lafleur	1				1
Amankwash	3				3	Sommerton	1				1
Opponents	3				3	Wannell	1				1
Leak	2				2	Young	1				1

SWINDON SUPERMARINE MATCH RESULTS 2019-20

Date	Comp	H/A	Opponents	Att:	Result	Goalscorers	Pos	No.
Aug 10	Sth PS	H	Walton Casuals	241	W 3 - 2	Campbell 62 Simpson 89 90		1
13	Sth PS	A	Hartley Wintney	228	W 2 - 1	Fleetwood 72 Williams 88		2
17	Sth PS	A	Truro City	431	L 0 - 1		9	3
24	Sth PS	H	Salisbury	389	D 2 - 2	Fleetwood 62 McDonagh 89	8	4
26	Sth PS	A	Merthyr Town	509	L 1 - 3	Simpson 77	12	5
31	Sth PS	H	Poole Town	271	L 0 - 1		16	6
Sept 7	FAC1Q	A	**Wantage Town**	168	W 3 - 0	**Liddiard 1 Edge 36 Fleetwood 84**	16	7
14	Sth PS	A	Taunton Town	539	D 1 - 1	Fleetwood 63	17	8
21	FAC2Q	H	**Bath City**	461	L 0 - 4			9
28	Sth PS	A	Dorchester Town	389	D 1 - 1	Dinsley 34	16	10
Oct 5	Sth PS	H	Chesham United	249	W 2 - 1	Hooper 5 Fleetwood 89	13	11
8	Sth PS	H	Blackfield & Langley	153	W 3 - 0	Campbell 27 McDonagh 38 Williams 64	10	12
12	Sth PS	H	Farnborough	278	W 3 - 2	McDonagh 12 Williams 57 Campbell 65	7	13
15	Sth PS	A	Metroploitan Police	139	W 3 - 2	Hopkins 30 Williams 81 Spalding 90	7	14
19	Sth PS	A	Tiverton Town	278	L 0 - 2		8	15
30	FAT1Q	H	**Thatcham Town**	139	L 1 - 4	**McDonagh 65**		16
Nov 2	Sth PS	H	Gosport Casuals	161	W 1 - 0	Fleetwood 42	6	17
9	Sth PS	A	Harrow Borough	146	W 3 - 2	Campbell 75 82 Hopkins 84	4	18
16	Sth PS	H	Hendon	311	W 2 - 0	Williams 26 32	4	19
23	Sth PS	A	Beaconsfield Town	80	D 0 - 0		5	20
30	Sth PS	H	Weston-s-Mare	402	W 3 2	Williams 9 Liddiard 29 Spalding 36	5	21
Dec 7	Sth PS	A	Wimborne	238	W 2 - 0	McDonagh 24 Henshall 58	5	22
Jan 1	Sth PS	H	Merthyr Town	333	D 2 - 2	McDonagh 34 71	5	23
4	Sth PS	A	Walton Casuals	183	W 4 - 2	McDonagh 25 78 Hopkins 35 Spalding 42	4	24
11	Sth PS	H	Hartley Wintney	309	W 3 - 2	Williams 19 McDonagh 69 85	4	25
18	Sth PS	A	Salisbury	650	W 2 - 0	Williams 50 54	4	26
21	Sth PS	H	Dorchester Town	217	W 1 0	Campbell 62	4	27
25	Sth PS	H	Truro City	341	L 1 - 3	Campbell 75	4	28
Feb 1	Sth PS	A	Poole Town	334	L 0 - 2		4	29
8	Sth PS	H	Taunton Town	278	L 1 - 2	McDonagh 35	4	30
11	Sth PS	A	Chesham United	354	W 2 - 1	Hopkins 62 Liddiard 63	3	31
15	Sth PS	A	Yate Town	162	L 0 - 2		4	32
22	Sth PS	A	Farnborough	328	W 1 - 0	Williams 90	3	33
25	Sth PS	H	Hayes & Yeading U	217	D 1 - 1	Spalding 47	3	34
Mar 7	Sth PS	A	Hayes & Yeading U	211	L 0 - 1		5	35

GOALSCORERS	SG	CSG	Pens	Hat tricks	Total		SG	CSG	Pens	Hat tricks	Total
McDonagh	9	4			12	Henshall	1				1
Williams	10	3			11	Hooper	1				1
Campbell	6	2			7						
Fleetwood	6	2			6						
Hopkins	3				4						
Spalding	4				4						
Liddiard	3				3						
Simpson	2				3						
Dinsley	1				1						
Edge	1				1						

TAUNTON TOWN MATCH RESULTS 2019-20

Date	Comp	H/A	Opponents	Att:	Result	Goalscorers	Pos	No.
Aug 10	Sth PS	A	Gosport Borough	342	L 0 - 3			1
14	Sth PS	H	Yate Town	545	L 0 - 4			2
17	Sth PS	H	Chesham United	500	W 3 - 2	Wright 13 34 Kite 70	17	3
24	Sth PS	A	Wimborne Town	365	W 3 - 0	Wright 20 Neal 36 72 (pen)	12	4
26	Sth PS	H	Tiverton Town	1068	W 3 - 1	Wright 27 White 37 Smith 50	10	5
31	Sth PS	A	Harrow Borough	155	D 1 - 1	Adelsbury 43	9	6
Sept 7	FAC1Q	A	**Winchester City**	234	W 3 - 0	Sullivan x3	9	7
14	Sth PS	H	Swindon Supermarine	539	D 1 - 1	Sullivan 16	9	8
17	Sth PS	A	Dorchester Town	348	D 2 - 2	Neal 31 Price 90		9
21	FAC2Q	A	**Havant & Waterlooville**	473	L 1 - 2	White 90		10
28	Sth PS	A	Metroplotan Police	142	D 1 - 1	Neal 55	8	11
Oct 5	Sth PS	H	Farnborough	604	W 3 - 1	Chamberlain 63 Sullivan 64 Adelsbury 82	6	12
12	Sth PS	H	Hayes & Yeading United	701	W 2 - 1	Chamberlain 37 Neal 55	5	13
15	Sth PS	A	Salisbury	584	L 1 - 2	Neal 83	6	14
19	Sth PS	A	Walton Casuals	192	W 5 - 1	Sullivan 28 Kite 37 Wright 39 66 Palmer 90	6	15
23	Sth PS	H	Truro City	612	W 2 - 0	Davis (og) 14 Grimes 63	4	16
26	FAT1Q	A	**Wimborne Town**	232	D 2 - 2	Neal 73 (pen) Kite 80		17
29	FAT1Qr	H	**Wimborne Town**	315	W 4 - 1	Neal 40 Hall 57 Wright 69 Chamberlain 82		18
Nov 9	FAT2Q	H	**Aveley**	473	D 3 - 3	Price 15 Kite 28 Brett 75		19
11	FAT2Qr	A	**Aveley**	167	L 1 - 2	Price 90		20
16	Sth PS	H	Blackfield & Langley	538	W 4 - 0	Neal 6 Brett 10 Wright 80 Short 87	5	21
30	Sth PS	A	Poole Town	414	W 1 - 0	Neal 74	5	22
Dec 7	Sth PS	H	Beaconsfield Town	499	W 3 - 0	Neal 52 56 Wright 26	5	23
14	Sth PS	H	Metropolitan Police	540	W 4 - 3	Neal 24 63 Price 15 Wright 55	5	24
26	Sth PS	H	Weston-s-Mare	801	L 1 - 2	Neal 65	4	25
Jan 1	Sth PS	A	Tiverton Town	853	L 2 - 3	Adelsbury 3 Neal 6	5	26
4	Sth PS	H	Gosport Borough	552	W 3 - 2	Brett 6 Sullivan 73 Chamberlain 75	5	27
11	Sth PS	A	Yate Town	263	L 1 - 4	Brett 26	5	28
18	Sth PS	H	Wimborne Town	558	W 3 - 0	Sullivan 38 Neal 45 Chamberlain 80	5	29
25	Sth PS	A	Chesham United	551	D 1 - 1	Wright 25	5	30
Feb 1	Sth PS	H	Harrow Borough	602	W 3 - 2	Sullivan 5 Short 67 Brett 71	5	31
8	Sth PS	A	Swindon Supermarine	318	W 2 - 1	Brett 56 Sullivan 68	4	32
11	Sth PS	A	Merthyr Town	304	L 2 - 4	Chamberlain 2 49	6	33
22	Sth PS	A	Hayes & Yeading United	223	D 2 - 2	Demkiv 23 Sullivan 68	6	34
Mar 4	Sth PS	H	Hendon	378	D 3 - 3	Kite 22 Wright 62 81	5	35
7	Sth PS	A	Truro City	661	D 1 - 1	White 12	5	36
11	Sth PS	A	Farnborough	143	L 0 - 4		5	37

GOALSCORERS	SG	CSG	Pens	Hat tricks	Total		SG	CSG	Pens	Hat tricks	Total
Neal	14	6	2		17	Grimes	1				1
Wright	10				13	Hall	1				1
Sullivan	8			1	10	Kite	1				1
Chamberlain	6				7	Opponents	1				1
Brett	5				5	Palmer	1				1
Kite	5				5	Smith	1				1
Price	4	2			4						
Adelsbury	3				3						
White	3				3						
Short	2				2						

TIVERTON TOWN MATCH RESULTS 2019-20

Date	Comp	H/A	Opponents	Att:	Result		Goalscorers	Pos	No.
Aug 13	Sth PS	H	Hayes & Yeading United	232	D	2 - 2	Landricombe 5 Koszela 46		1
17	Sth PS	A	Poole Town	403	W	2 - 1	Dyer 88 Allen 90 (pen)		2
20	Sth PS	A	Walton Casuals	186	W	3 - 1	Grimes 70 Allen 75 Lewington 90	2	3
24	Sth PS	H	Beaconsfield Town	204	W	6 - 1	Smerdon 21 57 Lewington 27 Shephard 32 Koszela 38 Allen 43 (pen)	1	4
26	Sth PS	A	Taunton Town	1068	L	1 - 3	Colwell 68	3	5
31	Sth PS	H	Salisbury	327	D	3 - 3	Bastin 9 Colwell 18 Landricombe 85	5	6
Sept 7	FAC1Q	A	Burnham	143	W	3 - 2	Allen 14 (pen) 88 Lewington 75		7
14	Sth PS	A	Hartley Wintney	212	W	4 - 1	Drage 37 (og) Bastin 47 Lewington 63 Allen 90	4	8
18	Sth PS	H	Merthyr Town	468	W	1 - 0	Allen 16 (pen)	4	9
21	FAC2Q	H	Bristol Manor Farm	241	L	2 - 4	Key 35 Dyer 72		10
28	Sth PS	A	Farnborough	289	W	7 - 0	Elliott 20 53 Smerdon 35 Lewington 42 44 67 Rogers 82	3	11
Oct 5	Sth PS	H	Dorchester Town	303	W	2 - 1	Lewington 54 90	1	12
12	Sth PS	A	Wimborne Town	344	W	3 - 0	Allen 34 90 Smerdon 86	1	13
16	Sth PS	H	Yate Town	261	L	0 - 2		1	14
19	Sth PS	H	Swindon Supermarine	278	W	2 - 0	Dyer 57 Bastin 68	1	15
22	Sth PS	A	Weston-super-Mare	560	L	2 - 3	Key 9 Bastin 34	2	16
29	FAT1Q	A	Yate Town	153	D	3 - 3	Lewington 7 58 Bastin 10		17
Nov 6	FAT1Qr	H	Yate Town	156	D	3 - 3	Bastin 52 Allen 105 Key 109 (Lost 1-4 on pens aet)		18
16	Sth PS	H	Metropolitan Police	275	W	2 - 1	Lewington 43 Bastin 48	2	19
23	Sth PS	A	Hendon	202	W	2 - 1	Bastin 52 Key 67	2	20
30	Sth PS	H	Gosport Corough	233	L	2 - 3	Colwell 80 Key 88	3	21
Dec 7	Sth PS	A	Harrow Borough	150	W	5 - 1	Key 11 Allen 26 90 Bastin 64 Shephard 70	3	22
17	Sth PS	A	Blackfield & Langley	78	W	1 - 0	Bastin 6	2	23
21	Sth PS	A	Dorchester Town	247	W	5 - 1	Shephard 6 43 Allen 55 Fletcher 67 Bastin 72	3	24
26	Sth PS	A	Truro City	576	D	3 - 3	Fletcher 7 19 Allen 48	1	25
Jan 1	Sth PS	H	Taunton Town	853	W	3 - 2	Shepherd 13 Bastin 38 Fletcher 90	1	26
4	Sth PS	A	Hayes & Yeading United	236	D	0 - 0		1	27
7	Sth PS	H	Poole Town	270	L	0 - 1		2	28
25	Sth PS	H	Walton Casuals	232	D	2 - 2	Fletcher 39 Allen 85	3	29
Feb 1	Sth PS	A	Salisbury	642	D	2 - 2	Fletcher 23 Bastin 25	3	30
8	Sth PS	H	Hartley Whitney	248	W	2 - 0	Fletcher 15 Bastin 28	3	31
22	Sth PS	H	Wimborne Town	301	D	2 - 2	Beckinsale 15 Fletcher 30	4	32
Mar 3	Sth PS	A	Beaconsfield Town	65	L	0 - 4		4	33

GOALSCORERS	SG	CSG	Pens	Hat tricks	Total		SG	CSG	Pens	Hat tricks	Total
Allen	12	3	4		15	Koszela	2				2
Bastin	14	6			14	Landricombe	2				2
Lewington	6	2		1	12	Beckinsale	1				1
Fletcher	7	4			8	Grimes	1				1
Key	6	3			6	Opponents	1				1
Shephard	4				5	Rogers	1				1
Smerden	3				4						
Colwell	3				3						
Dyer	3				3						
Elliott	1				2						

TRURO CITY MATCH RESULTS 2019-20

Date	Comp	H/A	Opponents	Att:	Result	Goalscorers	Pos	No.
Aug 10	Sth PS	A	Metropolitan Police	159	W 2 - 0	Law 22 Thompson 39		1
13	Sth PS	H	Dorchester Town	470	W 3 - 0	Mbayo 35 Jephcott 78 Keats 89		2
17	Sth PS	H	Swindon Supermarine	421	W 1 - 0	Jephcott	1	3
24	Sth PS	A	Chesham United	401	L 1 - 2	Thompson 12	2	4
26	Sth PS	H	Weston super Mare	551	L 0 - 2			5
31	Sth PS	A	Farnborough	329	W 2 - 0	Ward 4 Rooney 45	2	6
Sept 7	FAC1Q	H	Wimborne	363	W 2 - 1	Ward 25 Yetton 68	2	7
14	Sth PS	H	Gosport Borough	412	W 1 - 0	Rooney 90	2	8
18	Sth PS	A	Wimborne Town	266	D 2 - 2	Pettefer (og) 34 Jephcott 83 (pen)		9
21	FAC2Q	A	Hereford	1115	L 2 - 5	Law 9 Thompson 15	4	10
28	Sth PS	H	Hayes & Yeading	340	W 3 - 0	Harvey 16 30 Jephcott 84	4	11
Oct 5	Sth PS	A	Yate Town	267	W 3 - 0	Harvey 18 Thompson 45 Rooney 84	3	12
12	Sth PS	A	Harrow Borough	197	W 2 - 1	Harvey 23 65	2	13
15	Sth PS	H	Poole Town	428	D 3 - 3	Jephcott 53 Harvey 60 Law 90	2	14
19	Sth PS	H	Hendon	428	W 2 - 1	Ward 5 Jephcott 18	2	15
21	Sth PS	A	Taunton Town	612	L 0 - 2		3	16
Nov 5	FAT1Q	H	Blackfield & Langley	131	D 1 - 1			17
9	FAT1Qr	A	Blackfield & Langley	57	L 1 - 3			18
16	Sth PS	H	Hartley Wintney	412	W 2 - 0	Jephcott 1 Harvey 55	3	19
23	Sth PS	A	Blackfield & Langley	91	W 2 - 0	Harvey 38 78	3	20
30	Sth PS	A	Beaconsfield	83	W 1 - 0	Battle 32	1	21
Dec 7	Sth PS	H	Walton Casuals	312	W 5 - 1	Harvey 13 18 88 Battle 45 Thompson 70	1	22
14	Sth PS	A	Hayes & Yeading	237	W 1 - 0	Jephcott 11	1	23
26	Sth PS	A	Tiverton Town	576	D 3 - 3	Dean 14 Mbayo 66 Gafaiti 90	2	24
Jan 1	Sth PS	H	Weston-s-Mare	651	L 2 - 3	Rooney 14 Dickson 72	3	25
4	Sth PS	H	Metropolitan Police	444	W 4 - 0	Battle 45 Swann 55 73 Yetton 86	2	26
11	Sth PS	A	Dorchester Town	334	W 3 - 2	Swan 7 Dean 54 Rooney 75	1	27
18	Sth PS	H	Chesham United	620	L 0 - 1		2	28
25	Sth PS	A	Swindon Supermarine	341	W 3 - 1	Swan 43 53 Harvey 84	1	29
Dec 1	Sth PS	H	Farnborough Town	516	W 2 - 1	Harvey 57 Swann 67	1	30
8	Sth PS	A	Gosport Borough	305	L 0 - 1		2	31
18	Sth PS	A	Saklisbury	414	W 3 - 0	Harvey 49 74 Law 53	2	32
22	Sth PS	H	Harrow Borough	347	W 4 - 1	Harvey 26 76 Dean 49 Swan 59	1	33
29	Sth PS	A	Hendon	304	W 4 - 1	North 29 (og) Swan 67 83 Mbayo 71	1	34
Mar 7	Sth PS	H	Taunton Town	661	D 1 - 1	Harvey 64	1	35

GOALSCORERS	SG	CSG	Pens	Hat tricks	Total		SG	CSG	Pens	Hat tricks	Total
Harvey	12	4		1	19	Opponents	2				2
Swan	6				9	Yetton	2				2
Jephcott	8		1		8	Dixon	1				1
Rooney	5				5	Gafaiti	1				1
Thompson	4				5	Keats	1				1
Law	4				4						
Battle	3	2			3						
Dean	3				3						
Mbayo	3				3						
Ward	3				3						

WALTON CASUALS MATCH RESULTS 2019-20

Date	Comp	H/A	Opponents	Att:	Result	Goalscorers	Pos	No.
Aug 10	Sth PS	A	Swindon Supermarine	241	L 2 - 3	Morrison 36 Gordon 67 (pen)		1
13	Sth PS	H	Farnborough	211	L 0 - 2			2
17	Sth PS	H	Tiverton Town	186	L 1 - 3	Grant 20	21	3
26	Sth PS	H	Harrow Borough	207	L 1 - 2	Amu 87		4
31	Sth PS	A	Wimborne Town	263	L 1 - 4	Murphy-McVey 90		5
Sept 8	FAC1Q	A	Kingstonian	376	L 0 - 2			6
14	Sth PS	H	Weston-s-Mare	196	W 2 - 1	Gordon 40 Johnson 84	21	7
18	Sth PS	A	Metropolitan Police	150	W 3 - 0	Howe 45 47 Ofosu 86		8
21	Sth PS	A	Yate Town	180	W 2 - 0	Ward 3 5	14	9
28	Sth PS	H	Merthyr Town	293	W 2 - 1	Fitzpatrick 55 Fox 90	11	10
Oct 12	Sth PS	A	Hartley Witney	198	L 0 - 1		13	11
15	Sth PS	H	Gosport Borough	184	D 1 - 1	Fitzpatrick 80	14	12
19	Sth PS	H	Taunton	192	L 1 - 5	Howe 38	16	13
22	Sth PS	A	Hendon	154	L 0 - 2		16	14
26	FAT1Q	A	Worthing	356	L 1 - 2	Gordon 45		15
Nov 2	Sth PS	A	Beaconsfield Town	77	W 2 1	Ewington 71 Pearce 90	16	16
19	Sth PS	A	Dorchester Town	338	D 2 2	Ewington 73 Gogonas 87	14	17
23	Sth PS	H	Poole Town	144	L 0 - 3		17	18
26	Sth PS	A	Blackfield & Langley	60	D 2 - 2	Grant 27 Howe 87	16	19
30	Sth PS	H	Salisbury City	249	W 2 - 1	Howe 5 Brown 89	13	20
Dec 7	Sth PS	A	Truro City	312	L 1 - 5	Howe 60	14	21
14	Sth PS	A	Merthyr Town	363	W 2 - 0	Howe 66 Gogonas 90	12	22
17	Sth PS	H	Hayes & Yeading	178	L 2 - 3	Gordon 28 Fox 80	12	23
21	Sth PS	H	Blackfield & Langley	164	L 2 - 3	Gasson 31 Tomasso (og) 47	13	24
26	Sth PS	H	Chesham United	183	L 1 - 6	Howe 81	14	25
Jan 1	Sth PS	A	Harrow Borough	170	L 0 - 2		16	26
4	Sth PS	H	Swindon Supermarine	183	L 2 - 4	Grant 37 Gordon 62	18	27
11	Sth PS	A	Farnborough Town	282	L 1 - 2	Howe 60	18	28
18	Sth PS	H	Yate Town	124	D 1 - 1	Brown 14	18	29
25	Sth PS	A	Tiverton Town	232	D 2 - 2	Brown 18 Mason 71	20	30
Feb 1	Sth PS	H	Wimborne Town	161	L 0 - 2		20	31
8	Sth PS	A	Weston-s-Mare	490	L 0 - 1		20	32
15	Sth PS	A	Gosport Borough	178	L 1 - 2	Brown 78	20	33
22	Sth PS	H	Hartley Whitney	175	L 0 - 3		20	34
Mar 7	Sth PS	H	Hendon	174	D 1 - 1	Dos Santos	20	35

GOALSCORERS	SG	CSG	Pens	Hat tricks	Total		SG	CSG	Pens	Hat tricks	Total
Howe	8	4			9	Brown	1				1
Gordon	4		1		5	Don Santos	1				1
Brown	4	2			4	Gasson	1				1
Grant	3				3	Johnson	1				1
Ewington	2	2			2	Morrison	1				1
Fitzpatrick	2				2	Murphy-McVey	1				1
Fox	2				2	Ofosu	1				1
Gogonas	2				2	Opponents	1				1
Ward	1				2	Pearce	1				1
Amu	1				1						

WESTON-SUPER-MARE MATCH RESULTS 2019-20

Date	Comp	H/A	Opponents	Att:	Result	Goalscorers	Pos	No.
Aug 10	Sth PS	H	Hendon	518	D 2 - 2	McCootie 41 Whitehead 90		1
13	Sth PS	A	Merthyr Town	492	D 1 - 1	Laird 90		2
20	Sth PS	A	Hayes & Yeading United	171	W 2 - 1	Randall 11 Whitehead 57	10	3
24	Sth PS	H	Poole Town	579	D 1 - 1	Tindle 16	11	4
26	Sth PS	A	Truro City	551	W 2 - 0	Richards (og) McCootie 38	6	5
31	Sth PS	H	Beaconsfield Town	516	W 1 - 0	McCootie 59	3	6
Sept 7	FAC1Q	H	Fareham	342	W 3 - 0	Maishanskyj McCootie (2)		7
14	Sth PS	A	Walton Casuals	196	L 1 - 2	Pearce 25	6	8
18	Sth PS	H	Salisbury	518	D 3 - 3	Howe 12 McCootie 23 Randall 76	3	9
21	FAC2Q	H	Merthyr Town	355	W 2 - 1	Laird 26 Hendy 44		10
28	Sth PS	A	Wimborne Town	293	L 1 - 2	Randall 78	7	11
Oct 5	FAC3Q	A	Kingstonian	358	D 1 - 1	Laird 90 (pen)		12
8	FAC3Qr	H	Kingstonian	272	L 1 - 4	Dowling 22		13
12	Sth PS	H	Dorchester Town	561	W 6 - 0	Howe 12 84 Laird 30 38 50 Randall 7	7	14
15	Sth PS	A	Blackfield & Langley	63	L 1 - 2	Waite 35	9	15
19	Sth PS	A	Metropolitan Police	122	L 1 - 2	Laird 66	10	16
22	Sth PS	H	Tiverton Town	560	W 3 - 2	Laird 3 Maddern 47 McCootie 79	9	17
26	FAT1Q	A	AFC Totton	148	L 2 - 3	Randall 16 Jones 96		18
29	Sth PS	H	Harrow Borough	460	D 1 - 1	Randall 42	9	19
Nov 16	Sth PS	H	Chesham United	599	L 1 - 2	Laird 14	10	20
30	Sth PS	A	Swindon Supermarine	402	L 2 - 3	Laird 54 90	15	21
Dec 7	Sth PS	H	Farnborough	493	L 1 - 3	Parsons 45	16	22
17	Sth PS	A	Yate Town	223	W 2 - 1	Waite 29 81	15	23
21	Sth PS	A	Harrow Borough	118	W 4 - 0	Ash 4 Waite 33 67 90	13	24
26	Sth PS	A	Taunton Town	801	W 2 - 1	Waite 51 Ash 74	12	25
Jan 1	Sth PS	H	Truro Town	651	W 3 - 2	Laird 38 90 Symons 90	10	26
4	Sth PS	A	Hendon	218	L 0 - 4		10	27
7	Sth PS	H	Hartley Wintney	403	W 2 - 1	Humphries 35 Waite 54	9	28
25	Sth PS	H	Hayes & Yeading United	540	L 1 - 5	McCootie 66	10	29
28	Sth PS	A	Gosport Borough	172	L 0 - 1		10	30
Feb 1	Sth PS	A	Beaconsfield Town	71	D 2 - 2	Knowles 61 Ash 65	10	31
8	Sth PS	H	Walton Casuals	490	W 1 - 0	Tindle 45	10	32
11	Sth PS	H	Wimborne Town	374	W 5 - 0	Waite 17 23 72 Hendy 19 Jones 90	9	33
22	Sth PS	A	Dorchester Town	282	W 2 - 1	Knowles 15 Symons 40	8	34

GOALSCORERS	SG	CSG	Pens	Hat tricks	Total		SG	CSG	Pens	Hat tricks	Total
Laird	9		1		13	Whitehead	2				2
Waite	6		2		11	Dowling	1				1
McCootie	7	3			8	Humphries	1				1
Randall	6	2			6	Jones	1				1
Ash	3				3	Madden	1				1
Howe	2				3	Maishanskyi	1				1
Hendy	2				2	Opponents	1				1
Knowles	2				2	Parsons	1				1
Symons	2				2	Pearce	1				1
Tindle	2				2						

WIMBORNE TOWN MATCH RESULTS 2019-20

Date	Comp	H/A	Opponents	Att:	Result	Goalscorers	Pos	No.
Aug 10	Sth PS	H	Hartley Wintney	286	D 0 - 0			1
13	Sth PS	A	Blackfield & Langley	147	L 0 - 1			2
17	Sth PS	A	Hendon	189	D 1 - 1	Roberts 67	19	3
20	Sth PS	H	Taunton Town	365	L 0 - 3		19	4
24	Sth PS	A	Poole Town	768	L 1 - 3	Roberts 38	19	5
31	Sth PS	H	Walton Casuals	263	W 4 - 1	Burbidge 66 68 Bayston 82 Lee 87	18	6
Sept 7	**FAC1Q**	**A**	**Truro City**	**363**	**L 1 - 2**	**Bayston 67**		7
14	Sth PS	A	Beaconsfield Town	77	W 4 - 0	Lee 20 27 Penny 69 (pen) Burbidge 85	14	8
17	Sth PS	H	Truro City	266	D 2 - 2	Penny 62 (pen) Maybury 69	14	9
28	Sth PS	H	Weston -s-Mare	293	W 2 - 1	Bayston 51 Lee 90	9	10
Oct 5	Sth PS	A	Merthyr Town	434	L 1 - 3	Byrne 55	12	11
12	Sth PS	H	Tiverton Town	344	L 0 - 3		12	12
16	Sth PS	A	Farnborough	221	L 1 - 2	Wilson 47		13
19	Sth PS	A	Chesham United	348	L 0 - 1		18	14
22	Sth PS	H	Dorchester Town	361	W 2 - 1	Bayston 72 Lee 78	16	15
26	**FAT1Q**	**H**	**Taunton Town**	**232**	**D 2 - 2**	**Bayston 46 55**		16
29	**FAT1Qr**	**A**	**Taunton Town**	**315**	**L 1 - 4**	**Roberts 3**		17
Nov 2	Sth PS	H	Yate Town	235	W 2 - 0	Lee 66 72	13	18
16	Sth PS	H	Gosport Booroug	406	L 1 - 2	Diaz 21	13	19
23	Sth PS	A	Harrow Borough	113	W 1 - 0	Shepherd 74	10	20
26	Sth PS	A	Metropolitan Police	89	D 2 - 2	Lee 45 Bayston 59	10	21
30	Sth PS	A	Hayes & Yeading	201	L 1 - 3	Lee 90	11	22
Dec 7	Sth PS	H	Swindon Supermarine	238	L 0 - 2		12	23
26	Sth PS	A	Salisbury	536	L 1 - 3	Bayston 33	17	24
Jan 2	Sth PS	H	Poole Town	720	W 2 - 1	Lee 63 Young 90	16	25
4	Sth PS	A	Hartley Wintney	262	D 2 - 2	Burbidge 16 Lee 29 (pen)	16	26
11	Sth PS	H	Blackfield & Langley	317	W 2 - 0	Poole 39 Diaz 70	16	27
18	Sth PS	A	Taunton Town	558	L 0 - 3		17	28
25	Sth PS	H	Hendon	314	L 0 - 2		17	29
Feb 1	Sth PS	A	Walton Casuals	161	W 2 - 0	Lee 52 Burbidge 89	14	30
8	Sth PS	H	Beaconsfield Town	299	W 2 - 0	Bayston 4 Burbidge 61	14	31
11	Sth PS	H	Weston-s-Mare	374	L 0 - 5		14	32
22	Sth PS	A	Tiverton Town	301	D 2 - 2	Lee 4 Davidson 18	15	33
25	Sth PS	H	Merthyr Town	188	D 0 - 0		13	34
29	Sth PS	H	Chesham United	368	L 1 - 2	Young 36	13	35
Mar 7	Sth PS	A	Dorchester Town	406	L 0 - 1		13	36

GOALSCORERS	SG	CSG	Pens	Hat tricks	Total		SG	CSG	Pens	Hat tricks	Total
Lee	10	2			13	Maybury	1				1
Bayston	7	2			8	Poole	1				1
Burbidge	4	2			6	Shepherd	1				1
Roberts	3				3	Wilson	1				1
Diaz	2				2						
Penny	1	2	2		2						
Young	2				2						
Byrne	1				1						
Davidson	1				1						
Lee	1				1						

YATE TOWN MATCH RESULTS 2019-20

Date	Comp	H/A	Opponents	Att:	Result	Goalscorers	Pos	No.
Aug 10	Sth PS	H	Blackfield & Langley	205	L 1 - 4	Mehew 61 (pen)		1
14	Sth PS	A	Taunton Town	545	W 4 - 0	Spokes 1 60 Peare 53 Ollis 89		2
17	Sth PS	A	Poole Town	434	L 0 - 3		15	3
24	FACP	H	Exmouth Town	246	D 2 - 2	Mehew 36 80		4
26	Sth PS	A	Salisbury	632	L 2 - 3	Bryant 39 Lee 56	17	5
31	Sth PS	H	Hendon	247	D 2 - 2	Peare 52 Spokes 90	19	6
Sept 3	FACPr	A	Exmouth Town	451	L 0 - 2			7
14	Sth PS	A	Hayes & Yeading United	200	L 1 - 2	Ford 48	20	8
21	Sth PS	H	Walton Casuals	180	L 0 - 2		21	9
28	Sth PS	A	Chesham United	369	L 2 - 4	Kamara 16 Britton 21	22	10
Oct 5	Sth PS	H	Truro City	257	L 0 - 3			11
8	Sth PS	H	Hartley Wintmey	167	W 2 - 1	Britton 25 90	22	12
12	Sth PS	H	Metropolitan Police	192	W 1 - 0	Britton 90	20	13
16	Sth PS	A	Tiverton Town	261	W 2 - 0	Langworthy 15 55	17	14
19	Sth PS	A	Dorchester Town	378	L 0 - 2		17	15
22	Sth PS	H	Farnborough	170	L 0 - 1		17	16
29	FAT1Q	H	Tiverton Town	153	D 3 - 3			17
Nov 2	Sth PS	A	Wimborne	235	L 0 - 2		19	18
6	FAT1Qr	A	Tiverton Town		D 3 - 3	(Won 4-1 on pens aet)		19
9	FAT2Q	H	AFC Totton	230	W 6 - 3	Webb 11 Britton 38 43 65 Peare 75 Mehew 85		20
16	Sth PS	A	Beaconsfield Town	119	D 1 - 1	Guest 12	19	21
23	FAT3Q	A	Braintree Town	202	W 2 - 1			22
30	Sth PS	H	Harrow Borough	153	W 2 - 1	Webb 40 Bryant 68	19	23
Dec 7	Sth PS	A	Gosport Borough	219	D 1 - 1	Lee 9	19	24
14	FAT1P	A	Eastleigh	353	L 1 - 6	Twyman 73		25
17	Sth PS	H	Weston-s -Mare	223	L 1 - 2	Malshanskyj 33	19	26
26	Sth PS	A	Merthyr Town	519	L 1 - 2	Bell 57	20	27
Jan 1	Sth PS	H	Salisbury	340	L 2 - 4	Spokes 55 83 (pen)	20	28
4	Sth PS	A	Blackfield & Langley	103	L 0 - 2		20	29
7	Sth PS	A	Taunton Town	263	W 4 - 1	Peare 10 Bell 17 90 Low 50	20	30
18	Sth PS	A	Walton Casuals	124	D 1 - 1	Conway 24	20	31
21	Sth PS	H	Chesham United	146	W 4 - 1	Bell 19 48 Guest 46 Conway 76	18	32
25	Sth PS	H	Poole Town	259	D 1 - 1	Bell 88	19	33
Feb 1	Sth PS	A	Hendon	234	L 1 - 2	Taylor 59	19	34
8	Sth PS	H	Hayes & Yeading United	236	L 0 - 2		19	35
18	Sth PS	H	Swindon Supermarine	162	W 2 - 0	Bell 21 Corrick 60	19	36
22	Sth PS	A	Metropolitan Police	118	L 0 - 2		19	37
Mar 7	Sth PS	A	Farnborough	193	L 0 - 4		19	38

GOALSCORERS	SG	CSG	Pens	Hat tricks	Total		SG	CSG	Pens	Hat tricks	Total
Bell	54	2			7	Webb	2				2
Britton	5	2	1		7	Corrick	1				1
Spokes	3		1		5	Ford	1				1
Mehew	3		1		4	Kamara	1				1
Peare	4				4	Low	1				1
Bryant	1				2	Maklshanskyj	1				1
Conway	2				2	Ollis	1				1
Guest	2				2	Taylor	1				1
Langworthy	2				2	Twyman	1				1
Lee	2				2						

COMBINED COUNTIES LEAGUE

RECENT CHAMPIONS
2017: Hartley Wintney **2018:** Westfield **2019:** Chertsey Town

PREMIER DIVISION

		P	W	D	L	F	A	GD	Pts
1	Ascot United	32	22	2	8	63	37	26	68
2	Spelthorne Sports	31	18	5	8	63	40	23	59
3	Knaphill	29	17	7	5	63	28	35	58
4	Frimley Green	32	15	7	10	58	53	5	52
5	Southall	28	14	8	6	52	31	21	50
6	Molesey	31	17	2	12	48	38	10	50*
7	Abbey Rangers	30	14	7	9	50	34	16	49
8	Sutton Common Rovers	25	13	4	8	68	45	23	43
9	Cobham	30	13	4	13	37	36	1	43
10	Egham Town	31	12	4	15	55	60	-5	40
11	Colliers Wood United	26	11	5	10	40	40	0	38
12	Badshot Lea	27	11	3	13	50	46	4	36
13	Balham	27	11	3	13	58	56	2	36
14	Redhill	26	12	0	14	44	49	-5	36
15	Camberley Town	28	11	3	14	32	53	-21	36
16	Sheerwater	30	10	5	15	53	67	-14	35
17	Guildford City	31	8	4	19	28	52	-24	28
18	Hanworth Villa	29	7	6	16	36	54	-18	27
19	Raynes Park Vale	24	7	5	12	32	40	-8	26
20	Banstead Athletic	24	7	4	13	27	47	-20	24*
21	CB Hounslow United	33	5	6	22	32	83	-51	21

DIVISION ONE

		P	W	D	L	F	A	GD	Pts
1	Jersey Bulls	27	27	0	0	99	7	92	81
2	Farnham Town	28	19	4	5	48	26	22	61
3	Walton & Hersham	28	16	3	9	79	54	25	51
4	Tooting Bec	29	14	7	8	64	42	22	49
5	Fleet Spurs	29	15	2	12	56	41	15	47
6	Bedfont & Feltham	26	13	5	8	58	39	19	44
7	Sandhurst Town	25	12	8	5	56	39	17	44
8	Kensington & Ealing Borough	24	13	1	10	51	49	2	40
9	Epsom & Ewell	26	11	5	10	51	50	1	38
10	Bagshot	28	9	6	13	45	55	-10	33
11	AFC Hayes	22	9	4	9	51	50	1	31
12	Cove	26	9	4	13	42	72	-30	31
13	Dorking Wanderers Res	27	8	6	13	57	68	-11	30
14	FC Deportivo Galicia	30	8	6	16	50	90	-40	30
15	Westside	22	8	4	10	49	38	11	28
16	Ash United	26	9	0	17	41	68	-27	27
17	British Airways	29	7	5	17	42	77	-35	26
18	Eversley & California	26	4	8	14	31	53	-22	20
19	Chessington & Hook United	23	4	8	11	38	57	-19	17*
20	Godalming Town	27	3	6	18	42	75	-33	15

PREMIER CHALLENGE CUP

HOLDERS: FRIMLEY GREEN

ROUND 1

Egham Town	v	Raynes Park Vale	0-2
Tooting Bec	v	Bedfont & Feltham	2-4
FC Deportivo Galicia	v	AFC Hayes	2-9
Badshot Lea	v	Redhill	3-1 aet
Spelthorne Sports	v	Chessington & Hook United	6-2
Godalming Town	v	CB Hounslow United	0-4
Eversley & California	v	Balham	2-4
Guildford City	v	Hanworth Villa	2-3
Colliers Wood United	v	British Airways	4-2

ROUND 2

Abbey Rangers	v	Raynes Park Vale	1-0
Bedfont & Feltham	v	Knaphill	HW
Banstead Athletic	v	AFC Hayes	0-1
Sheerwater	v	Epsom & Ewell	4-2
Sandhurst Town	v	Cove	2-1
Badshot Lea	v	Dorking Wanderers Res	0-2
Molesey	v	Kensington & Ealing Borough	3-1
Sutton Common Rovers	v	Spelthorne Sports	2-1
CB Hounslow United	v	Balham	3-4
Frimley Green	v	Ascot United	3-7 aet
Hanworth Villa	v	Jersey Bulls	2-3
Cobham	v	Fleet Spurs	2-4
Ash United	v	Bagshot	2-2, 4-1p
Westside	v	Southall	2-1
Camberley Town	v	Colliers Wood United	2-1 aet
Farnham Town	v	Walton & Hersham	3-0

ROUND 3

Abbey Rangers	v	Bedfont & Feltham	4-1
AFC Hayes	v	Sheerwater	P-P
Sandhurst Town	v	Dorking Wanderers Res	1-4
Molesey	v	Sutton Common Rovers	2-2, 4-1p
Balham	v	Ascot United	1-2
Jersey Bulls	v	Fleet Spurs	3-1
Ash United	v	Westside	2-1 aet
Camberley Town	v	Farnham Town	0-3

QUARTER FINALS

Abbey Rangers	v	AFC Hayes/Sheerwater
Dorking Wanderes Res	v	Molesey
Ascot United	v	Jersey Bulls
Ash United	v	Farnham Town

PREMIER DIVISION	1	2	3	4	5	6	7	8	9	10	11	12	13	14	15	16	17	18	19	20	21
1 Abbey Rangers		1-2	2-3	1-0	1-2	0-0		1-0		2-0	2-4	0-0	3-3	2-2	2-1	2-1	2-0		1-2	1-0	0-1
2 Ascot United	2-1		1-0		1-0	2-3	3-2	2-0	3-0	3-1		0-3	1-3	2-3	1-2		2-3	2-1	2-0	2-1	
3 Badshot Lea		1-3		0-3	1-3	5-0		1-3	0-1	4-1	5-0	3-2			0-2	3-2	1-4	4-1			1-1
4 Balham	2-3	1-2			4-1	4-1	1-0	0-0	1-2	4-3	3-2		3-1		1-2			2-2	1-1	1-4	2-3
5 Banstead Athletic	0-5	0-4				1-2	1-1		1-0		1-2	0-1		0-3		2-0			0-3	1-1	
6 Camberley Town	0-4			1-2	3-2		3-1		0-2	1-4	1-0					1-3	0-1	0-3	0-0	1-2	0-4
7 CB Hounslow United	1-3		0-2		2-5	1-1		1-3	5-1	0-2		3-1	3-0	1-4	0-0	1-0	1-4	2-2		0-3	0-5
8 Cobham	1-2	0-2	2-1	3-2		1-2	2-0		2-0		2-0		2-2	0-1	1-3	2-1	1-2	0-0	2-0		0-2
9 Colliers Wood United		2-3					2-2	1-0		2-1	2-3	4-1	2-2			2-2		3-2	1-2		
10 Egham Town	3-0	0-3	1-0	1-6	3-3	2-3	1-0	0-1	3-0		1-2	2-2	1-3	0-3			4-2				4-1
11 Frimley Green	1-1	1-1	3-1	4-2		0-2	1-3	1-2	2-1	2-1		0-0		3-2	4-2	1-2	5-1	3-0	2-1	1-3	2-0
12 Guildford City		0-1	0-3	0-1		1-2	3-0		0-0	0-2			2-1	0-4	1-2	2-0	1-4	2-1	0-1	1-2	
13 Hanworth Villa		1-1	0-2		0-1	1-2		2-3		0-2	0-0	2-1		1-3	0-1		4-1	0-3	0-2	0-3	2-3
14 Knaphill	0-0	0-2	4-1	2-1	0-0	3-0	0-0		0-0	3-1		4-0	2-2		3-1	4-2		3-3	0-2	2-0	
15 Molesey	1-0			4-0	3-0	1-0	5-0	1-0	0-5	1-3	3-1		0-2	0-1			2-1	0-2	2-0	6-0	1-3
16 Raynes Park Vale	1-4	0-4					4-1		3-0	3-0	1-1				1-0				0-3	0-2	1-1
17 Redhill		1-2				2-1	3-0	0-3	1-3	0-2		3-1	4-0	0-2	3-0				0-5	3-4	
18 Sheerwater	1-1	4-2	3-1	3-5	3-2	1-2	1-0	1-2			1-2	2-1	2-0		0-2	1-5	1-0				4-4
19 Southall		1-0	1-1		0-1		1-0	1-1	1-3	4-4	2-2	1-0	1-1			3-1	1-2	5-1			
20 Spelthorne Sports		1-2	2-2	3-2			4-0	2-0	0-1	2-2	4-1	4-0	1-2	2-1	0-0	0-0	3-1	5-2	0-3		
21 Sutton Common Rovers	0-3		1-4	7-4	4-0		12-1	2-0			0-1		0-4	3-1	2-0	1-2	3-0	5-5	2-3		

DIVISION ONE	1	2	3	4	5	6	7	8	9	10	11	12	13	14	15	16	17	18	19	20
1 AFC Hayes		7-3	3-3							3-0		0-0	1-5	3-1	1-2					4-2
2 Ash United				4-1		3-1	4-2	1-4	1-2	2-1	1-2		2-1			2-1	0-8		1-4	2-1
3 Bagshot	1-4	1-2		0-0	2-3	1-1			2-1		1-0	3-0	0-1	3-3		2-0	2-3	2-1		3-1
4 Bedfont & Feltham	5-2	3-1	3-0				3-0	3-4			0-1	3-0		1-1	0-3	2-3	0-0	2-2	2-0	3-0
5 British Airways	4-1	1-3	1-5	1-1			3-3	0-2	2-0		1-5	2-3		0-2	4-2	0-4		0-2	0-6	0-3
6 Chessington & Hook United			3-3	3-0				0-2			1-1	0-2	2-4			1-2	2-2	4-3	3-4	1-1
7 Cove	3-3		1-2						0-6	2-2	3-1	0-7	2-3	2-1	3-1	0-1	2-0	2-1	0-2	3-3
8 Dorking Wanderers Reserves	2-5		1-0		1-4	5-1	1-1		1-1		1-1	6-2	0-1			4-5		0-4	3-6	1-5
9 Epsom & Ewell		1-4	2-1		0-5	3-0		4-0		2-2		0-2	3-0	3-5	5-2	2-0	1-1	2-2		3-2
10 Eversley & California	1-1		4-0	0-5	2-3	2-2		2-1			1-1	2-1	0-2	2-2		2-2		0-2	1-2	0-2
11 Farnham Town	0-1	3-1	2-1		1-1	1-0		2-0		1-0		1-1	2-0	1-0	0-2	3-1	1-4			3-1
12 FC Deportivo Galicia		1-0	2-4	4-3	2-0	6-2	4-3	2-2	2-3	1-1			4-1	3-3	0-6	2-3	4-4		0-3	0-7
13 Fleet Spurs	0-1	3-2	2-0	1-2	2-0	1-2			2-1	1-1	1-3	5-0			4-2	1-2	0-0	2-4	4-0	2-1
14 Godalming Town		4-2			2-1	2-4	3-4	2-2	0-2		1-2	3-0	0-5		0-5		1-2	1-5	2-2	
15 Jersey Bulls	7-2	3-0	7-1	3-0	2-0	6-0	7-0	5-0	2-0	5-1	4-0		4-0	2-0		4-0	4-1		1-0	
16 Kensington & Ealing Borough	3-2	2-1	3-1		2-3				3-1	3-0			4-2	1-5			2-3	2-1		
17 Sandhurst Town		2-1	2-2	2-5	4-0	1-0	1-2	1-2		3-1		4-1		2-1					1-1	3-2
18 Tooting Bec	3-2	3-0		1-2	3-3	2-2	4-1	3-2	2-1		1-2	5-1	2-1	2-1	0-1	3-1			1-3	
19 Walton & Hersham	2-1	5-1	1-0	3-4	7-3		8-2	3-4	6-3	3-0	0-1				0-3	0-5	2-2	1-1		
20 Westside	2-0			2-2			4-2	1-3			6-0				0-1	2-1		0-0	3-4	

Belper United v Kimberley MW 0-0. Photos Bill Wheatcroft.

EAST MIDLANDS COUNTIES LEAGUE

RECENT CHAMPIONS
2017: West Bridgford 2018: Dunkirk 2019: Selston

PREMIER DIVISION	P	W	D	L	F	A	GD	Pts
1 Sherwood Colliery	27	20	4	3	72	34	38	64
2 Heanor Town	26	19	5	2	84	29	55	62
3 Eastwood Community	29	19	4	6	77	38	39	61
4 Dunkirk	28	18	7	3	67	33	34	61
5 Hucknall Town	27	14	9	4	75	36	39	51
6 West Bridgford	26	11	7	8	45	43	2	40
7 Gedling Miners Welfare	27	12	3	12	59	56	3	39
8 Graham Street Prims	26	11	6	9	46	46	0	39
9 Radford	27	12	3	12	45	52	-7	39
10 Barrow Town	26	10	3	13	58	53	5	33
11 Ingles	26	10	3	13	36	49	-13	33
12 Belper United	27	9	4	14	40	58	-18	31
13 Clifton All Whites	25	8	6	11	43	42	1	30
14 Rainworth MW	28	7	8	13	41	52	-11	29
15 Clipstone	29	8	4	17	39	65	-26	28
16 Kimberley Miners Welfare	27	5	12	10	43	53	-10	27
17 Teversal	25	5	3	17	32	73	-41	18
18 Shirebrook Town	28	5	3	20	30	80	-50	18
19 Borrowash Victoria	26	3	4	19	25	65	-40	10*

LEAGUE CUP

HOLDERS: NEWARK FLOWSERVE

ROUND 1
Eastwood Community	v	Teversal	8-3
Hucknall Town	v	Ingles	2-2, 3-4p
Heanor Town	v	Belper United	2-3

ROUND 2
Sherwood Colliery	v	Gedling MW	3-1
Rainworth MW	v	Shirebrrok Town	3-1
Radford	v	Clifton All Whites	0-0, 2-4p
Dunkirk	v	Belper United	2-3
Barrow Town	v	Eastwood Community	3-2
Kimberley MW	v	Clipstone	2-0
Borrowash Victoria	v	West Bridgford	1-5
Graham Street Prims	v	Ingles	0-3

QUARTER FINALS
Barrow Town	v	Sherwood Community	2-2, 9-8p
West Bridgford	v	Clifton All Whites	3-1
Belper United	v	Kimberley MW	3-1
Rainworth MW	v	Inlges	3-0

SEMI FINALS
Belper United	v	Rainworth MW
West Bridgford	v	Barrow Town

Results Grid

		1	2	3	4	5	6	7	8	9	10	11	12	13	14	15	16	17	18	19
1	Barrow Town		3-1	2-2			6-2	1-2	2-3		2-4	2-3	0-1		1-1	2-1	2-2	3-0	4-1	3-4
2	Belper United			0-1	1-0	2-5	1-0	7-1		2-5	1-2		0-0	0-2	4-2		2-1	2-0		
3	Borrowash Victoria		2-4		1-2		0-4	1-2			1-5	1-4	4-0		2-4	2-3		0-3	2-0	
4	Clifton All Whites		5-0	1-0			0-1		1-2	1-1	1-3	3-3	1-2	1-1		2-1	1-4	1-2	8-3	1-2
5	Clipstone	2-1	1-0	1-1	2-3		3-4	2-3	3-1	0-1	1-1	1-7		1-1	2-0	5-2		0-1		1-4
6	Dunkirk	4-1		3-1		1-0		2-2	3-2	0-1	1-1		0-0	3-2	2-1		3-3		6-1	5-0
7	Eastwood Community	2-0	3-2	3-0	3-2	6-0	2-3		3-2	4-0	4-0		3-1	0-1	6-3	3-0	1-2	5-2	4-0	3-1
8	Gedling Miners Welfare	3-1	0-2	4-0	3-0	3-2	1-2			3-3	1-1	2-3		1-1	1-2	2-1		0-1	4-2	
9	Graham Street Prims	4-1		4-0		1-1	0-0	1-1	3-2		3-1	1-1	1-0	1-4			2-1	5-1	0-1	
10	Heanor Town		6-0	0-0		5-0	2-2		5-0	3-1		4-0	3-2	4-1	2-0		2-4			
11	Hucknall Town	5-1		3-0	3-3		3-3		5-1	0-1			2-0	4-0	0-2	4-0	3-1		5-2	2-0
12	Ingles	3-1	5-1	2-1		1-0		0-2		1-1	0-7	1-0		0-3		0-2	1-3		2-0	0-1
13	Kimberley Miners Welfare		1-1	3-0		0-2	1-2		1-4	7-2	0-4	4-4			1-1	0-3	5-1	0-4	1-1	
14	Radford	0-5	3-1	3-0	2-1	5-1		1-1	1-4	2-1	1-4		3-2	0-0		2-1	1-2	3-0	3-1	1-4
15	Rainworth MW	2-4	2-2	1-2	0-0		1-1	3-2	4-1	2-1	0-2	0-0	2-2		2-2				1-3	2-0
16	Sherwood Colliery	1-2	2-0		2-1	4-0	2-1	2-0	2-3	4-2		1-1		4-3	5-0	1-0		2-1	3-1	2-0
17	Shirebrook Town	0-6	1-2	1-1	0-2	0-4	0-4	1-3	1-5			2-10	1-3	3-3	2-0	2-1	1-6		1-2	1-1
18	Teversal		4-1		1-1	0-2	0-3		1-4	1-4	1-5	1-1	1-4							
19	West Bridgford	0-2	1-1	3-1		2-0	3-0					2-4	2-2	2-0	2-2		3-3	2-0	2-2	

EASTERN COUNTIES LEAGUE

RECENT CHAMPIONS

2017: Mildenhall Town **2018:** Coggeshall Town **2019:** Histon

PREMIER DIVISION

		P	W	D	L	F	A	GD	Pts
1	Stowmarket Town	28	23	5	0	95	17	78	74
2	Norwich United	27	18	5	4	73	26	47	59
3	Stanway Rovers	28	18	5	5	70	32	38	59
4	Newmarket Town	27	16	3	8	69	40	29	51
5	Wroxham	25	14	5	6	37	18	19	47
6	Brantham Athletic	31	15	2	14	44	54	-10	47
7	Woodbridge Town	28	14	3	11	71	61	10	45
8	Mildenhall Town	28	14	2	12	53	41	12	44
9	Long Melford	30	13	4	13	51	61	-10	43
10	Whitton United	28	12	6	10	49	55	-6	42
11	FC Clacton	28	11	6	11	61	48	13	39
12	Godmanchester Rovers	25	12	2	11	51	52	-1	38
13	Kirkley & Pakefield	28	10	3	15	43	48	-5	33
14	Haverhill Rovers	28	8	6	14	45	65	-20	30
15	Swaffham Town	27	8	5	14	33	62	-29	29
16	Thetford Town	30	9	2	19	52	86	-34	29
17	Walsham Le Willows	28	7	3	18	42	65	-23	24
18	Ely City	30	6	6	18	37	72	-35	24
19	Hadleigh United	27	5	5	17	36	69	-33	20
20	Gorleston	27	6	2	19	40	80	-40	20

FIRST DIVISION NORTH

		P	W	D	L	F	A	GD	Pts
1	Mulbarton Wanderers	28	21	4	3	78	30	48	67
2	Lakenheath	28	19	4	5	66	32	34	61
3	Downham Town	29	18	5	6	70	37	33	59
4	March Town United	28	17	4	7	77	37	40	55
5	Fakenham Town	28	17	2	9	72	37	35	53
6	Norwich CBS	27	16	4	7	67	34	33	52
7	Sheringham	30	15	3	12	66	52	14	48
8	Ipswich Wanderers	28	13	6	9	65	36	29	45
9	Debenham LC	26	14	2	10	50	48	2	44
10	Great Yarmouth Town	26	11	7	8	35	28	7	40
11	Diss Town	28	13	1	14	50	54	-4	40
12	Needham Market Res	28	9	6	13	51	72	-21	33
13	AFC Sudbury Res	29	9	5	15	60	66	-6	32
14	Leiston Res	27	10	1	16	56	86	-30	31
15	Cornard United	27	9	3	15	41	60	-19	30
16	Framlingham Town	28	8	4	16	55	70	-15	28
17	Haverhill Borough	27	8	3	16	45	63	-18	27
18	Kings Lynn Town Res	27	7	4	16	43	63	-20	25
19	Felixstowe & Walton Utd Res	28	5	2	21	21	89	-68	17
20	Wisbech St Mary	29	2	4	23	32	106	-74	10

FIRST DIVISION SOUTH

		P	W	D	L	F	A	GD	Pts
1	White Ensign	25	17	4	4	71	30	41	55
2	Lopes Tavares	22	16	2	4	53	22	31	50
3	Little Oakley	24	15	3	6	74	31	43	48
4	May & Baker	24	15	3	6	54	38	16	48
5	Holland	25	13	6	6	50	39	11	45
6	Barkingside	24	14	2	8	48	47	1	44
7	Halstead Town	25	13	3	9	52	40	12	42
8	Wormley Rovers	25	12	3	10	40	41	-1	39
9	Coggeshall United	21	11	5	5	46	23	23	38
10	Harwich & Parkeston	26	10	7	9	44	41	3	37
11	Benfleet	27	11	4	12	59	66	-7	37
12	Wivenhoe Town	25	11	3	11	54	40	14	36
13	Frenford	26	10	5	11	43	39	4	35
14	Burnham Ramblers	28	7	6	15	42	53	-11	27
15	Hackney Wick	26	5	5	16	32	58	-26	20
16	Brightlingsea Regent Res	27	3	3	21	32	88	-56	12
17	Newbury Forest	22	2	3	17	30	67	-37	9
18	Fire United	20	1	3	16	17	78	-61	6

Leyton Athletic withdrew after one game.

CHALLENGE CUP

HOLDERS: LONG MELFORD

ROUND 1

Haverhill Borough	v	Ely City	2-2, 9-10p
Lakenheath	v	Downham Town	2-1
Holland	v	Ipswich Wanderers	1-5
Framlingham Town	v	Diss Town	3-0
Brightlingsea Regent Res	v	Stanway Rovers	0-6
May & Baker	v	Burnham Ramblers	2-0
Harwich & Parkeston	v	Wivenhoe Town	3-2
King's Lynn Town Res	v	Thetford Town	1-4
Newbury Forest	v	Hackney Wick	2-2, 1-2p
Benfleet	v	Fire United	3-1
Cornard United	v	Halstead Town	4-5
Little Oakley	v	Felixstowe & Walton United	5-1
Frenford	v	Lopes Tavares	1-2
Barkingside	v	White Ensign	1-4
Swaffham Town	v	Wisbech St Mary	4-0
Gorleston	v	Norwich CBS	1-1, 4-5p
Fakenham Town	v	Sheringham	5-2
Long Melford	v	Hadleigh United	4-2
Leiston Res	v	Debenham LC	6-3

ROUND 2

Ely City	v	Godmanchester Rovers	0-2
Mildenhall Town	v	Lakenheath	1-0
Wroxham	v	Norwich United	1-2
Walsham Le Willows	v	Kirkley & Pakefield	2-1
FC Clacton	v	Ipswich Wanderers	1-2
Woodbridge Town	v	Framlingham Town	5-1
Stanway Rovers	v	May & Baker	4-0
Brantham Athletic	v	Harwich & Pakeston	4-1
Thetford Town	v	Haverhill Rovers	3-4
Hackney Wick	v	Benfleet	2-1
Halstead Town	v	Little Oakley	2-4
Lopes Tavsres	v	White Ensign	1-1, 3-1
Swaffham Town	v	Newmarlet Town	3-1
Norwich CBS	v	Fakenham Town	5-1
Long Melford	v	Whitton United	2-2, 5-4p
Stowmarket Town	v	Lesiton Res	7-0

ROUND 3

Godmanchester Rovers	v	Mildenhall Town	0-1
Norwich United	v	Walsham Le Willows	HW
Ipswich Wanderers	v	Woodbridge Town	4-1
Stanway Rovers	v	Brantham Athletic	3-1
Haverhill Rovers	v	Hackney Wick	1-2
Little Oakley	v	Lopes Tavares	2-0
Swaffham Town	v	Norwich CBS	2-1
Long Melford	v	Stowmarket Town	0-2

QUARTER FINALS

Mildenhall Town	v	Norwich United	1-4
Ipswich Wanderers	v	Stnway Rovers	0-2
Hackney Wick	v	Little Oakley	2-1
Swaffham Town	v	Stowmarket Town	0-3

SEMI FINALS

Norwich United	v	Stanway Rovers
Hackney Wick	v	Stowmarket Town

PREMIER DIVISION

#	Team	1	2	3	4	5	6	7	8	9	10	11	12	13	14	15	16	17	18	19	20
1	Brantham Athletic			3-0	0-2	3-1		2-0	2-1	3-2	1-0	2-0	1-3	0-4	0-5		3-1	1-2	0-2		2-1
2	Ely City	2-0		1-4	1-1	4-1	2-3	1-1	1-5	1-2	3-1	2-3	1-1	0-0			2-3		1-5		0-1
3	FC Clacton	3-1			2-3	8-0	1-1	5-1		3-0	2-3		0-0	2-2			5-5	2-1	5-3		0-0
4	Godmanchester Rovers	2-1	5-1	1-0		4-0	1-1	0-2	3-0					4-3	1-3		3-1		3-1		
5	Gorleston		1-2	3-1	4-5		1-1		1-0	0-1	3-2		0-3	2-4		1-3	0-2	6-0		1-7	2-0
6	Hadleigh United	0-2		1-3				6-2		0-4	1-2			2-3	1-3	0-1	2-3	3-2		2-1	
7	Haverhill Rovers	0-2	2-3	1-0	6-2				1-1	1-4	3-4	1-1	2-2	2-1	0-1	2-1	3-1	4-2			
8	Kirkley & Pakefield	0-1	1-1	3-1	4-1		3-0			4-0	4-0	2-1	0-1		0-3		0-2	1-0	5-2		1-2
9	Long Melford	0-3	3-1	1-1	3-2		6-1	1-1			0-2		1-9		3-0	1-3	5-0	1-1	0-4		1-0
10	Mildenhall Town	4-0	3-0		3-2	2-1	2-1	1-2		3-0			1-2		0-0	3-1	6-1	1-3			0-1
11	Newmarket Town			3-1	3-1	3-1	4-0	2-1	2-1	4-1	1-2		2-1	0-0	2-4	7-0	4-2	5-1	10-2	1-3	
12	Norwich United	2-0	4-1			8-0	4-1	5-0	1-1	2-3	0-1			0-3	5-1		2-0	1-1	7-0		1-1
13	Stanway Rovers	7-1			5-0	4-0	4-0	2-1	3-2	2-1	2-1	4-4			0-3	2-0	2-1		0-2	3-1	1-0
14	Stowmarket Town	3-0	7-1	2-1	3-0		3-0	3-0	7-0	4-2	2-1	2-0		2-1		1-1	4-1		1-1	7-0	
15	Swaffham Town	1-4	2-2	1-3	2-1	4-2		1-1		1-2	1-4		1-2	0-2	0-5		1-1	2-2	1-3		2-1
16	Thetford Town		0-1		1-3	1-0	2-2	3-2	1-2		3-2	3-4	2-3		0-7	1-2		2-1	1-5	3-6	0-4
17	Walsham Le Willows	0-2	4-0	5-2		0-3	1-3	3-4	3-1	1-2		1-1	0-2	1-2		2-3			0-1	2-2	
18	Whitton United	2-2	3-2	1-4		4-2	2-1		2-0	2-1	2-0	1-1	1-2		0-4			1-4			0-3
19	Woodbridge Town	3-1	1-0	1-2		4-4	3-3	5-2	4-1	1-2		2-0	0-4		3-1	4-1	5-1	0-2			1-3
20	Wroxham	1-1	2-0	1-0	2-1		4-0		3-1	1-1		0-0		0-1			1-2	2-1		1-0	

DIVISION ONE NORTH

#	Team	1	2	3	4	5	6	7	8	9	10	11	12	13	14	15	16	17	18	19	20
1	AFC Sudbury Res		0-3	5-0	7-1		0-3	3-0	1-2	0-0	1-1	0-4	3-3	1-4			0-2	5-3	1-2	1-2	7-2
2	Cornard United			1-2	0-3			3-1	2-0	3-0	2-0	1-4	1-1	1-2	2-4	3-2	0-7		1-2	1-2	2-0
3	Debenham LC	2-4			0-1	0-1	2-0		3-1	5-2	0-1	3-0		1-0		0-3	1-4	1-1	1-1		
4	Diss Town	0-2		0-2		3-2		1-0	4-0	2-0	0-3	5-0	0-3	2-4					1-1	3-1	2-1
5	Downham Town	5-0	3-0	5-1	2-1		2-1				2-0	0-0		0-3	4-2	0-3	1-1	7-1	2-0	5-1	5-1
6	Fakenham Town	4-1	2-1		6-1	0-2		8-1	2-2		4-3	1-2	2-1	2-0	2-1		3-1				5-0
7	Felixstowe & Walton United Res		0-3	0-3	0-3	0-4	0-7		0-2	1-0	2-1		3-2	0-4	0-1	1-2	0-4	2-1	1-2	0-8	
8	Framlingham Town	3-0	2-0	3-5	2-3	0-2	1-2	8-2		1-3	1-0	5-5	0-3		1-6				1-4	2-2	
9	Great Yarmouth Town	2-1	0-0	0-1	0-3	1-1	1-1		2-1		-		3-2		0-1	4-0	3-0				
10	Haverhill Borough		4-2		2-1		0-7	0-0	3-1	0-3			7-1	2-3	5-2		3-5	2-1			3-1
11	Ipswich Wanderers	1-3	7-1	0-3		0-0		2-2	2-3	1-1	3-1			0-1	8-0	3-0		1-0			3-0
12	Kings Lynn Town Res				5-2	1-3	1-2		0-1		2-0				2-2	1-1	4-0			2-1	3-2
13	Lakenheath	3-1	2-2	2-3	4-0	0-2			4-2		1-0	4-0		1-0	0-0	1-3	6-1	3-1	2-1		0-0
14	Leiston Res	2-2		3-1	8-2		4-1	3-2	0-4		0-5	2-4	5-4			1-8	2-3	1-2		0-5	
15	March Town United	5-0		4-3		1-0	3-0		1-2	1-1	5-2	2-1	0-1	7-3			6-1	2-0	0-2		
16	Mulbarton Wanderers	3-3	4-1	4-1	1-0	1-0	1-0		1-3	3-0	3-1			6-0	4-2			1-1	4-1	1-0	5-1
17	Needham Market Res	3-0	4-1		3-2	3-3	2-3	2-1	2-2		3-2	1-1	3-1	2-2		2-4	0-2			2-0	2-2
18	Norwich CBS			3-4	4-1		6-0	4-2	0-0	2-0		2-0	3-5	1-2	2-2	4-0	5-1			2-3	3-1
19	Sheringham		2-4	2-3	2-0	0-5	1-0	5-1	3-1	1-0	4-0	2-1	3-6		4-2	0-1			0-3		6-1
20	Wisbech St Mary	1-8		2-4	1-5	0-2		3-0	4-5	1-1	1-3	0-5	4-0	1-3	0-6	0-6	0-5		0-5	2-2	

DIVISION ONE SOUTH

#	Team	1	2	3	4	5	6	7	8	9	10	11	12	13	14	15	16	17	18
1	Barkingside		2-1	2-1	2-2				1-0	4-4	1-3				0-4	4-0	0-4	3-2	2-1
2	Benfleet	3-2		6-1	2-1	0-2			2-3	1-8	2-2	5-1	3-3	1-2	2-3	3-0			
3	Brightlingsea Regent Res	1-3	1-4		0-4	1-5		0-0		1-5	0-1		1-5		3-1	3-2	2-3	1-1	3-4
4	Burnham Ramblers	3-1		2-1		1-4	5-0	1-2	1-1	0-1	3-2	3-3	0-2	0-1		3-1	2-4	1-4	
5	Coggeshall United	4-2	2-0				9-0	2-1				1-1				1-1	2-2	0-1	1-3
6	Fire United				3-1	0-3			1-2	0-5	1-4	2-8							1-3
7	Frenford		0-1	2-3	5-1		2-2		5-1	1-1		3-1	4-1	0-3	2-3	2-1	0-1	3-2	
8	Hackney Wick		0-3	0-2	5-2	1-1	0-1	2-1		2-1	2-4	0-1	2-2		0-2	1-2	1-4	4-2	0-3
9	Halstead Town		1-2	2-3	4-0	1-0	0-2	5-0	0-0				3-2	2-2	2-1	2-1		2-0	0-5
10	Harwich & Parkeston		2-0	2-2			2-2	2-2	3-0	3-0		1-1	1-3	1-1	2-2	3-1	1-7	2-0	3-0
11	Holland		2-4	1-1	6-1	3-1	2-1		2-1	3-2	1-0	2-1		0-2	4-1	1-1	1-0		0-2
12	Little Oakley		5-2	9-1	2-1	4-1	1-0	2-0	1-1	1-1		1-2			8-0	4-1	3-1	7-0	
13	Lopes Tavares		1-2	0-1		2-0		5-0	2-1	3-1	3-0		1-0			5-1		3-4	2-0
14	May & Baker		3-0	4-4	3-0	1-3		3-2	2-1		3-1	2-1	1-3	2-1		3-0	3-2		2-0
15	Newbury Forest		1-2	5-7	4-2	3-1		2-2	2-3	3-4		0-1							0-3
16	White Ensign		5-1	4-0	1-1	2-1	5-0		0-1	4-1	1-0	3-1		4-2	1-2	2-1		0-0	6-0
17	Wivenhoe Town		1-3	2-1	3-0	1-1	3-0	6-0	4-1	6-2		2-0		1-2	5-1		3-4		0-2
18	Wormley Rovers		1-0	2-3	2-0	1-2	1-1		2-0	0-1	3-2	4-2	0-3			0-0	1-1		

ESSEX SENIOR LEAGUE

Recent Champions
2017: Barking **2018:** Great Wakering Rovers **2019:** Hullbridge Sports

PREMIER DIVISION	P	W	D	L	F	A	GD	Pts
1 Saffron Walden Town	29	20	6	3	69	28	41	66
2 Hashtag United	26	21	2	3	66	27	39	65
3 Walthamstow	26	20	3	3	73	17	56	63
4 Hadley	26	17	6	3	80	24	56	57
5 Stansted	27	16	2	9	55	36	19	50
6 Takeley	24	13	4	7	46	34	12	43
7 Hoddesdon Town	27	11	8	8	50	35	15	41
8 Redbridge FC	25	12	2	11	57	56	1	38
9 Woodford Town FC	28	10	4	14	43	48	-5	34
10 Cockfosters	26	10	4	12	42	47	-5	34
11 West Essex	24	9	4	11	51	51	0	31
12 Clapton	27	9	4	14	40	59	-19	31
13 Ilford	28	8	6	14	31	50	-19	30
14 St Margaretsbury	28	6	8	14	36	48	-12	26
15 Sporting Bengal United	26	8	4	14	44	62	-18	25*
16 Enfield FC	26	6	6	14	36	66	-30	24
17 Southend Manor	26	6	5	15	28	61	-33	23
18 Tower Hamlets	27	6	4	17	36	65	-29	22
19 Sawbridgeworth Town	28	2	2	24	30	99	-69	8

LEAGUE CHALLENGE CUP

HOLDERS: STANSTED

PRELIMINARY ROUND

Walthamstow	v	Tower Hamlets	3-0
Clapton	v	Saffron Walden Town	0-1
Takeley	v	Hashtag United	0-2

ROUND 1

St Margaretsbury	v	Walthamstow	0-2
Saffron Walden Town	v	Cockfosters	4-3
Woodford Town	v	West Essex	1-1, 2-3p
Hashtag United	v	Sawbridgeworth Town	0-0, 3-1p
Hadley	v	Stansted	2-0
Sporting Bengal United	v	Ilford	2-3
Southend Manor	v	Hoddesdon Town	0-2
Redbridge	v	Enfield	4-0

QUARTER FINALS

Walthamstow	v	Cockfosters	0-2
West Essex	v	Hashtag United	2-2, 4-5p
Hadley	v	Ilford	4-1
Hoddesdon Town	v	Redbridge	P-P

SEMI FINALS

Cockfosters	v	Hashtag United
Hadley	v	Hoddesdon Town or Redbridge

HELLENIC LEAGUE

RECENT CHAMPIONS
2017: Thame United 2018: Thatcham Town 2019: Wantage Town

PREMIER DIVISION	P	W	D	L	F	A	GD	Pts
1 Westfields	26	20	6	0	81	24	57	66
2 Binfield	22	17	2	3	55	23	32	53
3 Fairford Town	23	16	1	6	57	37	20	49
4 Shrivenham	27	13	4	10	53	52	1	43
5 Brackley Town Saints	27	12	2	13	49	46	3	38
6 Longlevens AFC	25	11	4	10	52	41	11	37
7 Burnham	27	12	1	14	42	42	0	37
8 Easington Sports	23	11	3	9	35	35	0	36
9 Flackwell Heath	24	9	6	9	41	40	1	33
10 Reading City	26	9	6	11	32	35	-3	33
11 Windsor	26	9	5	12	53	55	-2	32
12 Lydney Town	25	9	5	11	29	35	-6	32
13 Bishops Cleeve	21	9	4	8	48	32	16	31
14 Virginia Water	26	8	5	13	42	48	-6	29
15 Tuffley Rovers	21	7	7	7	47	50	-3	28
16 Royal Wootton Bassett Town	27	8	4	15	50	65	-15	28
17 Brimscombe & Thrupp	24	6	9	9	36	49	-13	27
18 Ardley United	26	5	8	13	38	68	-30	23
19 Holmer Green	26	2	4	20	24	87	-63	10

DIVISION ONE EAST	P	W	D	L	F	A	GD	Pts
1 Risborough Rangers	23	20	3	0	67	12	55	63
2 Abingdon United	24	14	7	3	67	27	40	49
3 Holyport	23	14	6	3	71	34	37	48
4 Wokingham & Emmbrook	22	13	3	6	47	18	29	42
5 Chalvey Sports	28	12	4	12	53	51	2	40
6 Milton United	25	12	3	10	63	55	8	39
7 Long Crendon	23	12	2	9	47	35	12	38
8 Didcot Town Dev'	27	10	5	12	45	58	-13	35
9 Kidlington Dev'	24	10	4	10	56	46	10	34
10 Wallingford Town	25	9	7	9	38	34	4	34
11 Penn & Tylers Green	21	9	3	9	56	35	21	30
12 Marlow United	22	9	3	10	45	40	5	30
13 Thame Rangers	24	6	8	10	37	48	-11	26
14 AFC Aldermaston	19	5	8	6	34	37	-3	23
15 Woodley United	25	3	4	18	31	78	-47	13
16 Langley	23	3	2	18	30	94	-64	11
17 Abingdon Town	20	2	0	18	15	100	-85	6

Chinnor withdrew before the season started.

DIVISION ONE WEST	P	W	D	L	F	A	GD	Pts
1 Malvern Town	22	17	2	3	107	32	75	53
2 Hereford Pegasus	24	16	4	4	79	39	40	52
3 Hereford Lads Club	21	13	6	2	76	28	48	45
4 Shortwood United	23	11	6	6	59	31	28	39
5 Cheltenham Saracens	18	13	0	5	53	32	21	39
6 Malmesbury Victoria	21	12	2	7	57	31	26	38
7 Thornbury Town	16	12	0	4	55	29	26	36
8 Wellington	21	11	3	7	53	33	20	36
9 Clanfield 85	18	10	4	4	42	32	10	34
10 Moreton Rangers	22	9	3	10	42	46	-4	30
11 Stonehouse Town	18	7	1	10	33	36	-3	22
12 Cirencester Town Dev'	24	5	4	15	35	68	-33	19
13 Tytherington Rocks	24	4	3	17	28	76	-48	15
14 Bourton Rovers	23	3	2	18	27	74	-47	11
15 Newent Town	19	2	3	14	25	62	-37	9
16 New College Swindon	20	0	1	19	9	131	-122	1

DIVISION TWO NORTH	P	W	D	L	F	A	GD	Pts
1 Southam United	17	16	0	1	71	17	54	48
2 Adderbury Park	15	10	3	2	35	16	19	33
3 Headington Amateurs	18	9	4	5	44	29	15	31
4 Woodstock Town	16	9	4	3	39	27	12	31
5 Heyford Athletic	12	6	3	3	40	12	28	21
6 Easington Sports Dev'	11	6	1	4	20	15	5	19
7 Buckingham Athletic Dev'	12	4	3	5	20	23	-3	15
8 Banbury United Dev'	15	4	1	10	28	47	-19	13
9 Chinnor	12	3	1	8	17	31	-14	10
10 Moreton Rangers Res'	10	2	3	5	7	18	-11	9
11 Long Crendon Res'	13	2	2	9	16	45	-29	8
12 Old Bradwell United Dev'	12	2	1	9	12	35	-23	7
13 Risborough Rangers Res'	13	1	2	10	10	44	-34	5

DIVISION TWO SOUTH	P	W	D	L	F	A	GD	Pts
1 Penn & Tylers Green Dev	13	13	0	0	59	10	49	39
2 Yateley United	16	11	2	3	39	29	10	35
3 Wokingham & Emmbrook Res	15	10	2	3	50	20	30	32
4 Hazlemere Sports	16	7	4	5	34	29	5	25
5 Aston Clinton	13	7	2	4	32	28	4	23
6 Wallingford Town Res	16	7	2	7	42	51	-9	23
7 Chalvey Sports Res'	16	6	0	10	29	41	-12	18
8 Chalfont Wasps	14	4	1	9	23	37	-14	13
9 AFC Aldermaston Res	13	4	0	9	20	33	-13	12
10 Taplow United	15	3	3	9	19	46	-27	12
11 Stokenchurch	13	3	2	8	27	37	-10	11
12 Virginia Water Dev'	12	3	1	8	19	28	-9	10

DIVISION TWO WEST	P	W	D	L	F	A	GD	Pts
1 Letcombe	13	10	1	2	33	18	15	31
2 Highworth Town Res'	12	9	1	2	54	15	39	28
3 Faringdon Town	14	8	3	3	32	16	16	27
4 Shrivenham Dev'	13	8	0	5	46	29	17	24
5 Fairford Town Res'	14	7	1	6	32	31	1	22
6 Wantage Town Dev'	13	6	3	4	33	21	12	21
7 Newent Town Res	11	6	1	4	26	22	4	19
8 Kintbury Rangers Res'	14	5	2	7	30	27	3	17
9 Swindon Robins	15	4	2	9	24	44	-20	14
10 Clanfield 85 Dev'	14	0	5	9	20	51	-31	5
11 Shortwood United Dev'	15	1	1	13	21	77	-56	4

LEAGUE CHALLENGE CUP

HOLDERS: ASCOT UNITED

QUARTER FINALS

Binfield	v	Fairford Town	
Reading City	v	Flackwell Heath	
Bishops Cleeve/Tuffley Rovers	v	Wellington	
Moreton Rangers	v	Risborough Rangers	0-1

PREMIER DIVISION	1	2	3	4	5	6	7	8	9	10	11	12	13	14	15	16	17	18	19
1 Ardley United			2-1	1-1		3-0	1-2		1-1	0-0	1-5		0-2	1-3		3-3	3-1	1-3	3-3
2 Binfield	4-2		4-2			4-1	4-0	1-2	5-1	2-1		1-0	1-1				2-0	2-3	2-0
3 Bishops Cleeve				4-0	2-2	2-1			0-2	6-1	4-1				6-1	4-0		0-2	
4 Brackley Town Saints	2-0	0-1	0-3		1-2	0-1	4-3		1-0	7-0	0-2	2-0				1-3	2-1		3-2
5 Brimscombe & Thrupp	4-4	0-1	0-1	1-4				0-1		2-2	0-3	1-0	1-1	3-1	1-3	4-3		3-3	
6 Burnham	3-0	0-2		4-1	1-1		0-1	0-3	5-0	3-0		0-1	2-0		0-2		4-1	0-2	1-0
7 Easington Sports	3-0	1-3		0-1		1-3		0-2			0-3		1-0	3-0			2-1		3-1
8 Fairford Town	7-1		4-4			2-4	1-2		2-0	4-1	3-2	3-1	3-0		2-6	4-2		0-2	3-0
9 Flackwell Heath	4-0			1-2		2-2				2-0	2-2	1-2	3-1		1-2		1-1	3-6	3-2
10 Holmer Green			3-6	0-4	0-7		2-0	0-0			0-2			3-3		3-4	2-1		
11 Longlevens AFC			1-1		0-0	6-2	1-2	3-0				2-3	0-2	1-3	6-1	3-2		1-3	1-4
12 Lydney Town	5-2		1-1	1-0	0-2			1-3	0-3	2-0	1-1		2-1	2-1			0-0	2-2	
13 Reading City		0-1		3-1	0-1	1-0	1-5	1-3	1-1	3-0		2-1		0-2	3-1		0-2		0-1
14 Royal Wootton Bassett Town	2-2	0-1	3-0	2-5	4-2	1-3		0-1	2-1	7-3	2-1		2-2		2-3	1-1	1-3	1-6	2-4
15 Shrivenham	2-2	2-2	2-0	1-0	3-3	1-0	0-2	5-1		0-1	2-1	1-1	3-1			2-3	4-3	1-3	
16 Tuffley Rovers		4-1		3-3		3-0	1-3	2-3	2-1		1-0	2-2							3-3
17 Virginia Water	0-i		3-2	1-1	2-0	4-2	3-1		4-0	1-3		0-4	5-1	0-2	2-2				3-3
18 Westfields	5-1		2-1	2-1	6-0		1-1		1-1	6-0	4-1	0-0		3-2	2-0	5-1	3-0		5-0
19 Windsor	2-3	0-5		7-2		1-2			0-3	5-1		3-0	0-1	3-1	4-2	2-2	2-0	1-1	

DIVISION ONE EAST	1	2	3	4	5	6	7	8	9	10	11	12	13	14	15	16	17
1 Abingdon Town		1-5		1-8		0-5	1-7	2-0	1-4		1-9			0-3			
2 Abingdon United	8-0		2-2	1-1	3-2		2-1		2-1			1-1	4-0	2-1	2-0	2-1	
3 AFC Aldermaston	2-1	1-1		3-1							4-5	3-2		0-0	2-3		1-1
4 Chalvey Sports	9-1	0-2	2-3		1-3	3-3	2-1	2-3	1-2		2-1	0-5	0-4	3-2	1-0	0-0	3-2
5 Didcot Town Development	3-2	1-7	1-0			2-4	0-1	4-2	2-0	1-1	2-2	1-3	0-5	2-2	0-0		3-0
6 Holyport	6-0		2-1	1-2	4-0		8-3	7-4	2-0				2-4	3-0	1-1	3-0	
7 Kidlington Development	3-0		5-6	2-0	2-1	2-2			3-1	7-0			1-2	3-4	2-2	0-3	4-0
8 Langley	4-1	0-11	2-2	0-3	1-3		1-3		0-5	0-5		0-5		3-3		1-6	4-3
9 Long Crendon		2-0		5-3	5-0	0-3					1-2	2-1	0-1	5-2	0-0	2-1	5-0
10 Marlow United	5-0	2-4		1-1	3-1	4-1					2-4	2-3	1-1	4-0			1-3
11 Milton United	6-1	2-0	1-1	0-1	1-3	2-4	3-1	7-0	2-2	5-1			0-6	1-2	1-0	0-2	
12 Penn & Tylers Green		4-4			1-2	2-2	1-2	8-0		1-2	3-2				1-1	1-2	6-0
13 Risborough Rangers		2-1	3-0	3-1	3-1	0-0	4-1	2-0	4-0	3-0		3-0		2-0	5-1	1-0	6-1
14 Thame Rangers			2-2	1-0	0-3	0-0	1-1	4-2	1-2	0-2	2-3	1-2			1-1		4-1
15 Wallingford Town	8-0	1-2	1-1		3-2		1-1	2-1	1-2	1-0	2-3	3-1				2-0	2-1
16 Wokingham & Emmbrook	4-0	0-0	2-0	1-2		2-3	1-2	2-0	3-1	3-0	5-1	3-0					
17 Woodley United	1-2	1-1		0-1	2-2	2-5		4-2		4-3		0-6	1-2	2-2	0-2	1-6	

DIVISION ONE WEST	1	2	3	4	5	6	7	8	9	10	11	12	13	14	15	16
1 Bourton Rovers			2-4	1-7	0-4	0-1	0-6	1-3				4-2		2-3		1-4
2 Cheltenham Saracens	3-1		2-1	7-2	1-3		2-0	2-1					3-0		4-1	4-3
3 Cirencester Town Dev'	1-1	1-5		3-3	0-6	0-5	2-3	3-6	2-1	2-1	7-2	0-4			2-1	2-3
4 Clanfield 85	2-1		5-1		1-1	2-2			4-0			3-1			2-1	2-1
5 Hereford Lads Club	6-0	1-5		2-1			3-3	6-0			0-0				2-1	5-1
6 Hereford Pegasus	6-1	6-2	1-0		2-2		3-1	1-7	7-0		5-1	3-1	6-0	2-1	3-1	2-3
7 Malmesbury Victoria	3-1		3-1	1-1						13-0	3-1	2-1		1-2	2-1	3-1
8 Malvern Town	7-1	4-2	6-1		1-2	3-3	3-1		3-1	14-0	4-3	3-0	5-0	6-1	8-0	
9 Moreton Rangers	2-0	2-1	3-2	3-4	3-3	1-4	1-1			8-1	1-2		4-0	1-2	1-0	1-0
10 New College Swindon	1-3					1-3	0-4	0-10				1-6	0-5	0-6	1-1	0-9
11 Newent Town	2-2		1-2	1-3	0-6	1-3	1-4	1-7	1-3	2-0		1-1			2-3	1-5
12 Shortwood United	1-0	0-2	0-0	0-1	4-4		2-0	3-1	3-1	14-1			2-1	2-1	7-1	3-3
13 Stonehouse Town	4-1	0-3	3-0			1-4	5-0	0-1		8-1	2-1	0-0				0-1
14 Thornbury Town		4-1		3-2	2-0	5-3	4-2	3-5		8-1					7-0	
15 Tytherington Rocks	1-4	2-4	2-1		0-10	2-2	4-2	1-4	1-1	3-0			1-3			0-2
16 Wellington	1-0		1-1						2-1	8-0	1-1	1-3		1-3	2-0	

MIDLAND FOOTBALL LEAGUE

RECENT CHAMPIONS

2017: Alvechurch **2018:** Bromsgrove Sporting **2019:** Ilkeston Town

PREMIER DIVISION

		P	W	D	L	F	A	GD	Pts
1	Coventry United	29	19	5	5	60	31	29	62
2	Sporting Khalsa	26	18	1	7	66	27	39	55
3	Romulus	29	17	4	8	65	38	27	55
4	Newark Flowserve	30	17	3	10	60	42	18	54
5	Heather St John's	26	15	5	6	49	27	22	50
6	Walsall Wood	24	14	4	6	47	30	17	46
7	Boldmere St Michaels	29	13	6	10	50	44	6	45
8	Stourport Swifts	29	12	8	9	42	39	3	44
9	Long Eaton United	26	11	5	10	59	50	9	38
10	Highgate United	29	12	5	12	45	48	-3	38*
11	South Normanton Athletic	26	10	7	9	40	40	0	37
12	Worcester City	26	10	6	10	52	41	11	36
13	A F C Wulfrunians	31	10	6	15	50	57	-7	36
14	Coventry Sphinx	25	9	7	9	38	57	-19	34
15	Tividale	23	7	6	10	29	32	-3	27
16	Haughmond	29	7	5	17	40	69	-29	26
17	Racing Club Warwick	24	6	6	12	25	54	-29	24
18	Lye Town	28	5	3	20	31	62	-31	18
19	Gresley	26	3	7	16	29	51	-22	16
20	Selston	25	2	7	16	29	67	-38	13

DIVISION ONE

		P	W	D	L	F	A	GD	Pts
1	Leicester Road	32	25	4	3	96	23	73	79
2	Brocton	31	21	2	8	91	43	48	65
3	Studley	27	18	5	4	62	23	39	59
4	Uttoxeter Town	27	19	1	7	65	35	30	58
5	Lichfield City	29	17	3	9	64	39	25	54
6	Atherstone Town	23	15	3	5	71	26	45	48
7	Kirby Muxloe	28	12	4	12	51	53	-2	40
8	Hinckley AFC	25	11	5	9	46	38	8	38
9	Rocester	28	10	6	12	43	54	-11	36
10	Stapenhill	26	10	5	11	50	40	10	35
11	G N P Sports	24	11	2	11	39	45	-6	35
12	NKF Burbage	28	11	2	15	46	55	-9	35
13	Ashby Ivanhoe	23	11	1	11	43	43	-10	34
14	Heath Hayes	28	10	3	15	48	58	-10	33
15	Coventry Copsewood	29	9	2	18	40	67	-27	29
16	Cadbury Athletic	27	8	3	16	43	56	-13	27
17	Paget Rangers	28	7	5	16	43	73	-30	26
18	Nuneaton Griff	31	7	5	19	35	85	-50	26
19	Chelmsley Town	30	7	3	20	28	78	-50	24
20	Stafford Town	30	4	4	22	28	88	-60	16

DIVISION TWO

		P	W	D	L	F	A	GD	Pts
1	Solihull United	24	18	1	5	79	35	44	55
2	Northfield Town	20	13	4	3	60	19	41	43
3	Knowle	19	13	3	3	49	27	22	42
4	Coton Green	22	12	1	9	58	43	15	37
5	Boldmere S & S Falcons	21	10	4	7	54	31	23	34
6	Feckenham	16	10	3	3	44	18	26	33
7	F C Stratford	17	10	2	5	38	24	14	32
8	Coventry Alvis	15	7	2	6	38	30	8	23
9	Fairfield Villa	18	7	2	9	29	41	-12	23
10	Earlswood Town	13	6	1	6	20	21	-1	19
11	Hampton	17	5	3	9	29	36	-7	18
12	Barnt Green Spartak	15	5	3	7	28	36	-8	18
13	Alcester Town	16	4	3	9	26	45	-19	15
14	Lane Head	23	2	2	19	33	97	-64	8
15	Redditch Borough	15	2	1	12	20	51	-31	7
16	Bolehall Swifts	17	2	1	14	9	60	-51	7

DIVISION THREE

		P	W	D	L	F	A	GD	Pts
1	Sutton United	17	14	2	1	63	14	49	44
2	Inkberrow	18	13	3	2	70	23	47	42
3	F C Shush	18	10	2	6	44	34	10	32
4	Welland	18	10	2	6	41	33	8	32
5	Continental Star	24	11	1	12	63	64	-1	31 *
6	Coventry Plumbing	12	9	1	2	45	18	27	28
7	Coventrians	14	7	4	3	37	25	12	25
8	Birmingham Tigers	15	7	3	5	32	18	14	24
9	Enville Athletic	16	6	4	6	32	23	9	22
10	Central Ajax	13	6	4	3	24	21	3	22
11	W L V Sport	19	7	1	11	31	54	-23	22
12	Leamington Hibernian	20	6	2	12	29	50	-21	20
13	Upton Town	19	5	5	9	23	44	-21	20
14	A F C Solihull	18	5	3	10	29	37	-8	18
15	Castle Vale Town	25	4	3	18	30	83	-53	15
16	Shipston Excelsior	20	2	2	16	26	78	-52	8

LEAGUE CUP

HOLDERS: ROMULUS

ROUND 1

Gresley	v	Selston	4-4, 2-4p
Uttoxeter Town	v	Stafford Town	5-2
Kirby Muxloe	v	NKF Burbage	4-3
Brocton	v	Rocester	4-0
Lichfield City	v	Hinckley AFC	2-3
Heather St John's	v	Ashby Ivanhoe	1-2
AFC Wulfrunians	v	Tividale	2-3
FC Stratford	v	GNP Sports	1-0
Sporting Khalsa	v	Haughmond	5-1
Paget Rangers	v	Lye Town	1-5
Chelmsley Town	v	Studley	4-3

ROUND 2

Bolehill Swifts	v	Selston	AW
South Normanton Athletic	v	Newark Flowserve	C-C
Long Eaton United	v	Stapenhill	3-3, 4-2p
Walsall Wood	v	Uttoxeter Town	1-2
Coton Green	v	Coventry Copsewood	1-8
Kirby Muxloe	v	Coventry United	2-4
Leicester Road	v	Atherston Town	0-0, 4-3p
Nuneaton Griff	v	Coventry Sphinx	1-1, 4-3p
Brocton	v	Heath Hayes	2-1
Hinckley AFC	v	Ashby Ivanhoe	3-2
Tividale	v	FC Stratford	4-1
Sporting Khalsa	v	Worcester City	1-2
Cadbury Athletic	v	Lye Town	1-1, 3-4p
Chelmsley Town	v	Romulus	1-1, 2-4p
Stourport Swifts	v	Boldmere St Michaels	2-1
Racing Club Warwick	v	Highgate United	0-0, 4-2p

ROUND 3

	v		
Long Eaton United	v	Uttoxeter Town	
Coventry Copsewood	v	Coventry United	0-3
Leicester Town	v	Nuneaton Griff	4-1
Brocton	v	Hinckley AFC	
Tividale	v	Worcester City	0-1
Lye Town	v	Romulus	0-3
Stourport Swifts	v	Racing Club Warwick	3-0
Selston	v	South Normanton or Newark	

QUARTER FINALS

Romulus	v	Coventry United	
Brocton or Hinckley AFC	v	Worcester City	
Stourport Swifts	v	Long Eaton or Uttoxeter	
Leicester Road	v	Selston or Sth Normanton or Newark	

Midland Division One game between Chelmsley Town (blue & white stripes) v Hinckley AFC which Hinckley won 5-0. Photo Bill Wheatcroft.

Midland Premier - Glancing header from Smith (Newark) to score the second against Selston. Photo Keith Clayton.

PREMIER DIVISION

#	Team	1	2	3	4	5	6	7	8	9	10	11	12	13	14	15	16	17	18	19	20
1	A F C Wulfrunians		2-1	0-1		2-3	1-0	1-3	3-1	6-4	2-0	1-3	1-2	2-4	1-1	1-2	1-2	2-2		2-0	1-2
2	Boldmere St Michaels	1-2			1-1	1-1	4-1	1-2	3-0	2-1	0-1	1-4	3-0	1-1	3-0	3-1	0-1	2-1		1-2	3-2
3	Coventry Sphinx							1-2		2-2		2-3	2-0		1-1	0-0		1-1	2-0	0-8	3-2
4	Coventry United	4-3				4-3	0-2	1-0	3-0	3-1	6-0	4-1	1-1		6-0	2-1		3-1	1-0	1-3	2-0
5	Gresley			3-3	0-0			0-1	1-1	1-3		1-3	0-1	1-1	1-2	1-2	1-4		1-3	3-0	
6	Haughmond	2-2	2-4	1-3	2-4	2-0		1-4			2-2	2-3		2-1	3-1	3-2	2-5	0-1	2-1		
7	Heather St. John's	0-1	1-2	1-2		2-1	1-1			0-1	4-1		2-1	4-0	2-1		1-1	1-1	1-0	2-2	2-0
8	Highgate United	2-1	2-2	3-2	2-3	4-1	2-1	0-2					1-2	2-1	2-0	1-1	2-0	2-1	3-1	0-1	2-2
9	Long Eaton United		3-3	6-2	2-1		5-0	1-5	1-2			2-1	2-2	2-2		1-1		2-3	3-0	1-2	4-0
10	Lye Town	0-1		2-3	1-2		0-1		2-3	2-1		0-1		1-2	1-0		1-2	2-0	1-1	0-5	0-1
11	Newark Flowserve	2-1		8-1	0-0	1-0	2-0			1-3	3-2		5-0	0-2	3-2	0-1	4-1	0-0			4-3
12	Racing Club Warwick	0-0	5-1	3-1	0-1	2-2	1-0			3-2	3-2			1-3			0-2				
13	Romulus	6-2	1-2	1-1		2-0	3-1			1-3	2-0	1-0			3-2	2-4	3-1	3-0	3-0	3-0	2-2
14	Selston	2-5		1-3	0-1		2-2		3-2	3-2	0-3		1-3				3-3	1-1	0-2		1-4
15	South Normanton Athletic			1-2	1-3				3-1	0-2	4-1		1-1				3-1	3-1	3-1		1-1
16	Sporting Khalsa	3-1	2-0	5-0	2-0		7-0			3-1		2-0	3-0	2-3	7-0	3-1		2-1	0-1	3-0	4-0
17	Stourport Swifts		0-0	4-1	3-1	2-0		3-2	2-0			2-0	1-0	2-1	3-2	1-1				1-2	
18	Tividale	2-0			0-0	1-1		2-2		3-1		2-1		1-1	2-1	1-1		1-2			0-1
19	Walsall Wood	0-0	0-2		1-2	4-2	3-2		1-1		3-3	2-0			5-0		3-0	2-1			
20	Worcester City	2-2	3-0		0-1		3-1	0-1	2-2	1-3	6-0	3-2	9-0	3-0		1-0		0-0			

DIVISION ONE

#	Team	1	2	3	4	5	6	7	8	9	10	11	12	13	14	15	16	17	18	19	20
1	Ashby Ivanhoe			1-3	2-0		3-1		3-6				4-1		1-0		2-0		0-1		
2	Atherstone Town	5-1		2-0			1-2			3-0				3-1	3-0	7-1	5-0	7-0			2-5
3	Brocton	2-0			4-1	7-1	2-1	3-1			3-0	2-1	0-2	1-2	14-0	2-1	5-1		0-2		1-2
4	Cadbury Athletic	1-0	3-3	0-1		3-0	4-0	1-2		2-2		1-5	2-1		4-2	5-0		3-2			0-3
5	Chelmsley Town	1-1	0-2	1-3				3-1	1-4	0-5	0-2	1-4	2-1		0-0		3-1	3-0	1-1		2-5
6	Coventry Copsewood	3-2	1-4	1-2		1-0		2-3		3-2	0-3	1-6		3-2	3-4	3-1	1-2	1-1	1-3		0-2
7	G N P Sports	1-2		1-3	3-1		0-3			4-1	0-3			5-1	1-2	2-1	1-0	1-1			
8	Heath Hayes		1-1	1-4	0-3	1-0	3-0				1-3	0-2	1-0	2-1	2-4		6-1	1-6	1-2		3-1
9	Hinckley AFC	3-0		2-1		4-0	2-0		2-1		5-3	0-4		0-3	1-0	2-0	2-2	1-2	1-3		1-2
10	Kirby Muxloe	1-2	2-1	3-5	5-2	3-1			3-2	0-0		1-3		3-1		5-0	3-1	3-1	0-3		
11	Leicester Road	0-1	4-1		5-0	5-0	3-2	7-1	2-1		1-0		1-1	2-2	5-2	2-1	1-0	1-0	4-0		4-4
12	Lichfield City	4-0	0-2	1-1		5-0	2-1	3-1	0-2	1-3	4-0			3-2		2-3	3-2	4-3	1-1		2-0
13	NKF Burbage	1-2	2-0	2-4	2-1		3-0		1-2		2-1	0-2	3-4			3-0	1-3		1-0		1-2
14	Nuneaton Griff		1-6	2-1	2-1	3-0	1-2	0-0	4-1	1-2		0-4	0-6	1-2		0-0	1-1	1-1	0-4		0-1
15	Paget Rangers	5-1		2-5	1-1	1-3	0-2	2-3	3-2	1-1	0-0	0-6		6-2	5-0		0-4		1-1		0-4
16	Rocester		1-6	4-5	2-1	2-0	1-1	0-3	1-1	3-1	2-2	0-1	2-1	4-0	0-1			2-1			4-3
17	Stafford Town	0-4	0-3	0-5	1-0	0-3	5-0	1-2	1-1	2-1	1-2	0-6		2-2		2-5					0-3
18	Stapenhill	0-1		2-2	3-1	4-0		1-0	2-1	1-1	0-4	0-2	2-3		4-0	1-1	6-0			0-2	
19	Studley	4-0	1-1		2-1	7-0		3-1	4-1	1-1		0-0	1-3	3-0	5-2	3-0	2-0	4-0			2-0
20	Uttoxeter Town			3-0	3-1	2-0	1-3		3-0	3-2	4-1	0-1		0-2	4-2	2-1	3-0	5-2	2-1		

DIVISION TWO

#	Team	1	2	3	4	5	6	7	8	9	10	11	12	13	14	15	16
1	Alcester Town			3-5	1-1	2-5	2-1	2-3	0-3								
2	Barnt Green Spartak	0-2		2-1							0-4	2-2	1-7				
3	Boldmere Sports & Social Falcons	2-1	4-1		5-0	0-2			2-3	2-0	2-4	0-0	2-2	3-0		6-0	1-2
4	Bolehall Swifts								0-2	0-3			4-1	0-5			0-4
5	Coton Green	3-3	1-4	0-3	4-0			2-1	4-0	1-2	0-3	1-2	10-2	1-3	5-3	3-2	
6	Coventry Alvis		2-0			5-0			1-2	1-1	2-3			4-1	4-3		1-5
7	Earlswood Town	1-1			1-3	0-1			1-3				2-1	0-1			2-0
8	F C Stratford	0-3	1-1			2-0		2-1		2-0	4-2		1-2	7-1			2-0
9	Fairfield Villa			1-2	2-2	3-0					1-1	3-0		2-3	2-6		1-3
10	Feckenham	5-1	1-2			7-0	3-0	2-1					2-3		0-0	3-0	3-0
11	Hampton			4-1	0-8	2-0	2-4		2-3		0-1		0-2	2-2	0-1	3-1	4-4
12	Knowle	2-1	2-0	1-1		1-3				4-3	6-1			4-0	2-0	4-3	
13	Lane Head	2-4	1-9	1-3	4-1	0-5	3-5	0-1	1-2	2-3	3-6					3-5	1-2
14	Northfield Town	5-0		2-1	4-0		4-5		2-3		0-0		2-2	6-0		4-1	2-0
15	Redditch Borough		3-3	4-0				0-1				0-5	0-2		0-5		0-5
16	Solihull United	7-0		3-2	8-1	4-1	3-1	4-3	2-1	5-1		2-1	3-1	9-0		2-0	

Midland League Premier Division - Hennessy (Heather St Johns) gets in his shot off against Hinckley.
Photo Keith Clayton.

Midland League Premier - Potts (Newark) gets in his shot under pressure from Lavelle-Moore (Basford).
Photo Keith Clayton.

NORTH WEST COUNTIES LEAGUE

RECENT CHAMPIONS
2017: Atherton Collieries 2018: Runcorn Linnets 2019: City of Liverpool

PREMIER DIVISION	P	W	D	L	F	A	GD	Pts
1 1874 Northwich	29	22	5	2	79	27	52	71
2 Rylands	30	20	3	7	62	32	30	63
3 Bootle	27	19	2	6	66	37	29	59
4 Charnock Richard	31	20	2	9	73	50	23	59*
5 Ashton Athletic	29	16	5	8	64	38	26	53
6 Longridge Town	26	17	2	7	62	44	18	53
7 Runcorn Town	31	14	9	8	55	41	14	51
8 Irlam	27	13	4	10	50	42	8	43
9 Squires Gate	32	13	4	15	56	68	-12	43
10 Northwich Victoria	28	11	7	10	57	43	14	40
11 Whitchurch Alport	29	10	8	11	43	44	-1	38
12 Avro	30	11	4	15	49	55	-6	37
13 Winsford United	29	9	5	15	51	57	-6	32
14 Congleton Town	30	8	7	15	54	60	-6	31
15 Barnoldswick Town	27	8	4	15	40	62	-22	28
16 Skelmersdale United	31	7	6	17	48	60	-12	27
17 Padiham	28	7	5	16	31	55	-24	26
18 Burscough	30	7	5	18	25	67	-42	26
19 Litherland REMYCA	31	5	7	19	30	77	-47	22
20 Hanley Town	30	5	6	19	34	70	-36	21

DIVISION ONE NORTH	P	W	D	L	F	A	GD	Pts
1 Lower Breck	29	21	4	4	95	38	57	67
2 AFC Liverpool	29	17	6	6	91	43	48	57
3 Shelley	31	17	6	8	67	47	20	57
4 Emley	27	17	5	5	68	43	25	56
5 Golcar United	28	14	4	10	71	49	22	46
6 Ashton Town	29	14	4	11	68	54	14	46
7 Prestwich Heys	29	14	4	11	49	48	1	46
8 Pilkington	30	14	2	14	62	61	1	44
9 AFC Blackpool	29	13	2	14	58	60	-2	41
10 Holker Old Boys	30	12	4	14	55	63	-8	40
11 Daisy Hill	31	11	5	15	63	86	-23	38
12 Chadderton	29	11	3	15	56	66	-10	36
13 AFC Darwen	32	14	4	14	65	74	-9	35*
14 Nelson	28	10	5	13	47	57	-10	35
15 Garstang	29	11	1	17	57	69	-12	34
16 Cleator Moor Celtic	26	8	7	11	52	64	-12	31
17 Atherton Laburnum Rovers	29	8	7	14	36	58	-22	31
18 Bacup Borough	27	7	6	14	50	58	-8	27
19 Steeton	29	7	5	17	40	75	-35	26
20 St Helens Town	31	7	4	20	53	90	-37	25

DIVISION ONE SOUTH	P	W	D	L	F	A	GD	Pts
1 Vauxhall Motors	31	27	1	3	83	28	55	82
2 FC Oswestry Town	30	21	3	6	68	37	31	66
3 Stone Old Alleynians	30	18	5	7	65	32	33	59
4 Wythenshawe Town	27	17	5	5	71	25	46	56
5 Abbey Hey	29	16	5	8	56	44	12	53
6 West Didsbury & Chorlton	28	14	5	9	51	34	17	47
7 Eccleshall	29	14	3	12	55	47	8	45
8 Cheadle Town	30	13	5	12	50	47	3	44
9 Stockport Town	29	13	4	12	57	52	5	40*
10 Maine Road	30	11	5	14	57	54	3	38
11 Cheadle Heath Nomads	30	10	5	15	44	59	-15	35
12 Wythenshawe Amateurs	26	10	4	12	38	34	4	34
13 Cammell Laird 1907	29	9	7	13	56	58	-2	34
14 New Mills	28	9	6	13	49	63	-14	33
15 Abbey Hulton United	31	10	1	20	40	80	-40	31
16 Sandbach United	26	10	0	16	37	45	-8	30
17 Barnton	29	9	1	19	30	59	-29	28
18 Ellesmere Rangers	28	7	5	16	37	73	-36	26
19 Alsager Town	28	6	7	15	31	63	-32	25
20 St Martins	28	5	3	22	34	75	-41	18

THE MACRON CUP

HOLDERS: 1874 NORTHWICH

ROUND 1

Bootle	v	Eccleshall	3-2
Rylands	v	Barnton	5-0
Skelmersdale United	v	Irlam	1-3
Abbey Hey	v	Holker Old Boys	2-1
Ashton Town	v	Golcar United	5-1
Avro	v	Vauxhall Motors	0-6
Bacup Borough	v	Charnock Richard	1-1, 3-1p
Burscough	v	Ashton Athletic	0-5
Cheadle Heath Nomads	v	1874 Northwich	1-5
Congleton Town	v	AFC Darwen	2-3
Daisy Hill	v	AFC Blackpool	3-6
Emley AFC	v	Squires Gate	2-1
Garstang	v	Stockport Town	1-1, 4-2p
Hanley Town	v	Abbey Hutton United	1-2
Lower Beck	v	Cammell Laird 1907	2-1
Maine Road	v	FC Oswestry Town	3-0
Northwich Victoria	v	Barnoldswick Town	3-1
Padiham	v	St Martins	9-1
Pilkington	v	Steeton	1-3
Prestwich Heys	v	Winsford United	1-0
Runcorn Town	v	Atherton LR	5-0
Sandbach United	v	AFC Liverpool	2-4
Shelley	v	Wythenshawe Town	3-2
St Helens Town	v	Nelson	2-1
Stone Old Alleynians	v	Litherland REMYCA	1-2
West Didsbury & Chorlton	v	New Mills	3-1
Wythenshawe Amateurs	v	Chadderton	2-1
Ellesmere Rangers	v	Cleator Moor Celtic	3-2

ROUND 2

Ashton Athletic	v	Ashton Town	4-2
Abbey Hey	v	Bacup Borough	2-1
Garstang	v	Steeton	4-2
Litherland REMYCA	v	Bootle	2-0
Longridge Town	v	Vauxhall Motors	0-3
Lower Breck	v	Maine Road	2-4
Northwich Victoria	v	Runcorn Town	0-2
Rylands	v	Padiham	4-3
St Helens Town	v	AFC Blackpool	0-1
West Didsbury & Chorlton	v	Alsager Town	6-1
Prestwich Heys	v	AFC Darwen	2-1
AFC Liverpool	v	Abeey Hulton United	2-0
Whitchurch Alpot	v	Shelley	2-3
1874 Northwich	v	Irlam	4-0
Wythenshawe Amateurs	v	Cheadle Town	3-2
Emley AFC	v	Ellesmere Rangers	1-2

ROUND 3

AFC Blackpool	v	Ellesmere Rangers	1-2
Ashton Athletic	v	Wythenshawe Amateurs	6-0
Prestwich Heys	v	AFC Liverpool	0-2
Rylands	v	1874 Northwich	1-1, 2-3p
Shelley	v	Abbey Hey	3-2
Vauxhall Motors	v	Litherland REMYCA	1-2
West Didsbury & Chorlton	v	Runcorn Town	1-4
Maine Road	v	Garstang	2-0

QUARTER FINALS

Litherland REMYCA	v	AFC Liverpool	1-5
Maine Road	v	1874 Northwich	0-4
Ashton Athletic	v	Runcorn Town	2-2, 4-2p
Shelley	v	Ellesmere Rangers	3-2

THE REUSCH CHAMPIONS CUP FINAL

City of Liverpool	v	1874 Northwich	2-1

NWCP - Darr (Charnock) meets the cross... ...heads over Spencer (Rylands)... ...and into the net.

NWCP - Foster (Winsford) tries to block Bevan (Avro) with Green ready for the shot.

NWCP - Great save from Reid (Runcorn Town) against Longridge. Photos Keith Clayton.

PREMIER DIVISION

PREMIER DIVISION	1	2	3	4	5	6	7	8	9	10	11	12	13	14	15	16	17	18	19	20
1 1874 Northwich		0-0		2-0	0-0		2-1	5-0	2-1	2-4	3-2		4-1	1-0	1-1	2-1	1-0			3-1
2 Ashton Athletic	0-1		2-1	2-3		3-1			2-1	1-0		3-1	0-1		4-1	1-3	2-2	3-2	3-3	
3 Avro	1-1	1-2			3-4	5-2	1-0		3-1		1-2	0-2	0-1	2-2	0-1	3-2	3-2	1-2		
4 Bootle	1-4	0-4	7-2		3-1	4-1			1-1	3-0	3-2		1-0	4-0	0-3	1-1	7-3	1-0	1-0	
5 Barnoldswick Town	4-8	1-0				4-2	3-3		3-1	0-3	3-1		2-0	1-2			2-2	2-4	2-1	
6 Burscough	0-2	1-1	0-1	0-5	3-2		1-0	1-2	2-1	1-1	1-1		0-1	0-2	0-1	0-0		2-1	2-0	1-3
7 Congleton Town		0-0	1-5	0-3	5-0	1-1		3-1			1-3	2-4	4-0	4-3	4-2		3-1	2-3	1-1	4-3
8 Charnock Richard	0-5	3-2	1-3	3-1	2-1	0-1	1-3		4-0	2-0		2-2	2-0	4-3		3-1	4-0		4-0	4-1
9 Hanley Town	0-4	2-6	0-2	0-4	3-0		4-3	0-1			1-3	2-2		0-0	0-3	2-1		1-3		
10 Irlam		2-4	0-2		3-2		1-0	2-4	1-0		4-2			2-2	1-2	1-2	4-0		4-2	1-0
11 Longridge Town	2-1	2-3						3-2	4-3	4-2		2-1	2-1	3-2		4-1	1-0			5-3
12 Northwich Victoria	3-3		1-0	1-2	2-0	6-1	1-0	2-3	1-1	3-3	1-2		3-1	8-0		0-2	2-0	2-3	0-1	1-1
13 Padiham		0-1	1-1	1-3		1-0		1-1	2-0	0-2	2-0	1-1			1-1	0-2	1-3	2-4	1-2	1-4
14 Litherland REMYCA	0-9	1-7	0-2		1-0		3-0	2-5	4-1		0-5		0-2			0-3	0-3	0-0	0-3	1-3
15 Runcorn Town	2-3	0-1	4-1	2-0	3-0	5-0	2-2	1-3	1-1	1-2	3-1	2-0	3-3	1-1			0-0	2-1		2-2
16 Rylands		2-1	5-0	2-3	0-1		4-2	3-2		1-0		1-2	5-1	1-1	1-1		2-0	2-1	2-1	
17 Skelmersdale United	2-3				3-0	4-0	2-1	2-4	2-2	0-1	1-4	3-2			2-3			3-3	2-3	0-1
18 Squires Gate	0-4	0-4	2-1	2-4	3-1	0-1	2-1	2-1	1-2	1-5		2-1		1-0	2-0	0-3	3-1			3-1
19 Whitchurch Alport	0-1			0-1	1-1	4-0	1-1	0-3	4-1	1-1	1-2		1-1	0-3	0-2	1-1	3-2			
20 Winsford United	0-2	3-2	3-1			6-0	2-2	0-2	1-2		0-0		4-1	4-1	0-1	0-2	0-5	5-4	1-2	

DIVISION ONE NORTH

DIVISION ONE NORTH	1	2	3	4	5	6	7	8	9	10	11	12	13	14	15	16	17	18	19	20
1 AFC Blackpool		2-4	2-0	2-3	2-0	3-2	1-3	2-2		0-3		1-2	1-1	2-1	1-5	4-1	4-1	3-1		1-2
2 AFC Darwen	2-1		1-0	4-1	2-2	3-1	4-3	0-3	3-3	2-3	3-2		3-0	0-4	1-1	1-5	2-1	0-2		
3 AFC Liverpool	4-2	8-0		4-1		1-0	4-1	4-2	7-1	4-4	2-1	2-2	8-2		3-3	3-0	1-2		6-2	8-0
4 Atherton Laburnum Rovers	1-0	2-2	2-0			1-2	1-1	0-3	2-2		1-2	2-1		0-2	0-2	0-2		0-4	3-2	3-1
5 Ashton Town	2-0		5-1			5-3	2-3		3-0	2-2	1-2	1-6	1-0		5-0	3-2		5-0	4-1	1-1
6 Bacup Borough		1-2	0-0	1-3	2-0		5-1		3-3	2-2			4-2	1-2	2-3	1-0		0-1	4-0	
7 Chadderton	2-3	4-3			0-2	3-4		7-0	1-1	0-1	2-1	2-1	1-2	0-3			1-1	1-1	3-2	5-3
8 Cleator Moor Celtic		1-3	1-3		0-3	3-2	4-1		3-1	2-3	3-4	4-4		3-3		2-2	3-5	3-1		
9 Daisy Hill	1-2	4-1	1-4			3-1				2-4	3-0	1-0	1-3	0-6	2-3	3-1	3-2	1-3	2-1	0-0
10 Emley	4-1	3-1		2-3			1-0	1-1	4-2		2-1	1-4	3-2		2-1		4-1	1-3		5-1
11 Garstang		2-5	0-2		4-2	4-4			7-1	0-2		1-5		2-0	2-0	0-8	2-3	1-2		3-1
12 Golcar United	1-3	3-1		5-3	3-3		1-1			3-1	2-1		5-3			2-1	1-0		5-0	2-3
13 Holker Old Boys	2-6	1-6		1-0	3-3	2-0		1-3	8-0		0-2	2-1			1-2	1-1	2-0	1-0	4-1	1-3
14 Lower Breck	4-3	1-0	3-3	6-1	4-3		5-1		4-3	3-1	5-1	5-2	4-1		4-1	3-0	2-2		5-1	
15 Nelson	1-2		1-4	1-1	3-1		1-0	2-0	3-6		3-2					2-3	1-3	0-0	1-1	0-1
16 Pilkington	1-2		3-1	0-2	4-1	1-2	0-3	5-1	3-2	2-1	1-5	3-2	3-1	3-2					3-2	2-0
17 Prestwich Heys		2-1	1-0	2-0	3-1			0-3	0-0	3-1	1-0	1-2	0-4	0-2	4-0				2-2	2-1
18 Shelley		4-1			1-1	3-0	5-0	3-2	1-1		2-1		2-3	2-0	5-3	4-1	1-2		0-2	5-2
19 St Helens Town	4-2	3-2	2-2	2-2	3-1	1-2	4-2	6-0	3-8	2-3	1-5	0-2	0-0	0-8	0-1		1-3	2-3		3-1
20 Steeton		1-2	1-3	1-1	1-3		1-4	0-1		0-5	1-4	2-1	1-4	1-1		2-0	1-3	3-3	5-1	

DIVISION ONE SOUTH

DIVISION ONE SOUTH	1	2	3	4	5	6	7	8	9	10	11	12	13	14	15	16	17	18	19	20
1 Abbey Hey		2-0	1-1	4-2	2-1	1-4			1-1	2-1		3-0	2-1	3-1	2-0	2-4	1-3	3-3		1-1
2 Abbey Hulton United			1-0	1-1	1-3	1-3	3-2	0-2	0-4	2-1	2-6	5-3		1-4	2-0	2-5			0-1	0-9
3 Alsager Town	0-3	3-2			0-3	1-4		0-3	2-2	0-3	1-2	0-2	2-0	2-3	1-0	1-2		1-2	0-0	
4 Barnton	2-3	0-2	1-1		2-3	0-2	1-0	0-2	0-2		2-3		3-2	1-6	1-0		1-4	0-1		2-1
5 Cammell Laird 1907		3-1	2-3	0-2		1-1	2-0		2-2		4-1	4-5		4-2	2-3	2-3	1-2			3-3
6 Cheadle Heath Nomads	0-1	5-1	1-2	1-2	0-1			1-0	3-0	2-4		2-0	1-4	1-1	3-2	1-5		0-5	1-1	
7 Cheadle Town	0-1	4-1	1-2			3-1		2-2	3-0	1-5	2-1	1-1	1-0	1-2	0-1	2-1	0-1	2-1		0-7
8 Eccleshall	4-1	2-0	8-1		2-4	2-0	0-4		9-0	0-5	1-0	1-2			3-2	2-0	0-1	0-4	0-4	
9 Ellesmere Rangers	2-3	0-2		0-3	2-2					0-1	1-6	2-0	2-0	1-5	2-0	0-2	1-2	3-2		1-2
10 FC Oswestry Town	2-1	1-0	5-1	2-1	4-1	4-0	1-3		3-3		2-1		1-1	2-1	0-1	2-1	2-1	2-3	2-1	
11 Maine Road	2-2	1-2	1-1	3-0	3-0	4-1	2-2		6-1	3-1		1-2	1-2	0-3		1-3		1-1		
12 New Mills		6-1	1-1	1-0	4-4	1-1	1-2	0-3		2-3	1-1		1-3	1-2			1-3	3-3		2-4
13 Sandbach United	0-1	1-0	3-1	0-1	0-3		1-2		4-0		0-2			0-1		5-2	1-2		1-3	
14 Stone Old Alleynians	0-1	2-1		2-1	1-1	4-1	1-1	3-1	4-0	0-1	0-2		3-0			5-0		1-3	0-1	2-1
15 St Martins			2-2	1-2	2-0		1-6	0-2	4-2		1-2	3-1	2-3	1-4		2-3	0-4	2-2	0-3	0-0
16 Stockport Town	2-1	1-5		4-1	1-3	2-2	2-2	2-2	3-2	8-2	4-1		1-1	2-0			2-3	2-1	1-2	1-2
17 Vauxhall Motors	2-1		2-0	4-0		2-1	4-2	0-0	2-4		3-1	8-0	2-0		5-0	2-0		3-0		1-2
18 West Didsbury & Chorlton		5-0	4-1		2-1	0-0	2-1	4-0		0-3			0-2		1-0	0-1			2-1	1-1
19 Wythenshawe Amateurs	2-5	0-1		3-0	1-0		0-1	0-2		0-1		0-2	0-2	2-4	5-0		1-2	1-0		
20 Wythenshawe Town	3-2		5-0		5-0	2-0	3-0	3-0	1-2	3-1	4-0	1-2	3-1	2-0			0-1	2-2	1-0	

NWCP - Wright (Avro) gets a shot on target under pressure from Cotterell (Winsford).

NWCP - Darr (Charnock) Spencer (Rylands).
Photo Keith Clayton.

NWCP - Marshall (Winsford) beats Latham (Avro) to give Winsford the lead. Photos Keith Clayton.

NORTHERN COUNTIES EAST LEAGUE

RECENT CHAMPIONS

2017: Cleethorpes Town **2018:** Pontefract Collieries **2019:** Worksop Town

PREMIER DIVISION	P	W	D	L	F	A	GD	Pts
1 Staveley Miners Welfare	26	17	4	5	59	26	33	55
2 Liversedge	24	16	5	3	80	42	38	53
3 Yorkshire Amateur	26	16	5	5	60	27	33	53
4 Penistone Church	28	15	8	5	58	32	26	53
5 Bridlington Town	25	14	6	5	52	33	19	48
6 Hemsworth Miners Welfare	28	13	6	9	53	42	11	45
7 Maltby Main	28	13	4	11	44	46	-2	43
8 Garforth Town	28	12	5	11	54	58	-4	41
9 Grimsby Borough	26	13	1	12	59	53	6	40
10 Silsden	28	10	7	11	46	51	-5	37
11 Barton Town	27	11	3	13	51	51	0	36
12 Eccleshill United	25	11	2	12	47	45	2	35
13 Knaresborough Town	25	9	5	11	42	39	3	32
14 Thackley	26	9	5	12	48	53	-5	32
15 Handsworth	23	8	6	9	39	55	-16	30
16 AFC Mansfield	26	7	7	12	33	43	-10	28
17 Goole AFC	28	7	4	17	40	61	-21	25
18 Bottesford Town	27	7	2	18	43	71	-28	23
19 Albion Sports	25	6	4	15	39	55	-16	22
20 Athersley Recreation	27	3	3	21	29	93	-64	12

DIVISION ONE	P	W	D	L	F	A	GD	Pts
1 Winterton Rangers	27	19	2	6	48	24	24	59
2 Skegness Town	26	18	4	4	58	19	39	58
3 Selby Town	25	18	2	5	86	40	46	56
4 North Ferriby	26	15	7	4	45	17	28	52
5 Campion	24	15	3	6	67	37	30	48
6 Retford FC	28	12	8	8	52	46	6	44
7 Glasshoughton Welfare	26	14	1	11	58	47	11	43
8 Hallam	23	10	7	6	41	30	11	37
9 Swallownest	25	11	4	10	44	43	1	37
10 Nostell Miners Welfare	25	11	2	12	55	42	13	35
11 Dronfield Town	25	10	5	10	50	43	7	35
12 Armthorpe Welfare	28	10	4	14	39	47	-8	34
13 Parkgate	25	10	4	11	35	51	-16	34
14 Rossington Main	26	8	7	11	40	46	-6	31
15 Brigg Town	30	8	6	16	44	63	-19	30
16 Ollerton Town	26	7	7	12	41	39	2	28
17 Hall Road Rangers	24	8	4	12	44	52	-8	28
18 Worsbrough Bridge Athletic	24	6	5	13	40	50	-10	23
19 Harrogate Railway Athletic	25	5	1	19	33	68	-35	16
20 East Hull	26	0	1	25	16	132	-116	1

LEAGUE CUP

HOLDERS: WORKSOP TOWN

ROUND 1

Brigg Town	v	Campion	1-2
Parkgate	v	Skegness Town	2-3
Retford	v	Swallownest	2-3
Rossington Main	v	Glasshoughton Welfare	6-2
Barton Town	v	Liversedge	4-4, 2-4p
Bottesford Town	v	Handsworth	2-2, 6-5p
Eccleshall United	v	Thackley	3-1
North Ferriby	v	Selby Town	3-3, 3-5p

ROUND 2

Armthorpe Welfare	v	Knaresborough Town	1-3
Athersley Recreation	v	Rossington Main	0-5
Bottesford Town	v	Staveley MW	0-5
Bridlington Town	v	Silsden	2-3
Dronfield Town	v	Selby Town	2-2, 3-0p
Eccleshill United	v	Garforth Town	3-2
Harrogate Railway Ath	v	Nostell MW	2-3
Hemsworth MW	v	Campion	1-0
Liversedge	v	Goole AFC	2-2, 4-2p
Maltby Main	v	AFC Mansfield	2-2, 4-5p
Ollerton Town	v	Albion Sports	0-2
Penistone Church	v	Hall Road Rangers	2-1
Swallownest	v	Skegness Town	2-1
Winterton Rangers	v	Grimsby Borough	4-1
Worsborough Bridge Ath	v	East Hull	3-2
Yorkshire Amateur	v	Hallam	6-2

ROUND 3

AFC Mansfield	v	Rossington Main	3-2
Dronfield Town	v	Knaresborough Town	
Eccleshill United	v	Yorkshire Amateur	2-1
Hemsworth MW	v	Worsborough Bridge Ath	4-1
Penistone Church	v	Liversedge	
Silsden	v	Nostell MW	
Swallownest	v	Albion Sports	
Winterton Rangers	v	Staveley MW	3-1

NCEP - Burke (Staveley Miners Welfare) beats the Silsden keeper.

NCEP - Paylor (Hemsworth MW) heads home against Worsbrough Bridge. Photos Keith Clayton.

PREMIER DIVISION		1	2	3	4	5	6	7	8	9	10	11	12	13	14	15	16	17	18	19	20
1	AFC Mansfield		2-0		1-2	1-2	2-0	3-0			2-4	2-1	2-0	2-4	0-0	1-1	2-2	2-0		0-2	
2	Albion Sports	0-2		1-1	0-1				3-1			2-3	3-0		3-5	1-0	1-3	3-3		2-3	
3	Athersley Rec	1-1	1-8			1-2		0-8	1-4		4-1		1-5		3-3	0-3			0-2	0-4	3-5
4	Barton Town	3-0	3-0	4-3		5-0	0-2	1-3	3-1	2-1	2-3				2-4	0-2	0-0	3-0	1-0		0-3
5	Bottesford Town	5-0	3-2	2-3	3-4			0-2			1-5	2-5	2-2	0-0	2-4		1-3	1-3	0-3	3-2	
6	Bridlington Town	1-0		6-1	4-1	0-3		3-0	4-5	4-2	5-1	3-0		1-0	0-2		4-3	2-2	2-5	3-3	2-1
7	Eccleshill United	3-0	2-1		4-1				1-2	1-2		2-2			2-3	0-3		1-1	2-1		
8	Garforth Town	2-1			2-1	1-1	2-1			1-1	1-6	3-0	0-3		1-3	2-4		3-0		6-1	0-1
9	Goole AFC	2-2		6-0	2-1	2-1		4-2	0-5			2-3	2-4	1-2	2-6	0-1	0-1	3-2	2-4	0-2	1-4
10	Grimsby Borough	1-0	1-5	5-0	5-2	3-1		2-3	2-4	4-1					0-3	3-2			2-1	4-2	0-1
11	Handsworth	2-2		5-3	3-1			1-2		1-1				0-0	3-4	1-1		0-1		1-0	1-3
12	Hemsworth MW	2-1	0-0	0-1	2-1	5-2	0-1	4-1	1-1		2-1	0-0			2-1	2-3		3-2	0-1	3-2	
13	Knaresborough	0-1		1-1		0-0		1-1	3-1	3-0	10-1	1-3		2-4		1-3	2-4	3-0	2-1	2-5	
14	Liversedge	1-1	6-0		4-3				4-1		2-3	10-1		2-4			1-0	2-1			
15	Maltby Main	2-1	1-0		0-3	0-1	1-3	2-2	1-0	1-4		4-1	1-0	2-2			3-0	0-4	1-2	1-6	
16	Penistone Church	3-1	3-0		3-1	1-0	5-1		2-1	1-1	0-0	1-1	4-0	2-2	4-3			1-2	1-3	1-0	
17	Silsden	1-1	2-0	0-3			2-1	7-1	0-0		2-0		0-2	1-3	2-1				1-2	0-5	
18	Staveley MW	4-2	4-0	5-0	2-1	4-0	0-0		3-1		3-1		1-0	1-0			1-1	1-3		1-1	
19	Thackley	4-0		3-3	3-1		0-2		0-1	2-1		4-3			1-4	2-2	2-5		1-1		
20	Yorkshire Amateur	3-0		3-1			1-1	2-0	0-1	2-0	1-0	1-4	1-2	2-3	1-1	3-0	2-2	1-1			

DIVISION ONE		1	2	3	4	5	6	7	8	9	10	11	12	13	14	15	16	17	18	19	20
1	Armthorpe Welfare		1-2	2-1	3-0	1-2			1-2	1-0	2-1	0-3	0-1	2-2	0-1	0-4	0-3	2-3		1-0	
2	Brigg Town	1-4		1-1	1-2	6-2	1-4		0-5		1-1	3-0	0-5	1-2	2-1	2-2	1-5		0-4	1-2	
3	Campion	4-1	2-2			10-0		4-2	5-2	5-2		2-1	2-1		6-0			1-3			
4	Dronfield Town		1-1	2-0		5-0	1-2	2-2	1-3	4-1		1-0			2-4			1-3			6-1
5	East Hull	0-2	0-2	0-5			0-2		0-3	0-6	1-10	2-4					0-5	0-5			
6	Glasshoughton Welf			3-0	3-1	8-2			1-1	2-1	1-0	4-1	2-0	3-4	2-1	2-0	2-3		2-1	0-2	
7	Hall Road Rangers		1-1	0-6	9-0				0-3					3-1	2-2	4-2		2-3	1-3	1-3	
8	Hallam	1-0	3-1				3-1			5-0	1-1	3-2	0-0		1-3	0-2			0-1		3-3
9	Harrogate RA	1-3	3-2	1-1	1-2	3-0			1-2			3-1	1-2			1-5			2-3	2-3	
10	North Ferriby	3-2	3-1			3-1	2-1	2-0	1-1	5-0		1-0		1-0	0-0			1-1	2-0	0-1	2-1
11	Nostell MW			4-1	1-1	5-2		1-2		2-0			4-2	5-1		0-0	3-2	4-2	3-4	1-2	
12	Ollerton Town	1-1	0-1	3-0	1-3	2-1		2-3	0-0		1-3	1-3			2-2			1-0	1-1	1-1	
13	Parkgate	3-3	0-3		0-1		3-2	3-1	1-1	2-1	0-3				1-3		1-4	0-2	1-1		1-5
14	Retford FC	0-0	4-1		4-4	5-1	2-0	1-1	2-1	1-0	0-0	1-3		1-2			3-2	2-3	2-0	2-5	4-2
15	Rossington Main	0-2	1-2	3-3	1-1	3-2	4-2		1-3		3-2	1-2	2-0	0-1			2-0	1-1	1-2	2-0	
16	Selby Town	2-1	2-3	3-2	11-2	5-3	4-1		7-3	0-5	2-1	4-0				5-1		1-1	5-1	0-2	
17	Skegness Town	2-1	2-1	3-1	1-0	7-0	5-4	2-1	3-0	4-0	2-0			0-1	0-0	3-1	0-0			0-1	3-0
18	Swallownest	0-3		1-2	2-1	4-1		2-3		3-1		1-1				0-5				2-2	2-1
19	Winterton Rangers	1-2	2-1	1-3	0-2	6-0	3-0	1-0		2-0	0-2	0-2	1-0	3-0			0-1	1-0			1-0
20	Worsbrough Bridge	5-1	0-3		4-1		1-2		1-2		1-1			2-2	2-2	4-2	0-2	0-3			

NCEP - Thornton (Worsbrough Bridge) opens the scoring against Hemdworth MW.

NCEP - Kaine (Silsden) Burke (Staveley Miners Welfare). Photos Keith Clayton.

NORTHERN LEAGUE

RECENT CHAMPIONS
2017: South Shields **2018:** Dunston UTS **2019:** Dunston UTS

PREMIER DIVISION

		P	W	D	L	F	A	GD	Pts
1	Stockton Town	30	24	5	1	71	14	57	77
2	Shildon	30	20	4	6	75	38	37	64
3	Hebburn Town	31	19	5	7	82	48	34	62
4	North Shields	28	16	6	6	56	37	19	54
5	Newton Aycliffe	29	17	2	10	64	43	21	53
6	Consett	27	14	7	6	72	38	34	49
7	Guisborough Town	29	15	4	10	43	38	5	49
8	Newcastle Benfield	31	11	10	10	50	49	1	43
9	West Auckland Town	29	11	9	9	50	35	15	42
10	Billingham Town	30	12	6	12	54	54	0	42
11	Bishop Auckland	32	12	5	15	59	66	-7	41
12	Sunderland RCA	30	12	5	13	50	59	-9	41
13	Ryhope C.W.	30	9	9	12	45	64	-19	36
14	Seaham Red Star	28	7	8	13	43	67	-24	29
15	Ashington	29	8	5	16	33	61	-28	29
16	Whitley Bay	31	7	7	17	50	62	-12	28
17	Whickham	29	7	4	18	37	66	-29	25
18	Thornaby	29	5	7	17	34	67	-33	22
19	Penrith	29	5	5	19	32	69	-37	20
20	Northallerton Town	27	6	1	20	29	54	-25	19

DIVISION ONE

		P	W	D	L	F	A	GD	Pts
1	West Allotment Celtic	28	22	2	4	100	39	61	68
2	Redcar Athletic	30	20	5	5	63	33	30	65
3	Crook Town	29	19	3	7	73	34	39	60
4	Billingham Synthonia	30	18	2	10	64	42	22	56
5	Heaton Stannington	28	16	5	7	63	29	34	53
6	Ryton & Crawcrook Albion	30	16	4	10	60	39	21	52
7	Carlisle City	27	16	3	8	65	54	11	51
8	Tow Law Town	27	14	4	9	55	38	17	46
9	Jarrow	27	14	3	10	48	39	9	45
10	Easington Colliery	27	10	6	11	64	55	9	36
11	Birtley Town	27	11	3	13	36	38	-2	36
12	Willington	27	11	3	13	44	51	-7	36
13	Newcastle University	27	10	5	12	60	63	-3	35
14	Chester-Le-Street	29	11	1	17	40	60	-20	34
15	Bedlington Terriers	26	10	1	15	44	65	-21	31
16	Esh Winning	29	8	6	15	49	63	-14	30
17	Sunderland West End	29	7	6	16	38	62	-24	27
18	Washington	30	5	4	21	33	77	-44	19
19	Brandon United	27	3	6	18	27	78	-51	15
20	Durham City	26	2	2	22	19	86	-67	8

BROOKS MILESON MEMORIAL LEAGUE CUP

HOLDERS: WEST AUCKLAND TOWN

GROUP A

		P	W	D	L	F	A	GD	Pts
1	North Shields	4	3	1	0	15	5	10	10
2	Seaham Red Star	4	3	0	1	7	7	0	9
3	Heaton Stannington	4	2	1	1	14	7	7	7
4	Billingham Synthonia	4	1	0	3	7	14	-7	3
5	Newcastle University	4	0	0	4	7	17	-10	0

GROUP B

		P	W	D	L	F	A	GD	Pts
1	Ryhope CW	4	3	1	0	10	3	7	10
2	Sunderland RCA	4	3	0	1	16	4	12	9
3	Billingham Town	4	2	1	1	6	8	-2	7
4	Crook Town *	4	1	0	3	7	9	-2	0
5	Washington	4	0	0	4	2	17	-15	0

GROUP C

		P	W	D	L	F	A	GD	Pts
1	West Allotment Celtic	4	3	1	0	8	2	6	10
2	Ryton & Crawcrook Albion	4	2	1	1	5	2	3	7
3	Stockton Town	4	2	0	2	5	5	0	6
4	Ashington	4	1	0	3	11	9	2	3
5	Esh Winning	4	1	0	3	4	15	-11	3

GROUP D

		P	W	D	L	F	A	GD	Pts
1	Consett	4	4	0	0	15	5	10	12
2	Newcastle Benfield	4	3	0	1	14	5	9	9
3	Thornaby	4	2	0	2	14	10	4	6
4	Bedlington Terriers	4	1	0	3	8	10	-2	3
5	Brandon United	4	0	0	4	2	23	-21	0

GROUP E

		P	W	D	L	F	A	GD	Pts
1	West Auckland Town	4	3	1	0	8	4	4	10
2	Newton Aycliffe	4	3	0	1	11	3	8	9
3	Northallerton Town	4	2	1	1	9	4	5	7
4	Easington Colliery	4	1	0	3	6	13	-7	3
5	Redcar Athletic	4	0	0	4	4	14	-10	0

GROUP F

		P	W	D	L	F	A	GD	Pts
1	Shildon	4	4	0	0	15	3	12	12
2	Guisborough Town	4	2	1	1	10	5	5	7
3	Tow Law Town	4	2	1	1	8	9	-1	7
4	Carlisle City	4	1	0	3	6	13	-7	3
5	Willington	4	0	0	4	3	12	-9	0

GROUP G

		P	W	D	L	F	A	GD	Pts
1	Whickham	4	4	0	0	9	3	6	12
2	Jarrow	4	1	2	1	6	6	0	5
3	Penrith	4	1	1	2	6	7	-1	4
4	Sunderland West End	4	0	3	1	7	9	-2	3
5	Bishop Auckland	4	0	2	2	6	9	-3	2

GROUP H

		P	W	D	L	F	A	GD	Pts
1	Hebburn Town	4	4	0	0	23	1	22	12
2	Whitley Bay	4	3	0	1	14	4	10	9
3	Chester-Le-Street	4	2	0	2	5	8	-3	6
4	Birtley Town	4	1	0	3	6	22	-16	3
5	Durham City	4	0	0	4	4	17	-13	0

ROUND 3

Consett	v	Whitley Bay	3-3, 9-8p
Hebburn Town	v	Newcastle Benfield	0-2
Ryhope CW	v	Newton Aycliffe	1-2
Shildon	v	Jarrow	2-2, 5-4p
West Auckland Town	v	Sunderland RCA	3-0
North Shields	v	Ryton & Crawcrook Albion	3-2
West Allotment Celtic	v	Seaham Red Star	3-2
Whickham	v	Guisborough Town	1-4

QUARTER FINALS

Shildon	v	West Allotment Celtic	4-1
North Shields	v	Consett	
Guisborough Town	v	West Auckland Town	1-2
Newcastle Benfield	v	Newton Aycliffe	

SOUTH WEST PENINSULA LEAGUE

RECENT CHAMPIONS
2017: Tavistock **2018:** Plymouth Parkway **2019:** Tavistock

PREMIER EAST		P	W	D	L	F	A	GD	Pts
1	Brixham AFC	27	18	4	5	67	33	34	58
2	Ilfracombe Town	25	17	6	2	77	29	48	57
3	Torpoint Athletic	25	16	3	6	75	34	41	51
4	Ivybridge Town	26	15	5	6	51	42	9	50
5	Cullompton Rangers	25	13	8	4	76	37	39	47
6	Newton Abbot Spurs	26	15	2	9	61	38	23	47
7	Millbrook AFC	23	13	4	6	55	28	27	43
8	Bovey Tracey	20	13	3	4	87	26	61	42
9	Torridgeside AFC	26	11	4	11	60	55	5	37
10	Dartmouth AFC	24	9	10	5	47	43	4	37
11	Elburton Villa	27	9	7	11	45	51	-6	34
12	Honiton Town	22	8	4	10	36	46	-10	28
13	Elmore AFC	23	6	7	10	43	43	0	25
14	Crediton United	22	7	3	12	32	33	-1	24
15	Axminster Town	24	6	6	12	40	62	-22	24
16	Stoke Gabriel	30	7	3	20	46	98	-52	24
17	Plymouth Marjon	29	6	4	19	38	93	-55	22
18	Holsworthy AFC	26	5	6	15	40	70	-30	21
19	Torrington AFC	25	3	5	17	31	97	-66	14
20	Sidmouth Town	23	3	4	16	33	82	-49	13

PREMIER WEST		P	W	D	L	F	A	GD	Pts
1	Helston Athletic	26	25	0	1	100	22	78	75
2	St Austell	28	21	4	3	85	23	62	67
3	Saltash United	22	19	2	1	107	18	89	59
4	Mousehole	25	17	6	2	92	22	70	57
5	Bodmin Town	27	18	3	6	77	44	33	57
6	Newquay	28	15	3	10	72	47	25	48
7	Falmouth Town	23	14	3	6	73	36	37	45
8	Porthleven	23	9	5	9	43	46	-3	32
9	Liskeard Athletic	25	10	1	14	44	66	-22	31
10	Camelford	23	9	3	11	54	50	4	30
11	St Blazey	26	8	5	13	48	51	-3	29
12	Wendron United	24	9	2	13	44	60	-16	29
13	Dobwalls	22	8	4	10	50	60	-10	28
14	Wadebridge Town	25	6	6	13	51	72	-21	24
15	Launceston	23	7	2	14	42	57	-15	23
16	Penzance	25	5	5	15	27	68	-41	20
17	Callington Town	27	6	2	19	37	90	-53	20
18	St Dennis	25	5	3	17	33	91	-58	18
19	Sticker	28	5	1	22	38	113	-75	16
20	Godolphin Atlantic	27	4	2	21	27	108	-81	14

WALTER C PARSON LEAGUE CUP

HOLDERS: SALTASH UNITED

ROUND 1

Sidmouth Town	v	Dartmouth AFC	1-3
Plymouth Marjon	v	Honiton Town	4-2
Holsworthy AFC	v	Torrington AFC	2-0
Crediton United	v	Newton Abbot Spurs	3-0
Dobwells	v	Wendron United	6-3
Wadebridge Town	v	Mousehole	2-7
Penzance	v	Portleven	1-3
St Blazey	v	St Dennis	7-1

ROUND 2

Elmore AFC	v	Camelford	4-1
Ivybridge Town	v	Dartmouth AFC	0-1
Plymouth Marjon	v	Ilfracombe Town	2-1
Launceston	v	Holsworthy AFC	1-0
Callington Town	v	Cullompton Rangers	3-2 aet
Millbrook AFC	v	Liskeard Athletic	3-1
Saltash United	v	Torpoint Athletic	2-1
Helston Athletic	v	Bodmin Town	4-1
Crediton United	v	Dobwells	3-6
St Austell	v	Bovey Tracey	2-4
Sticker	v	Brixham AFC	1-5
Mousehole	v	Porthleven	2-0
Godolphin Atlantic	v	Falmouth Town	1-11
Stoke Gabriel	v	Torridgeside AFC	1-3
Axminster Town	v	St Blazey	2-3
Elburton Villa	v	Newquay	1-1, 11-10p

ROUND 3

Elmore AFC	v	Dartmouth AFC	4-0
Plymouth Marjon	v	Launceston	6-4
Callington Town	v	Millbrook AFC	2-5
Saltash United	v	Helston Athletic	2-1
Dobwells	v	Bovey Tracey	3-6
Brixham AFC	v	Mousehole	3-3, 3-5p
Falmouth Town	v	Torridgeside AFC	4-2
St Blazey	v	Elburton Villa	1-0

QUARTER FINALS

Elmore AFC	v	Plymouth Marjon	6-3
Millbrook AFC	v	Saltash United	2-0
Bovey Tracey	v	Mousehole	
Falmouth Town	v	St Blazey	3-2

#	PREMIER DIVISION EAST	1	2	3	4	5	6	7	8	9	10	11	12	13	14	15	16	17	18	19	20
1	Axminster Town		2-4	1-0	1-1			1-1	3-1		2-0				3-5	5-0	1-1			0-3	2-0
2	Bovey Tracey							4-1	3-1			4-0				10-0	9-3	1-1	3-1	1-2	11-1
3	Brixham AFC		2-1		3-0	2-2		3-0	2-1	4-0	3-0		0-1		4-2	3-1	2-0	2-1	3-2		6-0
4	Crediton United	5-0		0-1		2-0				3-1	1-3	1-2					4-0			0-0	0-1
5	Cullompton Rangers	9-0	1-5	1-2	3-0		3-1	7-1	2-1		4-1	1-1		2-1	1-0		3-1			3-3	2-2
6	Dartmouth AFC		2-2	1-1		3-3		4-1	3-2	2-2	1-1	1-1		3-2	2-1	1-1	2-2	3-2			4-1
7	Elburton Villa	2-1		3-0	0-0		2-1			4-3	1-1	1-2	1-1	1-1	0-1	0-1		5-3		4-3	
8	Elmore AFC					1-1				5-1	4-4	1-1	2-2	2-2		2-0		1-2		1-1	4-1
9	Holsworthy AFC	3-3		1-1	4-3	0-2		1-1			1-2			1-4	2-5		2-2	0-8	3-2		1-1
10	Honiton Town	2-3	0-2	0-6			2-3	2-1	3-2	2-0							3-1				2-2
11	Ilfracombe Town	4-1		3-4	2-1	1-1	4-1		2-0	5-1	2-0		1-1	3-0	2-1	5-0	7-1	8-4		7-3	7-1
12	Ivybridge Town	1-0	2-1	4-2	2-0	5-3		2-1	2-0	3-2		3-1		1-4	2-3	2-1	3-1	3-1		0-1	0-3
13	Millbrook AFC						1-0	0-0	1-1	2-1	2-0		3-1			5-1	5-0	2-3	3-1		
14	Newton Abbot Spurs	2-2		4-0	1-0		1-4	0-2	2-4	0-0	3-1			1-0		5-1	3-0	0-4		2-0	6-0
15	Plymouth Marjon	5-4	1-7	2-6	2-3	1-4	1-2		0-2	1-5	1-1	1-3	0-5				2-2	4-1	2-3	2-1	3-1
16	Sidmouth Town	2-1	1-8	1-4		1-5	0-0	2-6					1-3	0-4					1-2	0-1	4-3
17	Stoke Gabriel	3-2	3-2		1-2	1-12	5-1		1-2	1-4		0-4	2-2	3-2	0-3	0-1	3-2		0-3		1-3
18	Torridgeside AFC		0-7	1-1	3-2			4-2	0-3	2-1			0-2	4-1	4-2		11-0	0-5			8-0
19	Torrington AFC	2-2			3-1		2-2	0-3					2-2	2-5	0-5		2-4	0-3		P	

#	PREMIER DIVISION WEST	1	2	3	4	5	6	7	8	9	10	11	12	13	14	15	16	17	18	19	20
1	Bodmin Town		7-0	4-6		4-0		2-4	2-0	3-2	1-3	7-4	3-0			1-2	2-0	4-1	6-0	2-1	
2	Callington Town	0-0			0-2	1-3			4-2	4-1		1-4	2-0		0-8	0-4	0-7	5-0		0-5	5-1
3	Camelford	2-3	3-1		3-0	2-3	1-1		1-2	0-2	1-2		2-4	1-2			2-1				7-3
4	Dobwalls		4-2				4-1	1-3		0-3	0-10			0-4	0-3			6-0			4-0
5	Falmouth Town			5-0	5-4			1-2	6-2	0-0	4-2					5-0	4-1	5-0	3-4		
6	Godolphin Atlantic		1-3	0-8	2-5	3-2		0-4	2-1	0-3	0-3	0-6	1-2	0-4			2-3	1-2	0-7		
7	Helston Athletic		2-1	4-0	4-0	3-0			6-1	1-2	3-1	6-2	11-0	4-1			3-2		8-0		2-1
8	Launceston				2-2	1-7	0-1	0-3		4-1		1-4	2-0		0-2		3-4	9-1	3-1		0-2
9	Liskeard Athletic	0-3	3-3	1-2	3-2		1-0	1-6				1-2	2-1	0-2		0-6	0-1	5-1	6-3		
10	Mousehole	4-1	7-1	3-2			10-0	0-1		5-0		4-0	5-2	3-1	1-1	2-0			8-0	2-2	
11	Newquay	1-2	6-0	2-3				0-2		3-1	3-0		2-2	3-3	0-3	1-0	9-1	2-0	5-3	0-2	
12	Penzance	0-3		2-2			4-3	0-3	2-2			1-1		2-2		0-6	0-2	5-2	1-2	2-0	2-2
13	Porthleven		2-1	3-2	2-2	1-3		0-3		2-2	0-2						1-1	1-2	3-2		2-1
14	Saltash United	6-0	5-0		3-1		6-0		6-2		2-2	3-0	7-1			3-0	6-0		7-0	8-2	4-2
15	St Austell	3-3	4-1	1-1		2-1	5-1	0-2	2-1	6-1	1-1	1-0		2-0	0-3			10-0	3-0	1-0	
16	St Blazey	1-2	3-1	1-3	1-2	2-2	9-1	1-3		1-4			3-1		0-1			0-0	0-2		
17	St Dennis	0-2			4-4	2-2		2-5	3-1		0-6	0-2		2-3	1-6	1-3					2-3
18	Sticker	1-6	2-1		3-5	0-5	2-3					0-4	1-0		0-6	4-4	0-1			2-3	2-4
19	Wadebridge Town	2-2			2-2	0-4	1-1	3-5	1-2	2-3			1-0	1-4	0-9	2-7	2-2		4-1		2-2
20	Wendron United	1-2	4-0		0-3	4-3					0-4	0-2	1-2	2-1	0-5		1-4	5-0	3-2		

SOUTHERN COMBINATION FOOTBALL LEAGUE

RECENT CHAMPIONS

2017: Shoreham **2018:** Haywards Heath Town **2019:** Chichester City

PREMIER DIVISION	P	W	D	L	F	A	GD	Pts
1 Lancing	29	21	5	3	70	30	40	68
2 Eastbourne Town	28	19	5	4	79	25	54	62
3 Horley Town	29	19	4	6	66	37	29	61
4 Newhaven	27	18	6	3	69	39	30	60
5 Peacehaven & Telscombe	29	18	4	7	68	40	28	58
6 Eastbourne United	27	13	3	11	51	54	-3	42
7 Crawley Down Gatwick	27	12	5	10	49	47	2	41
8 AFC Uckfield Town	24	12	4	8	41	29	12	40
9 Langney Wanderers	28	10	9	9	46	49	-3	39
10 Steyning Town	29	9	9	11	40	40	0	36
11 Alfold	25	10	4	11	46	48	-2	34
12 Horsham YMCA	30	9	6	15	56	69	-13	33
13 Little Common	26	8	7	11	43	42	1	31
14 Pagham	31	9	4	18	34	56	-22	31
15 Lingfield	24	9	2	13	41	48	-7	29
16 Broadbridge Heath	28	8	5	15	37	70	-33	29
17 East Preston	27	7	4	16	42	60	-18	25
18 Saltdean United	27	7	4	16	32	53	-21	25
19 Hassocks	25	6	2	17	32	60	-28	20
20 Loxwood	28	1	6	21	37	83	-46	9

DIVISION ONE	P	W	D	L	F	A	GD	Pts
1 Littlehampton Town	22	20	2	0	91	15	76	62
2 AFC Varndeanians	24	17	6	1	67	30	37	57
3 Mile Oak	23	15	3	5	67	38	29	48
4 Wick	23	14	4	5	63	41	22	46
5 Bexhill United	23	11	6	6	55	34	21	39
6 Midhurst & Easebourne	21	11	4	6	49	44	5	37
7 Seaford Town	22	10	4	8	47	37	10	34
8 Selsey	23	10	4	9	51	42	9	34
9 Arundel	17	10	2	5	43	26	17	32
10 Worthing United	25	8	5	12	46	48	-2	29
11 Shoreham	19	6	2	11	25	42	-17	20
12 Southwick	21	5	4	12	38	47	-9	19
13 Roffey	21	6	1	14	38	54	-16	19
14 Hailsham Town	20	5	1	14	33	59	-26	16
15 Storrington Community	21	4	3	14	28	60	-32	15
16 Oakwood	21	3	1	17	25	77	-52	10
17 Billingshurst	22	3	0	19	16	88	-72	9

Sidlesham withdrew after seven games.

DIVISION TWO	P	W	D	L	F	A	GD	Pts
1 Montpelier Villa	20	17	2	1	83	22	61	53
2 Upper Beeding	21	14	4	3	72	22	50	46
3 Copthorne	21	13	2	6	65	30	35	41
4 Rustington	19	10	2	7	45	29	16	32
5 Jarvis Brook	17	9	3	5	44	24	20	30
6 St Francis Rangers	17	9	2	6	29	18	11	29
7 Littlehampton United	16	8	2	6	54	47	7	26
8 TD Shipley	11	7	1	3	35	19	16	22
9 Angmering Village	18	7	1	10	35	61	-26	22
10 Worthing Town	17	6	2	9	34	32	2	20
11 Bosham	20	6	1	13	30	76	-46	19
12 Rottingdean Village	17	3	3	11	29	56	-27	12
13 Ferring	22	2	2	18	21	92	-71	8
14 Brighton Electricity	18	1	3	14	22	70	-48	6

Cowfold withdrew after eight games.

PETER BENTLEY CHALLENGE CUP

HOLDERS: SALTDEAN UNITED

ROUND 1

Seaford Town	v	Mile Oak	1-3
Worthing United	v	Oakwood	0-4
Southwick	v	Hailsham Town	1-2
Wick	v	Billinghurst	2-0
Storrington Community	v	Midhurst & Easebourne	0-3
Sidlesham	v	Roffey	2-3

ROUND 2

Broadbridge Heath	v	Loxwood	2-4
East Preston	v	Arundel	3-1
Steyning Town Com	v	Horsham YMCA	4-0
Selsey	v	Horley Town	2-1 aet
Littlehampton Town	v	Alfold	7-1
Saltdean United	v	Lingfield	0-3
Hasocks	v	Langney Wanderers	2-4
Mile Oak	v	Shoreham	4-0
Eastbourne United A	v	Bexhill United	2-1
Pagham	v	Oakwood	2-0
AFC Uckfield Town	v	AFC Varndeanians	3-1
Hailsham Town	v	Little Common	0-5
Eastbourne Town	v	Peacehaven & Telscombe	1-2
Wick	v	Midhurst & Easebourne	4-2
Crawley Down Gatwick	v	Roffey	6-2
Newhaven	v	Lancing	1-3 aet

ROUND 3

Loxwood	v	East Preston	2-3 aet
Steyning Town Com	v	Selsey	4-2 aet
Littlehampton Town	v	Lingfield	1-0
Langney Wanderers	v	Mile Oak	1-2
Eastbourne United A	v	Pagham	4-0
AFC Uckfield Town	v	Little Common	3-1
Peacehaven & Telscombev	Wick		4-0
Crawley Down Gatwick	v	Lancing	0-1

QUARTER FINALS

East Preston	v	Steyning Town Community	2-0
Littlehampton Town	v	Mile Oak	2-0
Eastbourne United A	v	AFC Uckfield Town	1-3
Peacehaven & Telscombev	Lancing		3-2 aet

SEMI FINALS

East Preston	v	Littlehampton Town	
AFC Uckfield Town	v	Peacehaven & Telscombe	

PREMIER DIVISION

#	Team	1	2	3	4	5	6	7	8	9	10	11	12	13	14	15	16	17	18	19	20
1	AFC Uckfield Town			1-0			1-1	1-2			1-2		1-0				4-2	2-0		1-2	
2	Alfold	1-0		1-2	2-2	2-0		3-2		2-4	5-3							2-0	2-3	4-1	1-1
3	Broadbridge Heath		1-0		1-3	2-4	1-5	1-3	2-1	2-2			1-0	3-2	1-6	2-2	1-4		3-2	2-0	
4	Crawley Down Gatwick			1-2				0-1	3-2		1-1	1-2	1-3	1-1	4-1	3-2				5-1	0-0
5	East Preston	1-1			5-2		0-2		1-2	2-3		0-1		0-3		0-0	1-4	1-2	1-2	0-3	1-3
6	Eastbourne Town	2-0	3-1	3-0	0-1	5-1			4-1	1-2	5-0		2-2	4-0			3-4	3-0	3-1		1-1
7	Eastbourne United Association	3-1	3-1		4-0	0-4			4-1		4-1	1-2		2-1	4-1	3-1		2-2	1-2	1-0	1-1
8	Hassocks	0-4			2-1	0-7				0-2	3-2	1-2		1-3		6-2	2-3	2-0	0-1		2-1
9	Horley Town	0-1	3-3		5-1	3-1		3-0	2-0		2-1	1-0	3-1	0-2	1-0	8-0	1-4	4-1	2-1		3-2
10	Horsham YMCA	3-1	3-2	3-3	2-5	1-2	6-1	2-2	0-1			2-2		1-4	3-1	0-1		1-3			
11	Lancing	0-1	3-1	3-0	4-0	5-1	3-1	4-2	2-1	3-2	1-1		3-0	3-0		1-0	2-2	2-1		3-0	
12	Langney Wanderers	1-6	3-2	5-1	2-1	2-2	0-2	1-0	4-0	0-0	3-1			2-2	2-2	1-0	1-2	1-0	0-4		
13	Lingfield			4-2		0-2		6-0	3-2		3-4	1-5			0-2		1-2	2-3		0-1	0-2
14	Little Common	0-3	0-1		1-1	0-2	1-1	2-2		2-3	2-1	2-4		0-1		3-3	3-0	1-2		0-0	
15	Loxwood	2-2	1-3	1-1	3-4	1-5	2-4		3-0	2-2	3-4	0-3	2-2		1-3		2-3		1-4	0-1	3-6
16	Newhaven	1-0	4-0	2-0	1-3		1-1			1-0	2-3	3-1	3-3		0-0	5-1				5-1	
17	Pagham	0-1	3-1	3-1	0-2		0-3	1-2	1-0		2-1	3-3	2-2		1-4	2-0	2-3		1-0	0-3	2-0
18	Peacehaven & Telscombe	4-4	1-2	5-0	2-1			3-2		3-1	3-0	1-1	3-3	6-2	2-1		2-3	1-0		3-0	1-1
19	Saltdean United FC	0-1	2-4	1-1	0-2	3-3	1-2	5-1	1-1		1-4		2-0	1-3	1-2		1-1				0-1
20	Steyning Town Community	2-3	0-0	3-1	2-3	1-2	0-5			1-3	0-0	1-2	1-2	0-1		2-1	1-1	2-0	2-1	3-0	

DIVISION ONE

#	Team	1	2	3	4	5	6	7	8	9	10	11	12	13	14	15	16	17
1	AFC Varndeanians			1-4	2-2	3-1	3-1	2-2	2-1	3-0	7-0	2-1	3-2		3-0	4-1	1-1	3-1
2	Arundel			2-1		4-1			0-3								3-0	3-1
3	Bexhill United	2-2	3-1			2-1		2-2	2-0	5-1	4-0		2-0	5-2	2-0	7-0	2-2	3-5
4	Billingshurst	1-6	0-4	1-3		3-1	0-4			1-6	3-1	1-8				0-5		
5	Hailsham Town			1-2	0-0		0-1		0-3			0-2		0-2	6-4	4-2		
6	Littlehampton Town			3-1	10-0	7-1		6-0		3-1	5-0	5-0	5-2		1-0	6-0		2-1
7	Midhurst & Easebourne			3-1	4-1		0-5		5-2	4-3	0-3	1-1	1-1			3-0		3-0
8	Mile Oak	3-3		1-0	5-0	7-2	3-3	5-4		3-2	1-1	4-2			2-1		2-3	1-3
9	Oakwood	0-2	2-2		2-0	0-7		0-3	2-7		0-1	2-6	4-1	2-7	0-3			
10	Roffey		0-4			5-1	1-3	1-2	0-1				1-6				1-2	2-3
11	Seaford Town			3-1	0-1	4-0	1-2	1-2		4-2	2-1			1-1	3-1	3-0	3-0	0-0
12	Selsey		1-2		2-1	5-1	0-4	2-3	2-3	6-0	2-3	2-1		5-0	2-1	2-2	0-2	3-1
13	Shoreham			2-1	2-2	4-0		2-4	2-5	0-2	4-2				1-0	2-0		0-1
14	Southwick	0-2	1-2	2-2	2-1	6-1	0-6	1-1		5-1	1-1		3-0			1-3	3-3	0-6
15	Storrington Community	0-2	2-5		5-0			1-3	1-6	2-0	1-2		3-4				2-3	1-1
16	Wick	2-2	3-2				5-0	0-3	4-2	1-4		2-0	6-2	4-0	3-1			
17	Worthing United	3-5	3-5		1-0	4-2	1-2	1-2	0-3	3-4	2-2	1-1	2-0			1-1	1-2	

DIVISION TWO

#	Team	1	2	3	4	5	6	7	8	9	10	11	12	13	14
1	Angmering Village		5-1	3-1	3-2			3-1					3-4	0-0	2-3
2	Bosham	5-1		3-2	3-0	1-5	0-6		4-3	2-3	0-3	1-5			0-1
3	Brighton Electricity	2-6	1-1		1-3		2-1		1-2		1-9	1-2			1-10
4	Copthorne	7-0	7-0	3-1		7-0	0-1	8-0		2-1	2-1	2-2		3-2	2-1
5	Ferring	0-3	1-4	4-2			0-8	4-4	1-4	1-1	0-5	1-8	0-3	0-4	2-1
6	Jarvis Brook	6-1	H-W	2-2	4-0	7-1			2-1	2-1	2-2	0-1		2-2	1-2
7	Littlehampton United	6-0	8-1		2-3	7-1			4-2		1-0			2-3	3-1
8	Montpelier Villa AFC	2-0	17-1	4-1	3-2	6-0	5-1	11-2		5-1	3-2	3-1	2-0	1-1	4-2
9	Rottingdean Village	2-0		3-3	0-6	2-1		5-6	0-4			1-1		2-3	3-1
10	Rustington	5-0	4-1	3-1		2-0		0-1	2-0			3-1		0-4	2-4
11	St Francis Rangers	1-2	3-0	H-W		2-1		1-1		2-0				0-2	
12	TD Shipley	10-1			3-0				3-3					0-3	3-2
13	Upper Beeding	8-3		9-0	1-3	6-1	3-0	4-1	1-2	11-2	4-0	1-0	2-1		
14	Worthing Town		1-2		1-1	3-2				0-1	0-2		1-1		

SOUTHERN COUNTIES EAST LEAGUE

RECENT CHAMPIONS
2017: Ashford United **2018:** Sevenoaks Town **2019:** Cray Valley (PM)

PREMIER DIVISION

		P	W	D	L	F	A	GD	Pts
1	Beckenham Town	27	19	3	5	61	30	31	60
2	Corinthian	26	18	4	4	71	32	39	58
3	Chatham Town	28	17	5	6	68	35	33	56
4	Sheppey United	27	16	7	4	80	34	46	55
5	Tunbridge Wells	23	15	1	7	57	38	19	46
6	Hollands And Blair	28	11	9	8	56	37	19	42
7	Bearsted	25	11	4	10	68	52	16	37
8	Canterbury City	25	9	8	8	41	38	3	35
9	Welling Town	27	9	7	11	42	50	-8	34
10	Erith Town	26	9	6	11	38	41	-3	33
11	Deal Town	24	9	5	10	37	40	-3	32
12	Fisher	26	8	8	10	32	37	-5	32
13	Lordswood	26	9	5	12	36	43	-7	32
14	Glebe	22	8	5	9	41	39	2	29
15	K Sports	31	8	5	18	45	71	-26	29
16	Punjab United	28	6	6	16	36	51	-15	24
17	AFC Croydon Athletic	27	7	3	17	37	70	-33	24
18	Crowborough Athletic	28	6	5	17	32	82	-50	23
19	Erith & Belvedere	28	4	8	16	35	93	-58	20

Grennwich Borough withdrew in January.

DIVISION ONE

		P	W	D	L	F	A	GD	Pts
1	Kennington	26	17	4	5	73	35	38	55
2	Rusthall	25	17	3	5	72	33	39	54
3	Holmesdale	24	15	6	3	53	17	36	51
4	SC Thamesmead	26	13	6	7	60	33	27	45
5	Rochester United	23	14	3	6	54	33	21	45
6	FC Elmstead	24	13	6	5	48	34	14	45
7	Stansfeld	24	13	6	5	40	31	9	45
8	Croydon	24	12	3	9	51	39	12	39
9	Greenways	26	11	4	11	73	64	9	37
10	Lewisham Borough	26	11	4	11	51	58	-7	37
11	Sutton Athletic	25	9	6	10	53	43	10	33
12	Forest Hill Park	26	9	5	12	41	48	-7	32
13	Bridon Ropes	27	7	2	18	53	73	-20	23
14	Lydd Town	26	6	4	16	40	70	-30	22
15	Meridian VP	26	4	6	16	24	68	-44	18
16	Snodland Town	24	3	5	16	22	63	-41	14
17	Kent Football United	26	1	5	20	22	88	-66	8

LEAGUE CHALLENGE CUP

HOLDERS: CHATHAM TOWN

ROUND 1

Rochester United	v	Sheppey United	2-5
SC Thamesmead	v	Erith Town	3-3, 5-6p
Corinthian	v	Stansfield	6-1
AFC Croydon Athletic	v	Croydon	1-0
Holmesdale	v	Welling Town	4-3

(Holmesdale removed for playing ineligible players)

ROUND 2

Hollands & Blair	v	Chatham Town	1-2 aet
Canterbury City	v	Lydd Town	6-1
Bearsted	v	Sheppey United	4-0
K Sports	v	Lordswood	0-1
Snodland Town	v	Deal Town	2-3
Greenways	v	Kennington	1-4
Corinthian	v	Erith & Belvedere	1-0
Lewisham Borough	v	Forest Hill Park	0-2
Fisher	v	Erith Town	1-1, 3-5p
AFC Croydon	v	FC Elmstead	3-3, 3-4p

(FC Elmstead removed for playing an ineligible player)

Tunbridge Wells	v	Welling Town	5-2
Beckenham Town	v	Rusthall	0-2
Glebe	v	Greenwich Borough	3-0
Bridon Ropes	v	Kent Football United	7-0
Meridian VP	v	Sutton Athletic	0-3
Punjab United	v	Crowborough Athletic	1-0

ROUND 3

Canterbury City	v	Tunbridge Wells	0-2
Sutton Athletic	v	Forest HIll	4-1
Deal Town	v	Bearsted	2-2, AWp
Kennington	v	Lordswood	3-2
Bridon Ropes	v	Punjab United	2-3
Chatham Town	v	AFC Croydon	2-0
Corinthian	v	Erith Town	0-2
Glebe	v	Rusthall	1-0

QUARTER FINALS

Sutton Athletic	v	Tunbridge Wells	AW

(Sutton Athletic removed for playing an ineligible player earlier in the competition)

Punjab United	v	Glebe	1-1, AWp
Chatham Town	v	Erith Town	3-1
Kennington	v	Deal Town	3-1

SEMI FINALS (Over two legs)

Kennington	v	Chatham Town
Glebe	v	Tunbridge Wells
Chatham Town	v	Kennington
Tunbrideg Wells	v	Glebe

PREMIER DIVISION		1	2	3	4	5	6	7	8	9	10	11	12	13	14	15	16	17	18	19
1	AFC Croydon Athletic			1-6	2-1		2-1	0-3	1-2	4-2	2-0	A-A		3-3		1-6	0-3		2-5	0-1
2	Bearsted	2-2		2-1	2-2		3-3	6-1		8-1	1-0		3-4	4-3		1-2	3-0			1-3
3	Beckenham Town	4-0	4-2		1-2		4-1		3-2	3-0		1-3	2-1	1-0	4-2	2-1	2-2		2-0
4	Canterbury City	1-1	2-1	0-2		1-0	2-0		0-3	4-0	2-1	4-1				P-P		2-2	0-5	5-0
5	Chatham Town	2-1	3-1				5-3	3-0	4-1	1-1	0-2	0-0	3-0	3-2	3-2	4-0	2-1	3-2	5-1	0-0
6	Corinthian		2-1	2-1		3-1			2-0	10-0	5-0		3-2	2-2	4-1	4-1	4-1	3-1	2-1	1-2
7	Crowborough Athletic	2-5	0-8		2-1	0-6	2-3			2-1	2-2			1-0	2-1	0-0		0-5	1-3	0-4
8	Deal Town	2-1		0-2	0-0		3-0				1-2	0-0		1-1	4-1			0-1	1-2	2-2
9	Erith & Belvedere	1-0		1-1	2-2	1-8		2-2	1-2			0-1		5-2	0-3	1-1	0-4		4-2	2-7
10	Erith Town	3-0	1-2	1-3	2-3	1-2		2-1	3-1	1-1			2-0		5-0	3-3	2-1	0-2		1-1
11	Fisher	1-3	4-1	1-2		1-1	0-1	1-1	1-0	1-1	0-0		3-1	1-4	2-3		2-0		0-3	3-1
12	Glebe		3-1		4-0		5-2	0-2	2-1		1-1			5-0	1-1	1-2			2-3	1-1
13	Hollands And Blair	4-1		0-2	0-3	1-0	0-1	9-2		7-1	0-0	1-0			1-1	1-0	1-1	1-1	1-3	1-0
14	K Sports	3-1	2-3	1-2	2-1	3-2	1-1	2-1	2-2	7-0		2-3	0-1	0-0		4-0	0-4	1-7	0-1	
15	Lordswood	3-1			1-1		0-3	0-0	2-3	1-2		1-2	3-1	0-3	1-0		2-0	0-1	2-0	
16	Punjab United		0-3	0-0	1-1	2-3	2-3	0-2	1-2	2-2		2-3	1-1	1-3	3-0	0-1			3-0	2-1
17	Sheppey United	6-0	4-1	4-1	4-3	2-2	0-0		6-2	5-0	5-3	2-0	1-1	3-3	2-0		5-0		1-2	
18	Tunbridge Wells	3-1	4-4	1-2		2-0		4-1		P-P		2-1			7-0			1-4		
19	Welling Town	0-2	1-4	0-3	0-0		1-5	2-1	5-3			0-0			1-5	3-0	2-2	3-2	1-2	

DIVISION ONE		1	2	3	4	5	6	7	8	9	10	11	12	13	14	15	16	17
1	Bridon Ropes		2-6		1-2	1-3	1-2	3-6	4-1	4-1	4-2	1-2		2-3	2-2	0-4	1-2	2-3
2	Croydon			1-3	2-1		0-2	A-A	5-0	1-3	3-2	2-2	4-0	2-3	2-0	0-0	1-2	
3	FC Elmstead	4-1	2-1			1-2	2-1	2-1	2-1	4-1		5-1	1-1		2-1		0-2	1-1
4	Forest Hill Park	0-3	1-3	1-4		2-1	0-1		1-1	3-2	2-1	1-1	2-1	1-3	1-0		3-1	
5	Greenways		4-4		3-2		3-2	3-5	6-1	7-3	2-3	3-2	1-3	1-2	9-0	0-3	3-1	0-7
6	Holmesdale	4-1		3-1		2-0		0-1	1-1		2-0	5-0	2-0		4-0	1-0	3-0	4-0
7	Kennington	3-1	2-0	3-1	3-2	2-2	1-1		4-1	6-2	2-0		3-3	1-2	3-1			1-0
8	Kent Football United	1-2	1-4	2-2	2-6			0-5		0-1	3-4	1-4	0-5	1-4		0-3	1-1	
9	Lewisham Borough (Community)	3-2	0-3	4-1	4-1	1-1	1-5		1-1			5-0	0-3	0-3		1-1	0-1	2-1
10	Lydd Town	2-1	1-2	2-2		4-2	1-4	3-3		2-5		2-1			0-0	1-3	2-6	3-3
11	Meridian VP	3-2	0-2	1-3	0-0	0-8	0-0	0-7		0-2	2-1			1-2	0-4	2-2	0-2	
12	Rochester United	2-2		P-P	2-1	3-2	A-A	1-5	5-0		2-1	1-0		3-2	6-0	2-1		3-0
13	Rusthall	3-4	3-0		2-2	5-0	1-1	1-0	5-0	2-2	6-0	3-0	1-2		4-2	6-1		4-1
14	Snodland Town			0-1	0-2		2-2	0-1	4-1	3-4	0-2	1-1	0-5			2-1		
15	Sporting Club Thamesmead	5-2	4-0	2-2	2-2			4-3	1-2	1-2	5-1	3-1	2-0	4-1	4-0		1-1	1-1
16	Stansfeld	2-1		0-1	2-1	2-2		1-0	1-0	2-1	2-0		3-1	1-0	2-2			3-3
17	Sutton Athletic	2-3	1-3	1-1	3-1	3-5	1-1	1-2	7-0		3-0			2-3	3-0	2-0	2-0	

SPARTAN SOUTH MIDLANDS LEAGUE

RECENT CHAMPIONS

2017: London Colney **2018:** Welwyn Garden City **2019:** Biggleswade FC

PREMIER DIVISION

		P	W	D	L	F	A	GD	Pts
1	Colney Heath	30	22	2	6	58	18	40	68
2	Tring Athletic	31	20	2	9	80	34	46	62
3	Biggleswade United	31	18	5	8	69	44	25	59
4	Newport Pagnell Town	29	15	9	5	67	39	28	54
5	Oxhey Jets	29	14	8	7	50	42	8	50
6	Harpenden Town	29	15	4	10	56	46	10	49
7	Leighton Town	26	15	3	8	63	39	24	45*
8	Crawley Green	32	11	11	10	62	52	10	44
9	Eynesbury Rovers	29	12	7	10	51	37	14	43
10	Edgware Town	33	12	6	15	50	63	-13	42
11	Leverstock Green	28	12	2	14	31	48	-17	38
12	Baldock Town	29	11	3	15	42	54	-12	36
13	Potton United	28	10	5	13	41	53	-12	35
14	Dunstable Town	27	9	5	13	35	47	-12	32
15	Harefield United	27	8	7	12	41	48	-7	31
16	Arlesey Town	28	7	12	9	44	48	-4	30*
17	Broadfields United	29	8	6	15	38	65	-27	30
18	Aylesbury Vale Dynamos	26	8	5	13	36	54	-18	29
19	Wembley	29	6	9	14	33	46	-13	27
20	North Greenford United	24	5	4	15	30	57	-27	19
21	London Colney	28	3	5	20	28	71	-43	14

DIVISION ONE

		P	W	D	L	F	A	GD	Pts
1	New Salamis	29	20	5	4	117	41	76	65
2	St Panteleimon	27	20	5	2	88	33	55	65
3	Winslow United	27	18	1	8	81	50	31	55
4	Rayners Lane	28	16	7	5	78	56	22	55
5	Stotfold	26	17	3	6	68	25	43	54
6	Milton Keynes Robins	28	16	4	8	61	56	5	52
7	Shefford Town & Campton	31	16	1	14	73	66	7	49
8	London Lions	27	11	6	10	45	40	5	39
9	FC Broxbourne Borough	26	9	10	7	44	45	-1	37
10	Ampthill Town	28	9	8	11	56	75	-19	35
11	Amersham Town	27	10	2	15	47	76	-29	32
12	Buckingham Athletic	26	9	4	13	53	59	-6	31
13	Bedford	28	9	3	16	39	59	-20	30
14	Enfield Borough	29	9	3	17	49	71	-22	30
15	London Tigers	29	7	9	13	44	58	-14	29*
16	Langford	27	7	5	15	49	70	-21	26
17	Hillingdon Borough	27	6	6	15	38	72	-34	24
18	Park View	26	5	3	18	38	69	-31	18
19	Brimsdown	28	2	7	19	39	86	-47	13

Woodson Park withdrew after 11 games.

DIVISION TWO

		P	W	D	L	F	A	GD	Pts
1	Old Bradwell United	15	13	0	2	49	11	38	39
2	Pitstone & Ivinghoe	20	13	3	4	55	27	28	39*
3	Codicote	19	10	4	5	29	24	5	34
4	MK Gallacticos	16	8	3	5	49	34	15	27
5	Aston Clinton	15	8	3	4	38	26	12	27
6	Berkhamsted Raiders	17	8	1	8	43	35	8	25
7	Sarratt	18	6	6	6	29	30	-1	23*
8	Mursley United	14	7	1	5	30	32	-2	22*
9	New Bradwell St Peter FC	16	5	6	5	26	26	0	21
10	Tring Corinthians AFC	18	7	2	9	34	29	5	20*
11	Bovingdon	17	5	3	9	27	26	1	18
12	Unite MK	16	5	3	8	30	49	-19	18
13	Buckingham United	17	5	2	9	17	34	-17	17*
14	Totternhoe	16	4	4	8	20	30	-10	16
15	The 61 FC (Luton)	18	0	1	17	18	81	-63	1

CHALLENGE TROPHY

HOLDERS: BALDOCK TOWN

ROUND 1

Amersham Town	v	Grendon Rangers	HW
Wembley	v	London Tigers	1-0
Tring Corinthians	v	Old Bradwell United	0-6
Colney Heath	v	Sarratt	2-1
Harefield United	v	Buckingham United	5-0
Leverstock Green	v	New Bradwell St Peter	0-0, 2-4p
Aylesbury Vale Dyamos	v	Codicote	0-1
Rayners Lane	v	Harpenden Town	2-3
Arlesey Town	v	London Lions	2-1
Aston Clinton	v	Bovingdon	2-1
Eynesbury Rovers	v	Bedford	2-2, 1-4p
Mursley United	v	Park View	3-6
Newport Pagnell Town	v	Enfield Borough	2-0
Potton United	v	London Colney	0-0, 5-4p
Unite MK	v	Ampthill Town	0-2
Wodson Park	v	North Greenford United	0-1
MK Gallacticos	v	Langford	1-3
Broadfields United	v	Leighton Town	0-3
Edgware Town	v	Pitstone & Ivinghoe	3-1
Biggleswade United	v	Crawley Green	0-2
Baldock Town	v	Buckingham Athletic	4-1
FC Broxbourne Borough	v	Hillingdon Borough	4-5
Milton Keynes Robins	v	Oxhey Jets	7-4
St Panteleimon	v	Dunstable Town	4-1
New Salamis	v	Berkhamsted Raiders	3-2

Bye: Totternhoe, Tring Athletic, The 61 FC (Luton), Stotfold, Brimsdown, Shefford Town & Campton, Winslow United.

ROUND 2

Amersham Town	v	Wembley	2-2, 2-3p
Old Bradwell United	v	Colney Heath	2-1
Tottenhoe	v	Harefield United	0-3
New Bradwell St Peter	v	Codicote	0-2
Harpenden Town	v	Arlesey Town	0-1
Aston Clinton	v	Bedford	4-2
Park View	v	Tring Athletic	2-1
Newport Pagnell Town	v	The 61 FC (luton)	4-0
Stotfold	v	Potton United	AW
Ampthill Town	v	Brimsdown	9-0
Shefford Town & Campton	v	North Greenford United	1-1, 6-5p
Langford	v	Leighton Town	1-3
Edgware Town	v	Crawley Green	0-0, 7-8p
Baldock Town	v	Hillingdon Borough	AW
Milton Keynes Robins	v	St Panteleimon	1-1, 14-13p
Winslow United	v	New Salamis	AW

ROUND 3

Wembley	v	Old Bradwell United	0-3
Harefield United	v	Codicote	3-0
Arlesey Town	v	Aston Clinton	1-1, 4-3p
Park View	v	Newport Pagnell Town	3-1
Potton United	v	Ampthill Town	1-1, 3-1p
Shefford Town & Campton	v	Leighton Town	0-1
Crawley Green	v	Hillingdon Borough	2-3
Milton Keynes Robins	v	New Salamis	3-2

QUARTER FINALS

Old Bradwell United	v	Harefield United	2-0
Arlesey Town	v	Park View	2-0
Potton United	v	Leighton Town	4-0
Hillingdon Borough	v	Milton Keynes Robins	0-5

SEMI FINALS

Old Bradwell United	v	Arlesey Town	4-1
Potton United	v	Milton Keynes Robins	3-5

FINAL

Old Bradwell United	v	Milton Keynes Robins	

PREMIER DIVISION

#	Team	1	2	3	4	5	6	7	8	9	10	11	12	13	14	15	16	17	18	19	20	21
1	Arlesey Town		2-2	1-3		2-1	0-5	2-2					2-2	1-1	1-1	3-0	1-0	1-5	0-1	0-1	0-2	2-0
2	Aylesbury Vale Dynamos	3-3		4-1	1-3	1-1		2-0			2-1	2-2	0-1	2-4	0-4		2-4		2-1			1-0
3	Baldock Town		4-1		0-1	1-3	1-0	0-2		4-2		0-3	4-0		0-3	3-2				4-2	1-0	1-0
4	Biggleswade United		2-0	4-3		4-1	3-0	2-2	2-2	3-1	0-5		2-1	1-0	2-1	1-1	1-1		3-1	0-1		4-1
5	Broadfields United			1-2	1-3			1-4	2-2	1-0	0-5	1-1	1-0	3-2		1-0	1-4	3-3	0-3		1-3	0-2
6	Colney Heath	2-0	3-1	2-0		5-0		2-1	3-0	3-0	2-1	2-1	1-0	0-1	0-1		4-0			3-2		1-0
7	Crawley Green	2-3	2-0		0-6	5-2			1-2	1-2	2-2	2-1	3-2		7-1	3-3	4-1	1-1		0-1	2-4	2-2
8	Dunstable Town	0-4	0-1	2-1	0-0	0-3		0-0		2-1	2-1		2-2	0-3	2-3		3-4		5-2			1-0
9	Edgware Town	2-2	1-2	4-0	1-3	3-1	0-3	2-1	1-0		0-3		3-3		2-1		0-2	4-2	2-2	3-2	0-6	3-1
10	Eynesbury Rovers	2-1		2-0	4-1		1-2	2-2	2-1	0-2		3-0		0-1	2-2		2-1	1-1	2-3			
11	Harefield United				0-4		0-0	1-1	1-2	1-0			2-1	3-1		1-1	6-1	0-1		2-1		2-2
12	Harpenden Town	1-1	1-0	2-1	2-1	4-3	0-1			5-2	3-1	4-2		2-1	1-2	1-2	3-1			1-2	3-2	
13	Leighton Town		1-2	4-1	3-1		0-1	3-2		4-2	2-2	2-1			5-2	8-0				0-3	3-2	0-0
14	Leverstock Green			1-4	2-1	0-0	0-3	0-3		1-0	0-2	1-2	0-1				0-1	2-1	0-1	3-1		1-1
15	London Colney	0-3	4-2		0-0	4-1		1-3	1-2	1-2	0-1	1-2		0-4			1-3	2-2	1-3		0-1	
16	Newport Pagnell Town		1-1	2-2	4-3		1-1	0-0	4-1		0-1		2-4	4-0	6-0			3-1	0-1	6-0	0-2	1-0
17	North Greenford United	1-1		3-0	0-3								1-4	2-5					0-3	1-2	2-1	
18	Oxhey Jets	3-3	4-2		1-4	0-0	1-0		3-2	0-0	1-0	2-4	1-3		3-0						2-0	3-1
19	Potton United	2-2		1-1		1-2		1-2	0-2	2-1	2-2	4-0		0-1	1-2	1-1	2-1				2-5	1-1
20	Tring Athletic	2-1	4-0		4-1	1-2		1-0	0-0	2-0	4-1		1-2	6-0	5-1	2-2	6-1	3-1	5-1			1-0
21	Wembley	2-2		2-0		1-3	1-0		2-2	1-1	2-1	3-1	0-3			2-2		1-2	3-4			

DIVISION ONE

#	Team	1	2	3	4	5	6	7	8	9	10	11	12	13	14	15	16	17	18	19
1	Amersham Town		6-4	2-1	5-3	0-1	6-3		0-2	3-2		1-1	0-6		3-2	2-5	0-3	1-2		0-7
2	Ampthill Town	3-3		0-1	2-1	0-6	1-0	2-2	5-1			2-2	1-3		3-1	0-3	2-2	1-4		
3	Bedford	1-0	1-3		1-0	1-2	1-1	2-0				0-0	1-7	0-0	5-2	0-2		0-4	3-2	
4	Brimsdown	2-3		1-4		1-1	1-3	3-3	1-1	1-5	3-4	3-3		0-10	1-2	0-1	1-5		2-1	1-2
5	Buckingham Athletic		2-2	4-1	5-0				0-1		4-2	1-1	2-3	2-4	4-3		3-0	3-7	0-1	
6	Enfield Borough	0-1	3-6	2-3	7-0	5-3			1-4	0-2	3-2	0-0	2-1	0-1	1-1		2-1	2-5	0-3	
7	FC Broxbourne Borough	2-0	3-0	2-1	1-1	3-2				1-1	1-2	2-2	2-3	4-1	0-0	3-3	2-0		1-5	0-5
8	Hillingdon Borough	3-2		4-1		1-2	1-4	1-2		3-2		0-2	2-2	2-7		2-2	1-4	1-1		
9	Langford			4-1	1-0	4-3	3-4		1-0		2-2		0-3	3-3		1-2	2-7	0-1	0-5	2-5
10	London Lions	2-4		1-2		2-1		5-1	1-1	1-1			3-0	0-2	0-1	1-1		0-2	0-3	3-1
11	London Tigers	1-2	0-2	5-2	2-2	1-1	3-1	0-2	4-1	1-1	1-3			0-3	3-3		0-2	2-1	4-3	0-2
12	Milton Keynes Robins		3-3	1-0	4-3	2-3	2-0	1-1	3-0		3-1	3-1		1-5		4-1	1-6	3-2		
13	New Salamis	7-1	10-1			6-0		4-4	5-2	0-1	4-1	1-2			6-0	3-2	3-2	2-0	2-1	8-2
14	Park View	4-1			1-2	7-0			2-2	0-4	0-4	1-2	2-1	0-6			2-3	2-3	0-3	3-4
15	Rayners Lane	5-0	3-3	3-2	4-2		1-1	3-0		5-1	4-3		5-2	4-3	5-1			2-4	2-1	
16	Shefford Town & Campton	2-1	0-2	0-4	2-1		3-1	4-1	4-0	0-1		4-1	0-1	2-0	4-2			1-8		2-6
17	St Panteleimon	2-0	2-2	4-2	1-1	4-0			4-0	4-2	2-0	3-0		1-1	4-2	7-1	5-2			2-1
18	Stotfold		5-1	3-0		4-1	4-1	2-0	3-1	0-1	0-0		3-0		2-1	1-1	5-3	1-1		3-0
19	Winslow United		3-2	4-1	2-1	1-0	1-0		8-1	3-2	0-3	2-1	8-0	0-2	4-1	2-2	2-5	4-2		

DIVISION TWO

#	Team	1	2	3	4	5	6	7	8	9	10	11	12	13	14	15
1	Aston Clinton			1-4			3-4		5-1			2-0		1-1		3-2
2	Berkhamsted Raiders	5-3			3-2			1-3		0-2	2-1	0-2				10-1
3	Bovingdon	2-2	1-3		0-0	1-3	3-0	2-3		1-3	1-1	0-1		0-2		
4	Buckingham United	1-7		2-0		0-0	4-3			0-3	0-3	2-0				
5	Codicote	0-1	1-0	2-1	1-0			4-1	1-1	1-0	0-4		3-0			1-3
6	MK Gallacticos		3-1	3-0				3-3	1-11		2-0	6-0	6-1			7-0
7	Mursley United		3-2	V-V						1-5	2-2	1-4	5-3	2-0	2-4	
8	New Bradwell St Peter FC	0-0	4-2		0-1	2-4		0-2			1-2	1-1	3-1		0-0	
9	Old Bradwell United			2-1	3-0	3-0	1-0					4-1				
10	Pitstone & Ivinghoe				2-3	3-1	1-7		0-3			2-2	9-1	3-0	2-0	2-1
11	Sarratt		2-3		2-1	2-2		1-1		2-4			2-2	3-1		1-1
12	The 61 FC (Luton)	0-3	0-5	0-7		0-2		2-5		1-5	0-7			0-2	0-3	4-6
13	Totternhoe	4-3	4-2	0-1		1-1	1-1			0-1	0-1				3-2	
14	Tring Corinthians AFC	1-2	1-2	1-2	4-1	1-2	3-1		1-3	4-0	1-3	2-3	4-3	0-0		
15	Unite MK	1-2	2-2				2-2	3-0	2-3	0-6	0-3	3-1		3-2		

United Counties Divison One - Holwell Sports v Whittlesey Athletic 4-0. The first goal. Photo Bill Wheatcroft.

United Counties Division One - Holwell Sports v Whittlesey Athletic 4-0. Goal number three. Photo Bill Wheatcroft.

UNITED COUNTIES LEAGUE

RECENT CHAMPIONS
2017: Peterborough Sports **2018:** Yaxley **2019:** Daventry Town

PREMIER DIVISION	P	W	D	L	F	A	GD	Pts
1 Quorn	30	19	7	4	92	35	57	64
2 Shepshed Dynamo	25	19	3	3	65	15	50	60
3 Rugby Town	27	18	3	6	77	27	50	57
4 Loughborough University	27	17	5	5	66	22	44	56
5 Holbeach United	27	16	6	5	70	29	41	54
6 Deeping Rangers	27	14	7	6	74	47	27	49
7 Anstey Nomads	29	13	8	8	67	56	11	47
8 Rothwell Corinthians	24	12	5	7	44	28	16	41
9 Harborough Town	29	11	6	12	52	56	-4	39
10 Leicester Nirvana	24	10	7	7	45	44	1	37
11 Boston Town	28	10	7	11	48	50	-2	37
12 Wellingborough Town	27	10	7	10	48	52	-4	37
13 Lutterworth Town	27	9	5	13	54	61	-7	32
14 Peterborough Northern Star	28	9	4	15	43	58	-15	31
15 Oadby Town	26	7	8	11	27	40	-13	29
16 Northampton O.N.Chenecks	28	6	9	13	33	57	-24	27
17 Cogenhoe United	27	7	5	15	37	68	-31	26
18 Desborough Town	29	6	3	20	28	75	-47	21
19 Sleaford Town	28	3	2	23	21	120	-99	11
20 Pinchbeck United	27	1	3	23	19	70	-51	6

DIVISION ONE	P	W	D	L	F	A	GD	Pts
1 Bugbrooke St.Michael	29	22	6	1	65	23	42	72
2 Long Buckby AFC	29	21	4	4	87	37	50	67
3 Melton Town	26	19	5	2	74	20	54	62
4 Aylestone Park	30	18	7	5	82	37	45	61
5 Harrowby United	30	15	7	8	60	38	22	52
6 St Andrews	29	15	3	11	50	51	-1	48
7 Blackstones	29	14	4	11	78	52	26	46
8 Irchester United	27	13	5	9	59	43	16	44
9 Burton Park Wanderers	27	13	4	10	40	32	8	43
10 Holwell Sports	27	12	5	10	67	57	10	41
11 Wellingborough Whitworth	29	12	5	12	64	79	-15	41
12 Saffron Dynamo	22	11	2	9	48	35	13	35
13 Whittlesey Athletic	29	8	9	12	44	69	-25	33
14 Raunds Town	28	5	14		46	58	-12	32
15 Birstall United Social	30	9	3	18	50	62	-12	30
16 Rushden & Higham United	29	8	4	17	44	74	-30	28
17 Northampton Sileby Rangers	28	7	3	18	38	68	-30	24
18 Bourne Town	29	6	3	20	30	69	-39	21
19 Huntingdon Town	30	4	7	19	40	81	-41	19
20 Lutterworth Athletic	29	1	1	27	22	103	-81	4

LEAGUE CUP

HOLDERS: DAVENTRY TOWN

PRELIMINARY ROUND

Oadby Town	v	Quorn	1-4
Desborough Town	v	Wellingborough Whitworth	5-1
Rushden & Higham United	v	Rothwell Corinthians	2-6
Peterborough Northern Star	v	Huntingdon Town	2-2, 6-5p
Harrowby United	v	Bourne Town	6-0
Bugbrooke St Michael	v	Cogenhoe United	1-1, 3-1p
Rugby Town	v	Lutterworth Town	2-0
Anstey Nomads	v	Leicester Nirvana	1-0

ROUND 1

Quorn	v	St Andrews	2-2, 2-4p
Holwell Sports	v	Saffron Dynamo	2-3
Wellingborough Town	v	Desborough Town	5-2
Rothwell Corinthians	v	Northampton ON Chenecks	2-1
Shepshed Dyamo	v	Birstall United Social	2-1
Burton Park Wanderers	v	Harborough Town	2-2, 3-4p
Northampton Sileby Rangers	v	Irchester United	1-1, 4-5p
Peterborough Northern Star	v	Deeping Rangers	2-3
Blackstone	v	Sleaford Town	5-4
Holbeach United	v	Whittlesey Athletic	5-1
Harrowby United	v	Pinchbeck United	2-3
Melton Town	v	Boston Town	2-0
Long Buckby AFC	v	Raunds Town	4-1
Aylestone Park	v	Loughborough University	3-0
(Aylestone Park removed from the competition)			
Bugbrooke St Michael	v	Rugby Town	1-2
Lutterworth Athletic	v	Leicester Nirvana	2-8

ROUND 2

St Andrews	v	Saffron Dyamo	1-2
Wellingborough Town	v	Rothwell Corinthians	1-3
Shepshed Dynamo	v	Harborough Town	2-2, 4-2p
Irchester United	v	Deeping Rangers	1-4
Blackstone	v	Holbeach United	0-3
Pinchbeck United	v	Melton Town	1-5
Long Buckby AFC	v	Loughborough University	0-5
Rugby Town	v	Leicester Nirvana	0-2

QUARTER FINALS

Saffron Dynamo	v	Rothwell Corinthians	0-1
Shepshed Dynamo	v	Deeping Rangers	1-2
Holbeach United	v	Melton Town	3-1
Loughborough University	v	Leicester Nirvana	2-1

SEMI FINALS

Rothwell Corinthians	v	Deeping Rangers	3-1
Holbeach United	v	Lougborough University	1-0

FINAL

Rothwell Corinthians	v	Holbeach United

PREMIER DIVISION

PREMIER DIVISION	1	2	3	4	5	6	7	8	9	10	11	12	13	14	15	16	17	18	19	20
1 Anstey Nomads			4-2	5-9	5-2	2-0	0-2	2-2	0-0	3-1	3-2	1-1		2-0		1-1	1-5	1-1	9-0	
2 Boston Town	3-5		1-0	0-1	2-1	3-3	2-3		0-1	4-1	1-1	2-0		5-1	3-2	3-0	0-3	0-4		2-2
3 Cogenhoe United				3-3	1-0	0-2		0-2	0-1	4-3	1-1	0-0		2-1	0-5		1-2	1-4	3-2	3-2
4 Deeping Rangers		2-2	2-1		4-2	3-2	2-0			3-3	6-0	2-3	3-3	3-0	0-1		3-2	0-1	5-0	
5 Desborough Town	0-3	1-0				1-3	0-4	1-2		1-3	1-0		3-2	2-0	1-4	1-3	0-4	0-4		
6 Harborough Town	1-4	1-1	3-0		2-2		0-3	0-2	0-1	3-3	3-0	2-1	4-2			3-1	1-3	0-2		0-1
7 Holbeach United		1-0	6-0	2-2	1-1			2-0	0-5	6-2	4-1	0-0	4-0		1-1	1-0	3-1		9-0	
8 Leicester Nirvana		2-2		2-1	2-3	4-4	4-3						1-1		0-0				4-0	1-2
9 Loughborough University	4-0	4-1	4-0	3-0	3-0		0-0	1-1			5-1	3-1	3-1	3-1	0-4	0-1	2-1		13-0	
10 Lutterworth Town			5-2	2-3	0-1	2-2	1-0		5-2			1-1	5-1		2-0	0-4			2-4	2-3
11 Northampton O.N.Chenecks	2-3			1-1	1-0	2-3		3-2	1-0	1-1		0-1	1-1	2-2		0-4		1-1	4-1	1-1
12 Oadby Town	1-1			3-2	0-2			1-1	1-2				0-2	1-0					3-2	0-0
13 Peterborough Northern Star	3-1	2-4	2-3		2-0	1-3		1-3	3-2		2-1	1-0		3-1	1-2	1-1		1-3		1-3
14 Pinchbeck United	1-3		1-2	2-4		1-4	0-3	1-2			0-2	1-1	0-2				1-1	0-3	2-1	0-3
15 Quorn	2-0	1-2	3-2		2-0	6-1	2-2	7-3		5-1	3-3	4-0	3-0	7-0		2-2	3-3	2-1	4-0	5-1
16 Rothwell Corinthians	2-2	3-0		1-1			0-1	0-2	3-0		2-1	3-0	3-1						5-0	1-0
17 Rugby Town	3-0	3-1	0-0	4-3	12-0	2-0		3-0		2-1	0-1	4-0	1-0		1-3			0-1	8-0	6-1
18 Shepshed Dynamo	1-2		5-2			3-0	4-1	6-0	0-0	2-0	5-0	3-1		2-1	2-1	2-0	0-1			
19 Sleaford Town	2-2	2-2		0-2	1-0		0-7	0-4		0-5		1-4	0-4	2-1	0-5	1-3	1-2	0-5		
20 Wellingborough Town	3-2	0-2	4-4	2-6	2-2		1-2	1-1	0-3	0-1	2-0	1-2		2-0	3-3	5-1			3-1	

United Counties Division One - Birstall United Social v Holwell Sports 0-1. The winning goal. Photo Bill Wheatcroft.

DIVISION ONE

DIVISION ONE	1	2	3	4	5	6	7	8	9	10	11	12	13	14	15	16	17	18	19	20
1 Aylestone Park		2-1	1-1	5-0		0-1	3-3		1-1	2-2	4-1	6-0	2-2	2-0	2-1		1-1	1-0	6-3	6-0
2 Birstall United Social				4-0	0-0			0-1		1-2	3-6	5-1	2-2	0-2	6-3	0-2	2-1	0-1		2-1
3 Blackstones	2-3	3-2			2-3	2-1	0-2	3-2	4-0	4-2	2-3	5-1	0-1		4-1	4-2	1-2	4-1		
4 Bourne Town	0-3		3-3		0-2	0-1	2-0	0-2	0-0	1-4		1-2	1-1	4-3	4-3	0-2	0-1	0-6	1-2	
5 Bugbrooke St.Michael	2-1	2-0				3-1	4-1	4-2	1-0	2-0	0-0	1-0	2-1	4-2		2-3	5-0			0-0
6 Burton Park Wanderers		3-1		2-0	0-1		1-3	1-2			2-2	4-0		1-2	0-0		0-2		5-0	3-0
7 Harrowby United	3-2	3-0	2-1	3-0	1-1	0-0			2-2	1-2		2-1	0-1	2-0	4-2	3-1		3-0	9-1	2-2
8 Holwell Sports	2-6	2-3	4-9	2-1			1-1		4-4		1-1	4-0		4-1	1-1	4-1		4-0	6-0	4-2
9 Huntingdon Town	0-3	1-5	2-0	2-4	0-5	0-2	2-3	0-1			4-3	2-5	3-1	0-2	1-2		3-3	2-2		1-2
10 Irchester United	2-0	3-1	0-0		3-5	1-2		3-2	5-2		1-2			0-0	0-1		3-0	3-0	5-4	3-3
11 Long Buckby A	1-2		3-0	4-1	1-4	4-0	1-0	4-2	3-0	3-2		3-0			1-1		4-2	5-2	3-3	
12 Lutterworth Athletic	2-6	1-4	1-6	0-1	0-2	1-3	2-3	0-2		0-2	1-3		0-8	4-2		1-6	0-6		0-1	
13 Melton Town	1-0	3-0		2-0	1-1	4-0	4-0	6-4	1-0		1-3	3-0			5-0			4-0	4-1	
14 Northampton Sileby Rangers	2-3	1-0	1-6		0-2	1-2	3-2		0-3	1-4		0-4			6-0		1-3	0-2		4-4
15 Raunds Town		3-1	2-1	0-4	2-3	1-0			2-1	0-0	0-5	5-1	0-2			5-0	1-2	3-4	5-2	
16 Rushden & Higham United	1-6	3-0	1-1	4-1	0-1	1-1		4-1	0-0		0-5		1-7	3-2	0-1		1-4	2-0	0-3	0-2
17 Saffron Dynamo		3-2			1-1	1-2	1-0		7-1				0-2		3-0			1-2	5-1	
18 St Andrews	0-1	5-0	2-1	3-1			0-2	2-1		2-0	0-3	2-0			4-2	0-0			3-2	1-1
19 Wellingborough Whitworth		1-4	4-5		1-2	2-1	1-1		4-3	2-1	1-5	2-1		6-0		4-1	3-1	2-3		1-3
20 Whittlesey Athletic	2-2	1-1	0-4	3-0		1-2	1-0	3-3	1-2	1-5	0-4	1-1	3-1	2-2	2-1	3-3		1-4		

WESSEX LEAGUE

RECENT CHAMPIONS

2017: Portland United **2018:** Blackfield & Langley **2019:** Sholing

PREMIER DIVISION	P	W	D	L	F	A	GD	Pts
1 Alresford Town	30	22	2	6	74	41	33	68
2 AFC Stoneham	31	20	4	7	67	35	32	64
3 AFC Portchester	28	19	2	7	72	40	32	59
4 Christchurch	26	18	3	5	58	20	38	57
5 Lymington Town	30	16	4	10	67	44	23	52
6 Horndean	28	14	8	6	63	38	25	50
7 Bashley	29	15	3	11	58	41	17	48
8 Fareham Town	27	15	5	7	69	46	23	47*
9 Hamworthy United	31	14	5	12	70	57	13	47
10 Hamble Club	30	14	4	12	47	51	-4	46
11 Portland United	27	13	5	9	65	42	23	44
12 Fleet Town	29	10	7	12	58	53	5	37
13 Tadley Calleva	28	11	3	14	48	59	-11	36
14 Baffins Milton Rovers	23	11	2	10	44	40	4	35
15 Brockenhurst	28	10	4	14	51	49	2	34
16 Shaftesbury	30	7	3	20	38	79	-41	24
17 Solent University	28	5	5	18	46	97	-51	20
18 Bournemouth	27	4	4	19	23	65	-42	16
19 Cowes Sports	30	3	5	22	39	84	-45	14
20 Amesbury Town	28	3	2	23	30	106	-76	8*

DIVISION ONE	P	W	D	L	F	A	GD	Pts
1 United Services Portsmouth	28	20	4	4	86	33	53	64
2 Andover New Street	25	18	3	4	75	44	31	57
3 Bemerton Heath Harlequins	28	17	3	8	80	38	42	54
4 Hythe & Dibden	24	16	6	2	67	29	38	54
5 Downton	28	16	5	7	62	40	22	53
6 Alton	28	15	5	8	54	44	10	50
7 Newport (IoW)	26	15	3	8	73	36	37	48
8 Whitchurch United	31	12	3	16	55	59	-4	39
9 Laverstock & Ford	25	11	5	9	53	43	10	38
10 Petersfield Town	25	9	8	8	33	27	6	35
11 Andover Town	31	9	8	14	42	57	-15	35
12 Verwood Town	27	9	6	12	47	58	-11	33
13 Romsey Town	24	9	4	11	54	60	-6	31
14 Ringwood Town	29	6	10	13	50	66	-16	28
15 Fawley AFC	29	6	6	17	43	69	-26	24
16 New Milton Town	29	4	10	15	29	71	-42	22
17 East Cowes Victoria	25	5	5	15	30	64	-34	20
18 Totton & Eling	22	5	3	14	24	55	-31	18
19 Folland Sports	28	3	5	20	29	93	-64	14

Pewsey Vale withdrew after 14 games.

LEAGUE CUP

HOLDERS: BAFFINS MILTON ROVERS

ROUND 1

AFC Stoneham	v	Alton	8-0
East Cowes Victoria	v	New Milton Town	3-0
Fawley AFC	v	Lymington Town	0-4
Cowes Sports	v	Horndean	1-0
Totton & Eling	v	Solent University	4-1
Romsey Town	v	Hamworthy United	0-2
Alresford Town	v	Laverstock & Ford	3-2
Petersfield Town	v	Verwood Town	2-1

ROUND 2

Shafesbury	v	AFC Stoneham	0-1
Bemerton Heath Harlequins	v	Andover Town	6-0
Brockenhurst	v	East Cowes Victoria	2-1
Bashley	v	Baffins Milton Rovers	1-1, 3-4p
Fareham Town	v	Christchurch	1-3
Hythe & Dibden	v	Ringwood Town	7-3
Bournemouth	v	Downton	1-1, 6-5p
Whitchurch United	v	Lymington Town	0-1
Tadley Calleva	v	AFC Porchester	4-3p
Portland United	v	Fleet Town	5-0
Cowes Sports	v	Newport (IoW)	3-2
Totton & Eling	v	Andover New Street	1-0
Hamworthy United	v	Alresford Town	3-4
United Services Portsmouth	v	Folland Sports	2-1
Hamble Club	v	Pewsey Vale	1-0
Amesbury Town	v	Petersfield Town	1-3

ROUND 3

AFC Stoneham	v	Bemerton Heath Harlequins	2-2, 4-3p
Brockenhurst	v	Baffins Milton Rovers	2-3
Christchurch	v	Hythe & Dibden	2-2, 4-3p
Bournemouth	v	Lymington Town	2-1
Tadley Calleva	v	Portland United	1-4
Cowes Sports	v	Totton & Eling	1-4
Alresford Town	v	United Services Portsmouth	2-1
Hamble Club	v	Petersfield Town	2-1

QUARTER FINALS

AFC Stoneham	v	Baffins Milton Rovers	3-2
Christchurch	v	Bournemouth	4-0
Portland United	v	Totton & Eling	6-1
Alresford Town	v	Hamble Club	1-2

SEMI FINALS

AFC Stoneham	v	Christchurch
Portland United	v	Hamble Club

PREMIER DIVISION	1	2	3	4	5	6	7	8	9	10	11	12	13	14	15	16	17	18	19	20
1 AFC Portchester		1-2	0-1	6-2	3-2		6-1	3-1		1-2	0-1	3-2		3-2	2-1	0-2		4-0	5-2	5-1
2 AFC Stoneham	0-3		1-3	9-0	2-0	0-2	5-0		0-1	1-0	3-1	2-0	3-2	3-1	0-0	1-0	4-1		2-2	4-3
3 Alresford Town	4-1	0-1		3-0		2-1	4-1	3-3	3-1	2-0	0-1	2-1	2-0	5-0	0-2	4-1		4-2	6-2	3-1
4 Amesbury Town	0-2	1-3			0-5	1-5			0-4	0-2	3-1		1-3	2-1	1-5		1-3	0-3	2-2	0-4
5 Baffins Milton Rovers								0-1		3-1	2-3		2-0			1-4		3-0	3-2	0-1
6 Bashley		3-2	0-1	0-3	3-0			3-1	2-1	3-0		0-0	2-0	3-1	0-2	2-1	4-1	7-2	1-2	3-1
7 Bournemouth	0-1	0-1	2-4	1-0	0-1	1-4			1-0		3-3	0-2		0-3	0-0		0-3	0-2		
8 Brockenhurst		0-1		8-1		1-2	2-3		0-1				3-0	1-1	0-2	3-2	1-5		3-1	4-0
9 Christchurch			1-1		3-0	2-1	2-0					4-0	3-1	0-1	1-1		3-2	5-1	6-1	
10 Cowes Sports	1-3	1-5			2-2	1-1	1-4	2-4	0-2			1-4	4-4	0-2	2-3	1-6	0-4		1-0	1-2
11 Fareham Town	1-3		7-1		5-5	2-1	1-1	2-2	1-3	3-2		4-2		3-0	3-0	3-1		5-1	3-3	5-1
12 Fleet Town	2-2	2-2	2-3	4-1	2-3		4-0	0-1	2-0	2-2	0-3		3-2		1-1		0-3	2-0		3-4
13 Hamble Club	2-2	0-2		2-1	3-2	1-0	2-0	2-1	1-1	4-2	2-1	1-0		1-4			0-2	4-2		
14 Hamworthy United		2-2		3-2	1-2		2-1	3-2	0-2	5-2	4-0	1-3	5-0				1-1	4-1	8-1	1-3
15 Horndean	0-3		4-1	5-1			4-1	3-3		3-2		0-4	1-1	3-0			1-2	3-1	4-2	1-2
16 Lymington Town	3-4	2-0	0-2	3-0	2-4	4-1	0-0	3-0	0-1	3-2	2-2	1-4		4-2	1-1		2-1	3-0		5-2
17 Portland United	2-1		5-0	12-2	2-0	2-1	5-2	0-2	0-2	3-1			1-1	2-3	2-2			1-1	3-4	2-0
18 Shaftesbury	0-1	1-3	0-3	5-3	0-2		3-1	2-1	0-2		3-2	2-2	0-2	1-1	0-4	1-4			3-1	2-0
19 Solent University	3-4	0-3	0-3		0-2	3-3		0-2	0-6			2-5	3-4	1-7	3-3	0-3				2-4
20 Tadley Calleva		3-0	1-4	2-2		3-0		3-1	2-1	2-0		0-2	2-1	1-3	0-1	2-2	1-1		1-2	

DIVISION ONE	1	2	3	4	5	6	7	8	9	10	11	12	13	14	15	16	17	18	19
1 Alton		2-3	1-0	1-0		1-3	2-2	2-0	1-1	3-1	3-2	1-3	2-1			2-3	2-1	2-1	3-0
2 Andover New Street	0-0		2-1	2-3	1-4	5-2	4-3	6-1		4-2	1-0		3-1		5-1	6-3	1-1		
3 Andover Town	2-4			1-0	2-2	1-1	2-3	3-1	3-1	1-0	1-1	0-1	1-0		3-4	2-0	0-5	3-1	
4 Bemerton Heath Harlequins		9-1	4-2			5-1	2-1	8-0	0-3	1-0	8-1	2-1	1-2	5-2		3-0		1-1	5-2
5 Downton	4-2		1-0	1-0		2-2	3-0	3-2		2-4	2-0	4-0		1-1	2-1	0-1	0-2	2-0	3-1
6 East Cowes Victoria	2-5	1-4		1-1	3-6			1-0	0-2		0-4	1-0	1-0	1-4	0-1	0-3			1-1
7 Fawley AFC	0-1	0-5	1-0	4-2	1-1	0-2			7-2	0-4	0-3		2-4	1-1	4-3	2-5	1-1		3-5
8 Folland Sports	2-2			0-0	0-3	2-2				0-4	2-3		0-7	0-5	1-5	3-0	2-3	2-3	0-6
9 Hythe & Dibden		1-1	8-2		4-2		1-0	5-1		1-1		1-0		6-1	2-1		2-1	3-3	3-2
10 Laverstock & Ford		2-1	4-4	0-1	4-2		2-0	1-0			4-2		2-2	4-2		2-3	2-1	0-2	
11 New Milton Town	0-0	0-6	0-1			4-2	0-1	1-1	3-3	1-1		1-0	0-0	1-1	1-4	2-1	2-2	0-0	1-2
12 Newport (IoW)	3-0	2-3	3-0			6-1		6-0	2-1		7-1		0-2	1-1	3-3		0-0	1-2	2-0
13 Petersfield Town		2-4	0-0	1-2	2-1	2-1	1-1			1-1	2-0			1-1		3-0	1-3		0-1
14 Ringwood Town		0-3	1-2	1-1	2-1	0-0	4-1	3-2		3-3		1-1	3-5		2-3	1-4	1-4	1-2	4-0
15 Romsey Town		0-3	2-5	3-4		1-1	0-4		2-1	4-1	5-2	0-1	1-1			1-5	1-4		
16 Totton & Eling	0-3		1-1					0-2	3-2		2-6		1-1					0-4	0-2
17 United Services Portsmouth	4-1		4-0	3-0	2-4	1-0	5-2	5-0	2-3		7-0		1-1		5-3	4-1			4-2
18 Verwood Town		2-3	0-2	1-0	1-6	1-3		3-1	1-1		2-7	1-3		1-2	2-2	5-2	1-4		2-1
19 Whitchurch United	4-2	2-3	2-2	2-5	1-0		1-0	1-2	0-3		5-0	1-4	0-1	6-2	0-3	2-0	1-2	1-1	

WEST MIDLANDS (REGIONAL) LEAGUE

RECENT CHAMPIONS

2017: Haughmond **2018:** Wolverhampton Sporting Community **2019:** Tividale

PREMIER DIVISION

		P	W	D	L	F	A	GD	Pts
1	Shifnal Town	23	20	0	3	81	21	60	60
2	Bewdley Town	24	18	0	6	67	33	34	54
3	Dudley Town	27	16	4	7	69	46	23	52
4	Wolverhampton Casuals	23	14	7	2	49	10	39	49
5	Bilston Town Community	28	15	1	12	67	54	13	46
6	Pershore Town	27	11	6	10	56	47	9	39
7	Black Country Rangers	21	11	5	5	42	28	14	38
8	Darlaston Town (1874)	29	11	5	13	53	54	-1	38
9	Littleton	23	11	3	9	45	33	12	36
10	Wednesfield	23	11	3	9	31	31	0	36
11	Worcester Raiders	23	9	4	10	52	51	1	31
12	Wolverhampton Sporting Com	24	7	8	9	36	39	-3	29
13	AFC Bridgnorth	25	8	5	12	37	52	-15	29
14	Smethwick	23	7	4	12	33	49	-16	25
15	Shawbury United	23	7	4	12	27	46	-19	25
16	Wem Town	27	6	2	19	37	87	-50	20
17	Dudley Sports	25	3	3	19	21	79	-58	12
18	Cradley Town	24	3	2	19	29	72	-43	11

DIVISION ONE

		P	W	D	L	F	A	GD	Pts
1	Droitwich Spa	20	15	4	1	83	27	56	49
2	Old Wulfrunians	20	11	3	6	39	27	12	36
3	Allscott Heath	22	10	5	7	69	49	20	35
4	Wrens Nest	21	10	5	6	52	43	9	35
5	Wellington Amateurs	19	10	4	5	62	49	13	34
6	Gornal Colts	22	9	7	6	63	58	5	34
7	Team Dudley	25	10	4	11	55	51	4	34
8	Willenhall Town	20	8	5	7	45	43	2	29
9	Tipton Town	20	8	3	9	40	37	3	27
10	Sikh Hunters	21	8	2	11	45	64	-19	26
11	Bromyard Town	18	6	7	5	34	29	5	25
12	Wyrley	22	6	5	11	28	50	-22	23
13	F C Darlaston	20	5	2	13	36	51	-15	17
14	Bustleholme	22	5	2	15	29	64	-35	17
15	Gornal Athletic	20	4	4	12	35	73	-38	16

DIVISION TWO

		P	W	D	L	F	A	GD	Pts
1	A F C Bentley	14	10	2	2	61	22	39	32
2	Church Stretton	15	8	2	5	47	22	25	26
3	Ludlow	14	8	2	4	43	33	10	26
4	Newport Town	16	8	2	6	29	35	-6	26
5	Coven Athletic	15	7	2	6	41	40	1	23
6	Walsall Town Swifts	15	6	3	6	39	28	11	21
7	Warstones Wanderers	10	6	0	4	31	24	7	18
8	Telford Juniors	17	3	4	10	22	49	-27	13
9	Worcester Raiders Res	12	3	3	6	19	41	-22	12
10	AFC Bridgnorth Dev	14	1	2	11	9	47	-38	5

North West Counties Premier - Squires Gate FC. Photo Keith Clayton.

WESTERN LEAGUE

Recent Champions

2017: Bristol Manor Farm **2018:** Street **2019:** Willand Rovers

PREMIER DIVISION	P	W	D	L	F	A	GD	Pts
1 Tavistock	26	20	2	4	73	29	44	62
2 Plymouth Parkway	23	19	2	2	80	21	59	59
3 Bradford Town	22	19	1	2	69	20	49	58
4 Hallen	29	17	6	6	64	48	16	57
5 Exmouth Town	25	18	2	5	64	26	38	56
6 Shepton Mallet	27	17	4	6	66	31	35	55
7 Bitton	26	16	2	8	69	37	32	50
8 Bridgwater Town	27	13	7	7	65	40	25	46
9 Clevedon Town	29	12	5	12	58	62	-4	41
10 Roman Glass St George	29	12	4	13	62	47	15	40
11 Street	30	12	4	14	61	65	-4	40
12 Westbury United	28	12	3	13	53	42	11	39
13 Buckland Athletic	25	12	2	11	48	48	0	38
14 Keynsham Town	29	11	4	14	50	57	-7	37
15 Brislington	27	10	5	12	42	62	-20	35
16 Cribbs	27	8	3	16	37	66	-29	27
17 Cadbury Heath	30	6	7	17	34	78	-44	25
18 Chipping Sodbury Town	28	6	1	21	33	92	-59	19
19 Bridport	27	5	2	20	35	90	-55	17
20 Wellington	30	3	3	24	24	73	-49	12
21 Odd Down (BATH)	28	3	1	24	26	79	-53	10

DIVISION ONE	P	W	D	L	F	A	GD	Pts
1 Calne Town	26	18	2	6	47	21	26	56
2 Sherborne Town	25	17	2	6	58	33	25	53
3 Longwell Green Sports	27	16	4	7	64	38	26	52
4 Wells City	26	15	6	5	67	30	37	51
5 Ashton & Backwell United	26	15	6	5	42	39	3	51
6 Radstock Town	23	14	3	6	53	32	21	45
7 Corsham Town	26	13	3	10	44	50	-6	42
8 Wincanton Town	23	13	2	8	47	46	1	41
9 Oldland Abbotonians	22	10	6	6	30	33	-3	36
10 Cheddar	24	10	4	10	38	37	1	34
11 Bishops Lydeard	23	10	3	10	48	38	10	33
12 Lebeq United	27	11	1	15	52	62	-10	33*
13 Portishead Town	26	9	4	13	45	46	-1	31
14 Hengrove Athletic	25	9	4	12	24	48	-24	31
15 Almondsbury	24	8	4	12	35	40	-5	28
16 Warminster Town	24	8	2	14	41	40	1	26
17 Welton Rovers	25	7	4	14	33	44	-11	25
18 Devizes Town	26	3	7	16	34	57	-23	16
19 Bristol Telephones	25	4	2	19	34	70	-36	14
20 Bishop Sutton	25	3	3	19	27	59	-32	12

LES PHILLIPS CUP

HOLDERS: PLYMOUTH PARKWAY

PRELIMINARY ROUND

Sherborne Town	v	Radstock Town	2-4
Wincanton Town	v	Street	0-2
Cadbury Heath	v	Tavistock	1-2
Odd Down (Bath)	v	Lebeq United	3-0
Hengrove Athletic	v	Bristol Telephones	5-1
Almondsbury	v	Exmouth Town	1-4
Wellington	v	Roman Glass St George	0-3
Brislington	v	Bishop Sutton	1-0
Oldland Abbotonians	v	Portishead Town	1-2

ROUND 1

Devizes Town	v	Hallen	0-3
Radstock Town	v	Street	0-3
Buckland Athletic	v	Cheddar	0-2
Cribbs	v	Welton Rovers	1-0
Tavistock	v	Calne Town	4-0
Clevedon Town	v	Chipping Sodbury Town	4-2
Westbury United	v	Longwell Green Sports	0-1
Warminster Town	v	Portishead	5-0
Corsham Town	v	Wells City	0-4
Bridgwater Town	v	Odd Down (Bath)	5-2
Hengrove Athletic	v	Shepton Mallet	0-4
Exmouth Town	v	Plymouth Parkway	4-1
Roman Glass St George	v	Bridport	2-1
Bishops Lydeard	v	Keynsham Town	0-4
Brislington	v	Bradford Town	1-4
Ashton & Backwell United	v	Bitton	3-3, 3-5p

ROUND 2

Hallen	v	Street	2-1
Cheddar	v	Cribbs	2-1
Tavistock	v	Clevedon Town	3-1
Longwell Green Sports	v	Warminster Town	2-2, 3-4p
Wells City	v	Bridgwater Town	1-3
Shepton Mallet	v	Exmouth Town	1-2
Roman Glass St George	v	Keynsham Town	2-2, 4-3p
Bradford Town	v	Bitton	2-1

QUARTER FINALS

Hallen	v	Chedder	1-1, 4-3p
Tavistock	v	Warminster Town	01/04/20
Bridgwater Town	v	Exmouth Town	3-1
Roman Glass St George	v	Bradford Town	1-2

PREMIER DIVISION		1	2	3	4	5	6	7	8	9	10	11	12	13	14	15	16	17	18	19	20	21
1	Bitton				2-1	4-0	2-2	6-2			0-1	3-0			1-5				4-2		2-0	2-1
2	Bradford Town	2-1			4-2	6-1		5-0	4-0	2-0				4-2	4-0			2-1	2-3			2-1
3	Bridgwater Town	2-3			3-2		3-3	4-0		3-3	1-1		2-2	1-1		2-0	2-0	1-2	2-4		2-0	
4	Bridport	0-5	0-9	0-6		1-2	1-3	2-0			1-3	1-0	3-3	4-3	0-5	2-2	0-3		0-1			
5	Brislington		2-1	2-1			1-3	4-3	3-4	4-4	1-0			3-1		1-1		1-1	1-7	0-3	2-0	
6	Buckland Athletic	1-6	0-1		5-0	1-1		2-1	4-0	2-3	4-2										2-0	1-3
7	Cadbury Heath			3-3	1-2			2-1	2-2	2-1	1-5	2-2	0-3	0-0	0-5	2-1		1-2	2-7	1-0	1-4	
8	Chipping Sodbury Town	3-1	0-2	1-8	0-4					0-2	0-3	2-3	0-2		0-3	2-1		1-2	0-3	3-1	2-2	
9	Clevedon Town	1-2	1-4	2-1	4-3	0-2	2-3			3-0		2-4	4-3	3-1	0-2	2-1	2-2	1-6	1-2		2-0	
10	Cribbs	0-6	2-2	2-3		0-2	1-0		1-2	0-5		0-4	2-4	0-1	3-1		2-6	0-0	2-4		3-0	
11	Exmouth Town	2-0		0-0	4-1		4-2	2-0	7-1		5-0		0-0			2-1	2-1	5-0	4-2	2-0		
12	Hallen	1-5		4-6		5-0	4-3	5-0	2-0	2-1		4-1		1-0	0-5		1-3	2-1	1-1			2-1
13	Keynsham Town	1-1	3-1	0-1	4-2		0-1	3-1		3-4	2-5	1-0	1-2		0-3	2-1	0-2	2-1	2-5		2-0	2-6
14	Odd Down (BATH)	1-5	0-1	2-3		5-1	1-2	0-1	1-2	0-2	3-4		0-2	0-1		1-6				0-4	3-1	0-2
15	Plymouth Parkway	4-3			3-1	3-1		7-1	5-2			1-0	2-2	3-3	10-0		4-1		2-3	1-0		
16	Roman Glass St George	3-1	1-2			2-2	1-0	2-1	6-1	2-0		3-2	1-2	2-1	1-2			2-0	3-0	0-4	8-0	0-1
17	Shepton Mallet		0-1	1-0		4-1	4-2	1-1	6-0	1-1		4-0			4-0		4-1		3-2	0-4	2-1	2-1
18	Street	0-1	0-5		9-2		0-2		4-0	2-3	3-4	0-2	2-1	1-0	0-3	2-2	0-5			2-0	4-2	
19	Tavistock		2-4	1-0	2-0	1-0	5-0		4-3		3-0			2-1			4-2				3-0	1-1
20	Wellington	0-2		0-3		0-1	0-2	1-1		1-3		0-2	2-2			5-0	0-2		0-5	3-3	3-1	1-3
21	Westbury United	2-1		1-2	4-0	3-2		0-2	4-1		0-1		1-3		3-1	1-2		2-5	1-1	0-1	5-0	

DIVISION ONE		1	2	3	4	5	6	7	8	9	10	11	12	13	14	15	16	17	18	19	20
1	Almondsbury		0-1		2-1	4-0	1-0				0-0		0-2	3-4	1-2		1-3	0-3		3-2	1-3
2	Ashton & Backwell United	1-3			1-3		3-2	2-0	3-3	1-1		0-2	3-2	0-0	2-1	0-3		2-1		1-0	2-1
3	Bishop Sutton	2-5			2-3	1-1	2-3		1-2		0-4	1-3	0-1	3-1	1-2	4-0	1-2	2-2			
4	Bishops Lydeard	0-3		3-0		2-1	0-1		2-0			2-2		1-1		1-3	1-5			4-1	2-3
5	Bristol Telephones	1-2	2-3				1-0	2-4	3-3	3-0	0-2		0-1		2-3	0-3		1-5	1-3		
6	Calne Town		0-1	2-0		1-0				3-0	5-0	4-1		0-0	2-1	2-0			3-1	3-1	2-1
7	Cheddar		3-3	3-2	4-2		4-1		2-3	3-2	0-1		1-2			0-1	2-1		1-1		
8	Corsham Town	4-1			2-3	5-0	0-2	0-0		1-0	2-1			2-1	2-0		2-1	0-7		2-0	0-4
9	Devizes Town	1-1	0-1	0-0	1-4	5-2		1-4	0-1		3-0			0-1	0-3		1-3		2-2		
10	Hengrove Athletic		1-1	3-0	0-7			1-0		1-5		0-3		2-3	0-3	1-4	0-3	1-0	3-2		
11	Lebeq United		2-3		1-0	1-5	0-3	1-3	3-0	4-1	1-2		0-6	3-4		3-1			1-7	4-1	5-1
12	Longwell Green Sports		1-2	4-0		5-4	0-0	0-1	3-2	2-1	3-0	5-3		1-2		1-1	1-2			1-0	4-1
13	Oldland Abbotonians	1-0				0-3	1-2	1-0	1-1	0-0					1-1		3-1	1-4			
14	Portishead Town			4-1		3-0		0-1	0-2	2-2		3-2	3-5	0-1			2-5	1-1			2-3
15	Radstock Town	2-2		5-1	2-0		2-0	2-1	7-2			2-2	4-1		1-3			1-2			
16	Sherborne Town	3-1	5-0	4-0		2-1	1-2		1-1	4-1	2-0	2-1	2-2	2-0	3-2	2-3		0-3	2-4		3-1
17	Warminster Town				2-3	1-0	3-1			1-2	1-2	0-3		2-1	1-2	0-2		3-3	0-1	0-1	
18	Wells City	1-0	1-3	1-0	1-1		0-1	2-2		3-0	0-0	1-0	4-0	4-1	4-0		5-1	3-2		1-1	
19	Welton Rovers	0-0	1-2	0-3	1-0	6-0	1-2	4-0		2-1	0-1	3-2	0-3	1-2	1-5						
20	Wincanton Town	3-1	1-1	1-0	1-6	4-1				5-2	5-2			0-4	2-2	2-1	0-4		2-1	2-0	

STEP 7 DIVISIONS

TABLES AS THEY WERE WHEN THE SEASON WAS TERMINATED ON 26/03/2020

ANGLIAN COMBINATION

PREMIER DIVISION

		P	W	D	L	F	A	GD	Pts
1	Waveney	22	17	2	3	51	21	30	53
2	Mundford	23	16	4	3	63	33	30	52
3	Harleston Town	23	16	1	6	65	32	33	49
4	Norwich CEYMS	24	14	4	6	53	29	24	46
5	Long Stratton	24	13	2	9	59	41	18	41
6	UEA	22	13	2	7	43	34	9	41
7	Acle United	24	10	8	6	52	44	8	38
8	Caister	27	10	8	9	58	54	4	38
9	Beccles Town	24	10	1	13	46	44	2	31
10	Mattishall	21	9	3	9	40	33	7	30
11	Scole United	22	7	4	11	30	43	-13	25
12	Wroxham Res	22	7	3	12	33	40	-7	24
13	Bradenham Wands	22	6	4	12	34	60	-26	22
14	Hellesdon	25	6	2	17	44	57	-13	20
15	Blofield United	21	5	2	14	32	51	-19	17
16	St Andrews	22	0	0	22	9	96	-87	0

DIVISION ONE

		P	W	D	L	F	A	GD	Pts
1	Wymondham Town	26	21	1	4	72	33	39	64
2	Gorleston Res	23	15	2	6	48	24	24	47
3	Attleborough Town	23	15	0	8	64	29	35	45
4	Aylsham	23	13	5	5	52	26	26	44
5	Stalham Town	24	14	2	8	69	48	21	44
6	Yelverton	23	13	4	6	48	32	16	43
7	East Harling	26	11	8	7	47	40	7	40*
8	Easton	24	9	6	9	66	60	6	33
9	Kirkley & Pakefield Res	21	9	5	7	45	34	11	32
10	Sprowston Athletic	23	7	5	11	47	48	-1	26
11	Bungay Town	23	7	4	12	39	50	-11	25
12	Thetford Rovers	23	6	3	14	42	59	-17	21
13	Watton United	21	5	2	14	28	54	-26	17
14	Norwich United U21	25	3	5	17	31	79	-48	14
15	Fakenham Town Res	24	2	0	22	23	105	-82	3*

DIVISION TWO

		P	W	D	L	F	A	GD	Pts
1	Heacham	21	18	2	1	73	20	53	56
2	Brandon Town	23	15	3	5	54	31	23	48
3	Loddon United	20	13	4	3	49	18	31	43
4	Wells Town	19	10	5	4	52	28	24	35
5	Hingham Athletic	23	11	2	10	59	38	21	35
6	Gayton United	23	10	5	8	47	56	-9	35
7	Beccles Caxton	21	10	2	9	45	43	2	32
8	Holt United	20	8	7	5	42	29	13	31
9	Buxton	19	7	4	8	42	45	-3	25
10	Freethorpe	19	4	8	7	28	41	-13	20
11	North Walsham Town	21	5	5	11	31	50	-19	19*
12	Reepham Town	22	4	5	13	30	55	-25	17
13	Martham	21	4	5	12	34	65	-31	17
14	Caister Res	23	4	4	15	37	77	-40	15*
15	Swaffham Town Res	21	3	3	15	32	59	-27	12

DIVISION THREE

		P	W	D	L	F	A	GD	Pts
1	Earsham	22	15	4	3	49	25	24	49
2	Castle Acre Swifts	19	14	2	3	52	23	29	44
3	AC Mill Lane	18	13	1	4	69	19	50	40
4	Poringland Wands	21	11	4	6	45	33	12	37
5	Waveney Res	22	10	5	7	49	37	12	35
6	Attleborough Town Res	23	11	2	10	40	39	1	34*
7	Long Stratton Res	23	10	3	10	46	49	-3	33
8	Gt Yarmouth Town Res	24	11	1	12	35	45	-10	33*
9	Mattishall Res	21	10	1	10	43	35	8	30*
10	Bradenham Wands Res	22	10	1	11	47	48	-1	30*
11	Norwich CEYMS Res	23	9	2	12	49	53	-4	29
12	Hempnall	22	6	2	14	32	52	-20	20
13	Aylsham Res	24	4	7	13	36	58	-22	19
14	Horsford United	24	7	0	17	22	77	-55	18*
15	South Walsham	22	4	5	13	33	54	-21	17

DIVISION FOUR

		P	W	D	L	F	A	GD	Pts
1	Dussindale Rovers	22	19	2	1	88	14	74	59
2	Costessey Sports	24	16	2	6	75	45	30	50
3	UEA Res	24	16	0	8	60	30	30	48
4	Harleston Town Res	23	14	1	8	55	41	14	43
5	Beccles Town Res	19	12	3	4	48	23	25	39
6	St Andrews Res	22	11	3	8	49	33	16	36
7	Hemsby	22	10	3	9	63	48	15	33
8	Acle United Res	23	10	2	11	60	57	3	32
9	Belton	20	10	2	8	43	43	0	32
10	Gayton United Res	23	8	2	13	49	65	-16	26
11	Downham Town Res	26	8	4	14	56	61	-5	25*
12	Hellesdon Res	20	6	3	11	34	49	-15	19*
13	Holt United Res	25	6	3	16	54	67	-13	18*
14	Scole United Res	22	4	5	13	41	68	-27	17
15	Mundford Res	23	1	1	21	16	147	-131	3*

DIVISION FIVE NORTH

		P	W	D	L	F	A	GD	Pts
1	Longham	20	19	1	0	106	29	77	58
2	Sheringham Res	21	17	2	2	83	31	52	53
3	Dersingham Rovers	18	15	2	1	75	17	58	47
4	Easton Res	22	11	5	6	56	47	9	38
5	AFC Lynn Napier	25	11	3	11	60	51	9	35*
6	Blofield United Res	19	11	1	7	61	36	25	34
7	Wells Town Res	18	11	0	7	56	32	24	31*
8	Norwich Eagles	21	9	3	9	83	66	17	30
9	Narborough	24	9	2	13	51	65	-14	29
10	Hindringham Res	21	5	5	11	38	56	-18	20
11	Thorpe Village	23	6	0	17	37	94	-57	17*
12	Stalham Town Res	19	2	4	13	28	57	-29	9*
13	Necton	19	2	4	13	38	94	-56	9*
14	Reepham Town Res	24	3	0	21	39	136	-97	8*

DIVISION FIVE SOUTH

		P	W	D	L	F	A	GD	Pts
1	Mutford & Wrentham	19	19	0	0	104	16	88	57
2	Norton Athletic	23	18	1	4	78	25	53	55
3	Mulbarton Wands Res	18	15	2	1	82	29	53	47
4	Tacolneston	20	13	2	5	77	38	39	41
5	East Harling Res	21	12	1	8	67	49	18	37
6	Yelverton Res	21	11	3	7	56	36	20	36
7	Thetford Rovers Res	23	7	2	14	48	88	-40	23
8	Bungay Town Res	20	7	0	13	47	64	-17	21
9	Martham Res	20	6	2	12	31	81	-50	20
10	Wymondham Town Res	22	5	4	13	45	70	-25	19
11	AC Mill Lane Res	22	3	5	14	44	76	-32	13*
12	Freethorpe Res	20	3	3	14	23	76	-53	12
13	Poringland Wands Res	21	2	3	16	17	71	-54	7*

BEDFORDSHIRE COUNTY LEAGUE

PREMIER DIVISION

		P	W	D	L	F	A	GD	Pts
1	Stevington	18	13	5	0	45	18	27	44
2	Cranfield United	19	12	4	3	71	18	53	40
3	AFC Oakley	17	13	1	3	58	18	40	40
4	Queens Park Crescents	19	9	6	4	57	34	23	33
5	Flitwick Town	20	8	5	7	38	34	4	29
6	Riseley Sports	22	8	5	9	39	62	-23	29
7	Crawley Green Res	16	9	1	6	34	28	6	28
8	Caldecote	20	7	7	6	34	38	-4	28
9	Biggleswade United U23	21	7	5	9	40	41	-1	26
10	Biggleswade FC Res	17	7	2	8	33	24	9	22*
11	Marston Shelton Rovers	16	6	1	9	27	57	-30	19
12	Bedford Albion	19	5	2	12	35	50	-15	17
13	Shefford Town & Campton Res	18	3	5	10	22	41	-19	14
14	AFC Kempston Town & B'ford Col	17	3	3	11	22	41	-19	11*
15	Wilstead	19	2	2	15	20	71	-51	8

Ickwell & Old Warden withdrew before the start of the season.
Wootton Blue Cross withdrew in Jan 2020.

DIVISION ONE

		P	W	D	L	F	A	GD	Pts
1	Elstow Abbey	22	19	1	2	71	11	49	58
2	Cranfield United Res	21	16	0	5	78	17	48	48
3	Sporting Lewsey Park	20	14	3	3	76	12	46	45
4	Henlow	17	11	3	3	43	7	24	36
5	Flitwick Town Res	18	11	1	6	55	12	27	34
6	Lea Sports PSG	18	10	2	6	51	16	26	32
7	Ampthill Town Dev	15	8	1	6	30	14	-2	25
8	Totternhoe Res	16	7	0	9	30	26	-13	21
9	Bedford Sports Athletic	18	6	0	12	29	15	-10	17
10	Houghton Athletic	21	5	1	15	33	26	-13	16
11	AFC Kempston Town & BC Res	19	5	1	13	15	36	-40	16
12	Stotfold Dev	15	5	1	9	20	9	1	12
13	Kempston Athletic	16	3	2	11	17	21	-31	11
14	The 61 FC (Luton) Res	21	4	0	17	16	58	-89	11
15	Wilstead Res	15	4	0	11	18	23	-23	6

CAMBRIDGESHIRE COUNTY LEAGUE

PREMIER DIVISION

		P	W	D	L	F	A	GD	Pts
1	Cherry Hinton	18	13	3	2	55	19	36	42
2	Great Shelford	20	13	1	6	58	37	21	40
3	Foxton	21	12	1	8	54	36	18	37
4	Eaton Socon Team	21	11	3	7	48	28	20	36
5	Cambridge University Press	18	10	4	4	42	19	23	34
6	Eynesbury United	19	10	2	7	43	40	3	32
7	Over Sports	18	8	3	7	47	32	15	31
8	West Wratting	17	8	3	6	44	28	16	27
9	Hemingfords United	19	7	4	8	38	44	-6	25
10	Comberton United	19	6	5	8	37	33	4	23
11	Linton Granta	19	6	2	11	36	43	-7	20
12	Ely City Res	21	6	1	14	29	59	-30	19
13	Chatteris Town	20	3	1	16	21	89	-68	10
14	Fulbourn Institute	18	2	1	15	27	72	-45	4*

SENIOR A

		P	W	D	L	F	A	GD	Pts
1	Witchford 96	20	12	4	4	48	32	16	40
2	Gamlingay United	19	11	4	4	56	25	31	37
3	AFC Barley Mow	21	11	3	7	64	41	23	36
4	Milton	18	10	3	5	50	39	11	33
5	Cottenham United	20	9	5	6	45	29	16	32
6	Somersham Town	20	10	2	8	49	34	15	32
7	Orwell	16	10	1	5	52	25	27	31
8	March Town United Res	19	9	2	8	37	39	-2	29
9	Huntingdon United	18	9	1	8	46	27	19	28
10	Soham Town Rangers Res	19	8	2	9	27	39	-12	26
11	Bluntisham Rangers	19	6	1	12	33	62	-29	19
12	Hundon F.C. (Sat)	15	4	4	7	34	37	-3	16
13	Whittlesford United	19	3	6	10	27	50	-23	15
14	Fulbourn Institute Res	21	1	0	20	17	106	-89	-3*

SENIOR B

		P	W	D	L	F	A	GD	Pts
1	Thaxted Rangers	21	13	3	5	74	39	35	42
2	Isleham United	20	13	1	6	57	31	26	40
3	Newmarket Town F.C Res	20	12	3	5	53	36	17	39
4	Eaton Socon Res	18	13	0	5	49	35	14	39
5	Bassingbourn	17	12	2	3	45	25	20	38
6	Lakenheath F.C. Res	18	10	2	6	62	43	19	32
7	Linton Granta Res	18	9	3	6	48	38	10	30
8	St Ives Rangers	24	9	2	13	51	70	-19	29
9	Fordham	18	8	3	7	37	40	-3	27
10	Cambridge University Press Res	20	7	5	8	47	47	0	26
11	Sawston Rovers	20	7	3	10	35	43	-8	24
12	Duxford United	20	7	2	11	41	41	0	23
13	West Wratting Res	17	5	2	10	29	39	-10	17
14	Wisbech St Mary Res	21	3	1	17	22	90	-68	10
15	Girton United	18	0	2	16	8	41	-33	-7*

DIVISION 1A

		P	W	D	L	F	A	GD	Pts
1	Hardwick FC	16	8	3	5	39	32	7	27
2	Cherry Hinton Res	12	7	5	0	30	16	14	26
3	Steeple Morden	14	7	2	5	45	39	6	23
4	Comberton United Res	14	6	5	3	39	33	6	23
5	Mott MacDonald	14	5	6	3	27	24	3	21
6	Clare Town F.C.	14	4	4	6	28	30	-2	16
7	Meldreth	14	4	4	6	25	32	-7	16
8	Debden	10	4	2	4	21	18	3	14
9	Balsham	13	3	3	7	25	34	-9	12
10	Milton Res	10	3	2	5	29	32	-3	11
11	Cambourne Rovers	9	0	2	7	20	38	-18	2

DIVISION 1B

		P	W	D	L	F	A	GD	Pts
1	Brampton	12	10	2	0	41	13	28	32
2	Houghton & Wyton	13	10	0	3	36	21	15	30
3	Hemingfords United Res	12	6	3	3	27	18	9	21
4	Fenstanton	11	5	3	3	22	16	6	18
5	Alconbury	9	4	2	3	29	17	12	14
6	Swavesey Institute	13	4	2	7	15	31	-16	14
7	St Ives Town FC Res	10	4	0	6	18	26	-8	12
8	Godmanchester Rovers Res	10	3	2	5	20	22	-2	11
9	Gamlingay United Res	14	3	2	9	36	47	-11	11
10	Chatteris Town Res	10	3	1	6	12	32	-20	10
11	Ely City 'A'	12	2	1	9	15	28	-13	7

Central Midlands League Chairman's Cup Final - Pinxton v Bakewell Town 5-1.
Photo Bill Wheatcroft.

Central Midlands League South Division - Holbrook St Michaels v Pinxton 1-6. Photos Bill Wheatcroft.

DIVISION 2A

	P	W	D	L	F	A	GD	Pts
1 Great Shelford Res	15	14	1	0	42	10	32	43
2 Barrington	17	13	2	2	61	17	44	41
3 Litlington Athletic	19	12	2	5	53	39	14	38
4 Over Sports Res	17	11	4	2	55	21	34	37
5 Buckden	18	11	1	6	63	27	36	34
6 Foxton Res	18	9	2	7	49	46	3	29
7 Melbourn	19	9	1	9	43	44	-1	28
8 Suffolk Punch Haverhill	17	7	2	8	35	38	-3	23
9 Papworth	19	6	2	11	54	52	2	20
10 Whittlesford United Res	14	4	4	6	32	40	-8	16
11 Linton Granta A	21	5	1	15	36	69	-33	16
12 Great Paxton	15	4	2	9	21	46	-25	14
13 Steeple Morden Res	19	3	2	14	36	74	-38	11
14 Haverhill Rovers A	20	2	2	16	22	79	-57	5*

DIVISION 2B

	P	W	D	L	F	A	GD	Pts
1 AFC Walpole	13	11	1	1	55	15	40	34
2 March Town United A	15	8	1	6	41	38	3	25
3 Burwell Swifts	11	7	3	1	37	17	20	24
4 Wimblington	17	6	3	8	42	33	9	21
5 Outwell Swifts	8	6	2	0	26	8	18	20
6 Exning United F.C.	12	5	3	4	39	29	10	18
7 Burwell Tigers Men	15	5	3	7	31	35	-4	18
8 Soham United	11	4	2	5	24	39	-15	14
9 Fordham Res	11	4	1	6	30	28	2	13
10 Wisbech St Mary A	12	2	1	9	14	50	-36	7
11 Wisbech Town Acorns	17	1	4	12	20	67	-47	7

DIVISION 3A

	P	W	D	L	F	A	GD	Pts
1 Harston	13	12	0	1	57	15	42	36
2 Guilden Morden Team	15	11	1	3	52	31	21	34
3 Abington United	17	10	1	6	47	27	20	31
4 Cherry Hinton A team	13	9	1	3	47	27	20	28
5 Oakington Vikings Youth	14	8	1	5	33	23	10	25
6 Longstanton FC	14	7	2	5	39	27	12	23
7 Wickhambrook F.C.	11	7	1	3	33	22	11	22
8 Isleham United Res	16	6	3	7	43	44	-1	21
9 Clare Town F.C. Res	19	6	0	13	24	46	-22	18
10 Eaton Socon A Team	11	4	1	6	16	24	-8	13
11 Duxford United Res	16	3	1	12	22	59	-37	10
12 Cottenham United Res	15	3	1	11	12	49	-37	10
13 Hundon F.C. Res (Sat)	16	2	1	13	20	51	-31	7

DIVISION 3B

	P	W	D	L	F	A	GD	Pts
1 Guyhirn 1st	15	12	1	2	43	15	28	37
2 March Academy 1st	12	9	1	2	29	14	15	28
3 The Eagle (Ely)	14	8	2	4	35	22	13	26
4 Houghton & Wyton Res	12	8	1	3	39	31	8	25
5 Manea United	15	7	1	7	28	28	0	22
6 Benwick Athletic	8	6	1	1	23	6	17	19
7 St Ives Rangers Res	12	4	0	8	15	26	-11	12
8 Somersham Town Res	15	4	0	11	23	44	-21	12
9 Alconbury Res	15	3	1	11	31	42	-11	10
10 Bluntisham Rangers Res	16	2	0	14	25	63	-38	6

DIVISION 4A

	P	W	D	L	F	A	GD	Pts
1 Orwell Res	17	15	1	1	87	16	71	46
2 Hardwick FC Res	13	12	0	1	64	23	41	36
3 Sawston Rovers Res	16	11	0	5	58	29	29	33
4 Kedington F.C.	12	10	0	2	63	16	47	30
5 Harston Res	18	8	1	9	36	59	-23	25
6 Sawston United Res	12	7	1	4	35	21	14	22
7 Thurlow	18	6	0	12	31	60	-29	18
8 Cambridge Ambassadors	15	5	1	9	41	53	-12	16
9 Guilden Morden Res	13	5	1	7	23	43	-20	16
10 Barrington Res	16	5	1	10	20	54	-34	16
11 Bassingbourn Res	14	2	2	10	20	48	-28	5*
12 Thaxted Rangers Res	18	1	0	17	22	78	-56	3

DIVISION 4B

	P	W	D	L	F	A	GD	Pts
1 Barton Mills F.C.	17	14	2	1	79	20	59	44
2 Crusaders 2019	22	13	3	6	73	46	27	42
3 Stretham	17	12	4	1	76	24	52	40
4 Needingworth United Res	14	12	1	1	61	11	50	37
5 Histon Hornets	16	10	0	6	51	35	16	30
6 Mott MacDonald Res	19	7	3	9	47	47	0	24
7 Wilbraham	22	6	3	13	28	83	-55	21
8 Papworth Res	15	4	6	5	29	33	-4	18
9 Swavesey Institute Res	17	5	2	10	28	48	-20	17
10 Soham Town Rangers A	18	4	3	11	43	53	-10	15
11 Wicken	18	5	0	13	31	66	-35	15
12 Hemingfords United A	15	4	1	10	23	59	-36	13
13 Milton A Team	14	1	2	11	13	57	-44	5

DIVISION 4C

	P	W	D	L	F	A	GD	Pts
1 AFC Christchurch Magpies	11	8	2	1	33	10	23	26
2 Little Downham & Pymoor Swifts	9	8	1	0	46	8	38	25
3 Fen Tigers Engineers	13	6	2	5	28	27	1	20
4 Witchford 96 Res	9	6	1	2	36	8	28	19
5 Littleport Town	6	4	1	1	19	12	7	13
6 The Isle	11	3	2	6	20	24	-4	11
7 Benwick Athletic Res	12	3	2	7	20	31	-11	11
8 March Academy Res	15	2	1	12	13	70	-57	7
9 Chatteris Town A Team	8	1	0	7	8	33	-25	3

CENTRAL MIDLANDS LEAGUE

NORTH DIVISION

	P	W	D	L	F	A	GD	Pts
1 Newark Town	24	18	6	0	94	16	78	60
2 Dinnington Town	19	15	4	0	51	11	40	49
3 Retford United	18	12	4	2	63	21	42	40
4 Harworth Colliery	18	10	3	5	53	28	25	33
5 Staveley Miners Welfare Res	18	9	3	6	43	26	17	30
6 Thorne Colliery	19	7	4	8	37	38	-1	25
7 Phoenix	20	7	2	11	30	39	-9	23
8 Sutton Rovers 2007	18	6	3	9	38	45	-7	21
9 Crowle Colts	17	6	2	9	30	30	0	20
10 Collingham	19	5	5	9	25	35	-10	20
11 Dronfield Town Res	19	6	2	11	26	67	-41	20
12 AFC Bentley	18	6	1	11	20	36	-16	19
13 Appleby Frodingham	19	3	1	15	17	72	-55	10
14 Askern	20	3	0	17	16	79	-63	9

DIVISION ONE NORTH

	P	W	D	L	F	A	GD	Pts
1 St Josephs Rockware of Worksop	16	14	2	0	54	16	38	44
2 Boynton Sports	16	10	2	4	50	31	19	32
3 Nottingham	14	9	3	2	45	15	30	30
4 Epworth Town Colts	12	8	2	2	46	19	27	26
5 Harworth Colliery Res	16	7	1	8	39	39	0	22
6 Chesterfield Town	16	4	2	10	31	51	-20	14
7 Wakefield Res	15	4	1	10	36	47	-11	13
8 Linby Colliery Welfare Res	14	4	0	10	19	53	-34	12
9 Retford United Res	12	2	3	7	22	35	-13	9
10 Nottingham Education	11	2	2	7	15	31	-16	8
11 Selston Res	10	2	2	6	13	33	-20	8

SOUTH DIVISION

		P	W	D	L	F	A	GD	Pts
1	Sherwood Colliery Res	18	13	3	2	65	21	44	42
2	Clay Cross Town	15	13	1	1	59	13	46	40
3	Pinxton	17	12	3	2	53	21	32	39
4	Rowsley '86	17	12	2	3	59	19	40	38
5	Linby Colliery Welfare	20	8	9	3	35	22	13	33
6	Blidworth Welfare	20	6	7	7	33	54	-21	25
7	Swanwick Pentrich Road	13	7	2	4	32	22	10	23
8	Holbrook Sports	13	7	1	5	34	32	2	22
9	Holbrook St Michaels	15	7	1	7	28	34	-6	22
10	Ashland Rovers	22	6	3	13	45	72	-27	21
11	Teversal Res	16	6	2	8	22	34	-12	20
12	Mansfield Hosiery Mills	23	5	5	13	28	66	-38	20
13	Hilton Harriers	16	4	3	9	22	29	-7	15
14	Underwood Villa	16	2	4	10	21	43	-22	10
15	Arnold Town	18	2	4	12	29	52	-23	10
16	Mickleover RBL	17	2	2	13	23	54	-31	8

DIVISION ONE SOUTH

		P	W	D	L	F	A	GD	Pts
1	Mickleover Sports Res	15	12	0	3	69	19	50	36
2	Long Eaton United Com	14	10	1	3	65	22	43	31
3	Cromford & Wirksworth Town	13	9	2	2	31	18	13	29
4	Wirksworth Ivanhoe	12	8	3	1	35	16	19	27
5	Bakewell Town	14	8	2	4	32	31	1	26
6	FC Sez	14	7	3	4	43	27	16	24
7	Woodhouse Colts	16	5	5	6	34	42	-8	20
8	Holbrook Sports Res	11	2	1	8	14	40	-26	7
9	Ripley Town	11	2	1	8	11	37	-26	7
10	Holbrook St Michaels Res	9	1	3	5	13	21	-8	6
11	Heanor Town Res	11	1	2	8	13	31	-18	5
12	Borrowash Victoria Dev	14	0	1	13	15	71	-56	1

CHESHIRE LEAGUE

PREMIER DIVISION

		P	W	D	L	F	A	GD	Pts
1	Whaley Bridge Athletic	19	11	4	4	29	20	9	37
2	Crewe	16	11	2	3	42	18	24	35
3	Congleton VR	20	9	6	5	37	30	7	33
4	Eagle Sports	18	10	3	5	36	30	6	33
5	F.C. St. Helens	17	9	5	3	44	27	17	32
6	Middlewich Town	21	9	4	8	53	45	8	31
7	Billinge	19	7	8	4	28	24	4	29
8	Altrincham Res	20	8	3	9	43	33	10	27
9	Poynton	15	6	6	3	30	24	6	24
10	Greenalls PSO	20	7	3	10	35	43	-8	24
11	Daten	23	7	3	13	33	51	-18	24
12	Lostock Gralam	11	5	2	4	17	22	-5	17
13	Knutsford	20	4	3	13	25	36	-11	15
14	Broadheath Central	15	4	1	10	25	41	-16	13
15	Egerton	18	2	1	15	18	51	-33	7

LEAGUE ONE

		P	W	D	L	F	A	GD	Pts
1	Winstanley Warriors	17	14	2	1	70	31	39	44
2	Garswood United	16	12	3	1	67	22	45	39
3	Windle Labour FC	19	11	3	5	66	42	24	36
4	Vulcan FC	15	11	1	3	43	20	23	34
5	Maine Road Res.	22	7	6	9	44	55	-11	27
6	Malpas FC	17	7	3	7	54	41	13	24
7	Cheadle Town Res.	16	7	2	7	35	36	-1	23
8	Styal FC	12	6	3	3	36	28	8	21
9	Denton Town	16	6	3	7	36	47	-11	21
10	Ashton Athletic Res.	17	4	6	7	44	47	-3	18
11	Cuddington FC	18	5	2	11	49	56	-7	17
12	Cheadle Heath Nomads Res.	18	3	5	10	36	62	-26	14
13	Moore United	17	2	3	12	35	65	-30	9
14	Orford FC	14	0	2	12	12	75	-63	2

LEAGUE TWO

		P	W	D	L	F	A	GD	Pts
1	Winnington Avenue Y.C. 94	19	13	3	3	49	24	25	42
2	Knowsley South	17	12	1	4	65	22	43	37
3	Partington Village	13	11	1	1	63	18	45	34
4	Newton Athletic	16	10	2	4	58	32	26	32
5	Parklands	11	9	0	2	32	13	19	27
6	Pilkington Res.	19	8	1	10	48	67	-19	25
7	Sandbach United Res.	15	7	3	5	40	34	6	24
8	Holmes Chapel Hurricanes	17	5	3	9	38	61	-23	18
9	Golborne Sports	18	5	2	11	41	58	-17	17
10	St Helens Town Res.	19	5	1	13	43	62	-19	16
11	Rylands Res.	18	3	1	10	26	52	-26	10
12	Hartford FC	18	1	0	17	19	79	-60	3

DEVON FOOTBALL LEAGUE

NORTH-EAST DIVISION

		P	W	D	L	F	A	GD	Pts
1	Newtown	21	20	0	1	95	19		60
2	Exwick Villa	21	16	2	3	82	17		50
3	Alphington	18	12	2	4	79	30		38
4	St Martins	19	12	2	5	62	28		38
5	Heavitree United	16	11	1	4	44	29		34
6	Teignmouth	16	9	3	4	40	20		30
7	University of Exeter	15	9	1	5	48	25		28
8	Exmouth Town Res	18	9	1	8	35	36		28
9	Braunton	15	8	1	6	34	24		25
10	Budleigh Salterton	23	8	1	14	45	64		25
11	Liverton United	20	7	1	12	38	85		22
12	Chudleigh Athletic	17	3	4	10	25	50		13
13	Witheridge	17	4	0	13	24	58		12
14	Bovey Tracey Res	14	3	0	11	20	57		9
15	Topsham Town	18	1	2	15	23	86		5
16	Clyst Valley	18	0	1	17	18	84		1

SOUTH-WEST DIVISION

		P	W	D	L	F	A	GD	Pts
1	Buckland Athletic Res	19	16	2	1	71	22		50
2	Waldon Athletic	21	13	2	6	56	48		41
3	Paignton Saints	22	12	2	8	70	50		38
4	Kingsteignton Athletic	17	12	1	4	59	31		37
5	Watcombe Wanderers	21	11	2	8	57	35		35
6	Plympton Athletic	19	10	2	7	54	34		32
7	Totnes & Dartington SC	22	8	4	10	44	42		28
8	Newton Abbot Spurs Res	23	9	1	13	42	70		28
9	Tavistock Res	12	7	5	0	47	21		26
10	Roselands	24	8	2	14	50	95		26
11	Bere Alston United	20	6	4	10	41	51		22
12	Plymstock United	16	6	3	7	32	39		21
13	Lakeside Athletic	19	4	6	9	40	65		18
14	Plymouth Argyle Dev	20	4	5	11	36	48		17
15	Ottery St Mary AFC	18	4	4	10	31	48		16
16	Paignton Villa Res	19	2	3	14	24	55		9

DORSET PREMIER LEAGUE

		P	W	D	L	F	A	GD	Pts
1	Merley Cobham Sports	19	16	1	2	93	25	68	46*
2	Hamworthy Recreation	16	15	1	0	66	19	47	46
3	Westland Sports	18	14	1	3	50	25	25	43
4	Bournemouth Sports (Parley)	24	13	4	7	56	38	18	40*
5	Gillingham Town	24	13	0	11	58	42	16	39
6	Dorchester Sports	23	10	7	6	56	43	13	37
7	Balti Sports	23	10	7	6	50	37	13	37
8	Blandford United	18	10	4	4	55	31	24	34
9	Holt United	24	9	3	12	49	49	0	30
10	Corfe Castle	25	8	3	14	46	77	-31	27
11	Swanage Town & Herston	19	7	2	10	40	46	-6	23
12	Bridport Res	23	7	2	14	46	72	-26	23
13	Shaftesbury Town Res	20	6	4	10	41	58	-17	22
14	Sturminster Newton United	22	5	4	13	33	70	-37	19
15	Portland United Res	24	5	4	15	37	80	-43	16*
16	Wareham Rangers	21	4	3	14	37	62	-25	15
17	Sherborne Town Res	21	4	2	15	27	66	-39	14

ESSEX & SUFFOLK BORDER LEAGUE

PREMIER DIVISION

		P	W	D	L	F	A	GD	Pts
1	Stanway Pegasus	27	19	2	6	79	40	39	59
2	Great Bentley	22	15	4	3	58	40	18	49
3	Flitch United	24	13	5	6	45	45	0	44
4	Tiptree Heath	26	12	5	9	61	52	9	41
5	Gas Recreation	20	11	6	3	53	31	22	39
6	West Bergholt	22	12	3	7	55	41	14	39
7	Hatfield Peverel	24	11	3	10	63	47	16	36
8	Alresford Colne Rangers	22	10	4	8	41	37	4	34
9	Lawford Lads	25	10	4	11	44	44	0	34
10	Little Oakley Res	25	9	4	12	43	55	-12	31
11	Dedham Old Boys	25	8	5	12	36	59	-23	29
12	White Notley	24	7	4	13	50	51	-1	25
13	Tiptree Engaine	24	7	3	14	48	66	-18	24
14	Barnston	25	6	4	15	32	52	-20	22
15	Earls Colne	20	5	6	9	39	37	2	21
16	Brantham Athletic Res	27	3	4	20	39	89	-50	13

DIVISION ONE

		P	W	D	L	F	A	GD	Pts
1	Sudbury Sports F.C.	20	17	2	1	110	20	90	53
2	Tiptree Jobserve	20	14	5	1	57	16	41	47
3	Colne Athletic	20	15	1	4	70	20	50	46
4	Cressing United	23	15	1	7	64	31	33	46
5	Gosfield United	22	13	4	5	70	31	39	43
6	Stanway Pegasus Res	21	11	2	8	43	47	-4	35
7	FC Clacton	18	11	1	6	51	33	18	34
8	Belle Vue Social Club	24	10	3	11	52	65	-13	33
9	Boxted Lodgers	26	7	5	14	54	89	-35	26
10	Stanway Rovers Res	19	8	0	11	53	45	8	24
11	Bures United F.C.	22	7	3	12	44	48	-4	24
12	West Bergholt Res	22	6	5	11	40	58	-18	23
13	Alresford Colne Rangers Res	19	6	1	12	40	58	-18	19
14	Mersea Island	21	5	3	13	24	72	-48	18
15	Little Oakley A	22	3	0	19	23	92	-69	9
16	Wormingford Wanderers	19	2	2	15	19	89	-70	8

DIVISION TWO

		P	W	D	L	F	A	GD	Pts
1	Hedinghams United	22	15	3	4	72	22	50	48
2	Shrub End United	21	15	2	4	59	30	29	47
3	Tavern	21	13	5	3	52	27	25	44
4	Great Bentley Res	19	12	3	4	31	17	14	39
5	Cavendish F.C.	17	12	1	4	72	40	32	37
6	Tollesbury	21	11	4	6	51	43	8	37
7	Tiptree Jobserve Res	19	12	0	7	45	43	2	36
8	Gas Recreation Res	22	9	1	12	55	82	-27	28
9	Hatfield Peverel Res	21	8	3	10	48	44	4	27
10	Harwich Rangers	18	7	5	6	50	42	8	26
11	Elmden Rovers	23	8	2	13	64	65	-1	26
12	Tiptree Engaine Res	23	8	2	13	37	61	-24	26
13	Dedham Old Boys Res	23	3	8	12	34	50	-16	17
14	Rowhedge	20	5	2	13	21	37	-16	17
15	Brantham Athletic F.C. 'A'	21	2	3	16	24	72	-48	9
16	Wormingford Wanderers Res	17	2	0	15	14	54	-40	6

DIVISION THREE

		P	W	D	L	F	A	GD	Pts
1	St Osyth Saturday	24	20	0	4	95	33	62	60
2	Oyster	21	17	0	4	66	27	39	51
3	Lawford Lads Res	19	15	1	3	68	33	35	46
4	Harwich & Parkeston Res	19	15	0	4	89	37	52	45
5	Barnston Res	17	13	2	2	66	30	36	41
6	Stanway Athletic	21	11	1	9	75	33	42	34
7	Tiptree Heath Res	18	9	0	9	49	49	0	27
8	Kelvedon Social	22	7	4	11	39	52	-13	25
9	Flitch United Res	16	8	0	8	46	46	0	24
10	Little Clacton FC	19	4	4	11	43	59	-16	16
11	Hedinghams United Res	20	4	4	12	36	60	-24	16
12	Bradfield Rovers	22	4	1	17	23	106	-83	13
13	Cavendish F.C. Res	23	2	2	19	37	102	-65	8
14	Boxted Lodgers Res	19	1	1	17	29	94	-65	4

ESSEX OLYMPIAN LEAGUE

PREMIER DIVISION

		P	W	D	L	F	A	GD	Pts
1	Sungate	22	13	5	4	52	29	23	44
2	Leigh Ramblers	22	12	2	8	52	30	22	38
3	Buckhurst Hill	14	10	2	2	46	16	30	32
4	Catholic United	21	9	4	8	51	39	12	31
5	Kelvedon Hatch	20	9	3	8	41	45	-4	30
6	Springfield	20	9	1	10	44	49	-5	28
7	Rayleigh Town	16	8	1	7	33	33	0	25
8	Old Southendian	22	7	4	11	38	42	-4	25
9	Bishop's Stortford Swifts	20	7	2	11	35	43	-8	23
10	Canning Town	22	7	2	13	39	49	-10	23
11	Shenfield A.F.C.	18	6	4	8	30	35	-5	22
12	Basildon Town	15	7	0	8	27	48	-21	21
13	Hutton	14	5	3	6	27	32	-5	18
14	Harold Wood Athletic	18	5	3	10	28	53	-25	18

DIVISION ONE

		P	W	D	L	F	A	GD	Pts
1	Chingford Athletic	17	14	1	2	48	20	28	43
2	Old Chelmsfordians	17	11	4	2	54	19	35	37
3	Ongar Town	11	10	1	0	36	9	27	31
4	Lakeside	15	9	2	4	31	22	9	29
5	Galleywood	15	6	6	3	23	20	3	24
6	Rayleigh Town Res	13	7	2	4	35	30	5	23
7	Shoebury Town	18	3	8	7	38	49	-11	17
8	FC Hamlets	11	5	3	3	21	12	9	15*
9	Snaresbrook	10	4	1	5	19	25	-6	13
10	Ramsden Scotia	15	4	2	9	18	29	-11	12*
11	Manford Way	15	4	1	10	22	48	-26	11*
12	Herongate Athletic	15	2	2	11	26	53	-27	11*
13	Runwell Sports	14	3	1	10	22	26	-4	10
14	Toby	18	1	4	13	22	53	-31	7

DIVISION TWO

		P	W	D	L	F	A	GD	Pts
1	Leigh Town	15	14	1	0	44	13	31	43
2	Beacon Hill Rovers	15	12	0	3	43	17	26	36
3	Old Southendian Res	17	10	4	3	33	20	13	36*
4	Corinthians	14	10	1	3	52	24	28	31
5	May & Baker E.C. Res	17	8	1	8	48	44	4	28*
6	Laindon Orient	12	8	2	2	28	11	17	26
7	Epping Town	16	7	2	7	38	25	13	20*
8	Wakering Sports	16	5	4	7	37	34	3	19
9	Harold Wood Athletic Res	14	3	2	9	18	26	-8	11
10	Rochford Town	18	3	0	15	21	60	-39	9
11	AS Rawreth	16	3	0	13	20	63	-43	9
12	Ryan	18	1	3	14	20	65	-45	1*

DIVISION THREE

		P	W	D	L	F	A	GD	Pts
1	ACD United	18	13	4	1	48	19	29	43
2	Wakebury	19	12	3	4	56	31	25	39
3	Corinthians Res	15	11	2	2	51	25	26	37
4	Toby Res	18	9	2	7	40	31	9	29
5	Collier Row	14	9	1	4	36	25	11	28
6	Hutton Res	13	7	0	6	35	28	7	21
7	Leigh Town Res	14	6	2	6	30	33	-3	20
8	Buckhurst Hill Res	14	6	0	8	28	35	-7	18
9	Lakeside Res	14	4	2	11	34	48	-14	14
10	Basildon Town Res	15	4	1	10	23	41	-18	13
11	White Ensign Res	18	3	1	14	19	53	-34	10
12	Hullbridge Sports A	15	1	1	13	15	46	-31	4

DIVISION FOUR

		P	W	D	L	F	A	GD	Pts
1	Roydon	15	12	3	0	67	20	47	39
2	Chingford Athletic Dev	19	11	5	3	61	21	40	38
3	Ongar Town Res	7	7	0	0	42	41	1	28
4	Wakering Sports Res	16	8	3	5	34	26	8	27
5	Forest Glade	18	8	3	8	34	34	0	27
6	Catholic United Res	17	8	3	6	52	58	-6	27
7	Galleywood Res	14	6	2	6	36	26	10	20
8	Leytonstone United	15	6	1	8	24	31	-7	19
9	Laindon Orient Res	15	6	0	9	23	49	-26	18
10	Old Chelmsfordians Res	15	3	5	7	31	44	-13	17*
11	Shenfield A.F.C. Res	16	4	0	12	24	48	-24	12
12	Canning Town Res	18	2	4	12	30	60	-30	10

DIVISION FIVE

		P	W	D	L	F	A	GD	Pts
1	Bishop's Stortford Swifts Res	18	12	3	3	51	22	29	39
2	Springfield Res	14	9	1	4	51	22	29	28
3	Collier Row Res	15	8	1	6	47	32	15	25
4	Herongate Athletic Res	17	8	2	7	48	46	2	24*
5	Newbury Forest Res	15	8	0	7	33	31	2	24
6	Roydon Res	15	7	2	6	30	25	5	23
7	Old Barkabbeyans	16	6	3	7	39	39	0	21
8	Leigh Ramblers Res	20	7	0	13	44	51	-7	21
9	Shoebury Town Res	13	6	2	5	28	37	-9	20
10	Runwell Sports Res	16	6	0	10	26	38	-12	16*
11	Wakering Sports Dev	17	3	2	12	14	68	-54	11

GLOUCESTERSHIRE COUNTY LEAGUE

DIVISION ONE

		P	W	D	L	F	A	GD	Pts
1	Frampton United	22	15	5	2	59	21	38	50
2	Wick	20	15	1	4	46	26	20	46
3	Sharpness	22	14	4	4	39	20	19	46
4	Rockleaze Rangers	23	14	3	6	56	32	24	45
5	Gala Wilton	22	10	4	8	53	40	13	34
6	Hardwicke	22	10	4	8	38	36	2	34
7	Quedgeley Wanderers	25	10	4	11	43	50	-7	34
8	Little Stoke	23	10	0	13	44	46	-2	30
9	AEK Boco	18	8	4	6	40	23	17	28
10	Henbury	20	7	5	8	32	32	0	26
11	Bromley Heath United	18	5	3	10	26	39	-13	18
12	Ruardean Hill Rangers	19	4	4	11	29	43	-14	16
13	Broadwell Amateurs	22	4	4	14	27	55	-28	16
14	Hanham Athletic	22	4	4	14	22	52	-30	16
15	Patchway Town	20	4	1	15	22	61	-39	13

HAMPSHIRE PREMIER LEAGUE

SENIOR DIVISION

		P	W	D	L	F	A	GD	Pts
1	Infinity	24	20	4	0	85	21	64	64
2	Paulsgrove	28	17	6	5	76	41	35	57
3	Bush Hill	20	16	3	1	75	16	59	51
4	Fleetlands	23	14	4	5	71	36	35	46
5	Hayling United	25	14	4	7	59	31	28	46
6	Stockbridge	25	12	2	11	60	40	20	38
7	Liphook United	23	10	5	8	61	52	9	35
8	Overton United	25	10	3	12	50	55	-5	33
9	Colden Common	19	9	4	6	62	36	26	31
10	Clanfield	22	8	3	11	45	46	-1	27
11	Lyndhurst	22	6	3	13	29	76	-47	21
12	Liss Athletic	23	6	3	14	36	85	-49	21
13	Winchester Castle	24	5	3	16	30	61	-31	17*
14	Sway	23	5	2	16	37	81	-44	17
15	Chamberlayne Athletic	24	5	0	19	27	80	-53	15
16	Locks Heath	24	3	5	16	30	76	-46	14

DIVISION ONE

		P	W	D	L	F	A	GD	Pts
1	Denmead	20	13	4	3	43	16	27	43
2	Moneyfields Res	14	13	1	0	63	11	52	40
3	Andover New Street Swifts	18	12	0	6	41	25	16	36
4	Broughton	17	10	2	5	42	29	13	32
5	South Wonston Swifts	17	8	3	6	46	37	9	27
6	Headley United	20	7	3	10	40	44	-4	24
7	QK Southampton	16	6	5	5	35	30	5	23
8	Kingsclere	15	6	3	6	45	44	1	21
9	Michelmersh & Timsbury	16	6	2	8	34	41	-7	20
10	Upham	16	4	5	7	33	39	-6	17
11	AFC Petersfield	22	2	2	18	20	87	-67	8
12	Netley Central Sports	15	0	2	13	12	51	-39	2

HERTS SENIOR COUNTY LEAGUE

SENIOR PREMIER DIVISION

		P	W	D	L	F	A	GD	Pts
1	Letchworth Garden City Eagles	18	16	1	1	57	12	45	49
2	Sandridge Rovers	22	14	2	6	43	27	16	44
3	Royston Town Res	18	11	4	3	56	33	23	37
4	Oxhey Jets Res	16	10	2	4	41	26	15	32
5	Bush Hill Rangers	18	9	4	5	38	36	2	31
6	Hoddesdon Town Res	20	8	4	8	43	37	6	28
7	Chipperfield Corinthians	17	8	2	7	25	23	2	26
8	Colney Heath Res	18	8	2	8	33	43	-10	26
9	New River Athletic	15	7	0	8	27	30	-3	21
10	Cuffley Seniors	14	6	2	6	30	29	1	20
11	Ware Sports	18	5	4	9	34	45	-11	19
12	Cockfosters Res	20	5	3	12	27	46	-19	18
13	Belstone	19	4	1	14	20	37	-17	13
14	Hatfield Town	16	4	1	11	18	36	-18	13
15	Weston	17	1	2	14	16	48	-32	5

SENIOR DIVISION ONE

		P	W	D	L	F	A	GD	Pts
1	Rayners Lane Res	21	12	6	3	65	28	37	42
2	Glenn Sports	18	12	2	4	49	22	27	38
3	New Salamis Res	21	10	4	7	57	40	17	34
4	Hatfield United	21	10	3	8	43	37	6	33
5	Aldenham FC	22	9	5	8	40	40	0	32
6	Bovingdon Res	21	9	4	8	51	39	12	31
7	Oracle Components	20	9	3	8	42	42	0	30
8	Hinton	17	9	1	7	39	35	4	28
9	Oxhey	19	6	5	8	31	42	-11	23
10	Buntingford Town	21	7	2	12	28	45	-17	23
11	Evergreen FC	16	4	5	7	24	38	-14	17
12	Knebworth	14	4	5	5	20	36	-16	17
13	St Margaretsbury Res	21	4	5	12	35	57	-22	17
14	Old Parmiterians	18	3	4	11	25	48	-23	13

DIVISION TWO

		P	W	D	L	F	A	GD	Pts
1	Hertford Heath	21	14	3	4	69	27	42	45
2	Chipperfield Corinthians Res	15	11	2	2	58	18	40	35
3	Wheathampstead Wanderers	15	11	0	4	46	16	30	33
4	Ware Sports FC Res	20	9	3	8	51	53	-2	30
5	Lemsford	12	9	1	2	48	14	34	28
6	Letchworth Garden City Eagles Res	14	7	4	3	38	21	17	25
7	Hadley Saturday Veterans	15	8	0	7	35	32	3	24
8	Wormley Rovers Res	15	5	2	8	22	31	-9	17
9	Oxhey Res	12	5	2	5	21	30	-9	17
10	Hatfield Town Acadamy	16	4	4	8	27	38	-11	16
11	Cuffley Seniors Res	18	4	2	12	31	53	-22	14
12	Mill End Sports	21	2	3	16	27	106	-79	9
13	Bedmond Sports	16	2	2	12	23	57	-34	8

DIVISION THREE

		P	W	D	L	F	A	GD	Pts
1	Tring Town AFC	19	14	3	2	57	23	34	45
2	Sandridge Rovers Res	18	13	2	3	53	15	38	41
3	Oxhey Jets Vets	17	13	0	4	41	28	13	39
4	Baldock Town FC Res	16	12	1	3	51	21	30	37
5	Harpenden Rovers	19	10	0	9	54	41	13	30
6	Stevenage Borough Community	20	9	3	8	47	42	5	30
7	Hinton Res	19	10	0	9	43	55	-12	30
8	Hatfield Athletic	18	8	2	8	50	36	14	26
9	Sarratt Res	17	7	2	8	39	34	5	23
10	Stanmore Jafferys	18	7	1	10	33	49	-16	22
11	Buntingford Town Res	17	4	3	10	27	53	-26	15
12	Evergreen FC Res	17	4	1	12	31	46	-15	13
13	Knebworth Res	21	3	1	17	27	67	-40	10
14	Lemsford Res	16	2	1	13	17	60	-43	7
15	Oxhey Res	0	0	0	0	0	0	0	0

HUMBER PREMIER LEAGUE

		P	W	D	L	F	A	GD	Pts
1	South Cave United	24	18	4	2	57	20	37	58
2	Chalk Lane	24	18	1	5	72	22	50	55
3	Westella & Willerby AFC	24	17	3	4	57	39	18	54
4	Beverley Town	26	15	3	8	63	28	35	48
5	Pocklington Town	25	14	3	8	54	39	15	45
6	Walkington AFC	22	13	6	4	49	30	19	42
7	Hessle Rangers	21	10	3	8	49	46	3	33
8	Hull United	23	9	4	10	41	55	-14	31
9	LIV Supplies	21	8	5	8	53	50	3	29
10	Hedon Rangers	28	8	3	17	46	75	-29	27
11	Sculcoates Amateurs	21	7	5	9	33	33	0	26
12	Driffield Junior	22	7	3	12	31	53	-22	24
13	Hornsea Town	20	6	1	13	42	50	-8	19
14	Reckitts AFC	25	4	5	16	27	49	-22	17
15	Barton Town Res	22	4	2	16	24	55	-31	14
16	North Ferriby Res	26	3	4	19	29	83	-54	13

DIVISION ONE

		P	W	D	L	F	A	GD	Pts
1	Hessle Sporting Club	21	11	4	6	55	51	4	37
2	East Riding Rangers	19	10	6	3	39	24	15	36
3	Reckitts AFC Res	18	11	2	5	57	42	15	35
4	Kingfields FC	19	10	3	6	56	40	16	33
5	Brandesburton AFC	16	8	3	5	40	26	14	27
6	Driffield Evening Institute	17	8	3	6	43	34	9	27
7	Easington United	16	6	5	5	37	30	7	23
8	Bridlington Town Res	19	6	4	9	41	39	2	22
9	St Marys AFC	18	5	7	6	43	52	-9	22
10	Goole United AFC	16	6	3	7	29	38	-9	21
11	Blackburn Athletic	18	5	2	11	25	39	-14	17
12	Beverley Town Res	19	4	4	11	30	43	-13	16
13	Howden AFC HPL	16	2	2	12	23	60	-37	8

KENT COUNTY LEAGUE

PREMIER DIVISION

		P	W	D	L	F	A	GD	Pts
1	Staplehurst Monarchs United	20	18	1	1	72	14	58	52*
2	Kings Hill	19	15	0	4	55	18	37	45
3	Faversham Strike Force	22	13	4	5	54	35	19	43
4	Ide Hill	23	10	4	9	54	48	6	34
5	Farnborough O B Guild	21	10	3	8	53	42	11	33
6	Fleetdown United	22	10	3	9	44	34	10	33
7	Bromleians	18	10	3	5	41	34	7	33
8	Tudor Sports	17	9	3	5	34	24	10	27*
9	Hawkinge Town	20	7	3	10	36	75	-39	23*
10	K Sports Res	23	6	4	13	31	50	-19	22
11	Borden Village	17	5	5	7	32	34	-2	20
12	Stansfeld (O&B)	23	5	4	14	38	59	-21	19
13	Crockenhill	20	6	0	14	22	56	-34	18
14	Otford United	18	4	4	10	32	55	-23	16
15	New Romney	20	4	3	13	28	39	-11	15
16	Peckham Town	13	3	2	8	20	29	-9	11

DIVISION ONE CENTRAL & EAST

		P	W	D	L	F	A	GD	Pts
1	Thanet United	12	9	2	1	47	12	35	29
2	Lordswood Res	11	8	0	3	35	14	21	24
3	Hollands & Blair Res	12	7	2	3	26	20	6	23
4	Cuxton 1991	12	6	4	2	34	18	16	22
5	Rusthall Res	12	5	1	6	21	28	-7	16
6	Ashford FC	8	4	1	3	17	25	-8	13
7	Rochester City	12	3	3	6	26	32	-6	12
8	Guru Nanak	14	3	2	9	24	35	-11	10*
9	Snodland Town Res	12	2	4	6	16	34	-18	10
10	Lydd Town Res	13	2	1	10	26	54	-28	7

DIVISION ONE WEST

		P	W	D	L	F	A	GD	Pts
1	Red Velvet	17	10	6	1	57	28	29	36
2	Welling Park	18	11	3	4	37	22	15	36
3	Chipstead	14	10	3	1	53	18	35	33
4	Halls AFC	18	10	1	7	46	36	10	31
5	HFSP & Ten-Em-Bee	13	8	4	1	35	14	21	28
6	Bexley	16	8	4	4	43	23	20	28
7	Metrogas	16	8	3	5	39	31	8	27
8	Belvedere	17	6	4	7	39	42	-3	22
9	Sydenham Sports	13	4	3	6	27	36	-9	15
10	Club Langley	16	4	2	10	20	36	-16	14
11	South East Athletic	19	4	2	13	26	52	-26	14
12	Sutton Athletic Res	19	4	1	14	33	67	-34	13
13	AFC Mottingham	16	1	0	15	16	66	-50	3

DIVISION TWO CENTRAL & EAST

		P	W	D	L	F	A	GD	Pts
1	Tenterden Town	15	12	1	2	56	21	35	37
2	Deal Town Rangers	18	9	4	5	46	27	19	31
3	Sturry	10	7	2	1	41	11	30	23
4	Whitstable Town Res	14	7	2	5	39	27	12	20*
5	Larkfield And New Hythe Wanderers	14	6	0	8	39	47	-8	18
6	West Farleigh	15	5	2	8	37	34	3	17
7	Bearsted Res	13	5	2	6	26	24	2	17
8	Cuxton 1991 Res	11	4	1	6	27	33	-6	13
9	Southborough	13	3	3	7	22	34	-12	11*
10	Rochester City Res	17	3	1	13	30	105	-75	10

DIVISION TWO WEST

		P	W	D	L	F	A	GD	Pts
1	Sporting Club Thamesmead Res	22	13	6	3	79	42	37	45
2	Danson Sports	15	9	1	5	31	23	8	27*
3	Crayford Arrows	17	7	3	7	37	43	-6	27*
4	Drummond Athletic	16	8	2	6	32	32	0	26
5	Parkwood Rangers	16	7	3	6	38	24	14	24
6	Equinoccial	14	7	3	4	37	25	12	24
7	Stansfeld (O&B) Res	13	6	2	5	28	24	4	20
8	Tudor Sports Res	7	5	2	0	30	10	20	17
9	Long Lane	13	5	2	6	34	27	7	17
10	Orpington	18	4	3	11	33	55	-22	15
11	Dulwich Village	13	3	4	6	24	37	-13	13
12	Fleetdown United Res	17	3	2	12	28	59	-31	11
13	Johnson & Phillip	15	3	3	9	22	52	-30	8*

DIVISION THREE CENTRAL & EAST

		P	W	D	L	F	A	GD	Pts
1	Minster FC	14	14	0	0	81	7	74	42
2	Woodnesborough	16	11	2	3	40	23	17	35
3	Cinque Ports	14	10	1	3	47	19	28	31
4	Staplehurst Monarchs United Res	11	6	1	4	22	20	2	19
5	Canterbury City University	15	5	4	6	41	45	-4	19
6	New Romney Res	16	5	1	10	26	45	-19	16
7	Tankerton	17	4	3	10	21	46	-25	15
8	Lokomotiv Canterbury	12	4	1	7	16	35	-19	13
9	Gillingham Town	13	4	0	9	29	47	-18	12
10	Paddock Wood	16	1	3	12	32	68	-36	6

DIVISION THREE WEST

		P	W	D	L	F	A	GD	Pts
1	Meridian Sports FC	17	16	0	1	77	20	57	48
2	Farnborough OB Guild Res	15	12	2	1	56	18	38	38
3	Halstead United	11	11	0	0	48	5	43	33
4	Bridon Ropes Res	19	10	2	7	65	33	32	32
5	Long Lane Res	15	9	2	4	48	24	24	29
6	Bromleians Res	15	7	1	7	29	29	0	22
7	Greenways Aces	13	7	0	6	31	30	1	21
8	Metrogas Res	14	6	1	7	30	28	2	19
9	AFC Lewisham	16	6	0	10	23	54	-31	17*
10	Welling Town Res	19	5	1	13	32	52	-20	16
11	Bexley Res	15	3	4	8	23	50	-27	13
12	South East Athletic Res	18	3	1	14	29	71	-42	10
13	Danson Sports Res	21	1	2	18	24	101	-77	4*

LEICESTERSHIRE SENIOR LEAGUE

PREMIER DIVISION

		P	W	D	L	F	A	GD	Pts
1	Allexton & New Parks	22	19	3	0	106	31	75	60
2	Cottesmore AFC	20	16	1	3	63	31	32	49
3	Friar Lane & Epworth	22	11	5	6	56	41	15	38
4	Rugby Borough	19	11	3	5	62	36	26	36
5	Sileby Town	20	10	4	6	44	27	17	34
6	Blaby & Whetstone	21	10	2	9	55	45	10	32
7	Hathern	17	10	1	6	54	35	19	31
8	Asfordby	18	8	4	6	47	50	-3	28
9	Barlestone St Giles	18	8	2	8	34	35	-1	26
10	County Hall	21	8	1	12	44	56	-12	25
11	FC GNG	24	10	2	12	51	70	-19	23*
12	Thurnby Rangers	19	4	5	10	32	56	-24	17
13	FC Khalsa GAD	20	6	1	13	46	68	-22	16*
14	Ellistown	17	4	3	10	19	41	-22	15
15	Ashby Ivanhoe Knights	18	2	2	14	22	62	-40	8
16	Desford	19	3	1	18	17	68	-51	6

STEP 7 TABLES 2019/20

DIVISION ONE

		P	W	D	L	F	A	GD	Pts
1	Fleckney Athletic	19	13	4	2	66	26	40	43
2	Highfield Rangers	24	12	4	8	44	32	12	40
3	Anstey Nomads Swifts	22	13	0	9	65	49	16	39
4	Barrow Town Res	17	13	2	2	42	17	25	38
5	Birstall United Res	22	11	4	7	44	32	12	37
6	Magna 73	19	11	2	6	64	37	27	35
7	Holwell Sports Res	23	10	0	13	37	64	-27	30
8	Greenhill Y C	19	10	2	7	53	44	9	29
9	Earl Shilton Albion	19	9	2	8	42	40	2	29
10	Saffron Dynamo Res	16	8	3	5	40	24	16	27
11	Anstey Town	18	6	5	7	49	37	12	23
12	Kirby Muxloe Res	18	6	2	10	35	41	-6	20
13	Lutterworth Town Res	20	6	1	13	25	56	-31	19
14	Friar Lane & Epworth Res	18	3	3	12	21	54	-33	12
15	Ingles Res	15	4	2	9	28	43	-15	11
16	Loughborough	19	0	2	17	13	72	-59	2

DIVISION TWO

		P	W	D	L	F	A	GD	Pts
1	Northfield Emerald	17	16	1	0	102	14	88	46
2	Sileby Athletic	19	12	2	5	63	37	26	38
3	Sileby Town Res	19	11	2	6	40	31	9	35
4	Dunton & Broughton United	17	11	1	5	42	30	12	34
5	Blaby & Whetstone Res	17	10	3	4	56	20	36	33
6	St Andrews Res	20	12	2	6	62	51	11	32
7	Sporting Markfield	18	10	0	8	50	34	16	30
8	Rothley Imperial	20	8	3	9	46	38	8	27
9	Kibworth Town	16	8	3	5	39	31	8	27
10	Bottesford	19	8	3	8	39	34	5	27
11	Newbold Verdon	21	5	7	9	34	52	-18	22
12	Sutton Bonington	19	5	2	12	52	58	-6	17
13	Thurnby Rangers Dev	18	4	2	12	34	100	-66	14
14	Rugby Borough Res	20	4	3	13	38	69	-31	12
15	Cottesmore Dev	17	3	0	14	20	59	-39	9
16	Desford Dev	17	3	0	14	17	76	-59	3

LINCOLNSHIRE LEAGUE

		P	W	D	L	F	A	GD	Pts
1	Hykeham Town	20	15	5	0	60	21	39	50
2	Lincoln Moorlands Railway	17	14	0	3	63	20	43	42
3	Gainsborough Trinity Res	18	13	2	3	46	16	30	41
4	Louth Town	20	12	2	8	37	43	-6	32
5	Horncastle Town	18	9	4	5	40	28	12	31
6	Cleethorpes Town Res	15	8	0	7	42	33	9	24
7	Grimsby Borough Res	20	7	3	10	41	40	1	24
8	Immingham Town	17	6	4	7	43	41	2	22
9	Wyberton	15	6	4	5	21	19	2	22
10	Brigg Town CIC Res	20	5	2	13	35	57	-22	17
11	Sleaford Town Rangers	19	4	1	14	12	59	-47	13
12	Nettleham	16	3	2	11	27	39	-12	11
13	Lincoln United Dev	21	3	1	17	29	80	-51	10

LIVERPOOL PREMIER LEAGUE

		P	W	D	L	F	A	GD	Pts
1	MSB Woolton	21	19	1	1	88	26	62	60*
2	East Villa	18	15	0	3	77	28	49	45
3	BRNESC	18	15	0	3	76	32	44	45
4	Liverpool NALGO	16	13	1	2	67	24	43	40
5	Liver Academy	21	13	1	7	59	46	13	40
6	Waterloo Dock	18	11	2	5	63	48	15	35
7	Alder	20	8	2	10	54	57	-3	26
8	Sefton Athletic	19	8	2	9	48	58	-10	25*
9	Page Celtic	16	7	2	7	47	37	10	23
10	Lower Breck Res	21	6	3	12	47	56	-9	21
11	Bankfield Old Boys	20	5	5	10	36	63	-27	20
12	FC Pilchy	19	5	4	10	37	48	-11	19
13	Old Xaverians	17	4	5	8	22	33	-11	17
14	AFC Liverpool Res	21	3	1	17	41	89	-48	10
15	Alumni	23	3	1	19	32	110	-78	10
16	Waterloo Grammar School OB	20	3	2	15	40	79	-39	8*

DIVISION ONE

		P	W	D	L	F	A	GD	Pts
1	The Empress	19	15	3	1	90	35	55	48
2	Quarry Bank Old Boys	16	14	2	0	80	16	64	44
3	The Lute	16	13	2	1	64	21	43	41
4	Red Rum	18	11	0	7	41	35	6	33
5	Kirkby Town	20	10	1	9	80	54	26	31
6	FC Bernie Mays	16	10	1	5	59	39	20	31
7	BRNESC Res	16	9	0	7	37	56	-19	27
8	Stoneycroft	17	8	2	7	56	42	14	26
9	Marshalls Roby	16	6	4	6	53	34	19	22
10	AFC Kirkby	16	6	3	7	45	60	-15	21
11	Old Xaverians Res	18	4	3	11	28	67	-39	17*
12	Botanic	20	5	1	14	35	82	-47	16
13	Edge Hill Boys Club OB	17	3	2	12	23	50	-27	10*
14	ROMA	19	1	2	16	25	74	-49	8*
15	Liverpool Hibernia	16	2	0	14	22	73	-51	3*

MANCHESTER LEAGUE

PREMIER DIVISION

		P	W	D	L	F	A	GD	Pts
1	Dukinfield Town	23	16	2	5	58	25	33	50
2	Hindsford	24	13	6	5	63	38	25	45
3	Rochdale Sacred Heart	23	14	3	6	48	30	18	45
4	Bolton County	20	13	1	6	48	30	18	40
5	Springhead	21	11	7	3	49	35	14	40
6	Stockport Georgians	21	11	4	6	50	37	13	37
7	Heywood St James	20	11	0	9	51	54	-3	33
8	Pennington	20	9	4	7	48	40	8	31
9	Heyside	19	8	4	7	44	33	11	28
10	Chadderton Res	22	6	3	13	42	59	-17	21
11	Beechfield United	25	5	5	15	43	83	-40	19*
12	Walshaw Sports	19	5	3	11	31	48	-17	18
13	Royton Town	25	5	3	17	45	73	-28	18
14	Manchester Gregorians	23	3	7	13	38	54	-16	16
15	Old Altrinchamians	19	4	4	11	24	43	-19	16

DIVISION ONE

		P	W	D	L	F	A	GD	PTS
1	Elton Vale	17	14	0	3	64	22	42	42
2	Tintwistle Athletic	18	12	3	3	59	23	36	39
3	Atherton Town	18	13	0	5	43	22	21	39
4	Boothstown	17	12	1	4	65	30	35	37
5	Middleton Colts	20	11	1	8	59	41	18	34
6	Govan Athletic	19	10	1	8	33	31	2	31
7	Bolton Lads & Girls Club	22	8	3	11	45	53	-8	27
8	East Manchester	22	7	6	9	37	50	-13	27
9	Moorside Rangers	18	7	3	8	34	34	0	24
10	Wilmslow Albion	20	6	4	10	38	52	-14	22
11	Altrincham Hale	21	6	2	13	42	56	-14	20
12	Uppermill	16	5	1	10	29	46	-17	15
13	Leigh Athletic	22	1	1	20	24	112	-88	4

Radcliffe Juniors withdrew before the start of the season.

DIVISION TWO

		P	W	D	L	F	A	GD	PTS
1	Bolton United	19	13	0	6	57	30	27	39
2	AFC Monton	16	12	2	2	59	16	43	38
3	Rochdale Sacred Heart Res	17	12	2	3	70	31	39	38
4	Avro Res	16	12	1	3	54	19	35	37
5	Wythenshawe Amateurs Res	14	7	4	3	38	22	16	25
6	Hindsford Res	17	7	1	9	45	47	-2	22
7	FC Unsworth	12	5	2	5	40	32	8	17
8	Hindley Juniors	12	3	2	7	23	45	-22	11
9	Hollinwood	16	3	1	12	22	80	-58	10
10	Breightmet United	14	1	2	11	18	66	-48	5
11	Astley & Tyldesley	17	1	1	15	21	59	-38	4

Irlam Steel withdrew after ten games.

MID SUSSEX LEAGUE

PREMIER DIVISION

		P	W	D	L	F	A	GD	Pts
1	Charlwood	15	11	1	3	45	21	24	34
2	Lindfield	17	9	2	6	48	29	19	29
3	Balcombe	16	9	0	7	47	34	13	27
4	AFC Ringmer	16	8	3	5	25	24	1	27
5	Forest Row	12	8	1	3	32	19	13	25
6	Cuckfield Rangers	14	7	4	3	33	23	10	25
7	Westfield	15	7	2	6	28	40	-12	23
8	Hollington United	14	6	3	5	25	27	-2	21
9	Rotherfield	15	5	3	7	27	38	-11	18
10	Sporting Lindfield	15	5	2	8	22	33	-11	17
11	Eastbourne Rangers	17	5	1	11	31	46	-15	16
12	Willingdon Athletic	12	3	2	7	23	32	-9	8*
13	AFC Uckfield Town Res	16	1	2	13	32	52	-20	5

Burgess Hill Albion withdrew.

CHAMPIONSHIP

		P	W	D	L	F	A	GD	Pts
1	Sidley United	15	13	1	1	66	13	53	40
2	Ashurst Wood	21	13	1	7	64	49	15	40
3	Crawley Devils	18	11	3	4	49	27	22	36
4	Peacehaven & Telscombe Res	17	10	3	4	54	31	23	33
5	Ridgewood	18	9	2	7	34	30	4	29
6	West Hoathly	16	7	5	4	28	25	3	26
7	Mile Oak Res	16	7	2	7	30	42	-12	23
8	Roffey Res	12	6	0	6	25	27	-2	18
9	Hurstpierpoint	12	4	2	6	25	27	-2	14
10	Sovereign Saints	14	4	0	10	22	36	-14	12
11	Copthorne Res	15	2	4	9	21	47	-26	10
12	Polegate Town	13	2	1	10	12	38	-26	7
13	Nutley	15	0	2	13	12	50	-38	2

DIVISION ONE

		P	W	D	L	F	A	GD	Pts
1	Holland Sports	12	9	1	2	54	24	30	28
2	AFC Varndeanians Res	13	6	3	4	28	25	3	21
3	AFC Acorns	9	5	2	2	19	7	12	17
4	Buxted	9	4	4	1	23	12	11	16
5	Balcombe Res	13	4	4	5	28	32	-4	16
6	Lindfield Res	10	4	2	4	30	36	-6	14
7	Montpelier Villa AFC Res	12	5	0	7	27	40	-13	12*
8	Ardingly	11	2	2	7	17	32	-15	8
9	Ansty Sports & Social Club	7	0	0	7	9	27	-18	0

DIVISION TWO NORTH

		P	W	D	L	F	A	GD	Pts
1	Godstone	11	8	1	2	41	22	19	25
2	Burgess Hill Rhinos	14	7	4	3	33	24	9	25
3	Galaxy	11	7	0	4	30	24	6	21
4	South Park FC A	11	3	2	6	23	30	-7	11
5	Royal Earlswood	10	3	2	5	25	34	-9	11
6	Stones	12	2	3	7	22	30	-8	9
7	Crawley & Maidenbower	9	2	2	5	27	37	-10	8

DIVISION TWO SOUTH

		P	W	D	L	F	A	GD	Pts
1	Eastbourne Rangers Res	17	9	3	5	35	39	-4	30
2	Cuckfield Town	13	7	4	2	25	16	9	25
3	Ditchling	13	7	3	3	37	19	18	24
4	Willingdon Athletic Res	13	7	2	4	36	26	10	23
5	AFC Hurst	14	7	2	5	31	33	-2	23
6	Fletching	12	6	1	5	39	27	12	19
7	Cuckfield Rangers Res	12	5	2	5	27	21	6	17
8	AFC Varndeanians 3rds	16	4	3	9	31	47	-16	15
9	Portslade Athletic	17	3	5	9	27	37	-10	14
10	Bolney Rovers	9	3	2	4	23	29	-6	10*
11	Plumpton Athletic	12	2	1	9	21	38	-17	7

DIVISION THREE NORTH

		P	W	D	L	F	A	GD	Pts
1	DCK Maidenbower	14	12	1	1	50	18	32	38
2	Crawley Devils Res	16	7	6	3	44	42	2	27
3	East Grinstead Town 3rds	12	7	2	3	39	24	15	23
4	Crawley United	11	5	0	6	26	24	2	15
5	Horley A.F.C	11	4	2	5	31	40	-9	14
6	Ashurst Wood II	13	4	2	7	24	36	-12	14
7	Forest Row II	12	3	2	7	20	25	-5	11
8	Rotherfield II	13	1	0	12	17	42	-25	3

Dormansland Rockets withdrew.

DIVISION THREE SOUTH

		P	W	D	L	F	A	GD	Pts
1	Burgess Hill Albion Res	13	12	1	0	37	9	28	37
2	FC Sporting	16	10	3	3	44	27	17	33
3	Ridgewood Res	15	9	0	6	47	29	18	27
4	AFC Ringmer Res	13	8	2	3	39	16	23	26
5	Polegate Town Res	11	5	2	4	24	18	6	17
6	Wivelsfield Green	13	5	1	7	37	46	-9	16
7	Peacehaven & Telscombe 3rds	14	2	1	11	17	52	-35	7
8	Horsted Keynes	12	1	3	8	10	38	-28	6
9	Wisdom Sports	13	1	1	11	11	31	-20	4

AFC Uckfield Town 3rds withdrew.

DIVISION FOUR NORTH

		P	W	D	L	F	A	GD	Pts
1	Ifield Sports	13	13	0	0	58	19	39	36*
2	Ifield	13	6	3	4	35	28	7	21
3	Balcombe 3rds	11	5	3	3	30	20	10	18
4	AFC Acorns Res	10	5	2	3	31	24	7	17
5	Ifield Albion	9	5	0	4	21	26	-5	15
6	Handcross Village	10	5	0	5	16	26	-10	15
7	Cuckfield Town Res	11	2	3	6	19	28	-9	9
8	Lindfield III	9	2	2	5	20	30	-10	8
9	Scaynes Hill	11	2	1	8	23	38	-15	7
10	Copthorne A	11	2	0	9	19	33	-14	6

DIVISION FOUR SOUTH

		P	W	D	L	F	A	GD	PTS
1	Barcombe	12	11	0	1	48	19	29	33
2	Newick	8	8	0	0	29	8	21	24
3	Eastbourne Athletic	11	5	1	5	28	23	5	16
4	Maresfield Village	13	5	1	7	31	49	-18	16
5	Hurstpierpoint Res	11	4	1	6	30	28	2	13
6	Buxted Res	8	4	1	3	17	21	-4	13
7	Ditchling Res	11	3	2	6	23	33	-10	11
8	Willingdon Athletic 3rds	10	3	0	7	15	21	-6	9
9	AFC Uckfield Town 4ths	8	2	1	5	11	19	-8	7
10	Ansty Sports & Social Club Res	8	1	1	6	7	18	-11	4

DIVISION FIVE NORTH

		P	W	D	L	F	A	GD	Pts
1	Fairfield	15	9	1	5	37	26	11	28
2	Galaxy Res	16	8	3	5	54	37	17	27
3	Horley A.F.C. Res	13	7	3	3	38	31	7	24
4	Hartfield	12	7	2	3	29	23	6	23
5	Old Oxted Town	12	5	3	4	32	23	9	18
6	Ashurst Wood 3rds	14	5	3	6	31	26	5	18
7	East Grinstead Town 4ths	10	5	1	4	29	21	8	16
8	Crawley United Res	9	5	0	4	26	28	-2	15
9	Stones Res	13	5	1	9	26	46	-20	10
10	East Grinstead Meads	12	3	1	8	30	57	-27	10
11	Holland Sports Res	10	2	0	8	27	41	-14	6

DIVISION FIVE SOUTH

		P	W	D	L	F	A	GD	Pts
1	Keymer & Hassocks	11	10	1	0	47	12	35	31
2	AFC Ringmer 3rds	15	8	2	5	34	31	3	26
3	Cuckfield Rangers Dev	9	8	0	1	53	8	45	24
4	Portslade Athletic Res	16	7	1	8	35	46	-11	22
5	Scaynes Hill Res	12	7	0	5	26	25	1	21
6	West Hoathly Res	9	6	1	2	44	16	28	19
7	Fletching Res	10	4	1	5	17	29	-12	13
8	Ardingly Res	12	3	1	8	18	34	-16	10
9	Willingdon Athletic 4ths	14	3	1	10	20	58	-38	10
10	Fairfield Res	11	2	1	8	19	36	-17	7
11	Lindfield 4ths	11	2	1	8	19	37	-18	7

MIDDLESEX COUNTY LEAGUE

PREMIER DIVISION

		P	W	D	L	F	A	GD	Pts
1	Brentham FC	18	11	4	3	47	34	13	37
2	Cricklewood Wanderers	21	10	2	9	38	34	4	32
3	Hilltop FC	15	9	4	2	44	28	14	31
4	Larkspur Rovers	14	9	1	4	42	26	17	28
5	Clapton CFC	16	8	4	4	39	29	10	28
6	London Samurai	15	7	6	2	37	27	10	27
7	Pitshanger Dynamo	19	7	5	7	34	34	0	25
8	NW London	14	7	2	5	36	26	10	23
9	Hillingdon FC	13	6	1	6	33	38	-5	19
10	Stonewall	19	5	4	10	27	47	-20	19
11	Indian Gymkhana Club	17	5	3	9	43	48	-5	18
12	Sporting Hackney	17	5	2	10	28	39	-11	17
13	PFC Victoria London	14	3	5	6	27	31	-4	16
14	Kensington Dragons	14	5	1	8	20	30	-10	16
15	C.B. Hounslow United Res	15	1	1	13	19	44	-25	4

Lampton Park withdrew after 11 games.
Yeading Town withdrew after 4 games.

STEP 7 TABLES 2019/20

DIVISION ONE CENTRAL & EAST	P	W	D	L	F	A	GD	Pts
1 Jolof Sports Club	13	10	3	0	32	9	23	33
2 The Wilberforce Wanderers	11	7	3	1	28	15	13	24
3 Camden & Islington	14	7	2	5	34	18	16	23
4 FC Roast	12	6	0	6	26	27	-1	18
5 Priory Park Rangers	12	5	2	5	23	18	5	17
6 FC Soma	11	3	3	5	18	23	-5	12
7 Leatherhead Academy	13	3	1	9	23	42	-19	10
8 Eastfield	12	1	0	11	14	46	-32	3

The Curve withdrew after two games.
London City withdrew after nine games.

DIVISION ONE WEST	P	W	D	L	F	A	GD	Pts
1 AVA	13	12	0	1	52	11	41	36
2 Harrow Bhoys	13	9	2	2	31	21	10	29
3 Hampton Town	13	7	0	6	37	27	10	21
4 FC Deportivo Galicia Res	13	7	0	6	37	30	7	21
5 Pitshanger Dynamo Res	12	6	3	3	24	22	2	21
6 Newmont	16	5	1	10	32	41	-9	16
7 Kodak Harrow	10	5	0	5	26	20	6	15
8 London Rangers	12	4	2	6	23	34	-11	14
9 AFC Hanwell & Hayes	9	4	0	5	22	29	-7	12
10 South Kilburn	14	3	2	9	20	56	-36	11
11 Hammersmith	11	1	0	10	7	20	-13	3

NORTH RIDING LEAGUE

PREMIER DIVISION	P	W	D	L	F	A	GD	Pts
1 Boro Rangers	22	20	2	0	104	19	85	62
2 Yarm & Eaglescliffe	24	18	2	4	90	39	51	56
3 Stockton West End	25	18	2	5	90	46	44	56
4 Grangetown Boys Club	26	13	2	11	59	68	-9	41
5 Staithes Athletic	21	12	2	7	69	47	22	38
6 Thornaby Dubliners	23	12	2	9	64	46	18	38
7 Bedale	19	9	4	6	65	46	19	31
8 Redcar Town	23	8	6	9	34	32	2	30
9 Redcar Newmarket	21	8	3	10	43	52	-9	27
10 BEADS	21	7	5	9	67	54	13	26
11 Fishburn Park	23	7	5	11	40	42	-2	26
12 Thirsk Falcons	24	6	1	17	39	100	-61	19
13 St. Mary's 1947	21	4	5	12	39	72	-33	17
14 Stokesley Sports Club	22	4	2	16	36	92	-56	14
15 Kader	23	1	1	21	29	113	-84	4

DIVISION ONE	P	W	D	L	F	A	GD	Pts
1 Redcar Athletic Res	13	11	1	1	58	13	45	34
2 Boro Rangers Res	14	11	1	2	57	20	37	34
3 Loftus Athletic	15	8	1	6	41	38	3	25
4 Great Ayton United	12	6	2	4	37	30	7	20
5 Whitby Fishermens Society	10	5	1	4	49	28	21	16
6 New Marske	13	5	0	8	36	30	6	15
7 Lealholm	13	4	3	6	36	32	4	15
8 Stokesley SC AFC	13	3	3	7	33	33	0	12
9 Middlesbrough Rovers	15	0	0	15	12	135	-123	0

NORTHANTS COMBINATION

PREMIER DIVISION	P	W	D	L	F	A	GD	Pts
1 Kettering Nomads	17	14	2	1	56	6	43	44
2 Roade	17	14	1	2	65	13	40	43
3 Woodford United	19	11	3	5	54	9	32	36
4 Harpole	16	8	4	4	35	10	14	28
5 Moulton	18	9	1	8	55	22	11	28
6 Wollaston Victoria	15	9	0	6	47	13	16	27
7 Earls Barton United	17	7	6	4	44	20	14	27
8 Corby Stewarts & Lloyds	14	9	0	5	29	20	8	27
9 Thrapston Town	16	8	1	7	38	16	3	25
10 James King Blisworth	17	6	4	7	36	24	-7	22
11 Corby Pegasus	17	5	1	11	26	35	-31	16
12 FC Aztec	19	4	1	14	36	33	-40	13
13 Weldon United	15	3	3	9	27	20	-12	12
14 Spratton	17	3	1	13	22	36	-36	10
15 Heyford Athletic	18	1	2	15	21	42	-55	5

DIVISION ONE	P	W	D	L	F	A	GD	Pts
1 West Haddon Albion	17	11	1	5	40	43	-3	34
2 Duston Dynamo	13	10	1	2	55	26	29	31
3 AFC Houghton Magna	12	9	2	1	32	19	13	29
4 Moulton Spartak	14	7	3	4	34	23	11	24
5 Roade Res	13	7	2	4	46	28	18	23
6 Finedon Volta	16	6	3	7	45	31	14	21
7 Corby White Hart Loco's	12	6	3	3	30	22	8	21
8 Corby Strip Mills	18	7	0	11	36	59	-23	21
9 Bugbrooke St Michaels 'A'	10	5	1	4	19	17	2	16
10 Milton	15	4	1	10	21	37	-16	13
11 Higham Town	12	3	1	8	22	38	-16	10
12 Woodford Wolves	13	3	1	10	18	38	-20	10
13 Wollaston Victoria Res	14	2	1	11	32	49	-17	7

NORTHERN ALLIANCE

PREMIER DIVISION	P	W	D	L	F	A	GD	Pts
1 Newcastle Blue Star FC	15	12	2	1	52	20	32	38
2 AFC New Fordley	16	11	4	1	47	16	31	37
3 Blyth Town	15	11	3	1	47	14	33	36
4 Ponteland United	20	11	2	7	48	31	17	35
5 AFC Killingworth	13	11	1	1	56	19	37	34
6 Cullercoats	17	10	1	6	40	28	12	31
7 Winlaton Vulcans	19	9	3	7	56	32	24	30
8 Newcastle Chemfica	20	8	4	8	44	40	4	28
9 Percy Main Amateurs	20	8	3	9	42	42	0	27
10 Wallington	16	6	4	6	24	26	-2	22
11 Gateshead Rutherford AFC	20	5	3	12	38	49	-11	18
12 Alnwick Town	17	5	2	10	25	43	-18	17
13 Whitley Bay Res	19	5	1	13	39	63	-24	16
14 North Shields Athletic	20	3	6	11	30	48	-18	15
15 Shankhouse	17	4	2	11	30	58	-28	14
16 Seaton Delaval AFC	20	2	1	17	19	108	-89	7

DIVISION ONE	P	W	D	L	F	A	GD	Pts
1 Hebburn Town U23	19	13	2	4	58	24	34	41
2 Prudhoe Youth Club Seniors	17	12	3	2	58	24	34	39
3 Red Row Welfare	16	11	2	3	54	25	29	35
4 Whitburn & Cleadon	18	11	2	5	43	29	14	35
5 Wallsend Boys Club	21	8	4	9	46	51	-5	28
6 Blyth Spartans Res	16	8	2	6	50	25	25	26
7 Gosforth Bohemian	18	7	5	6	37	39	-2	26
8 Cramlington United	15	7	3	5	36	27	9	24
9 Whitley Bay Sporting Club	16	7	3	6	50	44	6	24
10 Bedlington	18	6	6	6	43	44	-1	24
11 Hexham	14	7	2	5	29	28	1	23
12 Rothbury	19	5	3	11	29	51	-22	18
13 Forest Hall	18	4	4	10	27	39	-12	16
14 FC United of Newcastle	19	5	1	13	37	65	-28	16
15 Seaton Burn	17	4	3	10	30	49	-19	15
16 Felling Magpies	19	2	1	16	22	85	-63	7

DIVISION TWO	P	W	D	L	F	A	GD	Pts
1 Haltwhistle Jubilee	15	13	0	2	54	17	37	39
2 Newcastle East End	19	12	1	6	50	31	19	37
3 Willington Quay Saints	19	11	3	5	55	34	21	36
4 AFC Newbiggin	17	11	2	4	45	26	19	35
5 Cramlington Town	18	10	2	6	52	36	16	32
6 Newcastle University Res	19	10	2	7	49	41	8	32
7 Jesmond	19	10	4	5	45	28	17	31*
8 Ellington	23	8	7	8	44	56	-12	31
9 Seaton Sluice	18	8	3	7	35	41	-6	27
10 Blyth	15	8	2	5	38	26	12	26
11 Spittal Rovers	18	5	5	8	41	41	0	20
12 Gateshead Redheugh 1957	17	5	3	9	34	42	-8	18
13 Wideopen & District	19	3	3	13	28	70	-42	12
14 Burradon	18	3	5	10	29	46	-17	11*
15 Stobswood Welfare	18	2	4	12	22	52	-30	10
16 Newcastle Blue Star Res	18	2	2	14	25	59	-34	8

NOTTINGHAMSHIRE SENIOR LEAGUE

PREMIER DIVISION

		P	W	D	L	F	A	GD	Pts
1	Bingham Town	23	17	4	2	75	29	46	55
2	Southwell City	26	15	7	4	79	36	43	52
3	Woodthorpe Park Rangers	23	16	3	4	77	32	45	51
4	Burton Joyce	22	16	3	3	54	23	31	51
5	AFC Dunkirk	25	15	5	5	76	40	36	50
6	Wollaton	25	15	5	5	57	21	36	50
7	Keyworth United	23	14	4	5	71	40	31	46
8	Cotgrave	22	11	3	8	51	38	13	36
9	Calverton Miners Welfare	24	9	3	12	48	53	-5	30
10	Stapleford Town	20	8	5	7	49	35	14	29
11	Awsworth Villa	20	6	5	9	44	48	-4	23
12	Attenborough	23	6	5	12	36	63	-27	23
13	Sandiacre Town	22	4	9	9	36	49	-13	21
14	Aslockton & Orston	20	5	4	11	28	55	-27	19
15	Magdala Amateurs	23	4	4	15	28	66	-38	16
16	FC Cavaliers	24	2	6	16	22	66	-44	12
17	Bilborough Town	24	3	3	18	23	77	-54	12
18	Eastwood CFC Dev	29	2	4	23	31	114	-83	10

DIVISION ONE

		P	W	D	L	F	A	GD	Pts
1	AFC Top Valley	20	18	2	0	78	19	59	56
2	Ruddington Village	16	12	3	1	41	16	25	39
3	West Bridgford AFC	18	12	0	6	57	38	19	36
4	Beeston	22	11	1	10	63	54	9	34
5	Radcliffe Olympic	18	10	2	6	55	47	8	32
6	Wollaton Res	23	9	5	9	45	55	-10	32
7	Gedling Southbank	18	8	3	7	43	43	0	27
8	Kirton Brickworks	23	7	4	12	45	57	-12	25
9	Ravenshead	16	7	1	8	32	33	-1	22
10	Bridgford United	19	7	0	12	49	59	-10	21
11	Radford Res	19	6	2	11	49	63	-14	20
12	Hucknall Town Dev	19	6	2	11	29	45	-16	20
13	Southwell City Res	17	5	3	9	27	46	-19	18
14	Kimberley Miners Welfare Res	19	4	2	13	34	54	-20	14
15	Robin Hood Colts	17	3	4	10	29	47	-18	13

DIVISION TWO

		P	W	D	L	F	A	GD	Pts
1	United Grays	23	17	3	3	81	22	59	54
2	Stapleford Town Res	21	16	1	4	75	34	41	49
3	Ruddington Village Res	20	15	2	3	54	33	21	47
4	Keyworth United Res	20	12	1	7	81	33	48	37
5	AFC Dunkirk Res	17	12	1	4	60	24	36	37
6	Cotgrave Res	23	10	2	11	57	70	-13	32
7	Pythian	19	8	4	7	51	47	4	28
8	Asha	15	8	3	4	40	24	16	27
9	Elston United	21	8	3	10	37	53	-16	27
10	Barrowby	18	8	2	8	48	35	13	26
11	Ravenshead Reds	19	7	2	10	41	64	-23	23
12	Beeston Old Boys Association	19	6	0	13	42	59	-17	18
13	Bingham Town Res	20	5	2	13	31	60	-29	17
14	Clifton All Whites Dev	19	4	2	13	37	76	-39	14
15	Burton Joyce Res	16	2	1	13	22	74	-52	7
16	Bilborough Town Community	18	0	3	15	22	71	-49	3

OXFORDSHIRE SENIOR LEAGUE

PREMIER DIVISION

		P	W	D	L	F	A	GD	Pts
1	Cropredy	15	12	1	2	43	19	24	37
2	Marston Saints	14	11	2	1	56	21	35	35
3	Kennington Athletic	17	10	5	2	40	26	14	35
4	Yarnton	16	8	1	7	34	33	1	25
5	Hanborough	15	7	3	5	27	21	6	24
6	Freeland	12	7	2	3	26	14	12	23
7	Garsington	16	6	4	6	27	40	-13	22
8	Horspath	14	7	0	7	29	36	-7	21
9	Bicester United	21	5	3	13	33	50	-17	18
10	Mansfield Road	13	5	2	6	23	32	-9	17
11	Chesterton	16	4	4	8	40	40	0	16
12	Launton Sports	18	4	3	11	30	41	-11	15
13	Charlton United	15	4	0	11	15	30	-15	12
14	Summertown Stars	18	2	6	10	27	47	-20	12

DIVISION ONE

		P	W	D	L	F	A	GD	Pts
1	Kirtlington FC	13	11	0	2	52	19	33	33
2	Middleton Cheney	13	9	1	3	36	21	15	28
3	Eynsham Association	14	8	1	5	26	17	9	25
4	Adderbury Park Res	13	7	3	3	28	22	6	24
5	Woodstock Town Dev	14	6	1	7	26	43	-17	19
6	Freeland Res	8	6	0	2	25	9	16	18
7	Kidlington FC "A"	15	4	4	7	29	32	-3	16
8	Chalgrove Cavaliers	12	3	2	7	16	20	-4	11
9	M.IN.I	12	2	0	10	29	44	-15	6
10	Kennington Athletic Res	14	2	0	12	11	51	-40	6

DIVISION TWO

		P	W	D	L	F	A	GD	Pts
1	Heyford Athletic Res	14	9	1	4	36	18	18	28
2	Yarnton Res	15	8	2	5	59	31	28	26
3	Mansfield Road Res	17	6	5	6	41	42	-1	23
4	Garsington Res	15	7	2	6	28	31	-3	23
5	Charlton United Res	16	5	6	5	18	20	-2	21
6	Chesterton Res	13	5	5	3	29	29	0	20
7	Launton Sports Res	15	6	1	8	25	35	-10	19
8	Marston Saints Res	15	5	3	7	19	29	-10	18
9	Horspath Res	15	3	6	6	20	25	-5	15
10	Chinnor Res	15	4	3	8	24	39	-15	15

PETERBOROUGH & DISTRICT LEAGUE

PREMIER DIVISION

		P	W	D	L	F	A	GD	Pts
1	Netherton United	16	13	1	2	75	21	54	40
2	Stamford Lions	17	13	1	3	64	18	46	40
3	Uppingham Town	21	13	0	8	42	43	-1	39
4	Peterborough North End Sports	16	11	3	2	58	20	38	36
5	Moulton Harrox	18	11	3	4	47	30	17	36
6	Thorney	15	10	3	2	43	21	22	33
7	Parson Drove	19	10	4	5	49	35	14	31*
8	Long Sutton Athletic	16	8	4	4	29	21	8	28
9	Holbeach United Res	20	8	2	10	51	46	5	26
10	ICA Sports	16	6	1	9	30	51	-21	19
11	Oakham United	21	4	3	14	30	57	-27	18*
12	Leverington Sports	22	5	3	14	35	63	-28	18
13	Peterborough Polonia	22	3	5	14	34	75	-41	14
14	Ketton	19	3	4	12	19	45	-26	13
15	Tydd	18	1	1	20	80	-60		4

DIVISION ONE

		P	W	D	L	F	A	GD	Pts
1	Crowland Town	20	15	1	4	80	28	52	46
2	Wittering Harriers	21	13	4	4	77	44	33	43
3	Eunice Huntingdon	22	13	4	5	60	43	17	43
4	Cardea	18	13	1	4	64	39	25	40
5	Stilton United	16	11	3	2	74	21	53	36
6	Eye United	15	11	1	3	44	20	24	34
7	Stamford Belvedere	21	10	1	9	43	46	-3	34*
8	Premiair	22	9	3	10	79	62	17	30
9	Moulton Harrox Res	18	8	3	7	42	41	1	27
10	Oundle Town	18	8	2	8	53	43	10	26
11	Kings Cliffe	21	6	3	12	51	77	-26	21
12	FC Peterborough	21	6	1	13	41	58	-17	18*
13	Whittlesey Athletic Res	18	4	3	11	29	67	-38	15
14	Peterborough Northern Star Res	20	2	1	17	29	79	-50	7
15	Spalding Town	21	0	1	20	18	116	-98	1

DIVISION TWO

		P	W	D	L	F	A	GD	Pts
1	Crowland Town Res	15	10	2	3	50	21	29	32
2	Netherton United Res	16	10	1	5	49	31	18	31
3	NECI FC	13	9	1	3	53	22	31	28
4	Warboys Town	12	7	4	1	53	14	39	25
5	Thorpe Wood Rangers	14	10	1	3	49	16	33	25*
6	Stamford Belvedere Res	17	7	2	8	29	48	-19	23
7	Long Sutton Athletic Res	16	4	2	10	22	48	-26	20*
8	Rippingale & Folkingham	11	4	4	3	30	23	7	19*
9	Leverington Sports Res	14	4	1	9	29	55	-26	13
10	Stamford Lions Res	15	3	1	11	19	50	-31	13*
11	Oakham United Res	13	0	1	12	11	66	-55	4*

DIVISION THREE

		P	W	D	L	F	A	GD	Pts
1	Ramsey Town	19	14	3	1	75	24	51	48*
2	Holbeach United Sports	17	15	1	0	58	16	42	48*
3	Farcet United	15	9	2	2	57	20	37	35*
4	Hampton	21	10	2	8	59	47	12	35*
5	Orton Rangers	15	8	2	3	36	30	6	32*
6	Parkside	21	9	1	10	43	60	-17	31*
7	Glinton & Northborough	17	6	2	7	42	34	8	26*
8	Premiair Res	22	8	1	13	60	67	-7	25
9	Tydd Res	20	6	3	10	33	52	-19	24*
10	Wittering Harriers Res	21	5	7	9	55	60	-5	22
11	FC Parson Drove Res	13	6	2	3	32	22	10	18*
12	FC Peterborough Res	17	3	1	11	26	62	-36	8*
13	Whittlesey Athletic 'A'	18	2	1	14	26	58	-32	6*
14	Uppingham Town Res	21	2	4	12	26	76	-50	6*

DIVISION FOUR

		P	W	D	L	F	A	GD	Pts
1	Casterton	18	16	1	1	88	31	57	49
2	Stilton United Res	15	13	0	2	64	16	48	39
3	Stanground Sports	11	10	1	0	64	11	53	31
4	Cardea Res	17	10	1	6	88	46	42	31
5	Hampton Res	19	9	0	9	47	38	9	30*
6	Dreams	19	11	0	7	115	53	62	29*
7	Huntingdon Rovers	18	8	1	9	57	80	-23	25
8	The Limetree	16	7	3	6	56	47	9	24
9	Kings Cliffe Res	18	6	3	9	56	58	-2	24*
10	Netherton United 'A'	21	7	2	12	78	89	-11	23
11	Peterborough City	15	6	2	7	49	51	-2	20
12	Thurlby Tigers	14	4	2	8	36	39	-3	14
13	Orton Rangers Res	19	2	2	15	42	110	-68	8
14	Holbeach Bank	18	0	0	18	11	182	-171	0

DIVISION FIVE

		P	W	D	L	F	A	GD	Pts
1	Deeping United	10	8	1	0	67	7	60	28*
2	Long Sutton Athletic 'A'	9	7	1	1	26	15	11	22
3	Park Farm Pumas	11	7	1	3	26	20	6	22
4	Parkside Res	11	6	0	4	26	40	-14	21*
5	Huntingdon Town Dev	10	6	0	4	39	13	26	18
6	Warboys Town Res	10	3	1	4	18	24	-6	16*
7	Cambridge	8	5	0	3	25	21	4	15
8	Sawtry	7	4	0	3	24	14	10	12
9	Rippingale & Folkingham Res	11	2	1	8	29	43	-14	7
10	NECI Res	9	2	1	5	19	26	-7	6*
11	Stamford Lions 'A'	8	2	0	6	15	31	-16	6
12	Spalding Town Res	7	2	0	5	11	28	-17	6
13	Dreams Res	10	3	0	4	15	33	-18	6*
14	Hampton 'A'	11	2	0	9	18	43	-25	6

SHEFFIELD & HALLAMSHIRE LEAGUE

PREMIER DIVISION

		P	W	D	L	F	A	GD	Pts
1	Swinton Athletic	18	17	1	0	86	14	72	52
2	Dodworth Miners Welfare	18	10	4	4	34	28	6	34
3	Ecclesfield Red Rose 1915	21	10	4	7	37	32	5	34
4	AFC Penistone Church	18	10	3	5	38	19	19	33
5	North Gawber Colliery	15	9	4	2	31	16	15	31
6	Grimethorpe LLUK	15	9	1	5	42	34	8	28
7	Stocksbridge Park Steels Res	19	8	4	7	39	33	6	28
8	Wombwell Main	16	8	4	4	39	33	6	28
9	Wakefield AFC	22	8	4	10	38	45	-7	28
10	High Green Villa	18	7	6	5	35	34	1	27
11	Oughtibridge W.M.S.C.	20	7	4	9	29	31	-2	25
12	Hepworth United	20	4	8	8	28	28	0	20
13	Houghton Main	17	6	1	10	33	48	-15	19
14	Burngreave	25	6	0	19	50	80	-30	18
15	Jubilee Sports	18	5	0	13	24	41	-17	15
16	Frecheville Davys	18	1	0	17	19	86	-67	3

DIVISION ONE

		P	W	D	L	F	A	GD	Pts
1	Wombwell Town	17	14	1	2	48	21	27	43
2	Handsworth FC Res	17	12	0	5	62	26	36	36
3	AFC Dronfield	17	11	1	5	39	27	12	34
4	Kiveton Park F.C.	14	8	1	5	32	24	8	25
5	South Kirkby Colliery	14	7	1	6	27	25	2	22
6	Sheffield Medics F.C.	15	7	0	8	36	32	4	21
7	Denaby Main JFC	13	6	1	6	23	20	3	19
8	Wombwell Main Dev	13	5	0	8	25	34	-9	15
9	Sheffield Union	17	5	1	11	27	41	-14	15*
10	New Bohemians	13	3	0	10	11	36	-25	9
11	United Worksop	14	0	2	12	20	64	-44	2

DIVISION TWO

		P	W	D	L	F	A	GD	Pts
1	South Elmsall United Services	15	12	1	2	63	22	41	37
2	Swinton Athletic Res	19	12	1	6	56	32	24	37
3	Sheffield FC Res	16	11	1	4	51	34	17	34
4	Kinsley Boys	15	11	0	4	56	27	29	33
5	Frecheville CA	14	8	3	3	54	30	24	27
6	Athersley Recreation Res	13	8	3	2	44	22	22	27
7	Houghton Main Res	15	6	1	8	30	33	-3	19
8	Bank End AFC	19	6	0	13	44	76	-32	18
9	Burngreave F.C. Res	19	5	1	13	40	80	-40	16
10	Jubilee Sports Dev	13	4	2	7	31	37	-6	14
11	Thurcroft Miners Institute	16	3	1	12	30	62	-32	10
12	Silkstone United	16	2	0	14	24	68	-44	6

SOMERSET COUNTY LEAGUE

PREMEIR DIVISION

		P	W	D	L	F	A	GD	Pts
1	Shirehampton	21	16	3	2	46	16	30	51
2	Clevedon United	21	11	7	3	39	19	20	40
3	Mendip Broadwalk	17	12	3	2	47	16	31	39
4	Middlezoy Rovers	23	9	10	4	45	34	11	37
5	Chilcompton Sports	17	10	3	4	47	29	18	33
6	Keynsham Town Res	23	10	3	10	46	32	14	33
7	Fry Club	22	9	6	7	49	54	-5	33
8	Watchet Town	18	8	4	6	39	32	7	28
9	Westfield	20	8	3	9	56	52	4	27
10	Nailsea United	18	6	7	5	29	29	0	25
11	Ilminster Town	18	7	3	8	30	41	-11	24
12	Nailsea & Tickenham	16	5	6	5	34	25	9	21
13	Stockwood Green	21	4	7	10	23	36	-13	19
14	Stockwood Wanderers	25	2	10	13	33	66	-33	16
15	Clutton	18	4	3	11	26	46	-20	15
16	Chard Town	19	3	3	13	27	57	-30	12
17	Worle	21	2	5	14	33	65	-32	11

DIVISION ONE

		P	W	D	L	F	A	GD	Pts
1	Winscombe	20	12	4	4	56	25	31	40
2	Timsbury Athletic	20	12	3	5	49	32	17	39
3	Burnham United	17	10	3	4	38	24	14	33
4	Uphill Castle	16	9	3	4	46	24	22	30
5	Street FC Res	19	8	6	5	43	31	12	30
6	Minehead AFC	18	6	5	7	29	32	-3	23
7	Saltford	17	7	2	8	24	28	-4	23
8	Wells City Res	15	6	3	6	31	25	6	21
9	Broad Plain House	13	6	3	4	20	20	0	21
10	Somerton Town	16	6	2	8	30	26	4	20
11	Staplegrove	16	4	4	8	26	44	-18	13
12	Wrington Redhill	13	4	0	9	15	39	-24	12
13	Nailsea & Tickenham Res	18	2	5	11	26	42	-16	11
14	Yatton & Cleeve United	16	3	1	12	21	62	-41	10

DIVISION TWO

		P	W	D	L	F	A	GD	Pts
1	Middlezoy Rovers Res	19	15	2	2	50	18	32	47
2	Welton Rovers Res	19	15	2	2	55	24	31	47
3	AFC Brislington	20	14	2	4	63	21	42	44
4	Hutton	17	10	2	5	46	29	17	32
5	Peasedown Miners Welfare	21	9	5	7	34	27	7	32
6	Cheddar Res	19	9	4	6	34	24	10	31
7	Castle Cary	20	9	4	7	38	30	8	31
8	Ashton & Backwell United Res	18	9	3	6	36	23	13	30
9	Imperial	20	9	1	10	44	44	0	28
10	Glastonbury	20	5	7	8	33	42	-9	22
11	Portishead Town Res	17	6	3	8	30	33	-3	21
12	Radstock Town Res	19	6	2	11	41	32	9	20
13	Frome Town Sports	17	4	4	9	28	52	-24	16
14	Brislington Res	20	4	4	12	27	58	-31	16
15	Fry Club Res	21	2	6	13	30	57	-27	11
16	Long Ashton	19	1	1	17	16	91	-75	4

DIVISION THREE

		P	W	D	L	F	A	GD	Pts
1	Chew Magna	19	15	3	1	72	24	48	48
2	Winscombe Res	20	12	4	4	45	26	19	40
3	Ashcott	17	12	2	3	40	20	20	38
4	Bishops Lydeard Res	17	12	1	4	71	24	47	37
5	Banwell	16	12	1	3	63	25	38	37
6	Combe St Nicholas	18	10	4	4	39	27	12	34
7	Burnham United Res	19	10	3	6	50	45	5	30*
8	Draycott	18	8	1	9	39	45	-6	25
9	Congresbury	17	7	3	7	37	41	-4	24
10	Cutters Friday	18	5	4	9	34	37	-3	19
11	Yatton & Cleeve United Res	20	4	6	10	40	61	-21	18
12	Nailsea United Res	18	5	2	11	34	49	-15	17
13	Somerton Town Res	20	5	2	13	36	58	-22	17
14	Clevedon United Res	15	3	2	10	20	41	-21	11
15	Stockwood Green Res	18	3	2	13	20	60	-40	8*
16	Tunley Athletic	20	1	2	17	24	81	-57	5

ST PIRAN LEAGUE

EAST DIVISION

		P	W	D	L	F	A	GD	Pts
1	AFC St Austell Res	21	17	2	2	72	19	53	53
2	St Mawgan	20	14	3	3	77	23	54	45
3	Polperro	21	14	2	5	87	40	47	44
4	Launceston Res	20	14	1	5	65	25	40	43
5	Saltash United Res	19	12	0	7	58	26	32	36
6	Saltash Borough	23	10	4	9	45	42	3	34
7	Morwenstow	17	10	2	5	47	42	5	32
8	Bude Town	20	10	3	7	47	34	13	30*
9	Torpoint Athletic Res	20	9	3	8	39	40	-1	30
10	Sticker Res	22	6	4	12	29	52	-23	22
11	Millbrook Res	12	5	3	4	18	16	2	18
12	Liskeard Athletic Res	19	4	2	13	24	42	-18	14
13	Callington Town Res	17	4	2	11	27	71	-44	14
14	Lanreath	22	2	2	18	26	97	-71	11*
15	Wadebridge Town Res	18	2	1	15	16	56	-40	7
16	St Dennis Res	13	2	0	11	19	71	-52	6

WEST DIVISION

		P	W	D	L	F	A	GD	Pts
1	Penryn Athletic	18	14	2	2	64	18	46	44
2	St Ives Town	19	14	1	4	57	24	33	43
3	Illogan RBL	19	12	1	6	42	28	14	37
4	St Day	17	11	2	4	43	23	20	35
5	Mullion	20	10	3	7	38	33	5	33
6	Perranporth	17	10	1	6	39	28	11	31
7	Falmouth Town Res	17	9	2	6	47	34	13	29
8	Hayle	18	8	4	6	34	28	6	28
9	Helston Athletic Res	20	6	3	11	33	42	-9	21
10	St Agnes	18	6	1	11	23	50	-27	19
11	Wendron United Res	19	4	5	10	35	49	-14	17
12	Perranwell	18	3	3	12	20	52	-32	12
13	Mousehole Res	17	2	5	10	30	48	-18	11
14	Redruth United	17	1	1	15	17	65	-48	4

St Just withdrew before the season kicked off.
Ludgvan withdrew after 12 matches.

STAFFORDSHIRE SENIOR LEAGUE

PREMIER DIVISION

		P	W	D	L	F	A	GD	Pts
1	Leek C.S.O.B.	15	13	0	2	39	14	25	39
2	Alsager Town Res	19	12	3	4	38	18	20	39
3	Brereton Social	22	11	5	6	57	47	10	38
4	Redgate Clayton	18	10	2	6	48	27	21	32
5	Foley Meir	12	9	1	2	36	18	18	28
6	Walsall Phoenix	19	9	0	10	40	44	-4	27
7	Audley & District	18	8	2	8	33	33	0	26
8	Wolstanton United Res	16	7	4	5	34	28	6	25
9	Hanley Town Res	14	7	1	6	31	28	3	22
10	Silverdale Athletic	15	5	5	5	31	22	9	20
11	Ashbourne	15	4	4	7	25	29	-4	16
12	Abbey Hulton United Res	16	4	0	12	22	40	-18	12
13	Cheadle Town Eleven	19	1	5	13	19	54	-35	8
14	Eastwood Hanley	20	0	6	14	25	76	-51	6

Stones Dominoes withdrew after four games.
Tunstall Town withdrew after 12 games.

DIVISION ONE

		P	W	D	L	F	A	GD	Pts
1	AFC Alsager	20	19	0	1	71	22	49	57
2	Ball Haye Green	17	13	0	4	48	19	29	39
3	Shenstone Pathfinder	16	9	3	4	39	22	17	36
4	Milton United	17	8	4	5	45	36	9	28
5	Market Drayton Tigers	14	9	0	5	34	23	11	27
6	Lichfield City Casuals	15	8	1	6	51	42	9	25
7	Whittington	17	6	0	11	31	37	-6	18
8	Chesterton	15	5	2	8	25	35	-10	17
9	Leek CSOB Res	17	6	2	9	38	49	-11	17
10	Redgate Clayton Res	15	4	2	9	31	32	-1	14
11	City of Stoke	16	4	2	10	35	56	-21	14
12	Keele University	18	4	2	12	32	76	-44	14
13	Hawkins Sports	17	2	2	13	26	57	-31	8

Bloxwich United withdrew after nine games.

DIVISION TWO

		P	W	D	L	F	A	GD	Pts
1	Walsall Phoenix Res	15	11	1	3	41	23	18	34
2	Madeley White Star	11	8	1	2	43	12	31	28*
3	Eastwood Hanley Dev	11	7	2	2	34	23	11	23
4	Audley & District Res	14	7	2	5	32	25	7	23
5	Ball Haye Green Res	12	6	2	4	25	25	0	23*
6	Hilton Harriers Res	12	4	4	4	27	22	5	16
7	Cheadle Town Res	13	2	5	6	25	32	-7	14*
8	Cannock United	11	4	0	7	17	35	-18	12
9	Staffordshire Victoria	11	1	2	8	24	45	-21	5
10	Wyrley Titans	11	1	1	10	20	46	-26	4

SUFFOLK & IPSWICH LEAGUE

SENIOR DIVISION

		P	W	D	L	F	A	GD	Pts
1	Crane Sports	18	15	3	0	71	14	57	48
2	Haughley United	19	12	3	4	56	24	32	39
3	Henley Athletic	19	12	3	4	50	22	28	39
4	Old Newton United	17	12	2	3	60	25	35	38
5	East Bergholt United	20	11	3	6	62	47	15	36
6	Claydon	20	10	5	5	43	34	9	35
7	Coplestonians	19	10	3	6	48	24	24	33
8	Bildeston Rangers	19	9	5	5	50	55	-5	32
9	Bourne Vale United	20	8	3	9	42	57	-15	27
10	Benhall St Mary	22	7	4	11	27	47	-20	25
11	Capel Plough	19	6	5	8	29	36	-7	23
12	Achilles	22	4	6	12	51	73	-22	18
13	Trimley Red Devils	19	3	4	12	27	48	-21	13
14	Leiston St Margarets	21	2	2	17	17	54	-37	8
15	Westerfield United	20	0	1	19	26	99	-73	-1*

DIVISION ONE

		P	W	D	L	F	A	GD	Pts
1	Ransomes Sports	19	17	1	1	71	7	64	52
2	Halesworth Town	17	16	0	1	59	14	45	48
3	Wickham Market	18	12	1	5	53	34	19	37
4	Sporting 87	15	12	0	3	42	22	20	36
5	Southwold Town	17	9	4	4	30	17	13	31
6	Grundisburgh	18	8	2	8	40	44	-4	26
7	Coddenham Athletic	20	7	4	9	37	49	-12	25
8	Stowupland Falcons	17	6	3	8	28	29	-1	21
9	Stanton	16	6	2	8	26	36	-10	20
10	Wenhaston United	18	4	4	10	25	45	-20	16
11	Bacton United 89	18	4	3	11	29	37	-8	15
12	AFC Kesgrave	19	4	1	14	32	64	-32	13
13	Barham Athletic	16	3	2	11	25	55	-30	8*
14	Mendlesham	20	1	3	16	17	61	-44	6

DIVISION TWO

		P	W	D	L	F	A	GD	Pts
1	Tattingstone United	20	15	2	3	68	29	39	47
2	Bedricks Worth	14	12	1	1	58	26	32	37
3	Bramford Road Old Boys	16	12	0	4	52	26	26	36
4	AFC YourShirts	16	10	2	4	34	24	10	32
5	Woolverstone United	17	9	2	6	41	46	-5	29
6	Ufford Sports	17	9	0	8	60	47	13	27
7	Saxmundham Sports	18	8	3	7	52	40	12	27
8	Cockfield United	15	8	2	5	35	19	16	26
9	Kirton Athletic	19	8	2	9	48	44	4	26
10	Ipswich Athletic	14	6	2	6	28	36	-8	20
11	Tacket Street BBOB	18	4	2	12	22	45	-23	14
12	Stonham Aspal	18	3	2	13	20	41	-21	11
13	Thurston	19	3	1	15	23	61	-38	8*
14	Somersham	17	1	1	15	21	78	-57	4

DIVISION THREE

		P	W	D	L	F	A	GD	Pts
1	Melton United	14	12	2	0	51	16	35	38
2	Elmswell	12	9	1	2	49	17	32	28
3	Kesgrave Kestrels	15	8	2	5	29	23	6	26
4	Witnesham Wasps	11	5	3	3	28	21	7	18
5	Occold	12	4	6	2	29	23	6	18
6	Ipswich Exiles	15	4	3	8	33	41	-8	15
7	Bardwell Sports	10	5	1	4	29	19	10	14*
8	Hope Church	16	4	1	11	23	47	-24	13
9	Stage	14	4	1	9	20	50	-30	13
10	Whitton United Social Club	11	2	0	9	11	26	-15	6
11	Wortham	10	3	0	7	22	41	-19	5*

DIVISION FOUR

		P	W	D	L	F	A	GD	Pts
1	Walsham Le Willows 'B'	17	15	2	0	83	18	65	47
2	Leiston 'A'	17	12	4	1	84	26	58	40
3	Bury Town Rams	19	11	2	6	58	50	8	35
4	Bourne Vale United Res	15	9	1	5	46	29	17	28
5	Ipswich Athletic Res	17	9	0	8	40	44	-4	27
6	Stowmarket Town 'A'	16	7	1	8	43	44	-1	22
7	Coddenham Athletic Res	17	6	3	8	37	37	0	21
8	Crane Sports Res	18	7	0	11	49	68	-19	21
9	Woolverstone United Res	17	6	1	10	33	51	-18	19
10	Tacket Street BBOB Res	18	5	2	11	31	68	-37	17
11	Bildeston Rangers Res	13	5	0	8	27	38	-11	15
12	AFC Kesgrave 'A'	18	5	0	13	36	68	-32	15
13	Stanton Res	18	4	2	12	28	54	-26	11*

SURREY ELITE INTERMEDIATE LEAGUE

		P	W	D	L	F	A	GD	Pts
1	NPL	18	11	2	5	49	28	21	35
2	Battersea Ironsides	16	10	4	2	45	21	24	34
3	AFC Cubo	18	10	4	4	41	20	21	34
4	Worcester Park	14	10	1	3	29	15	14	31
5	Spartans Youth	18	9	4	5	37	32	5	31
6	Lyne	19	8	3	8	32	43	-11	27
7	Horsley	16	7	2	7	35	33	2	23
8	Royal Holloway Old Boys	18	6	5	7	28	38	-10	23
9	Staines Lammas	15	5	4	6	29	29	0	19
10	Merrow	17	4	5	8	26	28	-2	17
11	Chessington KC	17	2	8	7	24	38	-14	14
12	Ripley Village	13	2	4	7	13	25	-12	10
13	AFC Spelthorne Sports	14	2	4	8	19	36	-17	10
14	Farleigh Rovers	15	1	4	10	17	38	-21	7

Old Rutlishians withdrew after 16 matches.

THAMES VALLEY LEAGUE

PREMEIR DIVISION

		P	W	D	L	F	A	GD	Pts
1	Berks County	19	13	2	4	56	20	36	41
2	Westwood Wanderers	18	13	2	3	43	22	21	41
3	Maidenhead Town	19	10	5	4	48	36	12	35
4	Woodcote	20	11	0	9	43	39	4	33
5	Reading City U23	16	9	4	3	23	11	12	31
6	Newbury	15	8	2	5	27	16	11	26
7	Finchampstead	18	7	5	6	31	31	0	26
8	Richings Park	15	7	5	5	29	24	5	22
9	Burghfield	15	6	3	6	26	25	1	21
10	Mortimer	18	5	4	9	25	34	-9	19
11	Cookham Dean	18	5	3	10	34	49	-15	18
12	Wraysbury Village	20	3	3	13	23	37	-14	15
13	Windlesham United	19	4	2	13	28	58	-30	14
14	Woodley United Royals	18	2	4	12	24	58	-34	10

DIVISION ONE

		P	W	D	L	F	A	GD	Pts
1	Wargrave	12	8	3	1	44	10	34	27
2	Reading YMCA Rapids	11	8	1	2	29	13	16	25
3	Slough Heating Laurencians	11	7	1	3	33	19	14	22
4	FC Imaan Lions	13	7	1	5	33	24	9	22
5	Hurst	12	6	1	5	24	20	4	19
6	Rotherfield United	14	5	2	7	17	23	-6	17
7	Eldon Celtic	12	4	2	6	16	32	-16	14
8	Mortimer Res	11	4	1	6	23	27	-4	13
9	Cookham Dean Res	11	4	0	7	15	25	-10	12
10	Westwood Wanderers Res	12	4	0	8	25	39	-14	12
11	Woodcote Res	13	3	0	10	18	45	-27	9

WEARSIDE LEAGUE

DIVISION ONE

		P	W	D	L	F	A	GD	Pts
1	Horden Community Welfare	23	18	1	4	59	14	45	55
2	Darlington Town	21	16	1	4	68	28	40	49
3	Gateshead Leam Rangers	21	15	1	5	46	28	18	46
4	Hebburn Town Res	21	14	1	6	52	24	28	43
5	FC Hartlepool	25	13	3	9	57	52	5	42
6	Wolviston	17	11	2	4	47	23	24	35
7	Richmond Town	19	11	2	6	41	24	17	35
8	Boldon CA	20	10	2	8	42	38	4	32
9	Durham United	26	7	3	16	42	58	-16	24
10	Farringdon Detached	24	8	0	16	42	83	-41	24
11	Silksworth Colliery Welfare	20	7	2	11	40	36	4	23
12	Darlington RA	24	5	6	13	45	58	-13	21
13	Annfield Plain	19	7	0	12	38	51	-13	21
14	Windscale	21	6	3	12	40	60	-20	21
15	West Auckland Tunns	24	4	3	17	25	72	-47	15
16	Coxhoe Athletic	19	3	4	12	31	66	-35	13

WEST CHESHIRE LEAGUE

DIVISION ONE

		P	W	D	L	F	A	GD	Pts
1	South Liverpool	16	12	4	0	63	21	42	40
2	Mossley Hill Athletic	14	9	5	0	37	17	20	32
3	Chester Nomads	14	9	1	4	40	33	7	28
4	Vauxhall Motors FC Res	17	9	0	8	38	28	10	27
5	Rainhill Town	21	8	3	10	40	44	-4	27
6	Marshalls	21	8	3	10	52	62	-10	27
7	Ashville	17	6	6	5	30	23	7	24
8	Newton (Wirral)	15	7	2	6	40	30	10	22*
9	Upton AA Reds	13	7	1	5	34	28	6	22
10	Maghull	16	6	3	7	34	26	8	21
11	Ellesmere Port Town	16	6	3	7	39	38	1	21
12	Redgate Rovers	17	6	1	10	38	32	6	19
13	Capenhurst Villa	17	6	0	11	22	50	-28	18
14	Neston Nomads	20	1	2	17	20	95	-75	5

Hale withdrew after five games.
Richmond Raith Rovers withdrew after five games.

DIVISION TWO

		P	W	D	L	F	A	GD	Pts
1	Prescot Cables Res	21	16	5	0	57	27	30	53
2	Mersey Royal	18	14	1	3	64	26	38	43
3	Heswall	18	12	4	2	68	27	41	40
4	Aintree Villa	15	12	2	1	46	11	35	38
5	West Kirby	19	11	1	7	46	50	-4	34
6	South Sefton Borough	18	9	1	8	51	40	11	28
7	Cheshire Lines	16	7	6	3	34	25	9	27
8	Ashville Res	18	7	1	10	28	36	-8	22
9	Mossley Hill Athletic Res	17	6	2	9	36	38	-2	20
10	Maghull Res	18	6	1	11	22	33	-11	19
11	South Liverpool Res	17	4	5	8	39	44	-5	17
12	Mallaby	18	4	3	11	35	65	-30	15
13	Rainhill Town Res	20	4	3	13	41	74	-33	15
14	Poulton Royal	21	4	2	15	34	65	-31	14
15	Litherland Remyca Dev	22	3	1	18	42	82	-40	10

DIVISION THREE

		P	W	D	L	F	A	GD	Pts
1	FC Bootle St Edmund's	20	17	3	0	81	24	57	54
2	Marine FC Res	24	15	4	5	77	41	36	49
3	Bootle Res	23	15	0	8	85	56	29	45
4	Poulton Vics FC	16	12	3	1	75	22	53	39
5	Willaston FC	24	13	0	11	59	53	6	39
6	Rainford United FC	19	12	2	5	83	44	39	38
7	Aintree Villa Res	24	11	3	10	48	53	-5	36
8	West Kirby Res	22	11	2	9	48	43	5	35
9	Marshalls Res	23	9	4	10	43	47	-4	31
10	Capenhurst Villa Res	19	8	2	9	44	50	-6	26
11	Helsby	16	6	5	5	41	36	5	23
12	Pensby FC	23	5	4	14	40	69	-29	19
13	Chester Nomads Res	26	5	3	18	40	79	-39	18
14	Ellesmere Port Town Res	16	5	2	9	24	47	-23	17
15	Heswall Res	18	2	4	12	26	58	-32	10
16	Neston Nomads Res	23	1	1	21	16	108	-92	4

WEST LANCASHIRE LEAGUE

PREMIER DIVISION

		P	W	D	L	F	A	GD	Pts
1	Fulwood Amateurs	24	18	1	5	93	39	54	55
2	Tempest United	21	13	3	5	55	32	23	42
3	Euxton Villa	22	13	2	7	64	38	26	41
4	Slyne with Hest	20	12	1	7	66	45	21	37
5	Thornton Cleveleys	21	12	3	6	54	27	27	36*
6	Lytham Town	20	12	0	8	50	37	13	36
7	Poulton	19	10	3	6	47	38	9	33
8	Hurst Green	23	10	2	11	54	46	8	32
9	Coppull United	20	9	4	7	40	39	1	31
10	CMB	24	10	1	13	59	66	-7	31
11	Turton	17	10	0	7	30	27	3	30
12	Blackpool Wren Rovers	19	9	0	10	34	39	-5	27
13	Burscough Richmond	22	6	3	13	34	39	-5	21
14	Southport Hesketh	19	4	3	12	36	53	-17	15
15	Vickerstown	21	2	3	16	32	66	-34	9
16	Whitehaven	22	2	1	19	20	137	-117	7

DIVISION ONE

		P	W	D	L	F	A	GD	PTS
1	Lostock St Gerards	20	15	5	0	67	27	40	50
2	Stoneclough	24	13	2	9	50	45	5	41
3	Wyre Villa	20	9	5	6	48	28	20	32
4	Croston Sports Club	20	9	5	6	44	45	-1	32
5	Horwich St Mary's Victoria	19	9	4	6	41	27	14	31
6	Askam United	22	8	7	7	40	39	1	31
7	Hawcoat Park	20	8	5	7	40	29	11	29
8	Millom	20	8	4	8	43	37	6	28
9	Kendal County	19	7	3	9	34	45	-11	24
10	Crooklands Casuals	22	7	3	12	33	55	-22	24
11	Milnthorpe Corinthians	14	6	5	3	28	22	6	23
12	Eagley	18	7	1	10	30	39	-9	22
13	Ulverston Rangers	20	3	7	10	35	50	-15	16
14	Hesketh Bank	21	3	7	11	38	67	-29	16
15	Haslingden St Mary's	15	2	3	10	24	40	-16	9

DIVISION TWO

		P	W	D	L	F	A	GD	PTS
1	Rossendale	24	20	3	1	82	26	56	63
2	Walney Island	23	18	2	3	88	32	56	56
3	Longridge Town Res	19	13	1	5	58	35	23	40
4	Freckleton	23	11	4	8	57	48	9	37
5	Furness Rovers	21	9	5	7	61	47	14	32
6	Charnock Richard Res	22	13	3	6	61	33	28	30*
7	Galgate	21	9	3	9	48	42	6	30
8	Storeys of Lancaster	23	8	1	14	42	86	-44	25
9	Furness Cavaliers	20	7	2	11	34	53	-19	23
10	Kendal United	17	5	7	5	32	28	4	22
11	Dalton United	18	5	4	9	42	50	-8	19
12	Garstang Res	21	5	4	12	46	68	-22	19
13	Mill Hill St Peters	25	6	4	15	44	81	-37	19*
14	Burscough Dynamo	20	5	2	13	32	64	-32	17
15	Burnley United	17	4	4	9	35	40	-5	16
16	Chipping	22	4	3	15	36	65	-29	15

WEST YORKSHIRE LEAGUE

PREMIER DIVISION

		P	W	D	L	F	A	GD	Pts
1	Beeston St Anthony	19	17	2	0	48	17	31	53
2	Ilkley Town	18	12	2	4	57	26	31	38
3	Field	21	11	5	5	44	29	15	38
4	Horbury Town	19	12	1	6	41	27	14	37
5	Newsome	23	10	4	9	44	40	4	34
6	Hunslet Club	16	10	2	4	37	20	17	32
7	Huddersfield Amateur	21	9	3	9	46	41	5	30
8	Headingley	18	8	3	7	33	29	4	27
9	Whitkirk Wanderers	20	7	2	11	42	50	-8	23
10	Knaresborough Town	21	6	4	11	32	58	-26	22
11	Hall Green United	18	6	2	10	29	44	-15	20
12	Boroughbridge	19	5	3	11	31	40	-9	18
13	Carlton Athletic	17	5	2	10	36	39	-3	17
14	Robin Hood Athletic	17	4	4	9	25	38	-13	16
15	Sherburn White Rose	19	1	1	17	20	67	-47	4

DIVISION ONE

		P	W	D	L	F	A	GD	Pts
1	Shelley	21	13	4	4	64	28	36	43
2	Wetherby Athletic	25	13	4	8	63	48	15	43
3	Otley Town	19	11	5	3	55	29	26	38
4	Rawdon Old Boys	18	11	5	2	46	24	22	38
5	Kirk Deighton Rangers	21	10	8	3	43	31	12	38
6	Hartshead	20	11	3	6	56	40	16	36
7	Campion	21	10	6	5	55	41	14	36
8	Salts	19	10	3	6	61	33	28	33
9	Glasshoughton Rock	21	9	5	7	56	45	11	32
10	Pool	19	7	3	9	38	42	-4	24
11	Aberford Albion	21	7	2	12	46	61	-15	23
12	East End Park	22	5	5	12	42	59	-17	20
13	Featherstone Colliery	21	4	3	14	37	81	-44	15
14	Kippax	22	4	2	16	25	77	-52	14
15	Wyke Wanderers	19	3	4	12	24	45	-21	13
16	Oxenhope Recreation	17	4	0	13	27	54	-27	12

DIVISION TWO

		P	W	D	L	F	A	GD	Pts
1	Brighouse Sports Old Boys	16	10	2	4	56	36	20	32
2	Overthorpe Sports Club	19	8	4	7	49	45	4	28
3	Ripon City	13	8	1	4	38	22	16	25
4	Swillington Saints	15	7	4	4	43	29	14	25
5	Altofts	17	7	4	6	35	37	-2	25
6	Kellingley Welfare	16	7	4	5	43	46	-3	25
7	Rothwell	19	8	1	10	45	54	-9	25
8	Old Centralians	15	6	4	5	34	32	2	22
9	Huddersfield YM	12	5	4	3	29	20	9	19
10	Harrogate Railway Athletic	15	5	4	6	34	37	-3	19
11	Leeds Modernians	14	4	3	7	17	27	-10	15
12	Tingley Athletic	14	3	2	9	31	44	-13	11
13	Howden Clough	11	0	3	8	14	39	-25	3

WILTSHIRE LEAGUE

PREMIER DIVISION

		P	W	D	L	F	A	GD	Pts
1	Corsham Town Res	22	13	5	4	58	30	28	44
2	Shrewton United	20	13	3	4	62	30	32	42
3	Kintbury Rangers	20	12	5	3	60	27	33	41
4	Wroughton	15	12	3	0	58	13	45	39
5	Melksham Town Res	20	11	4	5	55	30	25	37
6	Purton	22	10	5	7	53	39	14	35
7	Royal Wootton Bassett Town Dev	22	10	5	7	42	33	9	32*
8	Cricklade Town	20	9	1	10	52	52	0	28
9	Frome Collegians AFC	22	6	6	10	43	48	-5	24
10	Marlborough Town	22	6	4	12	35	57	-22	22
11	Trowbridge Town	16	6	2	8	36	28	8	20
12	Stratton Juniors	19	5	3	11	24	48	-24	18
13	Malmesbury Victoria Dev	18	4	2	12	29	64	-35	14
14	Pewsey Vale	18	3	2	13	16	82	-66	9*
15	Ludgershall Sports	16	1	0	15	17	59	-42	3
	Holt withdrew.								

YORK LEAGUE

PREMIER DIVISION

		P	W	D	L	F	A	GD	Pts
1	Dringhouses	16	14	1	1	81	17	64	43
2	Thorpe United	18	12	4	2	56	22	34	40
3	Wigginton GH	16	12	2	2	57	18	39	38
4	Old Malton	19	11	2	6	49	33	16	35
5	Dunnington	23	12	3	8	49	40	9	35*
6	Huntington Rovers	18	9	3	6	52	45	7	30
7	Easingwold Town	23	9	3	11	62	56	6	30
8	Kirkbymoorside	20	8	3	9	55	56	-1	27
9	Tadcaster Magnets	16	8	2	6	48	36	12	26
10	Poppleton United	18	7	2	9	45	44	1	23
11	Copmanthorpe	20	5	3	12	39	60	-21	18
12	Hemingbrough United	17	4	4	9	28	38	-10	16
13	F1 Racing	21	5	0	16	47	73	-26	15
14	Church Fenton	19	0	0	19	12	142	-130	0

DIVISION ONE

		P	W	D	L	F	A	GD	Pts
1	Strensall Tigers	21	15	4	2	81	22	59	49
2	Osbaldwick	20	10	3	7	64	35	29	33
3	Rawcliffe	15	9	5	1	43	23	20	32
4	Pocklington Town Res	17	9	3	5	43	28	15	30
5	Malt Shovel	17	8	5	4	36	29	7	29
6	Haxby Town	22	9	4	9	61	59	2	29
7	Marston Green	21	8	3	10	52	48	4	27
8	Stamford Bridge	17	8	3	6	42	38	4	27
9	Tockwith	14	7	1	6	28	23	5	22
10	Riccall United	19	4	7	8	28	47	-19	19
11	Malton & Norton	20	5	3	12	39	64	-25	18
12	Cliffe	18	5	3	10	41	82	-41	18
13	Bishopthorpe United	16	5	2	9	48	64	-16	17
14	Harrison Signs	19	2	2	15	23	67	-44	8

DIVISION TWO

		P	W	D	L	F	A	GD	Pts
1	The Beagle	17	11	3	3	38	30	8	36
2	Cawood	14	10	2	2	46	23	23	32
3	Wombleton Wanderers	15	9	1	5	52	19	33	28
4	Pollington	14	8	2	4	46	34	12	26
5	Rufforth United	18	8	1	9	42	49	-7	25
6	Civil Service	11	6	4	1	40	17	23	19*
7	Clifford	12	6	1	5	28	27	1	19
8	Bubwith White Swan	15	5	3	7	42	41	1	18
9	Barmby Moor	18	6	2	10	28	68	-40	17*
10	Heslington	16	4	3	9	30	39	-9	15
11	Wilberfoss	14	5	0	9	27	39	-12	15
12	Wheldrake	16	4	1	11	37	50	-13	13
13	Brooklyn	16	3	3	10	32	52	-20	12

DIVISION THREE

		P	W	D	L	F	A	GD	Pts
1	York St Johns University	18	14	2	2	92	25	67	44
2	Garforth WMC	14	10	2	2	77	21	56	32
3	Helperby United	15	10	2	3	77	25	52	32
4	Walnut Tree	14	10	2	2	64	23	41	32
5	Fulford United	11	6	1	4	34	31	3	19
6	Crayke United	13	5	1	7	38	45	-7	16
7	Bishop Wilton	14	4	2	8	31	52	-21	14
8	York Railway Institute	16	4	0	12	34	74	-40	12
9	Duncombe Park	11	4	2	5	27	39	-12	11*
10	Selby Olympia	13	1	1	11	25	76	-51	4
11	Lner Builders	15	1	1	13	17	105	-88	1*

YORKSHIRE AMATEUR LEAGUE

SUPREME DIVISION

		P	W	D	L	F	A	GD	Pts
1	Farsley Celtic Juniors	16	15	0	1	65	13	52	45
2	Littletown	19	13	0	6	63	25	38	39
3	Calverley United	21	12	1	8	52	44	8	37
4	Horsforth St. Margarets	13	11	0	2	49	11	38	33
5	Stanley United	17	11	0	6	63	37	26	33
6	Ryburn United	18	9	4	5	37	29	8	31
7	Route One Rovers	20	9	4	7	57	50	7	31
8	Leeds Medics & Dentists	22	9	4	9	36	39	-3	31
9	Toller FC	20	9	3	8	56	58	-2	27*
10	Athletico FC	24	7	4	13	49	63	-14	25
11	Wortley FC	14	7	0	7	37	36	1	21
12	Alwoodley FC	16	5	5	6	28	24	4	20
13	Steeton	16	3	1	12	25	56	-31	10
14	Drighlington	21	1	3	17	22	110	-88	6
15	Lower Hopton	17	1	1	15	18	62	-44	4

PREMIER DIVISION

		P	W	D	L	F	A	GD	Pts
1	Gildersome Spurs O.B.	14	10	1	3	63	27	36	31
2	Middleton	14	10	0	4	54	33	21	30
3	Collegians	17	6	4	7	50	39	11	22
4	Leeds City FC	13	7	0	6	31	32	-1	21
5	Ealandians	16	6	3	7	29	32	-3	21
6	Wibsey	13	7	0	6	28	35	-7	21
7	St Bedes	17	6	2	9	47	65	-18	20
8	Stanningley Old Boys	15	6	2	7	23	48	-25	20
9	Morley Town AFC	16	5	2	9	48	57	-9	17
10	Shire Academics	14	5	0	9	33	37	-4	15
11	Whitkirk Wanderers	5	2	0	3	12	13	-1	6

CHAMPIONSHIP

		P	W	D	L	F	A	GD	Pts
1	Horsforth St. Margarets Res	13	11	0	2	60	13	47	33
2	Beeston Juniors	18	10	1	7	51	56	-5	31
3	Leeds Medics & Dentists Res	19	9	3	7	45	35	10	30
4	Mount St Marys	10	9	1	0	45	17	28	28
5	PFC	17	9	0	8	55	59	-4	27
6	Golcar United	9	8	0	1	41	10	31	24
7	Colton Athletic	15	8	0	7	33	31	2	24
8	Woodkirk Valley	12	7	0	5	39	27	12	21
9	Dewsbury Rangers	13	4	1	8	31	39	-8	13
10	Ealandians Res	17	4	1	12	27	65	-38	13
11	Idle FC	12	3	1	8	22	37	-15	10
12	Leeds Independent	19	0	2	17	14	74	-60	2

DIVISION ONE

		P	W	D	L	F	A	GD	Pts
1	Beeston St Anthony	11	8	1	2	40	19	21	25
2	Fairbank United	11	7	3	1	41	25	16	24
3	Lepton Highlanders	12	7	1	4	36	26	10	22
4	Athletico Res	14	6	2	6	40	43	-3	19*
5	Thornesians	15	5	1	9	38	68	-30	16
6	Leeds City FC Res	13	4	3	6	29	29	0	15
7	Horsforth St. Margarets 3rds	13	7	2	4	42	22	20	14*
8	Alwoodley Res	10	4	1	5	31	33	-2	13
9	Tyersal	12	4	1	7	33	41	-8	13
10	Shire Academics Res	13	3	3	7	23	33	-10	12
11	Farsley Celtic Juniors Res	12	3	2	7	27	41	-14	11

DIVISION TWO

		P	W	D	L	F	A	GD	Pts
1	Morley Town AFC Res	16	11	1	4	55	30	25	34
2	Middleton Park	15	10	1	4	56	21	35	31
3	Norristhorpe	16	10	1	5	64	43	21	31
4	North Leeds	14	7	3	4	43	36	7	24
5	Leeds City FC III	11	6	2	3	33	31	2	20
6	Sandal Wanderers	15	5	2	8	40	43	-3	17
7	Gildersome Spurs O.B. Res	15	4	5	6	28	44	-16	17
8	Trinity & All Saints Old Boys	17	5	2	10	37	57	-20	17
9	Leeds Medics & Dentists 3rds	13	4	1	8	13	28	-15	13
10	Huddersfield Amateur	14	3	4	7	29	46	-17	13
11	Prospect FC	14	4	1	9	31	53	-22	13
12	Horsforth St. Margarets 4ths	12	4	3	5	30	27	3	10*

DIVISION THREE

		P	W	D	L	F	A	GD	Pts
1	Littletown Res	14	12	0	2	48	19	29	36
2	Norristhorpe Res	14	9	2	3	61	30	31	29
3	Wortley Res	11	9	1	1	65	9	56	28
4	Morley Town AFC III	15	7	2	6	28	41	-13	23
5	Savile United FC	15	6	4	5	42	31	11	22
6	Shire Academics III	12	6	3	3	37	29	8	21
7	Ealandians III	16	4	2	10	34	68	-34	14
8	Garforth Rangers	13	3	3	7	27	38	-11	12
9	Tingley Athletic	12	3	1	8	20	41	-21	10
10	Woodkirk Valley Res	16	3	0	13	26	78	-52	9
11	Lepton Highlanders Res	14	4	2	8	34	38	-4	8*

DIVISION FOUR

		P	W	D	L	F	A	GD	Pts
1	Colton Athletic Res	16	12	2	2	61	29	32	38
2	Farnley Sports FC	14	8	2	4	66	42	24	26
3	Middleton Park U23's	11	8	2	1	38	18	20	26
4	Morley Town AFC Dev	12	6	2	4	38	28	10	20
5	St Bedes Res	15	6	2	7	45	45	0	20
6	Tyersal Res	14	6	1	7	48	56	-8	19
7	Calverley United Res	10	5	1	4	36	28	8	16
8	Leeds Modernians	13	3	3	7	27	33	-6	12
9	Old Batelians	13	3	3	7	36	50	-14	12
10	Old Centralians	13	3	5	5	40	39	1	11*
11	Thornesians Res	12	3	2	7	22	55	-33	11
12	North Leeds Res	15	3	1	11	24	58	-34	10

DIVISION FIVE

		P	W	D	L	F	A	GD	Pts
1	West End Park	16	12	2	2	63	26	37	38
2	Colton Athletic III	13	8	2	3	37	24	13	26
3	Shire Academics IV	12	8	0	4	43	24	19	24
4	Farnley Sports Res	14	8	0	6	44	42	2	21*
5	Dewsbury Rangers U23's	14	5	4	5	37	36	1	19
6	Huddersfield Amateur Res	16	5	3	8	43	54	-11	18
7	Leeds Modernians Res	11	5	1	5	29	39	-10	16
8	Thornesians III	12	5	0	7	32	39	-7	15
9	St Bedes Academy	13	4	3	6	35	45	-10	15
10	Leeds City FC IV	13	4	1	8	32	36	-4	13
11	Old Centralians Academics	14	5	1	8	34	43	-9	13*
12	Beeston Juniors Res	14	3	1	10	27	48	-21	10

STEP 8+ LEAGUE TABLES

ALDERSHOT & DISTRICT FOOTBALL LEAGUE

SENIOR DIVISION

		P	W	D	L	F	A	GD	Pts
1	Fleet Spurs A	12	6	3	3	37	26	11	21
2	Frimley Select	11	6	2	3	38	28	10	20
3	Ropley	10	4	5	1	35	23	12	17
4	Sandhurst Sports	8	5	1	2	21	18	3	16
5	Wey Valley	10	3	3	4	28	32	-4	12
6	Traco Athletic	9	2	4	3	21	20	1	10
7	Yateley United Res	12	3	1	8	14	25	-11	10
8	Headley United Res	12	3	1	8	18	40	-22	10

DIVISION ONE

		P	W	D	L	F	A	GD	Pts
1	Rushmoor Community	12	11	0	1	67	13	54	33
2	Yateley United A	14	8	1	5	37	31	6	25
3	Normandy	9	8	0	1	47	13	34	24
4	Mytchett Athletic	11	7	1	3	40	19	21	22
5	Farnborough North End	13	5	1	7	28	50	-22	16
6	Letef Select	9	4	1	4	23	18	5	13
7	Hartland Athletic	9	4	1	4	23	26	-3	13
8	Wey Valley Res	9	2	1	6	19	38	-19	7
9	AFC Laffans	11	2	1	8	21	50	-29	7
10	Fleet Spurs Zeppelins	13	0	1	12	18	65	-47	1

BASINGSTOKE & DISTRICT FOOTBALL LEAGUE

DIVISION ONE

		P	W	D	L	F	A	GD	Pts
1	Twentyten	9	6	2	1	36	17	19	20
2	Hook	12	5	4	3	21	17	4	19
3	Renegades	8	5	2	1	27	11	16	17
4	Overton Utd Res	10	5	2	3	30	23	7	17
5	Silchester Village	6	4	0	2	14	9	5	12
6	AFC Berg	9	3	1	5	18	27	-9	10
7	AFC Aldermaston A	12	2	2	8	21	41	-20	8
8	Tadley Calleva Dev	7	2	1	4	17	15	2	7
9	Oakridge	9	2	0	7	11	35	-24	6

DIVISION TWO

		P	W	D	L	F	A	GD	Pts
1	CK Andover	9	8	1	0	30	10	20	25
2	Overton Utd A	7	5	1	1	36	18	18	16
3	North Warnborough	8	5	0	3	33	15	18	15
4	Basingstoke Athletic	7	4	2	1	17	12	5	14
5	Herriard Sports	9	4	2	3	22	23	-1	14
6	AFC Berg Res	10	3	2	5	19	24	-5	11
7	Chineham	8	3	1	4	19	23	-4	10
8	Renegades Res	8	2	0	6	11	35	-24	6
9	AFC Aldermaston Dev	7	1	1	5	13	25	-12	4
10	Tidworth Town	7	0	0	7	8	23	-15	0

BRISTOL AND DISTRICT LEAGUE

SENIOR DIVISION

		P	W	D	L	F	A	GD	Pts
1	St Nicholas	11	8	3	0	50	11	39	27
2	Wick (Saturday) Res	10	7	1	2	33	17	16	22
3	Cribbs A Team	11	6	2	3	41	22	19	20
4	Oldland Abbotonians Res	12	6	2	4	37	28	9	20
5	Mendip Broadwalk Res	12	5	1	6	24	23	1	16
6	Nicholas Wanderers Res	10	4	3	3	22	21	1	15
7	Fry Club A Team	12	3	3	6	26	38	-12	12
8	AEK Boco A Team	8	3	1	4	20	33	-13	10
9	Henbury Res	9	3	0	6	16	28	-12	9
10	Patchway Town Res	11	0	0	11	5	53	-48	0

DIVISION ONE

		P	W	D	L	F	A	GD	Pts
1	Stapleton A	11	11	0	0	44	6	38	33
2	Highridge United Res	10	6	2	2	34	23	11	20
3	Real Thornbury	10	6	0	4	30	17	13	18
4	Lawrence Rovers	10	5	3	2	26	23	3	18
5	Chipping Sodbury Town A	10	5	2	3	24	19	5	17
6	Longwell Green Sports A	11	5	0	6	28	28	0	15
7	AFC Mangotsfield District	11	4	2	5	17	16	1	14
8	Totterdown United Res	12	4	0	8	25	42	-17	12
9	Seymour United Res	10	3	1	6	17	22	-5	10
10	Hanham Athletic Res	11	2	0	9	19	43	-24	6
11	Greyfriars Athletic Res	10	1	2	7	15	40	-25	5

DIVISION TWO

		P	W	D	L	F	A	GD	Pts
1	Old Sodbury	16	16	0	0	53	11	42	48
2	Hambrook Res	14	12	0	2	32	7	25	36
3	Bristol Barcelona	15	11	1	3	44	24	20	34
4	Bradley Stoke Town Res	18	9	1	8	52	36	16	28
5	Iron Acton Res	15	7	2	6	37	28	9	23
6	Brimsham Green	18	7	2	9	39	38	1	23
7	Thornbury Town Res	13	6	0	7	32	18	14	18
8	Olveston United Res	16	5	3	8	36	38	-2	18
9	Sea Mills Park Res	14	3	3	8	18	35	-17	12
10	Tormarton FC	12	3	1	8	11	24	-13	10
11	Lion	15	3	1	11	16	46	-30	10
12	Hartcliffe	18	3	0	15	36	101	-65	9

DIVISION THREE

		P	W	D	L	F	A	GD	Pts
1	Roman Glass St George A	12	10	0	2	33	20	13	30
2	Mendip Broadwalk A	12	9	2	1	39	19	20	29
3	Shaftesbury Crusade Res	14	8	3	3	59	15	44	27
4	Cribbs B Team	14	7	3	4	32	23	9	24
5	Pucklechurch Sports Res	13	7	1	5	41	24	17	22
6	Fry Club B Team	15	6	3	6	38	37	1	21
7	Westerleigh Sports	14	6	2	6	32	35	-3	20
8	Nicholas Wanderers A	14	6	2	6	32	37	-5	20
9	Bradley Stoke Town A	10	5	1	4	24	17	7	16
10	Stoke Lane Athletic	14	4	1	9	32	36	-4	13
11	Greyfriars Athletic A	16	2	2	12	21	57	-36	8
12	Bendix	14	0	2	12	15	78	-63	2

DIVISION FOUR

		P	W	D	L	F	A	GD	Pts
1	Winterbourne United Res	15	14	1	0	58	15	43	43
2	Oldland Abbotonians Colts	17	9	4	4	66	36	30	31
3	Hanham Athletic Vets	12	9	1	2	57	26	31	28
4	DRG SV Frenchay Res	11	9	1	1	44	15	29	28
5	Hanham Abbotonians	13	8	2	3	33	22	11	26
6	Highridge United A	11	7	2	2	35	16	19	23
7	Fishponds Athletic	17	5	3	9	35	43	-8	18
8	Fry Club C Team	13	5	1	7	29	35	-6	16
9	AFC Grace	16	4	2	10	33	66	-33	14
10	AFC Mangotsfield District Res	14	3	3	8	18	30	-12	12
11	Iron Acton A	15	3	0	12	21	57	-36	9
12	Seymour United A	14	2	2	10	15	41	-26	8
13	Crosscourt United	12	1	0	11	10	52	-42	3

DIVISION FIVE

		P	W	D	L	F	A	GD	Pts
1	Thornbury Town A	12	10	2	0	45	13	32	32
2	Longwell Green Sports B	14	10	0	4	49	24	25	30
3	De Veys Res	15	7	2	6	43	40	3	23
4	Real St George	12	6	2	4	37	26	11	20
5	St Nicholas Res	15	5	4	6	42	40	2	19
6	Wick A	13	6	1	6	40	41	-1	19
7	Lawrence Rovers Res	9	4	3	2	36	26	10	15
8	Brimsham Green Res	11	5	0	6	23	34	-11	15
9	Phoenix, The	13	4	1	8	32	41	-9	13
10	Bradley Stoke Town B	12	4	1	7	21	39	-18	13
11	Lion Res	14	1	0	13	24	68	-44	3

BRISTOL AND SUBURBAN LEAGUE

PREMIER ONE

		P	W	D	L	F	A	GD	Pts
1	Stoke Gifford United	13	11	1	1	63	13	50	34
2	Filton Athletic	15	9	2	4	33	18	15	29
3	Avonmouth (Saturday)	11	9	1	1	35	8	27	28
4	Bristol Spartak	13	9	1	3	28	23	5	28
5	Easton Cowboys	16	7	1	8	35	35	0	22
6	Rockleaze Rangers Res	16	7	0	9	35	35	0	21
7	Old Cothamians	10	6	2	2	30	11	19	20
8	Parson Street Old Boys	12	6	2	4	38	23	15	20
9	AFC Mangotsfield	15	6	0	9	27	39	-12	18
10	Bristol Bilbao	16	5	0	11	17	45	-28	15
11	Old Georgians	16	3	6	7	13	30	-17	9
12	St Aldhelms	10	1	2	7	13	42	-29	5
13	Southmead CS Athletic	14	0	2	12	15	60	-45	2

PREMIER TWO

		P	W	D	L	F	A	GD	Pts
1	North Bristol United	15	13	0	2	53	14	39	39
2	Lawrence Weston Athletic	15	11	2	2	53	26	27	35
3	Stoke Rangers	14	10	1	3	45	23	22	31
4	MPK Lofts	13	9	2	2	37	21	16	29
5	Wessex Wanderers	16	8	4	4	38	29	9	28
6	Stockwood Wanderers Res	14	7	1	6	31	36	-5	22
7	Keynsham Town A	18	6	1	11	37	54	-17	19
8	AFC Brislington Res	13	5	1	7	23	43	-20	16
9	Ridings High	16	5	0	11	28	43	-15	15
10	Ashton United	14	3	4	7	21	28	-7	13
11	Bristol Telephones	12	3	2	7	26	27	-1	11
12	Almondsbury Res	15	3	1	11	31	48	-17	10
13	Wanderers (Saturday)	13	1	1	11	18	49	-31	4

DIVISION ONE

		P	W	D	L	F	A	GD	Pts
1	Redbridge Saturday	13	12	0	1	51	20	31	36
2	Jamaica Bell, The	17	9	4	4	39	25	14	31
3	AFC Mangotsfield Res	12	9	2	1	33	17	16	29
4	Bromley Heath United Res	15	9	1	5	38	28	10	28
5	Old Cothamians Res	11	6	1	4	25	18	7	19
6	Stoke Gifford United Res	11	5	2	4	24	23	1	17
7	Cosmos UK	13	6	0	7	27	34	-7	17*
8	Rockleaze Rangers A	15	4	3	8	32	34	-2	15
9	Little Stoke Res	8	4	1	3	25	14	11	13
10	Park Knowle	9	3	2	4	22	21	1	11
11	Easton Cowboys Res	13	1	2	10	19	50	-31	5
12	Avonmouth Res	9	1	0	8	12	39	-27	3
13	Corinthian Sports	12	0	2	10	12	36	-24	2

DIVISION TWO

		P	W	D	L	F	A	GD	Pts
1	Filton Athletic Res	15	9	2	4	43	19	24	29
2	Rockleaze Rangers B	14	9	2	3	54	34	20	29
3	Broad Plain House Res	9	8	1	0	28	7	21	25
4	Imperial Res	12	8	0	4	38	23	15	24
5	AFC Mangotsfield A	12	6	4	2	29	19	10	22
6	Lawrence Weston	14	7	1	6	36	31	5	22
7	St Aldhelms Res	11	7	1	3	35	36	-1	22
8	Fishponds Old Boys	15	5	2	8	40	39	1	17
9	Lawrence Weston Athletic Res	16	5	2	9	29	49	-20	17
10	Easton Athletic	14	4	3	7	40	48	-8	15
11	Lockleaze Community	16	3	2	11	36	60	-24	11
12	Bristol Phoenix s	11	1	3	7	22	31	-9	6
13	Old Georgians Res	11	1	1	9	16	50	-34	4

DIVISION THREE

		P	W	D	L	F	A	GD	Pts
1	AFC Whitchurch	14	13	0	1	64	20	44	39
2	Socius United	15	9	1	5	57	49	8	28
3	Cutters Friday Res	13	8	1	4	54	34	20	25
4	Stokeside FC	11	7	2	2	47	31	16	23
5	Cadbury Heath Res	15	7	2	6	39	28	11	23
6	MPK Lofts Res	12	6	3	3	32	28	4	21
7	Avonmouth A	12	5	2	5	39	49	-10	17
8	Parson Street Old Boys Res	8	4	1	3	29	26	3	13
9	Wessex Wanderers Res	13	4	1	8	27	51	-24	13
10	Brandon Sports	17	4	0	13	39	79	-40	12
11	Easton Cowboys A	11	3	0	8	38	38	0	9
12	FC Union Bristol	15	1	1	13	34	66	-32	4

DIVISION FOUR

		P	W	D	L	F	A	GD	Pts
1	Little Stoke A	14	11	1	2	68	18	50	34
2	Bedminster Down	15	10	4	1	57	24	33	34
3	Brentry Athletic	17	10	4	3	52	29	23	34
4	Rockleaze Rangers C	16	9	5	2	49	26	23	32
5	Valhalla	14	8	1	5	40	32	8	25
6	Cutters Friday A	13	6	4	3	28	19	9	22
7	Bromley Heath United A	11	6	2	3	27	29	-2	20
8	Stoke Gifford United A	14	4	5	5	43	34	9	17
9	Eastville Rangers	13	5	2	6	32	34	-2	17
10	Kellaway Rangers	10	4	0	6	21	30	-9	12
11	TC Sports	16	3	2	11	21	54	-33	11
12	Hanham Abbotonians Res	13	2	1	10	29	44	-15	7
13	Bristol Phoenix Res	14	2	0	12	13	69	-56	6
14	Corinthian Sports Res	14	1	1	12	17	55	-38	4

BRISTOL PREMIER COMBINATION LEAGUE

PREMIER DIVISION

		P	W	D	L	F	A	GD	Pts
1	Cribbs Res	14	13	1	0	57	19	38	40
2	Shaftesbury Crusade	14	6	4	4	27	25	2	22
3	Winterbourne United	11	7	0	4	36	26	10	21
4	Seymour United	12	5	4	3	26	22	4	19
5	Olveston United	11	5	3	3	20	24	-4	18
6	Totterdown United	11	3	5	3	26	27	-1	14
7	Pucklechurch Sports	13	4	1	8	19	30	-11	13
8	Highridge United	11	4	0	7	29	33	-4	12
9	Longwell Green Sports Res	15	2	4	9	32	36	-4	10
10	Chipping Sodbury Town Res	11	3	1	7	21	36	-15	10
11	Lebeq	11	3	1	7	15	30	-15	10

DIVISION ONE

		P	W	D	L	F	A	GD	Pts
1	Bristol Manor Farm Res	11	9	1	1	35	17	18	28
2	Nicholas Wanderers	13	8	2	3	36	16	20	26
3	Bradley Stoke Town	16	6	5	5	40	30	10	23
4	AEK Boco Res	12	6	4	2	35	19	16	22
5	Hallen Res	11	6	3	2	36	22	14	21
6	Hambrook	11	5	3	3	31	22	9	18
7	De Veys	12	4	2	6	22	39	-17	14
8	Iron Acton	12	4	1	7	25	32	-7	13
9	Shirehampton Res	10	2	3	5	13	24	-11	9
10	DRG SV Frenchay	11	2	1	8	7	30	-23	7
11	Greyfriars Athletic	11	0	1	10	15	44	-29	1

BROMLEY AND SOUTH LONDON FOOTBALL LEAGUE

PREMIER DIVISION

		P	W	D	L	F	A	GD	Pts
1	Old Roan	12	9	2	1	57	15	42	29
2	BALMA	13	9	1	3	47	17	30	28
3	FC Greenwich	13	8	1	4	43	28	15	25
4	Eltham Town	11	8	1	2	45	32	13	25
5	AMG Ballerz	13	6	2	5	46	28	18	20
6	Bermondsey Town	14	5	1	8	38	47	-9	16
7	West Bromley Albion	12	3	6	3	23	45	-22	12
8	Leyton Athletic Res	13	1	2	10	21	39	-18	5
9	Elite Performance	11	1	1	11	14	83	-69	4

DIVISION ONE

		P	W	D	L	F	A	GD	Pts
1	Teviot Rangers	12	10	0	2	38	13	25	30
2	Russellers	11	6	1	4	26	19	7	19
3	Eltham Town Res	9	4	2	3	19	20	-1	14
4	Agenda	12	4	2	6	27	33	-6	14
5	Welling Park Res	13	3	2	8	26	44	-18	11
6	Ground Hoppers	6	3	1	2	14	15	-1	10
7	Red Velvet Res	9	2	3	4	20	24	-4	9
8	Farnborough OBG 3rds	8	2	1	5	20	22	-2	7

DIVISION TWO

		P	W	D	L	F	A	GD	Pts
1	Eden Park	13	10	0	3	49	22	27	30
2	Erith & Belvedere FC Res	14	8	3	3	34	30	4	27
3	Farnborough OBG 4ths	12	7	0	5	35	28	7	21
4	Eltham Eagles	10	7	0	3	23	16	7	21
5	South Dulwich	10	6	2	2	34	17	17	20
6	Crofton Albion	10	5	1	4	23	22	1	16
7	New Russellers A	11	4	1	6	15	17	-2	13
8	GL	13	2	1	10	17	35	-18	7
9	Wickham Park	9	1	1	7	16	31	-15	4
10	Beckenham	10	1	1	8	11	39	-28	4

DIVISION THREE

		P	W	D	L	F	A	GD	Pts
1	TNS United	15	14	0	1	71	21	50	42
2	STC Sports	13	12	1	0	56	23	33	37
3	Teviot Rangers Res	17	10	1	6	50	29	21	31
4	Eltham Eagles Res	18	9	3	6	49	51	-2	30
5	Matagalpa	17	8	2	7	40	37	3	26
6	Charlton Athletic Deaf	15	7	3	5	41	36	5	24
7	Slade Green Knights	16	7	2	7	39	35	4	23
8	Dulwich Village Res	18	5	4	9	37	42	-5	19
9	Catford	17	5	3	9	34	47	-13	18
10	Latter Day Saints	18	5	0	13	46	60	-14	15
11	FC Peak	18	4	1	13	32	77	-45	13
12	South East Athletic A	18	1	1	16	21	58	-37	5

STEP 8+ LEAGUE TABLES

CENTRAL & SOUTH NORFOLK LEAGUE

DIVISION ONE

		P	W	D	L	F	A	GD	Pts
1	Briston	14	12	2	0	65	17	48	38
2	Dussindale Rovers Res	16	11	3	2	45	23	22	36
3	Hethersett Athletic	16	10	2	4	28	22	6	32
4	Hockering	17	7	6	4	39	39	0	27
5	Dereham Taverners	13	6	4	3	30	24	6	22
6	Watton United Res	16	5	2	9	32	33	-1	17
7	Norwich Medics	15	5	1	9	21	30	-9	16
8	Redgrave Rangers	13	5	0	8	25	33	-8	15
9	Rockland United	16	2	6	8	22	38	-16	12
10	UEA 'A'	15	3	2	10	25	34	-9	11
11	Castle Acre Swifts Res	17	3	2	12	18	57	-39	11

DIVISION TWO

		P	W	D	L	F	A	GD	Pts
1	Brandon Town Res	12	10	2	0	44	7	37	32
2	Wensum Albion	14	10	1	3	34	21	13	31
3	Feltwell United	12	9	2	1	34	15	19	29
4	Briston Res	13	7	2	4	36	24	12	23
5	Yaxham	13	5	2	6	22	30	-8	17
6	Longham Res	15	4	2	9	35	52	-17	14
7	Bridgham United	15	3	3	9	28	39	-11	12
8	Gressenhall	16	3	1	12	24	49	-25	10
9	Tacolneston Res	14	2	3	9	20	40	-20	9

DIVISION THREE

		P	W	D	L	F	A	GD	Pts
1	Rockland United Res	15	14	0	1	96	24	72	42
2	Sprowston Athletic Res	17	13	1	3	72	20	52	40
3	Cockers	15	11	1	3	56	21	35	34
4	Hempnall Res	14	8	3	3	45	21	24	27
5	Litcham Youth Club	16	7	5	4	39	33	6	26
6	Bowthorpe Rovers	16	8	2	6	36	35	1	26
7	Bar 33	17	5	0	12	30	50	-20	15
8	Hockering Res	14	4	1	9	32	52	-20	13
9	Narborough Res	16	1	2	13	8	45	-37	5
10	AFC Weeting	18	0	1	17	13	126	-113	1

DIVISION FOUR

		P	W	D	L	F	A	GD	Pts
1	Hornets	18	13	3	2	52	27	25	42
2	Lakenheath Casuals	17	12	3	2	66	19	47	39
3	Costessey Sports Res	17	12	3	2	59	31	28	39
4	Firside Athletic	17	10	4	3	62	27	35	34
5	West Row Gunners	18	8	7	3	61	37	24	31
6	Diligent	15	7	2	6	32	29	3	23
7	Weasenham	15	7	1	7	42	31	11	22
8	Home Care United	18	6	3	9	45	50	-5	21
9	Redgrave Rangers Res	18	5	2	11	38	78	-40	17
10	Viking	17	4	2	11	41	57	-16	14
11	Necton Res	18	2	0	16	32	87	-55	6
12	Colkirk	18	2	0	16	18	75	-57	6

CHELTENHAM ASSOCIATION FOOTBALL LEAGUE

DIVISION ONE

		P	W	D	L	F	A	GD	Pts
1	Tewkesbury Town	14	10	2	2	47	21	26	32
2	Malvern Vale	18	8	3	7	45	33	12	27
3	Dowty Dynamos	15	8	1	6	31	25	6	25
4	Whaddon United	11	7	3	1	41	11	30	24
5	Kings	15	7	3	5	29	21	8	24
6	Prestbury Rovers	13	7	2	4	28	21	7	23
7	Bishops Cleeve FC A	10	7	1	2	31	17	14	22
8	Shurdington Rovers	13	5	2	6	25	30	-5	17
9	Bredon Res	14	5	1	8	21	40	-19	15*
10	Cheltenham Civil Service Res	12	4	2	6	25	23	2	14
11	Southside Star	13	3	5	5	28	29	-1	14
12	Hanley Swan	12	4	2	6	23	35	-12	14
13	AFC Renegades	15	3	4	8	28	42	-14	13
14	Newton	13	0	1	12	10	64	-54	0*

DIVISION TWO

		P	W	D	L	F	A	GD	Pts
1	Prestbury Rovers Res	14	11	1	2	52	25	27	33*
2	Smiths Barometrics Athletic Res	13	10	2	1	35	14	21	32
3	Gala Wilton Res	14	8	2	4	47	23	24	26
4	Windyridge Rovers	10	6	1	3	24	21	3	19
5	St Pauls United	13	5	3	5	39	20	19	18
6	Leckhampton Rovers	12	6	0	6	28	28	0	18
7	Brockworth Albion Res	13	4	3	6	19	29	-10	15
8	Welland Res	13	5	0	8	24	34	-10	14*
9	Fintan	14	4	1	9	33	42	-9	13
10	Pittville United	15	3	1	11	17	52	-35	10
11	Andoversford Res	13	3	0	10	16	46	-30	9

DIVISION THREE

		P	W	D	L	F	A	GD	Pts
1	Smiths Barometrics Athletic 3rds	15	11	1	3	49	27	22	34
2	FC Lakeside Res	11	11	0	0	60	18	42	33
3	Cheltenham United	17	9	2	6	54	40	14	29
4	Cheltenham Civil Service 3rds	15	9	1	5	45	31	14	28
5	Charlton Rovers Res	8	5	2	1	24	16	8	17
6	303 Squadron	12	4	2	6	23	39	-16	14
7	Worcester City Royals	11	4	1	6	27	24	3	13
8	Southside Star FC Res	12	4	1	7	29	41	-12	13
9	Tewkesbury Town Res	16	4	0	12	34	61	-27	12
10	Falcons Res	14	3	1	10	29	48	-19	10
11	Malvern Vale FC Res	13	2	1	10	23	52	-29	7

DIVISION FOUR

		P	W	D	L	F	A	GD	Pts
1	Tewkesbury Athletic	17	11	1	5	50	23	27	34
2	Winchcombe Town Res	15	9	3	3	43	20	23	30
3	AFC Cheltenham	10	9	1	0	61	14	47	28
4	Kempsey Corinthians	10	9	0	1	39	9	30	27
5	Fintan Res	12	6	4	2	37	29	8	22
6	Woodmancote United	12	7	0	5	35	38	-3	21
7	Apperley	12	6	0	6	25	31	-6	17*
8	Gala Wilton 3rds	14	5	0	9	29	43	-14	14*
9	AFC Renegades Res	13	4	1	8	32	66	-34	13
10	Cheltenham Saracens 3rds	13	4	1	8	27	46	-19	11*
11	Bishops Cleeve FC Dev	10	2	2	6	23	23	0	8
12	Charlton Rovers 3rds	14	2	1	11	27	55	-28	6*
13	Pittville United Res	14	1	2	11	16	47	-31	4*

CORNWALL COMBINATION LEAGUE

		P	W	D	L	F	A	GD	Pts
1	Pendeen Rovers	19	17	0	2	62	15	47	51
2	Porthleven Res	18	15	0	3	50	14	36	45
3	Hayle Res	21	14	1	6	73	27	46	43
4	Ruan Minor	18	14	0	4	56	28	28	42
5	St Day Res	21	9	2	10	39	63	-24	29
6	Lizard Argyle	18	8	1	9	30	27	3	25
7	RNAS Culdrose	16	7	3	6	40	29	11	24
8	Penryn Athletic Res	16	7	3	6	37	33	4	21*
9	Rosudgeon	18	6	3	9	42	45	-3	21
10	Marazion	20	5	3	12	31	52	-21	18
11	Wendron United Thirds	16	5	2	9	24	34	-10	17
12	Helston Athletic Thirds	15	3	1	11	19	47	-28	10
13	St Agnes Res	15	2	1	12	16	55	-39	7
14	Perranporth Res	19	3	0	16	30	80	-50	0*

Carharrack withdrew after nine games.

DEVON & EXETER LEAGUE

PREMIER DIVISION	P	W	D	L	F	A	GD	Pts
1 Okehampton Argyle	19	16	1	2	73	25	48	49
2 Feniton	20	12	2	6	49	31	18	38
3 Lapford	17	11	3	3	53	22	31	36
4 Cronies	13	11	1	1	44	14	30	34
5 Lyme Regis	15	10	0	5	52	27	25	30
6 Beer Albion	16	9	3	4	36	25	11	30
7 Bampton	13	9	1	3	44	20	24	28
8 University of Exeter Res	15	8	2	5	44	44	0	26
9 Whipton & Pinhoe	16	8	0	8	32	35	-3	24
10 Upottery	17	6	3	8	31	40	-9	21
11 Colyton	18	5	3	10	29	39	-10	18
12 Seaton Town	22	5	3	14	40	71	-31	18
13 Chagford	16	4	2	10	33	53	-20	14
14 Kentisbeare	19	3	3	13	31	54	-23	12
15 Hatherleigh Town	15	0	4	11	21	57	-36	4
16 Sidmouth Town Res	17	1	1	15	16	71	-55	4

DIVISIOn ONE	P	W	D	L	F	A	GD	Pts
1 Exwick Villa Res	15	12	1	2	69	25	44	37
2 Thorverton	12	8	2	2	36	14	22	26
3 Chard Town Res	15	7	3	5	35	24	11	24
4 Crediton United Res	15	7	1	7	32	28	4	22
5 Newtown Res	16	6	4	6	34	47	-13	22
6 Wellington Res	16	5	6	5	34	29	5	21
7 Alphington Res	13	6	2	5	30	25	5	20
8 University of Exeter 3rds	13	5	4	4	27	23	4	19
9 Winchester	10	6	1	3	23	20	3	19
10 Dawlish United	13	5	1	7	30	42	-12	15*
11 Bow Amateur Athletic Club	12	3	4	5	21	26	-5	13
12 Lympstone	17	2	4	11	14	44	-30	10
13 Tipton St John	13	1	1	11	12	50	-38	4

DIVISION TWO	P	W	D	L	F	A	GD	Pts
1 Elmore Res	13	13	0	0	70	6	64	39
2 Beer Albion Res	18	11	2	5	61	31	30	35
3 University of Exeter 4ths	16	10	3	3	48	32	16	33
4 East Budleigh	18	10	1	7	44	33	11	31
5 Otterton	15	9	3	3	42	34	8	30
6 Sandford	16	8	2	6	53	36	17	26
7 Halwill	15	8	2	5	39	42	-3	26
8 Tedburn St Mary	17	6	3	8	36	45	-9	21
9 Uplowman Athletic	13	5	2	6	27	33	-6	17
10 Newton St Cyres	15	5	2	8	30	44	-14	17
11 Alphington 3rds	16	4	4	8	29	44	-15	16
12 Honiton Town Res	18	3	2	13	37	71	-34	11
13 Clyst Valley Res	14	2	0	12	21	53	-32	5*
14 Heavitree United Res	14	2	0	12	23	56	-33	5*

DIVISION THREE	P	W	D	L	F	A	GD	Pts
1 North Tawton	16	8	3	5	31	37	-6	27
2 Exmouth Spartans	14	8	2	4	59	33	26	26
3 University of Exeter 5ths	11	8	1	2	37	23	14	25
4 Dunkeswell Rovers	13	7	2	4	34	30	4	23
5 Halwill Res	12	6	3	3	46	29	17	21
6 Lyme Regis Res	15	6	2	7	31	32	-1	20
7 Winkleigh	11	6	1	4	37	25	12	19
8 Teignmouth Res	12	6	1	5	31	29	2	18*
9 Hemyock	15	4	4	7	22	29	-7	16
10 Westexe Park Rangers	9	4	2	3	25	16	9	14
11 Axmouth United	12	3	2	7	20	29	-9	11
12 Pinhoe	12	2	0	10	20	45	-25	6
13 Upottery Res	13	1	3	9	19	55	-36	6

DIVISION FOUR	P	W	D	L	F	A	GD	Pts
1 Central	20	12	1	7	61	32	29	37
2 Cranbrook	14	9	2	3	54	22	32	29
3 Devon Yeoman	13	9	1	3	33	25	8	28
4 Culm United	15	9	1	5	28	36	-8	28
5 Kentisbeare Res	15	9	1	5	55	32	23	27*
6 Millwey Rise	14	9	0	5	45	31	14	27
7 Feniton Res	15	8	0	7	36	31	5	24
8 St Martins Res	14	5	4	5	31	25	6	19
9 Sidmouth Town 3rds	12	6	0	6	37	45	-8	18
10 Sampford Peverell	14	5	1	8	39	43	-4	16
11 Bampton Res	14	5	0	9	36	36	0	14*
12 Colyton Res	15	3	0	12	26	82	-56	9
13 Cheriton Fitzpaine	17	1	1	15	22	63	-41	4

DIVISION FIVE	P	W	D	L	F	A	GD	Pts
1 Exmouth Rovers	14	14	0	0	61	10	51	42
2 Royal Oak	12	9	2	1	40	13	27	29
3 Broadclyst	13	9	1	3	54	21	33	28
4 East Budleigh Res	13	6	2	5	36	25	11	20
5 University of Exeter 6ths	10	6	0	4	27	26	1	18
6 Exeter United	13	5	3	5	31	32	-1	18
7 Witheridge Res	11	4	1	6	23	28	-5	13
8 Bravehearts	13	3	0	10	30	63	-33	9
9 Awliscombe	10	2	1	7	9	26	-17	7
10 Farway United	6	2	0	4	6	14	-8	6
11 Amory Green Rovers	11	2	0	9	24	56	-32	6
12 Lapford Res	12	1	2	9	13	40	-27	5

DIVISION SIX	P	W	D	L	F	A	GD	Pts
1 Bishop Blaize FC	12	12	0	0	42	12	30	36
2 Elmore 3rds	14	9	1	4	57	35	22	28
3 Topsham Town Res	14	8	2	4	39	38	1	26
4 Dawlish United Res	11	7	1	3	39	19	20	22
5 Chagford Res	14	6	2	6	34	41	-7	20
6 Winchester Res	8	5	1	2	28	10	18	16
7 Offwell Rangers FC	11	4	3	4	27	21	6	15
8 Cullompton Rangers Res	10	2	4	4	20	25	-5	10
9 Seaton Town Res	13	3	1	9	18	41	-23	9*
10 Otterton Res	16	2	2	12	31	64	-33	7*
11 Bradninch	13	1	1	11	21	50	-29	4

DIVISION SEVEN	P	W	D	L	F	A	GD	Pts
1 Okehampton Argyle Res	19	16	3	0	123	16	107	51
2 Central Res	20	13	3	4	80	47	33	42
3 AFC Exe	12	11	1	0	64	12	52	34
4 Cheriton Fitzpaine AFC Res	17	10	1	6	50	39	11	31
5 University of Exeter 7ths	13	10	0	3	52	21	31	30
6 Devon Yeoman Res	16	8	2	6	51	44	7	26
7 Countess Wear Rovers	21	7	2	12	38	49	-11	23
8 Culm United Res	13	6	3	4	43	35	8	21
9 Lympstone Res	18	6	2	10	40	54	-14	19*
10 Sandford Res	16	4	4	8	36	58	-22	16
11 Priory	15	4	2	9	30	47	-17	14
12 Sidmouth Town 4ths	16	3	3	10	26	57	-31	12
13 HT Dons	13	3	1	9	22	49	-27	10
14 City Raiders AFC	21	0	1	20	10	137	-127	1

DIVISION EIGHT	P	W	D	L	F	A	GD	Pts
1 Broadclyst Ress	16	14	0	2	79	20	59	42
2 Witheridge 3rds	17	13	1	3	62	24	38	40
3 Ottery St Mary AFC Res	17	11	2	4	51	23	28	35
4 Kenn Valley United	20	11	0	9	95	52	43	33
5 Bow Amateur Athletic Club Res	17	10	2	5	51	40	11	32
6 Exmouth Town 3rds	17	9	2	6	71	56	15	29
7 University of Exeter 8ths	14	9	0	5	46	31	15	27
8 Newton St Cyres Res	13	6	1	6	38	37	1	19
9 Bradninch Ress	19	4	2	13	37	75	-38	14
10 Millwey Rise Res	14	4	1	9	19	41	-22	13
11 Amory Green Rovers Res	16	4	0	11	24	70	-46	13
12 Westexe Park Rangers Res	11	4	0	7	19	30	-11	12
13 Dawlish United 3rds	18	5	0	13	45	76	-31	11*
14 Tedburn St Mary Res	13	0	2	13	27	89	-62	6

STEP 8+ LEAGUE TABLES

DORSET LEAGUE

SENIOR DIVISION

	P	W	D	L	F	A	GD	Pts
1 Poole Borough	15	10	3	2	44	23	21	33
2 Mere Town FC	11	9	1	1	42	9	33	28
3 Tisbury United	13	9	1	3	41	18	23	28
4 Sturminster Marshall	15	8	4	3	46	25	21	28
5 Broadstone FC Seniors	18	9	1	8	48	44	4	28
6 Westland Sports Res	18	8	2	8	46	51	-5	26
7 Cranborne	19	8	2	9	42	55	-13	26
8 Stalbridge	17	8	1	8	38	33	5	25
9 Merley Cobham Sports Res	16	6	1	9	30	49	-19	19
10 Beaminster	13	5	3	5	30	20	10	18
11 Chickerell United	14	6	0	8	32	25	7	18
12 Wincanton Town Res	13	3	2	8	25	49	-24	11
13 AFC Blandford	13	2	1	10	30	60	-30	6*
14 Dorchester Sports Res	15	3	0	12	28	61	-33	5*

DIVISION ONE

	P	W	D	L	F	A	GD	Pts
1 Hamworthy Recreation Res	14	13	0	1	66	21	45	39
2 Allendale	14	10	2	2	45	24	21	32
3 Bournemouth Sports Res	19	10	1	8	54	44	10	31
4 Upwey and Broadwey	12	9	1	2	38	18	20	28
5 Blandford United Res	16	8	2	6	37	31	6	26
6 Alderholt	15	7	4	4	43	36	7	25
7 Gillingham Town Dons	12	7	1	4	57	24	33	22
8 Wool United Team	15	6	2	7	32	43	-11	20
9 Wareham Rangers Res	16	4	2	10	24	57	-33	14
10 Swanage Town And Herston Res	14	3	0	11	28	37	-9	9
11 Balti Sports Res	10	3	0	7	23	33	-10	9
12 Portland Town	11	2	0	9	20	41	-21	6
13 Boscombe Polonia	14	1	1	12	18	76	-58	3*

DIVISION TWO

	P	W	D	L	F	A	GD	Pts
1 Canford United	17	14	1	2	72	21	51	43
2 Bridport 3rd Team	18	13	3	2	49	17	32	42
3 Shaftesbury Town Colts	15	13	1	1	66	19	47	40
4 Bournemouth Sports Lions	20	11	2	7	56	36	20	35
5 Piddlehinton United	16	9	4	3	35	22	13	31
6 Milborne Port Res	15	8	0	7	31	34	-3	24
7 Broadmayne	18	7	2	9	32	52	-20	23
8 Donhead United	17	7	1	9	49	50	-1	22
9 Corfe Mullen United Utd	16	5	4	7	31	35	-4	19
10 Gillingham Town Phoenix	15	5	2	8	30	41	-11	17
11 Broadstone FC Seniors Res	17	3	5	9	26	48	-22	14
12 Maiden Newton & Cattistock	15	4	1	10	26	44	-18	13
13 Allendale Res	15	4	0	11	24	49	-25	12
14 Portesham United	16	5	0	11	33	48	-15	11*
15 Wool United Reserve Team	18	1	4	13	30	74	-44	7

DIVISION THREE

	P	W	D	L	F	A	GD	Pts
1 Puddletown	21	18	1	2	85	25	60	56
2 Bere Regis	20	15	3	2	81	31	50	48
3 Bournemouth Sports Phoenix	24	12	5	7	77	44	33	41
4 Redlands Rebels	19	12	2	5	65	52	13	38
5 Handley Sports	19	11	3	5	55	28	27	36
6 Portland United Youth Panthers	19	10	3	6	52	42	10	33
7 Poole Bay Team	20	10	2	8	59	50	9	32
8 Okeford United	16	8	2	6	36	27	9	26
9 Portland Town Res	16	7	3	6	41	33	8	24
10 Chickerell United Res	17	6	6	5	38	37	1	24
11 Marnhull	25	6	2	17	42	95	-53	20
12 Sturminster Newton United Res	19	4	6	9	36	47	-11	18
13 Milborne Sports	18	3	3	12	43	56	-13	12
14 Corfe Castle Res	18	2	4	12	23	49	-26	10
15 Donhead United Res	19	3	2	14	44	106	-62	10*
16 Piddlehinton United Res	18	2	2	14	23	78	-55	8

DIVISION FOUR

	P	W	D	L	F	A	GD	Pts
1 Porton Sports FC	18	11	4	3	54	23	31	37
2 D.I. United	14	11	2	1	40	11	29	35
3 Poole Borough Res	14	10	1	3	67	28	39	31
4 Chickerell United Youth Colts	15	8	4	3	31	23	8	28
5 Lytchett Matravers	14	8	2	4	55	26	29	26
6 Shillingstone	18	5	6	7	40	46	-6	21
7 Poole Bay Res	16	6	2	8	50	41	9	20
8 Wyke Regis	12	6	2	4	32	26	6	20
9 Crossways Spitfires	17	6	2	9	40	47	-7	20
10 Portland United Youth Panthers Res	17	5	3	9	31	54	-23	18
11 Tisbury United Res	15	4	5	6	21	35	-14	17
12 Portland Town Dev	15	5	1	9	22	50	-28	16
13 Puddletown FC Res	20	4	3	13	20	61	-41	15
14 Alderholt Res	13	4	3	6	25	35	-10	11
15 Okeford United Res	14	3	3	8	29	51	-22	11*

EAST CORNWALL PREMIER LEAGUE

PREMIER DIVISION

	P	W	D	L	F	A	GD	Pts
1 Mount Gould	17	15	1	1	89	15	74	46
2 St Dominick	17	13	1	3	97	19	78	40
3 Torpoint Athletic 3rds	19	12	3	4	46	32	14	39
4 Foxhole Stars	17	12	2	3	72	24	48	38
5 St Minver	15	9	5	1	58	20	38	32
6 Veryan	16	9	4	3	50	29	21	31
7 St Cleer	16	9	2	5	53	33	20	29
8 St Stephen	16	7	4	5	50	37	13	25
9 Newquay Res	22	5	8	9	43	67	-24	23
10 Roche	15	6	3	6	30	39	-9	21
11 Gerrans & St Mawes Utd	18	6	3	9	32	52	-20	21
12 Plymouth Marjon Res	18	5	4	9	28	47	-19	19
13 Looe Town FC	17	5	2	10	33	51	-18	17
14 North Petherwin	17	6	1	10	30	46	-16	16*
15 Padstow United	23	2	6	15	23	103	-80	12
16 St Teath	17	2	0	15	18	75	-57	6
17 St Blazey Res	18	1	1	16	17	80	-63	1*

HALIFAX & DISTRICT LEAGUE

PREMIER DIVISION

	P	W	D	L	F	A	GD	Pts
1 Sowerby Bridge	13	11	2	0	56	18	38	35
2 Shelf	15	10	2	3	52	26	26	32
3 Shelf United	14	10	0	4	51	27	24	30
4 Hebden Royd Red Star	12	7	2	3	46	23	23	23
5 Greetland	14	7	0	7	26	31	-5	21
6 Midgley United	14	5	4	5	37	33	4	19
7 AFC Illingworth St Mary's	17	4	1	12	38	97	-59	13
8 Northowram	16	3	3	10	33	48	-15	12
9 Denholme United	12	3	2	7	18	35	-17	11
10 Sowerby United	15	2	2	11	22	41	-19	8

DIVISION ONE

	P	W	D	L	F	A	GD	Pts
1 AFC Crossleys	13	10	1	2	59	15	44	31
2 Ryburn United	13	8	4	1	36	25	11	28
3 Calder 76	13	9	0	4	38	21	17	24*
4 St Columbas	13	6	3	4	30	25	5	21
5 Salem	13	6	1	6	45	43	2	19
6 Shelf United Res	14	3	2	9	24	52	-28	11
7 Midgley United Res	13	2	2	9	17	36	-19	8
8 Northowram Res	12	1	1	10	10	42	-32	4*

DIVISION TWO

	P	W	D	L	F	A	GD	Pts
1 Hebden Royd Red Star Res	15	13	1	1	76	30	46	40
2 Ivy House	16	12	0	4	86	34	52	36
3 Flying Dutchman	17	10	2	5	63	45	18	32
4 AFC Crossleys Res	14	8	0	6	53	38	15	24
5 Sowerby Bridge Res	13	7	0	6	39	30	9	21
6 Shelf FC Res	16	7	0	9	46	57	-11	21
7 Sowerby United Res	16	6	3	8	28	45	-17	21
8 Calder 76 Res	13	6	1	6	29	39	-10	19
9 Greetland Res	15	5	1	9	22	40	-18	16
10 St Columbas Res	15	3	1	11	23	53	-30	10
11 Warley Rangers 2017	17	2	1	14	24	78	-54	7

HUDDERSFIELD AND DISTRICT ASSOCIATION FOOTBALL LEAGUE

DIVISION ONE

	P	W	D	L	F	A	GD	Pts
1 Linthwaite Athletic	21	16	3	2	84	36	48	51
2 Heywood Irish Centre	17	12	1	4	49	24	25	37
2 Berry Brow	17	11	2	4	66	30	36	35
3 Honley	15	10	2	3	52	22	30	32
4 Holmbridge	15	8	4	3	34	21	13	28
5 Linthwaite Athletic	11	8	2	1	32	10	22	26
6 Newsome	14	7	2	5	35	39	-4	23
7 Skelmanthorpe A.	14	6	3	5	35	26	9	21
8 Scholes A.	15	6	2	7	23	24	-1	20
9 Shepley	18	4	2	12	27	45	-18	14
10 Slaithwaite United	16	3	2	11	11	42	-31	11
11 Fothergill & Whittles	18	3	1	14	25	36	-11	10
12 Diggle	18	1	1	16	19	89	-70	4

DIVISION TWO

		P	W	D	L	F	A	GD	Pts
1	AFC Lindley	18	12	3	3	48	22	26	39
2	Almondbury Woolpack	19	13	0	6	64	52	12	39
3	Shelley	20	12	1	7	72	34	38	37
4	Junction	16	11	1	4	53	26	27	34
5	Dalton Dynamoes	13	9	1	3	38	18	20	28
6	Britannia Sports	15	9	1	5	40	33	7	28
7	Netherton	16	7	2	7	41	31	10	23
8	Hepworth United	17	6	1	10	29	46	-17	19
9	Cumberworth	15	5	2	8	32	46	-14	17
10	Kirkheaton Rovers	19	4	1	14	27	68	-41	13
11	Lepton Highlanders	18	3	1	14	22	56	-34	10
12	H.V.Academicals	16	2	2	12	19	53	-34	8

DIVISION THREE

		P	W	D	L	F	A	GD	Pts
1	Meltham Athletic	16	10	0	6	49	38	11	30
2	Kirkburton	13	8	4	1	48	19	29	28
3	Grange Moor Saints A.	13	8	3	2	45	28	17	27
4	AFC Dalton	14	8	3	3	37	25	12	27
5	Scissett	13	7	5	1	40	18	22	26
6	Huddersfield YM	14	7	4	3	54	24	30	25
7	Moorside	17	7	3	7	41	52	-11	24
8	Deighton	16	4	4	8	45	61	-16	16
9	Sporting C.A.V.	15	4	3	8	44	47	-3	15
10	Brook Motors	16	2	2	12	25	70	-45	8
11	Hade Edge A.	15	0	1	14	13	59	-46	1

DIVISION FOUR

		P	W	D	L	F	A	GD	Pts
1	Mount	14	8	3	3	39	32	7	27
2	Flockton	10	7	1	2	37	14	23	22
3	Cartworth Moor A.	12	6	1	5	24	20	4	19
4	Brighouse Athletic	10	5	0	5	23	26	-3	15
5	Wooldale Wanderers	7	4	0	3	14	6	8	12
6	Uppermill	12	2	2	8	23	40	-17	8
7	Almondbury Athletic	11	2	1	8	11	33	-22	7

HARROGATE AND DISTRICT FOOTBALL LEAGUE

PREMIER DIVISION

		P	W	D	L	F	A	GD	Pts
1	Harlow Hill	18	13	5	0	69	22	47	44
1	Bardsey	15	10	1	4	47	24	23	31
2	Bramhope A	10	9	1	0	55	14	41	28
3	Harlow Hill	14	8	2	4	50	22	28	26
4	Bedale AFC Res	12	7	3	2	50	23	27	24
5	Grangefield Old Boys	12	7	3	2	32	12	20	24
6	Ventus Yeadon Celtic	14	6	2	6	35	32	3	20
7	Pannal Sports	17	3	4	10	31	63	-32	13
8	Beckwithshaw Saints	13	3	0	10	23	59	-36	9
9	Hampsthwaite	16	3	1	12	29	88	-59	9*
10	Kirkstall Crusaders	11	1	3	7	23	38	-15	6

DIVISION ONE

		P	W	D	L	F	A	GD	Pts
1	Ripon City Res	12	11	1	0	78	11	67	34
2	Hampsthwaite United	13	11	0	2	67	20	47	33
3	Harrogate Old Boys	18	9	4	5	61	55	6	31
4	Burley Trojans	15	8	3	4	37	35	2	27
5	Boroughbridge Dev	14	8	2	4	49	31	18	26
6	Kirkby Malzeard	14	6	4	4	39	24	15	22
7	Dalton Athletic	15	6	1	8	36	40	-4	18*
8	Thirsk Falcons Develop	15	5	2	8	34	64	-30	17
9	Beckwithshaw Saints Res	17	5	0	12	36	63	-27	15
10	Harlow Hill Res	17	5	0	12	23	44	-21	14*
11	Wetherby Athletic Res	16	0	1	15	25	98	-73	1

LOWESTOFT & DISTRICT LEAGUE

DIVISION ONE

		P	W	D	L	F	A	GD	Pts
1	Spexhall	21	18	2	1	86	25	61	56
2	Carlton Colville Town	19	18	0	1	96	25	71	54
3	Waveney A	22	14	3	5	72	32	40	45
4	Kirkley & Pakefield U23	21	14	2	5	72	30	42	44
5	Mariners	23	9	5	9	69	58	11	32
6	Loddon United Res	19	9	4	6	65	32	33	31
7	& Last	20	8	3	9	51	51	0	27
8	Beccles Caxton Res	20	7	6	7	43	51	-8	27
9	Earsham Res	23	7	6	10	50	55	-5	21*
10	Bungay Town A	20	6	0	14	35	74	-39	18
11	Redwood United	21	4	2	15	51	87	-36	14
12	Norton Athletic Res	20	2	3	15	29	74	-45	9
13	Crusaders	21	1	0	20	20	145	-125	3

DIVISION ONE

		P	W	D	L	F	A	GD	Pts
1	Kirkley & Pakefield B	20	16	2	2	90	26	64	50
2	Mutford & Wrentham Res	21	14	2	5	82	40	42	44
3	Whitehorse	20	13	0	7	73	42	31	39
4	Gunton	21	13	2	6	101	36	65	38*
5	AFC Waveney	20	11	3	6	54	37	17	36
6	Carlton Colville Town Res	20	10	3	7	66	50	16	33
7	AFC Oulton	19	9	4	6	78	43	35	31
8	Beccles Town A	21	7	1	13	46	68	-22	22
9	Southwold Town Res	20	7	3	10	49	41	8	21*
10	Spexhall Huntsman & Hounds Res	18	6	2	10	43	53	-10	17*
11	Hawthorn United	20	2	0	18	25	135	-110	6
12	Corton Development	20	0	2	18	24	160	-136	-10*

MIDLANDS REGIONAL ALLIANCE

PREMIER DIVISION

		P	W	D	L	F	A	GD	Pts
1	Melbourne Dynamo	14	14	0	0	65	10	55	42
2	Little Eaton	15	8	3	4	43	33	10	27
3	Castle Donington	12	8	2	2	40	23	17	26
4	Allestree	14	8	0	6	36	23	13	24
5	Tibshelf	14	7	1	6	43	31	12	22
6	Derby Singh Brothers	13	8	1	4	32	25	7	22*
7	Rolls-Royce Leisure	15	6	3	6	27	25	2	21
8	Moira United	14	5	4	5	33	32	1	19
9	Mayfield	15	5	3	7	31	38	-7	18
10	Stapenhill Development	14	5	2	7	28	38	-10	17
11	Shirebrook Rangers	14	4	4	6	21	28	-7	16
12	Rowsley '86 Res	13	3	2	8	17	42	-25	11
13	Ashbourne Res	16	2	4	10	19	53	-34	10
14	Cromford & Wirksworth Town Res	17	2	1	14	14	48	-34	7

DIVISION ONE

		P	W	D	L	F	A	GD	Pts
1	Real Madina	14	11	0	3	58	31	27	33
2	Sleetmoor United	10	9	1	0	44	12	32	28
3	Melbourne Dynamo Res	14	9	1	4	50	25	25	28
4	Netherseal St Peter's Sports	13	6	2	5	33	31	2	20
5	Little Eaton Res	12	5	2	5	38	27	11	17
6	Holbrook St Michaels Juniors	12	5	2	5	39	31	8	17
7	Willington	9	5	0	4	27	17	10	15
8	Derby Athletic	11	3	1	7	26	33	-7	10
9	Burton United	15	3	1	11	14	75	-61	10
10	Castle Donington Res	10	4	0	6	24	34	-10	9*
11	Sherwin	16	2	2	12	37	74	-37	8

DIVISION TWO

		P	W	D	L	F	A	GD	Pts
1	Acorn Albion	12	11	0	1	72	6	66	33
2	Asha Res	14	8	0	6	38	28	10	24
3	Bargate Rovers	10	7	2	1	32	13	19	23
4	Wirksworth Ivanhoe Res	10	6	1	3	28	11	17	19
5	Cromford & Wirksworth Town Dev	13	5	3	5	25	39	-14	18
6	Stenson	9	5	2	2	23	12	11	17
7	Willington Res	12	5	0	7	26	44	-18	15
8	South Normanton Colts	13	5	2	6	33	51	-18	15
9	G A D Khalsa Sports	10	3	0	7	25	61	-36	9
10	Punjab United	9	2	1	6	13	20	-7	4*
11	South Normanton United	10	1	0	8	18	48	-30	3

STEP 8+ LEAGUE TABLES

MID-SOMERSET LEAGUE

PREMIER DIVISION

		P	W	D	L	F	A	GD	Pts
1	Coleford Athletic	16	10	0	6	86	38	48	30
2	Peasedown Albion	12	9	1	2	55	17	38	28
3	Purnell Sports	11	7	1	3	63	18	45	22
4	Westhill Sports	14	7	1	6	59	28	31	22
5	Bath Villa	10	7	0	3	50	17	33	21
6	Westfield Res	11	6	0	5	43	30	13	18
7	Victoria Sports	14	6	0	8	38	37	1	18
8	Pilton United	7	5	1	1	23	12	11	16
9	Evercreech Rovers	13	2	0	11	15	91	-76	5*
10	High Littleton	14	0	0	14	11	155	-144	0

DIVISION ONE

		P	W	D	L	F	A	GD	Pts
1	Weston	12	10	0	2	55	10	45	30
2	Peasedown Albion Res	12	9	2	1	42	31	11	29
3	Wells City A	8	7	0	1	44	11	33	21
4	Chilcompton Sports Res	9	5	1	3	26	27	-1	16
5	Belrose	9	4	1	4	16	20	-4	13
6	Chew Magna Res	9	4	1	4	16	24	-8	13
7	Wessex	12	4	0	8	27	30	-3	12
8	Somer Valley Sports	13	3	1	9	19	43	-24	10
9	Timsbury Athletic Res	8	2	0	6	8	20	-12	6
10	Clutton Res	10	0	0	10	8	45	-37	-1*

DIVISION TWO

		P	W	D	L	F	A	GD	Pts
1	Mendip Rangers	13	9	2	2	32	17	15	29
2	Farrington Gurney	9	6	2	1	42	16	26	20
3	Meadow Rangers	13	6	1	6	48	39	9	19
4	Frome Collegians Res	9	6	1	2	22	13	9	19
5	Pilton United Res	11	6	1	4	22	18	4	19
6	Peasedown Albion A	9	5	1	3	30	23	7	16
7	Stoke Rovers	7	4	1	2	22	10	12	13
8	Saltford Res	11	3	2	6	16	26	-10	9*
9	Timsbury Athletic A	12	2	2	8	15	40	-25	8
10	Coleford Athletic Res	12	2	1	9	23	39	-16	7
11	Glastonbury Res	10	1	2	7	10	41	-31	2*

DIVISION THREE

		P	W	D	L	F	A	GD	Pts
1	Haydon Sports	13	11	1	1	58	7	51	34
2	Mells & Vobster	14	10	2	2	61	17	44	32
3	FC Lantokay	14	9	3	2	46	24	22	29*
4	Shepton Mallet Res	13	9	1	3	41	20	21	28
5	Paulton Rovers FC Res	11	8	0	3	29	17	12	24
6	Chilcompton Sports A	13	4	2	7	30	44	-14	14
7	Westfield A	12	3	1	8	13	33	-20	10
8	Somer Valley Sports Res	15	1	2	12	15	55	-40	5
9	Evercreech Rovers Res	8	0	1	7	9	42	-33	1
10	Chilcompton United	11	0	1	10	8	51	-43	1

NORTH WEST NORFOLK LEAGUE

DIVISION ONE

		P	W	D	L	F	A	GD	Pts
1	Snettisham	15	13	1	1	76	22	54	40
2	Birchwood	16	8	4	4	68	23	45	28
3	Terrington Tigers Youth	13	8	1	4	33	23	10	25
4	Heacham Res	13	7	1	5	26	21	5	22
5	Gayton United 'A'	15	6	4	5	38	40	-2	22
6	Dersingham Rovers Res	11	7	0	4	36	19	17	21
7	Denver	15	7	0	8	39	40	-1	21
8	King's Lynn Town "A"	17	6	2	9	47	35	12	20
9	Reffley Youth	14	5	2	7	34	26	8	17
10	Ingoldisthorpe	15	3	1	11	26	74	-48	10
11	AFC Lynn Napier Res	16	2	0	14	9	109	-100	6

DIVISION TWO

		P	W	D	L	F	A	GD	Pts
1	Marshland Saints	13	10	1	2	52	13	39	31
2	KLSC	13	10	1	2	62	33	29	31
3	Clenchwarton	13	8	2	3	23	18	5	26
4	Docking Rangers	14	8	1	5	61	33	28	25
5	West Winch William Burt	13	6	3	6	36	37	-1	21
6	Watlington Sports & Social Club	13	6	1	6	42	30	12	19
7	Terrington Tigers Youth Res	13	3	3	7	25	43	-18	12
8	South Creake	13	2	1	10	21	61	-40	7
9	Ingoldisthorpe Res	13	0	1	12	5	59	-54	1

DIVISION THREE

		P	W	D	L	F	A	GD	Pts
1	Heacham Social Club	13	12	1	0	80	16	64	37
2	Castle Rising	14	12	1	1	47	14	33	37
3	Woottons (The)	14	9	1	4	55	41	14	28
4	Marshland Saints Res	17	6	6	5	32	41	-9	24
5	West Winch William Burt Res	17	7	2	8	57	45	12	23
6	KLSC Res	16	7	1	8	37	38	-1	22
7	Docking Rangers Res	17	6	2	9	43	49	-6	20
8	Hunstanton Town	16	6	1	9	37	39	-2	19
9	Watlington Sports & Social Club Res	15	5	1	9	40	64	-24	16
10	Reffley Youth Res	14	4	3	7	31	62	-31	15
11	Hungate Rovers Youth	15	0	1	14	5	55	-50	1

PERRY STREET AND DISTRICT LEAGUE

PREMIER DIVISION

		P	W	D	L	F	A	GD	Pts
1	Merriott Rovers	11	10	0	1	40	12	28	30
2	Winsham United	9	8	0	1	30	16	14	24
3	South Petherton	8	6	0	2	28	11	17	18
4	Chard United	9	2	3	4	14	20	-6	9
5	West & Middle Chinnock	8	3	0	5	19	23	-4	8*
6	Misterton	10	2	1	7	16	26	-10	7
7	Halstock	8	2	1	5	14	25	-11	7
8	Ilminster Town Res	7	2	0	5	10	19	-9	6
9	Thorncombe	8	1	1	6	10	29	-19	4

DIVISION ONE

		P	W	D	L	F	A	GD	Pts
1	Hawkchurch	10	8	1	1	31	9	22	25
2	Crewkerne Rangers	8	6	1	1	24	8	16	19
3	Waytown Hounds	11	6	0	5	33	20	13	18
4	Forton Rangers	10	5	3	2	32	23	9	18
5	Misterton Res	12	5	3	4	16	20	-4	18
6	Shepton Beauchamp	11	4	4	3	21	16	5	16
7	South Petherton Res	11	5	1	5	24	24	0	16
8	Pymore	10	4	1	5	22	22	0	13
9	Uplyme	12	1	1	10	17	47	-30	4
10	Charmouth	11	1	1	9	13	44	-31	4

DIVISION TWO

		P	W	D	L	F	A	GD	Pts
1	Combe St Nicholas Res	13	11	1	1	44	15	29	34
2	Dowlish Wake & Donyatt	12	10	0	2	42	22	20	30
3	Lyme Regis Rovers	9	8	0	1	27	8	19	24
4	Shepton Beauchamp Res	13	5	2	6	27	36	-9	17
5	Chard United Res	11	5	1	5	26	26	0	16
6	Netherbury	13	4	3	6	22	30	-8	15
7	Winsham United Res	11	4	1	6	33	32	1	13
8	Forton Rangers Res	10	4	0	6	14	18	-4	12
9	Donyatt United	12	3	1	8	27	38	-11	10
10	Ilminster Town A Team	8	3	0	5	22	22	0	9
11	Crewkerne Rangers Res	9	2	1	6	16	35	-19	7
12	Chard Rangers	11	2	0	9	25	43	-18	6

DIVISION THREE

		P	W	D	L	F	A	GD	Pts
1	Kingsbury Episcopi	13	10	2	1	66	21	45	32
2	Combe St Nicholas A	11	9	1	1	39	8	31	28
3	Merriott Dynamos	10	7	1	2	42	14	28	22
4	Merriott Saints	11	5	0	6	36	25	11	15
5	Ilminster Town B	10	5	0	5	24	25	-1	14*
6	Thorncombe Res	9	3	1	5	23	34	-11	10
7	Farway United Res	7	2	3	2	9	17	-8	8
8	Chard Rangers Res	11	1	1	9	7	62	-55	4
9	Crewkerne Rangers A	12	1	0	11	12	52	-40	3

PLYMOUTH & WEST DEVON FOOTBALL LEAGUE

PREMIER DIVISION

		P	W	D	L	F	A	GD	Pts
1	The Windmill	12	11	1	0	80	10	70	34
2	Millbridge Res	12	9	2	1	64	19	45	29
3	Millbridge	14	7	0	7	49	40	9	21
4	Saltram Athletic	13	6	2	5	55	31	24	20
5	Signal Box Oak Villa	10	5	3	2	30	29	1	18
6	Pennycross Sporting Club	9	5	0	4	35	28	7	15
7	Central Park Rangers	12	4	3	5	28	30	-2	15
8	Activate	14	4	1	9	34	54	-20	13
9	Plymouth Hope	10	2	1	7	19	32	-13	7
10	Horrabridge Rangers	14	0	1	13	16	137	-121	1

SOUTH DEVON LEAGUE

PREMIER DIVISION

		P	W	D	L	F	A	GD	Pts
1	East Allington United	15	9	4	2	50	21	29	31
2	Torbay Police	13	8	3	2	47	27	20	27
3	Ipplepen Athletic	14	8	3	3	32	29	3	27
4	Meadowbrook Athletic	11	8	1	2	27	17	10	25
5	Salcombe Town	10	7	1	2	43	15	28	22
6	Brixham AFC Res	14	7	1	6	29	28	1	22
7	Plympton Athletic Res	15	6	1	8	24	32	-8	19
8	Broadmeadow ST	13	5	1	7	30	39	-9	16
9	Buckland Athletic Dev	12	5	0	7	28	26	2	15
10	Newton Abbot 66	16	4	2	10	25	45	-20	14
11	Ivybridge Town Res	12	4	0	8	20	34	-14	12
12	Buckfastleigh Rangers	11	3	2	6	22	26	-4	11
13	Beesands Rovers	12	0	1	11	12	50	-38	1

DIVISION ONE

		P	W	D	L	F	A	GD	Pts
1	Harbertonford	14	11	0	3	64	27	37	33
2	Abbotskerswell	15	11	0	4	39	20	19	33
3	Stoke Gabriel Res	12	10	0	2	44	15	29	30
4	Watts Blake Bearne	9	8	1	0	51	16	35	25
5	Kingskerswell & Chelston	13	8	0	5	44	29	15	24
6	Barton Athletic	9	7	2	0	45	6	39	23
7	Chudleigh Athletic Res	13	7	1	5	37	26	11	22
8	Waldon Athletic Res	15	7	0	8	28	33	-5	18*
9	Paignton Villa Res	12	5	1	6	37	35	2	16
10	Riviera United	11	3	2	6	32	41	-9	11
11	Buckfastleigh Rangers Res	14	3	2	9	19	44	-25	11
12	Kingsteignton Athletic Res	12	2	2	8	21	48	-27	8
13	Watcombe Wanderers Res	16	1	0	15	20	74	-54	3
14	Dittisham United	13	0	1	12	8	75	-67	-2*

DIVISION TWO

		P	W	D	L	F	A	GD	Pts
1	Upton Athletic	15	12	2	1	49	16	33	38
2	Galmpton United	16	11	4	1	52	12	40	37
3	Paignton Saints Res	15	11	2	2	54	29	25	35
4	Babbacombe Corinthians	15	8	3	5	42	37	5	24
5	Ilsington Villa	14	7	2	5	39	26	13	23
6	Torquay Town	16	7	2	7	43	37	6	23
7	Ipplepen Athletic Res	14	6	2	6	38	31	7	20
8	Torbay Police Res	12	6	2	4	37	33	4	20
9	Dartmouth Res	13	4	2	7	23	35	-12	14
10	Broadhempston United	14	3	2	9	19	45	-26	11
11	Newton Rovers	14	3	1	10	28	41	-13	10
12	Kingsbridge & Kellaton United	14	1	1	12	13	70	-57	4
13	Newton Abbot 66 Res	10	0	1	9	15	40	-25	-2*

DIVISION THREE

		P	W	D	L	F	A	GD	Pts
1	East Allington United Res	14	9	2	3	40	17	23	29
2	Bishopsteignton United	11	9	1	1	42	22	20	28
3	Torquay Town Res	10	7	2	1	37	21	16	23
4	Brixham AFC 3rd	14	6	4	4	33	25	8	22
5	Newton Abbot Spurs 3rd	12	7	2	3	47	23	24	20*
6	Chudleigh Athletic 3rds	13	6	0	7	38	37	1	18
7	Barton Athletic Res	8	5	1	2	38	15	23	16
8	Newton Rovers Res	9	4	2	3	18	16	2	14
9	Watts Blake Bearne Res	9	3	0	6	16	24	-8	9
10	Totnes & Dartington SC Res	10	2	3	5	26	37	-11	9
11	Kingsteignton Athletic 3rds	16	2	3	11	20	67	-47	9
12	Teign Village	11	2	2	7	17	36	-19	8
13	Babbacombe Corinthians Res	11	1	0	10	15	47	-32	3

SOUTHAMPTON FOOTBALL LEAGUE

PREMIER DIVISION

		P	W	D	L	F	A	GD	Pts
1	Braishfield	8	6	2	0	22	3	19	20
2	Alderbury	6	4	2	0	20	11	9	14
3	Durley	8	3	3	2	13	12	1	12
4	Compton	7	3	2	2	11	11	0	11
5	Knightwood United	6	3	1	2	16	15	1	10
6	Bishops Waltham	7	3	1	3	15	14	1	10
7	Priory Rovers	9	2	2	5	20	21	-1	8
8	Montefiore Halls	11	0	1	10	8	38	-30	1

SENIOR DIVISION ONE

		P	W	D	L	F	A	GD	Pts
1	Whiteley Wanderers	7	6	1	0	25	6	19	19
2	Warsash Wasps	11	6	1	4	32	25	7	19
3	Comrades	12	5	2	5	21	18	3	17
4	Redlynch & W Utd	11	4	3	4	15	23	-8	15
5	Hedge End Town	8	4	2	2	18	11	7	14
6	Itchen Saints	5	4	1	0	18	9	9	13
7	BTC Soton	4	1	1	2	12	6	6	4
8	Polygon	6	0	1	5	11	24	-13	1
9	Hamble United	8	0	0	8	3	33	-30	0

STROUD & DISTRICT LEAGUE
(TABLE BASED ON POINTS PER GAME)

DIVISION ONE

		P	W	D	L	F	A	GD	PPG	Pts
1	Dursley Town	14	12	1	1	53	17	36	2.64	37
2	Ramblers	15	12	0	3	50	26	24	2.40	36
3	Tredworth Tigers	13	10	1	2	45	25	20	2.38	31*
4	Tetbury Town	14	8	0	6	40	26	14	1.71	24
5	Randwick	16	7	4	5	40	37	3	1.56	25
6	Quedgeley Wanderers Res	18	8	4	6	49	46	3	1.56	28
7	Rodborough Old Boys	16	5	5	6	32	42	-10	1.25	20
8	Chalford Res	15	5	2	8	37	37	1	1.13	17
9	Old Richians	13	4	1	8	25	41	-16	1.00	13
10	Minchinhampton	14	3	3	8	20	32	-12	0.86	12
11	Kingswood	18	2	2	14	24	75	-51	0.44	8
12	Hardwicke Res	14	2	1	11	18	30	-12	0.29	4*

DIVISION TWO

		P	W	D	L	F	A	GD	PPG	Pts
1	Chesterton	13	11	1	1	45	12	33	2.62	34
2	Kingsway Rovers	11	7	2	2	31	12	19	2.09	23
3	Wickwar Wanderers	14	8	3	3	35	23	12	1.93	27
4	Tuffley Rovers 3rds	13	7	2	4	28	24	4	1.77	23*
5	Longlevens 3rds	13	7	0	6	27	25	2	1.62	21
6	Wotton Rovers	14	7	1	6	35	37	-2	1.57	22
7	Eastcombe	17	7	1	9	37	36	1	1.29	22
8	Taverners Res	13	5	1	7	29	33	-4	1.23	16
9	Upton St Leonards Res	14	5	2	7	32	35	-3	1.21	17*
10	Sharpness Res	14	5	1	8	30	38	-8	1.14	16
11	Cam Bulldogs Res	16	5	2	9	37	54	-17	1.06	17
12	Tibberton United	12	0	0	12	15	52	-37	0.00	0

DIVISION THREE

		P	W	D	L	F	A	GD	PPG	Pts
1	Horsley United	12	10	1	1	45	15	30	2.58	31
2	Avonvale United	14	11	0	3	47	20	27	2.36	33
3	Hempsted	15	10	0	5	55	29	26	2.00	30
4	Longford	13	8	2	3	32	14	18	2.00	26
5	Charfield Res	13	7	1	5	35	31	4	1.69	22
6	Uley	15	6	1	8	29	33	-4	1.27	19
7	Trident	15	5	2	8	37	34	3	1.13	17
8	Hardwicke 3rds	14	4	3	7	23	44	-21	1.07	15
9	Barnwood United Res	13	4	3	6	25	51	-26	0.92	12*
10	Cotswold Rangers	12	2	2	8	19	38	-19	0.67	8
11	Tetbury Town Res	14	0	1	13	12	50	-38	0.07	1

STEP 8+ LEAGUE TABLES

DIVISION FOUR

		P	W	D	L	F	A	GD	PPG	Pts
1	Painswick	16	14	0	2	96	19	77	2.62	42
2	North Nibley	18	13	2	3	79	24	55	2.28	41
3	Abbeymead Rovers Res	14	9	1	4	51	23	28	2.00	28
4	Quedgeley Wanderers 3rds	12	8	0	4	30	27	3	2.00	24
5	Kingsway Rovers Res	8	5	0	3	38	18	20	1.88	15
6	Frampton United 3rds	13	6	1	6	66	39	27	1.46	19
7	Stonehouse Town 3rds	15	6	1	8	44	41	3	1.27	19
8	Tuffley Rovers 4ths	14	5	2	7	21	29	-8	1.21	17
9	Rodborough Old Boys Res	16	5	4	7	48	32	16	1.19	19
10	Old Richians Res	10	3	0	7	14	44	-30	0.60	6*
11	Saintbridge	12	3	1	8	20	40	-20	0.08	1*
12	Alkerton Rangers (and Woodchester)	18	0	0	18	16	187	-171	0.00	0

DIVISION FIVE

		P	W	D	L	F	A	GD	PPG	Pts
1	Berkeley Town Res	13	11	1	1	36	12	24	2.62	34
2	Cashes Green	13	9	1	3	46	16	30	2.15	28
3	Kings Stanley Res	14	9	1	4	48	29	19	2.00	28
4	Dursley Town Res	12	8	0	4	36	29	7	2.00	24
5	Longlevens 4ths	11	6	0	5	35	29	6	1.64	18
6	Gloster Rovers	12	5	0	7	23	27	-4	1.25	15
7	Minchinhampton Res	15	4	4	7	29	32	-3	1.07	16
8	Cotswold Rangers Res	10	2	3	5	17	34	-17	0.90	9
9	Randwick Res	12	3	1	8	18	40	-22	0.83	10
10	Chalford 3rds	11	2	2	7	21	24	-3	0.73	8
11	Tuffley Rovers 5ths	11	1	1	9	13	50	-37	0.36	4

DIVISION SIX

		P	W	D	L	F	A	GD	PPG	Pts
1	Stroud United	14	11	3	0	46	12	34	2.57	36
2	Sharpness 3rds	15	10	1	4	48	25	23	2.07	31
3	Cam Bulldogs 3rds	14	7	3	4	41	32	9	1.71	24
4	Brockworth Albion 3rds	14	7	2	5	34	20	14	1.64	23
5	Hillesley	12	6	2	4	32	23	9	1.42	17*
6	Rodborough Old Boys 3rds	13	3	6	4	22	29	-7	1.15	15
7	Eastcombe Res	14	3	6	5	34	34	0	1.07	15
8	Leonard Stanley Res	13	4	1	8	18	37	-19	1.00	13
9	Chalford 4ths	14	3	4	7	21	49	-28	0.93	13
10	Ramblers Res	12	3	2	7	13	23	-10	0.67	8*
11	Longford Res	15	2	2	11	28	53	-25	0.53	8

DIVISION SEVEN

		P	W	D	L	F	A	GD	PPG	Pts
1	Cam Everside Wanderers	10	8	0	2	34	15	19	2.40	24
2	Cashes Green Res	14	10	1	3	51	32	19	2.21	31
3	Dursley Town 3rds	12	8	1	3	52	28	24	2.08	25
4	Uley Res	13	8	1	4	52	34	18	1.92	25
5	Tetbury Town 3rds	13	8	1	4	40	29	11	1.69	22*
6	Horsley United Res	13	7	1	5	32	29	3	1.69	22
7	Stonehouse Town 4ths	14	7	2	5	30	33	-3	1.43	20*
8	Painswick Res	13	3	0	10	22	43	-21	0.69	9
9	Uley 3rds	16	2	0	14	25	68	-43	0.38	6
10	Randwick 3rds	14	1	1	12	21	48	-27	0.29	4*

SURREY COUNTY INTERMEDIATE LEAGUE (WESTERN)

PREMIER DIVISION

		P	W	D	L	F	A	GD	Pts
1	Ottershaw	19	10	5	4	50	33	17	35
2	Shottermill & Haslemere	19	10	3	6	36	28	8	33
3	Guildford United	14	10	2	2	46	22	24	32
4	Hambledon	18	9	5	4	55	33	22	32
5	Manorcroft United	17	10	2	5	49	36	13	32
6	Lightwater United	19	8	5	6	45	46	-1	29
7	Keens Park Rangers	18	7	2	9	38	33	5	23
8	Hersham	16	7	1	8	30	34	-4	22
9	Cranleigh	17	6	4	7	28	37	-9	22
10	West End Village	16	6	1	9	30	37	-7	19
11	Milford & Witley	20	4	5	11	29	48	-19	17
12	Chiddingfold	15	3	7	5	32	41	-9	16
13	Knaphill Athletic	16	5	1	10	31	44	-13	16
14	University of Surrey	20	4	3	13	29	56	-27	15

SURREY SOUTH EASTERN COMBINATION

DIVISION ONE

		P	W	D	L	F	A	GD	Pts
1	West Fulham	13	11	2	0	46	16	30	35
2	Wandgas Sport	12	9	1	2	37	24	13	28
3	Earlsfield United	13	6	4	3	23	17	6	22
4	AFC Tooting Bec	16	6	3	7	32	30	2	21
5	Goldfingers	13	7	0	6	19	29	-10	21
6	AFC Walcountians	11	6	2	3	24	17	7	20
7	Kew Park Rangers	14	6	1	7	23	26	-3	19
8	Frenches Athletic	15	4	2	9	31	42	-11	14
9	Balham Res	14	3	2	9	22	28	-6	11
10	AMY	16	2	5	9	21	44	-23	11
11	Westminster Casuals	13	2	4	7	18	23	-5	10

Hanworth Sports withdrew after four games.

SWINDON & DISTRICT FOOTBALL LEAGUE

PREMIER DIVISION

		P	W	D	L	F	A	GD	Pts
1	The Globe	12	9	2	1	69	20	49	29
2	Nalgo Sports Club	14	8	2	4	57	27	30	26
3	Ruby Removals	10	8	1	1	48	19	29	25
4	Blunsdon	11	8	1	2	38	14	24	25
5	Highworth Town Dev	12	7	2	3	43	17	26	23
6	Wroughton Res	14	6	2	6	40	38	2	20
7	Paragon	14	6	1	7	31	42	-11	19
8	Sportz Central	12	5	1	6	29	40	-11	16
9	Redhouse	13	4	2	7	48	40	8	14
10	Ashton Keynes	11	3	2	6	36	28	8	11
11	Swindon Supermarine Dev	10	3	2	5	23	48	-25	11
12	Wheatsheaf Stratton	8	1	0	7	13	58	-45	3
13	The Regent	13	0	0	13	9	93	-84	0

DIVISION ONE

		P	W	D	L	F	A	GD	Pts
1	Chiseldon	16	11	2	3	48	27	21	35
2	Priory Vale	14	11	1	2	52	11	41	34
3	Bassett Bulldogs	13	9	1	3	48	17	31	28
4	Swindon A	12	7	3	2	40	9	31	24
5	Swindon Centurions 2019	15	7	1	7	35	42	-7	22
6	Lower Stratton	13	6	1	6	32	31	1	19
7	Marlborough Town Res	15	6	0	9	37	47	-10	18
8	North Swindon	13	4	2	7	22	48	-26	14
9	Ramsbury	11	4	1	6	37	38	-1	13
10	Down Ampney	13	4	1	8	20	29	-9	13
11	Cricklade Town Res	10	2	4	4	21	25	-4	10
12	Moredon	14	3	1	10	23	74	-51	10
13	Spectrum	13	2	2	9	20	37	-17	8

FC Abbeymeads withdrew.

TAUNTON LEAGUE

DIVISION ONE

		P	W	D	L	F	A	GD	Pts
1	FC Castlemoat	15	13	1	1	73	19	54	37 *
2	Westonzoyland	14	12	0	2	40	12	28	36
3	Wembdon	15	10	2	3	57	25	32	32
4	Creech Cougars	12	7	1	4	38	24	14	22
5	Redgate	17	6	2	9	33	48	-15	20
6	Galmington	18	5	4	9	42	55	-13	19
7	Stogursey	17	5	3	9	36	50	-14	18
8	North Petherton	12	5	2	5	27	35	-8	17
9	North Curry	15	5	0	10	31	39	-8	15
10	Watchet Town Res	14	4	1	9	18	47	-29	7 *
11	Alcombe Rovers	15	2	0	13	21	62	-41	-3 *

DIVISION TWO

		P	W	D	L	F	A	GD	Pts
1	Wellington A	17	13	1	3	74	34	40	40
2	Bridgwater Sports	16	12	3	1	52	17	35	39
3	Wyvern United	17	11	1	5	72	35	37	34
4	Staplegrove Crusaders	14	9	3	2	46	18	28	30
5	Wembdon Res	17	7	6	4	33	29	4	27
6	White Eagles (Taunton)	17	7	3	7	50	58	-8	24
7	Minehead AFC Res	15	6	3	6	27	34	-7	21
8	Middlezoy Rovers Athletic	19	6	3	10	42	51	-9	21
9	Porlock	14	5	4	5	46	35	11	19
10	Bridgwater Grasshoppers	18	3	5	10	33	64	-31	14
11	Bridgwater & Albion	16	3	4	9	26	60	-34	13
12	Norton Fitzwarren	18	2	6	10	23	43	-20	12
13	Dulverton Town	14	0	2	12	17	63	-46	2

DIVISION THREE

		P	W	D	L	F	A	GD	Pts
1	Staplegrove Spartans	17	16	0	1	106	18	88	48
2	FC Castlemoat Res	19	13	3	3	88	37	51	42
3	Nether Stowey	17	14	0	3	79	30	49	42
4	Galmington Res	20	9	3	8	54	52	2	30
5	North Petherton Res	15	9	1	5	38	26	12	28
6	Minehead AFC Colts	16	7	2	7	51	57	-6	20 *
7	Old Inn 98	17	6	2	9	58	68	-10	20
8	Bridgwater Sports Res	18	6	1	11	48	60	-12	13 *
9	Porlock Res	13	4	1	8	26	54	-28	13
10	Exmoor Rangers	13	3	1	9	19	46	-27	10
11	Bridgwater & Albion Res	18	3	2	13	18	67	-49	8 *
12	Norton Fitzwarren Res	17	1	2	14	24	94	-70	5
	Cannington withdrew.								

TROWBRIDGE & DISTRICT FOOTBALL LEAGUE

DIVISION ONE

		P	W	D	L	F	A	GD	Pts
1	Marshfield	13	11	1	1	50	15	35	34
2	Devizes Town Res	15	10	4	1	49	21	28	34
3	Heytesbury	12	8	1	3	47	15	32	25
4	Warminster United	12	7	3	2	36	17	19	24
5	Calne Town Res	14	7	2	5	33	35	-2	23
6	Three Daggers	11	5	1	5	25	27	-2	16
7	Freshford United	16	4	2	10	22	44	-22	13 *
8	Hilperton United	10	3	1	6	22	22	0	10
9	Melksham Town 'A'	15	3	1	11	16	43	-27	10
10	Semington Magpies	11	3	0	8	21	40	-19	9
11	Warminster Town Res	13	1	2	10	16	58	-42	5

DIVISION TWO

		P	W	D	L	F	A	GD	Pts
1	KEW PR	12	12	0	0	71	10	61	36
2	Staverton United	13	9	1	3	50	31	19	28
3	Westbury United Res	14	9	0	5	40	34	6	27
4	Calne Eagles	15	7	2	6	38	25	13	21 *
5	Dilton Marsh Wanderers	13	7	0	6	26	46	-20	21
6	Trowbridge Town Res	14	5	3	6	41	36	5	18
7	Aces	15	4	0	11	22	45	-23	12
8	The Stiffs	15	3	0	12	26	76	-50	9
9	Seend United	13	2	2	9	34	45	-11	7 *
	Barford Hornets FC withdrew.								
	Greyhound FC withdrew.								

WAKEFIELD & DISTRICT LEAGUE

PREMIER DIVISION

		P	W	D	L	F	A	GD	Pts
1	Beechwood Santos	9	8	1	0	36	8	28	25
2	Fieldhead Hospital	13	7	0	6	35	42	-7	21
3	Snydale Athletic	14	6	2	6	35	30	5	20
4	Nostell Miners Welfare	9	6	0	3	30	18	12	18
5	Red Lion Alverthorpe	11	6	0	5	27	23	4	18
6	Royston Cross	11	4	3	4	26	21	5	16
7	Hanging Heaton	12	4	0	8	29	39	-10	12
8	Durkar	13	3	2	8	21	42	-21	11
9	Crofton Sports	12	3	1	8	17	33	-16	10

DIVISION ONE

		P	W	D	L	F	A	GD	Pts
1	Howden Clough	17	11	1	5	49	35	14	34
2	West End Terriers	12	11	0	1	49	15	34	33
3	Ambience A	12	10	1	1	37	14	23	31
4	Great Preston A	12	9	1	2	44	26	18	28
5	Ossett Dynamos	13	6	1	6	35	36	-1	19
6	Waterloo	8	4	1	3	22	26	-4	13
7	Pontefract Sports & Social	14	3	1	10	19	42	-23	10
8	United Power Castleford	14	2	2	10	17	37	-20	8
9	Fieldhead Hospital Res	15	2	1	12	24	46	-22	7
10	Rocking Horse	13	2	1	10	27	46	-19	6*

DIVISION TWO

		P	W	D	L	F	A	GD	Pts
1	Thornhill United	16	12	0	4	92	35	57	36
2	Last Orders	14	13	0	1	79	20	59	35*
3	Hemsworth Town	14	11	0	3	59	30	29	33
4	AFC Sheaf	12	10	0	2	59	24	35	30
5	Overthorpe Sports Club	17	7	1	9	44	56	-12	22
6	Crofton Sports Res	13	7	0	6	33	29	4	21
7	Snydale Athletic Res	15	7	0	8	59	47	12	18*
8	New Carlton	15	2	2	11	32	55	-23	8
9	FC Broadway	17	2	1	14	33	89	-56	7
10	City of Wakefield	13	0	0	13	11	116	-105	0

WITNEY & DISTRICT LEAGUE

PREMIER DIVISION

		P	W	D	L	F	A	GD	Pts
1	Carterton	10	8	0	2	24	8	16	24
2	Stonesfield	10	7	1	2	34	16	18	22
3	Hailey	8	7	0	1	30	12	18	21
4	Carterton Rangers	12	4	3	5	21	22	-1	15
5	Spartan Rangers	14	5	0	9	25	49	-24	15
6	Carterton Town A	9	3	2	4	19	24	-5	11
7	Tower Hill	8	3	1	4	18	18	0	10
8	Minster Lovell	10	2	2	6	19	27	-8	8
9	Milton	8	2	1	5	16	26	-10	7
10	Charlbury Town	7	1	2	4	11	15	-4	5

DIVISION ONE

		P	W	D	L	F	A	GD	Pts
1	Minster Lovell Res	10	7	2	1	32	23	9	26*
2	Enstone	10	7	3	0	40	12	28	21*
3	Hailey Res	10	5	3	2	18	20	-2	18
4	Bampton Utd	8	5	2	1	27	12	15	17
5	Witney Royals	11	4	2	5	22	21	1	14
6	Chadlington	9	4	1	4	22	14	8	13
7	Bourton Rovers	11	2	1	8	19	34	-15	7
8	Middle Barton	10	2	0	8	12	33	-21	6
9	Kingham All Blacks	11	2	0	9	15	38	-23	6

DIVISION TWO

		P	W	D	L	F	A	GD	Pts
1	Hook Norton	13	11	0	2	59	27	32	33
2	Carterton Res	12	7	2	3	29	17	12	23
3	Charlbury Town Res	12	6	3	3	32	29	3	21
4	Brize Norton	13	7	0	6	38	44	-6	21
5	Wootton Sports	11	6	1	4	25	15	10	19
6	Spartan Rangers Res	13	6	1	6	30	35	-5	19
7	Ducklington	12	5	2	5	29	27	2	17
8	Siege	13	3	1	9	27	36	-9	10
9	Carterton Town B	11	2	2	7	26	28	-2	8
10	Eynsham SSC	12	2	0	10	15	52	-37	6

DIVISION THREE

		P	W	D	L	F	A	GD	Pts
1	Bletchington	14	13	0	1	68	6	62	39
2	Aston	13	9	0	4	44	27	17	27
3	Wootton Sports Res	15	7	1	7	34	29	5	22
4	FC Mills	14	6	1	7	30	39	-9	19
5	Chadlington Res	11	5	2	4	14	20	-6	17
6	Bourton Rovers Res	10	5	0	5	19	26	-7	15
7	Chipping Norton Town	10	4	2	4	24	26	-2	14
8	Kingham All Blacks Res	12	4	2	6	19	31	-12	14
9	Stonesfield Res	12	3	1	8	23	38	-15	10
10	Witney Royals Res	15	1	4	10	24	57	-33	6

STEP 8+ LEAGUE TABLES

DIVISION FOUR

		P	W	D	L	F	A	GD	Pts
1	East Oxford Rangers	12	11	0	1	57	13	44	33
2	Milton Res	11	10	1	0	49	13	36	31
3	Spartan Rangers A	16	6	2	8	36	57	-21	20
4	Hailey A	11	6	1	4	33	23	10	19
5	FC Ascott Rangers	10	6	0	4	25	19	6	18
6	Brize Norton Res	13	5	2	6	40	38	2	17
7	Bampton Utd Res	11	5	1	5	23	28	-5	16
8	Sherborne Harriers	13	2	1	10	30	52	-22	7
9	FC Ascott	13	0	0	13	15	65	-50	05
	Brize Norton Res	20	10	3	7	57	44	13	33
6	Milton-U-Wychwood Res	20	10	2	8	73	41	32	32
7	Bampton United Res	20	10	2	8	49	37	12	32
8	Eynsham SSC Res	20	8	1	11	46	58	-12	25
9	FC Ascott	20	6	4	10	49	53	-4	21*
10	Spartan Rangers A	20	3	1	16	37	100	-63	10
11	FC Ascott Rangers	20	2	1	17	18	76	-58	7

YEOVIL AND DISTRICT LEAGUE
(BASED ON POINTS PER GAME)

PREMIER DIVISION

		P	W	D	L	F	A	GD	PPG	Pts
1	Templecombe Rovers	11	7	4	0	28	10	18	2.27	25
2	Queen Camel	12	8	2	2	28	12	16	2.17	26
3	Milborne Port	12	7	3	2	58	14	44	2.00	24
4	Stoke Sub Hamdon	7	3	1	3	13	13	0	1.43	10
5	Odcombe	8	3	2	3	19	20	-1	1.38	11
6	Pen Mill Athletic	12	4	3	5	30	36	-6	1.25	15
7	Martock United	14	5	2	7	25	42	-17	1.21	17
8	Wagtail Athletic	11	3	2	6	25	28	-3	1.00	11
9	Castle Cary Res	13	0	1	12	11	62	-51	0.08	1

DIVISION ONE

		P	W	D	L	F	A	GD	PPG	Pts
1	Manor Athletic	11	10	0	1	44	6	38	2.73	30
2	AFC Strode	13	8	3	2	38	24	14	2.08	27
3	Ashcott Res	8	4	1	3	18	10	8	1.62	13
4	AFC Huish	13	6	2	5	29	31	-2	1.54	20
5	Barwick	10	3	1	6	13	19	-6	1.00	10
6	Bruton United	10	3	0	7	14	41	-27	0.90	9
7	Ilchester	8	2	1	5	16	15	1	0.88	7
8	Keinton Park Rangers	13	1	4	8	19	45	-26	0.54	7

DIVISION TWO

		P	W	D	L	F	A	GD	PPG	Pts
1	Wyndham Athletic FC	12	10	0	2	39	11	28	2.50	30
2	South Cheriton United	12	8	2	2	41	16	25	2.17	26
3	Pen Mill Athletic Res	12	8	1	3	28	25	3	2.08	25
4	Zeals FC	12	7	0	5	42	31	11	1.75	21
5	Milborne Port A	11	4	2	5	20	25	-5	1.27	14
6	Odcombe Res	14	3	3	8	32	37	-5	0.86	12
7	Barwick Res	12	2	1	9	13	44	-31	0.58	7
8	Stoke Sub Hamdon Res	13	1	3	9	19	45	-26	0.46	6

YORKSHIRE AMATEUR LEAGUE

SUPREME DIVISION

		P	W	D	L	F	A	GD	Pts
1	Farsley Celtic Juniors	16	15	0	1	65	13	52	45
2	Littletown	19	13	0	6	63	25	38	39
3	Calverley United	21	12	1	8	52	44	8	37
4	Horsforth St. Margarets	13	11	0	2	49	11	38	33
5	Stanley United	17	11	0	6	63	37	26	33
6	Ryburn United	18	9	4	5	37	29	8	31
7	Route One Rovers	20	9	4	7	57	50	7	31
8	Leeds Medics & Dentists	22	9	4	9	36	39	-3	31
9	Toller FC	20	9	3	8	56	58	-2	27*
10	Athletico FC	24	7	4	13	49	63	-14	25
11	Wortley FC	14	7	0	7	37	36	1	21
12	Alwoodley FC	16	5	5	6	28	24	4	20
13	Steeton	16	3	1	12	25	56	-31	10
14	Drighlington	21	1	3	17	22	110	-88	6
15	Lower Hopton	17	1	1	15	18	62	-44	4

PREMIER DIVISION

		P	W	D	L	F	A	GD	Pts
11	Gildersome Spurs O.B.	14	10	1	3	63	27	36	31
2	Middleton	14	10	0	4	54	33	21	30
3	Collegians	17	6	4	7	50	39	11	22
4	Leeds City FC	13	7	0	6	31	32	-1	21
5	Ealandians	16	6	3	7	29	32	-3	21
6	Wibsey	13	7	0	6	28	35	-7	21
7	St Bedes	17	6	2	9	47	65	-18	20
8	Stanningley Old Boys	15	6	2	7	23	48	-25	20
9	Morley Town AFC	16	5	2	9	48	57	-9	17
10	Shire Academics	14	5	0	9	33	37	-4	15
11	Whitkirk Wanderers	5	2	0	3	12	13	-1	6

CHAMPIONSHIP

		P	W	D	L	F	A	GD	Pts
1	Horsforth St. Margarets Res	13	11	0	2	60	13	47	33
2	Beeston Juniors	18	10	1	7	51	56	-5	31
3	Leeds Medics & Dentists Res	19	9	3	7	45	35	10	30
4	Mount St Marys	10	9	1	0	45	17	28	28
5	PFC	17	9	0	8	55	59	-4	27
6	Golcar United	9	8	0	1	41	10	31	24
7	Colton Athletic	15	8	0	7	33	31	2	24
8	Woodkirk Valley	12	7	0	5	39	27	12	21
9	Dewsbury Rangers	13	4	1	8	31	39	-8	13
10	Ealandians Res	17	4	1	12	27	65	-38	13
11	Idle FC	12	3	1	8	22	37	-15	10
12	Leeds Independent	19	0	2	17	14	74	-60	2

DIVISION ONE

		P	W	D	L	F	A	GD	Pts
1	Beeston St Anthony	11	8	1	2	40	19	21	25
2	Fairbank United	11	7	3	1	41	25	16	24
3	Lepton Highlanders	12	7	1	4	36	26	10	22
4	Athletico Res	14	6	2	6	40	43	-3	19*
5	Thornesians	15	5	1	9	38	68	-30	16
6	Leeds City FC Res	13	4	3	6	29	29	0	15
7	Horsforth St. Margarets 3rds	13	7	2	4	42	22	20	14*
8	Alwoodley Res	10	4	1	5	31	33	-2	13
9	Tyersal	12	4	1	7	33	41	-8	13
10	Shire Academics Res	13	3	3	7	23	33	-10	12
11	Farsley Celtic Juniors Res	12	3	2	7	27	41	-14	11

DIVISION TWO

		P	W	D	L	F	A	GD	Pts
1	Morley Town AFC Res	16	11	1	4	55	30	25	34
2	Middleton Park	15	10	1	4	56	21	35	31
3	Norristhorpe	16	10	1	5	64	43	21	31
4	North Leeds	14	7	3	4	43	36	7	24
5	Leeds City FC 3rds	11	6	2	3	33	31	2	20
6	Sandal Wanderers	15	5	2	8	40	43	-3	17
7	Gildersome Spurs O.B. Res	15	4	5	6	28	44	-16	17
8	Trinity & All Saints Old Boys	17	5	2	10	37	57	-20	17
9	Leeds Medics & Dentists 3rds	13	4	1	8	13	28	-15	13
10	Huddersfield Amateur	14	3	4	7	29	46	-17	13
11	Prospect FC	14	4	1	9	31	53	-22	13
12	Horsforth St. Margarets 4ths	12	4	3	5	30	27	3	10*

DIVISION THREE

		P	W	D	L	F	A	GD	Pts
1	Littletown Res	14	12	0	2	48	19	29	36
2	Norristhorpe Res	14	9	2	3	61	30	31	29
3	Wortley Res	11	9	1	1	65	9	56	28
4	Morley Town AFC III	15	7	2	6	28	41	-13	23
5	Savile United FC	15	6	4	5	42	31	11	22
6	Shire Academics III	12	6	3	3	37	29	8	21
7	Ealandians III	16	4	2	10	34	68	-34	14
8	Garforth Rangers	13	3	3	7	27	38	-11	12
9	Tingley Athletic	12	3	1	8	20	41	-21	10
10	Woodkirk Valley Res	16	3	0	13	26	78	-52	9
11	Lepton Highlanders Res	14	4	2	8	34	38	-4	8*

DIVISION FOUR

		P	W	D	L	F	A	GD	Pts
1	Colton Athletic Res	16	12	2	2	61	29	32	38
2	Farnley Sports FC	14	8	2	4	66	42	24	26
3	Middleton Park Under 23's	11	8	2	1	38	18	20	26
4	Morley Town AFC Dev	12	6	2	4	38	28	10	20
5	St Bedes Res	15	6	2	7	45	45	0	20
6	Tyersal Res	14	6	1	7	48	56	-8	19
7	Calverley United Res	10	5	1	4	36	28	8	16
8	Leeds Modernians	13	3	3	7	27	33	-6	12
9	Old Batelians	13	3	3	7	36	50	-14	12
10	Old Centralians	13	3	5	5	40	39	1	11*
11	Thornesians Res	12	3	2	7	22	55	-33	11
12	North Leeds Res	15	3	1	11	24	58	-34	10

DIVISION FIVE

		P	W	D	L	F	A	GD	Pts
1	West End Park	16	12	2	2	63	26	37	38
2	Colton Athletic III	13	8	2	3	37	24	13	26
3	Shire Academics IV	12	8	0	4	43	24	19	24
4	Farnley Sports Res	14	8	0	6	44	42	2	21*
5	Dewsbury Rangers U23's	14	5	4	5	37	36	1	19
6	Huddersfield Amateur Res	16	5	3	8	43	54	-11	18
7	Leeds Modernians Res	11	5	1	5	29	39	-10	16
8	Thornesians III	12	5	0	7	32	39	-7	15
9	St Bedes Academy	13	4	3	6	35	45	-10	15
10	Leeds City FC IV	13	4	1	8	32	36	-4	13
11	Old Centralians Academics	14	5	1	8	34	43	-9	13*
12	Beeston Juniors Res	14	3	1	10	27	48	-21	10

ISLAND FOOTBALL

GUERNSEY LEAGUE

PRIAULX LEAGUE

		P	W	D	L	F	A	GD	Pts
1	Northerners AC	16	14	1	1	49	18	31	43
2	St Martins AC	16	10	3	3	48	23	25	33
3	Alderney	16	8	1	7	34	26	8	25
4	UCF Sylvans	15	7	3	5	52	31	21	24
5	Manzur	16	7	3	6	37	32	5	24
6	Rovers AC	16	6	3	7	31	36	-5	21
7	Belgrave Wanderers	13	5	3	5	32	33	-1	18
8	Vale Recreation	16	4	1	11	33	37	-4	13
9	Rangers FAC	18	1	0	17	18	98	-80	3

DIVISION ONE

		P	W	D	L	F	A	GD	Pts
1	Rovers AC	7	5	0	2	27	21	6	15
2	St Martins AC	6	4	1	1	27	12	15	13
3	UCF Sylvans	9	4	1	4	27	27	0	13
4	Red Lion North	8	4	0	4	14	15	-1	12
5	Belgrave Wanderers	7	3	2	2	24	18	6	11
6	Manzur	8	2	1	5	21	30	-9	7
7	Vale Recreation	9	2	1	6	21	38	-17	7

DIVISION TWO

		P	W	D	L	F	A	GD	Pts
1	UCF Sylvans	9	8	0	1	29	5	24	24
2	Rovers AC	9	6	0	3	21	15	6	18
3	Manzur	8	5	2	1	33	20	13	17
4	Rocquaine Pirates	10	4	1	5	19	28	-9	13
5	Rangers FAC	10	3	1	6	26	33	-7	10
6	London House Bels	8	3	0	5	29	24	5	9
7	St Martins AC	10	3	0	7	22	37	-15	9
8	Northerners AC	10	3	0	7	22	39	-17	9

DIVISION THREE

		P	W	D	L	F	A	GD	Pts
1	Manor Farm Saints	10	10	0	0	55	15	40	30
2	Rovers AC	11	9	1	1	46	20	26	28
3	Thrive Physiotherapy FC	13	7	1	5	41	29	12	22
4	Rangers FAC	11	7	0	4	46	29	17	21
5	Vale Recreation	10	4	0	6	31	24	7	12
6	CF Independant	10	4	0	6	23	37	-14	12
7	Police	10	3	1	6	20	36	-16	10
8	UCF Sylvans	10	2	1	7	21	43	-22	7
9	Geomarine Rovers	11	0	0	11	9	59	-50	0

JERSEY FOOTBALL COMBINATION
(BASED ON POINTS PER GAME)

PREMIER DIVISION

		P	W	D	L	F	A	GD	PPG	Pts
1	JTC Jersey Wanderers	13	11	1	1	36	11	25	2.62	34
2	St Ouen	14	10	2	2	32	16	16	2.29	32
3	St Paul's	12	8	3	1	38	15	23	2.25	27
4	St Clement	10	5	1	4	26	18	8	1.60	16
5	Grouville	11	3	4	4	21	23	-2	1.36	15
6	St Peter	13	5	1	7	26	33	-7	1.23	16
7	Rozel Rovers	13	4	5	4	21	29	-8	1.23	14
8	St Brelade	13	4	1	8	26	36	-10	1.00	13
9	Sporting Academics	15	3	3	9	23	38	-15	0.80	12
10	St Lawrence	14	0	1	13	14	44	-30	0.07	1

CHAMPIONSHIP

		P	W	D	L	F	A	GD	PPG	Pts
1	St Ouen	10	9	0	1	49	16	33	2.70	27
2	St John	11	6	4	1	32	18	14	2.00	22
3	First Tower United	11	6	2	3	22	12	10	1.82	20
4	Rozel Rovers	8	3	2	3	25	22	3	1.38	11
5	JTC Jersey Wanderers	10	4	0	6	13	23	-10	1.20	12
6	St Clement	11	4	0	7	24	37	-13	1.09	12
7	St Peter	12	3	0	9	22	33	-11	0.75	9
8	St Lawrence	7	1	0	6	7	33	-26	0.43	3

DIVISION ONE

		P	W	D	L	F	A	GD	PPG	Pts
1	St Peter	7	6	0	1	24	16	8	2.57	18
2	St Brelade	9	7	0	2	34	20	14	2.33	21
3	Grouville	9	6	1	2	32	15	17	2.11	19
4	St Ouen	9	6	0	3	32	12	20	2.00	18
5	St John	10	2	2	6	9	27	-18	0.80	8
6	Sporting Academics	8	1	1	6	10	35	-25	0.50	4
7	Sports Club of Jersey	10	1	0	9	16	22	-6	0.30	3

AMATEUR FOOTBALL ASSOCIATION

ARTHURIAN LEAGUE

PREMIER DIVISION

		P	W	D	L	F	A	GD	Pts
1	Old Carthusians	15	12	1	2	59	17	42	37
2	Kings College Wimbledon	15	11	3	1	45	13	32	36
3	Old Etonians	17	8	5	4	36	24	12	29
4	Old Alleynians AFC	17	7	5	5	48	40	8	26
5	Old Bradfieldians	16	8	1	7	55	45	10	25
6	Old Tonbridgians	17	6	5	6	37	39	-2	23
7	Old Harrovians	18	5	5	8	40	53	-13	20
8	Old Foresters	16	5	3	8	23	40	-17	18
9	Old Chigwellians	17	2	1	14	26	76	-50	7
10	Old Salopians	14	1	3	10	18	40	-22	3*

DIVISION ONE

		P	W	D	L	F	A	GD	Pts
1	Old Brentwoods	15	11	1	3	72	27	45	34
2	Old Cholmeleians	16	9	5	2	45	26	19	32
3	Old Wykehamists	14	9	2	3	50	23	27	29
4	Lancing Old Boys	15	7	4	4	36	45	-9	25
5	Old Westminsters	17	6	4	7	51	44	7	22
6	Old Marlburians	16	6	3	7	40	51	-11	21
7	Old Reptonians	15	5	2	8	25	37	-12	17
8	Old Malvernians	15	4	2	9	26	43	-17	14
9	Old Berkhamstedians	16	3	5	8	26	52	-26	14
10	Old Radleians	17	2	4	11	31	54	-23	10

DIVISION TWO

		P	W	D	L	F	A	GD	Pts
1	Old Carthusians II	15	13	1	1	57	14	43	40
2	Old Etonians II	16	8	3	5	43	29	14	27
3	Old Rugbeians	13	8	1	4	31	23	8	25
4	Old Harrovians II	13	7	2	4	40	30	10	23
5	Old Merchant Taylors	15	5	2	8	30	42	-12	17
6	Old Aldenhamians	16	4	5	7	27	46	-19	17
7	Old Chigwellians II	14	5	2	7	22	27	-5	16*
8	Old Sennockians	13	3	1	8	23	33	-11	10
9	Old Foresters II	14	1	3	10	22	50	-28	2*

STEP 8+ LEAGUE TABLES

DIVISION THREE

		P	W	D	L	F	A	GD	Pts
1	Old Johnians FC	16	13	2	1	62	23	39	41
2	Old Columbans	14	10	1	3	47	30	17	28*
3	Old Suttonians SV	16	9	1	6	48	32	16	28
4	Old Epsomians	15	6	6	3	34	37	-3	24
5	Old Tonbridgians II	14	7	2	5	41	29	12	23
6	Kings College Wimbledon II	16	5	2	9	25	33	-8	17
7	Old Carthusians III	16	4	1	11	31	58	-27	13
8	Old Wellingtonians	15	3	3	9	32	43	-11	6*
9	Lancing Old Boys II	14	1	2	11	17	52	-35	5

DIVISION FOUR

		P	W	D	L	F	A	GD	Pts
1	Old Kimboltonians	13	9	2	2	47	22	25	29
2	Old Alleynians AFC II	12	9	1	2	46	18	28	28
3	Old Brentwoods II	10	8	1	1	29	14	15	25
4	Old Shirburnians	12	6	0	6	24	30	-6	18
5	Old King's Scholars	13	4	3	6	24	28	-4	15
6	Old Harrovians III	14	4	3	7	19	40	-21	15
7	Old Stoics	13	4	2	7	31	37	-6	14
8	Old Bancroftians AFC	14	3	2	9	20	31	-11	11
9	Old Salopians II	13	2	2	9	18	38	-20	8

DIVISION FIVE NORTH

		P	W	D	L	F	A	GD	Pts
1	Old Cholmeleians II	8	6	1	1	44	18	26	19
2	Old Albanians SA	8	6	0	2	33	17	16	18
3	Old Brentwoods III	8	3	0	5	19	37	-18	9
4	Old Haberdashers	9	3	1	5	28	28	0	7*
5	Old Merchant Taylors II	9	2	0	7	16	40	-24	6

DIVISION FIVE SOUTH

		P	W	D	L	F	A	GD	Pts
1	Old Alleynians AFC III	12	10	0	2	48	23	25	30
2	Old Westminsters II	12	6	2	4	36	21	15	20
3	Old Amplefordians	11	6	2	3	26	22	4	20
4	Old Berkhamstedians II	11	5	0	6	30	34	-4	15
5	Old Eastbournians	12	3	5	4	26	31	-5	14
6	Old Wykehamists II	12	3	1	8	20	35	-15	10
7	Old Kingstonians KGS	12	2	2	8	24	44	-20	8

NORTHERN IRELAND TABLES 2019-20

NORTHERN IRELAND FOOTBALL LEAGUE

Premiership

		P	W	D	L	F	A	GD	Pts
1	Linfield	31	22	3	6	71	24	47	69
2	Coleraine	31	19	8	4	64	24	40	65
3	Crusaders	31	17	8	6	66	30	36	59
4	Cliftonville	31	18	5	8	48	22	26	59
5	Glentoran	31	17	7	7	60	33	27	58
6	Larne	31	16	8	7	59	29	30	56
7	Glenavon	31	10	5	16	46	71	-25	35
8	Carrick Rangers	31	10	2	19	34	47	-13	32
9	Dungannon Swifts	31	8	6	17	36	76	-40	30
10	Ballymena United	31	7	6	18	34	54	-20	27
11	Warrenpoint Town	31	5	3	23	26	85	-59	18
12	Institute	31	2	9	20	23	72	-49	15

Championship

		P	W	D	L	F	A	GD	Pts
1	Portadown	31	20	6	5	72	30	42	66
2	Loughgall	31	19	5	7	66	40	26	62
3	Ballinamallard United	30	19	3	8	71	34	37	60
4	Ards	31	15	7	9	65	44	21	52
5	Newry City	30	15	6	9	55	32	23	51
6	Dundela	31	13	7	11	43	49	-6	46
7	Ballyclare Comrades	30	11	7	12	53	49	4	40
8	HW Welders	31	10	5	16	52	63	-11	35
9	Queens University	31	11	1	19	59	69	-10	34
10	Dergview	30	8	5	17	38	54	-16	29
11	PSNI	30	7	2	21	40	98	-58	23
12	Knockbreda	30	6	4	20	34	86	-52	22

Premier Intermediate League

		P	W	D	L	F	A	GD	Pts
1	Annagh United	14	10	3	1	32	14	18	33
2	Portstewart	14	8	6	0	28	13	15	30
3	Dollingstown	13	8	1	4	31	15	16	25
4	Bangor	12	6	2	4	30	21	9	20
5	Newington	11	5	3	3	16	18	-2	18
6	Armagh City	14	3	5	6	15	26	-11	14
7	Banbridge Town	12	3	4	5	16	20	-4	13
8	Lisburn Distillery	13	3	4	6	13	25	-12	13
9	Moyola Park	12	3	1	8	21	28	-7	10
10	Limavady United	13	2	3	8	21	32	-11	9
11	Tobermore United	12	2	2	8	14	25	-11	8

BALLYMENA & PROVINCIAL LEAGUE

Intermediate Division

		P	W	D	L	F	A	GD	Pts
1	Dunloy	21	19	2	0	65	24	41	59
2	Wakehurst FC	20	12	2	6	56	38	18	38
3	St James Swifts	15	12	1	2	56	15	41	37
4	Glebe Rangers	19	11	2	6	35	23	12	35
5	Ballymoney Utd	16	9	3	4	44	28	16	30
6	Cookstown Youth	19	8	4	7	40	42	-2	28
7	Belfast Celtic	11	9	0	2	51	15	36	27
8	Coagh Utd	16	8	2	6	46	37	9	26
9	Donegal Celtic	18	5	3	10	33	56	-23	18
10	Brantwood FC	16	4	4	8	32	38	-6	16
11	Ballynure OB	21	4	4	13	32	59	-27	16
12	Chimney Corner	16	4	0	12	24	49	-25	12
13	Cookstown RBL	18	2	0	16	29	60	-31	6
14	Desertmartin	18	1	1	16	16	75	-59	4

Junior Division One

		P	W	D	L	F	A	GD	Pts
1	Rathcoole	8	7	0	1	35	11	24	21
2	Killymoon Rangers	10	6	3	1	30	12	18	21
3	Woodlands	10	4	3	3	28	25	3	15
4	Cookstown Olympic	11	4	2	5	28	34	-6	14
5	FC Whiteabbey	9	4	2	3	16	23	-7	14
6	Ballynure OB 'B'	14	3	5	6	29	43	-14	14
7	St James Swifts IIs	9	4	1	4	29	21	8	13
8	Castle Star	7	2	2	3	16	17	-1	8
9	Antrim Rovers	12	1	2	9	21	46	-25	5
	Desertmartin Swifts withdrew								

Junior Division Two

		P	W	D	L	F	A	GD	Pts
1	3rd Ballyclare OB	14	9	3	2	41	23	18	30
2	Ballyclare North End	15	9	3	3	45	28	17	30
3	Cookstown Youth Colts	15	10	0	5	44	30	14	30
4	Brantwood Res	13	9	0	4	46	24	22	27
5	North Belfast Utd	13	7	0	6	36	27	9	21
6	St James Swifts IIIs	15	6	3	6	44	37	7	21
7	North United	16	6	3	7	37	49	-12	21
8	Carrick Athletic	16	5	2	9	37	48	-11	17
9	Loughside FC	14	4	1	9	17	40	-23	13
10	68th Newtownabbey OB	17	1	1	15	21	62	-41	4

Junior Division Three

		P	W	D	L	F	A	GD	Pts
1	Greenisland 3rds	13	11	0	2	71	21	50	33
2	Belfast Celtic Swifts	9	9	0	0	50	10	40	27
3	Cookstown RBL Res	12	7	2	3	40	19	21	23
4	Red Star	12	6	2	4	28	26	2	20
5	Rathcoole Res	14	6	0	8	41	39	2	18
6	Rooftop IIIs	11	4	1	6	26	34	-8	13
7	Grange Rangers	13	3	1	9	19	39	-20	10
8	Newington Rangers	13	2	4	7	17	43	-26	10
9	North Ballymena Rangers Ath	13	1	2	10	11	72	-61	5
	Mallusk Athletic withdrew.								
	St Malachy's OB withdrew								

NORTHERN IRELAND FOOTBALL

MID ULSTER LEAGUE

		At suspension			Ave. Projected	
Intermediate A		P	Pts	GD	P	Pts
1	Banbridge Rangers	17	42		26	64
2	Ballymacash Rangers	15	31		26	54
3	Crewe United	17	33		26	50
4	Windmill Stars	15	26		26	45
5	Oxford Sunnyside	17	29		26	44
6	Rectory Rangers	21	32		26	40
7	Moneyslane	16	24	7	26	39
8	Valley Rangers	16	24	5	26	39
9	Bourneview Mill	19	28		26	38
10	Hanover	17	21		26	32
11	Richhill AFC	15	17		26	29
12	Tandragee Rovers	19	16		26	22
13	Fivemiletown United	15	10		26	17
14	Laurelvale	21	8		26	10

Intermediate B		P	Pts	GD	P	Pts
1	St Marys	16	38		24	57
2	Markethill Swifts	14	32		24	55
3	Lurgan Town	15	31		24	50
4	Ambassadors	15	29		24	46
5	Dromore Amateurs	16	30		24	45
6	Tullyvallen	19	30		24	38
7	Dungannon Tigers	17	27		24	38
8	Seagoe	14	19	3	24	33
9	Lower Maze	16	22	-11	24	33
10	AFC Craigavon	17	15		24	21
11	Seapatrick	15	10		24	16
12	Craigavon City	18	10		24	13
13	Broomhedge Maghaberry	16	5		24	8

Division One		P	Pts	GD	P	Pts
1	Ballyoran	11	28		22	56
2	Coalisland Athletic	15	34		22	50
3	Caledon Rovers	14	26		22	41
4	Sandy Hill	18	31		22	38
5	Hill Street	19	29		22	34
6	Newmills	13	19		22	32
7	Portadown BBOB	17	21		22	27
8	Banbridge YCOB	15	18	3	22	26
9	Glenavy	20	24	-24	22	26
10	Derryhirk United	12	12		22	22
11	Armagh Celtic	16	14		22	19
12	Lurgan BBOB	16	12		22	17

Division Two		P	Pts	GD	P	Pts
1	Armagh Blues	12	31		20	52
2	Annalong	13	32		20	49
3	United LT	17	32		20	38
4	Ballyvea	15	23	21	20	31
5	Scarva Rangers	14	22	15	20	31
6	Hillsborough Boys	12	16		20	27
7	West End Hibs	16	21		20	26
8	Red Star	16	19		20	24
9	Goodyear	15	11		20	15
10	Keady Celtic	13	9		20	14
11	Donacloney	15	10		20	13

Division Three		P	Pts	GD		P	Pts
1	Gilford Crusaders	14	39			18	50
2	Glenavy Youth	14	34			18	44
3	Moira Albion	13	21			18	29
4	The Dons	14	21			18	27
5	Armagh Rovers	13	19			18	26
6	Dungannon Rovers	14	19			18	24
7	Tollymore United	13	15			18	21
8	Magheralin Village	17	17			18	18
9	Damolly	11	9			18	15
10	Castlecaulfield	15	7			18	8

Division Four		P	Pts	GD		P	Pts
1	Banbridge Rangers	17	42			26	64
2	Ballymacash Rangers	15	31			26	54
3	Crewe United	17	33			26	50
4	Windmill Stars	15	26			26	45
5	Oxford Sunnyside	17	29			26	44
6	Rectory Rangers	21	32			26	40
7	Moneyslane	16	24	7		26	39
8	Valley Rangers	16	24	5		26	39
9	Bourneview Mill	19	28			26	38
10	Hanover	17	21			26	32
11	Richhill AFC	15	17			26	29
12	Tandragee Rovers	19	16			26	22
13	Fivemiletown United	15	10			26	17
14	Laurelvale	21	8			26	10

NORTHERN AMATEUR LEAGUE

Premier Division		P	W	D	L	F	A	GD	Pts
1	Ballynahinch Olympic	18	14	0	4	48	23	25	42
2	Crumlin Star	13	11	1	1	44	11	33	34
3	East Belfast	11	11	0	0	44	6	38	33
4	Crumlin United	17	9	3	5	41	29	12	30
5	Derriaghy C C	18	9	3	6	33	33	0	30
6	Ards Rangers	17	8	4	5	42	28	14	28
7	Shankill United	21	9	1	11	41	50	-9	28
8	Killyleagh Y.C	13	6	2	5	29	20	9	20
9	Immaculata F.C.	15	6	2	7	30	31	-1	20
10	Larne Tech O.B.	12	5	2	5	27	21	6	17
11	Rathfriland Rangers	9	5	0	4	33	19	14	15
12	Islandmagee	18	4	2	12	39	52	-13	14
13	1st Bangor Old Boys	17	3	2	12	23	49	-26	11
14	Drumaness Mills	23	0	0	23	23	125	-102	0

Division One A		P	W	D	L	F	A	GD	Pts
1	Rosario Y.C.	20	15	2	3	43	15	28	47
2	Dunmurry Rec	21	13	4	4	46	26	20	43
3	Dromara Village	16	11	2	3	42	26	16	35
4	Abbey Villa	16	10	3	3	37	19	18	33
5	Comber Rec F.C.	20	10	3	7	44	31	13	33
6	Albert Foundry F.C.	20	9	5	6	41	37	4	32
7	Grove United	17	10	2	5	45	25	20	29*
8	Malachians	21	7	4	10	47	56	-9	25
9	Sirocco Wks	22	7	2	13	39	46	-7	23
10	Lisburn Rangers	20	5	5	10	31	43	-12	20
11	Kilmore Rec	20	6	4	10	44	40	4	19*
12	Newcastle	19	6	1	12	27	44	-17	19
13	Orangefield Old Boys	20	3	6	11	28	43	-15	15
14	Downpatrick F.C.	20	2	1	17	20	83	-63	7

Division One B

		P	W	D	L	F	A	GD	Pts
1	Ballywalter Rec. F.C.	20	14	3	3	55	35	20	45
2	Aquinas FC	19	13	3	3	62	19	43	42
3	Dunmurry Y. M.	19	10	5	4	56	34	22	35
4	18th Newtownabbey O.B.	15	11	2	2	58	38	20	35
5	St Lukes F.C.	16	9	4	3	51	29	22	31
6	Bangor Amateurs F.C.	21	8	6	7	55	49	6	30
7	Barn United	16	8	2	6	50	46	4	26
8	Downshire YM	18	7	4	7	40	31	9	25
9	Bryansburn Rangers	20	8	1	11	39	54	-15	25
10	Portaferry Rovers	17	7	3	7	32	48	-16	24
11	Dundonald	24	5	7	12	33	48	-15	22
12	Colin Valley F.C.	18	5	0	13	31	47	-16	15
13	Mossley F.C.	20	3	3	14	25	68	-43	12
14	Ballynahinch United	21	0	5	16	27	68	-41	5

Division One C

		P	W	D	L	F	A	GD	Pts
1	Rosemount Rec	24	21	1	2	95	32	63	64
2	Greenisland F.C.	21	17	2	2	66	15	51	53
3	St Oliver Plunkett F.C.	19	15	1	3	62	28	34	46
4	Woodvale F.C.	20	10	4	6	60	45	15	34
5	Holywood F.C.	19	10	3	6	50	39	11	33
6	Saintfield United	21	8	5	8	57	50	7	29
7	Suffolk F.C.	15	9	1	5	42	30	12	28
8	Tullycarnet FC	19	7	2	10	43	42	1	23
9	Bloomfield F.C.	22	5	6	11	39	49	-10	21
10	Shorts FC	22	4	5	13	37	64	-27	17
11	Wellington Rec	24	4	4	16	50	83	-33	16
12	Iveagh United	20	4	2	14	15	80	-65	14
13	Bangor Swifts	24	2	2	20	33	92	-59	8

Division Two A

		P	W	D	L	F	A	GD	Pts
1	Portavogie Rangers F.C.	15	12	1	2	53	18	35	37
2	Willowbank FC	11	11	0	0	67	10	57	33
3	Lower Shankill FC	20	8	4	8	48	56	-8	28
4	Nortel	14	8	2	4	45	25	20	26
5	Ford	18	8	1	9	42	55	-13	25
6	Donaghadee F.C.	13	7	2	4	37	18	19	23
7	Queens Grads.	17	7	1	9	39	45	-6	22
8	Shamrock FC	11	7	1	3	51	27	24	19*
9	Finaghy F.C.	15	6	1	8	33	37	-4	19
10	St Patricks Y.M. F.C.	15	4	3	8	28	47	-19	15
11	Ballysillan Swifts	20	3	3	14	40	81	-41	12
12	Uni of Ulster at Jordanstown	17	2	1	14	16	80	-64	7

Division Two B

		P	W	D	L	F	A	GD	Pts
1	Ravenhill YM FC	16	13	1	2	48	17	31	40
2	Bangor Y.M.	20	11	3	6	55	38	17	36
3	Kelvin Old Boys	13	10	1	2	48	19	29	31
4	Beann Mhádagháin FC	12	9	1	2	37	16	21	28
5	Castlewellan Town FC	13	5	4	4	27	25	2	19
6	Tullymore Swifts	16	6	1	9	35	35	0	19
7	Civil Service	17	5	1	10	27	47	-20	19
8	St Teresas Y.C.	16	5	3	8	38	36	2	18
9	St Matthews	17	5	3	9	30	34	-4	18
10	Newtownbreda F C	17	4	5	8	35	49	-14	18
11	Kircubbin F.C.	16	5	0	11	22	58	-36	15
12	Queens University 11's	17	3	3	11	25	53	-28	12

Division Two C

		P	W	D	L	F	A	GD	Pts
1	Newhill FC	18	12	3	3	57	20	37	39
2	St Mary's	16	10	1	5	45	23	22	31
3	Suffolk Swifts	17	9	0	8	42	32	10	27
4	4th Newtownabbey F.C.	17	8	3	6	40	47	-7	27
5	Belfast Celtic YM	9	8	0	1	28	6	22	24
6	Taughmonagh YM FC	12	7	3	2	43	22	21	24
7	Carryduff Colts	13	6	3	4	28	27	1	21
8	22nd Old Boys	16	4	6	6	26	38	-12	18
9	Réalta naCromóige	18	6	0	12	36	58	-22	15*
10	Rooftop	14	5	1	8	26	37	-11	13*
11	Groomsport	13	2	2	9	17	46	-29	8
12	Whitehead Eagles	17	1	2	14	21	53	-32	5

NORTHERN IRELAND INTERMEDIATE LEAGUE

		P	W	D	L	F	A	GD	Pts
1	Newbuildings Utd	4	4	0	0	12	3	9	12
2	Newtowne	9	3	3	3	18	16	2	12
3	Strabane Athletic	6	4	0	2	12	10	2	12
4	Dungiven	5	3	2	0	12	7	5	11
5	Ardstraw	6	3	1	2	14	12	2	10
6	Magherafelt Sky Blues	7	1	1	5	8	19	-11	4
7	Maiden City	7	0	1	6	8	17	-9	1

IRISH CUP

HOLDERS: CRUSADERS

ROUND 1

Albert Foundry	v	Bloomfield	3-1
Annagh United	v	Derriaghy Cricket Club	4-1
Armagh City	v	1st Bangor Old Boys	7-0
Ballynahinch Olympic	v	Bangor	2-3
Banbridge Town	v	Dungiven	2-1
Barn United	v	Oxford Sunnyside	0-3
Belfast Celtic	v	Dromore Amateurs	9-1
Bryansburn Rangers	v	Crumlin United	1-3
Chimney Corner	v	Laurelvale	5-1
Comber Recreation	v	Bangor Amateurs	2-0
Cookstown Royal British Legion	v	Glebe Rangers	2-3
Cookstown Youth	v	Newington	0-5
Craigavon City	v	Seapatrick	5-0
Crumlin Star	v	Kilmore Recreation	8-0
Downshire Young Men	v	Rectory Rangers	2-0
Dromara Village	v	Coagh United	3-6
East Belfast	v	St Mary's	3-1
Fivemiletown United	v	Ardstraw	2-3
Grove United	v	Newcastle	2-4
Holywood	v	Newbuildings United	1-4
Iveagh United	v	Lurgan Town	1-3
Limavady United	v	Ballynure Old Boys	3-0
Maiden City	v	Bourneview Mill	3-2
Malachians	v	Moneyslane	1-2
Mossley	v	Markethill Swifts	4-1
Moyola Park	v	Colin Valley	11-0
Rosario Youth	v	Killyleagh Youth	0-1
Rosemount Recreation	v	Dunmurry Recreation	2-3
Saintfield United	v	Banbridge Rangers	0-2
Sirocco Works	v	Seagoe	2-2, 3-4p
St James' Swifts	v	Abbey Villa	4-1
St Oliver Plunkett	v	Ballymacash Rangers	2-2, 2-3p
Suffolk	v	St Luke's	3-0

NORTHERN IRELAND FOOTBALL

Trojans	v	Desertmartin	3-1
Tullyvallen	v	Dunloy	2-2, 3-4p
Wakehurst	v	Ards Rangers	3-1
Woodvale	v	Windmill Stars	5-1

ROUND 2

Glebe Rangers	v	Chimney Corner	1-1, 3-4p
Aquinas	v	Craigavon City	2-1
Ardstraw	v	Wakehurst	4-1
Armagh City	v	Dunloy	2-1 aet
Ballymacash Rangers	v	Dunmurry Young Men	2-1
Ballymoney United	v	East Belfast	2-3
Banbridge Rangers	v	Bangor	0-3
Brantwood	v	Moyola Park	4-3aet
Comber Recreation	v	Coagh United	2-4
Crewe United	v	Crumlin United	3-4
Dollingstown	v	Lower Maze	5-0
Dunmurry Recreation	v	Newbuildings United	3-2
Greenisland	v	Albert Foundry	2-0
Islandmagee	v	Shorts	5-2
Killyleagh Youth	v	Downshire Young Men	1-0
Limavady United	v	Immaculata	2-0
Lisburn Distillery	v	Strabane Athletic	3-2
Lurgan Town	v	St James' Swifts	0-4
Maiden City	v	Tullycarnet	1-3
Moneyslane	v	Mossley	9-0
Newcastle	v	Banbridge Town	0-5
Newtowne	v	Newington	0-2
Portstewart	v	Belfast Celtic	0-1
Rathfriland Rangers	v	Seagoe	4-2
Richhill	v	Valley Rangers	0-3
Shankill United	v	Lisburn Rangers	1-4
Suffolk	v	Larne Tech Old Boys	1-4
Tandragee Rovers	v	18th Newtownabbey OB	5-7aet
Tobermore United	v	Oxford Sunnyside	7-1
Woodvale	v	Annagh United	1-7

ROUND 3

18th Newtownabbey OB	v	Coagh United	2-3
Ardstraw	v	Islandmagee	1-2
Banbridge Town	v	Dunmurry Recreation	2-1
Belfast Celtic	v	Annagh United	3-1
Brantwood	v	Crumlin United	4-3
Chimney Corner	v	Valley Rangers	0-3
Crumlin Star	v	Greenisland	1-0
Dollingstown	v	Lisburn Distillery	2-1
Hanover	v	Killyleagh Youth	3-2
Limavady United	v	Aquinas	3-0
Moneyslane	v	Bangor	1-5
Newington	v	East Belfast	0-3
Rathfriland Rangers	v	Lisburn Rangers	3-0
St James' Swifts	v	Ballymacash Rangers	0-4
Tobermore United	v	Larne Tech Old Boys	1-3
Tullycarnet	v	Armagh City	4-3

ROUND 4

Banbridge Town	v	Ballymacash Rangers	3-2
Belfast Celtic	v	Larne Tech Old Boys	2-1
Brantwood	v	Rathfriland Rangers	2-5
Coagh United	v	Crumlin Star	0-1
Dollingstown	v	Tullycarnet	6-0
East Belfast	v	Islandmagee	7-1
Limavady United	v	Bangor	1-3
Valley Rangers	v	Hanover	1-5

ROUND 5

Ards	v	Carrick Rangers	1-3
Ballinamallard United	v	Dollingstown	1-0
Ballyclare Comrades	v	Harland & Wolff Welders	2-1
Ballymena United	v	Crumlin Star	2-0
Banbridge Town	v	East Belfast	2-2, 5-4p
Cliftonville	v	Hanover	6-0
Crusaders	v	Dundela	3-0
Glenavon	v	Coleraine	0-2
Glentoran	v	Portadown	2-2, 5-4p
Institute	v	Dungannon Swifts	2-3
Knockbreda	v	Dergview	3-2
Larne	v	Belfast Celtic	8-0
Loughgall	v	Rathfriland Rangers	1-2
Newry City	v	Bangor	3-1
Queen's University	v	Linfield	2-1
Warrenpoint Town	v	PSNI	3-1

ROUND 6

Ballyclare Comrades	v	Larne	0-1
Carrick Rangers	v	Crusaders	1-5
Cliftonville	v	Rathfriland Rangers	3-1
Coleraine	v	Banbridge Town	3-0
Dungannon Swifts	v	Newry City	4-2
Knockbreda	v	Ballinamallard United	2-5
Queen's University	v	Glentoran	2-3
Warrenpoint Town	v	Ballymena United	1-2

QUARTER FINALS

Ballinamallard United	v	Ballymena United	0-2
Dungannon Swifts	v	Cliftonville	1-2
Glentoran	v	Crusaders	2-1
Larne	v	Coleraine	2-3

SEMI FINALS

Ballymena United	v	Coleraine
Cliftonville	v	Glentoran

SCOTTISH TABLES 2019-20

HIGHLAND LEAGUE

		P	W	D	L	F	A	GD	Pts
1	Brora Rangers	26	24	0	2	96	14	82	72
2	Inverurie Loco Works	28	19	2	7	80	40	40	59
3	Fraserburgh	23	17	4	2	79	23	56	55
4	Rothes	23	17	2	4	53	22	31	53
5	Buckie Thistle	24	17	2	5	64	35	29	53
6	Formartine United	23	14	2	7	62	21	41	44
7	Forres Mechanics	27	13	4	10	67	49	18	43
8	Nairn County	22	12	3	7	39	41	-2	39
9	Keith	27	10	4	13	50	65	-15	34
10	Wick Academy	25	9	5	11	38	47	-9	32
11	Deveronvale	27	9	4	14	42	56	-14	31
12	Huntly	27	6	6	15	35	73	-38	24
13	Strathspey Thistle	22	6	1	15	29	54	-25	19
14	Turriff United	27	5	3	19	33	83	-50	18
15	Clachnacuddin	27	4	4	19	27	63	-36	16
16	Lossiemouth	28	4	1	23	22	87	-65	13
17	Fort William	20	3	1	16	18	61	-43	10

LOWLAND LEAGUE

		P	W	D	L	F	A	GD	Pts
1	Kelty Hearts	25	22	2	1	95	17	78	68
2	Bonnyrigg Rose	24	20	2	2	70	22	48	62
3	East Stirlingshire	26	17	2	7	77	29	48	53
4	BSC Glasgow	22	16	3	3	58	21	37	51
5	The Spartans	25	16	1	8	49	32	17	49
6	Civil Service Strollers	23	12	3	8	40	38	2	39
7	East Kilbride	23	11	4	8	43	24	19	37
8	Caledonian Braves	26	11	3	12	57	55	2	36
9	Cumbernauld Colts	27	10	6	11	49	50	-1	36
10	University of Stirling	25	9	4	12	28	44	-16	31
11	Gala Fairydean Rovers	25	7	6	12	39	55	-16	27
12	Berwick Rangers	24	6	6	12	32	41	-9	24
13	Gretna 2008	24	2	6	16	21	62	-41	12
14	Edinburgh University	25	2	6	17	18	66	-48	12
15	Dalbeattie Star	23	3	2	18	19	68	-49	11
16	Vale of Leithen	23	2	2	19	18	89	-71	8

EAST OF SCOTLAND LEAGUE

PREMIER DIVISION

		P	W	D	L	F	A	GD	Pts
1	Bo'ness United	21	14	5	2	42	22	20	47
2	Broxburn Athletic	19	11	5	3	40	29	11	38
3	Hill of Beath Hawthorn	18	10	5	3	45	20	25	37
4	Tranent Juniors	20	10	4	6	37	25	12	34
5	Camelon Juniors	20	10	4	6	38	33	5	34
6	Dundonald Bluebell	18	8	3	7	46	35	11	27
7	Penicuik Athletic	18	8	3	7	37	32	5	27
8	Musselburgh Athletic	21	8	3	10	42	42	0	27
9	Jeanfield Swifts	16	8	2	6	36	28	8	26
10	Linlithgow Rose	17	7	3	7	41	37	4	24
11	Dunbar United	21	6	5	10	32	39	-7	23
12	Crossgates Primrose	21	6	5	10	37	55	-18	23
13	Sauchie Juniors	22	6	5	11	33	44	-11	20
14	Blackburn United	20	5	3	12	22	44	-22	18
15	Whitehill Welfare	18	4	4	10	20	35	-15	16
16	Newtongrange Star	22	4	3	15	32	60	-28	15

SOUTH OF SCOTLAND LEAGUE

		P	W	D	L	F	A	GD	Pts
1	Threave Rovers	20	17	2	1	70	17	53	53
2	Stranraer Reserves	16	14	1	1	55	14	41	43
3	Abbey Vale	17	13	2	2	62	17	45	41
4	Bonnyton Thistle	20	12	4	4	60	34	25	40
5	Mid-Annandale	23	12	4	7	70	56	14	40
6	Newton Stewart	22	10	4	8	50	52	-2	34
7	Nithsdale Wanderers	18	7	4	7	50	42	8	25
8	Heston Rovers	22	7	4	11	45	52	-7	25
9	St Cuthbert Wanderers	23	6	5	12	43	55	-12	23
10	Caledonian Braves Res	19	6	3	10	30	48	-18	21
11	Lochar Thistle	22	5	4	13	32	55	-23	19
12	Upper Annandale	18	6	0	12	30	56	-26	18
13	Wigtown & Bladnoch	22	4	4	14	33	80	-47	16
14	Lochmaben	21	4	3	14	24	55	-31	15
15	Creetown	17	3	4	10	21	42	-21	13

NORTH CALEDONIAN LEAGUE

		P	W	D	L	F	A	GD	Pts
1	Invergordon	13	11	0	2	60	12	48	33
2	Thurso	13	9	2	2	44	23	21	29
3	Golspie Sutherland	11	8	2	1	60	16	44	26
4	St Duthus	12	8	0	4	46	15	31	24
5	Orkney	10	6	2	2	43	11	32	20
6	Halkirk United	15	5	2	8	34	45	-11	17
7	Inverness Athletic	15	4	0	11	34	50	-16	12
8	Bunillidh Thistle	11	2	0	9	12	57	-45	6
9	Bonar Bridge	14	0	0	14	10	114	-104	0

SJFA EAST REGION

Superleague North

		P	W	D	L	F	A	GD	Pts
1	Carnoustie Panmure	19	15	3	1	60	21	39	48
2	Broughty Athletic	19	12	4	3	51	24	27	40
3	Lochee United	16	12	1	3	41	18	23	37
4	Downfield Juniors	18	7	5	6	24	25	-1	26
5	Dundee North End	18	6	4	8	34	41	-7	22
6	Luncarty	21	6	3	12	40	51	-11	21
7	Tayport	17	6	2	9	33	40	-7	20
8	Kirriemuir Thistle	19	4	4	11	35	55	-20	16
9	Scone Thistle	19	5	1	13	16	46	-30	16
10	Forfar West End	18	3	5	10	24	37	-13	14

SUPERLEAGUE SOUTH

		P	W	D	L	F	A	GD	Pts
1	Livingston United	20	11	3	6	44	27	17	36
2	Pumpherston Juniors	18	11	2	5	45	32	13	35
3	Whitburn Juniors	19	10	2	7	51	41	10	32
4	Thornton Hibs	18	9	3	6	47	26	21	31
5	Armadale Thistle	17	10	1	6	42	28	14	31
6	Fauldhouse United	16	9	3	4	33	28	5	30
7	Bathgate Thistle	14	5	2	7	29	25	4	17
8	Harthill Royal	17	4	2	11	18	43	-25	14
9	Kennoway Star Hearts	19	4	1	14	32	56	-24	13
10	Lochore Welfare	16	2	2	12	17	52	-35	8

Martyniuk (Bonnyrigg) gets in his cross under pressure from O'Neill (Vale of Leithen) (Lowland).

McGachie (Bonnyrigg) gets to the ball first (Lowland). Photos Keith Clayton.

PREMIER NORTH

		P	W	D	L	F	A	GD	Pts
1	Dundee East Craigie	19	17	2	0	82	19	63	53
2	Blairgowrie Juniors	21	15	3	3	69	36	33	48
3	Dundee Violet	22	12	1	9	40	43	-3	37
4	Arbroath Victoria	19	11	2	6	42	29	13	35
5	Brechin Victoria	20	8	2	10	44	49	-5	26
6	Lochee Harp	22	5	3	14	31	46	-15	18
7	Coupar Angus	22	5	1	16	30	76	-46	16
8	Forfar Albion	23	3	2	18	25	65	-40	11

PREMIER SOUTH

		P	W	D	L	F	A	GD	Pts
1	Rosyth	22	16	1	5	65	31	34	49
2	Newburgh Juniors	24	14	3	7	67	55	12	45
3	Stoneyburn Juniors	18	13	3	2	69	24	45	42
4	Kirkcaldy & Dysart	19	9	6	4	34	25	9	33
5	Lochgelly Albert	25	9	5	11	57	64	-7	32
6	Sauchie Community	21	8	7	6	34	37	-3	31
7	Syngenta	25	8	5	12	52	59	-7	29
8	Linlithgow Rose Community	25	6	10	9	39	53	-14	28
9	Bo'ness United Juniors	23	6	4	13	37	41	-4	22
10	West Calder United	20	0	0	20	15	80	-65	0

SJFA NORTH REGION

SUPERLEAGUE

		P	W	D	L	F	A	GD	Pts
1	Banks o' Dee	16	16	0	0	74	5	62	48
2	Culter	16	10	4	2	39	10	21	34
3	Hermes	16	10	4	2	40	6	19	34
4	Nairn St Ninian	21	8	7	6	44	35	-6	31
5	Bridge of Don Thistle	17	9	3	5	41	18	15	30
6	Dyce Juniors	18	7	6	5	34	13	6	27
7	Montrose Roselea	20	8	4	8	36	21	8	25*
8	Deveronside	20	7	4	9	41	23	-4	25
9	Colony Park	21	6	3	12	38	39	-25	21
10	Aberdeen East End	20	6	6	8	27	17	-5	18*
11	Banchory St Ternan	14	4	6	4	14	9	-8	18
12	Hall Russell United	19	2	7	10	25	26	-16	13
13	Ellon United	19	3	4	12	27	34	-28	13
14	Maud Juniors	17	2	0	15	17	35	-39	6

DIVISION ONE

		P	W	D	L	F	A	GD	Pts
1	Aberdeen University	19	12	3	4	48	21	17	39
2	Sunnybank	20	11	4	5	52	21	18	37
3	Stonehaven Juniors	18	10	2	6	46	20	18	32
4	Fraserburgh United	16	9	3	4	38	13	14	30
5	Longside	20	9	3	8	55	22	11	30
6	Stoneywood Parkvale	13	7	1	5	32	9	11	22
7	Dufftown	15	4	2	9	21	24	-14	14
8	Buckie Rovers	14	2	3	9	25	33	-18	9
9	Buchanhaven Hearts	17	1	1	15	19	27	-57	4

DIVISION TWO

		P	W	D	L	F	A	GD	Pts
1	Burghead Thistle	16	13	0	3	53	9	33	39
2	Forres Thistle	15	12	2	1	53	15	35	38
3	Newmachar United	18	10	1	7	48	22	7	31
4	Islavale	15	9	3	4	41	16	18	30
5	Spey Valley United	15	8	0	7	31	9	2	24
6	New Elgin	17	7	2	8	33	15	-1	23
7	Cruden Bay Juniors	18	6	3	9	39	28	-3	21
8	Glentanar	17	2	1	14	22	29	-33	7
9	Whitehills	17	1	0	16	19	38	-58	3

SJFA WEST REGION

PREMIERSHIP

		P	W	D	L	F	A	GD	Pts
1	Kilwinning Rangers	25	16	5	4	51	38	13	53
2	Pollok	22	13	3	6	48	22	26	42
3	Auchinleck Talbot	16	13	2	1	51	15	36	41
4	Irvine Meadow XI	22	12	2	8	36	35	1	38
5	Clydebank	28	11	4	13	42	45	-3	37
6	Glenafton Athletic	20	11	3	6	39	30	9	36
7	Beith Juniors	21	9	7	5	40	35	5	34
8	Kilbirnie Ladeside	24	10	3	11	44	44	0	33
9	Cumnock Juniors	25	9	5	11	39	45	-6	32
10	Rossvale	25	10	2	13	33	39	-6	32
11	Largs Thistle	25	9	4	11	41	44	-3	31
12	Hurlford United	19	8	5	6	29	26	3	29
13	Troon	24	6	4	14	31	51	-20	22
14	Benburb	20	5	4	17	27	39	-12	19
15	Rutherglen Glencairn	17	3	3	11	26	42	-16	12
16	Kirkintilloch Rob Roy	17	2	0	15	8	35	-27	6

CHAMPIONSHIP

		P	W	D	L	F	A	GD	Pts
1	Darvel	21	17	2	2	62	25	37	53
2	Cumbernauld United	22	15	2	5	63	30	33	47
3	Blantyre Victoria	18	15	1	2	66	34	32	46
4	Renfrew	23	13	3	7	59	40	19	42
5	Shotts Bon Accord	18	11	1	6	47	31	16	34
6	Arthurlie	23	10	1	12	46	41	5	31
7	Neilston Juniors	18	9	4	5	26	24	2	31
8	Whitletts Victoria	23	8	3	12	48	57	-9	27
9	Kilsyth Rangers	16	8	2	6	41	36	5	26
10	Dalry Thistle	17	7	2	8	35	41	-6	23
11	Gartcairn Juniors	21	5	6	10	46	56	-10	21
12	Petershill	21	6	2	13	32	51	-19	20
13	St Roch's	18	5	3	10	30	39	-9	18
14	Cambuslang Rangers	21	4	5	12	34	55	-21	17
15	Craigmark Burntonians	22	4	5	13	33	58	-25	17
16	Irvine Victoria	24	3	4	17	26	76	-50	13

DIVISION ONE

		P	W	D	L	F	A	GD	Pts
1	Ardrossan Winton Rovers	22	14	2	6	49	29	20	44
2	Lanark United	23	13	5	5	56	47	9	44
3	Shettleston	19	13	4	2	50	19	31	43
4	Port Glasgow Juniors	24	13	4	7	45	29	16	43
5	Lesmahagow Juniors	25	13	3	9	55	43	12	42
6	Greenock Juniors	22	10	5	7	51	40	11	35
7	Carluke Rovers	26	10	3	13	53	53	0	33
8	Glasgow Perthshire	21	8	5	7	63	48	15	32
9	Larkhall Thistle	22	10	2	10	51	56	-5	32
10	Bellshill Athletic	19	10	1	8	41	34	7	31
11	Girvan	19	7	3	9	42	47	-5	24
12	Maryhill	21	7	2	12	41	70	-29	23
13	Kello Rovers	21	6	3	12	31	42	-11	21
14	Wishaw Juniors	19	5	3	11	26	39	-13	18
15	East Kilbride Thistle	21	4	5	12	27	46	-19	17
16	Royal Albert	22	2	4	16	36	75	-39	10

SCOTTISH FOOTBALL

DIVISION TWO		P	W	D	L	F	A	GD	Pts
1	Vale of Leven	24	14	5	5	68	37	31	47
2	Yoker Athletic	22	13	3	6	54	32	22	42
3	Muirkirk Juniors	19	14	0	5	50	28	22	42
4	Maybole Juniors	23	13	1	9	63	48	15	40
5	Johnstone Burgh	14	13	0	1	51	11	40	39
6	Ashfield	17	12	1	4	66	36	30	37
7	Thorniewood United	19	11	2	6	54	24	30	35
8	Forth Wanderers	18	11	0	7	40	26	14	33
9	Annbank United	22	10	2	10	47	59	-12	32
10	Vale of Clyde	21	9	2	10	51	35	16	29
11	St Anthony's	20	8	2	10	32	44	-12	26
12	Saltcoats Victoria	24	3	7	14	24	54	-30	16
13	Newmains United	19	5	1	13	25	67	-42	16
14	Lugar Boswell Thistle	21	2	2	17	22	66	-44	8
15	Ardeer Thistle	23	0	2	21	24	104	-80	2

SCOTTISH JUNIOR CUP

HOLDERS: AUCHINLECK TALBOT

ROUND 1

Kilwinning Rangers	v	Dundee Violet	2-1
Maybole	v	Benburb	2-3
Neilston	v	Yoker Athletic	4-2
Newburgh	v	Whitburn	0-6

ROUND 2

Linlithgow Rose Com.	v	Fraserburgh United	3-2
Stonehaven	v	Glentanar	4-0
Carluke Rovers	v	Clydebank	1-3
Girvan	v	Tayport	5-5
Scone Thistle	v	Lochee Harp	3-0
Lochore Welfare	v	Brechin Victoria	1-2
Arbroath Victoria	v	Islavale	0-1
Troon	v	Montrose Roselea	3-1
Glasgow Perthshire	v	Broughty Athletic	1-2
Johnstone Burgh	v	Armadale Thistle	4-2
Lugar Boswell Thistle	v	Newmachar United	3-0
Dundee North End	v	Whitburn	4-1
Sauchie Juniors Com.	v	Hermes	1-2
Maryhill	v	Forfar West End	2-4
Ardeer Thistle	v	Rutherglen Glencairn	0-11
St Roch's	v	Renfrew	0-0
Kirkcaldy & Dysart	v	Saltcoats Victoria	1-1
New Elgin	v	St Anthony's	1-2
Gartcairn	v	Lanark United	5-2
Dyce	v	Sunnybank	2-1
Aberdeen East End	v	Port Glasgow	3-1
Blantyre Victoria	v	Muirkirk	2-0
Spey Valley United	v	Lesmahagow	0-5
Glenafton Athletic	v	West Calder United	13-0
Aberdeen University	v	Dalry Thistle	4-5
Livingston United	v	Shotts Bon Accord	0-1
Fauldhouse United	v	Carnoustie Panmure	2-1
Irvine Victoria	v	Kello Rovers	0-3
Largs Thistle	v	Luncarty	1-0
Vale of Clyde	v	Darvel	0-2
Syngenta	v	Shettleston	1-6
Kennoway Star Hearts	v	Larkhall Thistle	0-1
Kilwinning Rangers	v	Bridge of Don Thistle	2-2
Irvine Meadow	v	Buchanhaven Hearts	AW
Cambuslang Rangers	v	Harthill Royal	7-0
Cumbernauld United	v	Hurlford United	0-1
Blairgowrie	v	Stoneywood Parkvale	1-2
Ardrossan Winton Rovers	v	Royal Albert	3-0
Downfield	v	Greenock	2-1
Arthurlie	v	Beith	1-5
Forfar Albion	v	Bathgate Thiste	4-5
Bellshill Athletic	v	Auchinleck Talbot	0-7
Forres Thistle	v	Pollok	0-3

Dundee East Craigie	v	Nairn St Ninian	6-1
Kilbirnie Ladeside	v	Vale of Leven	3-1
Neilston	v	Forth Wanderers	4-4
Burghead Thistle	v	Lochgelly Albert	2-2
Cumnock	v	Rossvale	0-2
Petershill	v	Newmains United	6-0
Thornton Hibs	v	Rosyth	3-1
Hall Russell United	v	Lochee United	0-3
Kirkintilloch Rob Roy	v	Pumpherston	2-1
Dufftown	v	East Kilbride Thistle	2-1
Cruden Bay	v	Banchory St Ternan	0-4
Colony Park	v	Ashfield	3-6
Craigmark Burntonians	v	Kilsyth Rangers	0-2
Wishaw	v	Culter	1-1
Deveronside	v	Benburb	0-0
Annbank United	v	Whitletts Victoria	1-6
Ellon United	v	Bo'ness United Junior	0-0
Buckie Rovers	v	Stoneyburn	2-1
Longside	v	Whitehills	6-1
Maud	v	Kirriemuir Thistle	0-3
Thorniewood United	v	Banks O' Dee	2-6

REPLAYS

Tayport	v	Girvan	2-0
Renfrew	v	St Roch's	0-1
Saltcoats Victoria	v	Kirkcaldy & Dysart	0-2
Bridge of Don Thistle	v	Kilwinning Rangers	3-1
Forth Wanderers	v	Neilston	3-3, 3-5p
Lochgelly Albert	v	Burghead Thistle	3-4
Benburb	v	Deveronside	11-0
Bo'ness United Junior	v	Ellon United	2-2, 2-4p
Culter	v	Wishaw	4-2

ROUND 3

Aberdeen East End	v	Scone Thistle	1-1
Ashfield	v	Lugar Boswell Thistle	4-1
Auchinleck Talbot	v	Forfar West End	3-0
Banchory St Ternan	v	Larkhall Thistle	1-6
Bathgate Thiste	v	Irvine Meadow	1-3
Beith	v	Whitletts Victoria	7-2
Benburb	v	Dyce	2-1
Brechin Victoria	v	Neilston	0-2
Bridge of Don Thistle	v	Ardrossan Winton Rovers	4-1
Broughty Athletic	v	St Anthony's	5-1
Buckie Rovers	v	Blantyre Victoria	1-7
Burghead Thistle	v	Kirkintilloch Rob Roy	0-2
Cambuslang Rangers	v	Dundee East Craigie	2-1
Culter	v	Rossvale	0-1
Dalry Thistle	v	Dundee North End	1-2
Dufftown	v	Johnstone Burgh	1-4
Dundee Downfield	v	Tayport	3-4
Gartcairn	v	Kilbirnie Ladeside	1-0
Islavale	v	Rutherglen Glencairn	3-4
Kirkcaldy & Dysart	v	Darvel	1-2
Kirriemuir Thistle	v	Largs Thistle	3-1
Lesmahagow	v	St Roch's	0-2
Linlithgow Rose Com.	v	Pollok	0-2
Longside	v	Stoneywood Parkvale	1-6
Petershill	v	Clydebank	1-0
Shettleston	v	Kello Rovers	0-0
Shotts Bon Accord	v	Hurlford United	2-2
Stonehaven	v	Ellon United	0-4
Thornton Hibs	v	Fauldhouse United	1-2
Troon	v	Kilsyth Rangers	5-4
Glenafton Athletic	v	Banks O' Dee	2-1
Lochee United	v	Hermes	3-1

REPLAYS

Hurlford United	v	Shotts Bon Accord	3-1
Kello Rovers	v	Shettleston	3-1
Scone Thistle	v	Aberdeen East End	1-1, 2-4p

ROUND 4

Aberdeen East End	v	Beith	1-4
Blantyre Victoria	v	Darvel	3-4
Cambuslang Rangers	v	Broughty Athletic	0-3
Gartcairn	v	Ellon United	7-0
Hurlford United	v	Benburb	3-0
Irvine Meadow	v	Glenafton Athletic	0-0
Johnstone Burgh	v	St Roch's	2-3
Kirriemuir Thistle	v	Tayport	1-2
Larkhall Thistle	v	Kello Rovers	1-3
Neilston	v	Lochee United	1-1
Petershill	v	Rutherglen Glencairn	2-2
Pollok	v	Troon	2-1
Stoneywood Parkvale	v	Ashfield	4-1
Rossvale	v	Auchinleck Talbot	1-2
Bridge of Don Thistle	v	Fauldhouse United	2-3
Dundee North End	v	Kirkintilloch Rob Roy	0-2

REPLAYS

Glenafton Athletic	v	Irvine Meadow	1-1, 2-4p
Lochee United	v	Neilston	1-3
Rutherglen Glencairn	v	Petershill	0-4

ROUND 5

Auchinleck Talbot	v	Tayport	2-1
Broughty Athletic	v	St Roch's	2-1
Hurlford United	v	Gartcairn	5-1
Kello Rovers	v	Irvine Meadow	2-1
Kirkintilloch Rob Roy	v	Neilston	0-1
Petershill	v	Darvel	1-1
Pollok	v	Fauldhouse United	4-0
Stoneywood Parkvale	v	Beith	0-4

REPLAY

Darvel	v	Petershill	2-1

QUARTER FINALS

Beith	v	Kello Rovers	4-1
Neilston	v	Pollok	1-4
Darvel	v	Broughty Athletic	2-2
Broughty Athletic	v	Darvel	
Auchinleck Talbot	v	Hurlford United	

SEMI FINALS

First leg

Beith	v	Darvel or Broughty Athletic
Pollok	v	Auchinleck Talbot or Hurlford United

Second leg

Auchinleck Talbot or Hurlford United	v	Pollok
Darvel or Broughty Athletic	v	Beith

Baur (Bonnyrigg) Healy (Berwick).

Brian (Berwick) heads clear under Bonnyrigg pressure.

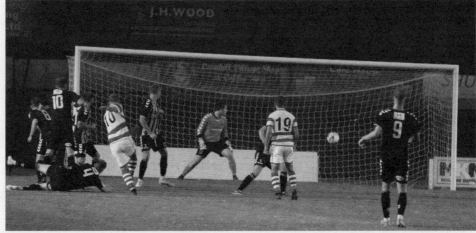

Currie (Bonnyrigg) sends his free kick past Brennan (Berwick) for number five. Photos Keith Clayton.

WELSH TABLES 2019-20

CYMRU PREMIER (Formerly Welsh Premier)

		P	W	D	L	F	A	GD	Pts
1	Connah's Quay Nomads	26	16	8	2	47	19	28	56
2	The New Saints	26	16	4	6	69	27	42	52
3	Bala Town	26	15	4	7	53	23	30	49
4	Barry Town United	25	12	6	7	35	29	6	42
5	Caernarfon Town	26	11	5	10	36	38	-2	38
6	Newtown	25	10	5	10	25	30	-5	35
7	Cardiff Metropolitan University	25	9	8	8	30	29	1	35
8	Cefn Druids	25	10	5	10	37	39	-2	35
9	Aberystwyth Town	26	7	6	13	36	55	-19	27
10	Pen-y-Bont	25	5	6	14	29	48	-19	21
11	Carmarthen Town	25	4	6	15	28	49	-21	18
12	Airbus UK Broughton	26	4	5	17	28	67	-39	17

After 22 games the League splits into two. The top six then play each other twice again and the bottom six do the same. However, once split, no team can climb back into the top six no matter what points they finish on.

CYMRU NORTH

		P	W	D	L	F	A	GD	Pts
1	Prestatyn Town	24	21	2	1	84	18	66	65
2	Flint Town United	22	15	4	3	59	22	37	49
3	Guilsfield	21	13	4	4	44	26	18	43
4	Colwyn Bay	24	14	5	5	44	30	14	47
5	Bangor City	22	10	7	5	27	25	2	37
6	Conwy Borough	23	9	6	8	43	44	-1	33
7	Llanrhaeadr-ym-Mochnant	21	9	3	9	35	34	1	30
8	Penrhyncoch	23	10	2	11	29	35	-6	32
9	Ruthin Town	23	7	7	9	29	34	-5	28
10	Buckley Town	20	7	3	10	24	41	-17	24
11	Gresford Athletic	22	7	5	10	34	34	0	26
12	Llandudno	21	6	4	11	32	38	-6	22
13	Llangefni Town	24	5	6	13	22	47	-25	21
14	Porthmadog	23	4	6	13	28	46	-18	18
15	Corwen	22	3	5	14	26	51	-25	14
16	Llanfair United	21	2	3	16	23	58	-35	9

Rhyl went into administration in April - all results expunged.

CYMRU SOUTH

		P	W	D	L	F	A	GD	Pts
1	Swansea University	25	17	5	3	56	31	25	56
2	Haverfordwest County	25	17	4	4	58	26	32	55
3	Briton Ferry Llansawel	24	15	2	7	65	36	29	47
4	STM Sports	22	12	3	7	51	34	17	39
5	Cambrian & Clydach Vale B.G.C.	23	11	7	5	41	31	10	40
6	Llanelli Town	26	12	4	10	47	51	-4	40
7	Ammanford	25	12	1	12	44	47	-3	37
8	Goytre United	25	10	6	9	40	41	-1	36
9	Pontypridd Town	25	9	8	8	52	41	11	35
10	Afan Lido	25	10	4	11	47	47	0	34
11	Llantwit Major	24	7	6	11	34	39	-5	27
12	Undy Athletic	21	7	2	12	29	38	-9	23
13	Cwmbran Celtic	22	6	4	12	29	44	-15	22
14	Taff's Well	25	6	3	16	40	64	-24	21
15	Cwmamman United	22	5	2	15	22	55	-33	17
16	Caerau (Ely)	21	1	5	15	22	52	-30	8

WELSH LEAGUE
Division One

		P	W	D	L	F	A	GD	Pts
1	Trefelin Boys & Girls Club	20	17	3	0	64	23	41	54
2	Port Talbot Town	18	10	5	3	33	16	17	35
3	Risca United	16	10	3	3	32	24	8	33
4	Goytre	18	9	5	4	46	22	24	32
5	Garden Village	20	8	5	7	25	29	-4	29
6	Caldicot Town	18	8	2	8	27	25	2	26
7	Penydarren BGC	13	7	3	3	26	22	4	24
8	Ton Pentre	19	6	4	9	31	42	-11	22
9	Bridgend Street	15	6	3	6	35	25	10	21
10	Pontardawe Town	16	5	4	7	22	28	-6	19
11	Abergavenny Town	20	5	3	12	25	42	-17	18
12	Aberbargoed Buds	15	4	4	7	25	31	-6	16
13	Monmouth Town	17	4	2	11	27	39	-12	14
14	AFC Llwydcoed	16	3	5	8	20	33	-13	14
15	Croesyceiliog	13	3	4	6	19	27	-8	13
16	Dinas Powys	18	2	3	13	28	57	-29	9

Division Two

		P	W	D	L	F	A	GD	Pts
1	Ynysygerwn	19	13	3	3	53	18	35	42
2	Ynyshir Albion	18	12	2	4	44	25	19	38
3	Trethomas Bluebirds	17	11	3	3	54	25	29	36
4	Abertillery Bluebirds	20	11	3	6	42	29	13	36
5	Newport City	21	10	4	7	46	34	12	34
6	Penrhiwceiber Rangers	13	10	1	2	34	15	19	31
7	Pontyclun	16	9	3	4	46	18	28	30
8	West End	19	8	2	9	40	41	-1	26
9	Chepstow Town	16	7	2	7	38	32	6	23
10	Treharris Athletic Western	19	6	4	9	35	36	-1	22
11	Tredegar Town	15	6	2	7	19	20	-1	20
12	Treowen Stars	16	4	2	10	17	36	-19	14
13	Panteg	14	4	1	9	19	38	-19	13
14	AFC Porth	15	3	0	12	14	51	-37	9
15	Aberdare Town	15	2	2	11	11	54	-43	8
16	Albion Rovers	13	0	0	13	8	48	-40	-3*

WELSH NATIONAL LEAGUE
Premier

		P	W	D	L	F	A	GD	Pts
1	Cefn Albion	20	14	3	3	60	32	28	45
2	Holywell Town	17	13	3	1	62	8	54	42
3	Rhostyllen	18	13	2	3	64	28	36	41
4	Queens Park	20	12	4	4	48	25	23	40
5	Mold Alexandra	17	11	3	3	50	33	17	36
6	Brymbo	18	10	2	6	54	34	20	32
7	Saltney Town	20	9	3	8	39	31	8	30
8	Penycae	21	9	2	10	35	38	-3	29
9	Llay Welfare	18	8	4	6	28	28	0	28
10	Llanuwchllyn	17	8	3	6	31	29	2	27
11	Rhydymwyn	17	6	2	9	26	39	-13	20
12	Plas Madoc	17	4	6	7	24	44	-20	18
13	Rhos Aelwyd	19	4	4	11	19	45	-26	16
14	Chirk AAA	16	2	2	12	23	46	-23	8
15	Brickfield Rangers	17	1	2	14	22	65	-43	2*
16	Castell Alun Colts	22	0	1	21	19	79	-60	1

Cymru Premier - Hood (Barry) gets the ball past Wilson (Penybont) for the winner. Photo Keith Clayton.

WELSH LEAGUE CUP

ROUND 1
NORTH

Buckley Town	v Rhyl	0–2
Ruthin	v Guilsfield	0–3
Prestatyn Town	v Llanrhaeadr	4–2
Gresford Athletic	v Colwyn Bay	1–0
Conwy Borough	v Bangor City	0–1
Llanfair United	v Llangefni Town	3–1
Berriew	v Corwen	0–2

SOUTH

Afan Lido	v Cwmbran Celtic	0–1
Pontypridd Town	v STM Sports	2–3
Undy Athletic	v Cwmamman United	2–2, 4-5p
Swansea University	v Llantwit Major	0–1
Goytre United	v Caerau (Ely)	3–0
Ammanford	v Penrhyncoch	2–1
Briton Ferry Llansawel	v Taffs Well	3–1

ROUND 2
NORTH

Corwen	v Caernarfon Town	0–2
Bala Town	v Gresford Athletic	7–0
Rhyl	v Connah's Quay Nomads	0–2
Airbus UK Broughton	v Llanfair United	4–0
Cefn Druids	v Prestatyn Town	1–2
Bangor City	v The New Saints	1-1, 4-2p
Flint Town United	v Portmadog	5–1
Guilsfield	v Llandudno	1–0

SOUTH

Cambrian & Clydach Vale B.&G.C.	v Aberystwyth Town	3–4
Haverfordwest County	v Barry Town United	1-1, 5-4p
Newtown	v Ammanford	2–0
Carmarthen Town	v Cwmamman United	4–1
Llanwit Major	v Cardiff Met.	1–2
Pen-y-Bont	v Goytre United	4–1
Briton Ferry Llansawel A.F.C.	v Llanelli Town	1-1, 4-1p
STM Sports	v Cwmbran Celtic	4–0

ROUND 3

Briton Ferry	v Carmarthen Town	0–2
STM Sports	v Haverfordwest County	1-1, 7-6p
Guilsfield	v Connah's Quay Nomads	1-1, 3-5p
Cardiff Met.	v Aberystwyth Town	0–1
Caernarfon Town	v Prestatyn Town	1–4
Flint Town United	v Airbus UK Broughton	2–1
Newtown	v Pen-y-Bont	2–1
Bala Town	v Bangor City	1-1, 7-6p

QUARTER FINAL

Newtown	v STM Sports	2-2, 3-4p
Carmarthen Town	v Aberystwyth Town	0–3
Connah's Quay Nomads	v Flint Town United	4–1
Prestatyn Town	v Bala Town	1–2

SEMI FINAL

Connah's Quay Nomads	v Bala Town	2–0
STM Sports	v Aberystwyth Town	2–1

FINAL 01/02/2020

Connah's Quay Nomads	v STM Sports	3–0

WELSH FOOTBALL

Division One

		P	W	D	L	F	A	GD	Pts
1	Hawarden Rangers	12	10	0	2	57	15	42	30
2	Coedpoeth United	10	6	3	1	37	16	21	21
3	New Brighton Villa	13	6	3	4	37	24	13	21
4	Llangollen Town	12	7	0	5	29	20	9	21
5	Cefn Mawr Rangers	9	7	0	2	22	13	9	21
6	Halkyn & Flint Mountain	11	5	1	5	25	22	3	16
7	Lex XI	11	4	2	5	27	27	0	14
8	Mynydd Isa Spartans	9	3	3	3	20	18	2	12
9	Overton Recreational	13	2	0	11	22	51	-29	6
10	Johnstown Youth	12	0	0	12	4	74	-70	-3*

NORTH EAST WALES LEAGUE

		P	W	D	L	F	A	GD	Pts
1	Brymbo Victoria	15	10	3	2	74	28	46	33
2	Chirk Town	14	10	2	2	57	19	38	32
3	Penyffordd Lions	14	8	3	3	48	28	20	27
4	Caerwys	12	7	1	4	40	20	20	22
5	CPD Sychdyn	13	6	1	6	38	22	16	19
6	Borras Park Albion	14	5	2	7	33	40	-7	17
7	Acton	13	5	1	7	52	30	22	16
8	Mold Town United	13	3	3	7	52	46	6	12
9	Bellevue	16	0	0	16	12	173	-161	0

WELSH ALLIANCE

Division One

		P	W	D	L	F	A	GD	Pts
1	Holyhead Hotspur	18	15	1	2	55	23	32	46
2	Glan Conwy	22	12	3	7	43	29	14	39
3	Denbigh Town	17	12	2	3	53	19	34	38
4	Llanrwst United	17	12	2	3	44	24	20	38
5	Llandudno Albion	20	11	3	6	50	31	19	36
6	Greenfield	18	11	2	5	33	17	16	35
7	Penrhyndeudraeth	23	10	3	10	46	48	-2	33
8	Bodedern Athletic	18	10	1	7	35	24	11	31
9	Nantlle Vale	18	6	8	4	37	29	8	26
10	Llanberis	20	8	2	10	31	47	-16	26
11	Llanrug United	17	6	4	7	34	30	4	22
12	Mynydd Llandegai	21	5	6	10	35	50	-15	21
13	Blaenau Amateurs	19	6	2	11	33	55	-22	20
14	St Asaph City	23	3	8	12	25	45	-20	17
15	Llandyrnog United	21	3	3	15	26	64	-38	12
16	Prestatyn Sports	20	0	2	18	27	72	-45	2

Division Two

		P	W	D	L	F	A	GD	Pts
1	Y Felinheli	18	12	5	1	64	35	29	41
2	Penmaenmawr Phoenix	21	12	5	4	47	27	20	41
3	Gaerwen	20	11	5	4	58	30	28	38
4	Llannefydd	17	11	3	3	49	22	27	36
5	Pwllheli	17	9	4	4	45	29	16	31
6	Gwalchmai	20	9	4	7	47	42	5	31
7	Kinmel Bay	19	8	4	7	45	51	-6	28
8	Barmouth & Dyffryn United	16	7	3	6	36	32	4	24
9	Llandudno Amateurs	22	4	8	10	44	65	-21	20
10	Amlwch Town	19	5	3	11	32	54	-22	18
11	Aberffraw	18	5	2	11	31	47	-16	17
12	Llandudno Junction	18	5	3	10	39	51	-12	15*
13	Mochdre Sports	18	3	5	10	27	42	-15	14
14	Pentraeth	23	3	4	16	39	76	-37	13

Holyhead Town were removed from the Division after 11 games.

GWYNEDD LEAGUE

		P	W	D	L	F	A	GD	Pts
1	Bangor 1876	16	16	0	0	115	9	106	48
2	Trearddur Bay Bulls	17	12	2	3	65	17	48	38
3	Menai Bridge Tigers	15	11	1	3	47	19	28	34
4	Nefyn United	14	10	2	2	47	18	29	32
5	Waunfawr	18	10	1	7	51	40	11	31
6	Llangoed & District	20	9	3	8	63	45	18	30
7	Bro Goronwy	16	9	2	5	34	26	8	29
8	Talysarn Celts	14	8	2	4	41	32	9	26
9	Bontnewydd	17	8	1	8	55	54	1	25
10	Glantraeth	15	5	2	8	30	46	-16	17
11	Caergybi	15	4	4	7	27	42	-15	16
12	Ogwen Tigers	19	5	1	13	32	60	-28	16
13	Llanystumdwy	20	4	2	14	41	82	-41	14
14	Bethesda Athletic	17	3	1	13	34	83	-49	10
15	Llanerchymedd	19	0	0	19	13	122	-109	0

ANGLESEY LEAGUE

		P	W	D	L	F	A	GD	Pts
1	Cemaes Bay	16	13	2	1	98	19	79	41
2	Holyhead Hotspur Reserves	17	12	3	2	61	26	35	39
3	Mountain Rangers	15	12	2	1	78	16	62	38
4	Llanfairpwll	15	9	2	4	40	31	9	26*
5	Valley Athletic	14	8	0	6	41	30	11	21*
6	Bodorgan	16	4	4	8	39	43	-4	16
7	Arriva Bangor	14	5	3	6	45	40	5	15*
8	Pentraeth Reserves	15	3	1	11	27	46	-19	10
9	Cefni	17	7	1	9	35	57	-22	4*
10	Holyhead Town Reserves	15	1	1	13	21	87	-66	4
11	Llandegfan	16	1	1	14	16	106	-90	4

MID WALES LEAGUE

Division One

		P	W	D	L	F	A	GD	Pts
1	Llanidloes Town	23	19	3	1	68	22	46	60
2	Builth Wells	20	14	2	4	47	19	28	44
3	Llandrindod Wells	19	13	4	2	43	22	21	43
4	Bow Street	22	12	4	6	36	22	14	40
5	Caersws	19	11	1	7	56	28	28	34
6	Welshpool Town	17	10	2	5	49	34	15	32
7	Berriew	16	7	4	5	47	23	24	25
8	Montgomery Town	18	6	5	7	25	32	-7	23
9	Kerry	23	6	5	12	46	61	-15	23
10	Aberaeron	20	6	5	9	29	50	-21	23
11	Carno	22	5	7	10	26	40	-14	22
12	Four Crosses	19	4	5	10	27	46	-19	17
13	Radnor Valley	16	5	1	10	17	23	-6	16
14	Tywyn Bryncrug	20	3	2	15	25	69	-44	11
15	Llansantffraid Village	22	1	2	19	17	67	-50	5

Hay St Mary's withdrew after six games.

Division Two

		P	W	D	L	F	A	GD	Pts
1	Penparcau	17	14	0	3	68	22	46	42
2	Machynlleth	18	13	3	2	63	24	39	42
3	Newbridge-on-Wye	18	13	2	3	70	19	51	41
4	Waterloo Rovers	15	11	2	2	43	19	24	35
5	Dolgellau Athletic	16	11	1	4	46	22	24	34
6	Rhayader Town	19	8	6	5	58	35	23	30
7	Borth United	19	8	5	6	35	27	8	29
8	Aberystwyth University	19	8	4	5	42	37	5	28
9	Forden United	17	8	2	7	47	29	18	26
10	Dyffryn Banw	16	6	2	8	20	32	-12	20
11	Churchstoke	18	4	3	11	29	47	-18	15
12	Abermule	21	3	2	16	31	70	-39	11
13	Presteigne St. Andrews	19	2	0	17	34	90	-56	6
14	Knighton Town	22	1	0	21	19	132	-113	-3*

VALE OF CLYWD & CONWY LEAGUE

Premier Division

		P	W	D	L	F	A	GD	Pts
1	Rhuddlan Town	16	13	2	1	70	24	46	41
2	Abergele	15	8	5	2	48	26	22	29
3	Bro Cernyw	15	9	2	4	28	23	5	29
4	Llanfairfechan Town	13	9	1	3	53	17	36	28
5	Llansannan	11	7	2	2	33	20	13	23
6	Meliden	11	4	2	5	17	21	-4	14
7	Cerrig-y-Drudion	11	3	4	4	17	28	-11	13
8	Y Glannau	15	3	2	10	29	49	-20	11
9	Llandudno Athletic	10	3	1	6	17	29	-12	10
10	Llanelwy Athletic	15	2	3	10	32	61	-29	9
11	Rhos United	16	1	0	15	12	58	-46	3

Division One

		P	W	D	L	F	A	GD	Pts
1	North Football Association	12	10	2	0	60	21	39	32
2	Llysfaen	11	9	2	0	64	14	50	29
3	Llandudno Amateurs Res	14	7	4	3	45	31	14	25
4	Llanfairfechan Town Res	17	7	2	8	47	51	-4	23
5	Penrhyn Bay Dragons	12	5	4	3	43	35	8	19
6	Denbigh Development	14	5	3	6	43	47	-4	18
7	Betws-y-Coed	12	6	0	6	23	36	-13	18
8	Machno United	12	4	0	8	31	47	-16	12
9	Henllan	14	2	1	11	27	54	-27	7
10	Rhyl All Stars	14	2	0	12	33	80	-47	6

PEMBROKESHIRE LEAGUE

Division One

		P	W	D	L	F	A	GD	Pts
1	Hakin United	13	12	0	1	81	14	67	36
2	Monkton Swifts	13	11	1	1	64	17	47	34
3	Carew	15	11	0	4	54	25	29	33
4	Merlins Bridge	13	9	1	3	60	21	39	28
5	Goodwick United	11	9	0	2	43	19	24	27
6	Clarbeston Road	15	7	0	8	47	44	3	21
7	Fishguard Sports	10	6	0	4	32	18	14	18
8	Narberth	14	5	1	8	32	63	-31	16
9	Neyland	12	4	0	8	29	43	-14	12
10	Pennar Robins	18	3	1	14	26	73	-47	10
11	St Clears	12	0	3	9	12	52	-40	3
12	Saundersfoot Sports	16	0	1	15	17	108	-91	1

Division Two

		P	W	D	L	F	A	GD	Pts
1	St Ishmaels	15	10	3	2	41	15	26	33
2	Merlins Bridge II	17	10	1	6	51	29	22	31
3	Hundleton	13	8	3	2	49	23	26	27
4	Hakin United II	16	8	3	5	42	28	14	27
5	Kilgetty	12	7	3	2	29	15	14	24
6	Herbrandston	16	6	2	8	33	42	-9	20
7	Pennar Robins II	17	6	2	9	33	56	-23	20
8	Milford United	13	4	6	3	25	18	7	18
9	Solva	17	5	3	9	35	52	-17	18
10	Broad Haven	13	4	1	8	34	46	-12	13
11	Lawrenny	18	3	4	11	31	64	-33	13
12	Johnston	15	3	3	9	33	48	-15	12

Division Three

		P	W	D	L	F	A	GD	Pts
1	Monkton Swifts II	16	16	0	0	95	30	65	48
2	Milford Athletic	16	11	1	4	51	24	27	34
3	Camrose	17	10	1	6	49	42	7	31
4	Clarbeston Road II	18	10	0	8	42	55	-13	30
5	Carew II	15	8	0	7	49	27	22	24
6	Cosheston AFC	14	7	2	5	47	37	10	23
7	Haverfordwest CC	13	6	1	6	37	35	2	19
8	Fishguard Sports II	15	6	1	8	29	32	-3	19
9	Goodwick United II	17	6	0	11	34	41	-7	18
10	Pendine	6	4	0	2	17	12	5	12
11	Pembroke Boro	18	3	1	14	55	95	-40	10
12	Letterston	17	0	1	16	28	103	-75	-2*

Division Four

		P	W	D	L	F	A	GD	Pts
1	Broad Haven II	14	12	2	0	56	21	35	38
2	Tenby	14	12	1	1	118	12	106	37
3	Milford United II	17	10	1	6	43	35	8	31
4	Neyland II	16	9	1	6	55	38	17	28
5	St Florence	16	7	3	6	60	59	1	24
6	Haverfordwest CC II	15	7	4	4	61	43	18	22*
7	Camrose II	18	6	3	9	35	57	-22	21
8	Pennar Robins III	17	5	1	11	33	59	-26	19
9	St Ishmaels II	15	3	4	8	34	63	-29	13
10	Narberth II	15	3	6	6	24	33	-9	12
11	Solva II	17	4	0	13	30	96	-66	12
12	St Clears II	16	3	2	11	33	66	-33	11

Division Five

		P	W	D	L	F	A	GD	Pts
1	Carew III	14	9	1	4	51	17	34	28
2	Hundleton II	15	8	4	3	48	26	22	28
3	Angle	15	8	2	5	49	27	22	26
4	Milford Athletic II	14	8	2	4	43	25	18	26
5	Newport Tigers	15	8	2	5	40	33	7	26
6	Pembroke Boro II	14	7	0	7	46	67	-21	21
7	Herbrandston II	16	5	1	10	40	54	-14	16
8	Saundersfoot Sports II	11	5	1	5	28	50	-22	16
9	Kilgetty II	12	5	2	5	34	22	12	14*
10	Johnston II	13	5	1	7	27	39	-12	10*
11	Lawrenny II	17	2	0	15	18	64	-46	6

WELSH CUP

HOLDERS: THE NEW SAINTS

FIRST QUALIFYING ROUND
NORTH

Amlwch Town	v	Holywell Town	3–5
Bangor 1876	v	Llandudno Athletic	4–1
Brickfield Rangers	v	New Brighton Villa	2–7
Bro Goronwy	v	Blaenau Ffestiniog Amateur	4–5 aet
Castell Alun Colts	v	Llangollen Town	4–0
Cefn Mawr Rangers	v	CPD Sychdyn	5–4
Coedpoeth United	v	Rhostyllen	3–2 aet
CPD Aberffraw	v	Llandudno Junction	3–1
CPD Llannefydd	v	Gwalchmai	7–2

WELSH FOOTBALL

Gaerwen	v Llanrwst United	2–3
Played at Llanrwst United		
Glan Conwy	v Pentraeth	8–2
Llandyrnog United	v Lex XI	4–2
Llanfairfechan Town	v Kinmel Bay	5–3
Mynydd Isa Spartans	v Llanuwchllyn	5–1
Mynydd Llandegai	v Menai Bridge Tigers	w/o
Nefyn United	v Llandudno Amateurs	6–4
Penycae	v Caerwys	6–0
Penmaenmawr Phoenix	v Mochdre Sports	0–2
Played at Mochdre Sports		
Rhosllanerchrugog	v Plas Madoc	2–12
Rhydymwyn	v Hawarden Rangers	3–2 aet

Central

Abermule	v Barmouth & Dyffryn United	0–1
Borth United	v Machynlleth	6–2
Churchstoke	v Waterloo Rovers	1–6
Kerry	v Dolgellau Athletic	1–4
Llansantffraid Village	v Four Crosses	0–2
Montgomery Town	v Hay St Mary's	3–1
Penparcau	v Tywyn Bryncrug	2–1
Rhayader Town	v Bow Street	2–1 aet

SOUTH

Abertillery Bluebirds	v Dinas Powys	4–0
AFC Porth	v CRC Olympic	0–2
Played at Taff's Well		
Blaenrhondda	v Ynyshir Albions	0–2
Played at 3G Cambrain		
Cardiff Draconians	v Panteg	7–0
Played at Panteg		
Cefn Cribwr BC	v Ynysygerwn	3–1
Cwmbach Royal Stars	v Newcastle Emlyn	2–1
Cwmbran Town	v Tredegar Town	1–2
Ely Rangers	v Risca United	3–4
Fairwater	v Aberystwyth Exiles	8–2
FC Cwmaman	v Penrhiwceiber Rangers	3–2
Lucas Cwmbran	v Ton & Gelli BGC	4–2
Merthyr Saints	v Quar Park Rangers	4–0
Newport City	v Chepstow Town	3–4 aet
Newport Civil Service	v Caerphilly Athletic	5–2
Newport Corinthians	v Canton Liberal	6–4
Pencoed Athletic BGC	v Trebanog	2-2, 4-2p
Penlan Club	v Aberdare Town	3–0
Played at Trefelin B.G.C.		
Penydarren BGC	v Treharris Athletic Western	4–1
Pill YMCA	v Cardiff Corinthians	1–3
Played at Cardiff Corinthians		
Pontyclun	v Trefelin BGC	0–1
Sully Sports	v Caerleon	2–3
Treforest	v Vale United	1–2
Treowen Stars	v AFC Llwydcoed	3–5 aet
Trethomas Bluebirds	v AFC Whitchurch	2–1
Wattsville	v Clwb Cymric	2–3
West End	v Baglan Dragons	0–1

SECOND QUALIFYING ROUND

NORTHEAST

Brymbo	v Rhos Aelwyd	4–2
Cefn Albion	v Chirk AAA	4–5 aet
Coedpoeth United	v Llandyrnog United	4–2
Denbigh Town	v Mynydd Isa Spartans	2–3
Greenfield	v Plas Madoc	4–3
Holywell Town	v New Brighton Villa	8–2
Llay Welfare	v Penycae	2–3 aet
Mold Alexandra	v Castell Alun Colts	8–0
Saltney Town	v Rhydymwyn	1–3
Cefn Mawr Rangers	v FC Queens Park	1–4

NORTHWEST

Aberffraw	v Glan Conwy	2–1
Bangor 1876	v Penrhyndeudraeth	6–2
Holyhead Hotspur	v Holywell Town	3–1
Llannefydd	v Llanrwst United	2–0
Llanrug United	v Llanfairfechan Town	5–0
Mochdre Sports	v Blaenau Ffestiniog Amateur	2–4
Nefyn United	v Mynydd Llandegai	7–4
Played at Mynydd Llandegai		
Nantlle Vale	v Bodedern Athletic	2–1
Prestatyn Sports	v Llandudno Albion	4–2
St Asaph City	v Llanberis	1–3

Central

Caersws	v Dolgellau Athletic	5–3
Barmouth & Dyffryn United	v Llanidloes Town	0–1
Four Crosses	v Rhayader Town	3–1
Llandrindod Wells	v Carno	5–2
Montgomery Town	v Berriew	2–1 aet
Radnor Valley	v Penparcau	2–4
Waterloo Rovers	v Welshpool Town	5–4
Aberaeron	v Borth United	4–2 aet
Played at North United		

SOUTHEAST

Risca United	v Tredegar Town	1–2
Abertillery Bluebirds	v Lucas Cwmbran	3–1
Builth Wells	v Bridgend Street	1–0
Chepstow Town	v Clwb Cymric	4–2
Goytre	v Caerleon	1–1, 4-5p
Newport Corinthians	v Abergavenny Town	0–2
Trethomas Bluebirds	v Croesyceiliog	2–4
Aberbargoed Buds	v Caldicot Town	1–0
Monmouth Town	v Newport Civil Service	6–2
Played at Newport Civil Service		

SOUTHWEST

AFC Llwydcoed	v Cefn Cribwr	1–2
Cardiff Draconians	v Pencoed Athletic BGC	3–0
CRC Olympic	v Cardiff Corinthians	2–3
Fairwater	v Garden Village	0–3
FC Cwmaman	v Baglan Dragons	5–1
Penydarren BGC	v Pontardawe Town	2–3
Cwmbach Royal Stars	v Penlan Club	1–2
Played at Penlan Club		
Trefelin BGC	v Port Talbot Town	3–0
Vale United	v Ton Pentre	1–5
Ynyshir Albions	v Merthyr Saints	3–1

FIRST ROUND

NORTH

Bangor 1876	v Penycae	3–3, 3-2p
Blaenau Ffestiniog Amateur	v Buckley Town	0–2
Chirk AAA	v Llannefydd	0–3
Coedpoeth United	v Gresford Athletic	0–5
Conwy Borough	v Ruthin Town	1–2
Corwen	v Colwyn Bay	2–3
Flint Town United	v Four Crosses	9–0
Greenfield	v Caersws	3–1
Guilsfield	v Brymbo	2–1

Holyhead Hotspur	v	Montgomery Town	4–2
Holywell Town	v	Llandudno	2–3
Llanrhaeadr	v	Prestatyn Town	1–4
Nantlle Vale	v	Rhydymwyn	2–0
Nefyn United	v	Bangor City	0–2
Prestatyn Sports	v	FC Queens Park	2–3
Rhyl	v	Llangefni Town	2–0
Waterloo Rovers	v	Mold Alexandra	1–8
Porthmadog	v	Llanberis	7–0
Played at Llanberis			
Aberffraw	v	Llanrug United	0–1
Played at Llanrug United			
Llanfair United	v	Myndd Isa Spartans	5–3
Played at Myndd Isa Spartans			

SOUTH

Cambrian BGC	v	Ynyshir Albions	7–3
Aberbargoed Buds	v	Aberaeron	3–1
Abertillery Bluebirds	v	Penparcau	3–1
Afan Lido	v	Monmouth Town	3–1
Ammanford	v	Cardiff Draconians	4–1
Briton Ferry Llansawel	v	Undy Athletic	2–2, 3-4p
Builth Wells	v	Ton Pentre	2–3
Cefn Cribwr	v	Tredegar Town	2–1 aet
Chepstow Town	v	Taffs Well	3–2
Croesyceiliog	v	Abergavenny Town	2–1
Cwmbran Celtic	v	Pontardawe Town	2–3 aet
FC Cwmaman	v	STM Sports	2–6
Garden Village	v	Goytre United	1–3
Haverfordwest County	v	Penlan Social	5–3
Llanwit Major	v	Llandrindod Wells	0–1
Penrhyncoch	v	Cardiff Corinthians	2–1 aet
Pontypridd Town	v	Caerau (Ely)	3–1
Swansea University	v	Caerleon	4–1
Trefelin BGC	v	Llanidloes Town	2–2, 3-4p
Llanelli Town	v	Cwmamman United	2–1

SECOND ROUND
NORTH

Bangor 1876	v	Ruthin Town	0–2
Bangor City	v	Prestatyn Town	0–3
Llannefydd	v	Guilsfield	1–5
Greenfield	v	Flint Town United	1–3
Holyhead Hotspur	v	Buckley Town	0–3
Porthmadog	v	Gresford Athletic	4–1
Llandudno	v	Llanfair United	4–1
Mold Alexandra	v	Llanrug United	8–1
Nantlle Vale	v	Colwyn Bay	0–1
Rhyl	v	FC Queens Park	3–0

SOUTH

Abertillery Bluebirds	v	Llanidloes Town	4–3
Afan Lido	v	Aberbargoed Buds	2–1
Ammanford	v	Ton Pentre	3–1
Goytre United	v	Cefn Cribwr	6–4
Haverfordwest County	v	Cambrian & Clydach Vale	1–2
Llanelli Town	v	Penrhyncoch	0–1
Pontypridd Town	v	Llandrindod Wells	1–0
Undy Athletic	v	Swansea University	5–6
Chepstow Town	v	STM Sports	0–5
Pontardawe Town	v	Croesyceiliog	6–1

THIRD ROUND

Carmarthen Town	v	Ammanford	0–4
Colwyn Bay	v	Airbus UK Broughton	1–0 aet
Abertillery Bluebirds	v	Connah's Quay Nomads	0–3
Aberystwyth Town	v	Ruthin Town	2–1
Afan Lido	v	Llandudno	5–1
Barry Town United	v	Newtown	0–1
Cardiff Metropolitan University	v	Pontypridd Town	1–0
Cefn Druids	v	Guilsfield	2–0
Flint Town United	v	Bala Town	2–0
Goytre United	v	Caernarfon Town	0–4
Penrhyncoch	v	Prestatyn Town	1–2
Pen-y-Bont	v	Porthmadog	2-2

Match abandoned in extra time due to serious injury.

Pen-y-Bont	v	Porthmadog	6–1
Pontardawe Town	v	Buckley Town	3–1
Rhyl	v	STM Sports	2–0
Swansea University	v	Cambrian & Clydach Vale	3–0
The New Saints	v	Mold Alexandra	9–0

FOURTH ROUND

Ammanford	v	Caernarfon Town	0–4
Flint Town United	v	Colwyn Bay	3–2
Pen-y-Bont	v	Cardiff Metropolitan University	1–2
Cefn Druids	v	Pontardawe Town	2–0
Connah's Quay Nomads	v	Afan Lido	8–0
Newtown	v	Rhyl	4–1
Swansea University	v	Prestatyn Town	0–1
The New Saints	v	Aberystwyth Town	3–0

QUARTER-FINALS

Caernarfon Town	v	Cefn Druids	4–0
Connah's Quay Nomads	v	Cardiff Metropolitan University	1–2
The New Saints	v	Newtown	6–1
Flint Town United	v	Prestatyn Town	0–1

SEMI-FINALS

Caernarfon Town	v	Cardiff Metropolitan University	
Prestatyn Town	v	The New Saints	

Wood (Penybont) gets back at Cummings (Barry).

Main Stand - Penybont

Kinsella (Penybont) just fails to make contact with a Kane cross. Photos Keith Clayton.

ENGLAND C

Due to COVID-19 there were no fixtures during the 2019-20 season

RESULTS SUMMARY 1979 - 2020	P	W	D	L	F	A
Barbados	1	1	0	0	2	0
Belgium	6	3	1	2	8	7
Bermuda	1	1	0	0	6	1
Bosnia & Herzegovina	1	0	0	1	2	6
Cyprus U21	1	0	0	1	1	2
Czech Republic U21	1	0	2	0	2	2
Finland U21	4	2	0	2	4	5
Estonia	1	1	0	0	1	0
Estonia U23	4	3	0	1	7	5
Grenada	1	0	1	0	1	1
Gibraltar	4	3	0	1	8	7
Holland	19	14	5	0	40	8
Hungary	2	0	1	1	3	5
Iraq	1	0	0	1	1	5
Irish Premier League XI	1	0	0	1	1	3
Italy	18	5	8	4	24	22
Jordan U23	1	1	0	0	1	0
Latvia U23	1	0	0	1	0	1
Malta	1	1	0	0	4	0
Norway U21	1	0	0	1	1	2
Panjab	1	1	0	0	2	1
Poland	1	1	0	0	2	1
Portugal	1	0	0	1	0	1
Republic of Ireland	13	10	0	3	30	11
Republic of Ireland U21	1	1	0	0	2	1
Republic of Ireland Amateurs	1	0	0	1	2	4
Russia	1	0	0	1	0	4
Scotland	15	10	3	2	30	15
Slovakia U21/U23	3	0	0	3	3	9
Sparta Prague B	1	0	2	0	2	2
Turkey U23	2	0	0	2	0	3
Ukraine	1	1	0	0	2	0
USA	2	1	1	0	2	1
Wales	24	13	7	4	34	20
Wales C	2	1	1	0	5	4
TOTALS	**139**	**74**	**32**	**34**	**233**	**160**

ENGLAND'S RESULTS 1979 - 2020

BARBADOS
02.06.08	Bridgetown	2 - 0

BELGIUM
11.02.03	KV Ostend	1 - 3
04.11.03	Darlington	2 - 2
15.11.05	FC Racing Jets	2 - 0
19.05.09	Oxford United	0 - 1
09.02.11	Luton Town	1 - 0
12.09.12	Gemeentalijk Sportstadion	2 - 1

BERMUDA
04.06.13	Hamilton	6 - 1

BOSNIA & HERZEGOVINA
16.09.08	Grbavia Stadium	2 - 6

CYPRUS U21
17.02.15	Larnaca	1 - 2

CZECH REPUBLIC UNDER-21
19.11.13	Home	2 - 2

ESTONIA
12.10.10		1 - 0

UNDER-23
18.11.14	FC Halifax Town	4 - 2
15.11.16	A Le Coq Arena, Tallinn	2 - 1
10.10.18	Leyton Orient FC	1 - 0
05.06.19	Kadrioru Stadium	0 - 2

FINLAND UNDER-21
14.04.93	Woking	1 - 3
30.05.94	Aanekoski	0 - 2
01.06.07	FC Hakka	1 - 0
15.11.07	Helsinki	2 - 0

GIBRALTAR
27.04.82	Gibraltar	3 - 2
31.05.95	Gibraltar	3 - 2
21.05.08	Colwyn Bay	1 - 0
15.11.11	Gibraltar	1 - 3

GRENADA
31.05.08	St. George's	1 - 1

HOLLAND
03.06.79	Stafford	1 - 0
07.06.80	Zeist	2 - 1
09.06.81	Lucca	2 - 0
03.06.82	Aberdeen	1 - 0
02.06.83	Scarborough	6 - 0
05.06.84	Palma	3 - 3
13.06.85	Vleuten	3 - 0
20.05.87	Kirkaldy	4 - 0
11.04.95	Aalsmeer	0 - 0
02.04.96	Irthlingborough	3 - 1
18.04.97	Appingedam	0 - 0
03.03.98	Crawley	2 - 1
30.03.99	Genemuiden	1 - 1
21.03.00	Northwich	1 - 0
22.03.01	Wihemina FC	3 - 0
24.04.02	Yeovil Town	1 - 0
25.03.03	BV Sparta 25	0 - 0
16.02.05	Woking	3 - 0
29.11.06	Burton Albion	4 - 1

HUNGARY
15.09.09	Szekesfehervar	1 - 1
28.05.14	Budapest	2 - 4

IRAQ
27.05.04	Macclesfield	1 - 5

IRISH PREMIER LEAGUE XI
13.02.07	Glenavon FC	1 - 3

ITALY
03.06.80	Zeist	2 - 0
13.06.81	Montecatini	1 - 1
01.06.82	Aberdeen	0 - 0
31.05.83	Scarborough	2 - 0
09.06.84	Reggio Emilia	0 - 1
11.06.85	Houten	2 - 2
18.05.87	Dunfermline	1 - 2
29.01.89	La Spezia	1 - 1
25.02.90	Solerno	0 - 2
05.03.91	Kettering	0 - 0
01.03.99	Hayes	4 - 1
01.03.00	Padova	1 - 1
20.11.02	AC Cremonese	3 - 2
11.02.04	Shrewsbury	1 - 4
10.11.04	US Ivrea FC	1 - 0
15.02.06	Cambridge United	3 - 1
12.11.08	Benevento	2 - 2
28.02.12	Fleetwood Town	1 - 1

JORDAN UNDER-23
04.03.14	Jordan	1 - 0

LATVIA UNDER-23
10.09.13	Latvia	0 - 1

MALTA UNDER-21
17.02.09	Malta	4 - 0

NORWAY UNDER-21
01.06.94	Slemmestad	1 - 2

PANJAB
28.05.17	Solihull Moors	1 - 2

POLAND
17.11.09	Gradiszk Wielpolski	2 - 1

PORTUGAL
19.05.11	Sixfields Stadium	0 - 1

REPUBLIC OF IRELAND
24.05.86	Kidderminster	2 - 1
26.05.86	Nuneaton	2 - 1
25.05.90	Dublin	2 - 1
27.05.90	Cork	3 - 0
27.02.96	Kidderminster	4 - 0
25.02.97	Dublin	0 - 2
16.05.02	Boston	1 - 2
20.05.03	Merthyr Tydfil	4 - 0
18.05.04	Deverondale	2 - 3
24.05.05	Cork	1 - 0
23.05.06	Eastbourne Boro'	2 - 0
22.05.07	Clachnacuddin	5 - 0
26.05.10	Waterford United	2 - 1

UNDER-21
01.06.15	Galway	2 - 1

AMATEURS
27.05.18	Whitehall Stadium	2 - 4

RUSSIA
05.06.12	Russia	0 - 4

SCOTLAND
31.05.79	Stafford	5 - 1
05.06.80	Zeist	2 - 4
11.06.81	Empoli	0 - 0
05.06.82	Aberdeen	1 - 1
04.06.83	Scarborough	2 - 1
07.06.84	Modena	2 - 0
15.06.85	Harderwijk	1 - 3
23.05.87	Dunfermline	2 - 1
18.05.02	Kettering	2 - 0
24.05.03	Carmarthen Town	0 - 0
23.05.04	Deverondale	3 - 1
28.05.05	Cork	3 - 2
27.05.06	Eastbourne Boro'	2 - 0
25.05.07	Ross County	3 - 0
22.05.08	Colwyn Bay	1 - 0

SLOVAKIA UNDER-21/23
24.05.14	Slovakia	0 - 1
05.06.16	Sutton United	3 - 4
08.11.17	Ziar nad Hronon Stadium	0 - 4

SPARTA PRAGUE B
21.05.14	Prague	2 - 2

TURKEY U23
05.02.13	Dartford FC	0 - 1
14.10.14	Istanbul	0 - 2

UKRAINE
22.03.16	Kiev	2 - 0

USA
20.03.02	Stevenage Boro.	2 - 1
09.06.04	Charleston USA	0 - 0

WALES
27.03.84	Newtown	1 - 2
26.03.85	Telford	1 - 0
18.03.86	Merthyr Tydfil	1 - 3
17.03.87	Gloucester	2 - 2
15.03.88	Rhyl	2 - 0
21.03.89	Kidderminster	2 - 0
06.03.90	Merthyr Tydfil	0 - 0
17.05.91	Stafford	1 - 2
03.03.92	Aberystwyth	1 - 0
02.03.93	Cheltenham	2 - 1
22.02.94	Bangor	2 - 1
28.02.95	Yeovil Town	1 - 0
23.05.99	St Albans	2 - 1
16.05.00	Llanelli	1 - 1
13.02.01	Rushden & Dia.	0 - 0
14.05.02	Boston	1 - 1
22.05.03	Merthyr Tydfil	2 - 0
20.05.04	Keith FC	0 - 2
26.05.05	Cork	1 - 0
25.05.06	Eastbourne Boro'	1 - 1
27.05.07	Clachnacuddin	3 - 0
21.02.08	Exeter City	2 - 1
24.05.08	Rhyl	3 - 0
15.09.10	Newtown FC	2 - 2

WALES C
20.03.18	Barry FC	3 - 2
20.03.19	Salford City FC	2 - 2

GOALSCORERS 1979 - 2020

13 GOALS...

Carter, Mark

7 GOALS...

Cole, Mitchell

6 GOALS...

Ashford, Noel

5 GOALS...

Davison, Jon

Williams, Colin

4 GOALS...

Culpin, Paul

D'Sane, Roscoe

Johnson, Jeff

Mackhail-Smith, Craig

Norwood, James

3 GOALS...

Adamson, David

Guinan, Steve

Grayson, Neil

Hatch, Liam

Kirk, Jackson

Morison, Steve

Morrison, Michael

Okenabirhie, Fejiri (Hatrick)

Opponents

Taylor, Matt

Watkins, Dale

2 GOALS...

Alford, Carl

Barnes-Homer, Matthew

Barrett, Keith

Bishop, Andrew

Burgess, Andrew

Casey, Kim

Cordice, Neil

Elding, Anthony

Gray, Andre

Hayles, Barry

Hill, Kenny

Howell, David

John, Louis

McQueen, Darren

Mutrie, Les

Patmore, Warren

Pearson, Matty

Richards, Justin

Seddon, Gareth

Southam, Glen

Watson, John

Weatherstone, Simon

Whitbread, Barry

Yiadom, Andy

1 GOAL...

Agana, Tony

Anderson, Dale

Ashton, John

Beautyman, Harry

Benson, Paul

Berry

Blackburn, Chris

Boardman, Jon

Bogle, Omar

Bolton, Jimmy

Boyd, George

Bradshaw, Mark

Briscoe, Louis

Brown, Paul

Browne, Corey

Carey-Bertram, Daniel

Carr, Michael

Cavell, Paul

Charles, Lee

Charley, Ken

Charnock, Kieran

Constable, James

Crittenden, Nick

Davies, Paul

Day, Matt

Densmore, Shaun

Drummond, Stewart

Fleming, Andrew

Franks, Franks

Furlong, Paul

Grant, John

Guthrie, Kurtis

Harrad, Shaun

Hine, Mark

Holland, Jack

Holroyd, Chris

Humphreys, Delwyn

Howells, Jake

Jackson, Kayden

Jackson, Marlon

James, Kingsley

Jennings, Connor

Kennedy, John

Kerr, Scott

Kimmins, Ged

King, Simon

Leworthy, David

Lowe, Jamal

McDougald, Junior

McFadzean, Kyle

Mayes, Bobby

Moore, Neil

Moore, Luke

Newton, Sean

O'Keefe, Eamon

Oli, Dennis

Pavey, Alfie

Penn, Russell

Pennell, Luke

Pitcher, Geoff

Porter, Max

Ricketts, Sam

Robbins, Terry

Roberts, Jordan

Robinson, Mark

Roddis, Nick

Rodgers, Luke

Rodman, Alex

Rogers, Paul

Ryan, Tim

Sarcevic, Antoni

Sellars, Neil

Shaw, John

Sheldon, Gareth

Simpson, Josh

Sinclair, Dean

Smith, Ian

Smith, Ossie

Spencer, Scott

Stansfield, Adam

Stephens, Mickey

Stott, Steve

Taylor, Steve

Thurgood, Stuart

Tubbs, Matthew

Venables, David

Walker, Thomas

Watkins, Adam

Way, Darren

Webb, Paul

Whitehouse, Elliott

Wilcox, Russ

Willoughby, Kurt

MANAGERS 1979 - 2020

		P	W	D	L	F	A	*Win%
1979	Howard Wilkinson	2	2	0	0	6	1	-
1980 - 1984	Keith Wright	17	9	5	3	30	16	53
1985 - 1988	Kevin Verity	12	7	2	3	23	15	58
1989 - 1996	Tony Jennings	19	10	4	5	27	18	53
1997	Ron Reid	2	0	1	1	0	2	-
1998 - 2002	John Owens	14	8	5	1	22	10	57
2002 -	Paul Fairclough	74	39	13	22	125	95	53

*Calculated for those who managed for 10 games or more.

the
FOOTBALL
ASSOCIATION
COMPETITIONS

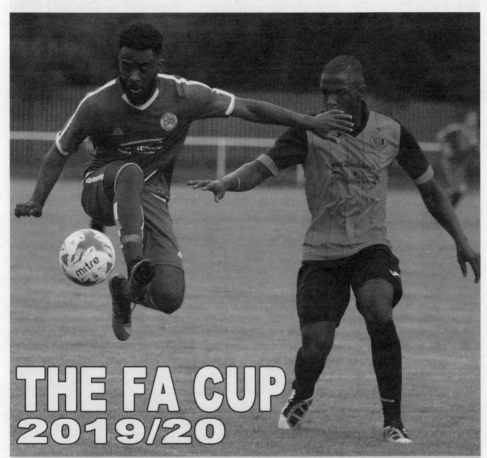

THE FA CUP
2019/20

FAC - EP - Kapendi (Hanley) Hollis (Leicester Road). Photo Keith Clayton.

FAC - EP - Ashton (Hanley) beats Highland (Leicester Road) and hits the crossbar. Photo Keith Clayton

FAC - EP - This time Ashton gets the ball past Highland. Photo Keith Clayton.

FAC - EP - Connor Hefferman of Hollands & Blair skips past Glebes Chris Edwards. Photo Alan Coomes

EXTRA PRELIMINARY ROUND
SATURDAY 10 AUGUST 2019 - WINNERS RECEIVE £2,250 LOSERS RECEIVE £750

No	Home		Away	Score	Att
1	Consett	v	Dunston	1-1	451
	Dunston	v	Consett (13/8)	5-2	398
2	Newton Aycliffe	v	Northallerton Town	0-2	
3	Kendal Town	v	Hemsworth MW	0-4	
4	Shildon	v	Garforth Town	0-0	
	Garforth Town	v	Shildon (13/8)	3-2	165
5	Whitley Bay	v	Hebburn Town	1-7	438
6	Ashington	v	Albion Sports	2-0	231
7	Billingham Town	v	Yorkshire Amateur	3-0	158
8	West Auckland Town	v	Bridlington Town	1-3	
9	North Shields	v	Guisborough Town	2-2	250
	Guisborough Town	v	North Shields (14/8)	1-0	304
10	Bishop Auckland	v	Thornaby	0-2	240
11	Sunderland RCA	v	Sunderland Ryhope CW	0-0	318
	Sunderland Ryhope CW	v	Sunderland RCA (13/8)	1-2	
12	Seaham Red Star	v	Penrith	4-2	
13	Harrogate Railway Athletic	v	Whickham	1-10	
14	Nostell MW	v	Stockton Town	2-2	155
	Stockton Town	v	Nostell MW (14/8)	5-1	396
15	Hall Road Rangers	v	Goole	0-3	
16	Knaresborough Town	v	Newcastle Benfield	0-3	
17	Vauxhall Motors	v	Winsford United	1-2	150
18	Charnock Richard	v	Lower Breck	2-1	185
19	Thackley	v	Handsworth Parramore	1-4	85
20	Longridge Town	v	Barnoldswick Town	6-1	392
21	Irlam	v	Ashton Athletic	4-0	138
22	Skelmersdale United	v	Penistone Church (9/8)	1-1	99
	Penistone Church	v	Skelmersdale United (14/8)	2-5	
23	Northwich Victoria	v	Silsden	2-2	188
	Silsden	v	Northwich Victoria (13/8)	3-4	166
24	AFC Liverpool	v	Burscough	2-3	
25	Avro	v	Litherland Remyca	3-4	
26	Runcorn Town	v	Rylands	2-0	
27	Squires Gate	v	West Didsbury & Chorlton	1-2	79
28	Clitheroe	v	1874 Northwich	1-2	
29	Eccleshill United	v	Bootle	2-1	89
30	Athersley Recreation	v	Padiham	0-4	
31	City of Liverpool	v	Campion	3-1	286
32	Liversedge	v	Abbey Hey	5-1	95
33	Coventry Sphinx	v	Coventry United	1-1	
	Coventry United	v	Coventry Sphinx (14/8)	0-1	160
34	Lye Town	v	Lutterworth Town	0-3	127
35	Worcester City	v	Stone Old Alleynians (11/8)	4-1	276
36	Romulus	v	Wolverhampton Casuals	0-0	
	Wolverhampton Casuals	v	Romulus (13/8)	1-2aet	132
37	Lichfield City	v	Highgate United	3-2	95
38	Haughmond	v	Walsall Wood	3-2	
39	Atherstone Town	v	Stourport Swifts	1-3	
40	Congleton Town	v	Westfields	1-1	
	Westfields	v	Congleton Town (13/8)	4-1	132
41	Hanley Town	v	Leicester Road	2-3	
42	Boldmere St Michaels	v	Daventry Town	3-1	77
43	Tividale	v	Wednesfield	2-1	105
44	Racing Club Warwick	v	AFC Wulfrunians	0-2	149
45	Dunkirk	v	Gresley	1-1	73
	(tie awarded to Gresley – Dunkirk removed)				
46	Sporting Khalsa	v	Rugby Town	5-4	
47	Heather St Johns	v	Wolverhampton SC	2-0	
48	Malvern Town	v	Whitchurch Alport	1-2	146
	(at Westfields FC)				
49	Hallam	v	Staveley MW (11/8)	0-2	
50	Radford	v	Heanor Town	0-7	88
51	Winterton Rangers	v	Grimsby Borough	2-1	
52	Quorn	v	Sherwood Colliery	1-2	
53	Shepshed Dynamo	v	Maltby Main	2-4	
54	Leicester Nirvana	v	Oadby Town	2-1	83
55	Worksop Town	v	Melton Town	1-2	
56	Sleaford Town	v	AFC Mansfield	0-7	
57	Mulbarton Wanderers	v	Boston Town	0-0	
	Boston Town	v	Mulbarton Wanderers (13/8)	4-2	
58	South Normanton Athletic	v	Selston	5-0	
59	Bottesford Town	v	Long Eaton United	2-8	
60	Barton Town	v	Carlton Town	3-2	
61	Anstey Nomads	v	Kirby Muxloe	0-3	
62	Loughborough University	v	Ilkeston Town	3-1	
	(at Loughborough Dynamo FC)				
63	Potton United	v	Ely City	1-2	82
64	March Town United	v	Norwich United	2-1	
65	Walsham Le Willows	v	Peterborough Northern Star	1-2	56
66	Eynesbury Rovers	v	Wellingborough Town	3-3	
	Wellingborough Town	v	Eynesbury Rovers (13/8)	4-1	
67	Desborough Town	v	Histon	1-3	128
68	Thetford Town	v	Rothwell Corinthians	0-1	
69	Biggleswade	v	Mildenhall Town	4-1	
70	Holbeach United	v	Fakenham Town	2-0	60
71	Bugbrooke St Michaels	v	Norwich CBS	1-0	
72	Biggleswade United	v	Swaffham Town	1-0	82
73	Harborough Town	v	Deeping Rangers	1-2	152
74	Newmarket Town	v	Arlesey Town	2-2	
	Arlesey Town	v	Newmarket Town (13/8)	1-0	133
75	Gorleston	v	Pinchbeck United	1-0	
76	Northampton On Chenecks	v	Godmanchester Rovers (11/8)	2-3	90
77	Great Yarmouth Town	v	Wellingborough Whitworth	4-2	
78	Kirkley & Pakefield	v	Wroxham (11/8)	2-2	
	Wroxham	v	Kirkley & Pakefield (14/8)	3-2	136
79	Walthamstow	v	Sporting Bengal United	5-0	
80	Hackney Wick	v	Framlingham Town (9/8)	1-3	
	(at Framlingham Town FC)				
81	Haverhill Rovers	v	Colney Heath	1-6	
82	Crawley Green	v	Takeley	2-5	37
83	Hadley	v	Redbridge	4-2	68
84	Hoddesdon Town	v	Brantham Athletic (11/8)	2-1	121
	(at Ware FC)				
85	Woodbridge Town	v	Coggeshall United	1-0	
86	Barkingside	v	Stansted (11/8)	4-1	
87	Clapton	v	Stowmarket Town	0-6	
	(at Aveley FC)				
88	Hullbridge Sports	v	Stanway Rovers	1-2	108
89	London Colney	v	Hadleigh United	2-0	
90	Sawbridgeworth Town	v	Halstead Town	1-3	
91	FC Clacton	v	St Margaretsbury	3-0	
92	Southend Manor	v	Long Melford	0-0	
	Long Melford	v	Southend Manor (14/8)	3-3aet	
	(Long Melford won 5-4 on kicks from the penalty mark)				
93	Leyton Athletic	v	Cockfosters	0-1	
	(at Cockfosters FC)				
94	Stotfold	v	Harpenden Town	3-1	
95	Ilford	v	Harwich & Parkeston	1-2	
96	Woodford Town	v	White Ensign (9/8)	1-1	
	White Ensign	v	Woodford Town (14/8)	3-1aet	
97	West Essex	v	Whitton United (11/8)	1-2	
	(at Redbridge FC)				
98	Saffron Walden Town	v	Baldock Town	1-0	232
99	Fairford Town	v	Enfield	3-2	79
100	AFC Hayes	v	Wembley	1-1	62
	Wembley	v	AFC Hayes (13/8)	3-2	71

FAC - EP - This Slimbridge player looks to evade two Edgware challenges. Photo Peter Barnes.

FAC - EP - Hollands & Blairs Ben Brown and Harry Goodger out jump Glebes Aaron Fray. Photo Alan Coomes.

EXTRA PRELIMINARY ROUND

	Home		Away	Score	Att
101	Clanfield 85	v	Shortwood United	1-3	79
102	Dunstable Town	v	Chipping Sodbury Town	3-2	112
103	Slimbridge	v	Edgware Town	1-0	77
104	Tuffley Rovers	v	North Greenford United	1-1	86
	North Greenford United	v	Tuffley Rovers (13/8)	2-1	56
105	Royal Wotton Bassett Town	v	Aylesbury Vale Dynamos	1-1	79
	Aylesbury Vale Dynamos	v	Royal Wotton Bassett Town (13/8)	1-0	204
106	Abingdon United	v	Brimscombe & Thrupp	1-2	97
107	London Tigers	v	Thame Rangers	0-2	
108	Newport Pagnell Town	v	Cheltenham Saracens	6-2	130
109	Leverstock Green	v	Ardley United	1-1	95
	Ardley United	v	Leverstock Green (13/8)	3-1	66
110	Oxhey Jets	v	Flackwell Heath	0-4	96
111	Burnham	v	Tring Athletic (13/8)	2-1	107
112	Bishop's Cleeve	v	Easington Sports	3-0	55
113	Wantage Town	v	Brackley Town Saints	1-1	111
	Brackley Town Saints	v	Wantage Town (14/8)	1-2	116
114	Leighton Town	v	Thornbury Town	4-1	
115	Shrivenham	v	Holmer Green	1-1	38
	Holmer Green	v	Shrivenham (13/8)	1-1aet	78
	(Shrivenham won 5-4 on kicks from the penalty mark)				
116	Harefield United	v	Lydney Town	3-0	93
117	Longlevens	v	Malmesbury Victoria	3-0	
118	Winslow United	v	Roman Glass St George (11/8)	2-3	278
119	AFC Croydon Athletic	v	Virginia Water	1-0	
120	Loxwood	v	Abbey Rangers	1-1	
	Abbey Rangers	v	Loxwood (13/8)	2-0	78
121	Balham	v	Rusthall (9/8)	1-0	
122	Crawley Down Gatwick	v	Newhaven	0-2	72
123	Cray Valley (PM)	v	Chatham Town	2-1	
124	Erith & Belvedere	v	Peacehaven & Telscombe (11/8)	1-1	133
	Peacehaven & Telscombe	v	Erith & Belvedere (13/8)	1-1aet	210
	(Erith & Belvedere won 5-3 on kicks from the penalty mark)				
125	Bridon Ropes	v	Broadfields United	3-1	
126	Tunbridge Wells	v	Pagham	1-1	
	Pagham	v	Tunbridge Wells (13/8)	0-2	92
127	Corinthian	v	Little Common	1-2	54
128	Walton & Hersham	v	Southall	2-4	
129	Horley Town	v	Bearsted	2-2	
	Bearsted	v	Horley Town (13/8)	0-2	
130	Egham Town	v	Lancing	2-2	
	Lancing	v	Egham Town (13/8)	4-4aet	87
	(Egham Town won 4-3 on kicks from the penalty mark)				
131	Lordswood	v	Steyning Town Community	0-1	62
132	CB Hounslow United	v	Sheerwater	2-1	
133	Horsham YMCA	v	Croydon	2-1	90
134	Saltdean United	v	Eastbourne United	6-1	157
135	Chertsey Town	v	Cobham	1-1	
	Cobham	v	Chertsey Town (13/8)	2-4	
136	Tower Hamlets	v	Selsey	2-1	
137	Chichester City	v	Erith Town	3-1	
138	Bexhill United	v	Eastbourne Town (9/8)	1-6	210
	(at Eastbourne Town FC)				
139	Hassocks	v	Langney Wanderers	2-0	
140	Arundel	v	Banstead Athletic	2-0	
141	Redhill	v	K Sports	2-1	
142	Glebe	v	Hollands & Blair	3-1	
143	Colliers Wood United	v	Shoreham	2-3	
144	Sheppey United	v	East Preston	4-1	148
145	Guildford City	v	Tooting Bec	3-2	
146	Punjab United	v	Broadbridge Heath	0-1	
	(Live on BBC Sport)				
147	Sutton Athletic	v	Deal Town	3-2	
148	Sutton Common Rovers	v	Molesey (9/8)	1-1	
	Molesey	v	Sutton Common Rovers (13/8)	0-1	
149	Spelthorne Sports	v	Lingfield	1-1	
	Lingfield	v	Spelthorne Sports (13/8)	0-4	80
	(at East Grinstead Town FC)				
150	Greenwich Borough	v	Canterbury City	2-3	
151	Crowborough Athletic	v	AFC Vardeanians	1-2	155
152	Welling Town	v	AFC Uckfield Town	1-4	
153	Hanworth Villa	v	Fisher	3-2	
154	Beckenham Town	v	Raynes Park Vale	4-3	
155	Solent University	v	Portland United	0-3	29
156	Shaftesbury	v	Knaphill	1-4	
157	Cowes Sports	v	Lymington Town	0-4	
158	Fleet Town	v	Farnham Town	2-2	138
	Farnham Town	v	Fleet Town (13/8)	1-2	
159	Brockenhurst	v	AFC Stoneham	0-2	
160	Bournemouth	v	Frimley Green	2-1	81
161	Windsor	v	Reading City	0-3	132
162	Bemerton Heath Harlequins	v	Andover New Street	3-3	
	Andover New Street	v	Bemerton Heath Harlequins (13/8)	3-2	144
163	Sholing	v	Tadley Calleva	1-0	
164	Ascot United	v	Badshot Lea	2-2	
	(at Badshot Lea FC)				
	Badshot Lea	v	Ascot United (13/8)	2-1	123
165	Binfield	v	United Services Portsmouth	3-2	143
166	Romsey Town	v	Hamble Club	1-5	
167	Amesbury Town	v	Christchurch	2-7	
168	Westbury United	v	Fareham Town	0-1	87
169	Hamworthy United	v	Bashley	3-0	110
170	AFC Portchester	v	Hythe & Dibden	2-2	80
	Hythe & Dibden	v	AFC Portchester (13/8)	3-2	122
171	Horndean	v	Camberley Town	5-3	
172	Alresford Town	v	Baffins Milton Rovers	0-0	73
	Baffins Milton Rovers	v	Alresford Town (14/8)	2-1	110
173	Cheddar	v	Bradford Town	2-3	
174	Bitton	v	Bridport	2-1	74
175	Wellington AFC	v	Cribbs	1-1	
	(at Cribbs FC)				
	Cribbs	v	Wellington AFC (13/8)	5-1	
176	Keynsham Town	v	Brislington	0-1	177
177	Exmouth Town	v	Barnstaple Town	2-0	301
178	Saltash United	v	Clevedon Town	1-2	
179	Plymouth Parkway	v	Buckland Athletic (9/8)	1-0	181
180	Willand Rovers	v	AFC St Austell	2-1	
181	Tavistock	v	Hengrove Athletic	3-0	85
182	Street	v	Odd Down	4-1	100
183	Shepton Mallet	v	Cadbury Heath	3-1	105
184	Bridgwater Town	v	Hallen	1-0	129

FAC - EP - Midfield action against Edgware in front of the Slimbridge clubhouse. Photo Peter Barnes

FAC - EP - Action from the tie between South Normanton and Selston. Photo Bill Wheatcroft.

PRELIMINARY ROUND
SATURDAY 24 AUGUST 2019 - WINNERS RECEIVE £2,890 LOSERS RECEIVE £960

#	Home		Away	Score	Att
1	Dunston	v	Goole	2-2	291
	Goole	v	Dunston (3/9)	1-4	283
2	Newcastle Benfield	v	Workington	1-0	248
3	Seaham Red Star	v	Guisborough Town	3-1	
4	Billingham Town	v	Ossett United	3-4	
5	Whickham	v	Thornaby (23/8)	1-2	
6	Garforth Town	v	Colne	0-4	188
7	Ashington	v	Marske United	1-3	252
8	Sunderland RCA	v	Hemsworth MW	1-0	114
9	Pickering Town	v	Bridlington Town	3-1	179
10	Brighouse Town	v	Morpeth Town	2-2	
	Morpeth Town	v	Brighouse Town (3/9)	3-2	503
11	Pontefract Collieries	v	Hebburn Town	1-1	147
	Hebburn Town	v	Pontefract Collieries (3/9)	0-4	
12	Frickley Athletic	v	Tadcaster Albion	0-1	157
13	Northallerton Town	v	Stockton Town	0-3	302
14	Widnes	v	Mossley	2-2	108
	Mossley	v	Widnes (3/9)	2-3	186
15	City of Liverpool	v	Skelmersdale United	2-1	378
16	Sheffield	v	Litherland Remyca	2-1	184
17	Eccleshill United	v	Glossop North End	1-1	77
	Glossop North End	v	Eccleshill United (3/9)	3-1	177
18	Stalybridge Celtic	v	West Didsbury & Chorlton	0-0	352
	West Didsbury & Chorlton	v	Stalybridge Celtic (3/9)	2-3	553
19	Ramsbottom United	v	Winsford United	3-3	
	Winsford United	v	Ramsbottom United (2/9)	1-3	352
20	Charnock Richard	v	Longridge Town	1-1	234
	Longridge Town	v	Charnock Richard (28/8)	0-2	
21	Trafford	v	Burscough	2-0	221
22	Liversedge	v	Droylsden	1-0	118
23	Atherton Collieries	v	Runcorn Linnets	2-1	
24	1874 Northwich	v	Handsworth Parramore	6-0	227
25	Northwich Victoria	v	Prescot Cables	2-1	
26	Stocksbridge Park Steels	v	Irlam	2-3	125
27	Padiham	v	Marine	1-1	199
	Marine	v	Padiham (3/9)	3-0	345
28	Radcliffe	v	Runcorn Town	0-0	200
	Runcorn Town	v	Radcliffe (4/9)	2-1	188
29	Kidsgrove Athletic	v	Newcastle Town	1-1	152
	Newcastle Town	v	Kidsgrove Athletic (3/9)	1-2	210
30	Mickleover Sports	v	Coventry Sphinx (23/8)	3-0	249
31	Coleshill Town	v	Whitchurch Alport	0-3	83
32	Tividale	v	Chasetown	0-5	168
33	AFC Wulfrunians	v	Leek Town	0-1	
34	Stourport Swifts	v	Boldmere St Michaels	0-0	108
	Boldmere St Michaels	v	Stourport Swifts (2/9)	4-1	183
35	Bromsgrove Sporting	v	Leicester Road	2-1	684
36	Bedworth United	v	Halesowen Town	1-1	178
	Halesowen Town	v	Bedworth United (26/8)	3-1	377
37	Belper Town	v	Sporting Khalsa	1-1	191
	Sporting Khalsa	v	Belper Town (3/9)	1-3aet	
38	Romulus	v	Market Drayton Town	6-0	
39	Heather St Johns	v	Worcester City	1-0	249
40	Gresley	v	Sutton Coldfield Town	1-2	153
41	Lichfield City	v	Haughmond	3-0	122
42	Westfields	v	Lutterworth Town	2-3	141
43	Barton Town	v	Grantham Town	1-3	207
44	Loughborough Dynamo	v	Sherwood Colliery	2-2	
	Sherwood Colliery	v	Loughborough Dynamo (3/9)	0-1	
45	Melton Town	v	Cleethorpes Town	1-3	405
46	Boston Town	v	Leicester Nirvana	0-0	93
	Leicester Nirvana	v	Boston Town (27/8)	0-1	
47	Heanor Town	v	AFC Mansfield	0-0	
	AFC Mansfield	v	Heanor Town (3/9)	2-1	
48	Long Eaton United	v	South Normanton Athletic	1-1	68
	South Normanton Athletic	v	Long Eaton United (3/9)	1-0	
49	Maltby Main	v	Loughborough University	4-1	
50	Winterton Rangers	v	Kirby Muxloe	0-1	
51	Staveley MW	v	Lincoln United	2-1	141
52	Spalding United	v	Dereham Town	2-4	144
53	Great Yarmouth Town	v	Rothwell Corinthians (23/8)	0-2	
54	Peterborough Sports	v	Bugbrooke St Michaels	7-0	
55	Gorleston	v	Kempston Rovers	0-1	107
56	Bedford Town	v	Deeping Rangers	0-1	207
57	Wisbech Town	v	Ely City	2-2	179
	Ely City	v	Wisbech Town (3/9)	0-4	
58	March Town United	v	Wellingborough Town	2-1	
59	Corby Town	v	Holbeach United	4-0	348
60	Wroxham	v	Stamford	2-4	148
61	Cambridge City	v	Barton Rovers	0-2	145
62	Arlesey Town	v	Peterborough Northern Star	2-0	102
63	Biggleswade	v	Yaxley	4-0	124
64	Bury Town	v	Histon	1-2	
65	Godmanchester Rovers	v	St Neots Town	1-1	
	St Neots Town	v	Godmanchester Rovers (3/9)	3-1	231
66	Soham Town Rangers	v	Biggleswade United	2-0	109
67	Walthamstow	v	Great Wakering Rovers	2-0	
68	Cockfosters	v	Coggeshall Town	0-4	
69	Harwich & Parkeston	v	Romford	0-2	
70	Long Melford	v	Colney Heath	0-2	
71	Hadley	v	Hoddesdon Town	2-0	84
72	London Colney	v	Halstead Town	5-0	
73	Whitton United	v	Hertford Town	2-1	
74	AFC Sudbury	v	Felixstowe & Walton United	2-1	
75	FC Romania	v	Ware (25/8)	3-3	68
	Ware	v	FC Romania (3/9)	2-1	
76	Grays Athletic	v	Heybridge Swifts	5-2	
77	FC Clacton	v	Witham Town	1-1	
	Witham Town	v	FC Clacton (3/9)	3-2aet	
78	Barking	v	Aveley (23/8)	2-1	198
	(at Aveley FC)				
79	Stotfold	v	Canvey Island	0-2	101
80	Bowers & Pitsea	v	Barkingside	4-2	156
81	Saffron Walden Town	v	Maldon & Tiptree	1-2	
82	Harlow Town	v	Brentwood Town	1-1	175
	Brentwood Town	v	Harlow Town (3/9)	2-1	203

FAC - P - Pontefract Collieries 1 v 1 Hebburn Town. Photo Bill Wheatcroft.

FAC - 1Q - Longlevens 0-2 Portland United. Photo Peter Barnes.

PRELIMINARY ROUND
SATURDAY 24 AUGUST 2019 - WINNERS RECEIVE £2,890 LOSERS RECEIVE £960

No	Home		Away	Score	
83	Tilbury	v	Stanway Rovers	3-1	
84	Wingate & Finchley	v	Welwyn Garden City	2-0	121
85	Cheshunt	v	Stowmarket Town	1-0	
86	Basildon United	v	Framlingham Town	7-1	98
87	Waltham Abbey	v	Woodbridge Town	4-0	112
88	Takeley	v	White Ensign	3-3	119
	White Ensign	v	Takeley (4/9)	2-3aet	
89	Cirencester Town	v	North Greenford United	5-0	100
90	Aylesbury Vale Dynamos	v	North Leigh	4-5	113
91	Shrivenham	v	Chalfont St Peter	0-2	27
92	Longlevens	v	Northwood	1-0	75
93	Wantage Town	v	Thame Rangers	2-2	19
	Thame Rangers	v	Wantage Town(4/9)	2-4aet	
94	Bishop's Cleeve	v	Kidlington	1-4	64
95	Dunstable Town	v	Shortwood United (25/8)	4-1	152
96	Highworth Town	v	Ardley United	3-0	114
97	Marlow	v	Cinderford Town	2-4	
98	Fairford Town	v	Hanwell Town	2-3	103
99	Wembley	v	Berkhamsted	2-3	68
100	Didcot Town	v	Roman Glass St George	2-1	141
101	Thame United	v	Leighton Town	3-3	101
	Leighton Town	v	Thame United (3/9)	2-1	212
102	Evesham United	v	Harefield United (25/8)	2-1	270
103	Slimbridge	v	Burnham	1-1	82
	Burnham	v	Slimbridge (3/9)	1-1aet	120
	(Burnham won 5-4 on kicks from the penalty mark)				
104	Brimscombe & Thrupp	v	Aylesbury United	1-3	117
105	AFC Dunstable	v	Hayes & Yeading United	0-0	121
	Hayes & Yeading United	v	AFC Dunstable (3/9)	2-1aet	168
106	Newport Pagnell Town	v	Flackwell Heath	1-2	145
107	Tooting & Mitcham United	v	Faversham Town	1-0	
108	Sittingbourne	v	Uxbridge	2-0	
109	Horsham YMCA	v	Egham Town	2-1	110
110	Little Common	v	Three Bridges	2-1	54
111	Cray Wanderers	v	Hythe Town (25/8)	5-0	230
112	Sutton Athletic	v	Ashford Town (Middx)	6-0	140
113	Sutton Common Rovers	v	Eastbourne Town (23/8)	3-0	102
114	Steyning Town Community	v	Ramsgate	1-4	
115	Herne Bay	v	AFC Croydon Athletic	2-2	262
	AFC Croydon Athletic	v	Herne Bay (3/9)	0-1	
116	Chertsey Town	v	Erith & Belvedere	5-1	
117	Sheppey United	v	Glebe	3-1	172
118	Whitehawk	v	Saltdean United (23/8)	2-0	350
119	Cray Valley (PM)	v	Whyteleafe	0-2	
120	Whitstable Town	v	Newhaven	3-1	219
121	Burgess Hill Town	v	Sevenoaks Town	0-3	209
122	VCD Athletic	v	AFC Uckfield Town	3-3	56
	AFC Uckfield Town	v	VCD Athletic (3/9)	1-1aet	
	(VCD Athletic won 5-4 on kicks from the penalty mark)				
123	Bedfont Sports Club	v	Hanworth Villa	3-2	
124	Redhill	v	Balham	1-4	
125	South Park	v	Canterbury City	2-1	
126	East Grinstead Town	v	Abbey Rangers	0-1	
127	Tower Hamlets	v	Horsham	1-6	
128	Arundel	v	Shoreham	1-0	120
129	Beckenham Town	v	Ashford United	0-1	
130	Phoenix Sports	v	Staines Town	0-6	111
131	Southall	v	Spelthorne Sports	1-2	102
132	Bridon Ropes	v	Chichester City	2-7	87
133	Chipstead	v	Hassocks	0-0	64
	Hassocks	v	Chipstead (3/9)	2-3	154
134	Guildford City	v	AFC Vardeanians	1-2	134
135	Haywards Heath Town	v	Tunbridge Wells	2-1	146
136	CB Hounslow United	v	Horley Town	0-3	
137	Hastings United	v	Broadbridge Heath	2-1	
138	Portland United	v	Hamworthy United	4-3	229
139	Hythe & Dibden	v	Horndean	2-1	148
140	Hamble Club	v	Sholing	0-1	
141	Reading City	v	Moneyfields	0-3	
	(at Moneyfields FC)				
142	Christchurch	v	Badshot Lea (23/8)	1-2	157
143	Fleet Town	v	Baffins Milton Rovers	3-0	
144	Bournemouth	v	Bracknell Town	0-5	100
145	Binfield	v	Lymington Town	3-2	127
146	Thatcham Town	v	Andover New Street	7-1	240
147	Blackfield & Langley	v	AFC Totton (23/8)	2-1	157
148	Winchester City	v	AFC Stoneham (23/8)	1-1	259
	AFC Stoneham	v	Winchester City (3/9)	1-3	202
149	Basingstoke Town	v	Westfield	0-2	
150	Knaphill	v	Fareham Town	0-1	
151	Plymouth Parkway	v	Paulton Rovers	5-2	184
152	Yate Town	v	Exmouth Town	2-2	246
	Exmouth Town	v	Yate Town (3/9)	2-0	451
153	Bridgwater Town	v	Brislington	7-0	
154	Cribbs	v	Bideford	0-1	88
155	Clevedon Town	v	Bristol Manor Farm	2-5	172
156	Tavistock	v	Frome Town	2-1	
157	Shepton Mallet	v	Melksham Town	1-1	196
	Melksham Town	v	Shepton Mallet (2/9)	2-3	311
158	Bradford Town	v	Larkhall Athletic	3-1	171
159	Street	v	Willand Rovers	1-5	149
160	Bitton	v	Mangotsfield United	2-3	170

FAC - 1Q - Dean (Sunderland RCA) dominates his area against Dunston. Photo Keith Clayton.

FAC - 1Q - Page (Dunston) shoots past Moan (Sunderland RCA). Photo Keith Clayton.

FIRST QUALIFYING ROUND

SATURDAY 7 SEPTEMBER 2019 - WINNERS RECEIVE £4,500 LOSERS RECEIVE £1,500

1	Thornaby	v	Ossett United	2-2	
	Ossett United	v	Thornaby (10/9)	6-0	265
2	1874 Northwich	v	Pickering Town	2-0	305
3	Scarborough Athletic	v	Marske United	1-1	
	Marske United	v	Scarborough Athletic (10/9)	1-2	550
4	Lancaster City	v	Northwich Victoria	0-0	261
	Northwich Victoria	v	Lancaster City (11/9)	1-2	310
5	FC United of Manchester	v	Atherton Collieries	2-2	1216
	Atherton Collieries	v	FC United of Manchester (10/9)	0-1	
6	Dunston	v	Sunderland RCA	0-0	392
	Sunderland RCA	v	Dunston (11/9)	0-5	262
7	Liversedge	v	Stockton Town	0-2	286
8	Newcastle Benfield	v	Runcorn Town	2-3	
9	Warrington Town	v	City of Liverpool	2-2	612
	City of Liverpool	v	Warrington Town (10/9)	0-4	1099
10	Charnock Richard	v	Irlam	0-4	209
11	Widnes	v	Whitby Town	0-4	153
12	Tadcaster Albion	v	Ashton United	2-2	361
	Ashton United	v	Tadcaster Albion (10/9)	4-2	
13	Stalybridge Celtic	v	Marine	0-2	294
14	Trafford	v	Bamber Bridge	3-0	298
15	Glossop North End	v	Pontefract Collieries	1-3	222
16	South Shields	v	Colne	0-0	1157
	Colne	v	South Shields (10/9)	1-0	231
17	Maltby Main	v	Ramsbottom United	1-5	
18	Morpeth Town	v	Hyde United	3-1	551
19	Seaham Red Star	v	Witton Albion	0-1	272
20	Kirby Muxloe	v	Boston Town	0-1	112
21	Lutterworth Town	v	Hednesford Town	0-3	
22	Halesowen Town	v	Lichfield City	7-1	635
23	South Normanton Athletic	v	Coalville Town	0-1	
24	Tamworth	v	Nuneaton Borough	3-1	1047
25	Loughborough Dynamo	v	Heather St Johns	1-0	
26	Barwell	v	AFC Mansfield	4-1	149
27	Romulus	v	Buxton	0-4	
28	Banbury United	v	Gainsborough Trinity	2-2	473
	Gainsborough Trinity	v	Banbury United (10/9)	1-0	321
29	Matlock Town	v	Basford United	2-1	
30	Stratford Town	v	Boldmere St Michaels	6-1	180
31	Rushall Olympic	v	Sheffield	3-1	259
32	Belper Town	v	Alvechurch	1-0	329
33	Nantwich Town	v	Grantham Town	3-1	359
34	Kidsgrove Athletic	v	Cleethorpes Town	2-1	193
35	Sutton Coldfield Town	v	Redditch United	1-1	218
	Redditch United	v	Sutton Coldfield Town (10/9)	1-3	205
36	Stafford Rangers	v	Mickleover Sports	3-0	519
37	Bromsgrove Sporting	v	Stourbridge	0-1	1205
38	Whitchurch Alport	v	Leek Town	0-2	797
39	Chasetown	v	Staveley MW	1-0	237
40	Wingate & Finchley	v	London Colney	4-1	111
41	Soham Town Rangers	v	Whitton United	3-0	158
42	Takeley	v	Potters Bar Town	0-1	
43	Deeping Rangers	v	AFC Sudbury	2-2	
	AFC Sudbury	v	Deeping Rangers (10/9)	2-3	
44	Enfield Town	v	AFC Rushden & Diamonds	1-0	501
45	Kings Langley	v	Barking	3-1	281
46	Hornchurch	v	Kempston Rovers	6-0	240
47	Cheshunt	v	Brightlingsea Regent	1-0	
48	Stamford	v	Witham Town	1-0	
49	Biggleswade	v	Tilbury	2-1	164
50	Basildon United	v	Coggeshall Town	2-1	104
51	Royston Town	v	Rothwell Corinthians	7-2	
52	Histon	v	Maldon & Tiptree	0-3	165
53	Waltham Abbey	v	Canvey Island	2-2	151
	Canvey Island	v	Waltham Abbey (10/9)	2-1	176
54	Colney Heath	v	Corby Town	1-3	
55	Dunstable Town	v	Bishop's Stortford	3-5	221
56	Grays Athletic	v	March Town United	3-1	
	(tie awarded to March Town United – Grays Athletic removed)				
57	Barton Rovers	v	Romford	4-0	146
58	Aylesbury United	v	Walthamstow (8/9)	0-3	208
59	St Ives Town	v	Berkhamsted	2-1	151
60	Ware	v	Leiston	5-1	
61	East Thurrock United	v	Peterborough Sports	1-1	161
	Peterborough Sports	v	East Thurrock United (10/9)	3-2	162
62	Wisbech Town	v	Hitchin Town	1-2	255
63	Bowers & Pitsea	v	Brentwood Town	2-1	158
64	St Neots Town	v	Biggleswade Town	2-2	288
	Biggleswade Town	v	St Neots Town (11/9)	2-0	
65	Hadley	v	Arlesey Town	3-2	127
66	Dereham Town	v	Needham Market	1-1	
	Needham Market	v	Dereham Town (10/9)	2-1	234
67	Lowestoft Town	v	Leighton Town	2-0	388
68	Whitstable Town	v	Folkestone Invicta	0-4	503
69	Chesham United	v	Fleet Town	4-2	289
70	Whyteleafe	v	Merstham	1-0	233
71	Chertsey Town	v	Sheppey United	4-1	260
72	Chichester City	v	Chalfont St Peter	2-0	
73	Hartley Wintney	v	Spelthorne Sports	3-0	192
74	Bracknell Town	v	Carshalton Athletic	0-2	
75	Kingstonian	v	Walton Casuals (8/9)	2-0	376
76	Leatherhead	v	Lewes	2-2	305
	Lewes	v	Leatherhead (11/9)	2-2aet	395
	(Lewes won 3-1 on kicks from the penalty mark)				
77	Hanwell Town	v	Staines Town	2-3	
78	South Park	v	Badshot Lea	1-3	
79	Tooting & Mitcham United	v	AFC Vardeanians	3-1	
80	Whitehawk	v	Abbey Rangers	0-1	330
81	Hastings United	v	Worthing	3-3	
	Worthing	v	Hastings United (10/9)	3-2	510
82	Haywards Heath Town	v	Hayes & Yeading United	0-1	167
83	Harrow Borough	v	Binfield	5-0	121
84	Horley Town	v	Balham	1-3	
85	Cray Wanderers	v	Bedfont Sports Club (8/9)	2-1	225
86	Westfield	v	Chipstead	0-1	126
87	Haringey Borough	v	Herne Bay	3-0	
88	Corinthian Casuals	v	Sevenoaks Town	4-0	235
89	Sutton Common Rovers	v	Beaconsfield Town (6/9)	1-3	139
90	Ashford United	v	Farnborough	0-3	
91	Ramsgate	v	Arundel	0-0	
	Arundel	v	Ramsgate (10/9)	0-4	194
92	Sutton Athletic	v	Flackwell Heath	1-1	100
	Flackwell Heath	v	Sutton Athletic (10/9)	3-1	141
93	VCD Athletic	v	Moneyfields	1-2	
94	Bognor Regis Town	v	Sittingbourne	3-0	
95	Little Common	v	Hendon	0-1	119
96	Horsham YMCA	v	Margate	1-2	
97	Metropolitan Police	v	Horsham	1-1	154
	Horsham	v	Metropolitan Police (10/9)	3-2	445
98	Weston Super Mare	v	Fareham Town	3-0	342
99	Cinderford Town	v	Bideford	5-3	133
100	Didcot Town	v	Poole Town	0-1	257
101	Truro City	v	Wimborne Town	2-1	363
102	Plymouth Parkway	v	Merthyr Town	0-1	201
103	Bridgwater Town	v	Bristol Manor Farm	1-3	
104	Winchester City	v	Taunton Town	0-3	
105	Willand Rovers	v	North Leigh	1-2	
106	Burnham	v	Tiverton Town	2-3	143
107	Hythe & Dibden	v	Kidlington	2-4	192
108	Tavistock	v	Shepton Mallet	3-3	
	Shepton Mallet	v	Tavistock (10/9)	1-2	247
109	Highworth Town	v	Exmouth Town	4-2	190
110	Wantage Town	v	Swindon Supermarine	0-3	168
111	Longlevens	v	Portland United	0-2	146
112	Thatcham Town	v	Salisbury	2-3	661
	(Live on BBC Sport)				
113	Cirencester Town	v	Gosport Borough	1-0	138
114	Evesham United	v	Dorchester Town (8/9)	0-2	320
115	Mangotsfield United	v	Blackfield & Langley	0-5	169
116	Sholing	v	Bradford Town	3-0	201

FAC - 2Q - Belper Town 0 v 0 Witton Albion. Photo Bill Wheatcroft.

FAC - 2Q - Hereford 5-2 Truro Photo Peter Barnes.

SECOND QUALIFYING ROUND
SATURDAY 21 SEPTEMBER 2019 - WINNERS RECEIVE £6,750 LOSERS RECEIVE £2,250

#	Home		Away	Score	Att
1	Marine	v	Dunston	1-2	396
2	Southport	v	Scarborough Athletic	5-2	875
3	Chester	v	Altrincham	1-1	1804
	Altrincham	v	Chester (24/9)	1-0	952
4	Curzon Ashton	v	Blyth Spartans	4-4	189
	Blyth Spartans	v	Curzon Ashton (24/9)	1-0	481
5	Bradford (Park Avenue)	v	Morpeth Town	2-4	217
6	Irlam	v	York City	0-2	773
	(Live on BBC Sport)				
7	Ashton United	v	Pontefract Collieries	1-0	192
8	Colne	v	Ossett United	0-0	252
	Ossett United	v	Colne (24/9)	0-4	377
9	1874 Northwich	v	Whitby Town	0-1	357
10	FC United of Manchester	v	Warrington Town	1-2	1263
11	Trafford	v	Darlington	1-3	795
12	Gateshead	v	Ramsbottom United	6-0	480
13	Guiseley	v	Stockton Town	1-0	483
14	Lancaster City	v	Spennymoor Town	0-5	294
15	Runcorn Town	v	Farsley Celtic	1-3	168
16	Alfreton Town	v	King's Lynn Town	1-1	335
	King's Lynn Town	v	Alfreton Town (24/9)	2-1	712
17	Stamford	v	Boston United	0-4	671
18	Leamington	v	Chasetown	2-2	395
	Chasetown	v	Leamington (24/9)	1-2aet	339
19	Kettering Town	v	Sutton Coldfield Town	1-1	423
	Sutton Coldfield Town	v	Kettering Town (24/9)	2-1	222
20	Belper Town	v	Witton Albion	0-0	503
	Witton Albion	v	Belper Town (24/9)	0-1aet	279
21	Loughborough Dynamo	v	Tamworth	0-3	416
22	AFC Telford United	v	Nantwich Town	0-3	718
23	Rushall Olympic	v	Gainsborough Trinity	2-0	249
24	Halesowen Town	v	Stratford Town	4-1	611
25	Boston Town	v	Leek Town	0-4	110
26	Buxton	v	Corby Town	5-0	264
27	Matlock Town	v	Kidsgrove Athletic	1-2	377
28	Hednesford Town	v	Barwell	3-2	393
29	Kidderminster Harriers	v	Stafford Rangers	0-0	950
	Stafford Rangers	v	Kidderminster Harriers (24/9)	3-0	663
30	Coalville Town	v	Stourbridge	1-2	315
31	Beaconsfield Town	v	Hemel Hempstead Town	1-0	211
32	Corinthian Casuals	v	Chelmsford City	2-0	374
33	Kingstonian	v	March Town United (25/9)	3-0	227
34	Walthamstow	v	Abbey Rangers	1-1	245
	Abbey Rangers	v	Walthamstow (24/9)	2-1	190
35	Balham	v	Royston Town	3-5	233
36	Tonbridge Angels	v	Eastbourne Borough	1-2	538
37	Margate	v	Concord Rangers	3-1	360
38	Hendon	v	Deeping Rangers	3-2	195
39	St Ives Town	v	Canvey Island	0-0	187
	Canvey Island	v	St Ives Town (24/9)	3-2aet	194
40	Maidstone United	v	Cheshunt	4-1	1129
41	Potters Bar Town	v	Hornchurch	2-0	184
42	Bishop's Stortford	v	Peterborough Sports	1-2	296
43	Dulwich Hamlet	v	Bognor Regis Town	6-1	1394
44	Flackwell Heath	v	Slough Town	0-3	484
45	Billericay Town	v	Basildon United	1-0	1106
46	Tooting & Mitcham United	v	Dorking Wanderers	1-0	326
47	Hadley	v	Ramsgate	1-0	202
48	Lewes	v	Bowers & Pitsea	1-2	479
49	Cray Wanderers	v	Soham Town Rangers (22/9)	5-2	184
50	Harrow Borough	v	Carshalton Athletic	0-1	157
51	Biggleswade	v	Chertsey Town (22/9)	1-3	272
52	Biggleswade Town	v	Ware	1-2	199
53	Badshot Lea	v	Hayes & Yeading United	0-4	189
54	Lowestoft Town	v	Needham Market	4-0	495
55	Barton Rovers	v	Hitchin Town	0-1	381
56	Enfield Town	v	Braintree Town	2-0	532
57	Maldon & Tiptree	v	Wingate & Finchley	4-2	116
58	Moneyfields	v	Whyteleafe	0-2	153
59	Hartley Wintney	v	Chichester City	0-0	205
	Chichester City	v	Hartley Wintney (24/9)	1-0	232
60	Horsham	v	Dartford	0-2	902
61	St Albans City	v	Worthing	2-2	473
	Worthing	v	St Albans City (24/9)	1-3	637
62	Kings Langley	v	Folkestone Invicta	4-0	335
63	Haringey Borough	v	Staines Town	5-0	343
64	Farnborough	v	Wealdstone	0-5	404
65	Welling United	v	Chipstead	7-0	388
66	Chesham United	v	Hampton & Richmond Borough	1-2	430
67	Weston Super Mare	v	Merthyr Town	2-1	355
68	Sholing	v	Weymouth	0-3	515
69	Hereford	v	Truro City	5-2	1116
70	Portland United	v	Salisbury	0-1	574
71	Havant & Waterlooville	v	Taunton Town	2-1	473
72	Cirencester Town	v	Chippenham Town	2-2	336
	Chippenham Town	v	Cirencester Town (24/9)	4-3aet	349
73	Tavistock	v	Highworth Town	4-0	189
74	Tiverton Town	v	Bristol Manor Farm	2-4	241
75	Poole Town	v	Hungerford Town	2-1	427
76	Swindon Supermarine	v	Bath City	0-4	461
77	Oxford City	v	North Leigh	7-0	334
78	Kidlington	v	Gloucester City	0-5	197
79	Brackley Town	v	Cinderford Town	4-0	385
80	Blackfield & Langley	v	Dorchester Town	1-0	161

FAC - 3Q - Tamworth 0-0 Hereford Photo Peter Barnes.

FAC - 4Q - Potters Bar Town 1 v 1 Barnet in front of a record crowd of 2011. Photo Bill Wheatcroft.

FAC - 4Q - Tamworth 0-3 Darlington Photo Peter Barnes.

THIRD QUALIFYING ROUND
SATURDAY 5 OCTOBER 2019 - WINNERS RECEIVE £11,250 LOSERS RECEIVE £3,750

#	Home		Away	Score	Att
1	Ashton United	v	Spennymoor Town	2-6	283
2	Halesowen Town	v	Altrincham	0-2	1235
	(Live on BBC Sport)				
3	Hednesford Town	v	Blyth Spartans	4-2	616
4	Nantwich Town	v	Morpeth Town	1-0	476
5	Peterborough Sports	v	Guiseley	1-0	435
6	Leek Town	v	King's Lynn Town	0-2	790
7	Whitby Town	v	Gloucester City	1-1	273
	Gloucester City	v	Whitby Town (7/10)	1-3	273
8	Kidsgrove Athletic	v	Gateshead	0-1	322
9	Stourbridge	v	Stafford Rangers	2-1	1048
10	Belper Town	v	Rushall Olympic	2-1	528
11	Buxton	v	York City	1-2	901
12	Tamworth	v	Hereford	0-0	1206
	Hereford	v	Tamworth (8/10)	0-0aet	1271
	(Tamworth won 3-1 on kicks from the penalty mark)				
13	Dunston	v	Colne	2-3	586
14	Farsley Celtic	v	Southport	0-5	411
15	Leamington	v	Darlington	0-2	605
16	Sutton Coldfield Town	v	Boston United	0-1	497
17	Brackley Town	v	Warrington Town	2-0	452
18	Oxford City	v	Hampton & Richmond Borough	2-0	347
19	Lowestoft Town	v	Carshalton Athletic	1-2	500
20	Dulwich Hamlet	v	Eastbourne Borough	3-0	606
21	Canvey Island	v	Bowers & Pitsea	1-1	387
	Bowers & Pitsea	v	Canvey Island (8/10)	1-1aet	452
	(Bowers & Pitsea won 5-3 on kicks from the penalty mark)				
22	Bristol Manor Farm	v	Wealdstone	0-0	422
	Wealdstone	v	Bristol Manor Farm (8/10)	4-0	524
23	Kingstonian	v	Weston Super Mare	1-1	358
	Weston Super Mare	v	Kingstonian (8/10)	1-4	248
24	Haringey Borough	v	Cray Wanderers	1-0	344
25	Welling United	v	Tavistock	4-1	491
26	Maldon & Tiptree	v	Chertsey Town	6-1	225
27	Chippenham Town	v	Slough Town	3-3	606
	Slough Town	v	Chippenham Town (8/10)	2-3	631
28	Salisbury	v	Margate	2-4	743
29	Abbey Rangers	v	Whyteleafe	0-2	272
30	Kings Langley	v	Corinthian Casuals	3-0	362
31	Ware	v	Potters Bar Town	1-2	387
32	Hayes & Yeading United	v	Hendon	5-4	289
33	Royston Town	v	Beaconsfield Town	2-1	407
34	Tooting & Mitcham United	v	Poole Town	0-2	434
35	Havant & Waterlooville	v	Hadley	3-0	515
36	Billericay Town	v	Bath City	4-2	678
37	Blackfield & Langley	v	Dartford	1-4	360
38	Weymouth	v	St Albans City	4-1	974
39	Chichester City	v	Enfield Town	1-0	515
40	Maidstone United	v	Hitchin Town	2-1	1253

FOURTH QUALIFYING ROUND
SATURDAY 19 OCTOBER 2019 - WINNERS RECEIVE £18,750 LOSERS RECEIVE £6,250

#	Home		Away	Score	Att
1	Hednesford Town	v	Boston United	0-1	891
2	Gateshead	v	Colne	5-0	878
3	Barrow	v	Solihull Moors	0-1	1523
4	Whitby Town	v	Stourbridge	1-1	1171
	Stourbridge	v	Whitby Town (21/10)	3-2	1092
5	Hartlepool United	v	Brackley Town	1-0	2506
6	Nantwich Town	v	Kings Lynn Town	1-0	742
7	Chorley	v	Spennymoor Town	2-0	859
8	Southport	v	Altrincham	1-3	1507
9	Tamworth	v	Darlington	0-3	1358
10	York City	v	Stockport County (5.20)	2-0	2870
	(Live on BT Sport)				
11	Notts County	v	Belper Town	2-1	5729
12	Chesterfield	v	Wrexham (1.00)	1-1	2199
	Wrexham	v	Chesterfield (22/10)	1-0	2220
13	FC Halifax Town	v	Harrogate Town	1-2	1241
14	AFC Fylde	v	Peterborough Sports	6-1	687
15	Whyteleafe	v	Chippenham Town	0-3	512
16	Haringey Borough	v	Yeovil Town (29/10)	0-3	857
	(19/10 – tie abandoned)				
17	Havant & Waterlooville	v	Dulwich Hamlet	1-2	826
18	Ebbsfleet United	v	Woking	1-1	750
	Woking	v	Ebbsfleet United (22/10)	0-1	916
19	Welling United	v	Eastleigh	0-0	511
	Eastleigh	v	Welling United (22/10)	4-2	803
20	Bromley	v	Aldershot Town	4-3	1408
21	Maidstone United	v	Kings Langley	4-1	1449
22	Maidenhead United	v	Wealdstone	1-1	891
	Wealdstone	v	Maidenhead United (22/10)	0-2	835
23	Oxford City	v	Margate	2-1	442
24	Bowers & Pitsea	v	Chichester City	1-2	531
25	Hayes & Yeading United	v	Poole Town	1-1	416
	Poole Town	v	Hayes & Yeading United (22/10)	2-3	1066
26	Royston Town	v	Maldon & Tiptree	1-3	1152
27	Potters Bar Town	v	Barnet (12.30)	1-1	2011
	(Live on BBC Sport)				
	Barnet	v	Potters Bar Town (22/10)	3-1	1466
28	Torquay United	v	Boreham Wood	3-2	1952
29	Sutton United	v	Billericay Town	1-1	789
	Billericay Town	v	Sutton United (22/10)	5-2	1113
30	Weymouth	v	Dover Athletic	1-2	1506
31	Dartford	v	Kingstonian	2-3	850
32	Carshalton Athletic	v	Dagenham & Redbridge	2-1	726

FAC - 1P - Barnett (Eastleigh) heads home the equaliser against Stourbridge. Photo Keith Clayton.

FAC - 2P - Hulme (Altrincham) tries to sneak a goal past MacGillivray (Portsmouth). Photo Keith Clayton.

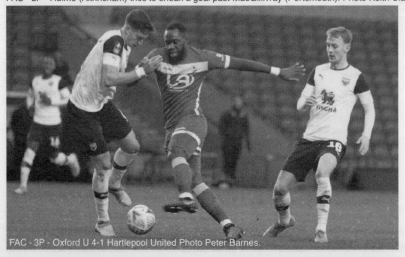

FAC - 3P - Oxford U 4-1 Hartlepool United Photo Peter Barnes.

FIRST ROUND PROPER
SATURDAY 9 NOVEMBER 2019 - WINNERS RECEIVE £36,000

1	Ipswich Town	v	Lincoln City	1-1	11598
	Lincoln City	v	Ipswich Town (20/11)	0-1	6781
2	Oxford City	v	Solihull Moors	1-5	667
3	Crawley Town	v	Scunthorpe United	4-1	1706
4	Harrogate Town	v	Portsmouth (11/11)	1-2	3408
	(Live on BT Sport 1)				
5	Colchester United	v	Coventry City	0-2	2919
6	Sunderland	v	Gillingham	1-1	7892
	Gillingham	v	Sunderland (19/11)	1-0	3561
	(Live on BBC Two)				
7	Dulwich Hamlet	v	Carlisle United (8/11)	1-4	3336
8	Bolton Wanderers	v	Plymouth Argyle	0-1	6992
9	York City	v	Altrincham (10/11)	0-1	3222
10	Wrexham	v	Rochdale (10/11)	0-0	3274
	Rochdale	v	Wrexham (19/11)	1-0	1628
11	Maidstone United	v	Torquay United	1-0	2330
12	Leyton Orient	v	Maldon & Tiptree (10/11)	1-2	3425
13	Chippenham Town	v	Northampton Town (10/11)	0-3	2625
14	Yeovil Town	v	Hartlepool United (12/11)	1-4	2361
15	Cambridge United	v	Exeter City	1-1	2302
	Exeter City	v	Cambridge United (19/11)	1-0	2719
16	Stourbridge	v	Eastleigh	2-2	1846
	Eastleigh	v	Stourbridge (19/11)	3-0	1509
17	Salford City	v	Burton Albion	1-1	2724
	Burton Albion	v	Salford City (19/11)	4-1	1479
18	Forest Green Rovers	v	Billericay Town	4-0	1419
19	Bristol Rovers	v	Bromley (10/11)	1-1	3649
	Bromley	v	Bristol Rovers (19/11)	0-1	4558
	(Live on BT Sport 1)				
20	Ebbsfleet United	v	Notts County	2-3	1206
21	Walsall	v	Darlington	2-2	2882
	Darlington	v	Walsall (20/11)	0-1	3106
	(Live on BT Sport 1)				
22	Nantwich Town	v	AFC Fylde	0-1	1554
23	AFC Wimbledon	v	Doncaster Rovers	1-1	2777
	Doncaster Rovers	v	AFC Wimbledon (19/11)	2-0	3413
24	Hayes & Yeading United	v	Oxford United (10/11)	0-2	1501
	(Live on BT Sport 1)				
25	Shrewsbury Town	v	Bradford City	1-1	3764
	Bradford City	v	Shrewsbury Town (19/11)	0-1	3888
26	Grimsby Town	v	Newport County	1-1	2086
	Newport County	v	Grimsby Town (20/11)	2-0	2053
	(Live on BBC Wales)				
27	Gateshead	v	Oldham Athletic (10/11)	1-2	2199
28	Mansfield Town	v	Chorley	1-0	2418
29	Dover Athletic	v	Southend United (10/11)	1-0	1754
	(Live on BT Sport 1)				
30	Tranmere Rovers	v	Wycombe Wanderers	2-2	3849
	Wycombe Wanderers	v	Tranmere Rovers (20/11)	1-2aet	2929
31	Carshalton Athletic	v	Boston United	1-4	1859
32	Cheltenham Town	v	Swindon Town	1-1	3456
	Swindon Town	v	Cheltenham Town (19/11)	0-1	4596
33	Accrington Stanley	v	Crewe Alexandra	0-2	1655
34	Barnet	v	Fleetwood Town (10/11)	0-2	1100
35	Macclesfield Town	v	Kingstonian (10/11)	0-4	996
36	Maidenhead United	v	Rotherham United	1-3	1924
37	Blackpool	v	Morecambe	4-1	5371
38	Milton Keynes Dons	v	Port Vale	0-1	3598
39	Stevenage	v	Peterborough United	1-1	2981
	Peterborough United	v	Stevenage (19/11)	2-0	3593
	Chichester City			Bye	

SECOND ROUND PROPER
SATURDAY 30 NOVEMBER 2019 - WINNERS RECEIVE £54,000

1	Blackpool	v	Maidstone United (1/12)	3-1	3977
2	Portsmouth	v	Altrincham	2-1	8539
3	Shrewsbury Town	v	Mansfield Town	2-0	3678
4	Coventry City	v	Ipswich Town (1/12)	1-1	2878
	Ipswich Town	v	Coventry City (10/12)	1-2	6515
5	Kingstonian	v	AFC Fylde	0-2	1460
6	Tranmere Rovers	v	Chichester City (1/12)	5-1	4370
	(Live on BT Sport 1)				
7	Walsall	v	Oxford United	0-1	3224
8	Exeter City	v	Hartlepool United (1/12)	2-2	3638
	Hartlepool United	v	Exeter City (10/12)	1-0aet	2398
9	Eastleigh	v	Crewe Alexandra (5.30)	1-1	1806
	(Live on BT Sport 1)				
	Crewe Alexandra	v	Eastleigh (10/12)	3-1	2184
10	Forest Green Rovers	v	Carlisle United	2-2	1504
	Carlisle United	v	Forest Green Rovers (10/12)	1-0	1736
11	Solihull Moors	v	Rotherham United (2/12)	3-4	2317
	(Live on BT Sport 1)				
12	Gillingham	v	Doncaster Rovers (1/12)	3-0	3216
13	Rochdale	v	Boston United (1/12)	0-0	2583
	Boston United	v	Rochdale (16/12)	1-2	4910
	(Live on BT Sport 1)				
14	Peterborough United	v	Dover Athletic (1/12)	3-0	4239
15	Oldham Athletic	v	Burton Albion	0-1	2858
16	Maldon & Tiptree	v	Newport County (29/11)	0-1	1876
	(Live on BBC Two)				
17	Crawley Town	v	Fleetwood Town (1/12)	1-2	2000
18	Cheltenham Town	v	Port Vale	1-3	2725
19	Northampton Town	v	Notts County (1/12)	3-1	4489
20	Bristol Rovers	v	Plymouth Argyle (1/12)	1-1	6215
	Plymouth Argyle	v	Bristol Rovers (17/12)	0-1	6585
	(Live on BT Sport 1)				

THIRD ROUND PROPER
SATURDAY 4 JANUARY 2020 - WINNERS RECEIVE £135,000

1	Leicester City	v	Wigan Athletic	2-0	30330
2	Queens Park Rangers	v	Swansea City (5/1)	5-1	6712
3	Fulham	v	Aston Villa	2-1	12980
4	Chelsea	v	Nottingham Forest (5/1)	2-0	40492
5	Wolverhampton Wanderers	v	Manchester United	0-0	31381
	Manchester United	v	Wolverhampton W (15/1)	1-0	67025
	(Live on BT Sport 1)				
6	Charlton Athletic	v	West Bromwich Albion (5/1)	0-1	6426
7	Rochdale	v	Newcastle United (14/1)	1-1	8593
	Newcastle United	v	Rochdale	4-1	29786
8	Cardiff City	v	Carlisle United	2-2	5282
	Carlisle United	v	Cardiff City (15/1)	3-4	4381
9	Oxford United	v	Hartlepool United	4-1	6240
10	Sheffield United	v	AFC Fylde (5/1)	2-1	11133
11	Southampton	v	Huddersfield Town	2-0	20091
12	Liverpool	v	Everton (5/1)	1-0	50786
	(Live on BBC One)				
13	Bristol City	v	Shrewsbury Town	1-1	9730
	Shrewsbury Town	v	Bristol City (14/1)	1-0	7194
14	AFC Bournemouth	v	Luton Town	4-0	10064
15	Brighton & Hove Albion	v	Sheffield Wednesday	0-1	20349
16	Bristol Rovers	v	Coventry City (5/1)	2-2	7000
	Coventry City	v	Bristol Rovers (14/1)	3-0	2693
17	Crewe Alexandra	v	Barnsley (5/1)	1-3	5158
18	Manchester City	v	Port Vale	4-1	52433
19	Middlesbrough	v	Tottenham Hotspur (5/1)	1-1	26693
	(Live on BT Sport 1)				
	Tottenham Hotspur	v	Middlesbrough (14/1)	2-1	49202
	(Live on BBC One)				
20	Reading	v	Blackpool	2-2	10181
	Blackpool	v	Reading (14/1)	0-2	5213
21	Watford	v	Tranmere Rovers	3-3	14373
	Tranmere Rovers	v	Watford (23/1)	2-1aet	10039
22	Preston North End	v	Norwich City	2-4	7616
23	Millwall	v	Newport County	3-0	6009
24	Crystal Palace	v	Derby County (5/1)	0-1	15507
25	Rotherham United	v	Hull City	2-3	6044
26	Brentford	v	Stoke City	1-0	7575
27	Fleetwood Town	v	Portsmouth	1-2	2145
28	Arsenal	v	Leeds United (6/1)	1-0	58403
	(Live on BBC One)				
29	Gillingham	v	West Ham United (5/1)	0-2	10913
	(Live on BT Sport 1)				
30	Burton Albion	v	Northampton Town (5/1)	2-4	3810
31	Burnley	v	Peterborough United	4-2	8043
32	Birmingham City	v	Blackburn Rovers	2-1	7330

FAC - 1P - Forest GR v Billericay Town Photo Peter Barnes.

FAC - 1P - Grocott (Stourbridge) gets the second goal against Eastleigh. Photo Keith Clayton.

FAC - 2P - Northampton 3-0 Notts County Photo Peter Barnes.

FOURTH ROUND PROPER
SATURDAY 25 JANUARY 2020 - WINNERS RECEIVE £180,000

1	Tranmere Rovers	v	Manchester United (26/1)	0-6	13779
2	Hull City	v	Chelsea	1-2	24109
3	Southampton	v	Tottenham Hotspur	1-1	29282
	Tottenham Hotspur	v	Southampton (5/2)	3-2	56046
	(Live on BT Sport 1)				
4	Queens Park Rangers	v	Sheffield Wednesday (24/1)	1-2	11871
5	AFC Bournemouth	v	Arsenal (27/1)	1-2	10308
6	Northampton Town	v	Derby County (24/1)	0-0	7798
	Derby County	v	Northampton Town (4/2)	4-2	15860
7	Brentford	v	Leicester City	0-1	12221
8	Millwall	v	Sheffield United	0-2	12653
9	Reading	v	Cardiff City	1-1	12798
	Cardiff City	v	Reading (4/2)	3-3aet	4832
	(Reading won 4-1 on kicks from the penalty mark)				

10	West Ham United	v	West Bromwich Albion	0-1	58911
11	Burnley	v	Norwich City	1-2	8071
12	Coventry City	v	Birmingham City	0-0	21193
	Birmingham City	v	Coventry City (4/2)	2-2aet	11680
	(Birmingham City won 4-1 on kicks from the penalty mark)				
13	Manchester City	v	Fulham (26/1)	4-0	39223
14	Newcastle United	v	Oxford United	0-0	52221
	Oxford United	v	Newcastle United (4/2)	2-3	11520
	(Live on BBC One)				
15	Portsmouth	v	Barnsley	4-2	13286
16	Shrewsbury Town	v	Liverpool (26/1)	2-2	9510
	Liverpool	v	Shrewsbury Town (4/2)	1-0	52399

FIFTH ROUND PROPER
WEDNESDAY 5 FEBRUARY 2020 - WINNERS RECEIVE £360,000

1	Sheffield Wednesday	v	Manchester City (4/3)	0-1	20995
	(Live on BBC One)				
2	Reading	v	Sheffield United (3/3)	1-2aet	15129
3	Chelsea	v	Liverpool (3/3)	2-0	40103
	(Live on BBC One)				
4	West Bromwich Albion	v	Newcastle United (3/3)	2-3	21803
5	Leicester City	v	Birmingham City (4/3)	1-0	27181

6	Derby County	v	Manchester United (5/3)	0-3	31379
	(Live on BT Sport 1)				
7	Tottenham Hotspur	v	Norwich City (4/3)	1-1aet	58007
	(Norwich City won 3-2 on kicks from the penalty mark)				
8	Portsmouth	v	Arsenal (2/3) 0-2		18839
	(Live on BT Sport 1)				

QUARTER FINALS
WINNERS RECEIVE £720,000

SUN 28 JUNE					
1	Sheffield United	v	Arsenal	1-2	0
2	Newcastle United	v	Manchester City	0-2	0

SAT 27 JUNE					
3	Norwich City	v	Manchester United	1-2 (aet)	0
SUN 28 JUNE					
4	Leicester City	v	Chelsea	0-1	0

SEMI FINALS
WINNERS RECEIVE £1,800,000   LOSERS RECEIVE £900,000

SUN 19 JULY - at Wembley Stadium				
1	Manchester United	v	Chelsea	1-3

SAT 18 JULY - at Wembley Stadium				
2	Arsenal	v	Manchester City	2-0

THE FINAL
SAT 1 AUGUST   WINNERS RECEIVE £3.6m   RUNNERS-UP £1.8m

ARSENAL	2	1	CHELSEA
Aubameyang 28 (pen) 67			Pulisic 5

AT WEMBLEY STADIUM ~ ATTENDANCE: Behind Closed Doors

FAC - 1P - Rendell (Eastleigh) crashes home the equaliser against Stourbridge. Photo Keith Clayton.

FAC - 2P - Spectacular take by Sanchez (Rochdale) against Boston. Photo Keith Clayton.

FAC - 1P - Jaakkola (Bristol Rovers) blocks Bush (Bromley). Photo Keith Clayton.

FAC - 1P - Lloyd (Stourbridge) heads home the first goal against Eastleigh. Photo Keith Clayton.

FAC - 1P - Huddart (Bromley) saves while Holland keeps Nichols (Bristol Rovers) at bay. Photo Keith Clayton.

FAC - 1Q - McNab (Sunderland RCA) clears from Marrs (Dunston). Photo Keith Clayton.

FAC - 2P - Brilliant save from Jaaskelainnen (Crewe) keeps out Barnett (Eastleigh). Photo Keith Clayton.

THE FA TROPHY 2019-20

EXTRA PRELIMINARY ROUND
SATURDAY 28 SEPTEMBER 2019 - WINNERS RECEIVE £1,500 LOSERS RECEIVE £500

#	Home		Away	Score	Att
1	Colne	v	Marske United	2-1	179
2	Cleethorpes Town	v	Frickley Athletic	1-0	
3	Runcorn Linnets	v	Marine	1-0	
4	City of Liverpool	v	Tadcaster Albion (1/10)	1-1	301
	Tadcaster Albion	v	City of Liverpool (8/10)	6-1	
5	Ossett United	v	Widnes	1-0	287
6	Clitheroe	v	Sheffield	2-1	272
7	Daventry Town	v	Kidsgrove Athletic	1-1	
	Kidsgrove Athletic	v	Daventry Town (30/9)	2-0	89
8	Lincoln United	v	Bury Town	1-3	175
9	Chasetown	v	Spalding United	5-1	139
10	Dereham Town	v	Halesowen Town	1-2	
11	Biggleswade	v	Bedford Town	2-2	
	Bedford Town	v	Biggleswade (1/10)	1-0aet	
12	Carlton Town	v	St Neots Town	3-1	92
13	Kempston Rovers	v	Wisbech Town	0-1	102
14	Stamford	v	Loughborough Dynamo	5-1	
15	Heybridge Swifts	v	Hertford Town	4-1	
16	Maldon & Tiptree	v	Felixstowe & Walton United	5-0	120
17	Ramsgate	v	Haywards Heath Town	2-2	
	Haywards Heath Town	v	Ramsgate (1/10)	1-0	102
18	Bracknell Town	v	Coggeshall Town	2-1	
19	Chichester City	v	Three Bridges	2-1	
20	Hullbridge Sports	v	Barton Rovers	2-4	
21	Harlow Town	v	Hanwell Town	1-1	143
	Hanwell Town	v	Harlow Town (1/10)	4-1	64
22	Welwyn Garden City	v	Canvey Island	1-4	186
23	Faversham Town	v	Chertsey Town	1-3	
24	Chalfont St Peter	v	Whitstable Town	0-1	
25	Bristol Manor Farm	v	Moneyfields	7-1	
26	Thame United	v	Kidlington	1-1	
	Kidlington	v	Thame United (2/10)	1-2	65
27	Basingstoke Town	v	North Leigh	4-3	
28	Mangotsfield United	v	Slimbridge	1-2	

PRELIMINARY ROUND
SATURDAY 12 OCTOBER 2019 - WINNERS RECEIVE £2,250 LOSERS RECEIVE £750

#	Home		Away	Score	Att
1	Tadcaster Albion	v	Brighouse Town (15/10)	1-2aet	
	(tie awarded to Tadcaster Albion – Brighouse Town removed)				
2	Pontefract Collieries	v	Glossop North End	2-0	
3	Clitheroe	v	Prescot Cables	0-3	395
4	Pickering Town	v	Stocksbridge Park Steels (13/10)	1-1	130
	Stocksbridge Park Steels	v	Pickering Town (15/10)	1-3aet	
5	Trafford	v	Runcorn Linnets	0-3	352
6	Ramsbottom United	v	Colne	1-3	
7	Worksop Town	v	Kendal Town	2-1	410
8	Cleethorpes Town	v	Mossley	2-4	
	(tie awarded to Cleethorpes Town – Mossley removed from Competition)				
9	Dunston	v	Ossett United	3-2	314
10	Droylsden	v	Workington	1-1	
	Workington	v	Droylsden (15/10)	3-1	401
11	Soham Town Rangers	v	Bury Town	3-0	217
12	Sutton Coldfield Town	v	Yaxley	2-1	240
13	Newcastle Town	v	Leek Town	2-5	334
14	Evesham United	v	Halesowen Town	1-1	382
	Halesowen Town	v	Evesham United (15/10)	3-0	389
15	Chasetown	v	Coleshill Town	3-0	232
16	Belper Town	v	Stamford	0-3	
17	Histon	v	Corby Town	0-0	213
	Corby Town	v	Histon (16/10)	4-1	290
18	Cambridge City	v	Market Drayton Town (13/10)	2-1	
19	Kidsgrove Athletic	v	Wisbech Town	1-0	155
20	Carlton Town	v	Bedford Town	3-2	119
21	Bedworth United	v	Ilkeston Town	3-1	
22	Staines Town	v	Heybridge Swifts	0-2	
23	Aylesbury United	v	Sevenoaks Town	2-2	134
	Sevenoaks Town	v	Aylesbury United (15/10)	2-4	
24	Grays Athletic	v	Bedfont Sports Club (6/11)	0-1	
	(12/10 – tie ordered to be replayed)				
25	Whitehawk	v	Romford	2-1	267
26	Whitstable Town	v	Ware	2-2	282
	Ware	v	Whitstable Town (15/10)	1-0aet	182
27	Hanwell Town	v	AFC Dunstable	2-4	134
28	Brentwood Town	v	Basildon United	2-3	159
29	Sittingbourne	v	South Park	1-0	157
30	Chipstead	v	FC Romania	2-1	74
31	VCD Athletic	v	AFC Sudbury	1-4	80
32	Great Wakering Rovers	v	Westfield	3-5	71
33	Uxbridge	v	Northwood	4-1	
34	East Grinstead Town	v	Aveley (15/10)	0-5	73
35	Berkhamsted	v	Herne Bay	5-0	179
36	Whyteleafe	v	Tooting & Mitcham United	1-3	174
37	Burgess Hill Town	v	Phoenix Sports	0-2	325
38	Barton Rovers	v	Chichester City	4-2	95
39	Ashford United	v	Witham Town	2-2	
	Witham Town	v	Ashford United (15/10)	0-2aet	
40	Barking	v	Guernsey (1.30)+	2-1	118
41	Hythe Town	v	Hastings United	1-2	366
42	Maldon & Tiptree	v	Cray Valley (PM)	5-2	156
43	Tilbury	v	Waltham Abbey	6-2	80
44	Ashford Town (Middx)	v	Canvey Island	1-1	
	Canvey Island	v	Ashford Town (Middx) (15/10)	5-0	156
45	Haywards Heath Town	v	Bracknell Town	2-1	96
46	Marlow	v	Chertsey Town	1-0	202
47	Highworth Town	v	Cinderford Town	1-1	140
	Cinderford Town	v	Highworth Town (15/10)	2-1	
48	Barnstable Town	v	Thatcham Town	1-3	113
49	Paulton Rovers	v	Willand Rovers	0-3	103
	(tie awarded to Paulton Rovers – Willand Rovers removed from Competition)				
50	Slimbridge	v	AFC Totton	0-1	87
51	Melksham Town	v	Wantage Town (1.00)	2-0	205
52	Frome Town	v	Bideford	2-1	252
53	Didcot Town	v	Larkhall Athletic	0-2	252
54	Cirencester Town	v	Basingstoke Town	2-3	137
55	Winchester City	v	Thame United (15/10)	3-3	98
	Thame United	v	Winchester City (22/10)	5-3	102
56	Sholing	v	Bristol Manor Farm	2-1	112

FAT - 1Q - Kings Langleys Jorrell Johnson shields the ball from Harry Harding of Phoenix Sports.
Photo Alan Coomes.

FAT - 2Q - Peterborough Sports 2-0 Whitby Town. Photo Bill Wheatcroft.

FIRST QUALIFYING ROUND
SATURDAY 27 OCTOBER 2019 - WINNERS RECEIVE £2,450 LOSERS RECEIVE £800

#	Home		Away	Score	Att
1	Buxton	v	Hyde United	3-2	360
2	Prescot Cables	v	Pickering Town (29/10)	0-0	
	Pickering Town	v	Prescot Cables (5/11)	0-3	
3	Whitby Town	v	Worksop Town (29/10)	4-1	
4	Lancaster City	v	Witton Albion	1-0	288
5	Nantwich Town	v	Bamber Bridge (29/10)	2-1	243
6	Atherton Collieries	v	Scarborough Athletic (29/10)	3-2	
7	Morpeth Town	v	Cleethorpes Town	6-1	502
8	Runcorn Linnets	v	Pontefract Collieries (29/10)	5-3	
9	Tadcaster Albion	v	Workington (5/11)	0-1	225
10	Warrington Town	v	Ashton United	0-1	327
11	Dunston	v	Gainsborough Trinity (29/10)	0-4	216
12	Radcliffe	v	FC United of Manchester (29/10)	0-2	523
13	Kidsgrove Athletic	v	Colne (28/10)	0-1	
14	Stalybridge Celtic	v	South Shields (29/10)	0-2	203
15	Redditch United	v	Corby Town	4-2	200
16	AFC Rushden & Diamonds	v	Banbury United	0-0	315
	Banbury United	v	AFC Rushden & Diamonds (29/10)	1-2	
17	Leek Town	v	Chasetown (29/10)	2-0	268
18	Halesowen Town	v	Stamford (29/10)	2-2	306
	Stamford	v	Halesowen Town (5/11)	0-3	
19	Stourbridge	v	Nuneaton Borough (29/10)	2-1	423
20	Peterborough Sports	v	Alvechurch (29/10)	1-0	170
21	Biggleswade Town	v	Bedworth United	2-1	
22	Cambridge City	v	Needham Market	0-3	163
23	Carlton Town	v	Matlock Town (30/10)	1-2	
24	Lowestoft Town	v	Coalville Town	2-4	264
25	Basford United	v	Mickleover Sports	3-0	352
26	St Ives Town	v	Soham Town Rangers	0-0	231
	Soham Town Rangers	v	St Ives Town (29/10)	3-0	202
27	Grantham Town	v	Rushall Olympic	5-3	
28	Tamworth	v	Leiston	4-0	385
29	Sutton Coldfield Town	v	Stafford Rangers	2-1	196
30	Stratford Town	v	Hednesford Town (29/10)	1-2	210
31	Bromsgrove Sporting	v	Barwell (29/10)	2-7	
32	Folkestone Invicta	v	Lewes	2-0	
33	AFC Sudbury	v	Harrow Borough	2-0	
34	Haywards Heath Town	v	Aylesbury United	3-1	109
35	Carshalton Athletic	v	Merstham	3-1	286
36	Uxbridge	v	Bognor Regis Town	1-3	186
37	Westfield	v	Beaconsfield Town	1-0	67
38	Hitchin Town	v	Bedfont Sports (9/11)	1-1	
	Bedfont Sports	v	Hitchin Town (12/11)	1-1aet	71
	(Bedfont Sports won 5-4 on kicks from the penalty mark)				
39	Ashford United	v	Barton Rovers	1-2	201
40	Hornchurch	v	Berkhamsted	3-1	133
41	Haringey Borough	v	Horsham	3-0	
42	Maldon & Tiptree	v	Cray Wanderers	3-0	145
43	Bishop's Stortford	v	Enfield Town	1-1	317
	Enfield Town	v	Bishop's Stortford (29/10)	4-2aet	204
44	Heybridge Swifts	v	Potters Bar Town	1-2	
45	Brightlingsea Regent	v	Royston Town	1-2	
46	Metropolitan Police	v	Tilbury	4-3	104
47	Leatherhead	v	Ware	3-0	225
48	Aveley	v	Bowers & Pitsea	3-0	
49	Sittingbourne	v	Tooting & Mitcham United	0-1	180
50	Chipstead	v	Canvey Island	3-3	
	Canvey Island	v	Chipstead (29/10)	2-1	151
51	Whitehawk	v	Hendon	4-1	207
52	Barking	v	Margate	0-0	110
	Margate	v	Barking (29/10)	2-0	159
53	Wingate & Finchley	v	Hayes & Yeading United	1-1	126
	Hayes & Yeading United	v	Wingate & Finchley (29/10)	2-1	109
54	Kingstonian	v	Corinthian Casuals	4-2	417
55	AFC Dunstable	v	Hastings United	0-4	
56	Phoenix Sports	v	Kings Langley	3-5	
57	Cheshunt	v	East Thurrock United	1-2	
58	Basildon United	v	Chesham United	5-3	96
59	Worthing	v	Walton Casuals	2-1	
60	Yate Town	v	Tiverton Town (29/10)	3-3	153
	Tiverton Town	v	Yate Town (6/11)	3-3aet	
	(Yate Town won 4-1 on kicks from the penalty mark)				
61	Melksham Town	v	Basingstoke Town	1-0	206
62	Truro City	v	Blackfield & Langley (5/11)	1-1	
	Blackfield & Langley	v	Truro City (9/11)	3-1	57
63	Poole Town	v	Hartley Wintney (29/10)	0-1	261
64	Thame United	v	Frome Town	1-2	74
65	Marlow	v	Sholing	0-0	110
	Sholing	v	Marlow (29/10)	2-0	135
66	Salisbury	v	Dorchester Town	3-3	342
	Dorchester Town	v	Salisbury (29/10)	0-3	336
67	Paulton Rovers	v	Larkhall Athletic (29/10)	1-1	96
	Larkhall Athletic	v	Paulton Rovers (6/11)	1-3	
68	Wimborne Town	v	Taunton Town	2-2	
	Taunton Town	v	Wimborne Town (29/10)	4-1	
69	Swindon Supermarine	v	Thatcham Town (29/10)	1-4	
70	Gosport Borough	v	Farnborough	3-1	243
71	AFC Totton	v	Weston Super Mare	3-2aet	
72	Cinderford Town	v	Merthyr Town (29/10)	2-2	175
	Merthyr Town	v	Cinderford Town (5/11)	4-5aet	

FAT - 2Q - Peterborough Sports score direct from a free-kick against Whitby Town. Photo Bill Wheatcroft.

FAT - 3Q - Gloucester City 0-2 Bradford (Park Avenue). Photo Peter Barnes.

Bradford Park Avenue take the lead against Gloucester City in the FA Trophy

FAT - 3Q - Gloucester City 0-2 Bradford (Park Avenue). Photo Peter Barnes.

SECOND QUALIFYING ROUND
SATURDAY 9 NOVEMBER 2019 - WINNERS RECEIVE £3,000 LOSERS RECEIVE £1,000

#	Home		Away	Score	Att
1	Halesowen Town	v	Grantham Town	2-1	403
2	Matlock Town	v	Ashton United	1-0	
3	Atherton Collieries	v	Morpeth Town	2-1	
4	Sutton Coldfield Town	v	Hednesford Town	1-5	
5	Peterborough Sports	v	Whitby Town	2-0	
6	South Shields	v	AFC Rushden & Diamonds	4-0	934
7	Barwell	v	Redditch United (12/11)	3-3	129
	Redditch United	v	Barwell (19/11)	3-2	
8	Colne	v	Buxton	3-1	191
9	Runcorn Linnets	v	Prescot Cables	1-1	408
	Prescot Cables	v	Runcorn Linnets (12/11)	1-2	
10	FC United of Manchester	v	Basford United	3-1	
11	Nantwich Town	v	Coalville Town (12/11)	0-1	208
12	Leek Town	v	Workington	1-3	321
13	Tamworth	v	Gainsborough Trinity	3-5	515
14	Stourbridge	v	Lancaster City (12/11)	2-2	315
	Lancaster City	v	Stourbridge (23/11)	1-2	
15	Margate	v	Tooting & Mitcham United	0-4	312
16	Haringey Borough	v	Canvey Island	2-1	
17	Yate Town	v	AFC Totton	6-3	230
18	Royston Town	v	Haywards Heath Town	7-0	225
19	Bognor Regis Town	v	East Thurrock United	3-1	
20	Westfield	v	Hartley Wintney	1-1	122
	Hartley Wintney	v	Westfield (12/11)	2-1	
21	Basildon United	v	Hornchurch	1-6	
22	Taunton Town	v	Aveley	3-3	
	Aveley	v	Taunton Town (11/10)	2-1	
23	Worthing	v	AFC Sudbury	1-4	521
24	Hastings United	v	Whitehawk	2-2	470
	Whitehawk	v	Hastings United (12/11)	1-2	157
25	Carshalton Athletic	v	Frome Town (12/11)	5-3	
26	Sholing	v	Barton Rovers (12/11)	2-1	116
27	Blackfield & Langley	v	Kingstonian (13/11)	0-3	85
28	Maldon & Tiptree	v	Folkestone Invicta (13/11)	4-3	196
29	Salisbury	v	Kings Langley	2-1	445
30	Hayes & Yeading United	v	Soham Town Rangers (13/11)	4-2	144
31	Bedfont Sports	v	Paulton Rovers (19/11)	0-5	
32	Enfield Town	v	Thatcham Town	5-0	248
33	Gosport Borough	v	Melksham Town	4-2	235
34	Cinderford Town	v	Potters Bar Town	1-0	103
35	Needham Market	v	Leatherhead	1-2	203
36	Metropolitan Police	v	Biggleswade Town	2-2	123
	Biggleswade Town	v	Metropolitan Police (19/11)	1-0	92

THIRD QUALIFYING ROUND
SATURDAY 23 NOVEMBER 2019 - WINNERS RECEIVE £3,750 LOSERS RECEIVE £1,250

#	Home		Away	Score	Att
1	Curzon Ashton	v	Kidderminster Harriers	3-0	266
2	York City	v	Altrincham	0-1	
3	Workington	v	Farsley Celtic	0-1	
4	Hednesford Town	v	Coalville Town	2-1	354
5	Runcorn Linnets	v	FC United of Manchester	0-3	962
6	Darlington	v	Gainsborough Trinity	2-1	770
7	Gloucester City	v	Bradford (Park Avenue) (24/11)	0-2	251
8	Blyth Spartans	v	Alfreton Town	1-1	
	Alfreton Town	v	Blyth Spartans (3/12)	1-3	
9	Brackley Town	v	Chester	0-1	334
10	Stourbridge	v	South Shields (26/11)	1-1	
	South Shields	v	Stourbridge (3/12)	4-0	612
11	Guiseley	v	AFC Telford United	0-4	345
12	Matlock Town	v	Redditch United	2-0	
13	Colne	v	Southport	2-3	312
14	King's Lynn Town	v	Hereford	0-0	846
	Hereford	v	King's Lynn Town (26/11)	0-3	715
15	Atherton Collieries	v	Boston United	1-0	
16	Peterborough Sports	v	Kettering Town	0-3	346
17	Halesowen Town	v	Gateshead	1-0	546
18	Leamington	v	Spennymoor Town	2-1	
19	Dulwich Hamlet	v	Chippenham Town	2-2	
	Chippenham Town	v	Dulwich Hamlet (26/11)	1-2	245
20	Bath City	v	Gosport Borough	0-0	528
	Gosport Borough	v	Bath City (27/11)	2-3aet	306
21	Sholing	v	Paulton Rovers (3/12)	0-0	105
	Paulton Rovers	v	Sholing (14/12)	1-2	136
22	Tonbridge Angels	v	Bognor Regis Town	2-1	
23	Weymouth	v	Hastings United	1-0	753
24	Chelmsford City	v	Hungerford Town	2-1	
25	Havant & Waterlooville	v	Cinderford Town	3-1	385
26	Carshalton Athletic	v	Tooting & Mitcham United	2-1	
27	Enfield Town	v	Maldon & Tiptree	4-3	278
28	Braintree Town	v	Yate Town	1-2	202
29	Biggleswade Town	v	Aveley	1-4	
30	Kingstonian	v	AFC Sudbury	2-1	294
31	Eastbourne Borough	v	Hartley Wintney	3-1	278
32	Leatherhead	v	Dorking Wanderers	0-3	734
33	Concord Rangers	v	Slough Town	0-0	201
	Slough Town	v	Concord Rangers (26/11)	2-3	295
34	Maidstone United	v	Dartford	2-2	1255
	Dartford	v	Maidstone United (26/11)	0-1	701
35	Haringey Borough	v	Hemel Hempstead Town	1-4	
36	Wealdstone	v	Royston Town	2-3	
37	Oxford City	v	Hornchurch	1-1	228
	Hornchurch	v	Oxford City	4-4aet	
	(Hornchurch won 4-1 on kicks from the penalty mark)				
38	Billericay Town	v	Hampton & Richmond Borough (26/11)	1-2	
39	Welling United	v	St Albans City	3-1	
40	Salisbury	v	Hayes & Yeading United	4-3	454

FAT - 2P - Notts County 2-1 Dagenham & Redbridge. Photo Peter Barnes.

FAT - 4P - Notts County 5-0 Aveley. Photo Peter Barnes.

FIRST ROUND PROPER
SATURDAY 14 DECEMBER 2019 - WINNERS RECEIVE £4,500 LOSERS RECEIVE £1,500

1	Solihull Moors	v	Darlington	2-2	500
	Darlington	v	Solihull Moors (8/1)	1-0	
2	South Shields	v	Southport	2-2	776
	Southport	v	South Shields (17/12)	3-1	372
3	Bradford (Park Avenue)	v	Halesowen Town	2-2	285
	Halesowen Town	v	Bradford (Park Avenue) (17/12)	2-0	
4	Harrogate Town	v	Hartlepool United+	3-2	803
5	Stockport County	v	Blyth Spartans	4-2	1436
6	Chesterfield	v	Notts County (1.00)+	0-1	931
7	Hednesford Town	v	Chester	0-0	
	Chester	v	Hednesford Town (17/12)	2-1	
8	FC Halifax Town	v	Wrexham+	4-0	752
9	AFC Telford United	v	Leamington (17/12)	0-5	
10	Farsley Celtic	v	Altrincham	2-2	253
	Altrincham	v	Farsley Celtic (17/12)	1-2aet	536
11	Matlock Town	v	Chorley	2-2	
	Chorley	v	Matlock Town (17/12)	2-2aet	229
	(Matlock Town won 4-3 on kicks from the penalty mark)				
12	FC United of Manchester	v	Kettering Town	2-1	
13	AFC Fylde	v	Curzon Ashton+	1-0	
14	Atherton Collieries	v	Barrow	2-2	
	Barrow	v	Atherton Collieries (7/1)	2-0	861
15	Yeovil Town	v	Welling United	3-1	1554
16	Hornchurch	v	Dulwich Hamlet	1-0	454
17	King's Lynn Town	v	Dover Athletic+	2-2aet	776
	(King's Lynn Town won 4-2 on kicks from the penalty mark)				
18	Carshalton Athletic	v	Aveley	3-3	
	Aveley	v	Carshalton Athletic (16/12)	2-0	
19	Eastleigh	v	Yate Town	6-1	353
20	Tonbridge Angels	v	Hampton & Richmond Borough	2-2	
	Hampton & Richmond Borough	v	Tonbridge Angels (17/12)	2-0	238
21	Barnet	v	Weymouth	2-1	624
22	Kingstonian	v	Woking (15/12)	3-1	655
23	Chelmsford City	v	Havant & Waterlooville	2-1	
24	Enfield Town	v	Ebbsfleet United	0-2	417
25	Eastbourne Borough	v	Salisbury	2-2	
	Salisbury	v	Eastbourne Borough (7/1)	1-0	354
26	Maidenhead United	v	Hemel Hempstead Town	4-2	
27	Sutton United	v	Dagenham & Redbridge	1-1	429
	Dagenham & Redbridge	v	Sutton United (17/12)	3-2aet	417
28	Maidstone United	v	Concord Rangers	2-3	881
29	Torquay United	v	Aldershot Town	5-1	1068
30	Bath City	v	Sholing (17/12)	2-0	
31	Dorking Wanderers	v	Bromley	3-0	759
32	Royston Town	v	Boreham Wood	2-0	428

SECOND ROUND PROPER
SATURDAY 11 JANUARY 2020 - WINNERS RECEIVE £5,250 LOSERS RECEIVE £1,750

1	Dorking Wanderers	v	Stockport County	1-1	
	Stockport County	v	Dorking Wanderers (14/1)	0-4	1121
2	Kingstonian	v	Leamington	1-1	529
	Leamington	v	Kingstonian (14/1)	1-0	308
3	AFC Fylde	v	Southport	4-1	
4	Royston Town	v	Chester	3-0	818
5	Darlington	v	Harrogate Town	0-2	
6	Yeovil Town	v	Hampton & Richmond Borough	4-0	1689
7	Ebbsfleet United	v	King's Lynn Town	1-0	
8	Halesowen Town	v	Maidenhead United	2-2	892
	Maidenhead United	v	Halesowen Town (21/1)	1-3	
9	Notts County	v	Dagenham & Redbridge	2-1	
10	Chelmsford City	v	Salisbury	4-0	
11	Torquay United	v	FC Halifax Town	1-2	
12	Eastleigh	v	Matlock Town	2-1	718
13	Concord Rangers	v	Bath City	1-1	
	Bath City	v	Concord Rangers (28/1)	1-2	437
14	Farsley Celtic	v	Barnet	1-1	
	Barnet	v	Farsley Celtic (28/1)	2-0	333
15	Hornchurch	v	Aveley	1-2	589
16	Barrow	v	FC United of Manchester	7-0	1892

THIRD ROUND PROPER
SATURDAY 8 FEBRUARY 2020 - WINNERS RECEIVE £6,000 LOSERS RECEIVE £2,000

1	Ebbsfleet United	v	Royston Town	0-2aet	900
2	Concord Rangers	v	Leamington	2-2aet	417
	(Concord Rangers won 4-3 on kicks from the penalty mark)				
3	Harrogate Town	v	Eastleigh	2-0	947
4	FC Halifax Town	v	Halesowen Town	0-1	1483
5	Barnet	v	Barrow	3-0	763
6	Dorking Wanderers	v	AFC Fylde	2-4	1529
7	Aveley	v	Chelmsford City	3-1	811
8	Yeovil Town	v	Notts County	1-2	1946

FOURTH ROUND PROPER
SATURDAY 29 FEBRUARY 2020 - WINNERS RECEIVE £7,500 LOSERS RECEIVE £2,500

1	Barnet	v	Halesowen Town	1-2aet	1483
2	Notts County	v	Aveley (12.30)	5-0	4893
3	Concord Rangers	v	Royston Town (3/3)	2-1aet	852
4	AFC Fylde	v	Harrogate Town	2-3aet	

SEMI FINALS
WINNERS RECEIVE £15,000 LOSERS RECEIVE £5,000

Halesowen Town	v	Harrogate Town
Harrogate Town	v	Halesowen Town
Concord Rangers	v	Notts County
Notts County	v	Concord Rangers

FAT - 1Q - Kings Langleys Kane Farrell clears from Jack Hopkins of Phoenix Sports. Photo Alan Coomes.

FAT - 2Q - Peterborough Sports 2-0 Whitby Town. Photo Bill Wheatcroft.

FAT - 3Q - Gloucester City 0-2 Bradford (Park Avenue). Photo Peter Barnes.

FAT - 4P - Notts County 5-0 Aveley. Photo Peter Barnes.

PAST FINALS

1970   **MACCLESFIELD TOWN 2 (Lyons, B Fidler)**   **TELFORD UNITED 0**   **Att: 28,000**
Northern Premier League   *Southern League*
Macclesfield: Cooke, Sievwright, Bennett, Beaumont, Collins, Roberts, Lyons, B Fidler,Young, Corfield, D Fidler.
Telford: Irvine, Harris, Croft, Flowers, Coton, Ray,Fudge, Hart, Bentley, Murray, Jagger.   Ref: K Walker

1971   **TELFORD UTD 3 (Owen, Bentley, Fudge)**   **HILLINGDON BORO. 2 (Reeve, Bishop)**   **Att: 29,500**
Southern League   *Southern League*
Telford: Irvine, Harris, Croft, Ray, Coton, Carr, Fudge, Owen, Bentley, Jagger ,Murray.
Hillingdon B.: Lowe, Batt, Langley, Higginson, Newcombe, Moore, Fairchild,Bishop, Reeve, Carter, Knox.   Ref: D Smith

1972   **STAFFORD RANGERS 3 (Williams 2, Cullerton)**   **BARNET 0**   **Att: 24,000**
Northern Premier League   *Southern League*
Stafford R.: Aleksic, Chadwick, Clayton, Sargeant, Aston, Machin, Cullerton, Chapman,Williams, Bayley, Jones.
Barnet: McClelland, Lye, Jenkins, Ward, Embrey, King, Powell, Ferry, Flatt, Easton, Plume .   Ref: P Partridge

1973   **SCARBOROUGH 2 (Leask, Thompson)**   **WIGAN ATHLETIC 1 (Rogers) aet**   **Att:23,000**
Northern Premier League   *Northern Premier League*
Scarborough: Garrow, Appleton, Shoulder, Dunn, Siddle, Fagan, Donoghue, Franks,Leask (Barmby), Thompson, Hewitt.
Wigan: Reeves, Morris, Sutherland, Taylor,Jackson, Gillibrand, Clements, Oats (McCunnell), Rogers, King, Worswick.   Ref: H Hackney

1974   **MORECAMBE 2 (Richmond, Sutton)**   **DARTFORD 1 (Cunningham)**   **Att: 19,000**
Northern Premier League   *Southern League*
Morecambe: Coates, Pearson, Bennett, Sutton, Street, Baldwin, Done, Webber,Roberts (Galley), Kershaw, Richmond.
Dartford: Morton, Read, Payne, Carr, Burns,Binks, Light, Glozier, Robinson (Hearne), Cunningham, Halleday.   Ref: B Homewood

1975(1) **MATLOCK TOWN 4 (Oxley, Dawson, T Fenoughy, N Fenoughy)**   **SCARBOROUGH 0**   **Att: 21,000**
Northern Premier League   *Northern Premier League*
Matlock: Fell, McKay, Smith, Stuart, Dawson, Swan, Oxley, N Fenoughy, Scott, T Fenoughty, M Fenoughty.
Scarborough: Williams, Hewitt, Rettitt, Dunn, Marshall, Todd, Houghton, Woodall, Davidson, Barnby, Aveyard.   Ref: K Styles

1976   **SCARBOROUGH 3 (Woodall, Abbey, Marshall(p))**   **STAFFORD R. 2 (Jones 2) aet**   **Att: 21,000**
Northern Premier League   *Northern Premier League*
Scarborough: Barnard, Jackson, Marshall, H Dunn, Ayre (Donoghue), HA Dunn, Dale,Barmby, Woodall, Abbey, Hilley.
Stafford: Arnold, Ritchie, Richards, Sargeant,Seddon, Morris, Chapman, Lowe, Jones, Hutchinson, Chadwick.   Ref: R Challis

1977   **SCARBOROUGH 2 (Dunn(p), Abbey)**   **DAGENHAM 1 (Harris)**   **Att: 21,500**
Northern Premier League   *Isthmian League*
Scarborough: Chapman, Smith, Marshall (Barmby), Dunn, Ayre, Deere, Aveyard,Donoghue, Woodall, Abbey, Dunn.
Dagenham: Hutley, Wellman, P Currie, Dunwell,Moore, W Currie, Harkins, Saul, Fox, Harris, Holder.   Ref: G Courtney

1978   **ALTRINCHAM 3 (King, Johnson, Rogers)**   **LEATHERHEAD 1 (Cook)**   **Att: 20,000**
Northern Premier League   *Isthmian League*
Altrincham: Eales, Allan, Crossley, Bailey, Owens, King, Morris, Heathcote,Johnson, Rogers, Davidson (Flaherty).
Leatherhead: Swannell, Cooper, Eaton, Davies,Reid, Malley, Cook, Salkeld, Baker, Boyle (Bailey).   Ref: A Grey

1979   **STAFFORD RANGERS 2 (A Wood 2)**   **KETTERING TOWN 0**   **Att: 32,000**
Northern Premier League   *Southern League*
Stafford: Arnold, F Wood, Willis, Sargeant, Seddon, Ritchie, Secker, Chapman, A Wood, Cullerton, Chadwick (Jones).
Kettering: Lane, Ashby, Lee, Eastell, Dixey,Suddards, Flannagan, Kellock, Phipps, Clayton, Evans (Hughes).   Ref: D Richardson

1980(2) **DAGENHAM 2 (Duck, Maycock)**   **MOSSLEY 1 (Smith)**   **Att: 26,000**
Isthmian League   *Northern Premier League*
Dagenham: Huttley, Wellman, Scales, Dunwell, Moore, Durrell, Maycock, Horan,Duck, Kidd, Jones (Holder).
Mossley: Fitton, Brown, Vaughan, Gorman, Salter, Polliot, Smith, Moore, Skeete, O'Connor, Keelan (Wilson).   Ref: K Baker

1981(3) **BISHOP'S STORTFORD 1 (Sullivan)**   **SUTTON UNITED 0**   **Att: 22,578**
Isthmian League   *Isthmian League*
Bishop's Stortford: Moore, Blackman, Brame, Smith (Worrell), Bradford, Abery, Sullivan,Knapman, Radford, Simmonds, Mitchell.
Sutton Utd.: Collyer, Rogers, Green, J Rains,T Rains, Stephens (Sunnucks), Waldon, Pritchard, Cornwell, Parsons, Dennis.   Ref: J Worrall

1982   **ENFIELD 1 (Taylor)**   **ALTRINCHAM 0**   **Att: 18,678**
Alliance Premier League   *Alliance Premier League*
Enfield: Jacobs, Barrett, Tone, Jennings, Waite, Ironton, Ashford, Taylor,Holmes, Oliver (Flint), King.   Ref: B Stevens
Altrincham: Connaughton, Crossley, Davison, Bailey, Cuddy, King (Whitbread), Allan, Heathcote, Johnson, Rogers, Howard.

Notes:
1   The only occasion three members of the same family played in the same FA Trophy Final team.
2   The first of the Amateurs from the Isthmian League to win the FA Trophy.
3   Goalkeeper Terry Moore had also won an Amateur Cup Winners Medal with Bishop's Stortford in 1974.
       All games played at Wembley (old & new) unless stated.

1983 **TELFORD UTD** 2 (Mather 2)   **NORTHWICH VICTORIA** 1 (Bennett)   Att: 22,071
Alliance Premier League   *Alliance Premier League*
Telford: Charlton, Lewis, Turner, Mayman (Joseph), Walker, Easton, Barnett,Williams, Mather, Hogan, Alcock.
Northwich: Ryan, Fretwell, Murphy, Jones, Forshaw, Ward, Anderson, Abel (Bennett), Reid, Chesters, Wilson.   Ref: B Hill

1984 **NORTHWICH VICTORIA** 1 (Chester)   **BANGOR CITY** 1 (Whelan)   Att: 14,200
Replay **NORTHWICH VICTORIA** 2 (Chesters(p), Anderson) BANGOR CITY 1 (Lunn)   Att: 5,805 (at Stoke)
Alliance Premier League   *Alliance Premier League*
Northwich: Ryan, Fretwell, Dean, Jones, Forshaw (Power 65), Bennett, Anderson,Abel, Reid, Chesters, Wilson.   Ref: J Martin
Bangor: Letheren, Cavanagh, Gray, Whelan, Banks,Lunn, Urqhart, Morris, Carter, Howat, Sutcliffe (Westwood 105) . Same in replay.

1985 **WEALDSTONE** 2 (Graham, Holmes)   **BOSTON UNITED** 1 (Cook)   Att: 20,775
Alliance Premier League   *Alliance Premier League*
Wealdstone: Iles, Perkins, Bowgett, Byatt, Davies, Greenaway, Holmes, Wainwright,Donnellan, Graham (N Cordice 89), A Cordice.
Boston: Blackwell, Casey, Ladd,Creane, O'Brien, Thommson, Laverick (Mallender 78), Simpsom, Gilbert, Lee, Cook.   Ref: J Bray

1986 **ALTRINCHAM** 1 (Farrelly)   **RUNCORN** 0   Att: 15,700
Gola League   *Gola League*
Altrincham: Wealands, Gardner, Densmore, Johnson, Farrelly, Conning, Cuddy,Davison, Reid, Ellis, Anderson. Sub: Newton.
Runcorn: McBride, Lee, Roberts,Jones, Fraser, Smith, S Crompton (A Crompton), Imrie, Carter, Mather, Carrodus.   Ref: A Ward

1987 **KIDDERMINSTER HARRIERS** 0   **BURTON ALBION** 0   Att: 23,617
Replay **KIDDERMINSTER HARRIERS** 2 (Davies 2)   **BURTON ALBION** 1 (Groves)   Att: 15,685 (at West Brom)
Conference   *Southern League*
Kidderminster: Arnold, Barton, Boxall, Brazier (sub Hazlewood in rep), Collins (sub Pearson 90 at Wembley), Woodall, McKenzie,
O'Dowd, Tuohy, Casey, Davies. sub:Jones.
Burton: New, Essex, Kamara, Vaughan, Simms, Groves, Bancroft, Land, Dorsett, Redfern, (sub Wood in replay), Gauden.
Sub: Patterson.   Ref: D Shaw

1988 **ENFIELD** 0   **TELFORD UNITED** 0   Att: 20,161
Replay **ENFIELD** 3 (Furlong 2, Howell)   **TELFORD UNITED** 2 (Biggins, Norris(p))   Att: 6,912 (at W Brom)
Conference   *Conference*
Enfield: Pape, Cottington, Howell, Keen (sub Edmonds in rep), Sparrow (sub Hayzleden at Wembley), Lewis (sub Edmonds at
Wembley), Harding, Cooper, King,Furlong, Francis.
Telford: Charlton, McGinty, Storton, Nelson, Wiggins, Mayman (sub Cunningham in rep (sub Hancock)), Sankey, Joseph, Stringer (sub
Griffiths at Wembley, Griffiths in replay), Biggins, Norris.   Ref: L Dilkes

1989 **TELFORD UNITED** 1 (Crawley)   **MACCLESFIELD TOWN** 0   Att: 18,102
Conference   *Conference*
Telford: Charlton, Lee, Brindley, Hancock, Wiggins, Mayman, Grainger, Joseph, Nelson, Lloyd, Stringer. Subs: Crawley, Griffiths.
Macclesfield: Zelem, Roberts, Tobin, Edwards, Hardman, Askey, Lake, Hanton, Imrie, Burr, Timmons. Subs: Devonshire, Kendall.

1990 **BARROW** 3 (Gordon 2, Cowperthwaite)   **LEEK TOWN** 0   Att: 19,011
Conference   *Northern Premier League*
Barrow: McDonnell, Higgins, Chilton, Skivington, Gordon, Proctor, Doherty (Burgess), Farrell (Gilmore), Cowperthwaite, Lowe, Ferris.
Leek: Simpson, Elsby (Smith), Pearce, McMullen, Clowes, Coleman (Russell),Mellor, Somerville, Sutton, Millington, Norris   Ref: T Simpson

1991 **WYCOMBE W.** 2 (Scott, West)   **KIDDERMINSTER HARRIERS** 1 (Hadley)   Att: 34,842
Conference   *Conference*
Wycombe: Granville, Crossley, Cash, Kerr, Creaser, Carroll, Ryan, Stapleton,West, Scott, Guppy (Hutchinson).   Ref: J Watson
Kidderminster: Jones, Kurila, McGrath, Weir, Barnett, Forsyth, Joseph (Wilcox), Howell (Whitehouse), Hadley, Lilwall, Humphries

1992 **COLCHESTER UTD*** 3 (Masters, Smith, McGavin)   **WITTON ALBION** 1 (Lutkevitch)   Att: 27,806
Conference   *Conference*
Colchester: Barrett, Donald, Roberts, Knsella, English, Martin, Cook, Masters,McDonough (Bennett 65), McGavin, Smith.   Ref: K P Barratt
Witton: Mason, Halliday, Coathup, McNeilis, Jim Connor, Anderson, Thomas, Rose, Alford, Grimshaw (Joe Connor), Lutkevitch (McCluskie)

1993 **WYCOMBE W*.** 4 (Cousins, Kerr, Thompson, Carroll) **RUNCORN** 1 (Shaughnessy)   Att: 32,968
Conference   *Conference*
Wycombe: Hyde, Cousins, Cooper, Kerr, Crossley, Thompson (Hayrettin 65),Carroll, Ryan, Hutchinson, Scott, Guppy. Sub: Casey.
Runcorn: Williams, Bates, Robertson, Hill, Harold (Connor 62), Anderson, Brady (Parker 72), Brown, Shaughnessy, McKenna, Brabin

1994 **WOKING** 2 (D Brown, Hay)   **RUNCORN** 1 (Shaw (pen))   Att: 15,818
Conference   *Conference*
Woking: Batty, Tucker, L Wye, Berry, Brown, Clement, Brown (Rattray 32), Fielder, Steele, Hay (Puckett 46), Walker.   Ref: Paul Durkin
Runcorn: Williams, Bates, Robertson, Shaw, Lee, Anderson, Thomas, Connor, McInerney (Hill 71), McKenna, Brabin. Sub: Parker

1995 **WOKING** 2 (Steele, Fielder)   **KIDDERMINSTER HARRIERS** 1 aet (Davies)   Att: 17,815
Conference   *Conference*
Woking: Batty, Tucker, L Wye, Fielder, Brown, Crumplin (Rattray 42), S Wye, Ellis, Steele, Hay (Newberry 112), Walker. (Sub: Read(gk)
Kidderminster: Rose, Hodson, Bancroft, Webb, Brindley (Cartwright 94), Forsyth, Deakin, Yates, Humphreys (Hughes 105), Davies,
Purdie. Sub: Dearlove (gk)   Ref: D J Gallagher

1996   MACCLESFIELD TOWN 3 (Payne, OG, Hemmings) **NORTHWICH VICTORIA 1 (Williams)**   Att: 8,672
        Conference   *Conference*
Macclesfield: Price, Edey, Gardiner, Payne, Howarth(C), Sorvel, Lyons, Wood (Hulme 83), Coates, Power, Hemmings (Cavell 88).
Northwich: Greygoose, Ward, Duffy, Burgess (Simpson 87), Abel (Steele), Walters, Williams, Butler (C), Cooke, Humphries, Vicary.
Ref: M Reed

1997   WOKING 1 (Hay 112)   **DAGENHAM & REDBRIDGE 0**   Att: 24,376
        Conference   *Isthmian League*
Woking: Batty, Brown, Howard, Foster, Taylor, S Wye, Thompson (sub Jones 115), Ellis, Steele (L Wye 108), Walker, Jackson (Hay 77).
Dagenham: Gothard, Culverhouse, Connor, Creaser, Jacques (sub Double 75), Davidson, Pratt (Naylor 81), Parratt, Broom, Rogers,
Stimson (John 65).   Ref: J Winter

1998   CHELTENHAM TOWN 1 (Eaton 74)   **SOUTHPORT 0**   Att: 26,387
        Conference   *Conference*
Cheltenham: Book, Duff, Freeman, Banks, Victory, Knight (Smith 78), Howells, Bloomer, Walker (sub Milton 78), Eaton, Watkins. Sub:
Wright.
Southport: Stewart, Horner, Futcher, Ryan, Farley, Kielty, Butler, Gamble, Formby (sub Whittaker 80), Thompson (sub Bollard 88),
Ross. Sub: Mitten.   Ref: G S Willard

1999   KINGSTONIAN 1 (Mustafa 49)   **FOREST GREEN ROVERS 0**   Att: 20,037
        Conference   *Conference*
Kingstonian: Farrelly, Mustafa, Luckett, Crossley, Stewart, Harris, Patterson, Pitcher, Rattray, Leworthy (Francis 87), Akuamoah. Subs
(not used): John, Corbett, Brown, Tranter
Forest Green Rovers: Shuttlewood, Hedges, Forbes, Bailey (Smart 76), Kilgour, Wigg (Cook 58), Honor (Winter 58), Drysdale,
McGregor, Mehew, Sykes. Subs (not used): Perrin, Coupe   Ref: A B Wilkie

2000   KINGSTONIAN 3 (Akuamoah 40, 69, Simba 75)   **KETTERING TOWN** 2 (Vowden 55, Norman 64p)   Att: 20,034
        Conference   *Conference*
Kingstonian: Farelly, Mustafa, Luckett, Crossley, Stewart (Saunders 77), Harris, Kadi (Leworthy 83), Pitcher, Green (Basford 86),
Smiba, Akuamoah. Subs (not used): Hurst, Allan
Kettering Town: Sollit, McNamara, Adams, Perkins, Vowden, Norman (Duik 76), Fisher, Brown, Shutt, Watkins (Hudson 46), Setchell
(Hopkins 81). Subs (not used): Ridgway, Wilson   Ref: S W Dunn

2001   CANVEY ISLAND 1 (Chenery)   **FOREST GREEN ROVERS 0**   Att: 10,007
        Isthmian League   *Conference*   at Villa Park
Forest Green Rovers: Perrin, Cousins, Lockwood, Foster, Clark, Burns, Daley, Drysdale (Bennett 46), Foster (Hunt 75), Meecham,
Slater. Subs (not used): Hedges, Prince, Ghent
Canvey Island: Harrison, Duffy, Chenery, Bodley, Ward, Tilson, Stimson (Tanner 83), Gregory, Vaughan (Jones 76), Parmenter. Subs
(not used): Bennett, Miller, Thompson.   Ref: A G Wiley

2002   YEOVIL TOWN 2 (Alford, Stansfield)   **STEVENAGE BOROUGH 0**   Att: 18,809
        Conference   *Conference*   at Villa Park
Yeovil Town: Weale, Lockwood, Tonkin, Skiverton, Pluck (White 51), Way, Stansfield, Johnson, Alford (Giles 86),
Crittenden (Lindegaard 83), McIndoe. Subs (not used): O'Brien, Sheffield
Stevenage Borough: Wilkerson, Hamsher, Goodliffe, Trott, Fraser, Fisher, Wormull (Stirling 71), Evers (Williams 56), Jackson, Sigere
(Campbell 74), Clarke. Subs (not used): Campbell, Greygoose   Ref: N S Barry

2003   BURSCOUGH 2 (Martindale 25, 55)   **TAMWORTH 1 (Cooper 78)**   Att: 14,265
        Northern Premier   *Southern Premier*   at Villa Park
Burscough: Taylor, Teale, Taylor, Macauley (White 77), Lawless, Bowen, Wright, Norman, Martindale (McHale 80), Byrne (Bluck 84),
Burns. Subs (not used): McGuire (g/k) Molyneux.
Tamworth: Acton, Warner, Follett, Robinson, Walsh, Cooper, Colley, Evans (Turner 64), Rickards (Hatton 88), McGorry,
Sale (Hallam 54). Subs (not used): Grocutt, Barnes (g/k).   Ref: U D Rennie

2004   HEDNESFORD TOWN 3 (Maguire 28, Hines 53, Brindley 87) **CANVEY ISLAND 2 (Boylan 46, Brindley 48 og)**   Att: 6,635
        Southern Premier   *Isthmian Premier Champions*   at Villa Park
Hednesford Town: Young, Simkin, Hines, King, Brindley, Ryder (Barrow 59), Palmer, Anthrobus, Danks (Piearce 78), Maguire,
Charie (Evans 55). Subs (not used): Evans (g/k) McGhee.
Canvey Island: Potter, Kennedy, Duffy, Chenery, Cowan, Gooden (Dobinson 89), Minton, Gregory (McDougald 80), Boylan,
Midgley (Berquez 73), Ward. Subs (not used): Theobald, Harrison (g/k).
Ref: M L Dean

2005   GRAYS ATHLETIC 1 (Martin 65) Pens: 6   **HUCKNALL TOWN 1 (Ricketts 75) Pens: 5**   Att: 8,116
        Conference South   *Conference North*   at Villa Park
Grays Athletic: Bayes, Brennan, Nutter, Stuart, Matthews, Thurgood, Oli (Powell 80), Hopper (Carthy 120), Battersby (sub West 61),
Martin, Cole. Subs (not used): Emberson, Bruce..
Hucknall Town: Smith, Asher, Barrick (Plummer 30), Hunter, Timons, Cooke, Smith (Ward 120), Palmer (Heathcote 94), Ricketts,
Bacon, Todd. Subs (not used): Winder, Lindley.   Ref: P Dowd

2006   GRAYS ATHLETIC 2 (Oli, Poole)   **WOKING 0**   Att: 13,997
        Conference   *Conference*   at Upton Park
Grays Athletic: Bayes, Sambrook, Nutter, Stuart, Hanson, Kightly (Williamson 90), Thurgood, Martin, Poole, Oli, McLean.
Subs (not used): Eyre (g/k), Hooper, Olayinka, Mawer.
Woking: Jalal, Jackson, MacDonald, Nethercott (Watson 60), Hutchinson, Murray, Smith (Cockerill 60), Evans (Blackman 85),
Ferguson, McAllister, Justin Richards. Subs (not used): Davis (g/k), El-Salahi.
                                                                            Ref: Howard Webb (Sheffield)

2007 **STEVENAGE BOROUGH** 3 (Cole, Dobson, Morrison) **KIDDERMINSTER HARRIERS** 2 (Constable 2) **Att: 53,262**
Conference   *Conference*   **(New Trophy record)**
Stevenage Borough: Julian, Fuller, Nutter, Oliver, Gaia, Miller, Cole, Morrison, Guppy (Dobson 63), Henry, Beard.
Subs not used: Potter, Slabber, Nurse, McMahon.
Kidderminster Harriers: Bevan, Kenna, Hurren, Creighton, Whitehead, Blackwood, Russell, Penn, Smikle (Reynolds 90),
Christie (White 75) , Constable.
Subs not used: Taylor, Sedgemore, McGrath.   Ref: Chris Foy (Merseyside)

2008 **EBBSFLEET UNITED** 1 (McPhee)   **TORQUAY UNITED** 0   **Att: 40,186**
Blue Square Premier   *Blue Square Premier*
Ebbsfleet United: Cronin, Hawkins, McCarthy, Smith, Opinel, McPhee, Barrett, Bostwick, Long (MacDonald 84), Moore, Akinde.
Subs not used: Eribenne, Purcell, Ricketts, Mott.
Torquay United: Rice, Mansell, Todd, Woods, Nicholson, D'Sane (Benyon 66), Hargreaves, Adams, Zebroski, Sills (Hill 88),
Phillips (Stevens 46). Subs not used: Hockley and Robertson.   Ref: Martin Atkinson (West Riding)

2009 **STEVENAGE BOROUGH** 2 (Morison, Boylan)   **YORK CITY** 0   **Att: 27,102**
Blue Square Premier   *Blue Square Premier*
Stevenage Borough: Day, Henry, Bostwick, Roberts, Wilson, Mills, Murphy, Drury, Vincenti (Anaclet 86), Boylan, Morison.
Subs not used: Bayes, Albrighton, Maamria and Willock.
York City:Ingham, Purkiss, McGurk, Parslow, Pejic, Mackin, Greaves(McWilliams 74), Rusk (Russell 80), Brodie, McBreen (Sodje 60),
Boyes. Subs not used – Mimms and Robinson.   Referee: Michael Jones.

2010 **BARROW** 2 (McEvilly 79, Walker 117)   **STEVENAGE BOROUGH** 1 (Drury 10)   **Att: 21,223**
Blue Square Premier   *Blue Square Premier*
Barrow: Stuart Tomlinson, Simon Spender, Paul Jones, Phil Bolland, Paul Edwards, Simon Wiles (sub Carlos Logan 63rd min),
Robin Hulbert, Andy Bond, Paul Rutherford (sub Mark Boyd 109th min), Jason Walker, Gregg Blundell (sub Lee McEvilly 73rd min).
Subs not used – Tim Deasy and Mike Pearson.
Stevenage Borough: Chris Day (sub Ashley Bayes 90th min), Ronnie Henry, Jon Ashton, Mark Roberts, Scott Laird,
Joel Byrom (sub Lawrie Wilson 58th min), David Bridges, Michael Bostwick, Andy Drury, Chris Beardsley (sub Charlie Griffin 64th min),
Yemi Odubade. Subs not used – Stacey Long and Peter Vincenti.
Man of the match - Paul Rutherford.   Referee Lee Probert.

2011 **DARLINGTON** 1 (Senior 120)   **MANSFIELD TOWN** 0   **Att: 24,668**
Blue Square Premier   *Blue Square Premier*
Darlington: Sam Russell, Paul Arnison, Ian Miller, Liam Hatch, Aaron Brown, Jamie Chandler, Chris Moore, Marc Bridge-Wilkinson (sub
Paul Terry 100th min), Gary Smith (sub Arman Verma 38th min), John Campbell (sub Chris Senior 75th min), Tommy Wright.
Subs not used – Danzelle St Louis-Hamilton (gk) and Phil Gray.
Mansfield Town: Alan Marriott, Gary Silk, Stephen Foster, Tom Naylor, Dan Spence, Louis Briscoe, Tyrone Thompson, Kyle Nix, Adam
Smith (sub Ashley Cain 95th min), Adam Murray (sub Danny Mitchley 108th min), Paul Connor
Subs not used – Paul Stonehouse and Neil Collett (gk)
Man of the match - Jamie Chandler.   Referee Stuart Atwell

2012 **YORK CITY** 2 (Blair 61, Oyebanjo 68)   **NEWPORT COUNTY** 0   **Att: 19,844**
Blue Square Premier   *Blue Square Premier*
York City: Michael Ingham, Jon Challinor, Chris Smith, Daniel Parslow, Ben Gibson, Matty Blair, Lanre Oyebanjo, Patrick McLaughlan
(sub Jamal Fyfield 82nd min), James Meredith, Ashley Chambers (Adriano Moke (89th min), Jason Walker (Jamie Reed 90th min).
Subs not used – Paul Musselwhite (g/k), Michael Potts.
Newport County: Glyn Thompson, David Pipe, Ismail Yakubu, Gary Warren, Andrew Hughes, Sam Foley, Lee Evans, Nat Jarvis (sub
Jake Harris 68th min), Max Porter (sub Darryl Knights 79th min), Romone Rose (sub Elliott Buchanan 68th min), Lee Minshull.
Subs not used – Matthew Swan (g/k), Paul Rodgers.
Man of the match - Lanre Oyebanjo.   Referee Anthony Taylor

2013 **WREXHAM** 1 (Thornton 82 (pen))   **GRIMSBY TOWN** 1 (Cook 71)   **Att: 35,226**
Wrexham won 4-1 on kicks from the penalty mark after extra time.
Blue Square Premier   *Blue Square Premier*
Wrexham: Chris Maxwell, Stephen Wright, Martin Riley, Jay Harris, Danny Wright, Brett Ormerod (Robert Ogleby 77 min),
Andy Morrell (Adrian Cieslewicz 61 min), Dean Keates, Johnny Hunt, Chris Westwood, Kevin Thornton (Joe Clarke 89 min).
Subs not used - Andy Coughlin (gk) Glen Little.
Grimsby Town: Sam Hatton, Aswad Thomas, Shaun Pearson, Ian Miller, Joe Colbeck, Craig Disley, Frankie Artus, Andy Cook, James
McKeown, Ross Hannah (Andi Thanoj 55 min), Marcus Marshall (Richard Brodie 87 min).
Subs not used - Jamie Devitt, Bradley Wood, Lenell John-Lewis.   Referee Jonathan Moss

2014 **CAMBRIDGE UNITED** 4 (Bird 38, Donaldson 50,59, Berry 78 (pen)) **GOSPORT BOROUGH** 0   **Att: 18,120**
Conference Premier   *Conference South*
Cambridge United: Will Norris, Greg Taylor, Jock Coulson (Tom Bonner 87 min), Ian Miller, Ryan Donaldson, Tom Champion,
Richard Tait, Liam Hughes (Nathan Arnold 73 min), Luke Berry, Ryan Bird, Josh Gillies (Andy Pugh 61 min).
Subs not used - Kevin Roberts, Mitch Austin.
Gosport Borough: Nathan Ashmore, Lee Molyneaux, Andy Forbes, Jamie Brown (Rory Williams 57 min), Brett Poate, Sam Pearce,
Josh Carmichael, Danny Smith, Tim Sills (Dan Woodward 57 min), Justin Bennett, Michael Gosney (Dan Wooden 72 min).
Subs not used - Ryan Scott, Adam Wilde.

Referee Craig Pawson

2015 NORTH FERRIBY UNITED 3 (King 76 (pen), Kendall 86, 111) **WREXHAM** 3 (Moult 11, 118, Harris 59) **Att: 14,548**
Conference North   *Conference National*
North Ferriby United: Adam Nicklin, Sam Topliss, Danny Hone, Matt Wilson, Josh Wilde (Nathan Peat 90), Liam King,
Adam Bolder (Nathan Jarman 62), Russell Fry (Ryan Kendall 80), Danny Clarke, Tom Denton, Jason St Juste.
Subs not used - Tom Nicholson and Mark Gray.
Wrexham: Andy Coughlin, Steve Tomassen, Manny Smith, Blaine Hudson, Neil Ashton, Jay Harris, Dean Keates (Robbie Evans 73),
Joe Clarke (Andy Bishop 102), Kieron Morris (Wes York 87), Louis Moult, Connor Jennings.
Subs not used - Mark Carrington and Luke Waterfall.   Referee Michael Oliver

2016 FC HALIFAX TOWN 1 (McManus 48)   **GRIMSBY TOWN** 0   **Att: 46,781** (Inaugural Non-League finals day)
Conference National   *Conference National*
FC Halifax Town: Sam Johnson, Matty Brown, Hamza Bencherif, Kevin Roberts, James Bolton, Nicky Wroe, Jake Hibbs,
Scott McManus (Kingsley James 73), Josh McDonald (Sam Walker 63), Jordan Burrow, Richard Peniket (Connor Hughes 86).
Subs not used - Jordan Porter and Shaquille McDonald.
Grimsby Town: James McKeown, Richard Tait (Danny East 81), Shaun Pearson, Aristote Nsiala, Gregor Robertson,
Andy Monkhouse (Jon-Paul Pitman 68), Craig Disley, Craig Clay (Nathan Arnold 63), Jon Nolan, Omar Bogle, Padraig Amond.
Subs not used - Josh Gowling and Josh Venney.   Referee Lee Mason

2017 YORK CITY 3 (Parkin 8, Oliver 22, Connolly 86)   **MACCLESFIELD TOWN** 2 (Browne 13, Norburn 45+1)
Conference National   *Conference National*   **Att: 38,224** (Combined Trophy/Vase att.)
York City: Kyle Letheren, Asa Hall (Aidan Connolly 69), Yan Klukowski (Adriano Moke 46), Hamza Bencherif, Danny Holmes (Shaun Rooney 76)
Amari Morgan-Smith, Simon Heslop, Sean Newton, Daniel Parslow, Jon Parkin, Vadaine Oliver.
Subs not used - Luke Simpson, Scott Fenwick.
Macclesfield Town: Scott Flinders, Andy Halls, David Fitzpatrick, Neill Byrne (John McCombe 68), George Pilkington, Rhys Browne, Chris Holroyd,
Kingsley James, Ollie Norburn (Anthony Dudley 89), Mitch Hancox (Luke Summerfield 86), Danny Whitaker.
Subs not used - Craig Ross, Danny Whitehead.   Referee Paul Tierney

2018 BRACKLEY TOWN 1, 5p (R Johnson 90+6 (og))   **BROMLEY** 1, 4p (Bugiel 19)
Conference National North   *Conference National*   **Att: 31,430** (Combined Trophy/Vase att.)
Brackley Town: Danny Lewis, Matt Lowe, Connor Franklin (Ellis Myles 77), Shane Byrne, Alex Gudger, Gareth Dean (c), Glenn Walker,
James Armson, Lee Ndlovu (Andy Brown 53), Aaron Williams, Adam Walker..
Subs not used - Luke Graham, Theo Streete, Steve Diggin.
Bromley: David Gregory, Jack Holland (c), Raymond Raymond, Louis Dennis (Brandon Hanlan 68), Adam Mekki (Ben Chorley 72), Jordan Higgs,
Tyrone Sterling, George Porter (Josh Rees 61), Roger Johnson, Frankie Sutherland, Omar Bugiel.
Subs not used - Alan Dunne, Dan Johnson.   Referee Chris Kavanagh

2019 AFC FYLDE 1 (Rowe 60 (direct free-kick))   **LEYTON ORIENT** 0
Conference National   *Conference National*   **Att: 42,962** (Combined Trophy/Vase att.)
AFC Fylde: Jay Lynch, Arlen Birch (Tom Crawford 90), Neil Byrne (c) (Tom Brewitt 12), Jordan Tunnicliffe, Zaine Francis-Angol, Danny Philliskirk,
Ryan Croasdale, Nick Haughton (Tim Odusina 74), Alex Reid, Andy Bond, Danny Rowe.
Subs not used - Russell Griffiths, James Hardy.
Leyton Orient: Dean Brill, Jamie Turley (Jordan Maguire-Drew 46), Marvin Ekpiteta, Josh Coulson, Daniel Happe (Matt Harrold 68), Joe Widdowson,
Craig Clay, James Brophy, John McAnuff (c) (Charlie Lee 78), Josh Koroma, Macauley Bonne.
Subs not used - Sam Sargeant, Sam Ling.   Referee Andrew Madley

Dagenham & Redbridge striker Mitch Brundle scores in the 75th minute @ Meadow Lane

FAT - 2P - Notts County 2-1 Dagenham & Redbridge. Photo Peter Barnes.

THE FA VASE 2019-20

FIRST QUALIFYING ROUND
SATURDAY 31 AUGUST 2019 - WINNING CLUB TO RECEIVE £550 LOSING CLUB TO RECEIVE £175

No	Home		Away	Score	Att
1	Whitley Bay	v	Barnoldswick Town	1-2	308
2	Birtley Town	v	Jarrow	2-5	
3	Harrogate Railway Athletic	v	West Allotment Celtic	0-4	
4	Willington	v	Albion Sports	0-2	
5	Garstang	v	Sunderland West End+	1-2	
6	Northallerton Town	v	Stokesley SC+	7-0	128
7	Shildon	v	Tow Law Town	3-0	
8	Chester-Le-Street Town	v	Garforth Town	1-2	
9	Knaresborough Town	v	Washington+	2-1	109
10	Whitehaven	v	Billingham Synthonia	0-9	
11	Billingham Town	v	Heaton Stannington	2-1	161
12	Penrith	v	Guisborough Town	0-1	135
13	Stockton Town	v	Ashington	4-0	405
14	Thackley	v	Carlisle City	3-2	83
15	Crook Town	v	Brandon United	2-1	
16	Whickham	v	Squires Gate (1/9)	1-2aet	
17	Nelson	v	Seaham Red Star	1-3aet	
18	AFC Blackpool	v	Redcar Athletic	2-1	
19	Padiham	v	Bedlington Terriers	5-0	120
20	Longridge Town	v	Newcastle University+	5-2	
21	Newton Aycliffe	v	Silsden	2-1	
22	Easington Colliery	v	Holker Old Boys+	4-1	
23	Eccleshill United	v	Thornaby	0-4	69
24	Yorkshire Amateur (at Farsley Celtic FC)	v	Alnwick Town+	1-0	
25	Esh Winning	v	Campion+	3-2	
26	Sunderland Ryhope CW	v	North Shields	2-0	
27	Prestwich Heys	v	1874 Northwich	1-0	
28	Swallownest	v	Vauxhall Motors	0-2	
29	Worsbrough Bridge Athletic	v	Hall Road Rangers (1/9)	5-6	116
30	Retford United	v	Daisy Hill+	3-2	
31	Skelmersdale United (at New Mills FC)	v	New Mills	5-2	
32	Handsworth Parramore	v	Shelley (1/9)	4-0	
33	Ashton Athletic	v	AFC Darwen	3-2	
34	Bacup Borough	v	Grimsby Borough	1-2	46
35	St Helens Town	v	Rossington Main (1/9)	1-2	70
36	Cammell Laird 1907	v	Charnock Richard	2-3	103
37	Parkgate	v	Chadderton	2-3	
38	Retford	v	Barton Town	1-3	103
39	Wythenshawe Town	v	Goole	5-2	
40	Nostell MW	v	AFC Liverpool+	4-1	72
41	Staveley MW	v	Cheadle Town+	2-5	124
42	Litherland Remyca	v	Glasshoughton Welfare (1/9)	3-6aet	67
43	Harworth Colliery	v	Stockport Town	1-3	
44	Cheadle Heath Nomads	v	Ashton Town	5-3	
45	Maine Road	v	Maltby Main	5-2	
46	AFC Emley	v	Burscough (1/9)	1-1aet	177
	Burscough	v	AFC Emley (4/9)	1-2	76
47	Brigg Town	v	Armthorpe Welfare	2-0	
48	Pilkington	v	Atherton LR	3-2aet	
49	Rylands	v	Athersley Recreation	6-0	97
50	Liversedge	v	Hallam	2-1	
51	West Didsbury & Chorlton	v	Egerton		
	(walkover for West Didsbury & Chorlton – Egerton not accepted into the Competition)				
52	Avro	v	Selby Town	0-2	
53	Abbey Hulton United	v	Tipton Town+	3-2	
54	Boldmere St Michaels	v	Stourport Swifts	3-2	81
55	Heather St Johns	v	Hereford Pegasus+	3-0	49
56	Bromyard Town	v	Uttoxeter Town	0-4	
57	Stafford Town	v	Tividale	1-3	78
58	Leicester Road	v	Dudley Sports	3-1	43
59	Racing Club Warwick	v	AFC Bridgnorth	4-0	
60	FC Oswestry Town	v	Bustleholme	4-0	
61	Highgate United	v	Ellistown	11-1	
62	Bewdley Town	v	Alsager Town	1-2	70
63	Malvern Town (at Evesham United FC)	v	Pershore Town (1/9)	1-1aet	
	Pershore Town	v	Malvern Town (3/9)	0-2	207
64	Heath Hayes	v	Ashby Ivanhoe	1-2aet	
65	Eccleshall	v	Hanley Town	2-3aet	
66	FC Stratford	v	Chelmsley Town	3-2	
67	Bolehall Swifts	v	Coventry Copsewood	0-5	
68	GNP Sports	v	Littleton+ (30/8)	3-2	
69	Nuneaton Griff	v	Wellington Amateurs	5-3aet	40
70	Stapenhill	v	Dudley Town	0-2	
71	St Martins	v	Shifnal Town (30/8)	0-3	
72	Wolverhampton Casuals	v	Bilston Town Community	2-1	
73	Haughmond	v	Stone Old Alleynians	3-1	51
74	Gresley	v	Winsford United	1-0	
75	Lichfield City	v	Romulus	5-2	
76	Sandbach United	v	Wem Town	13-0	
77	Studley	v	Brocton	3-2	
78	Wellington FC	v	Worcester City	0-5	117
79	Wolverhampton SC	v	Cradley Town	3-0	
80	Hinckley	v	Ellesmere Rangers+	2-1	121
81	Coton Green	v	Shawbury United	0-3	
82	Wednesfield	v	Droitwich Spa	0-2	
83	Coventry Sphinx	v	AFC Wulfrunians	2-1	76
84	County Hall	v	Newark Flowserve	1-3	
85	Radford	v	Cottesmore Amateurs S&S	1-3	
86	Holbeach United	v	Lincoln Moorlands Railway	3-2	
87	Bourne Town	v	Sleaford Town	4-2	
88	Kirby Muxloe	v	Oakham United	3-2aet	
89	FC Bolsover	v	Long Eaton United		
	(walkover for Long Eaton United – FC Bolsover removed)				
90	Harrowby United	v	Belper United	3-1	
91	Shirebrook Town	v	Arnold Town	3-2aet	
92	Quorn	v	Boston Town	6-1	
93	Horncastle Town	v	Sherwood Colliery	0-2	
94	Dunkirk	v	Oadby Town	1-0	22
95	AFC Mansfield	v	Graham Street Prims	1-0	
96	Melton Town	v	Gedling MW	2-4aet	
97	Barrow Town	v	Friar Lane & Epworth	5-3	
98	Pinxton	v	Birstall United Social	2-3	
99	Hucknall Town	v	Holbrook Sports	4-3aet	113
100	Aylestone Park	v	Loughborough University (30/8)	0-3	
101	Holwell Sports	v	Heanor Town	1-2	
102	South Normanton Athletic	v	Ollerton Town	7-0	
103	FC GNG	v	Clifton All Whites+	0-9	
104	Saffron Dynamo	v	Rainworth MW (1/9)	0-2	
105	Kimberley MW	v	Clipstone	2-1	46
106	Borrowash Victoria	v	West Bridgford	1-2	
107	Selston	v	Teversal (1/9)	3-1	
108	Newmarket Town	v	Gorleston	2-1	
109	Norwich CBS	v	March Town United	1-2	
110	Downham Town	v	Netherton United (1/9)	0-4	
111	Framlingham Town	v	Great Yarmouth Town+	1-1aet	
	(Great Yarmouth Town won 4-2 on kicks from the penalty mark)				
112	Fakenham Town	v	Norwich United	0-4	
113	Walsham Le Willows	v	Lakenheath+ (30/8)	2-1	95
114	Mildenhall Town	v	Swaffham Town	2-0	
115	Debenham LC	v	Wisbech St Mary+	2-0	
116	Diss Town	v	Huntingdon Town	1-3	121
117	Ely City	v	Peterborough Northern Star	4-6aet	
118	Park View	v	West Essex + (4/9)	1-4	
	(30/8 – match abandoned due to serious injury, 87 mins, 1-1)				
119	Wodson Park	v	Sawbridgeworth Town+	2-1	18
120	Holland	v	Baldock Town	0-2	
121	FC Broxbourne Borough	v	Barkingside	3-0	
122	Clapton (at Aveley FC)	v	Catholic United+ (30/8)	1-6	
123	New Salamis	v	Codicote+	4-0	
124	Hadleigh United	v	Stotfold	6-2	
125	Hoddesdon Town (at Ware FC)	v	Stanway Rovers	1-2	67
126	Long Melford	v	Little Oakley	1-0	
127	Cockfosters	v	Coggeshall United	1-2aet	
128	Woodford Town	v	St Margaretsbury+	1-2	
129	Ilford	v	Enfield	1-2	
130	Takeley	v	Burnham Ramblers	6-1	40
131	Halstead Town	v	Haverhill Borough	1-3	
132	FC Clacton	v	Southend Manor+	3-0	
133	Benfleet	v	Haverhill Rovers (1/9)	2-5	
134	Wivenhoe Town	v	Clapton Community	5-1	
135	White Ensign	v	Cornard United (1/9)	1-0	
136	Colney Heath	v	London Lions+	4-0	
137	Lopes Tavares London	v	Harwich & Parkeston	2-0	

FAV - 1Q - Pinxton 2 - 3 Birstall United Social. Photo Bill Wheatcroft.

FAV - 1Q - SC Thamesmeads Chris Hubbard shields the ball from Sutton Athletics George Bryan. Photo Alan Coomes.

FIRST QUALIFYING ROUND

138	London Colney	v	Brimsdown+	3-1	
139	Sporting Bengal United	v	Wormley Rovers+	0-1	
140	Hackney Wick (at Haringey Borough FC)	v	May & Baker Eastbrook (30/8) Community	6-3	
141	Potton United	v	Frenford	0-6	87
142	Hashtag United	v	Leyton Athletic	2-0	
143	Ipswich Wanderers	v	Enfield Borough	0-3	
144	Crawley Green	v	Ampthill Town	4-2	68
145	Risborough Rangers	v	Easington Sports	6-0	111
146	Holmer Green	v	Raunds Town	0-1	41
147	Irchester United	v	North Greenford United (1/9)	0-3	40
148	Long Crendon	v	Langley (1/9)	4-3	
149	Wellingborough Town	v	Wellingborough Whitworth	4-1	
150	Bedford	v	Burton Park Wanderers+	2-0	35
151	Burnham	v	Harborough Town	2-4	87
152	Eynesbury Rovers	v	Harpenden Town+	2-0	92
153	Winslow United	v	Rushden & Higham United	7-1	82
154	Chinnor	v	Broadfields United		
	(walkover for Broadfields United – Chinnor withdrawn)				
155	Rugby Borough	v	British Airways+	2-1	
156	Leighton Town	v	Bugbrooke St Michael	3-0	144
157	Leverstock Green	v	Aylesbury Vale Dynamos	1-1aet	
	Aylesbury Vale Dynamos	v	Leverstock Green (3/9)	3-1	78
158	Lutterworth Town	v	Pitshanger Dynamo	7-1	
159	Holyport	v	Unite MK (1/9)	3-2	
160	Ardley United	v	Northampton On Chenecks	1-3	38
161	Chalvey Sports	v	Wembley (1/9)	0-1	
162	Flackwell Heath	v	Arlesey Town	3-1	64
163	AFC Hayes	v	Dunstable Town	3-1	
164	Hanworth Villa	v	Marston Shelton Rovers+	5-1	
165	St Panteleimon	v	Long Buckby	3-4	58
166	Bedfont & Feltham	v	Lutterworth Athletic+	5-0	
167	Rothwell Corinthians	v	Desborough Town	2-0	83
168	Hillingdon	v	Rayners Lane+	5-1	
169	NW London	v	Harefield United	0-2	
170	Hillingdon Borough	v	Kensington & Ealing Borough	3-2	
171	Amersham Town	v	Thame Rangers	2-1	35
172	Ascot United (at Fleet Town FC)	v	Fleet Town (30/8)	3-3aet	174
	Fleet Town	v	Ascot United (3/9)	1-3	153
173	Tytherington Rocks	v	Newent Town	0-2	
174	Shrivenham	v	Milton United+ (30/8)	3-2	55
175	Cove	v	Fleet Spurs	0-1	
176	Fairford Town	v	Abingdon Town	5-1	43
177	Frimley Green	v	Lydney Town	3-1	
178	Thornbury Town	v	Cheltenham Saracens	6-2	100
179	Shortwood United	v	Tuffley Rovers	5-0	75
180	New College Swindon	v	Royal Wootton Bassett Town (30/8)	0-7	
181	Clanfield 85	v	Sandhurst Town	7-3	83
182	Wokingham & Emmbrook	v	Chipping Sodbury Town (1/9)	2-1	217
183	Abingdon United	v	Eversley & California	1-0	41
184	Binfield	v	Virginia Water (30/8)	1-0aet	129
185	Malmesbury Victoria (at Woodley United FC)	v	Woodley United+	3-0	30
186	Banstead Athletic	v	Greenwich Borough	2-2aet	
	Greenwich Borough	v	Banstead Athletic (3/9)	3-2	
187	Little Common	v	K Sports	1-2	38
188	Egham Town	v	FC Elmstead	3-2	41
189	Wick	v	Colliers Wood United	0-4aet	
190	Lydd Town	v	Raynes Park Vale	5-5aet	
	Raynes Park Vale	v	Lydd Town (3/9)	2-0aet	
191	Kent Football United	v	Snodland Town	0-1aet	
192	Saltdean United	v	Lordswood	0-2	
193	Tooting Bec	v	Walton & Hersham (1/9)	2-4	
194	Epsom & Ewell	v	Kennington+	1-4	70
195	Molesey	v	Greenways	4-3aet	
196	Littlehampton United	v	Bexhill United (1/9)	1-5	
197	AFC Varndeanians	v	Loxwood+	2-2aet	
	(Loxwood won 4-2 on kicks from the penalty mark)				
198	Farnham Town	v	Langney Wanderers	2-1	63
199	Sporting Club Thamesmead	v	Sutton Athletic	3-2	52
200	Littlehampton Town	v	Tunbridge Wells (1/9)	0-4	130
201	Southwick	v	Billingshurst	1-2	34
202	Erith & Belvedere	v	Fire United+	3-0	58
203	Rochester United	v	Mile Oak	0-3	
204	Ash United	v	Badshot Lea	1-2	
205	Shoreham	v	Crowborough Athletic	0-3	

206	Holmesdale	v	Sheerwater	2-1	
207	Crawley Down Gatwick	v	East Preston	5-4aet	58
208	CB Hounslow United	v	Beckenham Town	2-3	
209	Bagshot	v	Broadbridge Heath (1/9)	2-0	
210	Bridon Ropes	v	Pagham+	2-2aet	40
	(Bridon Ropes won 4-3 on kicks from the penalty mark)				
211	Meridian VP	v	Hassocks (1/9)	0-2	30
212	Godalming Town	v	Hailsham Town	2-1	
213	Storrington Community	v	Knaphill	0-6	
214	Sheppey United	v	AFC Croydon Athletic	2-0	147
215	Seaford Town	v	Eastbourne United+	2-1	
216	Forest Hill Park	v	Westside+	1-2aet	24
217	Lingfield	v	Horley Town	1-2	61
218	Guildford City	v	Glebe	0-3	82
219	Peacehaven & Telescombev	v	Steyning Town Community	2-2aet	161
	Steyning Town Community	v	Peacehaven & Telescombe (3/9)	0-3	127
220	Cobham	v	PFC Victoria London+	3-2	
221	AFC Spelthorne Sports	v	Spelthorne Sports+	1-4	
222	Balham	v	Rusthall	1-2	52
223	Lancing	v	Chessington & Hook United	3-2	90
224	Erith Town	v	Welling Town	2-2aet	27
	Welling Town	v	Erith Town (4/9)	2-0	
225	Midhurst & Easebourne	v	Alfold+	3-1	
226	Punjab United	v	Selsey	5-0	
227	Sidlesham	v	Stansfeld	1-1aet	
	Stansfeld	v	Sidlesham (3/9)	1-3	68
228	Lymington Town (at AFC Totton)	v	Fawley	5-2aet	54
229	Fareham Town	v	Whitchurch United (30/8)	2-0	
230	Folland Sports	v	East Cowes Victoria Athletic	0-1	
231	Alton	v	Andover New Street	2-1	
232	Hamble Club	v	Totton & Eling (30/8)	4-0	
233	Bashley	v	Bridport	3-0	
234	Bemerton Heath Harlequins	v	Alresford Town	1-2aet	
235	Solent University	v	Bradford Town	2-7	
236	United Services Portsmouth	v	Sherborne Town	2-3	43
237	Calne Town	v	Downton	1-3	63
238	New Milton Town	v	AFC Portchester	1-4	
239	Andover Town	v	Westbury United+	1-4	
240	Swanage Town & Herston	v	Dorchester Sports+	0-1	40
241	Devizes Town	v	Stockbridge	1-0	48
242	Cowes Sports	v	Shaftesbury	2-0	
243	Ringwood Town	v	Verwood Town	1-1aet	86
	Verwood Town	v	Ringwood Town (3/9)	2-0	
244	Amesbury Town	v	Christchurch	1-4	
245	Petersfield Town	v	AFC Stoneham	1-0	82
246	Pewsey Vale	v	Laverstock & Ford+	0-1	70
247	Clevedon Town	v	Roman Glass St George	1-2	70
248	Almondsbury	v	Buckland Athletic	2-4	30
249	Bishops Lydeard	v	Bodmin Town	1-3	44
250	Shepton Mallet	v	Wellington AFC+	4-0	92
251	Bristol Telephones	v	Falmouth Town	1-3	50
252	Ivybridge Town	v	Bishop Sutton	4-1aet	123
253	Cullompton Rangers	v	Newquay	2-0	73
254	St Blazey	v	Godolphin Atlantic	5-3	
255	Elburton Villa	v	Saltash United	1-5	141
256	Keynsham Town	v	Helston Athletic	0-1	
257	Tavistock	v	Hallen	4-1	
258	Street	v	Crediton United	3-0	108
259	Hengrove Athletic	v	Radstock Town+	0-1	44
260	Cadbury Heath	v	Longwell Green Sports	3-0	102
261	Wells City	v	Millbrook	5-3	
262	Welton Rovers	v	Newton Abbot Spurs+	0-4	62
263	Bovey Tracey	v	Liskeard Athletic+	3-1	
264	Porthleven	v	Callington Town	7-0	
265	Ilfracombe Town	v	Torpoint Athletic	1-2	
266	Odd Down	v	Portishead Town+	1-2aet	
267	Launceston	v	Cheddar+	0-2	
268	Exmouth Town	v	Brislington	3-2	

+ - penalties agreed, no replay

FAV - 2Q - Egham Town keeper Tristan Thomas gathers from Holmesdales Samuel Adenola. Photo Alan Coomes.

FAV - 2Q - Fairford Town 6-1 Shortwood Town. Photo Peter Barnes.

SECOND QUALIFYING ROUND

SATURDAY 14 SEPTEMBER 2019 - WINNING CLUB TO RECEIVE £725 LOSING CLUB TO RECEIVE £250

No	Home		Away	Score	
1	Thornaby	v	Thackley	2-1	89
2	Steeton	v	Seaham Red Star	2-3	63
3	Durham City	v	Stockton Town	0-2	
4	Easington Colliery	v	Shildon	1-2	
5	Ryton & Crawcrook Albion	v	Yorkshire Amateur+	2-4	93
6	Esh Winning	v	Billingham Town	2-3	
7	Jarrow	v	Newton Aycliffe	2-1	
8	Sunderland West End	v	Padiham	0-1	
9	Albion Sports	v	Guisborough Town	1-5	56
10	Northallerton Town	v	Barnoldswick Town	2-3	131
11	Squires Gate	v	West Allotment Celtic	1-4	52
12	Longridge Town	v	AFC Blackpool	3-1	
13	Billingham Synthonia	v	Knaresborough Town	1-2	119
14	Garforth Town	v	Sunderland Ryhope CW	0-2	139
15	Cleator Moor Celtic	v	Crook Town	0-2	
16	Skelmersdale United	v	Wythenshawe Town (13/9)	1-2	
17	Ashton Athletic	v	Liversedge	5-1	68
18	Chadderton	v	Brigg Town	1-2	
19	Runcorn Town	v	West Didsbury & Chorlton	0-1	
20	Cheadle Heath Nomads	v	Vauxhall Motors	1-2	
21	Wythenshawe Amateurs	v	Selby Town	1-3	
22	Grimsby Borough	v	Dronfield Town	3-2	
23	Stockport Town	v	Abbey Hey	1-2	
24	Lower Breck	v	Pilkington+	4-3	92
25	Handsworth Parramore	v	Glasshoughton Welfare (15/9)	1-2	
26	Hall Road Rangers	v	Maine Road	4-6	
27	Nostell MW	v	Barton Town	4-2	76
28	Retford United	v	Bottesford Town	2-4aet	
29	Rylands	v	Rossington Main	4-2	88
30	Cheadle Town	v	East Yorkshire Carnegie	4-0	
31	Prestwich Heys	v	Charnock Richard	2-3aet	
32	AFC Emley	v	Winterton Rangers (13/9)	0-2	120
33	Hinckley	v	Rocester	2-3	159
34	Shawbury United	v	Gornal Athletic	3-0	
35	Malvern Town	v	NKF Burbage	5-2	
	(at Stourport Swifts FC)				
36	Gresley	v	FC Oswestry Town	3-2	126
37	Tividale	v	Droitwich Spa	1-2	97
38	Heather St Johns	v	Coventry Copsewood+	5-2	52
39	Abbey Hulton United	v	Alsager Town	2-2aet	
	Alsager Town	v	Abbey Hulton United (17/9)	3-1	102
40	FC Stratford	v	GNP Sports+	2-2aet	
	(GNP Sports won 4-3 on kicks from the penalty mark)				
41	Black Country Rangers	v	Leicester Road	0-8	
42	Whitchurch Alport	v	Nuneaton Griff	4-1	168
43	Atherstone Town	v	Paget Rangers	3-1	
44	Ashby Ivanhoe	v	Sandbach United	0-3	
45	Boldmere St Michaels	v	Willenhall Town	4-1	104
46	Worcester City	v	Highgate United	2-0	304
47	Uttoxeter Town	v	Wolverhampton SC	1-0	
48	Studley	v	Racing Club Warwick	1-2	54
49	Shifnal Town	v	Haughmond	0-1	87
50	Coventry Sphinx	v	Hanley Town	4-5	89
51	Lichfield City	v	Wolverhampton Casuals	4-2	
52	Smethwick	v	Dudley Town (13/9)	0-1	
	(at Tividale FC)				
53	Barrow Town	v	St Andrews	3-2	
54	Dunkirk	v	Anstey Nomads	2-1	51
55	Clifton All Whites	v	Holbeach United	1-3	40
56	Newark Flowserve	v	Skegness Town	5-1	
57	Loughborough University	v	Ingles	1-1aet	
	Ingles	v	Loughborough University (19/9)	1-2aet	
58	Quorn	v	Shirebrook Town	5-0	
59	Blaby & Whetstone Athleticv	v	Kimberley MW	0-2	52
60	Blidworth Welfare	v	Sherwood Colliery	0-5	71
61	AFC Mansfield	v	Rainworth MW	3-2	
62	South Normanton Athletic	v	Kirby Muxloe	2-1	
63	Long Eaton United	v	Blackstones	3-0	74
64	West Bridgford	v	Selston	5-0	
65	Clay Cross Town	v	Gedling MW	2-2aet	85
	Gedling MW	v	Clay Cross Town (17/9)	2-3	91
66	Heanor Town	v	Birstall United Social	2-1	
67	Bourne Town	v	Hucknall Town	1-2	128
68	Harrowby United	v	Cottesmore Amateurs S&S+	1-2	
69	Kirkley & Pakefield	v	Debenham LC	1-0	
70	Huntingdon Town	v	Mulbarton Wanderers	2-1	48
71	Netherton United	v	Wroxham	2-3	
72	Thetford Town	v	Peterborough Northern Star	0-5	82
73	March Town United	v	Walsham Le Willows	4-3aet	
74	Mildenhall Town	v	Newmarket Town	1-1aet	230
	Newmarket Town	v	Mildenhall Town (17/9)	3-3aet	
	(Mildenhall Town won 7-6 on kicks from the penalty mark)				
75	Great Yarmouth Town	v	Norwich United	0-3	
76	FC Clacton	v	Redbridge	4-1	
77	Enfield	v	Enfield Borough	2-1	43
	(at Bishop's Stortford FC)				
78	London Colney	v	Baldock Town	2-4	
79	West Essex	v	Brantham Athletic	2-4	
80	White Ensign	v	Newbury Forest	3-0	
81	Coggeshall United	v	Long Melford (15/9)	1-0	
82	Langford	v	Hackney Wick+	1-1aet	
	(Hackney Wick won 4-2 on kicks from the penalty mark)				
83	Whitton United	v	St Margaretsbury	2-1	23
84	Takeley	v	Wormley Rovers+	3-0	38
85	Lopes Tavares London	v	Catholic United	3-1	
86	New Salamis	v	Tower Hamlets (13/9)	2-0	73
87	Frenford	v	Hashtag United	3-2	129
88	Hadleigh United	v	Haverhill Borough	5-2	64
89	Colney Heath	v	Haverhill Rovers	2-0	
90	FC Broxbourne Borough	v	Wivenhoe Town+	4-1	29
91	Stanway Rovers	v	Wodson Park	7-1	
92	Long Crendon	v	Leighton Town (15/9)	2-5	
93	Bedford	v	Bedfont & Feltham	0-4	32
94	Broadfields United	v	Hanworth Villa (13/9)	5-1	
95	Harefield United	v	Rothwell Corinthians	1-3	55
96	Wembley	v	Risborough Rangers	1-3	55
97	Buckingham Athletic	v	Hillingdon+	6-0	53
98	Harborough Town	v	Hillingdon Borough	3-3aet	126
	Hillingdon Borough	v	Harborough Town (17/9)	1-2	
99	Northampton On Chenecksv	v	Northampton Sileby Rangers	3-1	
100	Cricklewood Wanderers	v	Long Buckby (15/9)	1-4	
101	Wellingborough Town	v	Holyport	1-0	
102	Raunds Town	v	Flackwell Heath	1-2	
103	Aylesbury Vale Dynamos	v	Rugby Borough+	3-1	71
104	North Greenford United	v	Oxhey Jets	0-2	56
105	Edgware Town	v	Eynesbury Rovers (15/9)	0-2	83
106	Lutterworth Town	v	Amersham Town	6-0	44
107	Crawley Green	v	Winslow United+	4-0	61
108	AFC Hayes	v	London Tigers	2-0	50
109	Abingdon United	v	Reading City	3-1	
110	Fairford Town	v	Shortwood United	6-1	60
111	Wokingham & Emmbrook	v	Thornbury Town (15/9)	0-1	220
112	Frimley Green	v	Ascot United	0-3	
113	Malmesbury Victoria	v	Camberley Town	2-1	164
114	Longlevens	v	Newent Town	2-1	
115	Milton Keynes Robins	v	Fleet Spurs	4-1	

FAV - 1P - Harries (Longridge) gets in a shot on the Crook goal. Photo Keith Clayton.

Striker Ryan Lovell scores for Wellingborough Town against Takeley

FAV - 1P - Wellingborough Town 4-3 Takeley. Photo Peter Barnes.

SECOND QUALIFYING ROUND

116	Shrivenham	v	Clanfield 85	2-2aet	42
	Clanfield 85	v	Shrivenham (17/9)	1-5	46
117	AFC Aldermaston	v	Binfield	1-3	
118	Tadley Calleva	v	Royal Wootton Bassett Town	1-0	
119	Sidlesham	v	Kennington+	2-4	
120	Crawley Down Gatwick	v	Mile Oak	4-6	54
121	Midhurst & Easebourne	v	Crowborough Athletic	0-2	
122	Hassocks	v	Horley Town	1-6	62
123	Seaford Town	v	FC Deportivo Galicia	2-0	
124	Hollands & Blair	v	Deal Town	1-2	
125	Westside	v	Bexhill United	3-2	
126	Molesey	v	Greenwich Borough (17/9)	0-2	
	(14/9 – abandoned after 80 minutes due to serious injury, 0-0)				
127	Erith & Belvedere	v	Oakwood (15/9)	9-2	60
128	Sporting Club Thamesmead	v	Billingshurst+	3-1	40
129	Knaphill	v	Tunbridge Wells	2-2aet	
	Tunbridge Wells	v	Knaphill (17/9)	5-1	
130	Raynes Park Vale	v	Walton & Hersham	4-1	
131	Beckenham Town	v	Farnham Town	6-0	
132	Peacehaven & Telscombe	v	Spelthorne Sports	3-2aet	152
133	Lancing	v	Worthing United+	7-0	75
134	Arundel	v	Welling Town	1-7	62
135	Croydon	v	Colliers Wood United	1-3	133
136	Punjab United	v	Loxwood+	3-2	32
137	Cobham	v	Badshot Lea	2-4	
138	Lordswood	v	Sheppey United	0-1	
139	Redhill	v	Bagshot	4-3	50
140	Snodland Town	v	Bridon Ropes+	3-2	
141	Rusthall	v	Godalming Town	2-1	
142	K Sports	v	Glebe	0-3	48
143	Holmesdale	v	Egham Town	0-1	
144	Corsham Town	v	Romsey Town	1-3	69
145	Bradford Town	v	Hamble Club	1-0	
146	Hythe & Dibden	v	AFC Portchester	2-3	79
147	Alton	v	Westbury United	1-2	
148	Devizes Town	v	Newport (IW)	1-3	52
149	Dorchester Sports	v	Christchurch	2-4	
150	Bashley	v	Lymington Town	1-4	
151	Warminster Town	v	Alresford Town	2-1	110
152	East Cowes Victoria Athletic	v	Fareham Town	3-2	
153	Cowes Sports	v	Verwood Town+	7-3	132
154	Laverstock & Ford	v	Brockenhurst	0-4	78
155	Sherborne Town	v	Petersfield Town	2-2aet	
	Petersfield Town	v	Sherbourne Town (17/9)	1-0	92
156	Downton	v	Wincanton Town	2-1	
157	Camelford	v	Ashton & Backwell United+	2-1	43
158	St Blazey	v	Falmouth Town	1-3	
159	Cheddar	v	Tavistock+	0-5	
160	Shepton Mallet	v	Street	5-2	
161	Cadbury Heath	v	Exmouth Town	1-5	82
162	Radstock Town	v	Bovey Tracey+	2-3	
163	Ivybridge Town	v	Roman Glass St George+	2-3	96
164	Sidmouth Town	v	Cullompton Rangers	0-5	
165	Bodmin Town	v	Buckland Athletic	0-4	81
166	Wells City	v	Newton Abbot Spurs	1-2	72
167	Torpoint Athletic	v	Portishead Town+	4-1aet	109
168	Saltash United	v	Porthleven	2-1	112
169	Helston Athletic	v	Axminster Town+	2-0	142

FIRST ROUND PROPER

SATURDAY 12 OCTOBER 2019 - WINNING CLUB TO RECEIVE £825 LOSING CLUB TO RECEIVE £275

1	Jarrow	v	Vauxhall Motors	1-2aet	
2	Bottesford Town	v	West Allotment Celtic	4-2aet	63
3	Nostell MW	v	Wythenshawe Town	0-2	73
4	Seaham Red Star	v	Yorkshire Amateur	1-3	
5	Thornaby	v	Billingham Town	4-0	400
6	Shildon	v	West Didsbury & Chorlton	2-0	257
7	Longridge Town	v	Crook Town	4-2	
8	Knaresborough Town	v	Stockton Town	2-3aet	503
9	Penistone Church	v	Bridlington Town	1-2	
10	Rylands	v	Bootle	3-0	181
11	Selby Town	v	Cheadle Town	5-1	
12	Padiham	v	Bishop Auckland	0-1	283
13	Abbey Hey	v	Barnoldswick Town	0-5	165
14	Sunderland Ryhope CW	v	Ashton Athletic	2-0	74
15	Chadderton	v	Guisborough Town	1-3	138
16	Winterton Rangers	v	Consett	2-5	
17	Maine Road	v	Glasshoughton Welfare	4-2aet	130
18	Charnock Richard	v	Lower Breck	2-5	185
19	Grimsby Borough	v	Hemsworth MW	4-0	90
20	Leicester Road	v	Walsall Wood	1-2aet	
21	Droitwich Spa	v	Whitchurch Alport+	2-0	
22	Newark Flowserve	v	Heather St Johns	2-1	
23	GNP Sports	v	Malvern Town	2-4aet	
24	Alsager Town	v	Lutterworth Town	1-2	
25	South Normanton Athletic	v	Holbeach United	1-0	
26	Kimberley MW	v	Sherwood Colliery	0-4	
27	Lichfield City	v	Dudley Town	1-2aet	
28	Atherstone Town	v	Sandbach United	3-1	275
29	Brackley Town Saints	v	West Bridgford	2-3aet	
30	Shawbury United	v	Uttoxeter Town	0-0aet	
	Uttoxeter Town	v	Shawbury United (15/10)	4-0	
31	Heanor Town	v	Boldmere St Michaels	3-0	
32	Gresley	v	Rugby Town	0-1	205
33	Pinchbeck United	v	Worcester City	0-3	
34	AFC Mansfield	v	Hanley Town	2-1aet	
35	Haughmond	v	Loughborough University (11/10)	1-3aet	61
36	Dunkirk	v	Hucknall Town	2-1	113
37	Racing Club Warwick	v	Long Eaton United	2-3	148
38	Clay Cross Town	v	Cottesmore Amateurs S&S+	3-1	
39	Barrow Town	v	Congleton Town	1-2	
40	Quorn	v	Rocester+	5-3	
41	New Salamis	v	Eynesbury Rovers	1-6	
42	March Town United	v	Rothwell Corinthians	0-1	144
43	Stansted	v	Aylesbury Vale Dynamos	5-1	80
44	Risborough Rangers	v	FC Clacton	0-2	316
45	Tring Athletic	v	Woodbridge Town	1-3	156
46	Broadfields United	v	Walthamstow	1-3	48
47	Mildenhall Town	v	Crawley Green	4-1	145
48	Norwich United	v	Peterborough Northern Star+	4-1aet	131
49	AFC Hayes	v	FC Broxbourne Borough	1-3	
50	Flackwell Heath	v	Colney Heath	2-3aet	67
51	Leighton Town	v	Hadleigh United	2-1	174
52	White Ensign	v	Buckingham Athletic (13/10)	4-1	
53	Hadley	v	Milton Keynes Robins+	0-2	56
54	Wroxham	v	Baldock Town	6-2	155
55	Northampton On Chenecks	v	Kirkley & Pakefield	2-3aet	
56	Whitton United	v	Long Buckby	1-3	
57	Huntingdon Town	v	Frenford	2-3aet	48

FAV - 1P - Wellingborough Town 4-3 Takeley. Photo Peter Barnes.

FAV - 2P - Fishers Adebola Oluwo volleys just over against Glebe. Photo Alan Coomes.

FIRST ROUND PROPER

No	Home		Away	Score	Att
58	Biggleswade United	v	Saffron Walden Town (11/10)	4-4aet	184
	Saffron Walden Town	v	Biggleswade United (15/10)	5-1	209
59	Wellingborough Town	v	Takeley	4-3	150
60	Oxhey Jets	v	Hackney Wick+	7-0	57
61	Harborough Town	v	Enfield	4-1	
62	Coggeshall United	v	Brantham Athletic	1-0	
63	Lopes Tavares London	v	Stanway Rovers	2-3	
64	Southall	v	Tunbridge Wells (13/10)	4-4aet	
	Tunbridge Wells	v	Southall (15/10)	1-3	
65	Chatham Town	v	Beckenham Town	1-1aet	425
	Beckenham Town	v	Chatham Town (16/10)	2-2aet	
	(Chatham Town won 7-6 on kicks from the penalty mark)				
66	Egham Town	v	Binfield (15/10)	0-4	73
67	Raynes Park Vale	v	Horndean (15/10)	2-2aet	49
	Horndean	v	Raynes Park Vale (22/10)	1-2	
	(12/10 – tie abandoned after 70 mins due to waterlogged pitch, 0-0 – new date Tue 15 Oct 7.45)				
68	Sheppey United	v	Corinthian	0-2	168
69	Peacehaven & Telscombe	v	Glebe	3-5	
70	Welling Town	v	Erith & Belvedere	5-1	
71	Westside	v	Deal Town (23/10)	3-4	
72	Bedfont & Feltham	v	Colliers Wood United	3-1	
73	Sporting Club Thamesmead	v	Ascot United (11/10)	1-5	105
74	Fisher	v	Greenwich Borough	3-0	175
75	Kennington	v	Crowborough Athletic (13/10)+	4-2	277
76	Punjab United	v	Newhaven	0-3	
77	Mile Oak	v	Redhill	1-2	112
78	Seaford Town	v	Horley Town	1-0	
79	Rusthall	v	Lancing	0-2	208
80	Sutton Common Rovers	v	Snodland Town+	5-1	61
81	Eastbourne Town	v	Horsham YMCA	4-2	
82	Christchurch	v	Brimscombe & Thrupp	3-1	89
83	Bradford Town	v	Lymington Town	1-0	
84	Cullompton Rangers	v	AFC Portchester	0-1	
85	Newport (IW)	v	Bridgwater Town+	0-2	
86	Westbury United	v	Badshot Lea	0-1	71
87	Malmesbury Victoria	v	Roman Glass St George	3-5	127
88	Torpoint Athletic	v	Saltash United	1-4	189
89	Tavistock	v	Shepton Mallet+	4-1	
90	Warminster Town	v	East Cowes Victoria Athletic	3-2	133
91	Bitton	v	Tadley Calleva (15/10)	6-1	136
92	Bournemouth	v	Petersfield Town (15/10)	1-2	87
93	Longlevens	v	Cowes Sports+	1-0aet	70
94	Romsey Town	v	Plymouth Parkway (16/10)	1-3	123
95	Bishop's Cleeve	v	Brockenhurst	2-3	120
96	Helston Athletic	v	Falmouth Town	1-5	689
97	Camelford	v	Buckland Athletic	1-2	116
98	Bovey Tracey	v	Abingdon United (26/10)	3-1	93
	(tie awarded to Abingdon United – Bovey Tracey removed)				
99	Downton	v	Thornbury Town+	0-4	
100	Shrivenham	v	Fairford Town	2-3	83
101	Exmouth Town	v	Portland United	2-0	211
102	Newton Abbot Spurs	v	Westfields	0-8	200

SECOND ROUND PROPER

SATURDAY 2 NOVEMBER 2019 - WINNING CLUB TO RECEIVE £900 LOSING CLUB TO RECEIVE £300

No	Home		Away	Score	Att
1	Selby Town	v	Bridlington Town (19/11)	2-4	
	(at Bridlington Town FC)				
2	Bishop Auckland	v	West Auckland Town	0-1aet	517
3	Hebburn Town	v	Sunderland RCA	3-0	
4	Irlam	v	Consett	2-5	181
5	Congleton Town	v	Maine Road	3-2	144
6	Stockton Town	v	Barnoldswick Town	2-0	627
7	Northwich Victoria	v	Wythenshawe Town	5-5aet	
	Wythenshawe Town	v	Northwich Victoria (5/11)	2-1	
8	Lower Breck	v	Shildon	2-1	
9	Vauxhall Motors	v	Sunderland Ryhope CW	4-1	
10	Yorkshire Amateur	v	Bottesford Town	5-4	
11	Newcastle Benfield	v	Guisborough Town	4-0	235
12	Rylands	v	Grimsby Borough	0-1	87
13	Longridge Town	v	Thornaby	6-4	
14	Newark Flowserve	v	Rugby Town	3-0	
15	Lye Town	v	Droitwich Spa	2-1	
16	Wellingborough Town	v	Dudley Town	1-0	
17	Malvern Town	v	Loughborough University (13/11)	5-4aet	387
18	Lutterworth Town	v	Eastwood Community (5/11)	4-2aet	75
19	AFC Mansfield	v	Long Buckby	3-1	72
20	Walsall Wood	v	Uttoxeter Town (5/11)	3-1	
21	Leicester Nirvana	v	Westfields (12/11)	1-2	
22	West Bridgford	v	Heanor Town	0-2	
23	Sporting Khalsa	v	Quorn	3-1	
24	Coventry United	v	Long Eaton United	1-0	125
25	Clay Cross Town	v	Sherwood Colliery (5/11)	3-1	188
26	Worcester City	v	Dunkirk (6/11)	3-1	187
27	Harborough Town	v	Atherstone Town	1-6	343
28	Shepshed Dynamo	v	Cadbury Athletic (5/11)	4-1	128
29	South Normanton Athletic	v	Rothwell Corinthians (19/11)	3-1	
	(at Rothwell Corinthians FC)				
30	White Ensign	v	Wroxham (6/11)	2-5	
	(at Wroxham FC) (3/11 – tie abandoned after 75 mins due to floodlight failure, 0-3)				
31	Woodbridge Town	v	Godmanchester Rovers	5-2	
32	Norwich United	v	Kirkley & Pakefield	1-2	
33	Stansted	v	Mildenhall Town	1-0	142
34	Newport Pagnell Town	v	Coggeshall United	4-2	106
35	Saffron Walden Town	v	FC Clacton	3-4	
36	Leighton Town	v	FC Broxbourne Borough	6-1	
37	Deeping Rangers	v	Stanway Rovers	1-3	116
38	Milton Keynes Robins	v	Eynesbury Rovers	1-6	
39	Colney Heath	v	Stowmarket Town	0-1	
40	Fisher	v	Glebe	1-2	116
41	Abbey Rangers	v	Ascot United (5/11)	2-2aet	
	Ascot United	v	Abbey Rangers (12/11)	7-0	
42	Frenford	v	Lancing	1-3	
43	Raynes Park Vale	v	Sutton Common Rovers	0-4	52
	(at Sutton Common Rovers FC)				
44	Binfield	v	Redhill	3-1	92
45	Walthamstow	v	AFC Uckfield Town	2-3	74
46	Corinthian	v	Canterbury City	2-0	71
47	Windsor	v	Eastbourne Town	1-7	171
48	Deal Town	v	Oxhey Jets	3-1aet	
49	Southall	v	Seaford Town (3/11)	3-1	100
50	Welling Town	v	Bedfont & Feltham	3-1aet	
51	Bearsted	v	Chatham Town (12/11)	0-1	141
52	Kennington	v	Newhaven	1-6	199
53	Warminster Town	v	AFC Portchester	3-1	
54	Baffins Milton Rovers	v	Bradford Town (6/11)	2-3	86
55	Falmouth Town	v	Longlevens	3-2aet	
56	AFC St Austell	v	Buckland Athletic	0-1	
57	Tavistock	v	Exmouth Town (6/11)	6-1	
58	Saltash United	v	Bridgwater Town (13/11)	0-2aet	
59	Brockenhurst	v	Plymouth Parkway	0-3	181
60	Thornbury Town	v	Cribbs (3/11)	1-3aet	
61	Christchurch	v	Badshot Lea (5/11)	2-1	101
62	Petersfield Town	v	Roman Glass St George (5/11)	1-2	137
63	Abingdon United	v	Hamworthy United	1-6	39
64	Bitton	v	Fairford Town (5/11)	4-0	106

FAV - 3P - Glebes Jamie Philpot (stripes) and Newhavens Robbie Keith tussle for the ball. Photo Alan Coomes.

FAV - 4P - South Normanton 1 - 3 Wroxham. Photo Bill Wheatcroft.

THIRD ROUND PROPER
SATURDAY 30 NOVEMBER 2019 - WINNING CLUB TO RECEIVE £1,125 LOSING CLUB TO RECEIVE £375

1	Bridlington Town	v	Stockton Town	1-4aet		17	Woodbridge Town	v	Stanway Rovers	1-1aet
2	Vauxhall Motors	v	Newcastle Benfield	2-0	134		Stanway Rovers	v	Woodbridge Town (3/12)	0-4
3	Lower Breck	v	Hebburn Town	1-5	152	18	Stowmarket Town	v	Stansted	4-0
4	Wythenshawe Town	v	Consett	1-1aet	302	19	FC Clacton	v	Eynesbury Rovers	1-2
	Consett	v	Wythenshawe Town (7/12)	1-0	404	20	Chatham Town	v	Welling Town	1-0
5	Congleton Town	v	Longridge Town	2-2aet	225	21	Deal Town	v	Southall	2-0	296
	Longridge Town	v	Congleton Town (4/12)	2-0		22	Glebe	v	Newhaven	1-0
6	West Auckland Town	v	Yorkshire Amateur	2-1		23	Corinthian	v	Ascot United	2-1	75
7	Coventry United	v	Grimsby Borough (4.00)	4-2	122	24	Lancing	v	Sutton Common Rovers	3-3aet
8	Westfields	v	Lutterworth Town	1-3	126		Sutton Common Rovers	v	Lancing (7/12)	1-0	98
9	Worcester City	v	Shepshed Dynamo	2-1	344	25	Leighton Town	v	Eastbourne Town	2-1
10	Heanor Town	v	Sporting Khalsa	2-4		26	Binfield	v	AFC Uckfield Town	4-0	133
11	Lye Town	v	Walsall Wood	0-2	115	27	Bradford Town	v	Bridgwater Town	4-3aet
12	Malvern Town	v	Atherstone Town	3-3aet		28	Bitton	v	Cribbs	2-1	70
	Atherstone Town	v	Malvern Town (4/12)	10-0	222	29	Hamworthy United	v	Plymouth Parkway	1-4
13	AFC Mansfield	v	Newark Flowserve (3/12)	1-3		30	Christchurch	v	Falmouth Town	2-1	238
14	South Normanton Athletic	v	Clay Cross Town	2-1		31	Tavistock	v	Buckland Athletic	1-2
15	Newport Pagnell Town	v	Kirkley & Pakefield	0-2	117	32	Roman Glass St George	v	Warminster Town (2.00)	1-2
16	Wroxham	v	Wellingborough Town	1-0aet						

FOURTH ROUND PROPER
SATURDAY 11 JANUARY 2020 - WINNING CLUB TO RECEIVE £1,875 LOSING CLUB TO RECEIVE £625

1	Worcester City	v	Coventry United (15/1)+	2-1	452	10	Chatham Town	v	Corinthian	1-2aet	528
2	Stockton Town	v	Atherstone Town	0-1	719	11	Eynesbury Rovers	v	Leighton Town	3-4	469
3	Vauxhall Motors	v	Hebburn Town	0-1	175	12	Deal Town	v	Binfield	1-1aet	111
4	Longridge Town	v	Newark Flowserve	5-1			Binfield	v	Deal Town (18/1)	3-3aet	348
5	Consett	v	Lutterworth Town	3-1			(Deal Town won 7-6 on kicks from the penalty mark)				
6	West Auckland Town	v	Walsall Wood	1-0		13	Bitton	v	Warminster Town	3-1	199
7	South Normanton Athletic	v	Wroxham	1-3		14	Woodbridge Town	v	Plymouth Parkway	0-1	
8	Sporting Khalsa	v	Kirkley & Pakefield	2-0aet		15	Buckland Athletic	v	Bradford Town	1-2	174
9	Stowmarket Town	v	Glebe	3-0		16	Christchurch	v	Sutton Common Rovers	1-2	196

FIFTH ROUND PROPER
SATURDAY 8 FEBRUARY 2020 - WINNING CLUB TO RECEIVE £2,250 LOSING CLUB TO RECEIVE £750

1	Corinthian	v	Sporting Khalsa	3-0	246	5	Longridge Town	v	Hebburn Town	0-1aet	692
2	Bradford Town	v	Leighton Town	1-3	463	6	Wroxham	v	Stowmarket Town	2-0	1041
3	Consett	v	Deal Town	2-0	866	7	Bitton	v	Sutton Common Rovers	2-1	209
4	Plymouth Parkway	v	West Auckland Town	2-1	671	8	Atherstone Town	v	Worcester City	1-1aet	842
							Worcester City	v	Atherstone Town (12/2)	1-1aet
							(Atherstone Town won 5-4 on kicks from the penalty mark)			

QUARTER FINALS
SATURDAY 29 FEBRUARY 2020 - WINNING CLUB TO RECEIVE £4,125 LOSING CLUB TO RECEIVE £1,375

1	Corinthian	v	Leighton Town (7/3)	4-1	351	3	Atherstone Town	v	Consett (7/3)	1-3aet	
2	Wroxham	v	Bitton	0-4	978	4	Hebburn Town	v	Plymouth Parkway	2-0	1705

SEMI FINALS
1ST LEG SATURDAY ?? / 2ND LEG SATURDAY ?? 2020 - WINNERS RECEIVE £5,500 LOSING CLUB TO RECEIVE £1,750

Bitton	v	Consett
Consett	v	Bitton

Corinthian	v	Hebburn Town
Hebburn Town	v	Corinthian

FAV - 4P - Ryan Sawyer of Corinthian tries to block a cross from Chathams Matt Bodkin. Photo Alan Coomes.

FAV - 4P - Grant Holt celebrates one of his hat-trick goals for Wroxham against South Normanton. Photo Bill Wheatcroft.

FAV - 2Q - Egham Towns keeper Tristan Thomas saves from Holmesdales Samuel Adenola. Photo Alan Coomes.

FAV - 1P - Billy Brown (stripes) chips the ball past Greenwich Borough keeper Ryan Coltress-Reynolds to score for Fisher. Photo Alan Coomes.

FAV - 1Q - Pinxton 2 - 3 Birstall United Social. Photo Bill Wheatcroft.

FAV - 1P - Fishers Billy Brown (stripes) takes on Greenwich Boroughs Alex Nelson. Photo Alan Coomes.

PAST FINALS

1975 HODDESDON TOWN 2 *(South Midlands)*   **EPSOM & EWELL** 1 *(Surrey Senior)*   **Att: 9,500**
Sedgwick 2   Wales   Ref: Mr R Toseland
Hoddesdon: Galvin, Green, Hickey, Maybury, Stevenson, Wilson, Bishop, Picking, Sedgwick, Nathan, Schofield
Epsom & Ewell: Page, Bennett, Webb, Wales, Worby, Jones, O'Connell, Walker, Tuite, Eales, Lee

1976 BILLERICAY TOWN 1 *(Essex Senior)*   **STAMFORD** 0 (aet) *(United Counties)*   **Att: 11,848**
Aslett   Ref: Mr A Robinson
Billericay: Griffiths, Payne, Foreman, Pullin, Bone, Coughlan, Geddes, Aslett, Clayden, Scott, Smith
Stamford: Johnson, Kwiatkowski, Marchant, Crawford, Downs, Hird, Barnes, Walpole, Smith, Russell, Broadbent

1977 BILLERICAY TOWN 1 *(Essex Senior)*   **SHEFFIELD** 1 (aet) *(Yorkshire)*   **Att: 14,000**
Clayden   Coughlan og   Ref: Mr J Worrall
Billericay: Griffiths, Payne, Bone, Coughlan, Pullin, Scott, Wakefield, Aslett, Clayden,Woodhouse, McQueen. Sub: Whettell
Sheffield: Wing, Gilbody, Lodge, Hardisty, Watts, Skelton, Kay, Travis, Pugh, Thornhill,Haynes. Sub: Strutt

Replay BILLERICAY TOWN 2   **SHEFFIELD** 1   **Att: 3,482**
Aslett, Woodhouse   Thornhill   at Nottingham Forest
Billericay: Griffiths, Payne, Pullin, Whettell, Bone, McQueen, Woodhouse, Aslett, Clayden, Scott, Wakefield
Sheffield: Wing, Gilbody, Lodge, Strutt, Watts, Skelton, Kay, Travis, Pugh, Thornhill, Haynes

1978 NEWCASTLE BLUE STAR 2 *(Wearside)*   **BARTON ROVERS** 1 *(South Midlands)*   **Att: 16,858**
Dunn, Crumplin   Smith   Ref: Mr T Morris
Newcastle: Halbert, Feenan, Thompson, Davidson, S Dixon, Beynon, Storey, P Dixon, Crumplin, Callaghan, Dunn. Sub: Diamond
Barton Rovers: Blackwell, Stephens, Crossley, Evans, Harris, Dollimore, Dunn, Harnaman, Fossey, Turner, Smith. Sub: Cox

1979 BILLERICAY TOWN 4 *(Athenian)*   **ALMONDSBURY GREENWAY** 1 *(Glos. Co)*   **Att: 17,500**
Young 3, Clayden   Price   Ref: Mr C Steel
Billericay: Norris, Blackaller, Bingham, Whettell, Bone, Reeves, Pullin, Scott, Clayden,Young, Groom. Sub: Carrigan
Almondsbury: Hamilton, Bowers, Scarrett, Sulllivan, Tudor, Wookey, Bowers, Shehean, Kerr, Butt, Price. Sub: Kilbaine

1980 STAMFORD 2 *(United Counties)*   **GUISBOROUGH TOWN** 0 *(Northern Alliance)*   **Att: 11,500**
Alexander, McGowan   Ref: Neil Midgeley
Stamford: Johnson, Kwiatkowski, Ladd, McGowan, Bliszczak I, Mackin, Broadhurst, Hall,Czarnecki, Potter, Alexander. Sub: Bliszczak S
Guisborough: Cutter, Scott, Thornton, Angus, Maltby, Percy, Skelton, Coleman, McElvaney,Sills, Dilworth. Sub: Harrison

1981 WHICKHAM 3 *(Wearside)*   **WILLENHALL** 2 (aet) *(West Midlands)*   **Att: 12,000**
Scott, Williamson, Peck og   Smith, Stringer   Ref: Mr R Lewis
Whickham: Thompson, Scott, Knox, Williamson, Cook, Ward, Carroll, Diamond, Cawthra,Robertson, Turnbull. Sub: Alton
Willenhall: Newton, White, Darris, Woodall, Heath, Fox, Peck, Price, Matthews, Smith,Stringer. Sub: Trevor

1982 FOREST GREEN ROVERS 3 *(Hellenic)*   **RAINWORTH M.W** 0 *(Notts Alliance)*   **Att: 12,500**
Leitch 2, Norman   Ref: Mr K Walmsey
Forest Green: Moss, Norman, Day, Turner, Higgins, Jenkins, Guest, Burns, Millard, Leitch, Doughty. Sub: Dangerfield
Rainworth M.W: Watson, Hallam, Hodgson, Slater, Sterland, Oliver, Knowles, Raine, Radzi, Reah, Comerford. Sub: Robinson

1983 V.S. RUGBY 1 *(West Midlands)*   **HALESOWEN TOWN** 0 *(West Midlands)*   **Att: 13,700**
Crawley   Ref: Mr B Daniels
VS Rugby: Burton, McGinty, Harrison, Preston, Knox, Evans, ingram, Setchell, Owen,Beecham, Crawley. Sub: Haskins
Halesowen Town: Coldicott, Penn, Edmonds, Lacey, Randall, Shilvock, Hazelwood, Moss, Woodhouse,P Joinson, L Joinson. Sub: Smith

1984 STANSTED 3 *(Essex Senior)*   **STAMFORD** 2 *(United Counties)*   **Att: 8,125**
Holt, Gillard, Reading   Waddicore, Allen   Ref: Mr T Bune
Stanstead: Coe, Williams, Hilton, Simpson, Cooper, Reading, Callanan, Holt, Reevs,Doyle, Gillard. Sub: Williams
Stamford: Parslow, Smitheringate, Blades, McIlwain, Lyon, Mackin, Genovese, Waddicore,Allen, Robson, Beech. Sub: Chapman

1985 HALESOWEN TOWN 3 *(West Midlands)*   **FLEETWOOD TOWN** 1 *(N W Counties)*   **Att: 16,715**
L Joinson 2, Moss   Moran   Ref: Mr C Downey
Halesowen: Coldicott, Penn, Sherwood, Warner, Randle, Heath, Hazlewood, Moss (Smith),Woodhouse, P Joinson, L Joinson
Fleetwood Town: Dobson, Moran, Hadgraft, Strachan, Robinson, Milligan, Hall, Trainor, Taylor(Whitehouse), Cain, Kennerley

1986 HALESOWEN TOWN 3 *(West Midlands)*   **SOUTHALL** 0 *(Isthmian 2 South)*   **Att: 18,340**
Moss 2, L Joinson   Ref: Mr D Scott
Halesowen: Pemberton, Moore, Lacey, Randle (Rhodes), Sherwood, Heath, Penn, Woodhouse, PJoinson, L Joinson, Moss
Southall: Mackenzie, James, McGovern, Croad, Holland, Powell (Richmond), Pierre,Richardson, Sweales, Ferdinand, Rowe

1987 ST. HELENS 3 *(N W Counties)*   **WARRINGTON TOWN** 2 *(N W Counties)*   **Att: 4,254**
Layhe 2, Rigby   Reid, Cook   **Ref: Mr T Mills**
St Helens: Johnson, Benson, Lowe, Bendon, Wilson, McComb, Collins (Gledhill), O'Neill,Cummins, Lay, Rigby. Sub: Deakin
Warrington: O'Brien. Copeland, Hunter, Gratton, Whalley, Reid, Brownville (Woodyer), Cook,Kinsey, Looker (Hill), Hughes

1988 COLNE DYNAMOES 1 *(N W Counties)*   **EMLEY** 0 *(Northern Counties East)*   **Att: 15,000**
Anderson   **Ref: Mr A Seville**
Colne Dynamoes: Mason, McFafyen, Westwell, Bentley, Dunn, Roscoe, Rodaway, Whitehead (Burke),Diamond, Anderson, Wood (Coates)
Emley: Dennis, Fielding, Mellor, Codd, Hirst (Burrows), Gartland (Cook), Carmody,Green, Bramald, Devine, Francis

1989 TAMWORTH 1 *(West Midlands)*   **SUDBURY TOWN** 1 (aet) *(Eastern)*   **Att: 26,487**
Devaney   Hubbick   **Ref: Mr C Downey**
Tamworth: Bedford, Lockett, Atkins, Cartwright, McCormack, Myers, Finn, Devaney, Moores,Gordon, Stanton. Subs: Rathbone, Heaton
Sudbury Town: Garnham, Henry, G Barker, Boyland, Thorpe, Klug, D Barker, Barton, Oldfield,Smith, Hubbick. Subs: Money, Hunt
Replay TAMWORTH 3   **SUDBURY TOWN** 0   **Att: 11,201**
Stanton 2, Moores   **at Peterborough**
Tamworth: Bedford, Lockett, Atkins, Cartwright, Finn, Myers, George, Devaney, Moores,Gordon, Stanton. Sub: Heaton
Sudbury Town: Garnham, Henry, G Barker, Boyland, Thorpe, Klug, D Barker, Barton, Oldfield,Smith, Hubbick. Subs: Money, Hunt

1990 YEADING 0 *(Isthmian 2 South)*   **BRIDLINGTON TOWN** 0 (aet) *(N Co East)*   **Att: 7,932**
                                                                                                    Ref: Mr R Groves
Yeading: Mackenzie, Wickens, Turner, Whiskey (McCarthy), Croad, Denton, Matthews, James(Charles), Sweates, Impey, Cordery
Bridlington: Taylor, Pugh, Freeman, McNeill, Warburton, Brentano, Wilkes (Hall), Noteman,Gauden, Whiteman, Brattan (Brown)
Replay YEADING 1   **BRIDLINGTON TOWN** 0   **Att: 5,000**
Sweales   **at Leeds Utd FC**
Yeading: Mackenzie, Wickens, Turner, Whiskey, Croad (McCarthy), Schwartz, Matthews,James, Sweates, Impey (Welsh), Cordery
Bridlington: Taylor, Pugh, Freeman, McNeill, Warburton, Brentano, Wilkes (Brown), Noteman,Gauden (Downing), Whiteman, Brattan

1991 GRESLEY ROVERS 4 *(West Midlands)*   **GUISELEY** 4 (aet) *(Northern Co East)*   **Att: 11,314**
Rathbone, Smith 2, Stokes   Tennison 2, Walling, A Roberts   **Ref: Mr C Trussell**
Gresley: Aston, Barry, Elliott (Adcock), Denby, Land, Astley, Stokes, K Smith, Acklam,Rathbone, Lovell (Weston)
Guiseley: Maxted, Bottomley, Hogarth, Tetley, Morgan, McKenzie, Atkinson (Annan),Tennison, Walling, A Roberts, B Roberts
Replay GUISELEY 3   **GRESLEY ROVERS** 1   **Att: 7,585**
Tennison, Walling, Atkinson   Astley   **at Bramall Lane**
Guiseley: Maxted, Annan, Hogarth, Tetley, Morgan, McKenzie (Bottomley), Atkinson,Tennison (Noteman), Walling, A Roberts, B Roberts
Gresley: Aston, Barry, Elliott, Denby, Land, Astley, Stokes (Weston), K Smith, Acklam, Rathbone, Lovell (Adcock)

1992 WIMBORNE TOWN 5 *(Wessex)*   **GUISELEY** 3 *(Northern Premier Div 1)*   **Att: 10,772**
Richardson, Sturgess 2, Killick 2   Noteman 2, Colville   **Ref: Mr M J Bodenham**
Wimborne: Leonard, Langdown, Wilkins, Beacham, Allan, Taplin, Ames, Richardson, Bridle,Killick, Sturgess (Lovell), Lynn
Guiseley: Maxted, Atkinson, Hogarth, Tetley (Wilson), Morgan, Brockie, A Roberts,Tennison, Noteman (Colville), Annan, W Roberts

1993 BRIDLINGTON TOWN 1 *(NPL Div 1)*   **TIVERTON TOWN** 0 *(Western)*   **Att: 9,061**
Radford   **Ref: Mr R A Hart**
Bridlington: Taylor, Brentano, McKenzie, Harvey, Bottomley, Woodcock, Grocock, A Roberts, Jones, Radford (Tyrell), Parkinson. Sub: Swailes
Tiverton Town: Nott, J Smith, N Saunders, M Saunders, Short (Scott), Steele, Annunziata, KSmith, Everett, Daly, Hynds (Rogers)

1994 DISS TOWN 2 *(Eastern)*   **TAUNTON TOWN** 1 *(Western)*   **Att: 13,450**
Gibbs (p), Mendham   Fowler   **Ref: Mr K. Morton**
Diss Town: Woodcock, Carter, Wolsey (Musgrave), Casey (Bugg), Hartle, Smith, Barth, Mendham, Miles, Warne, Gibbs
Taunton Town: Maloy, Morris, Walsh, Ewens, Graddon, Palfrey, West (Hendry), Fowler, Durham, Perrett (Ward), Jarvis

1995 ARLESEY TOWN 2 *(South Midlands)*   **OXFORD CITY** 1 *(Ryman 2)*   **Att: 13,670**
Palma, Gyalog   S Fontaine   **Ref: Mr G S Willard**
Arlesey: Young, Cardines, Bambrick, Palma (Ward), Hull, Gonsalves, Gyalog, Cox, Kane,O'Keefe, Marshall (Nicholls). Sub: Dodwell
Oxford: Fleet, Brown (Fisher), Hume, Shepherd, Muttock, Hamilton (Kemp), Thomas, Spittle, Sherwood, S Fontaine, C Fontaine. Sub: Torres

1996 BRIGG TOWN 3 *(N Co East)*   **CLITHEROE** 0 *(N W Counties)*   **Att: 7,340**
Stead 2, Roach   **Ref: Mr S J Lodge**
Brigg: Gawthorpe, Thompson, Rogers, Greaves (Clay), Buckley (Mail), Elston, C Stead, McLean, N Stead (McNally), Flounders, Roach
Clitheroe: Nash, Lampkin, Rowbotham (Otley), Baron, Westwell, Rovine, Butcher, Taylor (Smith), Grimshaw, Darbyshire, Hill (Dunn)

1997 WHITBY TOWN 3 *(Northern)*   **NORTH FERRIBY UTD.** 0 *(N Co East)*   **Att: 11,098**
Williams, Logan, Toman   **Ref: Graham Poll**
North Ferriby: Sharp, Deacey, Smith, Brentano, Walmsley, M Smith, Harrison (Horne), Phillips (Milner), France (Newman), Flounders, Tennison
Whitby Town: Campbell, Williams, Logan, Goodchild, Pearson, Cook, Goodrick (Borthwick), Hodgson, Robinson, Toman (Pyle), Pitman (Hall)

1998 TIVERTON TOWN 1 *(Western)*   **TOW LAW TOWN** 0 *(Northern Division 1)*   Att: 13,139
Varley   Ref: M A Riley
Tiverton Town: Edwards, Felton, Saunders, Tatterton, Smith J, Conning, Nancekivell (Rogers), Smith K (Varley), Everett, Daly, Leonard (Waters)
Tow Law Town: Dawson, Pickering, Darwent, Bailey, Hague, Moan, Johnson, Nelson, Suddick, Laidler (Bennett), Robinson.

1999 TIVERTON TOWN 1 *(Western)*   **BEDLINGTON TERRIERS** 0 *(Northern)*   Att: 13, 878
Rogers 88   Ref: W. C. Burns
Bedlington Terriers: O'Connor, Bowes, Pike, Boon (Renforth), Melrose, Teasdale, Cross, Middleton (Ludlow), Gibb, Milner, Bond. Subs:
Pearson, Cameron, Gowans
Tiverton Town: Edwards, Fallon, Saunders, Tatterton, Tallon, Conning (Rogers), Nancekivell (Pears), Varley, Everett, Daly, Leonard. Subs:
Tucker, Hynds, Grimshaw

2000 DEAL TOWN 1 *(Kent)*   **CHIPPENHAM TOWN** 0 *(Western)*   Att: 20,000
Graham 87   Ref: D Laws
Deal Town: Tucker, Kempster, Best, Ash, Martin, Seager, Monteith, Graham, Lovell, Marshall, Ribbens. Subs: Roberts, Warden, Turner
Chippenham Town: Jones, James, Andrews, Murphy, Burns, Woods, Brown, Charity, Tweddle, Collier, Godley. Subs: Tiley, Cutler

2001 TAUNTON TOWN 2 *(Western)*   **BERKHAMPSTED TOWN** 1 *(Isthmian 2)*   (at Villa Park) Att: 8,439
Fields 41, Laight 45   Lowe 71   Ref: E. K. Wolstenholme
Taunton Town: Draper, Down, Chapman, West, Hawkings, Kelly, Fields (Groves), Laight, Cann (Tallon), Bastow, Lynch (Hapgood).
Subs: Ayres, Parker
Berkhampsted Town: O'Connor, Mullins, Lowe, Aldridge, Coleman, Brockett, Yates, Adebowale, Richardson, Smith, Nightingale.
Subs: Ringsell, Hall, Knight, Franklin, Osborne

2002 WHITLEY BAY 1 *(Northern)*   **TIPTREE UNITED** 0 *(Eastern)*   (at Villa Park) Att: 4742
Chandler 97   Ref: A Kaye
Whitley Bay: Caffrey, Sunderland, Walmsley, Dixon (Neil), Anderson, Locker, Middleton, Bowes (Carr), Chandler, Walton, Fenwick (Cuggy).
Subs: Cook, Livermore
Tiptree United: Haygreen, Battell, Wall, Houghton, Fish, Streetley (Gillespie), Wareham (Snow), Daly, Barefield, Aransibia (Parnell), Brady.
Subs: Powell, Ford.

2003 BRIGG TOWN 2 *(Northern Co.East)*   **A.F.C SUDBURY** 1 *(Eastern Counties)* (at Upton Park) Att: 6,634
Housham 2, Carter 68   Raynor 30   Ref: M Fletcher
Brigg Town:- Steer, Raspin, Rowland, Thompson, Blanchard, Stones, Stead (Thompson 41), Housham,
Borman (Drayton 87), Roach, Carter. Subs (not used) Nevis, Gawthorpe.
AFC Sudbury:- Greygoose, Head (Norfolk 63), Spearing, Tracey, Bishop, Anderson (Owen 73), Rayner,
Gardiner (Banya 79), Bennett, Claydon, Betson. Subs (not used) Taylor, Hyde.

2004 WINCHESTER CITY 2 *(Wessex)*   **A.F.C SUDBURY** 0 *(Eastern Counties)* (at St Andrews) Att: 5,080
Forbes 19, Smith 73 (pen)   Ref: P Crossley
Winchester City:- Arthur, Dyke (Tate 83), Bicknell, Redwood, Goss, Blake, Webber, Green, Mancey, Forbes (Rogers 70),
Smith (Green 90). Subs (not used) - Lang and Rastall.
AFC Sudbury:- Greygoose, Head, Wardley, Girling, Tracey, Norfolk, Owen (Banya 62), Hyde (Calver 57), Bennett, Claydon,
Betson (Francis 73n). Subs (not used) - Rayner, Nower.

2005 DIDCOT TOWN 3 *(Hellenic)*   **A.F.C SUDBURY** 2 *(Eastern Counties)*(at White Hart Lane) Att: 8,662
Beavon (2), Wardley (og)   Wardley, Calver (pen)   Ref: R Beeeby
Didcot Town:- Webb, Goodall, Heapy, Campbell, Green, Parrott, Hannigan, Ward, Concannon (Jones 88), Beavon (Bianchini 90), Powell.
Subs (not used) – Cooper, Allen, Spurrett.
AFC Sudbury:- Greygoose, Girling, Wardley, Bennett, Hyde (Hayes 78), Owen (Norfolk 65), Claydon (Banya 59), Head, Calver, Betson,
Terry Rayner. Subs (not used) – Howlett, Nower.

2006 NANTWICH TOWN 3 *(NWC 1)*   **HILLINGDON BOROUGH** 1 *(Spartan S.Mids P.)*(at St Andrews) Att: 3,286
Kinsey (2), Scheuber   Nelson
Nantwich Town:- Hackney, A.Taylor, T.Taylor, Smith, Davis, Donnelly, Beasley, Scheuber (Parkinson 69), Kinsey (Marrow 69),
Blake (Scarlett 86) and Griggs. Subs (not used): O'Connor and Read.
Hillingdon Borough:- Brown, Rundell (Fenton 80),Kidson, Phillips, Croft, Lawrence, Duncan (Nelson 46), Tilbury, Hibbs,
Wharton (Lyons 38). Subs (not used): O'Grady, White.

2007 TRURO 3 *(Western Division 1)*   **AFC TOTTON** 1 *(Wessex Division 1)* Att: 27,754 (New Vase record)
Wills (2), Broad   Potter   Ref: P Joslin
AFC Totton: Brunnschweiler, Reacord, Troon (Stevens 60), Potter (Gregory 82), Bottomley, Austen, Roden, Gosney, Hamodu (Goss 89), Osman, Byres.
Subs not used: Zammit, McCormack.
Truro City: Stevenson, Ash, Power, Smith, Martin (Pope 84), Broad, Wills, Gosling, Yetton, Watkins, Walker (Ludlam 90).
Subs not used: Butcher, Routledge, Reski.

2008 KIRKHAM & WESHAM 2 *(North West Co. Div.2)* **LOWESTOFT TOWN** 1 *(Eastern Co. Premier)* Att: 19,537
Walwyn (2)   Thompson (og)   Ref: A D'Urso
Kirkham and Wesham: Summerfield, Jackson (Walwyn 79), Keefe (Allen 55), Thompson, Shaw, Eastwood, Clark, Blackwell, Wane, Paterson (Sheppard 90), Smith. Subs not used: Moffat and Abbott
Lowestoft Town: Reynolds, Poppy, Potter, Woodrow, Saunders, Plaskett (McGee 79), Godbold, Darren Cockrill (Dale Cockrill 46), Stock, Hough, King (Hunn 55). Subs not used: McKenna and Rix.

2009 WHITLEY BAY 2 *(Northern Division One)* **GLOSSOP NORTH END** 0 *(North West Co. Prem)* Att: 12,212
Kerr, Chow   Ref: K Friend
Whitley Bay: Burke, Taylor, Picton, McFarlane (Fawcett 60), Coulson, Ryan, Moore, Robson, Kerr, Chow (Robinson 73), Johnston (Bell 60). Subs not used: McLean and Reay.
Glossop North End: Cooper, Young, Kay, Lugsden, Yates, Gorton, Bailey (Hind 57), Morris, Allen (Balfe 65), Hamilton (Bailey 72), Hodges. Subs not used: Whelan and Parker.

2010 WHITLEY BAY 6 *(Northern Division One)* **WROXHAM** 1 *(Eastern Counties Premier Division)* Att: 8,920
Chow 21(sec), Easthaugh 16 (og), Kerr, Johnston,   Cook 12   Ref: A Taylor
Robinson, Gillies
Whitley Bay: Terry Burke, Craig McFarlane, Callum Anderson, Richard Hodgson, (sub Lee Picton 69th min), Darren Timmons, Leon Ryan, Adam Johnston (sub Joshua Gillies 77th min), Damon Robson, Lee Kerr, Paul Chow (sub Phillip Bell 61st min), Paul Robinson. Subs not used – Tom Kindley and Chris Reid.
Wroxham: Scott Howie, Gavin Pauling (sub Ross Durrant 57th min), Shaun Howes, Graham Challen, Martin McNeil (sub Josh Carus 46th min), Andy Easthaugh (sub Owen Paynter 69th min), Steve Spriggs, Gavin Lemmon, Paul Cook, Danny White, Gary Gilmore. Subs not used – Danny Self and Gareth Simpson.

2011 WHITLEY BAY 3 *(Northern Division One)* **COALVILLE TOWN** 2 *(Midland Alliance)* Att: 8,778
Chow 28, 90, Kerr 61   Moore 58, Goodby 80   Ref: S Mathieson
Whitley Bay: Terry Burke, Craig McFarlane (sub Steve Gibson 90th min), Callum Anderson, Darren Timmons, Gareth Williams (sub David Coulson 68th min), Damon Robson, Lee Kerr, Paul Chow, Paul Robinson, David Pounder (sub Brian Smith 68th min), Gary Ormston. Subs not used – Kyle Hayes (gk) and Brian Rowe. Coalville Town: Sean Bowles, Ashley Brown (sub Matthew Gardner 88th min), Cameron Stuart, Adam Goodby, Zach Costello, Lee Miveld, Callum Woodward, Anthony Carney (sub Craig Attwood 90th min), Ryan Robbins (sub Ashley Wells 66th min), Matt Moore, Jerome Murdock. Subs not used – Richard Williams (gk) and James Dodd.

2012 DUNSTON UTS 2 *(Northern Division One)* **WEST AUCKLAND TOWN** 0 *(Northern Division One)* Att: 5,126
Bulford 32, 79   Ref: R East
Dunston UTS: Liam Connell, Ben Cattenach, Terry Galbraith, Michael Robson, Chris Swailes, Kane Young, Steven Shaw, Michael Dixon, Stephen Goddard (sub Sreven Preen 84th min), Andrew Bulford (sub Danny Craggs 88th min), Lee McAndrew. *Subs not used* – Andrew Clark (g/k), Ian Herron, Jack Burns.
West Auckland Town: Mark Bell, Neil Pattinson, Andrew Green, Jonny Gibson, John Parker, Mark Stephenson (sub Daniel Hindmarsh 76th min), Stuart Banks, Mark Hudson, Mattie Moffatt, Michael Rae, Adam Nicholls (sub Martin Young 60th min). *Subs not used* – Daryll Hall, Ross Preston, Matthew Coad.

2013 SPENNYMOOR TOWN 2 *(Northern Division One)* **TUNBRIDGE WELLS** 1 *(Kent League)* Att: 16,751
Cogdon 18, Graydon 80   Stanford 78   Ref: M Naylor
Spennymoor Town: Robert Dean, Kallum Griffiths, Leon Ryan, Chris Mason, Stephen Capper, Keith Graydon, Lewis Dodds, Wayne Phillips (Anthony Peacock 64 min), Joe Walton (Andrew Stephenson 73 min), Mark Davison, (Michael Rae 76 min), Gavin Congdon. *Subs not used* - David Knight (g/k), Steven Richardson.
Tunbridge Wells: Chris Oladogba, Jason Bourne, Scott Whibley, Perry Spackman, Lewis Mingle, Jon Pilbeam (Richard Sinden 85 min), Andy McMath, Joe Fuller (Tom Davey 58 min), Andy Irvine, Carl Connell (Jack Harris 58 min), Josh Stanford. *Subs not used* - Michael Czanner (gk), Andy Boyle.

2014 SHOLING 1 *(Wessex Premier Division - 1st)* **WEST AUCKLAND TOWN** 0 *(Northern Division One - 5th)* Att: 5,432
McLean 71   Ref: D Coote
Sholing: Matt Brown, Mike Carter, Marc Diaper, Peter Castle (Dan Miller 53 min), Lee Bright, Tyronne Bowers (Kevin Brewster 75 min), Barry Mason, Lewis Fennemore (Alex Sawyer 78 min), Lee Wort, Byron Mason, Marvin McLean. *Subs not used* - Ashley Jarvis, Nick Watts.
West Auckland Town: Jordan Nixon, Neil Pattinson, Andrew Green (Jonathan Gibson 63 min), Daryll Hall, Lewis Galpin, Brian Close, Shaun Vipond (Stuart Banks 76 min), Robert Briggs, Mattie Moffat (Steven Richardson 74 min). John Campbell, Dennis Knight. *Subs not used* - Paul Garthwaite, Adam Wilkinson..

2015 NORTH SHIELDS 2 *(Northern Division One - 4th)* **GLOSSOP NORTH END** 1 *(North West Co. Premier - 1st)* Att: 9,674
Bainbridge 80, Forster 96   Bailey 55   Ref: A Madley
North Shields: Christopher Bannon, Stuart Donnison, John Parker, Kevin Hughes, John Grey, James Luccock (Ryan Carr 59), Ben Richardson, Mciahel McKeown, Dean Holmes (Adam Forster 69), Denver Morris, Gareth Bainbridge (Kieran Wrightson 107). *Subs not used* - Curtis Coppen and Marc Lancaster.
Glossop North End: Greg Hall, Michael Bowler, Matthew Russell, Kevin Lugsden, Dave Young, Martin Parker, Lee Blackshaw (Samuel Grimshaw 69), Samuel Hare (Samuel Hind 82), Tom Bailey, Kieran Lugsden, Eddie Moran (Daniel White 60). *Subs not used* - Benjamin Richardson and Richard Gresty.

2016 MORPETH TOWN 4 *(Northern Division One - 4th)*   **HEREFORD** 1 *(Midland League - 1st)*   **Att: 46,781**
Swailes 34, Carr 47, Taylor 59, Bell 92   Purdie 2   *(Inaugural Non-League finals day)*
Ref: S Atwelly

Morpeth Town: Karl Dryden, Stephen Forster, James Novak, Ben Sayer, Chris Swailes, Michael Hall, Sean Taylor (sub Damien Mullen 78),
Keith Graydon, Luke Carr (sub Shaun Bell 88), Michael Chilton (sub Steven Anderson 69), Jordan Fry.
Subs not used - Dale Pearson and Niall Harrison.
Hereford: Martin Horsell, Jimmy Oates, Joel Edwards, Rob Purdie, Ryan Green, Aaron Birch, Pablo Haysham, Mike Symons,
Jamie Willets (sub John Mills 70), Joe Tumelty (sub Mustapha Bundu 55), Sirdic Grant.
Subs not used - Nathan Summers, Dylan Bonella and Ross Staley.

2017 SOUTH SHIELDS 4 *(Northern Division One - 1st)*   **CLEETHORPES TOWN** 0 *(Northern Counties East Premier - 1st)*   **Att: 38,224**
Finnigan 43 (pen), Morse 80, Foley 86, 89   *(Combined FA Trophy/Vase att.)*
Ref: D England

South Shields: Liam Connell, Alex Nicholson, Darren Lough, Jon Shaw, Dillon Morse, Julio Arca, Andrew Stephenson (sub Robert Briggs 56),
Wayne Phillips (sub Barrie Smith 82), Gavin Congdon, Carl Finnigan (sub Michael Richardson 71), David Foley.
Subs not used - Louis Storey and Darren Holden.
Cleethorpes Town: Liam Higton, Tim Lowe, Peter Winn, Liam Dickens, Matt Bloomer, Matty Coleman (sub Luke Mascall 70),
Liam Davis (sub Jack Richardson 73), Alex Flett, Marc Cooper (Andy Taylor 61), Brody Richardson, Jon Oglesby.
Subs not used - Gary King and Kieran Wressell.

2018 THATCHAM TOWN 1 *(Hellenic Premier - 1st)*   **STOCKTON TOWN** 0 *(Northern League D1 - 6th)*   **Att: 31,430**
Cooper-Clark 23 (pen)   *(Combined FA Trophy/Vase att.)*
Ref: J Brooks

Thatcham Town: Chris Rackley, Lewis Brownhill, Curtis Angell, Tom Melledew (c) (Ashliegh James 81), Baboucarr Jarra, Tom Moran, Harrison Bayley,
Shane Cooper-Clark (Rose Cook 89), Gavin James, Ekow Elliott, Jordan Brown (Jemel Johnson 70).
Subs not used - Harry Grant, Gareth Thomas.
Stockton Town: Michael Arthur, Joe Carter (Matthew Garbutt 61), James Ward (Adam Nicholson 79), Nathan Mulligan, Dale Mulligan, Tom Coulthard (c),
Kevin Hayes, Fred Woodhouse, Jamie Owens, James Risbrough, Chris Stockton (Sonni Coleman 67).
Subs not used - Alan Cossavella, Chris Dunwell.

2019 CHERTSEY TOWN 3 *(Combined Counties Prem - 1st)*   **CRAY VALLEY (PM)** 1 *(Southern Counties East Prem - 1st)*   **Att: 42,962**
Flegg 38, Baxter 105 (pen), Rowe 117   Tomlin 36   *(Combined FA Trophy/Vase att.)*
Ref: R Joyce

Chertsey Town: Nick Jupp, Sam Flegg, Michael Peacock, Quincy Rowe, Mason Welch-Turner, Kevin Maclaren (Dave Taylor 79), Lubomir Guentchev,
Sam Murphy, Lewis Driver (Andy Crossley 83), Dale Binns (Lewis Jackson 97), Jake Baxter (John Pomroy 118).
Subs not used - Lewis Gallifent, Michael Kinsella, Danny Bennell.
Cray Valley (PM): Andy Walker, Denzel Gayle, Cem Tumkaya (Brad Potter 106), Ashley Sains (Calum Willock 112), Liam Hickey, Danny Smith,
Ryan Flack (Josh James 72), Paul Semakula, Anthony Edgar, Gavin Tomlin, Kevin Lisbie (Francis Babalola 100).
Subs not used - Deren Ibrahim, Tyler Myers, Lea Dawson.

All Finals at Wembley unless otherwise stated.

FAV - 1P - Turner (Longridge) shoots under pressure from Gavin (Crook). Photo Keith Clayton.

FAV - 1P - Wellingborough Town 4-3 Takeley. Photo Peter Barnes.

FAV - 1Q - Shortwood United 5-0 Tuffley Rovers. Photo Peter Barnes.

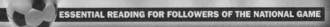
ESSENTIAL READING FOR FOLLOWERS OF THE NATIONAL GAME

BUY IT IN YOUR NEWSAGENTS EVERY SUNDAY

BE CLOSE TO THE PASSION

PRELIMINARY ROUND

1 Carlisle City v Consett (3/9) 3-3aet 83
(Carlisle City won 3-2 on kicks from the penalty mark)
2 Gateshead v South Shields (6/9) 2-3 216
3 Chester-Le-Street Town v Stockton Town (3/9) 0-3
4 Penrith v Cleator Moor Celtic (5/9) 9-0 37
5 Workington v Hebburn Town (5/9) 3-2aet 107
6 Guisborough Town v Morpeth Town (5/9) 0-11 60
7 North Shields v Shildon
(walkover for North Shields – Shildon withdrawn)
8 Bootle v Abbey Hey
(walkover for Bootle – Abbey Hey withdrawn)
9 St Helens Town v AFC Blackpool (8/9) 0-2 31
10 Sandbach United v Witton Albion (4/9) 6-2
11 Litherland Remyca v Garstang (2/9) 4-1 73
12 Radcliffe v Skelmersdale United (4/9) 8-1
13 West Didsbury & Chorlton v Cheadle Town (5/9) 2-5 68
(at Cheadle Town FC)
14 Irlam v Mossley (3/9) 10-0 85
15 Southport v Wythenshawe Amateurs (6/9) 6-0
16 Ashton Athletic v Prescot Cables (2/9) 4-1 57
17 Ashton Town v Vauxhall Motors (3/9) 1-5 50
18 FC United of Manchester v Stalybridge Celtic (4/9) 4-0 112
19 Altrincham v Curzon Ashton 2-2aet
(Curzon Ashton won 4-3 on kicks from the penalty mark)
20 City of Liverpool v Padiham (4/9) 4-1 60
(at Litherland Remyca FC)
21 Egerton v Lancaster City
(walkover for Lancaster City – Egerton not accepted into the Competition)
22 Warrington Town v Buxton (4/9) 1-2 31
23 Retford v Frickley Athletic (5/9) 0-2 68
24 Stocksbridge Park Steels v Grimsby Borough (5/9) 2-0 75
25 Hall Road Rangers v Selby Town (3/9) 1-3
26 Steeton v Handsworth Parramore (4/9) 0-3
27 Silsden v Staveley MW (2/9) 3-0 61
28 Brigg Town v Scarborough Athletic (5/9) 4-1
29 Harrogate Railway Athletic v Retford United (3/9) 3-1
30 Sheffield v Rossington Main (5/9) 7-1 47
31 Bradford (Park Avenue) C. v Brighouse Town (5/9) 1-4 69
32 Garforth Town v Farsley Celtic (5/9) 2-1 49
33 York City v Pontefract Collieries (4/9) 3-0
34 Cleethorpes Town v Guiseley (4/9) 0-7
35 Bottesford Town v Eccleshill United (5/9) 1-1aet 71
(Eccleshill United won 2-1 on kicks from the penalty mark)
36 Dronfield Town v Athersley Recreation (5/9) 1-4 33
37 Dunkirk v Grantham Town (5/9) 2-2aet 96
(Grantham Town won 3-0 on kicks from the penalty mark)
38 Bourne Town v Leicester Nirvana (3/9) 0-4
39 Stamford v Belper Town
(walkover for Stamford – Belper Town withdrawn)
40 Matlock Town v Anstey Nomads (4/9) 1-2
41 Mickleover Sports v Harrowby United
(walkover for Mickleover Sports – Harrowby United withdrawn)
42 Long Eaton United v Borrowash Victoria (5/9) 4-1 56
43 Deeping Rangers v Hinckley (5/9) 7-2 51
44 Lincoln United v Blaby & Whetstone Athletic (4/9)0-0aet
(Lincoln United won 4-3 on kicks from the penalty mark)
45 Eastwood Community v Lutterworth Athletic (6/9) 2-1
46 Leek Town v Coleshill Town
(walkover for Coleshill Town – Leek Town withdrawn)
47 Lye Town v Ellesmere Rangers (2/9) 3-1
48 Stafford Rangers v Leamington (4/9) 2-1 53
49 Coton Green v Hednesford Town (5/9) 0-3
50 Coventry Sphinx v Newcastle Town (5/9) 5-6aet
51 Alvechurch v Bedworth United (2/9) 4-1 80
52 Lichfield City v Chelmsley Town (2/9) 6-0 40
53 Boldmere St Michaels v Paget Rangers (3/9) 3-1 105
54 Atherstone Town v Bromsgrove Sporting
(walkover for Bromsgrove Sporting - Atherstone Town withdrawn)
55 Rushall Olympic v Shawbury United (3/9) 3-1 58
56 Bromyard Town v Stratford Town (2/9) 0-5
57 Halesowen Town v Tamworth (4/9) 3-2 171
58 Bustleholme v Bilston Town Community (3/9) 4-0
59 Stourport Swifts v Tipton Town (4/9) 10-0 59
60 AFC Telford United v Hereford (5/9) 2-3
(at Market Drayton Town FC)

61 Newport Pagnell Town v Daventry Town (5/9) 0-5 112
62 St Neots Town v Barton Rovers (4/9) 4-0 51
63 Bugbrooke St Michaels v Rothwell Corinthians (5/9) 2-2aet 45
(Bugbrooke St Michaels won 3-0 on kicks from the penalty mark)
64 Brackley Town v Wellingborough Town (2/9) 0-1 72
65 Biggleswade United v Leighton Town
(walkover for Leighton Town – Biggleswade United withdrawn)
66 Winslow United v Buckingham Athletic (5/9) 1-2 55
67 Netherton United v Hitchin Town (3/9) 1-4
68 Godmanchester Rovers v Stotfold (4/9) 1-2
69 Corby Town v Royston Town (2/9) 1-9 60
70 Kettering Town v Kempston Rovers (2/9) 4-2aet 43
71 Rugby Town v Wellingborough Whitworth (4/9) 6-1
72 AFC Rushden & Diamondsv Peterborough Sports (4/9) 2-3
73 Gorleston v Wroxham (5/9) 2-1aet 83
74 Hadleigh United v Wisbech St Mary (4/9) 1-6
75 Ely City v Stowmarket Town (5/9) 4-2
76 Whitton United v AFC Sudbury (5/9) 0-5
77 Walsham Le Willows v Framlingham Town (5/9) 2-1 42
78 Newmarket Town v Dereham Town (3/9) 3-6
79 Mildenhall Town v King's Lynn Town (5/9) 1-3 79
80 Cornard United v Bury Town (5/9) 0-6
81 Haverhill Rovers v Ipswich Wanderers (5/9) 8-2
82 Long Melford v Leiston (5/9) 2-0
83 Fakenham Town v Needham Market (5/9) 0-15
84 Saffron Walden Town v Lowestoft Town (5/9) 3-1 87
85 Histon v Lakenheath (5/9) 1-2aet
86 Cambridge City v Swaffham Town (2/9) 1-0 73
(at Huntingdon Town FC)
87 St Albans City v Aveley (5/9) 1-2aet 38
88 Harpenden Town v Grays Athletic (5/9) 4-5aet 47
89 Codicote v Hornchurch (5/9) 1-8 45
(at Hornchurch FC)
90 Wodson Park v Ware
(walkover for Ware – Wodson Park withdrawn)
91 Heybridge Swifts v Witham Town (2/9) 4-3aet 95
92 Great Wakering Rovers v Enfield Town (5/9) 0-3 36
93 St Margaretsbury v Ilford (5/9) 1-0
94 Barkingside v Redbridge (2/9) 1-3 43
95 Welwyn Garden City v Takeley (5/9) 6-5
96 Stanway Rovers v Sawbridgeworth Town (6/9) 3-2
97 Woodford Town v FC Broxbourne Borough (3/9) 2-0
98 Bowers & Pitsea v Cheshunt (2/9) 7-1 83
99 Brightlingsea Regent v Brentwood Town (5/9) 1-3
100 Tilbury v Hertford Town (6/9) 0-5 118
101 Colney Heath v Chelmsford City (2/9) 2-1
102 Bishop's Stortford v Romford (3/9) 0-6 44
103 Wingate & Finchley v Cockfosters (3/9) 2-2aet 127
(Wingate & Finchley won 4-2 on kicks from the penalty mark)
104 Barking v Braintree Town (5/9) 1-3 54
105 Hayes & Yeading United v Ashford Town (Middx) (4/9) 3-0 53
106 Spelthorne Sports v Hendon (3/9) 3-2
107 London Tigers v Hampton & Richmond Borough (11/9) 3-5
(at Hampton & Richmond Borough FC)
108 Uxbridge v Balham (4/9) 1-0
109 Hanworth Villa v Harefield United (3/9) 9-0
110 Staines Town v Beaconsfield Town (4/9) 0-6
111 North Greenford United v Burnham (4/9) 2-1 48
112 Edgware Town v Chalfont St Peter (4/9) 3-1
113 Wealdstone v CB Hounslow United (4/1) 2-1
114 Cray Wanderers v VCD Athletic (4/9) 4-3
115 Carshalton Athletic v K Sports (2/9) 1-2
116 Hastings United v Punjab United (5/9) 2-1aet
117 Corinthian v Folkestone Invicta (2/9) 3-1 74
118 East Grinstead Town v Glebe (3/9) 1-3
119 Eastbourne Borough v Eastbourne Town (6/9) 6-0
120 Tooting & Mitcham United v Dartford (4/9) 0-8
121 Sittingbourne v AFC Croydon Athletic (3/9) 5-0 80
122 Maidstone United v Dulwich Hamlet (5/9) 3-6 214
123 Phoenix Sports v Tonbridge Angels (4/9) 0-1 101
124 Welling United v FC Elmstead (5/9)
(match abandoned, 94th minute,6-5 – Welling United & FC Elmstead removed from the Competition - subject to appeal)
125 Ramsgate v Crowborough Athletic (3/9) 3-0
(tie awarded to Crowborough Athletic – Ramsgate removed)
126 Margate v Tower Hamlets (6/9) 3-4aet 105

No	Home		Away (date)	Score	Ref
127	Badshot Lea	v	Welling Town		
	(walkover for Badshot Lea – Welling Town withdrawn)				
128	Cray Valley (PM)	v	Bridon Ropes (2/9)	2-1	
129	Hollands & Blair	v	Whyteleafe (4/9)	0-5	
130	East Preston	v	Newhaven (5/9)	1-0	52
131	Sutton Common Rovers	v	Worthing (2/9)	5-4aet	
132	Worthing United	v	Guildford City (4/9)	3-0	48
133	Whitehawk	v	Walton Casuals (2/9)	1-3	
134	Steyning Town Community	v	Godalming Town (6/9)	3-1	156
135	Chipstead	v	Arundel (3/9)	2-1	154
136	Horley Town	v	Shoreham (5/9)	1-2	
137	Chertsey Town	v	Metropolitan Police (4/9)	2-1	
138	Redhill	v	Lewes (5/9)	1-2	92
139	Abbey Rangers	v	Pagham (5/9)	3-2aet	40
140	Raynes Park Vale	v	Chichester City (5/9)	4-3aet	
141	South Park	v	Bognor Regis Town (2/9)	1-1aet	41
	(Bognor Regis Town won 4-2 on kicks from the penalty mark)				
142	Corinthian Casuals	v	Kingstonian (9/9)	0-6	122
143	Leatherhead	v	Haywards Heath Town (4/9)	7-0	56
144	Lancing	v	Chessington & Hook United (3/9)	2-0	
145	Berkhamsted	v	Bracknell Town (3/9)	5-5aet	44
	(Berkhamsted won 4-2 on kicks from the penalty mark)				
146	Hungerford Town	v	Tring Athletic (4/9)	1-1aet	
	(Hungerford Town won 4-3 on kicks from the penalty mark)				
147	Wokingham & Emmbrook	v	Thatcham Town (3/9)	3-2	
148	Thame United	v	Easington Sports (4/9)	1-2	
	(at Easington Sports FC)				
149	Binfield	v	Camberley Town (4/9)	0-9	47
150	Farnborough	v	Kings Langley (4/9)	0-3	
151	Kidlington	v	Hemel Hempstead Town (5/9)	0-7	37
152	Fleet Town	v	Aylesbury Vale Dynamos (2/9)	1-2aet	
153	Reading City	v	Ardley United (6/9)	4-1	
154	Holmer Green	v	Tadley Calleva (5/9)	1-2	44
155	Havant & Waterlooville	v	Winchester City (5/9)	1-2	126
156	Basingstoke Town	v	Dorchester Town (3/9)	0-1	
157	Salisbury	v	Andover Town (4/9)	2-4	101
158	Bournemouth	v	Alton (4/9)	0-6	36
159	Hamble Club	v	Ringwood Town (2/9)	7-1	
160	AFC Totton	v	Fareham Town		
	(walkover for AFC Totton – Fareham Town withdrawn)				
161	AFC Portchester	v	Wimborne Town (3/9)	1-2	
162	Brockenhurst	v	Pewsey Vale (5/9)	15-1	67
163	Poole Town	v	Moneyfields (4/9)	1-2	152
164	Totton & Eling	v	Sholing (5/9)	1-8	
165	Slimbridge	v	Malvern Town (2/9)	3-2	72
166	Bishop's Cleeve	v	New College Swindon (2/9)	3-4	
167	Chippenham Town	v	Gloucester City (2/9)	3-0	
168	Shrivenham	v	Cirencester Town (5/9)	0-4	
169	Cinderford Town	v	Tuffley Rovers (5/9)	3-1	90
170	Clanfield 85	v	Yate Town		
	(walkover for Clanfield 85 – Yate Town withdrawn)				
171	Wells City	v	Street (3/9)	2-10	
172	Bristol Manor Farm	v	Odd Down (4/9)	2-1	
173	Weston Super Mare	v	Radstock Town		
	(walkover for Weston Super Mare – Radstock withdrawn)				
174	Bridgwater Town	v	Keynsham Town		
	(walkover for Bridgwater Town – Keynsham Town withdrawn)				
175	Clevedon Town	v	Mangotsfield United (2/9)	1-7	72
176	Paulton Rovers	v	Brislington (5/9)	1-3	
177	Longwell Green Sports	v	Helston Athletic		
	(walkover for Helston Athletic – Longwell Green Sports withdrawn)				
178	Cribbs	v	Welton Rovers (5/9)	3-0	38
179	Portishead Town	v	Bitton (5/9)	1-2	

FIRST ROUND QUALIFYING

No	Home		Away (date)	Score	Ref
1	Stockton Town	v	North Shields (16/9)	2-4aet	113
2	Seaham Red Star	v	Darlington (5/9)	2-1	65
3	Carlisle City	v	South Shields (19/9)	0-10	82
4	Workington	v	Penrith (19/9)	7-2	130
5	Spennymoor Town	v	Morpeth Town (19/9)	1-3	216
6	Hyde United	v	Marine (20/9)	3-3aet	114
	(Marine won 5-4 on kicks from the penalty mark)				
7	AFC Blackpool	v	Litherland Remyca (16/9)	2-3	
8	Sandbach United	v	Ashton Athletic (19/9)	2-3	
9	Irlam	v	Southport (19/9)	4-2	85
10	Nantwich Town	v	FC United of Manchester (18/9)	2-2aet	117
	(Nantwich Town won 4-3 on kicks from the penalty mark)				
11	Radcliffe	v	City of Liverpool (19/9)	3-9	62
12	Curzon Ashton	v	Vauxhall Motors (24/9)	11-1	
13	Cheadle Town	v	Buxton (19/9)	0-2	
14	Clitheroe	v	Chester (18/9)	1-4	100
15	Lancaster City	v	Bootle (18/9)	4-1	60
16	Shelley	v	Athersley Recreation (16/9)	0-4	42
17	Handsworth	v	Tadcaster Albion (16/9)	0-1	
18	AFC Emley	v	Frickley Athletic (16/9)	4-3	79
19	Eccleshill United	v	Brigg Town (18/9)	2-1	98
20	Harrogate Railway Athletic	v	Harworth Colliery (17/9)	5-1	67
21	Sheffield	v	Stocksbridge Park Steels (19/9)	4-2	98
22	Guiseley	v	Garforth Town (17/9)	2-0	150
23	Silsden	v	York City (18/9)	0-5	137
24	Selby Town	v	Brighouse Town (16/9)	1-0	
25	Anstey Nomads	v	Leicester Nirvana (18/9)	1-9	43
26	Mickleover Sports	v	Aylestone Park (18/9)	5-0	51
27	Deeping Rangers	v	Harborough Town (19/9)	3-1	38
28	Basford United	v	Gresley (18/9)	4-2aet	106
29	West Bridgford	v	Eastwood Community (19/9)	2-3	85
30	Long Eaton United	v	Boston United (17/9)	5-2	
31	Stamford	v	Lincoln United (16/9)	6-0	
32	Grantham Town	v	Alfreton Town (17/9)	2-1	
33	Stafford Rangers	v	Worcester City (18/9)	2-1	70
34	Hednesford Town	v	Lye Town (18/9)	1-2aet	61
35	Alvechurch	v	Haughmond (16/9)	1-2	45
36	Rushall Olympic	v	Bustleholme (17/9)	3-2	58
37	Sutton Coldfield Town	v	Bromsgrove Sporting (17/9)	1-3	58
38	Romulus	v	Coleshill Town (19/9)	1-0	
39	Racing Club Warwick	v	Newcastle Town (19/9)	3-1	105
40	Lichfield City	v	Boldmere St Michaels (16/9)	2-0	45
41	Stourport Swifts	v	Stourbridge (18/9)	0-1	82
42	Hereford	v	Stratford Town (19/9)	4-1	70
43	Kidderminster Harriers	v	Halesowen Town (17/9)	2-2aet	
	(Halesowen Town won 6-5 on kicks from the penalty mark)				
44	St Ives Town	v	Biggleswade Town (16/9)	4-2	84
45	Wellingborough Town	v	Peterborough Northern Star (19/9)	13-1	63
46	Rugby Borough	v	Daventry Town (16/9)	4-1	162
47	AFC Dunstable	v	Buckingham Athletic (19/9)	7-0	41
48	Hitchin Town	v	Eynesbury Rovers		
	(walkover for Hitchin Town – Eynesbury Rovers withdrawn)				
49	Stotfold	v	St Neots Town (18/9)	3-2aet	55
50	Peterborough Sports	v	Kettering Town (19/9)	3-2	
51	Leighton Town	v	Rugby Town (19/9)	1-2	
52	Bugbrooke St Michaels	v	Royston Town (19/9)	3-0	
53	Felixstowe & Walton United	v	Cambridge City (19/9)	1-0	76
54	AFC Sudbury	v	Woodbridge Town (19/9)	3-0	56
55	Norwich United	v	Gorleston (19/9)	2-0	
56	Lakenheath	v	Dereham Town (19/9)	2-7	
57	King's Lynn Town	v	Brantham Athletic (16/9)	6-2	
58	Bury Town	v	Wisbech St Mary (19/9)	5-2	51
59	Saffron Walden Town	v	Long Melford (19/9)	4-0	118
60	Walsham Le Willows	v	Needham Market (19/9)	4-5	42
61	Ely City	v	Haverhill Rovers (19/9)	7-1	55
62	Hornchurch	v	Haringey Borough (17/9)	3-0	38
63	Ware	v	Grays Athletic (18/9)	7-1	
64	Enfield Town	v	Billericay Town (16/9)	6-1	71
65	Stanway Rovers	v	Bowers & Pitsea (19/9)	0-6	
66	Braintree Town	v	Welwyn Garden City (18/9)	2-6	89
67	Romford	v	Aveley (23/9)	0-4	76
	(at Aveley FC)				
68	Colney Heath	v	Heybridge Swifts (23/9)	3-2	
69	St Margaretsbury	v	Redbridge (19/9)	0-3	55
70	Brentwood Town	v	Wingate & Finchley (19/9)	2-1	
71	Hertford Town	v	Concord Rangers (19/9)	2-3	
72	Walthamstow	v	Woodford Town (19/9)	2-7	91
73	Edgware Town	v	Spelthorne Sports (18/9)	6-1	31
74	Uxbridge	v	Brimsdown (16/9)	10-0	
75	North Greenford United	v	Hanworth Villa (18/9)	0-5	41
76	Hanwell Town	v	Hayes & Yeading United (18/9)	1-0	
77	Bedfont Sports Club	v	Windsor (16/9)	3-2	
78	Wealdstone	v	Northwood (18/9)	4-1	
79	Beaconsfield Town	v	Hampton & Richmond Boro (19/9)	3-4	47
80	Tower Hamlets	v	Hastings United (26/9)	0-4	53
	(at Hastings United FC)				

81	Glebe	v Dartford (19/9)	3-4aet	
82	Holmesdale	v Faversham Town (20/9)	0-8	
83	Badshot Lea	v Whitstable Town (17/9)	2-3	47
84	Croydon	v Whyteleafe (18/9)	3-1	44
85	Fisher	v Chatham Town		

(walkover for Chatham Town – Fisher withdrawn)

86	Hackney Wick	v Welling United or FC Elmstead		

(walkover for Hackney Wick – Welling United & FC Elmstead removed from the Competition)

87	K Sports	v Eastbourne Borough (16/9)	2-0	47
88	Cray Wanderers	v Ashford United (18/9)	4-2	44
89	Dulwich Hamlet	v Cray Valley (PM) (18/9)	1-0	
90	Tonbridge Angels	v Sittingbourne (18/9)	2-1	
91	Crowborough Athletic	v Corinthian (20/9)	0-4	
92	Worthing United	v Mile Oak (16/9)	0-1	
93	Walton Casuals	v Sutton Common Rovers (16/9)	0-1	
94	Chipstead	v Walton & Hersham (20/9)	5-2	34
95	Abbey Rangers	v Kingstonian (19/9)	0-1	
96	Dorking Wanderers	v Lewes (19/9)	1-0	155
97	Burgess Hill Town	v East Preston (16/9)	1-0	65
98	Knaphill	v Steyning Town Community (17/9)	4-0	
99	Shoreham	v Chertsey Town (19/9)	1-3	
100	Leatherhead	v Ash United (18/9)	4-1	56
101	Lancing	v Raynes Park Vale (18/9)	0-6	
102	Three Bridges	v Bognor Regis Town (16/9)	6-4aet	
103	Easington Sports	v Hungerford Town (16/9)	4-3	64
104	Camberley Town	v Ascot United (19/9)	5-1	
105	Fleet Spurs	v Cove (19/9)	1-0	40
106	Leverstock Green	v Tadley Calleva (19/9)	5-0	40
107	Oxford City	v Aylesbury Vale Dynamos (20/9)	4-0	90
108	Kings Langley	v Hartley Wintney (18/9)	3-2	42
109	Wokingham & Emmbrook	v Hemel Hempstead Town (19/9)	2-2aet	55

(Hemel Hempstead Town won 4-2 on kicks from the penalty mark)

110	Berkhamsted	v Reading City (18/9)	1-6	33
111	Winchester City	v Wimborne Town (19/9)	3-5	

(at Whitchurch United FC)

112	Dorchester Town	v Alton (18/9)	4-0	140
113	AFC Totton	v Brockenhurst (19/9)	3-4	
114	Sholing	v Moneyfields (16/9)	2-4	88
115	Andover Town	v Hamble Club (16/9)	4-0	
116	AFC Stoneham	v Christchurch (16/9)	8-0	
117	Clanfield 85	v Chippenham Town (19/9)	0-4	52
118	Cinderford Town	v Evesham United (17/9)	1-3	
119	Slimbridge	v New College Swindon (16/9)	4-2	
120	Cirencester Town	v Malmesbury Victoria (19/9)	3-0	50
121	Street	v Helston Athletic (24/9)	1-1aet	48

(Helston Athletic won 4-3 on kicks from the penalty mark)

122	Bristol Manor Farm	v Bridgwater Town (17/9)	2-3	49
123	Brislington	v Cribbs (25/9)	3-0	

(16/9 – tie abandoned after 44 mins, 0-4 – due to serious injury to player)

124	Elburton Villa	v Bitton (20/9)	2-3aet	101
125	Weston Super Mare	v Mangotsfield United (24/9)	2-3aet	
126	Bath City	v Frome Town (16/9)	5-0	195

SECOND ROUND QUALIFYING

1	Morpeth Town	v Workington (10/10)	9-1	
2	Seaham Red Star	v Hartlepool United (3/10)	0-7	120
3	South Shields	v North Shields (30/9)	3-1	
4	Nantwich Town	v Ashton Athletic (2/10)	6-5aet	131
5	Chorley	v Chester (30/9)	2-3aet	131
6	Stockport County	v Irlam (2/10)	3-2	181
7	AFC Fylde	v Lancaster City (2/10)	9-2	

(at Kellemargh Park)

8	Marine	v Curzon Ashton (3/10)	3-7aet	135
9	Litherland Remyca	v City of Liverpool (30/9)	3-1	48
10	Buxton	v FC Halifax Town (2/10)	1-5	
11	Harrogate Railway Athletic	v Selby Town (2/10)	4-3	68
12	Harrogate Town	v AFC Emley (30/9)	8-3	70
13	Eccleshill United	v Sheffield (10/10)	0-7	75

(at Sheffield FC)

14	York City	v Guiseley (2/10)	2-3	
15	Athersley Recreation	v Tadcaster Albion (3/10)	2-0	
16	Basford United	v Grantham Town (4/10)	3-1	
17	Chesterfield	v Mickleover Sports (30/9)	3-1	207
18	Deeping Rangers	v Eastwood Community (3/10)	2-1	67
19	Stamford	v Long Eaton United (30/9)	1-4	

20	Notts County	v Leicester Nirvana (1/10)	8-1	224
21	Haughmond	v Stourbridge (3/10)	2-0	51
22	Wrexham	v Solihull Moors (2/10)	5-2	114
23	Bromsgrove Sporting	v Rushall Olympic (3/10)	2-3	81
24	Romulus	v Halesowen Town (30/9)	6-2	
25	Stafford Rangers	v Lye Town (9/10)	1-1aet	67

(Stafford Rangers won 3-1 on kicks from the penalty mark)

26	Racing Club Warwick	v Lichfield City (3/10)	2-1	88
27	Stotfold	v Ely City (2/10)	4-2aet	40
28	St Ives Town	v AFC Dunstable (30/9)	0-3	60
29	Hitchin Town	v Peterborough Sports (2/10)	8-4	
30	Bugbrooke St Michaels	v Rugby Town (3/10)	0-5	
31	Wellingborough Town	v Rugby Borough (3/10)	2-5	78
32	AFC Sudbury	v Felixstowe & Walton United (3/10)	11-0	74
33	Saffron Walden Town	v Needham Market (3/10)	0-5	100
34	King's Lynn Town	v Bury Town (30/9)	6-4	
35	Dereham Town	v Norwich United (3/10)	5-0	94
36	Bowers & Pitsea	v Concord Rangers (4/10)	4-2	120
37	Hornchurch	v Dagenham & Redbridge (3/10)	11-0	49
38	Aveley	v Welwyn Garden City (30/9)	2-1	64
39	Colney Heath	v Woodford Town (30/9)	1-3	
40	Ware	v Enfield Town (2/10)	1-0	
41	Redbridge	v Brentwood Town (21/10)	0-9	
42	Hanworth Villa	v Hampton & Richmond Borough (3/10)	3-0	
43	Barnet	v Edgware Town (2/10)	3-1	322
44	Uxbridge	v Hanwell Town (3/10)	4-3	
45	Wealdstone	v Bedfont Sports Club (23/10)	1-0	64

(2/10 – tie ordered to be replayed)

46	Boreham Wood	v Maidenhead United (1/10)	0-3	89
47	Hackney Wick	v Croydon (4/10)	2-8	
48	Dover Athletic	v Tonbridge Angels (2/10)	2-2aet	

(Dover Athletic won 4-2 on kicks from the penalty mark)

49	Dartford	v Chatham Town (1/10)	5-4aet	190
50	Bromley	v Corinthian (1/10)	6-1	
51	Faversham Town	v Cray Wanderers (1/10)	1-2	63
52	Whitstable Town	v K Sports (3/10)	1-4	
53	Dulwich Hamlet	v Hastings United (9/10)	4-3	
54	Kingstonian	v Raynes Park Vale (2/10)	7-1	

(at Colliers Wood United FC)

55	Mile Oak	v Sutton United (4/10)	2-3	47
56	Burgess Hill Town	v Dorking Wanderers (30/9)	0-4	87
57	Knaphill	v Three Bridges (1/10)	3-2	
58	Sutton Common Rovers	v Chipstead (4/10)	3-1aet	
59	Chertsey Town	v Leatherhead (30/9)	4-1	121
60	Camberley Town	v Easington Sports (4/10)	5-1	
61	Hemel Hempstead Town	v Reading City (9/10)	1-6	53
62	Oxford City	v Kings Langley (1/10)	4-0	66
63	Leverstock Green	v Fleet Spurs (3/10)	4-0	
64	Dorchester Town	v AFC Stoneham (2/10)	0-5	85
65	Aldershot Town	v Yeovil Town (30/9)	2-6	
66	Wimborne Town	v Brockenhurst (2/10)	3-4	80
67	Andover Town	v Moneyfields (30/9)	2-0	
68	Eastleigh	v Woking (2/10)	3-3aet	128

(Eastleigh won 5-3 on kicks from the penalty mark)

69	Bath City	v Cirencester Town (1/10)	3-0	
70	Evesham United	v Hereford (3/10)	0-4	
71	Slimbridge	v Chippenham Town (30/9)	2-0	98
72	Mangotsfield United	v Bitton (2/10)	5-0	79
73	Bridgwater Town	v Torquay United (30/9)	2-1	69
74	Brislington	v Helston Athletic (2/10)	0-5	

THIRD ROUND QUALIFYING

1	Litherland Remyca	v FC Halifax Town (16/10)	1-4	110
2	Stockport County	v Hartlepool United (16/10)	0-6	189
3	Wrexham	v Sheffield (16/10)	3-2	102
4	Morpeth Town	v AFC Fylde (17/10)	4-0	
5	Athersley Recreation	v Chester (17/10)	2-8	
6	Guiseley	v Curzon Ashton (15/10)	1-3	
7	Harrogate Railway Athletic	v Nantwich Town (22/10)	2-3aet	39
8	South Shields	v Harrogate Town (14/10)	5-1	
9	Long Eaton United	v Racing Club Warwick (15/10)	4-1	
10	Basford United	v Notts County (18/10)	0-5	355
11	Romulus	v Chesterfield (18/10)	2-3aet	
12	Deeping Rangers	v Haughmond (17/10)	0-6	76
13	Stafford Rangers	v Rugby Town (14/10)	1-5	89
14	Rushall Olympic	v Rugby Borough (14/10)	4-2	75
15	Ware	v Needham Market (16/10)	4-1	
16	Hitchin Town	v King's Lynn Town (16/10)	3-4	124

17	AFC Dunstable	v	Dereham Town (17/10)	0-1	79
18	Stotfold	v	Bowers & Pitsea (17/10)	2-4	66
19	AFC Sudbury	v	Hornchurch (17/10)	2-0	
20	Woodford Town	v	Brentwood Town (31/10)	5-5aet	

(Brentwood Town won 5-4 on kicks from the penalty mark)

21	K Sports	v	Dulwich Hamlet (14/10)	1-4	39
22	Reading City	v	Wealdstone (30/10)	2-0	
23	Dover Athletic	v	Hanworth Villa (30/10)	0-5	133
24	Barnet	v	Camberley Town (16/10)	4-1	144
25	Uxbridge	v	Knaphill (14/10)	5-3	
26	Sutton United	v	Croydon (18/10)	2-3	345
27	Dorking Wanderers	v	Dartford (17/10)	3-2	
28	Sutton Common Rovers	v	Leverstock Green (14/10)	1-0	
29	Maidenhead United	v	Cray Wanderers (21/10)	6-2	
30	Aveley	v	Bromley	1-1aet	

(Aveley won 4-3 on kicks from the penalty mark)

31	Chertsey Town	v	Kingstonian (16/10)	3-7	167
32	Bath City	v	Slimbridge (14/10)	3-0	
33	Mangotsfield United	v	Eastleigh (23/10)	0-1	56
34	AFC Stoneham	v	Hereford (14/10)	2-2aet	

(Hereford won 4-2 on kicks from the penalty mark)

35	Helston Athletic	v	Brockenhurst (14/10)	8-2	165
36	Yeovil Town	v	Andover Town (17/10)	1-3	194
37	Bridgwater Town	v	Oxford City (15/10)	2-0	

FIRST ROUND PROPER

1	South Shields	v	Morecambe (30/10)	2-1	
2	Morpeth Town	v	Chester (29/10)	1-0	80
3	Fleetwood Town	v	FC Halifax Town (30/10)	5-0	238
4	Accrington Stanley	v	Hartlepool United (4/11)	1-2	
5	Bradford City	v	Rochdale (29/10)	3-0	252
6	Salford City	v	Carlisle United (30/10)	2-3	250
7	Sunderland	v	Tranmere Rovers (29/10)	3-1	

(at Eppleton CW)

8	Oldham Athletic	v	Nantwich Town (29/10)	4-1	399
9	Curzon Ashton	v	Blackpool (29/10)	2-1	235
10	Macclesfield Town	v	Crewe Alexandra (31/10)	2-3	209
11	Grimsby Town	v	Rugby Town (1/11)	1-0	
12	Shrewsbury Town	v	Port Vale (30/10)	1-0	159
13	Rushall Olympic	v	Lincoln City (6/11)	0-4	200
14	Haughmond	v	Rotherham United (31/10)	1-3	81
15	Long Eaton United	v	Wrexham (29/10)	3-5	
16	Chesterfield	v	Burton Albion (4/11)	1-2	274
17	Mansfield Town	v	Doncaster Rovers (29/10)	4-3	150
18	Coventry City	v	Walsall (30/10)	1-2	327

(at Leamington FC)

19	Notts County	v	Scunthorpe United (5/11)	0-1aet	180
20	Milton Keynes Dons	v	Ware (29/10)	0-2	
21	Southend United	v	Cambridge United (31/10)	1-2	277
22	Stevenage	v	Brentwood Town (12/11)	5-1	204
23	Ipswich Town	v	King's Lynn Town (6/11)	6-1	267
24	Northampton Town	v	Colchester United (30/10)	1-2	
25	Dereham Town	v	Peterborough United (31/10)	0-1aet	296
26	AFC Sudbury	v	Bowers & Pitsea (29/10)	2-1	141
27	Sutton Common Rovers	v	Uxbridge (28/10)	1-3	183
28	AFC Wimbledon	v	Leyton Orient (29/10)	5-0	436
29	Gillingham	v	Hanworth Villa (29/10)	2-3	
30	Reading City	v	Oxford United (6/11)	0-1aet	300
31	Barnet	v	Dorking Wanderers (30/10)	4-2	207
32	Maidenhead United	v	Kingstonian (30/10)	2-1	
33	Dulwich Hamlet	v	Crawley Town		

(walkover for Dulwich Hamlet – Crawley Town withdrawn)

34	Croydon	v	Aveley (6/11)	1-0	68
35	Cheltenham Town	v	Eastleigh (30/10)	3-2	171
36	Forest Green Rovers	v	Helston Athletic (29/10)	5-0	
37	Bridgwater Town	v	Newport County (29/10)	0-1	213
38	Portsmouth	v	Hereford (26/10)	5-1	294
39	Swindon Town	v	Bristol Rovers (29/10)	1-3	324
40	Plymouth Argyle	v	Exeter City (25/10)	0-1	
41	Bath City	v	Andover Town (5/11)	3-2aet	

BYE – Bolton Wanderers

SECOND ROUND PROPER

1	Lincoln City	v	Wrexham (23/11)	3-0	
2	South Shields	v	Hartlepool United (22/11)	3-2	
3	Crewe Alexandra	v	Grimsby Town (13/11)	2-0	
4	Mansfield Town	v	Rotherham United (13/11)	4-2aet	
5	Scunthorpe United	v	Morpeth Town (13/11)	2-1	174
6	Burton Albion	v	Bolton Wanderers (13/11)	1-1aet	275

(Bolton Wanderers won 3-1 on kicks from the penalty mark)

7	Curzon Ashton	v	Oldham Athletic (12/11)	3-2	433
8	Carlisle United	v	Bradford City (11/10)	2-3aet	
9	Walsall	v	Fleetwood Town (5/11)	0-3	283
10	Shrewsbury Town	v	Sunderland (15/11)	2-5	154
11	Cheltenham Town	v	Portsmouth (13/11)	8-4	
12	Croydon	v	Bath City (18/11)	2-0	
13	Ipswich Town	v	Exeter City (16/11)	2-1	331
14	Colchester United	v	Oxford United (19/11)	3-4	
15	Dulwich Hamlet	v	Forest Green Rovers (18/11)	1-9	
16	Ware	v	Maidenhead United (13/11)	1-3	
17	Stevenage	v	Peterborough United (21/11)	3-1aet	233
18	Barnet	v	Cambridge United (13/11)	3-2	184
19	Bristol Rovers	v	AFC Sudbury (5/11)	2-1	219
20	Hanworth Villa	v	AFC Wimbledon (18/11)	1-5	
21	Uxbridge	v	Newport County (11/10)	3-4	

THIRD ROUND PROPER

| 1 | Manchester City | v | Swansea City (19/12) | 3-0 | 374 |

(at Academy Stadium)

| 2 | Sunderland | v | Birmingham City (12/12) | 1-4 | |

(at Eppleton CW)

| 3 | Cardiff City | v | Ipswich Town (14/12) | 2-1aet | |
| 4 | Cheltenham Town | v | Arsenal (18/12) | 0-0aet | |

(Arsenal won 4-2 on kicks from the penalty mark)

| 5 | Stevenage | v | Aston Villa (10/12) | 0-0aet | 406 |

(Aston Villa won 4-2 on kicks from the penalty mark)

| 6 | Bradford City | v | Stoke City (12/12) | 3-3aet | |

(Bradford City won 5-4 on kicks from the penalty mark)

| 7 | Manchester United | v | Lincoln City (13/12) | 2-0 | 628 |

(at Leigh Sports Village)

8	Wigan Athletic	v	Croydon (17/12)	8-1	240
9	Preston North End	v	Bristol City (16/12)	2-0	504
10	Sheffield United	v	AFC Wimbledon (17/12)	2-1	336
11	Fulham	v	South Shields (11/12)	10-1	

(at Fulham FC Training Ground)

12	Norwich City	v	Newcastle United (10/12)	3-2	
13	Bristol Rovers	v	Southampton (11/12)	1-3	509
14	Luton Town	v	Sheffield Wednesday (11/12)	2-3	281
15	Blackburn Rovers	v	Newport County (17/12)	3-1	485
16	Chelsea	v	Huddersfield Town (18/12)	4-0	692

(at Kingsmeadow)

17	Mansfield Town	v	Queens Park Rangers (16/12)	3-1aet	247
18	Reading	v	Crystal Palace (12/12)	2-4	227
19	Wolverhampton Wanderers	v	Nottingham Forest (18/12)	3-0	
20	Fleetwood Town	v	Watford (3/12)	2-2aet	174

(Fleetwood Town won 4-3 on kicks from the penalty mark)

| 21 | Brighton & Hove Albion | v | Leicester City (6/12) | 3-2 | 306 |

(at Crawley Town FC)

| 22 | Middlesbrough | v | Forest Green Rovers (11/12) | 1-1aet | 378 |

(Middlesbrough won 5-4 on kicks from the penalty mark)

| 23 | Tottenham Hotspur | v | Liverpool (2/12) | 4-2 | 865 |

(at Stevenage FC)

24	Leeds United	v	Hull City (5/12)	3-1	
25	Bolton Wanderers	v	Millwall (4/12)	0-7	207
26	Crewe Alexandra	v	Barnsley (5/12)	1-2	
27	Oxford United	v	Maidenhead United (20/12)	1-0	168

(at Oxford City FC)

28	AFC Bournemouth	v	Barnet (11/12)	4-3	448
29	Curzon Ashton	v	Burnley (17/12)	0-5	
30	West Ham United	v	Charlton Athletic (13/12)	3-3aet	

(Charlton Athletic won 5-4 on kicks from the penalty mark – at Dagenham & Redbridge FC)

| 31 | Derby County | v | Everton (4/12) | 1-0 | |
| 32 | West Bromwich Albion | v | Scunthorpe United (10/12) | 3-0 | 295 |

FOURTH ROUND PROPER

| 1 | Norwich City | v | Manchester United (21/1) | 0-2 | 3241 |
| 2 | Leeds United | v | Sheffield Wednesday (9/1) | 2-2aet | |

(Leeds United won 5-4 on kicks from the penalty mark – at Tadcaster Albion FC)

| 3 | AFC Bournemouth | v | Cardiff City (14/1) | 1-0 | 438 |
| 4 | Arsenal | v | Southampton (9/1) | 1-0 | |

(at Boreham Wood FC)

| 5 | West Bromwich Albion | v | Middlesbrough (7/1) | 4-1 | 300 |
| 6 | Manchester City | v | Aston Villa (15/1) | 2-1 | 532 |

(at Academy Stadium)

| 7 | Blackburn Rovers | v | Charlton Athletic (20/1) | 1-0 | 498 |

FIRST ROUND

1	Northamptonshire (at Daventry Town FC)	v	Durham (2/11)	0-5	
2	Staffordshire (at Wolverhampton Wanderers FC, Jack Haywood Training Ground)	v	East Riding (1/12)	7-2	
3	Westmorland (at Kendal Town FC)	v	Shropshire (27/10)	0-2	
4	London (at Bromley FC)	v	Devon (27/10)	2-6	
5	Kent (at Chatham Town FC)	v	Guernsey (3/11)	2-1	
6	Gloucestershire (at Oaklands Park)	v	Bedfordshire (20/10)	0-3	
7	Cornwall (at Callywith College)	v	Jersey (26/10)	0-2	85
8	Cheshire (at Vauxhall Motors FC)	v	Isle of Man (3/11)	2-4aet	
9	Cumberland (at West Riding County FA)	v	West Riding (9/11)	1-2	
10	North Riding (at Kader FC)	v	Northumberland (23/11)	1-3	51
11	Amateur Football Alliance (at Hertfordshire FA)	v	Sheffield & Hallamshire (16/11)	7-3	42
12	Middlesex (at Uxbridge FC)	v	Berks & Bucks (3/11)	5-2	

Counties receiving a bye to the Second Round: Essex, Manchester, Norfolk, Sussex.

SECOND ROUND

1	Isle of Man (walkover for Isle of Man – Manchester withdrawn)	v	Manchester		
2	Northumberland (at Whitley Park)	v	Norfolk (4/1)	0-4	
3	Staffordshire (at Rushall Olympic FC)	v	Durham (22/12)	0-5	50
4	West Riding (tie awarded to West Riding – Shropshire removed)	v	Shropshire		
5	Bedfordshire (at Kempston Rovers FC)	v	Sussex (8/12)	0-1	
6	Essex (at Aveley FC)	v	Kent (8/12)	4-1	

PREVIOUS TEN FINALS

2019	Manchester	v	Norfolk	3-0
2018	Norfolk	v	Staffordshire	2-0
2017	Middlesex	v	Cornwall	2-1
2016	Liverpool	v	Sussex	2-0
2015	Cheshire	v	Middlesex	3-2
2014	Lancashire	v	Suffolk	3-2 aet
2013	Bedfordshire	v	Manchester	4-4, 4-2p
2012	Essex	v	West Riding	4-2 aet
2011	Norfolk	v	Staffordshire	4-2
2010	Kent	v	Sheffield & Hallamshire	1-0

7	Devon (at Devon FA)	v	Middlesex (23/11)	7-2	
8	Jersey (at Springfield Stadium)	v	Amateur Football Alliance (7/12)	1-2	

THIRD ROUND

1	West Riding (at West Riding FA)	v	Norfolk (18/1)	1-3	
2	Essex (at Aveley FC)	v	Isle of Man (12/1)	3-1	
3	Sussex (at Sussex FA)	v	Durham (19/1)	8-1	
4	Devon (at Devon County FA)	v	Amateur Football Alliance (11/1)	4-0	112

SEMI FINALS

1	Devon (at Tavistock FC)	v	Sussex (9/2)	0-1	
2	Norfolk (at The FDC, Norfolk FA)	v	Essex (7/2)	2-1	250

THE FINAL

Sussex	v	Norfolk

FA YOUTH CUP

8	Oxford United (at Preston North End FC)	v	Preston North End (20/1)	0-2	557
9	Millwall	v	Fleetwood Town (8/1)	3-1	411
10	Wolverhampton Wanderers	v	Crystal Palace (16/1)	2-1	
11	Chelsea (at Aldershot Town FC)	v	Bradford City (15/1)	5-0	180
12	Derby County	v	Brighton & Hove Albion (8/1)	1-2	
13	Wigan Athletic	v	Tottenham Hotspur (8/1)	2-0	668
14	Birmingham City (at Leamington FC)	v	Barnsley (15/1)	2-1	
15	Mansfield Town	v	Burnley (16/1)	0-3	432
16	Sheffield United	v	Fulham (15/1)	1-2	383

FIFTH ROUND PROPER

1	Burnley (at Curzon Ashton FC)	v	West Bromwich Albion (28/1)	2-0	
2	AFC Bournemouth	v	Millwall (4/2)	2-3	648
3	Blackburn Rovers	v	Preston North End (18/2)	4-2	978
4	Arsenal (at Boreham Wood FC)	v	Brighton & Hove Albion (6/2)	4-3	720
5	Manchester City (at Academy Stadium)	v	Fulham (6/2)	1-0	722
6	Wigan Athletic (at Lancashire FA)	v	Birmingham City (5/2)	4-0	366
7	Chelsea (at Aldershot Town FC)	v	Wolverhampton Wanderers (10/2)	7-0	201
8	Manchester United	v	Leeds United (5/2)	1-0	4263

SIXTH ROUND PROPER

1	Manchester City (at Academy Stadium)	v	Burnley (4/3)	1-0	673
2	Chelsea	v	Millwall (27/2)	1-0	2898
3	Manchester United	v	Wigan Athletic (28/2)	2-1	3681
4	Blackburn Rovers	v	Arsenal (6/3)	4-1	776

SEMI FINALS

1	Blackburn Rovers	v	Manchester City
2	Chelsea	v	Manchester United

THE FINAL

Blackburn or Man City	v	Chelsea or Man Utd

PREVIOUS TEN FINALS

				Aggregate Score
2019	Liverpool	v	Manchester City	1-1, 5-3p
2018	Chelsea	v	Arsenal	7-1
2017	Chelsea	v	Manchester City	6-2
2016	Chelsea	v	Manchester City	4-2
2015	Chelsea	v	Manchester City	5-2
2014	Chelsea	v	Fulham	7-6
2013	Norwich City	v	Chelsea	4-2
2012	Chelsea	v	Blackburn Rovers	4-1
2011	Manchester Utd	v	Sheffield United	4-1
2010	Chelsea	v	Aston Villa	3-2

FIRST ROUND

1 Billingham The Merlin v Witton Park Rose & Crown (13/10) 1-5
(at Wolviston FC)

2 Crossflatts Village v Hartlepool WHTDSOB (13/10)1-2 65
(at Silsden AFC)

3 Newton Aycliffe Iron Horse v Boro Walkers (13/10) 2-1 65
(at Shildon AFC)

4 Dawdon Welfare Park v Greenside 1-5
(at Dawdon CW)

5 Norton George & Dragon v Stella Dons
(walkover for Norton George & Dragon – Stella Dons withdrawn)

6 Burradon & New Fordley v Peterlee Catholic Club (13/10)2-2aet
(Peterlee Catholic Club won 4-3 on kicks from the penalty mark)
(at Bedlington Terriers FC)

7 Bransty Rangers v Blackhall Cricket Club
(walkover for Blackhall Cricket Club – Bransty Rangers withdrawn)

8 Oyster Martyrs v Wellington Westgate (13/10) 11-1
(at Bootle FC)

9 HT Sports v Mottram (20/10) 6-2
(tie reversed – at Litherland Sports Park)

10 Oakenshaw v Home Bargains 0-11 20
(at Bradford (Park Avenue) FC)

11 Kensington Fields v Mayfair 0-4
(at Jeffrey Humble Playing Fields)

12 FC Hounds v Leeds City Rovers (13/10) 2-3 50
(tie awarded to FC Walkers Hounds – Leeds City Rovers removed)

13 Canada v BRNESC 3-2 58
(at Lower Breck)

14 Queens Park v Dock 2-4
(at Vauxhall Motors FC)

15 Shepherds Arms v Bolton Woods (20/10) 11-2 38
(at Claybourn Ground)

16 Lobster v Campfield 2-3
(at St John Bosco College)

17 Dengo United v Linthwaite 1-3
(at St John Bosco College)

18 The Brow v Allerton 3-0
(at Lower Breck)

19 Pineapple v AFC Bull 4-3aet
(tie awarded to AFC Bull – Pineapple removed)

20 Quarry Green v Main Line Social 4-4aet
(Main Line Social won 5-4 on kicks from the penalty mark – at Kirkby Leisure Centre)

21 Custys v Western Avenue 1-2 40
(at Heron Eccles Football Hub)

22 Armley CC v Kirkdale (13/10) 1-3
(at West Leeds Activity Centre)

23 FC Dovecot v LIV Supplies 6-2
(at South Liverpool FC)

24 Huyton Cons v West Bowling 6-0
(at Simpson Ground)

25 Melling Victoria v Kent (27/10) 3-1
(at Kirkby Leisure Centre) (6/10 – tie ordered to be replayed)

26 Rolls Royce v FC Lion (27/10) 0-3
(at Rolls Royce Leisure)

27 Messingham Junior Trinity v Wigston Willow
(walkover for Messingham Junior Trinity – Wigston Willow withdrawn)

28 Anstey Sports Bar v Phoenix Gedling (20/10) 7-1 43
(at Anstey Nomads FC)

29 Joker v Joeys Old Boys
(walkover for Joker – Joeys Old Boys withdrawn)

30 Long Whatton v Attenborough Cavaliers 2-3 59
(at Shepshed Dynamo FC)

31 Long Eaton TNI v Oadby Athletic 4-3aet
(tie reversed – at Aylestone Park FC)

32 RHP Sports & Social v Crusader 0-5 52
(at YMCA Sports Village)

33 Sporting Dynamo v AFC Dowhan 3-6aet
(at Ibstock Welfare FC)

34 FC Poplar v Sileby Athletic 4-2
(at Derby Road Playing Fields)

35 AFC Jacks v Austin Ex Apprentices 6-2aet
(at Sporting Khalsa FC)

36 Black Horse (Redditch) v Digby Rangers 2-1 150
(at Highgate United FC)

37 Callow End v Sportsman 3-4
(at Pershore Town FC)

38 Waggon & Horses v Perrywood 0-5
(at Ribbesford Meadows)

39 Chaddesley Ravens v Codsall Legion Sundats 1-7 49
(at Stourport Swifts FC)

40 Hampton v OJM 0-5
(at Hampton Sports Club)

41 Flaunden v Larkspur Rovers 2-1 50
(at Bovingdon FC)

42 NLO v FC Bentons
(tie awarded to NLO - FC Bentons removed - subject to appeal)

43 Heritage United v Old Southall 1-6
(at Somerdale Pavilion)

44 Shire United v Reed Rangers 3-0
(at Hanworth Villa FC)

45 Rectory Rovers v AFC Links 4-4aet
(AFC Links won 9-8 on kicks from the penalty mark – at James Hornsby School)

46 Global v Asianos 1-5 18
(at Redbridge FC)

47 Lambeth All Stars v Priest Hill (29/9) 5-0
(at Croydon FC)

48 Palmers v Barnes Albion
(walkover for Palmers – Barnes Albion withdrawn)

49 Sauce v Mile End Baiteze Squad 0-7
(at Simon Langton Boys School)

50 Putney Town v Portland 0-6
(at Colliers Wood United FC)

51 Harrow Sports v Hashtag United (Sunday) 4-2
(at Tooting & Mitcham United FC)

52 Barnes AFC v Sporting Club de Mundial
(walkover for Sporting Club de Mundial – Barnes AFC withdrawn)

53 Highgate Albion v Blacksmiths 3-2
(at Tither Farm Sports & Social Club)

54 Massie Warriors v Gym United 0-6
(at Kingsway Rec)

55 Bishop's Stortford Swifts v Priory Sports 1-3
(at Silver Leys)

56 Brewery Tap v Broadwalk Pines United 1-4
(at Hitchin Town FC)

57 Crawley Green (Sunday) v Caddington Social 2-1
(at Crawley Green Rec)

58 Borussia Martlesham v Wixams Wanderers
(walkover for Wixams Wanderers – Borussia Martlesham withdrawn)

59 St Joseph's (Luton) v Club Lewsey 2-1
(at Arlesey Town FC)

60 Falcons v Skew Bridge (13/10) 4-2 20
(at Bottisham Sports Centre FC)

61 East Christchurch SSC v Broadwater
(walkover for East Christchurch SSC – Broadwater withdrawn)

62 Rudgwick Panthers v AFC Portchester (Sunday) 4-2
(tie reversed – at AFC Portchester)

63 Talbot Rangers v Loch & Quay 3-2
(at Lymington Town FC)

Club receiving exemption to the Second Round: Birstall Stamford

SECOND ROUND

1 Greenside v Witton Park Rose & Crown (17/11) 5-1
(at Consett AFC)

2 Peterlee Catholic Club v Messingham Junior Trinity 17-1 45
(at New Ferens Park)

3 Dock v HT Sports 4-3aet 88
(at Vauxhall Motors FC)

4 Campfield v The Brow (2.00) 2-0
(at Simpson Ground)

5 Norton George & Dragon v FC Dovecot (1.30) 3-6 52
(at Stockton Town FC)

6 Blackhall CC v Western Avenue (2.00) 0-1aet
   (at Blackhall Welfare Park)
7 Hartlepool WHTDSOB v Huyton Cons 3-2
   (at Hartlepool FC)
8 Shepherds Arms v Kirkdale 4-3 33
   (at AFC Emley)
9 Mayfair v Newton Aycliffe Iron Horse (2.30)2-1
   (at Anfield Sports Community Centre)
10 FC Walkers Hounds v AFC Bull
   (walkover for FC Walkers Hounds – AFC Bull withdrawn)
11 Home Bargains v Linthwaite 6-1
   (at Alder Road)
12 Canada v Oyster Martyrs (11.00) 0-1 126
   (at Lower Breck)
13 Melling Victoria v Main Line Social 3-1
   (at Kirby Leisure Centre)
14 Perrywood v Attenborough Cavaliers (17/11)5-3aet
   (at Neel Park)
15 Long Eaton TNI v AFC Dowhan 2-1
   (at Assterdale Sports Ground)
16 Birstall Stamford v AFC Jacks (17/11) 1-5 81
   (at Birstall United FC)
17 OJM v Codsall Legion Sundats (2.00)5-1
   (at Sporting Khalsa FC)
18 Crusader v FC Poplar 7-0
   (at Dunkirk FC)
19 Black Horse (Redditch) v Anstey Sports Bar (17/11) 4-0
   (at Coleshill Town FC)
20 Joker v FC Lion (17/11) 5-1
   (at Maltby Main FC)
21 Broadwalk Pines United v AFC Links 8-1
   (at Arlesey Town FC)
22 Flaunden v Crawley Green (Sunday) (17/11)1-3
   (at Bovingdon FC)
23 Priory Sports v Asianos 10-3
   (at Maldon & Tiptree FC)
24 Lambeth All Stars v NLO (17/11) 4-3
   (at Tooting & Mitcham United FC)
25 Highgate Albion v Palmers 5-2
   (at Tithe Farm Sports & Social)
26 Harrow Sports v Portland (2.00) 1-2
   (at Tooting & Mitcham United FC)
27 Sporting Club de Mundial v Old Southall 6-1 55
   (at Hackney Marshes)
28 Wixams Wanderers v Gym United (2.00) 4-3
   (at Shefford Town FC)
29 Falcons v St Joseph's (Luton) 0-3
   (at Cambourne Sports & Fitness Centre)
30 Shire United v Mile End Baiteze Squad (17/11)2-1
   (at Hanworth Villa FC)
31 Rudgwick Panthers v East Christchurch
   (walkover for East Christchurch – Rudgwick Panthers withdrawn)
32 Talbot Rangers v Sportsman 5-1
   (at Lymington Town FC)

THIRD ROUND

1 Hartlepool WHTDSOB v Peterlee Catholic Club 2-4
   (at Hartlepool FC)
2 Western Avenue v Melling Victoria 0-2
   (at Litherland Sports Centre)
3 FC Dovecot v Campfield 1-3
   (at Prescot Cables FC)
4 Oyster Martyrs v FC Walkers Hounds (12.00) 8-0
   (at St John Bosco School)
5 Dock v Home Bargains 2-1
   (at Vauxhall Motors FC)
6 Mayfair v Greenside 3-1
   (at Anfield Sports & Community Centre)
7 Crusader v Shepherds Arms (15/12) 3-8
   (at Basford United FC)

8 AFC Jacks v Joker 2-1 40
   (at Sporting Khalsa FC)
9 Long Eaton TNI v Black Horse (Redditch) 0-2
   (at Graham St Prims FC)
10 Perrywood v OJM 3-5
   (at Neel Park)
11 Talbot Rangers v Shire United 1-0
   (at Lymington Town FC)
12 Highgate Albion v East Christchurch (1.30) 5-1
   (at Sun Sports & Social)
13 St Joseph's (Luton) v Lambeth All Stars 3-0
   (at Arlesey Town FC)
14 Broadwalk Pines United v Wixams Wanderers 1-2
   (at AFC Dunstable)
15 Crawley Green (Sunday) v Portland 2-6
   (at Barton Rovers FC)
16 Sporting Club de Mundial v Priory Sports 2-0
   (at Hackney Marshes)

FOURTH ROUND

1 Mayfair v Campfield 0-1
   (at Anfield Sports Centre)
2 Peterlee Catholic Club v OJM 6-3aet
   (at Horden CW FC)
3 Oyster Martyrs v Black Horse (Redditch) 0-1aet
   (at St John Bosco)
4 Shepherds Arms v Dock 1-2
   (at Liversedge FC)
5 Melling Victoria v AFC Jacks 0-0aet
   (AFC Jacks won 4-2 on kicks from the penalty mark)
6 St Joseph's (Luton) v Sporting Club de Mundial 2-1
   (at Arlesey Town FC)
7 Talbot Rangers v Portland 0-1
   (at Lymington Town FC)
8 Wixams Wanderers v Highgate Albion 2-2aet
   (Wixham Wanderers won 4-2 on kicks from the penalty mark - at Shefford Town FC)

FIFTH ROUND

1 Portland v Dock (23/2) 1-0
   (at AFC Croydon Athletic)
2 Wixams Wanderers v Peterlee Catholic Club 1-2
   (at Shefford Town FC)
3 St Joseph's (Luton) v Black Horse (Redditch) (23/2) 4-1 54
   (at Arlesey Town FC)
4 AFC Jacks v Campfield 1-3
   (at Sporting Khalsa FC)

SEMI FINALS

1 Peterlee Catholic Club v Campfield
   (at Harrogate Town FC)
2 St Joseph's (Luton) v Portland
   (at Maidenhead United FC)

THE FA WOMEN'S CUP

EXTRA PRELIMINARY ROUND

1	Washington	v	Redcar Town	0-13	
	(at Northumbria Centre)				
2	Wakefield Trinity	v	Farsley Celtic	0-3	
	(at Hemsworth MW FC)				
3	Mossley Hill	v	Burnley Belvedere		
	(walkover for Mossley Hill – Burnley Belvedere withdrawn)				
4	Notts County	v	Cleethorpes Town	11-1	
	(at Ilkeston Town FC)				
5	Port Vale	v	Lye Town	9-0	57
	(at Dimensions Sports & Leisure Centre)				
6	Corby Town	v	Bungay Town	1-2	42
	(at Corby Town FC)				
7	New London Lionesses	v	Comets	5-4	
	(at Brunel University Sports Park)				
8	Bishop's Stortford	v	Hartham United	1-5	
	(at Bishop's Stortford FC)				
9	Ashford Town (Middx)	v	Denham United	4-1	
	(at Ashford Town (Middx) FC)				
10	Burgess Hill Town	v	Eastbourne United	3-2	
	(at Burgess Hill Town FC)				

PRELIMINARY ROUND

1	Penrith	v	Bishop Auckland	2-4	
	(at Penrith AFC)				
2	Boro Rangers	v	South Shields	1-3	
	(at Herlingshaw Centre)				
3	Carlisle United	v	Hartlepool United	1-11	
	(at Creighton Rugby Club)				
4	Redcar Town	v	Lumley	5-0	
	(at Redcar Town FC)				
5	Blyth Town	v	Workington Reds	2-1	
	(at Blyth Town FC)				
6	Alnwick Town	v	Sunderland West End	3-5	
	(at Alnwick Town FC)				
7	Wetherby Athletic	v	Harrogate Town	0-10	
	(at Wetherby Athletic FC)				
8	Ossett United	v	Rotherham United	5-1	93
	(at Ossett United FC)				
9	Ripon City	v	Yorkshire Amateur	0-4	
	(at Ripon City AFC)				
10	Bridlington Rovers	v	Bradford Park Avenue	4-2	
	(at Bridlington Rovers FC)				
11	Hepworth United	v	Pride Park	5-1	
	(at Hepworth United FC)				
12	Farsley Celtic	v	Thackley	3-0	
	(at Farsley Celtic FC)				
13	Oughtbridge WM	v	Sheffield Wednesday	2-1	107
	(at Oughtbridge WM Sports Ground)				
14	Blackburn Community	v	West Kirby	6-1	
	(at QEGS Playing Fields)				
15	Northwich Vixens	v	Bury	13-2	
	(at Witton Albion FC)				
16	Curzon Ashton	v	Mossley Hill	2-2aet	
	(Mossley Hill won 4-2 on kicks from the penalty mark - at Failsworth Sports Centre)				
17	Tameside United	v	Fleetwood Town Wrens	1-5	
	(at Hyde United FC)				
18	Manchester Stingers	v	Merseyrail	0-6	
	(at Whalley Range AFC)				
19	FC United of Manchester	v	Tranmere Rovers	5-0	92
	(at FC United of Manchester)				
20	Accrington Girls & Ladies	v	Altrincham	1-3	
	(at Livingstone Road)				
21	Didsbury	v	West Didsbury & Chorlton	4-2	
	(at West Didsbury & Chorlton FC)				
22	Accrington Stanley Community	v	Morecambe	1-8	
	(at St Christopher COE High School)				
23	Wythenshawe Amateurs	v	Crewe Alexandra	0-8	
	(at Wythenshawe Amateurs FC)				
24	Boston United	v	Loughborough Students		
	(walkover for Loughborough Students – Boston United withdrawn)				
25	AFC Leicester	v	Grimsby Borough	1-3	
	(at Judgemeadow Community College)				
26	Rise Park	v	Notts County	3-2aet	
	(at Arnold Town FC)				
27	Coalville Town	v	Hykeham Town	1-11	
	(at Coalville Town FC)				
28	Worksop Town	v	Mansfield Town	0-9	
	(at Manton Sports)				
29	Dronfield Town	v	Leicester City	1-2	
	(at Dronfield Town FC)				
30	Lutterworth Athletic	v	Chesterfield	0-12	
	(at Lutterworth Athletic FC)				
31	Sherwood	v	Arnold Eagles (1.00)	0-7	27
	(at Forest Sports Zone)				
32	Oadby & Wigston	v	Lincoln Moorlands Railway	5-1	
	(at Meadow Sports Ground)				
33	Arnold Town	v	Woodlands	1-4	
	(at Arnold Town FC)				
34	Kidderminster Harriers	v	Leek Town	3-4	
	(at Lea Castle Sports Ground)				
35	Port Vale	v	Knowle	8-1	59
	(at Dimensions Leisure Centre)				
36	Droitwich Spa	v	Sedgley & Gornal United		
	(walkover for Droitwich Spa – Sedgley & Gornal United withdrawn)				
37	Solihull Sporting	v	Rugby Town	7-1	50
	(at Chelmsley Town FC)				
38	Crusaders	v	Sandwell	5-2	
	(at Rowheath Pavillion)				
39	Tamworth	v	Shrewsbury Town	2-3	
	(at Tamworth FC)				
40	Kingfisher	v	Cookley Sports	2-4	
	(at Tudor Grange Academy)				
41	Kidsgrove Athletic	v	Solihull Ladies United	3-5	
	(at Kidsgrove Athletic FC)				
42	Coundon Court	v	Sutton Coldfield Town	2-3	
	(at University of Warwick)				
43	Wyrley	v	Shifnal Town	2-4	
	(at Wyrley Juniors FC)				
44	Stockingford AA Pavilion	v	Stourbridge	2-1	216
	(at Stockingford AA Pavilion)				
45	Coventry Sphinx	v	AFC Telford United	2-1aet	
	(at Coventry Sphinx FC)				
46	Wroxham	v	Kettering Town	6-2	65
	(at Wroxham FC)				
47	Haverhill Rovers	v	King's Lynn Town	1-3	
	(at Haverhill Rovers FC)				
48	St Ives Town	v	Histon	0-1	
	(at St Ives Town FC)				
49	AFC Sudbury	v	Harlow Town	0-8	
	(at AFC Sudbury)				
50	Riverside	v	Bungay Town	0-15	
	(at Queens Park)				
51	Peterborough United	v	Thrapston Town	14-0	
	(at Mick George Training Academy)				

52	Fulbourn Institute Bluebirdsv	Wymondham Town	0-5	
	(at Fulbourn Recreation Ground)			
53	Netherton United v	Newmarket Town	1-3	
	(at Netherton United FC)			
54	Clapton Community v	Margate	6-3	310
	(at Clapton Community FC)			
55	Aylesford v	Dulwich Hamlet	2-1	
	(at Kings Hill FC)			
56	Fulham v	New London Lionesses (2.30)	3-1	
	(at Motspur Park)			
57	Dartford v	Hackney	5-0	130
	(at Dartford FC)			
58	Whyteleafe v	Millwall Lionesses	3-6	
	(at Whyteleafe FC – tie awarded to Whyteleafe – Millwall Lionesses removed			
	from Competition)			
59	Victoire v	Herne Bay (2.30)	4-3	
	(at Herne Bay FC)			
60	Meridian v	Regents Park Rangers	1-3	40
	(at The Victory Academy)			
61	Sutton United v	Islington Borough	0-1	
	(at Sutton United FC)			
62	Phoenix Sports v	Haringey Borough	5-1	
	(at Phoenix Sports FC)			
63	Long Lane v	Ashford	0-11	
	(at Kidbrooke Playing Fields)			
64	Watford Ladies Dev v	Hemel Hempstead Town	4-2	
	(at Bovingdon FC)			
65	Hitchin Belles v	Bowers & Pitsea	1-6	
	(at St Christopher School)			
66	Royston Town v	Wodson Park	4-1	85
	(at Royston Town FC)			
67	Bedford v	Colney Heath	1-3	
	(at Bedford Town FC)			
68	Houghton Athletic v	AFC Dunstable	0-1	
	(at Kingsway Recreation Ground)			
69	Hartham United v	St Albans	0-5	
	(at Hertfordshire FA)			
70	Luton Town v	Leigh Ramblers	7-0	
	(at The Brache)			
71	Abbey Rangers v	Hampton & Richmond Boro	4-3aet	
	(at Abbey Rangers FC)			
72	Queens Park Rangers Dev v	Wargrave	11-0	
	(at QPR FC Training Ground)			
73	Banbury United v	Walton Casuals	1-2	
	(at Banbury United FC)			
74	Abingdon United v	Brentford	7-0	108
	(at Abingdon Town FC)			
75	Ascot United v	Abingdon Town	2-3	
	(at Abingdon Town FC)			
76	Ashford Town (Middx) v	Oxford City	5-2	
	(at Ashford Town (Middx) FC)			
77	Wantage Town v	Wycombe Wanderers	0-14	
	(at Wantage Town FC)			
78	Steyning Town v	Newhaven	1-5	
	(at Steyning Town CFC)			
79	Oakwood v	AFC Littlehampton	6-1	
	(at Horley Town FC)			
80	Pagham v	Worthing	2-3	
	(at Pagham FC)			
81	Godalming Town v	Eastbourne Town	1-2	
	(at Godalming Town FC)			
82	Milford & Witley v	Tunbridge Wells Foresters	1-5	
	(at Chiddingfold FC)			

83	Burgess Hill Town v	Saltdean United	2-4aet	
	(at Burgess Hill Town FC)			
84	Mole Valley v	Bexhill United	7-0	
	(at Dorking Wanderers FC)			
85	New Milton Town v	Newbury	3-1	50
	(at New Milton Town FC)			
86	Shanklin v	Alton (1.30)	1-0	37
	(at Shanklin FC)			
87	Bournemouth Sports v	Winchester City Flyers	1-3aet	
	(at Chapel Gate)			
88	Eastleigh v	Moneyfields	1-2	
	(at Eastleigh FC)			
89	AFC Bournemouth v	Feniton	6-0	
	(at Verwood Town FC)			
90	Almondsbury v	Longlevens	2-0	
	(at Almondsbury Playing Field)			
91	Weston Super Mare v	Middlezoy Rovers	1-4	
	(at Weston Super Mare FC)			
92	AEK Boco v	Ilminster Town	0-4	
	(at AEK Boco FC)			
93	Sherborne Town v	Keynsham Town Development	10-0	
	(at Sherborne Town FC)			
94	Royal Wootton Bassett Town v	Chipping Sodbury Town	7-0	
	(at Royal Wootton Bassett Town FC)			
95	Swindon Spitfires v	Portishead Town	1-7	51
	(at Watchfield Sports Pavilion)			
96	Bideford v	St Agnes	5-2	
	(at Bideford AFC)			
97	Marine Academy Plymouthv	AFC St Austell	1-0aet	
	(at Ivybridge Town FC)			
98	Torquay United v	RNAS Culdrose	3-0	
	(at South Devon College Sports Centre)			

FIRST QUALIFYING ROUND

1	Harrogate Town v	Fleetwood Town Wrens	5-0	
	(at Harrogate Town FC)			
2	Redcar Town v	Bishop Auckland	2-0	
	(at Redcar Town FC)			
3	Yorkshire Amateur v	Hartlepool United	0-5	
	(at Yorkshire Amateur AFC)			
4	Morecambe v	FC United of Manchester (6/10)	1-4	
	(tie reversed – at venue FC United of Manchester)			
5	Altrincham v	Didsbury	4-2	53
	(at Egerton Sports Club)			
6	Hepworth United v	Blackburn Community	1-8	
	(at Hepworth United FC)			
7	Farsley Celtic v	Merseyrail	2-1	
	(at Farsley Celtic FC)			
8	Bridlington Rovers v	Ossett United	0-7	
	(at Bridlington CYP)			
9	Sunderland West End v	Mossley Hill	4-4aet	
	(Mossley Hill won 5-4 on kicks from the penalty mark)			
10	Blyth Town v	South Shields	0-1	
	(at Blyth Town FC)			
11	Droitwich Spa v	Shifnal Town	0-3	
	(at King George Playing Fields)			
12	Stockingford AA Pavilion v	Coventry Sphinx	1-5	72
	(at Stockingford AA Pavilion FC)			
13	Shrewsbury Town v	Leek Town	1-3	
	(at Shrewsbury Town in the Community)			
14	Sutton Coldfield Town v	Solihull Sporting	5-0	
	(at Sutton Coldfield Town FC)			

15	Arnold Eagles	v	Northwich Vixens	2-3	
	(at Calverton MW FC)				
16	Oadby & Wigston	v	Crewe Alexandra	2-3	60
	(at Oadby & Wigston FC)				
17	Chesterfield	v	Cookley Sports	2-0	
	(at Glapwell FC)				
18	Peterborough United	v	Oughtbridge WM	3-0	
	(at Mick George Training Academy)				
19	Woodlands	v	Hykeham Town	2-1	
	(at Borrowash Victoria FC)				
20	Rise Park	v	Grimsby Borough	3-2	
	(at Arnold Town FC)				
21	Leicester City	v	Port Vale	3-2aet	40
	(at Linwood Playing Fields)				
22	Solihull Ladies United	v	Loughborough Students	2-1	
	(at Chelmsley Town FC)				
23	Mansfield Town	v	Crusaders	4-2	
	(at Mansfield Town FC)				
24	Harlow Town	v	King's Lynn Town	3-1	
	(at Harlow Town FC)				
25	Watford Ladies Development	v	Newmarket Town	0-2	
	(at Bovingdon FC)				
26	Histon	v	St Albans	0-4	
	(at Histon FC)				
27	Colney Heath	v	Royston Town	2-5	
	(at Colney Heath FC)				
28	AFC Dunstable	v	Bowers & Pitsea	2-2aet	
	(Bowers & Pitsea won 3-2 on kicks from the penalty mark)				
29	Luton Town	v	Bungay Town	6-0	64
	(at Brache Training Ground)				
30	Wroxham	v	Wymondham Town	3-2	108
	(at Wroxham FC)				
31	Victoire	v	Islington Borough	0-4	
	(at Croygas Sports Club)				
32	Clapton Community	v	Oakwood	2-3	
	(at Wadham Lodge Sports Ground)				
33	Fulham	v	Mole Valley (2.30)	5-1	
	(at Fulham FC Training Ground)				
34	Ashford	v	Eastbourne Town	4-1	30
	(at The North School)				
35	Dartford	v	Newhaven	4-0	143
	(at Dartford FC Community 3G Pitch)				
36	Regents Park Rangers	v	Wycombe Wanderers	0-3	
	(at Barns Elms Playing Fields)				
37	QPR Girls Development	v	Abbey Rangers	8-0	
	(at QPR FC Training Ground)				
38	Whyteleafe	v	Worthing (29/9)	0-1	
	(at Whyteleafe FC)				
39	Abingdon United	v	Aylesford	2-1	87
	(at Abingdon United FC)				
40	Tunbridge Wells Foresters	v	Phoenix Sports	1-4	
	(at Otford Recreation Ground)				
41	Abingdon Town	v	Walton Casuals	4-3	
	(at Abingdon Town FC)				
42	Ashford Town (Middx)	v	Saltdean United	0-1	
	(at Ashford Town (Middx) FC)				
43	Shanklin	v	Sherborne Town	0-12	
	(at Shanklin FC)				
44	AFC Bournemouth	v	New Milton Town	10-0	
	(at Verwood Town FC)				
45	Royal Wootton Bassett Town	v	Torquay United	8-0	
	(at Royal Wootton Bassett Town FC)				
46	Marine Academy Plymouth	v	Almondsbury	1-0	
	(at Ivybridge Town FC)				
47	Portishead Town	v	Middlezoy Rovers	3-1aet	
	(at Portishead Town FC)				
48	Winchester Flyers	v	Bideford	9-2	60
	(at Winchester City FC)				
49	Ilminster Town	v	Moneyfields	1-4	
	(at Ilminster Town FC)				

SECOND QUALIFYING ROUND

1	Hartlepool United	v	Blackburn Community	4-3	
	(at East Durham College)				
2	Bolton Wanderers	v	Newcastle United	1-2	
	(at Atherton Collieries FC)				
3	Redcar Town	v	Norton & Stockton Ancients (13/10)	1-3	
	(at Redcar Town FC)				
4	Harrogate Town	v	Chorley	0-2	
	(at Harrogate Town AFC)				
5	FC United of Manchester	v	Brighouse Town (13/10)	1-5	93
	(at FC United of Manchester)				
6	Barnsley	v	Bradford City	5-1	
	(at Barnsley FC Academy)				
7	Chester-Le-Street Town	v	Doncaster Rovers Belles	4-2	
	(at Chester-Le-Street Town FC)				
8	Leeds United	v	South Shields (3.00)	4-1	50
	(at Thorp Arch)				
9	Mossley Hill	v	Stockport County (13/10)	1-3	
	(at Mossley Hill Athletic Club)				
10	Durham Cestria	v	Ossett United	5-1	
	(at The Graham Sports Centre)				
11	Farsley Celtic	v	Liverpool Feds (13/10)	1-4	
	(6/10 - tie abandoned after 45 mins due to waterlogged pitch - at Farsley Celtic FC)				
12	Burton Albion	v	Leicester United (20/10)	0-3	
	(at Rocester FC)				
13	Woodlands	v	Rise Park (17/10)	2-1aet	
	(at Borrowash Victoria FC)				
14	Mansfield Town	v	Birmingham & West Midlands	0-6	
	(at Mansfield Town FC)				
15	Leek Town	v	Leicester City Ladies	6-0	
	(at Leek Town FC)				
16	Wolverhampton Wanderers	v	Shifnal Town	10-0	140
	(at AFC Wulfrunians)				
17	Lincoln City	v	Solihull Moors	7-0	
	(at Ashby Avenue)				
18	Chesterfield	v	Bedworth United	1-3	
	(at Glapwell FC)				
19	Northwich Vixens	v	Altrincham (20/10)	5-1	64
	(at Egerton FC)				
20	Leafield Athletic	v	Sporting Khalsa	2-5	94
	(at Dickens Heath Sports Club)				
21	Sutton Coldfield Town	v	Solihull Ladies United	3-2	
	(at Sutton Coldfield Town FC)				
22	Coventry Sphinx	v	Crewe Alexandra	0-5	
	(at Coventry Sphinx FC)				
23	The New Saints	v	Long Eaton United	6-1	
	(at TNS FC)				
24	Stevenage	v	Peterborough United (2.30)	1-2	111
	(at Letchworth County Ground)				
25	Newmarket Town	v	Luton Town	0-4	
	(at Newmarket Town FC)				
26	Harlow Town	v	Wroxham	4-3aet	
	(at Harlow Town FC)				

27	Norwich City (at Norwich United FC)	v	Cambridge United (13/10)	3-2	
28	Cambridge City (at Ely City FC)	v	St Albans (13/10)	4-3aet	130
29	Ipswich Town (at Felixstowe & Walton United FC)	v	Royston Town (13/10)	7-0	
30	Wycombe Wanderers (at Flackwell Heath College)	v	Worthing	3-1	
31	Kent Football United (at Kent Football United FC)	v	Actonians	1-3	
32	Dartford (at Dartford FC)	v	Billericay Town	0-7	118
33	Ashford (at Charing Playing Fields)	v	AFC Wimbledon	0-7	
34	QPR Girls Development (at QPR FC Training Ground)	v	Oakwood	9-1	
35	Enfield Town (at Enfield Town FC)	v	Islington Borough	4-0	
36	Maidenhead United (at Maidenhead United FC)	v	Bowers & Pitsea	1-2	
37	Fulham (Fulham won 3-0 on kicks from the penalty mark – at Fulham FC Training Ground)	v	Saltdean United (2.30)	1-1aet	50
38	Abingdon Town (at Abingdon Town FC)	v	Chesham United	0-4	
39	AFC Basildon (at Canvey Island FC)	v	Phoenix Sports	8-2	
40	Abingdon United (at Abingdon United FC)	v	Leyton Orient	1-4	
41	Exeter City (at Cullompton Rangers FC)	v	Sherborne Town	7-1	58
42	Portishead Town (at Portishead Town FC)	v	Royal Wootton Bassett Town	1-0	
43	Winchester Flyers (at Winchester City FC)	v	Poole Town	2-3	
44	Marine Academy Plymouth (at Ivybridge Town FC)	v	Southampton Women's FC	0-2	
45	Southampton FC Women (at AFC Totton)	v	Buckland Athletic (13/10)	8-0	148
46	Moneyfields (Moneyfields won 4-2 on kicks from the penalty mark – at Moneyfields FC)	v	Larkhall Athletic	2-2aet	73
47	Cheltenham Town (at Petersfield Park)	v	Brislington	5-0	
48	Swindon Town (at Fairford Town FC)	v	AFC Bournemouth	2-3	58

THIRD QUALIFYING ROUND

1	Northwich Vixens (at Park Stadium)	v	Liverpool Feds (3/11)	2-7	
2	Leeds United (at Leeds United Training Ground)	v	Barnsley	0-3	130
3	Chester-Le-Street Town (at Chester-Le-Street Town FC)	v	Newcastle United	3-1	
4	Hartlepool United (at East Durham College)	v	Chorley	0-8	
5	Norton & Stockton Ancients (at Norton & Stockton Ancients FC)	v	Durham Cestria (3/11)	2-6	60
6	Stockport County (Brighouse Town won 4-2 on kicks from the penalty mark - at Stockport Sports Village)	v	Brighouse Town	2-2aet	46
7	Peterborough United (at Mick George Training Academy)	v	The New Saints	2-3	

8	Sporting Khalsa (at Sporting Khalsa FC)	v	Lincoln City	1-3	
9	Bedworth United (at Bedworth United FC)	v	Woodlands	2-4	45
10	Leicester United (at Melton Sports Village)	v	Leek Town (3/11)	0-1	
11	Birmingham & West Midlands (at Romulus FC)	v	Crewe Alexandra	1-2	
12	Sutton Coldfield Town (at Sutton Coldfield Town FC)	v	Wolverhampton Wanderers	1-5	
13	Harlow Town (at Harlow Town FC)	v	Billericay Town	1-2	
14	Cambridge City (at Ely City FC)	v	AFC Basildon	3-7	73
15	Ipswich Town (at Felixstowe & Walton United FC)	v	Norwich City	6-1	
16	Bowers & Pitsea (at Bowers & Pitsea FC)	v	Luton Town	0-3	
17	Actonians (at Middlesex FA)	v	Fulham	3-1	
18	QPR Girls Development (at QPR FC Training Ground)	v	Leyton Orient	1-2	
19	Enfield Town (at Enfield Town FC)	v	AFC Wimbledon	1-2	
20	Chesham United (at Chesham United FC)	v	Wycombe Wanderers	3-0	
21	Portishead Town (Portishead Town won 3-1 on kicks from the penalty mark - at Portishead Town FC)	v	Moneyfields	1-1aet	53
22	Southampton Women's FC (at Romsey Town FC)	v	AFC Bournemouth (3/11)	3-1	
23	Southampton FC Women (at AFC Totton)	v	Poole Town	11-0	213
24	Cheltenham Town (at Cheltenham Saracens FC)	v	Exeter City (3/11)	4-3	

FIRST ROUND

1	Crewe Alexandra (at Cumberland Sports Arena)	v	Barnsley	1-2aet	
2	Liverpool Feds (at Jericho Lane Football Hub)	v	Brighouse Town (2.00)	0-4	
3	Durham Cestria (at The Graham Sports Centre)	v	Chester-Le-Street Town	1-3	
4	The New Saints (at Telford College)	v	Chorley	0-4	
5	Leek Town (at Leek Town FC)	v	Lincoln City	1-2aet	
6	Wolverhampton Wanderers (at AFC Wulfrunians)	v	Luton Town	4-1	90
7	Woodlands (at Friesland School)	v	Billericay Town (17/11)	0-13	
8	Ipswich Town (at Felixstowe & Walton United FC)	v	AFC Basildon	5-0	
9	Cheltenham Town (at Cheltenham Saracens FC)	v	Leyton Orient (17/11)	0-1	
10	Actonians (at Middlesex FA)	v	AFC Wimbledon (2.00)	2-1	
11	Chesham United (at Chesham United FC)	v	Southampton FC Women	0-1	
12	Southampton Womens FC (at Romsey Town FC)	v	Portishead Town (2.00)	4-0	

SECOND ROUND

1	Chorley	v	Brighouse Town (8/12)	1-2aet	60
	(at Chorley FC)				
2	Derby County	v	Nottingham Forest	2-3	
	(at Mickleover Sports FC)				
3	Barnsley	v	Sheffield (3.00)	4-0	
	(at Barnsley FC Academy)				
4	Sunderland	v	Middlesbrough (8/12)	4-3	
	(at Hebburn Town FC)				
5	Stoke City	v	Huddersfield Town (8/12)	1-1aet	
	(Huddersfield Town won 4-3 on kicks from the penalty mark - at Norton Sports Club)				
6	Wolverhampton Wanderers	v	Fylde	0-1	
	(at AFC Wulfrunians)				
7	Chester-Le-Street Town	v	Loughborough Foxes (8/12)	0-4	40
	(at Chester-Le-Street Town FC)				
8	Burnley	v	Hull City (8/12)	2-1	
	(at Padiham FC)				
9	West Bromwich Albion	v	Lincoln City (8/12)	2-0	
	(at Walsall Wood FC)				
10	Hounslow	v	Cardiff City (2.00)	0-6	15
	(at Uxbridge FC)				
11	Keynsham Town	v	Watford	0-3	
	(at Keynsham Town FC)				
12	Yeovil Town	v	Southampton FC Women (3.00)	1-1aet	
	(Southampton FC Women won 5-4 on kicks from the penalty mark - at Dorchester Town FC)				
13	Portsmouth	v	Leyton Orient (8/12)	6-1	137
	(at Baffins Milton Rovers FC)				
14	Southampton Women's FC	v	MK Dons (2.00)	1-1aet	
	(Southampton Women's FC won 3-2 on kicks from the penalty mark - at Romsey Town FC)				
15	Oxford United	v	Plymouth Argyle (2.00)	3-4aet	
	(at Oxford City FC)				
16	Chichester City	v	Ipswich Town	0-6	116
	(at Selsey FC)				
17	Billericay Town	v	Gillingham	2-1	
	(at Billericay Town FC)				
18	Actonians	v	Crawley Wasps (2.00)	3-1	
	(at Middlesex FA)				

THIRD ROUND

1	Fylde	v	Sunderland (12/1)	1-4	
	(at Kellamergh Park)				
2	Burnley	v	Nottingham Forest	2-1	138
	(at Padiham FC)				
3	Loughborough Foxes	v	Huddersfield Town (2.00)	2-3	57
	(at Loughborough University)				
4	Brighouse Town	v	Barnsley (2.00)	0-1	321
	(at Brighouse Town FC)				
5	Ipswich Town	v	Portsmouth	1-0	
	(at Felixstowe & Walton United FC)				
6	Watford	v	Plymouth Argyle (2.00)	5-0	
	(at Kings Langley FC)				
7	Cardiff City	v	Southampton FC Women (2.00)	1-2	215
	(at Centre of Sporting Excellence)				
8	Southampton Women's FC	v	West Bromwich Albion (2.00)	3-1	
	(at Winklebury Football Complex)				
9	Billericay Town	v	Actonians (12/1)	3-2	
	(at Aveley FC)				

FOURTH ROUND

1	West Ham United	v	Arsenal	0-2	
	(at Rush Green)				
2	Manchester United	v	Manchester City (25/1)	2-3	1948
	(at Leigh Sports Village – Live on BBC iPlayer & Red Button)				
3	Lewes	v	Billericay Town	1-1aet	
	(Lewes won 5-4 on kicks from the penalty mark – at Lewes FC)				
4	Charlton Athletic	v	Chelsea (2.00)	0-4	844
	(at VCD Athletic FC)				
5	Everton	v	London Bees	1-0	
	(at Southport FC)				
6	Burnley	v	Leicester City	1-3	
	(at Padiham FC)				
7	Sheffield United	v	Birmingham City	0-3	
	(at Chesterfield FC)				
8	London City Lionesses	v	Reading (2.00)	0-5	
	(at Dartford FC)				
9	Bristol City	v	Durham	1-0aet	
	(at Stoke Gifford Stadium)				
10	Tottenham Hotspur	v	Barnsley	5-0	621
	(at The Hive)				
11	Huddersfield Town	v	Ipswich Town	1-4	1115
	(at Huddersfield Town FC)				
12	Southampton FC Women	v	Coventry United	1-4	4150
	(at Southampton FC)				
13	Southampton Women's FC	v	Crystal Palace (2/2)	0-4	
	(tie reversed – at Carshalton Athletic FC)				
	(26/1 – tie abandoned due to waterlogged pitch – tie ordered to be replayed at Crystal Palace LFC)				
14	Sunderland	v	Watford	2-0	226
	(at Hebburn Town FC)				
15	Liverpool	v	Blackburn Rovers	8-1	
	(at Bamber Bridge FC)				
16	Aston Villa	v	Brighton & Hove Albion (3.00)	2-3	
	(at Boldmere St Michaels FC)				

FIFTH ROUND

1	Bristol City	v	Everton (17/2)	0-5	
	(at Bristol City FC)				
2	Coventry United	v	Tottenham Hotspur (17/2)	0-5	
	(at Coventry United FC)				
3	Leicester City	v	Reading (20/2)	2-1aet	354
	(at Quorn FC)				
4	Crystal Palace	v	Brighton & Hove Albion (25/2)	0-3	
	(at Bromley FC)				
5	Manchester City	v	Ipswich Town	10-0	
	(at Academy Stadium)				
6	Arsenal	v	Lewes (23/2)	2-0	
	(at Boreham Wood FC – Live on BBC Red Button, BBC iPlayer & The FA Player)				
7	Sunderland	v	Birmingham City	0-1	
	(at Eppleton CW FC)				
8	Chelsea	v	Liverpool (17/2)	1-0	2630
	(at Kingsmeadow)				

QUARTER FINALS

1	Brighton & Hove Albion	v	Birmingham City
	(at Crawley Town FC)		
2	Everton	v	Chelsea
	(at Walton Hall Park)		
3	Arsenal	v	Tottenham Hotspur
4	Leicester City	v	Manchester City
	(at Quorn FC)		

FIRST ROUND

1. Yorkshire Amateur v North Riding (28/9) 6-0
   (at Nostell MW FC)

2. Wearside v West Cheshire (28/9) 1-2aet
   (at Boldon CA FC)

3. Isle of Man v Cheshire (28/9) 1-2
   (at The Bowl, Douglas)

4. West Yorkshire v Manchester (25/9) 4-1
   (at Nostell MW FC)

5. Liverpool County Premier v York (28/9) 4-2
   (at Liverpool County FA)

6. Anglian Combination v Cambridgeshire County (24/9) 2-3

7. Lincolnshire v Northants Combination (28/9)3-3aet 28
   (Lincolnshire won 4-3 on kicks from the penalty mark – at Sleaford Town FC)

8. Bedfordshire County v Staffordshire County (5/10) 0-7
   (at Cranfield United FC)

9. Suffolk & Ipswich v Peterborough & District (28/9)1-4 70
   (at Hadleigh United FC)

10. Amateur Comb v Essex Olympian (28/9) 2-1 37
    (at Uxbridge FC)

11. Herts Senior County v Kent County (21/9) 4-2 52

12. Essex & Suffolk Border v Southern Combination (28/9) 1-0
    (at Harwich & Parkeston FC)

13. Thames Valley Premier v Southern Amateur (28/9) 0-4 37
    (at Rivermoor Stadium)

14. Dorset Premier v Mid Sussex
    (walkover for Dorset Premier – Mid Sussex withdrawn)

15. Hampshire Premier v Guernsey (28/9) 1-5 45
    (at Stockbridge FC)

16. Jersey Comb v Somerset County (28/9) 7-0 257
    (at Springfield Stadium)

SECOND ROUND

1. Liverpool County Premier v West Cheshire (16/11) 0-3
   (at Liverpool County FA)

2. Staffordshire County v Cambridgeshire County (16/11) 6-2
   (at Hanley Town FC)

3. West Yorkshire v Lincolnshire (23/11) 12-1
   (at West Riding County FA)

4. Cheshire v Yorkshire Amateur (23/11) 1-1aet 81
   (Cheshire won 4-3 on kicks from the penalty mark)

5. Amateur Combination v Jersey Combination (16/11)1-2aet
   (at Sutton United FC)

6. Peterborough & District v Herts Senior County (23/11) 2-1
   (at FC Parson Drove)

7. Essex & Suffolk Border v Southern Amateur (9/11) 1-3 76
   (at Little Oakley FC)

8. Guernsey v Dorset Premier (16/11) 3-3aet
   (Dorset Premier won 5-4 on kicks from the penalty mark)

THIRD ROUND

1. Staffordshire County v West Yorkshire (7/3) 3-2 136
   (at Hanley Town FC)

2. Cheshire v West Cheshire County 1-3
   (at Hyde United FC)

3. Dorset Premier v Peterborough & District (22/2)1-0
   (at Sherborne Town FC)

4. Jersey Combination v Southern Amateur (29/2) 2-0 219
   (at Springfield Stadium)

SEMI FINALS

1. Dorset Premier v Jersey Combination
   (at Sherborne Town FC)

2. West Cheshire County v Staffordshire County (14/3) 2-1 75
   (at Vauxhall Motors FC)

THE FINAL

1. Dorset Premier v West Cheshire County
   or Jersey Combination

UEFA REGIONS' CUP
INTERMEDIATE ROUND 2018/19

GROUP 2 - BUZAU COUNTY

		P	W	D	L	F	A	GD	Pts
1	West Slovakia	3	1	2	0	7	4	3	5
2	Buzau County	3	1	1	1	5	7	-2	4
3	North Riding	3	0	3	1	5	5	0	3
4	Munster/Ulster	3	0	2	1	3	4	-1	2

16th September 2018

West Slovakia v **North Riding** 2-2

Hollcek 13 Pilny 79   McQueeney 46 Rose 50

19th September 2018

North Riding v Buzau County 2-2

Rose 79 (pen)   Babageanu 33 Visteanu 62
Bellamy 90+7 (pen)

22nd September 2018

North Riding v Munster/Ulster 1-1

Keenan 17   Ryan 87

21 DAYS of Positivity

DAY 01
Enjoyment and Positivity
Try three things that make your session positive: Allow enjoyment, be positive and smile

DAY 02
How well do you know your Players?
Take some time to get to know your players better

DAY 03
This is a Safe Place
Think about how you react when a mistake is made, encourage creativity and experimentation

DAY 04
What do your Players want from Training
Fun, fitness or because they love it, consider the reasons your players are there

DAY 05
Make Matchday about Learning
Provide equal opportunities and focus on communication

DAY 06
How to deal with Winning and Losing
Look for opportunities to show how to deal with adversity and frustration with dignity and respect

DAY 07
Are You a Role Model
So much of young player's behaviour on matchday mimics that of the coach, refresh yourself with our code of conduct

DAY 08
Arrival Activities: Get Players Moving
Tag, small-sided games or movement activities are all fun, engaging and active ways to start your session

DAY 09
Routines and Boundaries
Having consistent coaching routines can help create a safe place for young players to learn

DAY 10
When are we Playing a Game
Small-sided games give players lots of touches of the ball and the chance to attack and defend

DAY 11
How to Include Goalkeeper in Coaching Sessions
What individual challenges can you give to your goalkeeper within a group practice?

DAY 12
Improving Strengths
Write down the strengths of five players in your squad? How can you challenge them to improve their strengths?

DAY 13
What are You Looking For?
More specific observation will lead to more specific and relevant feedback.

DAY 14
'Drop Off' 'Squeeze' 'Get Tight'
Having a consistent way of talking about football is one way to link training and matchday

DAY 15
One Size Doesn't Fit All
To get the most out of each individual try tailoring your training tasks for specific players

DAY 16
How to Work as a Coaching Pair
Defining coaching roles is crucial. If one coach 'leads' the session, the other coach is free to focus on individuals

DAY 17
Effective Observation
Stand back and carefully watch two or three players, what did you learn about the group you didn't already know?

DAY 18
Communication Styles
Using a variety of communication methods is one way you can cater for the different needs in your group

DAY 19
Countdown to Kickoff
Before each game players should be given the chance to spend time together, warm-up and think about the game

DAY 20
Half-Time
Let players have a drink, ask their thoughts, pick out positive moments for praise, finish with a positive message

DAY 21
Full-Time
Is a chance for you to help the players make sense of the matchday experience, highlight positive moments and provide constructive feedback

Visit TheFA.com/Respect to find out more   #WeOnlyDoPositive   RESPECT

THE NON-LEAGUE CLUB DIRECTORY 2020-21

FA National League System Club Allocations - Steps 1 - 6

(Correct at the time of going to press 02/08/2020)

ALDERSHOT TOWN
The Shots   **Club Colours** Red & blue

Founded 1992

Club Contact Details 01252 320 211   admin@theshots.co.uk

Previous Names: None

Previous Leagues: Isthmian 1992-2003. Conference 2003-2008. Football League 2008-13.

2019-20 Season
Nat   18 after PPG
FAC   4Q
FAT   1P

Record
P 41 W 12 D 10 L 19

Top Goalscorer
Chilsett (9)

10-11		11-12		12-13		13-14		14-15		15-16		16-17		17-18		18-19	
FL 2	14	FL 2	11	FL 2	24	Conf	19	Conf	18	Nat	15	Nat	5	Nat	5	Nat	21
FAC	2P	FAC	2P	FAC	4P	FAC	4Qr	FAC	2Pr	FAC	1Pr	FAC	4Q	FAC	1P	FAC	1Pr
FLC	1P	FLC	4P	FLC	1P	FAT	QF	FAT	1P	FAT	1P	FAT	1Pr	FAT	1P	FAT	1Pr

LEAGUE HONOURS:
Isthmian League Division Three 1992-93, Division One 97-98, Premier Division 2002-03. Conference 2007-08.

COUNTY FA HONOURS: Hampshire Senior Cup 1998-99, 99-2000, 01-02, 02-03, 06-07.

CLUB RECORDS
FA Cup (As a non-League side) Third Round Proper - 2006-07. (Football League side) Fourth Round Proper - 2012-13.
FA Trophy Semi-Finals 2003-04, 07-08.   **FA Vase** Quarter-Finals 1993-94.
Victory: 8-0 v Bishop's Stortford (A) Isthmian Premier 05/09/1998
Defeat: 0-6 v Worthing (A) Isthmian League Cup 02/03/99
Goalscorer: Mark Butler - 155 (1992-98)
Appearances: Jason Chewings - 489 (August 1994 - May 2004)
Additional: Paid an undisclosed record fee to Woking for Marvin Morgan (05/2008)
Received £130,000 from Crewe Alexandra for Joel Grant (11/2008)

GROUND: EBB Stadium, High street, Aldershot, GU11 1TW
Ground Capacity: 7,025   **Seats:** 2,676   **Covered:** 5,975   **Clubhouse:** Yes   **Shop:** Yes
Previous Grounds: None
Record Attendance: 7,500 v Brighton & Hove Albion, FA Cup 1st Round, 18/11/2000

ALTRINCHAM
The Robins   **Club Colours** Red & white stripes

Founded 1891

Club Contact Details 0161 928 1045   office@altrinchamfootballclub.co.uk

Previous Names: Rigby Memorial Club 1891-93. Merged with the 'Grapplers' to form Broadheath FC 1893-1903.

Previous Leagues: Manchester (Founder members) 1893-1911. Lancashire Combination 1911-19. Cheshire County (FM) 1919-68. Northern Premier (FM) 1968-79, 97-99, 00-04, 17-18. Alliance/Conference/National (FM) 1979-97, 99-00, 04-17.

2019-20 Season
Nat N   5 after PPG
FAC   1P
FAT   1Pr

Record
P 44 W 24 D 11 L 9

Top Goalscorer
Hulme (19)

10-11		11-12		12-13		13-14		14-15		15-16		16-17		17-18		18-19	
Conf	22	Conf N	8	Conf N	4	Conf N	3	Conf	17	Nat	22	Nat N	22	NP P	1	Nat N	5
FAC	4Q	FAC	2Q	FAC	1Pr	FAC	2Q	FAC	1P	FAC	2P	FAC	1P	FAC	3Q	FAC	4Q
FAT	2P	FAT	3Q	FAT	1P	FAT	1P	FAT	3P	FAT	2P	FAT	1Pr	FAT	1Pr	FAT	1P

LEAGUE HONOURS:
Manchester 1904-05, 06-07. Cheshire 1965-66, 66-67. Football Alliance 1979-80, 80-81. Northern Premier League Premier Division 1998-99, 2017-18.

COUNTY FA Cheshire Amateur Cup 1903-04.
HONOURS: Cheshire Senior Cup Winners 1904-05, 33-34, 66-67, 81-82, 98-99, 04-05, 08-09.

CLUB RECORDS
FA Cup Fourth Round Proper 1985-86
FA Trophy Winners 1977-78, 85-86
Victory: 14-2 v Sale Holmfield, Cheshire Amateur Cup, 05/12/1903
Defeat: 1-13 v Stretford (H) - 04.11.1893
Goalscorer: Jack Swindells - 252 (1965-71)
Appearances: John Davison - 677 (1971-86)
Additional: Transfer fee paid - £15k to Blackpool for Keith Russell. Received - £50k from Leicester for Kevin Ellison

GROUND: The J Davidson Stadium, Moss Lane, Altrincham, Cheshire WA15 8AP
Ground Capacity: 6,085   **Seats:** 1,323   **Covered:** Yes   **Clubhouse:** Yes   **Shop:** Yes
Previous Grounds: Pollitts Field 1903-10.
Record Attendance: 10,275 - Altrincham Boys v Sunderland Boys English Schools Shield 28/02/1925.
Nearest Railway Station Altrincham - Approx. 10min walk from the ground
Bus Route Arriva 263 & Stagecoach X41

BARNET

The Bees   **Club Colours** Amber and black

Founded 1885

Club Contact Details 020 8381 3800   tellus@thehivelondon.com

2019-20 Season
Nat   7 after PPG
FAC   1P
FAT   4P

Record
P 45 W 19 D 14 L 12

Top Goalscorer
Akinola (17)

Previous Names: New Barnet 1885-88. Barnet 1888-1902 (folded). Barnet Alston 1904-19.

Previous Leagues: Post 1945 - Athenian 1945-65. Southern 1965-79. Conference 1979-91, 2001-05, 13-15. Football League 1991-2001, 05-13.

10-11		11-12		12-13		13-14		14-15		15-16		16-17		17-18		18-19	
FL 2	22	FL 2	22	FL 2	23	Conf	8	Conf	1	FL 2	15	FL 2	15	FL 2	24	Nat	12
FAC	1Pr	FAC	2P	FAC	1P	FAC	1P	FAC	1P	FAC	2P	FAC	1P	FAC	1P	FAC	4Pr
FLC	1P	FLC	2P	FLC	1P	FAT	2P	FAT	1Pr	FLC	2P	FLC	1P	FLC	2P	FAT	4P

LEAGUE HONOURS:
Athenian League 1931-32, 32-33, 46-47, 58-59, 63-64, 64-65. Southern League Division One 1965-66, Division One South 1977-78. Football Conference 1990-91, 2004-05, 2014-15.

COUNTY FA HONOURS: Herts Senior Cup 1985-86, 90-91, 91-92, 92-93, 95-96, 2006-07, 10-11.

CLUB RECORDS
FA Cup (As a non-League side) 4th Rnd Proper Replay - 2018-19. (FL) 4th Rnd Proper - 2006-07, 07-08.
FA Am Cup Winners 1945-46   **FA Trophy** Finalists 1971-72
Victory: 7-0 v Blackpool Division 3 11/11/2000
Defeat: 1-9 v Peterborough Division 3 05/09/1998
Goalscorer: Arthur Morris - 403 (1927-36)
Appearances: Les Eason - 648 (1965-74, 77-78)

GROUND: The Hive, Camrose Avenue, Edgware, Middlesex, HA8 6AG
Ground Capacity: 6,500   **Seats:** 3,434   **Covered:** 5,176   **Clubhouse:** Yes   **Shop:** Yes
Previous Grounds: Underhill 1907-2013
Record Attendance: 11,026 v Wycombe Wanderers FA Amateur Cup 01/01/1953
Nearest Railway Station Canons Park Underground (Jubilee line) is a 5 min walk away.
Bus Route 340, 186 & 79 from Edgware to Canons Park.

BOREHAM WOOD

The Wood   **Club Colours** White & black

Founded 1948

Club Contact Details 0208 953 5097   matt@borehamwoodfootballclub.co.uk

2019-20 Season
Nat   5 after PPG
FAC   4Q
FAT   1P

Record
P 41 W 17 D 12 L 12

Top Goalscorer
Tshimanga (19)

Previous Names: Boreham Wood Rovers and Royal Retournez amalgamated in 1948 to form today's club

Previous Leagues: Mid Herts 1948-52, Parthenon 1952-57, Spartan 1957-66, Athenian 1966-74, Isthmian 1974-2004, Southern 2004-10.

10-11		11-12		12-13		13-14		14-15		15-16		16-17		17-18		18-19	
Conf S	14	Conf S	8	Conf S	9	Conf S	13	Conf S	2	Nat	19	Nat	11	Nat	4	Nat	20
FAC	4Q	FAC	2Q	FAC	1P	FAC	1Pr	FAC	4Q	FAC	1Pr	FAC	1Pr	FAC	2P	FAC	1P
FAT	1P	FAT	1P	FAT	1Pr	FAT	3Q	FAT	3Q	FAT	1P	FAT	QF	FAT	2Pr	FAT	2P

LEAGUE HONOURS:
Athenian League Division Two 1968-69, Division One 73-74. Isthmian League Division Two 1976-77, Division One 1994-95, 2000-01. Southern Division One East 2005-06.

COUNTY FA HONOURS: Herts Senior cup 1971-72, 98-99, 2001-02, 07-08, 13-14, 18-19.
HONOURS: Herts Charity Cup 1980-81, 83-84, 85-86, 88-89, 89-90. London Challenge Cup 1997-98.

CLUB RECORDS
FA Cup Second Round Proper - 1996-97, 97-98, 2017-18.
FA Trophy Semi-Finals - 2005-06
Goalscorer: Mickey Jackson
Appearances: Dave Hatchett - 714
Additional: Received £5,000 from Dagenham & Redbridge for Steve Heffer

GROUND: Meadow Park, Broughinge Road, Boreham Wood WD6 5AL
Ground Capacity: 4,502   **Seats:** 1,700   **Covered:** 2,800   **Clubhouse:** Yes   **Shop:** Yes
Previous Grounds: Eldon Avenue 1948-63
Record Attendance: 4,030 v Arsenal - Friendly 13/07/2001
Nearest Railway Station Elstree & Boreham Wood.

BROMLEY
The Ravens or The Lillywhites   **Club Colours** White and black

Founded 1892

NATIONAL LEAGUE

Club Contact Details 020 8460 5291   info@bromleyfc.net

Previous Names: None

Previous Leagues: South London, Southern, London, West Kent, South Surburban, Kent, Spartan 1907-08, Isthmian 1908-11, 52-2007, Athenian 1919-1952

2019-20 Season
Nat 13 after PPG
FAC 1Pr
FAT 1P

Record
P 42 W 15 D 11 L 16

Top Goalscorer
Cheek (15)

10-11	11-12	12-13	13-14	14-15	15-16	16-17	17-18	18-19
Conf S 11	Conf S 17	Conf S 15	Conf S 3	Conf S 1	Nat 14	Nat 10	Nat 9	Nat 11
FAC 3Qr	FAC 1P	FAC 1P	FAC 3Q	FAC 1P	FAC 4Q	FAC 4Q	FAC 1P	FAC 1P
FAT 3Q	FAT 3Q	FAT 3P	FAT 3Q	FAT 2P	FAT 1P	FAT 2P	FAT F	FAT 1P

LEAGUE HONOURS:
Spartan 1907-08. Isthmian League 1908-09, 09-10, 53-54, 60-61. Athenian League 1922-23, 48-49, 50-51. Conference South 2014-15.

COUNTY FA HONOURS: Kent Senior Cup 1949/50, 76-77, 91-92, 96-97, 2005-06, 06-07. Kent Amateur Cup x12. London Senior Cup 1909-10, 45-46, 50-51, 2002-03, 12-13.

CLUB RECORDS
FA Cup Second Round Proper 1937-38, 45-46.
FA Trophy Third Round Proper 1999-00, 2012-13.
Victory: 13-1 v Redhill - Athenian League 1945-46
Defeat: 1-11 v Barking - Athenian League 1933-34
Goalscorer: George Brown - 570 (1938-61)
Appearances: George Brown
Additional: Received £50,000 from Millwall for John Goodman

GROUND: The Stadium, Hayes Lane, Bromley, Kent BR2 9EF
Ground Capacity: 5,000 **Seats:** 1,300 **Covered:** 2,500 **Clubhouse:** Yes **Shop:** Yes
Previous Grounds: White Hart Field. Widmore Road. Plaistow Cricket Ground.
Record Attendance: 10,798 v Nigeria - 1950

CHESTERFIELD
The Spireites   **Club Colours** Blue & white

Founded 1866

Club Contact Details 01246 269 300   fans@chesterfield-fc.co.uk

Previous Names: Chesterfield Town 1891-1915, Chesterfield Municipal 1915-20.

Previous Leagues: Sheffield & District 1892-96. Midland 1896-99, 1909-15, 19-20. Football League 1899-1909, 1921-2018.

2019-20 Season
Nat 20 after PPG
FAC 4Qr
FAT 1P

Record
P 41 W 11 D 12 L 18

Top Goalscorer
Fondop-Talum (11)

10-11	11-12	12-13	13-14	14-15	15-16	16-17	17-18	18-19
FL 2 1	FL 1 22	FL 2 8	FL 2 1	FL 1 6	FL 1 18	FL 1 24	FL 2 23	Nat 14
FAC 2P	FAC 1P	FAC 2P	FAC 2P	FAC 4P	FAC 2Pr	FAC 2P	FAC 1P	FAC 2P
FLC 1P	FLC 1P	FLC 1P	FLC 1P	FLC 1P	FLC 1P	FLC 1P	FLC 1P	FAT 3P

LEAGUE HONOURS:
Midland 1909-10, 19-20. League Division Three North 1930-31, 35-36, Division Four/League Two 69-70, 84-85, 2010-11, 13-14.

COUNTY FA HONOURS: Derbyshire Senior Cup 1898-99, 1920-21, 21-22, 24-25, 32-33, 36-37, 2017-18.

CLUB RECORDS
FA Cup (As a non-League side) Second Round Proper - 2018-19. (Football League side) Semi-Finals 1996-97 (r).
FA Trophy Third Round Proper 2018-19.
Appearances: Mark Allott - 385 (League) 2001-12.
Goalscorer: Jack Lester - 92 (League) 2007-13.
Victory: 8-1 v Barrow 13/11/1926 and v Gateshead 25/04/1931.

GROUND: The Proact Stadium, 1866 Sheffield Road, Whittington Moor, Chesterfield S41 8NZ
Ground Capacity: 10,000 **Seats:** 10,000 **Covered:** Yes **Clubhouse:** Yes **Shop:** Yes
Previous Grounds: Athletic Ground 1866-72. Saltergate (Recreation Ground) 1872-2010.
Record Attendance: 30,561 (Saltergate) v Tottenham, 12/02/1938. 10,089 (1866 Sheffield Rd) v Rotherham United.
Nearest Railway Station Chesterfield

DAGENHAM & REDBRIDGE

The Daggers   **Club Colours** Red & blue

Founded 1992

2019-20 Season
Nat   17 after PPG
FAC   4Q
FAT   1P

Record
P 41 W 12 D 12 L 17

Top Goalscorer
Balanta & Brundle (8)

Club Contact Details   0208 592 1549   info@daggers.co.uk

Previous Names: Formed by the merger of Dagenham and Redbridge Forest

Previous Leagues: Football Conference 1992-96, 2000-2007. Isthmian 1996-2000. Football League 2007-16.

	10-11		11-12		12-13		13-14		14-15		15-16		16-17		17-18		18-19	
	FL 1	21	FL 2	19	FL 2	22	FL 2	9	FL 2	14	FL 2	23	Nat	4	Nat	11	Nat	18
	FAC	1Pr	FAC	3Pr	FAC	1P	FAC	1P	FAC	1Pr	FAC	3P	FAC	1Pr	FAC	4Qr	FAC	4Q
	FLC	1P	FLC	1P	FLC	1P	FLC	1P	FLC	1P	FLC	1P	FAT	1P	FAT	1P	FAT	2P

LEAGUE HONOURS:
Isthmian League Premier Division 1999-2000. Football Conference 2006-07.

COUNTY FA HONOURS: Essex Senior Cup 1997-98, 2000-01.

CLUB RECORDS
FA Cup Fourth Round Proper 2002-03.
FA Trophy Finalists 1996-97.
Victory: 8-1 v Woking, Football Conference, 19.04.94.
Defeat: 0-9 v Hereford United, Football Conference, 27.02.04.
Goalscorer: Danny Shipp - 105
Appearances: Tony Roberts - 507
Additional: Transfer fee received: £470,000 Dwight Gayle to Peterborough United

GROUND: Chigwell Construction Stadium, Victoria Road, Dagenham, Essex RM10 7XL
Ground Capacity: 6,078   **Seats:** 2,200   **Covered:** Yes   **Clubhouse:** Yes   **Shop:** Yes
Previous Grounds: None
Record Attendance: 5,949 v Ipswich Town (05/01/2002) FA Cup Third Round Proper
Nearest Railway Station Dagenham East Underground (District line), exit left and take fifth turning on the left 400 metres away.
Bus Route The 103 runs from Romford Station and stops outside the ground.

DOVER ATHLETIC

The Whites   **Club Colours** White & black

Founded 1983

2019-20 Season
Nat   11 after PPG
FAC   2P
FAT   1P

Record
P 42 W 17 D 10 L 15

Top Goalscorer
Effiong (16)

Club Contact Details   01304 822 373   enquiries@doverathletic.com

Previous Names: Dover F.C. until club folded in 1983

Previous Leagues: Southern 1983-93, 2002-04, Conference 1993-2002, Isthmian 2004-2009

	10-11		11-12		12-13		13-14		14-15		15-16		16-17		17-18		18-19	
	Conf S	7	Conf S	7	Conf S	3	Conf S	5	Conf	8	Nat	5	Nat	6	Nat	8	Nat	13
	FAC	3P	FAC	4Q	FAC	3Qr	FAC	2P	FAC	3P	FAC	1P	FAC	1Pr	FAC	4Qr	FAC	1P
	FAT	3Q	FAT	3Q	FAT	3Qr	FAT	3P	FAT	QFr	FAT	QF	FAT	1Pr	FAT	3P	FAT	2P

LEAGUE HONOURS:
Southern League Southern Division 1987-88, Premier Division 1989-90, 92-93.
Isthmian League Division One South 2007-08, Premier Division 2008-09.

COUNTY FA HONOURS: Kent Senior Cup 1990-91, 2016-17.

CLUB RECORDS
FA Cup Third Round Proper 2010-11, 14-15.
FA Trophy Semi-Finals 1997-98.
Victory: 7-0 v Weymouth - 03/04/1990
Defeat: 1-7 v Poole Town
Goalscorer: Lennie Lee - 160
Appearances: Jason Bartlett - 520+
Additional: Paid £50,000 to Farnborough Town for David Lewworthy August 1993
Received £50,000 from Brentford for Ricky Reina 1997

GROUND: Crabble Athletic Ground, Lewisham Road, Dover, Kent CT17 0JB
Ground Capacity: 6,500   **Seats:** 1,010   **Covered:** 4,900   **Clubhouse:** Yes   **Shop:** Yes
Previous Grounds: None
Record Attendance: 4,186 v Oxford United - FA Cup 1st Round Proper November 2002
Nearest Railway Station Main line - Dover Priory 2 miles away. Kearsney Station is a 10-15 minute walk from the ground.

EASTLEIGH
The Spitfires   **Club Colours** Blue

Founded 1946

Club Contact Details 02380 613 361   admin@eastleighfc.com

Previous Swaythling Athletic 1946-59
Names: Swaythling 1973-80
Previous Southampton Junior & Senior 1946-59, Hampshire 1950-86, Wessex 1986-2003,
Leagues: Southern 2003-04, Isthmian 2004-05

2019-20 Season
Nat   16 after PPG
FAC   2Pr
FAT   3P

Record
P 46 W 15 D 16 L 15

Top Goalscorer
Barnett (12)

	10-11	11-12	12-13	13-14	14-15	15-16	16-17	17-18	18-19
	Conf S 8	Conf S 12	Conf S 4	Conf S 1	Conf 4	Nat 7	Nat 15	Nat 14	Nat 7
FAC	4Q	3Q	3Q	3Q	2P	3Pr	3P	4Q	4Q
FAT	3P	3Q	3Q	3Q	1P	2P	1P	1P	1P

LEAGUE HONOURS:
Southampton Senior (West) 1949-50. Hampshire Division Three 1950-51, 53-54, Division Two 1967-68.
Wessex Division One 2002-03. Conference South 2013-14.

COUNTY FA
HONOURS: Hampshire Intermediate Cup 1950-51, Senior Cup 2011-12.

CLUB RECORDS
FA Cup Third Round Proper 2015-16 (r), 16-17.
FA Trophy Quarter Finals 2013-14.   **FA Vase**   Fourth Round 1982-83, 90-91, 94-95.
Victory: 12-1 v Hythe & Dibden (H) - 11/12/1948
Defeat: 0-11 v Austin Sports (A) - 01.01.1947
Goalscorer: Johnnie Williams - 177
Appearances: Ian Knight - 611
Additional: Paid £10,000 to Newport (I.O.W.) for Colin Matthews

GROUND: The Silverlake Stadium 'Ten Acres', Stoneham Lane, Eastleigh SO50 9HT
Ground Capacity: 3,000   **Seats:** 2,700   **Covered:** Yes   **Clubhouse:** Yes   **Shop:** Yes
Previous Grounds: Southampton Common. Walnut Avenue >1957.
Record Attendance: 5,250 v Bolton Wanderers, FA Cup Third Round 09/01/2016

FC HALIFAX TOWN
The Shaymen   **Club Colours** Blue and white trim

Founded 1911

Club Contact Details 01422 341 222   tonyallen@fchalifaxtown.com

Previous
Names: Halifax Town 1911-2008 then reformed as F.C. Halifax Town
Previous Yorkshire Combination 1911-12, Midland 1912-21, Football League (FM Division Three North)1921
Leagues: -93, 98-2002, Conference 1993-98, 2002-08

2019-20 Season
Nat   6 after PPG
FAC   4Q
FAT   3P

Record
P 42 W 19 D 7 L 16

Top Goalscorer
C King (10)

	10-11	11-12	12-13	13-14	14-15	15-16	16-17	17-18	18-19
	NP P 1	Conf N 3	Conf N 5	Conf 5	Conf 9	Nat 21	Nat N 3	Nat 16	Nat 15
FAC	4Q	1P	4Qr	1P	1P	1P	2Pr	4Q	2P
FAT	2Q	3Qr	QFr	1P	QF	F	3Qr	2P	2Pr

LEAGUE HONOURS:
Conference 1997-98. Northern Premier League Division One North 2009-10, Premier Division 2010-11.

COUNTY FA
HONOURS: West Riding County Cup 2012-13.

CLUB RECORDS
FA Cup Fifth Round Proper 1932-33, 52-53 as Halifax Town. Second Round Proper 2016-17 (r) as FC Halifax Town.
FA Trophy Winners 2015-16
Victory: 12-0 v West Vale Ramblers - FA Cup 1st Qualifying Road 1913-14
Defeat: 0-13 v Stockport County - Division 3 North 1933-34
Goalscorer: Ernie Dixon - 132 (1922-30)
Appearances: John Pickering - 402 (1965-74)
Additional: Recorded a 30 game unbeaten run at The Shay between 18/04/2009 - 20/11/2010 (W 24 D 6 F 79 A 20).
                      Fee paid - £150,000 for Chris Tate, July 1999. Fee Received - £350,000 for Geoff Horsfield, October 1998.

GROUND: The Shay Stadium, Shay Syke, Halifax HX1 2YT
Ground Capacity: 10,401   **Seats:** 5,830   **Covered:** Yes   **Clubhouse:** Yes   **Shop:** Yes
Previous Grounds: Sandhall Lane 1911-15, Exley 1919-21.
Record Attendance: 36,885 v Tottenham Hotspur - FA Cup 5th Round 14/02/1953
Nearest Railway Station Halifax - 5-10min walk from the ground.

HARTLEPOOL UNITED
Monkey Hangers   **Club Colours** Blue & white

Founded 1908

Club Contact Details 01429 272 584   enquiries@hartlepoolunited.co.uk

Previous Names: Hartlepools United 1908-68. Hartlepool 1968-77.

Previous Leagues: North Eastern 1908-21. Football League 1921-2017.

2019-20 Season
Nat 12 after PPG
FAC 3P
FAT 1P

Record
P 45 W 17 D 14 L 14

Top Goalscorer
Toure (13)

10-11		11-12		12-13		13-14		14-15		15-16		16-17		17-18		18-19	
FL 1	16	FL 1	13	FL 1	23	FL 2	19	FL 2	22	FL 2	16	FL 2	23	Nat	15	Nat	16
FAC	3P	FAC	1P	FAC	1P	FAC	2Pr	FAC	2P	FAC	3P	FAC	2P	FAC	1P	FAC	1Pr
FLC	2P	FLC	1P	FLC	1P	FLC	1P	FLC	1P	FLC	2P	FLC	1P	FAT	1P	FAT	2P

LEAGUE HONOURS:
None

COUNTY FA HONOURS: None

CLUB RECORDS
FA Cup 4th Rd Proper 1954-55(r), 77-78, 88-89(r), 92-93, 2004-05(r), 08-09 as a League club. 1st Rd Proper 2017-18, 18-19(r) as a N-Lge Club.
FA Trophy 2nd Round Proper 2018-19
Goalscorer: Joshie Fletcher - 111
Appearances: Ritchie Humphreys - 543 (Includes a run of 234 consecutive appearances)

GROUND: The Super 6 Stadium (Victoria Park), Clarence Road, Hartlepool TS24 8BZ
Ground Capacity: 7,865 **Seats:** 4,359 **Covered:** Yes   **Clubhouse:** Yes **Shop:** Yes
Previous Grounds: None
Record Attendance: 17,264 v Manchester United, FA Cup Third Round Proper, 1957
Nearest Railway Station Hartlepool is about half a mile away.

KING'S LYNN TOWN
The Linnets   **Club Colours** Yellow & blue

Founded 2010

Club Contact Details 01553 760 060   office@kltown.co.uk

Previous Names: King's Lynn Town formed in 2010 after King's Lynn FC folded.

Previous Leagues: United Counties 2010-12. Northern Premier 2012-15. Southern 2015-19.

2019-20 Season
Nat N 1 after PPG
FAC 4Q
FAT 2P

Record
P 40 W 22 D 10 L 8

Top Goalscorer
Marriott (30)

10-11		11-12		12-13		13-14		14-15		15-16		16-17		17-18		18-19	
UCL P	2	UCL P	2	NP1S	1	NP P	11	NP P	18	SthP	9	SthP	13	SthP	2	SthPC	2
		FAC	4Q	FAC	1Qr	FAC	1Q	FAC	4Q	FAC	3Q	FAC	3Q	FAC	2Q	FAC	3Q
FAV	SF	FAV	2P	FAT	3P	FAT	1Q	FAT	3Q	FAT	2Q	FAV	1P	FAT	1Q	FAT	1Qr

LEAGUE HONOURS:
Northern Premier Division One South 2012-13.
National North 2019-20 (Based on PPG).

COUNTY FA HONOURS: Norfolk Senior Cup 2016-17.

CLUB RECORDS
FA Cup Fourth Qualifying Round 2011-12, 14-15, 19-20.   **FA Vase** Semi-finals 2010-11.
FA Trophy Third Round Proper 2012-13.
Victory: 7-1 v Gosport Borough (A), Southern Premier, 06/02/2018

GROUND: The Walks Stadium, Tennyson Road, King's Lynn PE30 5PB
Ground Capacity: 8,200 **Seats:** 1,400 **Covered:** 5,000 **Clubhouse:** Yes **Shop:** Yes
Previous Grounds: None
Record Attendance:
Nearest Railway Station King's Lynn - 5min walk away.
Bus Route Serviced by Eastern Counties & Norfolk Green

MAIDENHEAD UNITED
Magpies   **Club Colours** Black & white

Founded 1870

Club Contact Details 01628 636 314   social@maidenheadunitedfc.org

Previous Names: After WWI Maidenhead F.C and Maidenhead Norfolkians merged to form Maidenhead Town >1920.

Previous Leagues: Southern (FM) 1894-1902, 2006-07, West Berkshire 1902-04, Gr. West Suburban 04-22, Spartan 1922-39, Gr. West Comb. 1939-45, Corinthian 45-63, Athenian 63-73, Isthmian 73-2004, Conference 04-06.

2019-20 Season
Nat   21 after PPG
FAC   1P
FAT   2Pr

Record
P 44 W 14 D 7 L 23

Top Goalscorer
Whitehall (15)

10-11		11-12		12-13		13-14		14-15		15-16		16-17		17-18		18-19	
Conf S	19	Conf S	20	Conf S	19	Conf S	18	Conf S	18	Nat S	7	Nat S	1	Nat	12	Nat	19
FAC	4Q	FAC	1Pr	FAC	3Q	FAC	2Q	FAC	3Qr	FAC	1Pr	FAC	2Q	FAC	1P	FAC	1P
FAT	3Q	FAT	1Pr	FAT	1P	FAT	3P	FAT	2Pr	FAT	2P	FAT	3Q	FAT	3Pr	FAT	1P

LEAGUE HONOURS:
West Berkshire 1902-03. Spartan 1926-27, 31-32, 33-34. Corinthian 1957-58, 60-61, 61-62. National South 2016-17.

COUNTY FA HONOURS: Berks & Bucks Senior Cup 1894-95, 95-96, 1911-12, 27-28, 29-30, 30-31, 31-32, 38-39, 45-46, 55-56, 56-57, 60-61, 62-63, 65-66, 69-70, 97-98, 98-99, 2001-02, 02-03, 09-10, 14-15, 16-17. Wycombe Senior Cup

CLUB RECORDS
FA Cup As United - First Round Proper 1960-61, 62-63, 63-64, 71-72, 2006-07, 07-08, 11-12 (r), 15-16 (r), 18-19.
FA Trophy Quarter-finals 2003-04   **FA Vase** Second Round Proper 1989-90
Victory: 14-1 v Buckingham Town - FA Amateur Cup 06/09/1952
Defeat: 0-14 v Chesham United (A) - Spartan League 31/03/1923
Goalscorer: George Copas - 270 (1924-35). Most goals in a season: Jack Palethorpe - 65 in 39 apps (1929-30).
Appearances: Bert Randall - 532 (1950-64)
Additional: Received £5,000 from Norwich City for Alan Cordice 1979

GROUND: York Road, Maidenhead, Berkshire SL6 1SF
Ground Capacity: 4,500   **Seats:** 550   **Covered:** 2,000   **Clubhouse:** Yes   **Shop:** Yes
Previous Grounds: Kidwells Park (Norfolkians)
Record Attendance: 7,989 v Southall - FA Amateur Cup Quarter final 07/03/1936
Nearest Railway Station Maidenhead - 200 yards from the ground.

NOTTS COUNTY
The Magpies   **Club Colours** Black & white

Founded 1862

Club Contact Details 0115 952 9000   office@nottscountyfc.co.uk

Previous Names: None

Previous Leagues: Football League (FM) 1888-2019

2019-20 Season
Nat   3 after PPG
FAC   2P
FAT

Record
P 47 W 24 D 12 L 11

Top Goalscorer
Wootton (19)

10-11		11-12		12-13		13-14		14-15		15-16		16-17		17-18		18-19	
FL 1	19	FL 1	7	FL 1	12	FL 1	20	FL 1	21	FL 2	7	FL 2	16	FL 2	5	FL 2	23
FAC	4Pr	FAC	4P	FAC	2Pr	FAC	1P	FAC	1Pr	FAC	1P	FAC	2Pr	FAC	4Pr	FAC	1P
FLC	3P	FLC	1P	FLC	1P	FLC	2P	FLC	1P	FLC	2P	FLC	1P	FLC	1P	FLC	1P

LEAGUE HONOURS:
Football League Division Two 1896-97, 1913-14, 22-23, Division Three South 1930-31, 49-50, Division Four 1970-71, Division Three 1997-98, League Two 2009-10.

COUNTY FA HONOURS:

CLUB RECORDS
FA Cup Winners 1893-94.
FA Trophy Semi Finals 2019-20 (At the time of going to press the Semi Finals had yet to be played)
Victory: (League) 11-1 v Newport County, Division Three South, 15/01/1949
Victory: (Cup) 15-0 v Rotherham Town, FA Cup 1st Round Proper, 24/10/1885
Goalscorer: (League) Les Bradd - 125 (1967-78). In a season: Tom Keetley - 39 (1930-31)
Appearances: (League) Albert Iremonger - 564 (1904-26)

GROUND: Meadow Lane Stadium, Meadow Lane, Nottingham NG2 3HJ
Ground Capacity: 19,841   **Seats:** 19,841   **Covered:** Yes   **Clubhouse:** Yes   **Shop:** Yes
Previous Grounds: 1862-63 Park Hollow, 63-73 Meadows Cket Gd, 73-77, 94-1910 Trent Bridge, 77-78 Beeston Cket Gd, 80–94 Castle Gd
Record Attendance: 47,310 v York City, FA Cup Six Round, 12/03/1955
Nearest Railway Station The ground is 10min walk from Nottingham train station.
Bus Route None directly to the ground only to Nottingham's coach station on Station Street, the ground is a short walk from there.

SOLIHULL MOORS

Moors   **Club Colours** Blue with yellow

Founded 2007

Club Contact Details 0121 705 6770   info@solihullmoorsfc.co.uk

Previous Names: Today's club was formed after the amalgamation of Solihull Borough and Moor Green in 2007.

Previous Leagues: None

2019-20 Season
Nat   9 after PPG

FAC   2P

FAT   1Pr

Record
P 45 W 17 D 13 L 15

Top Goalscorer
McCallum (9)

	10-11	11-12	12-13	13-14	14-15	15-16	16-17	17-18	18-19
	Conf N 7	Conf N 19	Conf N 9	Conf N 8	Conf N 12	Nat N 1	Nat 16	Nat 18	Nat 2
FAC	3Q	4Q	3Q	4Q	2Q	3Q	2P	1P	2Pr
FAT	3Q	1P	2P	3Q	1P	1P	1P	2P	4P

LEAGUE HONOURS:
National North 2015-16.

COUNTY FA HONOURS: Birmingham Senior Cup 2015-16.

CLUB RECORDS

FA Cup Second Round Proper 2016-17(r) 18-19(r) 19-20
FA Trophy Fourth Round Proper 2018-19
Victory: 7-2 v Corby Town, Conference North, 12/02/2011.
Defeat: 0-9 v Tranmere Rovers, National, 08/04/2017.
Appearances: Carl Motteram - 71 (2007-08)

GROUND: The Automated Technology Group Stadium, Damson Park, Damson Parkway, Solihull B91 2PP

Ground Capacity: 5,500 **Seats:** 2,131 **Covered:** Yes **Clubhouse:** Yes **Shop:** Yes
Previous Grounds: None
Record Attendance: 3,681 v Leyton Orient, National, 22/04/2019.
Nearest Railway Station Solihull & Birmingham within 3 miles away.
Bus Route Nos. X12 or 966 from Town Centre.

STEVENAGE

The Boro   **Club Colours** Red & white

Founded 1976

Club Contact Details 01438 223 223   info@stevenagefc.com

Previous Names: Stevenage Borough >2010.

Previous Leagues: Chiltern Youth 1976. Wallspan Southern Combination. United Counties 1980-84. Isthmian 1984-94. Conference 1994-2010. Football League 2010-20.

2019-20 Season
FL 2   24 after PPG

FAC   1Pr

FLC   1P

Record
P 45 W 6 D 15 L 24

Top Goalscorer
C Carter (6)

	10-11	11-12	12-13	13-14	14-15	15-16	16-17	17-18	18-19
	FL 2 6	FL 1 6	FL 1 18	FL 1 24	FL 2 6	FL 2 18	FL 2 10	FL 2 16	FL 2 10
FAC	4P	5Pr	1P	4P	1Pr	2P	1P	3Pr	1P
FLC	1P	1P	2P	1P	1P	1P	2P	1P	1P

LEAGUE HONOURS:
United Counties Division One 1980-81. Isthmian Division Two North 1985-86, 90-91, Division One 91-92, Premier 93-94. Conference 1995-96, 2009-10.

COUNTY FA HONOURS: Herts Charity Cup 1996-97. Herts Senior Cup 2008-09.

CLUB RECORDS

FA Cup (As a non-League club) Fourth Round Proper 1997-98(r). (As a League club) Fifth Round Proper 2011-12(r).
FA Trophy Winners 2006-07, 08-09, runners up 01-02, 09-10.   **FA Vase**   Quarter Finals 1985-86.
Appearances: Ronnie Henry - 502.
Goalscorer: Martin Gittings - 217 in 377 appearances. Scored 40 goals during the 1991-92 season.
Victory: 8-0 v Runcorn, Conference, 25/11/1995.
Defeat: 1-7 v Chesham United, Isthmian Premier, 21/10/1992.

GROUND: The Lamex Stadium, Broadhall Way, Stevenage SG2 8RH

Ground Capacity: 7,100 **Seats:** 2,190 **Covered:** 6,500 **Clubhouse:** Yes **Shop:** Yes
Previous Grounds: King George V playing fields 1976-80.
Record Attendance: 8,040 v Newcastle United (1-1), FA Cup Fourth Round, 25/01/1998
Nearest Railway Station Stevenage - Shuttle bus from Stop N takes you to the ground.
Bus Route Arriva services plus club Shuttle from Stop K at the bus station.

STOCKPORT COUNTY
County or Hatters   **Club Colours** Blue and white

Founded 1883

Club Contact Details 0161 286 8888   mark.lockyear@stockportcounty.com

2019-20 Season
Nat   8 after PPG
FAC   4Q
FAT   2Pr

Record
P 43 W 17 D 11 L 15

Top Goalscorer
Osborne (9)

Previous Names: Heaton Norris Rovers 1883-88, Heaton Norris 1888-90.

Previous Leagues: Lancashire 1863-1900. Football League 1900-2011.

10-11	11-12	12-13	13-14	14-15	15-16	16-17	17-18	18-19
FL 2 24	Conf 16	Conf 21	Conf N 14	Conf N 11	Nat N 9	Nat N 8	Nat N 5	Nat N 1
FAC 1Pr	FAC 4Q	FAC 1P	FAC 3Q	FAC 4Q	FAC 2Q	FAC 1P	FAC 3Qr	FAC 2P
FLC 1P	FAT 1Pr	FAT 2Pr	FAT 2Pr	FAT 2Pr	FAT 3Q	FAT 2Pr	FAT 4Pr	FAT SF

LEAGUE HONOURS:
Lancashire 1899-1900.
League Division Three North 1921-22, 36-37, Division Four 1966-67. National North 2018-19.

COUNTY FA HONOURS: Manchester S.C. 1897-98,98-99, 1914-15,22,23. Cheshire Medal 1922-23,24-25,28-29,29-30,30-31. Ches' Bowl 1933-34,48-49, 52-53,55-56,56-57,58-59,60-61,62-63. Ches' S.C.1905-06,46-47,48-49,65-66,2015-16. Ches' Prem. Cup 1969-70,70-71, 2010-11.

CLUB RECORDS
FA Cup Fifth Round Proper 1934-35, 49-50, 2000-01.
FA Trophy Semi-finals 2018-19.
Victory: 13-0 v Halifax Town, Division Three North 06/01/1934.
Defeat: 0-9 v Everton Reserves, Lancashire League, 09/12/1893.
Goalscorer: (League) Jack Connor - 132, 1951-56.
Appearances: (League) Andy Thorpe - 555, 1978-86, 88-92.
Additional: Paid, £800,000 for Ian Moore from Nottingham Forest, 07/1998.
          Received, £1,600,000 for Alun Armstrong from Middlesbrough, 02/1998.

GROUND: Edgeley Park, Hardcastle Road, Stockport SK3 9DD
Ground Capacity: 10,800   **Seats:** 10,800   **Covered:** Yes   **Clubhouse:** Yes   **Shop:** Yes
Previous Grounds: Heaton Norris Recreation Ground & other various locations 1883-89. Green Lane 1889-1902.
Record Attendance: 27,833 v Liverpool, FA Cup 5th Round 11/02/1950. 10,273 (all seated) v Leeds United, 28/12/2008.
Nearest Railway Station Stockport - Approx. half a mile from the ground.

SUTTON UNITED
The U's   **Club Colours** Amber & brown

Founded 1898

Club Contact Details 0208 644 4440   info@suttonunited.net

2019-20 Season
Nat   15 after PPG
FAC   4Qr
FAT   1Pr

Record
P 42 W 12 D 16 L 14

Top Goalscorer
Beautyman (17)

Previous Names: Club formed after the merger of Sutton Guild Rovers and Sutton Association (formerley Sutton St Barnabas FC).

Previous Leagues: Sutton Junior, Southern Suburban, Athenian 1921-63, Isthmian 1963-86, 91-99, 2000-04, 2008-11, Conference 1999-2000, 04-08.

10-11	11-12	12-13	13-14	14-15	15-16	16-17	17-18	18-19
Isth P 1	Conf S 4	Conf S 6	Conf S 2	Conf S 15	Nat S 1	Nat 12	Nat 3	Nat 9
FAC 1Q	FAC 2P	FAC 2Q	FAC 1P	FAC 3Q	FAC 4Q	FAC 5P	FAC 1P	FAC 1Pr
FAT 1Pr	FAT 3Q	FAT 3P	FAT 3Q	FAT 1P	FAT 3Pr	FAT 3Pr	FAT 3P	FAT 2P

LEAGUE HONOURS:
Athenian League 1927-28, 45-46, 57-58. Isthmian League 1966-67, 84-85, 85-86, 98-99, 2010-11. National League South 2015-16.

COUNTY FA HONOURS: London Senior Cup 1957-58, 82-83. Surrey Senior Cup 1945-46, 64-65, 67-68, 69-70, 79-80, 82-83, 83-84, 84-85, 85 -86,

CLUB RECORDS
FA Cup Fifth Round Proper 2016-17
FA Trophy Runners-up 1980-81
Victory: 11-1 v Clapton - 1966 and v Leatherhead - 1982-83 both Isthmian League
Defeat: 0-13 v Barking - Athenian League 1925-26
Goalscorer: Paul McKinnon - 279
Appearances: Larry Pritchard - 781 (1965-84)
Additional: Received £100,000 from AFC Bournemouth for Efan Ekoku 1990

GROUND: Borough Sports Ground, Gander Green Lane, Sutton, Surrey SM1 2EY
Ground Capacity: 5,013   **Seats:** 765   **Covered:** 1,250   **Clubhouse:** Yes   **Shop:** Yes
Previous Grounds: Western Road, Manor Lane, London Road, The Find
Record Attendance: 14,000 v Leeds United - FA Cup 4th Round 24/01/1970
Nearest Railway Station West Sutton a few minutes walk from the ground.
Bus Route 413

TORQUAY UNITED

The Gulls **Club Colours** Yellow

Founded 1899

Club Contact Details 01803 328 666 reception@torquayunited.com

Previous Names: Torquay United & Ellacombe merged to form Torquay Town 1910, then merged with Babbacombe to form Torquay United in 1921

Previous Leagues: Western 1921-27. Football League 1927-2007, 09-14. Conference 2007-09.

2019-20 Season
Nat 14 after PPG

FAC 1P

FAT 2P

Record
P 40 W 16 D 6 L 18

Top Goalscorer
Reid (22)

	10-11		11-12		12-13		13-14		14-15		15-16		16-17		17-18		18-19	
	FL 2	7	FL 2	5	FL 2	19	FL 2	24	Conf	13	Nat	18	Nat	17	Nat	22	Nat S	1
	FAC	4P	FAC	2P	FAC	1P	FAC	1P	FAC	4Q	FAC	4Q	FAC	4Qr	FAC	4Q	FAC	1P
	FLC	1P	FLC	1P	FLC	1P	FLC	1P	FAT	SF	FAT	QF	FAT	1P	FAT	1P	FAT	1P

LEAGUE HONOURS:
Torquay & District 1909-09. Plymouth & District 1911-12. Southern Western Section 1926-27. National South 2018-19.

COUNTY FA HONOURS: Devon Senior Cup 1910-11, 21-22. Devon Bowl/Devon St Luke's Bowl 1933-34, 34-35, 36-37,45-46, 47-48, 48-49, 54-55 (shared), 57-58, 60-61, 69-70, 70-71, 71-72, 95-96 (shared), 97-98, 2006-07.

CLUB RECORDS

FA Cup Fourth Round Proper 1948-49, 54-55, 70-71, 82-83, 89-90, 2008-09, 10-11.

FA Trophy Finalists 2007-08

Victory: 9-0 v Swindon Town, Division Three South, 08/03/1952

Defeat: 2-10 v Fulham, Division Three South, 07/09/1931

Goalscorer: Sammy Collins - 219 in 379 games (1948-58) Scored 40 during the 1955-56 season.

Appearances: Dennis Lewis - 443 (1947-59)

Additional: Paid £75,000 for Leon Constantine from Peterborough United, December 2004.
Received £650,000 from Crewe for Rodney Jack, July 1998.

GROUND: Plainmoor, Torquay, Devon TQ1 3PS

Ground Capacity: 6,500 **Seats:** 2,950 **Covered:** Yes **Clubhouse:** Yes **Shop:** Yes

Previous Grounds: Recreation Ground. Cricketfield Road > 1910.

Record Attendance: 21,908 v Huddersfield Town, FA Cup 4th Rnd, 29/01/1955.

Nearest Railway Station Torre, 25 mins away. Main Torquay 2+ miles away.

WEALDSTONE

The Stones **Club Colours** Blue & white

Founded 1899

Club Contact Details 07790 038 095

Previous Names: None

Previous Leagues: Willesden & District 1899-1906, 08-13, London 1911-22, Middlesex 1913-22, Spartan 1922-28, Athenian 1928 -64, Isthmian 1964-71, 95-2006, 2007-14. Southern 1971-79, 81-82, 88-95, Conference 1979-81, 82-88

2019-20 Season
Nat S 1 after PPG

FAC 4Qr

FAT 3Q

Record
P 39 W 24 D 5 L 10

Top Goalscorer
Lafayette (15)

	10-11		11-12		12-13		13-14		14-15		15-16		16-17		17-18		18-19	
	Isth P	12	Isth P	4	Isth P	3	Isth P	1	Conf S	12	Nat S	13	Nat S	8	Nat S	11	Nat S	7
	FAC	3Qr	FAC	1Q	FAC	2Q	FAC	3Q	FAC	2Qr	FAC	1P	FAC	4Q	FAC	3Q	FAC	4Q
	FAT	1Pr	FAT	SF	FAT	3Qr	FAT	2Qr	FAT	2P	FAT	1P	FAT	3P	FAT	SF	FAT	1P

LEAGUE HONOURS:
Athenian 1951-52. Southern Division One South 1973-74, Southern Division 1981-82. Conference 1984-85. Isthmian Division Three 1996-97, Premier 2013-14. National South 2019-20.

COUNTY FA HONOURS: Middlesex Junior Cup 1912-13. Senior 1929-30, 37-38, 40-41, 41-42, 42-43, 45-46, 58-59, 62-63, 63-64, 67-68, 84-85. Charity Cup 1929-30, 30-31, 37-38, 38-39, 49-50, 63-64, 68-68, 03-04, 10-11 Prem Cup 2003-04, 07-08, 08-09, 10-11. London Senior 1961-62.

CLUB RECORDS

FA Cup Third Round Proper 1977-78. **FA Vase** Third Round Proper 1997-98.

FA Trophy Winners 1984-85. **FA Am Cup** Winners 1965-66.

Victory: 22-0 v The 12th London Regiment (The Rangers) - FA Amateur Cup 13/10/1923

Defeat: 0-14 v Edgware Town (A) - London Senior Cup 09/12/1944

Goalscorer: George Duck - 251

Appearances: Charlie Townsend - 514

Additional: Became the first club to win the 'Non-League Double' when they won the Conference and FA Trophy in 1984-85.
Paid £15,000 to Barnet for David Gipp. Received £70,000 from Leeds United for Jermaine Beckford.

GROUND: Grosvenor Vale, Ruislip, Middlesex HA4 6JQ

Ground Capacity: 3,607 **Seats:** 329 **Covered:** 1,166 **Clubhouse:** Yes **Shop:** No

Previous Grounds: Locket Road, Belmont Road, Lower Mead Stadium 1922-91, Watford FC, Yeading FC, Edgware Town, Northwood FC

Record Attendance: 13,504 v Leytonstone - FA Amateur Cup 4th Round replay 05/03/1949 (at Lower Mead)

Nearest Railway Station Ruislip and Ruislip Gardens both walking distance.

Bus Route E7

WEYMOUTH
The Terras   **Club Colours** Claret & blue

Founded 1890

Club Contact Details 01305 785 558   info@theterras.co.uk

2019-20 Season
Nat S   3 after PPG
FAC   4Q
FAT   1P

Record
P 42 W 21 D 13 L 8

Top Goalscorer
Baggie (11)

Previous Names: None

Previous Leagues: Dorset, Western 1907-23, 28-49, Southern 1923-28, 49-79, 89-2005, Alliance/Conference 1979-89, 2005-10.

10-11		11-12		12-13		13-14		14-15		15-16		16-17		17-18		18-19	
SthP	18	SthP	17	SthP	9	SthP	12	SthP	7	SthP	7	SthP	10	SthP	5	SthPS	1
FAC	2Q	FAC	2Q	FAC	2Q	FAC	2Q	FAC	4Q	FAC	4Qr	FAC	1Q	FAC	3Q	FAC	1Qr
FAT	2Q	FAT	2P	FAT	2Q	FAT	2Q	FAT	1Pr	FAT	3Q	FAT	1Pr	FAT	1Q	FAT	2Pr

LEAGUE HONOURS:
Dorset 1897-98, 1913-14, Division One 1921-22. Western Division One 1922-23, 36-37, 37-38, Division Two 33 -34. Southern 1964-65, 65-66, Southern Division 1997-98, Southern Premier South 2018-19. Conference South 2005-06.

COUNTY FA HONOURS: Dorset Senior Cup x12 - Firstly in 1985-86 and most recently in 2016-17.

CLUB RECORDS
FA Cup Fourth Round Proper 1961-62.
FA Trophy Quarter-finals 1973-74, 76-77(r).
Goalscorer: W 'Farmer' Haynes - 275
Appearances: Tony Hobsons - 1,076
Additional: Paid £15,000 to Northwich Victoria for Shaun Teale
Received £100,000 from Tottenham Hotspur for Peter Guthrie 1988
Defeat: 0-9 v Rushden & Diamonds, Conference South, 21/02/2009 - this was a game which, due to an administration issue, the club had to field their U18 team.

GROUND: Bob Lucas Stadium, Radipole Lane, Weymouth DT4 9XJ
Ground Capacity: 6,600   **Seats:** 900   **Covered:** Yes   **Clubhouse:** Yes   **Shop:** Yes
Previous Grounds: Recreation Ground > 1987.
Record Attendance: 4,995 v Manchester United - Ground opening 21/10/97
Nearest Railway Station Weymouth - 2.2km
Bus Route 3 & X53 stop outside the ground

WOKING
The Cards   **Club Colours** Red, white & black

Founded 1889

Club Contact Details 01483 772 470   admin@wokingfc.co.uk

2019-20 Season
Nat   10 after PPG
FAC   4Qr
FAT   1P

Record
P 41 W 15 D 11 L 15

Top Goalscorer
Hyde (16)

Previous Names: None

Previous Leagues: West Surrey 1895-1911. Isthmian 1911-92.

10-11		11-12		12-13		13-14		14-15		15-16		16-17		17-18		18-19	
Conf S	5	Conf S	1	Conf	12	Conf	9	Conf	7	Nat	12	Nat	18	Nat	21	Nat S	2
FAC	P	FAC	3Q	FAC	4Q	FAC	4Q	FAC	1P	FAC	4Q	FAC	2P	FAC	2Pr	FAC	3P
FAT	3P	FAT	3Q	FAT	2P	FAT	2P	FAT	3Pr	FAT	QF	FAT	1Pr	FAT	1P	FAT	1Pr

LEAGUE HONOURS:
West Surrey 1895-96. Isthmian League Division Two South 1986-87, Premier Division 1991-92. Conference South 2011-12.

COUNTY FA HONOURS: Surrey Senior Cup 1912-13, 26-27, 55-56, 56-57, 71-72, 90-91, 93-94, 95-96, 99-00, 03-04, 2011-12, 13-14, 16-17.

CLUB RECORDS
FA Cup Fourth Round Proper 1990-91.   **FA Am Cup** Winners 1957-58.
FA Trophy Winners 1993-94, 94-95, 96-97, Runners-up 2005-06.
Victory: 17-4 v Farnham - 1912-13
Defeat: 0-16 v New Crusaders - 1905-06
Goalscorer: Charlie Mortimore - 331 (1953-65)
Appearances: Brian Finn - 564 (1962-74)
Additional: Paid £60,000 to Crystal Palace for Chris Sharpling
Received £150,000 from Bristol Rovers for Steve Foster

GROUND: The Laithwaite Community Stadium, Kingfield Road, Woking, Surrey GU22 9AA
Ground Capacity: 6,000   **Seats:** 2,500   **Covered:** 3,900   **Clubhouse:** Yes   **Shop:** Yes
Previous Grounds: Wheatsheaf, Ive Lane (pre 1923)
Record Attendance: 6,000 v Swansea City - FA Cup 1978-79 and v Coventry City - FA Cup 1996-97
Nearest Railway Station Woking - about 15 mins from the ground.
Bus Route 34 & 462

WREXHAM

The Robins   **Club Colours** Red & white

Founded 1864

Club Contact Details 01978 891 864   info@wrexhamfc.tv

2019-20 Season
Nat   19 after PPG

FAC   1Pr

FAT   1P

Record
P 45 W 13 D 13 L 19

Top Goalscorer
Grant (8)

Previous Names: Wrexham Athletic for the 1882-83 season only

Previous Leagues: The Combination 1890-94, 1896-1906, Welsh League 1894-96, Birmingham & District 1906-21, Football League 1921-2008

	10-11		11-12		12-13		13-14		14-15		15-16		16-17		17-18		18-19	
	Conf	4	Conf	2	Conf	5	Conf	17	Conf	11	Nat	8	Nat	13	Nat	10	Nat	4
	FAC	4Q	FAC	3Pr	FAC	1P	FAC	2P	FAC	3P	FAC	4Q	FAC	4Qr	FAC	4Q	FAC	2Pr
	FAT	2P	FAT	1P	FAT	F	FAT	2P	FAT	F	FAT	2P	FAT	1P	FAT	1P	FAT	2P

LEAGUE HONOURS:
Welsh Senior League 1894-95, 95-96. Combination 1900-01, 01-02, 02-03, 04-05.
Football League Division Three 1977-78.

COUNTY FA HONOURS: Denbighshire & Flintshire (Soames) Charity Cup 1894-95, 98-99, 1902-03, 04-05, 05-06, 08-09.

CLUB RECORDS
FA Cup Quarter-Finals 1973-74, 77-78, 96-97
FA Trophy Winners 2012-13
Victory: 10-1 v Hartlepool United - Division Four 03/03/62
Defeat: 0-9 v v Brentford - Division Three
Goalscorer: Tommy Bamford - 201 (1928-34)
Appearances: Arfon Griffiths - 591 (1959-61 & 62-79)
Additional: Paid £800,000 to Birmingham City for Bryan Hughes March 1997
               Received £212,000 from Liverpool for Joey Jones October 1978

GROUND: Racecourse Ground, Mold road, Wrexham LL11 2AH
Ground Capacity: 10,771 **Seats:** 10,771 **Covered:** Yes   **Clubhouse:** Yes **Shop:** Yes
Previous Grounds: Rhosddu Recreation Ground during the 1881-82 and 1882-83 seasons.
Record Attendance: 34,445 v Manchester United - FA Cup 4th Round 26/01/57
Nearest Railway Station Wrexham General is right next to the ground.

YEOVIL TOWN

The Glovers   **Club Colours** Green & white

Founded 1895

Club Contact Details 01935 423 662

2019-20 Season
Nat   4 after PPG

FAC   1P

FAT   3P

Record
P 43 W 20 D 9 L 14

Top Goalscorer
Murphy (20)

Previous Names: Yeovil Casuals 1895-1907. Yeovil Town & Petters United >1946.

Previous Leagues: Somerset Senior. Dorset District. Bristol Charity. Western. Southern 1946-79. Alliance 1979-85. Isthmian 1985-88, 95-97. Conference 1988-95, 97-2002. Football League 2002-19.

	10-11		11-12		12-13		13-14		14-15		15-16		16-17		17-18		18-19	
	FL 1	14	FL 1	7	FL 1	4	FLCh	24	FL 1	24	FL 2	20	FL 2	20	FL 2	19	FL 2	24
	FAC	2P	FAC	2Pr	FAC	4P	FAC	4P	FAC	3P	FAC	3Pr	FAC	1Pr	FAC	4P	FAC	1P
	FLC	1P	FLC	1P	FLC	2P	FLC	2P	FLC	1P	FLC	1P	FLC	2P	FLC	1P	FLC	1P

LEAGUE HONOURS:
Somerset Sen 1896-97, 1901-02, 12-13, 20-21. Dorset Dist 08-09. Bristol Charity 21-22.
Western 21-22, 24-25, 29-30, 34-35. Southern Western Div. 23-24, 31-32, 34-35. Premier 54-55, 63-64, 70-71. Isthmian Premier Division 1987-88, 96-97. Conference 2002-03. Football League 2 2004-05.

COUNTY FA HONOURS: Somerset Professional/Premier Cup x25 firstly in 1912-13 and most recently in 2004-05.

CLUB RECORDS
FA Cup Fifth Round Proper 1948-49
FA Trophy Winners 2001-02
Goalscorer: Johnny Hayward - 548 (1906-28). Most league goals Dave Taylor - 284 (1960-69).
Appearances: Len Harris - 691 (1958-72)

GROUND: Huish Park, Lufton Way, Yeovil BA22 8YF
Ground Capacity: 9,565 **Seats:** 5,212 **Covered:** Yes   **Clubhouse:** Yes **Shop:** Yes
Previous Grounds: Pen Mill Athletic Ground. Huish > 1990.
Record Attendance: 9,527 v Leeds United, League One, 25/04/2008
Nearest Railway Station Pen Mill Junction and Yeovil Junction - taxi ride away from the ground.
Bus Route No.68 from the above stations takes you to the town centre where you can get the First traveller No.1 to near the

AFC FYLDE
The Coasters   **Club Colours** White

Founded 1988

Club Contact Details 01772 682 593   info@afcfylde.co.uk

Previous Names: Wesham FC and Kirkham Town amalgamated in 1988 to form Kirkham & Wesham > 2008.

Previous Leagues: West Lancashire > 2007. North West Counties 2007-09. Northern Premier 2009-14.

2019-20 Season
Nat   23 after PPG
FAC   3P
FAT   4P

Record
P 45 W 15 D 12 L 18

Top Goalscorer
Williams (15)

	10-11	11-12	12-13	13-14	14-15	15-16	16-17	17-18	18-19
	NP1N 5	NP1N 1	NP P 5	NP P 2	Conf N 2	Nat N 3	Nat N 1	Nat 7	Nat 5
FAC	P	FAC 2Qr	FAC 1P	FAC 2Q	FAC 1P	FAC 1P	FAC 2Q	FAC 2Pr	FAC 4Q
FAT	P	FAT 1Q	FAT 3Q	FAT 3Q	FAT 3P	FAT 3P	FAT 1Pr	FAT 1P	FAT F

LEAGUE HONOURS:
West Lancashire League 1999-2000, 00-01, 01-02, 03-04, 04-05, 05-06, 06-07.
North West Counties League 2008-09. Northern Premier Division One North 2011-12.
National North 2016-17.

COUNTY FA HONOURS: Lancashire FA Challenge Trophy 2010-11, 12-13, 13-14. Lancashire Amateur Shield 2000-01, 03-04, 04-05, 05-06.
Northern Inter Counties Cup 2004-05, 05-06, 06-07.

CLUB RECORDS
FA Cup Third Round Proper 2019-20   **FA Vase**   Winners 2007-08
FA Trophy Winners 2018-19
Victory: 10-0 v Droylsden (A), Northern Premier League Premier Division, 29/10/2013
Goalscorer: Danny Rowe - 192 August 2014 - 16/01/2020 (293 apps). Bradley Barnes scored five in the club's record 10-0 win over Droylsden

GROUND: Mill Farm, Coronation Way, Wesham, Preston PR4 3JZ
Ground Capacity: 6,000   **Seats:** 6,000   **Covered:** Yes   **Clubhouse:** Yes   **Shop:** Yes
Previous Grounds: Coronation Road > 2006. Kellamergh Park 2006-2016.
Record Attendance: 3,858 v Chorley, National League North, 26/12/2016.
Nearest Railway Station Kirkham & Wesham half a mile away.
Bus Route No. 61

AFC TELFORD UNITED
The Bucks   **Club Colours** White and navy

Founded 1892

Club Contact Details 01952 640 064   enquiries@afctu.co.uk

Previous Names: Wellington Town 1892-1969. AFC Telford United was formed when Telford United folded in May 2004

Previous Leagues: Shropshire 1892-98. Birmingham & District 1898-1901, 02-06, 08-38, 39-45. The Combination 1901-02. Cheshire County 1938-39, 45-58. Southern 1958-79. Alliance/Conference 1979-2004. Northern Premier 2004-06.

2019-20 Season
Nat N   14 after PPG
FAC   2Q
FAT   1P

Record
P 37 W 12 D 9 L 16

Top Goalscorer
Dinanga (13)

	10-11	11-12	12-13	13-14	14-15	15-16	16-17	17-18	18-19
	Conf N 2	Conf 20	Conf 24	Conf N 1	Conf 22	Nat N 18	Nat N 17	Nat N 14	Nat N 8
FAC	3Qr	FAC 1P	FAC 4Qr	FAC 2Q	FAC 2P	FAC 2Q	FAC 2Qr	FAC 1P	FAC 3Q
FAT	3P	FAT 2P	FAT 2P	FAT 1Pr	FAT 2P	FAT 1P	FAT 1P	FAT 1P	FAT SF

LEAGUE HONOURS:
Birmingham & District 1920-21, 34-35, 35-36, 39-40. Cheshire County 1945-46, 46-47, 51-52.
National North 2013-14.

COUNTY FA Birmingham Senior Cup 1946-47. Walsall Senior Cup 1946-47.
HONOURS: Shropshire Senior Cup 2008-09, 13-14, 16-17.

CLUB RECORDS
FA Cup Fifth Round Proper 1984-85. As AFC Telford United - Second Round Proper 2014-15.
FA Trophy Winners 1970-71, 82-83. As AFC Telford United - Semi-Finals 2008-09, 18-19.
Victory: 7-0 v Runcorn (A) - Northern Premier League Division One, 17/04/06.
Defeat: 1-6 v Guiseley (A) - Conference North, 01/04/14.
Goalscorer: Andy Brown - 56 (2008-12)
Appearances: Ryan Young - 367 (2007-14)
Additional: Paid £5,000 to Tamworth for Lee Moore 08/12/06
     Received £25,000 from Burnley for Duane Courtney 31/08/05

GROUND: New Bucks Head Stadium, Watling Street, Wellington, Telford TF1 2TU
Ground Capacity: 6,380   **Seats:** 2,200   **Covered:** 4,800   **Clubhouse:** Yes   **Shop:** Yes
Previous Grounds: None - Renovation of the old Bucks Head started in 2000 and was completed in 2003.
Record Attendance: 5,710 vs Burscough 28/04/2007
Nearest Railway Station Wellington (Shropshire) - 20min walk to ground.
Bus Route 44 - every 10 mins from Town centre.

ALFRETON TOWN

The Reds   **Club Colours** All red

Founded 1959

Club Contact Details   01773 830 277   a.raisin@alfretontownfc.com

Previous Names: Formed when Alfreton Miners Welfare and Alfreton United merged.

Previous Leagues: Central Alliance 1959-61. Midland 1961-82. Northern Counties East 1982-87, 99-02. Northern Premier 1987-99, 02-04.

2019-20 Season
Nat N   13 after PPG

FAC   2Qr

FAT   3Qr

Record
P 36 W 12 D 6 L 18

Top Goalscorer
Morgan-Smith (16)

	10-11	11-12	12-13	13-14	14-15	15-16	16-17	17-18	18-19
	Conf N 1	Conf 15	Conf 13	Conf 11	Conf 21	Nat N 10	Nat N 18	Nat N 17	Nat N 15
	FAC 2Qr	FAC 1P	FAC 2P	FAC 1P	FAC 4Qr	FAC 4Q	FAC 1Pr	FAC 3Q	FAC 1P
	FAT 3Pr	FAT 3P	FAT 1P	FAT 1P	FAT 2P	FAT 3Q	FAT 2P	FAT 3Q	FAT 3Q

LEAGUE HONOURS:
Midland 1969-70, 73-74, 76-77. Northern Counties East 1986-87, 2001-02
Northern Premier League Division One 2002-03. Conference North 2010-11

COUNTY FA HONOURS: Derbyshire Senior Cup 1960-61, 69-70, 72-73, 73-74, 81-82, 94-95, 2001-02, 02-03, 15-16, 18-19

CLUB RECORDS

FA Cup Second Round Proper 2008-09, 12-13   **FA Vase**   Fifth Round Proper 1999-00

FA Trophy Fourth Round Proper 2002-03 (r), 2004-05

Victory: 15-0 v Loughborough Midland League 1969-70

Defeat: 1-9 v Solihull - FAT 1997. 0-8 v Bridlington - 1992

Goalscorer: John Harrison - 303

Appearances: John Harrison - 561

Additional: Paid £2,000 to Worksop Town for Mick Goddard
           Received £150,000 from Swindon Town for Aden Flint, January 2011

GROUND: The Impact Arena, North Street, Alfreton, Derbyshire DE55 7FZ

Ground Capacity: 3,600   **Seats:** 1,500   **Covered:** 2,600   **Clubhouse:** Yes   **Shop:** Yes

Previous Grounds: None

Record Attendance: 5,023 v Matlock Town - Central Alliance 1960

Nearest Railway Station Alfreton - Approx. 15min walk from the ground

Bus Route 150, 55 , 9.1, 9.3, Rainbow One

BLYTH SPARTANS

Spartans   **Club Colours** Green and white

Founded 1899

Club Contact Details   01670 352 373   generalmanager@blythspartans.com

Previous Names: None

Previous Leagues: Northumberland 1901-07, Northern All. 1907-13, 46-47, North Eastern 1913-39, Northern Com. 1945-46, Midland 1958-60, Northern Counties 1960-62, Northern 1962-94, NPL 1994-2006, 13-17. Conference 2006-13.

2019-20 Season
Nat N   21 after PPG

FAC   3Q

FAT   1P

Record
P 39 W 8 D 7 L 24

Top Goalscorer
Roberts (17)

	10-11	11-12	12-13	13-14	14-15	15-16	16-17	17-18	18-19
	Conf N 9	Conf N 21	NP P 16	NP P 8	NP P 6	NP P 2	NP P 1	Nat N 10	Nat N 6
	FAC 2Q	FAC 1P	FAC 2Qr	FAC 1Q	FAC 3P	FAC 1Q	FAC 2Q	FAC 2Q	FAC 4Q
	FAT QF	FAT 3Q	FAT 1Q	FAT 2Q	FAT 2Qr	FAT 3Q	FAT 3Qr	FAT 2P	FAT 3P

LEAGUE HONOURS:
North Eastern 1935-36. Northern 1972-73, 74-75, 75-76, 79-80, 80-81, 81-82, 82-83, 83-84, 86-87, 87-88. Northern Division 1 1994-95. Northern Premier Premier Division 2005-06, 16-17.

COUNTY FA HONOURS: Northumberland Senior Cup 2014-15, 16-17.

CLUB RECORDS

FA Cup Fifth Round Proper 1977-78(r).

FA Trophy Quarter-finals 1979-80(r), 82-83(r), 2010-11.

Victory: 18-0 v Gateshead Town - Northern Alliance 28/12/1907

Defeat: 0-10 v Darlington - North Eastern League 12/12/1914

Appearances: Robbie Dale (pictured) became Blyth's record appearance holder during the 2018-19 season.

Additional: Received £30,000 from Hull City for Les Mutrie

Goalscorer: Jeff Hunter scored 63 during the 1946-47 season, revised to 58 after his five against Prudhoe East Park were chalked off when their record was expunged having failed to finish the season.

GROUND: Croft Park, Blyth, Northumberland NE24 3JE

Ground Capacity: 4,435   **Seats:** 563   **Covered:** 1,000   **Clubhouse:** Yes   **Shop:** Yes

Previous Grounds: None

Record Attendance: 10,186 v Hartlepool United - FA Cup 08/12/1956

Nearest Railway Station Cramlington five miles from the ground - the X9 bus runs from Cramlington to Blyth.

Bus Route X9 from Cramlington. 308 from Whitley Bay.

BOSTON UNITED

The Pilgrims **Club Colours** Amber and black

Founded 1933

Club Contact Details 01205 364 406 admin@bufc.co.uk

Previous Names: Reformed as Boston United when Boston Town folded in 1933

Previous Leagues: Midland 1933-58, 62-64, Southern 1958-62, 98-2000, United Counties 1965-66, West Midlands 1966-68, NPL 1968-79, 93-98, 2008-10, Alliance/Conference 1979-93, 2000-02, 07-08, Football League 2002-07.

2019-20 Season
Nat N 3 after PPG
FAC 2Pr
FAT 3Q

Record
P 41 W 22 D 8 L 11

Top Goalscorer
Thewlis (17)

	10-11	11-12	12-13	13-14	14-15	15-16	16-17	17-18	18-19
	Conf N 3	Conf N 11	Conf N 16	Conf N 6	Conf N 3	Nat N 5	Nat N 15	Nat N 9	Nat N 11
FAC	2Q	2Qr	4Q	3Q	3Q	2Q	3Q	4Qr	2Q
FAT	2P	2P	1Pr	2P	1Pr	3Q	3Q	3Qr	1P

LEAGUE HONOURS:
Central Alliance League 1961-62. United Counties League 1965-66. West Midlands League 1966-67, 67-68. Northern Premier League 1972-73, 73-74, 76-77, 77-78. Southern League 1999-2000. Conference 2001-02.

COUNTY FA HONOURS: Lincolnshire Senior Cup 1934-35, 36-37, 37-38, 45-46, 49-50, 54-55, 55-56, 56-57, 59-60, 76-77, 78-79, 85-86, 87-88, 88-89, 05-06. East Anglian Cup 1960-61.

CLUB RECORDS
FA Cup Third Round Proper 1971-72, 73-74 (r), 2004-05 (r)
FA Trophy Final 1984-85
Victory: 12-0 v Spilsby Town - Grace Swan Cup 1992-93
Defeat: 2-9 v AFC Fylde - (A) National North, 19/11/2017
Goalscorer: Chris Cook - 181
Appearances: Billy Howells - 500+
Additional: Paid £30,000 to Scarborough for Paul Ellender, 08/2001
Received £50,000 from Bolton Wanderers for David Norris 2000

GROUND: Jakemans Community Stadium, Pilgrim Way, Wyberton, Boston PE21 7NH
Ground Capacity: 5,000 **Seats:** Yes **Covered:** Yes **Clubhouse:** Yes **Shop:** Yes
Previous Grounds: Jakemans Stadium, York Street 1933-2020.
Record Attendance: 11,000 v Derby County, FA Cup Third Round Proper Replay, 09/01/1974
Nearest Railway Station Boston
Bus Route B13 to Tytton Lane West

BRACKLEY TOWN

Saints **Club Colours** Red and white

Founded 1890

Club Contact Details 01280 704 077 janenebutters@brackleytownfc.co.uk

Previous Names: N/A

Previous Leagues: Oxfordshire Senior. North Bucks & District. Banbury & District. Hellenic 1977-83, 94-97, 99-2004. United Counties 1983-84. Southern 1997-99.

2019-20 Season
Nat N 4 after PPG
FAC 4Q
FAT 3Q

Record
P 39 W 18 D 13 L 8

Top Goalscorer
Ndlovu (20)

	10-11	11-12	12-13	13-14	14-15	15-16	16-17	17-18	18-19
	SthP 9	SthP 1	Conf N 3	Conf N 7	Conf N 18	Nat N 19	Nat N 7	Nat N 3	Nat N 3
FAC	2Q	1Q	3Q	2P	3Q	1Pr	2P	4Qr	3Q
FAT	3Q	1P	1P	3Qr	3Q	3Q	QF	F	4P

LEAGUE HONOURS:
United Counties Division One 1983-84. Hellenic Premier Division 1996-97, 2003-04. Southern Division One Midlands 2006-07, Premier Division 2011-12.

COUNTY FA HONOURS: Northamptonshire Senior Cup 2010-11, 11-12, 14-15.

CLUB RECORDS
FA Cup Second Round Proper 2013-14, 16-17. **FA Vase** Third Round Proper 1987-88.
FA Trophy Winners 2017-18
Goalscorer: Paul Warrington - 320
Appearances: Terry Muckelberg - 350
Additional: Received £2,000 from Oxford City for Phil Mason 1998

GROUND: St James Park, Churchill Way, Brackley NN13 7EJ
Ground Capacity: 3,500 **Seats:** 600 **Covered:** 1,500 **Clubhouse:** Yes **Shop:** Yes
Previous Grounds: Manor Road 1890-1968. Buckingham Road 1968-74.
Record Attendance: 2,604 v FC Halifax Town, Conference North Play-off final, 12/05/13.
Nearest Railway Station Banbury - Approx. 10 miles from the ground.
Bus Route Stagecoach No. 500 from Banbury.

BRADFORD (PARK AVENUE)

Avenue

Club Colours Green and white

Founded 1863

Club Contact Details 01274 674 584   info@bpafc.com

2019-20 Season
Nat N   22 after PPG
FAC   2Q
FAT   1Pr

Record
P 37 W 6 D 6 L 25

Top Goalscorer
Knight (6)

Previous Names: Bradford FC. 1863-1907. Reformed as a Sunday club in 1974, then as a Saturday club in 1988.

Previous Leagues: West York. 1895-98. Yorkshire 98-99. Southern 1907-08. Football Lge 08-70. NPL 70-74, 95-04, 05-12. Bradford Am Sun. 74-76. Bradford Sun.All. 76-92. W. Riding Co. Am. 88-89. Cen Mids 89-90. NWC 90-95. Conf 2004-05

10-11	11-12	12-13	13-14	14-15	15-16	16-17	17-18	18-19
NP P 3	NP P 4	Conf N 7	Conf N 10	Conf N 13	Nat N 14	Nat N 16	Nat N 7	Nat N 7
FAC 1Q	FAC 1P	FAC 1P	FAC 4Qr	FAC 2Qr	FAC 3Qr	FAC 2Q	FAC 3Qr	FAC 3Q
FAT 1Q	FAT 1Qr	FAT 3Q	FAT 2P	FAT 1P	FAT 2Pr	FAT 3Q	FAT 3Qr	FAT 3Q

LEAGUE HONOURS:
West Yorkshire 1895-96 (Shared). Football League Division Three North 1927-28.
North West Counties Div.One 1994-95
Northern Premier Division One 2000-01, Division One North 2007-08.

COUNTY FA HONOURS: West Riding Senior Cup x9. West Riding County Cup 1990-91, 2014-15, 15-16.

CLUB RECORDS

FA Cup Quarter-finals 1912-13, 19-20, 45-46.   **FA Vase** Second Round Proper 1994-95.
FA Trophy Fourth Round Proper 1998-99.
Victory: 11-0 v Derby Dale - FA Cup 1908
Defeat: 0-7 v Barnsley - 1911
Goalscorer: Len Shackleton - 171 (1940-46)
Appearances: Tommy Farr - 542 (1934-50)
Additional: Paid £24,500 to Derby County for Leon Leuty 1950
Received £34,000 from Derby County for Kevin Hector 1966

GROUND: Horsfall Stadium, Cemetery Road, Bradford, West Yorkshire BD6 2NG
Ground Capacity: 3,500   **Seats:** 1,800   **Covered:** 2,000   **Clubhouse:** Yes   **Shop:** Yes
Previous Grounds: Park Ave 1907-73,87-88, Valley Parade 1973-74, Bingley Road, Hope Ave, Ave Rd, Bramley, Mount Pleasant
Record Attendance: 2,100 v Bristol City - FA Cup 1st Round 2003
Nearest Railway Station Bradford Foster Square or Bradford Interchange
Bus Route From Interchange - 681 (682 Eve & Sun)

CHESTER

The Blues

Club Colours Blue & white

Founded 2010

Club Contact Details 01244 371 376   info@chesterfc.com

2019-20 Season
Nat N   6 after PPG
FAC   2Qr
FAT   2P

Record
P 39 W 17 D 11 L 11

Top Goalscorer
Asante (19)

Previous Names: Formed after the demise of Chester City, which itself was formed in 1983 after the original Chester of 1885 folded.

Previous Leagues: Northern Premier League 2010-12.

10-11	11-12	12-13	13-14	14-15	15-16	16-17	17-18	18-19
NP1N 1	NP P 1	Conf N 1	Conf 21	Conf 12	Nat 17	Nat 19	Nat 23	Nat N 9
		FAC 3Qr	FAC 4Q	FAC 2Pr	FAC 4Q	FAC 4Q	FAC 4Q	FAC 3Q
	FAT 2P	FAT 3Qr	FAT 1P	FAT 1Pr	FAT 3P	FAT 2P	FAT 2P	FAT 3Qr

LEAGUE HONOURS:
Northern Premier League Division One North 2010-11, Premier Division 2011-12. Conference North 2012-13.

COUNTY FA HONOURS: Cheshire Senior Cup 2012-13.

CLUB RECORDS

FA Cup Fourth Qualifying Round 2013-14, 15-16, 16-17, 17-18
FA Trophy Third Round Proper 2015-16
Goalscorer: League - Michael Wilde - 41 (2010-12)
Appearances: League - Craig Mahon - 187 (2013-)

GROUND: Swansway Chester Stadium, Bumpers Lane, Chester CH1 4LT
Ground Capacity: 5,376   **Seats:** 4,170   **Covered:** Yes   **Clubhouse:** Yes   **Shop:** Yes
Previous Grounds: None
Record Attendance: 5,009 v Northwich Victoria, April 2012
Nearest Railway Station Chester - 2.5 miles away.
Bus Route No.10A from City Centre Bus Exchange.

CHORLEY
Magpies

Founded 1875

Club Colours Black and white

Club Contact Details 01257 230 007   graham.watkinson@chorleyfc.com

2019-20 Season
Nat   24 after PPG
FAC   1P
FAT   1P

Record
P 41 W 5 D 15 L 21

Top Goalscorer
Holroyd (8)

Previous Names: Founded as a Rugby Union side in 1875 then switched to football in 1883.

Previous Leagues: Lancashire Jr 1889-90. Lancashire All 1890-94. Lancashire 1894-1903. Lancashire Comb 1903-68, 69-70. NPL (FM) 1968-69, 70-72, 82-88, 90-2014. Cheshire Co 1972-82. Conference 1988-90.

10-11	11-12	12-13	13-14	14-15	15-16	16-17	17-18	18-19
NP1N 3	NP P 3	NP P 8	NP P 1	Conf 4	Nat N 8	Nat N 6	Nat N 6	Nat N 2
FAC P	FAC 1Qr	FAC 2Q	FAC 2Q	FAC 4Qr	FAC 4Qr	FAC 3Qr	FAC 1P	FAC 1Pr
FAT 3Q	FAT 1Q	FAT 1Q	FAT 3P	FAT 2Pr	FAT 3Qr	FAT 1P	FAT 1P	FAT 3Q

LEAGUE HONOURS:
Lancashire Alliance 1892-93. Lancashire 1896-97, 98-99. Lancashire Combination 1919-20, 22-23, 27-28, 28-29, 32-33, 33-34, 39-40, 45-46, 59-60, 60-61, 63-64. Cheshire County 1975-76, 76-77, 81-82. Northern Premier League Premier 1987-88, 2013-14.

COUNTY FA HONOURS: Lancashire FA Trophy (Record 18 times) 1893-94, 1908-09, 23-24, 39-40, 45-46, 57-58, 58-59, 60-61, 63-64, 64-65, 75-76, 79-80, 81-82, 82-83, 2011-12, 14-15, 15-16, 17-18.

CLUB RECORDS
FA Cup Second Round Proper 1986-87, 90-91.
FA Trophy Semi-finals 1995-96.
Victory: 14-1 v Morecambe, April 1946.
Goalscorer: Peter Watson - 372 (1958-66).
Additional: Received £30,000 from Newcastle United for David Eatock 1996.

GROUND: Victory Park Stadium, Duke Street, Chorley, Lancashire PR7 3DU
Ground Capacity: 3,550   **Seats:** 900   **Covered:** 2,800   **Clubhouse:** Yes   **Shop:** Yes
Previous Grounds: Dole Lane 1883-1901, Rangletts Park 1901-05, St George's Park 1905-20.
Record Attendance: 9,679 v Darwen, FA Cup Fourth Qualifying Round, 15/11/1932.
Nearest Railway Station Chorley - half a mile from the ground.
Bus Route Bus station half a mile from the ground.

CURZON ASHTON
The Nash

Founded 1963

Club Colours Royal blue and

Club Contact Details 0161 330 6033   rob@curzon-ashton.co.uk

2019-20 Season
Nat N   20 after PPG
FAC   2Qr
FAT   1P

Record
P 37 W 9 D 11 L 17

Top Goalscorer
Miller (7)

Previous Names: Club formed when Curzon Road Methodists and Ashton Amateurs merged, and were initially known as Curzon Amateurs.

Previous Leagues: Manchester Amateur. Manchester > 1978. Cheshire (FM of Div.2) 1978-82. North West Counties (FM) 1983-87, 98-2007. Northern Premier (FM) 1987-97, 2007-15. Northern Counties East 1997-98.

10-11	11-12	12-13	13-14	14-15	15-16	16-17	17-18	18-19
NP1N 4	NP1N 2	NP1N 7	NP1N 1	NP P 4	Nat N 11	Nat N 14	Nat N 18	Nat N 18
FAC 1Qr	FAC Pr	FAC 2Q	FAC 3Q	FAC 3Q	FAC 2Q	FAC 1Pr	FAC 2Q	FAC 3Q
FAT 1P	FAT 3Q	FAT 1Q	FAT 1P	FAT 2Q	FAT 2P	FAT 2P	FAT 3Q	FAT 3Q

LEAGUE HONOURS:
Manchester Amateur Division One 1963-64, 65-66. Manchester Premier Division 1977-78. Northern Premier Division One North 2013-14, Premier Division Play-off 2014-15.

COUNTY FA HONOURS: Manchester Premier Cup 1981-82, 83-84, 85-86, 87-87, 89-90.

CLUB RECORDS
FA Cup Second Round Proper 2008-09.   **FA Vase** Semi-finals 1979-80, 2006-07.
FA Trophy Second Round Proper 2015-16.
Victory: 10-1 v Wakefield, 2012-13
Defeat: 0-8 v Bamber Bridge
Goalscorer: Rod Lawton - 376
Appearances: Alan Sykes

GROUND: Tameside Stadium, Richmond Street, Ashton-u-Lyme OL7 9HG
Ground Capacity: 4,000   **Seats:** 527   **Covered:** 1,100   **Clubhouse:** Yes   **Shop:** Yes
Previous Grounds: National Park 1963-2004. Stalybridge Celtic FC 2004-05.
Record Attendance: 3,210 v FC United of Manchester, North West Counties Challenge Cup Final, 03/05/07.
Nearest Railway Station Ashton-under-Lyne - Approx. one mile from ground.
Bus Route Also 5mins from Ashton West Metrolink.

DARLINGTON 1883

The Quakers   **Club Colours** Black and white

Founded 1883

Club Contact Details 01325 363 777   Dave.watson@darlingtonfc.org

Previous Names: Darlington FC 1883-2012

Previous Leagues: Northern League 1883-1908, 2012-13, North Eastern 1908-21, Football League 1921-89, 91-2010, Conference 1989-90, 10-12.

2019-20 Season
Nat N   10 after PPG

FAC   1Pr
FAT   2P

Record
P 42 W 19 D 8 L 15

Top Goalscorer
Campbell (16)

	10-11	11-12	12-13	13-14	14-15	15-16	16-17	17-18	18-19
	Conf 7	Conf 22	NL 1 1	NP1N 2	NP1N 2	NP P 1	Nat N 5	Nat N 12	Nat N 18
	FAC 2P	FAC 4Qr			FAC 1Qr	FAC 1Q	FAC 2Q	FAC 2Q	FAC 2Q
	FAT F	FAT 1P		FAT 1Qr	FAT 2Q	FAT 2Q	FAT 3Qr	FAT 3Q	FAT 3Q

LEAGUE HONOURS:
Northern 1895-96, 99-1900, 2012-13. North Eastern 1912-13, 20-21. Football League Division Three North 1924-25, Division Four 1990-91. Conference 1989-90. Northern Premier League Premier Division 2015-16.

COUNTY FA HONOURS: Durham Challenge Cup 1884-85, 90-91, 92-93, 96-97, 1919-20, 99-2000.

CLUB RECORDS
FA Cup Fifth Round Proper 1910-11, 57-58.
FA Trophy Winners 2010-11.
Victory: 13-1 v Scarborough, FA Cup, 24/10/1891
Defeat: 0-10 v Doncaster Rovers - Division 4 25/01/1964
Goalscorer: Alan Walsh - 100, Jerry Best - 80
Appearances: Ron Greener - 490, John Peverell - 465, Brian Henderson - 463
Additional: Paid £95,000 to Motherwell for Nick Cusack January 1992.
         Received £400,000 from Dundee United for Jason Devos October 1998

GROUND: Blackwell Meadows, Grange Road, Darlington DL1 5NR
Ground Capacity: 3299   **Seats:** 588   **Covered:** Yes   **Clubhouse:** Yes   **Shop:**
Previous Grounds: Feethams 1883-2003. Darlington Arena 2003-12. Bishop Auckland 2012-16.
Record Attendance: 21,023 v Bolton Wanderers - League Cup 3rd Round 14/11/1960
Nearest Railway Station Darlington - 1.5 miles away
Bus Route 13B

FARSLEY CELTIC

The Celt Army   **Club Colours** Green & white

Founded 2010

Club Contact Details 0113 255 7292   office@farsleyceltic.com

Previous Names: Farsley AFC 2010-15.

Previous Leagues: Northern Counties East 2010-11. Northern Premier 2011-19.

2019-20 Season
Nat N   11 after PPG

FAC   3Q
FAT   2Pr

Record
P 41 W 17 D 8 L 16

Top Goalscorer
Spencer (10)

	10-11	11-12	12-13	13-14	14-15	15-16	16-17	17-18	18-19
	NCEP 1	NP1N 4	NP1N 14	NP1N 7	NP1N 12	NP1N 9	NP1N 2	NP P 5	NP P 1
			FAC 1Qr	FAC P	FAC 2Q	FAC 1Q	FAC 3Q	FAC 1Q	FAC 2Q
		FAT 1Qr	FAT Pr	FAT P	FAT 1Q	FAT 1Q	FAT 1P	FAT 1Qr	FAT 1P

LEAGUE HONOURS:
Northern Counties East Premier Division 2010-11.
Northern Premier League Premier Division 2018-19.

COUNTY FA HONOURS: West Riding County Cup 2016-17.

CLUB RECORDS
FA Cup Third Qualifying Round 2016-17.
FA Trophy Second Round Proper 2019-20(r).
Victory: 8-0 v Arnold Town (H) Northern Counties East Premier 2010-11.
Defeat: 5-1 v Tadcaster Albion, President's Cup Final 27/04/11.

GROUND: The Citadel, Newlands, Pudsey, Leeds, LS28 5BE
Ground Capacity: 4,000   **Seats:** 300   **Covered:** 1,500   **Clubhouse:** Yes   **Shop:** Yes
Previous Grounds: None
Record Attendance: 11,000 v Tranmere Rovers, FA Cup First Round Proepr, 1974-75 (at Elland Road)
Nearest Railway Station New Pudsey - 1km
Bus Route Town Street - stop 500m away

GATESHEAD
Tynesiders, The Heed   **Club Colours** White & black

Founded 1930

Club Contact Details 01914 783 883   info@gateshead-fc.com

2019-20 Season
Nat N   7 after PPG
FAC   1P
FAT   3Q

Record
P 38 W 17 D 11 L 10

Top Goalscorer
Kayode, O'Donnell & Preston (8)

Previous Names: Gateshead AFC (formerly South Shields)1930-73. Gateshead Town 1973-74. Gateshead Utd (formerly South Shields) 1974-77.

Previous Leagues: Football League 1930-60, NCE 60-62, North Regional 62-68, Northern Prem 68-70, 73-83, 85-86, 87-90, Wearside 70-71, Midland 71-72, Northern Comb 73-74. Alliance/Conf 1983-85, 86-87, 90-98.

	10-11		11-12		12-13		13-14		14-15		15-16		16-17		17-18		18-19	
	Conf	15	Conf	8	Conf	17	Conf	3	Conf	10	Nat	9	Nat	8	Nat	17	Nat	17
	FAC	1P	FAC	2P	FAC	4Q	FAC	1Pr	FAC	3P	FAC	4Q	FAC	4Qr	FAC	2P	FAC	1P
	FAT	SF	FAT	QF	FAT	3P	FAT	2P	FAT	3Pr	FAT	QFr	FAT	2P	FAT	SF	FAT	1P

LEAGUE HONOURS:
Northern Regional 1963-64. Northern Premier League 1982-83, 85-86.

COUNTY FA HONOURS: Durham Senior Professional Cup 1930-31, 48-49, 501-51, 54-55, 58-59. Durham Challenge Cup 2010-11 (Reserve

CLUB RECORDS
FA Cup Quarter Finals 1952-53 as a League club. Third Round Proper 2014-15 as a Non-League Club.
FA Trophy Semi-Finals 2010-11
Victory: 8-0 v Netherfield - Northern Premier League
Defeat: 0-9 v Sutton United - Conference 22/09/90
Goalscorer: Paul Thompson - 130
Appearances: James Curtis - 506 (2003-present)
Additional: Record transfer fee paid: £9,000 - Paul Cavell, Dagenham & Redbridge 1994
Record transfer fee received: £150,000 Lee Novak, Huddersfield Town 2009

GROUND: The International Stadium, Neilson Road, Gateshead NE10 0EF
Ground Capacity: 11,795 **Seats:** 11,795 **Covered:** 7,271 **Clubhouse:** Yes **Shop:** Yes
Previous Grounds: Redheugh Park 1930-71
Record Attendance: 11,750 v Newcastle United - Friendly 07/08/95
Nearest Railway Station Gateshead Stadium Metro stop 5min walk away.
Bus Route 27, 93, 94

GLOUCESTER CITY
The Tigers   **Club Colours** Red & amber

Founded 1883

Club Contact Details info@gcafc.co.uk

2019-20 Season
Nat N   17 after PPG
FAC   3Qr
FAT   3Q

Record
P 34 W 10 D 7 L 17

Top Goalscorer
Hanks (11)

Previous Names: Gloucester 1883-86,1889-1901, Gloucester Nomads 1888-89, Gloucester YMCA 1910-25, Gloucester City 1902-10,1925 to date

Previous Leagues: Bristol & District (now Western) 1893-96, Gloucester & Dist. 1897-1907, North Gloucestershire 1907-10, Gloucestershire Northern Senior (FM) 1920-34, Birmingham Comb 1934-39, Southern 1939-2000

	10-11		11-12		12-13		13-14		14-15		15-16		16-17		17-18		18-19	
	Conf N	14	Conf N	14	Conf N	11	Conf N	17	Conf N	14	Nat N	15	Nat N	10	Nat S	14	Nat S	17
	FAC	2Q	FAC	4Qr	FAC	1P	FAC	1P	FAC	4Q	FAC	4Q	FAC	3Qr	FAC	2Q	FAC	4Q
	FAT	3P	FAT	3Qr	FAT	3Q	FAT	1P	FAT	3Qr	FAT	3Qr	FAT	3Q	FAT	3Q	FAT	3Q

LEAGUE HONOURS:
Gloucester & District Division One 1897-98, 99-1900, 03-04. North Gloucestershire Division One 1907-08, 08-09 Gloucestershire Northern Senior 1933-34. Southern League Midland Division 1988-89.

COUNTY FA HONOURS: Glos Junior Cup 1902-03. Glos Senior Amateur Cup 1931-32. Glos Senior Cup 1937-38, 49-50, 50-51, 52-53, 54-55, 55-56, 57-58, 65-66, 68-69, 70-71, 74-75, 78-79, 79-80, 81-82, 82-83, 83-84, 90-91, 92-93.

CLUB RECORDS
FA Cup Second Round Proper 1989-90 (r).   **Welsh Cup** Quarter-finals 1958-59 (r).
FA Trophy Semi-finals 1996-97 (r)
Victory: 12-1 v Bristol Saint George, April 1934
Defeat: 0-14 v Brimscombe FC, January 1923
Goalscorer: Jerry Causon - 206 (1930-36)
Appearances: Tom Webb - 675+ (2001 to date)
Additional: Paid £25,000 to Worcester City for Steve Ferguson 1990-91
Received £25,000 from AFC Bournemouth for Ian Hedges 1990

GROUND: Meadow Park, Sudmeadow Road, Hempsted, Gloucester GL2 5HS
Ground Capacity: 3,208 **Seats:** 700 **Covered:** Yes **Clubhouse:** Yes **Shop:** Yes
Previous Grounds: Longlevens 1934-64. Horton Rd 64-86. Meadow Pk 86-2007. FGR 07-08. Cirencester T. 08-10. Cheltenham 10-17. Evesham United 17-20.
Record Attendance: Longlevens: 10,500 v Tottenham - Friendly 1956. Meadow Park: 4,500 v Dagenham & Red. - FAT 3rd Q Rnd
Nearest Railway Station Gloucester - six min walk to Station Road (see below)
Bus Route Station Road (Stop Q) No.8 to Sainsbury's Supermarket - 5min walk from there.

GUISELEY
The Lions   **Club Colours** White and navy   **Founded** 1909

Club Contact Details 01943 873 223 (Office) 872 872 (Club)   admin@guiseleyafc.co.uk

Previous Names: None

Previous Leagues: Wharfedale, Leeds, West Riding Counties, West Yorkshire, Yorkshire 1968-82, Northern Counties East 1982-91, Northern Premier 1991-2010

2019-20 Season
Nat N   9 after PPG
FAC   3Q
FAT   3Q

Record
P 36 W 15 D 8 L 13

Top Goalscorer
Martin (17)

	10-11	11-12	12-13	13-14	14-15	15-16	16-17	17-18	18-19
	Conf N 5	Conf N 2	Conf N 2	Conf N 5	Conf N 5	Nat 20	Nat 20	Nat 24	Nat N 19
FAC	1P	3Q	1Pr	2Q	4Q	4Qr	4Qr	2P	2P
FAT	QF	3P	2P	3P	1P	3Pr	2P	1P	3Qr

LEAGUE HONOURS: Wharfedale 1912-13. Yorkshire Division Two 1975-76. Northern Counties East 1990-91. Northern Premier League Division One 1993-94, Premier Division 2009-10.

COUNTY FA HONOURS: West Riding County Cup 1978-79, 79-80, 80-81, 93-94, 95-96, 2004-05, 10-11, 11-12.

CLUB RECORDS
FA Cup First Round Proper 1991-92, 94-95, 99-00, 02-03, 10-11, 12-13(r)   **FA Vase** Winners 1990-91(r), Runners-up 91-92.
FA Trophy Semi-Finals 1993-94.
Misc: Highest points total gained - 93 - Northern Premier League Division One (1st) 1993-94 and Premier (3rd) 1994-95.

GROUND: Nethermoor Park, Otley Road, Guiseley, Leeds LS20 8BT
Ground Capacity: 4,200   **Seats:** 500   **Covered:** 1,040   **Clubhouse:** Yes   **Shop:** Yes
Previous Grounds: None
Record Attendance: 2,486 v Bridlington Town - FA Vase Semi-final 1st Leg 1989-90
Nearest Railway Station Nethermoor is about 5 min walk away.
Bus Route There are two bus stops directly outside.

HEREFORD
The Bulls   **Club Colours** White and black   **Founded** 2014

Club Contact Details 01432 268 257   info@herefordfc.co.uk

Previous Names: Formed in 2014 after the demise of Hereford United who folded during the 2014-15 season.

Previous Leagues: Midland 2015-16. Southern 2016-18.

2019-20 Season
Nat N   16 after PPG
FAC   3Qr
FAT   3Qr

Record
P 40 W 10 D 15 L 15

Top Goalscorer
Mooney & Vincenti (5)

	10-11	11-12	12-13	13-14	14-15	15-16	16-17	17-18	18-19
						MidL 1	Sthsw 1	SthP 1	Nat N 17
FAC							3Q	2P	3Q
FAT/FAV						FAV F	P	1P	2P

LEAGUE HONOURS: Midland League 2015-16. Southern Division One South & West 2016-17, Premier Division 17-18.

COUNTY FA HONOURS: Herefordshire County Cup 2015-16, 17-18

CLUB RECORDS
FA Cup Second Round Proper 2017-18   **FA Vase** Runners-up 2015-16
FA Trophy Second Round Proper 2018-19
Victory: 8-0 v Heanor Town - Midland League 23/04/16 & v Godalming Town (H), FAC 1Q, 02/09/2017.
Defeat: 4-5 v Coleshill Town - Midland League 2015-16.
Goalscorer: John Mills

GROUND: Edgar Street, Hereford HR4 9JU
Ground Capacity: 8,843   **Seats:** 2,761   **Covered:** 6,082   **Clubhouse:** Yes   **Shop:** Yes
Previous Grounds: None
Record Attendance: 4,712 v AFC Telford United, FA Cup 1P, 04/11/2017.
Nearest Railway Station Hereford - 0.6km
Bus Route 476 & 492

KETTERING TOWN

The Poppies   **Club Colours** Red & black

Founded 1872

Club Contact Details 01536 217 006   info@ketteringtownfc.com

2019-20 Season
Nat N   19 after PPG
FAC   2Qr
FAT   1P

Record
P 35 W 8 D 12 L 15

Top Goalscorer
Nti (6)

Previous
Names: Kettering > 1924

Previous Midland 1892-1900, also had a team in United Counties 1896-99, Southern 1900-30, 1950-79, 2001
Leagues: -02, 12-19. Birmingham 1930-50, Alliance/Conference 1979-2001, 02-03, 04-12. Isthmian 2003-04.

10-11		11-12		12-13		13-14		14-15		15-16		16-17		17-18		18-19	
Conf	14	Conf	24	SthP	22	SthC	3	SthC	1	SthP	6	SthP	9	SthP	4	SthPC	1
FAC	4Q	FAC	1P	FAC	2Q	FAC	P	FAC	2Q	FAC	3Qr	FAC	4Q	FAC	4Qr	FAC	4Q
FAT	1Pr	FAT	1P	FAT	1Q	FAT	1Q	FAT	1Q	FAT	2Q	FAT	2Q	FAT	1Q	FAT	2Q

LEAGUE HONOURS:
Midland 1895-96, 99-1900. United Counties 1904-05, 38-39. Southern 1927-28, 56-57, 72-73, 2001-02, Division One Central 2014-15, Premier Central 2018-19. National North 2007-08.

COUNTY FA
HONOURS: Northamptonshire Senior Cup 2016-17, 17-18.

CLUB RECORDS
FA Cup Fourth Round Proper 1988-89, 2008-09.
FA Trophy Runners-up 1978-79, 1999-2000.
Victory: 16-0 v Higham YMCI - FA Cup 1909
Defeat: 0-13 v Mardy - Southern League Division Two 1911-12
Goalscorer: Roy Clayton - 171 (1972-81)
Appearances: Roger Ashby
Additional: Paid £25,000 to Macclesfield for Carl Alford 1994.
Recieved £150,000 from Newcastle United for Andy Hunt

GROUND: Latimer Park, Burton Latimer, Kettering NN15 5PS
Ground Capacity: 2,500   **Seats:** 332   **Covered:** Yes   **Clubhouse:** Yes   **Shop:** Yes
Previous Grounds: North Park, Green Lane, Rockingham Road > 2011. Nene Park 2011-13.
Record Attendance: 11,536 v Peterborough - FA Cup 1st Round replay 1958-59
Nearest Railway Station Kettering - 4.1km
Bus Route Station Road - stop 150m away

KIDDERMINSTER HARRIERS

Harriers   **Club Colours** Red and white

Founded 1886

Club Contact Details 01562 823 931   info@harriers.co.uk

2019-20 Season
Nat N   15 after PPG
FAC   2Qr
FAT   3Q

Record
P 36 W 10 D 9 L 17

Top Goalscorer
Chambers (13)

Previous
Names: Kidderminster Harriers and Football Club 1886-90. Kidderminster FC 1890-1891.

Previous B'ham & Dist (FM) 1889-90, 91-1939, 47-48, 60-62. Midland 1890-91. Southern 1939-45, 48-60, 72
Leagues: -83. B'ham Comb 1945-47. West Mids (Reg) 1962-72. Conference 1983-2000. Football Lg 2000-05.

10-11		11-12		12-13		13-14		14-15		15-16		16-17		17-18		18-19	
Conf	6	Conf	6	Conf	2	Conf	7	Conf	16	Nat	23	Nat N	2	Nat N	4	Nat N	10
FAC	4Q	FAC	4Qr	FAC	1P	FAC	4P	FAC	4Q	FAC	4Q	FAC	1P	FAC	1P	FAC	3Q
FAT	1P	FAT	3P	FAT	2P	FAT	1P	FAT	2P	FAT	1P	FAT	3Q	FAT	2Pr	FAT	3Q

LEAGUE HONOURS:
Birmingham & District 1937-38. West Midlands (Regional) 1964-65, 68-69, 69-70, 70-71.
Conference 1993-94, 1999-2000.

COUNTY FA Worcestershire Senior Cup (27 times) Firstly in 1895-96 and most recently 2016-17. Birmingham Senior Cup (7x) Firstly in 1933-34
HONOURS: and most recently in 1966-67. Staffordshire Senior Cup (4x) Firstly in 1980-81 and most recently in 1984-85.

CLUB RECORDS
FA Cup Fifth Round Proper 1993-94   **Welsh Cup** Finalists 1985-86, 1988-89
FA Trophy Winners 1986-87; Runners-up 1990-91, 94-95, 2006-07
Victory: 25-0 v Hereford (H), Birmingham Senior Cup First Round, 12/10/1889
Defeat: 0-13 v Darwen (A), FA Cup First Round Proper, 24/01/1891
Goalscorer: Peter Wassell - 448 (1963-74)
Appearances: Brendan Wassell - 686 (1962-74)
Additional: Paid £80,000 to Nuneaton Borough for Andy Ducros July 2000
Recieved £380,000 from W.B.A. for Lee Hughes July 1997

GROUND: Aggborough Stadium, Hoo Road, Kidderminster DY10 1NB
Ground Capacity: 6,444   **Seats:** 3,140   **Covered:** 3,062   **Clubhouse:** Yes   **Shop:** Yes
Previous Grounds: Chester Road 1886-87.
Record Attendance: 9,155 v Hereford United, FA Cup First Round Proper, 27/11/48
Nearest Railway Station Kidderminster - half a mile from the ground.
Bus Route 192 & 42

LEAMINGTON
The Brakes   **Club Colours** Gold and black

Founded 1892

Club Contact Details 01926 430 406   info@leamingtonfc.co.uk

Previous Names: Leamington Town 1892-1937, Lockheed Borg & Beck 1944-46, Lockheed Leamington 1946-73, AP Leamington 1973-88

Previous Leagues: B'ham Comb, B'ham & Dist, West Mids (Reg), Midland Counties, Southern, Midland Combination, Midland Alliance 2005-07. Southern 2007-13, 15-17. Football Conference 2013-15.

2019-20 Season
Nat N 18 after PPG
FAC 3Q
FAT 3P

Record
P 40 W 13 D 11 L 16

Top Goalscorer
March (22)

	10-11	11-12	12-13	13-14	14-15	15-16	16-17	17-18	18-19
	SthP 5	SthP 7	SthP 1	Conf N 13	Conf N 21	SthP 3	SthP 2	Nat N 19	Nat N 13
FAC	1Qr	2Q	2Q	2Qr	3Qr	1Qr	1Q	3Qr	2Q
FAT	3Q	1Q	1Qr	2P	3Q	1Pr	1Q	1P	2P

LEAGUE HONOURS:
Birmingham & Dist 1961-62. West Mids Regional 1962-63. Midland Co 1964-65. Southern League 1982-83, 2012-13, Division One Midlands 2008-09. Midland Comb Div Two 2000-01, Premier Div 2004-05. Midland All 2006-07.

COUNTY FA HONOURS: Birmingham Senior Cup 2016-17, 18-19.

CLUB RECORDS
FA Cup First Round Proper 2005-06   **FA Vase** Quarter-finals 2006-07
FA Trophy Third Round Proper 2019-20
Goalscorer: Josh Blake - 187
Appearances: Josh Blake - 406

GROUND: Phillips 66 Community Stadium, Harbury Lane, Whitmarsh, Leamington CV33 9QB
Ground Capacity: 2,300   **Seats:** 294   **Covered:** 720   **Clubhouse:** Yes   **Shop:** Yes
Previous Grounds: Old Windmill Ground
Record Attendance: 1,380 v Retford United - 17/02/2007
Nearest Railway Station Leamington Spa - 3 miles away
Bus Route Nos. 65 & 66

SOUTHPORT
The Sandgrounders   **Club Colours** Yellow & black

Founded 1881

Club Contact Details 01704 533 422   secretary@southportfc.net

Previous Names: Southport Central 1888-1918, Southport Vulcan 1918-21.

Previous Leagues: Preston & District, Lancashire 1889-1903, Lancashire Combination 1903-11, Central 1911-21, Football League 1921-78, Northern Premier 1978-93, 2003-04, Conference 1993-2003.

2019-20 Season
Nat N 12 after PPG
FAC 4Q
FAT 2P

Record
P 39 W 16 D 8 L 15

Top Goalscorer
Morgan (13)

	10-11	11-12	12-13	13-14	14-15	15-16	16-17	17-18	18-19
	Conf 21	Conf 7	Conf 20	Conf 18	Conf 19	Nat 16	Nat 23	Nat N 15	Nat N 14
FAC	1P	1P	4Q	1P	3P	4Q	1Pr	2Q	2Pr
FAT	1Pr	1P	QF	1P	1Pr	2P	2P	3Qr	1P

LEAGUE HONOURS:
Football League Division Four 1972-73. Northern Premier League Premier Division 1992-93. Conference North 2004-05, 2009-10.

COUNTY FA HONOURS: Lancs Senior Cup 1904-05. Lancs Junior Cup 1919-20, 92-93, 96-97, 97-98, 2001-01, 05-06, 07-08, 09-10. Liverpool Senior Cup 1930-31, 31-32, 43-44, 62-63, 74-75, 90-91, 92-93, 98-99, 2011-12.

CLUB RECORDS
FA Cup Quarter-Finals 1930-31. As a Non-League side - Third Round Proper 1998-99, 2014-15.
FA Trophy Runners-up 1998-98
Victory: 8-1 v Nelson - 01/01/31
Defeat: 0-11 v Oldham Athletic - 26/12/62
Goalscorer: Alan Spence - 98
Appearances: Arthur Peat - 401 (1962-72)
Additional: Paid £20,000 to Macclesfield Town for Martin McDonald

GROUND: Merseyrail Community Stadium, Haig Avenue, Southport, Merseyside PR8 6JZ
Ground Capacity: 6,008   **Seats:** 1,660   **Covered:** 2,760   **Clubhouse:** Yes   **Shop:** Yes
Previous Grounds: Sussex Road Sports Ground, Scarisbrick New Road 1886-1905, Ash Lane (later named Haig Ave)
Record Attendance: 20,010 v Newcastle United - FA Cup 1932
Nearest Railway Station Meols Cop - 1mile away. Southport - 1.5miles away.
Bus Route 44 Arriva from the Southport Station.

SPENNYMOOR TOWN

The Moors   **Club Colours** Black and white   **Founded** 2005

Club Contact Details   01388 827 248

Previous Names: Evenwood Town and Spennymoor United merged to form today's club in 2005.

Previous Leagues: Northern League 2005-14. Northern Premier 2014-17.

2019-20 Season
Nat N   8 after PPG
FAC   4Q
FAT   3Q

Record P 38 W 17 D 10 L 11

Top Goalscorer Taylor (24)

	10-11	11-12	12-13	13-14	14-15	15-16	16-17	17-18	18-19
	NL 1 1	NL 1 1	NL 1 2	NL 1 1	NP1N 5	NP1N 2	NP P 2	Nat N 8	Nat N 4
	FAC 1Q	FAC 3Q	FAC 2Q	FAC 1Q	FAC 4Qr	FAC 2Q	FAC 1P	FAC 2Q	FAC 2Q
	FAV 5P	FAV 3P	FAV 2Q	FAV F	FAT 1P	FAT 3Q	FAT 1Q	FAT 4Pr	FAT 3P

LEAGUE HONOURS:
Northern League Division One 2009-10, 2010-11, 2011-12, 2013-14, Division Two 2006-07.

COUNTY FA HONOURS: Durham Challange Cup 2011-12.

CLUB RECORDS

FA Cup First Round Proper 1956-57, 2016-17.   **FA Vase** Winners 2012-13.
FA Trophy First Round Proper 2014-15.
Victory: 10-0 v Billingham Town (H), Northern League Division One, 18/03/2014
Defeat: 2-8 v Clitheroe (A), FA Cup 2nd Qualifying Round, 29/09/2007
Goalscorer: Gavin Cogdon - 103
Appearances: Lewis Dodds - 227
Additional: Northern League record points tally of 109 during 2012-13.

GROUND: The Brewery Field, Durham Road, Spennymoor DL16 6JN

Ground Capacity: 3,000   **Seats:** 224   **Covered:** 800   **Clubhouse:** Yes   **Shop:** Yes
Previous Grounds: None
Record Attendance: 2,670 v Darlington, Northern League 2012-13.
Nearest Railway Station Durham
Bus Route No.6 from Durham Bus Station in Durham Town Centre (15min journey)

YORK CITY

Minstermen   **Club Colours** Red and navy blue   **Founded** 1922

Club Contact Details   01904 624 447 / 559 500   enquiries@yorkcityfootballclub.co.uk

Previous Names: None

Previous Leagues: Midland 1922-29. Football League 1929-2004, 2012-16. Conference 2004-12.

2019-20 Season
Nat N   2 after PPG
FAC   1P
FAT   3Q

Record P 40 W 22 D 9 L 9

Top Goalscorer Burrow (15)

	10-11	11-12	12-13	13-14	14-15	15-16	16-17	17-18	18-19
	Conf 8	Conf 4	FL 2 17	FL 2 7	FL 2 18	FL 2 24	Nat 21	Nat N 11	Nat N 12
	FAC 3P	FAC 4Q	FAC 1Pr	FAC 1Pr	FAC 1Pr	FAC 1P	FAC 4Qr	FAC 3Q	FAC 1P
	FAT 1P	FAT F	FLC 1P	FLC 1P	FLC 1P	FLC 2P	FAT F	FAT 1P	FAT 1P

LEAGUE HONOURS:
Football League Division Four 1983-84, Third Division Play-offs 1992-93.
Conference Premier Play-offs 2011-12.

COUNTY FA HONOURS: North Riding Senior Cup 1949-50, 56-57, 69-70, 79-80, 87-88. 88-89, 95-96, 98-99, 99-00, 05-06, 09-10.

CLUB RECORDS

FA Cup Semi-Finals 1954-55.
FA Trophy Winners 2011-12, 16-17. Runners-up 08-09.
Victory: 9-1 v Southport - Division Three North 1957
Defeat: 0-12 v Chester City - Division Three North 1936
Goalscorer: Norman Wilkinson - 143 (1954-66)
Appearances: Barry Jackson - 539 (1958-70)
Additional: Paid £140,000 to Burnley for Adrian Randall December 1995
Received £950,000 from Sheffield Wednesday for Richard Cresswell 25/03/1999

GROUND: Bootham Crescent, York YO30 7AQ

Ground Capacity: 8,256   **Seats:** 3,409   **Covered:** Yes   **Clubhouse:** Yes   **Shop:** Yes
Previous Grounds: Fulfordgate 1922-32. New 8,000 all-seater stadium, at Monks Cross, open during 2019-20 season.
Record Attendance: 28,123 v Huddersfield Town - FA Cup Sixth Round Proper 1938
Nearest Railway Station York - 20 min walk away.   **NOTE:** At the time of going to press the club were unsure if they would be
Bus Route 2 & 5A   moving into their new 8,000 all seater stadium at Monks Cross for 2020/21.

BATH CITY
The Romans   **Club Colours** Black & white

Founded 1889

Club Contact Details 01225 423 087   info@bathcityfootballclub.co.uk

2019-20 Season
Nat S   4 after PPG

FAC   3Q

FAT   2Pr

Record
P 43 W 21 D 11 L 11

Top Goalscorer
T Smith (15)

Previous Names: Bath AFC 1889-92. Bath Railway FC 1902-05. Bath Amateurs 1913-23 (Reserve side)

Previous Leagues: Western 1908-21. Southern 1921-79, 88-90, 97-2007. Football League Division Two North 1939-45. Alliance/Conference 1979-88, 90-97.

10-11		11-12		12-13		13-14		14-15		15-16		16-17		17-18		18-19	
Conf	10	Conf	23	Conf S	11	Conf S	7	Conf S	14	Nat S	14	Nat S	9	Nat S	9	Nat S	5
FAC	4Qr	FAC	1Pr	FAC	3Qr	FAC	4Q	FAC	4Q	FAC	3Qr	FAC	4Q	FAC	4Qr	FAC	4Q
FAT	2P	FAT	3P	FAT	1P	FAT	3Q	FAT	SF	FAT	3Q	FAT	1P	FAT	1P	FAT	1P

LEAGUE HONOURS:
Western Division Two 1928-29, Premier 1933-34. Southern Premier Division 1959-60, 77-78, 2006-07.

COUNTY FA HONOURS: Somerset Premier Cup 1929-30, 33-34, 35-36, 51-52, 52-53, 57-58, 59-60, 65-66, 67-68, 69-70, 77-78, 80-81, 81-82, 83-84, 84-85, 85-86, 88-89, 89-90, 93-94, 94-95, 2007-08.

CLUB RECORDS
FA Cup Third Round Proper 1963-64 (r), 93-94 (r).
FA Trophy Semi-Finals 2014-15.
Victory: 8-0 v Boston United - 1998-99
Defeat: 0-9 v Yeovil Town - 1946-47
Goalscorer: Paul Randall - 106
Appearances: David Mogg - 530
Additional: Paid £15,000 to Bristol City for Micky Tanner.
Received £80,000 from Southampton for Jason Dodd.

GROUND: Twerton Park, Twerton, Bath, Somerset BA2 1DB
Ground Capacity: 8,880   **Seats:** 1,006   **Covered:** 4,800   **Clubhouse:** Yes   **Shop:** Yes
Previous Grounds: The Belvoir Ground 1889-92 & 1902-15. Lambridge Show Ground 1919-32.
Record Attendance: 18,020 v Brighton & Hove Albion - FA Cup 1960
Nearest Railway Station Bath Spa - 2 miles from ground or Avon Street - 1 mile
Bus Route No.5 - every 12mins from Town Centre.

BILLERICAY TOWN
Town or Blues   **Club Colours** All blue

Founded 1880

Club Contact Details 01277 286 474   info@billericaytownfc.co.uk

2019-20 Season
Nat S   17 after PPG

FAC   1P

FAT   3Q

Record
P 38 W 11 D 14 L 13

Top Goalscorer
Robinson (20)

Previous Names: Billericay FC.

Previous Leagues: Romford & Dist 1890-1914, Mid Essex 1918-47, South Essex Comb 1947-66, Essex Olympian 1966-71, Essex Senior 1971-77, Athenian 1977-79. Isthmian 1979-2012. Conference 2012-13.

10-11		11-12		12-13		13-14		14-15		15-16		16-17		17-18		18-19	
Isth P	11	Isth P	1	Conf S	21	Isth P	10	Isth P	8	Isth P	9	Isth P	8	Isth P	1	Nat S	8
FAC	2Qr	FAC	3Q	FAC	3Qr	FAC	2Q	FAC	3Q	FAC	1Qr	FAC	4Q	FAC	1Pr	FAC	1Pr
FAT	3Q	FAT	3Q	FAT	1P	FAT	2Qr	FAT	1Q	FAT	1Q	FAT	2Q	FAT	4P	FAT	1P

LEAGUE HONOURS:
Chelmsford & District Division Three 1932-33. Essex Olympian 1969-70, 70-71.
Essex Senior 1972-73, 74-75, 75-76. Athenian 1977-78, 78-79.
Isthmian Division Two 1979-80, Premier Division 2011-12.

COUNTY FA HONOURS: Essex Senior Cup 1975-76, 2010-11, 17-18. Essex Senior Trophy 1977-78, 79-80, 2017-18.

CLUB RECORDS
FA Cup First Round Proper 1997-98, 2004-05, 07-08, 18-19(r), 19-20.   **FA Vase** Winners 1975-76, 76-77, 78-79.
FA Trophy Fifth Round Proper 2000-01.
Victory: 11-0 v Stansted (A) - Essex Senior League 05/05/1976
Defeat: 3-10 v Chelmsford City (A) - Essex Senior Cup 04/01/1993
Goalscorer: Freddie Claydon - 273
Appearances: J Pullen - 418
Additional: Leon Gutzmore scored 51 goals during the 1997-98 season.
Received £22,500+ from West Ham United for Steve Jones November 1992

GROUND: New Lodge, Blunts Wall Road, Billericay CM12 9SA
Ground Capacity: 3,500   **Seats:** 424   **Covered:** 2,000   **Clubhouse:** Yes   **Shop:** Yes
Previous Grounds: None
Record Attendance: 3,841 v West Ham United - Opening of Floodlights 1977
Nearest Railway Station Billericay - 1.4km
Bus Route London Road - stop 300m away

BRAINTREE TOWN

The Iron   **Club Colours** Orange & blue

Founded 1898

Club Contact Details 01376 345 617   braintreeTFC@aol.com

Previous Names: Manor Works 1898-1921, Crittall Athletic 1921-68, Braintree and Crittall Athletic 1968-81, Braintree 1981-83.

Previous Leagues: N.Essex 1898-1925, Essex & Suffolk B 1925-29, 55-64, Spartan 28-35, Eastern Co. 35-37, 38-39, 52-55, 70-91, Essex Co. 37-38, London 45-52, Gt London 64-66, Met 66-70, Southern 91-96, Isthmian 96-2006

2019-20 Season

Nat S   21 after PPG

FAC   2Q

FAT   3Q

Record
P 37 W 10 D 5 L 22

Top Goalscorer
Akinwande (6)

	10-11		11-12		12-13		13-14		14-15		15-16		16-17		17-18		18-19	
	Conf S	1	Conf	12	Conf	9	Conf	6	Conf	14	Nat	3	Nat	22	Nat S	6	Nat	23
	FAC	3Q	FAC	4Q	FAC	1P	FAC	1Pr	FAC	1P	FAC	1Pr	FAC	2P	FAC	3Q	FAC	4Q
	FAT	1P	FAT	2Pr	FAT	1Pr	FAT	2P	FAT	3Pr	FAT	2P	FAT	3Pr	FAT	1Pr	FAT	1P

LEAGUE HONOURS:
North Essex 1905-06, 10-11, 11-12. Eastern Counties League 1936-37, 83-84, 84-85.
Essex & Suffolk Border 1959-60. Isthmian League Premier Division 2005-06. Conference South 2010-11.

COUNTY FA HONOURS: Essex Senior Cup 1995-96. Essex Senior Trophy 1986-87.

CLUB RECORDS

FA Cup Second Round Proper 2016-17

FA Trophy Fifth Round Proper 2001-02 (r)   **FA Vase**   Fifth Round Proper 1984-85 (r)

Victory: 12-0 v Thetford - Eastern Counties League 1935-36

Defeat: 0-14 v Chelmsford City (A) - North Essex League 1923

Goalscorer: Chris Guy - 211 (1963-90). Gary Bennett scored 57 goals during season 1997-98

Appearances: Paul Young - 524 (1966-77)

Additional: Received £10,000 from Brentford for Matt Metcalf and from Colchester United for John Cheesewright

GROUND: Cressing Road Stadium, off Clockhouse Way, Braintree CM7 3DE

Ground Capacity: 4,222   **Seats:** 553   **Covered:** 1,288   **Clubhouse:** Yes   **Shop:** Yes

Previous Grounds: The Fiar Field 1898-1903, Spalding Meadow 1903-23.

Record Attendance: 4,000 v Tottenham Hotspur - Testimonial May 1952

Nearest Railway Station Braintree - less than a mile from the ground.

Bus Route 133, 38A & 70

CHELMSFORD CITY

City or Clarets   **Club Colours** Claret and white

Founded 1878

Club Contact Details 01245 290 959

Previous Names: Chelmsford FC 1878-1938.

Previous Leagues: North Essex (FM) 1895-1900. South Essex 1900-13. Athenian (FM) 1912-22. Middlesex Co 1922-38. Essex & Suffolk Border 1923-24. London 1924-35. Eastern Co (FM) 1935-38. Southern 1938-2004. Isthmian 2004-08

2019-20 Season

Nat S   10 after PPG

FAC   2Q

FAT   3P

Record
P 39 W 14 D 11 L 14

Top Goalscorer
Jeffers (15)

	10-11		11-12		12-13		13-14		14-15		15-16		16-17		17-18		18-19	
	Conf S	4	Conf S	6	Conf S	5	Conf S	17	Conf S	10	Nat S	15	Nat S	4	Nat S	3	Nat S	4
	FAC	2P	FAC	2Pr	FAC	2P	FAC	2Q	FAC	4Qr	FAC	3Q	FAC	2Q	FAC	1P	FAC	2Q
	FAT	3Q	FAT	1P	FAT	3P	FAT	3Q	FAT	3Q	FAT	1P	FAT	3Pr	FAT	3Qr	FAT	3Q

LEAGUE HONOURS:
Middlesex County 1923-24. London League 1930-31. Southern League 1930-40 (joint), 45-46, 67-68, 71-72. Division One South 88-89. Isthmian League Premier Division 2007-08.

COUNTY FA HONOURS: Essex Senior Cup 1892-93, 1901-02, 85-86, 88-89, 92-93, 2002-03, 08-09 16-17. East Anglian Cup 1924-25, 26-27, 28-29. Essex Professional Cup 1957-58, 69-70, 70-71, 73-74, 74-75.

CLUB RECORDS

FA Cup Fourth Round Proper 1938-39.

FA Trophy Semi-Finals 1969-70.

Victory: 10-1 v Bashley (H) - Southern League 26/04/2000

Defeat: 1-10 v Barking (A) - FA Trophy 11/11/1978

Goalscorer: Tony Butcher - 286 (1956-71)

Appearances: Tony Butcher - 560 (1956-71)

Additional: Paid £10,000 to Dover Athletic for Tony Rogers, 1992 and to Heybridge Swifts for Kris Lee ,2001
Received £50,000 from Peterborough United for David Morrison, 1994

GROUND: Melbourne Community Stadium, Salerno Way, Chelmsford CM1 2EH

Ground Capacity: 3,000   **Seats:** 1,300   **Covered:** 1,300   **Clubhouse:** Yes   **Shop:** Yes

Previous Grounds: New Writtle Street 1938-97, Maldon Town 1997-98, Billericay Town 1998-2005

Record Attendance: 3,201 v AFC Wimbledon, 15/03/2008.

Nearest Railway Station Chelmsford - take bus or taxi to ground.

Bus Route No. 54 and 56 opposite the train station.

CHIPPENHAM TOWN

The Bluebirds   **Club Colours** All royal blue

Founded 1873

Club Contact Details 01249 650 400

Previous Names: None

Previous Leagues: Western 1904-06, 30-65, 73-2001. Wiltshire Senior. Wiltshire Premier. Hellenic 1968-73. Southern 2001-17.

2019-20 Season
Nat S   14 after PPG
FAC   1P
FAT   3Qr

Record
P 43 W 13 D 15 L 15

Top Goalscorer
Chambers (8)

	10-11		11-12		12-13		13-14		14-15		15-16		16-17		17-18		18-19	
	SthP	7	SthP	11	SthP	15	SthP	18	SthP	11	SthP	8	SthP	1	Nat S	1	Nat S	13
	FAC	2Q	FAC	1Q	FAC	4Q	FAC	1Q	FAC	3Q	FAC	4Q	FAC	3Q	FAC	2Q	FAC	4Qr
	FAT	2Qr	FAT	1P	FAT	2Q	FAT	2Q	FAT	2Q	FAT	1Q	FAT	2Q	FAT	3Q	FAT	3Qr

LEAGUE HONOURS:
Western League 1951-52.
Southern League Premier Division 2016-17.

COUNTY FA HONOURS: Wiltshire Senior Cup. Wiltshire Senior Shield x4.

CLUB RECORDS

FA Cup First Round Proper 1951-52, 2005-06(r), 19-20.   **FA Vase**   Runners-up 1999-2000.
FA Trophy Second Round Proper 2002-03, 09-10.
Victory: 9-0 v Dawlish Town (H) - Western League
Defeat: 0-10 v Tiverton Town (A) - Western League
Goalscorer: Dave Ferris
Appearances: Ian Monnery

GROUND: Hardenhuish Park, Bristol Road, Chippenham SN14 6LR
Ground Capacity: 3,000   **Seats:** 300   **Covered:** 1,000   **Clubhouse:** Yes   **Shop:** Yes
Previous Grounds: Played at four different locations before moving in to Hardenhuish on 24/09/1919.
Record Attendance: 4,800 v Chippenham United - Western League 1951
Nearest Railway Station Chippenham - 1km
Bus Route Bus stops within 200m of the ground.

CONCORD RANGERS

Beach Boys   **Club Colours** Yellow and blue

Founded 1967

Club Contact Details 01268 515 750   media@concordrangers.co.uk

Previous Names: None

Previous Leagues: Thundermite Boys League 1967-73. Vange & District 1973-79. Mid-Essex 1979-88. Essex Intermediate 1988-91. Essex Senior 1991-2008. Isthmian 2008-13.

2019-20 Season
Nat S   16 after PPG
FAC   2Q
FAT

Record
P 40 W 14 D 10 L 16

Top Goalscorer
Nouble & Sheriff 10

	10-11		11-12		12-13		13-14		14-15		15-16		16-17		17-18		18-19	
	Isth P	8	Isth P	14	Isth P	4	Conf S	9	Conf S	7	Nat S	10	Nat S	18	Nat S	17	Nat S	6
	FAC	3Q	FAC	2Qr	FAC	2Qr	FAC	4Q	FAC	1Pr	FAC	2Q	FAC	3Q	FAC	4Qr	FAC	4Q
	FAT	1Q	FAT	1Q	FAT	2Q	FAT	1P	FAT	2P	FAT	3Q	FAT	3Q	FAT	3Q	FAT	3Q

LEAGUE HONOURS:
Essex Intermediate League Division 2 1990-91. Essex Senior League 1997-98, 2003-04, 07-08.

COUNTY FA HONOURS: Essex Senior Cup 2013-14, 14-15, 15-16.

CLUB RECORDS

FA Cup First Round Proper 2014-15   **FA Vase**   Quarter-Finals 2007-08
FA Trophy Semi Finals 2019-20 (At the time of going to press the Semi Finals had not yet taken place).
Goalscorer: Tony Stokes - 120
Appearances: Steve King - 312 (2013-16)

GROUND: Aspect Arena, Thames Road, Canvey Island, Essex SS8 0HH
Ground Capacity: 3,250   **Seats:** 375   **Covered:** Yes   **Clubhouse:** Yes   **Shop:**
Previous Grounds: Waterside 70s-85
Record Attendance: 1,537 v Mansfield Town, FA Cup First Round Replay, 25/11/2014.
Nearest Railway Station Benfleet - Approx. 3 miles from the ground.
Bus Route First Buses operate a regular service to Thorney Bay Road, 5-10min walk from there

DARTFORD

The Darts   **Club Colours** White and black

Founded 1888

Club Contact Details 01322 299 991   info@dartfordfc.com

2019-20 Season
Nat S   6 after PPG
FAC   4Q
FAT   3Qr

Record

Top Goalscorer
McQueen (20)

Previous Names: None

Previous Leagues: Kent League (FM) 1894-96, 97-98, 99-1902, 09-14, 21-26, 93-96, Southern (FM) 1896-97, 1926-81, 82-84, 86-92, 96-2006. West Kent 1902-09. Alliance 1981-82, 84-86.

	10-11	11-12	12-13	13-14	14-15	15-16	16-17	17-18	18-19
	Conf S 10	Conf S 2	Conf 8	Conf 22	Conf 23	Nat S 8	Nat S 3	Nat S 2	Nat S 10
FAC	1Pr	4Q	4Qr	1P	2P	2Q	1P	1P	3Q
FAT	3P	3Pr	SF	1Pr	3Pr	3Q	2P	1Pr	3Qr

LEAGUE HONOURS:
Southern League Division 2 1896-97, Eastern Section 1930-31, 31-32, Southern Championship 30-31, 31-32, 73-74, 83-84, Southern Division 1980-81. West Kent 1908-09. Isthmian League Division One North 2007-08, Premier Division 2009-10.

COUNTY FA HONOURS: Kent Senior Cup 1930-31, 31-32, 32-33, 34-35, 46-47, 69-70, 72-73, 86-87, 87-88, 2010-11, 15-16. Kent Senior

CLUB RECORDS
FA Cup Third Round Proper 1935-36, 36-37.   **FA Vase** First Round Proper 1994-95.
FA Trophy Runners-up 1973-74.
Appearances: Steve Robinson - 692
Additional: Paid £6,000 to Chelmsford City for John Bartley
Received £25,000 from Redbridge Forest for Andy Hessenthaler

GROUND: Princes Park Stadium, Grassbanks, Darenth Road, Dartford DA1 1RT
Ground Capacity: 4,097   **Seats:** 642   **Covered:** Yes   **Clubhouse:** Yes   **Shop:** Yes
Previous Grounds: The Brent/Westgate House, Potters Meadow, Engleys Meadow, Summers Meadow, Watling Street
Record Attendance: 4,097 v Horsham YMCA - Isth Div 1 South 11/11/2006 and v Crystal Palace - Fr 20/07/07
Nearest Railway Station Dartford - bus ride away from the ground.
Bus Route Fasttrack B towards Bluewater/Dartford.

DORKING WANDERERS

Wanderers   **Club Colours** Red & white stripes

Founded 1999

Club Contact Details info@dorkingwanderers.com

2019-20 Season
Nat S   7 after PPG
FAC   2Q
FAT   3P

Record
P 43 W 18 D 9 L 16

Top Goalscorer
Prior (16)

Previous Names: None

Previous Leagues: Crawley & District 1999-2000. West Sussex 2000-2007. Sussex County 2007-2015. Isthmian 2015-19.

	10-11	11-12	12-13	13-14	14-15	15-16	16-17	17-18	18-19
	SxC3 1	SxC2 3	SxC1 20	SxC1 8	SxC1 2	Isth1S 2	Isth1S 2	Isth P 14	Isth P 1
FAC				Pr	2Qr	1Q	1Q	3Q	3Qr
FAV/FAT			2Q	2Qr	2Q	1Qr	P	3Q	1P

LEAGUE HONOURS:
West Sussex Division Four North 2000-01, Division Two North 2003-04, Premier Division 2006-07. Sussex County Division Three 2010-11. Isthmian Premier Division 2018-19.

COUNTY FA HONOURS: None

CLUB RECORDS
FA Cup Third Qualifying Round 2018-19(r).   **FA Vase** Second Qualifying Round 2012-13, 13-14(r), 14-15.
FA Trophy Third Round Proper 2019-20.

GROUND: Meadowbank Stadium, Mill Lane, Dorking RH4 1DX
Ground Capacity: 2,000   **Seats:** 472   **Covered:** Yes   **Clubhouse:** Yes   **Shop:**
Previous Grounds: Big Field Brockham 1999-2007. West Humble Playing Fields 2007-18.
Record Attendance: Unknown
Nearest Railway Station Dorking West and Dorking Deepdene
Bus Route 21 & 465

DULWICH HAMLET

Hamlet   **Club Colours** Navy and pink

Founded 1893

| **Club Contact Details** 020 7274 8707 |

Previous Names: None

Previous Leagues: Camberwell 1894-97. Southern Suburban 1897-1900, 01-07. Dulwich 1900-01. Spartan 1907-08. Isthmian 1907-2018.

2019-20 Season
Nat S   19 after PPG

FAC   1P
FAT   1P

Record
P 42 W 13 D 11 L 18

Top Goalscorer
Mills (18)

	10-11	11-12	12-13	13-14	14-15	15-16	16-17	17-18	18-19
	Isth1S 5	Isth1S 3	Isth1S 1	Isth P 6	Isth P 4	Isth P 5	Isth P 3	Isth P 2	Nat S 14
FAC	Pr	2Q	2Q	3Q	1Q	2Q	2Q	QFr	3Q
FAT	2Q	1Q	P	3Qr	2Q	2Q	2P	2Q	1P

LEAGUE HONOURS:
Dulwich 1899-00, 1900-01.
Isthmian League Premier Division 1919-20, 25-26, 32-33, 48-49, Division One 1977-78, Division One South 2012-13.

COUNTY FA Surrey Senior Cup x16, firstly in 1904-05 and most recently 74-75.
HONOURS: London Senior Cup x5, firstly in 1924-25 and most recently in 2003-04. London Challenge Cup 1998-99.

CLUB RECORDS
FA Cup First Round Proper 1925-26, 26-27, 27-28, 28-29, 29-30, 30-31(r), 32-33, 33-34(r), 34-35, 35-36, 36-37, 37-38, 48-49, 98-99, 2019-20.
FA Trophy Quarter-Finals 1979-80(r), 2016-17(r).   **FA Am Cup** Winners 1919-20, 31-32, 36-37.
Victory: 13-0 v Walton-on-Thames, Surrey Senior Cup, 1936-37
Defeat: 1-10 v Hendon, Isthmian league, 1963-64
Goalscorer: Edgar Kail - 427 (1919-33)
Appearances: Reg Merritt - 576 (1950-66)
Additional: Received £35,000 from Charlton Athletic for Chris Dickson 2007

GROUND: Champion Hill, Dog Kennell Hill, Edgar Kail Way SE22 8BD
Ground Capacity: 3,000   **Seats:** 500   **Covered:** 1,000   **Clubhouse:** Yes   **Shop:** Yes
Previous Grounds: Woodwarde Rd 1893-95, College Farm 95-96, Sunray Ave 1896-02, Freeman's Gd, Champ Hill 02-12, Champ Hill (old ord)12-92. Champion Hill 92-2018. T&M FC 18.
Record Attendance: 3,104 v Bath City, National South, 05/01/2019
Nearest Railway Station East Dulwich 200 yards. Denmark Hill 10 min walk. Herne Hill then bus 37 stops near ground. Mitcham Tram.
Bus Route Buses 40 & 176 from Elephant & Castle, 185 from Victoria.

EASTBOURNE BOROUGH

Borough   **Club Colours** All red

Founded 1964

| **Club Contact Details** 01323 766 265   info@ebfc.co.uk |

Previous Names: Langney FC 1964-68. Langney Sports 1968-2001.

Previous Leagues: Eastbourne & Dist 1964-73. Eastbourne & Hastings 1973-83. Sussex County 1983-2000. Southern 2000-2004.

2019-20 Season
Nat S   18 after PPG

FAC   3Q
FAT   1Pr

Record
P 38 W 10 D 15 L 13

Top Goalscorer
Luer & Walker (9)

	10-11	11-12	12-13	13-14	14-15	15-16	16-17	17-18	18-19
	Conf 23	Conf S 18	Conf S 12	Conf S 10	Conf S 11	Nat S 17	Nat S 11	Nat S	Nat S 18
FAC	4Q	4Q	3Qr	3Q	4Qr	4Q	1P	3Q	4Q
FAT	3Pr	3Qr	3Q	3Q	3Q	2P	3Qr	1P	1P

LEAGUE HONOURS:
Eastbourne & Hastings Premier Division 1981-82.
Sussex County League Division Three 1986-87, Division Two 1987-88, Division One 1999-2000, 02-03.

COUNTY FA
HONOURS: Sussex Senior Challenge Cup 2001-02, 08-09, 15-16.

CLUB RECORDS
FA Cup First Round Proper 2005-06, 07-08, 08-09(r), 16-17.   **FA Vase** Second Round Proper 1990-91, 91-92, 97-98.
FA Trophy Third Round Proper 2001-02, 02-03, 04-05, 10-11.
Victory: 11-1 v Crowborough, Sussex Senior Cup Quarter-final, 13/01/2009
Defeat: 0-8 v Sheppey United (A) - FA Vase 09/10/93 and v Peachaven & Tels (A) - Sussex Co. Div.1 09/11/93
Goalscorer: Nigel Hole - 146
Appearances: Darren Baker - 952 (1992-2013)
Additional: Paid £1,800 to Yeovil Town for Yemi Odoubade.
Received £25,000 from Oxford United for Yemi Odoubade.

GROUND: Langney Sports Club, Priory Lane, Eastbourne BN23 7QH
Ground Capacity: 4,151   **Seats:** 542   **Covered:** 2,500   **Clubhouse:** Yes   **Shop:** Yes
Previous Grounds: Local Recreation Grounds. Princes Park >1983.
Record Attendance: 3,770 v Oxford United - FA Cup 1st Round 05/11/05
Nearest Railway Station Pevensey & Westham - 15-20 mins walk.
Bus Route The LOOP Bus from the town centre.

EBBSFLEET UNITED

The Fleet **Club Colours** Red & white

Founded 1946

Club Contact Details 01474 533 796   info@eufc.co.uk

Previous Names: Gravesend United and Northfleet United merged in 1946 to form Gravesend and Northfleet > 2007

Previous Leagues: Southern 1946-79, 82-97. Alliance (FM) 1979-82. Isthmian 1997-2002.

2019-20 Season
Nat   22 after PPG
FAC   1P
FAT   3P

Record
P 45 W 13 D 13 L 19

Top Goalscorer
Ugwu (15)

	10-11		11-12		12-13		13-14		14-15		15-16		16-17		17-18		18-19	
	Conf S	3	Conf	14	Conf	23	Conf S	4	Conf S	8	Nat S	2	Nat S	2	Nat	6	Nat	8
FAC	1Pr		FAC	4Q		FAC	1P		FAC	4Qr		FAC	3Q		FAC	2Qr		FAC	4Q		FAC	1P		FAC	1Pr
FAT	2P		FAT	3P		FAT	3P		FAT	1P		FAT	3P		FAT	QF		FAT	1P		FAT	2Pr		FAT	1P

LEAGUE HONOURS:
Southern League 1957-58, Division One South 1974-75, Southern Division 1993-94.
Isthmian League Premier 2001-02.

COUNTY FA HONOURS: Kent Senior Cup 1948-49, 52-53, 80-81, 99-00, 00-01, 01-02, 07-08, 13-14

CLUB RECORDS
FA Cup Fourth Round Proper 1962-63
FA Trophy Winners 2007-08
Victory: 8-1 v Clacton Town - Southern League 1962-63
Defeat: 0-9 v Trowbridge Town - Southern League Premier Division 1991-92
Goalscorer: Steve Portway - 152 (1992-94, 97-2001)
Appearances: Ken Burrett - 537
Additional: Paid £8,000 to Wokingham Town for Richard Newbery 1996 and to Tonbridge for Craig Williams 1997
Received £35,000 from West Ham United for Jimmy Bullard 1998

GROUND: Stonebridge Road, Northfleet, Kent DA11 9GN
Ground Capacity: 4,184   **Seats:** 2,300   **Covered:** 3,000   **Clubhouse:** Yes   **Shop:** Yes
Previous Grounds: Gravesend United: Central Avenue
Record Attendance: 12,036 v Sunderland - FA Cup 4th Round 12/02/1963
Nearest Railway Station Northfleet - 300 yards from the ground.
Bus Route 480/490 or FASTRACK 'B' Service

HAMPTON & RICHMOND BOROUGH

Beavers or Borough   **Club Colours** Red & blue

HRBFC

Founded 1921

Club Contact Details 0208 979 2456   secretary@hamptonfc.net

Previous Names: Hampton 1921-99

Previous Leagues: Kingston & District 1921-33. South West Middlesex 1933-59. Surrey Senior 1959-64. Spartan 1964-71. Athenian 1971-73. Isthmian 1973-2007, 12-16. Conference 2007-12.

2019-20 Season
Nat S   8 after PPG
FAC   3Q
FAT   2P

Record
P 39 W 17 D 6 L 16

Top Goalscorer
Orsi-Dadamo (15)

	10-11		11-12		12-13		13-14		14-15		15-16		16-17		17-18		18-19	
	Conf S	18	Conf S	21	Isth P	13	Isth P	12	Isth P	15	Isth P	1	Nat S	7	Nat S	4	Nat S	15
FAC	3Q		FAC	3Q		FAC	3Q		FAC	4Q		FAC	1Q		FAC	1Q		FAC	3Q		FAC	4Q		FAC	1P
FAT	2P		FAT	3P		FAT	1Pr		FAT	3Q		FAT	1Q		FAT	3Q		FAT	3Qr		FAT	1Pr		FAT	3Q

LEAGUE HONOURS:
Surrey Senior 1963-64. Spartan 1964-65, 65-66, 66-67, 69-70. Isthmian Premier Division 2006-07, 2015-16.

COUNTY FA Middlesex Charity Cup 1969-70, 95-96, 97-98, 98-99. Middlesex Super Cup 1999-00, 06-07.
HONOURS: Middlesex Senior Cup 2005-06, 07-08, 11-12, 13-14, 16-17.

CLUB RECORDS
FA Cup First Round Proper 2000-01, 07-08.
FA Trophy Third Round Proper 2011-12.
Victory: 11-1 v Eastbourne United - Isthmian League Division 2 South 1990-91
Defeat: 0-13 v Hounslow Town - Middlesex Senior Cup 1962-63
Goalscorer: Peter Allen - 176 (1964-73)
Appearances: Tim Hollands - 750 (1977-95)
Additional: Paid £3,000 to Chesham United for Matt Flitter June 2000
Received £40,000 from Queens Park Rangers for Leroy Phillips

GROUND: Beveree Stadium, Beaver Close, Station Road, Hampton TW12 2BX
Ground Capacity: 3,500   **Seats:** 644   **Covered:** 800   **Clubhouse:** Yes   **Shop:** Yes
Previous Grounds: Moved to the Beveree Stadium in 1959
Record Attendance: 3,500 v Hayes & Yeading United, Conference South Play-off Final, 2008-09
Nearest Railway Station Hampton - less than half a mile from the ground.
Bus Route 111 & 216

HAVANT AND WATERLOOVILLE
Founded 1998

The Hawks **Club Colours** White & sky blue

Club Contact Details 02392 787 822   generalmanager@havantandwaterloovillefc.co.uk

Previous Names: Havant Town and Waterlooville merged in 1998

Previous Leagues: Southern 1998-2004. Conference/National 2004-16. Isthmian 2016-17.

2019-20 Season
Nat S 2 after PPG
FAC 4Q
FAT 1P
Record
P 40 W 22 D 10 L 8
Top Goalscorer
Ayunga (19)

	10-11	11-12	12-13	13-14	14-15	15-16	16-17	17-18	18-19
	Conf S 9	Conf S 19	Conf S 10	Conf S 6	Conf S 5	Nat S 20	Isth P 1	Nat S 1	Nat 22
FAC	1P	3Q	2Q	2Qr	1P	4Qr	3Q	4Q	4Q
FAT	3Qr	3Qr	2P	SF	2P	3P	3Q	1P	1Pr

LEAGUE HONOURS:
Southern League Southern Division 1998-99. Isthmian League Premier Division 2016-17. National South 2017-18.

COUNTY FA HONOURS: Hampshire Senior Cup 2015-16, 17-18.

CLUB RECORDS
FA Cup Fourth Round Proper 2007-08 (Eventually going out to Liverpool at Anfield 5-2)
FA Trophy Semi-finals 2013-14
Victory: 9-0 v Moneyfields - Hampshire Senior Cup 23/10/2001
Defeat: 0-5 v Worcester City - Southern Premier 20/03/2004
Goalscorer: James Taylor - 138
Appearances: James Taylor - 297
Additional: Paid £5,000 to Bashley for John Wilson
Received £15,000 from Peterborough United for Gary McDonald

GROUND: Westleigh Park, Martin Road, West Leigh, Havant PO9 5TH
Ground Capacity: 5,300 **Seats:** 710 **Covered:** Yes **Clubhouse:** Yes **Shop:** Yes
Previous Grounds: None
Record Attendance: 4,400 v Swansea City - FA Cup 3rd Round 05/01/2008
Nearest Railway Station Havant - within 2 miles of the ground.
Bus Route 20 & 21

HEMEL HEMPSTEAD TOWN
Founded 1885

The Tudors **Club Colours** All red

Club Contact Details 01442 259 777

Previous Names: Apsley End 1885-99. Hemel Hempstead 1899-1955, 72-99. Hemel Hempstead Town 1955-72. Merged with Hemel Hempstead United 1972.

Previous Leagues: West Herts 1885-99. Herts County 1899-1922. Spartan 1922-52. Delphian 1952-63. Athenian 1963-77. Isthmian 1977-2004. Southern 2004-14.

2019-20 Season
Nat S 11 after PPG
FAC 2Q
FAT 1P
Record
P 37 W 13 D 8 L 16
Top Goalscorer
Ashford (12)

	10-11	11-12	12-13	13-14	14-15	15-16	16-17	17-18	18-19
	SthP 15	SthP 19	SthP 4	SthP 1	Conf S 9	Nat S 6	Nat S 12	Nat S 5	Nat S 16
FAC	1Q	2Q	1Q	4Qr	1P	3Qr	4Qr	3Q	4Qr
FAT	1Q	2Q	1Qr	3Q	3P	1P	3Qr	3Qr	3P

LEAGUE HONOURS:
West Herts 1894-95, 97-98, 1904-05. Herts County 1899-1900. Spartan Division One 1933-34. Isthmian League Division Three 1997-98, Division Two 1999-2000. Southern Premier Division 2013-14.

COUNTY FA HONOURS: Herts Senior Cup 1905-06, 07-08, 08-09, 25-26, 2012-13, 14-15. Herts Charity Shield 1925-26, 34-35, 51-52,63-64, 76-77, 83-84. Herts Charity Cup 2004-05, 08-09, 09-10.

CLUB RECORDS
FA Cup First Round Proper 2014-15   **FA Vase** Third Round Proper 1999-00, 00-01
FA Trophy Third Round Proper 2018-19
Victory: 13-0 v RAF Uxbridge (A), Spartan Division One, 1933-34. and v Chipperfield Corinthians (H), St Mary's Cup QF, 2014-15.
Defeat: 1-13 v Luton Town, FA Cup First Qualifying Round, 05/10/1901.
Goalscorer: Dai Price
Appearances: John Wallace - 1012

GROUND: Vauxhall Road, Adeyfield Road, Hemel Hempstead HP2 4HW
Ground Capacity: 3,152 **Seats:** 300 **Covered:** 900 **Clubhouse:** Yes **Shop:** Yes
Previous Grounds: Salmon Meadow 1885-1928. Gees Meadow 1928-29. Crabtree Lane (Wood Lane Ground) 1929-72.
Record Attendance: 3,500 v Tooting & Mitcham - Amateur Cup 1962 (Crabtree Lane)
Nearest Railway Station Hemel Hempstead - Taxi ride away from the ground
Bus Route 320 from Stop 'A' outside the station

HUNGERFORD TOWN

The Crusaders · **Club Colours** White & black

Founded 1886

Club Contact Details 01488 682 939 · nmatthews@rhsystems.co.uk

2019-20 Season
Nat S   22 after PPG
FAC   2Q
FAT   3Q

Record
P 35 W 8 D 4 L 23

Top Goalscorer
Ferdinand (6)

Previous Names: None

Previous Leagues: Hungerford League. Newbury League (FM) 1909-39. Newbury & District. Swindon & District. Hellenic 1958-78, 2003-09. Isthmian 1978-2003. Southern 2009-16.

	10-11	11-12	12-13	13-14	14-15	15-16	16-17	17-18	18-19
	Sthsw 7	Sthsw 5	Sthsw 2	SthP 6	SthP 4	SthP 5	Nat S 6	Nat S 19	Nat S 19
FAC	3Q	2Qr	2Qr	3Q	1Q	1Qr	3Q	3Qr	3Q
FAT	1Qr	P	P	3P	1Qr	2P	3Q	3Q	3Q

LEAGUE HONOURS:
Newbury League 1912-13, 13-14, 19-20, 21-22.
Hellenic Division One 1970-71, Premier Division 2008-09.

COUNTY FA HONOURS: Berks & Bucks Senior Cup 1981-82. Basingstoke Senior Cup 2012-13, 14-15.

CLUB RECORDS
FA Cup First Round Proper 1979-80.   **FA Vase**   Semi-Finals 1977-78, 79-80, 88-89.
FA Trophy Third Round Proper 2014-15.
Goalscorer: Ian Farr - 268
Appearances: Dean Bailey and Tim North - 400+
Additional: Paid £4,000 to Yeovil Town for Joe Scott. Received £3,800 from Barnstaple Town for Joe Scott.
Isthmian representatives in Anglo Italian Cup 1981.

GROUND: Bulpitt Lane, Hungerford RG17 0AY
Ground Capacity: 2,500   **Seats:** 400   **Covered:** 400   **Clubhouse:** Yes   **Shop:** Yes
Previous Grounds: Hungerford Marsh Field.
Record Attendance: 1,684 v Sudbury Town - FA Vase Semi-final 1988-89
Nearest Railway Station Hungerford - Approx. one mile from the ground.
Bus Route Priory Close stop - 120m away

MAIDSTONE UNITED

The Stones · **Club Colours** Amber & black

Founded 1992

Club Contact Details 01622 753 817 · info@maidstoneunited.co.uk

2019-20 Season
Nat S   9 after PPG
FAC   2P
FAT   1P

Record
P 41 W 17 D 10 L 14

Top Goalscorer
Akanbi (11)

Previous Names: Maidstone Invicta > 1997

Previous Leagues: Kent County 1993-2001, Kent 2001-06. Isthmian 2006-15.

	10-11	11-12	12-13	13-14	14-15	15-16	16-17	17-18	18-19
	Isth P 20	Isth1S 6	Isth1S 2	Isth P 7	Isth P 1	Nat S 3	Nat 14	Nat 19	Nat 24
FAC	1Q	2Q	3Q	3Q	2P	1P	1Pr	2P	2P
FAT	3Q	P	2P	3Q	2Q	1P	1P	3Pr	4Pr

LEAGUE HONOURS:
Kent County Division Four 1993-94, Division Two 1994-95, Division One 1998-99, Premier 2001-02.
Kent 2000-02, 05-06. Isthmian Division One South 2006-07, Premier 2014-15.

COUNTY FA HONOURS: Kent Junior Cup 1994-95, Weald of Kent Charity Cup 1999-00, 00-01, Kent Senior Trophy 2002-03. Kent Senior Cup 2017-18, 18-19.

CLUB RECORDS
FA Cup Second Round Proper 2014-15, 18-19, 19-20.   **FA Vase**   Third Round Proper 2005-06(r)
FA Trophy Fourth Round Proper 2018-19(r)
Victory: 12-1 v Aylesford - Kent League 1993-94
Defeat: 2-8 v Scott Sports - 1995-96
Goalscorer: Richard Sinden - 98
Appearances: Tom Mills
Additional: Paid £2,000 for Steve Jones - 2000

GROUND: The Gallagher Stadium, James Whatman Way, Maidstone, Kent ME14 1LQ
Ground Capacity: 4,200   **Seats:** 792   **Covered:** 1,850   **Clubhouse:** Yes   **Shop:** Yes
Previous Grounds: London Rd 1993-01, Central Pk 01-02 & Bourne Pk 02-09 (S'bourne), 11-12, The Homelands (A'ford) 09-11.
Record Attendance: 3,560 v Oldham Athletic, FA Cup 2nd Round, 1 December 2018
Nearest Railway Station Maidstone East & Maidstone Barracks a walk away
Bus Route Nos. 101 or 155 from the Mall Bus Station

OXFORD CITY
The Hoops   **Club Colours** Blue & white   **Founded** 1990

Club Contact Details 01865 744 493

Previous Names: The original club, founded in 1882, folded in 1988 when they were evicted from their White House ground and did not reform until 1990.

Previous Leagues: South Midlands 1990-93. Isthmian 1993-2004. Southern 2004-05, 06-12. Spartan South Midlands 2005-06.

2019-20 Season
Nat S   13 after PPG

FAC   1P
FAT   3Qr

Record
P 40 W 14 D 11 L 15

Top Goalscorer
McEachran & Owusu (10)

	10-11	11-12	12-13	13-14	14-15	15-16	16-17	17-18	18-19
	SthP 14	SthP 2	Conf N 10	Conf N 20	Conf N 6	Nat S 12	Nat S 14	Nat S 16	Nat S 12
FAC	1Q	1Q	1Pr	2Q	4Q	3Q	2Qr	2P	1Pr
FAT	1Q	1Q	1Q	2P	3Q	3P	3Q	3Q	2P

LEAGUE HONOURS:
Spartan South Midlands Premier Division 1992-93, 2005-06.
Isthmian Division One 1995-96.

COUNTY FA HONOURS: Oxford Senior Cup 1996-97, 98-99, 99-00, 02-03, 17-18.

CLUB RECORDS
FA Cup Second Round Proper 2017-18
FA Trophy Third Round Proper 1999-00, 02-03, 15-16
FA Vase Runners-up 1994-95

GROUND: Court Place Farm, Marsh Lane, Marston, Oxford OX3 0NQ
Ground Capacity: 3,500   **Seats:** 520   **Covered:** 400   **Clubhouse:** Yes   **Shop:** Yes
Previous Grounds: Cuttleslowe Park 1990-91, Pressed Steel 1991-93.
Record Attendance: 2,276 v Oxford United, pre-season friendly, 08/07/2017
Nearest Railway Station Oxford - three miles from the ground.
Bus Route 14A from the Station to the ground.

SLOUGH TOWN
The Rebels   **Club Colours** Yellow & blue   **Founded** 1890

Club Contact Details 07792 126 124   gensec@sloughtownfc.net

Previous Names: Slough FC. Slough United.

Previous Leagues: Southern All 1892-93, Berks & Bucks 1901-05, Gt Western Suburban 09-19, Spartan 20-39, Herts & Middx 40-45, Corinthian 46-63, Athenian 63-73, Isthmian 73-90, 94-95, 98-2007, Conf 90-94, 95-98, Southern 2007-2018.

2019-20 Season
Nat S   5 after PPG

FAC   3Qr
FAT   3Qr

Record
P 41 W 18 D 11 L 12

Top Goalscorer
B Harris & Roberts(12)

	10-11	11-12	12-13	13-14	14-15	15-16	16-17	17-18	18-19
	SthC 5	SthC 2	SthC 6	SthC 5	SthP 16	SthP 17	SthP 5	SthP 3	Nat S 11
FAC	1Q	3Qr	1Pr	Pr	1Q	2Q	3Q	2P	2P
FAT	1Qr	P	1Qr	1Q	1Q	2Qr	2Q	3Qr	3Q

LEAGUE HONOURS:
Isthmian League 1980-81, 89-90. Athenian League x3.

COUNTY FA HONOURS: Berks & Bucks Senior Cup 1902-03, 19-20, 23-24, 26-27, 35-36, 54-55, 70-71, 71-72, 76-77, 80-81, 2018-19

CLUB RECORDS
FA Cup Second Round Proper 1970-71, 79-80, 82-83, 85-86(r), 86-87, 2004-05, 17-18, 18-19.
FA Trophy Semi-finals 1976-77, 97-98   **FA Am Cup** Runners-up 1972-73
Victory: 17-0 v Railway Clearing House - 1921-22
Defeat: 1-11 v Chesham Town - 1909-10
Goalscorer: Ted Norris - 343 in 226 appearances. Scored 84 during the 1925-26 season.
Appearances: Terry Reardon - 475 (1964-81)
Additional: Paid £18,000 to Farnborough Town for Colin Fielder
Received £22,000 from Wycombe Wanderers for Steve Thompson

GROUND: Arbour Park, Stoke Road, Slough SL2 5AY
Ground Capacity: 2,000   **Seats:** 250   **Covered:** Yes   **Clubhouse:** Yes   **Shop:** Yes
Previous Grounds: Dolphin Stad 1890-1936. Wrexham Park >2003. Stag Meadow W & Eton 03-07. Holloways Park B'field SYCOB 07-16.
Record Attendance: 1,401 v Hayes & Yeading United, Southern Premier, 29/08/2016
Nearest Railway Station Slough
Bus Route First Group 1, 13, 12, 14, 353.

ST ALBANS CITY
The Saints **Club Colours** Yellow & blue **Founded** 1908

Club Contact Details 01727 848 914

Previous Names: None

Previous Leagues: Herts County 1908-10. Spartan 1908-20. Athenian 1920-23. Isthmian 1923-2004. Conference 2004-11. Southern 2011-14.

2019-20 Season
Nat S   20 after PPG
FAC   3Q
FAT   3Q

Record
P 39 W 10 D 11 L 18

Top Goalscorer
Iaciofano (17)

	10-11	11-12	12-13	13-14	14-15	15-16	16-17	17-18	18-19
	Conf S 22	SthP 8	SthP 11	SthP 4	Conf S 13	Nat S 18	Nat S 10	Nat S 8	Nat S 9
	FAC 4Q	FAC 2Qr	FAC 3Q	FAC 1P	FAC 4Q	FAC 1P	FAC 1P	FAC 4Q	FAC 3Q
	FAT 1P	FAT 1Q	FAT 1Q	FAT 2P	FAT 3Qr	FAT 3Q	FAT 3Qr	FAT 2Pr	FAT 3Qr

LEAGUE HONOURS:
Herts County Western Division 1909-09, Western & Championship 09-10.
Spartan B Division 1909-10, Spartan 11-12. Athenian League 1920-21, 21-22.
Isthmian League 1923-24, 26-27, 27-28, Division One 1985-86.

COUNTY FA
HONOURS: London Senior Cup 1970-71.

CLUB RECORDS
FA Cup Second Round Proper 1968-69 (r), 80-81 (r), 96-97.
FA Trophy Semi-final 1998-99.
Victory: 14-0 v Aylesbury United (H) - Spartan League 19/10/1912
Defeat: 0-11 v Wimbledon (H) - Isthmian League 1946
Goalscorer: Wilfred Minter - 356 in 362 apps. (Top scorer for 12 consecutive seasons from 1920-32)
Appearances: Phil Wood - 900 (1962-85)
Additional: Wilfred Minter scored seven goals in an 8-7 defeat by Dulwich Hamlet, the highest tally by a player on the losing side of an FAC tie. Paid £6,000 to Yeovil Town for Paul Turner 1957. Received £92,759 from Southend United for Dean Austin 1990.

GROUND: Clarence Park, York Road, St. Albans, Herts AL1 4PL
Ground Capacity: 5,007 **Seats:** 667 **Covered:** 1,900 **Clubhouse:** Yes **Shop:** Yes
Previous Grounds: N/A
Record Attendance: 9,757 v Ferryhill Athletic - FA Amateur Cup 1926
Nearest Railway Station St. Albans City - 5-10 minute walk from the ground.
Bus Route 302, 321, 602 & 84

TONBRIDGE ANGELS
Angels **Club Colours** Blue and white **Founded** 1947

Club Contact Details 01732 352 417   charlie.cole@tonbridgeangels.co.uk

Previous Names: Tonbridge FC 1947-94.

Previous Leagues: Southern 1948-80, 93-2004, Kent 1989-93, Isthmian 2004-11, 14-19, Conference 2011-14.

2019-20 Season
Nat S   15 after PPG
FAC   2Q
FAT   1Pr

Record
P 35 W 10 D 10 L 15

Top Goalscorer
Turner (12)

	10-11	11-12	12-13	13-14	14-15	15-16	16-17	17-18	18-19
	Isth P 2	Conf S 9	Conf S 16	Conf S 21	Isth P 20	Isth P 4	Isth P 6	Isth P 11	Isth P 4
	FAC 1Q	FAC 2Q	FAC 2Q	FAC 3Q	FAC 2Q	FAC 2Q	FAC 4Q	FAC 1Q	FAC 2Q
	FAT 3Q	FAT 3Qr	FAT 2P	FAT 1Pr	FAT 3Qr	FAT 2Q	FAT 2Qr	FAT 1Qr	FAT 2Q

LEAGUE HONOURS:
Kent 1992-93.

COUNTY FA
HONOURS: Kent Senior Cup 1964-65, 74-75. Kent Senior Shield 1951-52, 55-56, 57-58, 58-59, 63-64.

CLUB RECORDS
FA Cup First Round Proper 1967-68, 72-73.   **FA Vase** Third Round Proper 1993-94.
FA Trophy Third Round Proper 2004-05(r).
Victory: 11-1 v Worthing - FA Cup 1951
Defeat: 2-11 v Folkstone - Kent Senior Cup 1949
Goalscorer: Jon Main scored 44 goals in one season including seven hat-tricks
Appearances: Mark Giham

GROUND: Longmead Stadium, Darenth Avenue, Tonbridge, Kent TN10 3JF
Ground Capacity: 3,000 **Seats:** 760+ **Covered:** 1,500 **Clubhouse:** Yes **Shop:** Yes
Previous Grounds: The Angel 1948-80
Record Attendance: 8,236 v Aldershot - FA Cup 1951 at The Angel.
Nearest Railway Station Tonbridge - 3.1km
Bus Route Heather Walk - stop 250m away

WELLING UNITED

The Wings   **Club Colours** Red & white

Founded 1963

Club Contact Details 0208 301 1196   info@wellingunited.com

Previous Names: None

Previous Leagues: Eltham & District Sunday 1963-71, Metropolitan 1971-75, London Spartan 1975-78, Athenian 1978-81, Southern 1981-86, 2000-04, Conference 1986-2000

2019-20 Season
Nat S   12 after PPG

FAC   4Qr

FAT   1P

Record
P 40 W 15 D 7 L 18

Top Goalscorer
Cook (11)

10-11		11-12		12-13		13-14		14-15		15-16		16-17		17-18		18-19	
Conf S	6	Conf S	3	Conf S	1	Conf	16	Conf	20	Nat	24	Nat S	16	Nat S	10	Nat S	3
FAC	2Q	FAC	2Q	FAC	4Q	FAC	2P	FAC	4Q	FAC	2P	FAC	4Q	FAC	2Q	FAC	4Q
FAT	1Pr	FAT	1P	FAT	3P	FAT	1P	FAT	1Pr	FAT	2P	FAT	2P	FAT	3P	FAT	3Qr

LEAGUE HONOURS:
Southern League Premier Division 1985-86. Conference South 2012-13.

COUNTY FA Kent Senior Cup 1985-86, 98-99, 2008-09.
HONOURS: London Senior Cup 1989-90. London Challenge Cup 1991-92.

CLUB RECORDS

FA Cup Third Round Proper 1988-89.   **FA Vase** Third Round Proper 1979-80.
FA Trophy Quarter-finals 1988-89, 2006-07.
Victory: 7-1 v Dorking - 1985-86
Defeat: 0-7 v Welwyn Garden City - 1972-73
Additional: Paid £30,000 to Enfield for Gary Abbott
Received £95,000 from Birmingham City for Steve Finnan 1995

GROUND: Park View Road Ground, Welling, Kent DA16 1SY
Ground Capacity: 4,000   **Seats:** 1,070   **Covered:** 1,500   **Clubhouse:** Yes   **Shop:** Yes
Previous Grounds: Butterfly Lane, Eltham 1963-77.
Record Attendance: 4,100 v Gillingham - FA Cup First Round Proper, 22nd November 1989
Nearest Railway Station Welling - 15-20 minute walk from the ground.
Bus Route Numbers 89, 486 and B16.

BISHOP'S STORTFORD

Nickname: Blues or Bishops **Club Colours:** Blue and white

Founded 1874

Club Contact Details
01279 306 456

Previous Names: None
Previous Leagues: East Herts 1896-97, 1902-06, 19-21, Stansted & Dist. 1906-19, Herts Co. 1921-25, 26-29, Herts & Essex Border 1925-26, Spartan 1929-51, Delphian (FM) 1951-63, Athenian 1963-71, Isthmian 1971-2004, Conference 2004-17, Southern 2017-18.

	10-11	11-12	12-13	13-14	14-15	15-16	16-17	17-18	18-19	19-20
	Conf S 16	Conf N 10	Conf N 17	Conf S 15	Conf S 16	Nat S 11	Nat S 21	SthP 18	Isth P 7	Isth P n&v
FAC	2Qr	4Q	1P	1P	2Qr	2Q	3Q	1Q	1Q	2Q
FAT	3Q	1P	1P	3Q	1P	3Q	3Q	2Q	2Q	1Qr

HONOURS / RECORDS

FA Comps: FA Amateur Cup 1973-74. FA Trophy 1980-81.
League: Stansted & District 1910-11, 12-13, 19-20. Spartan Division Two East 1931-32. Delphian 1954-55.
Athenian Division One 1965-66, Premier 69-70. Isthmian Division One 1980-81, 93-94.
County FA: Herts Senior Cup 1932-33, 58-59, 59-60, 63-64, 70-71, 72-73, 73-74, 75-76, 86-87, 2005-06, 09-10, 11-12.
London Senior Cup 1973-74.
Victory: 11-0 v Nettleswell & Buntwill - Herts Junior Cup 1911
Defeat: 0-13 v Cheshunt (H) - Herts Senior Cup 1926
Goalscorer: Post 1929 Jimmy Badcock - 123
Appearances: Phil Hopkins - 543

GROUND: ProKit Uk Stadium, Woodside Park, Dunmow Road, Bishop's Stortford CM23 5RG

Ground Capacity: 4,000 **Seats:** 525 **Covered:** 700 **Clubhouse:** Yes **Shop:** Yes
Previous Grounds: Silver Leys 1874-97. Hadham Rd 97-1900. Havers Lane 00-03. Laundry Field 03-19. Brazier's Field 1919-97.Shared>99
Record Attendance: 6,000 v Peterborough Utd - FAC 2nd Rnd 1972-73 and v Middlesbrough - FA Cup 3rd Rnd replay 1982-83

Nearest Railway Station Bishop's Stortford - 20 minute walk from ground.
Bus Route 508, 7 & 7A

BOGNOR REGIS TOWN

Nickname: The Rocks **Club Colours:** White & green

Founded 1883

Club Contact Details
01243 822 325

Previous Names: None
Previous Leagues: West Sussex 1896-1926, Brighton & Hove District 1926-27, Sussex County 1927-72, Southern League 1972-81, Isthmian 1982-2004, 2009-17, Conference 2004-09, 17-18.

	10-11	11-12	12-13	13-14	14-15	15-16	16-17	17-18	18-19	19-20
	Isth1S 2	Isth1S 2	Isth P 14	Isth P 3	Isth P 14	Isth P 2	Isth P 2	Nat S 22	Isth P 14	Isth P n&v
FAC	2Q	3Q	2Q	2Qr	1Qr	4Q	2Q	4Q	2Qr	2Q
FAT	3Qr	P	3Q	3Q	1Qr	SF	1Q	2P	2Qr	3Q

HONOURS / RECORDS

FA Comps: None
League: West Sussex 1920-21, 21-22, 22-23, 23-24, 24-25.
Sussex County Division One 1948-49 71-72, Division Two 70-71.
County FA: Sussex Professional Cup 1973-74.
Sussex Senior Cup 1954-55, 55-56, 79-80, 80-81, 81-82, 82083, 83084, 86-87, 2018-19.
Victory: 24-0 v Littlehampton - West Sussex League 1913-14
Defeat: 0-19 v Shoreham - West Sussex League 1906-07
Goalscorer: Kevin Clements - 216 (1978-89). On 16/12/14 Jason Prior scored his 100th goal for the club making it the fastest century of goals
Appearances: Mick Pullen - 967 (20 seasons)

GROUND: Nyewood Lane, Bognor Regis PO21 2TY

Ground Capacity: 4,100 **Seats:** 350 **Covered:** 2,600 **Clubhouse:** Yes **Shop:** Yes
Previous Grounds: None
Record Attendance: 3,642 v Swnsea City - FA Cup 1st Round replay 1984

Nearest Railway Station Bognor is within walking distance to the ground.
Bus Route 600 & 700

BOWERS & PITSEA

Founded 1946

Nickname: **Club Colours:** Red & white

Club Contact Details
01268 452 068

Previous Names: Bowers United > 2004.
Previous Leagues: Thurrock & Thameside Combination. Olympian. Essex Senior >2016.

	10-11	11-12	12-13	13-14	14-15	15-16	16-17	17-18	18-19	19-20
	ESen 14	ESen 15	ESen 19	ESen 14	ESen 2	ESen 1	Isth1N 6	Isth1N 3	IsthN 1	Isth P n&v
	FAC P	FAC EP	FAC EP	FAC EP	FAC 1Q	FAC EP	FAC Pr	FAC P	FAC 2Q	FAC 4Q
	FAV 2Q	FAV 2Q	FAV 1Q	FAV 1P	FAV 1P	FAV SF	FAT 1Q	FAT 1Qr	FAT EP	FAT 1Q

HONOURS / RECORDS
FA Comps: None
League: Thurrock & Thameside Combination 1958-59. Essex Senior 1980-81, 98-99, 2015-16.
     Isthmian North Division 2018-19.
County FA: None

Victory: 14-1 v Stansted, 2006-07
Defeat: 0-8 v Ford United, 1996-97
Goalscorer: David Hope scored 50 during the 1998-99 season.

GROUND: Len Salmon Stadium, Crown Avenue, Pitsea, Basildon SS13 2BE
Ground Capacity: 2,000   **Seats:** 200   **Covered:** 1,000   **Clubhouse:** Yes   **Shop:** Yes
Previous Grounds: Pitsea Market. Gun Meadow.
Record Attendance: 1,800 v Billericay Town, FA Vase.

Nearest Railway Station Pitsea - 1.7km
Bus Route Wilsner - stop 200m award

BRIGHTLINGSEA REGENT

Founded 1928

Nickname: The Rs   **Club Colours:** Red & black

Club Contact Details
01206 304 119

Previous Names: Brightlingsea Athletic & Brightlingsea Town merged to form Brightlingsea United 1928-2005. Merged with Regent Park Rangers.
Previous Leagues: Essex Senior 1972-91. Eastern Counties 1990-02, 2011-14. Essex & Suffolk Border 2002-2011.

	10-11	11-12	12-13	13-14	14-15	15-16	16-17	17-18	18-19	19-20
	EsSuP 1	EC1 5	EC1 3	ECP 2	Isth1N 6	Isth1N 8	Isth1N 1	Isth P 20	Isth P 13	Isth P n&v
				FAC EPr	FAC 1Q	FAC Pr	FAC 1Q	FAC 1Q	FAC 3Q	FAC 1Q
		FAV 1Q	FAV 3P	FAV 5P	FAT 1Q	FAT Pr	FAT 2Qr	FAT 1Q	FAT 3Qr	FAT 1Q

HONOURS / RECORDS
FA Comps: None
League: Essex & Suffolk Border Division One 1946-47, 60-61, Division Two 2005-06, Premier 10-11. Essex Senior 1988-89, 89-90.
     Isthmian Division One North 2016-17.
County FA: None

Best FA Cup   Third Qualifying Round 2018-19.
FA Trophy   Third Qualifying Round 2018-19(r).
FA Vase   Fifth Round Proper 2013-14.

GROUND: Tydal Stadium, North Road, Brightlingsea, Essex CO7 0PL
Ground Capacity: 2,500   **Seats:** 254   **Covered:** 1864   **Clubhouse:** Yes   **Shop:**
Previous Grounds: Bell Green (Bellfield Close). Recreation Ground (Regent Road) > 1920.
Record Attendance: 1,200 v Colchester United, friendly, 1988.

Nearest Railway Station Alresford - 4.8km
Bus Route Spring Chase - stop 300m away

CARSHALTON ATHLETIC

Founded 1905

Nickname: Robins   **Club Colours:** All red

Club Contact Details
020 8642 2551   secretary@carshaltonathletic.co.uk

Previous Names: Mill Lane Mission 1905-07.
Previous Leagues: Croydon & District 1905-10. Southern Suburban 1910-22. Surrey Senior (Founding Members) 1922-23. London 1923-46. Corinthian 1946-56. Athenian 1956-73. Isthmian 1973-2004. Conference 2004-06.

10-11		11-12		12-13		13-14		14-15		15-16		16-17		17-18		18-19		19-20	
Isth P	13	Isth P	16	Isth P	20	Isth P	23	Isth1S	20	Isth1S	10	Isth1S	6	Isth1S	1	Isth P	2	Isth P	n&v
FAC	4Qr	FAC	2Q	FAC	2Q	FAC	1Q	FAC	1Q	FAC	2Q	FAC	1Qr	FAC	2Q	FAC	P	FAC	4Q
FAT	2Q	FAT	3P	FAT	2Q	FAT	3Q	FAT	P	FAT	P	FAT	Pr	FAT	P	FAT	3Pr	FAT	1Pr

HONORS / RECORDS
FA Comps: None
League: Corinthian 1952-53, 53-54. Isthmian Division One South 2002-03, 17-18.

County FA: Surrey Intermediate Cup 1921-22, 31-32. Surrey Senior Shield 1975-76. Surrey Senior Cup 1988-89, 89-90, 91-92. London Challenge Cup 1991-92.
Victory: 13-0 v Worthing - Isthmian League Cup 28/01/1991
Defeat: 0-11 v Southall - Athenian League March 1963
Goalscorer: Jimmy Bolton - 242 during seven seasons
Appearances: Jon Warden - 504
Additional: Paid £15,000 to Enfield for Curtis Warmington. Received £30,000 from Crystal Palace for Ian Cox 1994

GROUND: War Memorial Sports Ground, Colston Avenue, Carshalton SM5 2PN

Ground Capacity: 8,000   **Seats:** 240   **Covered:** 4,500   **Clubhouse:** Yes   **Shop:** Yes
Previous Grounds: Various before moving to Colston Avenue during the 1920-21 season.
Record Attendance: 7,800 v Wimbledon - London Senior Cup, Jan 1959.

Nearest Railway Station Carshalton - 0.3km
Bus Route 127, 157 & S1

CHESHUNT

Founded 1946

Nickname: Ambers   **Club Colours:** Amber & black

Club Contact Details
01992 625 793   info@cheshuntfc.com

Previous Names: None
Previous Leagues: London 1946-51, 55-59, Delphian 1951-55, Aetolian 1959-62, Spartan 1962-64, 88-93, Athenian 1964-77, Isthmian 1977-87, 94-2005, Southern 2006-08.

10-11		11-12		12-13		13-14		14-15		15-16		16-17		17-18		18-19		19-20	
Isth1N	18	Isth1N	18	Isth1N	11	Isth1N	15	Isth1N	18	Isth1N	6	Isth1N	10	Isth1N	19	IsthSC	3	Isth P	n&v
FAC	1Q	FAC	Pr	FAC	Pr	FAC	P	FAC	P	FAC	P	FAC	1Q	FAC	2Q	FAC	1Qr	FAC	2Q
FAT	P	FAT	P	FAT	P	FAT	1Q	FAT	P	FAT	2Q	FAT	1Q	FAT	1Q	FAT	EPr	FAT	1Q

HONORS / RECORDS
FA Comps: None
League: London Division One 1947-48, 48-49, Premier 49-50, Division One 1948, 49. Spartan 1962-63. Athenian 1967-68, 75-76. Isthmian Division Two 2002-03.
County FA: London Charity Cup 1974. East Anglian Cup 1975. Herts Charity Cup 2006, 2008.

Defeat: 0-10 v Eton Manor - London League 17/04/1956
Goalscorer: Darrell Cox - 152 (1997-2005, 07-08, 2010)
Appearances: John Poole - 526 (1970-76, 79-83)
Additional: Received £10,000 from Peterborough United for Lloyd Opara

---

GROUND: Cheshunt Stadium, Theobalds Lane, Cheshunt, Herts EN8 8RU

Ground Capacity: 3,500   **Seats:** 424   **Covered:** 600   **Clubhouse:** Yes   **Shop:** No
Previous Grounds: Gothic Sports Ground 1946-47. College Road 1947-50. Brookfield Lane 1950-52, 53-58.
Record Attendance: 5,000 v Bromley - FA Amateur Cup 2nd Round 28/01/1950

Nearest Railway Station Theobalds Grove - 0.6km
Bus Route 217, 242, 279, 310 & 66

CORINTHIAN-CASUALS

Founded 1939

Nickname: Casuals   **Club Colours:** Chocolate and pink

Club Contact Details
020 8397 3368   secretary@ccfcltd.co.uk

Previous Names: Casuals and Corinthians merged in 1939
Previous Leagues: Isthmian 1939-84, Spartan 1984-96, Combined Counties 1996-97

	10-11		11-12		12-13		13-14		14-15		15-16		16-17		17-18		18-19		19-20	
Isth1S	20	Isth1S	13	Isth1S	14	Isth1S	17	Isth1S	13	Isth1S	6	Isth1S	4	Isth1S	5	Isth P	17	Isth P	n&v	
FAC	1Q	FAC	P	FAC	P	FAC	1Q	FAC	P	FAC	P	FAC	1Q	FAC	1Q	FAC	2Qr	FAC	3Q	
FAT	P	FAT	P	FAT	P	FAT	P	FAT	Pr	FAT	1P	FAT	1Q	FAT	2Q	FAT	1Q	FAT	1Q	

HONOURS / RECORDS

FA Comps: None

League: London Spartan Senior Division 1985-86.

County FA: Surrey Senior Cup 1953-54, 2010-11.

Goalscorer:	Cliff West - 215
Appearances:	Simon Shergold - 526
Best FA Cup	First Round Proper 1965-66, 83-84.
FA Amateur C	Runners-up 1955-56. **FA Trophy:** Second Round Proper 2002-03.
FA Vase	First Round Proper 1983-84.

GROUND: King George's Field, Queen Mary Close, Hook Rise South, KT6 7NA

Ground Capacity: 2,000   **Seats:** 161   **Covered:** 700   **Clubhouse:** Yes   **Shop:** Yes
Previous Grounds: Kingstonian's Richmond Road 1939-46. Polytechnic Ground in Chiswick 46-50. Oval 50-63. Dulwich Hamlet's Champion Hill 63-68,
Record Attendance: Tooting & Mitcham United's Sandy Lane 68-83, Molesey's Walton Road 83-84, 86-88. Wimbledon Park Athletics Stadium 84-86.

Nearest Railway Station Tolworth - 10-15 min walk
Bus Route K1 from new Malden, 265 from Putney, K2 from Hook or Kingston Hospital, 406 & 408 from Kingston and Epsom, 418 from Kingston

CRAY WANDERERS

Founded 1860

Nickname: Wanderers or Wands   **Club Colours:** Amber & black

Club Contact Details
020 8460 5291

Previous Names: Cray Old Boys (immediately after WW1); Sidcup & Footscray (start of WW2).
Previous Leagues: Kent 1894-1903, 06-07, 09-14, 34-38, 78-2004; West Kent & Sth Suburban (before WW1); London 20-34, 51-59; Kent Am 38-39, 46-51; South London All 43-46; Aetolian 59-64; Gr London 64-66; Metropolitan 66-71; Met. London 71-15; London Spartan 75-78.

	10-11		11-12		12-13		13-14		14-15		15-16		16-17		17-18		18-19		19-20	
Isth P	9	Isth P	9	Isth P	17	Isth P	24	Isth1N	16	Isth1N	4	Isth1S	11	Isth1S	3	IsthSE	1	Isth P	n&v	
FAC	2Qr	FAC	3Q	FAC	3Q	FAC	1Q	FAC	1Q	FAC	1Q	FAC	1Q	FAC	P	FAC	1Q	FAC	3Q	
FAT	2Q	FAT	1Q	FAT	3Q	FAT	1Q	FAC	3Q	FAT	P	FAT	2Q	FAT	3Q	FAT	P	FAT	1Q	

HONOURS / RECORDS

FA Comps: None

League: Kent 1901-02, 80-81, 2002-03, 03-04. London 1956-57, 57-58. Aetolian 1962-63. Greater London 1965-66. Metropolitan London 1974-75; London Spartan 1976-77, 77-78. Isthmian South East Division 2018-19.
County FA: Kent Amateur Cup 1930-31, 62-63, 63-64, 64-65. Kent Senior Trophy 1992-93, 2003-04.

Victory:	15-0 v Sevenoaks - 1894-95.
Defeat:	2-15 (H) and 0-14 (A) v Callenders Athletic - Kent Amateur League, 1947-48.
Goalscorer:	Ken Collishaw 274 (1954-1965)
Appearances	John Dorey - 454 (1961-72).
Additional:	Unbeaten for 28 Ryman League games in 2007-2008.

GROUND: Bromley FC, Hayes Lane, Bromley, Kent BR2 9EF

Ground Capacity: 5,000   **Seats:** 1,300   **Covered:** 2,500   **Clubhouse:** Yes   **Shop:** Yes
Previous Grounds: Northfield Farm (1950-51), Tothills (aka Fordcroft, 1951-1955), Grassmeade (1955-1973), Oxford Road (1973-1998).
Record Attendance: Grassmeade - 2,160 v Leytonstone, FAAm.R3, 1968-69; Oxford Road - 1,523 v Stamford, FAV QF 1979-80; Hayes Lane - 1,082 v AFC Wimbledon, 2004-05
Nearest Railway Station Bromley South - 1km
Bus Route Hayes Road - stop 160m away

EAST THURROCK UNITED

Founded 1969

Nickname: The Rocks   **Club Colours:** Amber & black

Club Contact Details
01375 644 166   secretary.eastthurrockunited@gmail.com

Previous Names: Corringham Social > 1969 (Sunday side)
Previous Leagues: South Essex Comb 1969-70. Greater London 1970-72. Metropolitan London 1972-75. London Spartan 1975-79. Essex Senior 1979-92. Isthmian 1992-2004, 05-16. Southern 2004-05. National 16-19.

10-11		11-12		12-13		13-14		14-15		15-16		16-17		17-18		18-19		19-20	
Isth1N	1	Isth P	10	Isth P	5	Isth P	20	Isth P	13	Isth P	3	Nat S	13	Nat S	15	Nat S	21	Isth P	n&v
FAC	2Qr	FAC	1P	FAC	4Qr	FAC	1Qr	FAC	1P	FAC	3Q	FAC	2Q	FAC	4Qr	FAC	2Q	FAC	1Qr
FAT	P	FAT	2Pr	FAT	2Qr	FAT	1Pr	FAT	3Q	FAT	1P	FAT	2P	FAT	3Pr	FAT	3Q	FAT	2Q

HONOURS / RECORDS

FA Comps: None

League: Metropolitan London Division Two 1972-73.
Isthmian League Division Three 1999-2000, Division One North 2010-11.
County FA: East Anglian Cup 2002-03.

Victory:	7-0 v Coggeshall (H) - Essex Senior League 1984
Defeat:	0-9 v Eton Manor (A) - Essex Senior League 1982
Goalscorer:	Graham Stewart - 102
Appearances:	Glen Case - 600+
Additional:	£22,000 from Leyton Orient for Greg Berry 1990

GROUND: Rookery Hill, Corringham, Essex SS17 9LB

Ground Capacity: 3,500 **Seats:** 160 **Covered:** 1,000 **Clubhouse:** Yes **Shop:** Yes
Previous Grounds: Billet, Stanford-le-Hope 1970-73, 74-76, Grays Ath 73-74, TilburyFC 77-82, New Thames Club 82-84.
Record Attendance: 1,661 vs Dulwich Hamlet, Isthmian League Premier Division Play-off final, 2016

Nearest Railway Station Stanford-le-Hope or Basildon.
Bus Route 100 - Stops 100 metres from the ground.

ENFIELD TOWN

Founded 2001

Nickname: ET's or Towners   **Club Colours:** White & blue

Club Contact Details
07787 875 650

Previous Names: Broke away from Enfield F.C. in 2001
Previous Leagues: Essex Senior 2001-2005. Southern 2005-2006.

10-11		11-12		12-13		13-14		14-15		15-16		16-17		17-18		18-19		19-20	
Isth1N	6	Isth1N	2	Isth P	16	Isth P	19	Isth P	7	Isth P	6	Isth P	4	Isth P	17	Isth P	10	Isth P	n&v
FAC	3Q	FAC	P	FAC	2Q	FAC	2Qr	FAC	2Qr	FAC	4Q	FAC	1Q	FAC	4Qr	FAC	1Q	FAC	3Q
FAT	2Q	FAT	1Q	FAT	3Q	FAT	2Q	FAT	1Q	FAT	2Q	FAV	2Q	FAT	1Q	FAT	2Q	FAT	1P

HONOURS / RECORDS

FA Comps: None

League: Essex Senior 2002-03, 04-05.

County FA: Middlesex Charity Cup 2001-02, 07-08.

Victory:	7-0 v Ilford (A) - 29/04/2003
Goalscorer:	Liam Hope - 108 (2009-15)
Appearances:	Rudi Hall

GROUND: Queen Elizabeth Stadium, Donkey Lane, Enfield EN1 3PL

Ground Capacity: 2,500 **Seats:** Yes **Covered:** Yes **Clubhouse:** Yes **Shop:** No
Previous Grounds: Brimsdown Rovers FC 2001-2010
Record Attendance: 969 v Tottenham Hotspur, friendly, November 2011.

Nearest Railway Station Southbury - 1.2km
Bus Route 191 towards Brimsdown from Enfield stops outside the ground.

FOLKESTONE INVICTA

Nickname: The Seasiders   **Club Colours:** Yellow & black

Founded 1936

Club Contact Details
01303 257 461

Previous Names: None
Previous Leagues: East Kent Amateur. Kent County Eastern Section. Kent 1990-98, Southern 1998-2004

10-11		11-12		12-13		13-14		14-15		15-16		16-17		17-18		18-19		19-20	
Isth P	22	Isth1S	4	Isth1S	5	Isth1S	2	Isth1S	2	Isth1S	1	Isth P	16	Isth P	4	Isth P	6	Isth P	n&v
FAC	2Qr	FAC	1Q	FAC	1Q	FAC	2Q	FAC	1Qr	FAC	1Qr	FAC	3Q	FAC	4Q	FAC	1Q	FAC	2Q
FAT	3Q	FAT	3Q	FAT	Pr	FAT	2Qr	FAT	2Qr	FAT	Pr	FAT	2Q	FAT	1Qr	FAT	3Q	FAT	1Q

HONOURS / RECORDS
FA Comps: None

League: Kent County Eastern Division One 1969-70, Premier 78-79. Kent Division Two 1991-92.
  Isthmian Division One South 2015-16.
County FA: Kent Intermediate Shield 1991-92.

Victory: 13-0 v Faversham Town - Kent League Division One, May 1995.
Defeat: 1-7 v Crockenhill - Kent League Division One, February 1993 & v Welling United, Kent Senior Cup, February 2009.
Goalscorer: James Dryden - 141
Appearances: Michael Everitt - 631

GROUND: The BuildKent Stadium, Cheriton Road CT19 5JU

Ground Capacity: 4,000   **Seats:** 900   **Covered:** Yes   **Clubhouse:** Yes   **Shop:** Yes
Previous Grounds: South Road Hythe > 1991, County League matches on council pitches
Record Attendance: 2,332 v West Ham United, benefit match, 1996-97.

Nearest Railway Station Folkestone West - 0.4km
Bus Route 71, 72, 73 & 17 from the Town Centre

HARINGEY BOROUGH

Nickname: Borough   **Club Colours:** Yellow & blue

Founded 1973

Club Contact Details
0208 888 9933

Previous Names: Edmonton & Haringey 1973-76. Haringey Borough 1976-95. Tufnell Park 1995-96.
Previous Leagues: Athenian 1973-84. Isthmian 1984-89. Spartan South Midlands 1989-2013. Essex Senior 2013-15.

10-11		11-12		12-13		13-14		14-15		15-16		16-17		17-18		18-19		19-20	
SSM P	8	SSM P	5	SSM P	9	ESen	2	ESen	1	Isth1N	15	Isth1N	5	Isth1N	4	Isth P	3	Isth P	n&v
FAC	P	FAC	P	FAC	EP	FAC	2Q	FAC	EP	FAC	1Q	FAC	1Q	FAC	4Q	FAC	4Q	FAC	4Q
FAV	1P	FAV	3P	FAV	2Q	FAV	3P	FAV	1Pr	FAT	2Qr	FAT	P	FAT	1P	FAT	1Qr	FAT	3Q

HONOURS / RECORDS
FA Comps: None

League: Essex Senior 2014-15.

County FA: London Senior Cup 1990-91

Best FA Cup   First Round Proper 2018-19.
FA Trophy   First Round Proper 2017-18.
FA Vase   Quarter Finals 1977-78.

GROUND: Coles Park, White Hart Lane, Tottenham, London N17 7JP

Ground Capacity: 2,500   **Seats:** 280   **Covered:** yes   **Clubhouse:** Yes   **Shop:** No
Previous Grounds: None
Record Attendance: 2,710 v AFC Wimbledon, FA Cup First Round Proper, 09/11/2018.

Nearest Railway Station White Hart Lane - 1.5km. Wood Green (UG) - 1.5km
Bus Route W3 stops outside the ground.

HORNCHURCH

Founded 2005

Nickname: The Urchins   **Club Colours:** Red and white

Club Contact Details
01708 220 080

Previous Names: Formed in 2005 after Hornchurch F.C. folded. AFC Hornchurch 2005-18.
Previous Leagues: Essex Senior 2005-06. Isthmian 2006-12. Conference 2012-13.

10-11		11-12		12-13		13-14		14-15		15-16		16-17		17-18		18-19		19-20	
Isth P	10	Isth P	2	Conf S	20	Isth P	5	Isth P	23	Isth1N	5	Isth1N	4	Isth1N	1	Isth P	15	Isth P	n&v
FAC	2Qr	FAC	1Q	FAC	2Q	FAC	4Q	FAC	1Qr	FAC	4Q	FAC	1Q	FAC	3Q	FAC	3Q	FAC	2Q
FAT	1P	FAT	2P	FAT	3Q	FAT	1Q	FAT	3Q	FAT	1Q	FAT	P	FAT	Pr	FAT	2Q	FAT	2P

HONOURS / RECORDS

FA Comps: None

League: Essex Senior 2005-06. Isthmian League Division One North 2006-07, 17-18.

County FA: Essex Senior Cup 2012-13.

Misc: Won the Essex League with a record 64 points in 2005-06
Best FA Cup First Round Proper 2008-09
FA Trophy Second Round Proper 2011-12
FA Vase Second Round Proper 2005-06

GROUND: The Stadium, Bridge Avenue, Upminster, Essex RM14 2LX

Ground Capacity: 3,500 **Seats:** 800 **Covered:** 1,400 **Clubhouse:** Yes **Shop:** Yes
Previous Grounds: None
Record Attendance: Not known

Nearest Railway Station Upminster Bridge Underground - 0.4km
Bus Route 248 & 370

HORSHAM

Founded 1881

Nickname: Hornets   **Club Colours:** Yellow & green

Club Contact Details
01403 458 854   admin@horshamfc.co.uk

Previous Names: None
Previous Leagues: West Sussex Senior, Sussex Co 1926-51, Metropolitan 1951-57, Corinthian 1957-63, Athenian 1963-73, Isthmian 1973-2015. Southern Combination 2015-16,

10-11		11-12		12-13		13-14		14-15		15-16		16-17		17-18		18-19		19-20	
Isth P	17	Isth P	22	Isth1S	15	Isth1S	16	Isth1S	24	SCom	1	Isth1S	16	Isth1S	15	IsthSE	2	Isth P	n&v
FAC	1Q	FAC	2Qr	FAC	2Q	FAC	3Q	FAC	1Q	FAC	Pr	FAC	P	FAC	2Q	FAC	3Qr	FAC	2Q
FAT	2Q	FAT	1Q	FAT	P	FAT	1Q	FAT	3Q	FAV	1P	FAT	1Q	FAT	P	FAT	3Q	FAT	1Q

HONOURS / RECORDS

FA Comps: None

League: West Sussex Senior 1899-00, 1900-01, 01-02, 25-26. Sussex County 1931-32, 32-33, 34-35, 36-37, 37-38, 46-47. Metropolitan 1951-52. Athenian Division Two 1969-70, Division One 72-73. Isthmian Division Three 1995-96. Southern Combination 2015-16.
County FA: Sussex Senior Cup 1933-34, 38-39, 49-50, 53-54, 71-72, 73-74, 75-76.

Victory: 16-1 v Southwick - Sussex County League 1945-46
Defeat: 1-11 v Worthing - Sussex Senior Cup 1913-14
Goalscorer: Mick Browning
Appearances: Mark Stepney
Additional: Paid £2,500 to Lewes for Lee Farrell, July 2007. Received £10,000 from Tonbridge Angels for Carl Rook, Dec 2008.

GROUND: Hop Oast, Worthing Road, Horsham RH13 0AX

Ground Capacity: **Seats:** Yes **Covered:** Yes **Clubhouse:** Yes **Shop:** Yes
Previous Grounds: Queens Street 1904-2008. Worthing FC 08-09. Horsham YMCA 2009-17. Culver Road (Sussex FA) 2017-19.
Record Attendance: 7,134 v Swindon - FA Cup First Round Proper, November 1966

Nearest Railway Station Horsham from which you can catch a bus to the stadium.
Bus Route No.98 from Roffey, Southwater and Horsham Railway and Bus Stations. No.23 can be taken from Crawley & Worthing.

KINGSTONIAN

Founded 1885

Nickname: The K's   **Club Colours:** Red and white hoops

Club Contact Details
020 8330 6869   secretary@kingstonian.com

Previous Names: Kingston & Suburban YMCA 1885-87, Saxons 1887-90, Kingston Wanderers 1893-1904, Old Kingstonians 1908-19
Previous Leagues: Kingston & District, West Surrey, Southern Suburban, Athenian 1919-29, Isthmian 1929-98, Conference 1998-2001

	10-11	11-12	12-13	13-14	14-15	15-16	16-17	17-18	18-19	19-20
Isth P	7	11	11	2	11	7	17	13	18	n&v
FAC	3Qr	1Q	2Q	1Q	3Q	2Q	1Q	2Q	1Q	4Q
FAT	2Q	1Q	1P	1Q	1Q	3Q	3Q	3Qr	1Qr	2Pr

HONOURS / RECORDS
FA Comps: FA Amateur Cup 1932-33. FA Trophy 1998-99, 99-2000.
League: Athenian League 1923-24, 25-26. Isthmian 1933-34, 36-37, 97-98, Division One South 2008-09.

County FA: Surrey Senior Cup 1910-11, 13-14, 25-26, 30-31, 31-32, 34-35, 38-39, 51-52, 62-63, 63-64, 66-67, 97-98, 2005-06.
London Senior Cup 1962-63, 64-65, 86-87.
Victory: 15-1 v Delft - 1951
Defeat: 0-11 v Ilford - Isthmian League 13/02/1937
Goalscorer: Johnnie Whing - 295 (1948-62)
Appearances: Micky Preston - 555 (1967-85)
Additional: Paid £18,000 to Rushden & Diamonds for David Leworthy 1997 Received £150,000 from West Ham for Gavin Holligan 1999

GROUND: Corinthian-Casuals FC, King George's Field, Queen Mary Close, Hook Rise South, KT6 7NA
Ground Capacity: 3,400   **Seats:** 125   **Covered:** Yes   **Clubhouse:** Yes   **Shop:** Yes
Previous Grounds: Several > 1921, Richmond Road 1921-89. Kingsmeadow 1989-2017. Leatherhead FC 2017-18.
Record Attendance: 8,760 v Dulwich Hamlet at Richmond Road 1933.

Nearest Railway Station Tolworth - 10-15 min walk
Bus Route K1 from new Malden, 265 from Putney, K2 from Hook or Kingston Hospital, 406 & 408 from Kingston and Epsom, 418 from Kingston

LEATHERHEAD

Founded 1946

Nickname: The Tanners   **Club Colours:** Green & white

Club Contact Details
01372 360 151

Previous Names: Club was formed when Leatherhead Rose and Leatherhead United merged in 1946.
Previous Leagues: Surrey Senior 1946-50, Metropolitan 1950-51, Delphian 1951-58, Corinthian 1958-63, Athenian 1963-72

	10-11	11-12	12-13	13-14	14-15	15-16	16-17	17-18	18-19	19-20
	Isth1S 4	Isth P 19	Isth1S 6	Isth1S 3	Isth P 10	Isth P 11	Isth P 13	Isth P 6	Isth P 8	Isth P n&v
FAC	P	4Qr	2Q	3Q	1Q	1Qr	1Q	2P	4Qr	1Qr
FAT	P	1Q	3Qr	2Q	3Q	1Q	1Q	2Q	1Q	3Q

HONOURS / RECORDS
FA Comps: None
League: Surrey Senior 1946-47, 47-48, 48-49, 49-50. Corinthian 1962-63. Athenian Division One 1963-64.

County FA: Surrey Senior Cup 1968-69. Surrey Senior Shield 1968-69. Surrey Intermediate Cup 1968-69.

Victory: 13-1 v Leyland Motors - Surrey Senior League 1946-47
Defeat: 1-11 v Sutton United
Goalscorer: Steve Lunn scored 46 goals during 1996-97
Appearances: P Caswell - 200
Additional: Paid £1,500 to Croydon for B Salkeld. Received £1,500 from Croydon for B Salkeld.

GROUND: Fetcham Grove, Guildford Road, Leatherhead, Surrey KT22 9AS
Ground Capacity: 3,400   **Seats:** 125   **Covered:** Yes   **Clubhouse:** Yes   **Shop:** Yes
Previous Grounds: None
Record Attendance: 5,500 v Wimbledon - 1976

Nearest Railway Station Leatherhead - half a mile away
Bus Route 21, 465 & 479

LEWES

Nickname: Rooks   **Club Colours:** Red & black

Founded 1885

Club Contact Details
01273 470 820

Previous Names: None
Previous Leagues: Mid Sussex 1886-1920, Sussex County 1920-65, Athenian 1965-77, Isthmian 1977-2004, Conference 2004-11.

10-11		11-12		12-13		13-14		14-15		15-16		16-17		17-18		18-19		19-20	
Conf S	21	Isth P	6	Isth P	19	Isth P	16	Isth P	19	Isth P	23	Isth1S	9	Isth1S	2	Isth P	11	Isth P	n&v
FAC	4Q	FAC	1Q	FAC	2Q	FAC	3Q	FAC	2Q	FAC	1Q	FAC	1Qr	FAC	1Q	FAC	3Q	FAC	2Q
FAT	3Q	FAT	2Q	FAT	2Qr	FAT	1Q	FAT	3Q	FAT	1Qr	FAT	1Q	FAT	3Q	FAT	3Qr	FAT	1Q

HONOURS / RECORDS

FA Comps: None

League: Mid Sussex 1910-11, 13-14. Sussex County 1964-65. Athenian Division Two 1967-68, Division One 1969-70.
Isthmian Division Two 2001-02, Division One South 2003-04. Conference South 2007-08.
County FA: Sussex Senior Cup 1964-65, 70-71, 84-85, 2000-01, 05-06.

Goalscorer: 'Pip' Parris - 350
Appearances: Terry Parris - 662
Additional: Paid £2,000 for Matt Allen
Received £2,500 from Brighton & Hove Albion for Grant Horscroft

GROUND: The Dripping Pan, Mountfield Road, Lewes, East Sussex BN7 2XA

Ground Capacity: 3,000   **Seats:** 600   **Covered:** 1,400   **Clubhouse:** Yes   **Shop:** Yes
Previous Grounds: Played at Convent Field for two seasons before WWI
Record Attendance: 2,500 v Newhaven - Sussex County League 26/12/1947

Nearest Railway Station Lewes - 0.3km
Bus Route Priory School - stop 100m away

MARGATE

Nickname: The Gate   **Club Colours:** Blue & white

Founded 1896

Club Contact Details
01843 221 769   secretary@margate-fc.com

Previous Names: Margate Town 1896-1929. Thanet United 1981-89.
Previous Leagues: Kent 1911-23, 24-28, 29-33, 37-38, 46-59. Southern 1933-37, 59-2001,
Conference 2001-05, 15-17. Isthmian 2005-15.

10-11		11-12		12-13		13-14		14-15		15-16		16-17		17-18		18-19		19-20	
Isth P	16	Isth P	15	Isth P	9	Isth P	11	Isth P	2	Nat S	19	Nat S	22	Isth P	7	Isth P	12	Isth P	n&v
FAC	2Qr	FAC	3Q	FAC	3Q	FAC	2Q	FAC	2Q	FAC	4Q	FAC	4Qr	FAC	4Q	FAC	2Q	FAC	4Q
FAT	2Q	FAT	2Qr	FAT	1Q	FAT	3Q	FAT	1Q	FAT	3Q	FAT	3Qr	FAT	3Q	FAT	1Q	FAT	2Q

HONOURS / RECORDS

FA Comps: None

League: Kent 1932-33, 37-38, 46-47, 47-48. Southern League Eastern Section & Championship 1935-36, Division One 1962-63,
Division One South 1977-78, Premier Division 2000-01.
County FA: Kent Senior Cup 1935-36, 36-37, 73-74, 93-94, 97-98, 2002-03, 03-04, 04-05.

Victory: 12-1 v Deal Cinque Ports, FA Cup 1Q, 1919-20 and v Erith & Belvedere, Kent League, 1927-28.
Defeat: 0-11 v AFC Bournemouth (A), FA Cup, 20/11/1971.
Goalscorer: Martin Buglione - 158
Appearances: Bob Harrop - 564
Additional: Paid £5,000 to Dover Athletic for Steve Cuggy

GROUND: Hartsdown Park, Hartsdown Road, Margate, Kent CT9 5QZ

Ground Capacity: 3,000   **Seats:** 400   **Covered:** 1,750   **Clubhouse:** Yes   **Shop:** Yes
Previous Grounds: At least six before moving to Hartsdown in 1929. Shared with Dover Ath. 2002-03 and Ashford Town 04-05.
Record Attendance: 14,169 v Tottenham Hotspur - FA Cup 3rd Round 1973

Nearest Railway Station Margate - 0.7 miles from the ground.
Bus Route 8 & 8X

MERSTHAM
Nickname: The Moatsiders   **Club Colours:** Yellow & black

Founded 1892

Club Contact Details
01737 644 046

Previous Names: None
Previous Leagues: Redhill & District. Surrey Intermediate. Surrey Senior 1965-78. London Spartan 1978-84. Combined Counties 1984-2008.

10-11		11-12		12-13		13-14		14-15		15-16		16-17		17-18		18-19		19-20	
Isth1S	19	Isth1S	9	Isth1S	12	Isth1S	7	Isth1S	4	Isth P	10	Isth P	20	Isth P	18	Isth P	5	Isth P	n&v
FAC	P	FAC	2Q	FAC	P	FAC	2Q	FAC	2Q	FAC	1Q	FAC	1P	FAC	1Q	FAC	1Qr	FAC	1Q
FAT	P	FAT	1Q	FAT	2Q	FAT	Pr	FAT	2Q	FAT	1Qr	FAT	2Q	FAT	1Qr	FAT	2Q	FAT	1Q

HONOURS / RECORDS
FA Comps: None

League: Redhill & District 1934-35, 35-36, 49-50, 50-51. Surrey Intermediate 1952-53. Surrey Senior 1971-72. Combined Counties Premier Division 2007-08.
County FA: East Surrey Junior Cup 1929-30. Surrey Senior Charity Cup 1976-77. East Surrey Charities Senior Cup 1979-80, 80-81. East Surrey Charity Cup 1998-99, 2004-05, 06-07. Surrey Senior Cup 2007-08, 15-16, 17-18.
Defeat: 1-8 v Aldershot Town, FA First Qualifying Round, 1996-97.
Best FA Cup First Round Proper 2016-17.
FA Trophy Second Qualifying Round 2009-10, 12-13, 16-17, 18-19.
FA Vase Quarter Finals 2007-08.

GROUND: Moatside Stadium, Weldon Way, Merstham, Surrey RH1 3QB
Ground Capacity: 2,500   **Seats:** 174   **Covered:** 100   **Clubhouse:** Yes   **Shop:** No
Previous Grounds: None
Record Attendance: 1,920 v Oxford United, FAC First Round Proper, 05/11/2016

Nearest Railway Station Merstham - 0.7km
Bus Route 405, 430 & 435

POTTERS BAR TOWN
Nickname: Grace or Scholars   **Club Colours:** Maroon & white

Founded 1960

Club Contact Details
01707 654 833

Previous Names: Mount Grace Old Scholars 1960-84. Mount Grace 1984-91.
Previous Leagues: Barnet & District 1960-65, North London Combination 1965-68, Herts Senior County 1968-91, Spartan South Midlands 1991-2005, Southern 2005-06, 13-17. Isthmian 2006-13.

10-11		11-12		12-13		13-14		14-15		15-16		16-17		17-18		18-19		19-20	
Isth1N	13	Isth1N	12	Isth1N	10	SthC	15	SthC	14	SthC	12	SthC	9	Isth1N	2	Isth P	16	Isth P	n&v
FAC	P	FAC	P	FAC	1Qr	FAC	P	FAC	P	FAC	2Q	FAC	4Q	FAC	2Qr	FAC	1Q	FAC	4Qr
FAT	1Qr	FAT	2Q	FAT	1Q	FAT	1Qr	FAT	Pr	FAT	Pr	FAT	P	FAT	2Qr	FAT	2Q	FAT	2Q

HONOURS / RECORDS
FA Comps: None

League: North London Combination Premier Division 1967-68. Herst Senior county Premier Division 1990-91. Spartan South Midlands Premier Division 1996-97, 2004-05.
County FA: None

Goalscorer: Micky Gray scored 51 during a single season. Richard Howard has come closest to that record having scored 49 goals during seasons 2004-05 and 2006-07 respectively.

Best FA Cup Fourth Qualifying Round 2006-07, 16-17.
FA Trophy Second Round Qualifying 2011-12, 17-18(r).
FA Vase Sixth Round Proper 1997-98.

GROUND: Pakex Stadium, Parkfield, Watkins Rise, Potters Bar EN6 1QB
Ground Capacity: 2,000   **Seats:** 150   **Covered:** 250   **Clubhouse:** Yes   **Shop:** Yes
Previous Grounds: None
Record Attendance: 2011 v Barnet - FA Cup Fourth Qualifying Round 2019-20 (4,000 watched a charity match in 1997)

Nearest Railway Station Potters Bar - 0.9km
Bus Route 298, 313 & 84

WINGATE & FINCHLEY

Founded 1991

Nickname: Blues   Club Colours: Blue & black

Club Contact Details
0208 446 2217

Previous Names: Wingate (founded 1946) and Finchley (founded late 1800s) merged in 1991
Previous Leagues: South Midlands 1991-95, Isthmian 1995-2004, Southern 2004-2006

10-11		11-12		12-13		13-14		14-15		15-16		16-17		17-18		18-19		19-20	
Isth1N	3	Isth P	13	Isth P	18	Isth P	21	Isth P	12	Isth P	13	Isth P	5	Isth P	9	Isth P	19	Isth P	n&v
FAC	Pr	FAC	1Q	FAC	2Q	FAC	1Qr	FAC	2Q	FAC	3Q	FAC	2Q	FAC	2Qr	FAC	1Q	FAC	2Q
FAT	1Q	FAT	1Q	FAT	2Qr	FAT	2Qr	FAT	1Q	FAT	1Q	FAT	1Pr	FAT	1P	FAT	2P	FAT	1Qr

HONOURS / RECORDS

FA Comps: None

League: None

County FA: London Senior Cup 2010-11.

Victory: 9-1 v Winslow, South Midlands League, 23/11/1991
Defeat: 0-9 v Edgware, Isthmian Division Two, 15/01/2000
Goalscorer: Marc Morris 650 (including with Wingate FC)
Appearances: Marc Morris 720 (including with Wingate FC)

GROUND: Maurice Rebak Stadium, Summers Lane, Finchley N12 0PD

Ground Capacity: 1,500   **Seats:** 500   **Covered:** 500   **Clubhouse:** Yes   **Shop:** No
Previous Grounds: None
Record Attendance: 528 v Brentwood Town (Division One North Play-Off) 2010/11

Nearest Railway Station New Southgate - 2.3km
Bus Route 134, 263 & 382

WORTHING

Founded 1886

Nickname: Rebels   Club Colours: All red

Club Contact Details
01903 233 444   secretary@worthingfc.com

Previous Names: None
Previous Leagues: West Sussex 1896-1904, 1905-14, 19-20, Brighton Hove & District 1919-20, Sussex County 1920-48, Corinthian 1948-63, Athenian 1963-77

10-11		11-12		12-13		13-14		14-15		15-16		16-17		17-18		18-19		19-20	
Isth1S	14	Isth1S	7	Isth1S	10	Isth1S	15	Isth1S	6	Isth1S	3	Isth P	15	Isth P	16	Isth P	9	Isth P	n&v
FAC	2Q	FAC	3Q	FAC	1Q	FAC	P	FAC	2Q	FAC	3Q	FAC	3Q	FAC	1Q	FAC	4Q	FAC	2Qr
FAT	1Q	FAT	2Q	FAT	P	FAT	P	FAT	2Q	FAT	1Q	FAT	2Pr	FAT	2Q	FAT	3Q	FAT	2Q

HONOURS / RECORDS

FA Comps: None

League: Sussex League 1920-21, 21-22, 26-27, 28-29, 30-31, 33-34, 38-39, 39-40. Sussex League West 1945-46.
Isthmian League Division Two 1981-82, 92-93, Division One 1982-83.
County FA: Sussex Senior Cup x21.

Victory: 25-0 v Littlehampton (H) - Sussex League 1911-12
Defeat: 0-14 v Southwick (A) - Sussex County League 1946-47
Goalscorer: Mick Edmonds - 276
Appearances: Mark Knee - 414
Additional: Received £7,500 from Woking for Tim Read 1990

GROUND: Woodside Road, Worthing, West Sussex BN14 7HQ

Ground Capacity: 3,650   **Seats:** 500   **Covered:** 1,500   **Clubhouse:** Yes   **Shop:** No
Previous Grounds: None
Record Attendance: 3,600 v Wimbledon - FA Cup 14/11/1936

Nearest Railway Station Worthing - 0.6km
Bus Route 23, 7, & 700

AFC SUDBURY

Nickname: Yellows or The Suds   **Club Colours:** Yellow & blue

Founded 1999

Club Contact Details
01787 376 213

Previous Names: Sudbury Town (1874) and Sudbury Wanderers (1958) merged in 1999
Previous Leagues: Eastern Counties 1999-2006, Isthmian 2006-08, Southern 2008-10.

	10-11	11-12	12-13	13-14	14-15	15-16	16-17	17-18	18-19	19-20
	Isth1N	7	Isth1N	8	Isth1N	17	Isth1N	10	Isth1N	3	Isth1N	1	Isth P	23	Isth1N	12	IsthN	8	IsthN	n&v
FAC	Pr	FAC	3Q	FAC	1Q	FAC	3Q	FAC	2Q	FAC	2Q	FAC	3Q	FAC	3Q	FAC	1Q
FAT	1P	FAT	1Q	FAT	P	FAT	3Qr	FAT	1P	FAT	2Q	FAT	2P	FAT	1Q	FAT	EP	FAT	3Q

HONOURS / RECORDS

FA Comps: None

League: Eastern Counties League 2000-01, 01-02, 02-03, 03-04, 04-05. Isthmian League Division One North 2015-16.

County FA: Suffolk Premier Cup 2001-02, 02-03, 03-04.

Goalscorer: Gary Bennett - 172
Appearances: Paul Betson - 376
Best FA Cup   First Round Proper 2000-01.
FA Trophy   First Round Proper 2006-07, 08-09, 10-11, 14-15.

GROUND: Brundon Lane, Sudbury CO10 7HN

Ground Capacity: 2,500 **Seats:** 200   **Covered:** 1,500   **Clubhouse:** Yes   **Shop:** Yes
Previous Grounds: The Priory Stadium
Record Attendance: 1,800

Nearest Railway Station Sudbury - 1.5km
Bus Route Bulmer Road - stop 100m away

AVELEY

Nickname: The Millers   **Club Colours:** All blue

Founded 1927

Club Contact Details
07946 438 540   craigjohnson.aveleyfc@gmail.com

Previous Names: Lodge Meadow 1927-51.
Previous Leagues: Thurrock Combination 1946-49, London 1949-57, Delphian 1957-63, Athenian 1963-73, Isthmian 1973-2004, Southern 2004-06

	10-11	11-12	12-13	13-14	14-15	15-16	16-17	17-18	18-19	19-20
	Isth P	19	Isth P	20	Isth P	5	Isth1N	13	Isth1N	9	Isth1N	12	Isth1N	7	Isth1N	14	IsthN	2	IsthN	n&v
FAC	1Q	FAC	2Q	FAC	2Q	FAC	1Q	FAC	3Q	FAC	3Q	FAC	P	FAC	P	FAC	P	FAC	P
FAT	1Q	FAT	1Q	FAT	P	FAT	P	FAT	P	FAT	P	FAT	P	FAT	1Q	FAT	2P	FAT	4P

HONOURS / RECORDS

FA Comps: None

League: London Division One 1950-51, Premier Division 54-55. Athenian 1970-71. Isthmian Division One North 2008-09.

County FA: Essex Thameside Trophy 1979-80, 2004-05, 06-07.

Victory: 11-1 v Histon - 24/08/1963
Defeat: 0-8 v Orient, Essex Thameside Trophy
Goalscorer: Jotty Wilks - 214
Appearances: Ken Riley - 422

GROUND: Parkside, Park Lane, Aveley RM15 4PX

Ground Capacity: 3,500 **Seats:** 424   **Covered:** Yes   **Clubhouse:** Yes   **Shop:** No
Previous Grounds: Lodge Meadow 1927-52. Mill Field 1952-2018.
Record Attendance: 3,741 v Slough Town - FA Amateur Cup 27/02/1971

Nearest Railway Station Purfleet
Bus Route 372 (Hornchurch to Lakeside) passes the ground.

BASILDON UNITED

Founded 1963

Nickname: The Bees   **Club Colours:** Yellow & black

Club Contact Details
01268 521 278

Previous Names: Armada Sports.
Previous Leagues: Grays & Thurrock. Greater London. Essex Senior. Athenian. Isthmian. Essex Senior >2018.

10-11	11-12	12-13	13-14	14-15	15-16	16-17	17-18	18-19	19-20
ESen 12	ESen 18	ESen 13	ESen 8	ESen 12	ESen 2	ESen 9	ESen 2	IsthN 17	IsthN n&v
FAC EP	FAC EP	FAC 1Q	FAC P	FAC P	FAC 1Q	FAC P	FAC P	FAC 1Q	FAC 2Q
FAV 2Q	FAV 1P	FAV 1Q	FAV 1Q	FAV 1Q	FAV 3P	FAV 3P	FAV 1P	FAT P	FAT 2Q

HONOURS / RECORDS

FA Comps: None
League: Essex Senior 1976-77, 77-78, 78-79, 79-80, 93-94.
  Isthmian Division Two 1983-84.
County FA: Essex Senior Trophy 1978-79.

Best FA Cup Third Qualifying Round 1983-84, 98-99.
FA Trophy Second Qualifying Round 1985-86.
FA Vase Quarter Finals 1980-81.

GROUND: Gardiners Close, Basildon SS14 3AW

Ground Capacity: 2,000   **Seats:** 400   **Covered:** 1,000   **Clubhouse:** Yes   **Shop:** No
Previous Grounds: Gloucester Park Bowl 1963-70.
Record Attendance: 4,000 v West Ham, ground opening 11/08/1970 (4,999 watched a West Ham XI open Gloucester Park Bowl)

Nearest Railway Station Basildon (C2C), 2 miles
Bus Route 5 (First), 400 metres from ground

BRENTWOOD TOWN

Founded 1954

Nickname: Blues   **Club Colours:** Sky blue & white

Club Contact Details
07768 006 370   info@brentwoodtownfc.co.uk

Previous Names: Manor Athletic, Brentwood Athletic, Brentwood F.C.
Previous Leagues: Romford & District, South Essex Combination, London & Essex Border, Olympian, Essex Senior

10-11	11-12	12-13	13-14	14-15	15-16	16-17	17-18	18-19	19-20
Isth1N 5	Isth1N 9	Isth1N 9	Isth1N 19	Isth1N 4	Isth P 22	Isth1N 14	Isth1N 21	IsthN 13	IsthN n&v
FAC 3Qr	FAC 1Qr	FAC 3Q	FAC 1Qr	FAC 2Q	FAC 4Q	FAC P	FAC P	FAC 1Q	FAC 1Q
FAV 1Q	FAV 1Q	FAV 3Qr	FAV P	FAV 1Qr	FAV 2Q	FAV P	FAT 3Q	FAT 2Qr	FAT P

HONOURS / RECORDS

FA Comps: None
League: Essex Senior 2000-01, 2006-07.

County FA: None

Best FA Cup Third Round Proper 1969-70.
FA Trophy First Round Proper 1969-70.
FA Vase First Round 2004-05, 06-07.

GROUND: The Arena, Brentwood Centre, Doddinghurst Road, Brentwood CM15 9NN

Ground Capacity: 1,000   **Seats:** 150   **Covered:** 250   **Clubhouse:** Yes   **Shop:** No
Previous Grounds: King George's Playing Fields (Hartswood), Larkins Playing Fields 1957-93
Record Attendance: 763 v Cheshunt, Isthmian Division One North, 23/04/2011.

Nearest Railway Station Shenfield - 2.1km
Bus Route Leisure Centre - stop 150m away

BURY TOWN

Nickname: The Blues   **Club Colours:** Blue & white

Founded 1872

Club Contact Details
01284 754 721

Previous Names: Bury St Edmunds 1872-1885, 1895-1908. Bury Town 1885-95. Bury United 1908-23.

Previous Leagues: Norfolk & Suffolk Border, Essex & Suffolk Border, Eastern Counties 1935-64, 76-87, 97-2006, Metropolitan 1964-71, Southern 1971-76, 87-97

10-11	11-12	12-13	13-14	14-15	15-16	16-17	17-18	18-19	19-20
Isth P 3	Isth P 5	Isth P 7	Isth P 15	Isth P 24	Isth1N 13	Isth1N 11	Isth1N 9	IsthN 6	IsthN n&v
FAC 3Q	FAC 2Q	FAC 4Q	FAC 1Q	FAC 1Q	FAC 2Q	FAC P	FAC P	FAC 1Q	FAC P
FAT 2Q	FAT 3Qr	FAT 1Qr	FAT 1P	FAT 1Q	FAT 1P	FAT 1Q	FAT 2Q	FAT EP	FAT P

HONOURS / RECORDS

FA Comps: None

League: Metropolitan 1965-66, 68-69. Eastern Counties1963-64. Southern Division One Central 2009-10

County FA: Suffolk Senior Cup 1936-37, 37-38, 38-39, 44-45, 84-85.
Suffolk Premier Cup x12 - Firstly in 1958-59 and most recently in 2013-14.

Goalscorer: Doug Tooley - 251 in nine seasons

Appearances: Dick Rayner - 610 over 12 seasons

Additional: Paid £1,500 to Chelmsford City for Mel Springett. Received £5,500 from Ipswich Town for Simon Milton

---

GROUND: Ram Meadow, Cotton Lane, Bury St Edmunds IP33 1XP

Ground Capacity: 3,500 **Seats:** 300 **Covered:** 1,500 **Clubhouse:** Yes **Shop:** Yes

Previous Grounds: Kings Road 1888-1976. Temporary Ground 1976-77.

Record Attendance: 2,500 v Enfield - FA Cup Fourth Qualifying Round 1986

Nearest Railway Station Bury St Edmunds - 0.7km

Bus Route 11, 15, 16, 385, 753 & 84

CAMBRIDGE CITY

Nickname: Lilywhites   **Club Colours:** Black and white

Founded 1908

Club Contact Details
07720 678 585   info@cambridge-city-fc.com

Previous Names: Cambridge Town 1908-51

Previous Leagues: Bury & District 1908-13, 19-20, Anglian 1908-10, Southern Olympian 1911-14, Southern Amateur 1913-35. Spartan 1935-50. Athenian 1950-58. Southern 1958-2004, 08-19. Conference 2004-08.

10-11	11-12	12-13	13-14	14-15	15-16	16-17	17-18	18-19	19-20
SthP 4	SthP 5	SthP 8	SthP 3	SthP 13	SthP 18	SthP 21	Sth1E 6	SthC 12	IsthN n&v
FAC 3Q	FAC 1Qr	FAC 1Pr	FAC 2Q	FAC 1Q	FAC 1Q	FAC 2Q	FAC 2Qr	FAC 1Q	FAC P
FAT 3Q	FAT 2Q	FAT 1Q	FAT 2Qr	FAT 1Q	FAT 1Q	FAT 1Q	FAT 1Q	FAT 1Q	FAT 1Q

HONOURS / RECORDS

FA Comps: None

League: Southern 1962-63, Southern Division 1985-86.

County FA: Suffolk Senior Cup 1909-10. East Anglian x9. Cambridgeshire Professional Cup 2012-13, 14-15, Invitational Cup 2014-15.

Goalscorer: Gary Grogan

Appearances: Mal Keenan

Additional: Paid £8,000 to Rushden & Diamonds for Paul Coe
Received £100,000 from Millwall for Neil Harris 1998

GROUND: Histon FC, Bridge Road, Impington, Cambridge CB24 9PH

Ground Capacity: 3,250 **Seats:** 450 **Covered:** Yes **Clubhouse:** Yes **Shop:** Yes

Previous Grounds: City Ground.

Record Attendance: 12,058 v Leytonstone - FA Amateur Cup 1st Round 1949-50

Nearest Railway Station Cambridge - the following buses run every 20 minutes,

Bus Route Citi 8 and Guided Busway routes A, B and C

CANVEY ISLAND

Founded 1926

Nickname: The Gulls **Club Colours:** Yellow & blue

Club Contact Details
01268 682 991

Previous Names: None

Previous Leagues: Southend & District, Thurrock & Thames Combination, Parthenon, Metropolitan, Greater London 1964-71, Essex Senior 1971-95, Isthmian 1995-2004, Conference 2004-06

10-11		11-12		12-13		13-14		14-15		15-16		16-17		17-18		18-19		19-20	
Isth P	6	Isth P	8	Isth P	8	Isth P	13	Isth P	17	Isth P	14	Isth P	22	Isth1N	6	IsthN	9	IsthN	n&v
FAC	3Qr	FAC	2Q	FAC	1Q	FAC	4Q	FAC	4Qr	FAC	1Q	FAC	2Qr	FAC	P	FAC	P	FAC	3Qr
FAT	1Q	FAT	3Q	FAT	3Qr	FAT	2Q	FAT	1Qr	FAT	2Q	FAT	1Q	FAT	P	FAT	1Q	FAT	2Q

HONOURS / RECORDS

FA Comps: FA Trophy 2000-01.

League: Thurrock Combination 1955-56. Greater London Division One 1967-68, 68-69. Essex Senior 1986-87, 92-93. Isthmian Division Two 1995-96, 97-98, Division One 1998-99, Premier Division 2003-04.

County FA: Essex Senior Cup 1998-99, 99-00, 01-02, 11-12.

Goalscorer: Andy Jones

Appearances: Steve Ward

Additional: Paid £5,000 to Northwich Victoria for Chris Duffy

Received £4,500 from Farnborough Town for Brian Horne

GROUND: Park Lane, Canvey Island, Essex SS8 7PX

Ground Capacity: 4,100 **Seats:** 500 **Covered:** 827 **Clubhouse:** Yes **Shop:** Yes

Previous Grounds: None

Record Attendance: 3,553 v Aldershot Town - Isthmian League 2002-03

Nearest Railway Station Leigh-on-Sea - 3.2km

Bus Route Transport Museum - stop 100m away

COGGESHALL TOWN

Founded 1878

Nickname: Seed Growers **Club Colours:** Red & black

Club Contact Details
01376 562 843   secretary@coggeshalltownfc.co.uk

Previous Names: None

Previous Leagues: North Essex 1899-1909. Colchester & District/Essex & Suffolk Border 1909-39, 58-72, 90-96, 2000-2016. North Essex. Braintree & Dist. Colchester & E Essex 1950-58. Essex Senior 1972-90. Essex Inter. 1996-98, 99-00. Eastern Co 2016-18.

10-11		11-12		12-13		13-14		14-15		15-16		16-17		17-18		18-19		19-20	
EsSu1	5	EsSu1	5	EsSu1	2	EsSuP	7	EsSuP	6	EsSuP	1	EC1	2	ECP	1	IsthN	4	IsthN	n&v
																FAC	3Q	FAC	EP
														FAV	2Q	FAT	EP	FAT	EP

HONOURS / RECORDS

FA Comps: None

League: North Essex x4. Essex & Suffolk Border Division II B 1909-10, 10-11, Division One 1962-63, Premier Division 1966-67, 67-68, 69-70, 2015-16. Eastern Counties Premier 2017-18.

County FA: Essex Intermediate Cup 1970-71.

Best FA Cup Third Qualifying Round 2018-19.

FA Trophy Extra Preliminary Round 2018-19, 19-20.

FA Vase Second Qualifying Round 2017-18.

GROUND: West Street, Coggeshall CO6 1NW

Ground Capacity: **Seats:** Yes **Covered:** Yes **Clubhouse:** Yes **Shop:**

Previous Grounds: Mynheer Park. Barnard Field 1880-81. Highfields Farm Park 1881-90, 95-1960. Fabians Field 1890-95.

Record Attendance: 1,124 v Tiptree United, Essex & Suffolk Border League, 1967-68.

Nearest Railway Station Kelvedon - 3.6km

Bus Route 70

DEREHAM TOWN
Nickname: Magpies **Club Colours:** Black & white

Founded 1884

Club Contact Details
01362 690 460 enquiries@derehamtownfc.co.uk

Previous Names: Dereham and Dereham Hobbies.
Previous Leagues: Norwich District. Dereham & District. Norfolk & Suffolk. Anglian Comb. Eastern Counties > 2013.

10-11		11-12		12-13		13-14		14-15		15-16		16-17		17-18		18-19		19-20	
ECP	2	ECP	10	ECP	1	Isth1N	7	Isth1N	7	Isth1N	9	Isth1N	18	Isth1N	8	IsthN	14	IsthN	n&v
FAC	EP	FAC	EP	FAC	3Qr	FAC	1Q	FAC	2Q	FAC	P	FAC	2Q	FAC	2Q	FAC	P	FAC	1Qr
FAV	1Q	FAV	1P	FAV	2P	FAT	1Q	FAT	2Q	FAT	P	FAT	P	FAT	Pr	FAT	P	FAT	EP

HONOURS / RECORDS
FA Comps: None

League: Anglian Combination Division One 1989-90, Premier Division 97-98. Eastern Counties Premier Division 2012-13.

County FA: Norfolk Senior Cup 2005-06, 06-07, 15-16.

Best FA Cup Third Qualifying Round replay 2012-13.
FA Trophy Second Qualifying Round 2014-15.
FA Vase Fifth Round Proper 2008-09.

GROUND: Aldiss Park, Norwich Road, Dereham, Norfolk NR20 3PX

Ground Capacity: 2,500 **Seats:** 150 **Covered:** 500 **Clubhouse:** Yes **Shop:** Yes
Previous Grounds: Bayfields Meadow. Recreation Ground >1996.
Record Attendance: 3000 v Norwich City, Friendly, 07/2001.

Nearest Railway Station Peterborough - take B excel bus towards Norwich City Centre, alight at Hornbeam Drive
Bus Route 8 & X1

FELIXSTOWE & WALTON UNITED
Nickname: Seasiders **Club Colours:** Red & white

Founded 2000

Club Contact Details
01394 282 627 secretary@felixstowefootball.co.uk

Previous Names: Felixstowe Port & Town and Walton United merged in July 2000.
Previous Leagues: Eastern Counties 2000-18.

10-11		11-12		12-13		13-14		14-15		15-16		16-17		17-18		18-19		19-20	
ECP	18	ECP	18	ECP	14	ECP	3	ECP	5	ECP	4	ECP	2	ECP	2	IsthN	11	IsthN	n&v
FAC	2Qr	FAC	P	FAC	Pr	FAC	P	FAC	1Q	FAC	EPr	FAC	3Q	FAC	EP	FAC	P	FAC	P
FAV	1P	FAV	P	FAV	2Q	FAV	1Q	FAV	1P	FAV	1Q	FAV	2P	FAV	1P	FAT	EP	FAT	EP

HONOURS / RECORDS
FA Comps: None
League: None

County FA: None

Best FA Cup Third Qualifying Round 2016-17.
FA Vase Second Round Proper 2011-12, 16-17.
FA Trophy Extra Preliminary Round 2018-19.

GROUND: Dellwood Avenue, Felixstowe IP11 9HT

Ground Capacity: 2,000 **Seats:** 200 **Covered:** 200 **Clubhouse:** Yes **Shop:** Yes
Previous Grounds: None
Record Attendance: 1,541 v Coggeshall Town, Eastern Counties Premier Division, 01/05/2018

Nearest Railway Station Felixstowe - 0.3km
Bus Route X7 - alight at Great eastern Square - ground is a 5min walk

GRAYS ATHLETIC

Founded 1890

Nickname: The Blues   **Club Colours:** All royal blue

Club Contact Details
07913 566 706   graysathleticfc@hotmail.co.uk

Previous Names: Grays Juniors 1890.
Previous Leagues: Grays & District. South Essex. Athenian 1912-14, 58-83. London 1914-24, 26-39,.Kent 1924-26. Corinthian 1945-58. Isthmian 1983-2004. Conference 2004-10

10-11		11-12		12-13		13-14		14-15		15-16		16-17		17-18		18-19		19-20	
Isth1N	10	Isth1N	5	Isth1N	1	Isth P	14	Isth P	6	Isth P	15	Isth P	24	Isth1N	16	IsthN	7	IsthN	n&v
FAC	2Qr	FAC	1Q	FAC	2Q	FAC	3Q	FAC	3Qr	FAC	4Qr	FAC	1Q	FAC	1Qr	FAC	P	FAC	1Q
FAT	3Qr	FAT	2Q	FAT	2Qr	FAT	3Q	FAT	2Q	FAT	3Qr	FAT	1Qr	FAT	1Qr	FAT	P	FAT	P

HONOURS / RECORDS
FA Comps: FA Trophy 2004-05, 05-06.
League: South Essex Division Two B 1908-09. Corinthian 1945-46. London Prmier (Amateur) 1914-15, Premier 1921-22, 26-27, 29-30. Isthmian Division Two South 1984-85, Division One North 2012-13. Conference South 2004-05.
County FA: Essex Senior Cup 1914-15, 20-21, 22-23, 44-45, 56-57, 87-88, 93-94, 94-95. East Anglian Cup 1944-45.

Victory: 12-0 v Tooting & Mitcham United - London League 24/02/1923
Defeat: 0-12 v Enfield (A) - Athenian League 20/04/1963
Goalscorer: Harry Brand - 269 (1944-52)
Appearances: Phil Sammons - 673 (1982-97)
Additional: Paid £12,000 to Welling United for Danny Kedwell. Received £150,000 from Peterborough United for Aaron McLean.

GROUND: Aveley FC, Parkside, Park Lane, Aveley RM15 4PX
Ground Capacity: 3,500   **Seats:** 424   **Covered:** Yes   **Clubhouse:** Yes   **Shop:** No
Previous Grounds: Recreation Ground Bridge Road. Rookery Hill (East Thurrock Utd). Rush Green Road. Mill Field (Aveley FC).
Record Attendance: 9,500 v Chelmsford City - FA Cup 4th Qualifying Round 1959

Nearest Railway Station Purfleet
Bus Route 372 (Hornchurch to Lakeside) passes the ground.

GREAT WAKERING ROVERS

Founded 1919

Nickname: Rovers   **Club Colours:** Green & white

Club Contact Details
01702 217 812

Previous Names: None
Previous Leagues: Southend & District 1919-81, Southend Alliance 1981-89, Essex Intermediate 1989-92, Essex Senior 1992-99, 2012-14, Isthmian 1999-2004, 14-17, Southern 2004-05.

10-11		11-12		12-13		13-14		14-15		15-16		16-17		17-18		18-19		19-20	
Isth1N	15	Isth1N	22	ESen	4	ESen	1	Isth1N	15	Isth1N	18	Isth1N	24	ESen	1	IsthN	15	IsthN	n&v
FAC	1Q	FAC	Pr	FAC	P	FAC	P	FAC	P	FAC	P	FAC	P	FAC	EP	FAC	2Q	FAC	P
FAT	1Q	FAT	P	FAV	1P	FAV	3P	FAT	P	FAT	P	FAT	P	FAV	3P	FAT	P	FAT	P

HONOURS / RECORDS
FA Comps: None
League: Essex Intermediate Division Three 1990-91, Division Two 91-92. Essex Senior 1994-95, 2013-14, 17-18.

County FA: None

Victory: 9-0 v Eton Manor - 27/12/1931
Defeat: 1-7 v Bowers United - Essex Senior League 01/04/1998
Appearances: John Heffer - 511
Best FA Cup Second Qualifying Round 1998-99, 2006-07, 18-19.
FA Trophy First Round Proper 2002-03, 04-05.   **FA Vase:** Fifth Round 1997-98, 2001-02.

GROUND: Burroughs Park, Little Wakering Hall Lane, Great Wakering SS3 0HH
Ground Capacity: 3,000   **Seats:** 250   **Covered:** Yes   **Clubhouse:** Yes   **Shop:**
Previous Grounds: Great Wakering Rec
Record Attendance: 1,150 v Southend United - Friendly 19/07/2006

Nearest Railway Station Shoeburyness - 3.2km
Bus Route Barrow Hall Rd (Little Wakering Rd) - 631m

HEYBRIDGE SWIFTS

Founded 1880

Nickname: Swifts **Club Colours:** Black & white

Club Contact Details
01621 852 978 secretaryhsfc@btinternet.com

Previous Names: Heybridge FC.
Previous Leagues: Essex & Suffolk Border, North Essex, South Essex, Essex Senior 1971-84

	10-11	11-12	12-13	13-14	14-15	15-16	16-17	17-18	18-19	19-20
	Isth1N 9	Isth1N 16	Isth1N 6	Isth1N 3	Isth1N 12	Isth1N 20	Isth1N 21	Isth1N 5	IsthN 5	IsthN n&v
FAC	Pr	1Q	2Q	4Q	P	1Q	1Qr	1P	2Q	P
FAT	Pr	P	P	1Q	1Q	2Qr	1Q	2P	EP	1Q

HONOURS / RECORDS
FA Comps: None
League: Essex & Suffolk Border Division Two (West) 1920-21, Division One 30-31. Essex Senior 1981-82, 82-83, 83-84.
Isthmian Division Two North 1989-90.
County FA: Essex Junior Cup 1931-32. East Anglian Cup 1993-94, 94-95.

Goalscorer: Arthur 'Stumpy' Moss - 193 (1948-60)
Appearances: John Pollard - 543
Additional: Paid £1,000 for Dave Rainford and for Lee Kersey
Received £35,000 from Southend United for Simon Royce

GROUND: Scraley Road, Heybridge, Maldon, Essex CM9 8JA
Ground Capacity: 3,000 **Seats:** 550 **Covered:** 1,200 **Clubhouse:** Yes **Shop:** Yes
Previous Grounds: Bentall's Sports Ground 1890-1964. Sadd's Athletic ground share 1964-66.
Record Attendance: 2,477 v Woking - FA Trophy Quarter-finals 1997.

Bus Route Scylla Close - stop 1km away

HISTON

Founded 1904

Nickname: The Stutes **Club Colours:** Red and black

Club Contact Details
01223 237 373 (Ground)

Previous Names: Histon Institute 1904-51.
Previous Leagues: Cambridgeshire 1904-48. Spartan 1948-60. Delphian 1960-63. Athenian 1963-65. Eastern Counties 1965-2000, 17-19.
Southern 2000-05, 14-17. Conference 2005-14.

	10-11	11-12	12-13	13-14	14-15	15-16	16-17	17-18	18-19	19-20
	Conf 24	Conf N 16	Conf N 19	Conf N 21	SthP 18	SthP 22	SthC 21	ECP 6	ECP 1	IsthN n&v
FAC	4Q	2Qr	3Qr	3Q	2Qr	1Q	2Q	EP	1Qr	1Q
FAT	1P	3Q	3Q	3Q	2Q	1Qr	Pr	FAV 2Q	FAV 2P	Pr

HONOURS / RECORDS
FA Comps: None
League: Spartan Division One Eastern 1950-51. Eastern Counties 1999-2000, 18-19. Southern League Premier 2004-05. Conference South 2006-07.
County FA: Cambridgeshire Professional Cup 2012-13, 15-16.

Victory: 11-0 v March Town - Cambridgeshire Invitation Cup 15/02/01
Defeat: 1-8 v Ely City - Eastern Counties Division One 1994
Goalscorer: Neil Kennedy - 292
Appearances: Neil Andrews and Neil Kennedy
Additional: Paid £6,000 to Chelmsford City for Ian Cambridge 2000. Received £30,000 from Man Utd for Guiliano Maiorana.

GROUND: Bridge Road, Impington, Cambridge CB24 9PH
Ground Capacity: 3,250 **Seats:** 450 **Covered:** 1,800 **Clubhouse:** Yes **Shop:** Yes
Previous Grounds: None
Record Attendance: 6,400 v King's Lynn - FA Cup 1956

Nearest Railway Station Cambridge - the following buses run every 20 minutes,
Bus Route Citi 8 and Guided Busway routes A, B and C

HULLBRIDGE SPORTS

Founded 1945

Nickname: The Bridge or Sports   **Club Colours:** Blue & white

Club Contact Details
01702 230 420

Previous Names: None
Previous Leagues: Southend & District. Southend Alliance.

	10-11	11-12	12-13	13-14	14-15	15-16	16-17	17-18	18-19	19-20
	ESen 9	ESen 11	ESen 15	ESen 9	ESen 4	ESen 11	ESen 11	ESen 15	ESen 1	IsthN n&v
	FAC EP	FAC EP	FAC EP	FAC P	FAC EP	FAC 2Q	FAC P	FAC Pr	FAC P	FAC EP
	FAV 2P	FAV 1P	FAV 1P	FAV 4P	FAV 4P	FAV 4P	FAV 2P	FAV 4P	FAV 2P	FAT EP

HONOURS / RECORDS

FA Comps: None

League: Southend & District Division Two 1951-52, Division Three 1956-57, Division One 1965-66. Essex Senior 2018-19.

County FA: None

Best FA Cup	Second Qualifying Round 2015-16.
FA Vase	Fourth Round Proper 2014-14, 14-15, 15-16, 17-18.
FA Trophy	Extra Preliminary Round 2019-20.

GROUND: Lower Road, Hullbridge, Hockley Essex SS5 6BJ

Ground Capacity: 1,500   **Seats:** 60   **Covered:** 60   **Clubhouse:** Yes   **Shop:** No
Previous Grounds: Originally played on land on the junction of Pooles Lane and Long Lane until 1980.
Record Attendance: 800 v Blackburn Rovers, FA Youth Cup 1999-00.

Nearest Railway Station Rayleigh, approx. 3 miles
Bus Route 20, bottom of the hill

MALDON & TIPTREE

Founded 1946

Nickname: The Jammers   **Club Colours:** Blue & red

Club Contact Details
01621 853 762

Previous Names: Maldon Town were rebranded in 2010.
Previous Leagues: Chelmsford & Mid-Essex. North Essex. Essex & Suffolk Border. Eastern Counties 1966-72. Essex Senior 1972-2004. Southern 2004-05.

	10-11	11-12	12-13	13-14	14-15	15-16	16-17	17-18	18-19	19-20
	Isth1N 8	Isth1N 11	Isth1N 2	Isth1N 9	Isth1N 19	Isth1N 7	Isth1N 2	Isth1N 7	IsthN 3	IsthN n&v
	FAC 2Q	FAC 3Q	FAC 2Qr	FAC 1Q	FAC P	FAC P	FAC 1Q	FAC 1Qr	FAC P	FAC 2P
	FAT P	FAT 3Q	FAT P	FAT 1Q	FAT P	FAT P	FAT 1Q	FAT 2Q	FAT 1Q	FAT 3Q

HONOURS / RECORDS

FA Comps: None

League: Mid-Essex Premier Division 1949-50, 50-51. Essex & Suffolk Border Premier Division 1965-66. Essex Senior 1984-85.

County FA: Essex Intermediate Cup 1951-52.

Best FA Cup	Second Round Proper 2019-20.
FA Trophy	Third Qualifying Round 2011-12, 19-20.
FA Vase	Semi Finals 2002-03.

GROUND: Park Drive, Maldon CM9 5JQ

Ground Capacity: 2,800   **Seats:** 155   **Covered:** 300   **Clubhouse:** Yes   **Shop:**
Previous Grounds: Sadd's Ground 1946-47. Promenade 1947-50. Farmbridge Road 1950-1994.
Record Attendance: 1,163 v AFC Sudbury, FA Vase semi-final 2003.

Nearest Railway Station Witham (6 miles) take a taxi. Chelmsford (11 miles) catch either the 31B or 31X bus
Bus Route 31B or 31X

ROMFORD

Nickname: Boro   **Club Colours:** Yellow & blue

Club Contact Details
07973 717 074

Founded 1876

Previous Names: Original club founded in 1876 folded during WW1, Reformed in 1929 folded again in 1978 and reformed in 1992
Previous Leagues: Essex Senior 1992-96, 2002-09. Isthmian 1997-2002.

10-11		11-12		12-13		13-14		14-15		15-16		16-17		17-18		18-19		19-20	
Isth1N	12	Isth1N	13	Isth1N	8	Isth1N	11	Isth1N	20	Isth1N	16	Isth1N	16	Isth1N	23	IsthN	19	IsthN	n&v
FAC	2Q	FAC	1Q	FAC	P	FAC	1Q	FAC	2Qr	FAC	Pr	FAC	1Q	FAC	1Q	FAC	1Q	FAC	1Q
FAT	3Q	FAT	P	FAT	1Q	FAT	P	FAT	Pr	FAT	1Q	FAT	2Q	FAT	P	FAT	EP	FAT	P

HONOURS / RECORDS
FA Comps: None
League: Essex Senior 1995-96, 2008-09. Isthmian Division Two 1996-97.

County FA: East Anglian Cup 1997-98.

Goalscorer: Danny Benstock. Vinny John scored 45 goals during season 1997-98.
Appearances: Paul Clayton - 396 (2006-15)
Victory: 9-0 v Hullbridge Sports, Essex Senior, 21/10/1995.
Misc: Mark Lord became the oldest player to play for the club aged 48yrs 90 days on 03/03/2015.

GROUND: Brentwood Town FC, The Arena, Brentwood Centre, Doddinghurst Road, Brentwood CM15 9NN

Ground Capacity: 3,500   **Seats:** 160   **Covered:** 1,000   **Clubhouse:** Yes   **Shop:** Yes
Previous Grounds: Hornchurch Stadium 1992-95. Rush Green 1995-96. Sungate 1996-2001. The Mill Field (Aveley FC). Thurrock FC. E.Thurrock
Record Attendance: 820 v Leatherhead - Isthmian Division Two

Nearest Railway Station Shenfield - 2.1km
Bus Route Leisure Centre - stop 150m away

SOHAM TOWN RANGERS

Nickname: Greens, Town or Rangers   **Club Colours:** Green & white stripes

Club Contact Details
01353 720 732

Founded 1947

Previous Names: Soham Town and Soham Rangers merged in 1947
Previous Leagues: Peterborough & District, Eastern Counties 1963-2008, Southern 2008-11.

10-11		11-12		12-13		13-14		14-15		15-16		16-17		17-18		18-19		19-20	
SthC	17	Isth1N	19	Isth1N	7	Isth1N	8	Isth1N	11	Isth1N	17	Isth1N	19	Isth1N	13	IsthN	16	IsthN	n&v
FAC	P	FAC	P	FAC	1Q	FAC	P	FAC	P	FAC	P	FAC	1Qr	FAC	1Qr	FAC	1Q	FAC	2Q
FAT	1Q	FAT	P	FAT	2Q	FAT	2Q	FAT	P	FAT	P	FAT	1Q	FAT	P	FAT	Pr	FAT	2Q

HONOURS / RECORDS
FA Comps: None
League: Peterborough & District 1959-60, 61-62. Eastern Counties Premier Division 2007-08.

County FA: Cambridgeshire Challenge Cup 1957-58. Cambridgeshire Invitation Cup 1990-91, 97-98, 98-99, 2005-06.

Best FA Cup   Third Qualifying Round 1970-71
FA Trophy   Second Qualifying Round 2012-13, 13-14
FA Vase   Fifth Round 2004-05

GROUND: Julius Martin Lane, Soham, Ely, Cambridgeshire CB7 5EQ

Ground Capacity: 2,000   **Seats:** 250   **Covered:** 1,000   **Clubhouse:** Yes   **Shop:** Yes
Previous Grounds: None
Record Attendance: 3,000 v Pegasus - FA Amateur Cup 1963

Nearest Railway Station Cambridge - catch Citi 1 towards Arbury alight at Jesus College, catch No.12 from Fair Street towards Ely.
Bus Route 12 - Julius Martin Lane - stop 200m away

TILBURY

Nickname: The Dockers   **Club Colours:** Black & white

Founded 1895

Club Contact Details
01375 843 093

Previous Names: None
Previous Leagues: Grays & District/South Essex, Kent 1927-31, London 1931-39, 46-50, 57-62, South Essex Combination (Wartime), Corinthian 1950-57, Delphian 1962-63, Athenian 1963-73, Isthmian 1973-2004, Essex Senior 2004-05

	10-11		11-12		12-13		13-14		14-15		15-16		16-17		17-18		18-19		19-20	
Isth1N	19	Isth1N	3	Isth1N	16	Isth1N	16	Isth1N	14	Isth1N	11	Isth1N	12	Isth1N	17	IsthN	10	IsthN	n&v
FAC	1Q	FAC	1Q	FAC	1Q	FAC	2Q	FAC	1Q	FAC	1Q	FAC	1Q	FAC	1Q	FAC	P	FAC	1Q
FAT	P	FAT	P	FAT	P	FAT	1Q	FAT	Pr	FAT	1P	FAT	Pr	FAT	P	FAT	P	FAT	1Q

HONOURS / RECORDS

FA Comps: None
League: London 1958-59, 59-60, 60-61, 61-62. Athenian Division One 1968-69. Isthmian Division Two 1975-76.

County FA: Essex Senior Cup x4. East Anglian Cup 2008-09.

Goalscorer: Ross Livermore - 282 in 305 games
Appearances: Nicky Smith - 424 (1975-85)
Additional: Received £2,000 from Grays Athletic for Tony Macklin 1990 and from Dartford for Steve Connor 1985
Best FA Cup Third Round Proper 1977-78 **FA Amateur Cup:** Quarter Finals 1946-47
FA Trophy Third Round Proper 1982-83 **FA Vase:** Fourth Round Proper 1988-89, 99-00

GROUND: Chadfields, St Chads Road, Tilbury, Essex RM18 8NL

Ground Capacity: 4,000   **Seats:** 350   **Covered:** 1,000   **Clubhouse:** Yes   **Shop:**
Previous Grounds: Orient Field 1895-46.
Record Attendance: 5,500 v Gorleston - FA Cup 1949

Nearest Railway Station Tilbury Town - 1.1km
Bus Route Raphael Avenue - stop 75m away

WITHAM TOWN

Nickname: Town   **Club Colours:** White & blue

Founded 1947

Club Contact Details
01376 511 198   withamtownfc@gmail.com

Previous Names: Witham Town Football Clubs did exist before both World Wars with both folding due to the conflicts.
Previous Leagues: Mid-Essex 1947-52. South Essex 1952-58. Essex & Suffolk Border 1958-71. Essex Senior 1971-87, 2009-12. Isthmian 1987-2009.

	10-11		11-12		12-13		13-14		14-15		15-16		16-17		17-18		18-19		19-20	
ESen	3	ESen	1	Isth1N	4	Isth1N	2	Isth P	22	Isth1N	19	Isth1N	13	Isth1N	11	IsthN	18	IsthN	n&v
FAC	Pr	FAC	P	FAC	1Q	FAC	2Qr	FAC	4Q	FAC	2Q	FAC	2Q	FAC	1Q	FAC	Pr	FAC	1Q
FAV	3P	FAV	3P	FAT	P	FAT	1Q	FAT	2Q	FAT	P	FAT	1Q	FAT	1Q	FAT	1Q	FAT	Pr

HONOURS / RECORDS

FA Comps: None
League: Braintree & District 1920-21, 24-25. Mid-Essex Division Three 1935-36, 47-48, Division Two 48-49. South Essex 1955-56. Essex & Suffolk Border 1964-65, 70-71. Essex Senior 1970-71, 85-86, 2011-12.
County FA: Essex Senior Trophy 1985-86.

Goalscorer: Colin Mitchell.
Appearances: Keith Dent.

GROUND: Spa Road, Witham CM8 1UN

Ground Capacity: 2,500   **Seats:** 157   **Covered:** 780   **Clubhouse:** Yes   **Shop:** No
Previous Grounds: Crittall Windows works ground 1949-75.
Record Attendance: 800 v Billericay Town, Essex Senior League, May 1976.

Nearest Railway Station Witham - 1.1km
Bus Route Cuppers Close - stop 200m away

ASHFORD TOWN (MIDDLESEX)

Founded 1958

Nickname: Ash Trees   **Club Colours:** Tangerine, white & black

Club Contact Details
01784 245 908

Previous Names: Ashford Albion 1958-64.
Previous Leagues: Hounslow & District 1964-68, Surrey Intermediate 1968-82, Surrey Premier 1982-90, Combind Counties 1990-2000, 14-16, Isthmian 20 00-04, 06-10, Southern 2004-06, 10-14, 16-18.

10-11		11-12		12-13		13-14		14-15		15-16		16-17		17-18		18-19		19-20	
SthC	16	SthC	9	SthC	10	SthC	22	CCP	3	CCP	2	SthC	10	Sth1E	12	IsthSC	11	IsthSC	n&v
FAC	1Qr	FAC	P	FAC	2Q	FAC	1Q	FAC	Pr	FAC	1Q	FAC	1Q	FAC	3Q	FAC	P	FAC	P
FAT	2P	FAT	2Q	FAT	1Qr	FAT	P	FAV	1P	FAV	1Pr	FAT	1Qr	FAT	2Qr	FAT	1Q	FAT	Pr

HONOURS / RECORDS

FA Comps: None
League: Surrey Intermediate (Western) Prmeier Division A 1974-75. Surrey Premier 1982-90.
Combined Counties 1994-95, 95-96, 96-97, 97-98, 99-00.
County FA: Middlesex Senior Charity Cup 1999-00, 11-12, 16-17. Aldershot Senior Cup 2002-03, 11-12.
Middlesex Premier Cup 2006-07. Surrey Senior Cup 2008-09.
Goalscorer: Andy Smith
Appearances: Alan Constable - 650
Additional: Received £10,000 from Wycombe Wanderers for Dannie Bulman 1997

GROUND: Robert Parker Stadium, Stanwell, Staines TW19 7BH

Ground Capacity: 2,550 **Seats:** 250 **Covered:** 250 **Clubhouse:** Yes **Shop:** No
Previous Grounds: Clockhouse Lane Recreation 1958-85.
Record Attendance: 992 v AFC Wimbledon - Isthmian League Premier Division 26/09/2006

Nearest Railway Station Heathrow Terminal 4 Underground - 1.5km
Bus Route Genesis Close - stop 400m away

BARKING

Founded 1880

Nickname: The Blues   **Club Colours:** All blue

Club Contact Details
0203 244 0069   secretary@barking-fc.co.uk

Previous Names: Barking Rov. Barking Woodville. Barking Working Lads Institute, Barking Institute. Barking T. Barking & East Ham United.
Previous Leagues: South Essex, London 1896-98, 1909-26. Athenian 1923-52. Isthmian. Southern. Essex Senior >2017.

10-11		11-12		12-13		13-14		14-15		15-16		16-17		17-18		18-19		19-20	
ESen	6	ESen	7	ESen	6	ESen	12	ESen	3	ESen	4	ESen	1	Isth1N	10	IsthN	12	IsthSC	n&v
FAC	P	FAC	EPr	FAC	EPr	FAC	Pr	FAC	EP	FAC	Pr	FAC	Pr	FAC	2Q	FAC	P	FAC	1Q
FAV	1P	FAV	1P	FAV	1P	FAV	2P	FAV	1Q	FAV	2P	FAV	1P	FAT	1Q	FAT	P	FAT	1Qr

HONOURS / RECORDS

FA Comps: None
League: South Essex Division One 1898-99, 1911-12, Division Two 1900-01. Division Two 1901-02. London Division One A 1909-10, Premier 1920-21. Athenian 1934-35. Isthmian Premier 1978-79. Essex Senior 2016-17.
County FA: Essex Senior Cup 1893-94, 95-96, 1919-20, 45-46, 62-63, 69-70, 89-90.
London Senior Cup 1911-12, 20-21, 26-27, 78-79.
Goalscorer: Neville Fox - 242 (1965-73).
Appearances: Bob Makin - 569.
Victory: 14-0 v Sheppey United, Mithras Cup, 02/12/1969
Best FA Cup Second Round Proper replay 1981-82. **FA Amateur Cup:** Finalists 1926-27.
FA Trophy Second Round Proper 1979-80. **FA Vase:** Fifth Round Proper 1996-97.

GROUND: Mayesbrook Park, Lodge Avenue, Dagenham RM8 2JR

Ground Capacity: 2,500 **Seats:** 200 **Covered:** 600 **Clubhouse:** Yes **Shop:** Yes
Previous Grounds: Barking Park Recreation Ground. Vicarage Field 1884-1973.
Record Attendance: 1,972 v Aldershot, FA Cup Second Round Proper, 1978.

Nearest Railway Station Upney (District Line), 2 miles
Bus Route 368 (50 yards) 5, 145, 364 (400 yards)

BEDFONT SPORTS

Founded 2000

Nickname: The Eagles **Club Colours:** Red & black

Club Contact Details
0208 831 9067 or 07967 370 109

Previous Names: Bedfont Sunday became Bedfont Sports in 2002 - Bedfont Eagles (1978) merged with the club shortly afterwards.
Previous Leagues: Hounslow & District 2003-04. Middlesex County 2004-09.

10-11		11-12		12-13		13-14		14-15		15-16		16-17		17-18		18-19		19-20	
CC1	4	CC1	2	CCP	13	CCP	17	CCP	16	CCP	13	CCP	8	CCP	2	IsthSC	12	IsthSC	n&v
		FAC	Pr	FAC	EP	FAC	P	FAC	EP	FAC	P	FAC	P	FAC	EP	FAC	P	FAC	1Q
FAV	1Q	FAV	1P	FAV	2Q	FAV	2Q	FAV	1P	FAV	1P	FAV	3Pr	FAV	1Q	FAT	P	FAT	2Q

HONOURS / RECORDS
FA Comps: None
League: Hounslow & District League Division One 2003-04

County FA: Middlesex County Premier Cup 2009-10

Best FA Cup	First Qualifying Round 2019-20
FA Vase	Third Round Proper 2016-17(r)
FA Trophy	Second Qualifying Round 2019-20

GROUND: Bedfont Sports Club, Hatton Road, Bedfont TW14 9QT

Ground Capacity: 3,000 **Seats:** Yes **Covered:** 200 **Clubhouse:** Yes **Shop:**
Previous Grounds: N/A
Record Attendance:

Nearest Railway Station Hatton Cross or Feltham BR
Bus Route London Transport 203, H25, H26

BRACKNELL TOWN

Founded 1896

Nickname: The Robins **Club Colours:** Red & white

Founded 1896
"The Robins"

Club Contact Details
01344 412 305

Previous Names: Old Bracknell Wanderers 1896-1962.
Previous Leagues: Ascot & District. Reading & District 1949-58. Great Western Comb. 1958-63, Surrey Senior 1963-70, Spartan 1970-75, London
Spartan 1975-84, Isthmian 1984-2004, Southern 2004-10, Hellenic 2010-18.

10-11		11-12		12-13		13-14		14-15		15-16		16-17		17-18		18-19		19-20	
Hel P	16	Hel P	21	Hel1E	5	Hel P	13	Hel P	9	Hel P	14	Hel P	2	Hel P	2	IsthSC	2	IsthSC	n&v
FAC	P	FAC	P	FAC	1Q	FAC	P	FAC	EP	FAC	1Q	FAC	P	FAC	P			FAC	1Q
FAV	2P	FAV	2Q	FAV	2Q	FAV	2Q	FAV	2Q	FAV	2Qr	FAV	1P	FAV	QF	FAT	1Qr	FAT	P

HONOURS / RECORDS
FA Comps: None
League: Ascot & District 1911-12, 32-33, Division Two 13-14. Surrey Senior 1969-70.
Spartan Senior Division 1980-81, Premier 1982-83. Isthmian Division Three 1993-94.
County FA: Berks & Bucks Senior Trophy 2016-17

Goalscorer:	Justin Day
Goalscorer:	James Woodcock
Best FA Cup	First Round Proper 2000-01
FA Trophy	First Round Proper 2002-03, 03-04, 04-05
FA Vase	Quarter Finals 2017-18

GROUND: Larges Lane, Bracknell RG12 9AN

Ground Capacity: 2,500 **Seats:** 150 **Covered:** 500 **Clubhouse:** Yes **Shop:** Yes
Previous Grounds: Field next to Downshire Arms. Station Field > 1933
Record Attendance: 2,500 v Newquay - FA Amateur Cup 1971

Nearest Railway Station Bracknell - 0.5km
Bus Route Larges Bridge Drive stop - 282m away

CHALFONT ST PETER

Founded 1926

Nickname: Saints   **Club Colours:** Red & green

Club Contact Details
01753 886 477

Previous Names: None

Previous Leagues: G W Comb 1948-58. Parthernon 1958-60. London 1960-62. Spartan 1962-75. London Spartan 1975-76. Athenian 1976-84. Isthmian 1984-2006. Spartan South Midlands 2006-11. Southern 2011-19.

10-11		11-12		12-13		13-14		14-15		15-16		16-17		17-18		18-19		19-20	
SSM P	1	SthC	12	SthC	16	SthC	14	SthC	16	SthC	6	SthC	18	Sth1E	9	IsthSC	14	IsthSC	n&v
FAC	P	FAC	1Q	FAC	3Qr	FAC	2Q	FAC	3Q	FAC	P	FAC	1Q	FAC	Pr	FAC	1Qr	FAC	1Q
FAV	2Pr	FAT	1Q	FAT	1Q	FAT	Pr	FAT	1Q	FAT	1Q	FAV	2Qr	FAT	1Qr	FAT	P	FAT	EP

HONOURS / RECORDS

FA Comps: None

League: Spartan Division Two 1975-76. Isthmian Division Two 1987-88. Spartan South Midlands Premier Division 2010-11.

County FA: Berks & Bucks Intermediate Cup 1952-53, 84-85.

Victory: 10-1 v Kentish Town (away) Spartan League Premier Division 23 Dec 2008
Defeat: 0-13 v Lewes (away) Isthmian Division 3, 7 Nov 2000
Appearances: Colin Davies

GROUND: Mill Meadow, Gravel Hill, Amersham Road, Chalfont St Peter SL9 9QX

Ground Capacity: 4,500   **Seats:** 220   **Covered:** 120   **Clubhouse:** Yes   **Shop:** Yes
Previous Grounds: Gold Hill Common 1926-49.
Record Attendance: 2,550 v Watford benefit match 1985

Nearest Railway Station Gerrards Cross - 2.3km
Bus Route The Waggon & Horses Pub - stop 250m away

CHERTSEY TOWN

Founded 1890

Nickname: Curfews   **Club Colours:** Royal blue & white stripes

Club Contact Details
01932 561 774

Previous Names: Chertsey 1890-1950.

Previous Leagues: West Surrey. Surrey Inter 1919-39. Surrey Senior 46-63. Metropolitan 63-66. Greater London 66-67. Spartan 67-75. London Spartan 75-76. Athenian 76-84. Isthmian 84-85, 86-2006. Combined Counties 85-86, 2006-11, 14-19. Southern 2011-14.

10-11		11-12		12-13		13-14		14-15		15-16		16-17		17-18		18-19		19-20	
CCP	2	SthC	17	SthC	20	SthC	21	CCP	20	CCP	18	CCP	19	CCP	15	CCP	1	IsthSC	n&v
FAC	2Q	FAC	2Q	FAC	P	FAC	2Q	FAC	EPr	FAC	P	FAC	1Q	FAC	P	FAC	EP	FAC	3Q
FAV	2P	FAT	3Q	FAT	1Q	FAT	1Q	FAV	1P	FAV	2Q	FAV	1Q	FAV	1Q	FAV	F	FAT	P

HONOURS / RECORDS

FA Comps: FA Vase 2018-19

League: Surrey Senior 1958-59, 60-61, 61-62. Combined Counties Premier 2018-19

County FA: Surrey Junior Cup 1896-97.

Goalscorer: Alan Brown (54) 1962-63.
FA Cup   Third Qualifying Round 1994-95
FA Trophy   Third Qualifying Round 2011-12
FA Vase   Finalists 2018-19

GROUND: Alwyns Lane, Chertsey, Surrey KT16 9DW

Ground Capacity: 2,500   **Seats:** 240   **Covered:** 760   **Clubhouse:** Yes   **Shop:** Yes
Previous Grounds: Pre 1929 - Willow Walk, Free Prae Road, Staines Lane and Chilsey Green.
Record Attendance: 2150 v Aldershot Town, Isthmian Div.2 04/12/93.

Nearest Railway Station Chertsey
Bus Route Abellio 446, 451, 461, 557

CHIPSTEAD

Nickname: Chips   **Club Colours:** Green, white & black

Founded 1906

Club Contact Details
01737 553 250

Previous Names: None
Previous Leagues: Surrey Intermediate 1962-82, Surrey Premier 1982-86, Combined Counties 1986-2007

10-11		11-12		12-13		13-14		14-15		15-16		16-17		17-18		18-19		19-20	
Isth1S	10	Isth1S	12	Isth1S	20	Isth1S	13	Isth1S	15	Isth1S	21	Isth1S	20	Isth1S	20	IsthSC	13	IsthSC	n&v
FAC	2Qr	FAC	2Q	FAC	1Q	FAC	3Q	FAC	1Qr	FAC	P	FAC	1Q	FAC	2Q	FAC	P	FAC	2Q
FAT	P	FAT	1Q	FAT	P	FAT	P	FAT	P	FAT	1Q	FAT	Pr	FAT	Pr	FAT	2Qr	FAT	1Qr

HONOURS / RECORDS

FA Comps: None

League: Combined Counties Premier 1989-90, 2006-07.

County FA: East Surrey Charity Cup 1960-61.

Goalscorer:	Mick Nolan - 124
Best FA Cup	Fourth Qualifying Round 2008-09
FA Trophy	Second Qualifying Round 2009-10, 18-19(r)
FA Vase	Third Round Proper 1997-98, 98-99

GROUND: High Road, Chipstead, Surrey CR5 3SF

Ground Capacity: 2,000   **Seats:** 150   **Covered:** 200   **Clubhouse:** Yes   **Shop:** Yes
Previous Grounds: None
Record Attendance: 1,170

Nearest Railway Station Coulsdon South from where a Taxi can be taken to the ground. Chipstead a dangerous 1.25m walk away
Bus Route 405 to Star Lane, Hooley. Ground is a further 20min walk from there

FC ROMANIA

Nickname: The Wolves   **Club Colours:** Yellow & red

Founded 2006

Club Contact Details
01992 625 793

Previous Names: None
Previous Leagues: Sunday London Weekend 2006-07. Essex Business Houses 2007-10. Middlesex County 2010-13. Essex Senior 2013-18.

10-11		11-12		12-13		13-14		14-15		15-16		16-17		17-18		18-19		19-20	
Midx1SE	2	MidxP	2	MidxP	2	ESen	5	ESen	6	ESen	3	ESen	3	ESen	3	IsthSC	16	IsthSC	n&v
								FAC	2Q	FAC	EP	FAC	EP	FAC	2Qr	FAC	2Q	FAC	Pr
				FAV	2Q	FAV	1Q	FAV	2Q	FAV	4P	FAV	3Pr	FAV	2Pr	FAT	P	FAT	P

HONOURS / RECORDS

FA Comps: None

League: None

County FA: None

Best FA Cup	Second Qualifying Round 2014-15, 17-18(r), 18-19
FA Vase	Fourth Round Proper 2015-16
FA Trophy	Preliminary Round 2018-19

GROUND: Cheshunt FC, Theobalds Lane, Cheshunt, Herts EN8 8RU

Ground Capacity: 3,500   **Seats:** 424   **Covered:** 600   **Clubhouse:** Yes   **Shop:**
Previous Grounds: Hackey Marshes 2006-07. Low Hall Rec Walthamstow 2007-10. Leyton Sport Centre 2010-12.
Record Attendance: Not known

Nearest Railway Station Theobalds Grove – 5 mins walk
Bus Route N279

HANWELL TOWN
Founded 1920

Nickname: Magpies **Club Colours:** Black & white

Club Contact Details
020 8998 1701

Previous Names: None
Previous Leagues: London 1924-27. Dauntless. Wembley & District. Middlesex County 1970-83. London Spartan/Spartan 1983-97. Spartan South Midlands (FM) 1997-2006, 2007-14. Southern 2006-07, 14-18.

10-11		11-12		12-13		13-14		14-15		15-16		16-17		17-18		18-19		19-20	
SSM P	15	SSM P	21	SSM P	6	SSM P	1	SthC	7	SthC	20	SthC	11	Sth1E	18	IsthSC	8	IsthSC	n&v
FAC	EP	FAC	EP	FAC	EP	FAC	EPr	FAC	P	FAC	3Q	FAC	2Qr	FAC	1Q	FAC	3Qr	FAC	1Q
FAV	1Q	FAV	1P	FAV	1Pr	FAV	5P	FAT	P	FAT	P	FAT	2Q	FAT	1Q	FAT	P	FAT	P

HONOURS / RECORDS
FA Comps: None
League: London Spartan Senior Division 1983-84. Spartan South Midlands Premier 2013-14.

County FA: London Senior Cup 1991-92, 92-93.

Goalscorer:	Keith Rowlands
Appearances:	Phil Player 617 (20 seasons)
Best FA Cup	Third Qualifying Round 2015-16, 18-19(r)
FA Trophy	Second Qualifying Round 2006-07, 16-17(r)
FA Vase	Fifth Round Proper 2013-14

GROUND: Preivale Lane, Perivale, Greenford, UB6 8TL

Ground Capacity: 1,250 **Seats:** 175 **Covered:** 600 **Clubhouse:** Yes **Shop:** No
Previous Grounds: Moved to Reynolds Field in 1981.
Record Attendance: 600 v Spurs, floodlight switch on, 1989.

Nearest Railway Station Perivale Underground - 0.6km
Bus Route Perivale Lane - stop 200m away

HARLOW TOWN
Founded 1879

Nickname: Hawks **Club Colours:** Red & white

Club Contact Details
01279 443 196 harlowtownfc@aol.com

Previous Names: Harlow & Burnt Mill 1898-1902.
Previous Leagues: East Hertfordshire > 1932, Spartan 1932-39, 46-54, London 1954-61, Delphian 1961-63, Athenian 1963-73, Isthmian 1973-92, 93-2004, Inactive 1992-93, Southern 2004-06

10-11		11-12		12-13		13-14		14-15		15-16		16-17		17-18		18-19		19-20	
Isth1N	4	Isth1N	7	Isth1N	21	Isth1N	4	Isth1N	2	Isth1N	3	Isth P	10	Isth P	21	Isth P	22	IsthSC	n&v
FAC	2Q	FAC	P	FAC	P	FAC	2Q	FAC	1Qr	FAC	4Q	FAC	2Q	FAC	3Qr	FAC	1Qr	FAC	Pr
FAT	1P	FAT	3Q	FAT	Pr	FAT	P	FAT	1Q	FAT	2Q	FAT	2P	FAT	3Q	FAT	2Q	FAT	EPr

HONOURS / RECORDS
FA Comps: None
League: East Herts Division One 1911-12, 22-23, 28-29, 29-30. Athenian Division One 1971-72. Isthmian Division One 1978-79, Division Two North 1988-89.
County FA: Essex Senior cup 1978-79

Victory:	14-0 v Bishop's Stortford - 11/04/1925
Defeat:	0-11 v Ware (A) - Spartan Division 1 East 06/03/1948
Goalscorer:	Dick Marshall scored 64 during 1928-29, Alex Read scored 52 during 2013-14.
Appearances:	Norman Gladwin - 639 (1951-70)

GROUND: The Harlow Arena, off Elizabeth Way, The Pinnacles, Harlow CM19 5BE

Ground Capacity: 3,500 **Seats:** 500 **Covered:** 500 **Clubhouse:** Yes **Shop:** Yes
Previous Grounds: Green Man Field 1879-60. Harlow Sportcentre 1960-2006.
Record Attendance: 9,723 v Leicester City - FA Cup 3rd Round replay 08/01/1980

Nearest Railway Station Canons Gate - 12min walk
Bus Route 381 & 6

HERTFORD TOWN

Founded 1901

Nickname: The Blues   **Club Colours:** All blue

Club Contact Details
01992 583 716

Previous Names: Port Vale Rovers 1901.
Previous Leagues: Herts Senior County 1908-20. Middlsex 1920-21. Spartan 1921-59. Delphian 1959-63. Athenian 1963-72. Eastern Counties 1972-73. Spartan South Midlands 1973-2017.

10-11		11-12		12-13		13-14		14-15		15-16		16-17		17-18		18-19		19-20	
SSM P	9	SSM P	16	SSM P	17	SSM P	16	SSM P	11	SSM P	8	SSM P	2	Isth1N	15	IsthSC	18	IsthSC	n&v
FAC	P	FAC	1Q	FAC	EP	FAC	1Q	FAC	1Q	FAC	EPr	FAC	P	FAC	2Q	FAC	1Q	FAC	P
FAV	1P	FAV	1Q	FAV	3P	FAV	1Q	FAV	1P	FAV	3P	FAV	1P	FAT	1Q	FAT	P	FAT	EP

HONOURS / RECORDS

FA Comps: None
League: Spartan Division One Eastern Section 1949-50. Delphian 1960-61, 61-62.

County FA: Herts Senior Cup 1966-67. East Anglian Cup 1962-63, 69-70.

Appearances:	Robbie Burns
Best FA Cup	Fourth Qualifying Round 1973-74
FA Trophy	Second Round Proper 1979-80
FA Vase	Third Round Proper 1986-87, 2003-04, 12-13, 15-16

GROUND: Hertingfordbury Park, West Street, Hertford SG13 8EZ

Ground Capacity: 6,500   **Seats:** 200   **Covered:** 1,500   **Clubhouse:** Yes   **Shop:** Yes
Previous Grounds: Hartham Park 1901-08.
Record Attendance: 5,000 v Kingstonian FA Am Cup 2nd Round 1955-56.

Nearest Railway Station Hertford North - 0.8km
Bus Route 310, 341, 351, 641 & H4

MARLOW

Founded 1870

Nickname: The Blues   **Club Colours:** All royal blue

Club Contact Details
01628 483 970

Previous Names: Great Marlow
Previous Leagues: Reading & District, Spartan 1908-10, 28-65, Gt Western Suburban, Athenian 1965-84, Isthmian 1984-2004. Southern 2004-12, 13-18. Hellenic 2012-13.

10-11		11-12		12-13		13-14		14-15		15-16		16-17		17-18		18-19		19-20	
SthC	11	SthC	22	Hel P	1	SthC	17	SthC	11	Sthsw	13	SthC	4	Sth1E	14	IsthSC	4	IsthSC	n&v
FAC	P	FAC	1Q	FAC	1Q	FAC	P	FAC	P	FAC	Pr	FAC	Pr	FAC	2Q	FAC	2Q	FAC	P
FAT	Pr	FAT	1Qr	FAV	2P	FAT	3Q	FAT	P	FAT	3Q	FAT	1Q	FAT	1Q	FAT	Pr	FAT	1Qr

HONOURS / RECORDS

FA Comps: None
League: Spartan 1937-38, Division Two West 1929-30. Isthmian Division One 1987-88. Hellenic Premier Division 2012-13.

County FA: Berks & Bucks Senior Cup x11

Goalscorer:	Kevin Stone
Appearances:	Mick McKeown - 500+
Additional:	Paid £5,000 to Sutton United for Richard Evans Received £8,000 from Slough Town for David Lay

GROUND: Alfred Davies Memorial Ground, Oak tree Road, Marlow SL7 3ED

Ground Capacity: 3,000   **Seats:** 250   **Covered:** 600   **Clubhouse:** Yes   **Shop:** No
Previous Grounds: Crown ground 1870-1919, Star Meadow 1919-24
Record Attendance: 3,000 v Oxford United - FA Cup 1st Round 1994

Nearest Railway Station Marlow - 1km
Bus Route Oak Tree Road - stop 100m away

NORTHWOOD

Nickname: Woods **Club Colours:** All red

Founded 1926

Club Contact Details
01923 827 148

enquiries@northwoodfc.com

Previous Names: Northwood United 1926-1945.
Previous Leagues: Harrow & Wembley 1932-69, Middlesex 1969-78, Hellenic 1979-84, London Spartan 1984-93, Isthmian 1993-2005, 2007-10, Southern 2005-07, 10-18.

10-11		11-12		12-13		13-14		14-15		15-16		16-17		17-18		18-19		19-20	
SthC	20	SthC	7	SthC	13	SthC	9	SthC	10	SthC	7	SthC	20	Sth1E	17	IsthSC	10	IsthSC	n&v
FAC	1Q	FAC	P	FAC	3Q	FAC	P	FAC	1Qr	FAC	2Q	FAC	P	FAC	P	FAC	1Qr	FAC	P
FAT	Pr	FAT	Pr	FAT	P	FAT	P	FAT	2Q	FAT	1Q	FAT	1Qr	FAT	P	FAT	P	FAT	P

HONOURS / RECORDS
FA Comps: None

League: Harrow, Wembley & District Premier 1932-33, 33-34, 34-35, 35-36, 36-37, 47-48, 48-49. Middlesex Premier 1977-78. Hellenic Division One 1978-79. Spartan Premier 1991-92. Isthmian Division One North 2002-03.
County FA: Middlesex Intermediate Cup 1978-79. Middlesex Senior Cup 2006-07, 15-16.

Victory: 15-0 v Dateline (H) - Middlesex Intermediate Cup 1973
Defeat: 0-8 v Bedfont - Middlesex League 1975
Goalscorer: Lawrence Yaku scored 61 goals during season 1999-2000
Appearances: Chris Gell - 493+

GROUND: Northwood Park, Chestnut Avenue, Northwood, Middlesex HA6 1HR
Ground Capacity: 3,075 **Seats:** 308 **Covered:** 932 **Clubhouse:** Yes **Shop:** No
Previous Grounds: Northwood Recreation Ground 1926-1928. Northwood Playing Fields 1928-1971.
Record Attendance: 1,642 v Chlesea - Friendly July 1997

Nearest Railway Station Northwood Hills Underground - 0.5m
Bus Route 282 & H11 to Northwood Hills

SOUTH PARK

Nickname: The Sparks **Club Colours:** All red

Founded 1897

Club Contact Details
01737 245 963

Previous Names: South Park & Reigate Town 2001-03.
Previous Leagues: Redhill & District. Crawley & District > 2006. Combined Counties 2006-14.

10-11		11-12		12-13		13-14		14-15		15-16		16-17		17-18		18-19		19-20	
CC1	3	CCP	8	CCP	4	CCP	1	Isth1S	14	Isth1S	11	Isth1S	8	Isth1S	13	IsthSC	17	IsthSC	n&v
FAC	1Q	FAC	P	FAC	4Q	FAC	1Qr	FAC	1Qr	FAC	2Q	FAC	2Q	FAC	P	FAC	P	FAC	1Q
FAV	2Q	FAV	4P	FAV	3P	FAV	3P	FAT	1Q	FAT	1Q	FAT	2P	FAT	Pr	FAT	P	FAT	P

HONOURS / RECORDS
FA Comps: None
League: Combined Counties Premier Division 2013-14.

County FA: Surrey Premier Cup 2010-11.

Best FA Cup Fourth Qualifying Round 2012-13
FA Vase Fourth Round Proper 2011-12
FA Trophy Second Round Proper 2016-17

GROUND: King George's Field, Whitehall Lane, South Park RH2 8LG
Ground Capacity: 2,000 **Seats:** 113 **Covered:** Yes **Clubhouse:** Yes **Shop:** Yes
Previous Grounds: Crescent Road. Church Road.
Record Attendance: 643 v Metropolitan Police, 20/10/2012

Nearest Railway Station Reigate - 2km
Bus Route Sandcross Lane - stop 200m away

STAINES TOWN

Founded 1892

Nickname: The Swans   **Club Colours:** Yellow and blue

Club Contact Details
01784 469 240

Previous Names: Staines Albany & St Peters Institute merged in 1895. Staines 1905-18, Staines Lagonda 1918-25, Staines Vale (WWII)

Previous Leagues: Great Western Suburban, Hounslow & District 1919-20, Spartan 1924-35, 58-71, Middlesex Senior 1943-52, Parthenon 1952-53, Hellenic 1953-58, Athenian 1971-73, Isthmian 1973-2009, 15-18. Conference 2009-15. Southern 2018-19.

	10-11		11-12		12-13		13-14		14-15		15-16		16-17		17-18		18-19		19-20	
	Conf S	15	Conf S	15	Conf S	18	Conf S	8	Conf S	21	Isth P	16	Isth P	12	Isth P	8	SthPS	22	IsthSC	n&v
FAC	4Q		4Q		2Q		1P		3Qr		1P		3Q		1Q		1Q		2Q	
FAT	3Q		2P		3Qr		1Pr		3Qr		1Q		1Q		1Q		1Q		P	

HONOURS / RECORDS

FA Comps: None

League: Spartan League 1959-60. Athenian League Division Two 1971-72, Division One 1974-75, 88-89.

County FA: Middlesex Senior cup 1975-76, 76-77, 77-78, 88-89, 90-91, 94-95, 97-98, 2009-10, 12-13. Barassi Cup 1975-76.

Victory: 14-0 v Croydon (A) - Isthmian Division 1 19/03/1994

Defeat: 1-18 - Wycombe Wanderers (A) - Great Western Suburban League 27/12/1909

Goalscorer: Alan Gregory - 122

Appearances: Dickie Watmore - 840

GROUND: Wheatsheaf Park, Wheatsheaf Lane, Staines TW18 2PD

Ground Capacity: 3,000   **Seats:** 300   **Covered:** 850   **Clubhouse:** Yes   **Shop:** Yes

Previous Grounds: Groundshared with Walton & Hersham and Egham Town whilst new Wheatsheaf stadium was built 2001-03.

Record Attendance: 2,860 v Stokcport County, FAC, 2007

Nearest Railway Station Staines - 1.3km

Bus Route Penton Hook Road - stop 100m away

TOOTING & MITCHAM UNITED

Founded 1932

Nickname: The Terrors   **Club Colours:** Black and white stripes

Club Contact Details
020 8685 6193

Previous Names: Tooting Town (Founded in 1887) and Mitcham Wanderers (1912) merged in 1932 to form Tooting & Mitcham FC.

Previous Leagues: London 1932-37, Athenian 1937-56

	10-11		11-12		12-13		13-14		14-15		15-16		16-17		17-18		18-19		19-20	
	Isth P	14	Isth P	21	Isth1S	16	Isth1S	11	Isth1S	11	Isth1S	17	Isth1S	1	Isth P	24	IsthSC	6	IsthSC	n&v
FAC	2Q		1Q		1Q		P		3Q		2Q		P		2Q		2Q		3Q	
FAT	1Q		1Q		P		P		P		1Q		1Q		1Q		EP		3Q	

HONOURS / RECORDS

FA Comps: None

League: Athenian 1949-50, 54-55. Isthmian 1975-76, 59-60, Division Two 2000-01, Division One South 2016-17.

County FA: London Senior Cup 1942-43, 48-49, 58-59, 59-60, 2006-07, 07-08, 15-16. Surrey Senior cup 1937-38, 43-44, 44-45, 52-53, 59-60, 75-76, 76-77, 77-78, 2007-07. Surrey Senior Shield 1951-52, 60-61, 61-62, 65-66.

Victory: 11-0 v Welton Rovers - FA Amateur Cup 1962-63

Defeat: 1-8 v Kingstonian - Surrey Senior Cup 1966-67

Goalscorer: Alan Ives - 92

Appearances: Danny Godwin - 470

Additional: Paid £9,000 to Enfield for David Flint. Received £10,000 from Luton Town for Herbie Smith.

GROUND: Imperial Fields, Bishopsford Road, Morden, Surrey SM4 6BF

Ground Capacity: 3,500   **Seats:** 612   **Covered:** 1,200   **Clubhouse:** Yes   **Shop:** Yes

Previous Grounds: Sandy Lane, Mitcham

Record Attendance: 17,500 v Queens Park Rangers - FA Cup 2nd Round 1956-57 (At Sandy Lane)

Nearest Railway Station Mitcham Tram Stop - 0.5km

Bus Route 280

UXBRIDGE

Founded 1871

Nickname: The Reds   **Club Colours:** Red & white

Club Contact Details
01895 443 557   sec@uxbridgefc.co.uk

Previous Names: Uxbridge Town 1923-45
Previous Leagues: Southern 1894-99, Greatt Western Suburban 1906-19, 20-23, Athenian 1919-20, 24-37, 63-82, Spartan 1937-38, London 1938-46, Great Western Comb. 1939-45, Corinthian 1946-63, Athenian 1963-82. Isthmian 1982-2004. Southern 2004-18.

10-11		11-12		12-13		13-14		14-15		15-16		16-17		17-18		18-19		19-20	
SthC	13	SthC	4	SthC	11	SthC	10	SthC	12	SthC	15	SthC	17	Sth1E	15	IsthSC	15	IsthSC	n&v
FAC	P	FAC	P	FAC	1Q	FAC	1Q	FAC	2Q	FAC	3Q	FAC	2Q	FAC	P	FAC	P	FAC	P
FAT	2P	FAT	1P	FAT	2Qr	FAT	P	FAT	2Q	FAT	P	FAT	1Q	FAT	P	FAT	EPr	FAT	1Q

HONOURS / RECORDS

FA Comps: None

League: Corinthian 1959-60.

County FA: Middlesex Senior Cup 1893-94, 95-96, 1950-51, 2000-01, Charity Cup 1907-08, 12-13, 35-36, 81-82, 2012-13, 13-14.
London Challenge Cup 1993-94, 96-97, 98-99.

Goalscorer: Phil Duff - 153

Appearances: Roger Nicholls - 1,054

Best FA Cup Second Round Proper 1873-74   **FA Amateur Cup:** Finalists 1897-98

FA Trophy Second Round Proper 1998-99, 99-2000, 00-01, 08-09

FA Vase Fourth Round Proper 1983-84

GROUND: Honeycroft, Horton Road, West Drayton, Middlesex UB7 8HX

Ground Capacity: 3,770   **Seats:** 339   **Covered:** 760   **Clubhouse:** Yes   **Shop:**
Previous Grounds: RAF Stadium 1923-48, Cleveland Road 1948-78
Record Attendance: 1,000 v Arsenal - Opening of the floodlights 1981

Nearest Railway Station West Drayton - 1km
Bus Route 350 & A10

WALTHAM ABBEY

Founded 1944

Nickname: Abbotts   **Club Colours:** Green and white hoops

Club Contact Details
01992 711 287

Previous Names: Abbey Sports amalgamated with Beechfield Sports in 1974 to form Beechfields. Club then renamed to Waltham Abbey in 1976
Previous Leagues: London Spartan/Spartan. Essex & Herts Border. Essex Senior.

10-11		11-12		12-13		13-14		14-15		15-16		16-17		17-18		18-19		19-20	
Isth1N	11	Isth1N	14	Isth1N	12	Isth1N	18	Isth1N	10	Isth1N	21	Isth1N	20	Isth1N	18	IsthSC	9	IsthSC	n&v
FAC	P	FAC	1Q	FAC	2Q	FAC	1Q	FAC	3Q	FAC	P	FAC	P	FAC	1Q	FAC	P	FAC	1Qr
FAT	P	FAT	Pr	FAT	1Q	FAT	1Q	FAC	2Q	FAT	2Q	FAT	1Q	FAT	1Q	FAT	EP	FAT	P

HONOURS / RECORDS

FA Comps: None

League: London Spartan Division One 1977-78, Senior Division 1978-79.

County FA: London Senior Cup 1998-99. Essex Senior Cup 2004-05.

Best FA Cup Third Qualifying Round 2014-15

FA Trophy First Qualifying Round 2006-07, 09-10, 12-13, 13-14

FA Vase Second Round Proper 1997-98

GROUND: Capershotts, Sewardstone Road, Waltham Abbey, Essex EN9 1NX

Ground Capacity: 3,500   **Seats:** 200   **Covered:** 500   **Clubhouse:** Yes   **Shop:** No
Previous Grounds: None
Record Attendance:

Nearest Railway Station Waltham Cross - 2km
Bus Route Catersfield - stop 100m away

WARE

Founded 1892

Nickname: Blues   **Club Colours:** Blue & white

Club Contact Details
01920 462 064

Previous Names: Ware Town.
Previous Leagues: East Herts, North Middlesex 1907-08, Herts County 1908-25, Spartan 1925-55, Delphian 1955-63, Athenian 1963-75, Isthmian 1975-2015. Southern 2015-16.

10-11		11-12		12-13		13-14		14-15		15-16		16-17		17-18		18-19		19-20	
Isth1N	14	Isth1N	21	Isth1N	19	Isth1N	21	Isth1N	10	SthC	11	Isth1N	22	Isth1N	20	IsthSC	7	IsthSC	n&v
FAC	P	FAC	P	FAC	1Q	FAC	P	FAC	P	FAC	P	FAC	P	FAC	2Q	FAC	1Q	FAC	3Q
FAT	P	FAT	P	FAT	P	FAT	Pr	FAT	1Q	FAT	P	FAT	2Q	FAT	1Q	FAT	P	FAT	1Q

HONOURS / RECORDS

FA Comps: None

League: East Herts 1897-88, 98-99, 99-1900, 02-03, 03-04, 05-06 (shared), 06-07. Herts County 1908-09, 21-22. Spartan Division Two B 1926-27, Division One 51-52, Premier 52-53. Isthmian Division Two 2005-06.

County FA: Herts Senior Cup 1898-99, 1903-04, 06-07, 21-22, 53-54. Herts Charity Shield 1926-27, 52-53, 56-57, 58-59, 62-63, 85-86. East Anglian Cup 1973-74.

Victory: 10-1 v Wood Green Town

Defeat: 0-11 v Barnet

Goalscorer: George Dearman scored 98 goals during 1926-27

Appearances: Gary Riddle - 654

GROUND: Wodson Park, Wadesmill Road, Ware, Herts SG12 0UQ

Ground Capacity: 3,300   **Seats:** 500   **Covered:** 312   **Clubhouse:** Yes   **Shop:** Yes
Previous Grounds: Highfields, Canons Park, London Road, Presdales Lower Park 1921-26
Record Attendance: 3,800 v Hendon - FA Amateur Cup, January 1957.

Nearest Railway Station Ware - 1.9km
Bus Route Wodson Park - stop 100m away

WESTFIELD

Founded 1953

Nickname: The Field   **Club Colours:** Amber & black

Club Contact Details
01483 771 106

Previous Names: None
Previous Leagues: Woking & District. Surrey Intermediate > 1962. Parthenon 1962-63. Surrey Senior 1963-78. Combined Counties (FM) 1978-2018.

10-11		11-12		12-13		13-14		14-15		15-16		16-17		17-18		18-19		19-20	
CC1	13	CC1	8	CC1	3	CCP	4	CCP	14	CCP	9	CCP	2	CCP	1	IsthSC	5	IsthSC	n&v
FAC	N/A	FAC	EP	FAC	EP	FAC	1Qr	FAC	P	FAC	EPr	FAC	EP	FAC	2Q	FAC	P	FAC	1Q
FAV	1Q	FAV	2Q	FAV	1Q	FAV	1P	FAV	2P	FAV	2Q	FAV	2Q	FAV	3P	FAT	Pr	FAT	2Qr

HONOURS / RECORDS

FA Comps: None

League: Surrey Senior League 1972-73, 73-74. Combined Counties Premier 2017-18.

County FA: Surrey County Junior Charity Cup 1954-55

Best FA Cup   Second Qualifying Round 2017-18

FA Vase   Fourth Round Proper 2000-01

FA Trophy   Second Qualifyig Round 2019-20(r)

GROUND: Woking Park, off Elmbridge Lane, Kingfield, Woking GU22 9BA

Ground Capacity: 1000   **Seats:** Yes   **Covered:** Yes   **Clubhouse:** Yes   **Shop:**
Previous Grounds: Moved to Woking Park in 1960
Record Attendance: 325 v Guernsey, Combined Counties Division One, 2011-12

Nearest Railway Station Woking
Bus Route Arriva 34, 35

ASHFORD UNITED

Founded 1930

Nickname: The Nuts & Bolts **Club Colours:** Green & white

Club Contact Details
01233 611 838 - info@ashfordunitedfc.com

Previous Names: Ashford Town 1930-2010.
Previous Leagues: Kent 1930-59. Southern 1959-2004. Isthmian 2004-10. Kent Invicta 2011-2013. Southern Counties East 2013-17.

10-11	11-12	12-13	13-14	14-15	15-16	16-17	17-18	18-19	19-20
	K_lv 5	K_lv 3	SCEP 2	SCEP 2	SCEP 3	SCEP 1	Isth1S 21	IsthSE 4	IsthSE n&v
		FAC P	FAC P	FAC P	FAC EP	FAC 1Q	FAC 1Q	FAC P	FAC 1Q
	FAV 1Qr	FAV 2Q	FAV 4P	FAV 4P	FAV QF	FAV 2P	FAT P	FAT EPr	FAT 1Q

HONOURS / RECORDS
FA Comps: None
League: Kent 1948-49. Southern Counties East 2016-17.

County FA: Kent Senior Cup 1958-59, 62-63, 92-93, 95-96. Kent Senior Trophy 2016-17.

Victory: 15-0 v Erith & Belvedere, Kent League, 28/04/1937.
Defeat: 3-14 v Folkestone Reserves, Kent League, 1933-34.
Goalscorer: Dave Arter - 197. Shaun Welford scored 48 goals during the 2016-17 season.
Stuart Zanone scored 7 v Lingfield (A), Southern Counties East, 24/03/2015.
Appearances: Peter McRobert - 765

GROUND: The Homelands, Ashford Road TN26 1NJ

Ground Capacity: 3,200 **Seats:** 500 **Covered:** Yes **Clubhouse:** Yes **Shop:**
Previous Grounds: Essella Park 1931-1987.
Record Attendance: At Essella Park - 6,525 v Crystal Palace, FAC 1st Rnd, 1959-60. At Homelands - 3,363 v Fulham, FAC 1st , 1994-95.

Nearest Railway Station Ham Street - 4.2km
Bus Route Smithfields Crossroads - stop 600m away

BURGESS HILL TOWN

Founded 1882

Nickname: Hillians **Club Colours:** Green & black

Club Contact Details
01444 871 514

Previous Names: Burgess Hill 1882-1969.
Previous Leagues: Mid Sussex >1958, Sussex County 1958-2003, Southern 2003-04

10-11	11-12	12-13	13-14	14-15	15-16	16-17	17-18	18-19	19-20
Isth1S 7	Isth1S 20	Isth1S 8	Isth1S 6	Isth1S 1	Isth P 21	Isth P 20	Isth P 23	Isth P 21	IsthSE n&v
FAC 2Q	FAC P	FAC P	FAC 2Q	FAC 4Q	FAC 1Q	FAC 4Qr	FAC 4Q	FAC 2Q	FAC P
FAT 1Q	FAT 1Q	FAT Pr	FAT Pr	FAT 2P	FAT 1Q	FAT 3Q	FAT 2Q	FAT 1Qr	FAT P

HONOURS / RECORDS
FA Comps: None
League: Mid-Sussex 1900-01, 03-04, 39-40, 56-57. Sussex County Division Two 1974-75, Division One 75-76, 96-97, 98-99, 2001-02, 02-03. Isthmian Division One South 2014-15.
County FA: Sussex Senior Cup 1883-84, 84-85, 85-86.

Goalscorer: Ashley Carr - 208
Appearances: Paul Williams - 499
Best FA Cup Fourth Qualifying Round 1999-2000, 08-09, 14-15, 16-17(r), 17-18.
FA Trophy Second Round Proper 2003-04, 04-05, 14-15.
FA Vase Quarter Finals 2001-02.

GROUND: Green Elephant Stadium, Leylands Park, Maple Drive, Burgess Hill, West Sussex RH15 8DL

Ground Capacity: 2,500 **Seats:** 408 **Covered:** Yes **Clubhouse:** Yes **Shop:** Yes
Previous Grounds: Moved to Leylands Park in 1969.
Record Attendance: 2,005 v AFC Wimbledon - Isthmian League Division One 2004-05

Nearest Railway Station Wivelsfield - 0.3m
Bus Route 270, 271 & 272

CHICHESTER CITY

Founded 2000

Nickname: Lillywhites   **Club Colours:** White & green

Club Contact Details
01243 533 368
secretary@chichestercityfc.co.uk

Previous Names: Chichester FC (pre 1948), Chichester City 1948-2000. Merged with Portfield in 2000, Chicester City United 2000-09
Previous Leagues: Sussex County/Southern Combination >2019

10-11	11-12	12-13	13-14	14-15	15-16	16-17	17-18	18-19	19-20
SxC1 14	SxC1 20	SxC1 19	SxC1 11	SxC1 14	SCP 5	SCP 3	SCP 6	SCP 1	IsthSE n&v
FAC EP	FAC EPr	FAC EP	FAC EP	FAC EP	FAC P	FAC EP	FAC EP	FAC EP	FAC 2P
FAV 1P	FAV 2P	FAV 2Q	FAV 1Q	FAV 1Q	FAV 1Q	FAV 4P	FAV 5P	FAV 2P	FAT P

HONOURS / RECORDS

FA Comps: None

League: Sussex County Division One 2003-04. Southern Combination Premier 2018-19.

County FA: Sussex RUR Cup 2006-07

FA Cup	Second Round Proper 2019-20 (Due to Bury folding, the club were the lucky ones to get a bye to the Second Round.)
FA Vase	Fifth Round Proper 2017-18
FA Trophy	Preliminary Round 2019-20

GROUND: Oaklands Park, Chichester, W Sussex PO19 6AR

Ground Capacity: 2,000   **Seats:** none   **Covered:** 200   **Clubhouse:** Yes   **Shop:** Yes
Previous Grounds: Church Road (Portfield) 2000-08.
Record Attendance: Not known

Nearest Railway Station Chichester - 1.2km
Bus Route University - stop 182m away

CRAY VALLEY PAPER MILLS

Founded 1919

Nickname: Millers   **Club Colours:** Green & black

Club Contact Details
07838 344 451

Previous Names: None
Previous Leagues: Sidcup & Kent 1919. Kent County Amateur >55. South London Alliance 55-91. Spartan 1991-97,
Spartan South Midlands 1997-98, London Intermediate 1998-01, Kent County 2001-11, Kent/Southern Co East 2011-19.

10-11	11-12	12-13	13-14	14-15	15-16	16-17	17-18	18-19	19-20
KC P 3	Kent P 11	Kent P 8	SCE 7	SCE 7	SCE 10	SCEP 4	SCEP 6	SCEP 1	IsthSE n&v
			FAC P	FAC EP	FAC P	FAC P	FAC 1Q	FAC 2Q	FAC P
		FAV 1Q	FAV 2Pr	FAV 2Q	FAV 1P	FAV 1Q	FAV 1P	FAV F	FAT P

HONOURS / RECORDS

FA Comps: None

League: Sidcup & Kent Division Two 1919-20. South Kent County Division Three (Western) 1933-37, Division One West 2002-03, Premier Division 2004-05. London Alliance Premier Division 1980-81. Southern Counties Premier 2018-19.
County FA: Kent Junior Cup 1921-22, 77-78, 80-81. Kent Intermediate Shield 2004-05.
London Intermediate Cup 2002-03, 03-04, 09-10. London Senior Cup 2016-17.

FA Cup	Second Qualifying Round 2018-19
FA Vase	Runners-up 2018-19
FA Trophy	Preliminary Round 2019-20

GROUND: Badgers Sports Ground, Middle Park Avenue, Eltham SE9 5HT

Ground Capacity: 1,000   **Seats:** 100   **Covered:** Yes   **Clubhouse:** Yes   **Shop:**
Previous Grounds: St Paul's Cray paper mills sports ground 1919-81. Played at many grounds until permanent move to Badgers.
Record Attendance: 663 v Canterbury City, FA Vase semi-final, 17/03/2019

Nearest Railway Station Mottingham - 30min walk from ground.
Bus Route 160 stops outside the ground.

EAST GRINSTEAD TOWN

Founded 1890

Nickname: The Wasps **Club Colours:** Amber & black stripes (Blue & yellow)

Club Contact Details
01342 325 885

Previous Names: East Grinstead 1890-1997.
Previous Leagues: Mid Sussex, Sussex County, Souhern Amateur 1928-35. Sussex County 1935-2014.

10-11		11-12		12-13		13-14		14-15		15-16		16-17		17-18		18-19		19-20	
SxC1	7	SxC1	9	SxC1	8	SxC1	2	Isth1S	22	Isth1S	20	Isth1S	18	Isth1S	22	IsthSE	13	IsthSE	n&v
FAC	1Q					FAC	EP	FAC	Pr	FAC	P	FAC	P	FAC	1Q	FAC	2Q	FAC	P
FAV	2Q			FAV	1Qr	FAV	2P	FAT	Pr	FAT	1Q	FAT	1Q	FAT	P	FAT	1Q	FAT	P

HONOURS / RECORDS
FA Comps: None
League: Mid-Sussex 1901-02, 36-37. Southern Amateur DivisioN Three 1931-32. Sussex County Division Two 2007-08.

County FA: Sussex RUR Cup 2003-04.

Appearances:	Guy Hill
Best FA Cup	Second Qualifying Round 1947-48, 50-51, 52-53, 71-72, 2018-19
FA Trophy	First Qualifying Round 2015-16, 16-17, 18-19
FA Vase	Third Round Proper 1974-75

GROUND: College Lane, East Court, East Grinstead RH19 3LS

Ground Capacity: 3,000 **Seats:** Yes **Covered:** Yes **Clubhouse:** Yes **Shop:** No
Previous Grounds: West Ground 1890-1962. King George's Field 1962-67.
Record Attendance: 2,006 v Lancing F A Am Cup, November 1947

Nearest Railway Station East Grinstead - 1.1km
Bus Route East Court - stop 100m away

FAVERSHAM TOWN

Founded 1884

Nickname: Lillywhites **Club Colours:** White & black

Club Contact Details
01795 591 000

Previous Names: Faversham Invicta, Faversham Services, Faversham Railway and Faversham Rangers pre War.
Previous Leagues: Kent 1884-1900, 1904-12, 24-34, 37-59, 66-71, 76-2003. Kent County 1934-37. Aetolian 1959-63. Greater London 1964-66.
Metropolitan London 1971-73. Athenian 1973-76. Kent County 2005-10.

10-11		11-12		12-13		13-14		14-15		15-16		16-17		17-18		18-19		19-20	
Isth1S	8	Isth1S	17	Isth1S	3	Isth1S	10	Isth1S	3	Isth1S	5	Isth1S	10	Isth1S	19	IsthSE	17	IsthSE	n&v
FAC	1Q	FAC	1Q	FAC	1Qr	FAC	2Q	FAC	2Q	FAC	1Qr	FAC	3Qr	FAC	2Q	FAC	1Q	FAC	P
FAT	1Q	FAT	2Q	FAT	1Q	FAT	P	FAT	1Q	FAT	P	FAT	1Q	FAT	P	FAT	P	FAT	P

HONOURS / RECORDS
FA Comps: None
League: Kent 1969-70, 70-71, 77-78, 89-90, Division Two 1895-96. Kent County 2009-10.

County FA: Kent Amateur Cup 1956-57, 58-59, 71-72, 72-73, 73-74. Kent Senior Trophy 1976-77, 77-78.

Best FA Cup	Third Qualifying Round 2016-17
FA Trophy	Second Qualifying Round 201-12
FA Vase	Third Round Proper 1991-92

GROUND: The Aquatherm Stadium, Salters Lane, Faversham Kent ME13 8ND

Ground Capacity: 2,000 **Seats:** 200 **Covered:** 1,800 **Clubhouse:** Yes **Shop:** No
Previous Grounds: Moved in to Salters Lane in 1948.
Record Attendance:

Nearest Railway Station Faversham - 0.5m
Bus Route 3 & 666

GUERNSEY

Nickname: Green Lions   **Club Colours:** Green & white

Founded 2011

Club Contact Details
01481 747 279

Previous Names: None
Previous Leagues: Combined Counties 2011-13.

10-11	11-12	12-13	13-14	14-15	15-16	16-17	17-18	18-19	19-20
	CC1 1	CCP 2	Isth1S 4	Isth1S 10	Isth1S 13	Isth1S 21	Isth1S 18	IsthSE 18	IsthSE n&v
			FAC 2Q	FAC P	FAC Pr	FAC Pr	FAC Pr	FAC Pr	
		FAV SF	FAT 1Q	FAT 1Q	FAT P	FAT P	FAT P		FAT P

HONOURS / RECORDS

FA Comps: None
League: Combined Counties Division One 2011-12.

County FA: None

Victory:	11-0 v Crawley Down Gatwick, Isthmian Division One South, 01/01/2014
Defeat:	0-8 v Merstham, Isthmian Division One South, 18/11/2014
Goalscorer:	Ross Allen - 239 in 226 appearances. (Scored 57 in all competitions during 2011-12)
FA Cup	Second Qualifying Round 2013-14 **FA Trophy** First Qualifying Round 2013-14 14-15
FA Vase	Semi Finals 2012-13

GROUND: Footes Lane Stadium, St Peter Port, Guernsey GY1 2UL

Ground Capacity: 5,000   **Seats:** 720   **Covered:** Yes   **Clubhouse:** Yes   **Shop:** No
Previous Grounds: None
Record Attendance: 4,290 v. Spennymoor Town, FA Vase semi-final first leg, 23/03/2013

Nearest Railway Station N/A
Bus Route Bus stops outside the ground

HASTINGS UNITED

Nickname: The U's or The Arrows   **Club Colours:** All white

Founded 1894

Club Contact Details
01424 444 635

Previous Names: Rock-a-Nore 1894-1921. Hastings and St Leonards Amateurs 1921-79. Hastings Town 1979-2002.
Previous Leagues: South Eastern 1904-05, Southern 1905-10, Sussex County 1921-27, 52-85, Southern Amateur 1927-46, Corinthian 1946-48

10-11	11-12	12-13	13-14	14-15	15-16	16-17	17-18	18-19	19-20
Isth P 18	Isth P 18	Isth P 22	Isth1S 5	Isth1S 19	Isth1S 7	Isth1S 5	Isth1S 9	IsthSE 3	IsthSE n&v
FAC 1Q	FAC 1Q	FAC 3P	FAC 1Q	FAC 2Q	FAC 3Q	FAC 3Q	FAC 1Q	FAC 3Q	FAC 1Qr
FAT 1Qr	FAT 1Q	FAT 1Q	FAT 1Q	FAT 2Q	FAT P	FAT 2Q	FAT 2Qr	FAT P	FAT 3Q

HONOURS / RECORDS

FA Comps: None
League: Southern Division Two B 1909-10, Southern Division 1991-92, Eastern Division 2001-01.
       Sussex County Division Two 1979-80.
County FA: Sussex Senior Cup 1935-36, 37-38, 95-96, 97-98.

Goalscorer:	Terry White scored 33 during 1999-2000
Additional:	Paid £8,000 to Ashford Town for Nicky Dent
	Received £50,000 from Nottingham Forest for Paul Smith

GROUND: The Pilot Field, Elphinstone Road, Hastings TN34 2AX

Ground Capacity: 4,050   **Seats:** 800   **Covered:** 1,750   **Clubhouse:** Yes   **Shop:** Yes
Previous Grounds: Bulverhythe Recreation > 1976
Record Attendance: 4,888 v Nottingham Forest - Friendly 23/06/1996

Nearest Railway Station Ore - 0.9km. Hastings - 1.9km.
Bus Route 2 & 21A

HAYWARDS HEATH TOWN

Founded 1888

Nickname: The Blues   **Club Colours:** Blue & white

Club Contact Details
07796 677 661

Previous Names: Haywards Heath Juniors 1888-94. Haywards Heath Excelsior 1894-95. Haywards Heath 1895-1989.
Previous Leagues: Mid-Sussex 1888-1927. Sussex County/Southern Combination 1927-52, 61-2018. Metropolitan 1952-61.

10-11	11-12	12-13	13-14	14-15	15-16	16-17	17-18	18-19	19-20
SxC3 8	SxC3 15	SxC3 2	SxC2 5	SxC2 9	SC1 1	SCP 2	SCP 1	IsthSE 5	IsthSE n&v
				FAC EP		FAC P	FAC 1Qr	FAC EP	FAC 1Q
	FAV 1Qr		FAV 2Q	FAV 1Q	FAV 2P	FAV 2P	FAV 2P	FAT P	FAT 2Q

HONOURS / RECORDS

FA Comps: None
League: Sussex County/Southern Combination 1949-50, 69-70, 2017-18, Eastern Division 45-46/ Division One 2015-16.

County FA: Sussex Senior Cup 1941-42, 57-58. Sussex RUR Cup 1943-44, 66-67, 74-75, 75-76. Sussex Intermediate Cup 2012-13

Best FA Cup	Fourth Qualifying Round 1945-46
FA Vase	Third Round Proper 1990-91
FA Trophy	Second Qualifying Round 2019-20

GROUND: Hanbury Park Stadium, Haywards Heath RH16 3PT

Ground Capacity: 2,000   **Seats:** Yes   **Covered:** Yes   **Clubhouse:** Yes   **Shop:**
Previous Grounds:
Record Attendance:

Nearest Railway Station Haywards HEath - 1.9km
Bus Route Market Square - stop 84m away

HERNE BAY

Founded 1886

Nickname: The Bay   **Club Colours:** Blue & white

Club Contact Details
01227 374 156

Previous Names: None.
Previous Leagues: East Kent. Faversham & Dist. Cantebury & Dist. Kent Am. Aetolian 1959-64. Athenian 1964-74.

10-11	11-12	12-13	13-14	14-15	15-16	16-17	17-18	18-19	19-20
Kent P 2	Kent P 1	Isth1S 19	Isth1S 18	Isth1S 9	Isth1S 8	Isth1S 17	Isth1S 12	IsthSE 15	IsthSE n&v
FAC EP	FAC 1Q	FAC P	FAC Pr	FAC 1Q	FAC 2Qr	FAC 2Qr	FAC 3Q	FAC 1Q	FAC 1Q
FAV 4P	FAV SF	FAT P	FAT 1Qr	FAT P	FAT 2Qr	FAT 1Qr	FAT P	FAT 2Q	FAT P

HONOURS / RECORDS

FA Comps: None
League: East Kent 1902-03, 03-04, 04-05, 05-06. Athenian Division Two 1970-71. Kent 1991-92, 93-94, 96-97, 97-98, 2011-12, Division Two 1954-55.
County FA: Kent Amateur Cup 1957-58. Kent Senior Trophy 1978-79, 1996-97.

Victory:	19-3 v Hythe Wanderers - Feb 1900.
Defeat:	0-11 v 7th Dragon Guards - Oct 1907.
Misc:	Most League Victories in a Season: 34 - 1996-97.

GROUND: Winch's Field, Stanley Gardens, Herne Bay CT6 5SG

Ground Capacity: 3,000   **Seats:** 200   **Covered:** 1,500   **Clubhouse:** Yes   **Shop:** Yes
Previous Grounds: Mitchell's Athletic Ground. Herne Bay Memorial Park.
Record Attendance: 2,303 v Margate, FA Cup 4th Qual. 1970-71.

Nearest Railway Station Herne Bay - 0.8km
Bus Route Triangle - alighting at Spenser Road East

HYTHE TOWN

Nickname: The Cannons   **Club Colours:** Red & white

Founded 1910

Club Contact Details
01303 264 932 / 238 256

Previous Names: Hythe Town 1910-1992, Hythe United 1992-2001
Previous Leagues: Kent Amateur League, Kent League, Southern League, Kent County League, Kent League.

10-11		11-12		12-13		13-14		14-15		15-16		16-17		17-18		18-19		19-20	
Kent P	1	Isth1S	8	Isth1S	4	Isth1S	8	Isth1S	16	Isth1S	4	Isth1S	7	Isth1S	7	IsthSE	7	IsthSE	n&v
FAC	1P	FAC	2Q	FAC	P	FAC	P	FAC	2Q	FAC	P	FAC	2Q	FAC	Pr	FAC	1Q	FAC	P
FAV	3P	FAT	2Q	FAT	1Qr	FAT	2Qr	FAT	1Q	FAT	P	FAT	1P	FAT	1Q	FAT	1Q	FAT	P

HONOURS / RECORDS

FA Comps: None
League: Kent County Eastern Division Two 1936-37, Division One 71-72, Premier Division 73-74, 74-75, 75-76.
Kent League 1988-89, 2010-11.
County FA: Kent Senior Cup 2011-12.
Kent Senior Trophy 1990-91.
Victory: 10-1 v Sporting Bengal, 2008-09
Defeat: 1-10 v Swanley Furness, 1997-98
Goalscorer: Dave Cook - 130
Appearances: John Walker - 354, Jason Brazier - 349, Dave Cook - 346, Lee Winfield - 344

GROUND: Reachfields Stadium, Fort Road, Hythe CT21 6JS

Ground Capacity: 3,000   **Seats:** 350   **Covered:** 2,400   **Clubhouse:** Yes   **Shop:** Yes
Previous Grounds: South Road 1910-77.
Record Attendance: 2,147 v Yeading, FA Vase Semi-Final, 1990.

Nearest Railway Station Hythe - 0.5km
Bus Route 10, 102, 104 & 16

PHOENIX SPORTS

Nickname: None   **Club Colours:** Green & black

Founded 1935

Club Contact Details
07795 182 927

Previous Names: St Johns Welling. Lakeside. Phoenix.
Previous Leagues: Spartan League. Kent County > 2011. Kent Invicta 2011-13. Southern Counties East 2013-15.

10-11		11-12		12-13		13-14		14-15		15-16		16-17		17-18		18-19		19-20	
KC P	5	K_lv	2	K_lv	1	SCE	6	SCE	1	Isth1N	14	Isth1N	8	Isth1N	11	IsthSE	9	IsthSE	n&v
								FAC	EPr	FAC	2Q	FAC	P	FAC	3Q	FAC	1Qr	FAC	P
						FAV	1P	FAV	5P	FAT	1Qr	FAT	2Q	FAT	P	FAT	Pr	FAT	1Q

HONOURS / RECORDS

FA Comps: None
League: Kent County Division One West 1999-2000, 2007-08, Division Two West 2004-05. Kent Invicta 2012-13.
Southern Counties East 2014-15.
County FA: London Senior Trophy 2017-18

Best FA Cup   Third Qualifying Round 2017-18
FA Trophy   Second Qualifying Round 2016-17
FA Vase   Fifth Round Proper 2014-15

GROUND: Mayplace Ground, Mayplace Road East, Barnehurst, Kent DA7 6JT

Ground Capacity: 2,000   **Seats:** 439   **Covered:** Yes   **Clubhouse:** Yes   **Shop:** No
Previous Grounds: Danson Park >1950.
Record Attendance: Not known

Nearest Railway Station Barnehurst - 1.1km
Bus Route 492 stops at the ground

RAMSGATE

Nickname: The Rams   **Club Colours:** All red

Founded 1945

Club Contact Details
01843 591 662

Previous Names: Ramsgate Athletic > 1972
Previous Leagues: Kent 1945-59, 1976-2005, Southern 1959-76

	10-11	11-12	12-13	13-14	14-15	15-16	16-17	17-18	18-19	19-20
	Isth1S 9	Isth1S 10	Isth1S 7	Isth1S 12	Isth1S 21	Isth1S 12	Isth1S 12	Isth1S 16	IsthSE 11	IsthSE n&v
FAC	Pr	Pr	P	P	1Q	P	1Q	2Q	3Q	2Q
FAT	1Qr	P	3Q	3Q	P	1Q	P	P	1Q	EPr

HONOURS / RECORDS

FA Comps: None

League: Kent Division One 1949-50, 55-56, 56-57, Premier 1998-99, 2004-05. Isthmian Division One 2005-06.

County FA: Kent Senior Shield 1960-61, 67-68, 68-69. Kent Senior Cup 1963-64. Kent Senior Trophy 1987-88, 88-89, 98-99.

Victory:	11-0 & 12-1 v Canterbury City - Kent League 2000-01
Goalscorer:	Mick Willimson
Best FA Cup	First Round Proper 1955-56, 2005-06
FA Trophy	Third Qualifying Round 1969-70, 75-76, 2008-09, 09-10, 12-13, 13-14
FA Vase	Quarter Finals 1999-2000

GROUND: Southwood Stadium, Prices Avenue, Ramsgate, Kent CT11 0AN

Ground Capacity: 2,500   **Seats:** 400   **Covered:** 600   **Clubhouse:** Yes   **Shop:** Yes
Previous Grounds: None
Record Attendance: 5,038 v Margate - 1956-57

Nearest Railway Station Ramsgate - 1km
Bus Route The Loop towards Ramsgate - alight at South Eastern Road

---

SEVENOAKS TOWN

Nickname: Town   **Club Colours:** Blue & black

Founded 1883

Club Contact Details
07876 444 274   secretary@sevenoakstownfc.co.uk

Previous Names: None.
Previous Leagues: Sevenoaks League. Kent Amateur/County. Kent/Southern Counties East >2018.

	10-11	11-12	12-13	13-14	14-15	15-16	16-17	17-18	18-19	19-20
	Kent P 7	Kent P 14	Kent P 17	SCE 16	SCE 8	SCE 5	SCEP 3	SCEP 1	IsthSE 10	IsthSE n&v
FAC	EP	P	EP	EP	EP	EPr	2Qr	1Q	1Qr	1Q
FAV	1Q	2Q	1P	1P	1Q	2Q	2Q	3P	1Q	
FAT										P

HONOURS / RECORDS

FA Comps: None

League: Kent County 1984-85, 95-96, 2002-03. Southern Counties East Premier 2017-18.

County FA:

Best FA Cup	Second Qualifying Round 2016-17(r)
FA Vase	Third Round Proper 2017-18
FA Trophy	First Qualifying Round 2018-19

GROUND: Greatness Park, Mill Lane, Sevenoaks TN14 5BX

Ground Capacity: 2,000   **Seats:** 150   **Covered:** 200   **Clubhouse:** Yes   **Shop:**
Previous Grounds: None
Record Attendance:

Nearest Railway Station Bat & Ball - 0.4km
Bus Route 308 & 402

SITTINGBOURNE

Nickname: Brickies   **Club Colours:** Red & black

Founded 1886

Club Contact Details
01795 410 777

Previous Names: Sittingbourne United 1881-86
Previous Leagues: Kent 1894-1905, 1909-27, 30-39, 46-59, 68-91, South Eastern 1905-09, Southern 1927-30, 59-67

10-11		11-12		12-13		13-14		14-15		15-16		16-17		17-18		18-19		19-20	
Isth1S	11	Isth1S	19	Isth1S	9	Isth1S	14	Isth1S	12	Isth1S	18	Isth1S	15	Isth1S	14	IsthSE	16	IsthSE	n&v
FAC	P	FAC	1Q	FAC	1Q	FAC	3Q	FAC	P	FAC	2Q	FAC	Pr	FAC	Pr	FAC	1Q	FAC	1Q
FAT	P	FAT	1Q	FAT	1Q	FAT	P	FAT	P	FAT	P	FAT	P	FAT	2Qr	FAT	1Q	FAT	P

HONOURS / RECORDS

FA Comps: None

League: Kent 1902-03, 57-58, 58-59, 75-76, 83-84, 90-91. Southern Southern Division 1992-93, 95-96.

County FA: Kent Senior Cup 1901-02, 28-29, 29-30, 57-58.

Victory: 15-0 v Orpington, Kent League 1922-23)
Defeat: 0-10 v Wimbledon, SL Cup 1965-66)
Additional: Paid £20,000 to Ashford Town for Lee McRobert 1993
                    Received £210,000 from Millwall for Neil Emblem and Michael Harle 1993

GROUND: Woodstock Park, Broadoak Road, Sittingbourne ME9 8AG
Ground Capacity: 3,000   **Seats:** 300   **Covered:** 600   **Clubhouse:** Yes   **Shop:** Yes
Previous Grounds: Sittingbourne Rec. 1881-90, Gore Court 1890-92, The Bull Ground 1892-1990. Central Park 1990-2001
Record Attendance: 5,951 v Tottenham Hotspur - Friendly 26/01/1993

Nearest Railway Station Sittingbourne - 3.1km
Bus Route Kent Science Park - stop 500m away

THREE BRIDGES

Nickname: Bridges   **Club Colours:** Yellow & black

Founded 1901

Club Contact Details
01293 442 000

Previous Names: Three Bridges Worth 1936-52. Three Bridges United 1953-64.
Previous Leagues: Mid Sussex, E Grinstead, Redhill & Dist 36-52. Sussex County/Southern Combintion >2012, 2017-18. Isthmian 2012-17.

10-11		11-12		12-13		13-14		14-15		15-16		16-17		17-18		18-19		19-20	
SxC1	5	SxC1	1	Isth1S	21	Isth1S	19	Isth1S	7	Isth1S	14	Isth1S	23	SCP	2	IsthSE	14	IsthSE	n&v
FAC	P	FAC	EP	FAC	P	FAC	1Q	FAC	Pr	FAC	P	FAC	P	FAC	P	FAC	P	FAC	P
FAV	3P	FAV	4Pr	FAT	2Q	FAT	2Q	FAT	1Q	FAT	P	FAT	P	FAV	1P	FAT	P	FAT	EP

HONOURS / RECORDS

FA Comps: None

League: Sussex County Division One 1953-54, 2011-12.

County FA: Sussex RUR Charity Cup 1982-83, 87-88, 2007-08

Appearances: John Malthouse
Best FA Cup   Second Qualifying Round 1982-83, 83-84, 2002-03
FA Vase   Fifth Round Proper 1981-82
FA Trophy   Preliminary Round 2018-19

GROUND: Jubilee Walk, Three Bridges Road, Crawley, RH10 1LQ
Ground Capacity: 3,500   **Seats:** 120   **Covered:** 600   **Clubhouse:** Yes   **Shop:**
Previous Grounds: None
Record Attendance: 2,000 v Horsham 1948

Nearest Railway Station Three Bridges - 0.4km
Bus Route Jubilee Walk - stop 71m away

VCD ATHLETIC

Founded 1916

Nickname: The Vickers   **Club Colours:** Green & white

Club Contact Details

01322 524 262   davejoyo@yahoo.co.uk

Previous Names: Vickers (Erith). Vickers (Crayford) Now Vickers Crayford Dartford Athletic.
Previous Leagues: Dartford & District. Kent County 1997-2009, 2010-13. Isthmian 2009-10.

10-11	11-12	12-13	13-14	14-15	15-16	16-17	17-18	18-19	19-20
Kent P 3	Kent P 3	Kent P 2	Isth1N 1	Isth P 18	Isth P 24	Isth1N 15	Isth1S 17	IsthSE 6	IsthSE n&v
FAC Pr	FAC 2Qr	FAC 1Q	FAC P	FAC 2Q	FAC 1Qr	FAC 2Q	FAC P	FAC P	FAC 1Q
FAV 2P	FAV 3Pr	FAV 1Pr	FAT Pr	FAT 1Q	FAT 2Q	FAT 1Q	FAT P	FAT 1Q	FAT P

HONOURS / RECORDS

FA Comps: None

League: Kent County 1952-53, 63-64, 96-97. Kent 2008-09. Isthmian Division One North 2013-14.

County FA: Kent Junior Cup 1926-27. Kent Amateur Cup 1961-62, 63-64. Kent Intermediate Cup 1995-96.
Kent Senior Trophy 2005-06, 08-09.
Best FA Cup Second Qualifying Round 2002-03, 08-09, 11-12(r), 14-15, 16-17
FA Trophy Second Qualifying Round 2015-16
FA Vase Fifth Round Proper 2005-06, 06-07

GROUND: Oakwood, Old Road, Crayford DA1 4DN

Ground Capacity: 1,180   **Seats:** Yes   **Covered:** Yes   **Clubhouse:** Yes   **Shop:** No
Previous Grounds: Groundshared with Thamesmead (5 seasons), Lordswood (2) and Greenwich Boro' (1) whilst waiting for planning at Oakwood.
Record Attendance: 13,500 Away v Maidstone, 1919.

Nearest Railway Station Crayford - 0.9km
Bus Route 492 & 96

WHITEHAWK

Founded 1945

Nickname: Hawks   **Club Colours:** Red and white

Club Contact Details

01273 601 244

Previous Names: Whitehawk & Manor Farm Old Boys untill 1960.
Previous Leagues: Brighton & Hove District >1952. Sussex County 1952-2010. Isthmian 2010-13. Conference/National 2013-18.

10-11	11-12	12-13	13-14	14-15	15-16	16-17	17-18	18-19	19-20
Isth1S 3	Isth1S 1	Isth P 1	Conf S 19	Conf S 4	Nat S 5	Nat S 17	Nat S 21	Isth P 20	IsthSE n&v
FAC 3Q	FAC 2Qr	FAC 2Qr	FAC 2Q	FAC 3Qr	FAC 2Pr	FAC 1Pr	FAC 2Q	FAC 3Q	FAC 1Q
FAT 1Q	FAT 1Q	FAT 3Q	FAT 2Pr	FAT 3Q	FAT 1P	FAT 2P	FAT 1P	FAT 1Q	FAT P

HONOURS / RECORDS

FA Comps: None

League: Sussex County League Division One 1961-62, 63-64, 83-84, 2009-10, Division Two 1967-68, 80-81.
Isthmian League Division One South 2011-12, Premier Division 2012-13.
County FA: Sussex Senior Cup 1950-51, 61-62, 2011-12, 14-15. Sussex RUR Charity Cup 1954-55, 58-59, 90-91.

Goalscorer: Billy Ford
Appearances: Ken Powell - 1,103
Victory: 14-0 v Southdown (H), Sussex Junior Cup Second Round, 27/03/1948.
Defeat: 2-13 v St Luke's Terrace Old Boys (A), Brighton & Hove District Division Two, 02/11/1946.
Misc: Scored 127 goals in 32 matches during the 1961-62 season.

GROUND: East Brighton Park, Wilson Avenue, Brighton BN2 5TS

Ground Capacity: 3,000   **Seats:** 800   **Covered:** Yes   **Clubhouse:** Yes   **Shop:** No
Previous Grounds: N/A
Record Attendance: 2,174 v Dagenham & Redbridge, FA Cup Second Round Proper replay, 6th December 2015.

Nearest Railway Station Brighton Central - two & half miles from the ground.
Bus Route B&H Bus No.7 or 27

WHITSTABLE TOWN

Founded 1886

Nickname: Oystermen or Natives   **Club Colours:** Red & white

Club Contact Details
01227 266 012

Previous Names: None

Previous Leagues: East Kent 1897-1909, Kent 1909-59, 67-2007, Aetolian 1959-60, 63-64, Kent Amateur 1960-62, 64-67, South East Anglian 1962-63, Isthmian 2007-16. Southern Counties East 2016-18.

10-11		11-12		12-13		13-14		14-15		15-16		16-17		17-18		18-19		19-20	
Isth1S	15	Isth1S	18	Isth1S	17	Isth1S	20	Isth1S	8	Isth1S	23	SCEP	5	SCEP	2	IsthSE	12	IsthSE	n&v
FAC	2Q	FAC	P	FAC	P	FAC	Pr	FAC	1Q	FAC	1Qr	FAC	Pr	FAC	EP	FAC	1Q	FAC	1Q
FAT	P	FAT	P	FAT	2Q	FAT	2P	FAT	P	FAT	P	FAV	1Qr	FAV	3P	FAT	1Q	FAT	P

HONOURS / RECORDS

FA Comps: None

League: Kent Division Two (Mid Kent) 1927-28, Division Two 33-34, 49-50, Premier Division 2006-07. Kent Amateur Eastern Division 1960-61

County FA:

Goalscorer: Barry Godfrey

Appearances: Frank Cox - 429 (1950-60)

Best FA Cup   Third Qualifying Round 1957-58, 88-89, 89-90

FA Trophy   Second Round Proper 2013-14

FA Vase   Fifth Round Proper 1996-97

GROUND: The Belmont Ground, Belmont Road, Belmont, Whitstable CT5 1QP

Ground Capacity: 3,000   **Seats:** 500   **Covered:** 1,000   **Clubhouse:** Yes   **Shop:** Yes

Previous Grounds: None

Record Attendance: 2,500 v Gravesend & Northfleet - FA Cup 19/10/1987.   **Previous Lges:** Greater London 1964-67, Kent 1967-2007. Isthmian 2007-16.

Nearest Railway Station Whitstable 400 yards away

Bus Route 4, 638 & Triangle

WHYTELEAFE

Founded 1946

Nickname: The Leafe   **Club Colours:** White with green

Club Contact Details
0208 660 5491

Previous Names: None

Previous Leagues: Caterham & Ed, Croydon. Thornton Heath & District. Surrey Interm. (East) 1954-58. Surrey Senior 1958-75. Spartan 1975-81. Athenian 1981-84. Isthmian 1984-2012.

10-11		11-12		12-13		13-14		14-15		15-16		16-17		17-18		18-19		19-20	
Isth1S	16	Isth1S	21	Kent P	6	SCE	1	Isth1S	5	Isth1S	15	Isth1S	14	Isth1S	8	IsthSE	8	IsthSE	n&v
FAC	P	FAC	Pr	FAC	EP	FAC	2Q	FAC	1Q	FAC	P	FAC	2Q	FAC	Pr	FAC	1Qr	FAC	4Q
FAT	Pr	FAT	1Q	FAV	1P	FAV	2P	FAT	2Q	FAT	P	FAT	P	FAT	P	FAT	1Q	FAT	P

HONOURS / RECORDS

FA Comps: None

League: Surrey Senior Premier Division 1968-69. Southern Counties East 2013-14.

County FA: Surrey Senior Cup 1968-69.

Misc: Paid £1,000 to Carshalton Athletic for Gary Bowyer
Received £25,000 for Steve Milton

Best FA Cup   First Round Proper 1999-2000

FA Trophy   Fourth Round Proper 1998-99

FA Vase   FiFth Round Proper 1980-81, 85-86

GROUND: 15 Church Road, Whyteleafe, Surrey CR3 0AR

Ground Capacity: 2,000   **Seats:** 400   **Covered:** 600   **Clubhouse:** Yes   **Shop:** Yes

Previous Grounds: None

Record Attendance: 2,210 v Chester City - FA Cup 1999-2000

Nearest Railway Station Whyteleafe South - 0.4km

Bus Route 407 & 434

ASHTON UNITED

Founded 1878

Nickname: Robins   **Club Colours:** Red and white

Club Contact Details
0161 339 4158

Previous Names: Hurst 1878-1947
Previous Leagues: Manchester, Lancashire Combination 1912-33, 48-64, 66-68, Midland 1964-66, Cheshire County 1923-48, 68-82, North West Counties 1982-92. NPL 92-2018. National 2018-19.

10-11		11-12		12-13		13-14		14-15		15-16		16-17		17-18		18-19		19-20	
NP P	14	NP P	12	NP P	10	NP P	5	NP P	3	NP P	3	NP P	11	NP P	2	Nat N	20	NP P	n&v
FAC	2Q	FAC	2Q	FAC	2Q	FAC	3Q	FAC	3Q	FAC	3Q	FAC	1Q	FAC	2Q	FAC	4Q	FAC	3Q
FAT	1Q	FAT	1Q	FAT	1Q	FAT	1Q	FAT	1Q	FAV	1P	FAT	1Q	FAT	2Pr	FAT	3Q	FAT	2Q

HONOURS / RECORDS

FA Comps: None

League: Manchester League 1911-12. Lancashire Combination 1916-17.
North West Counties Division Two 1987-88, Division One 1991-92.
County FA: Manchester Senior Cup 1894-95, 1913-14, 75-76, 77-78.
Manchester Premier Cup 1979-80, 82-83, 91-92, 2000-01, 01-02, 02-03. Manchester Challenge Shield 1992-93.
Victory: 11-3 v Stalybridge Celtic - Manchester Intermediate Cup 1955
Defeat: 1-11 v Wellington Town - Cheshire League 1946-47
Appearances: Micky Boyle - 462
Additional: Paid £9,000 to Netherfield for Andy Whittaker 1994
Received £15,000 from Rotherham United for Karl Marginson 1993

GROUND: Hurst Cross, Surrey Street, Ashton-u-Lyne OL6 8DY

Ground Capacity: 4,500   **Seats:** 250   **Covered:** 750   **Clubhouse:** Yes   **Shop:** Yes
Previous Grounds: Rose Hill 1878-1912
Record Attendance: 11,000 v Halifax Town - FA Cup 1st Round 1952

Nearest Railway Station Ashton-under-Lyne - 1.4km
Bus Route Kings Road - stop 50m away

ATHERTON COLLIERIES

Founded 1916

Nickname: Colls   **Club Colours:** Black & white

Club Contact Details
07968 548 056

Previous Names: None
Previous Leagues: Bolton Combination 1918-21, 52-71. Lancashire Alliance 1921. Manchester 1945-48. West Lancashire 1948-50. Lancashire Combination 1950-52, 71-78. Cheshire Co 1978-82. North West Co 1982-2017.

10-11		11-12		12-13		13-14		14-15		15-16		16-17		17-18		18-19		19-20	
NWC1	5	NWC1	4	NWC1	4	NWC1	5	NWC1	1	NWCP	3	NWCP	1	NP1N	10	NP1W	1	NP P	n&v
FAC	Pr	FAC	P	FAC	1Q	FAC	Pr	FAC	Pr	FAC	Pr	FAC	P	FAC	2Q	FAC	1Q	FAC	1Qr
FAV	2Q	FAV	2Q	FAV	1Q	FAV	1Q	FAV	2P	FAV	3P	FAV	5P	FAT	2Q	FAT	Pr	FAT	1Pr

HONOURS / RECORDS

FA Comps: None

League: Bolton Combination 1919-20, 36-37, 37-38, 38-39, 40-41, 44-45, 56-57, 58-59, 60-61, 64-65.
North West Counties Division Three 1986-87, Division One 2014-15, Premier 2016-17. NPL Division One West 2018-19.
County FA: Lancashire County FA Shield 1919-20, 22-23, 41-42, 45-46, 56-57, 64-65.

Best FA Cup Third Qualifying Round 1994-95
FA Vase Fifth Round 2016-17
FA Trophy First Round Proper 2019-20

GROUND: Alder Street, Atherton, Greater Manchester M46 9EY

Ground Capacity: 2,500   **Seats:** Yes   **Covered:** Yes   **Clubhouse:** Yes   **Shop:** No
Previous Grounds: None
Record Attendance: 3,300 in the Bolton Combination 1920's.

Nearest Railway Station Atherton - 0.7km
Bus Route High Street - stop 100m away

BAMBER BRIDGE

Founded 1952

Nickname: Brig   **Club Colours:** White & black

Club Contact Details
01772 909 690   admin@bamberbridgefc.com

Previous Names: None
Previous Leagues: Preston & District 1952-90, North West Counties 1990-93

10-11		11-12		12-13		13-14		14-15		15-16		16-17		17-18		18-19		19-20	
NP1N	7	NP1N	10	NP1N	9	NP1N	4	NP1N	3	NP1N	12	NP1N	11	NP1N	4	NP P	16	NP P	n&v
FAC	2Qr	FAC	1Q	FAC	2Q	FAC	1Qr	FAC	3Q	FAC	4Q	FAC	P	FAC	1Q	FAC	2Qr	FAC	1Q
FAT	2Q	FAT	1Q	FAT	P	FAT	P	FAT	1Q	FAT	P	FAT	1Q	FAT	1Q	FAT	1Q	FAT	1Q

HONOURS / RECORDS
FA Comps: None

League: Preston & District Premier Division 1980-81, 85-86, 86-87, 89-90. North West Counties Division Two 1991-92.
Northern Premier Premier Division 1995-96.
County FA: Lancashire FA Amateur Shield 1981-82, Trophy 1994-95.

Victory: 8-0 v Curzon Ashton - North West Counties 1994-95
Additional: Paid £10,000 to Horwich RMI for Mark Edwards
Received £15,000 from Wigan Athletic for Tony Black 1995

GROUND: Sir Tom Finney Stadium, Brownedge Road, Bamber Bridge PR5 6UX
Ground Capacity: 3,000   **Seats:** 554   **Covered:** 800   **Clubhouse:** Yes   **Shop:** Yes
Previous Grounds: King George V, Higher Wallton 1952-86
Record Attendance: 2,300 v Czech Republic - Pre Euro '96 friendly

Nearest Railway Station Lostock Hall - 0.9km. Bamber Bridge - 0.9km
Bus Route Irongate - stop 100m away

BASFORD UNITED

Founded 1900

Nickname: Community   **Club Colours:** All amber

Club Contact Details
0115 924 4491

Previous Names: None
Previous Leagues: Notts Alliance 1905-39, 1946-2004. Notts Amateur League 1939-46. Notts Amateur Alliance 2004-06. Notts Senior 2006-11.
Central Midlands 2011-12. East Midlands Counties 2012-13. Northern Counties East 2013-14. Midland League 2014-15.

10-11		11-12		12-13		13-14		14-15		15-16		16-17		17-18		18-19		19-20	
NottS	2	CMSth	1	EMC	1	NCEP	5	MFLP	1	NP1S	4	NP1S	6	NP1S	1	NP P	7	NP P	n&v
						FAC	1Q	FAC	Pr	FAC	2Q	FAC	P	FAC	3Q	FAC	1Q	FAC	1Q
				FAV	2P	FAV	2Q	FAV	2Q	FAT	2Q	FAT	P	FAT	1Q	FAT	1P	FAT	2Q

HONOURS / RECORDS
FA Comps: None

League: Notts Alliance 1905-06, 07-08, 19-20, Division One 1997-98. Central Midlands Southern 2011-12.
East Midland Counties 2012-13. Midland Football Premier Division 2014-15. Northern Premier Division One South 2017-18.
County FA: Notts Senior Cup 1946-47, 87-88, 2014-15, 15-16, 17-18, Intermediate Cup 2005-06.

Misc: Former club secretary, Wallace Brownlow, who took up the post when 19 in 1907, remained in the position until his
death in 1970 - a world record of 63 years.

GROUND: Mill Street Playing Field, Greenwich Avenue, off Bagnall Road, Basford, Nottingham NG6 0LD
Ground Capacity: 2,200   **Seats:** Yes   **Covered:** Yes   **Clubhouse:** Yes   **Shop:**
Previous Grounds: Old Peer Tree Inn, Dolly Tub > 1903, Catchems Corner 1903-30, Vernon Avenue 1930-34, Mill Street 1934-91.
Record Attendance: 3,500 v Grantham United, FACup 1937.

Nearest Railway Station Highbury Vale Tram Stop - 400m
Bus Route Christina Avenue - stop 150m away

BUXTON

Founded 1877

Nickname: The Bucks   **Club Colours:** Blue & white

Club Contact Details
01298 23197

Previous Names: None
Previous Leagues: Combination 1891-99. Manchester 1899-1932. Cheshire County 1932-40, 46-73.
Northern Premier 1973-98, 2006- Northern Counties East 1998-2006.

10-11	11-12	12-13	13-14	14-15	15-16	16-17	17-18	18-19	19-20
NP P 6	NP P 13	NP P 7	NP P 13	NP P 10	NP P 11	NP P 7	NP P 8	NP P 5	NP P n&v
FAC 4Q	FAC 2Q	FAC 4Q	FAC 2Q	FAC 3Q	FAC 3Qr	FAC 1Q	FAC 4Q	FAC 2Qr	FAC 3Q
FAT 1Q	FAT 2Q	FAT 1Pr	FAT 2Q	FAT 2Q	FAT 3Q	FAT 2Q	FAT 1Q	FAT 2Qr	FAT 2Q

HONOURS / RECORDS
FA Comps: None
League: Manchester 1931-32. Cheshire County 1972-73.
Northern Counties East 2005-06. Northern Premier Division One 2006-07.
County FA: Derbyshire Senior Cup 1938-39, 45-46, 56-57, 59-60, 71-72, 80-81, 85-86, 86-87, 2008-09, 11-12.

Goalscorer: Mark Reed - 251 (469 appearances)
Appearances: David Bainbridge - 642
Additional: Paid £5,000 to Hyde United for Gary Walker 1989
     Received £16,500 from Rotherham for Ally Pickering 1989

GROUND: The Silverlands, Buxton, Derbyshire SK17 6QH

Ground Capacity: 5,200   **Seats:** 490   **Covered:** 2,500   **Clubhouse:** Yes   **Shop:** Yes
Previous Grounds: The Park (Cricket Club) 1877-78. Fields at Cote Heath and Green Lane 1878-84.
Record Attendance: 6,000 v Barrow - FA Cup 1st Round 1962-63

Nearest Railway Station Higher Buxton - walking distance from the ground.

FC UNITED OF MANCHESTER

Founded 2005

Nickname: F.C.   **Club Colours:** Red/white/black

Club Contact Details
0161 769 2005   office@fc-utd.co.uk

Previous Names: None
Previous Leagues: North West Counties 2005-07. Northern Premier 2007-15. National 2015-19.

10-11	11-12	12-13	13-14	14-15	15-16	16-17	17-18	18-19	19-20
NP P 4	NP P 6	NP P 3	NP P 2	NP P 1	Nat N 13	Nat N 13	Nat N 16	Nat N 21	NP P n&v
FAC 2Pr	FAC 2Q	FAC 4Q	FAC 1Q	FAC 2Q	FAC 1P	FAC 3Qr	FAC 4Q	FAC 3Q	FAC 2Q
FAT 3Q	FAT 1P	FAT 2Q	FAT 1Qr	FAT QF	FAT 3Q	FAT 3Q	FAT 3Q	FAT 3Q	FAT 2P

HONOURS / RECORDS
FA Comps: None
League: North West Counties League Division Two 2005-06, Division One 2006-07.
Northern Premier League Division One North Play-off 2007-08, Premier Division 2014-15.
County FA: Manchester Premier Cup 2016-17, 17-18.

Victory: 10-2 v Castleton Gabriels 10/12/2005. 8-0 v Squires Gate 14/10/06, Glossop N.E. 28/10/06 & Nelson 05/09/10
Defeat: 0-5 v Harrogate Town, 20 February 2016
Goalscorer: Rory Patterson - 99 (2005-08). Simon Carden scored 5 goals against Castleton Gabriels 10/12/2005.
Appearances: Jerome Wright - 400
Additional: Longest unbeaten run (League): 22 games 03/12/2006 - 18/08/2007.

GROUND: Broadhurst Park, 310 Lightbowne Road, Moston, Manchester, M40 0FJ

Ground Capacity: 4,400   **Seats:** 696   **Covered:** Yes   **Clubhouse:** Yes   **Shop:** Yes
Previous Grounds: Gigg Lane(Bury FC) 2005-14. Bower Fold (Stalybridge C) Aug-Dec'14. Tameside Stad (Curzon A)
Record Attendance: 6,731 v Brighton & Hove Albion, FA Cup 2nd Round 08/12/2010 (Gigg Lane)

Nearest Railway Station Moston - 11min walk from the ground.
Bus Route Matchday Special and Shuttle Bus

GAINSBOROUGH TRINITY

Founded 1873

Nickname: The Blues   **Club Colours:** All blue

Club Contact Details
07500 838 068

Previous Names: Trinity Recreationists
Previous Leagues: Midland (FM) 1889-96, 1912-60, 61-68. Football League 1896-1912. Yorkshire 1960-61.
Northern Premier (FM) 1968-2004.

	10-11		11-12		12-13		13-14		14-15		15-16		16-17		17-18		18-19		19-20	
	Conf N	18	Conf N	4	Conf N	8	Conf N	16	Conf N	17	Nat N	18	Nat N	19	Nat N	20	NP P	6	NP P	n&v
	FAC	2Q	FAC	4Q	FAC	2Qr	FAC	2Q	FAC	4Q	FAC	1P	FAC	2Q	FAC	1P	FAC	3Q	FAC	2Q
	FAT	3Q	FAT	3Q	FAT	SF	FAT	3Q	FAT	1P	FAT	3Qr	FAT	3Qr	FAT	1P	FAT	1Qr	FAT	1P

HONOURS / RECORDS

FA Comps: None
League: Midland 1890-91, 1927-28, 48-49, 66-67.

County FA: Lincolnshire County Senior Cup 1889-90, 92-93, 94-95, 97-98, 1903-04, 04-05, 06-07, 10-11, 46-47, 47-48, 48-49,
50-51, 51-52, 57-58, 58-59, 63-64, 70-71, 2002-03, 15-16, 17-18. Lincolnshire Shield 2007-08.
Victory: 7-0 v Fleetwood Town and v Great Harwood Town
Defeat: 1-7 v Stalybridge Celtic - Northern Premier 2000-01 and v Brentford - FA Cup 03-04.
Additional: Paid £3,000 to Buxton for Stuart Lowe
    Received £30,000 from Lincoln City for Tony James

GROUND: The Martin & Co Arena, Gainsborough, Lincolnshire DN21 2QW

Ground Capacity: 4,340 **Seats:** 504 **Covered:** 2,500 **Clubhouse:** Yes **Shop:** Yes
Previous Grounds: Played at Bowling Green Ground and Sincil Bank when Northolme was being used for cricket.
Record Attendance: 9,760 v Scunthorpe United - Midland League 1948

Nearest Railway Station Gainsborough Central - less than half a mile away.
Bus Route 100 & 97

GRANTHAM TOWN

Founded 1874

Nickname: Gingerbreads   **Club Colours:** Black & white stripes

Club Contact Details
01476 591 818   psnixon@hotmail.com

Previous Names: Grantham FC 1874-1987.
Previous Leagues: Midland Amateur Alliance, Central Alliance 1911-25, 59-61, Midland Counties 1925-59, 61-72,
Southern 1972-79, 85-2006, Northern Premier 1979-85

	10-11		11-12		12-13		13-14		14-15		15-16		16-17		17-18		18-19		19-20	
	NP1S	5	NP1S	1	NP P	19	NP P	15	NP P	12	NP P	18	NP P	8	NP P	4	NP P	18	NP P	n&v
	FAC	Pr	FAC	3Q	FAC	2Q	FAC	1Qr	FAC	3Q	FAC	1Q	FAC	1Qr	FAC	2Q	FAC	2Qr	FAC	1Q
	FAT	P	FAT	1Q	FAT	1Q	FAT	1Qr	FAT	1Q	FAT	1Q	FAT	2Q	FAT	3Q	FAT	1Q	FAT	2Q

HONOURS / RECORDS

FA Comps: None
League: Midland Amateur 1910-11. Central Alliance 1924-25. Midland 1963-64, 70-71, 71-72.
Southern Division One North 1972-73, 78-79, Midland Division 97-98. Northern Premier Division One South 2011-12.
County FA: Lincolnshire Senior Cup 1884-85, 1971-72, 82-83, County Senior Cup 1936-37, Senior Cup 'A' 1953-54, 60-61, 61-62,
County Shield 2003-04, 04-05.
Victory: 13-0 v Rufford Colliery (H) - FA Cup 15/09/1934
Defeat: 0-16 v Notts County Rovers (A) - Midland Amateur Alliance 22/10/1892
Goalscorer: Jack McCartney - 416
Appearances: Chris Gardner - 664
Additional: Received £20,000 from Nottingham Forest for Gary Crosby

GROUND: South Kesteven Sports Stadium, Trent Road, Gratham NG31 7XQ

Ground Capacity: 7,500 **Seats:** 750 **Covered:** 1,950 **Clubhouse:** Yes **Shop:** Yes
Previous Grounds: London Road >1990-91. Spalding United FC 1990-91.
Record Attendance: 6,578 v Middlesbrough, FA Cup Third Round Proper, 1973-74.

Nearest Railway Station Grantham - 1.5km
Bus Route Meres Leisure Centre - stop 100m away

HYDE UNITED

Founded 1919

Nickname: The Tigers   **Club Colours:** Red & navy

Club Contact Details
0161 367 7273

Previous Names: Hyde United 1919-2010, Hyde F.C. 2010-15.
Previous Leagues: Lancashire & Cheshire 1919-21, Manchester 1921-30, Cheshire County 1930-68, 1970-82, Northern Premier 1968-70, 1983-2004. Football Conference 2004-15.

10-11	11-12	12-13	13-14	14-15	15-16	16-17	17-18	18-19	19-20
Conf N 19	Conf N 1	Conf 18	Conf 24	Conf N 22	NP P 22	NP1N 10	NP1N 3	NP P 10	NP P n&v
FAC 2Qr	FAC 3Q	FAC 4Qr	FAC 4Q	FAC 2Q	FAC 2Qr	FAC 2Q	FAC 1P	FAC 1Q	FAC 1Q
FAT 1P	FAT 1P	FAT 1Pr	FAT 1P	FAT 2P	FAT 1Qr	FAT P	FAT P	FAT 2Q	FAT 1Q

HONOURS / RECORDS

FA Comps: None

League: Manchester 1920-21, 21-22, 22-23, 28-29, 29-30. Cheshire 1954-55, 55-56, 81-82.
Northern Premier Division One North 2003-04, Premier Division 2004-05. Conference North 2011-12.
County FA: Cheshire Senior Cup 1945-46, 62-63, 69-70, 80-81, 89-90, 96-97. Manchester Senior Cup 1974-75, Premier Cup 1993-94, 94-95, 95-96, 98-99.
Victory: 13-1 v Eccles United, 1921-22.
Goalscorer: Pete O'Brien - 247. Ernest Gillibrand 86 goals during the 1929-30 season, including 7 against New Mills.
Appearances: Steve Johnson - 623 (1975-1988)
Additional: Paid £8,000 to Mossley for Jim McCluskie 1989
Received £50,000 from Crewe Alexandra for Colin Little 1995

GROUND: Ewen Fields, Walker Lane, Hyde SK14 5PL

Ground Capacity: 4,250   **Seats:** 530   **Covered:** 4,073   **Clubhouse:** Yes   **Shop:** Yes
Previous Grounds: None
Record Attendance: 7,600 v Nelson - FA Cup 1952

Nearest Railway Station Newton for Hyde - 0.8km
Bus Route Walker Lane - stop 110m away

LANCASTER CITY

Founded 1911

Nickname: Dolly Blues   **Club Colours:** Blue & white

Club Contact Details
01524 382 238   secretary@lancastercityfc.com

Previous Names: Lancaster Town 1911-37
Previous Leagues: Lancashire Combination 1911-70, Northern Premier League 1970-82, 87-2004, North West Counties 1982-87, Conference 2004-07

10-11	11-12	12-13	13-14	14-15	15-16	16-17	17-18	18-19	19-20
NP1N 8	NP1N 6	NP1N 13	NP1N 6	NP1N 11	NP1N 6	NP1N 1	NP P 17	NP P 12	NP P n&v
FAC P	FAC 3Q	FAC 1Q	FAC 2Qr	FAC 3Q	FAC 2Q	FAC 3Q	FAC 3Q	FAC 1Q	FAC 2Q
FAT 2Q	FAT P	FAT P	FAT 1Q	FAT Pr	FAT Pr	FAT 1Q	FAT 1P	FAT 1P	FAT 2Qr

HONOURS / RECORDS

FA Comps: None

League: Northern Premier Division One 1995-96, Division One North 2016-17.

County FA: Lancashire Junior Cup (ATS Challenge Trophy) 1927-28, 28-29, 30-31, 33-34, 51-52, 74-75.

Victory: 17-2 v Appleby, FA Cup, 1915.
Defeat: 0-10 v Matlock Town - Northern Premier League Division 1 1973-74
Goalscorer: David Barnes - 130, 1979-84, 88-91. Jordan Connerton scored 38 during the 2009-10 season.
Appearances: Edgar J Parkinson - 591, 1949-64.
Additional: Paid £6,000 to Droylsden for Jamie Tandy. Received £25,000 from Birmingham City for Chris Ward.

GROUND: Giant Axe, West Road, Lancaster LA1 5PE

Ground Capacity: 3,500   **Seats:** 513   **Covered:** 900   **Clubhouse:** Yes   **Shop:** Yes
Previous Grounds: None
Record Attendance: 7,506 v Carlisle United - FA Cup Fourth Qualifying Round, 17/11/1927

Nearest Railway Station Lancaster - 3min walk
Bus Route 41, 42 & 89

MATLOCK TOWN

Founded 1885

Nickname: The Gladiators **Club Colours:** Blue & white

Club Contact Details
01629 583 866

Previous Names: None
Previous Leagues: Midland Combination 1894-96, Matlock and District, Derbyshire Senior, Central Alliance 1924-25, 47-61, Central Combination 1934-35, Chesterfield & District 1946-47, Midland Counties 1961-69

	10-11	11-12	12-13	13-14	14-15	15-16	16-17	17-18	18-19	19-20
NP P	11	14	17	12	14	17	9	14	15	n&v
FAC	3Q	2Q	1Qr	2Q	1Q	1Qr	4Q	2Q	1Q	2Q
FAT	2Qr	3Q	2P	3Q	1Q	1P	2P	1Q	1Q	2P

HONOURS / RECORDS
FA Comps: FA Trophy 1974-75. Anglo Italian Non-League Cup 1979.

League: Central Alliance North Division 1959-60, 60-61. Midland Counties 1961-62, 68-69.

County FA: Derbyshire Senior Cup 1974-75, 76-77, 77-78, 83-84, 84-85, 91-92, 2003-04, 09-10, 14-15, 16-17.

Victory:	10-0 v Lancaster City (A) - 1974
Defeat:	0-8 v Chorley (A) - 1971
Goalscorer:	Peter Scott
Appearances:	Mick Fenoughty
Additional:	Paid £2,000 for Kenny Clark 1996. Received £10,000 from York City for Ian Helliwell.

GROUND: Causeway Lane, Matlock, Derbyshire DE4 3AR

Ground Capacity: 2,757 **Seats:** 560 **Covered:** 1,200 **Clubhouse:** Yes **Shop:** Yes
Previous Grounds: None
Record Attendance: 5,123 v Burton Albion - FA Trophy Semi-final, 1975

Nearest Railway Station Matlock - 0.3km
Bus Route Causeway Lane - stop 100m away

MICKLEOVER SPORTS

Founded 1948

Nickname: Sports **Club Colours:** Red & black

Club Contact Details
01332 512 826

Previous Names: Mickleover Old Boys 1948-93. Mickleover Sports
Previous Leagues: Derby & District Senior 1948-93. Central Midlands 1993-99, Northern Counties East 1999-2009

	10-11	11-12	12-13	13-14	14-15	15-16	16-17	17-18	18-19	19-20
NP P / NP1S	15	21	21	5	1	20	16	12	19	n&v
FAC	3Q	2Q	Pr	2Qr	3Q	1Q	2Q	3Q	3Q	1Q
FAT	2Q	1Q	P	2Q	3Q	1Q	3Qr	1Q	2Qr	1Q

HONOURS / RECORDS
FA Comps: None

League: Central Midlands Supreme Division 1998-99. Northern Counties East Division One 2002-03, Premier Division 2008-09. Northern Premier League Division One South 2009-10, 14-15.
County FA: None

Misc:	Won 16 consecutive League matches in 2009-10 - a Northern Premier League record
Best FA Cup	Third Qualifying Round 2010-11, 14-15, 17-18, 18-19
FA Trophy	Third Qualifying Round 2014-15, 16-17(r)
FA Vase	Fourth Round Proper 2000-01

GROUND: Mickleover Sports Club, Station Road, Mickleover Derby DE3 9FE

Ground Capacity: 1,500 **Seats:** 280 **Covered:** 500 **Clubhouse:** Yes **Shop:** Yes
Previous Grounds: None
Record Attendance: 1,074 v FC United of Manchester, Northern Premier League Premier Division, 02/10/10.

Nearest Railway Station Peartree - 5.1km
Bus Route Buxton Drive - stop 100m away

MORPETH TOWN

Founded 1909

Nickname: Highwaymen   **Club Colours:** Amber & black

Club Contact Details
07882 991 356

Previous Names: None
Previous Leagues: Northern Alliance 1936-1994. Northern League 1994-2018.

	10-11		11-12		12-13		13-14		14-15		15-16		16-17		17-18		18-19		19-20	
	NL 2	20	NL 2	4	NL 2	3	NL 2	17	NL 1	8	NL 1	4	NL 1	2	NL 1	2	NP1E	1	NP P	n&v
FAC	EP				EP		1Q		EP		P		3Q		EP		1Qr		3Q	
FAV	2Q		FAV	1Q	2P		5P		2P		F		4P		2P		FAT	P	FAT	2Q

HONOURS / RECORDS
FA Comps: FA Vase 2015-16.

League: Northern Alliance 1983-84, 93-94. Northern Division Two 1995-96.

County FA: Northumberland Benevolent Bowl 1978-79, 85-86. Northumberland Senior Cup 2006-07.

Best FA Cup Fourth Qualifying Round 1998-99
FA Trophy Preliminary Round 2018-19

GROUND: Craik Park, Morpeth Common, Morpeth, Northumberland NE61 2YX

Ground Capacity: 1,000   **Seats:** 100   **Covered:** Yes   **Clubhouse:** Yes   **Shop:**
Previous Grounds: Stobhill Cricket Hill. Storey Park 1954-94.
Record Attendance:

Nearest Railway Station Morpeth - 1.9km
Bus Route Whalton Road - stop 670m away

NANTWICH TOWN

Founded 1884

Nickname: The Dabbers   **Club Colours:** All green

Club Contact Details
01270 621 771   secretary@nantwichtownfc.com

Previous Names: Nantwich
Previous Leagues: Shropshire & Dist. 1891-92, Combination 1892-94, 1901-10, Cheshire Junior 1894-95, Crewe & Dist. 1895-97, North Staffs & Dist. 1897-1900, Cheshire 1900-01, Manchester 1910-12, 65-68, Lancs. Com. 1912-14, Cheshire Co. 1919-38, 68-82, Crewe & Dist. 1938-39, 47-48, Crewe Am. Comb. 1946-47, Mid-Cheshire 1948-65, North West Co. 1982-2007.

	10-11		11-12		12-13		13-14		14-15		15-16		16-17		17-18		18-19		19-20	
	NP P	17	NP P	10	NP P	14	NP P	19	NP P	15	NP P	8	NP P	5	NP P	15	NP P	4	NP P	n&v
FAC	2Q		1P		1Q		1Q		1Q		1Q		4Q		1P		2Qr		4Q	
FAT	1P		1Q		2Qr		3Q		2Q		SF		1P		1Q		1Q		2Q	

HONOURS / RECORDS
FA Comps: FA Vase 2005-06.

League: Mid-Cheshire 1963-64. Cheshire County 1980-81.

County FA: Crew Amateur Combination 1946-47. Cheshire Amateur Cup 1895-96, 1963-64.
Cheshire Senior Cup 1932-33, 75-76, 2007-08, 11-12, 17-18, 18-19.
Victory: 20-0 v Whitchurch Alexandra (home) 1900/01 Cheshire League Division 1, 5 April 1901
Defeat: 2-16 v Stalybridge Celtic (away) 1932/33 Cheshire County League, 22 Oct 1932
Goalscorer: John Scarlett 161 goals (1992/3 to 2005/6).
Bobby Jones scored 60 goals during season 1946-47, Gerry Duffy scored 42 during season 1961-62
Additional: Received £20,000 from Crewe Alexandra for Kelvin Mellor - Feb 2008

GROUND: Weaver Stadium, Water Lode, Kingsley Fields, Nantwich, CW5 5UP

Ground Capacity: 3,500   **Seats:** 350   **Covered:** 495   **Clubhouse:** Yes   **Shop:** Yes
Previous Grounds: London Road/Jackson Avenue (1884-2007)
Record Attendance: 5,121 v Winsford United - Cheshire Senior Cup 2nd Round 1920-21

Nearest Railway Station Nantwich - 1.1km
Bus Route Malbank School - stop 150m away

RADCLIFFE

Founded 1949

Nickname: The Boro Club Colours: Blue

Club Contact Details
0161 724 8346   secretary@radcliffefc.com

Previous Names: Radcliffe Borough >2018
Previous Leagues: South East Lancashire, Manchester 1953-63, Lancashire Combination 1963-71,
Cheshire County 1971-82, North West Counties 1982-97

	10-11	11-12	12-13	13-14	14-15	15-16	16-17	17-18	18-19	19-20
	NP1N 18	NP1N 15	NP1N 15	NP1N 18	NP1N 19	NP1N 18	NP1N 20	NP1N 20	NP1W 2	NP P n&v
FAC	1Q	3Q	Pr	1Q	1Q	P	1Q	1Q	2Q	Pr
FAT	2Qr	2Qr	1Q	1Q	P	2Q	P	P	P	1Q

HONOURS / RECORDS
FA Comps: None

League: South Lancashire Division Two 1950-51, Division One 51-52, Premier 80-81. North West Counties Division Two 1982-83, Division One 84-85. Northern Premier Division One 1996-97.
County FA: Manchester Premier Cup 2007-08.

Goalscorer: Ian Lunt - 147. Jody Banim scored 46 during a single season.
Appearances: Simon Kelly - 502
Additional: Paid £5,000 to Buxton for Gary Walker 1991
Received £20,000 from Shrewsbury Town for Jody Banim 2003

GROUND: Stainton Park, Pilkington Road, Radcliffe, Lancashire M26 3PE
Ground Capacity: 4,000 Seats: 350 Covered: 1,000 Clubhouse: Yes Shop: Yes
Previous Grounds: Ashworth Street. Bright Street > 1970.
Record Attendance: 2,495 v York City - FA Cup 1st Round 2000-01

Nearest Railway Station Radcliffe - 1.3km
Bus Route Lowe Street - 100m away

SCARBOROUGH ATHLETIC

Founded 2007

Nickname: The Seadogs Club Colours: Red & white

Club Contact Details
07538 903 723   club.secretary@scarboroughathletic.com

Previous Names: Formed after Scarborough F.C. folded in 2007.
Previous Leagues: Northern Counties East 2007-13.

	10-11	11-12	12-13	13-14	14-15	15-16	16-17	17-18	18-19	19-20
	NCEP 10	NCEP 3	NCEP 1	NP1S 7	NP1N 6	NP1N 20	NP1N 3	NP1N 2	NP P 8	NP P n&v
FAC	P	1Q	EP	2Q	2Q	P	P	4Q	1Qr	2Q
FAV/FAT	3P	1P	1P	3Q	1Q	P	P	P	1Q	1Q

HONOURS / RECORDS
FA Comps: None

League: Northern Counties East Division One 2008-09, Premier 2012-13.

County FA: None

Victory: 13-0 v Brodsworth, Northern Counties East, 2009-10.
Defeat: 0-6 v Thackley 16/04/2013 and AFC Telford United 16/11/2013.
Goalscorer: Ryan Blott - 231, including 42 scored during the 2008-09 season and 5 each against Yorkshire Amateur's (08/11/08) and Armthorpe Welfare (14/04/12).
Appearances: Ryan Blott - 376 (20/10/07 - 29/04/16).

GROUND: Scarborough Leisure Village, Ashburn Road YO11 2JW
Ground Capacity: 2,000 Seats: 250 Covered: Yes Clubhouse: Yes Shop: No
Previous Grounds: Queensgate - Bridlington FC >2017.
Record Attendance: 2,038 v Sheffield United, Opening of the new ground friendly, 15/07/2017.

Nearest Railway Station Scarborough - 1km
Bus Route 128, 7A & 843

SOUTH SHIELDS

Founded 1974

Nickname: Mariners   **Club Colours:** Claret & white

Club Contact Details
0191 454 7800

Previous Names: South Shields Mariners.
Previous Leagues: Northern Alliance 1974-76, Wearside 1976-95.

10-11		11-12		12-13		13-14		14-15		15-16		16-17		17-18		18-19		19-20	
NL 1	11	NL 1	13	NL 1	23	NL 2	17	NL 2	15	NL 2	1	NL 1	1	NP1N	1	NP P	2	NP P	n&v
FAC	Pr	FAC	Pr	FAC	1Q	FAC	Pr					FAC	EP	FAC	4Q	FAC	2Q	FAC	1Qr
FAV	1P	FAV	1P	FAV	1P	FAV	1P	FAV	2Q	FAV	3P	FAV	F	FAT	2Q	FAT	3Q	FAT	1Pr

HONOURS / RECORDS

FA Comps: FA Vase 2016-17.

League: Northern Alliance 1975-76. Wearside 1976-77, 92-93, 94-95. Northern Division Two 2015-16, Division One 2016-17.

County FA: Monkwearmouth Charity Cup 1986-87. Durham Senior Challenge Cup 2016-17.

Best FA Cup   Fourth Qualifying Round 2017-18
FA Trophy   Third Qualifying Round 2018-19

GROUND: Mariners Park, Shaftesbury Avenue, Jarrow, Tyne & Wear NE32 3UP

Ground Capacity: 3,500   **Seats:** Yes   **Covered:** Yes   **Clubhouse:** Yes   **Shop:** No
Previous Grounds: Filtrona Park (renamed Mariners Park in 2015) 1992-2013. Eden Lane 2013-15.
Record Attendance: 3,464 v Coleshill Town, FA Vase semi-final, 2016-17.

Nearest Railway Station Bede - 0.2km
Bus Route Taunton Avenue - stop 200m away

STAFFORD RANGERS

Founded 1876

Nickname: Rangers   **Club Colours:** Black & white

Club Contact Details
01785 602 430   secretary@staffordrangersfc.co.uk

Previous Names: None
Previous Leagues: Shropshire 1891-93, Birmingham 1893-96, N. Staffs. 1896-1900, Cheshire 1900-01, Birmingham Combination 1900-12, 46-52, Cheshire County 1952-69, N.P.L. 1969-79, 83-85, Alliance 1979-83, Conf. 1985-95, 2005-11. Southern >2005.

10-11		11-12		12-13		13-14		14-15		15-16		16-17		17-18		18-19		19-20	
Conf N	20	NP P	16	NP P	15	NP P	22	NP1S	6	NP1S	1	NP P	13	NP P	13	NP P	14	NP P	n&v
FAC	2Qr	FAC	2Q	FAC	2Q	FAC	2Q	FAC	1Qr	FAC	P	FAC	1Q	FAC	4Q	FAC	2Q	FAC	3Q
FAT	3Q	FAT	2Q	FAT	1P	FAT	1Q	FAT	1Q	FAT	1Qr	FAV	3Q	FAT	3Q	FAT	2Q	FAT	1Q

HONOURS / RECORDS

FA Comps: FA Trophy 1971-72.

League: Birmingham Combination 1912-13. Cheshire County 1968-69. Northern Premier 1971-72, 84-85, Division One South 2015-16. Southern Premeir Division 2002-03. Coference North 2005-06.

County FA: Staffordshire Senior Cup 1954-55, 56-57, 62-63, 71-72, 77-78, 86-87, 91-92, 2002-03, 04-05, 14-15, 17-18.

Victory: 15-0 v Kidsgrove Athletic - Staffordshire Senior Cup 2003
Defeat: 0-12 v Burton Town - Birmingham League 1930
Goalscorer: M. Cullerton - 176.   Les Box scored seven against Dudley Town, FA Cup, 06/09/1958.
Appearances: Jim Sargent
Additional: Paid £13,000 to VS rugby for S. Butterworth. Received £100,000 from Crystal Palace for Stan Collymore.

GROUND: Marston Road, Stafford ST16 3UF

Ground Capacity: 4,000   **Seats:** 530   **Covered:** Yes   **Clubhouse:** Yes   **Shop:** Yes
Previous Grounds: None
Record Attendance: 8,536 v Rotherham United - FA Cup 3rd Round 1975

Nearest Railway Station Stafford - 1.8km
Bus Route Co-operative Strret - stop 200m away

STALYBRIDGE CELTIC

Founded 1909

Nickname: Celtic   **Club Colours:** Royal blue & white

Club Contact Details
0161 338 2828   secretary@stalybridgeceltic.co.uk

Previous Names: None

Previous Leagues: Lancs & Cheshire Am. 1909-11. Lancashire Comb 1911-12, Central 1912-14, 15-21, Southern 1914-15, Football Lge 1921-23, Cheshire Co. 1923-82, North West Co. 1982-87, N.P.L. 1987-92, 98-2001, 02-04, Conference 1992-98, 01-02, 04-17.

10-11		11-12		12-13		13-14		14-15		15-16		16-17		17-18		18-19		19-20	
Conf N	10	Conf N	6	Conf N	13	Conf N	19	Conf N	19	Nat N	12	Nat N	21	NP P	22	NP P	17	NP P	n&v
FAC	4Q	FAC	2Q	FAC	4Q	FAC	2Q	FAC	2Q	FAC	1P	FAC	3Q	FAC	3Q	FAC	1Q	FAC	1Q
FAT	2P	FAT	2P	FAT	3Q	FAT	1P	FAT	3Qr	FAT	3Q	FAT	3Qr	FAT	3Q	FAT	3Q	FAT	1Q

HONOURS / RECORDS

FA Comps: None

League: Lancashire Combination Division Two 1911-12. Cheshire County 1979-80. North West Counties 1983-84, 86-87. Northern Premier League Premier Division 1991-92, 2000-01.

County FA: Manchester Senior Cup 1922-23.
Cheshire Senior Cup 1952-53, 2000-01.

Victory: 16-2 v Manchester NE - 01/05/1926 and v Nantwich - 22/10/1932

Defeat: 1-10 v Wellington Town - 09/03/1946

Goalscorer: Harry Dennison - 215. Cecil Smith scored 77 goals during the 1931-32 season

Appearances: Kevan Keelan - 395

Additional: Paid £15,000 to Kettering Town for Ian Arnold 1995. Received £16,000 from Southport for Lee Trundle.

GROUND: Bower Fold, Mottram Road, Stalybridge, Cheshire SK15 2RT

Ground Capacity: 6,500   **Seats:** 1,500   **Covered:** 2,400   **Clubhouse:** Yes   **Shop:** Yes

Previous Grounds: None

Record Attendance: 9,753 v West Bromwich Albion - FA Cup replay 1922-23

Nearest Railway Station Stalybridge - 1.5 miles from the ground.

Bus Route 236 & 237

WARRINGTON TOWN

Founded 1949

Nickname: The Wire   **Club Colours:** Yellow & blue

Club Contact Details
01925 653 044

Previous Names: Stockton Heath Albion 1949-61

Previous Leagues: Warrington & District 1949-52, Mid Cheshire 1952-78, Cheshire County 1978-82, North West Counties 1982-90 Northern Premier 1990-97

10-11		11-12		12-13		13-14		14-15		15-16		16-17		17-18		18-19		19-20	
NP1N	9	NP1N	11	NP1N	10	NP1N	3	NP1N	9	NP1N	1	NP P	10	NP P	3	NP P	3	NP P	n&v
FAC	3Q	FAC	2Q	FAC	2Q	FAC	2Qr	FAC	2P	FAC	P	FAC	1Q	FAC	3Qr	FAC	4Qr	FAC	3Q
FAT	P	FAT	Pr	FAT	P	FAT	P	FAT	P	FAT	3Q	FAT	1Q	FAT	3P	FAT	1Q	FAT	1Q

HONOURS / RECORDS

FA Comps: None

League: MId-Cheshire 1960-61. North West Counties 1989-90, Division Two 2000-01. Northern Premier Division One North 2015-16.

County FA: None

Goalscorer: Steve Hughes - 167

Appearances: Neil Whalley

Additional: Paid £50,000 to Preston North End for Liam Watson Received £60,000 from P.N.E. for Liam Watson
Players to progress - Roger Hunt, Liverpool legend and 1966 World Cup winner.

GROUND: Cantilever Park, Loushers Lane, Warrington WA4 2RS

Ground Capacity: 2,500   **Seats:** 350   **Covered:** 650   **Clubhouse:** Yes   **Shop:** Yes

Previous Grounds: Stockton Lane 1949-50, 55-56. London Road 1950-53. Loushers Lane 1953-55.

Record Attendance: 2,600 v Halesowen Town - FA Vase Semi-final 1st leg 1985-86

Nearest Railway Station Warrington Central - 2.3km

Bus Route Fairfield Gardens - stop 200m away

Owens (Witton) so close in the last minute at Basford.

Owens (Witton) Galinski (Basford).

Owens (Witton) De Girolamo (Buxton). Photos Keith Clayton.

WHITBY TOWN

Founded 1926

Nickname: Seasiders   **Club Colours:** All royal blue

Club Contact Details
Office: 01947 604 847

Previous Names: Whitby Whitehall Swifts and Whitby Town merged in 1926 to form Whitby United. Name changed to Whitby Town in 1949.
Previous Leagues: Northern 1926-97

	10-11	11-12	12-13	13-14	14-15	15-16	16-17	17-18	18-19	19-20
NP P	16	17	13	9	13	19	6	21	11	n&v
FAC	1Q	3Q	3Q	1Qr	1Qr	1Qr	2Q	2Q	1Q	4Qr
FAT	3Qr	1Q	3Q	1Q	1Q	2Q	2Q	1Q	1Q	2Q

HONOURS / RECORDS
FA Comps: FA Vase 1996-97.
League: Northern 1992-93, 96-97.
Northern Premier Division One 1997-98.
County FA: North Riding Senior Cup 1964-65, 67-68, 82-83, 89-90, 2004-05, 16-17.

Victory:	11-2 v Cargo Fleet Works - 1950
Defeat:	3-13 v Willington - 24/03/1928
Goalscorer:	Paul Pitman - 382
Appearances:	Paul Pitman - 468
Additional:	Paid £2,500 to Newcastle Blue Star for John Grady 1990. Received £5,000 from Gateshead for Graham Robinson 1997

GROUND: Turnbull Ground, Upgang Lane, Whitby, North Yorks YO21 3HZ
Ground Capacity: 3,500   **Seats:** 622   **Covered:** 1,372   **Clubhouse:** Yes   **Shop:** Yes
Previous Grounds: None
Record Attendance: 4,000 v Scarborough - North Riding Cup 18/04/1965

Nearest Railway Station Whitby - 1km
Bus Route Argyle Road - 120m away

WITTON ALBION

Founded 1887

Nickname: The Albion   **Club Colours:** Red & white stripes

Club Contact Details
01606 430 08

Previous Names: None
Previous Leagues: Lancashire Combination, Cheshire County > 1979, Northern Premier 1979-91, Conference 1991-94

	10-11	11-12	12-13	13-14	14-15	15-16	16-17	17-18	18-19	19-20
	NP1N 10	NP1N 3	NP P 4	NP P 16	NP P 22	NP1N 11	NP1S 2	NP P 7	NP P 9	NP P n&v
FAC	P	4Q	2Q	1Q	1Q	2Q	2Qr	1Q	4Q	2Qr
FAT	3Qr	3Q	2Q	2Q	2Qr	1Q	1Pr	1Q	3Q	1Q

HONOURS / RECORDS
FA Comps: None
League: Cheshire County 1948-49, 49-50, 53-54. Northern Premier Premier Division 1990-91.
County FA: Cheshire Senior Cup x7.

Victory:	13-0 v Middlewich (H)
Defeat:	0-9 v Macclesfield Town (A) - 18/09/1965
Goalscorer:	Frank Fidler - 175 (1947-50)
Appearances:	Brian Pritchard - 729
Additional:	Paid £12,500 to Hyde United for Jim McCluskie 1991. Received £11,500 from Chester City for Peter Henderson.

GROUND: Wincham Park, Chapel Street, Wincham, CW9 6DA
Ground Capacity: 4,813   **Seats:** 650   **Covered:** 2,300   **Clubhouse:** Yes   **Shop:** Yes
Previous Grounds: Central Ground (1910-1989)
Record Attendance: 3,940 v Kidderminster Harries - FA Trophy Semi-final 13/04/1991

Nearest Railway Station Northwich - 1.2km
Bus Route 89 & CAT9

BRIGHOUSE TOWN

Founded 1963

Nickname: Town   Club Colours: Orange & black

Club Contact Details
07483 119 054

Previous Names: Blakeborough
Previous Leagues: Huddersfield Works 1963-75. West Riding County Amateur 1975-08.

10-11	11-12	12-13	13-14	14-15	15-16	16-17	17-18	18-19	19-20
NCEP 16	NCEP 4	NCEP 2	NCEP 1	NP1N 14	NP1N 14	NP1N 9	NP1N 17	NP1E 3	NPNW n&v
FAC EP	FAC EP	FAC P	FAC 2Q	FAC 1Q	FAC 1Q	FAC 1Q	FAC P	FAC P	FAC P
FAV 1Pr	FAV 1Q	FAV 4P	FAV 3Pr	FAT P	FAT 1Q	FAT P	FAT P	FAT 1Q	FAT P

HONOURS / RECORDS
FA Comps: None
League: Hudersfield Works 1966-67, 68-69, 73-74, 74-75. West Riding County Amateur Premier Division 1990-91, 94-95, 95-96, 2000-01, 01-02, Division One 88-89. Northern Counties East Premier 2013-14.
County FA: West Riding county Cup 1991-92.

Best FA Cup	Second Qualifying Round 2013-14
FA Trophy	First Qualifying Round 2015-16
FA Vase	Fourth Round Proper 2012-13

GROUND: St Giles Road, Hove Edge, Brighouse, HD6 3PL

Ground Capacity: 1,000 **Seats:** 100 **Covered:** 200 **Clubhouse:** Yes **Shop:** No
Previous Grounds: Woodhouse Recreation Ground. Green Lane.
Record Attendance: 1,059 v Scarborough Athletic, Northern Counties East Premier Division, 13/04/2013.

Nearest Railway Station Brighouse - 2.5km
Bus Route 314

CITY OF LIVERPOOL

Founded 2015

Nickname: The Purps   Club Colours: All purple

Club Contact Details
07831 494 885   contact@colfc.co.uk

Previous Names: None
Previous Leagues: North West Counties 2016-19.

10-11	11-12	12-13	13-14	14-15	15-16	16-17	17-18	18-19	19-20
						NWC1 4	NWCP 4	NWCP 1	NPNW n&v
							FAC 1Q	FAC 2Q	FAC 1Qr
							FAV 3P	FAV 1P	FAT EPr

HONOURS / RECORDS
FA Comps: None
League: North West Counties Premier 2018-19.

County FA: None

Victory:	10-0 v Stockport Town, North West Counties Division One, 31/12/2016
FA Cup	Second Qualifying Round 2018-19
FA Vase	Third Round Proper 2017-18
FA Trophy	Extra Preliminary Round 2019-20(r)

GROUND: Vesty Road, off Bridle Road, Bootle, Liverpool L20 1NY

Ground Capacity: 1,750 **Seats:** Yes **Covered:** Yes **Clubhouse:** Yes **Shop:**
Previous Grounds: Sharing with Bootle FC (current agreement ends 2021). Hope to move in to a new 3,000 capacity stadium.
Record Attendance: 1,024 v Nantwich Town, FA Cup First Qualifying Round, 01/09/2017

Nearest Railway Station Aintree - 0.5km
Bus Route Arriva 15, 135 & 157

CLITHEROE

Nickname: The Blues **Club Colours:** All blue

Founded 1877

Club Contact Details
01200 423 344   secretary@clitheroefc.co.uk

Previous Names: Clitheroe Central 1877-1903.
Previous Leagues: Blackburn & District, Lancashire Combination 1903-04, 05-10, 25-82, North West Counties 1982-85

	10-11	11-12	12-13	13-14	14-15	15-16	16-17	17-18	18-19	19-20
	NP1N 6	NP1N 19	NP1N 8	NP1N 17	NP1N 13	NP1N 7	NP1N 7	NP1N 12	NP1W 18	NPNW n&v
FAC	P	2Q	1Q	P	1Q	1Q	P	1Q	1Q	EP
FAT	2Q	Pr	Pr	Pr	1Q	P	P	1Q	1Q	P

HONOURS / RECORDS

FA Comps: None

League: Lancashire Combination Division Two 1959-60, Division One 1979-80.
North West Counties Division Three 1983-84, Division Two 1984-85, Division One 1985-86, 2003-04.
County FA: Lancashire Challenge Trophy 1892-93, 1984-85.

Goalscorer: Don Francis
Appearances: Lindsey Wallace - 670
Additional: Received £45,000 from Crystal Palace for Carlo Nash.

GROUND: Shawbridge, off Pendle Road, Clitheroe, Lancashire BB7 1LZ

Ground Capacity: 2,000 **Seats:** 250 **Covered:** 1,400 **Clubhouse:** Yes **Shop:** No
Previous Grounds: None
Record Attendance: 2,050 v Mangotsfield - FA Vase Semi-final 1995-96

Nearest Railway Station Clitheroe - 0.6km
Bus Route Hayhurst Street - 50m away

COLNE

Nickname: The Reds **Club Colours:** Red & white

Founded 1996

Club Contact Details
01282 862 545   secretary@colnefootballclub.com

Previous Names: None
Previous Leagues: North West Counties 1996-2016.

	10-11	11-12	12-13	13-14	14-15	15-16	16-17	17-18	18-19	19-20
	NWCP 5	NWCP 8	NWCP 8	NWCP 9	NWCP 4	NWCP 1	NP1N 5	NP1N 8	NP1W 4	NPNW n&v
FAC	P	EP	EPr	EPr	EP	1Q	1Q	1Q	2Q	4Q
FAV	1P	1P	2Q	2Q	1P	2P	FAT P	FAT P	FAT EP	FAT 3Q

HONOURS / RECORDS

FA Comps: None

League: North West Counties League Division Two 2003-04, Premier Division 2015-16.

County FA: None

Goalscorer: Geoff Payton
Appearances: Richard Walton
Best FA Cup Fourth Qualifying Round 2019-20
FA Vase Semi Final 2003-04
FA Trophy Third Qualifyning Round 2019-20

GROUND: Harrison Drive, Colne, Lancashire BB8 9SL

Ground Capacity: 1,800 **Seats:** 160 **Covered:** 1,000 **Clubhouse:** Yes **Shop:** Yes
Previous Grounds: None
Record Attendance: 1,742 v AFC Sudbury F.A. Vase SF 2004. 2,762 (at Accrington Stanley) v FC United, NWC Challenge Cup, 13/11/05.
Nearest Railway Station Colne - 0.6km
Bus Route Tennyson Road - stop 100m away

DROYLSDEN

Founded 1892

Nickname: The Bloods   **Club Colours:** All red

Club Contact Details
0161 301 1352

Previous Names: None
Previous Leagues: Manchester, Lancashire Combination 1936-39, 50-68, Cheshire County 1939-50, 68-82,
North West Counties 1982-87, Northern Premier 1986-2004

10-11		11-12		12-13		13-14		14-15		15-16		16-17		17-18		18-19		19-20	
Conf N	8	Conf N	9	Conf N	21	NP P	24	NP1N	10	NP1N	19	NP1N	13	NP1N	13	NP1W	14	NPNW	n&v
FAC	2Pr	FAC	4Qr	FAC	2Q	FAC	1Q	FAC	2Q	FAC	3Q	FAC	Pr	FAC	2Q	FAC	Pr	FAC	P
FAT	3Pr	FAT	2P	FAT	3Q	FAT	1Q	FAT	P	FAT	P	FAT	Pr	FAT	3Q	FAT	1Qr	FAT	Pr

HONOURS / RECORDS

FA Comps: None
League: Manchester 1930-31, 32-33. North West Counties Division Two 1986-87. Northern Premier Division One 1998-99.
Conference North 2006-07.
County FA: Manchester Junior Cup 1922-23, Manchester Premier Cup x12 - Firstly in 1946-47 and most recently in 2009-10,
Manchester Senior Cup 1972-73, 75-76, 78-79.
Victory: 13-2 v Lucas Sports Club
Goalscorer: E. Gillibrand - 275 (1931-35)
Appearances: Paul Phillips - 326
Additional: Received £11,000 from Crewe Alexandra for Tony Naylor 1990
Defeat: 1-13 v Chorley, Northern Prmeier Premier Division, 05/04/2014.

GROUND: Market Street, Droylsden, M43 7AY

Ground Capacity: 3,000   **Seats:** 500   **Covered:** 2,000   **Clubhouse:** Yes   **Shop:** Yes
Previous Grounds: None
Record Attendance: 15,000 v Hyde United, Manchester League, 1921.

Nearest Railway Station Droylsden - 240m away
Bus Route Bus stops outside the ground

DUNSTON UTS

Founded 1975

Nickname: The Fed   **Club Colours:** All blue

Club Contact Details
0191 493 2935

Previous Names: Whickham Sports 1975-82. Dunston Mechanics 82-87. Dunston Federation Brewery 87-2007. Dunston Federation 07-09.
Previous Leagues: Newcastle City Amateur. Northern Amateur. Northern Combination 1980-87. Wearside 1987-91. Northern 91-2019.

10-11		11-12		12-13		13-14		14-15		15-16		16-17		17-18		18-19		19-20	
NL 1	7	NL 1	3	NL 1	5	NL 1	7	NL 1	6	NL 1	11	NL 1	15	NL 1	10	NL 1	1	NPNW	n&v
FAC	2Q	FAC	1Q	FAC	1Qr	FAC	P	FAC	2Q	FAC	1Q	FAC	2Q	FAC	P	FAC	4Q	FAC	4Q
FAV	QF	FAV	F	FAV	4P	FAV	QF	FAV	5Pr	FAV	5Pr	FAV	3P	FAV	2P	FAV	2P	FAT	1Q

HONOURS / RECORDS

FA Comps: FA Vase 2011-12.
League: Northern Amateur 1977-78. Northern Combination 1986-87. Wearside 1988-89, 89-90.
Northern Division Two 1992-93, Division One 2003-04, 04-05, 18-19.
County FA: None

Goalscorer: Paul King
Appearances: Paul Dixon
Best FA Cup Fourth Qualifying Round 2018-19 19-20
FA Vase Winners 2011-12
FA Trophy First Qualifying Round

GROUND: UTS Stadium, Wellington Road, Dunston, Gateshead NE11 9JL

Ground Capacity: 2,000   **Seats:** 150   **Covered:** 400   **Clubhouse:** Yes   **Shop:** No
Previous Grounds:
Record Attendance: 2,520 v Gateshead, FA Cup Fourth Qualifying Round, 20/10/2018

Nearest Railway Station Metrocentre - 0.9km. Dunston - 1km.
Bus Route Wellington Road - stop 24m away

KENDAL TOWN

Founded 1919

Nickname: The Mintcakes / The Field   **Club Colours:** Black and white stripes

Club Contact Details
01539 738 818

Previous Names: Netherfield AFC 1919-2000
Previous Leagues: Westmorland, North Lancashire Combination 1945-68, Northern Premier 1968-83, North West Counties 1983-87

10-11		11-12		12-13		13-14		14-15		15-16		16-17		17-18		18-19		19-20	
NP P	8	NP P	11	NP P	21	NP1N	10	NP1N	16	NP1N	15	NP1N	12	NP1N	18	NP1W	19	NPNW	n&v
FAC	1Q	FAC	3Q	FAC	3Q	FAC	P	FAC	Pr	FAC	2Q	FAC	P	FAC	1Q	FAC	1Q	FAC	EP
FAT	3Q	FAT	2Qr	FAT	1Qr	FAT	1Qr	FAT	P	FAT	1Q	FAT	2Q	FAT	1Q	FAT	P	FAT	P

HONOURS / RECORDS
FA Comps: None

League: Lancashire Combination 1948-49, 64-65.

County FA: Westmorlands Senior Cup x12. Lancashire Senior Cup 2002-03.

Victory: 11-0 v Great Harwood - 22/03/1947
Defeat: 0-10 v Stalybridge Celtic - 01/09/1984
Goalscorer: Tom Brownlee
Additional: Received £10,250 from Manchester City for Andy Milner 1995

GROUND: Parkside Road, Kendal, Cumbria LA9 7BL

Ground Capacity: 2,490   **Seats:** 450   **Covered:** 1000   **Clubhouse:** Yes   **Shop:** Yes
Previous Grounds: None
Record Attendance: 5,184 v Grimsby Town - FA Cup 1st Round 1955

Nearest Railway Station Kendal - 1.3km
Bus Route Castle Circle - stop 200m away

MARINE

Founded 1894

Nickname: Mariners   **Club Colours:** Gold & black

Club Contact Details
0151 924 1743

Previous Names: None
Previous Leagues: Liverpool Zingari, Liverpool County Combination, Lancashire Combination 1935-39, 46-69, Cheshire County 1969-79

10-11		11-12		12-13		13-14		14-15		15-16		16-17		17-18		18-19		19-20	
NP P	9	NP P	7	NP P	11	NP P	20	NP P	21	NP P	15	NP P	18	NP P	19	NP P	20	NPNW	n&v
FAC	1Qr	FAC	1Q	FAC	4Q	FAC	1Q	FAC	3Q	FAC	3Q	FAC	2Qr	FAC	2Q	FAC	4Q	FAC	2Q
FAT	2Q	FAT	3Q	FAT	1Q	FAT	2Q	FAT	2Q	FAT	3Q	FAT	1P	FAT	2P	FAT	1Q	FAT	EP

HONOURS / RECORDS
FA Comps: None

League: I Zingari Division Two 1901-02, Division One 02-03, 03-04, 09-10, 19-20, 20-21, 22-23. Liverpool Combination Division One 1927-28, 30-31, 33-34, 34-35, 43-44. Cheshire County 1973-74, 75-76, 76-77. Northern Premier Premier Division 1993-94, 84-95.
County FA: Lancashire Amateur Cup 1921-22, 25-26, 30-31, Junior Cup /Trophy 78-79, 87-88, 90-91, 99-00. Liverpool Challenge Cup 42-43, 44-45, 71-72, Non-League Cup 1968-69, 75-76, 76-77, Senior Cup 78-79, 84-85, 87-88, 89-90, 93-94, 99-00, 07-08.
Victory: 14-0 v Sandhurst - FA Cup 1st Qualifying Round 01/10/1938
Defeat: 2-11 v Shrewsbury Town - FA Cup 1st Round 1995
Goalscorer: Paul Meachin - 200
Appearances: Peter Smith 952
Additional: Paid £6,000 to Southport for Jon Penman October 1985. Received £20,000 from Crewe for Richard Norris 1996.

GROUND: College Road, Crosby, Liverpool L23 3AS

Ground Capacity: 3,185   **Seats:** 400   **Covered:** 1,400   **Clubhouse:** Yes   **Shop:** Yes
Previous Grounds: Waterloo Park 1894-1903
Record Attendance: 4,000 v Nigeria - Friendly 1949

Nearest Railway Station Blunellsands & Crosby - 0.5km
Bus Route Brompton Avenue - stop 175m away

MARSKE UNITED

Founded 1956

Nickname: The Seasiders **Club Colours:** Yellow & navy

Club Contact Details
07803 248 709   admin@marskeunitedfc.com

Previous Names: None
Previous Leagues: Local leagues 1956-76. Teeside 1976- 85. Wearside 1985-97. Northern League 1997-2018.

	10-11	11-12	12-13	13-14	14-15	15-16	16-17	17-18	18-19	19-20
	NL 2 3	NL 1 18	NL 1 19	NL 1 16	NL 1 1	NL 1 2	NL 1 5	NL 1 1	NP1E 10	NPNW n&v
FAC	1Q	P	P	4Q	1Qr	Pr	1Q	Pr	P	1Qr
FAV	2P	2Q	1Qr	1P	3P	4P	2P	SF	FAT 3Q	FAT EP

HONOURS / RECORDS

FA Comps: None

League: Teesside 1980-81, 84-85. Wearside 1995-96. Northern Division One 2014-15, 17-18.

County FA: None

Defeat:	3-9
Goalscorer:	Chris Morgan 169.
Appearances:	Mike Kinnair 583.
Victory:	16-0

GROUND: Mount Pleasant Avenue, Marske by the Sea, Redcar TS11 7BW

Ground Capacity: 2,500 **Seats:** Yes **Covered:** Yes **Clubhouse:** Yes **Shop:**
Previous Grounds: None
Record Attendance: 1,359 v Bedlington Terriers FA Vase.

Nearest Railway Station Marske - 0.4km
Bus Route Windy Hill Lane - stop 84m away

MOSSLEY

Founded 1903

Nickname: Lilywhites **Club Colours:** White & black

Club Contact Details
01457 832 369

Previous Names: Park Villa 1903-04, Mossley Juniors
Previous Leagues: Ashton, South East Lancashire, Lancashire Combination 1918-19, Cheshire County 1919-72,
Northern Premier 1972-95, North West Counties 1995-2004

	10-11	11-12	12-13	13-14	14-15	15-16	16-17	17-18	18-19	19-20
	NP1N 15	NP1N 14	NP1N 5	NP1N 15	NP1N 7	NP1N 13	NP1N 17	NP1N 19	NP1W 8	NPNW n&v
FAC	4Q	Pr	P	Pr	Pr	Pr	1Q	1Qr	2Q	Pr
FAT	2Q	P	1Qr	2Q	1Q	1Q	1Q	1Q	EP	P

HONOURS / RECORDS

FA Comps: None

League: Ashton & District 1911-12, 14-15. Northern Premier 1978-79, 79-80, Division One 2005-06.

County FA: Manchester Premier Cup 1937-38, 48-49, 60-61, 66-67, 67-68, 88-89, 90-91, 2011-12, 12-13, 14-15, 15-16. Manchester Challenge Trophy 2011-12.

Victory:	9-0 v Urmston, Manchester Shield, 1947
Defeat:	2-13 v Witton Albion, Cheshire League, 1926
Goalscorer:	David Moore - 235 (1974-84). Jackie Roscoe scored 58 during the 1930-31 season.
Appearances:	Jimmy O'Connor - 613 (1972-87)
Additional:	Paid £2,300 to Altrincham for Phil Wilson. Received £25,000 from Everton for Eamonn O'Keefe.

GROUND: Seel Park, Market Street, Mossley, Lancashire OL5 0ES

Ground Capacity: 4,000 **Seats:** 220 **Covered:** 1,500 **Clubhouse:** Yes **Shop:** Yes
Previous Grounds: Moved to Seel Park in 1911.
Record Attendance: 7,000 v Stalybridge Celtic 1950

Nearest Railway Station Mossley - 0.3km
Bus Route Stamford Street - 200m away

OSSETT UNITED

Founded 2018

Nickname: United   **Club Colours:** Blue

Club Contact Details
01924 272 960   secretary@ossettunited.com

Previous Names: Formed after the merger of Ossett Albion (1944) and Ossett Town (1936).
Previous Leagues: None

10-11	11-12	12-13	13-14	14-15	15-16	16-17	17-18	18-19	19-20
								NP1E 5	NPNW n&v
								FAC Pr	FAC 2Qr
								FAT 2Q	FAT P

HONOURS / RECORDS
FA Comps: None
League: None

County FA: West Riding County Cup 2018-19.

Best FA Cup   Second Qualifying Round 2019-20(r)
FA Trophy   Second Qualifying Round 2018-19

GROUND: Ingfield Stadium, Prospect Road, Ossett WF5 9HA

Ground Capacity: 1,950   **Seats:** 360   **Covered:** 1,000   **Clubhouse:** Yes   **Shop:** Yes
Previous Grounds: None
Record Attendance: 1,118 v AFC Guiseley, West Riding County Cup Final, 9/04/2019

Nearest Railway Station Dewsbury - 3.9km
Bus Route Prospect Road - stop 50m away

PICKERING TOWN

Founded 1888

Nickname: Pikes   **Club Colours:** All blue

Club Contact Details
01751 473 317

Previous Names: None
Previous Leagues: Beckett, York & District, Scarborough & District, Yorkshire 1972-82. Northern Counties East 1982-2018.

10-11	11-12	12-13	13-14	14-15	15-16	16-17	17-18	18-19	19-20
NCEP 7	NCEP 12	NCEP 5	NCEP 7	NCEP 11	NCEP 6	NCEP 2	NCEP 2	NP1E 16	NPNW n&v
FAC EP	FAC 1Qr	FAC EPr	FAC EP	FAC EP	FAC P	FAC Pr	FAC P	FAC P	FAC 1Q
FAV 2P	FAV 2Q	FAV 2P	FAV 2Q	FAV 2Q	FAV 1Q	FAV 2P	FAV 1P	FAT 3Qr	FAT 1Qr

HONOURS / RECORDS
FA Comps: None

League: Scarborough & District Division One 1930-31, 50-51. York Division Two 1953-54, Division One 55-56, 66-67, 69-70. Yorkshire Division Three 1973-74. Northern Counties East Division Two 1987-88.
County FA: North Riding Cup 1990-91. North Riding Senior Cup 2012-13.

Best FA Cup   Second Qualifying Round 1999-2000, 01-02, 03-04
FA Vase   Quarter Finals 2005-06
FA Trophy   Third Qualifying Round 2018-19(r)

GROUND: Recreation Club, off Mill Lane, Malton Road, Pickering YO18 7DB

Ground Capacity: 2,000   **Seats:** 200   **Covered:** 500   **Clubhouse:** Yes   **Shop:** Yes
Previous Grounds: Not known
Record Attendance: 1,412 v Notts County (friendly) in August 1991

Nearest Railway Station Pickering - 650m
Bus Route Millfield Close - stop 62m away

PONTEFRACT COLLIERIES

Founded 1958

Nickname: Colls   **Club Colours:** All blue

Club Contact Details
01977 600 818

Previous Names: None
Previous Leagues: West Yorkshire 1958-79. Yorkshire 1979-82. Northern Counties East 1982-2018.

10-11		11-12		12-13		13-14		14-15		15-16		16-17		17-18		18-19		19-20	
NCE1	5	NCE1	5	NCE1	5	NCE1	9	NCE1	2	NCEP	20	NCE1	2	NCEP	1	NP1E	2	NPNW	n&v
FAC	EP	FAC	P	FAC	EPr	FAC	EP	FAC	EP	FAC	P	FAC	1Q	FAC	P	FAC	P	FAC	2Q
FAV	2Q	FAV	1P	FAV	2Q	FAV	2Q	FAV	1Q	FAV	1Q	FAV	1Q	FAV	4P	FAT	P	FAT	1Q

HONOURS / RECORDS
FA Comps: None

League: Yorkshire Division Three 1981-82.
Northern Counties East Division One North 1983-84, Premier Division 2017-18.
County FA: Castleford & District FA Embleton Cup 1982-83, 86-87, 95-96, 99-2000, 05-06, 06-07, 07-08.

Best FA Cup   Second Qualifying Round 2019-20
FA Vase   Second Round Proper 2002-03
FA Trophy   First Qualifying Round 2019-20

GROUND: Beechnut Lane, Pontefract, WF8 4QE

Ground Capacity: 1,200   **Seats:** 300   **Covered:** 400   **Clubhouse:** Yes   **Shop:** Yes
Previous Grounds: Not known
Record Attendance: 1,000 v Hull City, floodlight opening 1987.

Nearest Railway Station pontefract Tanshelf - ¼ mile
Bus Route 113, 148, 149, 184, 28, 410

PRESCOT CABLES

Founded 1884

Nickname: Tigers   **Club Colours:** Amber & black

Club Contact Details
0151 426 0527

Previous Names: Prescot > 1995
Previous Leagues: Liverpool County Combination, Lancashire Combination 1897-98, 1918-20, 27-33, 36-76,
Mid Cheshire 1976-78, Cheshire County 1978-82, North West Counties 1982-2003

10-11		11-12		12-13		13-14		14-15		15-16		16-17		17-18		18-19		19-20	
NP1N	21	NP1N	16	NP1N	17	NP1N	20	NP1N	20	NP1N	16	NP1N	16	NP1N	5	NP1W	7	NPNW	n&v
FAC	1Qr	FAC	P	FAC	1Q	FAC	1Q	FAC	1Q	FAC	P	FAC	P	FAC	Pr	FAC	P	FAC	P
FAT	1Q	FAT	P	FAT	1Q	FAT	P	FAT	1Q	FAT	P	FAT	1Q	FAT	1Qr	FAT	2Q	FAT	2Qr

HONOURS / RECORDS
FA Comps: None

League: Lancashire Combination Division Two 1951-52, Premier 1956-57. Mid-Cheshire 1976-77.
Cheshire County Division Two 1979-80. North West Counties 2002-03.
County FA: Liverpool Challenge Cup 1927-28, 28-29, 29-30, 48-49, 61-62, 77-78. Liverpool Non-League Cup 1952-53, 58-59, 60-61.
Liverpool Senior Cup 2016-17, 17-18.
Victory: 18-3 v Great Harwood - 1954-55
Defeat: 1-12 v Morecambe - 1936-37
Goalscorer: Freddie Crampton
Appearances: Harry Grisedale

GROUND: Volair Park, Eaton Street, Prescot L34 6ND

Ground Capacity: 3,200   **Seats:** 500   **Covered:** 600   **Clubhouse:** Yes   **Shop:** Yes
Previous Grounds: None
Record Attendance: 8,122 v Ashton National - 1932

Nearest Railway Station Eccleston Park - 26min walk
Bus Route 10, 10A & 89

RAMSBOTTOM UNITED

Founded 1966

Nickname: The Rams   **Club Colours:** Blue & white

Club Contact Details
01706 822 799   secretary@rammyunited.co.uk

Previous Names: None
Previous Leagues: Bury Amateur 1966-69. Bolton Combination 1969-89. Manchester 1989-95. North West Counties 1995-2012.

	10-11		11-12		12-13		13-14		14-15		15-16		16-17		17-18		18-19		19-20	
	NWCP	2	NWCP	1	NP1N	6	NP1N	5	NP P	17	NP P	24	NP1N	14	NP1N	14	NP1W	5	NPNW	n&v
	FAC	1Q	FAC	1Q	FAC	1Q	FAC	2Q	FAC	1Q	FAC	1Q	FAC	P	FAC	P	FAC	Pr	FAC	2Q
	FAV	1P	FAV	2P	FAT	2Q	FAT	3Q	FAT	1P	FAT	1Qr	FAT	3Q	FAT	2Q	FAT	3Pr	FAT	P

HONOURS / RECORDS

FA Comps: None

League: Bolton Combination Division One 1972-73, Premier Division 76-77. Manchester Division One 1990-91. North West Counties Division Two 1996-97, Premier Division 2011-12.

County FA: None

Victory: 9-0 v Stantondale (H), NWCFL Division Two, 9th November 1996.
Defeat: 0-7 v Salford City (A), NWCFL Division One, 16th November 2002.
Goalscorer: Russell Brierley - 176 (1996-2003). Russell Brierley scored 38 during the 1999-2000 season.

GROUND: The Harry Williams Stadium, Acrebottom (off Bridge Street) BL0 0BS.

Ground Capacity: 2,000   **Seats:** Yes   **Covered:** Yes   **Clubhouse:** Yes   **Shop:** No
Previous Grounds: None
Record Attendance: 2,104 v FC United of Manchester, Northern Premier League Premier Division, 04/04/15.

Bus Route 472 & 474

RUNCORN LINNETS

Founded 2006

Nickname: Linnets   **Club Colours:** Yellow & green

Club Contact Details
08454 860 705   secretary@runcornlinnetsfc.co.uk

Previous Names: None
Previous Leagues: North West Counties 2006-18.

	10-11		11-12		12-13		13-14		14-15		15-16		16-17		17-18		18-19		19-20	
	NWCP	12	NWCP	5	NWCP	6	NWCP	2	NWCP	2	NWCP	2	NWCP	4	NWCP	1	NP1W	6	NPNW	n&v
	FAC	P	FAC	2Q	FAC	EPr	FAC	3Q	FAC	P	FAC	1Q	FAC	EP	FAC	P	FAC	P	FAC	P
	FAV	1P	FAV	1P	FAV	1P	FAV	1P	FAV	1P	FAV	2P	FAV	1P	FAV	3P	FAT	EP	FAT	3Q

HONOURS / RECORDS

FA Comps: None

League: North West Counties Premier 2017-18.

County FA: None

Best FA Cup   Third Qualifying Round 2013-14
FA Vase   Third Round Proper 2008-09, 17-18
FA Trophy   Third Qualifying Round 2019-20

GROUND: Millbank Linnets Stadium, Stockham Lane, Murdishaw, Runcorn, Cheshire WA7 6GJ

Ground Capacity: 1,600   **Seats:** Yes   **Covered:** Yes   **Clubhouse:** Yes   **Shop:**
Previous Grounds: Not known
Record Attendance: 1,037 v Witton Albion, pre season friendly July 2010

Nearest Railway Station Runcorn East - 1.2km
Bus Route Halton Arms stop - 62m away

TADCASTER ALBION

Founded 1892

Nickname: The Brewers / Taddy   **Club Colours:** White & blue

Club Contact Details
01904 606 000

Previous Names: John Smith's FC > 1923.
Previous Leagues: York, Harrogate, Yorkshire 1973-82. Northern Counties East 1982-2016.

10-11		11-12		12-13		13-14		14-15		15-16		16-17		17-18		18-19		19-20	
NCEP	4	NCEP	8	NCEP	6	NCEP	2	NCEP	3	NCEP	1	NP1N	19	NP1N	7	NP1E		NPNW	n&v
FAC	1Qr	FAC	2Q	FAC	3Q	FAC	EPr	FAC	P	FAC	P	FAC	2Q	FAC	P	FAC	1Q	FAC	1Qr
FAV	4P	FAV	2P	FAV	1Q	FAV	1Q	FAV	QFr	FAV	3P	FAT	P	FAT	P	FAT	Pr	FAT	1Q

HONOURS / RECORDS

FA Comps: None

League: York Division One 1909-10, 23-24, 32-33, Premier 47-48.
Northern Counties East Division One 2009-10, Premier Division 2015-16.

County FA: None

Victory:　　　13-0 v Blidworth Welfare, NCEL Division One, 1997-98
Defeat:　　　10-2 v Thackley, 1984-85

GROUND: Ings Lane, Tadcaster LS24 9AY

Ground Capacity: 2,000　**Seats:** 159　**Covered:** 259　**Clubhouse:** Yes　**Shop:** No
Previous Grounds: None
Record Attendance: 1,307 v Highworth Town, FA Vase, 2014-15.

Nearest Railway Station Ulleskelf - 4.3km
Bus Route John Smith's Brewery - stop 300m away

TRAFFORD

Founded 1990

Nickname: The North   **Club Colours:** All white

Club Contact Details
0161 747 1727

Previous Names: North Trafford 1990-94
Previous Leagues: Mid Cheshire 1990-92, North West Counties 1992-97, 2003-08, Northern Premier 1997-2003

10-11		11-12		12-13		13-14		14-15		15-16		16-17		17-18		18-19		19-20	
NP1N	14	NP1N	12	NP1N	4	NP P	10	NP P	23	NP1N	8	NP1N	6	NP1N	6	NP1W	9	NPNW	n&v
FAC	1Q	FAC	1Q	FAC	3Q	FAC	3Q	FAC	1Q	FAC	P	FAC	2Q	FAC	Pr	FAC	2Q	FAC	2Q
FAT	P	FAT	P	FAT	2Q	FAT	2Q	FAT	2Q	FAT	P	FAT	2Q	FAT	P	FAT	P	FAT	P

HONOURS / RECORDS

FA Comps: None
League: North West Counties Division One 1996-97, 2007-08.

County FA: Manchester Challenge Trophy 2004-05.

Victory:　　　10-0 v Haslingden St.Mary's (Lancs Amt Shield 1991)
Goalscorer:　　Scott Barlow - 100
Appearances:　Lee Southwood - 311
Additional:　　NWC League Record: 18 consecutive league wins in 2007-08
　　　　　　　　　Most Points In One Season: 95 points from 38 games 2007-08

GROUND: Shawe View, Pennybridge Lane, Flixton Urmston M41 5DL

Ground Capacity: 2,500　**Seats:** 292　**Covered:** 740　**Clubhouse:** Yes　**Shop:** Yes
Previous Grounds: None
Record Attendance: 803 v Flixton - Northern Premier League Division 1 1997-98. 2,238 (at Altrincham FC) FAC P v FC United
　　　　　　　　　02/09/07.
Nearest Railway Station Urmston - 0.3km
Bus Route 245 & 255

WIDNES

Nickname: Vikings   **Club Colours:** White & black

Founded 2003

Club Contact Details
07917 428 609

Previous Names: Formed as Dragons AFC in 2003. Widnes Dragons > 2012. Widnes Vikings 2012-14.
Previous Leagues: Junior Leagues 2003-12. West Cheshire 2012-13. North West Counties 2013-18.

10-11	11-12	12-13	13-14	14-15	15-16	16-17	17-18	18-19	19-20
		WCh3 4	NWC1 14	NWC1 16	NWC1 13	NWC1 1	NWCP 2	NP1W 12	NPNW n&v
							FAC EP	FAC EPr	FAC 1Q
				FAV 2Q		FAV 2Q	FAV 1Q	FAT EP	FAT EP

HONOURS / RECORDS
FA Comps: None
League: North West Counties Division One 2016-17.

County FA: None

Victory: (League) 8-0 v St Helens Town, 08/04/2017
Defeat: (League) 1-10 v Northwich Manchester Villa, 13/12/2014

GROUND: Lowerhouse Lane, Widnes, Cheshire WA8 7DZ
Ground Capacity: 13,350   **Seats:** Yes   **Covered:** Yes   **Clubhouse:** Yes   **Shop:**
Previous Grounds: The club moved to Halton Stadium in 2012.
Record Attendance: 462 v Charnock Richard, North West Counties Division One, 22/04/2017

Nearest Railway Station Widnes - 1.5km
Bus Route Cricketers Arms stop - 121m away

WORKINGTON

Nickname: Reds   **Club Colours:** Red and white

Founded 1921

Club Contact Details
01900 602 871

Previous Names: Workington AFC 1921-
Previous Leagues: North Eastern 1921-51, Football League 1951-77, Northern Premier 1977-2005. Conference 2005-14.

10-11	11-12	12-13	13-14	14-15	15-16	16-17	17-18	18-19	19-20
Conf N 11	Conf N 13	Conf N 14	'Conf N 22	NP P 2	NP P 5	NP P 4	NP P 11	NP P 21	NPNW n&v
FAC 4Qr	FAC 2Q	FAC 4Q	FAC 4Q	FAC 2Q	FAC 2Q	FAC 3Qr	FAC 2Q	FAC 3Qr	FAC P
FAT 3Qr	FAT 3Q	FAT 3Q	FAT 3Q	FAT 3Q	FAT 1Q	FAT 1Q	FAT 3Pr	FAT 1P	FAT 3Q

HONOURS / RECORDS
FA Comps: None
League: North West Counties 1998-99

County FA: Cumberland County Cup x25 (Most recently 2016-17).

Victory: 17-1 v Cockermouth Crusaders - Cumberland Senior League 19/01/1901
Defeat: 0-9 v Chorley (A) - Northern Premier League 10/11/1987
Goalscorer: Billy Charlton - 193
Appearances: Bobby Brown - 469
Additional: Paid £6,000 to Sunderland for Ken Chisolm 1956. Received £33,000 from Liverpool for Ian McDonald 1974.

GROUND: Borough Park, Workington, Cumbria CA14 2DT
Ground Capacity: 3,101   **Seats:** 500   **Covered:** 1,000   **Clubhouse:** Yes   **Shop:** Yes
Previous Grounds: Lonsdale Park 1921-37.
Record Attendance: 21,000 v Manchester United - FA Cup 3rd round 04/01/1958

Nearest Railway Station Workington - 0.6km
Bus Route Tesco - stop 100m away

BELPER TOWN

Nickname: The Nailers   **Club Colours:** Yellow & black

Founded 1883

Club Contact Details
01773 825 549

Previous Names: None

Previous Leagues: Derbyshire Senior (Founder members) 1890-1911. Notts & Derbyshire (FM) 1911-12. Central Alliance 1957-61, Midland Counties 1961-82, Northern Counties East 1982-97

10-11		11-12		12-13		13-14		14-15		15-16		16-17		17-18		18-19		19-20	
NP1S	14	NP1S	6	NP1S	3	NP1S	4	NP P	24	NP1S	13	NP1S	10	NP1S	16	NP1E	9	NPSE	n&v
FAC	P	FAC	P	FAC	2Qr	FAC	2Q	FAC	1Qr	FAC	1Q	FAC	2Q	FAC	Pr	FAC	1Q	FAC	4Q
FAT	P	FAT	2Q	FAT	2Q	FAT	1Q	FAT	1Q	FAT	1Qr	FAT	P	FAT	P	FAT	Pr	FAT	P

HONOURS / RECORDS

FA Comps: None

League: Central Alliance 1958-59. Midland Counties 1979-80. Northern Counties East 1984-85.

County FA: Derbyshire Senior Cup 1958-59, 61-62, 63-64, 79-80, 2007-08.

Victory:	15-2 v Nottingham Forest 'A' - 1956
Defeat:	0-12 v Goole Town - 1965
Goalscorer:	Mick Lakin - 231
Appearances:	Craig Smithurst - 678
Additional:	Paid £2,000 to Ilkeston Town for Jamie Eaton 2001. Received £2,000 from Hinckley United for Craig Smith.

GROUND: Christchurch Meadow, Bridge Street, Belper DE56 1BA

Ground Capacity: 2,650   **Seats:** 500   **Covered:** 850   **Clubhouse:** Yes   **Shop:** Yes
Previous Grounds: Acorn Ground > 1951
Record Attendance: 3,200 v Ilkeston Town - 1955

Nearest Railway Station Belper - 0.4km
Bus Route The Lion Hotel - stop 200m away

CARLTON TOWN

Nickname: The Millers   **Club Colours:** Yellow & blue

Founded 1904

Club Contact Details
01159 403 192

Previous Names: Sneinton FC

Previous Leagues: Notts Alliance, Central Midlands, Northern Counties East

10-11		11-12		12-13		13-14		14-15		15-16		16-17		17-18		18-19		19-20	
NP1S	8	NP1S	2	NP1S	12	NP1S	10	NP1S	18	NP1S	18	NP1S	19	NP1S	19	NP1E	19	NPSE	n&v
FAC	2Q	FAC	2Q	FAC	3Q	FAC	3Q	FAC	1Q	FAC	P	FAC	P	FAC	P	FAC	P	FAC	EP
FAT	1Qr	FAT	P	FAT	P	FAT	Pr	FAT	1Qr	FAT	2Q	FAT	1Q	FAT	1Q	FAT	2Q	FAT	1Q

HONOURS / RECORDS

FA Comps: None

League: Notts Alliance 1905-06, 07-08, 08-09, 09-10, Division Two 1984-85, Division One 1992-93.
Central Midlands Supreme Division 2002-03. Northern Counties East Division One 2005-06.

County FA: Notts Senior Cup 2012-13, 16-17.

Best FA Cup	Third Qualifying Round 2012-13, 13-14
Amateur Cup	Third Round Proper 1910-11, 19-20, 30-31
FA Trophy	Second Qualifying Round 2009-10, 15-16
FA Vase	Third Round Proper 2005-06

GROUND: Bill Stokeld Stadium, Stoke Lane, Gedling NG4 2QS

Ground Capacity: 1,500   **Seats:** 164   **Covered:** Yes   **Clubhouse:** Yes   **Shop:** No
Previous Grounds: Club played at several grounds before moving to Stoke Lane (Bill Stokeld Stadium) in the 1990s.
Record Attendance: 1,000 - Radio Trent Charity Match

Nearest Railway Station Carlton - 1.1km. Netherfield - 1.5km
Bus Route Stoke Lane - stop 50m away

CHASETOWN

Nickname: The Scholars **Club Colours:** Royal blue & white

Founded 1954

Club Contact Details
01543 682 222

Previous Names: Chase Terrace Old Scholars 1954-72
Previous Leagues: Cannock Youth 1954-58, Lichfield & District 1958-61, Staffordshire County 1961-72, West Midlands 1972-94, Midland Alliance 1994-2006, Southern 2006-09

10-11		11-12		12-13		13-14		14-15		15-16		16-17		17-18		18-19		19-20	
NP P	10	NP P	20	NP1S	5	NP1S	12	NP1S	13	NP1S	7	NP1S	17	NP1S	5	NP1W	13	NPSE	n&v
FAC	1Q	FAC	2Q	FAC	2Q	FAC	1Qr	FAC	1Qr	FAC	3Qr	FAC	2Q	FAC	2Q	FAC	1Qr	FAC	2Q
FAT	QF	FAT	2Q	FAT	2Q	FAT	1Q	FAT	3Q	FAT	Pr	FAT	P	FAT	2Q	FAT	1Q	FAT	1Q

HONOURS / RECORDS
FA Comps: None

League: West Midlands 1978. Midland Alliance 2004-05.

County FA: Walsall Senior Cup 1990-91, 92-93, 2004-05.

Victory: 14-1 v Hanford - Walsall Senior Cup 1991-92
Defeat: 1-8 v Telford United Reserves - West Midlands League
Goalscorer: Tony Dixon - 197. Mick Ward scored 39 goals during the 1987-88 season, whilst a player by the name of Keith Birch scored 11 in a 21-1 win over Lichfield Laundry.
Misc: Became the first club from the eighth tier of English football to reach the FA Cup Third Round Proper during the 2007-08 season.

GROUND: The Scholars, Church Street, Chasetown, Walsall WS7 3QL

Ground Capacity: 2,000 **Seats:** 151 **Covered:** 220 **Clubhouse:** Yes **Shop:** Yes
Previous Grounds: Burntwood Recreation
Record Attendance: 2,420 v Cardiff City - FA Cup Third Round Proper January 2008

Nearest Railway Station Hednesford - 6.4km
Bus Route Queen Street - stop 160m away

CLEETHORPES TOWN

Nickname: The Owls **Club Colours:** Blue & black

Founded 1998

Club Contact Details
01472 693 601

Previous Names: Lincolnshire Soccer School Lucarlys 1998-2008.
Previous Leagues: Lincolnshire 2003-05, 10-12. Central Midlands 2005-06. Humber Premier 2006-09. Northern Counties East 2012-17.

10-11		11-12		12-13		13-14		14-15		15-16		16-17		17-18		18-19		19-20	
Lincs	3	Lincs	1	NCE1	4	NCE1	1	NCEP	4	NCEP	3	NCEP	1	NP1S	10	NP1E	7	NPSE	n&v
								FAC	2Q	FAC	P	FAC	P	FAC	1Q	FAC	3Qr	FAC	1Q
						FAV	2P	FAV	2P	FAV	5P	FAV	F	FAT	3Q	FAT	1Q	FAT	1Q

HONOURS / RECORDS
FA Comps: None

League: Lincolnshire 2011-12. Northern Counties East Division One 2013-14, Premier 2016-17.

County FA: Lincolnshire Senior Trophy 2016-17.

Best FA Cup Second Qualifying Round 2014-15
FA Vase Runners-up 2016-17
FA Trophy Third Qualifying Round 2017-18

GROUND: The Linden Club, Clee Road, Grimsby DN32 8QL

Ground Capacity: 1,875 **Seats:** 190 **Covered:** Yes **Clubhouse:** Yes **Shop:**
Previous Grounds: None
Record Attendance: 1,154 v Bromsgrove Sporting, FA Vase Semi-Final second leg, 18/03/2017.

Nearest Railway Station Grimsby - then a 5 min walk to main bus station (see below).
Bus Route From the bus station, take either No.14 or No.13 bus.

FRICKLEY ATHLETIC

Founded 1910

Nickname: The Blues   **Club Colours:** All royal blue

Club Contact Details
01977 642 460

Previous Names: Frickley Colliery
Previous Leagues: Sheffield, Yorkshire 1922-24, Midland Counties 1924-33, 34-60, 70-76, Cheshire County 1960-70, Northern Premier 1976-80, Conference 1980-87

10-11		11-12		12-13		13-14		14-15		15-16		16-17		17-18		18-19		19-20	
NP P	18	NP P	19	NP P	18	NP P	21	NP P	19	NP P	7	NP P	22	NP1S	3	NP1E	12	NPSE	n&v
FAC	3Qr	FAC	3Q	FAC	3Q	FAC	2Q	FAC	1Q	FAC	2Q	FAC	1Q	FAC	1Q	FAC	2Q	FAC	P
FAT	1Q	FAT	1Q	FAT	1Q	FAT	1Q	FAT	1Q	FAT	1Q	FAT	1Q	FAT	1Q	FAT	1Q	FAT	EP

HONOURS / RECORDS

FA Comps: None

League: None

County FA: Sheffield & Hallamshire Senior Cup x14 - Firstly in 1927-28 and most recently in 2015-16.

Goalscorer: K Whiteley
Additional: Received £12,500 from Boston United for Paul Shirtliff and from Northampton Town for Russ Wilcox

---

GROUND: Westfield Lane, South Elmsall, Pontefract WF9 2EQ

Ground Capacity: 2,087   **Seats:** 490   **Covered:** 700   **Clubhouse:** Yes   **Shop:** Yes
Previous Grounds: None
Record Attendance: 5,800 v Rotherham United - FA Cup 1st Round 1971

Nearest Railway Station South Elmsall - 0.7km. Moorthorpe - 0.9km
Bus Route Westfield Lane - stop 100m away

GLOSSOP NORTH END

Founded 1886

Nickname: Peakites / The Hillmen   **Club Colours:** All royal blue

Club Contact Details
07740 265 711

Previous Names: Glossop North End 1886-1896 and Glossop FC 1898-1992. Reformed in 1992.
Previous Leagues: North Cheshire 1890-94. Combination 1894-96. Midland 1896-98. The Football League 1898-1918. Lancashire Comb. 1919 -20, 57-66. Manchester 1920-57, 66-78. Cheshire County (Founder member) 1978-82. North West Counties (FM)1982-2015.

10-11		11-12		12-13		13-14		14-15		15-16		16-17		17-18		18-19		19-20	
NWCP	14	NWCP	6	NWCP	13	NWCP	3	NWCP	1	NP1N	4	NP1N	8	NP1N	11	NP1W	17	NPSE	n&v
FAC	1Q	FAC	EP	FAC	P	FAC	1Q	FAC	2Q	FAC	1Qr	FAC	Qr	FAC	Pr	FAC	Pr	FAC	1Q
FAV	1P	FAV	3P	FAV	2Qr	FAV	2P	FAV	F	FAT	Pr	FAT	1Q	FAT	3Qr	FAT	EP	FAT	P

HONOURS / RECORDS

FA Comps: None

League: Manchester 1927-28. North West Counties Premier Division 2014-15.

County FA: Manchester FA Premier Cup 1996-97, 97-98. Derbyshire Senior Cup 2000-01.

Best FA Cup   First Round Proper 1896-97
FA Trophy   Third Qualifying Round 2017-18
FA Vase   Finalists 2014-15

GROUND: Surrey Street, Glossop, Derbys SK13 7AJ

Ground Capacity: 2,374   **Seats:** 209   **Covered:** 509   **Clubhouse:** Yes   **Shop:** Yes
Previous Grounds: Pyegrove. Silk Street. Water Lane. Cemetery Road. North Road 1890-1955.
Record Attendance: 10,736 v Preston North End F.A. Cup 1913-1914

Nearest Railway Station Glossop - 0.4km
Bus Route St Mary's Road - stop 300m away

ILKESTON TOWN

Founded 2017

Nickname: The Robins   **Club Colours:** Red & white

Club Contact Details
07876 492 902

Previous Names: None
Previous Leagues: Midland 2017-19.

10-11	11-12	12-13	13-14	14-15	15-16	16-17	17-18	18-19	19-20
							MFL1 2	MFLP 1	NPSE n&v
									FAC EP
							FAV 2P	FAT P	

HONOURS / RECORDS

FA Comps: None
League: Midland Premier 2018-19.

County FA: None

Victory:	8-1 v Loughborough University, Midland Premier, 27/04/2019
Defeat:	0-4 v Coventry Sphinx, Midland Premier, 15/12/2018
Best FA Cup	Extra Preliminary Round 2019-20
FA Vase	Second Round Proper 2018-19
FA Trophy	Preliminary Round 2019-20

GROUND: New Manor Ground, Awsworth Road, Ilkeston, Derbyshire DE7 8JF

Ground Capacity: 3,029   **Seats:** 550   **Covered:** 2,000   **Clubhouse:** Yes   **Shop:** Yes
Previous Grounds: None.
Record Attendance: Not known

Nearest Railway Station Ikeston
Bus Route 21, 27 & The Two

KIDSGROVE ATHLETIC

Founded 1952

Nickname: The Grove   **Club Colours:** All blue

Club Contact Details
01782 782 412

Previous Names: None
Previous Leagues: Buslem and Tunstall 1953-63, Staffordshire County 1963-66, Mid Cheshire 1966-90,
North West Counties 1990-2002

10-11	11-12	12-13	13-14	14-15	15-16	16-17	17-18	18-19	19-20
NP1S 7	NP1S 13	NP1S 18	NP1S 21	NP1S 20	NP1S 15	NP1S 12	NP1S 18	NP1W 10	NPSE n&v
FAC 2Q	FAC 4Q	FAC P	FAC 1Q	FAC P	FAC Pr	FAC 2Q	FAC 2Q	FAC 4Q	FAC 3Q
FAT Pr	FAT 1Q	FAT 1Q	FAT 2Q	FAT P	FAT 2Qr	FAT 2Q	FAT 2Q	FAT P	FAT 1Q

HONOURS / RECORDS

FA Comps: None
League: Staffordshire County Division Two 1963-64, Premier 65-66. Mid-Cheshire 1970-71, 77-78, 86-87, 87-88.
       North West Counties Premier Division 1997-98, 2001-02.
County FA: Staffordshire Senior Cup 2003-04, 06-07, 08-09, 10-11, 11-12.

Victory:	23-0 v Cross Heath W.M.C. - Staffordshire Cup 1965
Defeat:	0-15 v Stafford Rangers - Staffordshire Senior Cup 20/11/2001
Goalscorer:	Scott Dundas - 53 (1997-98)
Additional:	Paid £10,000 to Stevenage Borough for Steve Walters
	Received £3,000 for Ryan Baker 2003-04

GROUND: Hollinwood Road, Kidsgrove, Staffs ST7 1DH

Ground Capacity: 2,000   **Seats:** 1,000   **Covered:** 800   **Clubhouse:** Yes   **Shop:** Yes
Previous Grounds: Vickers and Goodwin 1953-60
Record Attendance: 1,903 v Tiverton Town - FA Vase Semi-final 1998

Nearest Railway Station Kidsgrove - 0.8km
Bus Route Grove Avenue - stop 200m away

LEEK TOWN

Nickname: The Blues   **Club Colours:** All blue

Founded 1946

Club Contact Details
01538 399 278

Previous Names: None
Previous Leagues: Staffordshire Co., Manchester 1951-54, 57-73, West Midlands (B'ham) 1954-56, Cheshire Co. 1973-82, North West Counties 1982-87, Northern Premier 1987-94, 95-97, Southern 1994-95, Conference 1997-99

10-11		11-12		12-13		13-14		14-15		15-16		16-17		17-18		18-19		19-20	
NP1S	16	NP1S	5	NP1S	10	NP1S	3	NP1S	2	NP1S	8	NP1S	9	NP1S	7	NP1W	3	NPSE	n&v
FAC	P	FAC	3Qr	FAC	3Q	FAC	Pr	FAC	4Q	FAC	1Qr	FAC	1Q	FAC	1Q	FAC	2Q	FAC	3Q
FAT	P	FAT	2Qr	FAT	2Qr	FAT	2P	FAT	2Qr	FAT	P	FAT	2Q	FAT	2Q	FAT	1Qr	FAT	2Q

HONOURS / RECORDS

FA Comps: None

League: Staffordshire County 1949-50, 50-51. Manchester 1951-52, 71-72, 72-73. Cheshire County 1974-75.
          Northern Premier Division One 1989-90, Premier Division 1996-97.
County FA: Staffordshire Senior Cup 1995-96.

Goalscorer: Dave Sutton - 144
Appearances: Gary Pearce - 447
Additional: Paid £2,000 to Sutton Town for Simon Snow
                          Received £30,000 from Barnsley for Tony Bullock

GROUND: Harrison Park, Macclesfield Road, Leek, Cheshire ST13 8LD

Ground Capacity: 3,600   **Seats:** 650   **Covered:** 3,000   **Clubhouse:** Yes   **Shop:** Yes
Previous Grounds: None
Record Attendance: 3,512 v Macclesfield Town - FA Cup 1973-74

Nearest Railway Station Congleton - 8.4 miles
Bus Route 109 & 18

LINCOLN UNITED

Nickname: United   **Club Colours:** White & red

Founded 1938

Club Contact Details
01522 609 674

Previous Names: Lincoln Amateurs > 1954
Previous Leagues: Lincolnshire 1945-46, 60-67, Lincoln 1946-60, Yorkshire 1967-82,
                          Northern Counties East 1982-86, 92-95, Central Midlands 1982-92

10-11		11-12		12-13		13-14		14-15		15-16		16-17		17-18		18-19		19-20	
NP1S	12	NP1S	18	NP1S	20	NP1S	17	NP1S	9	NP1S	5	NP1S	8	NP1S	8	NP1E	14	NPSE	n&v
FAC	2Q	FAC	P	FAC	P	FAC	P	FAC	1Q	FAC	2Q	FAC	4Q	FAC	1Q	FAC	P	FAC	P
FAT	1Qr	FAT	1Q	FAT	1Q	FAT	P	FAT	P	FAT	2Q	FAT	3Q	FAT	P	FAT	P	FAT	EP

HONOURS / RECORDS

FA Comps: None

League: Yorkshire Division Two 1967-68, Division One 70-71, 73-74. Central Midlands Supreme Division 1991-92.
          Northern Counties East Division One (South) 82-83, Division Two 1985-86, Division One 92-93, Premier Division 1994-95.
County FA: Lincolnshire Senior Cup 2016-17.

Victory: 12-0 v Pontefract Colliery - 1995
Defeat: 0-7 v Huddersfield Town - FA Cup 1st Round 16/11/1991
Goalscorer: Tony Simmons - 215
Appearances: Steve Carter - 447
Additional: Paid £1,000 to Hucknall Town for Paul Tomlinson Dec 2000. Received £3,000 from Charlton for Dean Dye July 1991.

GROUND: Ashby Avenue, Hartsholme, Lincoln LN6 0DY

Ground Capacity: 2,200   **Seats:** 400   **Covered:** 1,084   **Clubhouse:** Yes   **Shop:** Yes
Previous Grounds: Skew Bridge 1940s, Co-op Sports Ground > 1960s, Hartsholme Cricket Club > 1982
Record Attendance: 2,000 v Crook Town - FA Amateur Cup 1st Round 1968

Nearest Railway Station Hkeham - 2.1km
Bus Route Eccleshare Court - stop 75m away

LOUGHBOROUGH DYNAMO

Nickname: The Moes   **Club Colours:** Gold & black

Founded 1955

Club Contact Details
01509 215 972

Previous Names: None
Previous Leagues: Loughborough Alliance 1957-66, Leicestershire & District 1966-71, East Midlands 1971-72,
Central Alliance 1972-89, Leicestershire Senior 1989-2004, Midland Alliance 2004-08

	10-11	11-12	12-13	13-14	14-15	15-16	16-17	17-18	18-19	19-20
NP1S	17	8	16	14	14	20	20	14	NP1E 8	NPSE n&v
FAC	2Q	2Q	1Qr	P	P	P	P	1Q	P	2Q
FAT	P	P	P	P	2Q	P	P	P	Pr	EP

HONOURS / RECORDS

FA Comps: None

League: Loughborough Alliance Division Three 1959-60, Division One 64-65. Leicester & District Division One 1969-70.
Leicestershire Senior Division One 2001-02, Premier Division 2003-04.
County FA: Leicestershire Charity Cup 1987-88, 2003-04, 11-12, Senior Cup 2002-03, 03-04.

Best FA Cup	Second Qualifying Round 2010-11, 11-12, 19-20
FA Trophy	Second Qualifying Round 2014-15
FA Vase	Second Round Proper 2004-05

GROUND: Watermead Lane, Loughborough LE11 3TN

Ground Capacity: 1,500   **Seats:** 75   **Covered:** Yes   **Clubhouse:** Yes   **Shop:** No
Previous Grounds: None
Record Attendance: Not known

Nearest Railway Station Loughborough - 4.6km
Bus Route Nursery School - stop 500m away

MARKET DRAYTON TOWN

Nickname: None   **Club Colours:** All red

Founded 1969

Club Contact Details
07453 960 650

Previous Names: Little Drayton Rangers > 2003
Previous Leagues: West Midlands (Regional) 1969-2006, Midland Alliance 2006-09

	10-11	11-12	12-13	13-14	14-15	15-16	16-17	17-18	18-19	19-20
NP1S	18	16	15	19	19	11	14	21	NP1W 16	NPSE n&v
FAC	2Q	P	1Qr	P	1Q	1Q	P	1Q	P	P
FAT	1Qr	P	P	P	1Qr	P	1Q	P	EP	P

HONOURS / RECORDS

FA Comps: None

League: West Midlands (Regional) 2005-06. Midland Alliance 2008-09.

County FA: None

Victory:	(League) 9-0 Home vs. Racing Club Warwick 10/03/09
Best FA Cup	Second Qualifying Round 2007-08, 10-11
FA Trophy	First Qualifying Round 2010-11, 14-15, 15-16
FA Vase	Fifth Round Proper 2008-09

GROUND: Greenfields Sports Ground, Greenfields Lane, Market Drayton TF9 3SL

Ground Capacity: 1,000   **Seats:** Yes   **Covered:** Yes   **Clubhouse:** Yes   **Shop:** No
Previous Grounds: Not known
Record Attendance: 440 vs. AFC Telford, Friendly 11/07/09. 229 vs. Witton Albion, Unibond South 25/08/09

Nearest Railway Station Prees
Bus Route 164 - Cemetery Road Jct - stop 400m away

NEWCASTLE TOWN

Founded 1964

Nickname: The Castle   **Club Colours:** Blue & white

Club Contact Details
01782 662 350   secretary@newcastletownfc.co.uk

Previous Names: Parkway Hanley, Clayton Park & Parkway Clayton. Merged as NTFC in 1986.
Previous Leagues: Newcatle & District, Staffs Co & Mid Cheshire, North West Counties

10-11		11-12		12-13		13-14		14-15		15-16		16-17		17-18		18-19		19-20	
NP1S	2	NP1S	15	NP1S	17	NP1S	8	NP1S	3	NP1S	14	NP1S	7	NP1S	20	NP1W	15	NPSE	n&v
FAC	4Q	FAC	1Qr	FAC	P	FAC	1Qr	FAC	Pr	FAC	1Qr	FAC	P	FAC	1Q	FAC	P	FAC	P
FAT	1Q	FAT	1Qr	FAT	1Q	FAT	P	FAT	1Q	FAT	1Qr	FAT	P	FAT	1Qr	FAT	2Qr	FAT	P

HONOURS / RECORDS

FA Comps: None

League: Mid Cheshire Division Two 1982-83, 90-91, Division One 85-86. North West Counties Premier Division 2009-10.

County FA: Walsall Senior Cup 1993-94, 94-95. Staffordshire Senior Cup 2009-10.

Goalscorer: Andy Bott - 149
Appearances: Dean Gillick - 632

GROUND: Buckmaster Avenue, Newcastle-under-Lyme, Stoke-on-Trent ST5 3BX

Ground Capacity: 4,000   **Seats:** 300   **Covered:** 1,000   **Clubhouse:** Yes   **Shop:** Yes
Previous Grounds: None
Record Attendance: 3,948 v Notts County - FA Cup 1996

Nearest Railway Station Stafford - take the 101 towards Hanley and alight at The Orange Tree - ground 14min walk
Bus Route 101, 11H, 25 & 9

SHEFFIELD

Founded 1857

Nickname: The Club   **Club Colours:** Red & black

Club Contact Details
0114 362 7016

Previous Names: None
Previous Leagues: Yorkshire 1949-82

10-11		11-12		12-13		13-14		14-15		15-16		16-17		17-18		18-19		19-20	
NP1S	11	NP1S	4	NP1S	9	NP1S	16	NP1S	15	NP1S	17	NP1S	15	NP1S	15	NP1E	4	NPSE	n&v
FAC	4Qr	FAC	P	FAC	P	FAC	1Q	FAC	2Qr	FAC	Pr	FAC	1Q	FAC	P	FAC	P	FAC	1Q
FAT	1Qr	FAT	3Q	FAT	P	FAT	3Q	FAT	1Q	FAT	1Q	FAT	P	FAT	P	FAT	EPr	FAT	EP

HONOURS / RECORDS

FA Comps: FA Amateur Cup 1902-03.
League: Northern Counties East Division One 1988-89, 90-91.

County FA: Sheffield and Hallamshire Senior Cup 1993-94, 2004-05, 05-06, 07-08, 09-10.

Misc: Oldest Football Club in the World.
              Paid £1,000 to Arnold Town for David Wilkins. Received £1,000 from Alfreton for Mick Godber 2002.
Best FA Cup Fourth Round Proper 1877-78, 79-80.
FA Trophy Third Qualifying Round 2007-08, 11-12, 13-14
FA Vase Finalists 1976-77

GROUND: The Home of Football Stadium, Sheffield Road, Dronfield S18 2GD

Ground Capacity: 2,089   **Seats:** 250   **Covered:** 500   **Clubhouse:** Yes   **Shop:** Yes
Previous Grounds: Abbeydale Park, Dore 1956-89, Sheffield Amateur Sports Stadium, Hillsborough Park 1989-91, Don Valley Stadium 1991-97
Record Attendance: 2,000 v Barton Rovers - FA Vase Semi-final 1976-77

Nearest Railway Station Dronfield - 1.1km
Bus Route 43

SPALDING UNITED

Founded 1921

Nickname: Tulips **Club Colours:** Blue & yellow

Club Contact Details
01778 713 328

Previous Names: None

Previous Leagues: Peterborough, United Counties 1931-55,68-78,86-88,91-99,03-04, 11-14 Eastern Counties 1955-60, Central Alliance 1960-61, Midland Co. 1961-68, Northern Counties East 1982-86, Southern 1988-91, 99-03. NPL 2003-11.

10-11		11-12		12-13		13-14		14-15		15-16		16-17		17-18		18-19		19-20	
NP1S	22	UCL P	13	UCL P	3	UCL P	1	NP1S	7	NP1S	12	NP1S	3	NP1S	13	NP1E	18	NPSE	n&v
FAC	1Qr	FAC	EP	FAC	EP	FAC	2Q	FAC	2Q	FAC	3Qr	FAC	1Q	FAC	Pr	FAC	1Q	FAC	P
FAT	P	FAV	2P	FAV	5P	FAV	3P	FAT	1Qr	FAT	P	FAT	P	FAT	1Q	FAT	P	FAT	EP

HONOURS / RECORDS

FA Comps: None

League: Peterborough & District 1930-31. United Counties 1954-55, 75-75, 87-88, 98-99, 2003-04, 13-14.
Northern Counties East 1983-84.

County FA: Lincolnshire Senior Cup 1952-53.

Best FA Cup	First Round Proper 1957-58, 64-65
FA Trophy	Third Round Proper 1999-2000
FA Vase	Quarter Finals 1989-90, 96-97

GROUND: Sir Halley Stewart Playing Fields, Winfrey Avenue, Spalding PE11 1DA

Ground Capacity: 3,500 **Seats:** 1,000 **Covered:** 1,000 **Clubhouse:** Yes **Shop:** Yes
Previous Grounds: Stadium known as the Black Swan Ground before being renamed after Halley Stewart MP in 1954.
Record Attendance: 6,972 v Peterborough - FA Cup 1982

Nearest Railway Station Spalding - 0.2km
Bus Route Broad Street - stop 100m away

STAMFORD

Founded 1896

Nickname: The Daniels **Club Colours:** Red with white trim

Club Contact Details
01780 751 471

Previous Names: Stamford Town and Rutland Ironworks amalgamated in 1894 to form Rutland Ironworks > 1896

Previous Leagues: Peterborough, Northants (UCL) 1908-55, Central Alliance 1955-61, Midland counties 1961-72, United Counties 1972-98, Southern 1998-2007

10-11		11-12		12-13		13-14		14-15		15-16		16-17		17-18		18-19		19-20	
NP1S	19	NP1S	7	NP1S	4	NP P	18	NP P	20	NP P	21	NP1S	16	NP1S	6	NP1E	11	NPSE	n&v
FAC	2Q	FAC	P	FAC	2Q	FAC	4Q	FAC	2Q	FAC	2Q	FAC	1P	FAC	P	FAC	Pr	FAC	2Q
FAT	1Q	FAT	1Q	FAT	3Q	FAT	1Q	FAT	1Q	FAT	1Q	FAT	1Q	FAT	2Q	FAT	3Qr	FAT	1Q

HONOURS / RECORDS

FA Comps: FA Vase 1979-80.

League: United Counties 1911-12, 75-76, 77-78, 79-80, 80-81, 81-82, 96-97, 97-98.

County FA: Lincolnshire Senior Cup 2000-01, Senior Shield 2006-07, 08-09, 10-11, 13-14, 14-15.

Victory:	13-0 v Peterborough Reserves - Northants League 1929-30
Defeat:	0-17 v Rothwell - FA Cup 1927-28
Goalscorer:	Bert Knighton - 248
Appearances:	Dick Kwiatkowski - 462

GROUND: Borderville Sports Centre, Ryhall Road, Stamford PE9 1US

Ground Capacity: 2,000 **Seats:** 300 **Covered:** 1,250 **Clubhouse:** Yes **Shop:** Yes
Previous Grounds: Hanson's Field 1894-2014.
Record Attendance: 1,573 v Peterborough United, pre-season friendly, 10/07/2019.

Nearest Railway Station Stamford - 2.1km
Bus Route Gush Way - stop 300m away

STOCKSBRIDGE PARK STEELS

Founded 1986

Nickname: Steels   **Club Colours:** Yellow & royal blue

Club Contact Details
0114 288 8305 (Match days)

Previous Names: Stocksbridge Works and Oxley Park merged in 1986
Previous Leagues: Northern Counties East 1986-96

10-11	11-12	12-13	13-14	14-15	15-16	16-17	17-18	18-19	19-20
NP P 13	NP P 18	NP P 20	NP P 23	NP1S 17	NP1S 6	NP1S 4	NP1S 11	NP1E 13	NPSE n&v
FAC 2Q	FAC 3Q	FAC 1Q	FAC 1Qr	FAC P	FAC Pr	FAC P	FAC P	FAC P	FAC P
FAT 3Q	FAT 1Qr	FAT 1P	FAT 1Q	FAT P	FAT 1P	FAT 1P	FAT P	FAT P	FAT P

HONOURS / RECORDS

FA Comps: None

League: Northern Counties East Division One 1991-92, Premier Division 1993-94.

County FA: Sheffield Senior Cup 1951-52, 92-93, 95-96, 98-99, 2006-07, 08-09.

Victory: 17-1 v Oldham Town - FA Cup 2002-03
Defeat: 0-6 v Shildon
Goalscorer: Trevor Jones - 145
Appearances: Paul Jackson scored 10 v Oldham Town in the 2002-03 FA Cup - a FA Cup record
Received £15,000 from Wolverhampton Wanderers for Lee Mills

GROUND: Bracken Moor Lane, Stocksbridge, Sheffield S36 2AN

Ground Capacity: 3,500   **Seats:** 450   **Covered:** 1,500   **Clubhouse:** Yes   **Shop:** Yes
Previous Grounds: Stonemoor 1949-51, 52-53
Record Attendance: 2,050 v Sheffield Wednesday - opening of floodlights October 1991

Nearest Railway Station Tram - Meadowhall Interchange to Middlewood, then catch the SL1 alighting at Victoria Road.
Bus Route 201, 23 & SL1

SUTTON COLDFIELD TOWN

Founded 1879

Nickname: Royals   **Club Colours:** All blue

Club Contact Details
0121 354 2997   murralln@gmail.com

Previous Names: Sutton Coldfield F.C. 1879-1921
Previous Leagues: Central Birmingham, Walsall Senior, Staffordshire County, Birmingham Combination 1950-54,
West Midlands (Regional) 1954-65, 79-82, Midlands Combination 1965-79. Northern Premier 2010-18. Southern 2018-19.

10-11	11-12	12-13	13-14	14-15	15-16	16-17	17-18	18-19	19-20
NP1S 6	NP1S 12	NP1S 6	NP1S 6	NP1S 4	NP1S 12	NP P 20	NP P 24	SthC 5	NPSE n&v
FAC 1Q	FAC P	FAC 1Q	FAC 2Q	FAC 1Q	FAC 1Q	FAC 2Q	FAC 1Q	FAC 2Qr	FAC 3Q
FAT P	FAT 1Q	FAT P	FAT P	FAT P	FAT 1P	FAT 1Q	FAT 1Q	FAT EP	FAT 2Q

HONOURS / RECORDS

FA Comps: None

League: West Midlands League 1979-80. Midland Combination x2.
NPL Division One South Play-off 2014-15.
County FA: Birmingham Senior Cup 2010-11.

Goalscorer: Eddie Hewitt - 288
Appearances: Andy Ling - 550
Additional: Paid £1,500 to Gloucester for Lance Morrison, to Burton Albion for Micky Clarke and to Atherstone United for Steve
Farmer 1991. Received £25,000 from West Bromwich Albion for Barry Cowdrill 1979

GROUND: Central Ground, Coles Lane, Sutton Coldfield B72 1NL

Ground Capacity: 4,500   **Seats:** 200   **Covered:** 500   **Clubhouse:** Yes   **Shop:** Yes
Previous Grounds: Meadow Plat 1879-89, Coles Lane 1890-1919
Record Attendance: 2,029 v Doncaster Rovers - FA Cup 1980-81

Nearest Railway Station Sutton Coldfield - 1.1km
Bus Route Douglas Road - stop 100m away

WISBECH TOWN

Founded 1920

Nickname: Fenmen   **Club Colours:** All red

Club Contact Details
01945 581 511

Previous Names: None

Previous Leagues: Peterborough 1920-35. United Counties 1935-50, 2013-18. EC 1950-52, 70-97, 2003-13. Midland 1952-58. Southern 1958-70, 97-2002.

	10-11	11-12	12-13	13-14	14-15	15-16	16-17	17-18	18-19	19-20
	ECP 4	ECP 4	ECP 2	UCL P 7	UCL P 3	UCL P 8	UCL P 6	UCL P 2	NP1E 17	NPSE n&v
	FAC P	FAC 1Q	FAC 1Qr	FAC EP	FAC 1Q	FAC P	FAC P	FAC 1Q	FAC 1Q	FAC 1Q
	FAV 2P	FAV 4Pr	FAV 4P	FAV QF	FAV 3P	FAV 1P	FAV 1Qr	FAV 4P	FAT 1Qr	FAT P

HONOURS / RECORDS

FA Comps: None

League: United Counties 1946-47, 47-48. Southern Division one 1961-62. Eastern Counties 1971-72, 76-77, 90-91.

County FA: None

Goalscorer: Bert Titmarsh - 246 (1931-37)
Appearances: Jamie Brighty - 731
Best FA Cup Second Round Proper 1957-58, 97-98
FA Trophy Second Round Proper 1999-2000
FA Vase Semi Finals 1984-85, 85-86

GROUND: Fenland Stadium, Lynn Road, Wisbech PE14 7AL

Ground Capacity: **Seats:** 118   **Covered:** Yes   **Clubhouse:** Yes   **Shop:**

Previous Grounds: Played on several grounds before moving to Fenland Park in 1947, then moving to their new stadium in 2008.

Record Attendance: 8,044 v Peterborough United, Midland League 25/08/1957

Nearest Railway Station Watlington
Bus Route Pumping Station - stop 370m away

WORKSOP TOWN

Founded 1861

Nickname: Tigers   **Club Colours:** Amber & black

Club Contact Details
07952 365 224

Previous Names: None

Previous Leagues: Sheffield Association. Midland 1949-60, 61-68, 69-74, Northern Premier 1968-69, 74-2004, 2007-14, Conf. 2004-07. Northern Counties East 2014-19.

	10-11	11-12	12-13	13-14	14-15	15-16	16-17	17-18	18-19	19-20
	NP P 7	NP P 15	NP P 9	NP P 4	NCEP 2	NCEP 4	NCEP 13	NCEP 18	NCEP 1	NPSE n&v
	FAC 1Q	FAC 1Q	FAC 1Q	FAC 3Q	FAC EP	FAC EP	FAC Pr	FAC EP	FAC 1Q	FAC EP
	FAT 1P	FAT 2P	FAT 1P	FAT 1Q	FAV 4P	FAV 2P	FAV 2P	FAV 3P	FAV 2Q	FAT 1Q

HONOURS / RECORDS

FA Comps: None

League: Sheffield Association 1898-99 (joint), 47-48, 48-49. Midland 1921-22, 65-66, 72-73. Northern Counties east Premier 2018-19.

County FA: Sheffield & Hallamshire Senior Cup 1923-24, 52-53, 54-55, 65-66, 69-70, 72-73, 81-82, 84-85, 94-95, 96-97, 2002-03, 11-12

Victory: 20-0 v Staveley - 01/09/1984
Defeat: 1-11 v Hull City Reserves - 1955-56
Goalscorer: Kenny Clark - 287
Appearances: Kenny Clark - 347
Additional: Paid £5,000 to Grantham Town for Kirk Jackson. Received £47,000 from Sunderland for Jon Kennedy 2000.

GROUND: Babbage Way, Worksop S80 1UJ

Ground Capacity: 2,500   **Seats:** 200   **Covered:** 750   **Clubhouse:** Yes   **Shop:** Yes

Previous Grounds: Central Avenue, Sandy Lane, shared with Ilkeston Town (New Manor Ground)

Record Attendance: 8,171 v Chesterfield - FA Cup 1925 (Central Avenue)

Nearest Railway Station Worksop - 0.5km
Bus Route Grafton Street - stop 114m away

AFC RUSHDEN & DIAMONDS

Founded 2011

Nickname: The Diamonds   **Club Colours:** White & blue

Club Contact Details
01933 359 206   secretary@afcdiamonds.com

Previous Names: None
Previous Leagues: United Counties 2012-15. Southern 2015-16. Northern Premier 2016-17.

10-11	11-12	12-13	13-14	14-15	15-16	16-17	17-18	18-19	19-20
		UCL 1 2	UCL P 3	UCL P 1	SthC 5	NP1S 5	Sth1E 2	SthPC 9	SthPC n&v
			FAC 3Q	FAC 1Q	FAC 4Qr	FAC 3Q	FAC 2Qr	FAC 1Q	FAC 1Q
		FAV 3P	FAV 4P	FAV 2P	FAT P	FAT 2Q	FAT P	FAT 1Q	FAT 2Q

HONOURS / RECORDS
FA Comps: None
League: United Counties Premier Division 2014-15.

County FA: Northamptonshire Senior Cup 2015-16.

Victory:	9-0 v Buckingham Town (A) 15/12/12 and v Desborough Town (A) 21/02/15
Goalscorer:	Tom Lorraine - 54 in 150 appearances, 2014- present.
Appearances:	Brad Harris - 213, 2013 - present
Additional:	28 matches unbeaten, 13/01/2015 - 31/10/2015.

GROUND: Rushden & Higham United FC, Hayden Road, Rushden NN10 0HX

Ground Capacity: 2,654   **Seats:** 100   **Covered:** 250   **Clubhouse:** Yes   **Shop:** Yes
Previous Grounds: The Dog & Duck Wellingborough Town FC 2011-17.
Record Attendance: 1,162 v Barwell, 27/10/2015.

Nearest Railway Station Wellingborough and Bedford
Bus Route X46/X47, 49, 50, 26 to Rushden town centre a 10 min walk from the ground

ALVECHURCH

Founded 1929

Nickname: The Church   **Club Colours:** Amber & black.

Club Contact Details
0121 445 2929   info@alvechurchfc.club

Previous Names: Alvechurch FC >1993. Re-formed in 1994 as Alvechurch Villa > 1996.
Previous Leagues: Worcestershire Combination/Midland Combination 1961-73, 94-2003. West Midlands (Reg) 1973-78. Southern 1978-93.
Midland Alliance 2003-14. Midland Football League 2014-17. Northern Premier 2017-18.

10-11	11-12	12-13	13-14	14-15	15-16	16-17	17-18	18-19	19-20
MidAl 20	MidAl 13	MidAl 11	MidAl 13	MFLP 15	MFLP 2	MFLP 1	NP1S 2	SthPC 4	SthPC n&v
FAC EP	FAC 1Q	FAC EPr	FAC EP	FAC EP	FAC P	FAC P	FAC 3Q	FAC 2Q	FAC 1Q
FAV 2Q	FAV 2Q	FAV 2Q	FAV 3P	FAV 1Q	FAV 4P	FAV 2P	FAV 2Q	FAT 1Qr	FAT 1Q

HONOURS / RECORDS
FA Comps: None
League: Worcestershire Combination Division 1962-63, 64-65, 66-67. Midland Combination Division One 1971-72, Premier 2002-03.
West Midlands (Reg) Premier 1973-74, 74-75, 75-76, 76-77. Southern Midland Division 1980-81. Midland Football Premier 2016-17.
County FA: Worcestershire Senior Cup 1972-73, 73-74, 76-77, Senior Urn 2003-04, 04-05, 07-08, 12-13.

Victory:	13-0 v (A) Alcester Town.
Defeat:	0-9 v (H) Coalville Town.
Goalscorer:	Graham Allner. Keith Rostill scored 53 goals during the 2002-03 season.
Appearances:	Kevin Palmer.
Additional:	In 1971, the club played out the longest FA Cup tie in history when it took six games to beat Oxford City in the 4Q Round.

GROUND: Lye Meadow, Redditch Road, Alvechurch B48 7RS

Ground Capacity: 3,000   **Seats:** 100   **Covered:** 300   **Clubhouse:** Yes   **Shop:**
Previous Grounds: Played in the local park until moving to Lye Meadow.
Record Attendance: 13,500 v Enfield, FA Amateur Cup Quarter-final, 1964-65.

Nearest Railway Station Alvechurch - 0.7km
Bus Route Bus stops at the ground.

BANBURY UNITED

Founded 1931

Nickname: Puritans   Club Colours: Red

Club Contact Details
01295 263 354   bworsley@btinternet.com

Previous Names: Spencer Villa 1931-34. Banbury Spencer. Club reformed in 1965 as Banbury United
Previous Leagues: Banbury Junior 1933-34, Oxon Senior 1934-35, Birmingham Combination 1935-54,
West Midlands 1954-66, Southern 1966-90, Hellenic 1991-2000

10-11		11-12		12-13		13-14		14-15		15-16		16-17		17-18		18-19		19-20	
SthP	16	SthP	16	SthP	16	SthP	19	SthP	21	Sthsw	2	SthP	6	SthP	9	SthPC	17	SthPC	n&v
FAC	1Q	FAC	1Q	FAC	1Qr	FAC	1Q	FAC	2Q	FAC	P	FAC	3Q	FAC	3Q	FAC	2Q	FAC	1Qr
FAT	2Q	FAT	3Qr	FAT	1Qr	FAT	1Q	FAT	3Q	FAT	1Qr	FAT	1Q	FAT	2Qr	FAT	2Q	FAT	1Qr

HONOURS / RECORDS
FA Comps: None
League: Oxfordshire Junior Banbury Division 1933-34. Oxfordshire Senior 1934-35. Hellenic Premier 1999-2000.

County FA: Oxford Senior Cup 1978-79, 87-88, 2003-04, 05-06, 06-07, 14-15.

Victory: 12-0 v RNAS Culham - Oxon Senior Cup 1945-46
Defeat: 2-11 v West Bromwich Albion 'A' - Birmingham Combination 1938-39
Goalscorer: Dick Pike and Tony Jacques - 222 (1935-48 and 1965-76 respectively). Jacues also scored 62 in a single season, 1967-68.
Appearances: Jody McKay - 576
Additional: Paid £2,000 to Oxford United for Phil Emsden. Received £20,000 from Derby County for Kevin Wilson 1979.

GROUND: Station Approach, Banbury OX16 5AB
Ground Capacity: 4,000   **Seats:** 250   **Covered:** 250   **Clubhouse:** Yes   **Shop:** Yes
Previous Grounds: Middleton Road 1931-34.
Record Attendance: 7,160 v Oxford City - FA Cup 3rd Qualifying Round 30/10/1948

Nearest Railway Station Banbury - 0.2km
Bus Route 500 & S4

BARWELL

Founded 1992

Nickname: Canaries   Club Colours: Green & yellow

Club Contact Details
07961 905 141

Previous Names: Barwell Athletic FC and Hinckley FC amalgamated in 1992.
Previous Leagues: Midland Alliance 1992-2010, Northern Premier League 2010-11, 13-18. Southern 2011-13.

10-11		11-12		12-13		13-14		14-15		15-16		16-17		17-18		18-19		19-20	
NP1S	1	SthP	9	SthP	7	NP P	14	NP P	8	NP P	9	NP P	14	NP P	10	SthPC	16	SthPC	n&v
FAC	4Q	FAC	2Q	FAC	3Qr	FAC	1Q	FAC	4Q	FAC	1P	FAC	2Q	FAC	3Q	FAC	1Q	FAC	2Q
FAT	P	FAT	2Q	FAT	1Q	FAT	1Q	FAT	3Qr	FAT	1Q	FAT	2Q	FAT	2Q	FAT	1P	FAT	2Qr

HONOURS / RECORDS
FA Comps: None
League: Midland Alliance 2009-10.
Northern Premier Division One South 2010-11.
County FA: Leicestershire Challenge Cup 2014-15, 16-17.

Goalscorer: Andy Lucas
Appearances: Adrian Baker
Best FA Cup   First Round Proper 2015-16
FA Trophy   First Round Proper 2018-19
FA Vase   Semi Finals 2009-10

GROUND: Kirkby Road Sports Ground, Kirkby Road, Barwell LE9 8FQ
Ground Capacity: 2,500   **Seats:** 256   **Covered:** 750   **Clubhouse:** Yes   **Shop:** Yes
Previous Grounds: None
Record Attendance: 1,279 v Whitley Bay, FA Vase Semi-Final 2009-10.

Nearest Railway Station Hinckley - 7 miles away
Bus Route 158, 159 & 2

BIGGLESWADE TOWN
Founded 1874

Nickname: The Waders   **Club Colours:** Green & white

Club Contact Details
01767 318 802 (Matchdays)   michaeldraxler@hotmail.com

Previous Names: Biggleswade FC. Biggleswade & District.
Previous Leagues: Biggleswade & District 1902-20. Bedford & District. Northamptonshire/United Counties 1920-39 / 1951-55, 1963-80. Spartan 1945-51. Eastern Counties 1955-63. South Midlands/SSM 1980-2009.

10-11		11-12		12-13		13-14		14-15		15-16		16-17		17-18		18-19		19-20	
SthC	4	SthC	8	SthC	4	SthP	9	SthP	19	SthP	14	SthP	7	SthP	16	SthPC	7	SthPC	n&v
FAC	1Q	FAC	2Qr	FAC	1Q	FAC	1P	FAC	3Q	FAC	2Q	FAC	2Q	FAC	3Q	FAC	1Q	FAC	2Q
FAT	1Q	FAT	1Q	FAT	P	FAT	1Q	FAT	2Q	FAT	1Q	FAT	2Qr	FAT	1Q	FAT	2P	FAT	3Q

HONOURS / RECORDS
FA Comps: None
League: Biggleswade & District 1902-03. Spartan South Midlands Premier Division 2008-09.

County FA: Bedfordshire Senior Cup 1902-03, 07-08, 46-47, 50-51, 61-62, 62-63, 66-67, 73-74. Bedfordshire Premier Cup 2009. Bedfordshire Senior Challenge Cup 2012-13.
Victory: 12-0 v Newmarket Town (A), Eastern Counties.
Best FA Cup First Round Proper 2013-14
FA Trophy Second Round Proper 2018-19
FA Vase Quarter Finals 2008-09

GROUND: The Langford Road Stadium, Langford Road, Biggleswade SG18 9JT
Ground Capacity: 3,500 **Seats:** 300 **Covered:** 400 **Clubhouse:** Yes **Shop:**
Previous Grounds: Fairfield
Record Attendance: 2,000

Nearest Railway Station Biggleswade - 1km
Bus Route 188, 190, 200 & 74

BROMSGROVE SPORTING
Founded 2009

Nickname: The Rouslers   **Club Colours:** Red & white

Club Contact Details
01527 876 949   info@bromsgrovesporting.co.uk

Previous Names: None
Previous Leagues: Midland Combination 2010-14.

10-11		11-12		12-13		13-14		14-15		15-16		16-17		17-18		18-19		19-20	
MCm2	3	MCm1	3	MCmP	6	MCmP	2	MFL1	2	MFL1	2	MFL1	1	MFLP	1	SthC	2	SthPC	n&v
								FAC	Pr	FAC	P	FAC	P	FAC	P	FAC	P	FAC	1Q
						FAV	1P	FAV	3P	FAV	1P	FAV	SF	FAV	5P	FAT	EP	FAT	1Q

HONOURS / RECORDS
FA Comps: None
League: Midland Football League Division One 2016-17, Premier 2017-18.

County FA: Worcestershire Senior Urn 2017-18

Best FA Cup Preliminary Round 2014-15(r), 15-16, 16-17, 17-18, 18-19
FA Vase Semi Final 2016-17
FA Trophy Extra Preliminary Round 2018-19

GROUND: The Victoria Ground, Birmingham Road, Bromsgrove, Worcs, B61 0DR
Ground Capacity: 5,008 **Seats:** Yes **Covered:** Yes **Clubhouse:** Yes **Shop:** Yes
Previous Grounds: None
Record Attendance: 3,349 v Cleethorpes Town, FA Vase Semi Final First Leg, 11/03/2017

Nearest Railway Station Bromsgrove - 2km
Bus Route All Saints Road stop - 214m away

COALVILLE TOWN

Nickname: The Ravens   **Club Colours:** Black & white

Founded 1926

Club Contact Details
07496 792 650   coalvilletownfc@gmail.com

Previous Names: Ravenstoke Miners Ath. 1926-58. Ravenstoke FC 1958-95. Coalville 1995-98.
Previous Leagues: Coalville & Dist. Amateur. North Leicester. Leicestershire Senior. Midland Alliance > 2011. Northern Premier 2011-18.

	10-11	11-12	12-13	13-14	14-15	15-16	16-17	17-18	18-19	19-20
	MidAl 1	NP1S 14	NP1S 2	NP1S 2	NP1S 10	NP1S 3	NP P 17	NP P 20	SthPC 6	SthPC n&v
FAC	2Q	P	1Q	2Q	2Qr	2Q	2Q	2Q	3Qr	2Q
FAV/FAT	F	P	2Q	1Pr	P	1Q	1Q	1Q	3Q	3Q

HONOURS / RECORDS
FA Comps: None

League: Coalville & District Amateur 1952-53. North Leicestershire 1988-89, 89-90. Leicestershire Senior 2001-02, 02-03. Midland Football Alliance 2010-11.
County FA: Leicestershire Senior Cup 1999-00. Leicestershire Challenge Cup 2012-13, 17-18.

Appearances: Nigel Simms.
Additional: 153 goals scored during 2010-11 season.

GROUND: Owen Street Sports Ground, Owen St, Coalville LE67 3DA
Ground Capacity: 2,000   **Seats:** 240   **Covered:** 240   **Clubhouse:** Yes   **Shop:** Yes
Previous Grounds: None
Record Attendance: 1,500.

Nearest Railway Station Loughborough and Leicester
Bus Route Arriva No.137 can be taken to Coalville from both Loughborough and Leicester.

HEDNESFORD TOWN

Nickname: The Pitmen   **Club Colours:** White and black

Founded 1880

Club Contact Details
01543 422 870   office@hednesfordtownfc.com

Previous Names: Hednesford 1938-74
Previous Leagues: Walsall & District, Birmingham Comb. 1906-15, 45-53, West Mids 1919-39, 53-72, 74-84, Midland Counties 1972-74, Southern 1984-95, 2001-2005, 2009-11, Conference 1995-2001, 05-06, 13-16. Northern Premier 2006-09, 11-13, 16-19.

	10-11	11-12	12-13	13-14	14-15	15-16	16-17	17-18	18-19	19-20
	SthP 2	NP P 5	NP P 2	Conf N 4	Conf N 8	Nat N 21	NP P 15	NP P 16	NP P 13	SthPC n&v
FAC	1Q	1Q	3Q	3Qr	1P	2Q	3Q	1Q	2Q	4Q
FAT	1Q	1Q	2Qr	1P	1P	3Q	3Q	2Qr	2Qr	1Pr

HONOURS / RECORDS
FA Comps: FA Trophy 2003-04.
League: Birmingham Combination 1909-10, 50-51. West Midlands (Reg) 1940-41, 77-78. Southern League Premier Division 1994-95.
County FA: Staffordshire Senior Cup 1897-98, 1969-70, 73-74, 2012-13. Birmingham Senior Cup 1935-36, 2008-09, 12-13.
Victory: 12-1 v Redditch United - Birmingham Combination 1952-53
Defeat: 0-15 v Burton - Birmingham Combination 1952-53
Goalscorer: Joe O'Connor - 220 in 430 games
Appearances: Kevin Foster - 470
Additional: Paid £12,000 to Macclesfield Town for Steve Burr. Received £40,000 from Blackpool for Kevin Russell.

GROUND: Keys Park, Park Road, Hednesford, Cannock WS12 2DZ
Ground Capacity: 6,039   **Seats:** 1,011   **Covered:** 5,335   **Clubhouse:** Yes   **Shop:** Yes
Previous Grounds: The Tins 1880-1903. The Cross Keys 1903-95.
Record Attendance: 4,412 v FC United of Manchester, Northern Premier League Premier Division play-off final, 11/05/13.

Nearest Railway Station Hednesford - 1.6km
Bus Route Brickworks Road - stop 200m away

HITCHIN TOWN

Nickname: Canaries **Club Colours:** Yellow & green

Founded 1865

Club Contact Details
01462 459 028 (match days only)   roy.izzard@outlook.com

Previous Names: Hitchin FC 1865-1911. Re-formed in 1928
Previous Leagues: Spartan 1928-39, Herts & Middlesex 1939-45, Athenian 1945-63, Isthmian 1964-2004

	10-11	11-12	12-13	13-14	14-15	15-16	16-17	17-18	18-19	19-20
League	SthC 2	SthP 14	SthP 13	SthP 13	SthP 9	SthP 3	SthP 4	SthP 11	SthPC 18	SthPC n&v
FAC	2Qr	1Q	3Qr	1Qr	2Q	3Qr	2Qr	1Qr	1P	3Q
FAT	P	2Q	3Q	1Qr	1Qr	3Q	1P	1Q	1Q	1Qr

HONOURS / RECORDS
FA Comps: None
League: Spartan 1934-35. Isthmian League Division One 1992-93.

County FA: AFA Senior Cup 1931-32. London Senior Cup 1969-70. East Anglian Cup 1972-73. Herts Senior Cup x14 Most recently 2016-17.
Victory: 13-0 v Cowley and v RAF Uxbridge - both Spartan League 1929-30
Defeat: 0-10 v Kingstonian (A) and v Slough Town (A) - 1965-66 and 1979-80 respectively
Goalscorer: Paul Giggle - 214 (1968-86)
Appearances: Paul Giggle - 769 (1968-86)
Additional: Paid £2,000 to Potton United for Ray Seeking. Received £30,000 from Cambridge United for Zema Abbey, Jan 2000

GROUND: Top Field, Fishponds Road, Hitchin SG5 1NU

Ground Capacity: 5,000 **Seats:** 500 **Covered:** 1,250 **Clubhouse:** Yes **Shop:** Yes
Previous Grounds: None
Record Attendance: 7,878 v Wycombe Wanderers - FA Amateur Cup 3rd Round 08/02/1956

Nearest Railway Station Hitchin - 1.3km
Bus Route Buss stops outside the ground

KING'S LANGLEY

Nickname: Kings **Club Colours:** White & black

Founded 1886

Club Contact Details
07730 410 330

Previous Names: None
Previous Leagues: West Herts (Founder Member) 1891-1920, 22-34. Southern Olympian 1934-39. Hertfordshire County 1920-22, 46-52, 55-2001. Parthenon 1952-55. Spartan South Midlands 2001-2015.

	10-11	11-12	12-13	13-14	14-15	15-16	16-17	17-18	18-19	19-20
League	SSM1 3	SSM1 4	SSM1 6	SSM1 2	SSM P 1	SthC 1	SthP 20	SthP 21	SthPS 6	SthPC n&v
FAC		EP	EPr	1Q	Pr	P	2Q	2Q	2Qr	4Q
FAV/FAT	FAV 1Q	FAV 2Q	FAV 1Q	FAV 1Q	FAV 2P	FAT 1Q	FAT 3Q	FAT 1Q	FAT 1Q	FAT 2Q

HONOURS / RECORDS
FA Comps: None
League: West Herts Div.3 1911-12, Div.2 1919-20, 30-31, 34-35. Southern Olympian Div.1 1936-37. Herts County 1949-50, 51-52, 65-66, 66-67, Div.1 1975-76. Spartan South Midlands Div.2 2007-08, Premier 2014-15. Southern Div.1 Central 2015-16.
County FA: Herts Charity Shield 1966-67. Herts Intermediate Cup 2006-07, 07-08. Herts Senior Centenary Trophy 2011-12.

Misc: 47 consecutive matches unbeaten in all competitions between 15-09-07 and 15-10-08.

GROUND: Gaywood Park, Hempstead Road, Kings Langley Herts WD4 8BS

Ground Capacity: 1,963 **Seats:** Yes **Covered:** Yes **Clubhouse:** Yes **Shop:**
Previous Grounds: Groomes Meadow. Blackwell Meadow. Kings Langley Common. Home Park 1913-80.
Record Attendance: Not known   Oxhey, Rolls Royce & Buncefield Lane and Leavesden Hospital Ground between 1980-97.

Nearest Railway Station Kings Langley - 1.6km
Bus Route 500

LEISTON

Nickname: The Blues   **Club Colours:** All blue

Founded 1880

Club Contact Details
01728 830 308   info@leistonfc.co.uk

Previous Names: Leiston Works Athletic 1919-35.

Previous Leagues: North Suffolk. Suffolk & Ipswich. South East Anglian/East Anglian. Essex & Suffolk Border. Norfolk & Suffolk. Ipswich & District 1953-2001. Eastern Counties 2001-2011. Isthmian 2011-18.

10-11		11-12		12-13		13-14		14-15		15-16		16-17		17-18		18-19		19-20	
ECP	1	Isth1N	1	Isth P	12	Isth P	9	Isth P	9	Isth P	8	Isth P	7	Isth P	5	SthPC	19	SthPC	n&v
FAC	4Qr	FAC	1Q	FAC	2Q	FAC	1Q	FAC	2Q	FAC	3Q	FAC	4Q	FAC	3Q	FAC	2Q	FAC	1Q
FAV	QF	FAT	P	FAT	3Qr	FAT	1Q	FAT	1P	FAT	2Q	FAT	1Pr	FAT	2Q	FAT	3Q	FAT	1Q

HONOURS / RECORDS

FA Comps: None

League: Suffolk & Ipswich/Ipswich & District 1900-01, 01-02, 02-03, Division 2B 1937-38 / Division One 83-84. Eastern Counties Premier Division 2010-11. Isthmian Division One North 2011-12.

County FA: Suffolk Junior Cup 1894-95, 82-83, 83-84, Premier Cup 2017-18. East Anglian Cup 2007-08.

Goalscorer: Lee McGlone - 60 (League).

Appearances: Gareth Heath - 201 (League).

GROUND: Victory Road, Leiston IP16 4DQ

Ground Capacity: 2,250   **Seats:** 250   **Covered:** 500   **Clubhouse:** Yes   **Shop:**

Previous Grounds: Leiston Recreation Ground 1880-1921.

Record Attendance: 1,250 v Fleetwood Town, FA Cup First round Proper, 2008-09.

Nearest Railway Station Saxmundham - 6 miles

Bus Route Alde Valley Sixth Form - stop 300m away

LOWESTOFT TOWN

Nickname: The Trawler Boys or Blues   **Club Colours:** Blue & white

Founded 1880

Club Contact Details
01502 573 818   admin@lowestofttownfc.co.uk

Previous Names: Original club merged with Kirkley in 1887 to form Lowestoft and became Lowestoft Town in 1890

Previous Leagues: North Suffolk 1897-35, Eastern Counties 1935-2009. Isthmian 2009-2014, 16-18. Conference 2014-16.

10-11		11-12		12-13		13-14		14-15		15-16		16-17		17-18		18-19		19-20	
Isth P	4	Isth P	3	Isth P	2	Isth P	4	Conf N	16	Nat N	20	Isth P	11	Isth P	22	SthPC	14	SthPC	n&v
FAC	2Q	FAC	3Q	FAC	4Q	FAC	1Q	FAC	3Q	FAC	2Q	FAC	1Q	FAC	2Q	FAC	2Q	FAC	3Q
FAT	1P	FAT	1P	FAT	1Q	FAT	1Q	FAT	1P	FAT	1P	FAT	1Q	FAT	1Q	FAT	1Q	FAT	1Q

HONOURS / RECORDS

FA Comps: None

League: Eastern Counties League 1935-36 (shared), 37-38, 62-63, 64-65, 65-66, 66-67, 67-68, 69-70, 70-71, 77-78, 2005-06, 08-09. Isthmian League Division One North 2009-10.

County FA: Suffolk Senior Cup 1902-03, 22-23, 25-26, 31-32, 35-36, 46-47, 47-48, 48-49, 55-56, Premier Cup 1966-67, 71-72, 74-75, 78-79, 79-80, 99-00, 00-01, 04-05, 05-06, 08-09, 11-12, 14-15, 15-16. East Anglian Cup 1929-30, 70-71, 77-78.

Best FA Cup   First Round Proper 1926-27, 38-39, 66-67, 67-68, 77-78, 2009-10

FA Trophy   Second Round Proper 1971-72

FA Vase   Runners-up 2007-08

GROUND: Crown Meadow, Love Road, Lowestoft NR32 2PA

Ground Capacity: 3,250   **Seats:** 466   **Covered:** 500   **Clubhouse:** Yes   **Shop:** Yes

Previous Grounds: Crown Meadow Athletic Ground 1880-1889. North Denes 1889-94.

Record Attendance: 5,000 v Watford - FA Cup 1st Round 1967

Nearest Railway Station Lowestoft - 0.7km

Bus Route 99 & X1

NEEDHAM MARKET

Founded 1919

Nickname: The Marketmen   **Club Colours:** All red

Club Contact Details
01449 721 000   m.easlea@sky.com

Previous Names: None
Previous Leagues: Suffolk & Ipswich Senior, Eastern Counties. Isthmian 2010-2018.

	10-11	11-12	12-13	13-14	14-15	15-16	16-17	17-18	18-19	19-20
	Isth1N 2	Isth1N 4	Isth1N 16	Isth1N 5	Isth1N 1	Isth P 20	Isth P 9	Isth P 19	SthPC 11	SthPC n&v
FAC	3Q	2Q	1Q	4Q	3Q	1Qr	1Q	3Q	2Qr	2Q
FAT	1Qr	1Q	P	P	P	1Q	2Q	2Q	1P	2Q

HONOURS / RECORDS

FA Comps: None
League: Eastern Counties Premier Division 2009-10. Isthmian Division One North 2014-15.

County FA: Suffolk Senior Cup 1989-90, 2004-05. Suffolk & Ipswich Senior League 1995-96. East Anglian Cup 2006-07. Suffolk Premier Cup 2016-17.
Victory: 10-1 v I[swich Wanderers (A) , FA Cup Preliminary Round, 01/09/2007
Defeat: 2-6 v Lowestoft Town (A), FA Trophy First round Qualifier, 19/10/2010
Goalscorer: Craig Parker - 111 (2007-2011) Most goals in a season - Craig Parker 40 (2011-11).
Appearances: Rhys Barber - 334 (2006-2012)
Additional: Most goals scored in a season - 196 in 70 games (2007-08)

GROUND: Bloomfields, Quinton Road, Needham Market IP6 8DA

Ground Capacity: 2,250   **Seats:** 250   **Covered:** 250   **Clubhouse:** Yes   **Shop:** Yes
Previous Grounds: Young's Meadow 1919. Crowley Park >1996.
Record Attendance: 1,784 v Cambridge United, FAC Fourth Qualifying Round, 26/10/2013.

Nearest Railway Station Needham Market - 0.6km
Bus Route Quinton Road stop - 38m away

NUNEATON BOROUGH

Founded 1889

Nickname: The Boro / The Town   **Club Colours:** Blue and white

Club Contact Details
024 7634 9690

Previous Names: Nuneaton St. Nicholas 1889-1894. Nuneaton Town 1894-37. Nuneaton Borough 1937-2008.
Previous Leagues: Local 1894-1906. Birmingham Jr/Comb 06-15, 26-33, 38-52. Birmingham 19-24, 33-37. Central Am. 37-38. Birmingham 52-58. Southern 24-25, 58-79 81-82, 87-99, 2003-04, 08-10. Conference/National 79-81, 82-87, 99-03, 04-08, 10-19.

	10-11	11-12	12-13	13-14	14-15	15-16	16-17	17-18	18-19	19-20
	Conf N 6	Conf N 5	Conf 15	Conf 13	Conf 24	Nat N 6	Nat N 12	Nat N 13	Nat N 22	SthPC n&v
FAC	1P	4Q	1Pr	4Q	4Qr	3Q	2Q	3Q	2Qr	1Q
FAT	3Q	1P	1P	2Pr	1P	1P	3P	1P	3Q	1Q

HONOURS / RECORDS

FA Comps: None
League: Coventry & Dist. 1902-03. Coventry & North Warwicks' 1904-05. Birmingham Junior 1906-07, Combination 1914-15, 28-29, 30-31. Birmingham League North 1954-55, Div.One 55-56. Southern League Midland Div. 1981-82, 92-93, 95-96, Premier Division 1988-99.
County FA: Birmingham Senior Cup 1930-31, 48-49, 54-55, 59-60, 77-78, 79-80, 92-93, 2001-02, 09-10.

Victory: 11-1 - 1945-46 and 1955-56
Defeat: 1-8 - 1955-56 and 1968-69
Goalscorer: Paul Culpin - 201 (55 during season 1992-93)
Appearances: Alan Jones - 545 (1962-74)
Misc: Paid £35,000 to Forest green Rovers for Marc McGregor 2000

GROUND: Liberty Way, Nuneaton CV11 6RR

Ground Capacity: 4,614   **Seats:** 514   **Covered:** Yes   **Clubhouse:** Yes   **Shop:** Yes
Previous Grounds: Higham Lane/Rose Inn/Arbury Rd/Edward St. 1889-1903. Queens Rd 03-08. Newdegate Arms 08-15. Manor Pk 19-07.
Record Attendance: 22,114 v Rotherham Utd, FAC 3P 28/01/1967 (Manor Park). 3,480 v Luton Town, Conf. Prem., 22/02/14 (Liberty Way).
Nearest Railway Station Nuneaton - approx. 35min walk from the ground.
Bus Route 2 & 4

PETERBOROUGH SPORTS

Nickname: The Turbines   **Club Colours:** All blue

Founded 1919

Club Contact Details
01733 567 835

Previous Names: Brotherhoods Engineering Works 1919-99. Bearings Direct during 1999-2001.
Previous Leagues: Northants League (former UCL) 1919-23. Peterborough & District 1923-2013. United Counties 2013-17.
Northern Premier 2017-18.

10-11	11-12	12-13	13-14	14-15	15-16	16-17	17-18	18-19	19-20
	P&D P 3	P&D P 3	UCL 1 16	UCL 1 5	UCL 1 1	UCL P 1	NP1S 12	SthC 1	SthPC n&v
					FAC 1Qr	FAC 1Q	FAC 1Q	FAC 3Q	FAC 4Q
				FAV 2P	FAV 1Q	FAV 4P	FAT P	FAT P	FAT 3Q

HONOURS / RECORDS

FA Comps: None

League: Northants 1919-20, United Counties 1919-20, Division One 2015-16, Premier 2016-17.
Peterborough & Dist Division Three 1925-26, Division Three South 1980-81, Premier 2006-07. Southern Div1 Central 18-19.
County FA: Northants Junior Cup 2006-07, 15-16,

Best FA Cup   Fourth Qualifying Round 2019-20
FA Trophy   Third Qualifying Round 2019-20
FA Vase   Fourth Round Proper 2016-17

GROUND: Lincoln Road, Peterborough PE1 3HA

Ground Capacity: 1,500   **Seats:** Yes   **Covered:** Yes   **Clubhouse:** Yes   **Shop:** No
Previous Grounds: None
Record Attendance: Not known

Nearest Railway Station Peterborough - 3 miles
Bus Route 101 towards Bourne - alight at Boulevard Retail Park, 6min walk from there.

REDDITCH UNITED

Nickname: The Reds   **Club Colours:** Red & black

Founded 1891

Club Contact Details
01527 67450   info@redditchutdfc.co.uk

Previous Names: Redditch Town
Previous Leagues: Birmingham Combination 1905-21, 29-39, 46-53, West Midlands 1921-29, 53-72,
Southern 1972-79, 81-2004, Alliance 1979-80. Conference 2004-11.

10-11	11-12	12-13	13-14	14-15	15-16	16-17	17-18	18-19	19-20
Conf N 21	SthP 15	SthP 19	SthP 10	SthP 6	SthP 2	SthP 17	SthP 14	SthPC 15	SthPC n&v
FAC 4Q	FAC 1Q	FAC 1Q	FAC 1Qr	FAC 1Qr	FAC 1Q	FAV 2Q	FAC 2Q	FAC 1Q	FAC 1Qr
FAT 1P	FAT 1Q	FAT 1Q	FAT 1Q	FAT 3Q	FAT 1Q	FAV 2Q	FAT 1Q	FAT 1Q	FAT 3Q

HONOURS / RECORDS

FA Comps: None

League: Birmingham Combination 1913-14, 32-33, 52-53. Birmingham & District Southern Division 1954-55.
Southern Division One North 1975-76, Western Division 2003-04.
County FA: Worcestershire Senior Cup 1893-94, 29-30, 74-75, 76-76, 2007-08, 13-14.
Birmingham Senior Cup 1924-25, 31-32, 38-39, 76-77, 2004-05. Staffordshire Senior Cup 1990-91.
Misc: Paid £3,000 to Halesowen Town for Paul Joinson. Received £40,000 from Aston Villa for David Farrell.
Played nine games in nine days at the end of the 1997-98 season.

Victory: 7-1 v Farnborough (H), Southern Premier, 06/01/2018

GROUND: Bromsgrove Road, Redditch B97 4RN

Ground Capacity: 4,000   **Seats:** 400   **Covered:** 2,000   **Clubhouse:** Yes   **Shop:** Yes
Previous Grounds: HDA Sports Ground, Millsborough Road
Record Attendance: 5,500 v Bromsgrove Rovers - Wets Midlands League 1954-55

Nearest Railway Station Redditch - 0.4km
Bus Route Bus stops outside the ground

ROYSTON TOWN

Founded 1875

Nickname: The Crows   **Club Colours:** White & black

Club Contact Details

01763 241 204   secretary@roystontownfc.co.uk

Previous Names: None

Previous Leagues: Buntingford & District 1919-29. Cambridgeshire 1929-48. Herts County 1948-60, 63-77. South Midlands 1960-63, 77-84. Isthmian 1984-94. Spartan South Midlands 1994-2012.

10-11		11-12		12-13		13-14		14-15		15-16		16-17		17-18		18-19		19-20	
SSM P	3	SSM P	1	SthC	7	SthC	7	SthC	2	SthC	2	SthC	1	SthP	7	SthPC	10	SthPC	n&v
FAC	EP	FAC	P	FAC	1Qr	FAC	2Q	FAC	P	FAC	Pr	FAC	P	FAC	2Qr	FAC	1Q	FAC	4Q
FAV	2Pr	FAV	4P	FAT	1Qr	FAT	P	FAT	1Q	FAT	2Q	FAT	1Pr	FAT	3P	FAT	3Qr	FAT	4P

HONOURS / RECORDS

FA Comps: None

League: Cambridgeshire Division Two 1929-30. Herts County Division One 1969-70, 72-73, Premier 1976-77. South Midlands Division One 1977-78, 2008-09, Premier Division 2011-12. Southern Division One Central 2016-17.

County FA: Herts Charity Shield 1981-82, 96-97. Herts Intermediate Cup 1988-89.

Best FA Cup	Fourth Qualifying Round 2019-20
FA Trophy	Fourth Round Proper 2019-20
FA Vase	Fifth Round Proper 2009-10

GROUND: Garden Walk, Royston, Herts SG8 7HP

Ground Capacity: 1,900   **Seats:** 300   **Covered:** Yes   **Clubhouse:** Yes   **Shop:** No

Previous Grounds: Newmarket Road, Baldock Road and Mackerell Hall before acquiring Garden Walk in 1932.

Record Attendance: 876 v Aldershot Town, 1993-94.

Nearest Railway Station Royston - 0.7km

Bus Route St Mary's School - stop 150m away

RUSHALL OLYMPIC

Founded 1951

Nickname: The Pics   **Club Colours:** Gold and black

Club Contact Details

01922 641 021   philfisher.secretary@gmail.com

Previous Names: None

Previous Leagues: Walsall Amateur 1952-55, Staffordshire County (South) 1956-78, West Midlands 1978-94, Midland Alliance 1994-2005, Southern 2005-08. Northern Premier 2008-18.

10-11		11-12		12-13		13-14		14-15		15-16		16-17		17-18		18-19		19-20	
NP1S	3	NP P	8	NP P	6	NP P	7	NP P	9	NP P	10	NP P	12	NP P	8	SthPC	8	SthPC	n&v
FAC	Pr	FAC	4Q	FAC	1Q	FAC	4Q	FAC	2Q	FAC	3Q	FAC	2Q	FAC	3Qr	FAC	1Qr	FAC	3Q
FAT	2Q	FAT	1Q	FAT	1P	FAT	2Q	FAT	3Qr	FAT	2Qr	FAT	1Q	FAT	2Q	FAT	1Q	FAT	1Q

HONOURS / RECORDS

FA Comps: None

League: West Midlands (Reg) Division One 1979-80. Midland Alliance 2004-05.

County FA: Staffordshire Senior Cup 2015-16. Walsall Senior Cup 2015-16, 17-18.

Goalscorer: Graham Wiggin

Appearances: Alan Dawson - 400+

GROUND: Dales Lane off Daw End Lane, Rushall, Nr Walsall WS4 1LJ

Ground Capacity: 1,980   **Seats:** 200   **Covered:** 200   **Clubhouse:** Yes   **Shop:** Yes

Previous Grounds: Rowley Place 1951-75, Aston University 1976-79

Record Attendance: 2,000 v Leeds United Ex players

Nearest Railway Station Walsall - 3km.

Bus Route Royal Oak - stop 50m away

ST. IVES TOWN

Founded 1887

Nickname: The Ives   **Club Colours:** Red & white

Club Contact Details
01480 463 207   sitfcsecretary@aol.com

Previous Names: None
Previous Leagues: Cambridgeshire, Central Amateur, Hunts, Peterborough & District. United Counties > 2013.

	10-11	11-12	12-13	13-14	14-15	15-16	16-17	17-18	18-19	19-20
	UCL P 11	UCL P 3	UCL P 2	SthC 13	SthC 9	SthC 4	SthP 15	SthP 22	SthPC 13	SthPC n&v
	FAC EP	FAC Pr	FAC P	FAC 2Q	FAC Pr	FAC 2Q	FAC 1Q	FAC 2Q	FAC 3Q	FAC 2Qr
	FAV 4P	FAV QF	FAV 2Pr	FAT 2Q	FAT P	FAT 1Q	FAV 3Q	FAT 1Q	FAT 1Q	FAT 1Qr

HONOURS / RECORDS

FA Comps: None

League: Southern Division One Central Play-offs 2015-16.

County FA: Hunts Senior Cup 1900/01, 11-12, 22-23, 25-26, 29-30, 81-82, 86-87, 87-88, 2006-07, 08-09, 11-12, 15-16.
Hunts Premier Cup 2006-07, 08-09.
Victory: 0-6 v Stafford Rangers (A), FAT 1Q, 28/10/2017 & v Dorchester Town (A), Southern Premier, 16/12/2017
Best FA Cup Third Qualifying Round 2018-19
FA Vase Quarter Finals 2011-12
FA Trophy First Qualifying Round 2017-18, 18-19

GROUND: Westwood Road, St. Ives PE27 6DT

Ground Capacity: 2,000   **Seats:** Yes   **Covered:** Yes   **Clubhouse:** Yes   **Shop:** No
Previous Grounds: Meadow Lane.
Record Attendance: 1,523 v AFC Rushden & Diamonds, Southern Division One Central Play-off Final, 02/05/2016.

Nearest Railway Station Huntingdon - 6.2 miles
Bus Route B the busway - alight at Langley Close. 7min walk from there.

STOURBRIDGE

Founded 1876

Nickname: The Glassboys   **Club Colours:** Red and white

Club Contact Details
01384 394 040   clive1974eades@gmail.com

Previous Names: Stourbridge Standard 1876-87
Previous Leagues: West Midlands (Birmingham League) 1892-1939, 54-71, Birmingham Combination 1945-53,
Southern 1971-2000. Midland Alliance 2000-06. Southern 2006-14. Northern Premier 2014-18.

	10-11	11-12	12-13	13-14	14-15	15-16	16-17	17-18	18-19	19-20
	SthP 8	SthP 6	SthP 2	SthP 5	NP P 16	NP P 6	NP P 3	NP P 11	SthPC 3	SthPC n&v
	FAC 2Q	FAC 2P	FAC 1Qr	FAC 2P	FAC 3Qr	FAC 2P	FAC 3P	FAC 4Q	FAC 4Q	FAC 1Pr
	FAT 3Q	FAT 3Q	FAT 1Q	FAT 3Qr	FAT 2Q	FAT 3P	FAT 1Q	FAT 2P	FAT 1Q	FAT 3Qr

HONOURS / RECORDS

FA Comps: None

League: Birmingham 1923-24. Birmingham Combination 1951-52. Southern Division One North 1973-74, Midland Division 1990-91.
Midland Alliance 2001-02, 02-03.
County FA: Worcestershire Junior Cup 1927-28. Hereford Senior Cup 1954-55. Birmingham Senior Cup 1949-50, 58-59, 67-68,
2017-18. Worcestershire Senior Cup x11 - Firstly in 1904-05 and most recently in 2012-13.
Goalscorer: Ron Page - 269
Appearances: Ron Page - 427
Additional: Received £20,000 from Lincoln City for Tony Cunningham 1979

GROUND: War Memorial Athletic Ground, High Street, Amblecote DY8 4HN

Ground Capacity: 2,626   **Seats:** 250   **Covered:** 750   **Clubhouse:** Yes   **Shop:** Yes
Previous Grounds: None
Record Attendance: 5,726 v Cardiff City - Welsh Cup Final 1st Leg 1974

Nearest Railway Station Stourbridge - 1km
Bus Route Bus 246 from Dudley, 256 from Wolverhampton and 257 all pass the War Memorial Athletic Ground.

SthD1S - Evesham United v Bristol MF 0-0. Photo Bill Wheatcroft.

SthD1S - Rhodes (Cinderford) blocks a cross from Veal (Willand). Photo Keith Clayton.

STRATFORD TOWN

STFC

Nickname: The Town   **Club Colours:** All blue

Founded 1941

Club Contact Details
01789 269 336   stratfordtownfcsecretary@outlook.

Previous Names: Straford Rangers 1941-49. Stratford Town Amateurs 1964-70.
Previous Leagues: Local leagues > 1954. Worcestershire/Midland Combination 1954-57, 70-75, 77-94. Birmingham & District/West Midlands (Reg) 1957-70. Hellenic 1975-77. Midland Alliance (Founder Members) 1994-2013.

10-11		11-12		12-13		13-14		14-15		15-16		16-17		17-18		18-19		19-20	
MidAl	5	MidAl	8	MidAl	1	Sthsw	10	Sthsw	3	SthP	19	SthP	14	SthP	15	SthPC	5	SthPC	n&v
FAC	P	FAC	3Q	FAC	EP	FAC	P	FAC	P	FAC	1Q	FAC	1Q	FAC	3Qr	FAC	1Q	FAC	2Q
FAV	1P	FAV	1P	FAV	2Q	FAT	Pr	FAT	2Q	FAT	2Q	FAT	1Qr	FAT	2Q	FAT	1P	FAT	1Q

HONOURS / RECORDS
FA Comps: None
League: Worcestershire/Midland Combination 1956-57, 86-87.
        Midland Alliance 2012-13.
County FA: Birmingham Senior Cup 1962-63.

Best FA Cup   Third Qualifying Round 2004-05, 06-07, 11-12, 17-18(r)
Amateur Cup   Third Round 1962-63
FA Trophy   First Round Proper 2018-19
FA Vase   Fifth Round Proper 2008-09

GROUND: The DCS Stadium, Knights Lane, Tiddington, Stratford Upon Avon CV37 7BZ
Ground Capacity: 1,400   **Seats:** Yes   **Covered:** Yes   **Clubhouse:** Yes   **Shop:** Yes
Previous Grounds: A number of pitches before Alcester Road by the late 1940s where they stayed until 2007.
Record Attendance: 1,078 v Aston Villa, Birmingham Senior Cup, Oct. 1996.

Nearest Railway Station Stratford-upon-Avon - 2.8km
Bus Route Alveston Primary School - stop 50m away

TAMWORTH

Nickname: The Lambs   **Club Colours:** All red

Founded 1933

Club Contact Details
01827 657 98   clubsec@thelambs.co.uk

Previous Names: None
Previous Leagues: Birmingham Combination 1933-54. West Midlands (originally Birmingham & District League) 1954-72, 84-88. Southern 1972-79, 83-84, 89-2003. Northern Premier 1979-83. Conference/National 2003-18.

10-11		11-12		12-13		13-14		14-15		15-16		16-17		17-18		18-19		19-20	
Conf	19	Conf	18	Conf	19	Conf	23	ConfN	7	Nat N	7	Nat N	9	Nat N	21	SthPC	12	SthPC	n&v
FAC	2P	FAC	3P	FAC	4Q	FAC	2P	FAC	4Qr	FAC	2Q	FAC	2Q	FAC	2Q	FAC	1Q	FAC	4Q
FAT	1P	FAT	1P	FAT	3P	FAT	QF	FAT	3Q	FAT	1P	FAT	3Qr	FAT	3Pr	FAT	2Q	FAT	2Q

HONOURS / RECORDS
FA Comps: FA Vase 1988-89.
League: West Midlands League 1963-64, 65-66, 71-72, 87-88.
        Southern League Divison One Midland 1996-97, Premier Division 2002-03. Conference North 2008-09.
County FA: Staffordshire Senior Cup 1958-59, 63-64, 65-66, 2001-02.
        Birmingham Senior Cup 1960-61, 65-66, 68-69.
Victory: 14-4 v Holbrook Institue (H) - Bass Vase 1934
Defeat: 0-11 v Solihull (A) - Birmingham Combination 1940
Goalscorer: Graham Jessop - 195
Appearances: Dave Seedhouse - 869
Additional: Paid £7,500 to Ilkeston Town for David Hemmings, Dec 2000. Received £12,000 from Kidderminster H for Scott Rickards, 2003

GROUND: The Lamb Ground, Kettlebrook, Tamworth, Staffordshire B77 1AA
Ground Capacity: 4,565   **Seats:** 518   **Covered:** 1,191   **Clubhouse:** Yes   **Shop:** Yes
Previous Grounds: Jolly Sailor Ground 1933-34
Record Attendance: 5,500 v Torquay United - FA Cup 1st Round 15/11/69

Nearest Railway Station Tamworth - within walking distance of the ground.
Bus Route 110 & 765

OUT: Blackfield & Langley (Voluntary relegation - WexP).

BEACONSFIELD TOWN
Founded 1994

Nickname: The Rams   **Club Colours:** Red

Club Contact Details
01494 676 868   info@beaconsfieldtownfc.co.uk

Previous Names: Slough YCOB and Beaconsfield United merged in 1994. Beaconsfield SYCOB 1994-2017.
Previous Leagues: Spartan South Midlands 1004-2004, 07-08, Southern 2004-07.

10-11		11-12		12-13		13-14		14-15		15-16		16-17		17-18		18-19		19-20	
SthC	22	SthC	5	SthC	5	SthC	8	SthC	20	SthC	9	SthC	16	Sth1E	1	SthPS	12	SthPS	n&v
FAC	P	FAC	2Qr	FAC	P	FAC	1Q	FAC	2Q	FAC	1Q	FAC	4Q	FAC	1Q	FAC	3Q	FAC	3Q
FAT	1Q	FAT	P	FAT	Pr	FAT	P	FAT	P	FAT	P	FAT	1Q	FAT	2Qr	FAT	1P	FAT	1Q

HONOURS / RECORDS
FA Comps: None
League: Spartan South Midlands 2000-01, 03-04, 07-08. Southern Division One East 2017-18.

County FA: Berks and Bucks Senior Trophy 2003-04, Senior Cup 2012-13.

Goalscorer:	Allan Arthur
Appearances:	Allan Arthur
Best FA Cup	Fourth Qualifying Round 2016-17
FA Trophy	First Round Proper 2018-19
FA Vase	Second Round Proper 2003-04

GROUND: Holloways Park, Windsor Road, Beaconsfield, Bucks HP9 2SE

Ground Capacity: 2,900   **Seats:** Yes   **Covered:** Yes   **Clubhouse:** Yes   **Shop:** No
Previous Grounds: None
Record Attendance: Not known

Nearest Railway Station Beaconsfield - 2.8km
Bus Route 101, 104 & X74

CHESHAM UNITED
Founded 1917

Nickname: The Generals   **Club Colours:** Claret & blue

Club Contact Details
01494 783 964   secretary@cheshamunited.co.uk

Previous Names: Chesham Town and Chesham Generals merged in 1917 to form Chesham United.
Previous Leagues: Spartan 1917-47, Corinthian 1947-63, Athenian 1963-73, Isthmian 1973-2004

10-11		11-12		12-13		13-14		14-15		15-16		16-17		17-18		18-19		19-20	
SthP	6	SthP	4	SthP	3	SthP	2	SthP	12	SthP	13	SthP	11	SthP	8	SthPS	10	SthPS	n&v
FAC	2Qr	FAC	2Q	FAC	1Q	FAC	1Q	FAC	1Qr	FAC	2P	FAC	1P	FAC	2Q	FAC	2Q	FAC	2Q
FAT	1Qr	FAT	2Qr	FAT	2P	FAT	1P	FAT	1Q	FAT	1Pr	FAT	2Q	FAT	1P	FAT	2Q	FAT	1Q

HONOURS / RECORDS
FA Comps: None
League: Spartan 1921-22, 22-23, 24-25, 32-33. Isthmian Division Two North 1986-87, Division One 1986-87, 97-97, Premier Division 1992-93.
County FA: Berks & Bucks Senior Cup x13. Most recently 2017-18

Goalscorer:	John Willis
Appearances:	Martin Baguley - 600+
Additional:	Received £22,000 from Oldham Athletic for Fitz Hall
Victory:	13-1 v Merthyr Town (H), Southern Premier, 18/11/2017

GROUND: The Meadow, Amy Lane, Amersham Road, Chesham HP5 1NE

Ground Capacity: 5,000   **Seats:** 284   **Covered:** 2,500   **Clubhouse:** Yes   **Shop:** Yes
Previous Grounds: None
Record Attendance: 5,000 v Cambridge United - FA Cup 3rd Round 1979

Nearest Railway Station Chesham underground - 0.7km
Bus Route The Wild Rover Pub - stop 250m away

DORCHESTER TOWN

Founded 1880

Nickname: The Magpies   **Club Colours:** Black & white

Club Contact Details

01305 267 623   office@dorchestertownfc.co.uk

Previous Names: None
Previous Leagues: Dorset, Western 1947-72

10-11	11-12	12-13	13-14	14-15	15-16	16-17	17-18	18-19	19-20
Conf S 17	Conf S 11	Conf S 8	Conf S 22	SthP 17	SthP 12	SthP 18	SthP 19	SthPS 15	SthPS n&v
FAC 3Q	FAC 2Q	FAC 2P	FAC 2Q	FAC 4Q	FAC 1Qr	FAC 1Q	FAC 2Q	FAC 2Q	FAC 2Q
FAT 2Pr	FAT 3Q	FAT 1Pr	FAT 3Q	FAT 1Q	FAT 2Qr	FAT 2Q	FAT 2Q	FAT 2P	FAT 1Qr

HONOURS / RECORDS

FA Comps: None

League: Western Division One 1954-55. Southern Southern Division 1979-80, 86-87, Division One East 2002-03.

County FA: Dorset Senior Cup x12 - Firstly in 1950-51 and most recently in 2011-12.

Victory:	7-0 v Canterbury (A) - Southern League Southern Division 1986-87
Defeat:	0-13 v Welton Rovers (A) - Western League 1966
Appearances:	Mark Jermyn - 600+ over 14 seasons
Additional:	Denis Cheney scored 61 goals in one season. Paid £12,000 to Gloucester City for Chris Townsend 1990. Received £35,000 from Portsmouth for Trevor Sinclair.

GROUND: The Avenue Stadium, Weymouth Avenue, Dorchester DT1 2RY

Ground Capacity: 4,939 **Seats:** 710 **Covered:** 2,846 **Clubhouse:** Yes **Shop:** Yes
Previous Grounds: Council Recreation Ground, Weymouth Avenue 1908-1929, 1929-90, The Avenue Ground 1929
Record Attendance: 4,159 v Weymouth - Southern Premier 1999

Nearest Railway Station Dorchester South & West - 0.9km
Bus Route 10 & X12

FARNBOROUGH

Founded 1967

Nickname: Boro   **Club Colours:** Yellow and blue

Club Contact Details

0844 807 9900   info@farnboroughfc.co.uk

Previous Names: Farnborough Town 1967-2007
Previous Leagues: Surrey Senior 1968-72, Spartan 1972-76, Athenian 1976-77, Isthmian 1977-89, 99-2001, 15-16. Alliance/Conference 1989-90, 91-93, 94-99, 2010-15. Southern 1990-91, 93-94, 2007-10.

10-11	11-12	12-13	13-14	14-15	15-16	16-17	17-18	18-19	19-20
Conf S 2	Conf S 16	Conf S 13	Conf S 16	Conf S 20	Isth P 18	SthC 2	SthP 20	SthPS 9	SthPS n&v
FAC 4Qr	FAC 2Qr	FAC 2Q	FAC 2Qr	FAC 2Qr	FAC 2Qr	FAC 2Q	FAC 1Q	FAC 1Qr	FAC 2Q
FAT 3Q	FAT 1Pr	FAT 1P	FAT 3Qr	FAT 3P	FAT 1Qr	FAT P	FAT 3Q	FAT 1Q	FAT 1Q

HONOURS / RECORDS

FA Comps: None

League: Spartan 1972-73, 73-74, 74-75. London Spartan 1975-76. Athenian Division Two 1976-77. Isthmian Division Two 1978-79, Division One 84 -85, Premier 2000-01. Southern Premier 1990-91, 93-94, 2009-10, Division One South & West 2007-08.
County FA: Hampshire Senior Cup 1974-75, 81-82, 83-84, 85-86, 90-91, 2003-04, 05-06.

Victory:	7-0 v Newport (I.O.W.) (A) - Southern League Division 1 South & West 01/12/2007
Defeat:	0-4 v Hednesford Town (A) - Southern League Premier Division 04/03/2010
Goalscorer:	Dean McDonald - 35 (in 53+3 Appearances 2009-10)
Appearances:	Nic Ciardini - 147 (2007-10)

GROUND: The Rushmoor Stadium, Cherrywood Road, Farnborough, Hants GU14 8DU

Ground Capacity: 6,500 **Seats:** 627 **Covered:** 1,350 **Clubhouse:** Yes **Shop:** Yes
Previous Grounds: Queens Road Recreation ground.
Record Attendance: 2,230 v Corby Town - Southern Premier 21/03/2009

Nearest Railway Station Frimley - 0.7km
Bus Route 194

GOSPORT BOROUGH

Founded 1944

Nickname: The 'Boro' **Club Colours:** Yellow & blue

Club Contact Details
023 9250 1042   enquiries@gosportboroughfc.co.uk

Previous Names: Gosport Borough Athletic
Previous Leagues: Portsmouth & District 1944-45, Hampshire 1945-78. Southern 1978-92, 2007-13. Wessex 1992-2007. Conference 2013-17.

10-11	11-12	12-13	13-14	14-15	15-16	16-17	17-18	18-19	19-20
Sthsw 13	Sthsw 3	SthP 5	Conf S 12	Conf S 6	Nat S 9	Nat S 20	SthP 23	SthPS 19	SthPS n&v
FAC Pr	FAC P	FAC 4Qr	FAC 2Q	FAC 1P	FAC 3Qr	FAC 2Q	FAC 2Q	FAC 2Q	FAC 1Q
FAT P	FAT 1P	FAT 2Q	FAT F	FAT 2P	FAT 3Q	FAT 1P	FAT 2Q	FAT 1Q	FAT 3Qr

HONOURS / RECORDS

FA Comps: None
League: Portsmouth & District 1944-45. Hampshire 1945-46, 76-77, 77-78.
        Wessex 2006-07.
County FA: Hampshire Senior Cup 1987-88, 2014-15.

Victory: 19-1 v Widbrook United, Portsmouth Senior Cup, 2016-17.
Defeat: 0-9 v Gloucester City - Southern Premier Division 1989-90 and v Lymington & N.M. - Wessex Lge 99-2000
Goalscorer: Justin Bennett- 257
Appearances: Tony Mahoney - 765

GROUND: Privett Park, Privett Road, Gosport, Hampshire PO12 3SX

Ground Capacity: 4,500   **Seats:** 1,000   **Covered:** Yes   **Clubhouse:** Yes   **Shop:** Yes
Previous Grounds: None
Record Attendance: 4,770 v Pegasus - FA Amateur Cup 1953

Nearest Railway Station Portsmouth Harbour
Bus Route X5 (to Southampton) & 9/9A (to Fareham)

HARROW BOROUGH

Founded 1933

Nickname: Boro **Club Colours:** All red

Club Contact Details
0844 561 1347

Previous Names: Roxonian 1933-38, Harrow Town 1938-66
Previous Leagues: Harrow & District 1933-34, Spartan 1934-40, 45-58, West Middlesex Combination 1940-41, Middlesex Senior 1941-45,
        Delphian 1956-63, Athenian 1963-75. Isthmian 1975-2018.

10-11	11-12	12-13	13-14	14-15	15-16	16-17	17-18	18-19	19-20
Isth P 5	Isth P 17	Isth P 15	Isth P 18	Isth P 16	Isth P 17	Isth P 21	Isth P 12	SthPS 7	SthPS n&v
FAC 1P	FAC 2Q	FAC 1Q	FAC 1Q	FAC 4Qr	FAC 1Q	FAC 1P	FAC 1Q	FAC 1Q	FAC 2Q
FAT 1Q	FAT 2Qr	FAT 1Q	FAT 1Q	FAT 1Q	FAT 1Q	FAV 3Q	FAT 1Qr	FAT 1Q	FAT 1Q

HONOURS / RECORDS

FA Comps: None
League: Isthmian League 1983-84.

County FA: Middlesex Senior Cup 1982-83, 92-93, 2014-15. Middlesex Premier Cup 1981-82.
        Middlesex Senior Charity Cup 1979-80, 92-93, 2005-06, 06-07, 14-15.
Victory: 13-0 v Handley Page (A) - 18/10/1941
Defeat: 0-8 on five occasions
Goalscorer: Dave Pearce - 153
Appearances: Les Currell - 582, Colin Payne - 557, Steve Emmanuel - 522

GROUND: Earlsmead Stadium, Carlyon Avenue, South Harrow HA2 8SS

Ground Capacity: 3,068   **Seats:** 350   **Covered:** 1,000   **Clubhouse:** Yes   **Shop:** Yes
Previous Grounds: Northcult Road 1933-34.
Record Attendance: 3,000 v Wealdstone - FA Cup 1st Qualifying Road 1946

Nearest Railway Station Northolt Underground - 1.1km
Bus Route 114, 282, 487, H10, H9 & X140

HARTLEY WINTNEY

Founded 1897

Nickname: The Row   **Club Colours:** All orange

Club Contact Details
01252 843 586 (Clubhouse)

Previous Names: None
Previous Leagues: Basingstoke & District. Aldershot & District >1978. Founder members of the Home Counties League (renamed Combined Counties League) 1978- 2017.

10-11		11-12		12-13		13-14		14-15		15-16		16-17		17-18		18-19		19-20	
CC1	7	CC1	3	CCP	19	CCP	7	CCP	9	CCP	1	CCP	1	Sth1E	4	SthPS	8	SthPS	n&v
FAC	Pr	FAC	3Q	FAC	P	FAC	4Q	FAC	Pr	FAC	3Q	FAC	EP	FAC	2Q	FAC	1Q	FAC	2Qr
FAV	1Q	FAV	1P	FAV	1Q	FAV	2P	FAV	2Q	FAV	5P	FAV	2P	FAT	1P	FAT	1Qr	FAT	3Q

HONOURS / RECORDS
FA Comps: None
League: Combined Counties League 1982-83, 2015-16, 16-17.

County FA: None

Best FA Cup	Fourth Qualifying Round 2013-14
FA Vase	Fifth Round 2015-16
FA Trophy	First Qualifying Round 2018-19(r)

GROUND: Memorial Playing Fields, Green Lane, Hartley Wintney RG27 8DL

Ground Capacity: 1,500   **Seats:** 113   **Covered:** Yes   **Clubhouse:** Yes   **Shop:** Yes
Previous Grounds: Causeway Farm 1897-1953.
Record Attendance: 1,392 v AFC Wimbledon , Combined Counties League Premier, 25/01/03.

Nearest Railway Station Winchfield - 1.9km
Bus Route Green Lane - stop 100m away

HAYES & YEADING UNITED

Founded 2007

Nickname: United   **Club Colours:** Red & white

Club Contact Details
0208 573 2075   info@hyufc.com

Previous Names: Hayes - Botwell Mission 1909-29. Hayes and Yeading merged to form today's club in 2007
Previous Leagues: Isthmian. Conference 2007-16. Southern 2016-18.

10-11		11-12		12-13		13-14		14-15		15-16		16-17		17-18		18-19		19-20	
Conf	16	Conf	21	Conf S	17	Conf S	20	Conf S	19	Nat S	21	SthP	23	Sth1E	3	IsthSC	1	SthPS	n&v
FAC	1P	FAC	4Q	FAC	4Q	FAC	2Qr	FAC	2Q	FAC	2Q	FAC	2Q	FAC	3Q	FAC	2Q	FAC	4Qr
FAT	1P	FAT	1P	FAT	1P	FAT	1P	FAT	1P	FAT	3Qr	FAT	1Q	FAT	1Q	FAT	1P	FAT	3Q

HONOURS / RECORDS
FA Comps: None
League: Isthmian South Central 2018-19.

County FA: None

Victory:	8-2 v Hillingdon Borough (A) - Middlesex Senior Cup 11/11/08
Defeat:	0-8 v Luton Town (A) - Conference Premier 27/03/10
Goalscorer:	Josh Scott - 40 (2007-09)
Appearances:	James Mulley - 137 (2007-10)

GROUND: SKYex Community Stadium, Beaconsfield Road, Hayes UB4 0SL

Ground Capacity: 6,000   **Seats:** 2,500   **Covered:** 3,900   **Clubhouse:** Yes   **Shop:** Yes
Previous Grounds: Kingfield Stadium (Woking FC) 2012-13.
Record Attendance: 1,881 v Luton Town - Conference Premier 06/03/2010

Nearest Railway Station Hayes & Harlington - 5-10min taxi ride from ground
Bus Route From Uxbridge Underground take bus towards Shep Bush, alight at Springfield Rd

HENDON

Nickname: Dons or Greens **Club Colours:** Green and white

Founded 1908

Club Contact Details
020 8205 1645 Secretaryhendonfc@gmail.com

Previous Names: Christ Church Hampstead > 1908, Hampstead Town > 1933, Golders Green > 1946
Previous Leagues: Finchley & District 1908-11, Middlesex 1910-11, London 1911-14, Athenian 1914-63. Isthmian 1963-2018.

10-11		11-12		12-13		13-14		14-15		15-16		16-17		17-18		18-19		19-20	
Isth P	15	Isth P	7	Isth P	10	Isth P	8	Isth P	2	Isth P	19	Isth P	19	Isth P	3	SthPS	16	SthPS	n&v
FAC	1P	FAC	4Q	FAC	1P	FAC	2P	FAC	3Q	FAC	1Q	FAC	4Q	FAC	1Qr	FAC	3Q	FAC	3Q
FAT	2Q	FAT	1Q	FAT	1Q	FAT	1P	FAT	3Q	FAT	1Q	FAT	1Q	FAT	2P	FAT	2Q	FAT	1Q

HONOURS / RECORDS
FA Comps: FA Amateur Cup 1959-60, 64-65, 71-72. European Amateur Champions 1972-73.

League: Finchley & District Division Three 1908-09, DivisioN Two 09-10, Division One 10-11. Middlesex 1912-13, 13-14.
Athenian 1952-53, 55-56, 60-61. Isthmian 1964-65, 72-73.

County FA: London Senior Cup 1963-64, 68-69, 2008-09, 11-12 14-15. Middlesex Senior Cup x16 - Firstly in 1933-34 / Most recently 2017-18.
Middlesex Intermediate Cup 1964-65, 66-67, 72-73. London Intermediate Cup 1962-63, 64-65, 72-73, 75-76, 79-80.

Victory: 13-1 v Wingate - Middlesex County Cup 02/02/1957
Defeat: 2-11 v Walthamstowe Avenue, Athenian League 09/11/1935
Goalscorer: Freddie Evans - 176 (1929-35)
Appearances: Bill Fisher - 787 - (1940-64)
Additional: Received £30,000 from Luton Town for Iain Dowie

GROUND: Silver Jubilee Park, Townsend Lane, Kingsbury, London NW9 7NE

Ground Capacity: 3,070 **Seats:** 350 **Covered:** 1,000 **Clubhouse:** Yes **Shop:**
Previous Grounds: Claremont Road. Vale Farm (Wembley FC). Earlsmead (Harrow Borough FC).
Record Attendance: 9,000 v Northampton Town - FA Cup 1st Round 1952

Nearest Railway Station Hendon - 1.1km
Bus Route Queensbury Road - 700m away

MERTHYR TOWN

Nickname: Martyrs **Club Colours:** White & black

Founded 2010

Club Contact Details
01685 359 921 merthyrsec@gmail.com

Previous Names: None
Previous Leagues: Western League 2010-12.

10-11		11-12		12-13		13-14		14-15		15-16		16-17		17-18		18-19		19-20	
West1	1	WestP	1	Sthsw	3	Sthsw	2	Sthsw	1	SthP	10	SthP	3	SthP	17	SthPS	13	SthPS	n&v
FAC	EP	FAC	1Qr	FAC	3Q	FAC	1Q	FAC	P	FAC	2Q	FAC	3Q	FAC	2Q	FAC	2Q	FAC	2Q
FAV	2Q	FAV	2Q	FAT	1P	FAT	3Q	FAT	3Qr	FAT	3Qr	FAT	2Qr	FAT	2Qr	FAT	1Q	FAT	1Qr

HONOURS / RECORDS
FA Comps: None

League: Western League Division One 2010-11, Premier Division 2011-12.
Southern Division One South & West 2014-15.

County FA: None

Victory: 9-0 v Bishops Cleeve, Southern Division One South & West, 06/04/2015.
Defeat: 1-13 v Chesham United (A), Southern Premier, 18/11/2017

GROUND: Penydarren Park, Park Terrace CF47 8RF

Ground Capacity: 4,000 **Seats:** Yes **Covered:** Yes **Clubhouse:** Yes **Shop:**
Previous Grounds: Rhiw Dda'r (Taff's Well AFC) 2010-11.
Record Attendance: Not known

Nearest Railway Station Merthyr Tydfil - 0.6km
Bus Route St Mary's Church - stop 100m away

METROPOLITAN POLICE

Nickname: The Blues   **Club Colours:** All blue

Founded 1919

Club Contact Details
020 8398 7358

Previous Names: None
Previous Leagues: Spartan 1928-60, Metropolitan 1960-71, Southern 1971-78. Isthmian 1978-2018.

10-11		11-12		12-13		13-14		14-15		15-16		16-17		17-18		18-19		19-20	
Isth1S	1	Isth P	12	Isth P	6	Isth P	17	Isth P	5	Isth P	12	Isth P	18	Isth P		SthPS	3	SthPS	n&v
FAC	4Qr	FAC	1Q	FAC	1P	FAC	1Qr	FAC	2Q	FAC	1Qr	FAC	2Q	FAC	2Q	FAC	1P	FAC	1Qr
FAT	Pr	FAT	1Q	FAT	2Qr	FAT	2Q	FAT	3Q	FAT	3Q	FAV	1Q	FAT	3Q	FAT	1Qr	FAT	2Qr

HONOURS / RECORDS

FA Comps: None

League: Spartan League Eastern Division and overall 1928-29, 29-30, 36-37, 38-39, 46-47, 53-54, 54-55, Central Division 45-46. Isthmian League Division One South 2010-11.
County FA: Middlesex Senior Cup 1927-28, Surrey Senior Cup 1932-33, 2014-15. London Senior Cup 2009-10.

Victory: 10-1 v Tilbury - 1995
Defeat: 1-11 v Wimbledon - 1956
Goalscorer: Mario Russo
Appearances: Pat Robert

GROUND: Imber Court, Ember Lane, East Molesey, Surrey KT8 0BT

Ground Capacity: 3,100   **Seats:** 297   **Covered:** 1,800   **Clubhouse:** Yes   **Shop:** No
Previous Grounds: None
Record Attendance: 4,500 v Kingstonian - FA Cup 1934

Nearest Railway Station Thames Ditton - 0.8km
Bus Route 411

POOLE TOWN

Nickname: The Dolphins   **Club Colours:** Red & white

Founded 1890

Club Contact Details
01794 517 991   secretary@pooletownfc.co.uk

Previous Names: Poole Rovers and Poole Hornets merged in 1890 to form Poole FC > 1934 (Known as Poole & St. Mary's 1919-20).
Previous Leagues: Dorset 1896-1903, 04-05, 10-11. Hampshire 1903-04, 05-10, 11-23, 34-35, 96-2004. Western 1923-26, 30-34, 35-57. Southern 1926-30, 57-96, 2011-16. Wessex 2004-11. National 2016-18.

10-11		11-12		12-13		13-14		14-15		15-16		16-17		17-18		18-19		19-20	
WexP	1	Sthsw	2	Sthsw	1	SthP	7	SthP	2	SthP	1	Nat S	5	Nat S	20	SthPS	5	SthPS	n&v
FAC	4Q	FAC	3Q	FAC	P	FAC	4Qr	FAC	2Qr	FAC	4Q	FAC	2Q	FAC	3Q	FAC	4Q	FAC	4Qr
FAV	SF	FAT	1Qr	FAT	2Qr	FAT	2Q	FAT	1P	FAT	1Q	FAT	3Qr	FAT	3Q	FAT	3Q	FAT	1Q

HONOURS / RECORDS

FA Comps: None

League: Western 1956-57. Hampshire Division One 1999-00. Wessex Premier Division 2008-09, 09-10, 10-11. Southern Division One South & West 2012-13, Premier 2015-16.
County FA: Dorset Senior Cup 1894-95, 96-97, 98-99, 1901-02, 03-04, 06-07, 25-26, 26-27, 37-38, 46-47, 74-75, 88-89, 97-98, 2008 -09, 12-13, 13-14.
Victory: 12-0 v Welton Rovers (H) Western League 26/04/1939.
Defeat: 1-12 v Boscombe (A) Hampshire League (West) 20/12/1913.
Additional: Transfer fee paid £5,000 for Nicky Dent 1990.
                  Transfer fee received reported as £180,000 for Charlie Austin from Swindon Town 2009.

GROUND: Tatnam Ground, Oakdale School, School Lane, Poole BH15 3JR

Ground Capacity: 3,100   **Seats:** 268   **Covered:** Yes   **Clubhouse:** Yes   **Shop:** Yes
Previous Grounds: Ye Old Farm Ground. Wimborne Road Rec > 1933. Poole Stadium 1933-94. Hamworthy Utd 1994-96. Holt Utd 1996.
Record Attendance: 6,575 v Watford, FAC 1Pr, 1962-63 (at Poole Stadium). 2,203 v Corby, Southern Prem, 2014-15 (at Tatnam).

Nearest Railway Station Poole - 3/4 mile from the ground.
Bus Route 10, 6, M1, M2, X6 & X8

SALISBURY

Founded 2015

Nickname: The Whites   **Club Colours:** White and black

Club Contact Details
01722 776 655   info@salisburyfc.co.uk

Previous Names: None
Previous Leagues: Wessex 2015-16.

10-11	11-12	12-13	13-14	14-15	15-16	16-17	17-18	18-19	19-20
					WexP 1	Sthsw 2	Sth1W 2	SthPS 4	SthPS n&v
						FAC 2Q	FAC 2Q	FAC 2Qr	FAC 3Q
					FAV SF	FAT 1Q	FAT P	FAT 2P	FAT 2P

HONOURS / RECORDS
FA Comps: None
League: Wessex Premier Division 2015-16.

County FA: None

Victory: 9-1 v Bournemouth - Wessex Premier 25/08/15.
Defeat: 4-1 v AFC Porchester - Wessex Premier 30/04/16.
Goalscorer: Sam Wilson - 40 - 2015-16.
Appearances: Thomas Whelan - 54 - 2015-16.

GROUND: Raymond McEnhill Stadium, Partridge Way, Old Sarum SP4 6PU

Ground Capacity: 4,000   **Seats:** 500   **Covered:** 2,247   **Clubhouse:** Yes   **Shop:**
Previous Grounds: None
Record Attendance: 3,450 v Hereford FC, FA Vase Semi-final 2nd leg, 2015-16.

Nearest Railway Station Salisbury - 4km
Bus Route Bus stops outside the ground

SWINDON SUPERMARINE

Founded 1992

Nickname: Marine   **Club Colours:** All blue

Club Contact Details
01793 828 778   supermarinefc@aol.com

Previous Names: Club formed after the amalgamation of Swindon Athletic and Supermarine
Previous Leagues: Wiltshire, Hellenic1992-2001.

10-11	11-12	12-13	13-14	14-15	15-16	16-17	17-18	18-19	19-20
SthP 10	SthP 21	Sthsw 4	Sthsw 5	Sthsw 14	Sthsw 4	Sthsw 7	Sth1W 5	SthPS 11	SthPS n&v
FAC 2P	FAC 2Q	FAC 1Q	FAC P	FAC 2Q	FAC 1Q	FAC 3Q	FAC 3Q	FAC 2Qr	FAC 2Q
FAT 3Q	FAT 1P	FAT 1Q	FAT 1Q	FAT P	FAT 2Q	FAT 1Q	FAT 1Q	FAT 1Qr	FAT 1Q

HONOURS / RECORDS
FA Comps: None
League: Hellenic League Premier Division 1997-98, 2000-01.

County FA: Wiltshire Premier Shield 1996-97, 2006-07. Senior Cup 2016-17.

Goalscorer: Damon York - 136 (1990-98)
Appearances: Damon York - 314 (1990-98)
Additional: Paid £1,000 to Hungerford Town for Lee Hartson

GROUND: The Webbswood Stadium, South Marston, Swindon SN3 4BZ

Ground Capacity: 2,000   **Seats:** 325   **Covered:** Yes   **Clubhouse:** Yes   **Shop:** Yes
Previous Grounds: Supermarine: Vickers Airfield > Mid 1960s
Record Attendance: 1,550 v Aston Villa

Nearest Railway Station Swindon - 5.8km
Bus Route Stanton Fitzwarren Turn - stop 300m away

TAUNTON TOWN

Founded 1947

Nickname: The Peacocks

Club Colours: Claret and sky blue

Club Contact Details
01823 254 909

admin@tauntontown.com

Previous Names: Taunton > 1968
Previous Leagues: Western 1954-77, 83-2002, Southern 1977-83

	10-11	11-12	12-13	13-14	14-15	15-16	16-17	17-18	18-19	19-20
	Sthsw 9	Sthsw 17	Sthsw 18	Sthsw 8	Sthsw 4	Sthsw 3	Sthsw 4	Sth1W 1	SthP 2	SthPS n&v
FAC	1Q	1Qr	1Qr	Pr	1Q	2Qr	1Pr	1Qr	4Qr	2Q
FAT	Pr	1Q	1Q	2Q	P	Pr	3Q	1P	1Q	2Qr

HONOURS / RECORDS

FA Comps: FA Vase 2000-01.
League: Western League 1968-69, 89-90, 95-96, 98-99, 99-2000, 2000-01.
Southern Division One 2017-18.
County FA: Somerset Senior Cup 1969-70, Premier Cup 2002-03, 05-06, 13-14, 14-15, 16-17.

Victory: 12-0 v Dawlish Town (A) - FA Cup Preliminary Round 28/08/1993
Defeat: 0-8 v Cheltenham Town (A) - FA Cup 2nd Qualifying Round 28/09/1991
Goalscorer: Tony Payne. Reg Oram scored 67 in one season
Appearances: Tony Payne

GROUND: Wordsworth Drive, Taunton, Somerset TA1 2HG

Ground Capacity: 2,500 **Seats:** 300 **Covered:** 1,000 **Clubhouse:** Yes **Shop:** Yes
Previous Grounds: Mountfields. French Weir. Victoria Park. Huish Old Boys. Denman's Park > 1953.
Record Attendance: 3,284 v Tiverton Town - FA Vase Semi-final 1999

Nearest Railway Station Taunton - 1.4km
Bus Route Milford Road - stop 20m away

TIVERTON TOWN

Founded 1913

Nickname: Tivvy

Club Colours: All yellow

Club Contact Details
01884 252 397

jayrichdevon24@googlemail.com

Previous Names: Tiverton Athletic.
Previous Leagues: East Devon 1913-28. North Devon 1928-32. Exeter & District 1932-73. Western 1973-99.

	10-11	11-12	12-13	13-14	14-15	15-16	16-17	17-18	18-19	19-20
	SthP 20	Sthsw 9	Sthsw 16	Sthsw 3	Sthsw 16	Sthsw 8	Sthsw 3	SthP 6	SthPS 18	SthPS n&v
FAC	1Qr	P	P	P	1Qr	P	Pr	1Q	3Qr	2Q
FAT	1Q	3Q	1Q	3Qr	1Q	2Q	1Q	2Qr	2Q	1Qr

HONOURS / RECORDS

FA Comps: FA Vase 1997-98, 98-99.
League: East Devon Senior Division 1924-25, 25-26, 26-27, 27-28. North Devon 1931-32.
Exeter & District 1933-34, 64-65, 65-66. Western 1993-94, 94-95, 96-97, 97-98.
County FA: Devon Senior Cup 1955-56, 65-66.
Devon St Luke's Cup 1990-91, 91-92, 92-93, 93-94, 94-95, 96-97, 1999-2000, 02-03, 05-06, 16-17.
Victory: 14-1 v University College SW, 11/02/1933.
Defeat: 0-10 v Dawlish Town, 27/12/1969.
Goalscorer: Phil Everett - 378.
Appearances: Tom Gardner - 510.

GROUND: Ladysmead, Bolham Road, Tiverton, Devon EX16 6SG

Ground Capacity: 2,983 **Seats:** 520 **Covered:** 2,300 **Clubhouse:** Yes **Shop:** Yes
Previous Grounds: Athletic Ground (Amory Park) 1913-21. Elm Field (The Elms) 1921-46.
Record Attendance: 3,000 v Leyton Orient - FA Cup 1st Round Proper 12/11/1994.

Nearest Railway Station Tiverton Parkway - 2km
Bus Route Park Road - stop 300m away

TRURO CITY

Founded 1889

Nickname: City, White Tigers, The Tinmen **Club Colours:** All white

Club Contact Details
01872 225 400   info@trurocityfc.net

Previous Names: None

Previous Leagues: Cornwall County. Plymouth & District >1951. South Western (FM) 1951-2006. Western 2006-08. Southern 2008-11, 13-15. Conference 2011-13.

10-11		11-12		12-13		13-14		14-15		15-16		16-17		17-18		18-19		19-20	
SthP	1	Conf S	14	Conf S	22	SthP	17	SthP	3	Nat S	4	Nat S	19	Nat S	7	Nat S	20	SthPS	n&v
FAC	2Q	FAC	3Q	FAC	2Q	FAC	2Q	FAC	1Q	FAC	3Q	FAC	2Q	FAC	1P	FAC	2Qr	FAC	2Q
FAT	3Q	FAT	1P	FAT	3Q	FAT	1Q	FAT	3Q	FAT	2Pr	FAT	1Pr	FAT	3Q	FAT	2P	FAT	1Qr

HONOURS / RECORDS
FA Comps: FA Vase 2006-07.

League: Plymouth & District 1936-37. South Western League 1960-61, 69-70, 92-93, 95-96, 97-98. Western Div. One 2006-07, Premier Division 07-08. Southern Division One South & West 2008-09, Premier Division 2010-11.

County FA: Cornwall Senior Cup 1894-95, 1901-02, 02-03, 10-11, 23-24, 26-27, 27-28, 37-38, 58-59, 66-67, 69-70, 94-95, 97-98, 2005 -06, 06-07, 07-08.

Misc: 115 points & 185 goals, Western League Division One (42 games) 2006-07.

Became first British club to achieve five promotions in six seasons.

GROUND: Treyew Road, Truro TR1 2TH

Ground Capacity: 3,200   **Seats:** 1,675   **Covered:** Yes   **Clubhouse:** Yes   **Shop:** Yes

Previous Grounds: Truro School. Tolgarrick > mid-1900s Treyew Road Mid 1900s-2018. Plainmoor (Torquay) 18.

Record Attendance:

Nearest Railway Station Truro - 10min walk from the ground.

Bus Route 87, T1, T2 & U1

WALTON CASUALS

Founded 1948

Nickname: The Stags   **Club Colours:** Orange and black

Club Contact Details
01932 260 300   info@waltoncasuals.com

Previous Names: None

Previous Leagues: Surrey Intermediate 1948-69. Surrey Senior 1969-71. Suburban 1971-92. Surrey County 1992-95. Combined Counties 1995-2005.

10-11		11-12		12-13		13-14		14-15		15-16		16-17		17-18		18-19		19-20	
Isth1S	12	Isth1S	15	Isth1S	22	Isth1S	9	Isth1S	18	Isth1S	16	Isth1S	13	Isth1S	6	SthPS	17	SthPS	n&v
FAC	1Q	FAC	P	FAC	P	FAC	P	FAC	Pr	FAC	P	FAC	3Q	FAC	1Q	FAC	2Q	FAC	1Q
FAT	1Q	FAT	Pr	FAT	P	FAT	P	FAT	Pr	FAT	1Q	FAT	1Qr	FAT	1P	FAT	1Q	FAT	3Q	FAT	1Q

HONOURS / RECORDS
FA Comps: None

League: Surban Southern Section 1982-83, Premier B 2012-13. Combined Counties Premier Division 2004-05.

County FA: None

Goalscorer: Paul Mills - 111 in 123 appearances (1993-99).

Appearances: Lawrence Ennis - 288

Victory: 10-0 v Chessington United, Combined Counties Premier, 28/12/2004.

Defeat: 0-7 v Redhill, Surrey Senior Cup 1st Rnd, 08/12/98. v Chipstead, Combined Counties Premier, 09/11/2002. v Faversham Town, Isthmian Division One, 08/12/2012. v Faversham Town, Isthmian Division One, 09/04/2016.

GROUND: Elmbridge Sports Hub, Waterside Drive, Walton-on-Thames, Surrey KT12 2JP

Ground Capacity: 2,217   **Seats:** 153   **Covered:** 403   **Clubhouse:** Yes   **Shop:** Yes

Previous Grounds: Elm Grove Rec. 1948-69. Franklyn Road 69-71. Stompond Lane 71-72. Liberty Lane 72-80. Waterside Stadium 80-2015.

Record Attendance: 1,748 v AFC Wimbledon - Combined Counties League 12/04/2004   Moatside 2015-16. Church Road 2016-17.

Nearest Railway Station Both Walton and Hersham stations about 43min walk.

Bus Route Nos. 461 & 459 stop nearest the hub.

WESTON-SUPER-MARE

Nickname: Seagulls   **Club Colours:** White & black

Founded 1887

Club Contact Details
01934 621 618   enquiries@wsmafc.co.uk

Previous Names: Borough or Weston-super-Mare
Previous Leagues: Western League 1900-02, 10-18, 48-92. Bristol & District and Somerset County 1921-45. Southern 1992-04.

10-11	11-12	12-13	13-14	14-15	15-16	16-17	17-18	18-19	19-20
Conf S 12	Conf S 13	Conf S 7	Conf S 11	Conf S 17	Nat S 16	Nat S 15	Nat S 12	Nat S 22	SthPS n&v
FAC 3Q	FAC 4Q	FAC 3Qr	FAC 3Q	FAC 1P	FAC 4Q	FAC 2Q	FAC 2Q	FAC 1P	FAC 3Qr
FAT 3Q	FAT 3Q	FAT 3Q	FAT 1Pr	FAT 1P	FAT 2P	FAT 3Q	FAT 2Pr	FAT 1P	FAT 1Q

HONOURS / RECORDS
FA Comps: None

League: Western League 1991-92.

County FA: Somerset Senior Cup 1926-67.
               Somerset Premier Cup 2010-11, 11-12, 17-18.
Victory: 11-0 v Paulton Rovers
Defeat: 1-12 v Yeovil Town Reserves
Goalscorer: Matt Lazenby - 180
Appearances: Harry Thomas - 740
Additional: Received £20,000 from Sheffield Wednesday for Stuart Jones

---

GROUND: Winterstoke Road, Weston-super-Mare BS24 9AA

Ground Capacity: 3,500   **Seats:** 350   **Covered:** 2,000   **Clubhouse:** Yes   **Shop:** Yes
Previous Grounds: 'Great Ground' Locking Road >1955. Langford Road 1955-83. Woodspring Park 1983-2004.
Record Attendance: 2,949 v Doncaster Rovers, FA Cup First Round Proper, 18th November 2014.

Nearest Railway Station Weston-Super-Mare - 25-30 minute walk away.
Bus Route 3

WIMBORNE TOWN

Nickname: Magpies   **Club Colours:** Black and white

Founded 1878

Club Contact Details
01202 884 821   info@wimbornetownfc.co.uk

Previous Names: None
Previous Leagues: Dorset, Dorset Combination, Western 1981-86, Wessex 1986-2010

10-11	11-12	12-13	13-14	14-15	15-16	16-17	17-18	18-19	19-20
Sthsw 19	Sthsw 19	Sthsw 12	Sthsw 13	Sthsw 13	Sthsw 17	Sthsw 11	Sth1W 3	SthPS 14	SthPS n&v
FAC 1Q	FAC P	FAC P	FAC P	FAC 1Q	FAC 2Q	FAC Pr	FAC Pr	FAC 1Qr	FAC 1Q
FAT 1Qr	FAT P	FAT 2Q	FAT P	FAT 1P	FAT P	FAT 2Q	FAT 1Q	FAT 1Q	FAT 1Qr

HONOURS / RECORDS
FA Comps: FA Vase 1991-92.

League: Dorset Division One 1980-81. Wessex 1991-92, 93-94, 99-2000.

County FA: Dorset Minor Cup 1912-13, Senior Amateur Cup 1936-37, 63-64, Senior Cup 91-92, 96-97.

Goalscorer: Jason Lovell
Appearances: James Sturgess

GROUND: The Cuthbury, Cowgrove Road, Wimborne, Dorset BH21 4EL

Ground Capacity: 1,716   **Seats:** 275   **Covered:** 425   **Clubhouse:** Yes   **Shop:** Yes
Previous Grounds: None
Record Attendance: 3,250 v Bamber Bridge

Nearest Railway Station Poole - 8 miles
Bus Route First School - stop 400m away

SthD1S - Hannah (Cinderford) blocks the shot from Stamp (Willand) before Veal taps in.

SthD1S - Turl (Cinderford) Richards (Willand). Photos Keith Clayton.

YATE TOWN

Nickname: The Bluebells   **Club Colours:** White & navy blue

Founded 1906

Club Contact Details
01454 228 103   yatetownfootballclub@outlook.com

Previous Names: Yate Rovers 1906-1930s. Yate YMCA 1933-58.

Previous Leagues: Bristol Premier Combination > 1968, Gloucestershire County 1968-83, Hellenic 1983-89, 2000-03, Southern 1989-2000

10-11		11-12		12-13		13-14		14-15		15-16		16-17		17-18		18-19		19-20	
Sthsw	14	Sthsw	13	Sthsw	6	Sthsw	9	Sthsw	6	Sthsw	16	Sthsw	18	Sth1W	14	SthS	3	SthPS	n&v
FAC	P	FAC	2Qr	FAC	1P	FAC	3Qr	FAC	1Q	FAC	P	FAC	P	FAC	P	FAC	1Qr	FAC	Pr
FAT	P	FAT	2Q	FAT	Pr	FAT	Pr	FAT	P	FAT	P	FAT	1Q	FAT	1Q	FAT	1Qr	FAT	1P

HONOURS / RECORDS

FA Comps: None

League: Hellenic 1987-88, 88-89.

County FA: Gloucestershire Senior Cup 2004-05, 05-06.

Victory: 13-3 v Clevedon - Bristol Premier Combination 1967-68

Goalscorer: Kevin Thaws

Appearances: Gary Hewlett

Additional: Paid £2,000 to Chippenham Town for Matt Rawlings 2003
Received £15,000 from Bristol Rovers for Mike Davis

GROUND: Lodge Road, Yate, Bristol BS37 7LE

Ground Capacity: 2,300   **Seats:** 236   **Covered:** 400   **Clubhouse:** Yes   **Shop:** Yes

Previous Grounds: Yate Aerodrome 1954-60. Sunnyside Lane 1960-84.

Record Attendance: 2,000 v Bristol Rovers v Bristol Rovers Past XI - Vaughan Jones testimonial 1990

Nearest Railway Station Yate - 1km

Bus Route North Road - stop 100m away

Father and son supporters of Bristol Manor Farm who follow them home and away and apparently sing throughout each game, great characters. Photo Bill Wheatcroft.

AFC DUNSTABLE

Founded 1981

Nickname: Od's   **Club Colours:** All royal blue

Club Contact Details
01582 891 433   afcdunstable2016@gmail.com

Previous Names: Old Dunstablians 1981- 2004.
Previous Leagues: Dunstable Alliance 1981-83. Luton District & South Bedfordshire 1983-95. South Midlands/Spartan South Midlands 1995-2016.

10-11		11-12		12-13		13-14		14-15		15-16		16-17		17-18		18-19		19-20	
SSM1	2	SSM P	3	SSM P	8	SSM P	9	SSM P	3	SSM P	1	SthC	7	Sth1E	5	SthC	10	SthC	n&v
		FAC	P	FAC	2Qr	FAC	EP	FAC	P	FAC	1Q	FAC	2Q	FAC	P	FAC	Pr	FAC	Pr
FAV	2P	FAV	2Q	FAV	1P	FAV	1Qr	FAV	3P	FAV	4P	FAT	P	FAT	P	FAT	P	FAT	1Q

HONOURS / RECORDS
FA Comps: None
League: Spartan South Midlands Division Two 2003-04, 06-07, Premier Division 2015-16.

County FA: Bedfordshire Junior Cup 1989-90. Bedfordshire Senior Trophy 2006-07, 07-08. Bedfordshire Senior Cup 2016-17.

Best FA Cup	Second Qualifying Round 2012-13(r), 16-17
FA Trophy	Preliminary Round 2016-17, 17-18, 18-19
FA Vase	Fourth Round Proper 2015-16

GROUND: Creasey Park, Creasey Park Drive, Brewers Hill Road LU6 1BB
Ground Capacity: 3,200   **Seats:** 350   **Covered:** 1,000   **Clubhouse:** Yes   **Shop:** Yes
Previous Grounds: Manshead School 1981-94. Dunstable Cricket Club (Totternhoe) 1994-2009.
Record Attendance: Not known.

Nearest Railway Station Luton Leagrave - 4 miles
Bus Route 34, C & F77

AYLESBURY UNITED

Founded 1897

Nickname: The Ducks   **Club Colours:** Green & white

Club Contact Details
01296 487 367 (Office)   info@aylesburyunitedfc.co.uk

Previous Names: None
Previous Leagues: Post War: Spartan1908-51, Delphian 51-63, Athenian 63-76, Southern 76-88, 2004-10, Conf. 88-89, Isthmian 89-2004. Spartan South Midlands 2010-13.

10-11		11-12		12-13		13-14		14-15		15-16		16-17		17-18		18-19		19-20	
SSM P	6	SSM P	4	SSM P	2	SthC	12	SthC	13	SthC	19	SthC	13	Sth1E	13	SthC	15	SthC	n&v
FAC	1Q	FAC	Pr	FAC	Pr	FAC	2Q	FAC	P	FAC	P	FAC	P	FAC	3Q	FAC	1Qr	FAC	1Q
FAV	2P	FAV	2Q	FAV	1P	FAT	1Q	FAV	P	FAT	P	FAT	1Q	FAT	Pr	FAT	P	FAT	1Q

HONOURS / RECORDS
FA Comps: None
League: Spartan 1908-09, Western Division 28-29. Delphian 1953-54. Southern 1987-88.

County FA: Berks & Bucks Senior Cup 1913-14, 85-86, 96-97, 99-00. Berks & Bucks Senior Shield 2012-13.

Victory:	10-0 v Hornchurch & Upminster (H), Delphain League 17/04/1954
Defeat:	0-9 v Bishop's Stortford (A), Delphain League 08/10/1955
Goalscorer:	Cliff Hercules - 301 (1984-2002)
Appearances:	Cliff Hercules - 651+18 (1984-2002)

GROUND: Chesham United FC, The Meadow, Amy Lane, Chesham HP5 1NE
Ground Capacity: 5,000   **Seats:** 284   **Covered:** Yes   **Clubhouse:** Yes   **Shop:** No
Previous Grounds: Turnfurlong Lane. Buckingham Road >2006. Meadow View Park (Thame Utd) 2006-17.
Record Attendance: Turnfurlong Lane - 7,440 v Watford FAC 1st Rnd 1951-52. Buckingham Road - 6,031 v England 04/06/1988.

Nearest Railway Station Chesham underground - 0.7km
Bus Route The Wild Rover Pub - stop 250m away

BARTON ROVERS

Founded 1898

Nickname: Rovers   **Club Colours:** All royal blue

Club Contact Details
01582 707 772   bartonrovers@talktalk.net

Previous Names: None
Previous Leagues: Local village football leagues >1939. Luton & District 1947-54, South Midlands 1954-79, Isthmian 1979-2004

	10-11		11-12		12-13		13-14		14-15		15-16		16-17		17-18		18-19		19-20	
SthC	12		SthC	11		SthC	14		SthC	6		SthC	5		SthC	18		SthC	3		Sth1E	20		SthC	16		SthC	n&v
FAC	P		FAC	1Qr		FAC	1Q		FAC	2Qr		FAC	3Q		FAC	1Q		FAC	2Q		FAC	P		FAC	1Q		FAC	2Q
FAT	1Q		FAT	1Q		FAT	1Q		FAT	P		FAT	P		FAT	Pr		FAT	P		FAT	P		FAT	EP		FAT	2Q

HONOURS / RECORDS
FA Comps: None
League: South Midlands Division Two 1954-55, Division One 64-65, Premier 70-71, 71-72, 72-73, 74-75, 75-76, 76-77, 77-78, 78-79.

County FA: Bedfordshire Senior Cup 1971-72, 72-73, 80-81, 81-82, 89-90, 97-98, 98-99, 2014-15, Premier Cup 1995-96, Senior Challenge Cup 2015-16.
Goalscorer: Richard Camp - 152 (1989-98)
Appearances: Tony McNally - 598 (1988-2005)
Additional: Paid £1,000 to Hitchin Town for Bill Baldry 1980
Received £2,000 from AFC Wimbledon for Paul Barnes

GROUND: Luton Road, Barton-le-Clay, Bedford MK45 4LQ

Ground Capacity: 2,000   **Seats:** 160   **Covered:** 1,120   **Clubhouse:** Yes   **Shop:** Yes
Previous Grounds: None
Record Attendance: 1,900 v Nuneaton Borough - FA Cup 4th Qualifying Round 1976

Nearest Railway Station Harlington - 4.6km
Bus Route The Memorial - stop 200m away

BEDFORD TOWN

Founded 1989

Nickname: The Eagles   **Club Colours:** All blue

Club Contact Details
01234 831 558

Previous Names: Original Bedford Town founded in 1908 folded in 1982
Previous Leagues: South Midlands 1989-94, Isthmian 1994-2004, Southern 2004-06, Conference 2006-07

	10-11		11-12		12-13		13-14		14-15		15-16		16-17		17-18		18-19		19-20	
SthP	17		SthP	10		SthP	10		SthP	22		SthC	17		SthC	14		SthC	8		Sth1E	8		SthC	4		SthC	n&v
FAC	2Q		FAC	1Q		FAC	1Q		FAC	2Q		FAC	Pr		FAC	1Q		FAC	P		FAC	1Q		FAC	2Q		FAC	P
FAT	1Q		FAT	1Q		FAT	2Q		FAT	1Qr		FAT	3Qr		FAT	2Q		FAT	P		FAT	1Qr		FAT	2P		FAT	P

HONOURS / RECORDS
FA Comps: None
League: South Midlands Division One 1992-93, Premier Division 93-94. Isthmian Division Two 1998-99.

County FA: Bedfordshire Senior Cup 1994-95.

Defeat: 0-10 v Merthyr Tydfil, 1950-51, v Yeovil Town 1960-61
Goalscorer: Jason Reed. Joe Chamberlain scored 9 v Rushden Fosse, December 1911
Appearances: David Skinn
Victory: 9-0 v Weymouth, Southern League, 1954-55, v Poole 1958-59, v Ickleford, v Cardington

GROUND: The Eyrie, Meadow Lane, Cardington, Bedford MK44 3LW

Ground Capacity: 3,000   **Seats:** 300   **Covered:** 1,000   **Clubhouse:** Yes   **Shop:** Yes
Previous Grounds: Allen Park, Queens Park, Bedford Park Pitch 1991-93
Record Attendance: 3,000 v Peterborough United - Ground opening 06/08/1993. At Queens Park - 18,407 v Everton, FAC, 1965-66

Nearest Railway Station Bedford St Johns - 3.8km
Bus Route Meadow Lane - stop 150m away

SOUTHERN LEAGUE DIVISION ONE CENTRAL

BEDWORTH UNITED

Founded 1895

Nickname: Greenbacks   **Club Colours:** All green

Club Contact Details
02476 314 752   secretary@bedworthunitedfc.co.uk

Previous Names: Bedworth Town 1947-68
Previous Leagues: Birmingham Combination 1947-54, Birmingham/West Midlands 1954-72. Southern 1972-2013, 14-16. Northern Premier 2013-14, 16-18.

10-11		11-12		12-13		13-14		14-15		15-16		16-17		17-18		18-19		19-20	
SthC	15	SthC	3	SthP	21	NP1S	20	SthC	4	SthP	21	NP1S	11	NP1S	4	SthPC	22	SthC	n&v
FAC	2Q	FAC	1Q	FAC	2Q	FAC	P	FAC	2Qr	FAC	2Q	FAC	2Q	FAC	3Q	FAC	P	FAC	P
FAT	1Q	FAT	1Q	FAT	1Q	FAT	P	FAT	P	FAT	1Q	FAT	1Q	FAT	1Q	FAT	1Q	FAT	1Q

HONOURS / RECORDS
FA Comps: None
League: Birmingham Combination 1948-49, 49-50.

County FA: Birmingham Senior Cup 1978-79, 80-81, 81-82.

Goalscorer: Peter Spacey - 1949-69
Appearances: Peter Spacey - 1949-69
Additional: Paid £1,750 to Hinckley Town for Colin Taylor 1991-92
Received £30,000 from Plymouth Argyle for Richard Landon

GROUND: The Oval, Coventry Road, Bedworth CV12 8NN
Ground Capacity: 2,900   **Seats:** 300   **Covered:** 300   **Clubhouse:** Yes   **Shop:** Yes
Previous Grounds: British Queen Ground 1911-39
Record Attendance: 5,172 v Nuneaton Borough - Southern League Midland Division 23/02/1982

Nearest Railway Station Bedworth - 0.5km
Bus Route Bus stops at the Leisure Centre

BERKHAMSTED

Founded 2009

Nickname: Comrades   **Club Colours:** Yellow and blue

Club Contact Details
07525 872 914

Previous Names: None
Previous Leagues: Spartan South Midlands 2009-18.

10-11		11-12		12-13		13-14		14-15		15-16		16-17		17-18		18-19		19-20	
SSM1	1	SSM P	7	SSM P	11	SSM P	5	SSM P	6	SSM P	5	SSM P	8	SSM P	2	SthC	6	SthC	n&v
		FAC	1Qr	FAC	2Q	FAC	1Q	FAC	EP	FAC	P	FAC	EP	FAC	1Q	FAC	1Qr	FAC	1Q
FAV	2Q	FAV	2Q	FAV	2P	FAV	2P	FAV	1P	FAV	5P	FAV	4P	FAV	3P	FAT	1Q	FAT	1Q

HONOURS / RECORDS
FA Comps: None
League: Spartan South Midlands Division Two 2009-10, Division One 10-11.

County FA: Hertfordshire Charity Shield 2016-17

Victory: 12-1 v Stotfold, FA Cup Extra Preliminary Round, 05/08/2017
Defeat: 1-7 v Hanwell Town, Spartan South Midlands Premier Division, 2011-12

GROUND: Broadwater, Lower Kings Road, Berkhamsted HP4 2AL
Ground Capacity: 1,500   **Seats:** 170   **Covered:** 350   **Clubhouse:** Yes   **Shop:** Yes
Previous Grounds: None
Record Attendance: 366 v Slough Town, FA Cup First Qualifying Round, 02/09/2017

Nearest Railway Station Berkhamsted - 0.3km
Bus Route Castel Hill Avenue - stop 190m away

BIGGLESWADE FC

Nickname: FC   **Club Colours:** Green & white

Founded 2016

Club Contact Details

Previous Names: Based on Biggleswade Town's U18 side.
Previous Leagues: Spartan South Midlands 2016-19.

10-11	11-12	12-13	13-14	14-15	15-16	16-17	17-18	18-19	19-20
						SSM1 1	SSM P 5	SSM P 1	SthC n&v
							FAC EP	FAC P	FAC 2Q
						FAV 2P	FAV 4P	FAV 2P	FAT EPr

HONOURS / RECORDS

FA Comps: None
League: Spartan South Midlands Division One 2016-17, Premier Division 2018-19.

County FA: None

FA Cup	Second Qualifying Round 2019-20
FA Vase	Fourth Round Proper 2017-18
FA Tropjhy	Extra Preliminary Round 2019-20

GROUND: Biggleswade Town FC, Langford Road, Biggleswade SG18 9JT

Ground Capacity: 3,000   **Seats:** 300   **Covered:** Yes   **Clubhouse:** Yes   **Shop:**
Previous Grounds: None
Record Attendance: Not known

Nearest Railway Station Biggleswade - 1km
Bus Route Eldon Way - stop 260m away

COLESHILL TOWN

Nickname: The Coleman   **Club Colours:** White & blue

Founded 1894

Club Contact Details

01675 464 905   paul@unique-brass-finishes.co.uk

Previous Names: Coleshill & District. Coleshill FC. Coleshill United 1919.
Previous Leagues: Birmingham Youth & Old Boys 1906-07, 56-67. Sutton & Erdington 1907-08. Trent Valley 1912. Sutton & District 1919-56. Worcestershire Combination/Midland Combination 1967-2008. Midland Alliance 2008-2014.

10-11	11-12	12-13	13-14	14-15	15-16	16-17	17-18	18-19	19-20
MidAl 12	MidAl 16	MidAl 15	MidAl 4	MFLP 2	MFLP 5	MFLP 2	MFLP 2	SthC 9	SthC n&v
FAC 3Q	FAC Pr	FAC EPr	FAC EP	FAC 1Q	FAC 3Q	FAC 1Q	FAC 1Q	FAC EP	FAC P
FAV 1Q	FAV 1Q	FAV 1Q	FAV 4P	FAV 2P	FAV 4P	FAV SF	FAV 5P	FAT EP	FAT P

HONOURS / RECORDS

FA Comps: None
League: Sutton & District Division One 1952-53, 54-5. Birmingham Youth & Old Boys Suburban Division 1958-59. Midland Combination Division Two 1969-70, Premier 07-08.
County FA: Walsall Senior Cup 1982-83

Best FA Cup	Third Qualifying Round 2015-16
FA Vase	Semi Finals 2016-17
FA Trophy	Extra Preliminary Round 2018-19

GROUND: Pack Meadow, Packington Lane, Coleshill B46 3JJ

Ground Capacity: 2,000   **Seats:** 570   **Covered:**   **Clubhouse:** Yes   **Shop:**
Previous Grounds: Memorial Ground >1974
Record Attendance:

Nearest Railway Station Coleshill Parkway - 3.6km
Bus Route St Edmunds Primary School - 258m away

CORBY TOWN

Nickname: The Steelmen   **Club Colours:** Black and white

Founded 1948

Club Contact Details
01536 406 640   media@corbytownfc.co.uk

Previous Names: Stewart & Lloyds (Corby) > 1947
Previous Leagues: United Counties 1935-52. Midland 1952-58. Southern 1958-2009, 13-15. Football Conference 2009-13, 15-16. Northern Premier 2016-18.

10-11		11-12		12-13		13-14		14-15		15-16		16-17		17-18		18-19		19-20	
Conf N	13	Conf N	17	Conf N	20	SthP	11	SthP	1	Nat N	22	NP P	21	NP1S	9	SthC	3	SthC	n&v
FAC	1Pr	FAC	1P	FAC	4Q	FAC	1P	FAC	1Qr	FAC	2Qr	FAC	1Q	FAC	P	FAC	3Q	FAC	2Q
FAT	3Q	FAT	3Qr	FAT	2Pr	FAT	1Q	FAT	1Q	FAT	3Q	FAT	1Q	FAT	1Q	FAT	P	FAT	1Q

HONOURS / RECORDS

FA Comps: None

League: United Counties League 1950-51, 51-52. Southern League Premier Division 2008-09, 2014-15.

County FA: Northants Senior Cup 1950-51, 62-63, 75-76, 82-83, 2009-10, 12-13.

Goalscorer: David Holbauer - 159 (1984-95)
Appearances: Derek Walker - 601
Additional: Paid £2,700 to Barnet for Elwun Edwards 1981
                Received £20,000 from Oxford United for Matt Murphy 1993

GROUND: Steel Park, Jimmy Kane Way, Rockingham Road, Corby NN17 2FB

Ground Capacity: 3,893   **Seats:** 577   **Covered:** 1,575   **Clubhouse:** Yes   **Shop:** Yes
Previous Grounds: Occupation Road 1948-85.
Record Attendance: 2,240 v Watford - Friendly 1986-87

Nearest Railway Station Corby - 2.2km
Bus Route Dalton Road - stop 500m away

DAVENTRY TOWN

Nickname: Purple Army   **Club Colours:** Purple

Founded 1886

Club Contact Details
01327 311 239   club.secretary@dtfc.co.uk

Previous Names: None
Previous Leagues: Northampton Town (pre-1987), Northants Comb 1987-89, United Counties 1989-2010, 16-19. Southern 2010-15. Northern Premier 2015-16.

10-11		11-12		12-13		13-14		14-15		15-16		16-17		17-18		18-19		19-20	
SthC	2	SthC	16	SthC	8	SthC	4	SthC	19	NP1S	21	UCL 1	1	UCL P	10	UCL P	1	SthC	n&v
FAC	P	FAC	3Q	FAC	2Q	FAC	1P	FAC	1Q	FAC	P	FAC	EP	FAC	EP	FAC	1Q	FAC	EP
FAT	2Q	FAT	2Q	FAT	P	FAT	1P	FAT	P	FAT	P	FAV	1P	FAV	2Q	FAT	P	FAT	EP

HONOURS / RECORDS

FA Comps: None

League: Northants Combination Division One 1987-88, Premier 88-89.
          United Counties Division One 1989-90, 90-91, 2000-01, 2007-08, 16-17, Premier Division 2009-10, 18-19.
County FA: Northants Junior Cup 1930-31, 60-61.

FA Cup   First Round Proper 2013-14
FA Trophy   First Round Proper 2013-14
FA Vase   Fifth Round 2009-10

GROUND: Browns Road, Daventry, Northants NN11 4NS

Ground Capacity: 3,000   **Seats:** 250   **Covered:** 250   **Clubhouse:** Yes   **Shop:**
Previous Grounds: Hollow Ground.
Record Attendance: 850 v Utrecht (Holland) - 1989

Nearest Railway Station Northampton
Bus Route D3 towards Daventry from Rail Station approach road - alight at Cherwell, 7min walk from there.

DIDCOT TOWN

Founded 1907

Nickname: Railwaymen   **Club Colours:** Red & white

Club Contact Details
01235 813 138   info@didcottownfc.co.uk

Previous Names: Didcot Village and Northbourne Wanderers amalgamated to form Didcot Town in 1907.
Previous Leagues: Metropolitan 1957-63, Hellenic 1963-2006.

	10-11	11-12	12-13	13-14	14-15	15-16	16-17	17-18	18-19	19-20
	SthP 19	Sthsw 16	Sthsw 17	Sthsw 12	Sthsw 7	Sthsw 10	Sthsw 12	Sth1W 6	SthC 7	SthC n&v
FAC	3Q	1Qr	4Q	3Q	P	1P	P	1Q	2Qr	1Q
FAT	1Q	1P	3Q	Pr	1Pr	1Q	P	P	2Q	P

HONOURS / RECORDS

FA Comps: FA Vase 2004-05.

League: Hellenic Premier Division 1953-54, 2005-06, Division One 1976-77, 87-88.

County FA: Berks & Bucks Senior Trophy 2001-02, 02-03, 05-06.

Goalscorer:	Ian Concanon
Best FA Cup	First Round Proper 2015-16
FA Trophy	First Round Proper 2011-12, 14-15(r)

GROUND: Loop Meadow Stadium, Bowmont Water, Didcot OX11 7GA

Ground Capacity: 2,800   **Seats:** 350   **Covered:** 200   **Clubhouse:** Yes   **Shop:** Yes
Previous Grounds: Fleet Meadow. Edmonds Park. Cow Lane. Haydon Road. Station Road 1923-99.
Record Attendance: 2,707 - v Exeter City, FA Cup 1st Round, 08/11/2015

Nearest Railway Station Didcot Parkway - 0.4km
Bus Route X2 & X32

HALESOWEN TOWN

Founded 1873

Nickname: Yeltz   **Club Colours:** All blue

Club Contact Details
0121 629 0727   info@ht-fc.com

Previous Names: None
Previous Leagues: Birmingham & District/West Midlands 1892-1905, 06-11, 46-86, Birmingham Combination 1911-39. Southern 1986-12. Northern Premier 2012-18.

	10-11	11-12	12-13	13-14	14-15	15-16	16-17	17-18	18-19	19-20
	SthP 21	Sthsw 12	NP1S 7	NP1S 1	NP P 11	NP P 13	NP P 19	NP P 23	SthPC 21	SthC n&v
FAC		P	P	P	3Q	3Q	2Q	3Qr	2Q	2Q	3Q
FAT	1Q	P	2Q	1Q	1P	1Q	2Q	1Q	1Q	3Q

HONOURS / RECORDS

FA Comps: FA Vase 1984-85, 85-86.

League: West Midlands (Reg) 1946-47, 82-83, 83-84, 84-85, 85-86. Southern League Midland Division 1989-90, Western Division 2001-02. Northern Premier Division One South 2013-14.
County FA: Worcestershire Senior Cup 1951-52, 61-62, 2002-03, 04-05. Birmingham Senior Cup 1983-84, 97-98. Staffordshire Senior Cup 1988-89.

Victory:	13-1 v Coventry Amateurs - Birmingham Senior cup 1956
Defeat:	0-8 v Bilston - West Midlands League 07/04/1962
Goalscorer:	Paul Joinson - 369
Appearances:	Paul Joinson - 608
Additional:	Paid £7,250 to Gresley Rovers for Stuart Evans. Received £40,000 from Rushden & Diamonds for Jim Rodwell.

GROUND: The Grove, Old Hawne Lane, Halesowen B63 3TB

Ground Capacity: 3,150   **Seats:** 525   **Covered:** 930   **Clubhouse:** Yes   **Shop:** Yes
Previous Grounds: None
Record Attendance: 5,000 v Hendon - FA Cup 1st Round Proper 1954

Nearest Railway Station Old Hill - 1.8km
Bus Route Cranmoor Crescent - stop 50m away

KEMPSTON ROVERS

Founded 1884

Nickname: Walnut Boys   **Club Colours:** Red, white & black

Club Contact Details
01234 852 346   afckempston@yahoo.co.uk

Previous Names: Kempston Rovers 1884-2004. AFC Kempston Rovers 2004-16.
Previous Leagues: Bedford & District. Biggleswade & District. Bedfordshire & District County/South Midlands 1927-53.
United Counties 1957-2016.

10-11		11-12		12-13		13-14		14-15		15-16		16-17		17-18		18-19		19-20	
UCL 1	1	UCL P	10	UCL P	17	UCL P	12	UCL P	8	UCL P	1	SthC	6	Sth1E	7	SthC	13	SthC	n&v
FAC	1Q	FAC	EP	FAC	1Q	FAC	EP	FAC	P	FAC	P	FAC	2Qr	FAC	2Q	FAC	3Q	FAC	1Q
FAV	1Q	FAV	2Q	FAV	2Q	FAV	1Q	FAV	2P	FAV	2P	FAT	1Q	FAT	P	FAT	1Qr	FAT	EP

HONOURS / RECORDS

FA Comps: None

League: Bedford & District Division One 1907-08, 08-09, Division Two South 22-23, 33-34. Biggleswade & District 1910-11.
United Counties Premier Division 1957-58, 73-74, 2015-16, Division One 85-86, 2010-11, Division Two 1955-56,
County FA: Bedfordshire Senior Cup 1908-09, 37-38, 76-77, 91-92. Huntingdonshire Premier Cup 1999-2000, 00-01.

Best FA Cup   Fourth Qualifying Round 1978-79
FA Trophy   First Qualifying Round 2016-17, 18-19(r)
FA Vase   Fifth Round Proper 1974-75, 80-81

GROUND: Hillgrounds Leisure, Hillgrounds Road, Kempston, Bedford MK42 8SZ

Ground Capacity: 2,000   **Seats:** 100   **Covered:** 250   **Clubhouse:** Yes   **Shop:** Yes
Previous Grounds: None
Record Attendance: Not known

Nearest Railway Station Bedford - 1.3km
Bus Route Prentice Gardens - stop 100m away

KIDLINGTON

Founded 1909

Nickname: Greens   **Club Colours:** Green

Club Contact Details
01865 849 777

Previous Names: None.
Previous Leagues: Villages Leagues > 1945. Oxford City Junior 1945-51. Oxfordshire Senior 1951-54. Hellenic 1954-2016.

10-11		11-12		12-13		13-14		14-15		15-16		16-17		17-18		18-19		19-20	
Hel P	7	Hel P	18	Hel P	13	Hel P	6	Hel P	4	Hel P	1	SthC	12	Sth1W	12	SthC	18	SthC	n&v
FAC	EP	FAC	P	FAC	EPr	FAC	EPr	FAC	P	FAC	2Q	FAC	P	FAC	2Q	FAC	P	FAC	2Q
FAV	1P	FAV	2Q	FAV	3P	FAV	3P	FAV	1Q	FAV	QFr	FAT	P	FAT	1Q	FAT	P	FAT	EP

HONOURS / RECORDS

FA Comps: None

League: Oxfordshire Senior 1952-53. Hellenic Premier Division 2015-16.

County FA: Oxfordshire Intermediate Cup 1952-53, 69-70, 84-85.

Best FA Cup   Second Qualifying Round 2015-16, 17-18, 19-20
FA Trophy   First Qualifying Round 2017-18
FA Vase   Fifth Round 1976-77

GROUND: Yarnton Road, Kidlington, Oxford OX5 1AT

Ground Capacity: 2,086   **Seats:** Yes   **Covered:** Yes   **Clubhouse:** Yes   **Shop:** No
Previous Grounds: None
Record Attendance: 2,000 v Showbiz XI, 1973.

Nearest Railway Station Oxford Parkway - 1.9km
Bus Route Treeground Place - stop 100m away

NORTH LEIGH

Founded 1908

Nickname: The Millers   **Club Colours:** Yellow and black

Club Contact Details
01993 880 157

commercial@northleighfc.co.uk

Previous Names: None
Previous Leagues: Witney & District, Hellenic 1990-2008

	10-11	11-12	12-13	13-14	14-15	15-16	16-17	17-18	18-19	19-20
	Sthsw 6	Sthsw 6	Sthsw 9	Sthsw 7	Sthsw 8	Sthsw 9	Sthsw 6	Sth1W 18	SthC 17	SthC n&v
	FAC P	FAC 1Q	FAC 3Q	FAC 1Q	FAC P	FAC 3Q	FAC 4Q	FAC 1Qr	FAC P	FAC 2Q
	FAT 1Qr	FAT P	FAT 1Qr	FAT 1Q	FAT 1Q	FAT 1Q	FAT 1Pr	FAT P	FAT Pr	FAT EP

HONOURS / RECORDS

FA Comps: None

League: Witney & District Premier 1985-86, 86-87, 87-88, 88-89, 89-90. Hellenic Premier Division 2002-03, 07-08.

County FA: Oxfordshire Senior Cup 2011-12, 16-17.

Goalscorer:	P Coles
Appearances:	P King
Best FA Cup	Fourth Qualifying Round 2016-17
FA Trophy	First Round Proper 2016-17
FA Vase	Fourth Round Proper 2003-04

GROUND: Eynsham Hall Park, North Leigh, Witney, Oxon OX29 6SL

Ground Capacity: 1,500 **Seats:** 175 **Covered:** 200 **Clubhouse:** Yes **Shop:** No
Previous Grounds: None
Record Attendance: 426 v Newport County - FA Cup 3rd Qualifying Round 16/10/2004

Nearest Railway Station Combe - 3.3km
Bus Route 233

ST. NEOTS TOWN

Founded 1879

Nickname: Saints   **Club Colours:** Dark blue & light blue

Club Contact Details
01480 470 012

enquiries@stneotstownfc.co.uk

Previous Names: St Neots 1879-1924. St. Neots & District 1924-1957.
Previous Leagues: Biggleswade & Dist. Bedfordshire & Dist/South Midlands 1927-36, 46-49. United Co. 1936-39, 51-56, 66-69, 73-88, 94-2011. Metropolitan (Founder Members) 1949-51, 60-66. Central Alliance 1956-60. Eastern Co. 1969-73. Hunts Junior 1990-94.

	10-11	11-12	12-13	13-14	14-15	15-16	16-17	17-18	18-19	19-20
	UCL P 1	SthC 1	SthP 12	SthP 16	SthP 5	SthP 20	SthP 19	SthP 12	SthPC 20	SthC n&v
	FAC 1Q	FAC P	FAC 2Q	FAC 2Qr	FAC 1Qr	FAC 2Qr	FAC 1Qr	FAC 1Q	FAC 4Q	FAC 1Qr
	FAV 5P	FAT 2Q	FAT 1Q	FAT 2Q	FAT 3Qr	FAT 2Q	FAT 2Qr	FAT 2Q	FAT 2Q	FAT EP

HONOURS / RECORDS

FA Comps: None

League: South Midlands 1932-33. Metropolitan 1949-50. United Counties 1967-68, 2010-11, Division One 1994-95. Huntingdonshire 1990-91, 91-92, 92-93, 93-94. Southern Division One Central 2011-12.
County FA: Huntingdonshire Senior Cup x38 - Firstly in 1888-89 and most recently in 2017-18. Huntingdonshire Premier Cup 2001-02.
Misc: 105 points obtained in the 2010-11 season - a United Counties record.

In 1968-69 the club won the Huntingdonshire Senior Cup for the 12th consecutive time - an English record for Senior cups.

GROUND: Rowley Park, Kester Way, Cambridge Road, St Neots, PE19 6SN

Ground Capacity: 3,500 **Seats:** 250 **Covered:** 850 **Clubhouse:** Yes **Shop:** No
Previous Grounds: Town Common 1879-1899. Shortsands 1899-1988. Priory Park 1990-93. Old Rowley Park 1993-2008.
Record Attendance: 2,000 v Wisbech 1966

Nearest Railway Station St Neots - 06.km
Bus Route 150 & 66

THAME UNITED

Founded 1883

Nickname: Red Kites   **Club Colours:** Red & black

Club Contact Details
01844 214 401   jake@jcpc.org.uk

Previous Names: Thame F.C.
Previous Leagues: Oxon Senior. Hellenic 1959-88, 2006-17. South Midlands 1988-91. Isthmian 1991-2004. Southern 2004-06.

10-11		11-12		12-13		13-14		14-15		15-16		16-17		17-18		18-19		19-20	
Hel P	10	Hel P	9	Hel P	9	Hel P	10	Hel P	5	Hel P	6	Hel P	1	Sth1E	11	SthC	8	SthC	n&v
FAC	2Qr	FAC	2Q	FAC	P	FAC	EP	FAC	1Q	FAC	EPr	FAC	P	FAC	P	FAC	1Q	FAC	Pr
FAV	2Q	FAV	2Q	FAV	2P	FAV	2Q	FAV	2P	FAV	3P	FAV	1P	FAT	3Q	FAT	2Q	FAT	1Q

HONOURS / RECORDS
FA Comps: None
League: Hellenic 1961-62, 69-70, 2016-17, Division One East 2009-10. South Midlands League 1990-91. Isthmian Division Two 1994-95.
County FA: None

Appearances:	Steve Mayhew
Best FA Cup	Fourth Qualifying Round 2003-04, 04-05
FA Trophy	Third Round Proper 2002-03
FA Vase	Semi Finals 1998-99

GROUND: Meadow View Park, Tythrop Way, Thame, Oxon OX9 3RN

Ground Capacity: 3,000   **Seats:** Yes   **Covered:** Yes   **Clubhouse:** Yes   **Shop:**
Previous Grounds: Windmill Road 1883-2005. Aylesbury United FC 2005-06. AFC Wallingford 2006-11.
Record Attendance: 1,382 v Oxford United Jan 2011.

Nearest Railway Station Haddenham & Thame Parkway - 2.9km
Bus Route Queens Close - stop 350m away

WANTAGE TOWN

Founded 1892

Nickname: Alfredians   **Club Colours:** Green & white

Club Contact Details
01235 764 781 (Ground)   wantagetownnfc-secretary@outlook.com

Previous Names: None.
Previous Leagues: Swindon & District. North Berkshire. Reading & District. Hellenic > 2014, 17-19. Southern 2014-17.

10-11		11-12		12-13		13-14		14-15		15-16		16-17		17-18		18-19		19-20	
Hel P	1	Hel P	12	Hel P	2	Hel P	1	Sthsw	20	Sthsw	20	Sthsw	21	Hel P	4	Hel P	1	SthC	n&v
FAC	EP	FAC	P	FAC	1Q	FAC	P	FAC	1Qr	FAC	P	FAC	1Qr	FAC	P	FAC	2Qr	FAC	1Q
FAV	3P	FAV	3P	FAV	2P	FAV	2P	FAT	P	FAT	P	FAT	1Qr	FAV	2P	FAT	1Q	FAT	P

HONOURS / RECORDS
FA Comps: None
League: Swindon & District 1907-08, 33-34, 52-53, 55-56. North Berks Division One 1919-20, 21-22.
      Hellenic Division 1 East 1980-81, 03-04, Premier Division 2010-11, 13-14, 18-19.
County FA: Berks & Bucks Intermediate Cup 1954-55. Reading Senior Cup 1982-83.

FA Cup	Second Qualifying Round 2018-19
FA Trophy	First Qualifying Round 2016-17
FA Vase	Third Round Proper 1974-75, 83-84, 86-87, 2010-11, 11-12

GROUND: Alfredian Park, Manor Road, Wantage OX12 8DW

Ground Capacity: 1,500   **Seats:** 50   **Covered:** 300   **Clubhouse:** Yes   **Shop:**
Previous Grounds: Not known
Record Attendance: 550 v Oxford United, July 2003.

Nearest Railway Station Didcot Parkway
Bus Route From Parkway Station take the X32 Connector towards Wantage - alight at Market Place, 11min walk from there.

WELWYN GARDEN CITY

Founded 1921

Nickname: Citizens   **Club Colours:** Claret & sky blue

Club Contact Details
01707 329 358   welwyngardencityfc@gmail.com

Previous Names: Original club folded in 1935 and was reformed in 1937.

Previous Leagues: Mid-Herts 1922-26, 44-45. Beds & Dist 26-27. Spartan 27-35, 37-39, 45-51, 55-59. East, North & Mid-Herts Comb. 1939. Beds & Herts Comb 1940. London 51-55. Herts Senior Co 59-70. Greater London 70-71. Met London (FM) 71-73.

10-11		11-12		12-13		13-14		14-15		15-16		16-17		17-18		18-19		19-20	
SSM1	17	SSM1	17	SSM1	13	SSM1	4	SSM1	1	SSM P	4	SSM P	6	SSM P	1	SthC	14	SthC	n&v
FAC	EP							FAC	1Q	FAC	1Q	FAC	P	FAC	EP	FAC	P	FAC	P
FAV	2Q	FAV	1Q	FAV	1Q	FAV	3P	FAV	1P	FAV	1P	FAV	3P	FAV	3P	FAT	P	FAT	EP

HONOURS / RECORDS

FA Comps: None

League: South Midlands 1973-74, Division One 1981-82. Spartan South Midlands Division One 2014-15, Premier 17-18.

County FA: Hertfordshire FA Charity Shield 1927-28, 86-87, 87-88. Herts FA Senior Centenary Trophy 1984-85.

Best FA Cup	Third Qualifying Round 1998-99(r), 2005-06
FA Vase	Fourth Round Proper Replay 2005-06
FA Trophy	Preliminary Round 2018-19
Goalscorer:	Jason Caswell scored 51 goals during the 2014-15 season

GROUND: Herns Lane, Welwyn Garden City, Herts AL7 1TA

Ground Capacity: 2,500   **Seats:** Yes   **Covered:** Yes   **Clubhouse:** Yes   **Shop:**

Previous Grounds: Several before moving to Herns Lane in 1968

Record Attendance: Unknown

Nearest Railway Station Welwyn Garden City - 1.9km

Bus Route Hernes Way - stop 160m away

YAXLEY

Founded 1962

Nickname: The Cuckoos   **Club Colours:** Navy and orange

Club Contact Details
01733 244 928   info@yaxleyfc.com

Previous Names: Yaxley British Legion 1963-86. Coalite Yaxley 1986-90. Clarksteel Yaxley 1990.

Previous Leagues: Peterborough & District 1962-88. Eastern Counties (Founder Member) 1988-92. Huntingdonshire 1992-94. West Anglia 1994-95. United Counties 1995-2018.

10-11		11-12		12-13		13-14		14-15		15-16		16-17		17-18		18-19		19-20	
UCL P	16	UCL P	18	UCL P	12	UCL P	6	UCL P	4	UCL P	12	UCL P	3	UCL P	1	SthC	11	SthC	n&v
FAC	EP	FAC	EP	FAC	P	FAC	EP	FAC	EP	FAC	1Q	FAC	Pr	FAC	1Q	FAC	P	FAC	P
FAV	1Q	FAV	1P	FAV	1P	FAV	1Q	FAV	4P	FAV	3P	FAV	1P	FAV	3P	FAT	2Qr	FAT	P

HONOURS / RECORDS

FA Comps: None

League: Peterborough & District Division Three South 1968-69, Division Two 70-71, Premier 76-77, 83-84. West Anglia 1994-95. United Counties Division One 1996-97, Premier 2017-18.

County FA: Hunts Senior Cup 1974-75, 75-76, 82-83, 83-84, 98-99, 2003-04, 04-05, 07-08. Hunts Premier Cup 2004-05

Best FA Cup	Second Qualifying Round 2002-03, 06-07
FA Vase	Fourth Round Proper 2014-15
FA Trophy	Second Qualifying Round 2018-19(r)

GROUND: Leading Drove, Holme Road, Yaxley, Peterborough PE7 3NA

Ground Capacity: 1,500   **Seats:** 150   **Covered:** yes   **Clubhouse:** Yes   **Shop:** Yes

Previous Grounds: Middleton Road 1962-94

Record Attendance: 300v Wisbech Town, FA Vase Preliminary Round 1982-83

Nearest Railway Station Peterborough - 8 miles

Bus Route Churhc Street stop 300m away

AFC TOTTON

Founded 1886

Nickname: Stags   **Club Colours:** Blue and white

Club Contact Details
02380 868 981   enquiries@afctotton.com

Previous Names: Totton FC until merger with Totton Athletic in 1975
Previous Leagues: New Forest (Founder Members) 1904. Southampton Senior. Hampshire 1920-86, Wessex 1986-2008.

	10-11	11-12	12-13	13-14	14-15	15-16	16-17	17-18	18-19	19-20
	Sthsw 1	SthP 3	SthP 14	SthP 21	Sthsw 15	Sthsw 15	Sthsw 19	Sth1W 10	SthS 10	SthS n&v
FAC	P	2P	4Q	1Q	1Q	P	P	1Q	P	P
FAT	2Q	1Q	1P	1Q	1Q	P	Pr	Pr	2Q	2Q

HONOURS / RECORDS

FA Comps: None
League: New Forest 1905-06, 10-11, 13-14, 19-20, 25-26, 26-27, 47-48, 60-61, 61-62. Hampshire West 1924-25. Hampshire Division Two 1930-31, 66-67, Division One 81-82, 84-85. Wessex Premier Division 2007-08. Southern Division South & West 2010-11.
County FA: Hampshire Junior Cup 1913-14, Intermediate Cup 1946-47, 66-67, 81-82, 82-83, Senior Cup 2009-10, 10-11.

Appearances: Michael Gosney - 427
Best FA Cup Second Round Proper 2011-12
FA Trophy Third Qualifying Round 2006-07, 08-09(r)
FA Vase Runners-up 2008-09

GROUND: Testwood Stadium, Salisbury Road, Calmore, Totton SO40 2RW
Ground Capacity: 2,375 **Seats:** 500 **Covered:** 500 **Clubhouse:** Yes **Shop:** Yes
Previous Grounds: South Testwood Park 1886-1933.
Record Attendance: 2,315 v Bradford Park Avenue, 12/11/2011.

Nearest Railway Station Totton - 2.9km
Bus Route Cooks Lane - stop 300m away

BARNSTAPLE TOWN

Founded 1904

Nickname: Barum   **Club Colours:** Red

Club Contact Details
01271 343 469

Previous Names: Pilton Yeo Vale
Previous Leagues: North Devon, Devon & Exeter, South Western. Western >2016.

	10-11	11-12	12-13	13-14	14-15	15-16	16-17	17-18	18-19	19-20
	WestP 11	WestP 15	WestP 20	West1 3	West1 1	WestP 2	Sthsw 17	Sth1W 21	SthS 19	SthS n&v
FAC	EP	EP	EP	EP	EP	1Q	1Q	1Q	P	EP
FAV	2Q	FAV 3P	FAV 1P	FAV 2P	FAV 2Q	FAV 2P	FAT 1Q	FAT 1Q	FAT P	FAT P

HONOURS / RECORDS

FA Comps: None
League: North Devon 1904-05, 08-09. Exeter & District 1946-47. Western 1952-53, 79-80, Division One 1993-94, 2014-15.
County FA: Devon Pro Cup 1952-53, 62-63, 64-65, 67-68, 69-70, 71-72, 72-73, 74-75, 76-77, 77-78, 78-79, 79-80, 80-81. Devon St Lukes Cup 1987-88. Devon Senior Cup 1992-93.
Victory: 12-1 v Tavistock, F.A. Cup 3rd Qualifying Round 1954.
Defeat: 0-11 v Odd Down, Western, 25/04/2013.
Appearances: Ian Pope
Additional: Paid £4,000 to Hungerford Town for Joe Scott.
Received £6,000 from Bristol City for Ian Doyle.

GROUND: Mill Road, Barnstaple, North Devon EX31 1JQ
Ground Capacity: 2,000 **Seats:** 250 **Covered:** 1,000 **Clubhouse:** Yes **Shop:** Yes
Previous Grounds: None
Record Attendance: 6,200 v Bournemouth & Boscombe Athletic, FA Cup 1st Round, 1951-52.

Nearest Railway Station Barnstaple - 1km
Bus Route 21, 21A & 5B

BASINGSTOKE TOWN

Nickname: Dragons   **Club Colours:** All blue

Founded 1896

Club Contact Details

01256 327 575   admin@basingstoketown.net

Previous Names: The club was formed by the merger of Aldworth United and Basingstoke Albion in 1896.
Previous Leagues: Hampshire 1900-40, 45-71, Southern 1971-87, Isthmian 1987-2004. Conference 2004-16.

10-11	11-12	12-13	13-14	14-15	15-16	16-17	17-18	18-19	19-20
Conf S 13	Conf S 5	Conf S 14	Conf S 14	Conf S 3	Nat S 22	SthP 12	SthP 10	SthPS 20	SthS n&v
FAC 4Q	FAC 1P	FAC 3Q	FAC 2Q	FAC 1Pr	FAC 1P	FAC 2Q	FAC 1Qr	FAC 2Q	FAC P
FAT 1P	FAT 2P	FAT 3Q	FAT 1Pr	FAT 1Pr	FAT 3Q	FAT 3Q	FAT 1Q	FAT 3Q	FAT 1Q

HONOURS / RECORDS

FA Comps: None

League: Hampshire North Division 1911-12, 19-20, Division One 1967-68, 69-70, 70-71.
         Southern Southern Division 1984-85.
County FA: Hampshire Senior Cup 1970-71, 89-90, 95-96, 96-97, 2007-08, 13-14, 16-17.

Victory:	10-1 v Chichester City (H) - FA Cup 1st Qualifying Round 1976
Defeat:	0-8 v Aylesbury United - Southern League April 1979
Goalscorer:	Paul Coombs - 159 (1991-99)
Appearances:	Billy Coomb
Additional:	Paid £4,750 to Gosport Borough for Steve Ingham

GROUND: The Ark Cancer Charity Stadium, Western Way, Basingstoke RG22 6EZ

Ground Capacity: 2,402   **Seats:** 651   **Covered:** 2,000   **Clubhouse:** Yes   **Shop:** Yes
Previous Grounds: Castle Field 1896-1947
Record Attendance: 5,085 v Wycombe Wanderers - FA Cup 1st Round replay 1997-98

Nearest Railway Station Basingstoke - 2.6km
Bus Route Mansfield Road - 50m away

BIDEFORD

Nickname: The Robins   **Club Colours:** All red

Founded 1947

Club Contact Details

01237 474 974   enquiries@bidefordafc.com

Previous Names: Bideford Town
Previous Leagues: Devon & Exeter 1947-49, Western 1949-72, 75-2010, Southern 1972-75

10-11	11-12	12-13	13-14	14-15	15-16	16-17	17-18	18-19	19-20
Sthsw 10	Sthsw 1	SthP 20	SthP 8	SthP 15	SthP 23	Sthsw 10	Sth1W 8	SthS 9	SthS n&v
FAC P	FAC 2Q	FAC 2Q	FAC 2Q	FAC 2Q	FAC 2Q	FAC 1Q	FAC 3Q	FAC Pr	FAC 1Q
FAT 3Q	FAT 1Q	FAT 1Q	FAT 2Q	FAT 1Qr	FAT 3Q	FAT P	FAT P	FAT P	FAT P

HONOURS / RECORDS

FA Comps: None

League: Western 1963-64, 70-71, 71-72, 81-82, 82-83, 2001-02, 03-04, 04-05, 05-06, 09-10, Division Two 1951-52, Division Three
         1949-50. Southern Division One South & West 2011-12.
County FA: Devon Pro Cup 1960-61, 61-62, 63-64, 65-66, 66-67, 68-69, 70-71. Devon Senior Cup 1979-80.
         Devon St Lukes Bowl 1981-82, 83-84, 85-86, 95-96, 2009-10.

Victory:	16-1 v Soundwell, 1950-51
Defeat:	1-10 v Taunton Town, 1998-99
Goalscorer:	Tommy Robinson - 259
Appearances:	Derek May - 647

GROUND: The Sports Ground, Kingsley Road, Bideford EX39 2NG

Ground Capacity: 4,000   **Seats:** 375   **Covered:** 1,000   **Clubhouse:** Yes   **Shop:**
Previous Grounds: None
Record Attendance: 5,975 v Gloucester City - FA Cup 4th Qualifying Round 1949

Nearest Railway Station Barnstaple - 9 miles
Bus Route The Dairy - stop 100m away

BRISTOL MANOR FARM

Founded 1960

Nickname: The Farm   **Club Colours:** Red & black

Club Contact Details
0117 968 3571

Previous Names: None
Previous Leagues: Bristol Suburban 1964-69. Somerset Senior 1969-77. Western 1977-2017.

10-11		11-12		12-13		13-14		14-15		15-16		16-17		17-18		18-19		19-20	
WestP	7	WestP	8	WestP	18	WestP	2	WestP	4	WestP	3	WestP	1	Sth1W	9	SthS	15	SthS	n&v
FAC	2Qr	FAC	EPr	FAC	EP	FAC	2Qr	FAC	P	FAC	1Q	FAC	EPr	FAC	P	FAC	3Qr	FAC	3Qr
FAV	2P	FAV	2Q	FAV	2Q	FAV	1P	FAV	2P	FAV	QF	FAV	5P	FAT	1Q	FAT	1Q	FAT	P

HONOURS / RECORDS

FA Comps: None
League: Western Division One 1982-83, Premier 2016-17.

County FA: Gloucestershire Challenge Trophy 1987-88, 2015-16. Gloucestershire Amateur Cup 1989-90.

Appearances: M. Baird
Victory: 10-0 v Devizes Town, Les Phillips Cup, 19/11/2016.
Defeat: 0-11 v Bristol City, Community Match, 09/07/2017

GROUND: The Creek, Portway, Sea Mills, Bristol BS9 2HS

Ground Capacity: 1,700   **Seats:** 200   **Covered:** 350   **Clubhouse:** Yes   **Shop:** No
Previous Grounds: None
Record Attendance: 1,417 v Bristol City, pre-season friendly, 09/07/2017.

Nearest Railway Station Sea Mills - 0.3km
Bus Route Riverleaze - stop 50m away

CINDERFORD TOWN

Founded 1922

Nickname: The Foresters   **Club Colours:** Black and white

Club Contact Details
01594 824 080

Previous Names: None
Previous Leagues: Gloucestershire Northern Senior 1922-39, 60-62, Western 1946-59, Warwickshire Combination 1963-64, West Midlands 1965-69, Gloucestershire Co. 1970-73, 85-89, Midland Comb. 1974-84, Hellenic 1990-95

10-11		11-12		12-13		13-14		14-15		15-16		16-17		17-18		18-19		19-20	
Sthsw	12	Sthsw	10	Sthsw	10	Sthsw	15	Sthsw	9	Sthsw	1	SthP	24	Sth1W	13	SthS	5	SthS	n&v
FAC	3Q	FAC	2Q	FAC	1Qr	FAC	P	FAC	P	FAC	1Q	FAC	1Q	FAC	3Q	FAC	2Q	FAC	2Q
FAT	2Q	FAT	P	FAT	1Q	FAT	P	FAT	Pr	FAT	P	FAT	1Q	FAT	P	FAT	1Qr	FAT	3Q

HONOURS / RECORDS

FA Comps: None
League: Western Division Two 1956-57. Warwickshire Combination Western Division 1964-65. Hellenic Premier Division 1994-95. Southern Division One South & West 2015-16.
County FA: Gloucestershire Senior Amateur Cup North x6. Gloucestershire Junior Cup North 1980-81. Gloucestershire Senior Cup 2000-01.
Victory: 13-0 v Cam Mills - 1938-39
Defeat: 0-10 v Sutton Coldfield - 1978-79
Appearances: Russel Bowles - 528

GROUND: The Causeway, Edge Hills Road, Cinderford, Gloucestershire GL14 2QH

Ground Capacity: 2,200   **Seats:** 250   **Covered:** 1,000   **Clubhouse:** Yes   **Shop:** Yes
Previous Grounds: Mousel Lane, Royal Oak
Record Attendance: 4,850 v Minehead - Western League 1955-56

Nearest Railway Station Gloucester - 15 miles
Bus Route Forest High School - stop 200m away

CIRENCESTER TOWN

Founded 1889

Nickname: Centurions   **Club Colours:** Red & black

Club Contact Details
01285 654 543   enquiries@cirentownfc.com

Previous Names: None
Previous Leagues: Cheltenham 1889-1935. Gloucestershire Northern Senior 1935-68. Gloucestershire County (Founder Members) 1968-69. Hellenic 1969-96.

10-11		11-12		12-13		13-14		14-15		15-16		16-17		17-18		18-19		19-20	
SthP	13	SthP	22	Sthsw	11	Sthsw	1	SthP	8	SthP	15	SthP	22	Sth1W	7	SthS	2	SthS	n&v
FAC	1Qr	FAC	1Q	FAC	P	FAC	3Q	FAC	1Qr	FAC	2Q	FAC	2Q	FAC	P	FAC	3Q	FAC	2Q
FAT	1Pr	FAT	2Q	FAT	P	FAT	1Q	FAT	1Q	FAT	1Pr	FAT	1Q	FAT	1Qr	FAT	P	FAT	P

HONOURS / RECORDS
FA Comps: None
League: Cheltenham Division One 1927-28, 29-30, 48-49, 54-55, 55-56. Gloucestershire Northern Senior 1966-67, 67-68. Hellenic Division One 1973-74, Premier Division 95-96. Southern Division One South & West 2013-14.
County FA: Gloucestershire Senior Amateur Cup 1989-90. Gloucestershire Senior Challenge Cup 1995-96, 2015-16.

Misc: Paid £4,000 to Gloucester City for Lee Smith
Best FA Cup   Fourth Qualifying Round 2001-02, 03-04
FA Trophy   Third Round Proper 2002-03
FA Vase   Third Round Proper 1975-76, 76-77

GROUND: The Corinium Stadium, Kingshill Lane, Cirencester GL7 1HS

Ground Capacity: 2,564 **Seats:** 550   **Covered:** 1,250   **Clubhouse:** Yes   **Shop:** Yes
Previous Grounds: Smithfield Stadium >2002.
Record Attendance: 2,600 v Fareham Town - 1969

Nearest Railway Station Kemble - 6 miles
Bus Route Kingshill School - stop 150m away

EVESHAM UNITED

Founded 1945

Nickname: The Robins   **Club Colours:** Red and white

Club Contact Details
01386 442 303   eveshamunitedsecretary@hotmail.com

Previous Names: None
Previous Leagues: Worcester, Birmingham Combination, Midland Combination 1951-55, 65-92, West Midlands (Regional) 1955-62

10-11		11-12		12-13		13-14		14-15		15-16		16-17		17-18		18-19		19-20	
SthP	12	SthP	20	Sthsw	14	Sthsw	16	Sthsw	2	Sthsw	6	Sthsw	5	Sth1W	4	SthS	7	SthS	n&v
FAC	1Q	FAC	3Q	FAC	P	FAC	1Q	FAC	4Q	FAC	P	FAC	1Qr	FAC	Pr	FAC	P	FAC	1Q
FAT	2Q	FAT	1Qr	FAT	P	FAT	P	FAT	1Q	FAT	1Qr	FAT	2Q	FAT	P	FAT	EP	FAT	P

HONOURS / RECORDS
FA Comps: None
League: Midland Combination Premier Division 1991-92, Division One 1965-66, 67-68, 68-69. Southern Division One Midlands 2007-08.
County FA: Worcestershire Senior Urn 1976-77, 77-78, Senior Cup 2008-09, 17-18.

Victory: 11-3 v West Heath United
Defeat: 1-8 v Ilkeston Town
Goalscorer: Sid Brain
Appearances: Rob Candy
Additional: Paid £1,500 to Hayes for Colin Day 1992. Received £5,000 from Cheltenham Town for Simon Brain.

GROUND: Jubilee Stadium, Cheltenham Road, Evesham WR11 2LZ

Ground Capacity: 3,000 **Seats:** Yes   **Covered:** Yes   **Clubhouse:** Yes   **Shop:** Yes
Previous Grounds: The Crown Meadow > 1968, Common Reed 1968-2006. Ground shared with Worcester City 2006-12.
Record Attendance: 2,338 v West Bromwich Albion - Friendly 18/07/1992

Nearest Railway Station Evesham - 2.9km
Bus Route Lavender Walk - stop 400m away

FROME TOWN

Founded 1904

Nickname: The Robins   **Club Colours:** Red

Club Contact Details
01373 464 087   gary@frometownfc.co.uk

Previous Names: None
Previous Leagues: Wiltshire Premier 1904, Somerset Senior 1906-19, Western 1919, 63-2009

10-11	11-12	12-13	13-14	14-15	15-16	16-17	17-18	18-19	19-20
Sthsw 4	SthP 12	SthP 18	SthP 14	SthP 20	SthP 16	SthP 8	SthP 13	SthPS 21	SthS n&v
FAC 2Q	FAC 2Qr	FAC 2Q	FAC 1Qr	FAC 3Qr	FAC 1Qr	FAC 1Q	FAC 2Q	FAC 1Qr	FAC P
FAT 1Q	FAT 1Q	FAT 1Q	FAT 1Qr	FAT 1Q	FAT 3Qr	FAT 3Q	FAT 1Q	FAT 1Q	FAT 2Q

HONOURS / RECORDS
FA Comps: None
League: Somerset County 1906-07, 08-09, 10-11.
Western Division Two 1919-20, Division One 2001-02, Premier Division 1978-79.
County FA: Somerset Senior Cup 1932-33, 33-34, 50-51 Somerset Premier Cup 1966-67, 68-69 (shared), 82-83, 2008-09.

Victory: 7-2 v kings Langley (A), Southern Premier, 09/12/2017
Defeat: 0-7 v Gosport Borough (A), Southern Premier, 21/04/2018

GROUND: Badgers Hill, Berkley Road, Frome BA11 2EH

Ground Capacity: 2,331   **Seats:** 250   **Covered:** Yes   **Clubhouse:** Yes   **Shop:** Yes
Previous Grounds: None
Record Attendance: 8,000 v Leyton Orient - FA Cup 1st Round 1958

Nearest Railway Station Frome - 0.9km
Bus Route Bus stops outside the ground

HIGHWORTH TOWN

Founded 1893

Nickname: Worthians   **Club Colours:** Red and black

Club Contact Details
01793 766 263

Previous Names: None.
Previous Leagues: Cirencester & District. Swindon & District. Wiltshire Combination. Hellenic >2018.

10-11	11-12	12-13	13-14	14-15	15-16	16-17	17-18	18-19	19-20
Hel P 4	Hel P 6	Hel P 16	Hel P 11	Hel P 7	Hel P 7	Hel P 6	Hel P 3	SthS 14	SthS n&v
FAC 1Qr	FAC EP	FAC EP	FAC EP	FAC P	FAC P	FAC 2Q	FAC P	FAC EPr	FAC 2Q
FAV 1Q	FAV 2Pr	FAV 1Qr	FAV 1Q	FAV SF	FAV 3P	FAV 2P	FAV 1P	FAT EP	FAT Pr

HONOURS / RECORDS
FA Comps: None
League: Cirencester & District Division Two 1931-32. Swindon & District Division Three 1933-34, 54-55, Two 1955-56, One 1956-57, Premier 57-58, 58-59, 60-61, 61-62, 62-63, 63-64, 65-66, 66-67, 67-68. Hellenic Premier 2004-05.
County FA: Wiltshire Senior Cup 1963-64, 72-73, 95-96, 97-98.

Goalscorer: Kevin Higgs
Appearances: Rod Haines

GROUND: Elms Recreation Ground, Highworth SN6 7DD

Ground Capacity: 1,500   **Seats:** 150   **Covered:** 250   **Clubhouse:** Yes   **Shop:** No
Previous Grounds: Unknown
Record Attendance: 2,000 v QPR, opening of floodlights.

Nearest Railway Station Swindon - 7 miles
Bus Route Swindon Street stop - 90m away

LARKHALL ATHLETIC

Founded 1914

Nickname: Larks   **Club Colours:** All royal blue

Club Contact Details
01225 334 952

Previous Names: None
Previous Leagues: Somerset Senior. Western 1976-2014.

10-11		11-12		12-13		13-14		14-15		15-16		16-17		17-18		18-19		19-20	
WestP	1	WestP	3	WestP	5	WestP	1	Sthsw	5	Sthsw	11	Sthsw	13	Sth1W	15	SthS	13	SthS	n&v
FAC	P	FAC	1Q	FAC	1Qr	FAC	1Q	FAC	2Qr	FAC	2Qr	FAC	P	FAC	P	FAC	P	FAC	P
FAV	1Q	FAV	5P	FAV	5P	FAV	5P	FAT	P	FAT	1Q	FAT	P	FAT	1Q	FAT	Pr	FAT	1Qr

HONOURS / RECORDS

FA Comps: None

League: Western Division One 1988-89, 08-09, Premier Division 2010-11, 13-14.

County FA: Somerset Junior Cup 1962-63, Senior Cup 1975-76, 2003-04.

Victory:	8-0 v Oldland Abbotonians, 2007
Defeat:	1-6 v Exmouth Town, 2001
Goalscorer:	Ben Highmore scored 52 goals during the 2008-09 season.
Appearances:	Luke Scott - 600+ (as at July 2014)

GROUND: Plain Ham, Charlcombe Lane, Larkhall, Bath BA1 8DJ

Ground Capacity: 1,429   **Seats:** Yes   **Covered:** 50   **Clubhouse:** Yes   **Shop:** No
Previous Grounds: None
Record Attendance: 280 v Tunbridge Wells, FA Vase, Feb 2013

Nearest Railway Station Bath Spa - 2.8km
Bus Route Charlcombe Lane - stop 200m away

MANGOTSFIELD UNITED

Founded 1950

Nickname: The Field   **Club Colours:** Claret and sky blue

Club Contact Details
0117 956 0119   davidj693@hotmail.co.uk

Previous Names: None
Previous Leagues: Bristol & District 1950-67. Avon Premier Combination 1967-72. Western 1972-2000.

10-11		11-12		12-13		13-14		14-15		15-16		16-17		17-18		18-19		19-20	
Sthsw	3	Sthsw	14	Sthsw	13	Sthsw	11	Sthsw	10	Sthsw	14	Sthsw	8	Sth1W	16	SthS	16	SthS	n&v
FAC	2Q	FAC	P	FAC	1Q	FAC	2Q	FAC	1Q	FAC	1Q	FAC	P	FAC	P	FAC	P	FAC	1Q
FAT	Pr	FAT	2Qr	FAT	Pr	FAT	2Q	FAT	2Q	FAT	2Q	FAT	P	FAT	P	FAT	1Qr	FAT	EP

HONOURS / RECORDS

FA Comps: None

League: Bristol & District Div.7 1951-52, Div.6 52-53, Div.4 53-54, Div.3 54-55, Div.2 55-56, Premier Comb Div.1 68-69. Somerset Senior Div.3 74-75, Div.2 75-76, 97-98, Prem 2004-05. Western 1990-91. Southern Division One West 2004-05.
County FA: Gloucestershire Senior Cup 1968-69, 75-76, 2002-03, 12-13. Gloucestershire F.A. Trophy x6.
     Somerset Premier Cup 1987-88.

Victory:	17-0 v Hanham Sports (H) - 1953 Bristol & District League
Defeat:	3-13 v Bristol City United - Bristol & District League Division One
Goalscorer:	John Hill. **Appearances:** John Hill - 600+
Misc:	In the last 10 matches of the 2003/04 season, the club went 738 minutes (just over 8 games) without scoring and then finished the campaign with 13 goals in the last two, which included a 9-0 away win.

GROUND: Cossham Street, Mangotsfield, Bristol BS16 9EN

Ground Capacity: 3,038   **Seats:** 300   **Covered:** 800   **Clubhouse:** Yes   **Shop:** Yes
Previous Grounds: None
Record Attendance: 1,253 v Bath City - F.A. Cup 1974

Nearest Railway Station Bristol Parkway - 5 miles. Temple Meads - 7 miles.
Bus Route Cossham Street - stop 50m away

MELKSHAM TOWN

Founded 1876

Nickname: Town   **Club Colours:** Yellow and black

Club Contact Details
01225 302 977

Previous Names: Melksham FC 1876-1951.
Previous Leagues: Wiltshire (Founder Members) 1894-1974. Western 1974-2018.

10-11		11-12		12-13		13-14		14-15		15-16		16-17		17-18		18-19		19-20	
WestP	8	West1	2	WestP	13	WestP	7	WestP	1	WestP	5	WestP	3	WestP	2	SthS	12	SthS	n&v
FAC	EP	FAC	P	FAC	1Q	FAC	EPr	FAC	EPr	FAC	EPr	FAC	EP	FAC	EP	FAC	1Q	FAC	Pr
FAV	2P	FAV	2P	FAV	2Q	FAV	2Q	FAV	4P	FAV	2P	FAV	4Pr	FAV	QF	FAT	2Q	FAT	2Q

HONOURS / RECORDS

FA Comps: None

League: Wiltshire 1903-04, Premier 1993-94.
Western Division One 1979-80, 96-97, Premier Division 2014-15.
County FA: Wiltshire Senior Cup 1904-05, 69-70, 77-78, 2002-03, 07-08, 12-13, 13-14, 15-16.

Best FA Cup   Third Qualifying Round 1954-55, 57-58
FA Trophy   Second Qualifying Round 1982-83, 84085, 85-86, 87-87, 87-88, 2018-19
FA Vase   Quarter Finals 2017-18
Goalscorer: Gareth Lewis scored 72 goals during the 1968-69 season

---

GROUND: Oakfield Stadium, Eastern Way, Melksham SN12 7GU

Ground Capacity: 3,000   **Seats:** Yes   **Covered:** Yes   **Clubhouse:** Yes   **Shop:**
Previous Grounds: Challymead Common 1876-83. Old Bear Field 1883-1920. Conigre 1920-2017.
Record Attendance: 2,821 v Trowbridge Town, FA Cup 1957-58.

Nearest Railway Station Melksham - 2.7km
Bus Route New Road - stop 300m away

MONEYFIELDS

Founded 1987

Nickname: Moneys   **Club Colours:** Yellow and navy

Club Contact Details
02392 665 260   kat.close@ntlworld.com

Previous Names: Portsmouth Civil Service 1987-94.
Previous Leagues: Portsmouth 1987-91. Hampshire 1991-98. Wessex 1998-2017.

10-11		11-12		12-13		13-14		14-15		15-16		16-17		17-18		18-19		19-20	
WexP	7	WexP	4	WexP	4	WexP	9	WexP	4	WexP	8	WexP	2	Sth1E	10	SthS	4	SthS	n&v
FAC	P	FAC	1Qr	FAC	P	FAC	1Q	FAC	EP	FAC	P	FAC	1Q	FAC	1Q	FAC	3Q	FAC	2Q
FAV	3P	FAV	2Q	FAV	2P	FAV	3P	FAV	2Q	FAV	4P	FAV	2P	FAT	2Qr	FAT	P	FAT	EP

HONOURS / RECORDS

FA Comps: None

League: Portsmouth Premier 1990-91.
Hampshire Division Three 1991-92, Division Two 1992-93, Division One 1996-97.
County FA: Hampshire Intermediate 1991-92, 92-93.

Victory: 9-0 v Blackfield & Langley 01-02.
Goalscorer: Lee Mould - 86
Appearances: Matt Lafferty - 229

GROUND: Moneyfields Sports Ground, Moneyfield Ave, Copnor, Portsmouth PO3 6LA

Ground Capacity: 1,500   **Seats:** 150   **Covered:** 150   **Clubhouse:** Yes   **Shop:** Yes
Previous Grounds: Copnor Road 1987-94.
Record Attendance: 250 v Fareham, Wessex Division One 2005-06

Nearest Railway Station Hilsea - 1.6km
Bus Route Chichester Road - stop 400m away

PAULTON ROVERS

Founded 1881

Nickname: The Robins or Rovers   **Club Colours:** Claret and white

Club Contact Details
01761 412 907

Previous Names: None
Previous Leagues: Wiltshire Premier, Somerset Senior, Western

	10-11	11-12	12-13	13-14	14-15	15-16	16-17	17-18	18-19	19-20
	Sthsw 11	Sthsw 7	Sthsw 5	Sthsw 4	SthP 10	SthP 24	Sthsw 15	Sth1W 19	SthS 17	SthS n&v
FAC	2Q	P	Pr	P	2Qr	2Q	1Q	4Q	1Qr	P
FAT	2Q	2Q	Pr	1Q	2Q	1Q	P	2Q	P	P

HONOURS / RECORDS
FA Comps: None

League: None

County FA: Somerset Junior Cup 1898-99, Senior Cup x12 - Firstly in 1900-01 and most recently in 1974-75, Premier Cup 2012-13.

Goalscorer:	Graham Colbourne
Appearances:	Steve Tovey
Best FA Cup	First Round Proper 2009-10
FA Trophy	First Round Proper 2004-05
FA Vase	Fifth Round Proper 1989-90

GROUND: Athletic Ground, Winterfield Road, Paulton, Bristol BS39 7RF

Ground Capacity: 2,500   **Seats:** 253   **Covered:** 2,500   **Clubhouse:** Yes   **Shop:** Yes
Previous Grounds: Chapel Field, Cricket Ground, Recreation Ground
Record Attendance: 2,000 v Crewe Alexandra - FA Cup 1906-07

Nearest Railway Station Bath Spa - 13 miles
Bus Route Alexandra Park - stop 150m away

SHOLING

Founded 1884

Nickname: The Boatmen   **Club Colours:** Red & white stripes

Club Contact Details
07496 804 555   secretary@sholingfc.com

Previous Names: Woolston Works, Thornycrofts (Woolston) 1918-52, Vospers 1960-2003, Vosper Thorneycroft FC/VTFC 2003-10
Previous Leagues: Hampshire 1991-2004, Wessex 2004-09, 2013-14, 15-19. Southern 2009-13, 2014-15.

	10-11	11-12	12-13	13-14	14-15	15-16	16-17	17-18	18-19	19-20
	Sthsw 2	Sthsw 4	Sthsw 7	WexP 1	Sthsw 17	WexP 2	WexP 5	WexP 3	WexP 1	SthS n&v
FAC	2Qr	2Q	3Q	2Q	1Q	P	1Q	EP	2Qr	2Q
FAT	P	1Q	3Q	FAV F	FAV 3Q	FAV 2P	FAV 1P	FAV 3P	FAT 3Q	FAT 1P

HONOURS / RECORDS
FA Comps: FA Vase 2013-14.

League: Hampshire Premier Division 2000-01, 03-04.
Wessex Premier 2013-14, 18-19.
County FA: Southampton Senior Cup 2001-02, 03-04, 05-06, 06-07, 07-08, 09-10, 13-14, 16-17

Goalscorer:	George Diaper - 100+
FA Cup	Third Qualifying Round 2012-13
FA Trophy	First Round Proper 2019-20

GROUND: Portsmouth Road, Sholing, SO19 9PW

Ground Capacity: 1,400   **Seats:** 150   **Covered:** 250   **Clubhouse:** Yes   **Shop:**
Previous Grounds: Not known
Record Attendance: 150

Nearest Railway Station Netley - 1.9km
Bus Route Bus stop outside the ground.

SLIMBRIDGE

Nickname: The Swans   **Club Colours:** All blue

Founded 1899

Club Contact Details
01453 899 982   info@slimbridgeafc.co.uk

Previous Names: None
Previous Leagues: Stroud & District. Gloucester Northern. Gloucestershire County >2009. Hellenic 2009-2013. Western 2013-15.

10-11		11-12		12-13		13-14		14-15		15-16		16-17		17-18		18-19		19-20	
Hel P	5	Hel P	5	Hel P	6	WestP	16	WestP	3	Sthsw	18	Sthsw	20	Sth1W	20	SthS	18	SthS	n&v
		FAC	P	FAC	EP	FAC	EPr	FAC	P	FAC	2Q	FAC	2Q	FAC	P	FAC	Pr	FAC	Pr
FAV	1Q	FAV	1P	FAV	1Q	FAV	2Q	FAV	2Pr	FAT	P	FAT	P	FAT	P	FAT	P	FAT	P

HONOURS / RECORDS

FA Comps: None

League: Stroud & District Division Three 1951-52, Division Two 1952-53, Division one 1953-54, 98-99, Division Four 1989-90. Hellenic Division 1 West 2003-04, 09-10, Premier 06-07. Gloucester Northern 2007-08. Gloucestershire County 2008-09.
County FA: Gloucester Challenge Trophy 2003-04, 05-06, 06-07. Gloucester Northern Senior Cup 2000-01.

Victory: 12-1 v Cheltenham Civil Service, Reg Davis Cup, 18/08/2007
Defeat: 0-9 v Cinderford Town (A), 19/04/2018 and v Taunton Town (A), 24/04/2018
Goalscorer: Marvyn Roberts - 104 (in 221 appearances)
Appearances: Fred Ward - 505

GROUND: Thornhill Park, Cambridge, Glos GL2 7AF

Ground Capacity: 1,500   **Seats:** Yes   **Covered:** Yes   **Clubhouse:** Yes   **Shop:** Yes
Previous Grounds: Various venues around Slimbridge before moving to Wisloe Road (now Thornhill Park) in 1951.
Record Attendance: 525 v Shortwood United, Hellenic Premier, 24/08/2003.

Nearest Railway Station Cam & Dursley - 1 mile
Bus Route Wisloe Road - stop 300m away

THATCHAM TOWN

Nickname: Kingfishers   **Club Colours:** Blue and white

Founded 1895

Club Contact Details
01635 862 016

Previous Names: Thatcham 1895-1974.
Previous Leagues: Reading Temperance 1896-1953. Hellenic (founder member) 1953-82, Athenian 1982-84, London Spartan 1984-86, Wessex 1986-2006. Southern 2006-14.

10-11		11-12		12-13		13-14		14-15		15-16		16-17		17-18		18-19		19-20	
Sthsw	5	Sthsw	8	SthC	17	Sthsw	19	Hel P	12	Hel P	2	Hel P	4	Hel P	1	SthS	11	SthS	n&v
FAC	1Q	FAC	P	FAC	2Q	FAC	P	FAC	EPr	FAC	1Q	FAC	EP	FAC	2Q	FAC	Pr	FAC	1Q
FAT	P	FAT	2Qr	FAT	P	FAT	P	FAV	1P	FAV	2Q	FAV	3P	FAV	F	FAT	1Q	FAT	2Q

HONOURS / RECORDS

FA Comps: FA Vase 2017-18.

League: Reading Temperance Division Two 1905-06. Hellenic Division One 1958-59, 64-65, 72-73, Premier 1974-75, 2017-18. Wessex 1995-96.
County FA: Berks & Bucks Junior Cup 1935-36, Senior Cup 74-75, Senior Trophy 2004-05. Basingstoke Senior Cup 2008-09, 10-11, 11-12.
Best FA Cup   Fourth Qualifying Round 1996-97
FA Trophy   Second Qualifying Round 2008-09, 09-10, 11-12(r)
FA Vase   Winners 2017-18

GROUND: Waterside Park, Crookham Hill, Thatcham, Berks RG19 4PA

Ground Capacity: 2,500   **Seats:** 300   **Covered:** 300   **Clubhouse:** Yes   **Shop:** Yes
Previous Grounds: Station Road 1946-52, Lancaster Close 1952-92
Record Attendance: 1,400 v Aldershot - FA Vase

Nearest Railway Station Thatcham - 1.6km
Bus Route Vincent Road stop - 287m away

WILLAND ROVERS

Founded 1946

Nickname: Rovers   **Club Colours:** White and blue

Club Contact Details
01884 33885

Previous Names: None.
Previous Leagues: Devon & Exeter >1992. Devon County (Founder Members) 1992-2001. Western 2001-19.

10-11		11-12		12-13		13-14		14-15		15-16		16-17		17-18		18-19		19-20	
WestP	4	WestP	5	WestP	11	WestP	8	WestP	6	WestP	6	WestP	6	WestP	3	WestP	1	SthS	n&v
FAC	1Q	FAC	EP	FAC	EP	FAC	EP	FAC	4Q	FAC	EP	FAC	EPr	FAC	1Q	FAC	P	FAC	1Q
FAV	4P	FAV	4P	FAV	2P	FAV	1P	FAV	1Q	FAV	2Q	FAV	1P	FAV	2P	FAV	QF	FAT	P

HONOURS / RECORDS
FA Comps: None

League: Devon County 1998-99, 2000-01, Western Division One 2004-05, Premier 18-19.

County FA: None

Goalscorer:	Paul Foreman
FA Cup	Fourth Qualifying Round 2014-15
FA Vase	Quarter finals 2018-19

GROUND: Silver Street, Willand, Collumpton, Devon EX15 2RG

Ground Capacity: 1,000   **Seats:** 75   **Covered:** 150   **Clubhouse:** Yes   **Shop:**
Previous Grounds: Not known
Record Attendance: 650 v Newton Abbot 1992-3

Nearest Railway Station Tiverton Parkway - 3.2km
Bus Route Garage (Silver St) - stop 50m away

WINCHESTER CITY

Founded 1884

Nickname: The Capitals   **Club Colours:** Red & black

Club Contact Details
07768 828 918   secretary.wcfc@outlook.com

Previous Names: None
Previous Leagues: Hampshire 1898-71, 73-03. Southern 1971-73, 2006-09, 2012-13. Wessex 2003-06. 2009-12, 13-15.

10-11		11-12		12-13		13-14		14-15		15-16		16-17		17-18		18-19		19-20	
WexP	3	WexP	1	SthC	22	WexP	5	WexP	2	Sthsw	5	Sthsw	14	Sth1W	11	SthS	6	SthS	n&v
FAC	EP	FAC	P	FAC	1Q	FAC	1Q	FAC	3Q	FAC	2Qr	FAC	3Q	FAC	1Q	FAC	4Q	FAC	1Q
FAV	2Q	FAV	2P	FAT	P	FAV	1P	FAV	1P	FAT	1Q	FAT	3Q	FAT	P	FAT	EPr	FAT	Pr

HONOURS / RECORDS
FA Comps: FA Vase 2004.

League: Hampshire Division Two 1973-74, 91-92, Division One 2000-01, Premier Division 2002-03.
Wessex Division One 2003-04, 05-06, Premier Division 2011-12.
County FA: Hants Senior Cup 1930-31, 2004-05.

Goalscorer:	Andy Forbes.
Appearances:	Ian Mancey.

GROUND: Hillier Way, Winchester SO23 7SR

Ground Capacity: 3,000   **Seats:** 180   **Covered:** 275   **Clubhouse:** Yes   **Shop:** Yes
Previous Grounds: None
Record Attendance: 1,818 v Bideford, FA Vase Semi-final.

Nearest Railway Station Winchester - 0.9km
Bus Route Simonds Court - stop 250m away

OUT: Balham (LM - SCEP).

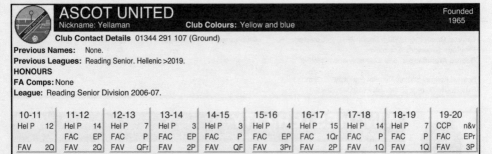

ABBEY RANGERS
Nickname:　　　　　　　Club Colours: Black & white
Founded 1976

Club Contact Details 01932 422 962　　　　　　　graham.keable@ntlworld.com

Previous Names: None
Previous Leagues: Surrey Elite 2011-2015
HONOURS
FA Comps: None
League: Surrey & Hants Border League 2004-05.
Surrey Intermediate League (Western) Division One 2008-09.

10-11	11-12	12-13	13-14	14-15	15-16	16-17	17-18	18-19	19-20
SuIP	SuEI 10	SuEI 7	SuEI 3	SuEI 4	CC1 3	CCP 10	CCP 17	CCP 3	CCP n&v
						FAC EP	FAC EP	FAC EP	FAC 3Q
					FAV 2P	FAV 3P	FAV 2Q	FAV 2P	FAV 2P

GROUND: Addlestone Moor, Addlestone, KT15 2QH
Capacity:　　**Seats:** Yes　**Covered:** Yes
Nearest Railway Station Addlestone
Bus Route No.461

ASCOT UNITED
Nickname: Yellaman　　　　　　Club Colours: Yellow and blue
Founded 1965

Club Contact Details 01344 291 107 (Ground)

Previous Names: None.
Previous Leagues: Reading Senior. Hellenic >2019.
HONOURS
FA Comps: None
League: Reading Senior Division 2006-07.

10-11	11-12	12-13	13-14	14-15	15-16	16-17	17-18	18-19	19-20
Hel P 12	Hel P 14	Hel P 7	Hel P 3	Hel P 3	Hel P 4	Hel P 15	Hel P 14	Hel P 7	CCP n&v
	FAC EP	FAC P	FAC EP	FAC P	FAC EP	FAC 1Qr	FAC P	FAC P	FAC EPr
FAV 2Q	FAV 2Q	FAV QFr	FAV 2P	FAV QF	FAV 3Pr	FAV 2P	FAV 1Q	FAV 1Q	FAV 3P

GROUND: Ascot Racecourse, Car Park 10, Winkfield Rd, Ascot SL5 7RA
Capacity: 1,150 **Seats:**　　**Covered:**　　**Shop:** Yes
Nearest Railway Station Ascot - 1.3km
Bus Route Hilltop Close (Cheapside Rd) stop - 934m

BADSHOT LEA
Nickname: Baggies　　　　　　Club Colours: Claret & sky blue
Founded 1907

Club Contact Details badshotleafootballclub.co.uk

Previous Names: None
Previous Leagues: Surrey Intermediate. Hellenic > 2008.
HONOURS
FA Comps: None
League: Surrey Intermediate Division One 1936-37, 37-38, 85-86, Division Two 92-93

10-11	11-12	12-13	13-14	14-15	15-16	16-17	17-18	18-19	19-20
CCP 6	CCP 17	CCP 7	CCP 15	CCP 8	CCP 17	CCP 21	CC1 3	CCP 9	CCP n&v
FAC EP	FAC P	FAC 3Q	FAC P	FAC P	FAC P	FAC P	FAC P	FAC EP	FAC 2Q
FAV 1Q	FAV 2Q	FAV 1Q	FAV 1Q	FAV 1Q	FAV 2Q	FAV 2Q	FAV 2Q	FAV 2P	FAV 2P

GROUND: Westfield Lane, Wrecclesham, Farnham, Surrey GU10 4PF
Capacity: 1,200 **Seats:** Yes　**Covered:** Yes
Nearest Railway Station Aldershot
Bus Route Stagecoach 18 from Aldershot bus station - about 28min journey via 31 stops to Westfield Lane.

PREMIER DIVISION

BANSTEAD ATHLETIC

Nickname: The A's   **Club Colours:** Amber & black

Founded 1944

Club Contact Details 01737 350 982   terrymolloy@leyfield.eclipse.co.uk

Previous Names: Banstead Juniors 1944-46.

Previous Leagues: Surrey Senior 1949-65. Spartan 1965-75. London Spartan 1975-79. Athenian 1979-85. Isthmian 1985-2006.

HONOURS

FA Comps: None

League: Surrey Senior League 1950-51, 51-52, 52-53, 53-54, 56-57, 64-65.
Combined Counties League Division One 2016-17.

	10-11		11-12		12-13		13-14		14-15		15-16		16-17		17-18		18-19		19-20	
CCP	17		CCP	22	CC1	17	CC1	12	CC1	6	CC1	6	CC1	1	CCP	19	CCP	8	CCP	n&v
FAC	P		FAC	1Q	FAC	EP	FAC		FAC		FAC	EPr	FAC	Pr	FAC	1Q	FAC	EP	FAC	EP
FAV	2Q		FAV	2Q	FAV	2Q	FAV	2Q	FAV	1P	FAV	2Q	FAV	1P	FAV	1Q	FAV	2P	FAV	1Qr

GROUND: Merland Rise, Tadworth, Surrey KT20 5JG

Capacity: 4000   **Seats:** 250   **Covered:** 800   **Shop:** Yes

Nearest Railway Station Tattenham Corner

Bus Route Metro 420 & 460

CAMBERLEY TOWN

Nickname: The Krooners   **Club Colours:** Red and white stripes

Founded 1895

Club Contact Details 01276 65 392

Previous Names: St Michael's FC (St Michael's Camberley) 1895-1901. Camberley & Yorktown 1901-46. Camberley 1946-67.

Previous Leagues: East & West Surrey (West Surrey) 1898-99, 1910-22. Aldershot Comb 1902-03. Ascot & Dist 1903-10. Surrey Senior 1922-73. Spartan 1973-75. Athenian 1975-77, 82-84. Isthmian 1977-82, 84-2006.

HONOURS

FA Comps: None

League: Ascot & Dist. 1904-05, 07-08, 08-09, 09-10. Aldershot Sen. Civilian 1912-13. West Surrey 1913-14. Surrey Senior 1930-31, 31-32, 32-33.

10-11		11-12		12-13		13-14		14-15		15-16		16-17		17-18		18-19		19-20	
CCP	4	CCP	6	CCP	16	CCP	2	CCP	2	CCP	3	CCP	6	CCP	7	CCP	16	CCP	n&v
FAC	P	FAC	P	FAC	P	FAC	1Qr	FAC	EP	FAC	EP	FAC	1Q	FAC	P	FAC	EP	FAC	EP
FAV	2P	FAV	1P	FAV	2Q	FAV	2Q	FAV	1P	FAT	QF	FAV	2P	FAV	1P	FAV	2Q	FAV	2Q

GROUND: Krooner Park, Wilton Road, Camberley, Surrey GU15 2QW

Capacity: 1,976   **Seats:** 196   **Covered:** 300   **Shop:** Yes

Nearest Railway Station Camberley

Bus Route Stagecoach 1

CB HOUNSLOW UNITED

Nickname: The Dragons   **Club Colours:** Green and black

Founded 1989

Club Contact Details 07958 718 930   cbhounslowunitedfc.com

Previous Names: CB United 1989-94. (Named after Cater Bank, a company owned by the father of the club chairman.)

Previous Leagues: Hounslow & District 1989-94. Middlesex County 1994-2006.

HONOURS

FA Comps: None

League: Combined Counties League Division One 2015-16.

10-11		11-12		12-13		13-14		14-15		15-16		16-17		17-18		18-19		19-20	
CC1	14	CC1	15	CC1	8	CC1	14	CC1	7	CC1	1	CCP	20	CCP	9	CCP	17	CCP	n&v
												FAC	1Q	FAC	P	FAC	P	FAC	P
								FAV	1Q	FAV	2Q	FAV	2Q	FAV	2Q	FAV	1P	FAV	1Q

GROUND: The Lair, Hounslow Sports Club, Green Lane, Hounslow TW4 6DH

Capacity: 1200   **Seats:** 100   **Covered:** Yes

Nearest Railway Station Hatton Cross (Underground) Piccadilly Line

Bus Route London Transport 423 stops almost opposite the ground, 482 & 203 stop on Grest South West Road close to Green Lane

COBHAM
Nickname: Hammers **Club Colours:** Red & black **Founded** 1892

Club Contact Details 07813 643 336

Previous Names: None
Previous Leagues: Kingston & District. Surrey Senior 1937-78.
HONOURS
FA Comps: None
League: Kingston & District Division One 1928-29, 29-30.

	10-11		11-12		12-13		13-14		14-15		15-16		16-17		17-18		18-19		19-20	
	CC1	8	CC1	11	CC1	11	CC1	16	CC1	11	CC1	7	CC1	11	CC1	2	CCP	14	CCP	n&v
	FAC	1Q	FAC	EPr	FAC	EPr											FAC	P	FAC	EPr
	FAV	1Q	FAV	1Q	FAV	2Q	FAV	2Q	FAV	2Q	FAV	2Q	FAV	2Q	FAV	1P	FAV	1P	FAV	2Q

GROUND: Leg O'Mutton Field, Anvil Lane, Cobham KT11 1AA
Capacity: 2000 **Seats:** 112 **Covered:** 200
Nearest Railway Station Cobham
Bus Route Green Line 715

COLLIERS WOOD UNITED
Nickname: The Wood **Club Colours:** Royal blue & black **Founded** 1874

Club Contact Details 0208 942 8062 collierswoodunited@yahoo.co.uk

Previous Names: Vandyke 1874-1997. Vandyke Colliers United 1997-99.
Previous Leagues: Wimbledon & Sutton. Surrey Intermediate. Surrey County Senior
HONOURS
FA Comps: None
League: Surrey County Premier League 1997-98.

	10-11		11-12		12-13		13-14		14-15		15-16		16-17		17-18		18-19		19-20	
	CCP	11	CCP	19	CCP	18	CCP	16	CCP	11	CCP	8	CCP	15	CCP	16	CCP	13	CCP	n&v
	FAC	EP	FAC	EPr	FAC	P	FAC	P	FAC	EP	FAC	EP	FAC	2Qr	FAC	Pr	FAC	EPr	FAC	EP
	FAV	3P	FAV	1P	FAV	3P	FAV	1Q	FAV	4P	FAV	3P	FAV	1Q	FAV	1Q	FAV	2Q	FAV	1P

GROUND: Wibbandune Sports Ground, Lincoln Green, Wimbledon SW20 0AA
Capacity: 2000 **Seats:** 102 **Covered:** 100 **Shop:** Yes
Nearest Railway Station Raynes Park
Bus Route London Transport 265

EGHAM TOWN
Nickname: Sarnies **Club Colours:** Red & white **Founded** 1877

Club Contact Details 01784 437 055

Previous Names: Runnymead Rovers 1877-1905. Egham F.C. 05-63.
Previous Leagues: West Surrey. Surrey Senior 1922-28, 33-39, 65-67. Spartan 1928-33, 67-74. Athenian 1964-77. Isthmian 1977-2004, 05-06, 18-19. Southern 2004-05, 13-18. Combined Counties 2006-13.
HONOURS
FA Comps: None
League: West Surrey 1921-22. Surrey Senior 1922-23. Spartan 1971-72. Athenian Division Two 1974-75. Combined Counties 2012-13.

	10-11		11-12		12-13		13-14		14-15		15-16		16-17		17-18		18-19		19-20	
	CCP	13	CCP	4	CCP	1	SthC	11	SthC	15	SthC	3	SthC	5	Sth1E	16	IsthSC	20	CCP	n&v
	FAC	EP	FAC	Pr	FAC	P	FAC	P	FAC	P	FAC	Pr	FAC	4Q	FAC	1Qr	FAC	2Qr	FAC	P
	FAV	2P	FAV	2P	FAV	1P	FAT	2Q	FAT	1Q	FAT	1Q	FAT	P	FAT	2Q	FAT	P	FAV	1P

GROUND: Runnymead Stadium, Tempest Road, Egham TW20 8XD
Capacity: 5500 **Seats:** 262 **Covered:** 3300
Nearest Railway Station Egham - 1km
Bus Route Charta Road - stop 200m away

FRIMLEY GREEN
Nickname: The Green   Club Colours: All blue   Founded 1919

Club Contact Details 01252 835 089

Previous Names: None
Previous Leagues: Surrey Senior 1960-74. London Spartan 1974-75. London Spartan 1975-81. Combined Counties 1981-94. Surrey County Premier 1999-2002.
HONOURS
FA Comps: None
League: Combined Counties Division One 2012-13.

	10-11	11-12	12-13	13-14	14-15	15-16	16-17	17-18	18-19	19-20
	CC1 15	CC1 10	CC1 1	CCP 12	CCP 21	CC1 12	CC1 13	CC1 7	CC1 2	CCP n&v
FAC	EP			FAC P	FAC EP	FAC EP			FAC P	FAC EP
FAV	2Q	FAV 1Q	FAV 2P	FAV 1Q	FAV 2Q	FAV 2Q	FAV 2Q	FAV 1P	FAV 1Q	FAV 2Q

GROUND: Frimley Green Rec. Ground, Frimley Green, Camberley GU16 6JY
Capacity: 2000   **Seats:** No   **Covered:** Yes
Nearest Railway Station Frimley
Bus Route Stagecoach 3, Arriva 49

GUILDFORD CITY
Nickname: The Sweeney   Club Colours: Red & white stripes   Founded 1996

Club Contact Details 01483 443 322

Previous Names: AFC Guildford 1996-2005. Guildford United 2005-06.
Previous Leagues: Surrey Senior. Combined Counties > 2012. Southern 2012-14.
HONOURS
FA Comps: None
League: Southern League 1937-38, 55-56, League cup 1962-63, 66-67. Combined Counties Division One 2003-04, Premier Division 2010-11, 11-12.

	10-11	11-12	12-13	13-14	14-15	15-16	16-17	17-18	18-19	19-20
CCP	1	CCP 1	SthC 9	Sthsw 22	CCP 17	CCP 14	CCP 16	CCP 12	CCP 7	CCP n&v
FAC	2Q	FAC EP	FAC 1Q	FAC P	FAC EP	FAC P	FAC 1Q	FAC 1Q	FAC EP	FAC P
FAV	4P	FAV 2P	FAT 1Q	FAT P	FAV 1P	FAV 1Q	FAV 1Q	FAV 1Q	FAV 2Q	FAV 1Q

GROUND: Spectrum Leisure Centre, Parkway, Guildford GU1 1UP
Capacity: 1,320   **Seats:** 255   **Covered:** Yes   **Shop:** Yes
Nearest Railway Station Guildford Main Line (2 miles) & Guildford (London Rd) (1 mile)
Bus Route Arriva 100

HANWORTH VILLA

Nickname: The Vilans   Club Colours: Red & white   Founded 1976

Club Contact Details 0208 831 9391   db1959@btinternet.com

Previous Names: None
Previous Leagues: Hounslow & District Lge. West Middlesex Lge. Middlesex County League.
HONOURS
FA Comps: None
League: Hounslow & District Div.1 & Prem. West Middlesex Division One & Division Two. Middlesex County 2002-03, 04-05.

	10-11	11-12	12-13	13-14	14-15	15-16	16-17	17-18	18-19	19-20
CCP	5	CCP 3	CCP 9	CCP 8	CCP 19	CCP 7	CCP 3	CCP 11	CCP 15	CCP n&v
		FAC 4Q	FAC P	FAC P	FAC Pr	FAC EP	FAC P	FAC P	FAC Pr	FAC P
FAV	2Q	FAV 3Pr	FAV 4P	FAV 4P	FAV 3P	FAV 1P	FAV 1Q	FAV 2P	FAV 1P	FAV 2Q

GROUND: Rectory Meadows, Park Road, Hanworth TW13 6PN
Capacity: 600   **Seats:** 100   **Covered:** Yes
Nearest Railway Station Feltham or Hampton
Bus Route London United 111 or H25

COMBINED COUNTIES

KNAPHILL
Nickname: The Knappers   Club Colours: Red and black
Founded 1924

Club Contact Details 01483 475 150

Previous Names: None
Previous Leagues: Woking & District. Surrey Intermediate (Western) > 2007
HONOURS
FA Comps: None
League: Woking & District League 1978-79.
Surrey Intermediate League Division Three 1980-81, Division One 2005-06, Premier 06-07.

10-11	11-12	12-13	13-14	14-15	15-16	16-17	17-18	18-19	19-20
CC1 9	CC1 12	CC1 12	CC1 3	CCP 13	CCP 5	CCP 14	CCP 8	CCP 11	CCP n&v
				FAC 1Q	FAC EP	FAC EPr	FAC 2Q	FAC EP	FAC P
	FAV 1Q	FAV 1Q	FAV 2P	FAV 2P	FAV 4P	FAV 3P	FAV 2Q	FAV 1Q	FAV 2Q

GROUND: Brookwood Country Park, Redding Way, Knaphill GU21 2AY
Capacity: 1,000 **Seats:** 100 **Covered:** Yes
Nearest Railway Station Brookwood or Woking
Bus Route Arriva 34, 35

MOLESEY
Nickname: The Moles   Club Colours: White & black
Founded 1946

Club Contact Details 020 8979 4823

Previous Names: None.
Previous Leagues: Surrey Intermediate 1946-53. Surrey Senior 1953-59. Spartan 1959-73. Athenian 1973-77. Isthmian 1977-2008, 15-19.
HONOURS Combined Counties 2008-15.
FA Comps: None
League: Surrey Intermediate 1946-47. Surrey Senior 1957-58. Combined Counties Premier Division 2014-15.

10-11	11-12	12-13	13-14	14-15	15-16	16-17	17-18	18-19	19-20
CCP 3	CCP 5	CCP 10	CCP 11	CCP 1	Isth1S 9	Isth1S 19	Isth1S 23	IsthSC 19	CCP n&v
FAC EP	FAC EP	FAC EP	FAC Pr	FAC P	FAC 1Q	FAC P	FAC P	FAC Pr	FAC EPr
FAV 1P	FAV 1P	FAV 1Q	FAV 1Q	FAV 2Q	FAT 3Q	FAT P	FAT P	FAT 1Q	FAV 2Q

GROUND: 412 Walton Road, West Molesey KT8 2JG
Capacity: 4,000 **Seats:** 160 **Covered:** Yes **Shop:** Yes
Nearest Railway Station Hampton - 1.5km
Bus Route Grange Road - stop 150m away

RAYNES PARK VALE
Nickname: The Vale   Club Colours: Blue and yellow
Founded 1995

Club Contact Details 0208 540 8843

Previous Names: Malden Vale and Raynes Park merged in 1995
Previous Leagues: None
HONOURS
FA Comps: None
League: Combined Counties Division One 2002-03.

10-11	11-12	12-13	13-14	14-15	15-16	16-17	17-18	18-19	19-20
CCP 15	CCP 9	CCP 11	CCP 10	CCP 15	CCP 15	CCP 23	CC1 5	CCP 5	CCP n&v
FAC P	FAC P	FAC Pr	FAC Pr	FAC Pr	FAC EP	FAC EP	FAC EP	FAC Pr	FAC EP
FAV 1P	FAV 1P	FAV 2Q	FAV 1P	FAV 1P	FAV 1Q	FAV 1Q	FAV 1Q	FAV 1Q	FAV 2P

GROUND: Grand Drive, Raynes Park SW20 9DZ
Capacity: 1500 **Seats:** 120 **Covered:** 100
Nearest Railway Station Raynes Park (9 mins away). **Underground:** Morden (take 163 bus for 10 mins, walk from Blenheim Road)
Bus Route London Buses 152 & 163

REDHILL
Nickname: Reds/Lobsters   **Club Colours:** Red & white   Founded 1894

Club Contact Details 01737 762 129

Previous Names: None
Previous Leagues: E & W Surrey. Spartan 1909-10. Southern Sub. London 1921-23. Athenian 1923-84. Sussex County 1984-2013. Isthmian 2013-15.
HONOURS
FA Comps: None
League: London League 1922-23. Athenian League 1924-25, 83-84.

	10-11	11-12	12-13	13-14	14-15	15-16	16-17	17-18	18-19	19-20
	SxC1 8	SxC1 10	SxC1 2	Isth1S 22	Isth1S 23	CCP 20	CC1 2	CCP 6	CCP 12	CCP n&v
FAC	EP	1Q	1Q	1Q	3Q	EP	P	P	EP	P
FAV	2Q	2Q	1Q	FAT P	FAT Pr	2Q	1Q	1Q	1P	2P

GROUND: Kiln Brow, Three Arch Road, Redhill, Surrey RH1 5AE
Capacity: 2,000   **Seats:** 150   **Covered:** 150   **Shop:** Yes
Nearest Railway Station Redhill (mainline) Earlswood
Bus Route 100, 400, 420, 430, 435, 460

SHEERWATER
Nickname: Sheers   **Club Colours:** All royal blue   Founded 1958

Club Contact Details 07791 612 008

Previous Names: None
Previous Leagues: Woking & District 1958-67. Surrey County Intermediate 1967-78. Surrey Senior 1972-78. Combined Counties 1978-82. Surrey Premier (FM) 1982-93, 94-2000. Surrey County Senior 2000-03.
HONOURS
FA Comps: None
League: Combined Counties Division One 2018-19

	10-11	11-12	12-13	13-14	14-15	15-16	16-17	17-18	18-19	19-20
	CC1 17	CC1 18	CC1 15	CC1 11	CC1 14	CC1 13	CC1 9	CC1 4	CC1 1	CCP n&v
FAC										EP
FAV									1P	1Q

GROUND: Woking FC, The Laithwaite Community Stadium, Kingfield Road, Woking, Surrey GU22 9AA
Capacity: 6,200   **Seats:** 2,500   **Covered:** 3,900
Nearest Railway Station Woking - about 15 mins from the ground.
Bus Route 34 & 462

SOUTHALL
Nickname: None   **Club Colours:** Red and white   Founded 1871

Club Contact Details enquiries@southallfc.com

Previous Names: Southall 1871-1975. Southall & Ealing Borough 1975-80.
Previous Leagues: West London (FM) 1892-93. Southern 1896-1905. Great Western Suburban 1907-14. Athenian 1919-73. Isthmian 1973-75, 80--2000. Combined Counties 2000-06. Middlesex County 2006-12. Spartan South Midlands 2012-18.
HONOURS
FA Comps: None
League: Great Western Suburban 1912-13. Athenian 1926-27. Spartan South Midlands Division One 2017-18.

	10-11	11-12	12-13	13-14	14-15	15-16	16-17	17-18	18-19	19-20
	MidxP 8	MidxP 3	SSM1 9	SSM1 11	SSM1 12	SSM1 12	SSM1 5	SSM1 1	CCP 4	CCP n&v
FAC								P	EP	P
FAV				1Q	2Q	1P	QF	2P	2P	3P

GROUND: Robert Parker Stadium, Short Lane, Stanwell TW19 7BH
Capacity: 3,000   **Seats:**   **Covered:**
Nearest Railway Station Greenford

SPELTHORNE SPORTS

Nickname: Spelly **Club Colours:** Navy & sky blue

Founded 1922

Club Contact Details 01932 961 055

Previous Names: None
Previous Leagues: Surrey Intermediate (West) > 2009. Surrey Elite Intermediate 2009-11.
HONOURS
FA Comps: None
League: Surrey Elite Intermediate League 2010-11. Combined Counties Division One 2013-14.

10-11		11-12		12-13		13-14		14-15		15-16		16-17		17-18		18-19		19-20	
SuEI	1	CC1	7	CC1	6	CCP	1	CCP	6	CCP	11	CCP	9	CCP	10	CCP	6	CCP	n&v
										FAC	P	FAC	P	FAC	EP	FAC	1Q	FAC	1Q
								FAV	1P	FAV	1Q	FAV	1Qr	FAV	1P	FAV	2P	FAV	1Q

GROUND: Spelthorne Sports Club, 296 Staines Rd West, Ashford Common, TW15 1RY
Capacity: 1,500 **Seats:** 50 **Covered:** Yes
Nearest Railway Station Sunbury
Bus Route 290 to outside the club.

SUTTON COMMON ROVERS

Nickname: Commoners **Club Colours:** All yellow

Founded 1978

Club Contact Details 020 8644 4440

Previous Names: Inrad FC. Centre 21 FC . SCR Plough, SCR Grapes, SRC Litten Tree, SCR Kingfisher, Mole Valley SCR >2015.
Previous Leagues: South Eastern Combination.
HONOURS
FA Comps: None
League: Combined Counties League Division One 2009-10.

10-11		11-12		12-13		13-14		14-15		15-16		16-17		17-18		18-19		19-20	
CCP	8	CCP	21	CC1	2	CCP	18	CCP	18	CCP	19	CCP	12	CCP	3	CCP	2	CCP	n&v
FAC	EP	FAC	EP	FAC	EPr	FAC	EP	FAC	P	FAC	EP	FAC	EPr	FAC	P	FAC	EP	FAC	1Q
FAV	1Q	FAV	2Q	FAV	2Q	FAV	2Q	FAV	1Q	FAV	4P	FAV	3P	FAV	1Q	FAV	2P	FAV	5P

GROUND: Sutton United FC, Gander Green Lane, Sutton. Surrey SM1 2EY
Capacity: 5,013 **Seats:** 765 **Covered:** 1,250 **Shop:** Yes
Nearest Railway Station West Sutton a few minutes walk from the ground.
Bus Route 413

DIVISION ONE

AFC HAYES
Nickname: The Brooks   **Club Colours:** Blue and white stripes   Founded 1976

Club Contact Details 020 8845 0110

HONOURS
FA Comps: None
League: Spartan South Midlands Premier South 1997-98.

10-11		11-12		12-13		13-14		14-15		15-16		16-17		17-18		18-19		19-20	
SthC	19	SthC	10	SthC	15	SthC	18	SthC	22	CCP	16	CCP	17	CCP	18	CCP	19	CC1	n&v
FAC	P	FAC	1Q	FAC	P	FAC	P	FAC	1Q	FAC	Pr	FAC	P	FAC	EP	FAC	EP	FAC	EPr
FAT	1Q	FAT	1Q	FAT	P	FAT	1Q	FAT	Pr	FAV	2Q	FAV	1Q	FAV	2Q	FAV	1Q	FAV	1P

GROUND: Farm Park, Kingshill Avenue, Hayes UB4 8DD
Nearest Railway Station Northholt or Haye & Harlington
Bus Route No.90

ASH UNITED
Nickname: Green Army   **Club Colours:** Green & red.   Founded 1911

Club Contact Details 01252 320 385 / 345 757

HONOURS
FA Comps: None
League: Combined Counties 1981-82, 86-87, 98-99.

10-11		11-12		12-13		13-14		14-15		15-16		16-17		17-18		18-19		19-20	
CCP	18	CCP	13	CCP	20	CCP	1	CC1	10	CC1	10	CC1	12	CC1	10	CC1	7	CC1	n&v
FAC	EP	FAC	EP	FAC	EP	FAC	EP	FAC	EP										
FAV	2Q	FAV	1Q	FAV	2P	FAV	1Q	FAV	1Q	FAV	1Q	FAV	1P	FAV	1Q	FAV	1Q	FAV	1Q

GROUND: Shawfield Stadium, Youngs Drive off Shawfield Road, Ash, GU12 6RE.
Nearest Railway Station Ash or Ash Vale
Bus Route Stagecoach 20A, 550

BAGSHOT
Nickname: **Club Colours:** Yellow & blue   Founded 1906

Club Contact Details 07971 147 315

HONOURS
FA Comps: None
League: Aldershot & District Division Two 2005-06, Division One 2008-09, Senior Division 2011-12, 12-13, 13-14, 15-16.

10-11		11-12		12-13		13-14		14-15		15-16		16-17		17-18		18-19		19-20	
A&DS	3	A&DS	1	A&DS	1	A&DS	1	A&DS	1	A&DS	1	CC1	8	CC1	19	CC1	13	CC1	n&v
														FAV	1Q	FAV	1Q	FAV	2Q

GROUND: Camberley Town FC, Krooner Park, Wilton Rd, Camberley GU15 2QW
Nearest Railway Station Camberley
Bus Route Stagecoach 1

BEDFONT & FELTHAM
Nickname: The Yellows   **Club Colours:** Yellow & blue   Founded 2012

Club Contact Details 020 8890 7264

HONOURS
FA Comps: None
League: None

10-11	11-12	12-13		13-14		14-15		15-16		16-17		17-18		18-19		19-20	
		CC1	13	CC1	5	CC1	5	CC1	2	CCP	22	CC1	17	CC1	5	CC1	n&v
						FAC	1Q	FAC	1Q	FAC	EP	FAC	EP	FAC	EP		
		FAV	2Q	FAV	1P	FAV	1Q	FAV	1Q	FAV	2Q	FAV	1Q	FAV	1P	FAV	2P

GROUND: The Orchard, Hatton Road, Bedfont TW14 9QT
Nearest Railway Station Hatton Cross (Piccadilly Line)
Bus Route London Transport 203, H25, H26

BRITISH AIRWAYS
Founded 1947

Nickname: **Club Colours:** Blue and white

Club Contact Details britishairwaysfc.co.uk

HONOURS
FA Comps: None
League: Middlesex County Premier Division 2012-13, 17-18.

10-11	11-12	12-13	13-14	14-15	15-16	16-17	17-18	18-19	19-20
LonCom 2	LonCom 1	MidxP 1	MidxP 7	MidxP 11	MidxP 6	MidxP 2	MidxP 1	CC1 10	CC1 n&v
								FAV 1Q	FAV 1Q

GROUND: Bedfont & Feltham FC, The Orchard, Hatton Road, Bedfont TW14 9QT
Nearest Railway Station Hatton Cross (Piccadilly Line)
Bus Route London Transport 203, H25, H26

CHESSINGTON & HOOK UNITED
Founded 1921

Nickname: Chessey **Club Colours:** Blue and white

Club Contact Details chufc.co.uk

HONOURS
FA Comps: None
League: Kingston & District Division Four 1922-23, Division Two 1955-56, Division One 1957-58.

10-11	11-12	12-13	13-14	14-15	15-16	16-17	17-18	18-19	19-20
CCP 12	CCP 20	CCP 17	CCP 22	CC1 3	CCP 21	CC1 5	CC1 13	CC1 9	CC1 n&v
FAC EP	FAC P	FAC P	FAC P	FAC 1Q	FAC 1Q	FAC Pr	FAC P		
FAV 1Q	FAV 1Q	FAV 2Q	FAV 2P	FAV 2P	FAV 1Q	FAV 1Qr	FAV 2Q	FAV 2Q	FAV 1Q

GROUND: Chalky Lane, Chessington, Surrey KT9 2NF
Nearest Railway Station Chessington South
Bus Route London United 71, 465

COVE
Founded 1897

Nickname: None **Club Colours:** Yellow and black

Club Contact Details 01252 543 615

HONOURS
FA Comps: None
League: Combined Counties League 2000-01.

10-11	11-12	12-13	13-14	14-15	15-16	16-17	17-18	18-19	19-20
CCP 9	CCP 11	CCP 3	CCP 5	CCP 4	CCP 22	CC1 17	CC1 18	CC1 18	CC1 n&v
FAC EPr	FAC EP	FAC P	FAC 1Q	FAC EP	FAC P	FAC EP			
FAV 1P	FAV 2Q	FAV 2Q	FAV 2P	FAV 1Q	FAV 1P	FAV 1Q	FAV 1Q	FAV 1Q	FAV 1Q

GROUND: Oak Farm Fields, 7 Squirrels Lane, Farnborough GU14 8PF
Nearest Railway Station Farnborough Main - 16min walk from there.

DORKING WANDERERS RESERVES
Founded 1999

Nickname: Wanderers **Club Colours:** Red & white

Club Contact Details info@dorkingwanderers.com

HONOURS
FA Comps: None
League: None

10-11	11-12	12-13	13-14	14-15	15-16	16-17	17-18	18-19	19-20
					CC1 15			CC1 11	CC1 n&v

GROUND: Meadowbank Stadium, Mill Lane, Dorking RH4 1DX
Nearest Railway Station Dorking West and Dorking Deepdene
Bus Route 21 & 455

EPSOM & EWELL
Nickname: E's or Salts **Club Colours:** Royal blue & white
Founded 1960

Club Contact Details 01737 553 250

HONOURS
FA Comps: None
League: Surrey Senior 1925-26, 26-27, 27-28, 74-75. London 1927-28. Isthmian Division Two 1977-78.

	10-11	11-12	12-13	13-14	14-15	15-16	16-17	17-18	18-19	19-20
CCP	10	14	5	3	7	4	4	21	8	CC1 n&v
FAC	1Q	P	1Q	EPr	Pr	EP	P	EP	Pr	
FAV	2Q	2Q	1Q	2Q	1P	1Q	2P	2P	1Q	1Q

GROUND: Leatherhead FC, Fetcham Grove, Guildford Road, Leatherhead, Surrey KT22 9AS
Nearest Railway Station Leatherhead - half a mile away
Bus Route 21, 465 & 479

EVERSLEY & CALIFORNIA
Nickname: The Boars **Club Colours:** Yellow and blue
Founded 1910

Club Contact Details eversleyandcalifornia.co.uk

HONOURS
FA Comps: None
League: Surrey Elite Intermediate 2008-09.

	10-11	11-12	12-13	13-14	14-15	15-16	16-17	17-18	18-19	19-20
CC1	11	5	4	2	9	5	6	9	16	n&v
FAC								EP		
FAV					2Q		2Q	1Q	1P	1Q

GROUND: ESA Sports Complex, Halls Way, off Fox Lane, Eversley RG27 0NS
Nearest Railway Station Fleet, Sandhurst

FARNHAM TOWN
Nickname: The Town **Club Colours:** Claret & sky blue
Founded 1906

Club Contact Details 01252 715 305

HONOURS
FA Comps: None
League: Surrey Intermediate 1929-30, 30-31. Surrey Senior 1965-66, 66-67, 67-68.
Combined Counties 1990-91, 91-92, Division One 2006-07.

	10-11	11-12	12-13	13-14	14-15	15-16	16-17	17-18	18-19	19-20
	CC1 2	CCP 12	CCP 8	CCP 15	CCP 10	CCP 10	CCP 18	CCP 22	CC1 4	CC1 n&v
FAC	P	P	EP	P	EP	1Q	P	P	EP	EPr
FAV	2Q	1P	2Q	1P	1Pr	1P	1Q	2P	2Q	2Q

GROUND: Memorial Ground, West Street, Farnham GU9 7DY
Nearest Railway Station Farnham
Bus Route Stagecoach 5, 14, 18, 19, 46, 64, 71, 536

FC DEPORTIVO GALICIA
Nickname: Depor **Club Colours:** Blue and white
Founded 1968

Club Contact Details fcdeportivogalicia.com

HONOURS
FA Comps: None
League: Middlesex County Premier Division 2016-17.

	10-11	11-12	12-13	13-14	14-15	15-16	16-17	17-18	18-19	19-20
	MidxP 7	MidxP 12	MidxP 13	MidxP 6	MidxP 12	MidxP 13	MidxP 1	CC1 12	CC1 14	CC1 n&v
FAV							1Q	2Q	1P	2Q

GROUND: Hatten Road, Feltham, Middlesex TW14 9JR
Nearest Railway Station Hatton Cross or Feltham BR
Bus Route London Transport 203, H25, H26

FLEET SPURS

Nickname: Spurs   Club Colours: Red and blue

Founded 1948

Club Contact Details fleetspurs.com

HONOURS
FA Comps: None
League: Surrey Premier A Division 1968-69. Aldershot Senior 1990-91.
         Hampshire Division Two 1997-98.

10-11		11-12		12-13		13-14		14-15		15-16		16-17		17-18		18-19		19-20	
Wex1	10	Wex1	7	Wex1	10	Wex1	12	Wex1	9	Wex1	12	Wex1	16	CC1	16	CC1	17	CC1	n&v
		FAC	EP	FAC	EP														
FAV	2Q	FAV	1Q	FAV	2Q	FAV	1Q	FAV	1Qr	FAV	1Q	FAV	2Q	FAV	1Q	FAV	2Q	FAV	2Q

GROUND: Kennels Lane, Farnborough Hampshire, GU14 0ST
Nearest Railway Station Fleet - take No.10 bus towards Farnborough - alight at Trunk Road, 5min walk from there.
Bus Route 10 & 7

GODALMING TOWN

Nickname: The G's   Club Colours: Yellow & green

Founded 1950

Club Contact Details 01483 417 520   godalmingtownfootballclub@gmail.com

HONOURS
FA Comps: None
League: Combined Counties Premier Division 1983-84, 2005-06.

10-11		11-12		12-13		13-14		14-15		15-16		16-17		17-18		18-19		19-20	
Isth1S	17	Isth1S	5	SthC	3	Sthsw	18	SthC	8	SthC	10	Isth1S	24	CCP	20	CC1	12	CC1	n&v
FAC	1Q	FAC	4Q	FAC	1Qr	FAC	P	FAC	1Qr	FAC	1Q	FAC	1Q	FAC	1Q	FAC	EP		
FAT	2Qr	FAT	2Q	FAT	P	FAT	P	FAT	P	FAT	P	FAT	P	FAV	2Q	FAV	1Q	FAV	2Q

GROUND: The Bill Kyte Stadium, Wey Court, Meadrow, Guildford, Surrey GU7 3JF
Nearest Railway Station Farncombe - 1/2 a mile from the ground.

JERSEY BULLS

Nickname: Bulls   Club Colours: Red & white

Founded 2018

Club Contact Details info@bulls.je   01534 449615 (Stadium)

HONOURS
FA Comps: None
League: None

10-11	11-12	12-13	13-14	14-15	15-16	16-17	17-18	18-19	19-20	
									CC1	n&v

GROUND: Springfield Stadium, Saint Helier, Jersey JE2 4LF

Bus Route No.15 from Jersey Airport.

KENSINGTON & EALING BOROUGH

Nickname: Club Colours: Green and white

Founded 2012

Club Contact Details

HONOURS
FA Comps: None
League: None

10-11	11-12	12-13	13-14		14-15		15-16		16-17		17-18		18-19		19-20	
			Midx2	3	Midx1SE	6	SSM2	5	SSM1	12	CC1	15	CC1	15	CC1	n&v
											FAV	1P	FAV	2P	FAV	1Q

GROUND: Hanwell Town FC, Preivale Lane, Perivale, Greenford, UB6 8TL
Nearest Railway Station Perivale Underground - 0.6km
Bus Route Perivale Lane - stop 200m away

SANDHURST TOWN
Nickname: Fizzers   **Club Colours:** Red and black   Founded 1910

Club Contact Details info@sandhursttownfc.org

HONOURS

FA Comps: None

League: Reading & Disttrict Division One 1932-33, Premier 33-34.
Aldershot & District Division One 1980-81.

	10-11	11-12	12-13	13-14	14-15	15-16	16-17	17-18	18-19	19-20
	CCP 7	CCP 15	CCP 21	CC1 13	CC1 16	CC1 11	Hel1E 8	Hel1E 4	CC1 6	CC1 n&v
	FAC EP	FAC EP	FAC EP	FAC EPr					FAC EPr	
	FAV 2Q	FAV 1Q	FAV 1P	FAV 1Q			FAV 1Q	FAV 1P	FAV 1Q	FAV 1Q

GROUND: Bottom Meadow, Memorial Ground, Yorktown Rd, GU47 9BJ
Nearest Railway Station Sandhurst - 0.9km
Bus Route Wellington Arms stop - 194m away

TOOTING BEC
Nickname: **Club Colours:** Black & white   Founded 2004

Club Contact Details

HONOURS

FA Comps: None

League: Surrey Elite Intermediate Division One 2009-10, Premier 2017-18.

	10-11	11-12	12-13	13-14	14-15	15-16	16-17	17-18	18-19	19-20
	SuEl 15	SuEl 13	SuEl 9	SuEl 7	SuEl 10	SuEl 7	SuEl 2	SuEl 1	CC1 3	CC1 n&v
										FAC EP
								FAV 2Q	FAV 1Q	FAV 1Q

GROUND: Imperial Fields, Bishopsford Road, Morden SM4 6BF
Nearest Railway Station Mitcham Junction - then take the tram to Mitcham Tram stop, ground an 8min walk from there.

WALTON & HERSHAM
Nickname: Swans   **Club Colours:** Red and white   Founded 1945

Club Contact Details waltonhersham2019@gmail.com

HONOURS

FA Comps: Amateur Cup 1972-73

League: Corinthian 1946-47, 47-48, 48-49. Athenian League 1968-69.

	10-11	11-12	12-13	13-14	14-15	15-16	16-17	17-18	18-19	19-20
	Isth1S 6	Isth1S 11	Isth1S 18	Isth1S 21	Isth1S 17	Isth1S 22	CCP 5	CCP 4	CCP 20	CC1 n&v
	FAC 1Q	FAC 1Q	FAC 1Qr	FAC P	FAC P	FAC P	FAC Pr	FAC Pr	FAC EP	FAC EP
	FAT P	FAT P	FAT 1Q	FAT P	FAT 1Q	FAT P	FAV 2P	FAV 3P	FAV 1P	FAV 2Q

GROUND: Waterside Drive, Walton-on-Thames, Surrey KT12 2JP
Nearest Railway Station Walton-on-Thames less a mile from the ground.

WESTSIDE
Nickname: **Club Colours:** Yellow & blue   Founded 1996

Club Contact Details westsidefc.co.uk

HONOURS

FA Comps: None

League: Surrey South Eastern Combination Division Two 2014-15, Division One 2015-16.

	10-11	11-12	12-13	13-14	14-15	15-16	16-17	17-18	18-19	19-20
	SSECI2 10	SSECI2 5	SSECI2 6	SSECI2 3	SSECI2 1	SSECI1 1	SuEl 6	SuEl 12	SuEl 4	CC1 n&v
								FAV 1Q	FAV 1Q	FAV 1P

GROUND: Chessington & Hook United FC, Chalky Lane, Chessington, Surrey KT9 2NF
Nearest Railway Station Chessington South
Bus Route London United 71, 465

BARROW TOWN
Nickname: The Riversiders   **Club Colours:** Red & black

Founded
Late

Club Contact Details 07904 289 690   newton-chris@sky.com

HONOURS
FA Comps: None
League: Leicester Senior Division One 1992-93.

10-11		11-12		12-13		13-14		14-15		15-16		16-17		17-18		18-19		19-20	
EMC	5	EMC	5	EMC	2	EMC	19	EMC	9	EMC	13	EMC	14	EMC	11	EMC	8	EMC	n&v
FAC	P	FAC	3Q	FAC	EP	FAC	EP	FAC	EP	FAC	EP								
FAV	1Q	FAV		FAV	1Q	FAV	2Q	FAV	2Q	FAV	2Q	FAV	1Q	FAV	1Q	FAV	1P	FAV	1P

GROUND: Riverside Park, Bridge Street, Quorn, Leicestershire LE12 8EN
Nearest Railway Station Barrow upon Soar - 1.7km
Bus Route 2 - alight at Crossley Close, 6min walk from there.

BELPER UNITED
Nickname: **Club Colours:** Green and black

Founded
1920

Club Contact Details pitchero.com/clubs/belperutdfc

HONOURS
FA Comps: None
League: Midlands Regional Alliance Premier Division 1985-86, 94-95,
Division One 2004-05.

10-11		11-12		12-13		13-14		14-15		15-16		16-17		17-18		18-19		19-20	
MidRAP	10	CMSth	9	CMSth	3	CMSth	10	CMSth	5	CMSth	2	EMC	13	EMC	5	EMC	10	EMC	n&v
														FAC	P	FAC	EP		
						FAV	1Q	FAV	1P	FAV	1Q	FAV	1Q	FAV	2Q	FAV	1P	FAV	1Q

GROUND: Christchurch Meadow, Bridge Street, Belper DE56 1BA
Nearest Railway Station Belper
Bus Route Transpeak towards Buxton - alight at Mill, 4min walk from there.

BORROWASH VICTORIA
Nickname: The Vics   **Club Colours:** Red & white stripes

Founded
1911

Club Contact Details 07540 938 780

HONOURS
FA Comps: None
League: Derby & District 1952-53. East Midlands regional Premier 1977-78.
Midland Division One 1980-81. Northern Counties East Div.1 South 1983-84.

10-11		11-12		12-13		13-14		14-15		15-16		16-17		17-18		18-19		19-20	
EMC	2	EMC	2	EMC	4	EMC	5	EMC	16	EMC	9	EMC	12	EMC	19	EMC	19	EMC	n&v
FAC	P	FAC	P	FAC	P	FAC	P	FAC	EP										
FAV	2Q	FAV	2Q	FAV	4P	FAV	2P	FAV	2P	FAV	1P	FAV	1Q			FAV	1Q	FAV	1Q

GROUND: Borrowash Road, Spondon, Derby DE21 7PH
Nearest Railway Station Spondon - 1.2km
Bus Route I4 & Indigo

CLIFTON ALL WHITES
Nickname: All Whites   **Club Colours:** All white

Founded
1963

Club Contact Details 07775 615 237

HONOURS
FA Comps: None
League: Notts Alliance Division One 1998-99. Central Midlands 2013-14.
Notts Senior Premier Division 2016-17.

10-11		11-12		12-13		13-14		14-15		15-16		16-17		17-18		18-19		19-20	
		NottS1	2	CMSth	4	CMSth	1	CMSth	8	NottSP	6	NottSP	1	EMC	12	EMC	12	EMC	n&v
										FAV	2Q	FAV	2Q	FAV	1Qr	FAV	1Qr	FAV	2Q

GROUND: Green Lane, Clifton, Nottingham NG11 9AZ
Nearest Railway Station Beeston - 3.2km
Bus Route Clifton Centre Tram Stop 426m from ground.

CLIPSTONE
Nickname: The Cobras   **Club Colours:** Black & white

Founded 1928

Club Contact Details 07792 113 376   enquiries@clipstonefc.co.uk

HONOURS

FA Comps: None

League: Central Midlands 1993-94, 96-97. Northern Counties East Division One 2014-15.

10-11	11-12	12-13	13-14	14-15	15-16	16-17	17-18	18-19	19-20
CM Su 9	CMN 4	NCE1 11	NCE1 7	NCE1 1	NCEP 13	NCEP 16	NCEP 22	EMC 18	EMC n&v
				FAC 1Q	FAC 1Q	FAC EP	FAC P	FAC P	
			FAV 2Q	FAV 2Q	FAV 1P	FAV 2Q	FAV 1P	FAV 1Q	FAV 1Q

GROUND: The Lido Ground, Clipstone Road East, Clipstone Village NG21 9AB

Nearest Railway Station Mansfield Woodhouse - 4.9km

Bus Route Station Road - stop 27m away

DUNKIRK
Nickname: The Boatmen   **Club Colours:** Red and black

Founded 1946

Club Contact Details 0115 985 0803

HONOURS

FA Comps: None

League: Notts Alliance Division Two 1981-82, Division One 1984-85.
Central Midlands Supreme Division 2004-05. East Midlands 2009-10, 17-18.

10-11	11-12	12-13	13-14	14-15	15-16	16-17	17-18	18-19	19-20
MidAl 8	MidAl 18	MidAl 10	MidAl 19	MFLP 19	MFLP 20	EMC 5	EMC 1	MFLP 19	EMC n&v
FAC 1Q	FAC EP	FAC P	FAC 1Q	FAC EP	FAC 3Q	FAC 1Q	FAC 1Q	FAC EP	FAC EP
FAV 3P	FAV 2Q	FAV 1P	FAV 2Q	FAV 2Q	FAV 2P	FAV 2Q	FAV 1P	FAV 2Q	FAV 2P

GROUND: Ron Steel Spts Ground, Lenton Lane, Clifton Bridge, Nottingham NG7 2SA

Nearest Railway Station Beeston - 2.3km

Bus Route 1, 48X, 49X & 901

EASTWOOD COMMUNITY
Nickname: Red Badgers   **Club Colours:** Red and black

Founded 2014

Club Contact Details 01773 432 414 / 07713 478 246

HONOURS

FA Comps: None

League: Central Midlands South 2017-18.

10-11	11-12	12-13	13-14	14-15	15-16	16-17	17-18	18-19	19-20
				CMSth 13	CMSth 10	CMSth 2	CMSth 1	EMC 6	EMC n&v
					FAV 1Q	FAV 2Q	FAV 2Q	FAV 2P	FAV 2P

GROUND: Chewton Street, Eastwood, Notts NG16 3HB

Nearest Railway Station Langley Mill via Chesterfield station. Walk to Acorn Centre to catch bus.

Bus Route Rainbow one bus from Acorn Centre. 11min journey via seven stops to Edward Road, ground 1min walk from there.

GEDLING MINERS WELFARE
Nickname: Miners   **Club Colours:** Yellow and royal blue

Founded 1919

Club Contact Details 0115 926 6300

HONOURS

FA Comps: None

League: Notts Alliance 1945-46, 49-50, 50-51, 51–52, 53-54, 55-56, 57-58, 58-59,
59-60, 60-61, Division Two 2000-01.

10-11	11-12	12-13	13-14	14-15	15-16	16-17	17-18	18-19	19-20
EMC 4	EMC 13	EMC 13	EMC 12	EMC 12	EMC 14	EMC 20	EMC 10	EMC 16	EMC n&v
FAC P	FAC EPr								
FAV 2Q	FAV 1Q	FAV 2Q	FAV 1Q	FAV 1P	FAV 1Q	FAV 1Q	FAV 1Q	FAV 1Q	FAV 2Q

GROUND: Plains Social Club, Plains Road, Mapperley, Nottingham NG3 5RH

Nearest Railway Station Carlton - 3.5km

Bus Route 45

GRAHAM STREET PRIMS
Nickname: Prims   **Club Colours:** Red & white   Founded 1904

Club Contact Details 07902 403 074

HONOURS
FA Comps: None
League: Central Alliance Premier Division 1970-71.
East Midlands Regional 1978-79.

	10-11	11-12	12-13	13-14	14-15	15-16	16-17	17-18	18-19	19-20
EMC	14	14	8	10	18	11	19	16	7	n&v
FAC				EP	EP					
FAV	2Q	1Q	1P	3P	1P	2Q	1Q	1Q	2Q	1Q

GROUND: The Gred Harding Ground, Borrowash Road, Spondon DE21 7PH
Nearest Railway Station Spondon - 1.2km
Bus Route Indigo - alight at Borrowash Road, 3min walk from there.

HEANOR TOWN
Nickname: The Lions   **Club Colours:** White & black   Founded 1883

Club Contact Details 07581 015 868

HONOURS
FA Comps: None
League: Central Midlands Supreme Division 1994-95, 96-97.
East Midlands Counties 2011-12.

	10-11	11-12	12-13	13-14	14-15	15-16	16-17	17-18	18-19	19-20
	EMC 3	EMC 1	NCEP 11	NCEP 8	NCEP 6	MFLP 6	MFLP 6	MFLP 13	EMC 4	EMC n&v
FAC	EPr	1Q	P	EP	EP	EP	1Q	EP	EP	P
FAV	2P	1Q	FAT 1Pr	1P	4P	2P	1P	1Q	1P	3P

GROUND: The Town Ground, Mayfield Avenue, Heanor DE75 7EN
Nearest Railway Station Langley Mill - 2km
Bus Route Sports Ground stop - 132m away

HUCKNALL TOWN
Nickname: The Town   **Club Colours:** Yellow and black   Founded 1987

Club Contact Details 07572 473 037

HONOURS
FA Comps: None
League: Central Midlands South Division 2018-19.

	10-11	11-12	12-13	13-14	14-15	15-16	16-17	17-18	18-19	19-20
	NP P 20	NP1S 11	NP1S 22	CMSth 13	CMSth 4	CMSth 3	CMSth 4	CMSth 3	CMSth 1	EMC n&v
FAC	1Q	1Q	P	EP						
FAT/FAV	FAT 1Q	FAT 1Q	FAT 2Q	FAV 1P		FAV 1P	FAV 3P	FAV 2Q	FAV 2P	FAV 1P

GROUND: Watnall Road, Hucknall, Notts NG15 6EY
Nearest Railway Station Hucknall
Bus Route 3A, 3C, C1, Connect, Green

INGLES
Nickname: **Club Colours:** Red and white   Founded 1972

Club Contact Details 07703 730 872

HONOURS
FA Comps: None
League: North Leicestershire Division Three 1973-74, Division Two 74-75, Premier 92-93, 95-96, 2013-14. Leicestershire Senior Premier Division 2017-18.

	10-11	11-12	12-13	13-14	14-15	15-16	16-17	17-18	18-19	19-20
				NLeiP 1	LeicSP 3	LeicSP 5	LeicSP 7	LeicSP 1	EMC 11	EMC n&v
FAV									2Q	2Qr

GROUND: The Dovecote, Little Haw Lane, Shepshed, Leicestershire LE12 9BN
Nearest Railway Station Loughborough
Bus Route Skylink - alight at the Bull Ring, 6min walk from there.

KIMBERLEY MINERS WELFARE
Nickname: Miners Club Colours: Red & black Founded 1926

Club Contact Details 07803 267 825

HONOURS

FA Comps: None

League: Spartan League 1947-48, 64-65, 65-66. Notts Amateur League 1985-86. Notts Alliance Division Two 1994-95, Division One 95-96.

	10-11	11-12	12-13	13-14	14-15	15-16	16-17	17-18	18-19	19-20
		NottSP 13	NottSP 5	NottSP 2	EMC 13	EMC 15	EMC 8	EMC 6	EMC 9	EMC n&v
								FAC P	FAC P	
						FAV 1Q	FAV 2Qr	FAV 2P	FAV 2Q	FAV 1P

GROUND: Kimberley MWFC, The Stag Ground, Kimberley, Nottingham NG16 2NB
Nearest Railway Station Ilkeston - 3.4km and Bulwell - 3.8km.
Bus Route Rainbow One

OLLERTON TOWN
Nickname: The Town Club Colours: Red and black Founded 1988

Club Contact Details craigemb99@gmail.com

HONOURS

FA Comps: None

League: Notts Alliance Division Two 1992-93, Division One 95-96. Central Midlands Premier Division 2007-08.

	10-11	11-12	12-13	13-14	14-15	15-16	16-17	17-18	18-19	19-20
	CM Su 13	CMN 7	CMN 6	CMN 8	CMN 10	CMN 2	NCE1 17	NCE1 15	NCE1 16	NCE1 n&v
	FAV 1Q	FAV 2Q	FAV 1Q	FAV 2Q		FAV 1Q	FAV 1Q	FAV 2Q	FAV 2Q	FAV 1Q

GROUND: The Lane, Walesby Lane, New Ollerton, Newark NG22 9UT
Nearest Railway Station Worksop
Bus Route Rosewood Centre - stop 214m away

RADFORD
Nickname: The Pheasants Club Colours: Claret and sky blue Founded 1964

Club Contact Details 0115 942 3250

HONOURS

FA Comps: None

League: East Midlands Regional League 1982-83.

	10-11	11-12	12-13	13-14	14-15	15-16	16-17	17-18	18-19	19-20
	EMC 19	EMC 17	EMC 19	EMC 15	EMC 3	EMC 2	EMC 7	EMC 7	EMC 5	EMC n&v
						FAC P	FAC EP	FAC EPr	FAC EP	FAC EP
	FAV 1Q	FAV 2Q	FAV 2Q	FAV 1Q	FAV 1Q	FAV 1P	FAV 2P	FAV 2Q	FAV 1Q	FAV 1Q

GROUND: Selhurst Street, Off Radford Road, Nottingham NG7 5EH
Nearest Railway Station Nottingham - 2.8km
Bus Route 77, 79B, Medlink & Rainbow One

RAINWORTH MINERS WELFARE
Nickname: The Wrens Club Colours: All white Founded 1922

Club Contact Details 01623 792 495

HONOURS

FA Comps: None

League: Notts Alliance 1971-72, 77-78, 78-79, 79-80, 80-81, 81-82, 82-83, 90-91, 95-96, 96-97.

	10-11	11-12	12-13	13-14	14-15	15-16	16-17	17-18	18-19	19-20
	NP1S 20	NP1S 19	NP1N 14	NP1S 15	NP1S 21	NCEP 9	NCEP 18	NCEP 10	EMC 17	EMC n&v
	FAC P	FAC P	FAC 1Qr	FAC Pr	FAC P	FAC EPr	FAC EP	FAC EP	FAC P	
	FAT Pr	FAT P	FAT 1Q	FAT P	FAT Pr	FAV 1Q	FAV 1Q	FAV 1Q	FAV 1Q	FAV 2Q

GROUND: Welfare Ground, Kirklington Road, Rainworth, Mansfield NG21 0JY
Nearest Railway Station Mansfield - 4¼ miles
Bus Route Garden Avenue - stop 24m away

SHERWOOD COLLIERY
Nickname: The Wood **Club Colours:** Black and blue
Founded 2008

Club Contact Details 07813 718 302

HONOURS
FA Comps: None
League: None

10-11	11-12	12-13	13-14	14-15	15-16	16-17	17-18	18-19	19-20
		CMN 15	CMN 11	CMN 17	CMN 5	CMN 3	CMN 2	EMC 3	EMC n&v
									FAC Pr
						FAV 2P	FAV 2Q	FAV 2Q	FAV 2P

GROUND: Debdale Lane, Mansfield Woodhouse, Mansfield NG19 7NS
Nearest Railway Station Mansfield Woodhouse - 6min walk from the ground.
Bus Route 1, 12B, 23 & 53

SHIREBROOK TOWN
Nickname: None **Club Colours:** Red and black
Founded 1985

Club Contact Details pitchero.com/clubs/shirebrooktownfootballclub

HONOURS
FA Comps: None
League: Central Midlands League Supreme Division 2000-01, 01-02.
Northern Counties East Division One 2003-04.

10-11	11-12	12-13	13-14	14-15	15-16	16-17	17-18	18-19	19-20
NCE1 13	NCE1 13	NCE1 6	NCE1 5	NCE1 4	NCE1 7	NCE1 18	NCE1 5	NCE1 18	EMC n&v
FAC 1Q	FAC Pr	FAC EP	FAC Pr	FAC EPr	FAC EP	FAC EPr		FAC EP	
FAV 1Q	FAV 2Q	FAV 2Pr	FAV 2Q	FAV 1Q	FAV 2P	FAV 2Q	FAV 1P	FAV 2Q	FAV 2Q

GROUND: Langwith Road, Shirebrook, Mansfield, NG20 8TF
Nearest Railway Station Shirebrook - 0.2km
Bus Route Langwith Road End - stop 36m away

TEVERSAL
Nickname: Tevie Boys **Club Colours:** Black and red
Founded 1918

Club Contact Details 01623 554 924

HONOURS
FA Comps: None
League: Central Midlands Division Two 1987-88.

10-11	11-12	12-13	13-14	14-15	15-16	16-17	17-18	18-19	19-20
NCE1 18	NCE1 15	NCE1 10	NCE1 15	NCE1 20	NCE1 14	NCE1 16	EMC 3	EMC 15	EMC n&v
FAC EPr		FAC EP	FAC EP					FAC EP	
FAV 1Q	FAV 2Q	FAV 2Q	FAV 2Q	FAV 1Q	FAV 2Q	FAV 1Q	FAV 2Q	FAV 2Q	FAV 1Q

GROUND: Teversal Grange Sports and Social Centre, Carnarvon Street, Teversal, NG17 3HJ
Nearest Railway Station Sutton Parkway - 4.5 miles
Bus Route Trent Barton No.241 from Mansfield bus station to Teversal (Carnarvon Street) - 1/4 mile walk to ground from there.

WEST BRIDGFORD
Nickname: **Club Colours:** Black & red
Founded 1990

Club Contact Details 07581 049 797   pitchero.com/clubs/westbridgfordfootballclub

HONOURS
FA Comps: None
League: East Midlands Counties 2016-17.

10-11	11-12	12-13	13-14	14-15	15-16	16-17	17-18	18-19	19-20
	NottS2 2	NottS1 5	NottS1 2	NottSP 2	NottSP 3	EMC 1	EMC 15	EMC 13	EMC n&v
							FAC EP		
						FAV 2Q	FAV 1Q	FAV 1Q	FAV 2P

GROUND: Regatta Way, Gamston, West Bridgford, Nottingham NG2 5AT
Nearest Railway Station Nottingham
Bus Route Mainline & The Cotgrave

PREMIER DIVISION

BRANTHAM ATHLETIC

Nickname: Blue Imps   **Club Colours:** All blue   Founded 1887

Club Contact Details 01206 392 506 (ground)   secretary@branthamathletic.com

Previous Names: Brantham & Stutton United 1996-98.
Previous Leagues: Eastern Counties. Suffolk & Ipswich.
HONOURS
FA Comps: None
League: Essex & Suffolk Border 1972-73, 73-74, 75-76, 76-77. Suffolk & Ipswich Senior League 2007-08.

	10-11	11-12	12-13	13-14	14-15	15-16	16-17	17-18	18-19	19-20
ECP	13	3	4	11	8	11	8	5	8	n&v
FAC	P	P	P	1Q	EPr	1Q	EP	P	2Q	EP
FAV	1Q	1P	1P	5P	4P	3P	1P	1Q	2Q	1P

GROUND: Brantham Leisure Centre, New Village, Brantham CO11 1RZ
Capacity: 1,200 **Seats:** 200 **Covered:** 200
Nearest Railway Station Manningtree - 1.5km
Bus Route Temple Pattle (Brooklands Close) - 120m

ELY CITY

Nickname: Robins   **Club Colours:** Red   Founded 1885

Club Contact Details 01353 662 035 (ground)   derek.oakey11@gmail.com

Previous Names: None.
Previous Leagues: Cambridgeshire 1901-02, 03-51. Peterborough & District 1951-58. Central Alliance 1958-60.
HONOURS
FA Comps: None
League: Peterborough & District 1955-56.
Eastern Counties Division One 1996-97.

	10-11	11-12	12-13	13-14	14-15	15-16	16-17	17-18	18-19	19-20
ECP	15	2	11	17	20	EC1 2	13	14	18	n&v
FAC	1Q	1Qr	Pr	EP	EP	EPr	EP	EP	EP	Pr
FAV	1Qr	1Q	1Q	4P	2Pr	1Q	2Q	5P	2P	1Q

GROUND: The Ellgia Stadium, Downham Road, Ely CB6 2SH
Capacity: 1,500 **Seats:** 200 **Covered:** 350 **Shop:** Yes
Nearest Railway Station Ely - 2.5km
Bus Route 12, 125, 39 & 9

FC CLACTON

Nickname: The Seasiders   **Club Colours:** White & royal blue   Founded 1892

Club Contact Details 07527 222 088 (ground)   secretaryfcclacton@gmail.com

Previous Names: Clacton Town > 2007
Previous Leagues: Eastern Counties 1935-37, 38-58. Essex County 1937-38. Southern League 1958-64.
HONOURS
FA Comps: None
League: North Essex D2 1898-99, 99-1900. Clacton & District 1905-06. South East Anglian D2 1907-08. Colchester & District D2 1909-10. East Anglian 1910-11. Southern D1 1959-60. Eastern Counties D1 1994-95, 98-99.

	10-11	11-12	12-13	13-14	14-15	15-16	16-17	17-18	18-19	19-20
ECP	16	15	20	15	16	10	20	18	6	n&v
FAC	Pr	Pr	P	2Qr	P	P	EP	EP	P	Pr
FAV	1P	1P	2Q	1Q	2Q	1P	1Q	1Q	3P	3P

GROUND: Rush Green Bowl, Rush Green Rd, Clacton-on-Sea CO16 7BQ
Capacity: 3,000 **Seats:** 200 **Covered:** Yes **Shop:** Yes
Nearest Railway Station Clacton-on-Sea - 1.8km
Bus Route 135, 5, 5A & 74

GODMANCHESTER ROVERS
Nickname: Goody/Rovers   **Club Colours:** Royal blue

Founded 1911

Club Contact Details 07734 136 419 (Ground)   secretary@godmanchesterroversfc.co.uk

Previous Names: None
Previous Leagues: Huntingdonshire County. Cambridgeshire >2002.
HONOURS
FA Comps: None
League: Eastern Counties League Division One 2011-12.

	10-11	11-12	12-13	13-14	14-15	15-16	16-17	17-18	18-19	19-20
	EC1 9	EC1 1	ECP 5	ECP 5	ECP 2	ECP 2	ECP 12	ECP 4	ECP 3	ECP n&v
FAC	EPr	P	P	P	P	P	Pr	EP	1Q	Pr
FAV	2P	3P	1P	1P	1Pr	1Pr	1P	2Q	4P	2P

GROUND: The David Wilson Homes Ground, Godmanchester, Huntingdon PE29 2LQ
Capacity: **Seats:** Yes   **Covered:** Yes
Nearest Railway Station Huntingdon - 3.1km
Bus Route 478 & X3

GORLESTON
Nickname: The Greens   **Club Colours:** Green

Founded 1887

Club Contact Details 01493 602 802 (Ground)   colin-bray@sky.com

Previous Names: None
Previous Leagues: Aldred/Yarmouth & District 1900-08. Norfolk & Suffolk/Anglian Combination 1908-35, 60-69. Eastern Counties 1935-60.
HONOURS
FA Comps: None
League: Yarmouth & District 1905-06, 07-08. Norfolk & Suffolk/Anglian Comb. 1920-21, 25-26, 29-30, 31-32, 32-33, 33-34, 34-35, 68-69. Eastern Counties 1952-53, 72-73, 79-80, 80-81, Division One 1995-96, 2010-11.

	10-11	11-12	12-13	13-14	14-15	15-16	16-17	17-18	18-19	19-20
	EC1 1	ECP 12	ECP 3	ECP 4	ECP 12	ECP 16	ECP 4	ECP 7	ECP 15	ECP n&v
FAC	EP	1Q	P	1Q	EP	EP	EP	1Q	EP	P
FAV	2P	2Q	1P	1P	1P	2P	4P	3P	2Q	1Q

GROUND: Emerald Park, Woodfarm Lane, Gorleston, Norfolk NR31 9AQ
Capacity: **Seats:** Yes   **Covered:** Yes
Nearest Railway Station Great Yarmouth
Bus Route 580, 881 & X1

HADLEIGH UNITED
Nickname: Brettsiders   **Club Colours:** Navy blue

Founded 1892

Club Contact Details 01473 822 165 (Ground)   waffhenderson@aol.com

Previous Names: None
Previous Leagues: Ipswich & District/Suffolk & Ipswich 1929-91.
HONOURS
FA Comps: None
League: Suffolk & Ipswich 1953-54, 56-57, 73-74, 76-77, 78-79, Division Two 1958-59. Eastern Counties 1993-94, 2013-14.

	10-11	11-12	12-13	13-14	14-15	15-16	16-17	17-18	18-19	19-20
	ECP 9	ECP 11	ECP 8	ECP 1	ECP 7	ECP 7	ECP 18	ECP 21	ECP 16	ECP n&v
FAC	P	P	1Q	1Q	1Q	EP	EP	P	P	EP
FAV	1P	1Q	QF	5P	2P	2Q	2Q	2Q	2Q	1P

GROUND: The Millfield, Tinkers Lane, Duke St, Hadleigh IP7 5NF
Capacity: 3,000   **Seats:** 250   **Covered:** 500
Nearest Railway Station Manningtree
Bus Route 91

HAVERHILL ROVERS
Nickname: Rovers   **Club Colours:** Red

Founded 1886

Club Contact Details 01440 702 137 (ground)   barbarajoneshrfc@outlook.com

Previous Names: None.

Previous Leagues: East Anglian. Essex & Suffolk Border.

HONOURS

FA Comps: None

League: Essex & Suffolk Border 1947-48, 62-63, 63-64.
Eastern Counties 1978-79.

10-11		11-12		12-13		13-14		14-15		15-16		16-17		17-18		18-19		19-20	
ECP	8	ECP	14	ECP	10	ECP	7	ECP	17	ECP	12	ECP	16	ECP	19	ECP	12	ECP	n&v
FAC	Pr	FAC	1Q	FAC	P	FAC	P	FAC	EPr	FAC	EP	FAC	EP	FAC	EP	FAC	Pr	FAC	2Q	FAC	EP
FAV	1P	FAV	1P	FAV	1P	FAV	1P	FAV	1Q	FAV	2Q	FAV	1Q	FAV	2Q	FAV	1Q	FAV	2Q	FAV	2Q

GROUND: The New Croft, Chalkstone Way, Haverhill, Suffolk CB9 0BW

Capacity: 3,000   **Seats:** 200   **Covered:** 200

Nearest Railway Station Cambridge - take 13 Gold towards Haverhill - alight at Chalkstone Way Underpass, 1min walk from there.

Bus Route 13, 13A, 15 & 18

KIRKLEY & PAKEFIELD
Nickname: The Kirks   **Club Colours:** Royal blue

Founded 1886

Club Contact Details 01502 513 549 (ground)   secretarykpfc@outlook.com

Previous Names: Kirkley. Kirkley & Waveney 1929-33. Merged with Pakefield in 2007.

Previous Leagues: North Suffolk. Norfolk & Suffolk. Anglian Combination.

HONOURS

FA Comps: None

League: North Suffolk 1894-95, 96-97, 1901-02, 05-06, 07-08, 08-09.
Anglian Combination Premier Division 2001-02, 02-03.

10-11		11-12		12-13		13-14		14-15		15-16		16-17		17-18		18-19		19-20	
ECP	12	ECP	13	ECP	12	ECP	12	ECP	4	ECP	5	ECP	11	ECP	10	ECP	5	ECP	n&v
FAC	EP	FAC	EP	FAC	P	FAC	P	FAC	P	FAC	2Q	FAC	P	FAC	EP	FAC	EPr	FAC	EPr
FAV	2P	FAV	1Q	FAV	1Q	FAV	2Q	FAV	2P	FAV	2P	FAV	1Q	FAV	2Q	FAV	2P	FAV	4P

GROUND: The Bungalow, Walmer Road, Lowestoft NR33 7LE

Capacity: 2,000   **Seats:** 150   **Covered:** 150   **Shop:** Yes

Nearest Railway Station Oulton Broad South - 1.8km

Bus Route 146 & 99

LONG MELFORD
Nickname: The Villagers   **Club Colours:** Black & white

Founded 1868

Club Contact Details 01787 312 187 (Ground)   richardjpowell@outlook.com

Previous Names: N/A

Previous Leagues: Essex & Suffolk Border > 2003

HONOURS

FA Comps: None

League: Essex & Suffolk Border Champions x5.
Eastern Counties Division One 2014-15.

10-11		11-12		12-13		13-14		14-15		15-16		16-17		17-18		18-19		19-20	
EC1	12	EC1	9	EC1	13	EC1	11	EC1	1	ECP	9	ECP	17	ECP	16	ECP	17	ECP	n&v
				FAC	P	FAC	EP			FAC	P	FAC	P	FAC	P	FAC	1Qr	FAC	P
FAV	2Q	FAV	1Q	FAV	1P	FAV	2Q	FAV	2Q	FAV	2Q	FAV	2Q	FAV	1Q	FAV	1Q	FAV	P

GROUND: Stoneylands Stadium, New Road, Long Melford, Suffolk CO10 9JY

Capacity: **Seats:** Yes   **Covered:** Yes

Nearest Railway Station Sudbury - 4.6km

Bus Route 236

MILDENHALL TOWN
Nickname: The Hall   **Club Colours:** Amber & black   Founded 1898

Club Contact Details 01638 713 449 (ground)   bhensby@talktalk.net

Previous Names: None
Previous Leagues: Bury & District. Cambridgeshire. Cambridgeshire Premier. Eastern Counties > 2017. Isthmian 2017-19.
HONOURS
FA Comps: None
League: Eastern Counties Premier Division 2016-17.

	10-11	11-12	12-13	13-14	14-15	15-16	16-17	17-18	18-19	19-20
	ECP 5	ECP 7	ECP 7	ECP 10	ECP 10	ECP 6	ECP 1	Isth1N 22	IsthN 20	ECP n&v
	FAC EP	FAC EP	FAC EP	FAC 1Qr	FAC 1Q	FAC 2Q	FAC EP	FAC 1Qr	FAC P	FAC EP
	FAV 1Q	FAV 2Q	FAV 1Q	FAT 1Pr	FAT 2Q	FAT 2P	FAT 2Q	FAT 3Q	FAT 1Q	FAV 2P

GROUND: Recreation Way, Mildenhall, Suffolk IP28 7HG
Capacity: 2,000   **Seats:** 100   **Covered:** 200   **Shop:** Yes
Nearest Railway Station Kennett
Bus Route 727

NEWMARKET TOWN
Nickname: The Jockeys   **Club Colours:** Yellow & royal blue   Founded 1877

Club Contact Details 01638 663 637 (ground)   domszary123@hotmail.com

Previous Names: None
Previous Leagues: Cambridgeshire Senior. Bury & District. Suffolk & Ipswich >1937. Eastern Counties 1937-52. Peterborough & District 1952-59.
HONOURS
FA Comps: None
League: Cambridgeshire Senior 1919-20. Bury & District 1926-27. Suffolk & Ipswich 1931-32, 32-33, 33-34. Peterborough & District 1957-58. Eastern Counties Division One 2008-09.

	10-11	11-12	12-13	13-14	14-15	15-16	16-17	17-18	18-19	19-20
	ECP 19	ECP 20	EC1 2	ECP 9	ECP 6	ECP 13	ECP 3	ECP 9	ECP 10	ECP n&v
	FAC P	FAC EP	FAC EP	FAC Pr	FAC 1Q	FAC P	FAC EP	FAC P	FAC 1Q	FAC EPr
	FAV 2Q	FAV 2Q	FAV 2Q	FAV 2P	FAV 2Q	FAV 1P	FAV 2Q	FAV 1P	FAV 1P	FAV 2Qr

GROUND: The Bloorie Stadium, Cricket Field Road, Off Cheveley Rd, Newmarket CB8 8BT
Capacity: 2,750   **Seats:** 144   **Covered:** 250   **Shop:** Yes
Nearest Railway Station Newmarket - 0.4km
Bus Route 11, 12,16, 18, 903 & 904

NORWICH UNITED
Nickname: Planters   **Club Colours:** Yellow & blue   Founded 1903

Club Contact Details 01603 716 963 (ground)   norwich.utd.fc@gmail.com

Previous Names: Poringland & District > 1987
Previous Leagues: Norwich & District. Anglian Combination. Eastern Counties >2016. Isthmian 2016-18.
HONOURS
FA Comps: None
League: Anglian Combination Premier Division 1988-99.
Eastern Counties Division One 1990-91, 01-02, Premier Division 2014-15, 15-16.

	10-11	11-12	12-13	13-14	14-15	15-16	16-17	17-18	18-19	19-20
	ECP 6	ECP 9	ECP 13	ECP 6	ECP 1	ECP 1	ECP 9	Isth1N 24	ECP 11	ECP n&v
	FAC Pr	FAC EP	FAC 1Q	FAC EP	FAC 2Qr	FAC Pr	FAC P	FAC P	FAC EP	FAC EP
	FAV 1P	FAV 2Q	FAV 2Q	FAV 4P	FAV 5P	FAT 2P	FAT P	FAT P	FAV 1Q	FAV 2P

GROUND: Plantation Park, Blofield, Norwich NR13 4PL
Capacity: 3,000   **Seats:** 100   **Covered:** 1,000   **Shop:** Yes
Nearest Railway Station Brundall - 2.1km
Bus Route Surgery (Plantation Rd) stop - 48m away.

STANWAY ROVERS

Nickname: Rovers **Club Colours:** Yellow

Founded 1956

Club Contact Details 01206 578 187 (ground) ivan_senter@tiscali.co.uk

Previous Names: None.
Previous Leagues: Colchester & East Essex. Essex & Suffolk Border. Eastern Counties >2018. Essex Senior 2018-19.
HONOURS
FA Comps: None
League: Colchester & East Essex Premier Division 1973-74. Essex & Suffolk Border Division Two 1981-82, 85-86. Eastern Counties Division One 2005-06.

	10-11		11-12		12-13		13-14		14-15		15-16		16-17		17-18		18-19		19-20	
ECP	7	ECP	5	ECP	9	ECP	13	ECP	3	ECP	3	ECP	6	ECP	8	ESen	15	ECP	n&v	
FAC	1Qr	FAC	EP	FAC	EP	FAC	EPr	FAC	EP	FAC	2Q	FAC	1Q	FAC	EP	FAC	P	FAC	P	
FAV	3P	FAV	2Q	FAV	2Q	FAV	2Q	FAV	5P	FAV	3P	FAV	2P	FAV	2Q	FAV	2Q	FAV	3Pr	

GROUND: Hawthorns, New Farm Road, Stanway, Colchester CO3 0PG
Capacity: 1,500 **Seats:** 100 **Covered:** 250 **Shop:** Yes
Nearest Railway Station Colchester - 3.7km
Bus Route 70 & 71

STOWMARKET TOWN

Nickname: Gold and Blacks **Club Colours:** Old Gold & black

Founded 1883

Club Contact Details 01449 612 533 (ground) davidwalker545@gmail.com

Previous Names: Stowuplands Corinthians. Stowmarket Corinthians. Stowmarket FC
Previous Leagues: Ipswich & District 1896-1925. Essex & Suffolk Border 1925-52.
HONOURS
FA Comps: None
League: Ipswich & District/Suffolk & Ipwich 1896-97, 97-98, 99-1900, 21-22. Essex & Suffolk Border 1950-51. Eastern Counties Division One 2016-17.

	10-11		11-12		12-13		13-14		14-15		15-16		16-17		17-18		18-19		19-20	
EC1	7	EC1	15	EC1	17	EC1	14	EC1	11	EC1	14	EC1	1	ECP	3	ECP	4	ECP	n&v	
		FAC	EP											FAC	Pr	FAC	EP	FAC	P	
FAV	2Q	FAV	2Q	FAV	1Q	FAV	2Q	FAV	2Q	FAV	2Q	FAV	1Q	FAV	2Q	FAV	4P	FAV	5P	

GROUND: Stowmarket Community S & S Club, Greens Meadow, Bury Road, Stowmarket, Suffolk IP14 1JQ
Capacity: **Seats:** Yes **Covered:** Yes
Nearest Railway Station Stowmarket - 1km
Bus Route 88

SWAFFHAM TOWN

Nickname: Pedlars **Club Colours:** Black & white

Founded 1892

Club Contact Details 01760 722 700 (ground) rayewart@aol.com

Previous Names: None
Previous Leagues: Anglian Combination
HONOURS
FA Comps: None
League: Anglian Combination Division Two 1973-74. Eastern Counties Division One 2000-01, Division One North 18-19.

	10-11		11-12		12-13		13-14		14-15		15-16		16-17		17-18		18-19		19-20	
EC1	15	EC1	13	EC1	9	EC1	7	EC1	2	ECP	18	ECP	21	ECP	4	EC1N	1	ECP	n&v	
						FAC	P	FAC	EP	FAC	EP	FAC	EP	FAC	EP	FAC	EP	FAC	P	
FAV	2Q	FAV	1Q	FAV	1P	FAV	1Pr	FAV	1Q	FAV	1P	FAV	1P	FAV	2Q	FAV	3Pr	FAV	1Q	

GROUND: The Pavillion, Shoemakers Lane, Swaffham, Norfolk PE37 7NS
Capacity: **Seats:** Yes **Covered:** Yes
Nearest Railway Station Peterborough - take A excel towards Norwich City Centre - alight at the Kings Arms, 10min walk from there.
Bus Route 6 & 61

THETFORD TOWN
Nickname: Brecklanders | Club Colours: Claret & blue | Founded 1883

Club Contact Details 01842 766 120 (Ground)   jackieskipp@live.co.uk

Previous Names: None
Previous Leagues: Norwich & District. Norfolk & Suffolk. Founder member of Eastern Counties League
HONOURS
FA Comps: None
League: Norfolk & Suffolk League 1954-55.

	10-11	11-12	12-13	13-14	14-15	15-16	16-17	17-18	18-19	19-20
	EC1 5	EC1 2	ECP 19	ECP 16	ECP 14	ECP 19	ECP 7	ECP 12	ECP 14	ECP n&v
FAC	EPr	EP	EP	P	P	P	EP	EP	P	EP
FAV	2Q	2P	2Q	1P	2Q	1Q	2P	2P	2P	2Q

GROUND: Recreation Ground, Mundford Road, Thetford, Norfolk IP24 1NB
Capacity: Seats: Yes   Covered: Yes
Nearest Railway Station Thetford - 0.5km
Bus Route 201, 84 & 86

WALSHAM LE WILLOWS
Nickname: The Willows | Club Colours: Yellow | Founded 1888

Club Contact Details 01359 259 298 (Ground)   gordonaross2@gmail.com

Previous Names: None
Previous Leagues: St Edmundsbury/Bury & District 1907-89. Suffolk & Ipswich 1989-2004.
HONOURS
FA Comps: None
League: Suffolk & Ipswich Senior Division 2001-02, 02-03. Eastern Counties Division One 2006-07.

	10-11	11-12	12-13	13-14	14-15	15-16	16-17	17-18	18-19	19-20
	ECP 17	ECP 17	ECP 6	ECP 8	ECP 15	ECP 14	ECP 14	ECP 17	ECP 9	ECP n&v
FAC	EP	Pr	EP	EP	EPr	EP	EPr	EPr	EP	EP
FAV	2P	1P	1Pr	2P	2Q	2Q	1P	2Q	2Q	2Q

GROUND: Walsham-le-Willows Sports Club, Sumner Road, Walsham-le-Willows IP31 3AH
Capacity: Seats: 100   Covered: 100

Bus Route 338

WHITTON UNITED
Nickname: The Boyos | Club Colours: Green and white | Founded 1926

Club Contact Details 01473 464 030 (Ground)   secretary@whittonunited.co.uk

Previous Names:
Previous Leagues: Essex & Border. Ispswich District. Suffolk & Ipswich.
HONOURS
FA Comps: None
League: Suffolk & Ipswich Senior 1946-47, 47-48, 65-66, 67-68, 91-92, 92-93. Eastern Counties Division One 2013-14.

	10-11	11-12	12-13	13-14	14-15	15-16	16-17	17-18	18-19	19-20
	EC1 2	EC1 3	EC1 7	EC1 1	ECP 11	ECP 20	EC1 11	EC1 3	ECP 13	ECP n&v
FAC		EP		Pr	P	P	EPr		P	1Q
FAV	2P	2P	1P	2Q	1P	1P	1Q	1P	2Q	1P

GROUND: King George V Playing Fields, Old Norwich Road, Ipswich IP1 6LE
Capacity: Seats: Yes   Covered: Yes
Nearest Railway Station Westerfield - 2.9km
Bus Route Maypole (Old Norwich Rd) - 52m away

WOODBRIDGE TOWN

Nickname: The Woodpeckers **Club Colours:** Black & white

Founded 1885

Club Contact Details 01394 385 308 (ground)   richardnscott@btinternet.com

Previous Names: None.

Previous Leagues: Ipswich & District. Suffolk & Ipswich.

HONOURS

FA Comps: None

League: Ipswich & District/Suffolk & Ipswich Senior 1912-13, 88-89, Division One 1986-87, 70-71. Eastern Counties Division One 2017-18.

10-11		11-12		12-13		13-14		14-15		15-16		16-17		17-18		18-19		19-20	
ECP	10	ECP	6	ECP	15	ECP	20	EC1	17	EC1	9	EC1	4	EC1	1	ECP	2	ECP	n&v
FAC	EP	FAC	EPr	FAC	EP	FAC	EP	FAC	EP					FAC	EP	FAC	1Q	FAC	P
FAV	2Q	FAV	1Pr	FAV	2Q	FAV	2Q	FAV	1P	FAV	2Q	FAV	2Q	FAV	2Q	FAV	2P	FAV	4P

GROUND: Notcutts Park, Fynn Road, Woodbridge IP12 4LS

Capacity: 3,000 **Seats:** 50   **Covered:** 200   **Shop:** No

Nearest Railway Station Woodbridge - 1.7km

Bus Route Ashton House (California) - 201m away

WROXHAM

Nickname: Yachtsmen   **Club Colours:** Royal blue

Founded 1892

Club Contact Details 01603 783 538 (ground)   ray.bayles@ntlworld.com

Previous Names: None

Previous Leagues: East Norfolk. Norwich City. East Anglian. Norwich & Dist. Anglian Comb.

HONOURS

FA Comps: None

League: Anglian County League 1981-82, 82-83, 83-84, 84-85, 86-87. Eastern Counties Division One 1988-89, Prem 91-92, 92-93, 93-94, 96-97, 97-98, 98-99, 2006-07, 11-12.

10-11		11-12		12-13		13-14		14-15		15-16		16-17		17-18		18-19		19-20	
ECP	3	ECP	1	Isth1N	14	Isth1N	22	Isth1N	8	Isth1N	22	Isth1N	23	ECP	13	ECP	7	ECP	n&v
FAC	Pr	FAC	3Q	FAC	1Q	FAC	1Q	FAC	2Q	FAC	1Q	FAC	P	FAC	EP	FAC	EPr	FAC	P
FAV	3P	FAV	1P	FAT	1Qr	FAT	1Q	FAT	P	FAT	P	FAT	1Q	FAV	2Q	FAV	1P	FAV	QF

GROUND: Trafford Park, Skinners Lane, Wroxham NR12 8SJ

Capacity: 2,500 **Seats:** 50   **Covered:** 250

Nearest Railway Station Hoveton & Wroxham - 1.6km

Bus Route 722, 724 and 717.

ESSENTIAL READING FOR FOLLOWERS OF THE NATIONAL GAME

BUY IT IN YOUR NEWSAGENTS EVERY SUNDAY

BE CLOSE TO THE PASSION

OUT: Felixstowe & Walton United Res (WD).

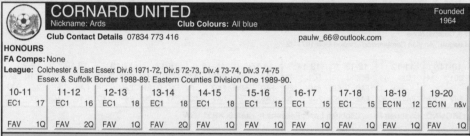

AFC SUDBURY RESERVES

Nickname: AFC   **Club Colours:** Yellow & blue   Founded 1999

Club Contact Details 01787 376 213   dave-afc@supanet.com

HONOURS
FA Comps: None
League: None

10-11	11-12	12-13	13-14	14-15	15-16	16-17	17-18	18-19	19-20
			EC1 16	EC1 14	EC1 10	EC1 18	EC1 11	EC1N 13	EC1N n&v

GROUND: Kings Marsh Stadium, Brundon Lane, Sudbury CO10 7HN
Nearest Railway Station Sudbury - 1.5km
Bus Route Bulmer Road - stop 100m away

CORNARD UNITED

Nickname: Ards   **Club Colours:** All blue   Founded 1964

Club Contact Details 07834 773 416   paulw_66@outlook.com

HONOURS
FA Comps: None
League: Colchester & East Essex Div.6 1971-72, Div.5 72-73, Div.4 73-74, Div.3 74-75
Essex & Suffolk Border 1988-89. Eastern Counties Division One 1989-90.

10-11	11-12	12-13	13-14	14-15	15-16	16-17	17-18	18-19	19-20
EC1 17	EC1 16	EC1 18	EC1 18	EC1 18	EC1 15	EC1 15	EC1 15	EC1N 12	EC1N n&v
FAV 1Q	FAV 2Q	FAV 1Q	FAV 2Q	FAV 1Q	FAV 1Q	FAV 1Q	FAV 1Q	FAV 1Q	FAV 1Q

GROUND: Backhouse Lane, Great Cornard, Sudbury, Suffolk CO10 0NL
Nearest Railway Station Sudbury - 2.2km

DEBENHAM LC

Nickname: The Hornets   **Club Colours:** Yellow & black   Founded 1991

Club Contact Details 01728 861 101 (ground)

HONOURS
FA Comps: None
League: Suffolk & Ipswich Division Seven 1991-92, Four 96-97, Three 99-2000, One 03-04.

10-11	11-12	12-13	13-14	14-15	15-16	16-17	17-18	18-19	19-20
ECP 22	EC1 7	EC1 15	EC1 12	EC1 7	EC1 13	EC1 12	EC1 7	EC1N 11	EC1N n&v
	FAC EP	FAC EP			FAC EP				
FAV 2Q	FAV 2Q	FAV 1Qr	FAV 1P	FAV 2Q	FAV 2Q	FAV 1Q	FAV 1Pr	FAV 1Pr	FAV 2Q

GROUND: Debenham Leisure Centre, Gracechurch Street, Debenham IP14 6BL

DISS TOWN

Nickname: Tangerines   **Club Colours:** Tangerine & navy   Founded 1888

Club Contact Details 01379 651 223 (ground)   pamdisstownfc@gmail.com

HONOURS
FA Comps: FA Vase 1993-94.
League: Anglian Combination Division One 1967-68, 73-74, Premier 76-77, 78-79.
Eastern Counties Division One 1991-92.

10-11	11-12	12-13	13-14	14-15	15-16	16-17	17-18	18-19	19-20
EC1 3	ECP 16	ECP 17	ECP 18	ECP 19	EC1 7	EC1 6	EC1 12	EC1N 15	EC1N n&v
FAC EP	FAC EP	FAC EP	FAC EP	FAC EP	FAC EP		FAC EP		
FAV 1Q	FAV 3P	FAV 2P	FAV 1P	FAV 1Q	FAV 1P	FAV 2Q	FAV 2Q	FAV 1Q	FAV 1Q

GROUND: Brewers Green Lane, Diss, Norfolk IP22 4QP
Nearest Railway Station Diss - 0.5 miles

DOWNHAM TOWN
Nickname: Town   Club Colours: Red   Founded 1881

Club Contact Details   george.dickson@me.com

HONOURS
FA Comps: None
League: Peterborough & District 1962-63, 73-74, 78-79, 86-87, 87-88.

10-11	11-12	12-13	13-14	14-15	15-16	16-17	17-18	18-19	19-20
EC1 16	EC1 14	EC1 16	EC1 17	EC1 9	EC1 16	EC1 14	EC1 9	EC1N 8	EC1N n&v
	FAV 2Q	FAV 2Q	FAV 1Q		FAV 2Q	FAV 2Q	FAV 1Q	FAV 1Q	FAV 1Q

GROUND: Memorial Field, Lynn Road, Downham Market PE38 9AU
Nearest Railway Station Downham Market - 1.25 miles

FAKENHAM TOWN
Nickname: Ghosts   Club Colours: Amber & black   Founded 1884

Club Contact Details 01328 851 735 (ground)   chilvers.paul@yahoo.com

HONOURS
FA Comps: None
League: Anglian Combination Division One 1971-72.

10-11	11-12	12-13	13-14	14-15	15-16	16-17	17-18	18-19	19-20
EC1 14	EC1 11	EC1 5	EC1 2	ECP 13	ECP 17	ECP 15	ECP 22	EC1N 6	EC1N n&v
		FAC EP	FAC EP	FAC EPr	FAC P	FAC EP	FAC EP	FAC EP	FAC EP
FAV 1Qr	FAV 1Q	FAV 2Q	FAV 2Q	FAV 2P	FAV 2Q	FAV 2Q	FAV 1Q	FAV 1Q	FAV 1Q

GROUND: Clipbush Park, Clipbush Lane, Fakenham, Norfolk NR21 8SW

Bus Route Sanders Coaches No.9

FRAMLINGHAM TOWN
Nickname: The Castlemen   Club Colours: Green & white   Founded 1887

Club Contact Details   fionawhatling@tiscali.co.uk

HONOURS
FA Comps: None
League: Suffolk & Ipswich Division Two 1980-81, Senior Division 91-92.

10-11	11-12	12-13	13-14	14-15	15-16	16-17	17-18	18-19	19-20
S&IS 10	S&IS 16	S&I1 10	S&I1 5	S&I1 2	S&IS 5	EC1 7	EC1 2	ECP 20	EC1N n&v
							FAC P	FAC EPr	FAC P
FAV 1P	FAV 2Q					FAV 1Q	FAV 2P	FAV 2Qr	FAV 1Q

GROUND: Framingham Sports Club, Badingham Road, Framlingham IP13 9HS

GREAT YARMOUTH TOWN
Nickname: The Bloaters   Club Colours: Yellow & black   Founded 1897

Club Contact Details 07776 147 508 (Secretary)   jglewsley@btinternet.com

HONOURS
FA Comps: None
League: Norfolk & Suffolk 1913-14, 26-27, 27-28. Eastern Counties 1968-69, Division One 2009-10.

10-11	11-12	12-13	13-14	14-15	15-16	16-17	17-18	18-19	19-20
ECP 14	ECP 21	EC1 10	EC1 8	EC1 4	EC1 3	ECP 5	ECP 15	ECP 19	EC1N n&v
FAC EP	FAC EP	FAC P	FAC EP	FAC P	FAC EP	FAC EP	FAC 1Q	FAC EP	FAC P
FAV 2Q	FAV 2Q	FAV 2Q	FAV 2P	FAV 3P	FAV 1P	FAV 1P	FAV 2Q	FAV 2P	FAV 2Q

GROUND: The Wellesley, Sandown Road, Great Yarmouth NR30 1EY
Nearest Railway Station Great Yarmouth - 1/2 mile away.

HAVERHILL BOROUGH

Nickname: Borough **Club Colours:** Blue

Founded 2011

Club Contact Details 01440 702 137 (Ground)

HONOURS

FA Comps: None

League: Essex & Suffolk Border Division One 2011-12.

10-11	11-12	12-13	13-14	14-15	15-16	16-17	17-18	18-19	19-20
	EsSu1 1	EsSuP 2	EC1 4	EC1 6	EC1 8	EC1 3	ECP 20	EC1N 16	EC1n n&v
				FAC 1Q	FAC EP		FAC 1Q	FAC EP	
			FAV 1Q	FAV 1P	FAV 1Q	FAV 1P	FAV 1Q	FAV 1P	FAV 2Q

GROUND: The New Croft, Chalkestone Way, Haverhill, Suffolk CB9 0BW

IPSWICH WANDERERS

Nickname: Wanderers **Club Colours:** All blue

Founded 1980

Club Contact Details 01473 720 691 (Ground)

HONOURS

FA Comps: None

League: Eastern Counties Division One 1997-98, 04-05.

10-11	11-12	12-13	13-14	14-15	15-16	16-17	17-18	18-19	19-20
EC1 10	EC1 12	EC1 4	EC1 3	ECP 9	ECP 15	ECP 10	ECP 23	EC1N 10	EC1N n&v
	FAC Pr	FAC EP	FAC P	FAC 1Qr	FAC 2Q	FAC EPr	FAC EP	FAC EP	
FAV 1P	FAV 2Q	FAV 1P	FAV 1P	FAV 2P	FAV 5Pr	FAV 2P	FAV 1Q	FAV 1Q	FAV 1Q

GROUND: SEH Sports Centre, Humber Doucy Lane, Ipswich IP4 3NR

Nearest Railway Station Derby Road (Ipswich) 2.1km.

KING'S LYNN TOWN RESERVES

Nickname: The Linnets **Club Colours:** Blue

Founded 1879

Club Contact Details 01553 760 060 (Ground) ncesar1947@yahoo.co.uk

HONOURS

FA Comps: None

League: None

10-11	11-12	12-13	13-14	14-15	15-16	16-17	17-18	18-19	19-20
				EC1 5	EC1 5	EC1 10	EC1 6	EC1N 14	EC1N n&v

GROUND: The Walks Stadium, Tennyson Road, King's Lynn PE30 5PB.

Nearest Railway Station King's Lynn - 5min walk away.

Bus Route Serviced by Eastern Counties & Norfolk Green

LAKENHEATH

Nickname: **Club Colours:** Green & white

Founded

Club Contact Details lakenheathfc.secretary@gmail.com

HONOURS

FA Comps: None

League: Cambridgeshire County Senior Division A 2007-08, Premier 10-11.

10-11	11-12	12-13	13-14	14-15	15-16	16-17	17-18	18-19	19-20
CamP 1	CamP 2	CamP 9	CamP 5	CamP 2	CamP 6	CamP 3	CamP 8	EC1N 5	EC1N n&v
									FAV 1Q

GROUND: The Nest, Wings Road, Lakenheath IP27 9HN

Nearest Railway Station Lakenheath 4.5km walk

Bus Route 201 from Mildenhall, 200 from Thetford

LEISTON RESERVES
Nickname: Blues   Club Colours: All blue   Founded 1880

Club Contact Details 01728 830 308 (ground)

HONOURS
FA Comps: None
League: None

10-11	11-12	12-13	13-14	14-15	15-16	16-17	17-18	18-19	19-20
				EC1 19	EC1 6	EC1 21	EC1 13	EC1N 9	EC1N n&v

GROUND: The LTAA, Victory Road, Leiston, Suffolk IP16 4DQ
Nearest Railway Station Saxmundham - 6 miles
Bus Route Alde Valley Sixth Form - stop 300m away

MARCH TOWN UNITED
Nickname: Hares   Club Colours: Amber & black   Founded 1885

Club Contact Details 01354 653 073 (ground)   chris@gbshealthandsafety.co.uk

HONOURS
FA Comps: None
League: United Counties Division One 1953-54. Eastern Counties 1987-88.

10-11	11-12	12-13	13-14	14-15	15-16	16-17	17-18	18-19	19-20
EC1 8	EC1 4	EC1 14	EC1 19	EC1 8	EC1 11	EC1 16	EC1 17	EC1N 4	EC1N n&v
FAC P	FAC Pr	FAC EP							FAC 1Q
FAV 1Q	FAV 1Q	FAV 1Q	FAV 2Q			FAV 2Q	FAV 1Q	FAV 2Q	FAV 1P

GROUND: GER Sports Ground, Robin Goodfellow Lane, March, Cambs PE15 8HS
Nearest Railway Station March - 0.7km
Bus Route Darthill Road stop - 290m away

MULBARTON WANDERERS
Nickname: Wanderers   Club Colours: Blue & black   Founded 2002

Club Contact Details 07545 470 130   j.nurse21@btinternet.com

HONOURS
FA Comps: None
League: Anglian Combination Division Five 2010-11, Division Four 11-12, Division One 14-15.

10-11	11-12	12-13	13-14	14-15	15-16	16-17	17-18	18-19	19-20
AnC5 1	AnC4 1	AnC3 2	AnC3 2	AnC1 1	AnCP 8	AnCP 3	AnCP 2	EC1N 3	EC1N n&v
									FAC EPr
							FAV 2Q		FAV 2Q

GROUND: Mulberry Park, Mulbarton Common, Norfolk NR14 8AE
Nearest Railway Station Norwich (6.5 miles away)
Bus Route Regular services from Norwich City centre to the village of Mulbarton.

NEEDHAM MARKET RESERVES
Nickname: The Marketmen   Club Colours: Red   Founded 1919

Club Contact Details 01449 721 000 (ground)   m.easlea@sky.com

HONOURS
FA Comps: None
League: None

10-11	11-12	12-13	13-14	14-15	15-16	16-17	17-18	18-19	19-20
			EC1 15	EC1 16	EC1 19	EC1 19	EC1 20	EC1N 17	EC1N n&v

GROUND: Bloomfields, Quinton Road, Needham Market IP6 8DA.
Nearest Railway Station Needham Market - 0.6km
Bus Route Quinton Road stop - 38m away

NORWICH CBS
Nickname: **Club Colours:** Sky blue

Founded 1888

Club Contact Details 01603 748 944 (ground)   norwichcbsfc@outlook.com

HONOURS
FA Comps: None
League: Anglian Combination Premier Division 2016-17.

10-11	11-12	12-13	13-14	14-15	15-16	16-17	17-18	18-19	19-20
AnCP 11	AnCP 4	AnCP 2	AnCP 2	AnCP 5	AnCP 2	AnCP 1	EC1 8	EC1N 7	EC1N n&v
									FAC EP
							FAV 4P	FAV 2P	FAV 1Q

GROUND: The FDC, Bowthorpe Park, Clover Hill Road, Norwich NR5 9ED

Bus Route Breckland Road stop - 176m away

SHERINGHAM
Nickname: The Shannocks **Club Colours:** Red

Founded 1897

Club Contact Details 07961 435261 (Secretary)   info@sheringhamfc.co.uk

HONOURS
FA Comps: None
League: Norfolk & Suffolk 1957-58. Anglian Combination Premier 1969-70, 2008-09, 18-19, Division Three 02-03, Division Two 03-04, Division One 04-05.

10-11	11-12	12-13	13-14	14-15	15-16	16-17	17-18	18-19	19-20
AnCP 10	AnCP 11	AnCP 14	AnCP 13	AnCP 16	AnC1 6	AnC1 11	AnC1 2	AnCP 1	EC1N n&v

GROUND: Sheringham Recreation, Weybourne Road, Sheringham NR26 8WD

WISBECH ST MARY
Nickname: The Saints **Club Colours:** Purple

Founded 1993

Club Contact Details 01945 410 243 (ground)   martin@jsholmes.com

HONOURS
FA Comps: None
League: Cambridgeshire County Division 1B 2008-09, Senior B 10-11,

10-11	11-12	12-13	13-14	14-15	15-16	16-17	17-18	18-19	19-20
CamSB 1	CamSA 3	CamP 7	CamP 8	CamP 15	CamP 5	EC1 13	EC1 18	EC1N 18	EC1N n&v
					FAV 2Q	FAV 1Q	FAV 2P	FAV 1Q	FAV 1Q

GROUND: ABC Meats Stadium, Beechings Close, Wisbech St Mary PE13 4SS

Bus Route St Mary's Close (High Rd) stop - 362m away

IN: Brimsdown (LM - SSM1).
OUT: Brightlingsea Regent Res (WD), Hackney Wicks (LM - SSM1).

DIVISION ONE SOUTH

BARKINGSIDE

Founded 1898

Nickname: The Side / Sky Blues   **Club Colours:** Sky blue

Club Contact Details 020 8552 3995   confclothing@aol.com

HONOURS
FA Comps: None
League: Spartan Premier Division 1996-97. Spartan South Midlands 1998-99.

10-11		11-12		12-13		13-14		14-15		15-16		16-17		17-18		18-19		19-20	
ESen	15	ESen	8	ESen	2	Isth1N	20	Isth1N	22	Isth1N	23	ESen	10	ESen	16	ESen	19	EC1S	n&v
FAC	EP	FAC	EP	FAC	EPr	FAC	P	FAC	1Q	FAC	P	FAC	P	FAC	EP	FAC	EPr	FAC	P
FAV	2Q	FAV	2Qr	FAV	1Q	FAT	P	FAT	2Q	FAT	P	FAV	2Q	FAV	2Q	FAV	2Q	FAV	1Q

GROUND: Cricketfield Stadium, 3 Cricklefield Place, Ilford IG1 1FY
Nearest Railway Station Ilford (underground) / Seven Kings (BR) ½ mile
Bus Route 86 outside ground

BENFLEET

Founded 1922

Nickname: **Club Colours:** Sky and navy blue

Club Contact Details 01268 682 991 (Canvey Island FC)

HONOURS
FA Comps: None
League: Essex Olympian Division One 1988-89, Division Two 2006-07, Division Three 15-16.

10-11		11-12		12-13		13-14		14-15		15-16		16-17		17-18		18-19		19-20	
EsxO1	5	EsxO1	11	EsxO1	9	EsxO1	11	EsxO2	Exp	EsxO3	1	EsxO2	3	EsxO2	4	EC1S	12	EC1S	n&v
																		FAV	1Q

GROUND: Canvey Island FC, Frost Financial Stadium, 1 Park Lane SS8 7PX
Nearest Railway Station Leigh-on-Sea - 3.2km
Bus Route Transport Museum - stop 100m away

BRIMSDOWN

Founded 2013

Nickname: The Limers   **Club Colours:** White

Club Contact Details   gulayermiya1996@googlemail.com

HONOURS
FA Comps: None
League: None

10-11	11-12	12-13	13-14		14-15		15-16		16-17		17-18		18-19		19-20	
			SSM2	13	SSM2	4	SSM1	15	SSM1	17	SSM1	11	SSM1	18	SSM1	n&v
							FAV	2Q			FAV	1Q	FAV	1P	FAV	1Q

GROUND: Tilbury FC, Chadfields, St Chads Road, Tilbury, Essex RM18 8NL
Nearest Railway Station Tilbury Town - 1.1km
Bus Route Raphael Avenue - stop 75m away

BURNHAM RAMBLERS

Founded 1900

Nickname: Ramblers   **Club Colours:** Blue & black

Club Contact Details 01621 784 383 (Ground)   martin.leno@btopenworld.com

HONOURS
FA Comps: None
League: Mid-Essex 1927-28, 54-55, 62-63. Essex Olympian 1966-67. Essex Senior League 2012-13.

10-11		11-12		12-13		13-14		14-15		15-16		16-17		17-18		18-19		19-20	
ESen	7	ESen	4	ESen	1	Isth1N	17	Isth1N	24	ESen	14	ESen	21	ESen	20	EC1S	13	EC1S	n&v
FAC	1Q	FAC	Pr	FAC	P	FAC	1Q	FAC	P	FAC	EP	FAC	EP	FAC	EP	FAC	EP		
FAV	2P	FAV	1P	FAV	2P	FAT	1Q	FAT	P	FAV	1Qr	FAV	2Q	FAV	1P	FAV	1Q	FAV	1Q

GROUND: Leslie Fields Stadium, Springfield Road CM0 8TE
Nearest Railway Station Burnham on Crouch (Greater Anglia).
Bus Route 31X (Eastern National)

COGGESHALL UNITED
Nickname: Weavers — Club Colours: Blue — Founded 2017

Club Contact Details 01376 562 962 (Ground) secretary@coggeshallunitedfc.co.uk

HONOURS
FA Comps: None
League: None

10-11	11-12	12-13	13-14	14-15	15-16	16-17	17-18	18-19	19-20
							EsSuP 2	EC1S 2	EC1S n&v
									FAC EP
								FAV 2Q	FAV 2P

GROUND: West Street, Coggeshall, Essex CO6 1NT

FIRE UNITED
Nickname: — Club Colours: Gold & blue — Founded 2012

Club Contact Details 02075 114 477 & 077446 952 176 (ground) fire_united_secretary@hotmail.com

HONOURS
FA Comps: None
League: None

10-11	11-12	12-13	13-14	14-15	15-16	16-17	17-18	18-19	19-20
		Midx1SE 9	Midx1SE 7	Midx1SE 12		Midx1SE 9	Midx1SE 4	EC1S 19	EC1S n&v
								FAV 1Q	FAV 1Q

GROUND: Terence MacMillan Stadium, Plaistow E13 8SD
Nearest Railway Station (Underground) District and Hammersmith & City
Bus Route 276 and 376

FRENFORD
Nickname: — Club Colours: Red & white — Founded 1945

Club Contact Details 020 8518 0992 (ground)

HONOURS
FA Comps: None
League: Ilford & District Premier 1975-76. Essex Olympian Division Two 1995-96, Premier 2011-12, 12-13.

10-11	11-12	12-13	13-14	14-15	15-16	16-17	17-18	18-19	19-20
EsxOP 3	EsxOP 1	EsxOP 1	EsxOP 3	EsxOP 7	EsxOP 7	EsxOP 5	EsxOP 2	EC1S 9	EC1S n&v
									FAV 2P

GROUND: Jack Carter Centre, The Drive, Ilford, Essex, IG1 3PS

HALSTEAD TOWN
Nickname: Humbugs — Club Colours: Black & white — Founded 1879

Club Contact Details 01787 472 082 (ground) halsteadtownfc@aol.com

HONOURS
FA Comps: None
League: Essex & Suffolk Border Premier Division 1957-58, 68-69, 77-78.
Eastern Counties 1994-95, 95-96, Division One 2002-03.

10-11	11-12	12-13	13-14	14-15	15-16	16-17	17-18	18-19	19-20
EC1 11	EC1 6	EC1 11	EC1 6	EC1 10	EC1 4	EC1 9	EC1 10	EC1S 3	EC1S n&v
FAC P	FAC EP	FAC P	FAC EP	FAC EPr		FAC 1Q	FAC 2Q		FAC P
FAV 2Q	FAV 1P	FAV 2Q	FAV 2Q	FAV 1Q	FAV 2Q	FAV 2Q	FAV 2Q	FAV 1Q	FAV 1Q

GROUND: Rosemary Lane, Broton Industrial Estate, Halstead, Essex CO9 1HR

HARWICH & PARKESTON
Nickname: Shrimpers   Club Colours: Black & white stripes   **Founded 1875**

Club Contact Details 01255 503 643

HONOURS
FA Comps: None
League: Essex & Suffolk Border Senior Division 1908-09, 13-14, 20-21, 21-22, 22-23, 28-29, 31-32, 32-33, 33-34. Eastern Counties 1935-36 (joint). Essex County 1937-38. Athenian Division Two 1964-65

10-11	11-12	12-13	13-14	14-15	15-16	16-17	17-18	18-19	19-20
EsSuP	EsSuP 2	EsSuP 5	EsSuP 3	EsSu1 5	EsSuP 9	EsSuP 6	EsSuP 10	EC1S 5	EC1S n&v
									FAC P
									FAV 1Q

GROUND: Royal Oak, Main Road, Dovercourt, Harwich CO12 4AA

HOLLAND
Nickname: Club Colours: Orange   **Founded 2006**

Club Contact Details 07778 142 118 (ground)   mark.sorrell@btinternet.com

HONOURS
FA Comps: None
League: Essex & Suffolk Border Division One 2008-09.

10-11	11-12	12-13	13-14	14-15	15-16	16-17	17-18	18-19	19-20
EsSuP 5	EsSuP 12	EsSuP 4	EsSuP 10	EsSuP 4	EsSuP 4	EC1 5	EC1 16	EC1S 11	EC1S n&v
							FAV 1P	FAV 2Q	FAV 1Q

GROUND: Eastcliff Sports Ground, Dulwich Road, Holland-on-Sea CO15 5HP
Nearest Railway Station Clacton-on-Sea - 1.7km

LITTLE OAKLEY
Nickname: The Acorns   Club Colours: Blue & black   **Founded 1947**

Club Contact Details 01255 880 370 (ground)

HONOURS
FA Comps: None
League: Essex & Suffolk Border Division One 1985-86, Premier Division 1986-87, 87-88, 92-93, 2003-04, 15-16, 16-17.

10-11	11-12	12-13	13-14	14-15	15-16	16-17	17-18	18-19	19-20
EsSuP 13	EsSuP 6	EsSuP 7	EsSuP 6	EsSuP 2	EsSuP 4	EsSuP 1	EC1 14	EC1S 7	EC1S n&v
							FAV 2Q	FAV 1Pr	FAV 1Q

GROUND: Memorial Ground, Harwich Road, Little Oakley, Harwich CO12 5ED
Nearest Railway Station Harwich International - 3.3km
Bus Route Mayes Lane stop - 173m away

LOPES TAVARES
Nickname: Club Colours: Red   **Founded 2015**

Club Contact Details 0300 124 0123/07756 417255   secretary.ltlondonfc@gmail.com

HONOURS
FA Comps: None
League: None

10-11	11-12	12-13	13-14	14-15	15-16	16-17	17-18	18-19	19-20
						EsxAIP 8	EsxAIP 5	EC1S 16	EC1S n&v
									FAV 1P

GROUND: Newham Leisure Centre, 281 Prince Regent Lane, London E13 8SD

MAY & BAKER E.C.
Nickname: Bakers   **Club Colours:** Red & black   Founded

Club Contact Details 0208 919 2156 / 3156   mwright@cvc.com

HONOURS
FA Comps: None
League: Essex Olympian Division One 2009/10.

10-11	11-12	12-13	13-14	14-15	15-16	16-17	17-18	18-19	19-20
EsxOP 6	EsxOP 11	EsxOP 8	EsxOP 10	EsxOP 9	EsxOP 11	EsxOP 3	EsxOP 7	EC1S 8	EC1S n&v
								FAV 2P	FAV 1Q

GROUND: Parkside, Park Lane, Aveley RM15 4PX
Nearest Railway Station Purfleet

NEWBURY FOREST
Nickname: **Club Colours:** Navy blue   Founded 2003

Club Contact Details 0208 550 3611   ron.dangerfield@newburyforestfc.co.uk

HONOURS
FA Comps: None
League: Romford & District Senior 2009-10.

10-11	11-12	12-13	13-14	14-15	15-16	16-17	17-18	18-19	19-20
		EsxO1 3	EsxOP 7	EsxOP 10	EsxOP 14	EsxO1 6	EsxO1 8	EC1S 17	EC1S n&v
					FAV 2Q	FAV 1Q		FAV 1P	FAV 2Q

GROUND: Redbridge FC, Oakside Stadium, Station Road, Barkingside, IG6 1NB
Nearest Railway Station Barkingside Underground - 186m
Bus Route Barkingside - 395m away

WHITE ENSIGN
Nickname: **Club Colours:** Red   Founded 1951

Club Contact Details 01702 217 812 (ground)

HONOURS
FA Comps: None
League: Essex Intermediate/Olympian Division Two 2002-03, Division One 03-04, 04-05, 06-07, 07-08.

10-11	11-12	12-13	13-14	14-15	15-16	16-17	17-18	18-19	19-20
EsxOP 12	EsxOP 8	EsxOP 7	EsxOP 13	EsxO1 2	EsxOP 5	EsxOP 12	EsxOP 4	EC1S 4	EC1S n&v
									FAC Pr
								FAV 1Q	FAV 2P

GROUND: Burroughs Park, Little Wakering Hall Lane, Great Wakering SS3 0HH
Nearest Railway Station Shoeburyness - 3.2km
Bus Route Barrow Hall Rd (Little Wakering Rd) - 631m

WIVENHOE TOWN
Nickname: The Dragons   **Club Colours:** Blue & white   Founded 1925

Club Contact Details   lorraineosman1969@yahoo.com

HONOURS
FA Comps: None
League: Brightlingsea & Dist 1932-33, 36-37, 47-48. Colchester & East Essex Prem 1952-53, 55-56, D1 59-60, 69-70. Essex & Suffolk D2 1971-72, D1 72-73, Prem 78-79. Isth D2N 1987-88, D1 1989-90. Eastern C. D1 2015-16.

10-11	11-12	12-13	13-14	14-15	15-16	16-17	17-18	18-19	19-20
ECP 20	ECP 19	ECP 18	ECP 19	ECP 18	EC1 1	ECP 19	ECP 24	EC1S 14	EC1S n&v
		FAC EPr	FAC EPr	FAC P	FAC EP	FAC EP	FAC EP	FAC EP	
	FAV 1Q	FAV 2Qr	FAV 1Q	FAV 1P	FAV 2Q	FAV 1Q	FAV 1Q	FAV 1Q	FAV 2Q

GROUND: Broad Lane Ground, Elmstead Road, Wivenhoe CO7 7HA
Nearest Railway Station Wivenhoe - 2.4km.
Bus Route No.62.

WORMLEY ROVERS

Nickname: **Club Colours:** Red & black

Founded 1921

Club Contact Details 01992 460 650 (ground)

HONOURS
FA Comps: None
League: Herts Senior County Division Three 1976-77, Division One 86-87.

10-11	11-12	12-13	13-14	14-15	15-16	16-17	17-18	18-19		19-20	
HertP 7	HertP 8	HertP 7	HertP 8	HertP 5	HertP 15	HertP 8	HertP 5	EC1S 10		EC1S n&v	
								FAV 1Q		FAV 2Q	

GROUND: Wormley Sports Club, Church Lane, Wormley EN10 6LB

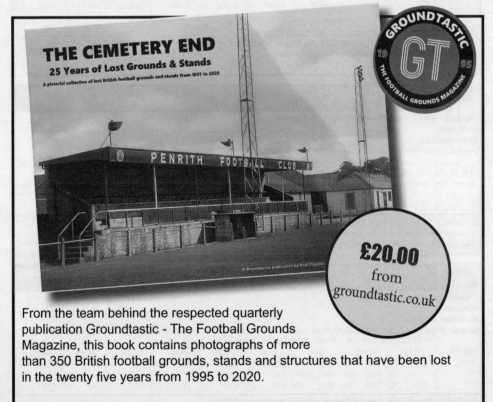

GROUNDTASTIC
GT
19 95
THE FOOTBALL GROUNDS MAGAZINE

THE CEMETERY END
25 Years of Lost Grounds & Stands
A pictorial collection of lost British football grounds and stands from 1995 to 2020

PENRITH FOOTBALL CLUB

A Groundtastic publication by Paul Claydon

£20.00
from
groundtastic.co.uk

From the team behind the respected quarterly publication Groundtastic - The Football Grounds Magazine, this book contains photographs of more than 350 British football grounds, stands and structures that have been lost in the twenty five years from 1995 to 2020.

It is a seminal work and promises to be a key point of reference for many years to come.

CLAPTON
Nickname: Tons   **Club Colours:** Red & white   Founded 1878

Club Contact Details 0203 652 2951 (ground)   secretary@claptonfc.com

Previous Names: None
Previous Leagues: Southern (FM). London. Isthmian (FM) 1905-2006.
HONOURS
FA Comps: FA Amateur Cup 1906-07, 08-09, 14-15, 23-24, 24-25.
League: Isthmian 1910-11, 22-23, Division Two 1982-83.

	10-11	11-12	12-13	13-14	14-15	15-16	16-17	17-18	18-19	19-20
ESen	17	17	18	10	8	7	2	6	11	n&v
FAC	EP	EP	EP	P	EPr	EP	P	1Q	EPr	EP
FAV	2Q	2Q	1P	1P	2Q	2Q	1Q	1P	2Q	1Q

GROUND: Terence MacMillan Stadium, Plaistow E13 8SD
Capacity: **Seats:**   **Covered:**   **Shop:** No
Nearest Railway Station (Underground) District and Hammersmith & City
Bus Route 276 and 376

COCKFOSTERS
Nickname: Fosters   **Club Colours:** All red   Founded 1921

Club Contact Details 0208 449 5833   graham.bint@btinternet.com

Previous Names: Cockfosters Athletic 1921-68.
Previous Leagues: Barnet 1921-30s. Wood Green 1930s-46. Northern Suburban Int. 1946-66. Hertfordshire County 1966-1991. Spartan 1991-97.
HONOURS Spartan South Midlands 1997-2019.
FA Comps: None
League: Wood green Division Two 1931-32, Division One 33-34, Premier 38-39. Northern Suburban Inter. Division One 1949-50, 60
-61, Premier 61-62. Hertfordshire Senior County Division One 1966-67, Premier 78-79, 80-81, 83-84

	10-11	11-12	12-13	13-14	14-15	15-16	16-17	17-18	18-19	19-20
SSM1/SSM P	15	9	2	8	18	9	3	20	18	n&v
FAC	Pr	P	P	1Qr	P	1Q	EP	1Q	EP	P
FAV	1P	1Q	2P	2P	1P	1Qr	2P	1P	1Q	1Q

GROUND: Cockfosters Sports Ground, Chalk Lane, Cockfosters, Herts EN4 9JG
Capacity: **Seats:** Yes   **Covered:** Yes
Nearest Railway Station New Barnet - 1.5km
Bus Route Cockfosters - stop 200m away

ENFIELD 1893 FC
Nickname: The E's   **Club Colours:** White & royal blue   Founded 1893

Club Contact Details 07957 647 820   enfieldfc@sky.com

Previous Names: Enfield Spartans > 1900. Enfield > 2007.
Previous Leagues: Tottenham & District. North Middlesex. London 1903-12, 20-21. Athenian 1912-14, 21-63. Isthmian 1963-81, 90-2005, 06-07.
HONOURS Conference 1981-90. Southern 2005-06.
FA Comps: FA Amateur Cup 1966-67, 69-70. FA Trophy 1981-82, 87-88.
League: Alliance 1982-83, 85-86. Essex Senior 2010-11.

	10-11	11-12	12-13	13-14	14-15	15-16	16-17	17-18	18-19	19-20
ESen	1	7	9	3	16	20	18	9	14	n&v
FAC	EP	Pr	EP	EPr	EP	EP	EP	EP	EP	EP
FAV	1P	4P	4P	4P	1P	1Q	2Q	3P	2P	1P

GROUND: The Harlow Arena, Elizabeth Way, Harlow, Essex CM19 5BE
Capacity: 3,500 **Seats:** 500 **Covered:** Yes
Nearest Railway Station Harlow Town, 1.2 miles
Bus Route No direct bus to the ground

HADLEY

Nickname: Bricks   **Club Colours:** Red and black

Founded 1882

Club Contact Details   info@hadleyfc.co.uk

Previous Names: None

Previous Leagues: Barnet & Dist. 1922-57, North Suburban 1957-70, Mid-Herts 1970-77, Herts Senior County 1977-85, 99-2007, Southern Olymian 1985-99, West Herts 2007-08. Spartan South Mildlands 08-19.

HONOURS

FA Comps: None

League: Mid-Herts Premier 1975-76, 76-77. Hertfordshire Senior County Division Three 1977-78, Division One 2001-02, Premier 2003-04, 04-05. West Hertfordshire 2007-08.

10-11	11-12	12-13	13-14	14-15	15-16	16-17	17-18	18-19	19-20
SSM P 14	SSM P 15	SSM P 12	SSM P 13	SSM P 9	SSM P 6	SSM P 19	SSM P 6	SSM P 3	ESen n&v
FAC EPr	FAC EPr	FAC P	FAC P	FAC EPr	FAC EP	FAC 3Qr	FAC 1Q	FAC 1Qr	FAC 3Q
FAV 2Q	FAV 1P	FAV 1Pr	FAV 2P	FAV 2Qr	FAV 1P	FAV 1Q	FAV 2Qr	FAV 2Q	FAV 1P

GROUND: Hadley Sports Ground, Brickfield Lane, Arkley, Barnet EN5 3LD
Capacity: 2,000 **Seats:** 150   **Covered:** 250   **Shop:** Yes
Nearest Railway Station Elstree & Borehamwood - 2.8km
Bus Route Brickfield Lane - stop 70m away

HASHTAG UNITED

Nickname: **Club Colours:** Blue & yellow

Founded 2016

Club Contact Details 0208 889 1415 (Matchday)   jay@hashtagunited.co.uk

Previous Names: Spencer FC.

Previous Leagues: Eastern Counties 2018-19

HONOURS

FA Comps: None

League: Eastern Counties Division One South 2018-19

10-11	11-12	12-13	13-14	14-15	15-16	16-17	17-18	18-19	19-20
								EC1S 1	ESen n&v
									FAV 2Q

GROUND: Bowers & Pitsea FC, Len Salmon Stadium, Crown Avenue, Pitsea, Basildon SS13 2BE
Capacity: 2,000 **Seats:** 200   **Covered:** 1,000
Nearest Railway Station Pitsea - 1.7km
Bus Route Wilsner - stop 200m away

HODDESDON TOWN

Nickname: Lilywhites   **Club Colours:** White & black

Founded 1879

Club Contact Details 07860 423 977   jdsinden1@gmail.com

Previous Names: None

Previous Leagues: Hertfordshire County 1920-25. Spartan 1925-75. London Spartan 1975-77. Athenian 1977-84. Spartan SM 1984-2018.

HONOURS

FA Comps: FA Vase 1974-75 (1st Winners).

League: Spartan 1970-71, Division One 1935-36, Division Two 'B' 1927-28.

10-11	11-12	12-13	13-14	14-15	15-16	16-17	17-18	18-19	19-20
SSM1 9	SSM1 3	SSM1 3	SSM P 6	SSM P 19	SSM P 3	SSM P 7	SSM P 12	ESen 9	ESen n&v
FAC EP	FAC EP	FAC EPr	FAC EPr	FAC P	FAC 3Qr	FAC P	FAC EP	FAC P	FAC P
FAV 1Q	FAV 1P	FAV 1P	FAV 2Q	FAV 2Q	FAV 1P	FAV 3P	FAV 1Q	FAV 2Q	FAV 1Q

GROUND: The Stewart Edwards Stadium, Lowfield, Park View, Hoddesdon, Herts. EN11 8PX
Capacity: 3,000 **Seats:** 150   **Covered:** Yes
Nearest Railway Station Broxbourne
Bus Route 310 - Hoddesdon High Street

ILFORD

Nickname: The Foxes Club Colours: Blue and white hoops Founded 1987

Club Contact Details 020 8514 8352

Previous Names: Reformed as Ilford in 1987 after the original club merged with Leytonstone in 1980.
Previous Leagues: Spartan 1987-94, Essex Senior 1996-2004, Isthmian 2004-05, 2006-13, Southern 2005-06.
HONOURS
FA Comps: FA Amateur Cup 1928-29, 29-30.
League: Isthmian 1906-07, 20-21, 21-22, Division Two 2004-05.

	10-11	11-12	12-13	13-14	14-15	15-16	16-17	17-18	18-19	19-20
	Isth1N 20	Isth1N 20	Isth1N 22	ESen 16	ESen 10	ESen 5	ESen 6	ESen 13	ESen 10	ESen n&v
	FAC 1Q	FAC Pr	FAC P	FAC EP	FAC EP	FAC P	FAC P	FAC P	FAC EP	FAC EP
	FAT 1Q	FAT P	FAT 1Q	FAV 1P	FAV 2Q	FAV 1P	FAV 1P	FAV 2Q	FAV 1Q	FAV 1Q

GROUND: Cricklefield Stadium, 486 High Road, Ilford, Essex IG1 1FY
Capacity: 3,500 Seats: 216 Covered: Yes Shop: No
Nearest Railway Station Seven Kings (BR), approx. ½ mile
Bus Route 86, outside ground

REDBRIDGE

Nickname: Motormen Club Colours: Royal blue Founded 1958

Club Contact Details r.holloway338@btinternet.com

Previous Names: Ford United 1958-2004
Previous Leagues: Aetolian 1959-64, Greater London 1964-71, Metropolitan London 1971-74, Essex Senior 1974-97, Isthmian 1997-2004, 05-16.
HONOURS Conference 2004-05.
FA Comps: None
League: Aetolian 1959-60, 61-62. Greater London 1970-71. Essex Senior 1991-92, 96-97.
Isthmian Division Three 1998-99, Division One 2001-02.

	10-11	11-12	12-13	13-14	14-15	15-16	16-17	17-18	18-19	19-20
	Isth1N 16	Isth1N 6	Isth1N 20	Isth1N 14	Isth1N 23	Isth1N 24	ESen 14	ESen 4	ESen 12	ESen n&v
	FAC 2Q	FAC 2P	FAC P	FAC P	FAC Pr	FAC P	FAC EP	FAC EP	FAC EP	FAC EP
	FAT 1Q	FAT 3Q	FAT 1Q	FAT P	FAT P	FAT 1Q	FAV 2Q	FAV 2Qr	FAV 3P	FAV 2Q

GROUND: Oakside Stadium, Station Road, Barkingside, Essex IG6 1NB
Capacity: 3,000 Seats: Covered:
Nearest Railway Station Barkingside Underground - 186m
Bus Route Barkingside - 395m away

SAFFRON WALDEN TOWN

Nickname: The Bloods Club Colours: Red & black Founded 1872

Club Contact Details 01799 520 980

Previous Names: Saffron Walden > 1967. Resigned from ECo in August 2011 rejoining for 2012-13 season.
Previous Leagues: Herts County 1955-71. Essex Senior 1971-74, 96-2003. Eastern Counties 1974-84 2004-11, 12-18. Isthmian 1984-96.
HONOURS
FA Comps: None
League: Essex Senior 1973-74, 99-00. Eastern Counties 1982-83.

	10-11	11-12	12-13	13-14	14-15	15-16	16-17	17-18	18-19	19-20
	EC1 6		EC1 6	ECP 5	EC1 3	ECP 8	ECP 9	ECP 11	ESen 4	ESen n&v
	FAC Pr			FAC EP	FAC Pr	FAC 1Q	FAC 1Q	FAC Pr	FAC 1Qr	FAC P
	FAV 2Q		FAV 2Q	FAV 2Q	FAT 4P	FAV 3P	FAV 1P	FAV 1Q	FAV 2Q	FAV 2P

GROUND: Catons Lane Stadium, Saffron Walden, Essex CB10 2DU
Capacity: Seats: Yes Covered: Yes
Nearest Railway Station Audley End - 3.5km
Bus Route Saffron Walden High Street

SAWBRIDGEWORTH TOWN
Nickname: Robins   Club Colours: Red & black   Founded 1897

Club Contact Details 01279 722 039

Previous Names: Sawbridgeworth > 1976.
Previous Leagues: Stortford. Spartan 1936-39, 46-53. Herts County. Essex Olympian.
HONOURS
FA Comps: None
League: Essex Olympian 1971-72.

	10-11	11-12	12-13	13-14	14-15	15-16	16-17	17-18	18-19	19-20
ESen	16	6	14	6	5	10	5	8	18	n&v
FAC		EP	EP	EP	EP	EP	1Q	EP	EP	EP
FAV	2Q	2Q	2Q	2Q	1Q	1Q	2Q	1P	1P	1Q

GROUND: Crofters End, West Road, Sawbridgeworth CM21 0DE
Capacity: 2,500   **Seats:** 175   **Covered:** 300
Nearest Railway Station Sawbridgeworth, approx. ½ mile
Bus Route 510 & 511, approx. ½ mile

SOUTHEND MANOR
Nickname: The Manor   Club Colours: Yellow & black   Founded 1955

Club Contact Details 07788 580 360   southendmanor@btinternet.com

Previous Names: None
Previous Leagues: Southend Borough Combination. Southend & District Alliance.
HONOURS
FA Comps: None
League: Southend Borough Combination 1971-72, 73-74, 78-79, 79-80, 80-81, 81-82.
Southend & District Alliance 1983-84, 84-85. Essex Senior 1990-91.

	10-11	11-12	12-13	13-14	14-15	15-16	16-17	17-18	18-19	19-20
ESen	5	2	7	19	18	16	7	14	17	n&v
FAC	P	4Q	1Q	EPr	EP	P	EPr	P	EP	EPr
FAV	2Q	3Pr	3P	2Q	2Q	2Qr	2Q	1Q	1P	1Q

GROUND: The Arena, Southchurch Park, Northumberland Crescent, Southend SS1 2XB
Capacity: 2,000   **Seats:** 500   **Covered:** 700   **Shop:** No
Nearest Railway Station Southend East (C2C), ½ mile to ground
Bus Route 7 & 8 (Arriva) to Woodgrange Drive, ¼ mile

SPORTING BENGAL UNITED
Nickname: Bengal Tigers   Club Colours: All royal blue   Founded 1996

Club Contact Details 020 8980 1885

Previous Names: None.
Previous Leagues: Asian League. London Intermediate. Kent 2003-11.
HONOURS
FA Comps: None
League: None

	10-11	11-12	12-13	13-14	14-15	15-16	16-17	17-18	18-19	19-20
	Kent P 15	ESen 10	ESen 11	ESen 13	ESen 20	ESen 12	ESen 19	ESen 10	ESen 8	ESen n&v
FAC			EPr	EPr	EP	EP	1Q	EP	Pr	EP
FAV		3P	1P	1P	1Q	2P	1P	1Q	2Q	1Q

GROUND: Mile End Stadium, Rhodeswell Rd, Off Burdett Rd E14 7TW
Capacity: 2,000   **Seats:** Yes   **Covered:** Yes
Nearest Railway Station Mile End – approx. 5 mins walk
Bus Route 277, 309, D6, D7 – outside ground

ST MARGARETSBURY
Nickname: The Bury   **Club Colours:** Red & black

Founded 1894

Club Contact Details 01920 870 473

Previous Names: Stanstead Abbots > 1962
Previous Leagues: East Herts, Hertford & District, Waltham & District 1947-48, Herts Senior County 1948-92. Spartan SM 1992-2018.
HONOURS
FA Comps: None
League: Spartan 1995-96.

	10-11	11-12	12-13	13-14	14-15	15-16	16-17	17-18	18-19	19-20
SSM P / ESen	SSM P 18	SSM P 12	SSM P 4	SSM P 4	SSM P 8	SSM P 19	SSM P 20	SSM P 16	ESen 7	ESen n&v
FAC	P	P	EP	1Q	P	P	EP	1Q	P	EP
FAV	1Q	2Q	2Q	1P	3P	1Q	3P	1Qr	1Q	2Q

GROUND: Recreation Ground, Station Road, St Margarets SG12 8EH
Capacity: 1,000 **Seats:** 60 **Covered:** 60
Nearest Railway Station St Margarets - 5mins from the ground

STANSTED
Nickname: Blues   **Club Colours:** Royal blue

Founded 1892

Club Contact Details 07921 403 842

Previous Names: None.
Previous Leagues: Spartan 1946-53. London 1953-56. Herts Premier 1956-71.
HONOURS
FA Comps: FA Vase 1983-84.
League: East Herts 1934-35. Essex Senior 2009-10.

	10-11	11-12	12-13	13-14	14-15	15-16	16-17	17-18	18-19	19-20
ESen	2	16	17	17	7	9	8	18	2	n&v
FAC	EP	1Q	EP	EPr	EP	Pr	EP	EP	P	EP
FAV	5P	2P	2Q	2Q	2Q	1Q	1Q	1Q	1Q	3P

GROUND: Hargrave Park, Cambridge Road, Stansted CM24 8BX
Capacity: 2,000 **Seats:** 200 **Covered:** 400 **Shop:** No
Nearest Railway Station Stansted Mountfitchet - ¼ mile
Bus Route 301 100 yards from ground

TAKELEY
Nickname: **Club Colours:** Royal blue

Founded 1904

Club Contact Details 01279 870 404   Takeleyfc@mail.com

Previous Names: None.
Previous Leagues: Essex Intermediate/Olympian.
HONOURS
FA Comps: None
League: Essex Olympian/Intermediate 1987-88, 2001-02, Division Two 1993-94.

	10-11	11-12	12-13	13-14	14-15	15-16	16-17	17-18	18-19	19-20
ESen	13	3	3	7	11	18	4	5	5	n&v
FAC	EP	EPr	P	EP	EP	EPr	EP	1Q	1Q	1Q
FAV	1P	2Q	2P	2P	1Q	2Qr	2Q	1P	1P	1P

GROUND: Station Road, Takeley, Bishop's Stortford CM22 6SQ
Capacity: 2,000 **Seats:** Yes **Covered:** Yes
Nearest Railway Station Stansted Airport (overground) Epping (underground)
Bus Route from Stansted Airport to Four Ashes Pub.

WALTHAMSTOW
Nickname: The Stags   **Club Colours:** Royal blue   Founded 1964

Club Contact Details 07748 983 792

Previous Names: Pennant 1964-88. Walthamstow Pennant 88-95. Merged with Leyton to form Leyton Pennant 95-2003. Waltham Forest 03-18.
Previous Leagues: Isthmian 2003-04, 06-14. Southern 2004-06.
HONOURS
FA Comps: None
League: None

	10-11	11-12	12-13	13-14	14-15	15-16	16-17	17-18	18-19	19-20
	Isth1N 21	Isth1N 17	Isth1N 18	Isth1N 23	ESen 9	ESen 19	ESen 12	ESen 17	ESen 3	ESen n&v
FAC	P	2Q	2Q	P	EP	EP	2Q	EPr	1Q	2Qr
FAT/FAV	FAT 1Q	FAT 1Q	FAT 1Q	FAT P	FAV 1P	FAV 2Q	FAV 1P	FAV 1Q	FAV 1Q	FAV 2P

GROUND: Wadham Lodge, Kitchener Road, Walthamstow E17 4JP
Capacity: 3,500 **Seats:** 216 **Covered:** Yes
Nearest Railway Station Walthamstow Central - Victoria Line/London Overground.
Bus Route 158

WEST ESSEX
Nickname: **Club Colours:** Red & black   Founded 1989

Club Contact Details 07956 557 438

Previous Names: None
Previous Leagues: Ilford & District 1989-94. Essex Business Houses 1994-2010. Middlesex County 2010-2016.
HONOURS
FA Comps: None
League: Essex Business Houses Division One 2008-09.
Middlesex County Division One (Central & East) 2010-11, Premier Division 2015-16.

	10-11	11-12	12-13	13-14	14-15	15-16	16-17	17-18	18-19	19-20
	Midx1SE 1	MidxP 11	MidxP 10	MidxP 9	MidxP 7	MidxP 1	ESen 13	ESen 7	ESen 13	ESen n&v
FAC								P	P	EP
FAV							1Q	2Q	1P	2Q

GROUND: Barking FC, Mayesbrook Park, Lodge Avenue, Dagenham RM8 2JR
Capacity: 2,500 **Seats:** 200 **Covered:** 600
Nearest Railway Station Barking. Upney (District Line) 2 miles
Bus Route 5, 62, 145, 364, 368

WOODFORD TOWN
Nickname: The Woods   **Club Colours:** Blue   Founded 2007

Club Contact Details

Previous Names: Mauritius Sports merged with Walthamstow Ave & Pennant 2007. Mauritius Sports Ass. 09-11. Haringey & Waltham Dev. 11-13. Grhouse London 13-15
Previous Leagues: London Intermediate 2001-03.   **Previous Names Cont:** Greenhouse Sports 15-16. Haringey & Waltham 16-17.
Middlesex County 2003-2007.
HONOURS
FA Comps: None
League: None

	10-11	11-12	12-13	13-14	14-15	15-16	16-17	17-18	18-19	19-20
	ESen 11	ESen 12	ESen 8	ESen 18	ESen 19	ESen 15	ESen 22	ESen 12	ESen 6	ESen n&v
FAC	EP	Pr	P	1Q						EPr
FAV	1Q	2P	1Qr	2Q		2P				1Q

GROUND: The Harlow Arena, Elizabeth Way, Harlow Essex CM19 5BE
Capacity: 3,500 **Seats:** Yes **Covered:** Yes
Nearest Railway Station Harlow Town, 1 mile

PREMIER DIVISION

ARDLEY UNITED
Nickname: None   **Club Colours:** All sky blue   Founded 1945

Club Contact Details 07711 009 198   sharon.smith23@talk21.com

Previous Names: None

Previous Leagues: Oxford Senior. Volunteered for relegation after 2016-17 season.

HONOURS

FA Comps: None

League: Banbury District & Lord Jersey FA Division One 1984-85. Oxfordshire Senior Division One 1988-89, Premier 1990-91. Hellenic Division One 1996-97, 97-98, Division One West 2017-18.

10-11		11-12		12-13		13-14		14-15		15-16		16-17		17-18		18-19		19-20	
Hel P	3	Hel P	3	Hel P	5	Hel P	2	Hel P	8	Hel P	13	Hel P	5	Hel1W	1	Hel P	17	Hel P	n&v
FAC	EP	FAC	Pr	FAC	P	FAC	1Qr	FAC	2Q	FAC	EP	FAC	P	FAC	EP	FAC	P	FAC	P
FAV	2Q	FAV	1P	FAV	3P	FAV	1Q	FAV	1P	FAV	1Q	FAV	2Q	FAV	1Q	FAV	1Q	FAV	1Q

GROUND: The Playing Fields, Fritwell Road, Ardley OX27 7PA
Capacity: 1,000 **Seats:** 100 **Covered:** 200 **Shop:** No
Nearest Railway Station Bicester North - 6.3km
Bus Route Water Lane stop - 121m away

BINFIELD
Nickname: Moles   **Club Colours:** All red   Founded 1892

Club Contact Details 07515 336 989   robchallis@binfieldfc.com

Previous Names: None.

Previous Leagues: Ascot & District. Great Western Combination. Reading & Dist. Chiltonian.

HONOURS

FA Comps: None

League: Great Western Combination 1946-47. Reading & District Division One 1975-76, 87-88, Division Two 86-87. Hellenic Division One East 2008-09.

10-11		11-12		12-13		13-14		14-15		15-16		16-17		17-18		18-19		19-20	
Hel P	2	Hel P	8	Hel P	3	Hel P	5	Hel P	6	Hel P	8	Hel P	8	Hel P	7	Hel P	9	Hel P	n&v
FAC	1Q	FAC	P	FAC	EP	FAC	2Q	FAC	EP	FAC	P	FAC	EP	FAC	P	FAC	2Q	FAC	1Q
FAV	2P	FAV	4P	FAV	3P	FAV	3P	FAV	2Q	FAV	1Qr	FAV	2Q	FAV	2Q	FAV	2Q	FAV	4Pr

GROUND: Stubbs Lane off Hill Farm Lane, Binfield RG42 5NR
Capacity: 1,500 **Seats:** yes **Covered:** yes
Nearest Railway Station Bracknell - 3.9km
Bus Route Church Lane North stop - 628m

BISHOP'S CLEEVE
Nickname: The Mitres   **Club Colours:** All Green   Founded 1905

Club Contact Details 01242 676 166 (Ground)   themitres@outlook.com

Previous Names: None

Previous Leagues: Cheltenham. North Gloucestershire. Hellenic 1983-2006. Southern 2006-18.

HONOURS

FA Comps: None

League: Cheltenham Division Two 1924-25, 30-31, 58-59, Division One 31-32, 34-35, 61-62, 63-64, 65-66, 66-67. Gloucestershire Northern Senior Division Two 1967-68, Division One 68-69, 69-70, 72-73. Hellenic Division One 1986-87.

10-11		11-12		12-13		13-14		14-15		15-16		16-17		17-18		18-19		19-20	
Sthsw	15	Sthsw	11	Sthsw	21	Sthsw	20	Sthsw	21	Sthsw	12	Sthsw	16	Sth1W	22	Hel P	4	Hel P	n&v
FAC	2Q	FAC	P	FAC	2Q	FAC	Pr	FAC	1Q	FAC	P	FAC	Pr	FAC	1Q	FAC	1Q	FAC	P
FAT	1Q	FAT	P	FAT	1Q	FAT	P	FAT	1Q	FAT	P	FAT	2Q	FAT	P	FAV	2Q	FAV	1P

GROUND: Kayte Lane, Bishop's Cleeve, Cheltenham GL52 3PD
Capacity: 1,500 **Seats:** 50 **Covered:** 50   Yes
Nearest Railway Station Cheltenham Spa - 4.9km
Bus Route Bus stops outside the ground

BRIMSCOMBE & THRUPP

Nickname: Lilywhites   **Club Colours:** White and blue

Founded 1886

Club Contact Details 07833 231 464   allanboulton370@btinternet.com

Previous Names: Brimscombe AFC 1886- late 1970s. Brimscombe and Thrupp merged.
Previous Leagues: Stroud & District. Gloucestershire Northern Senior. Gloucestershire County
HONOURS
FA Comps: None
League: Stroud & Dist. 1902-03, 06-07, 07-08, 12-13. Gloucestershire Northern Senior 1922-23, 30-31, 47-48, Division Two 2004 -05. Gloucestershire County 2010-11. Hellenic Division One West 2012-13.

10-11		11-12		12-13		13-14		14-15		15-16		16-17		17-18		18-19		19-20	
GlCo	1	Hel1W	4	Hel1W	1	Hel P	12	Hel P	10	Hel P	5	Hel P	7	Hel P	6	Hel P	2	Hel P	n&v
								FAC	EP	FAC	Pr	FAC	3Q	FAC	P	FAC	P	FAC	P
						FAV	2P	FAV	1P	FAV	3Pr	FAV	2Pr	FAV	1Q	FAV	1P	FAV	1P

GROUND: 'The Meadow', London Road, Brimscombe Stroud, Gloucestershire GL5 2SH
Capacity: 1,500   **Seats:** Yes   **Covered:** Yes
Nearest Railway Station Stroud - 2.9km
Bus Route Brewery Lane stop - 261m away

BURNHAM

Nickname: The Blues   **Club Colours:** Blue & white

Founded 1878

Club Contact Details 01628 668 654 (Ground)   burnhamfcsec@aol.com

Previous Names: Burnham & Hillingdon 1985-87
Previous Leagues: Hellenic 1971-77, 95-99, Athenian 1977-84, London Spartan 1984-85, Southern 1985-95, 99-16.
HONOURS
FA Comps: None
League: Hellenic 1975-76, 98-99, Division One East 2018-19. London Spartan 1984-85. Southern Division One Central 2012-13.

10-11		11-12		12-13		13-14		14-15		15-16		16-17		17-18		18-19		19-20	
SthC	14	SthC	15	SthC	1	SthP	20	SthP	23	Sthsw	21	Hel P	17	Hel P	20	Hel1E	1	Hel P	n&v
FAC	2Q	FAC	3Q	FAC	P	FAC	2Q	FAC	2Q	FAC	Pr	FAC	EP	FAC	EP	FAC	2Q	FAC	1Q
FAT	1Qr	FAT	Pr	FAT	2Q	FAT	2Q	FAT	2Qr	FAT	P	FAV	2Q	FAV	2Q	FAV	2Q	FAV	1Q

GROUND: The Gore, Wymers Wood Road, Burnham, Slough SL1 8JG
Capacity: 2,500   **Seats:** Yes   **Covered:** Yes   **Shop:** Yes
Nearest Railway Station Taplow - 1.9km
Bus Route Pink Lane stop - 239m away

EASINGTON SPORTS

Nickname: The Clan   **Club Colours:** Red & white

Founded 1946

Club Contact Details 07791 681 204   jamiehunter@hotmail.co.uk

Previous Names:
Previous Leagues: Warwick Combination.
HONOURS
FA Comps: None
League: Oxfordshire Senior Premier Division 1957-58, 58-59, Division One 1965-66. Hellenic Division One West 2018-19.

10-11		11-12		12-13		13-14		14-15		15-16		16-17		17-18		18-19		19-20	
Hel1W	11	Hel1W	6	Hel1W	8	Hel1W	9	Hel1W	4	Hel1W	5	Hel1W	4	Hel1W	3	Hel1W	1	Hel P	n&v
																FAC	P	FAC	EP
														FAV	1Q	FAV	2Q	FAV	1Q

GROUND: Addison Road, Banbury OX16 9DH
Capacity: 1,500   **Seats:** 50   **Covered:** Yes
Nearest Railway Station Banbury - 1.6km
Bus Route Springfield Avenu stop - 117m away

FAIRFORD TOWN
Nickname: The Reds   Club Colours: All red.

Founded 1891

Club Contact Details 01285 712 071 (Ground)   clake@fairfordtownfc.co.uk

Previous Names: None.
Previous Leagues: Cirencester & District. Swindon & District.
HONOURS
FA Comps: None
League: Swindon & District Prmeier Division 1964-65, 68-69.
Hellenic Division One A 1971-72, Division One West 2016-17.

	10-11		11-12		12-13		13-14		14-15		15-16		16-17		17-18		18-19		19-20	
Hel P	21	Hel P	20	Hel1W	4	Hel1W	4	Hel1W	14	Hel1W	4	Hel1W	1	Hel P	18	Hel P	13	Hel P	n&v
FAC	EPr	FAC	P	FAC	EP	FAC	EP	FAC	EP			FAC	EP	FAC	EPr	FAC	EP	FAC	P
FAV	1P	FAV	1P	FAV	1P	FAV	2Q	FAV	1Q	FAV	1P	FAV	1P	FAV	1Q	FAV	1Q	FAV	2P

GROUND: Cinder Lane, London Road, Fairford GL7 4AX
Capacity: 2,000 **Seats:** 100 **Covered:** 250 **Shop:** Yes
Nearest Railway Station Swindon or Kemble
Bus Route Hatherop Lane stop - 124m

FLACKWELL HEATH
Nickname: Heathens   Club Colours: All red.

Founded 1907

Club Contact Details 07932 952 538   joparsons19@sky.com

Previous Names: None.
Previous Leagues: High Wycombe & District 1907-50. Great Western Combination 1950-76. Hellenic 1976-82. Athenian 1982-84. Isthmian 1984-2007.
HONOURS
FA Comps: None
League: Great Western Combination Division Two 1950-51, Premier 1957-58, 62-63.
Hellenic Premier Division 2014-15.

	10-11		11-12		12-13		13-14		14-15		15-16		16-17		17-18		18-19		19-20	
Hel P	8	Hel P	4	Hel P	10	Hel P	8	Hel P	1	Hel P	3	Hel P	3	Hel P	5	Hel P	8	Hel P	n&v
FAC	P	FAC	EP	FAC	EP	FAC	EPr	FAC	3Q	FAC	EP	FAC	1Q	FAC	P	FAC	EP	FAC	2Q
FAV	2P	FAV	3P	FAV	1P	FAV	1Q	FAV	5P	FAV	2P	FAV	1P	FAV	1P	FAV	1P	FAV	1P

GROUND: Wilks Park, Magpie Lane, Heath End Rd, Flackwell Hth HP10 9EA
Capacity: 2,000 **Seats:** 150 **Covered:** Yes
Nearest Railway Station Bourne End - 3km
Bus Route Fernlea Close stop - 106m

HOLMER GREEN
Nickname: The Greens   Club Colours: All Green

Founded 1908

Club Contact Details 01494 711 485 (Ground)   j.ostinelli@sky.com

Previous Names: None
Previous Leagues: Chesham & District 1908-38, Wycombe Combination 1984-95, Chiltonian 1995-98. Spartan South Midlands 1998-2018.
HONOURS
FA Comps: None
League: Wycombe Combination 1971-72, 73-74, 76-77, 80-81. Chiltonian Prmeier 1984-85, 85-86, 93-94.
South Midlands Senior 1995-96. Spartan South Midlands 1998-99, Division One 2009-10.

	10-11		11-12		12-13		13-14		14-15		15-16		16-17		17-18		18-19		19-20	
SSM P	17	SSM P	20	SSM P	22	SSM P	12	SSM P	20	SSM P	7	SSM P	14	SSM P	14	Hel P	12	Hel P	n&v
		FAC	EP	FAC	EP	FAC	EP	FAC	Pr	FAC	EP	FAC	EP	FAC	EP	FAC	EP	FAC	EPr
FAV	1Q	FAV	1Q	FAV	2Q	FAV	2Q	FAV	1Pr	FAV	1Q	FAV	2P	FAV	1Q	FAV	1Q	FAV	1Q

GROUND: Airedale Park, Watchet Lane, Holmer Green, Bucks HP15 6UF
Capacity: 1,000 **Seats:** 25 **Covered:** yes
Nearest Railway Station Great Missenden - 4.3km
Bus Route Copners Drive - stop 350m away

LONGLEVENS AFC
Nickname: Levens **Club Colours:** Red & black
Founded 1954

Club Contact Details 01452 530 388 (Clubho) 07526 958 972 bill1853@outlook.com

Previous Names: None
Previous Leagues: Gloucestershire Northern Senior > 2011. Gloucestershire County 2011-14.
HONOURS
FA Comps: None
League: Gloucestershire Northern Division One 2008-09. Gloucestershire County 2012-13, 13-14. Hellenic Division One West 2014-15.

10-11	11-12	12-13	13-14	14-15	15-16	16-17	17-18	18-19	19-20
GlN1 4	GlCo 9	GlCo 1	GlCo 1	Hel1W 1	Hel P 10	Hel P 12	Hel P 9	Hel P 16	Hel P n&v
						FAC P	FAC P	FAC P	FAC 1Q
					FAV 1Q	FAV 2Q	FAV 1P	FAV 1P	FAV 2P

GROUND: Saw Mills End, Corinium Avenue, Gloucester GL4 3DG
Capacity: 500 **Seats:** Yes **Covered:** Yes
Nearest Railway Station Gloucester - 1.9km
Bus Route Budgen's Garage stop - 146m away

LYDNEY TOWN
Nickname: The Town **Club Colours:** Black & white
Founded 1911

Club Contact Details 01594 844 523 (Ground) rogersansom@outlook.com

Previous Names: None
Previous Leagues: Local leagues 1911-52. Gloucestershire Northern Senior 1952-80, 84-. Hellenic 1980-84. Gloucestershire County 2005-06.
HONOURS
FA Comps: None
League: Gloucesteeshire Northern Senior 1979-80. Gloucestershire County 2005-06. Hellenic League Division One West 2006-07.

10-11	11-12	12-13	13-14	14-15	15-16	16-17	17-18	18-19	19-20
Hel1W 5	Hel1W 13	Hel1W 10	Hel1W 2	Hel1W 3	Hel P 12	Hel P 9	Hel P 16	Hel P 11	Hel P n&v
FAC P	FAC EP					FAC EP	FAC EP	FAC 1Qr	FAC EP
FAV 1P	FAV 1P	FAV 2Q	FAV 2Q		FAV 2Q	FAV 1P	FAV 2Q	FAV 1Q	FAV 1Q

GROUND: Lydney Recreation Ground, Swan Road, Lydney GL15 5RU
Capacity: 1,000 **Seats:** Yes **Covered:** Yes
Nearest Railway Station Lydney Town - 144m
Bus Route Forest Parade - 156m away

READING CITY
Nickname: Mighty Moor **Club Colours:** Blue
Founded 2001

Club Contact Details 07918 880 777 media@readingcity.co.uk

Previous Names: Highmoor and Ibis merged to form today's club in 2001. Highmoor Ibis 2001-18.
Previous Leagues: Reading 2001-2011.
HONOURS
FA Comps: None
League: Reading Senior Division 2003-04, 10-11.

10-11	11-12	12-13	13-14	14-15	15-16	16-17	17-18	18-19	19-20
ReadS 1	Hel1E 2	Hel P 12	Hel P 4	Hel P 2	Hel P 11	Hel P 14	Hel P 17	Hel P 18	Hel P n&v
			FAC 1Q	FAC P	FAC 1P	FAC P	FAC P	FAC EPr	FAC P
		FAV 2Q	FAV 1P	FAV 1P	FAV 1P	FAV 1Q	FAV 1Q	FAV 1Q	FAV 2Q

GROUND: The Rivermoor, Scours Lane, Tilehurst, Reading RG30 6AY
Capacity: **Seats:** Yes **Covered:** Yes
Nearest Railway Station Tilehurst - 1.2km
Bus Route Cold Store stop - 277m away

ROYAL WOOTTON BASSETT

Nickname: Bassett   **Club Colours:** All blue

Founded 1882

Club Contact Details 01793 853 880 (Ground)   ian.thomas@wbtfc.co.uk

Previous Names: Wootton Bassett Town > 2015.

Previous Leagues: Vale of White 1898-99. Swindon & District 1899-1903. Wiltshire County 1903-08, 35-69, 76-88. Calne & District 1930. Wiltshire Combination 1969-76.

HONOURS

FA Comps: None

League: Calne & District 1931-32, 34-35, 35-36.
Wiltshire Division One 1958-59, Division Two 1984-85, Division One 1987-88.

10-11		11-12		12-13		13-14		14-15		15-16		16-17		17-18		18-19		19-20	
Hel P	15	Hel1W	5	Hel1W	2	Hel P	14	Hel P	11	Hel P	15	Hel P	11	Hel P	15	Hel P	10	Hel P	n&v
FAC	1Qr	FAC	EP	FAC	2Q	FAC	EP	FAC	P	FAC	EP	FAC	EP	FAC	EP	FAC	Pr		
FAV	1P	FAV	1Q	FAV	1Q	FAV	2Q	FAV	2Q	FAV	2Q	FAV	2Q	FAV	2P	FAV	2Q	FAV	2Q

GROUND: Gerrard Buxton Sports Ground, Malmesbury Road, Royal Wootton Bassett SN4 8DS
Capacity: 4,500 **Seats:** 550 **Covered:** 1,250 **Shop:** No

Bus Route The Farm stop - 69m

SHRIVENHAM

Nickname: Shrivvy   **Club Colours:** Blue & white

Founded 1900

Club Contact Details 07711 263 113   c.rawle@shrivenhamfc.co.uk

Previous Names: None.

Previous Leagues: North Berkshire.

HONOURS

FA Comps: None

League: North Berks Division Two 1994-95, Division One 1997-98, 2000-01.
Hellenic Division One West 2004-05.

10-11		1,1-12		12-13		13-14		14-15		15-16		16-17		17-18		18-19		19-20	
Hel P	20	Hel P	16	Hel P	19	Hel P	15	Hel P	19	Hel1W	8	Hel1W	7	Hel1W	2	Hel P	5	Hel P	n&v
FAC	EP	FAC	EP	FAC	P	FAC	EP	FAC	P	FAC	EP							FAC	P
FAT	1P	FAV	2Q	FAV	2Q	FAV	2Q	FAV	1Q	FAV	2Q	FAV	1Q			FAV	2Q	FAV	1P

GROUND: The Recreation Ground, Barrington Park, Shrivenham SN6 8BJ
Capacity: 1,500 **Seats:** Yes **Covered:** Yes

Bus Route Green (Townsend Rd) stop - 268m away

TUFFLEY ROVERS

Nickname: Rovers   **Club Colours:** Claret & blue

Founded 1929

Club Contact Details 07545 492 261   admin@tuffleyroversfc.co.uk

Previous Names: None

Previous Leagues: Gloucestershire County 1988-91, 2007-13. Hellenic 1991-06. Gloucestershire Northern 2006-07.

HONOURS

FA Comps: None

League: Gloucester County 1990-91. Gloucestershire Northern Division One 2006-07.

10-11		11-12		12-13		13-14		14-15		15-16		16-17		17-18		18-19		19-20	
GlCo	6	GlCo	3	GlCo	2	Hel1W	6	Hel1W	2	Hel P	17	Hel P	10	Hel P	10	Hel P	15	Hel P	n&v
										FAC	1Q	FAC	EP	FAC	1Q	FAC	EP	FAC	EPr
								FAV	1P	FAV	1Q	FAV	2P	FAV	1Q	FAV	2Qr	FAV	1Q

GROUND: Glevum Park, Lower Tuffley Lane, Tuffley, Gloucester GL2 5DT
Capacity: 1,000 **Seats:** 100 **Covered:** yes
Nearest Railway Station Gloucester - 3.5km
Bus Route Pearce Way stop - 197m away

VIRGINIA WATER
Founded 1920

Nickname: The Waters   Club Colours: Maroon

Club Contact Details 01753 860 656 (Ground)   gp738@hotmail.com

Previous Names:

Previous Leagues: Surrey Senior 1968-75. London Spartan 1975-79. Combined Counties 1979-87, 93-94. Surrey County Premier 1992-93, 94 -2002. Surrey Intermediate (West) 2002-10. Surrey Elite Intermediate 2010-17.

HONOURS

FA Comps: None

League: Surrey County Premier Division 1992-93, 96-97. Surrey Elite Intermediate 2016-17. Hellenic Division One East 2017-18.

10-11		11-12		12-13		13-14		14-15		15-16		16-17		17-18		18-19		19-20	
SuEl	6	SuEl	14	SuEl	11	SuEl	8	SuEl	7	SuEl	5	SuEl	1	Hel1E	1	Hel P	14	Hel P	n&v
																		FAC	EP
																FAV	2Q	FAV	1Q

GROUND: Windsor FC, Stag Meadow, St Leonards Road Windsor SL4 3DR
Capacity: 4,500 **Seats:** 450 **Covered:** 650
Nearest Railway Station Windsor & Eton Central - 1.5km
Bus Route Stag Meadow stop - 131m away

WESTFIELDS
Founded 1966

Nickname: The Fields   Club Colours: All Maroon & sky blue

Club Contact Details 07860 410 548   andrewmorris@westfieldsfc.com

Previous Names: None.

Previous Leagues: Herefordshire Sunday 1966-73. Worcester & Dist. 1973-78. West Midlands (Regional) 1978-04. Midland Alliance 2004-14. Midland 2014-19.

HONOURS

FA Comps: None

League: West Midlands (Regional) Division One 1986-87, Premier 2002-03.

10-11		11-12		12-13		13-14		14-15		15-16		16-17		17-18		18-19		19-20	
MidAl	6	MidAl	2	MidAl	2	MidAl	12	WMP	8	MFLP	16	MFLP	5	MFLP	12	MFLP	4		n&v
FAC	P	FAC	EP	FAC	2Qr	FAC	EP	FAC	P	FAC	1Q	FAC	1P	FAC	2Q	FAC	EP	FAC	P
FAV	3P	FAV	1P	FAV	1P	FAV	4P	FAV	3P	FAV	1P	FAV	3P	FAV	4P	FAV	3P	FAV	3P

GROUND: Allpay Park, Widemarsh Common, Hereford HR4 9NA
Capacity: 2,250 **Seats:** 220 **Covered:** 400 **Shop:** Yes
Nearest Railway Station Hereford - 1km
Bus Route Priory Place stop - 165m away

WINDSOR
Founded 1892

Nickname: The Royals   Club Colours: Red, white & green

Club Contact Details 01753 860 656 (Ground)   secretary@windsorfc.net

Previous Names: Formed when Windsor Phoenix and Windsor St. Albans merged in 1892. Windsor & Eton 1892-2011.

Previous Leagues: W.Berks, Gt Western, Suburban, Athenian 22-29,63-81, Spartan 29-39, Gt W.Comb. Corinthian 45-50, Met 50-60, Delphian 60-63, Isthmian 1963-2006, Southern 2006-11. Combined Counties 2011-17.

HONOURS

FA Comps: None

League: Athenian League 1979-80, 80-81. Isthmian League Division 1 1983-84. Southern League Division 1 South & West 2009-10.

10-11		11-12		12-13		13-14		14-15		15-16		16-17		17-18		18-19		19-20	
SthP	Exp	CCP	2	CCP	6	CCP	6	CCP	5	CCP	12	CCP	11	Hel P	8	Hel P	6	Hel P	n&v
FAC	1Q			FAC	1Q	FAC	P	FAC	P	FAC	EP	FAC	EP	FAC	EP	FAC	P	FAC	EP
FAT	2Q	FAV	2Q	FAV	1P	FAV	1P	FAV	1P	FAV	1P	FAV	1Q	FAV	QF	FAV	5P	FAV	2P

GROUND: Stag Meadow, St Leonards Road, Windsor, Berks SL4 3DR
Capacity: 4,500 **Seats:** 450 **Covered:** 650 **Shop:** Yes
Nearest Railway Station Windsor & Eton - 1.5km
Bus Route Stag Meadow stop - 131m away

OUT: Marlow United (WD)., Didcot Town Development (WD).

DIVISION ONE EAST

ABINGDON TOWN
Nickname: The Abbots　　　　Club Colours: Yellow and green
Founded 1870

Club Contact Details 07585 443 656　　　　sec@abingdontownfc.com

HONOURS
FA Comps: None
League: Oxford & District 1899-00, 1900-01. North Berks 1919-20, 22-23. Reading & District 1947-48. Spartan Premier 1988-89. Hellenic Premier 1956-57, 58-59, 59-60, 86-87, Division One 75-76.

10-11	11-12	12-13	13-14	14-15	15-16	16-17	17-18	18-19	19-20
Hel P 14	Hel P 11	Hel P 18	Hel P 20	NBk 1 3	NBk 1 5		Hel2E 7	Hel1E 12	Hel1E n&v
FAC EP	FAC Pr	FAC P	FAC EP						
FAV 2Q	FAV 1P	FAV 1Q	FAV 1P						FAV 1Q

GROUND: Culham Road, Abingdon OX14 3HP

ABINGDON UNITED
Nickname: The Yellows　　　　Club Colours: Yellow and blue
Founded 1946

Club Contact Details 01235 203 203　　　　secretaryaufc@virginmedia.com

HONOURS
FA Comps: None
League: North Berks 1952-53.

10-11	11-12	12-13	13-14	14-15	15-16	16-17	17-18	18-19	19-20
Sthsw 16	Sthsw 18	Sthsw 20	Hel P 17	Hel P 15	Hel P 19	Hel1W 2	Hel P 13	Hel P 19	Hel1E n&v
FAC P	FAC 1Q	FAC P	FAC EPr	FAC 2Q	FAC EP	FAC EPr		FAC EPr	FAC EP
FAT 1Q	FAT P	FAT P	FAV 1P	FAV 2Pr	FAV 1Q	FAV 1P	FAV 2Q	FAV 1P	FAV 1P

GROUND: The Northcourt, Northcourt Road, Abingdon OX14 1PL
Nearest Railway Station Radley - 2.5km
Bus Route Boundary House (Oxford Rd) stop - 215m

AFC ALDERMASTON
Nickname: The Atomics　　　　Club Colours: Red & black
Founded 1952

Club Contact Details 01189 824 454 (Ground)　　　　martin.desay@gmail.com

HONOURS
FA Comps: None
League: None

10-11	11-12	12-13	13-14	14-15	15-16	16-17	17-18	18-19	19-20
HantP 15	HantP 9	HantP 8	HantP 10	ReadP 5	ReadP 7	Hel1E 7	Hel1E 11	Hel1E 3	Hel1E n&v
							FAV 1Q		FAV 2Q

GROUND: AWE, Aldermaston, Reading RG7 4PR
Nearest Railway Station Midgham - 4km
Bus Route Calleva Park stop - 48m away

CHALVEY SPORTS
Nickname: The Stab-monks　　　　Club Colours: Blue & black
Founded 1885

Club Contact Details 07525 441 926

HONOURS
FA Comps: None
League: Great Western Combination 1954-55. East Berkshire Division One 1992-93, Premier 96-97. Hellenic Division Two East 2016-17, 17-18.

10-11	11-12	12-13	13-14	14-15	15-16	16-17	17-18	18-19	19-20
EBkP 10	EBkP 8	EBkP 7	EBkP 2	EBkP 2	EBkP 2	Hel2E 1	Hel2E 1	Hel1E 8	Hel1E n&v
									FAV 1Q

GROUND: Arbour Park, Stoke Road, Slough SL2 5AY
Nearest Railway Station Slough
Bus Route First Group 1, 13, 12, 14, 353.

www.nonleagueclubdirectory.co.uk　　701

HELLENIC LEAGUE

HOLYPORT
Nickname: The Villagers Club Colours: Claret & green Founded 1934

Club Contact Details 07515 789 415 richardtyrell@googlemail.com

HONOURS
FA Comps: None
League: Hayes & Giles Premier Division 1998-99, 99-2000, 01-02.
Hellenic Division One East 2010-11.

	10-11	11-12	12-13	13-14	14-15	15-16	16-17	17-18	18-19	19-20
	Hel1E 1	Hel P 13	Hel P 14	Hel P 18	Hel P 16	Hel1E 7	Hel1E 13	Hel1E 5	Hel1E 4	Hel1E n&v
	FAC EP	FAC EP	FAC EP	FAC EP	FAC EPr	FAC EP			FAC EP	
	FAV 2P	FAV 1Q	FAV 1P	FAV 2Q	FAV 1Q	FAV 1Qr	FAV 1Q	FAV 2Q	FAV 1Pr	FAV 2Q

GROUND: Summerleaze Village, 7 Summerleaze Road SL6 8SP
Nearest Railway Station Furze Platt - 1km
Bus Route Veterinary Hospital stop - 133m away

KIDLINGTON DEVELOPMENT
Nickname: Greens Club Colours: All green Founded 1909

Club Contact Details 01865 849 777 (Ground) barry.hiles@btinternet.com

HONOURS
FA Comps: None
League: None

10-11	11-12	12-13	13-14	14-15	15-16	16-17	17-18	18-19	19-20
							Hel1W 11	Hel1W 6	Hel1E n&v

GROUND: Yarnton Road, Kidlington, Oxford OX5 1AT
Nearest Railway Station Oxford Parkway - 1.9km
Bus Route Treeground Place stop - 63m away

LANGLEY
Nickname: The Villagers Club Colours: Red and white Founded

Club Contact Details 07935 046 504 langleyfc2016@gmail.com

HONOURS
FA Comps: None
League: East Berkshire Division One 2013-14, Premier Division 2016-17.

10-11	11-12	12-13	13-14	14-15	15-16	16-17	17-18	18-19	19-20
			EBk1 1	EBkP 5	EBkP 4	EBkP 1	EBkP 2	Hel2E 2	Hel1E n&v
									FAV 1Q

GROUND: Slough Town FC, Arbour Park, Stoke Road, Slough SL2 5AY
Nearest Railway Station Slough
Bus Route First Group 1, 13, 12, 14, 353.

LONG CRENDON
Nickname: The Robins Club Colours: Red and white Founded 1886

Club Contact Details 07937 423 781 admin@longcrendonfc.co.uk

HONOURS
FA Comps: None
League: Aylesbury & District Division Two 2014-15, Hellenic Division Two East 2018-19

10-11	11-12	12-13	13-14	14-15	15-16	16-17	17-18	18-19	19-20
			AyD2 9	AyD2 1	AyD1 2	AyDP 2	Hel2E 3	Hel2E 1	Hel1E n&v
									FAV 2Q

GROUND: Court Place Farm, Marsh Lane, Marston, Oxford OX3 0NQ
Nearest Railway Station Oxford - three miles from the ground.
Bus Route 14A from the Station to the ground.

MILTON UNITED
Nickname: Miltonians   **Club Colours:** Claret & sky blue

Founded 1909

Club Contact Details 01235 832 999   milton.united.fc@hotmail.co.uk

HONOURS
FA Comps: None
League: Hellenic 1990-91, Division One East 2013-14.

10-11		11-12		12-13		13-14		14-15		15-16		16-17		17-18		18-19		19-20	
Hel1E	4	Hel1E	14	Hel1E	14	Hel1E	1	Hel P	14	Hel P	18	Hel1W	12	Hel1E	13	Hel1E	10	Hel1E	n&v
FAC	EP	FAC	EP							FAC	1Q	FAC	P	FAC	EP				
FAV	1Q	FAV	2Q	FAV	2Q	FAV	1P	FAV	2Q	FAV	2Q	FAV	2Q	FAV	1Q	FAV	1Q	FAV	1Q

GROUND: The Heights, Potash Lane, Milton Heights, OX13 6AG
Nearest Railway Station Didcot Parkway - 4.7km. Appleford - 5.9km
Bus Route The Pack Horse stop - 69m away

PENN & TYLERS GREEN
Nickname: Penn   **Club Colours:** Blue & white

Founded 1905

Club Contact Details 01494 676 868   hsvlatta1955@yahoo.co.uk

HONOURS
FA Comps: None
League: Wycombe Comb. Div.A 1911-12, Div.2 35-36, 56,57, 60-61, North 39-40, Div.1 46-47, Div.3 55-56, Prem 62-63. Wycombe & Dist Sen 83 -84. Hellenic D1E 2015-16, 16-17

10-11		11-12		12-13		13-14		14-15		15-16		16-17		17-18		18-19		19-20	
Hel1E	10	Hel1E	12	Hel1E	4	Hel1E	5	Hel1E	9	Hel1E	1	Hel1E	1	Hel1E	3	Hel1E	9	Hel1E	n&v
																FAV	1Q		

GROUND: Beaconsfield Town FC, Holloways Park, Windsor Road HP9 2SE
Nearest Railway Station Beaconsfield - 2.8km

RISBOROUGH RANGERS
Nickname: Rangers or Boro   **Club Colours:** All red

Founded 1971

Club Contact Details 07855 958 236   nick@lloydlatchford.co.uk

HONOURS
FA Comps: None
League: None

10-11		11-12		12-13		13-14		14-15		15-16		16-17		17-18		18-19		19-20	
SSM2	5	SSM2	2	SSM2	4	SSM1	14	SSM1	5	SSM1	7	SSM1	6	SSM1	8	SSM1	7	Hel1E	n&v
										FAC	P	FAC	EP	FAC	EPr				
								FAV	2Q	FAV	2Q	FAV	1Q	FAV	1Q	FAV	1Q	FAV	1P

GROUND: " Windsors" Horsenden Lane, Princes Risborough. Bucks HP27 9NE
Nearest Railway Station Princes Rosborough - 0.2km
Bus Route Railway Station - stop 0.2km away

THAME RANGERS
Nickname: None   **Club Colours:** Red & black

Founded

Club Contact Details 01844 214 401   rjcarr5@btinternet.com

HONOURS
FA Comps: None
League: Wycombe & District Senior Division 2015-16.
Spartan South Midlands Division Two 2016-17.

10-11		11-12		12-13		13-14		14-15		15-16		16-17		17-18		18-19		19-20	
										WyDS	1	SSM2	1	Hel1E	8	Hel1E	2	Hel1E	n&v
																		FAC	Pr
																FAV	2P	FAV	1Q

GROUND: Meadow View Park, Tythrop Way, Thame OX9 3RN
Nearest Railway Station Haddenham & Thame Parkway - 2.9km
Bus Route Queens Close stop - 309m away

WALLINGFORD TOWN
Nickname: Wally   **Club Colours:** Red & white

Founded 1995

Club Contact Details 01491 835 044

HONOURS
FA Comps: None
League: None

10-11	11-12	12-13	13-14	14-15	15-16	16-17	17-18	18-19	19-20
NBk 1 4	NBk 1 11	NBk 1 9	NBk 1 9	NBk 1 4	NBk 1 6	NBk 1 3	Hel1E 7	Hel1E 7	Hel1E n&v
FAV 1P	FAV 1Q						FAV 2Q	FAV 1Q	

GROUND: Wallingford Sports Park, Hithercroft Road, Wallingford OX10 9RB
Nearest Railway Station Wallingford - 366m
Bus Route Moses Winter Way stop - 58m away

WOKINGHAM & EMMBROOK
Nickname: Satsumas   **Club Colours:** Orange and black

Founded 2004

Club Contact Details 07525 736 797   senior@wefc.club

HONOURS
FA Comps: None
League: Hellenic Division One East 2014-15.

10-11	11-12	12-13	13-14	14-15	15-16	16-17	17-18	18-19	19-20
Hel P 11	Hel P 10	Hel P 8	Hel1E 2	Hel1E 1	Hel P 20	Hel1E 12	Hel1E 6	Hel1E 6	Hel1E n&v
	FAC 1Q	FAC EP							
FAV 2Q	FAV 2Q	FAV 1P			FAV 1P				FAV 2Q

GROUND: Bracknell Town FC whilst work is done on Lowther Road
Nearest Railway Station Bracknell - 0.5km
Bus Route Larges Bridge Drive stop - 282m away

WOODLEY UNITED
Nickname: Woods or United   **Club Colours:** Sky blue

Founded 1904

Club Contact Details 0118 9453 555   info@woodleyunitedfc.co.uk

HONOURS
FA Comps: None
League: Wargrave & District 1909-10, 26-27. Reading & District Division Three 28-29, Division One 32-33, Division Two 50-51, Premier 57-58, 58
-59, 85-86. Reading Division Four Kennet 91-92, Division Three Kennet 92-93, Senior Division 2008-09.

10-11	11-12	12-13	13-14	14-15	15-16	16-17	17-18	18-19	19-20
Hel1E 5	Hel1E 5	Hel1E 3	Hel1E 14	Hel1E 8	Hel1E 13	Hel1E 2	Hel P 19	Hel1E 11	Hel1E n&v
							FAC EP	FAC EP	
			FAV 2Q	FAV 1Q	FAV 1Q	FAV 1Q	FAV 1Q	FAV 1Q	FAV 1Q

GROUND: Rivermoor Stadium, Scours Lane, Reading, Berkshire, RG30 6AY
Nearest Railway Station Tilehurst - 1.2km
Bus Route Cold Store stop - 277m away

DIVISION ONE WEST

BOURTON ROVERS
Nickname: Rovers   **Club Colours:** All blue

Founded 1894

Club Contact Details 01451 821 977

HONOURS
FA Comps: None
League: Hellenic Division Two West 2016-17

10-11	11-12	12-13	13-14	14-15	15-16	16-17	17-18	18-19	19-20
						Hel2W 1	Hel2W 2	Hel2W 5	Hel1W n&v

GROUND: Rissington Road, Bourton-on-the-Water, Cheltenham GL54 2EB
Nearest Railway Station Cirencester
Bus Route 801 - alight at Edinburgh Wool Shop, 11min walk from there.

CHELTENHAM SARACENS
Nickname: The Sarries   **Club Colours:** All blue

Founded 1964

Club Contact Details 07468 515 471   saracenschairman@outlook.com

HONOURS
FA Comps: None
League: Hellenic Division One 1999-2000.

10-11	11-12	12-13	13-14	14-15	15-16	16-17	17-18	18-19	19-20
Hel1W 3	Hel P 15	Hel P 11	Hel P 16	Hel P 20	Hel1W 2	Hel1W 14	Hel1W 10	Hel1W 2	Hel1W n&v
			FAC Pr	FAC P	FAC 1Q				FAC EP
FAV 1Q	FAV 1Q	FAV 1P	FAV 1Q	FAV 1Q	FAV 1Q			FAV 2Q	FAV 1Q

GROUND: Petersfield Park, Tewkesbury Road GL51 9DY
Nearest Railway Station Cheltenham Spa - 1.4km
Bus Route Moors Avenue stop - 171m away

CIRENCESTER TOWN DEV.
Nickname: Centurions   **Club Colours:** Red & black

Founded 2011

Club Contact Details 01285 654 543   scott.griffin@cirentownfc.com

HONOURS
FA Comps: None
League: None

10-11	11-12	12-13	13-14	14-15	15-16	16-17	17-18	18-19	19-20
		Hel2W 3	Hel2W 3	Hel1W 4	Hel1W 11	Hel1W 5	Hel1W 5	Hel1W 8	Hel1W n&v

GROUND: Corinium Stadium, Kingshill Lane, Cirencester Glos GL7 1HS
Nearest Railway Station Cirencester
Bus Route Kingshill School Grounds stop - 55m away

CLANFIELD 85
Nickname: Robins   **Club Colours:** All red

Founded 1890

Club Contact Details 01367 810 770   peter.osborne1@virgin.net

HONOURS
FA Comps: None
League: North Berks Division Two 1924-25.
Hellenic Division One 1969-70.

10-11	11-12	12-13	13-14	14-15	15-16	16-17	17-18	18-19	19-20
Hel1W 4	Hel1W 8	Hel1W 11	Hel1W 5	Hel1W 9	Hel1W 12	Hel1W 10	Hel1W 8	Hel1W 5	Hel1W n&v
FAC EP	FAC EP								FAC EP
FAV 2P	FAT 1P	FAV 1Q					FAV 2Q	FAV 2Q	FAV 2Q

GROUND: Radcot Road, Clanfield OX18 2ST

Bus Route Carter Institute stop - 399m away

HEREFORD LADS CLUB
Nickname: Lads Club **Club Colours:** Blue

Founded 1925

Club Contact Details 07557 128 790

HONOURS

FA Comps: None

League: Herefordshire Division One 2002-03.
West Midlands Division One 2016-17.

10-11	11-12	12-13	13-14	14-15	15-16	16-17	17-18	18-19	19-20
	WM2 2	WM2 3	WM1 10	WM1 5	WM1 2	WM1 1	WMP 12	WMP 7	Hel1W n&v
							FAV 1Q	FAV 2P	

GROUND: Widemarsh Common, Hereford HR4 9NA

Nearest Railway Station Hereford - 1km

Bus Route Priory Place - stop 150m away

HEREFORD PEGASUS
Nickname: The Redmen or Peggy **Club Colours:** Red and white

Founded 1955

Club Contact Details 07931 971 765   nikmarsh1982@gmail.com

HONOURS

FA Comps: None

League: Hellenic Division One 1984-85, 98-99.

10-11	11-12	12-13	13-14	14-15	15-16	16-17	17-18	18-19	19-20
Hel P 22	WMP 17	WMP 7	WMP 2	WMP 9	WMP 9	WMP 9	WMP 19	WMP 20	Hel1W n&v
FAC EPr	FAC EPr	FAC P	FAC EP	FAC EPr	FAC EP	FAC 2Q	FAV 1Q	FAV 1Q	FAV 1Q
FAV 2Q	FAV 1Q	FAV 1P	FAV 1Q	FAV 2P	FAV 1Q				

GROUND: Old School Lane, Hereford HR1 1EX

Nearest Railway Station Hereford - 1.3km

Bus Route Bus stops outside the ground

MALMESBURY VICTORIA
Nickname: The Vics **Club Colours:** Black & white

Founded 1896

Club Contact Details 01666 822 141   brendon@innov.co.uk

HONOURS

FA Comps: None

League: Wiltshire Premier 1999-00, 2014-15.

10-11	11-12	12-13	13-14	14-15	15-16	16-17	17-18	18-19	19-20
Hel1W 13	Hel1W 16	Hel1W 15	Hel1W 12	Wilt 1	Wilt 3	West1 9	West1 15	Hel1W 4	Hel1W n&v
									FAC EP
FAV 1Q			FAV 1Q	FAV 1P	FAV 2Q	FAV 1Q	FAV 2Q	FAV 2P	FAV 1P

GROUND: Flying Monk Ground, Gloucester Road, SN16 9JS

Bus Route Bus stops outside the Supermarket

MALVERN TOWN
Nickname: The Hillsiders **Club Colours:** Sky blue and claret

Founded 1947

Club Contact Details 01684 564 746   marg@malverntown.co.uk

HONOURS

FA Comps: None

League: Midland Combination Division One 1955-56.

10-11	11-12	12-13	13-14	14-15	15-16	16-17	17-18	18-19	19-20
MidAl 23	WMP 13	WMP 13	WMP 14	WMP 5	WMP 3	WMP 4	WMP 3	WMP 4	Hel1W n&v
FAC P	FAC EPr				FAC EP	FAC EP	FAC P	FAC P	FAC EP
FAV 1P	FAV 1Q	FAV 1Q	FAV 1Q	FAV 1Q	FAV 2Q	FAV 1P	FAV 1Q	FAV 1Q	FAV 3P

GROUND: Langlands Avenue, Malvern WR14 2EQ

Nearest Railway Station Great Malvern - 1.2km. Malvern Link - 1.5km

Bus Route Bus stops outside the ground

MORETON RANGERS
Nickname: The Townsmen   Club Colours: Claret and blue   Founded 1997

Club Contact Details 07568 469 120

HONORS
FA Comps: None
League: Cheltenham Division One 2009-10. Hellenic Division Two West 2018-19

10-11	11-12	12-13	13-14	14-15	15-16	16-17	17-18	18-19	19-20
					Hel2W 3	Hel2W 5	Hel2W 3	Hel2W 1	Hel1W n&v

GROUND: London Road, Moreton-in-Marsh, Glos GL56 0HN
Nearest Railway Station Moreton-in-Marsh - 1min walk away

NEWENT TOWN AFC
Nickname: The Daff's   Club Colours: Yellow & blue   Founded

Club Contact Details 01531 821 509 (Ground)   phil@calendarlady.co.uk

HONORS
FA Comps: None
League: North Gloucestershire Premier 2012-13. Hellenic Division Two West 2017-18

10-11	11-12	12-13	13-14	14-15	15-16	16-17	17-18	18-19	19-20
NGIP 6	NGIP 3	NGIP 1	GIN2 3	GIN1 14	GIN1 3	GIN1 7	Hel2W 1	Hel1W 9	Hel1W n&v
									FAV 2Q

GROUND: Wildsmith Meadow, Malswick, Newent GL18 1HE
Nearest Railway Station Gloucester
Bus Route 32

SHORTWOOD UNITED
Nickname: The Wood   Club Colours: Red and white   Founded 1900

Club Contact Details 07931 971 765   jimcunneen1951@gmail.com

HONORS
FA Comps: None
League: Gloucestershire 1981-82. Hellenic 1984-85, 91-92.

10-11	11-12	12-13	13-14	14-15	15-16	16-17	17-18	18-19	19-20
Hel P 6	Hel P 2	Sthsw 8	Sthsw 6	Sthsw 11	Sthsw 7	Sthsw 9	Sthsw 17	WestP 20	Hel1W n&v
FAC Pr	FAC Pr	FAC P	FAC 1P	FAC 3Qr	FAC 2Q	FAC P	FAC P	FAC EP	FAC P
FAV 2P	FAV QF	FAT 3Qr	FAT 1Q	FAT 1Q	FAT P	FAT P	FAT 3Q	FAV 2Q	FAV 2Q

GROUND: Meadowbank, Shortwood, Nailsworth GL6 0SJ

Bus Route Homefield Turn - stop 250m away

STONEHOUSE TOWN
Nickname: The Magpies   Club Colours: Black and white   Founded 1898

Club Contact Details 07849 551 656

HONORS
FA Comps: None
League: Dursley & Dist 1900-01. Stroud & Dist 1908-09, 20-12, 27-28. North Glos 1919-20. Glos Nth Senior 1934-35, 35-36, 36-37, Div.2 2008-09, Wiltshire 1967-68. Glos Co 1968-69. Western Div.2 1950-51.

10-11	11-12	12-13	13-14	14-15	15-16	16-17	17-18	18-19	19-20
						GlCo 3	GlCo 4	GlCo 3	Hel1W n&v

GROUND: Oldends Lane, Stonehouse, Glos GL10 2DG
Nearest Railway Station Stonehouse - 3min walk to Wycliffe College bus stop.
Bus Route No.61 (Woodmancote) from Wycliffe College 5min journey to Oldends Lane.

THORNBURY TOWN
Nickname: Thorns **Club Colours:** Red & black
Founded 1898

Club Contact Details 01454 413 645 (Ground)   pengelly.mike@gmail.com

HONOURS
FA Comps: None
League: Bristol Premier Combination x2. Gloucestershire County 2009-10, 17-18.

10-11	11-12	12-13	13-14	14-15	15-16	16-17	17-18	18-19	19-20
GlCo 13	GlCo 16	GlCo 14	GlCo 6	GlCo 4	GlCo 4	GlCo 4	GlCo 1	Hel1W 3	Hel1W n&v
									FAC EP
									FAV 2P

GROUND: Mundy Playing Fields, Kington Lane, Thornbury BS35 1NA
Nearest Railway Station Bristol Parkway - 40min bus journey from the ground.
Bus Route No.77 (Thornbury) to Rock Street - 14min walk to ground from there.

TYTHERINGTON ROCKS
Nickname: The Rocks **Club Colours:** Amber & black
Founded 1896

Club Contact Details 07837 555 776 (Ground)   tramar1618@btinternet.com

HONOURS
FA Comps: None
League: Iron Acton & District 1944-45. Bristol & Suburban Div.3 1949-50, Prem Div.2 93-94, Prem Div.1 96-97, Prem Div.1 97-98. Hellenic Div.1W 2011-12, 13-14.

10-11	11-12	12-13	13-14	14-15	15-16	16-17	17-18	18-19	19-20
Hel1W 8	Hel1W 1	Hel1W 3	Hel1W 1	Hel1W 15	Hel1W 14	Hel1W 15	Hel1W 14	Hel1W 11	Hel1W n&v
					FAV 2Qr	FAV 1Q	FAV 2Q	FAV 1Q	FAV 1Q

GROUND: Hardwicke Playing Field, Woodlands Road, Tytherington GL12 8UQ

Bus Route Stowell Hill Road stop - 102m away

WELLINGTON
Nickname: The Wellies **Club Colours:** Orange
Founded 1968

Club Contact Details 07842 186 643 (MD)   wellingtonherefordfc@gmail.com

HONOURS
FA Comps: None
League: West Midlands (Reg) Division One South 1998-99.

10-11	11-12	12-13	13-14	14-15	15-16	16-17	17-18	18-19	19-20
WMP 10	WMP 11	WMP 15	WMP 8	WMP 11	WMP 11	WMP 5	WMP 10	WMP 9	Hel1W n&v
FAC EPr	FAC EP	FAC P		FAC P			FAC EP		
FAV 1Q	FAV 2Q	FAV 1Q	FAV 1Q	FAV 1P	FAV 2Q	FAV 2Q	FAV 1P	FAV 1Pr	FAV 1Q

GROUND: Wellington Playing Field, Wellington, Hereford HR4 8AZ
Nearest Railway Station Hereford
Bus Route Wellington Village - stop 270m away

DIVISION TWO (SOUTH)	DIVISION TWO (WEST)	DIVISION TWO (EAST)	DIVISION TWO (NORTH)
Abingdon Town Res	Bourton Rovers Res	Chalfont Wasps	Adderbury Park
Abingdon Utd Dev	Cricklade Town Res	Chalvey Sports Dev'	Ardley United Dev
Aldermaston Res	Evesham Town Res	Chinnor	Aston Clinton
Clanfield Dev	Fairford Town Res	Cove Res	Banbury Utd
Faringdon Town	Hartpury College	FC Beaconsfield	Buckingham Ath Dev'
Highworth Town Res	Kington Town	Flackwell Heath Res	Easington Sports Res
Hungerford Swifts	Malvern Town Dev	Hazlemere	Headington Amat's
Kintbury Rangers	Moreton Rangers Dev	Holmer Green Dev'	Heyford Athletic
Letcombe	Newent Town Res	Penn & Tylers Green Dev	Kidlington Dev
Shrivenham Dev	SC Inkberrow	Stokenchurch	Long Crendon Res
Swindon Supermarine Dev	Shipston Excelsior	Taplow United	Old Bradwell Utd
Wallingford Town Res	Shortwood United Res	Westfield Res	Risborough Rangers Dev
Wantage Town	Slimbridge Res	Wokingham & Emm Res	Southam United
Woodcote SR	Tuffley Rovers Dev	Watlington Town	Thame United Res
		Yateley	Woodstock Town

OUT: South Normanton Athletic (WD).

AFC WULFRUNIANS
Nickname: The Wulfs   **Club Colours:** Red and black

Founded 2005

Club Contact Details 07765 141 410   birchkeith@yahoo.co.uk

Previous Names: None
Previous Leagues: West Midlands (Regional). Midland Alliance 2013-14.
HONOURS
FA Comps: None
League: West Midlands (Regional) League Division Two 2005-06, Premier Division 2008-09, 12-13.

	10-11	11-12	12-13	13-14	14-15	15-16	16-17	17-18	18-19	19-20
	WMP 3	WMP 5	WMP 1	MidAl 8	MFLP 7	MFLP 13	MFLP 17	MFLP 17	MFLP 12	MFLP n&v
FAC	EP	1Q	1Q	2Q	P	1Q	EP	Pr	EP	P
FAV	2Q	2Q	3P	2P	1Pr	4P	2P	1Pr	2Q	1Q

GROUND: Castlecroft Stadium, Castlecroft Road, Wolverhampton WV3 8NA
Capacity: 2,000 **Seats:** Yes **Covered:** Yes
Nearest Railway Station Wolverhampton - 5km
Bus Route Castlecroft Hotel stop - 218m away

BOLDMERE ST. MICHAELS
Nickname: The Mikes   **Club Colours:** White & black

Founded 1883

Club Contact Details 07866 122 254   clivefaulkner457@gmail.com

Previous Names: None.
Previous Leagues: West Midlands (Regional) 1949-63. Midland Combination. Midland Alliance > 2014.
HONOURS
FA Comps: None
League: Midland Combination Premier 1985-86, 88-89, 89-90.

	10-11	11-12	12-13	13-14	14-15	15-16	16-17	17-18	18-19	19-20
	MidAl 3	MidAl 12	MidAl 9	MidAl 2	MFLP 9	MFLP 11	MFLP 12	MFLP 14	MFLP 5	MFLP n&v
FAC	EP	1Q	EP	EP	1Q	EPr	P	1Q	EPr	1Q
FAV	2P	2P	2Q	2Q	1P	1P	2Q	2Q	2P	1P

GROUND: Trevor Brown Memorial Ground, Church Road, Boldmere B73 5RY
Capacity: 2,500 **Seats:** 230 **Covered:** 400
Nearest Railway Station Chester Road - 0.9km
Bus Route Church Road stop - 106m away

COVENTRY SPHINX
Nickname: Sphinx   **Club Colours:** Sky blue & white

Founded 1946

Club Contact Details 07979 233 845   sharon@coventrysphinx.co.uk

Previous Names: Armstrong Siddeley Motors. Sphinx > 1995.
Previous Leagues: Midland Combination. Midland Alliance 2007-14.
HONOURS
FA Comps: None
League: Midland Combination Premier 2006-07.

	10-11	11-12	12-13	13-14	14-15	15-16	16-17	17-18	18-19	19-20
	MidAl 16	MidAl 3	MidAl 14	MidAl 7	MFLP 18	MFLP 19	MFLP 10	MFLP 10	MFLP 9	MFLP n&v
FAC	2Q	P	P	2Q	Pr	P	EP	EP	EP	P
FAV	2P	2Q	2P	2Q	2P	2P	2Q	1Q	1Qr	2Q

GROUND: Sphinx Sports & Social Club, Sphinx Drive, Coventry CV3 1WA
Capacity: 1,000 **Seats:** Yes **Covered:** Yes
Nearest Railway Station Coventry - 2.6km
Bus Route Bulls Head Lane stop - 363m away

COVENTRY UNITED

Nickname: Cov United **Club Colours:** Red and green **Founded** 2013

Club Contact Details 07863 563 943 graham.wood@coventryunited.co.uk

Previous Names: None
Previous Leagues: Midland Combination 2013-14.
HONOURS
FA Comps: None
League: Midland Football League Division Two 2014-15, Division One 2015-16.

10-11	11-12	12-13	13-14	14-15	15-16	16-17	17-18	18-19	19-20
			MCm2 2	MFL2 1	MFL1 1	MFLP 8	MFLP 8	MFLP 8	MFLP n&v
						FAC 1Q	FAC EP	FAC EP	FAC EPr
					FAV 2P	FAV 1P	FAV 3Pr	FAV 4P	FAV 4P

GROUND: Coventry RFC, Butts Park Arena, The Butts, Coventry CV1 3GE
Capacity: 3,000 **Seats:** Yes **Covered:** Yes
Nearest Railway Station Coventry - 1km
Bus Route Albany Road stop - 156m away

GRESLEY

Nickname: The Moatmen **Club Colours:** Red & white **Founded** 2009

Club Contact Details 07733 055 212 ian.collins@gresleyfc.com

Previous Names: Gresley Rovers
Previous Leagues: East Midlands 2009-11. Midland Football Alliance 2011-12. Northern Premier 2012-19.
HONOURS
FA Comps: None
League: East Midlands Counties 2010-11. Midland Alliance 2011-12.

10-11	11-12	12-13	13-14	14-15	15-16	16-17	17-18	18-19	19-20
EMC 1	MidAl 1	NP1S 11	NP1S 9	NP1S 5	NP1S 16	NP1S 18	NP1S 17	NP1E 20	MFLP n&v
FAC 1Qr	FAC 1Q	FAC 3Q	FAC 2Qr	FAC Pr	FAC Pr	FAC 2Qr	FAC P	FAC P	FAC P
FAV 4P	FAV 5P	FAT 1Q	FAT 1P	FAT 3Q	FAT 1Q	FAT 1Q	FAT P	FAT P	FAV 1P

GROUND: The Moat Ground, Moat Street, Church Gresley, Derbyshire DE11 9RE
Capacity: 2,400 **Seats:** Yes **Covered:** Yes Yes

Bus Route Church Street - stop 200m away

HAUGHMOND

Nickname: Academicals **Club Colours:** White and black **Founded** 1980

Club Contact Details 07785 531 754 stuartlwilliams@btinternet.com

Previous Names: None
Previous Leagues: West Midlands >2017. Midland Football 2017-18. West Midlands 2018-19.
HONOURS
FA Comps: None
League: Shropshire County Premier Division 2010-11. West Midlands Division Two 2011-12, Premier Division 2016-17.

10-11	11-12	12-13	13-14	14-15	15-16	16-17	17-18	18-19	19-20
ShCP 1	WM2 1	WM1 4	WM1 2	WMP 8	WMP 5	WMP 1	MFLP 20	WMP 2	MFLP n&v
						FAC EP	FAC 2Qr	FAC 1Q	FAC P
					FAV 2P	FAV 1P	FAV 1P	FAV 1Q	FAV 1P

GROUND: Sundorne Sports Village, Sundorne Road, Shrewsbury. SY1 4RQ
Capacity: **Seats:** Yes **Covered:** Yes
Nearest Railway Station Shrewsbury - 2.6km
Bus Route Ta Centre stop - 109m away

HEATHER ST. JOHN'S
Nickname: **Club Colours:** All royal blue

Founded 1949

Club Contact Details 07952 633 331   adrianrock@hotmail.co.uk
Previous Names: Heather Athletic 1949-2007.
Previous Leagues: Midland Combination > 2011. Midland Alliance 2011-14.
HONOURS
FA Comps: None
League: Leicester & District Division One 1965-66., 69-70, 71-72.
Midland Combination Division One 2006-07, Premier 10-11. Midland Division One 2018-19.

10-11		11-12		12-13		13-14		14-15		15-16		16-17		17-18		18-19		19-20	
MCmP	1	MidAl	19	MidAl	20	MidAl	22	MFL1	16	MFL1	16	MFL1	8	MFL1	7	MFL1	1	MFLP	n&v
FAC	P					FAC	EP	FAC	EP							FAC	EP	FAC	1Q
FAV	3P			FAV	1P	FAV	2Q	FAV	2Q	FAV	1Q	FAV	1Q	FAV	1P	FAV	2P	FAV	1P

GROUND: St John's Park, Ravenstone Rd, Heather LE67 2QJ
Capacity: **Seats:** Yes   **Covered:** Yes

Bus Route Holyoake Drive stop - 160m away

HIGHGATE UNITED
Nickname: Red or Gate   **Club Colours:** All red

Founded 1948

Club Contact Details 07527 941 993   jimmymerry777@gmail.com
Previous Names: None.
Previous Leagues: Worcestershire/Midland Combination. Midland Alliance 2008-14.
HONOURS
FA Comps: None
League: Midland Combination Premier 1972-73, 73-74, 74-75.

10-11		11-12		12-13		13-14		14-15		15-16		16-17		17-18		18-19		19-20	
MidAl	18	MidAl	20	MidAl	19	MidAl	3	MFL1	1	MFLP	9	MFLP	7	MFLP	3	MFLP	14	MFLP	n&v
FAC	EP	FAC	P	FAC	EPr									FAC	2Q	FAC	EPr	FAC	1Q	FAC	EP
FAV	2Q	FAV	1P	FAV	2Q					FAV	2P	FAV	2Q	FAV	3P	FAV	1P	FAV	2Q

GROUND: The Coppice, Tythe Barn Lane, Shirley Solihull B90 1PH
Capacity: 2,000 **Seats:**   **Covered:**
Nearest Railway Station Whitlocks End - 0.4km
Bus Route Whitlocks End stop - 302m away

LONG EATON UNITED
Nickname: Blues   **Club Colours:** Blue and black

Founded 1956

Club Contact Details 07971 416 444   secretary@longeatonutd.co.uk
Previous Names: None
Previous Leagues: Central Alliance 1956-61, Mid Co Football Lge 1961-82, NCE 1982-89, 2002-14. Central Midlands 1989-2002
HONOURS
FA Comps: None
League: Northern Counties East Division One South 1984-85.

10-11		11-12		12-13		13-14		14-15		15-16		16-17		17-18		18-19		19-20	
NCEP	12	NCEP	15	NCEP	12	NCEP	11	MFLP	3	MFLP	18	MFLP	14	MFLP	9	MFLP	15	MFLP	n&v
FAC	EPr	FAC	EP			FAC	1Q	FAC	EP	FAC	1Q	FAC	P	FAC	EP	FAC	P	FAC	Pr
FAV	1Q	FAV	2P	FAV	3P	FAV	2P	FAV	1P	FAV	2P	FAV	3P	FAV	2Q	FAV	1P	FAV	2Q

GROUND: Grange Park, Station Road, Long Eaton, Derbys NG10 2EF
Capacity: 1,500 **Seats:** 450   **Covered:** 500   **Shop:** No
Nearest Railway Station Attenborough - 1.9km
Bus Route School stop - 158m away

LYE TOWN
Nickname: The Flyers   **Club Colours:** Blue & white   Founded 1930

Club Contact Details 07429 887 570   dprobbo@gmail.com

Previous Names: Lye & Wollescote 1930-31.
Previous Leagues: Worcestershire Combination 1931-39. Birmingham & Dist/West Midlands (Regional) 1947-62/1962-2014.
HONOURS
FA Comps: None
League: West Midlands (Regional) 2013-14.

10-11	11-12	12-13	13-14	14-15	15-16	16-17	17-18	18-19	19-20
WMP 11	WMP 15	WMP 2	WMP 1	MFLP 6	MFLP 8	MFLP 4	MFLP 16	MFLP 10	MFLP n&v
	FAC EP	FAC P	FAC P	FAC EP	FAC EPr	FAC P			FAC EP
FAV 2Q	FAV 1Q	FAV 1P	FAV 1Q	FAV 2Q	FAV 2Q	FAV 1Q		FAV 4P	FAV 3P

GROUND: Sports Ground, Stourbridge Road, Lye, Stourbridge, West Mids DY9 7DH
Capacity: 1,000   Seats: Covered:
Nearest Railway Station Lye - 0.5km
Bus Route Cemetery Road stop - 93m away

NEWARK FLOWSERVE
Nickname: Simmos   **Club Colours:** Orange   Founded 1901

Club Contact Details 07760 334 155   kmpnewark@aol.com

Previous Names: Worthington Simpsons >1998, IDP Newark 1998-2001.
Previous Leagues: Nottingham Alliance. Nottinghamshire Senior >2004, 2009-18. Central Midlands 2004-09. East Midlands Counties 2018-19.
HONOURS
FA Comps: None
League: Notts Alliance 1952-53, 65-66. Nottinghamshire Senior Premier Division 2017-18.

10-11	11-12	12-13	13-14	14-15	15-16	16-17	17-18	18-19	19-20
			NottS2 3	NottS1 2	NottSP	NottSP	NottSP 1	EMC 2	MFLP n&v
								FAV 1Q	FAV 4P

GROUND: Lowfields, Hawton Lane, Newark, Nottinghamshire NG24 3BU
Capacity: Seats: Yes   Covered: Yes
Nearest Railway Station Nottingham - walk to Eugene Gardens (Stop ME03).
Bus Route From Eugene Gardens take 90 Fosseway Flyer getting off at Princes Street in Newark - the ground is 1.5 miles.

RACING CLUB WARWICK
Nickname: Racers   **Club Colours:** Gold and black   Founded 1919

Club Contact Details 07926 188 553   pja.murphy@hotmail.co.uk

Previous Names: Warwick Saltisford Rovers > 1970.
Previous Leagues: Warwick. Leamington & District. West Midlands (regional) 1967-72. Midland Combination 1972-89, 2009-14. Southern 1989-2003. Midland Alliance 2003-09.
HONOURS
FA Comps: None
League: Warwick 1933-34, 34-35, 35-36. Leamington & District 37-38, 45-46, 46-47, 47-48. Midland Combination Premier Division 1987-88.

10-11	11-12	12-13	13-14	14-15	15-16	16-17	17-18	18-19	19-20
MCmP 19	MCmP 13	MCmP 17	MCmP 12	MFL1 18	MFL1 10	MFL1 6	MFL1 5	MFL1 2	MFLP n&v
								FAC 1Q	FAC EP
FAV 1Q	FAV 2P	FAV 2Q	FAV 1P	FAV 1Q	FAV 2P	FAV 1Q	FAV 3P	FAV 2Q	FAV 1P

GROUND: Townsend Meadow, Hampton Road, Warwick, Warwickshire CV34 6JP
Capacity: 1,300   Seats: Covered:
Nearest Railway Station Warwick Parkway - 1.4km
Bus Route Shakespeare Avenue stop - 131m away

ROMULUS
Nickname: The Roms   **Club Colours:** Red and white stripes/red/red

Founded 1979

Club Contact Details 07515 991 621   sarah.romulusfc@virginmedia.com

Previous Names: None
Previous Leagues: Midland Combination 1999-2004, Midland Alliance 2004-07, Southern 2007-2010. Northern Premier 2010-18.
HONOURS
FA Comps: None
League: Midland Combination Division One 1999-00, Premier Division 2003-04.

10-11		11-12		12-13		13-14		14-15		15-16		16-17		17-18		18-19		19-20	
NP1S	10	NP1S	20	NP1S	19	NP1S	11	NP1S	12	NP1S	10	NP1S	13	NP1S	22	MFLP	17	MFLP	n&v
FAC	1Q	FAC	1Q	FAC	P	FAC	P	FAC	1Q	FAC	P	FAC	1Qr	FAC	1Q	FAC	2Q	FAC	1Q
FAT	2Q	FAT	2Q	FAT	3Q	FAT	Pr	FAT	1Q	FAT	Pr	FAT	Pr	FAT	P	FAV	2P	FAV	1Q

GROUND: Vale Stadium, Farnborough Road, Castle Vale, Birmingham B35 7LQ
Capacity: **Seats:**   **Covered:**

SELSTON
Nickname: The Parishioners   **Club Colours:** Blue & black

Founded 1968

Club Contact Details 07973 364 188   clanclif@hotmail.co.uk

Previous Names: None
Previous Leagues: Midland Regional Alliance >2011. Notts Senior 2011-15. Central Midlands 2015-17. East Midlands Counties 2017-19.
HONOURS
FA Comps: None
League: Midland Regional Alliance Division Two 2007-08. Notts Senior 2013-14.
Central Midlands South Division 2015-16, 16-17. East Midlands Counties 2018-19.

10-11		11-12		12-13		13-14		14-15		15-16		16-17		17-18		18-19		19-20	
MidRA1	5	NottSP	11	NottSP	11	NottSP	1	NottSP	4	CMSth	1	CMSth	1	EMC	4	EMC	1	MFLP	n&v
																		FAC	EP
															FAV	1P	FAV	2Q

GROUND: Parish Hall, Mansfield Road, Selston, Nottinghamshire NG16 6EE
Capacity: **Seats:** Yes   **Covered:** Yes
Nearest Railway Station Kirkby in Ashfield - 4.5km

SPORTING KHALSA
Nickname: Sporting   **Club Colours:** Yellow & blue

Founded 1991

Club Contact Details 07976 220 444   manjit.gill@globeproperty.co.uk

Previous Names: None
Previous Leagues: Walsall & District Sunday 1991-96. West Midlands (Regional) 1996-97, 2005-15.
HONOURS
FA Comps: None
League: West Midlands (Regional) Premier Division 2014-15.

10-11		11-12		12-13		13-14		14-15		15-16		16-17		17-18		18-19		19-20	
WM1	3	WMP	14	WMP	11	WMP	6	WMP	1	MFLP	3	MFLP	3	MFLP	5	MFLP	3	MFLP	n&v
				FAC	Pr			FAC	P	FAC	4Q	FAC	P	FAC	Pr	FAC	P	FAC	P
FAV	1Q	FAV	1Q	FAV	1Q	FAV	2Q	FAV	2Qr	FAV	1P	FAV	QF	FAV	2P	FAV	5P	FAV	5P

GROUND: Aspray Arena, Noose Lane, Willenhall WV13 3BB
Capacity: 5,000 **Seats:** Yes **Covered:** Yes
Nearest Railway Station Wolverhampton - 3.9km
Bus Route Fibbersley Bridge stop - 125m away

STOURPORT SWIFTS
Nickname: Swifts **Club Colours:** Gold & black
Founded 1882

Club Contact Details 07780 997 758 ghaighway@hotmail.co.uk

Previous Names: None
Previous Leagues: Kidderminster/Worcestershire/West Midlands (Regional) > 1998, Midland Alliance 1998-2001, 12-14, Southern 2001-12.
HONOURS
FA Comps: None
League: Midland Alliance 2000-01.

10-11	11-12	12-13	13-14	14-15	15-16	16-17	17-18	18-19	19-20
Sthsw 17	Sthsw 21	MidAl 5	MidAl 10	MFLP 10	MFLP 10	MFLP 13	MFLP 15	MFLP 13	MFLP n&v
							FAC EPr	FAC 1Q	FAC Pr
							FAV 5P	FAV 2P	FAV 1Q

GROUND: Walshes Meadow, Harold Davis Drive, Stourport on Severn DY13 0AA
Capacity: 2,000 **Seats:** 250 **Covered:** 150 **Shop:** Yes
Nearest Railway Station Hartlebury - 4.2km
Bus Route Swimming Pool stop - 104m away

TIVIDALE
Nickname: The Dale **Club Colours:** Yellow and blue
Founded 1953

Club Contact Details 07939 234 813 leon@tividalefc.com

Previous Names: Tividale Hall Youth Club 1953-56
Previous Leagues: Warwickshire & West Midlands Alliance 1956-66. West Midlands (Regional) 1966- 2011. Midland Alliance 2011-14.
HONOURS
FA Comps: None
League: Warwickshire & West Midlands Alliance Premier 1964-65. West Midlands (Reg) Division One 1972-73, Premier Division 2010-11, 18-19. Midland Alliance 2013-14.

10-11	11-12	12-13	13-14	14-15	15-16	16-17	17-18	18-19	19-20
WMP 1	MidAl 4	MidAl 8	MidAl 1	NP1S 8	NP1S 22	MFLP 22	WMP 2	WMP 1	MFLP n&v
FAC EP	FAC EP	FAC 2Q	FAC 1Q	FAC 2Qr	FAC 1Q	FAC P	FAC 1Q	FAC EP	FAC P
FAV 1P	FAV 5P	FAV 2Q	FAV 2Q	FAT P	FAT P	FAV 1Q	FAV 1Q	FAV 2Q	FAV 2Q

GROUND: The Beeches, Packwood Road, Tividale, West Mids B69 1UL
Capacity: 3,000 **Seats:** 200 **Covered:** Yes
Nearest Railway Station Dudley Port - 1.6km
Bus Route Regent Road - stop 100m away

WALSALL WOOD

Nickname: Wood or Prims **Club Colours:** All Red
Founded 1915

Club Contact Details 07775 512 373 gevangelou67@gmail.com

Previous Names: Walsall Borough (formed when Walsall Wood & Walsall Sportsco merged) 1982-96.
Previous Leagues: Midland Combinataion 1986-92, 2006-13. Staffordshire Senior 1992-93. West Midlands 1993-2006. Mid Alliance 2013-14.
HONOURS
FA Comps: None
League: Worcestershire/Midland Combination 1951-52, 2012-13. Midland Football Division One 2017-18.

10-11	11-12	12-13	13-14	14-15	15-16	16-17	17-18	18-19	19-20
MidCo 9	MidCo 14	MidCo 1	MidAl 6	WMP 4	MFLP 7	MFLP 20	MFL1 1	MFLP 2	MFLP n&v
FAC EP	FAC EP		FAC 1Qr	FAC P	FAC EPr	FAC EP	FAC P	FAC 1Q	FAC EP
FAV 2Q	FAV 2Q	FAV QFr	FAV 2P	FAV 4Pr	FAV 3P	FAV 1P	FAV 3P	FAV 3P	FAV 4P

GROUND: Oak Park, Lichfield Road, Walsall Wood, Walsall WS9 9NP
Capacity: 1,000 **Seats:** Yes **Covered:** Yes

WORCESTER CITY

Nickname: City   **Club Colours:** Blue & white

Founded
1902

Club Contact Details 07811 076 933   kevinpreece1987@gmail.com

Previous Names: Formed when Berwick Rangers and Worcester Rovers amalgamated

Previous Leagues: Birmingham & District 1902-38. Southern 1938-79, 85-2004. Alliance 1979-85. Conference 2004-17.

HONOURS

FA Comps: None

League: Birmingham League 1913-14, 24-25, 28-29, 29-30.
Southern League Division One North 1967-68, 76-77, Premier 1978-79.

10-11		11-12		12-13		13-14		14-15		15-16		16-17		17-18		18-19		19-20	
Conf N	16	Conf N	7	Conf N	15	Conf N	15	Conf N	9	Nat N	17	Nat N	20	MFLP	4	MFLP	11	MFLP	n&v
FAC	3Q	FAC	2Q	FAC	4Q	FAC	4Qr	FAC	2Pr	FAC	1P	FAC	3Q	FAC	Pr	FAC	EPr	FAC	P
FAT	2Pr	FAT	3Q	FAT	3Q	FAT	2P	FAT	1P	FAT	1Pr	FAT	1P	FAV	2P	FAV	2P	FAV	5Pr

GROUND: The Victoria Ground, Birmingham Road, Bromsgrove B61 0DR

Capacity: 3,500 **Seats:** 400 **Covered:** Yes **Shop:** Yes

Nearest Railway Station Bromsgrove - two miles from the ground.

Bus Route 144/144a from Crowngate Bus Station

ASHBY IVANHOE
Nickname: The Knights   Club Colours: Blue and red

Founded 1948

Club Contact Details 07966 293 355   ctissington1962@btinternet.com

HONOURS
FA Comps: None
League: North Leicestershire 1994-95, 96-97, 98-99, 2002-03.
Leicestershire Senior Premier Division 2010-11.

10-11	11-12	12-13	13-14	14-15	15-16	16-17	17-18	18-19	19-20
LeicSP 1	LeicSP 8	LeicSP 4	LeicSP 3	EMC 6	EMC 3	EMC 10	EMC 17	EMC 14	MFL1 n&v
						FAC 1Q			
FAV 2Q	FAV 2Q				FAV 1Q	FAV 1P	FAV 2Q	FAV 2Q	FAV 2Q

GROUND: Lower Packington Road, Ashby de la Zouch LE65 1TS

ATHERSTONE TOWN
Nickname: The Adders   Club Colours: Red & white

Founded 2004

Club Contact Details 07980 037 883   trn700@aol.com

HONOURS
FA Comps: None
League: Midland Combination Division 1 2004-05, Premier Division 2005-06. Midland Alliance 2007-08.

10-11	11-12	12-13	13-14	14-15	15-16	16-17	17-18	18-19	19-20
SthC 21	MidAl 21	MCmP 9	MCmP 9	MFL1 13	MFL1 13	MFL1 4	MFL1 3	MFL1 3	MFL1 n&v
FAC Pr	FAC P	FAC EP	FAC 3Q	FAC EPr			FAC EP	FAC 2Q	FAC EP
FAT P	FAV 1P	FAV 1Q	FAV 1P	FAV 2Q	FAV 1Q	FAV 2Q	FAV 1P	FAV 2Q	FAV QF

GROUND: Sheepy Road, Atherstone, Warwickshire CV9 3AD
Nearest Railway Station Atherstone - 0.6km
Bus Route Lister Road stop - 118m away

BROCTON
Nickname: The Badgers   Club Colours: Green and white

Founded 1937

Club Contact Details 07791 841 774   terryhomer@yahoo.co.uk

HONOURS
FA Comps: None
League: Midland Combination Premier 2013-14.

10-11	11-12	12-13	13-14	14-15	15-16	16-17	17-18	18-19	19-20
MCmP 8	MCmP 6	MCmP 5	MCmP 1	MFLP 13	MFLP 15	MFLP 21	MFL1 17	MFL1 11	MFL1 n&v
FAC EPr	FAC EP	FAC EP	FAC 1Q	FAC Pr	FAC EP	FAC P	FAC 1Q		
FAV 2Q	FAV 3Pr	FAV 1Q	FAV 4P	FAV 4P	FAV 3P	FAV 2Q	FAV 2P	FAV 2P	FAV 1Q

GROUND: Silkmore Lane Sports Grd, Silkmore Lane, Stafford, Staffordshire ST17 4JH
Nearest Railway Station Stafford - 2km
Bus Route Silkmore Crescent stop - 30m away

CADBURY ATHLETIC
Nickname: Club Colours: Purple & white quarters/purple/white

Founded 1994

Club Contact Details 07827 963 212   cafc.sec@gmail.com

HONOURS
FA Comps: None
League: Midland Combination Division One 2013-14.

10-11	11-12	12-13	13-14	14-15	15-16	16-17	17-18	18-19	19-20
MCmP 6	MCmP 12	MCm1 3	MCm1 1	MFL1 6	MFL1 15	MFL1 5	MFL1 15	MFL1 8	MFL1 n&v
	FAC EP				FAC P		FAC EP		
FAV 1Q	FAV 1Q	FAV 1Q	FAV 1Q	FAV 1Q	FAV 1Q	FAV 1P	FAV 1Q	FAV 4P	FAV 2P

GROUND: Eckersall Road, Kings Norton, Birmingham, B38 8SR
Nearest Railway Station Kings Norton - 0.5km
Bus Route Meadow Hill Road stop - 266m away

CHELMSLEY TOWN
Founded 1927

Nickname: **Club Colours:** Sky blue, white & black

Club Contact Details 07837 509 752   louisehelenhughes@gmail.com

HONOURS
FA Comps: None
League: Midland Combination Division One 1987-88.

10-11	11-12	12-13	13-14	14-15	15-16	16-17	17-18	18-19	19-20
MCm2 11	MCm2 3	MCm1 13	MCm1 6	MCm2 6	MCm2 2	MCm1 17	MFL1 16	MFL1 12	MFL1 n&v
							FAV 2Q	FAV 1P	FAV 1Q

GROUND: Coleshill FC Pack Meadow, Packington Lane, Coleshill, B46 3JQ
Nearest Railway Station Coleshill Parkway - 3.6km
Bus Route St Edwards Primary School stop - 258m away

COVENTRY COPSEWOOD
Founded 1923

Nickname: The G's   **Club Colours:** All blue

Club Contact Details 07884 585 440   davide.wilson@hotmail.co.uk

HONOURS
FA Comps: None
League: Midland Combination Division One 1996-97.

10-11	11-12	12-13	13-14	14-15	15-16	16-17	17-18	18-19	19-20
MCmP 4	MCmP 3	MCmP 12	MCmP 16	MFL1 8	MFL1 11	MFL1 12	MFL1 13	MFL1 15	MFL1 n&v
FAV 2P	FAV 1P	FAV 1Q	FAV 1Q	FAV 1Q	FAV 1Q	FAV 1P	FAV 2Q	FAV 2Q	FAV 2Q

GROUND: Copsewood Sports & Social Club, Allard Way, Coventry CV3 1JP

GNP SPORTS
Founded 1983

Nickname: **Club Colours:** Red and black

Club Contact Details 07875 690 471   jasingh84@hotmail.com

HONOURS
FA Comps: None
League: Midland Division Three 2017-18

10-11	11-12	12-13	13-14	14-15	15-16	16-17	17-18	18-19	19-20
							MFL3 1	MFL2 2	MFL1 n&v
									FAV 1P

GROUND: Sphinx Drive, off Siddeley Drive, Coventry, CV3 1WA
Nearest Railway Station Coventry - 2.6km
Bus Route Bulls Head Lane stop - 363m away

HEATH HAYES
Founded 1965

Nickname: The Hayes   **Club Colours:** Blue

Club Contact Details 07974 851 604   tony.hhfc@gmail.com

HONOURS
FA Comps: None
League: Staffordshire County Division One 1977-78. West Midlands (Regional) Division One North 1998-99. Midland Combination Premier Division 2009-10.

10-11	11-12	12-13	13-14	14-15	15-16	16-17	17-18	18-19	19-20
MidAl 11	MidAl 14	MidAl 18	MidAl 8	MFLP 22	MFL1 8	MFL1 14	MFL1 14	MFL1 18	MFL1 n&v
FAC P	FAC EP	FAC P	FAC EP	FAC EP	FAC EP	FAC EP			
FAV 3P	FAV 1P	FAV 1Q	FAV 1Q	FAV 1Q	FAV 1Q	FAV 1Q	FAV 2Q	FAV 2Q	FAV 1Q

GROUND: Coppice Colliery Grd, Newlands Lane, Heath Hayes, Cannock, WS12 3HH
Nearest Railway Station Cannock - 2.7km
Bus Route Five Ways Inn stop - 253m away

HINCKLEY AFC

Nickname:
Club Colours: Red & blue
Founded 2014

Club Contact Details match.secretary@hinckleyafc.co.uk

HONOURS
FA Comps: None
League: None

10-11	11-12	12-13	13-14	14-15	15-16	16-17	17-18	18-19	19-20
				MFL1 3	MFL1 5	MFL1 2	MFL1 6	MFL1 16	MFL1 n&v
					FAC 2Q	FAC EPr	FAC 1Q	FAC EPr	
				FAV 1Q	FAV 1P	FAV 5P	FAV 4P	FAV 3P	FAV 2Q

GROUND: Barwell FC, Kirkby Road Sports Ground, Kirkby Road, Barwell LE9 8FQ
Nearest Railway Station Hinckley - 7 miles away

KIRBY MUXLOE

Nickname:
Club Colours: Blue
Founded 1910

Club Contact Details 07715 403 409   kirbymuxloefc@outlook.com

HONOURS
FA Comps: None
League: Leicestershire Senior Premier Division 2007-08.
East Midlands Counties 2008-09.

10-11	11-12	12-13	13-14	14-15	15-16	16-17	17-18	18-19	19-20
MidAl 9	MidAl 11	MidAl 12	MidAl 14	MFLP 5	UCL P 9	UCL P 18	UCL P 12	UCL P 19	MFL1 n&v
FAC P	FAC EP	FAC P	FAC P	FAC P	FAC Pr	FAC 2Q	FAC P	FAC EP	FAC 1Q
FAV 1Q	FAV 2Q	FAV 1P	FAV 1P	FAV 2Q	FAV 2Q	FAV 1P	FAV 2Q	FAV 1Q	FAV 2Q

GROUND: Kirby Muxloe Sports Club, Ratby Lane LE9 2AQ
Bus Route Kirby Corner - stop 55m away

LEICESTER ROAD

Nickname: The Knitters
Club Colours: Blue & red
Founded 2013

Club Contact Details 07814 414 726   stuart.millidge43@hotmail.com

HONOURS
FA Comps: None
League: None

10-11	11-12	12-13	13-14	14-15	15-16	16-17	17-18	18-19	19-20
				MFL2 2	MFL1 4	MFL1 3	MFL1 4	MFL1 5	MFL1 n&v
						FAC 1Qr	FAC P	FAC P	FAC P
					FAV 2Q	FAV 1P	FAV 1Q	FAV 1Qr	FAV 1P

GROUND: Leicester Road Stadium, Leicester Road, Hinckley, LE10 3DR
Nearest Railway Station Hinckley - 2.7km
Bus Route Leicester Road stop - 262m away

LICHFIELD CITY

Nickname:
Club Colours: All royal blue
Founded 1970

Club Contact Details 07779 295 033   darrenleaver@outlook.com

HONOURS
FA Comps: None
League: None

10-11	11-12	12-13	13-14	14-15	15-16	16-17	17-18	18-19	19-20
MCm2 4	MCm1 4	MCmP 10	MCmP 7	MFL1 12	MFL1 7	MFL1 7	MFL1 10	MFL1 4	MFL1 n&v
				FAC P		FAC P			FAC 1Q
				FAV 2Q	FAV 1Q	FAV 2P	FAV 1Q	FAV 1Q	FAV 1P

GROUND: Brownsfield Road, Lichfield, Staffs, WS13 6AY
Nearest Railway Station Lichfield Trent Valley High Level/Lichfield Trent Valley - 1.4km
Bus Route Netherstowe Lane stop - 78m away

NUNEATON GRIFF
Nickname: The Heartlanders — Club Colours: Blue & white — Founded 1972

Club Contact Details 07944 457 250   nuneatongriff@sky.com

HONOURS
FA Comps: None
League: Coventry Alliance Premier 1996-97, 97-98.
Midland Combination Premier Division 1999-2000, 00-01.

	10-11	11-12	12-13	13-14	14-15	15-16	16-17	17-18	18-19	19-20
	MCmP 2	MCmP 11	MCmP 4	MCmP 3	MFL1 17	MFL1 3	MFL1 10	MFL1 19	MFL1 19	MFL1 n&v
FAC	P	EP	2Q	EP	EP		FAC EPr			
FAV	1Q	1Q	2Q	2Q	1P	5P	3P	1Q	2Q	2Q

GROUND: The Pingles Stadium, Avenue Road, Nuneaton, Warwickshire CV11 4LX

PAGET RANGERS
Nickname: Bears or The Wee Gers — Club Colours: Gold and black — Founded 2011

Club Contact Details 07528 177 046   paterson_r3@sky.com

HONOURS
FA Comps: None
League: None

	10-11	11-12	12-13	13-14	14-15	15-16	16-17	17-18	18-19	19-20
				MCm2 3	MFL2 11	MFL2 4	MFL2 2	MFL1 12	MFL1 10	MFL1 n&v
FAV						1Q	2P	2Q	1P	2Q

GROUND: Central Ground, Coles Lane, Sutton Coldfield, B72 1NL

ROCESTER
Nickname: Romans — Club Colours: Amber & black — Founded 1876

Club Contact Details 07885 836 094   sam.goldsworthy@rocesterfc.net

HONOURS
FA Comps: None
League: Staffordshire Senior 1985-86, 86-87. West Mids (Regional) Division One 1987-88.
Midland Alliance 1998-99, 2003-04.

	10-11	11-12	12-13	13-14	14-15	15-16	16-17	17-18	18-19	19-20
	MidAl 14	MidAl 6	MidAl 13	MidAl 20	MFLP 12	MFLP 12	MFLP 16	MFLP 22	MFL1 14	MFL1 n&v
FAC	EP	1Q	P	EPr	EPr	Pr	P	EPr	EP	
FAV	1Q	1Q	4P	2P	1P	1P	2P	2Q	1Q	1P

GROUND: Hillsfield, Mill Street, Rocester, Uttoxeter ST14 5JX

Bus Route Ashbourne Road Garage stop - 152m away

STAFFORD TOWN
Nickname: Reds or Town — Club Colours: All red — Founded 1976

Club Contact Details 07789 110 923   staffordtown@hotmail.co.uk

HONOURS
FA Comps: None
League: Midland Combination Division Two 1978-79.
West Midlands (Regional) Division One 1993-94, Premier 1999-2000.

	10-11	11-12	12-13	13-14	14-15	15-16	16-17	17-18	18-19	19-20
	WMP 15	WMP 18	MCmP 11	MCmP 8	MFL1 14	MFL1 18	MFL1 16	MFL1 20	StfSP 5	MFL1 n&v
FAC				EP	P					
FAV	1Q	2P	2Q	2Q	1Q	2Q	1Q	1P	1Q	1Q

GROUND: Evans Park, Riverway, Stafford ST16 3TL
Nearest Railway Station Stafford - 1.1km
Bus Route Hatherton Street stop - 99m away

STAPENHILL
Nickname: The Swans **Club Colours:** All red

Founded 1947

Club Contact Details 07411 832 333   stapenhillsecretary@yahoo.com

HONOURS
FA Comps: None
League: Leicestershire Senior 1958-59, 59-60, 86-87, 88-89, 2006-07.

10-11	11-12	12-13	13-14	14-15	15-16	16-17	17-18	18-19	19-20
LeicSP 4	LeicSP 5	LeicS1 5	EMC 2	EMC 15	EMC 12	EMC 11	EMC 13	MFL1 13	MFL1 n&v
				FAC EPr					
		FAV 1Q	FAV 1Q	FAV 1Q	FAV 1Q	FAV 2Q	FAV 1Q	FAV 1Q	FAV 1Q

GROUND: Edge Hill, Maple Grove, Stapenhill DE15 9NN.
Nearest Railway Station Burton-on-Trent - 3km

STUDLEY
Nickname: Bees **Club Colours:** Sky blue and navy

Founded 1971

Club Contact Details 07745 310 077   bobtheat@hotmail.co.uk

HONOURS
FA Comps: None
League: Midland Combination Division One 1991-92.

10-11	11-12	12-13	13-14	14-15	15-16	16-17	17-18	18-19	19-20
MidAl 7	MidAl 17	MidAl 21	MCmP 6	MFL1 10	MFLP 12	MFLP 15	MFL1 9	MFL1 9	MFL1 n&v
FAC EP	FAC P	FAC P	FAC P	FAC EP					
FAV 1P	FAV 2Q	FAV 1Q	FAV 2Q	FAV 1P	FAV 2Q	FAV 1Q	FAV 2Q	FAV 2Q	FAV 2Q

GROUND: The Beehive, Abbeyfields Drive, Studley B80 7BF
Nearest Railway Station Redditch - 4.6km
Bus Route Red Hill Close stop - 49m away

UTTOXETER TOWN
Nickname: Town **Club Colours:** Yellow & blue

Founded 1983

Club Contact Details 07970 383 822   uttoxetertfc@gmail.com

HONOURS
FA Comps: None
League: None

10-11	11-12	12-13	13-14	14-15	15-16	16-17	17-18	18-19	19-20
			StfSP 2	MFL1 5	StfSP 6	MFL1 11	MFL1 11	MFL1 7	MFL1 n&v
					FAV 3P	FAV 2P	FAV 2Q	FAV 2Qr	FAV 2P

GROUND: Oldfields Sports Ground, Springfield Road, Uttoxeter, ST14 7JX
Nearest Railway Station Uttoxeter - 1.1km
Bus Route Smithfield Road stop - 178m away

PREMIER DIVISION

1874 NORTHWICH

Nickname: **Club Colours:** Green and black   Founded 2012

Club Contact Details 07975 679 624

Previous Names: None
Previous Leagues: None
HONOURS
FA Comps: None
League: None

10-11	11-12	12-13	13-14	14-15	15-16	16-17	17-18	18-19	19-20
			NWC1 3	NWCP 3	NWCP 4	NWCP 5	NWCP 7	NWCP 10	NWCP n&v
				FAC Pr	FAC P	FAC Pr	FAC 3Qr	FAC EPr	FAC 2Q
			FAV 1Q	FAV 3P	FAV 2P	FAV 2P	FAV SF	FAV 2P	FAV 1Q

GROUND: Townfield, Townfield Lane, Barnton Northwich, Cheshire CW8 4LH
Capacity: 6,000   **Seats:** Seats   **Covered:** Yes
Nearest Railway Station Greenbank
Bus Route No.4 from Northwich interchange. Embark at Beech Road which is a short walk from the ground.

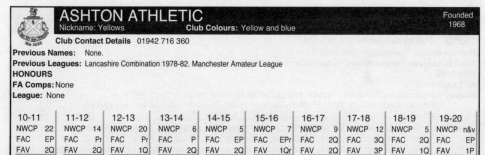

ASHTON ATHLETIC

Nickname: Yellows   **Club Colours:** Yellow and blue   Founded 1968

Club Contact Details   01942 716 360

Previous Names: None.
Previous Leagues: Lancashire Combination 1978-82. Manchester Amateur League
HONOURS
FA Comps: None
League: None

10-11	11-12	12-13	13-14	14-15	15-16	16-17	17-18	18-19	19-20
NWCP 22	NWCP 14	NWCP 20	NWCP 6	NWCP 5	NWCP 7	NWCP 9	NWCP 12	NWCP 5	NWCP n&v
FAC EP	FAC Pr	FAC Pr	FAC P	FAC EP	FAC EPr	FAC 2Q	FAC 3Q	FAC 2Q	FAC EP
FAV 2Q	FAV 2Q	FAV 1Q	FAV 2Q	FAV 2Q	FAV 1Qr	FAV 2Q	FAV 3P	FAV 1Q	FAV 1P

GROUND: Brocstedes Park, Downall Green, Ashton in Makerfield WN4 0NR
Capacity: 600   **Seats:** 100   **Covered:** 300
Nearest Railway Station Bryn - 1.6km.
Bus Route 156/157 St Helens/Bryn route

AVRO

Nickname: **Club Colours:** Blue, black and white   Founded 1936

Club Contact Details   07920 779 382

Previous Names:
Previous Leagues: Manchester.
HONOURS
FA Comps: None
League: Manchester Division One 1988-89, 2003-04, Premier 09-10, 10-11, 17-18.

10-11	11-12	12-13	13-14	14-15	15-16	16-17	17-18	18-19	19-20
MancP 1	MancP 6	MancP 5	MancP 9	MancP 3	MancP 9	MancP 11	MancP 1	NWC1N 2	NWCP n&v
									FAC EP
								FAV 3P	FAV 1Q

GROUND: Vestacare Stadium, White Bank Road, Oldham OL8 3JH
Capacity: **Seats:**   **Covered:**
Nearest Railway Station Manchester Victoria or Moston (mainline). Hollinwood (metrolink) 20 mins walk or 180 bus.
Bus Route No.180 from Oldham Street (Manchester City centre) to Hollins Road/Oak Road, then 5 mins down Oak Road to ground.

BARNOLDSWICK TOWN
Nickname: Town or Barlick **Club Colours:** All blue

Founded 1972

Club Contact Details 07528 410 204

Previous Names: Today's club formed after the merger of Barnoldswick United and Barnoldswick Park Rovers in 2003
Previous Leagues: Craven, East Lancashire, West Lancashire.
HONOURS
FA Comps: None
League: West Lancashire Division One 1998-99.

10-11		11-12		12-13		13-14		14-15		15-16		16-17		17-18		18-19		19-20	
NWCP	7	NWCP	4	NWCP	9	NWCP	16	NWCP	19	NWCP	9	NWCP	11	NWCP	9	NWCP	11	NWCP	n&v
		FAC	EP	FAC	EP	FAC	EPr	FAC	EP	FAC	EP	FAC	EPr	FAC	1Q	FAC	P	FAC	EP
FAV	2Q	FAV	2P	FAV	3P	FAV	2Q	FAV	2Q	FAV	2Q	FAV	1P	FAV	1Q	FAV	2Q	FAV	2P

GROUND: Silentnight Stadium, West Close Road, Barnoldswick, Colne, BB18 5LJ
Capacity: **Seats:** Yes   **Covered:** Yes
Nearest Railway Station Colne or Skipton
Bus Route Greenberfield Road stop - 97m away

BOOTLE
Nickname: Bucks **Club Colours:** All blue

Founded 1953

Club Contact Details 0151 525 4796

Previous Names: Langton Dock 1953 - 1973.
Previous Leagues: Liverpool Shipping. Lancashire Combination 1974-78. Cheshire County 1978-82. Liverpool County Combination 1982-2006.
HONOURS
FA Comps: None
League: Liverpool County Combination 1964-65, 65-66, 67-68, 68-69, 69-70, 70-71, 71-72, 72-73, 73-74.
Lancashire Comb. 1975-76, 76-77. Cheshire County Div.2 1978-79. North West Counties Div.1 2008-09.

10-11		11-12		12-13		13-14		14-15		15-16		16-17		17-18		18-19		19-20	
NWCP	6	NWCP	3	NWCP	3	NWCP	8	NWCP	7	NWCP	8	NWCP	2	NWCP	5	NWCP	2	NWCP	n&v
FAC	P	FAC	P	FAC	1Q	FAC	1Qr	FAC	EP	FAC	EP	FAC	P	FAC	EP	FAC	EP	FAC	EP
FAV	2P	FAV	2Q	FAV	2P	FAV	1P	FAV	1P	FAV	2Q	FAV	3P	FAV	2P	FAV	2Q	FAV	1P

GROUND: Vestey Road, Off Bridle Road, Bootle L30 1NY
Capacity: 1,750 **Seats:**   **Covered:** Yes
Nearest Railway Station Aintree - 0.5km
Bus Route Hereford Drive stop - 251m away

BURSCOUGH
Nickname: Linnets **Club Colours:** All green

Founded 1946

Club Contact Details 01704 896 776

Previous Names: None
Previous Leagues: Liverpool County Combination 1946-53, Lancashire Combination 1953-70, Cheshire County 1970-82,
North West Counties 1982-98, Northern Premier League 1998-2007, 09-17, Conference 2007-09.
HONOURS
FA Comps: FA Trophy 2002-03.
League: Lancashire Combination Division Two 1953-54. North West Counties Division One 1982-83. Northern Premier Premier Division 2006-07.

10-11		11-12		12-13		13-14		14-15		15-16		16-17		17-18		18-19		19-20	
NP P	19	NP P	22	NP1N	11	NP1N	14	NP1N	15	NP1N	5	NP1N	22	NWCP	18	NWCP	12	NWCP	n&v
FAC	1Q	FAC	1Qr	FAC	1Q	FAC	2Q	FAC	1Q	FAC	3Q	FAC	2Q	FAC	Pr	FAC	1Q	FAC	P
FAT	1Q	FAT	1Q	FAT	2Q	FAT	1Qr	FAT	P	FAT	1Pr	FAT	P	FAV	1P	FAV	2Q	FAV	1Qr

GROUND: New Stadium, Burscough L40 0SW
Capacity: **Seats:** Yes   **Covered:** Yes
Nearest Railway Station Burscough Bridge - 0.2km
Bus Route 2A

CHARNOCK RICHARD

Nickname: **Club Colours:** Green & white

Founded 1933

Club Contact Details 01257 792 558

Previous Names: None
Previous Leagues: Chorley Alliance (Sunday). Preston & District. West Lancashire >2016
HONOURS
FA Comps: None
League: Chorley Alliance 1947-48, 56-57. Preston & District 1960-61, 66-67, 67-68, 68-69, 89-90.
West Lancashire Division One 1997-98, Premier 2002-03, 08-09, 11-12, 12-13, 13-14, 14-15.

10-11	11-12	12-13	13-14	14-15	15-16	16-17	17-18	18-19	19-20
WLaP 2	WLaP 1	WLaP 1	WLaP 1	WLaP 1	WLaP 2	NWC1 2	NWCP 6	NWCP 6	NWCP n&v
							FAC EP	FAC Pr	FAC 1Q
						FAV 2P	FAV 1P	FAV 1P	FAV 1P

GROUND: Mossie Park, Charter Lane, Charnock Richard, Chorley PR7 5LZ
Capacity: **Seats:** Yes **Covered:** Yes
Nearest Railway Station Euxton Balshaw Lane - 3km
Bus Route Leeson Avenue stop - 299m away

CONGLETON TOWN

Nickname: Bears **Club Colours:** Black & white

Founded 1901

Club Contact Details 01260 274 460

Previous Names: Congleton Hornets
Previous Leagues: Crewe & District, North Staffs, Macclesfield, Cheshire County 1920-39, 46-65, 78-82. Mid Cheshire, NW Co, NPL
HONOURS
FA Comps: None
League: Crewe & District 1901-02, 02-03, 03-04. North Staffs & District 1919-20. Macclesfield & District 1939-40.
Mid Cheshire 1973-74, 75-76, 77-78.

10-11	11-12	12-13	13-14	14-15	15-16	16-17	17-18	18-19	19-20
NWCP 8	NWCP 11	NWCP 7	NWCP 10	NWCP 8	NWCP 6	NWCP 16	NWCP 15	NWCP 3	NWCP n&v
FAC Pr	FAC P	FAC P	FAC Pr	FAC Pr	FAC 2Q	FAC P	FAC P	FAC 1Q	FAC EPr
FAV 1Q	FAV 1Q	FAV 1P	FAV 4P	FAV 2P	FAV 1P	FAV 1P	FAV 2Qr	FAV 1Q	FAV 3Pr

GROUND: Ivy Gardens, Booth Street, Crescent Road, Congleton, Cheshire CW12 4GA
Capacity: 1,450 **Seats:** 250 **Covered:** 1,200 **Shop:** Yes
Nearest Railway Station Congleton - 1.9km
Bus Route Booth Street stop - 75m away

HANLEY TOWN

Nickname: **Club Colours:** All royal blue

Founded 1966

Club Contact Details 07977 519 498

Previous Names: None
Previous Leagues: London 1966-67. Staffordshire County Senior 1967-76. Mid-Cheshire 1976-88, 96-98.
Midland/Staffordshire County 1998-2013.
HONOURS
FA Comps: None
League: London 1966-67. Staffordshire County Div.2 67-68, Div.1 68-69, Premier 72-73, 75-76. Mid-Cheshire Div.1 81-82. Midland/Staffordshire County Senior 2004-05, 2006-07, 11-12, 12-13. North West Counties Div.1 2015-16.

10-11	11-12	12-13	13-14	14-15	15-16	16-17	17-18	18-19	19-20
StfSP 2	StfSP 1	StfSP 1	NWC1 4	NWC1 4	NWC1 1	NWCP 10	NWCP 8	NWCP 17	NWCP n&v
					FAC P	FAC EPr	FAC P	FAC EPr	FAC EP
				FAV 1P	FAV 1Q	FAV 1P	FAV 1P	FAV 1P	FAV 1P

GROUND: Potteries Park, Abbey Lane, Bucknall, Stoke-on-Trent, Staffordshire ST2 8AJ
Capacity: **Seats:** Yes **Covered:** Yes
Nearest Railway Station Stoke-on-Trent - 3.2km
Bus Route Abbey Lane stop - 229m away

IRLAM

Nickname: Mitchells/Shack **Club Colours:** All blue

Founded 1969

Club Contact Details 07969 946 277

Previous Names: Mitchell Shackleton.
Previous Leagues: Manchester Amateur. Manchester.
HONOURS
FA Comps: None
League: Manchester Amateur Division Three 1973-74, Division Two 74-75. Manchester Premier Division 2002-03.

10-11	11-12	12-13	13-14	14-15	15-16	16-17	17-18	18-19	19-20
NWC1 9	NWC1 10	NWC1 14	NWC1 10	NWC1 14	NWC1 2	NWCP 8	NWCP 13	NWCP 13	NWCP n&v
FAC EP	FAC EP	FAC P				FAC EP	FAC EP	FAC 2Q	FAC 2Q
FAV 2P	FAV 1Q	FAV 1Q	FAV 1Q	FAV 1Q	FAV 1Qr	FAV 1P	FAV 1P	FAV 5P	FAV 2P

GROUND: Silver Street, Irlam, Manchester M44 6JJ
Capacity: **Seats:** 150 **Covered:** Yes
Nearest Railway Station Flixton - 2.3km
Bus Route Silver Street stop - 23m away

LITHERLAND REMYCA

Nickname: The REMY **Club Colours:** Red and black

Founded 1959

Club Contact Details 0151 288 6288

Previous Names:
Previous Leagues: Liverpool County >2015.
HONOURS
FA Comps: None
League: Zingari Premier Division 1987-88, 93-94, 94-95, 95-96,
Division Two 2005-06. Liverpool County Division Two 2006-07.

10-11	11-12	12-13	13-14	14-15	15-16	16-17	17-18	18-19	19-20
LivCP 13	LivCP 15	LivCP 9	LivCP 5	NWC1 9	NWC1 9	NWC1 3	NWC1 2	NWCP 15	NWCP n&v
							FAC P	FAC EP	FAC P
				FAV 1Q	FAV 1P	FAV 1P	FAV 1P	FAV 1P	FAV 1Q

GROUND: Litherland Sports Park, Boundary Road, Litherland, Liverpool L21 7LA
Capacity: **Seats:** 100 **Covered:** Yes
Nearest Railway Station Aintree - 1.7km
Bus Route Moss Lane stop - 98m away

LONGRIDGE TOWN

Nickname: **Club Colours:** All red

Founded 1996

Club Contact Details 01772 786365 / 07710 514767

Previous Names:
Previous Leagues: Preston & District 1996-2009.
HONOURS
FA Comps: None
League: Preston & District Division Three 2003-04. West Lancashire Division One 2011-12, Premier 16-17.
North West Counties Division One North 2018-19.

10-11	11-12	12-13	13-14	14-15	15-16	16-17	17-18	18-19	19-20
WLa1 4	WLa1 1	WLaP 3	WLaP 12	WLaP 6	WLaP 4	WLaP 1	WLaP 3	NWC1N 1	NWCP n&v
									FAC Pr
								FAV 1Q	FAV 5P

GROUND: The Mike Riding Ground, Inglewhite Road, Longridge, Preston PR3 2NA
Capacity: **Seats:** Yes **Covered:** Yes
Nearest Railway Station Preston (7.7 miles)
Bus Route No.1 bus Preston to Berry Lane Longridge

NORTHWICH VICTORIA
Nickname: Vics, Greens or Trickies **Club Colours:** Green and white

Founded 1874

Club Contact Details 01606 43008

Previous Names: None

Previous Leagues: The Combination 1890-92, 1894-98, Football League 1892-94, Cheshire 1898-1900, Manchester 1900-12 Lancashire 1912-19, Cheshire County 1919-68, Northern Premier 1968-79, Conference 1979-2010

HONOURS

FA Comps: FA Trophy 1983-84.

League: Manchester 1902-03. Cheshire County 1956-57. Conference North 2005-06.

	10-11		11-12		12-13		13-14		14-15		15-16		16-17		17-18		18-19		19-20	
NP P	12	NP P	2	NP1S	8	NP1N	9	NP1N	4	NP1N	3	NP1S	22	NWCP	16	NWCP	4	NWCP	n&v
FAC	2Qr	FAC	2Q	FAC	Pr	FAC	1Q	FAC	1Qr	FAC	2P	FAC	P	FAC	EPr	FAC	P	FAC	1Qr
FAT	1P	FAT	3P	FAT	1Q	FAT	1Pr	FAT	1Qr	FAT	1Q	FAT	Pr	FAV	1Q	FAV	SF	FAV	2Pr

GROUND: Wincham Park, Chapel Street, Northwich CW9 6DA
Capacity: **Seats:** Yes **Covered:** Yes
Nearest Railway Station Northwich (1.3 miles)

PADIHAM
Nickname: Caldersiders **Club Colours:** All blue.

Founded 1878

Club Contact Details 01282 773 742

Previous Names: None

Previous Leagues: Lancashire Combination 1894-98, 1900-06, 10-16, 49-68, 77-82. East Lancs Am. North East Lancs. West Lancs. North West Counties > 2013. NPL 2013-15.

HONOURS

FA Comps: None

League: West Lancashire Division Two 1971-72, 76-77, Division One 1999-00. North West Counties 2012-13.

	10-11		11-12		12-13		13-14		14-15		15-16		16-17		17-18		18-19		19-20	
NWCP	4	NWCP	15	NWCP	1	NP1N	19	NP1N	22	NWCP	11	NWCP	7	NWCP	17	NWCP	18	NWCP	n&v
FAC	EP	FAC	EP	FAC	P	FAC	1Q	FAC	P	FAC	1Q	FAC	P	FAC	EP	FAC	EP	FAC	Pr
FAV	2Qr	FAV	2P	FAV	1Q	FAT	P	FAT	1Q	FAV	1Q	FAV	2P	FAV	1Q	FAV	2Qr	FAV	1P

GROUND: Arbories Memorial Sports Ground, Well Street, Padiham BB12 8LE
Capacity: 1,688 **Seats:** 159 **Covered:** Yes
Nearest Railway Station Hapton - 2.2km
Bus Route Memorial Park stop - 110m away

RUNCORN TOWN
Nickname: Town **Club Colours:** Sky and navy blue

Founded 1967

Club Contact Details 07808 737 773

Previous Names: Mond Rangers 1967-2005 (Amalgamated with ICI Weston 1974-75).

Previous Leagues: Runcorn Sunday 1967-73, Warrington & District 1973-84, West Cheshire 1984-10.

HONOURS

FA Comps: None

League: West Cheshire League Division Two 2006-07.

	10-11		11-12		12-13		13-14		14-15		15-16		16-17		17-18		18-19		19-20	
NWC1	2	NWCP	2	NWCP	4	NWCP	5	NWCP	13	NWCP	13	NWCP	3	NWCP	3	NWCP	7	NWCP	n&v
		FAC	1Q	FAC	1Q	FAC	P	FAC	3Q	FAC	P	FAC	EP	FAC	P	FAC	1Q	FAC	2Q
FAV	4P	FAV	4Pr	FAV	5P	FAV	2P	FAV	2P	FAV	3Pr	FAV	1P	FAV	1P	FAV	3P	FAV	2Q

GROUND: Sandy Lane, Weston Point, Runcorn WA7 4ET
Capacity: 1,530 **Seats:** Yes **Covered:** Yes
Nearest Railway Station Runcorn - 1.6km
Bus Route South Parade stop - 69m away

RYLANDS

Nickname: Club Colours: All blue Founded 1911

Club Contact Details 01925 635 880

Previous Names: Merged with Crosfields and became Crosfields/Rylands between 2008-10
Previous Leagues: Mid-Cheshire 1968-2007. Cheshire 2008-18.
HONOURS
FA Comps: None
League: Mid-Cheshire 1980-81, 83-84. North West Counties Division One South 2018-19.

10-11	11-12	12-13	13-14	14-15	15-16	16-17	17-18	18-19	19-20
Ches1 7	Ches1 12	Ches1 6	Ches1 8	ChesP 9	ChesP 14	ChesP 10	ChesP 11	NWC1S 1	NWCP n&v
									FAC EP
								FAV 2Q	FAV 2P

GROUND: Rylands Recreation Club, Gorsey Lane, Warrington WA2 7RZ
Capacity: 1345 Seats: Yes Covered: Yes
Nearest Railway Station Warrington Central (1.4 miles)
Bus Route No.3 from Warrington to Beresford Street

SKELMERSDALE UNITED

Nickname: Skem / Blueboys Club Colours: All blue Founded 1882

Club Contact Details pitchero.com/clubs/skelmersdaleunited

Previous Names: Skelmsdale Young Rovers. Skelmersdale Wesleyans.
Previous Leagues: Liverpool County Combination, Lancashire Combination 1891-93, 1903-07, 21-24, 55-56, 76-78,
Cheshire County 1968-71, 78-82, Northern Premier 1971-76, 06-19. North West Counties 1983-2006.
HONOURS
FA Comps: FA Amateur Cup 1970-71. Barassi Anglo-Italian Cup 1970-71.
League: Northern Premier Division One North 2013-14.

10-11	11-12	12-13	13-14	14-15	15-16	16-17	17-18	18-19	19-20
NP1N 2	NP1N 7	NP1N 1	NP P 6	NP P 7	NP P 16	NP P 24	NP1N 21	NP1W 20	NWCP n&v
FAC 2Q	FAC P	FAC 2Q	FAC 2Q	FAC 2Q	FAC 2Q	FAC 1Qr	FAC 1Q	FAC P	FAC P
FAT 1Q	FAT P	FAT 3P	FAT 1Q	FAT 1Q	FAT 1Pr	FAT 1Q	FAT P	FAT P	FAV 2Q

GROUND: JMO Sports Park, Liverpool Road, Skelmersdale WN8 8BX
Capacity: Seats: Yes Covered: Yes
Nearest Railway Station Rainford - 3.6 miles
Bus Route 310, 375 & 385

SQUIRES GATE

Nickname: Gate Club Colours: All blue. Founded 1948

Club Contact Details 01253 348 512

Previous Names: Squires Gate British Legion FC >1953.
Previous Leagues: Blackpool & District Amateur 1958-61. West Lancashire 1961-91.
HONOURS
FA Comps: None
League: Blackpool & District Amateur League Division One 1955-56, 56-57.
West Lancashire League Division Two 1980-81.

10-11	11-12	12-13	13-14	14-15	15-16	16-17	17-18	18-19	19-20
NWCP 9	NWCP 16	NWCP 21	NWCP 19	NWCP 6	NWCP 19	NWCP 19	NWCP 11	NWCP 8	NWCP n&v
FAC EP	FAC 1Qr	FAC EP	FAC EP	FAC 1Qr	FAC EPr	FAC 1Q	FAC 1Q	FAC 1Q	FAC EP
FAV 2Q	FAV 3P	FAV 2Q	FAV 2Q	FAV 1Q	FAV 2Q	FAV 1Q	FAV 1Q	FAV 2P	FAV 2Q

GROUND: Brian Addison Stadium, School Road, Marton, Blackpool, Lancs FY4 5DS
Capacity: 1,000 Seats: 100 Covered: Yes
Nearest Railway Station Squires Gate - 2.4km
Bus Route St Nicholas School stop - 75m away

WHITCHURCH ALPORT

Nickname: **Club Colours:** Red and white

Founded 1946

Club Contact Details

Previous Names: None

Previous Leagues: Cheshire. Mercian Regional League.

HONOURS

FA Comps: WFA Am Cup 1973-74

League: Shrewsbury & District 1947-48. Mid Cheshire 1969-70.

10-11		11-12		12-13		13-14		14-15		15-16		16-17		17-18		18-19		19-20	
Ches2	3	Ches2	7	MerRP	11	MerRP	5	MerRP	4	NWC1	18	NWC1	5	NWC1	4	NWCP	14	NWCP	n&v
														FAC	EP	FAC	P	FAC	1Q
												FAV	1Q	FAV	1Q	FAV	2Q	FAV	1P

GROUND: Yockings Park, Black Park Road, Whitchurch SY13 1PG

Capacity: **Seats:** Yes   **Covered:** Yes

Nearest Railway Station Whitchurch - 0.4km

Bus Route Railway Station stop - 501m away

WINSFORD UNITED

Nickname: Blues   **Club Colours:** Navy blue

Founded 1883

Club Contact Details 01606 558 447

Previous Names: Over Wanderers 1883-1887

Previous Leagues: The Combination 1902-04. Cheshire County 1919-40, 47-82. Northern Premier League 1987-2001.

HONOURS

FA Comps: None

League: Cheshire County 1920-21, 76-77.
North West Counties League Division Two 2006-07.

10-11		11-12		12-13		13-14		14-15		15-16		16-17		17-18		18-19		19-20	
NWCP	3	NWCP	7	NWCP	5	NWCP	14	NWCP	12	NWCP	14	NWCP	13	NWCP	14	NWCP	16	NWCP	n&v
FAC	EP	FAC	EPr	FAC	P	FAC	P	FAC	EP	FAC	EPr	FAC	1Qr	FAC	EP	FAC	EP	FAC	Pr
FAV	2Q	FAV	2P	FAV	3P	FAV	2Pr	FAV	1P	FAV	1P	FAV	1Q	FAV	2Q	FAV	1P	FAV	1Q

GROUND: The Barton Stadium, Kingsway, Winsford, Cheshire CW7 3AE

Capacity: 3,000 **Seats:** 200   **Covered:** 5,000   **Shop:** Yes

Nearest Railway Station Winsford - 1.2km

Bus Route Wesley Court stop - 34m away

IN: Bury AFC (New Club). **OUT:** Emley AFC (LM - NCE1).

AFC BLACKPOOL
Nickname: Mechanics **Club Colours:** Tangerine

Founded 1947

Club Contact Details 01253 761 721

HONOURS
FA Comps: None
League: West Lancashire League 1960-61, 61-62.
North West Counties League Division Three 1985/86, Division One 2010-11.

10-11		11-12		12-13		13-14		14-15		15-16		16-17		17-18		18-19		19-20	
NWC1	1	NWCP	9	NWCP	10	NWCP	13	NWCP	18	NWCP	22	NWC1	19	NWC1	7	NWC1N	13	NWC1N	n&v
		FAC	Pr	FAC	EP	FAC	EP	FAC	EP	FAC	1Q	FAC	EP						
FAV	2P	FAV	1Q	FAV	2Q	FAV	1P	FAV	1Q	FAV	1Q	FAV	2Q	FAV	1Q	FAV	2Q	FAV	2Q

GROUND: Jepson Way, Common Edge Road, Blackpool FY4 5DY
Nearest Railway Station Squires Gate - 2.2km
Bus Route Borough Boundary stop - 109m away

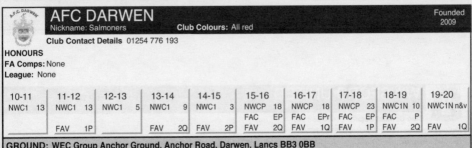

AFC DARWEN
Nickname: Salmoners **Club Colours:** All red

Founded 2009

Club Contact Details 01254 776 193

HONOURS
FA Comps: None
League: None

10-11		11-12		12-13		13-14		14-15		15-16		16-17		17-18		18-19		19-20	
NWC1	13	NWC1	13	NWC1	5	NWC1	9	NWC1	3	NWCP	18	NWCP	18	NWCP	23	NWC1N	10	NWC1N	n&v
										FAC	EP	FAC	EPr	FAC	EP	FAC	P		
		FAV	1P			FAV	2Q	FAV	2P	FAV	2Q	FAV	1Q	FAV	1P	FAV	2Q	FAV	1Q

GROUND: WEC Group Anchor Ground, Anchor Road, Darwen, Lancs BB3 0BB
Nearest Railway Station Darwen - 1.7km
Bus Route Birch Hall Avenue stop - 256m away

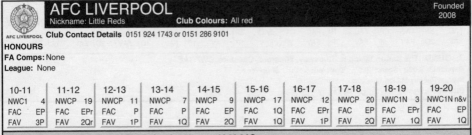

AFC LIVERPOOL
Nickname: Little Reds **Club Colours:** All red

Founded 2008

Club Contact Details 0151 924 1743 or 0151 286 9101

HONOURS
FA Comps: None
League: None

10-11		11-12		12-13		13-14		14-15		15-16		16-17		17-18		18-19		19-20	
NWC1	4	NWCP	19	NWCP	11	NWCP	7	NWCP	9	NWCP	17	NWCP	12	NWCP	20	NWC1N	3	NWC1N	n&v
FAC	EP	FAC	EPr	FAC	P	FAC	P	FAC	EP	FAC	1Q	FAC	EPr	FAC	EP	FAC	EPr	FAC	EP
FAV	3P	FAV	2Qr	FAV	1P	FAV	1Q	FAV	2Q	FAV	1Q	FAV	1P	FAV	2Q	FAV	1Q	FAV	1Q

GROUND: Marine FC, College Road, Crosby, Liverpool L23 3AS
Nearest Railway Station Blundellsands & Crosby - 0.5km
Bus Route Brompton Avenue stop - 175m away

ASHTON TOWN
Nickname: The Town **Club Colours:** All red

Founded 1953

Club Contact Details 01942 724 448

HONOURS
FA Comps: None
League: St Helens Combination Division Two 1957-58.
Warrington & District League Division One 1959-60, 60-61, 62-63, 63-64, 64-65, 69-70.

10-11		11-12		12-13		13-14		14-15		15-16		16-17		17-18		18-19		19-20	
NWC1	16	NWC1	18	NWC1	6	NWC1	12	NWC1	17	NWC1	11	NWC1	22	ChesP	6	NWC1N	9	NWC1N	n&v
FAC	EP					FAC	EP												
FAV	2Q	FAV	1Q	FAV	2Q	FAV	1Q	FAV	1P	FAV	2Q	FAV	1P	FAV	1Q	FAV	2Q	FAV	1Q

GROUND: Edge Green Street, Ashton-in-Makerfield, Wigan, WN4 8SL
Nearest Railway Station Bryn
Bus Route 600 or 601

ATHERTON L.R.
Nickname: The Panthers **Club Colours:** Yellow and royal blue
Founded 1956

Club Contact Details 01942 575 173

HONOURS
FA Comps: None
League: Bolton Combination Division Two A 1965-66.
North West Counties 1992-93, 93-94.

10-11	11-12	12-13	13-14	14-15	15-16	16-17	17-18	18-19	19-20
NWCP 10	NWCP 22	NWC1 13	NWC1 3	NWC1 12	NWC1 17	NWC1 20	NWC1 18	NWC1N 20	NWC1N n&v
FAC Pr	FAC P	FAC P							
FAV 1P	FAV 1P	FAV 1Q	FAV 1P		FAV 2Q	FAV 1P	FAV 1Q	FAV 2Q	FAV 1Q

GROUND: Crilly Park, Spa Road, Atherton, Manchester M46 9XG
Nearest Railway Station Atherton - 0.3km
Bus Route Devonshire Rad stop - 97m away

BACUP BOROUGH
Nickname: The Boro **Club Colours:** White and black
Founded 1875

Club Contact Details 01706 878 655

HONOURS
FA Comps: None
League: Lancashire Combination 1946-47.
North West Counties Division Two 2002-03.

10-11	11-12	12-13	13-14	14-15	15-16	16-17	17-18	18-19	19-20
NWCP 11	NWCP 17	NWCP 17	NWCP 21	NWCP 21	NWC1 5	NWC1 18	NWC1 17	NWC1N 8	NWC1N n&v
FAC 1Q	FAC EP	FAC P			FAC EP	FAC EP			
FAV 2P	FAV 2P	FAV 1Qr			FAV 2Q	FAV 2Q	FAV 2Q	FAV 2Q	FAV 1Q

GROUND: Brian Boys Stadium, Cowtoot Lane, Blackthorn, Bacup OL13 8EE

Bus Route Thorn Cp School stop - 119m away

BURY AFC
Nickname: The Shakers **Club Colours:** White & blue
Founded 2019

Club Contact Details 07754 125 768 buryafc.uk

HONOURS
FA Comps: None
League: None

10-11	11-12	12-13	13-14	14-15	15-16	16-17	17-18	18-19	19-20

GROUND: Radcliffe FC, Stainton Park, Pilkington Road, Radcliffe M26 3PE
Nearest Railway Station Radcliffe - 1.3km
Bus Route Lowe Street - 100m away

CHADDERTON
Nickname: Chaddy **Club Colours:** All red
Founded 1946

Club Contact Details 07506 104 005 (MD)

HONOURS
FA Comps: None
League: Manchester Amateur League 1955-56, Division One 1962-63.
Manchester League Division Two 1964-65, Division One 1966-67.

10-11	11-12	12-13	13-14	14-15	15-16	16-17	17-18	18-19	19-20
NWC1 6	NWC1 6	NWC1 12	NWC1 13	NWC1 6	NWC1 14	NWC1 9	NWC1 16	NWC1N 16	NWC1N n&v
FAC P	FAC EP	FAC P			FAC EP				
FAV 1Q	FAV 2Q	FAV 2Q	FAV 1P	FAV 4P	FAV 2P	FAV 1P	FAV 2Q	FAV 1Q	FAV 1P

GROUND: Andrew Street, Chadderton, Oldham, Greater Manchester OL9 0JT
Nearest Railway Station Freehold (Manc. Metrolink) - 1.1km
Bus Route Middleton Road stop - 133m away

CLEATOR MOOR CELTIC

Nickname: **Club Colours:** Green and white

Founded 1909

Club Contact Details 07710 251 421

HONOURS
FA Comps: None
League: None

10-11	11-12	12-13	13-14	14-15	15-16	16-17	17-18	18-19	19-20
Wear 15	Wear 7	Wear 4	Wear 4	Wear 3	Wear 4	Wear 3	Wear 2	NWC1N 11	NWC1N n&v
	FAV 1Q								FAV 2Q

GROUND: McGrath Park, Birks Road, Cleator Moor, Cumbria CA25 5HP
Nearest Railway Station Whitehaven
Bus Route Buses run on a regular basis from Whitehaven to Cleator Moor.

DAISY HILL
Nickname: The Daisies   **Club Colours:** All royal blue and white

Founded 1894

Club Contact Details 01942 818 544

HONOURS
FA Comps: None
League: Wigan & District 1896-97.
         Bolton Combination Premier Division 1962-63, 72-73, 75-76, 77-78.

10-11	11-12	12-13	13-14	14-15	15-16	16-17	17-18	18-19	19-20
NWC1 14	NWC1 12	NWC1 16	NWC1 18	NWC1 8	NWC1 12	NWC1 16	NWC1 21	NWC1N 19	NWC1N n&v
FAC EP		FAC EP							
FAV 1Q	FAV 1Q	FAV 2Q	FAV 1Q	FAV 1P	FAV 2P	FAV 2Q	FAV 1Q	FAV 2Q	FAV 1Q

GROUND: New Sirs, St James Street, Westhoughton, Bolton BL5 2EB
Nearest Railway Station Daisy Hill - 0.7km
Bus Route Hindley Road stop - 173m away

GARSTANG
Nickname: **Club Colours:** Red and black

Founded 1895

Club Contact Details 07501 119 458

HONOURS
FA Comps: None
League: West Lancashire Premier 2007-08, 17-18.

10-11	11-12	12-13	13-14	14-15	15-16	16-17	17-18	18-19	19-20
WLaP 13	WLaP 16	WLa1 2	WLaP 10	WLaP 5	WLaP 9	WLaP 4	WLaP 1	NWC1N 7	NWC1N n&v
								FAV 2P	FAV 1Q

GROUND: The Riverside, Lancaster Road, Garstang PR3 1EB
Nearest Railway Station Lancaster (12 miles) or Preston (14.5)
Bus Route From Preston/Lancaster/Blackpool stop High St.

GOLCAR UNITED
Nickname: **Club Colours:** green and black

Founded 1904

Club Contact Details 07825 744 829

HONOURS
FA Comps: None
League: West Riding County Amateur Premier Division 2004-05, 17-18, 18-19

10-11	11-12	12-13	13-14	14-15	15-16	16-17	17-18	18-19	19-20
WRCP 12	WRCP 7	WRCP 6	WRCP 6	WRCP 2	WRCP 7	WRCP 5	WRCP 1	WRCP 1	NWC1N n&v

GROUND: Longfield Avenue, Golcar, Huddersfield HD7 4AZ
Nearest Railway Station Huddersfield - 2.9 miles or Slaithwaite - 3.7 miles.
Bus Route 301/302 Golcar Circular.

HOLKER OLD BOYS
Nickname: Cobs   Club Colours: Green and white   Founded 1936

Club Contact Details 01229 828 176

HONOURS
FA Comps: None
League: West Lancashire 1986-87.

10-11	11-12	12-13	13-14	14-15	15-16	16-17	17-18	18-19	19-20
NWC1 3	NWC1 9	NWC1 7	NWC1 6	NWC1 5	NWC1 8	NWC1 17	NWC1 9	NWC1N 18	NWC1N n&v
FAC P	FAC P	FAC 1Q		FAC EPr	FAC P				
FAV 2Q	FAV 2Q	FAV 1Q	FAV 1P	FAV 1P	FAV 2Q	FAV 1P	FAV 1Q	FAV 1Q	FAV 1Q

GROUND: Rakesmoor, Rakesmoor Lane, Hawcoat, Barrow-in-Furness LA14 4QB
Nearest Railway Station Barrow-in-Furness - 2.6km
Bus Route Dunmail Raise stop - 151m away

LOWER BRECK
Nickname: Club Colours: Red and white   Founded 2010

Club Contact Details 0151 263 6186

HONOURS
FA Comps: None
League: Liverpool County Division Two 2012-13, Premier 17-18.

10-11	11-12	12-13	13-14	14-15	15-16	16-17	17-18	18-19	19-20
		LivC2 1	LivC1 4	LivCP 11	LivCP 3	LivCP 2	LivCP 1	NWC1N 4	NWC1N n&v
									FAC EP
								FAV 1P	FAV 3P

GROUND: Anfield Sports & Community Centre, Lower Breck Rd, Liverpool L6 0AG
Nearest Railway Station Liverpool Lime Street
Bus Route Arriva Bus 68 stops at the ground

NELSON
Nickname: Admirals   Club Colours: All blue   Founded 1883

Club Contact Details 01772 794 103

HONOURS
FA Comps: None
League: Lancashire 1895-96. Lancashire Combination 1949-50, 51-52. Football League Division Three North 1922-23. North West Counties Division One 2013-14.

10-11	11-12	12-13	13-14	14-15	15-16	16-17	17-18	18-19	19-20
	NWC1 15	NWC1 10	NWC1 1	NWCP 11	NWCP 16	NWCP 21	NWC1 22	NWC1N 14	NWC1N n&v
				FAC EP	FAC EP	FAC P	FAC EP	FAC EP	
		FAV 2Q	FAV 1P	FAV 2Qr	FAV 2Q	FAV 1Q	FAV 2Q	FAV 1P	FAV 1Q

GROUND: Little Wembley, Lomeshaye Way, Nelson, Lancs BB9 7BN.
Nearest Railway Station Nelson - 1km
Bus Route Business Village stop - 83m away

PILKINGTON
Nickname: Club Colours: Green   Founded 1938

Club Contact Details

HONOURS
FA Comps: None
League: Cheshire Premier Division 2018-19.

10-11	11-12	12-13	13-14	14-15	15-16	16-17	17-18	18-19	19-20
ChesP 2	ChesP 9	ChesP 13	ChesP 15	ChesP 16	Ches1 6	Ches1 3	Ches1 2	ChesP 1	NWC1N n&v
									FAV 2Q

GROUND: Ruskin Drive, Dentons Green, St Helens WA10 6RP
Nearest Railway Station St Helens Central
Bus Route The 37, 38 and 38A go past the end of Ruskin Drive.

PRESTWICH HEYS
Nickname: The Heys   **Club Colours:** Red and white   Founded 1938

Club Contact Details 0161 7773 8888 (MD)

HONOURS
FA Comps: None
League: Lancashire Combination 1970-71. Manchester Division One 1996-97, Premier Division 2004-05, 04-05, 05-06, 06-07, 15-16.

10-11	11-12	12-13	13-14	14-15	15-16	16-17	17-18	18-19	19-20
MancP 12	MancP 13	MancP 8	MancP 4	MancP 6	MancP 1	NWC1 8	NWC1 3	NWC1N 5	NWC1N n&v
								FAC P	
							FAV 1Q	FAV 2Pr	FAV 2Q

GROUND: Adie Moran Park, Sandgate Road, Whitefield M45 6WG
Nearest Railway Station Clifton - 3.5km
Bus Route Sandgate Road stop - 73m away

SHELLEY
Nickname: **Club Colours:** Red and black   Founded 1903

Club Contact Details 07931 853 881

HONOURS
FA Comps: None
League: Huddersfield & District Division Two A 1904-05, Division Two 28-29, 2000-01, Division Three 60-61, 86-87, 2010-11, Division Four 2009-10. West Yorkshire Division Two 2011-12.

10-11	11-12	12-13	13-14	14-15	15-16	16-17	17-18	18-19	19-20
HudD3 3	WYk2 1	WYk1 2	WYkP 12	WYkP 10	WYkP 11	WYkP 8	WYkP 10	NWC1N 12	NWC1N n&v
								FAV 2Q	FAV 1Q

GROUND: Storthes Hall, Huddersfield HD8 0WA
Nearest Railway Station Brockholes (2.5 miles), Stockmoor (2.3) Huddersfield (5.2)
Bus Route 398 Huddersfield Uni to Storthes Hall Park

ST HELENS TOWN
Nickname: Town or Saints   **Club Colours:** All blue   Founded 1946

Club Contact Details

HONOURS
FA Comps: FA Vase 1986-87.
League: Lancashire Combination Division Two 1950-51, Premier 1971-72 .

10-11	11-12	12-13	13-14	14-15	15-16	16-17	17-18	18-19	19-20
NWCP 17	NWCP 21	NWCP 19	NWCP 17	NWCP 20	NWC1 7	NWC1 13	NWC1 20	NWC1N 17	NWC1N n&v
FAC Pr	FAC EP	FAC EP	FAC EPr	FAC EP	FAC EP				
FAV 3P	FAV 2Q	FAV 1P	FAV 1Q	FAV 3P	FAV 2Q	FAV 1Q	FAV 1Q	FAV 1Q	FAV 1Q

GROUND: Ruskin Drive, Dentons Green, St Helens WA10 6RP
Nearest Railway Station St Helens Central - 1.9km
Bus Route Ruskin Drive stop - 153m away

STEETON
Nickname: **Club Colours:** All green   Founded 1905

Club Contact Details 01535 606 044

HONOURS
FA Comps: None
League: Keighley & District 1937-38, 38-39, 54-55. Craven & District 1959-60.
West Riding County Amateur Division Two 1988-89, 2000-01, Division One 2009-10.

10-11	11-12	12-13	13-14	14-15	15-16	16-17	17-18	18-19	19-20
WRCP 8	WRCP 6	WRCP 2	WRCP 5	WRCP 7	WRCP 10	WRCP 3	WRCP 3	NWC1N 15	NWC1N n&v
								FAV 1P	FAV 2Q

GROUND: Cougar Park, Royd Ings Avenue, Keighley BD21 3RF
Nearest Railway Station Keighly (0.8 miles)
Bus Route 662 (Bradford) & 760 (Leeds)

DIVISION ONE SOUTH

ABBEY HEY
Nickname: Red Rebels   **Club Colours:** Red and black
Founded 1902

Club Contact Details 0161 231 7147

HONOURS
FA Comps: None
League: Manchester Amateur League 1964-65. South East Lancashire 1966-67, 68-69.
Manchester League Division One 1970-71, Premier 1981-82, 88-89, 88-89, 91-92, 93-94, 94-95.

10-11		11-12		12-13		13-14		14-15		15-16		16-17		17-18		18-19		19-20	
NWC1	15	NWC1	3	NWC1	2	NWCP	20	NWCP	14	NWCP	10	NWCP	14	NWCP	19	NWCP	20	NWC1S	n&v
FAC	EPr			FAC	2Q	FAC	EP	FAC	EP	FAC	2Q	FAC	EP	FAC	1Qr	FAC	EP	FAC	EP
FAV	2Qr	FAV	2Q	FAV	1Q	FAV	1Q	FAV	2Q	FAV	1P	FAV	2Q	FAV	1Q	FAV	1Q	FAV	1P

GROUND: The Abbey Stadium, Goredale Avenue, Gorton, Manchester M18 7HD
Nearest Railway Station Ryder Brow - 0.5km
Bus Route Ryder Brow Road stop - 124m away

ABBEY HULTON UNITED
Nickname: **Club Colours:** Orange and black
Founded 1947

Club Contact Details 01782 570 302

HONOURS
FA Comps: None
League: Staffordshire County Senior Premier Division 2016-17.

10-11		11-12		12-13		13-14		14-15		15-16		16-17		17-18		18-19		19-20	
		StfSP	5	StfSP	4	StfSP	7	StfSP	3	StfSP	8	StfSP	1	NWC1	13	NWC1S	8	NWC1S	n&v
																		FAV	1Q	FAV	2Qr

GROUND: Birches Head Road, Abbey Hulton, Stoke-on-Trent ST2 8DD
Nearest Railway Station Stoke-on-Trent - 4.2km
Bus Route Woodhead Road stop - 262m away

ALSAGER TOWN
Nickname: The Bullets   **Club Colours:** White & black
Founded 1968

Club Contact Details 07888 750 532

HONOURS
FA Comps: None
League: None

10-11		11-12		12-13		13-14		14-15		15-16		16-17		17-18		18-19		19-20	
NWCP	20	NWCP	13	NWCP	15	NWCP	18	NWCP	17	NWCP	20	NWC1	7	NWC1	8	NWC1S	17	NWC1S	n&v
FAC	EP	FAC	EP	FAC	EP	FAC	EP	FAC	EP	FAC	1Q	FAC	P	FAC	EP				
FAV	2Q	FAV	1Q	FAV	2Q	FAV	2Q	FAV	1Q	FAV	3P	FAV	2Q	FAV	2P	FAV	1Q	FAV	1P

GROUND: Woodpark Stadium, Woodland Court, Alsager ST7 2DP
Nearest Railway Station Alsager - 0.9km
Bus Route Curzon Avenue stop - 374m away

BARNTON
Nickname: Villagers   **Club Colours:** Black and white
Founded 1946

Club Contact Details 07484 793 822

HONOURS
FA Comps: None
League: Mid-Cheshire/Cheshire 1979-80, 82-83, 88-89, 96-97, 97-98, 98-99, 99-2000, 2000-01, 01-02, 02-03, 04-05, Division Two 2012-13.

10-11		11-12		12-13		13-14		14-15		15-16		16-17		17-18		18-19		19-20	
Ches2	13	Ches2	13	Ches2	1	Ches1	5	NWC1	7	NWC1	3	NWCP	17	NWCP	22	NWC1S	12	NWC1S	n&v
												FAC	EP	FAC	EP	FAC	EP		
										FAV	2Q	FAV	2Q	FAV	2Q	FAV	2Q		

GROUND: Townfield, Townfield Lane, Barnton, Cheshire CW8 4LH
Nearest Railway Station Greenbank - 2.6km
Bus Route Crocus Street stop - 128m away

CAMMELL LAIRD 1907

Nickname: Lairds **Club Colours:** All royal blue

Founded 1907

Club Contact Details 0151 645 3121

HONOURS
FA Comps: None
League: West Cheshire x19 (Firstly in 1954-55 and most recently 2000-01).
North West Counties Division Two 2004-05, Division One 2005-06.

	10-11	11-12	12-13	13-14	14-15	15-16	16-17	17-18	18-19	19-20
	NP1N 19	NP1N 22	NP1N 2	NP1N 11	NWC1 2	NWCP 15	NWCP 22	NWC1 6	NWC1S 15	NWC1S n&v
	FAC P	FAC 1Q	FAC 1Q	FAC 2Q	FAC EP			FAC P		
	FAT 1Q	FAT P	FAT 3Q	FAT 1Q	FAV 1Q			FAV 1Q	FAV 1P	FAV 1Q

GROUND: Kirklands, St Peter's Road, Rock Ferry, Birkenhead CH42 1PY
Nearest Railway Station Rock Ferry - 0.7km
Bus Route St Peters Road stop - 58m away

CHEADLE HEATH NOMADS

Nickname: **Club Colours:** Maroon and blue

Founded 2004

Club Contact Details

HONOURS
FA Comps: None
League: Cheshire Premier 2014-15.

	10-11	11-12	12-13	13-14	14-15	15-16	16-17	17-18	18-19	19-20
	Ches1 16	Ches1 6	Ches1 12	Ches1 10	ChesP 1	ChesP 2	ChesP 5	ChesP 4	NWC1S 9	NWC1S n&v
										FAV 2Q

GROUND: The Heath, Norbreck Avenue, Cheadle, Stockport SK8 2ET
Nearest Railway Station Stockport
Bus Route 11, 11a and 309

CHEADLE TOWN

Nickname: **Club Colours:** Red and white

Founded 1961

Club Contact Details 0161 428 2510

HONOURS
FA Comps: None
League: Manchester Division One 1979-80.

	10-11	11-12	12-13	13-14	14-15	15-16	16-17	17-18	18-19	19-20
	NWC1 10	NWC1 8	NWC1 7	NWC1 11	NWC1 10	NWC1 6	NWC1 12	NWC1 12	NWC1S 16	NWC1S n&v
	FAC P	FAC P	FAC EPr	FAC EP			FAC 1Q			
	FAV 1Q	FAV 1P	FAV 1P	FAV 2P	FAV 1Q	FAV 2Q	FAV 1Q	FAV 1Q	FAV 2Qr	FAV 1P

GROUND: Park Road Stadium, Cheadle, Cheshire SK8 2AN
Nearest Railway Station Gatley - 1.8km
Bus Route Stockport Road stop - 161m away

ECCLESHALL

Nickname: The Eagles **Club Colours:** All royal blue

Founded 1971

Club Contact Details 01785 851 351 (MD)

HONOURS
FA Comps: None
League: Staffordshire County Premier 1982-83. Staffordshire Senior 1989-90.
Midland 2001-02, 02-03.

	10-11	11-12	12-13	13-14	14-15	15-16	16-17	17-18	18-19	19-20
	NWC1 11	NWC1 7	NWC1 15	NWC1 17	NWC1 15	NWC1 16	NWC1 21	NWC1 15	NWC1S 13	NWC1S n&v
	FAC 1Q	FAC Pr	FAC EP							
	FAV 1P	FAV 1Q	FAV 1P	FAV 2Q	FAV 1P	FAV 2Q	FAV 1Q	FAV 1Q	FAV 1Q	FAV 1Q

GROUND: Pershall Park, Chester Road, Eccleshall ST21 6NE
Nearest Railway Station Stafford - 8.5 miles
Bus Route Pershall Farm stop - 228m away

ELLESMERE RANGERS
Nickname: The Rangers   **Club Colours:** Sky blue & navy blue

Founded 1969

Club Contact Details 07947 864 357   john.edge2@homecall.co.uk

HONOURS
FA Comps: None
League: West Midlands (Reg) Division One 2005-06, Premier 2009-10.

	10-11		11-12		12-13		13-14		14-15		15-16		16-17		17-18		18-19		19-20	
MidAl	13		MidAl	15	MidAl	22	WMP	11	WMP	4	WMP	10	WMP	7	WMP	6	NWC1S	19	NWC1S n&v	
FAC	EP		FAC	EP	FAC	EP	FAC	P	FAC	EP	FAC	EP					FAC	EP		
FAV	2Q		FAV	2P	FAV	1Qr	FAV	2Q	FAV	EP	FAV	1P	FAV	1Q	FAV	1Q	FAV	1Q	FAV	1Q

GROUND: Beech Grove, Ellesmere, Shropshire SY12 0BZ
Nearest Railway Station Gobowen (7 miles)
Bus Route Lakelands School - stop 50m away

FC ISLE OF MAN
Nickname: **Club Colours:** Red & black

Founded 2019

Club Contact Details info@fcisleofman.im

HONOURS
FA Comps: None
League: None

10-11	11-12	12-13	13-14	14-15	15-16	16-17	17-18	18-19	19-20

GROUND: The Bowl, Pulrose Road, Douglas, Isle of Man IM2 1AD

Bus Route Island served by Bus Vannin and can be caught from the ferry port.

MAINE ROAD
Nickname: Blues   **Club Colours:** All sky blue.

Founded 1955

Club Contact Details 0161 861 0344

HONOURS
FA Comps: None
League: Manchester Amateur Sunday 1971-72. Manchester Premier 1982-83, 83-84, 84-85, 85-86.
North West Counties Division Two 1989-90.

10-11		11-12		12-13		13-14		14-15		15-16		16-17		17-18		18-19		19-20	
NWCP	13	NWCP	18	NWCP	2	NWCP	4	NWCP	15	NWCP	12	NWCP	15	NWCP	21	NWC1S	14	NWC1S n&v	
FAC	EPr	FAC	1Q	FAC	1Q	FAC	EP	FAC	EP	FAC	P	FAC	1Q	FAC	Pr	FAC	EP		
FAV	1Pr	FAV	2Q	FAV	1P	FAV	2P	FAV	1P	FAV	2Q	FAV	1Q	FAV	1Q	FAV	2Q	FAV	2P

GROUND: Brantingham Road, Chorlton-cum-Hardy M21 0TT
Nearest Railway Station Chorlton (Manc. Metrolink) - 768m
Bus Route Manley Road stop - 170m away

NEW MILLS
Nickname: The Millers   **Club Colours:** Amber & black

Founded pre1890

Club Contact Details 01663 747 435

HONOURS
FA Comps: None
League: Manchester Premier Division 1924, 26, 56, 63, 65, 66, 67, 68, 70, 71.
North West Counties Division Two 2007-08, Premier Division 2010-11.

10-11		11-12		12-13		13-14		14-15		15-16		16-17		17-18		18-19		19-20	
NWCP	1	NP1S	9	NP1N	3	NP1N	16	NP1N	21	NP1N	22	NWCP	20	NWC1	14	NWC1S	18	NWC1S n&v	
FAC	2Q	FAC	1Q	FAC	2Q	FAC	1Qr	FAC	P	FAC	P	FAC	EP	FAC	EP				
FAV	2P	FAT	P	FAT	3Q	FAT	P	FAT	2Q	FAT	P	FAV	2Q	FAV	1Q	FAV	1Q	FAV	1Q

GROUND: Church Lane, New Mills SK22 4NP
Nearest Railway Station New Mills Central - 0.7km
Bus Route School (Bus Park) stop - 72m away

SANDBACH UNITED
Nickname: **Club Colours:** Blue and white
Founded 2004

Club Contact Details 07974 710 924

HONOURS
FA Comps: None
League: None

10-11	11-12	12-13	13-14	14-15	15-16	16-17	17-18	18-19	19-20
StfSP	Ches2 5	Ches2 6	Ches2 2	ChesP 11	ChesP 4	NWC1 6	NWC1 5	NWC1S 7	NWC1S n&v
								FAC EP	
							FAV 2Q	FAV 1P	FAV 1P

GROUND: Hind Heath Road, Sandbach CW11 3LZ
Nearest Railway Station Sandbach - 1.4km
Bus Route Salt Line Way stop - 260m away

ST MARTINS
Nickname: Saints **Club Colours:** Yellow and black
Founded 1897

Club Contact Details 01691 684 840

HONOURS
FA Comps: None
League: Oswestry & District 1919-20, 52-53, 54-55. West Shropshire Alliance Division Three 1973-74, Premier 89-90, 2000-01. Shropshire County Division One 1997-98, 2007-08, Premier 2009-10.

10-11	11-12	12-13	13-14	14-15	15-16	16-17	17-18	18-19	19-20
WM2 2	WM2 5	WM1 16	WM1 14	WM1 3	WM1 6	WM1 8	WM1 4	NWC1S 11	NWC1S n&v
							FAV 1Q	FAV 1Q	FAV 1Q

GROUND: The Venue, Burma Road, Parkhall, Oswestry, Shrops. SY11 4AS
Nearest Railway Station Gobowen - 1.9 miles
Bus Route No.53, Oswestry/Gobowen/Ellesmere, bus stop is 500 yards from the ground.

STOCKPORT TOWN
Nickname: The Lions **Club Colours:** Red & white stripes
Founded 2014

Club Contact Details 0161 494 3140

HONOURS
FA Comps: None
League: None

10-11	11-12	12-13	13-14	14-15	15-16	16-17	17-18	18-19	19-20
					NWC1 4	NWC1 10	NWC1 10	NWC1S 10	NWC1S n&v
						FAV 1P	FAV 2Q	FAV 2Q	FAV 2Q

GROUND: Lambeth Grove, Woodley, Stockport SK6 1QX
Nearest Railway Station Woodley - 0.7km. Bredbury - 0.8km
Bus Route Hyde Road stop - 414m away

STONE OLD ALLEYNIANS
Nickname: **Club Colours:** White & black
Founded 1962

Club Contact Details 01785 761 891

HONOURS
FA Comps: None
League: Mid Staffordshire Division Two 1965-66, 80-81, Division One 71-72, 74-75, 78-79.

10-11	11-12	12-13	13-14	14-15	15-16	16-17	17-18	18-19	19-20
WM1 6	WM1 5	WM1 10	WM1 8	WM1 2	WMP 14	WMP 12	WMP 13	NWC1S 3	NWC1S n&v
									FAC EP
				FAV 2Q	FAV 2Q	FAV 2Qr	FAV 2Q	FAV 2Q	FAV 1Q

GROUND: Wellbeing Park, Yarnfield Lane, Yarnfield ST15 0NF
Nearest Railway Station Norton Bridge - 2.8km
Bus Route Labour-in-Vain Pub - stop 650m away

VAUXHALL MOTORS
Nickname: The Motormen   Club Colours: White and navy

Founded 1963

Club Contact Details 0151 327 2294

HONOURS

FA Comps: None

League: North West Counties Division Two 1988-89, 95-96, Division One 99-2000.

10-11	11-12	12-13	13-14	14-15	15-16	16-17	17-18	18-19	19-20
ConfN 17	ConfN 18	ConfN 12	ConfN 18	WCh1 4	WCh1 4	WCh1 8	WCh1 2	NWC1S 2	NWC1S n&v
FAC 1Pr	FAC 2Qr	FAC 2Q	FAC 4Q						FAC EP
FAT 3Q	FAT 1Pr	FAT 3Q	FAT 3Q	FAV 1Q	FAV 2Q	FAV 2Q	FAV 1Q	FAV 2P	FAV 4P

GROUND: Rivacre Road, Ellesmere Port, South Wirrall CH66 1NJ

Nearest Railway Station Overpool (1.4 miles) or Hooton (1.7)

Bus Route None near the ground

WEST DIDSBURY & CHORLTON
Nickname: West   Club Colours: White and black

Founded 1908

Club Contact Details

HONOURS

FA Comps: None

League: Lancashire & Cheshire Amateur Division Two 1987-88, Division One 88-89
Manchester League Division One 2010-11.

10-11	11-12	12-13	13-14	14-15	15-16	16-17	17-18	18-19	19-20
Manc1 1	MancP 7	NCE1 3	NWCP 12	NWCP 16	NWCP 5	NWCP 6	NWCP 10	NWCP 19	NWC1S n&v
			FAC Pr	FAC P	FAC EP	FAC P		FAC Pr	FAC Pr
	FAV 2Q	FAV 1Q	FAV 1P	FAV 1P	FAV 1P	FAV 2Q	FAV 1P	FAV 1Q	FAV 1P

GROUND: End of Brookburn Road, Chorlton, Manchester M21 8FE

Nearest Railway Station Chorlton Metrolink - 0.9 miles

Bus Route No.86 - Manchester Piccadilly Gardens to Barlow Moor road Bus Station.

WYTHENSHAWE AMATEURS
Nickname: The Ammies   Club Colours: Blue & white

Founded 1946

Club Contact Details 0161 428 0517

HONOURS

FA Comps: None

League: Lancashire & Cheshire Division Two 1954-55, Division One 56-57, Premier 61-62.
Manchester Division One 1972-73, Premier 89-90, 92-93, 2002-03.

10-11	11-12	12-13	13-14	14-15	15-16	16-17	17-18	18-19	19-20
MancP 8	MancP 9	MancP 13	MancP 8	MancP 7	MancP 10	MancP 2	MancP 2	NWC1S 4	NWC1S n&v
									FAV 2Q

GROUND: Hollyhedge Park, Altrincham Road, Wythenshawe M22 4US

Nearest Railway Station Benchill Metrolink

Bus Route 102, 103 to Altrincham Road from Manchester City Centre

WYTHENSHAWE TOWN
Nickname: Club Colours: Royal Blue

Founded 1946

Club Contact Details

HONOURS

FA Comps: None

League: Sth Manc & Wythen Div.2 1949-50. Lancs & Ches Div.C 1958-59, Div.3 59-60, Div.2 64-65, Div.1 66-67, 68-69, 69-70, 70-71. Manc Div.2 73-74, Div.1 2011-12. Cheshire Div.2 2014-15, Div.1 15-16.

10-11	11-12	12-13	13-14	14-15	15-16	16-17	17-18	18-19	19-20
Manc1 4	Manc1 1	MancP 10	MancP 15	Ches2 1	Ches1 1	ChesP 7	ChesP 8	NWC1S 5	NWC1S n&v
								FAV 1Q	FAV 3Pr

GROUND: Ericstan Park, Timpson Road, Wythenshawe M23 9LL

Nearest Railway Station Baguley tram stop is only a 5-10 minute walk from Ericstan Park.

Bus Route 11 / 11a / 109

AFC MANSFIELD
Nickname: The Bulls   **Club Colours:** All red   Founded 2012

Club Contact Details 07973 491 739

Previous Names: None
Previous Leagues: Central Midlands North 2012-14. Northern Counties East 2014-18.
HONOURS Northern Premier 2018-19 (demoted due to ground grading).
FA Comps: None
League: Central Midlands North 2013-14.

10-11	11-12	12-13	13-14	14-15	15-16	16-17	17-18	18-19	19-20
		CMN 2	CMN 1	NCE1 7	NCE1 2	NCEP 7	NCEP 3	NP1E 15	NCEP n&v
					FAC EP	FAC 3Q	FAC 3Q	FAC 2Q	FAC 1Q
			FAV 2Pr	FAV 5P	FAV 2Pr	FAV 4P	FAV 2P	FAT 2Qr	FAV 3P

GROUND: Forest Town Stadium, Clipstone Road West, Forest Town, Mansfield NG19 0EE
Capacity: **Seats:** Yes   **Covered:** Yes
Nearest Railway Station Mansfield - 2.7km
Bus Route School - stop 64m away

ALBION SPORTS
Nickname: Lions   **Club Colours:** Yellow and royal blue   Founded 1974

Club Contact Details 0113 255 7292   contact@albionsports.co.uk

Previous Names: None
Previous Leagues: Bradford Amateur Sunday 1974-2007. West Riding County Amateur 2007-11.
HONOURS
FA Comps: None
League: Bradford Amateur Sunday Premier Division 1995-96, 99-2000, 00-01, 02-03, 04-05, 05-06.
Northern Counties East Division One 2012-13.

10-11	11-12	12-13	13-14	14-15	15-16	16-17	17-18	18-19	19-20
WRCP 2	NCE1 4	NCE1 1	NCEP 6	NCEP 10	NCEP 11	NCEP 8	NCEP 14	NCEP 16	NCEP n&v
			FAC 1Q	FAC P	FAC EPr	FAC EPr	FAC 2Q	FAC Pr	FAC EP
		FAV 2Q	FAV 2Q	FAV 2Q	FAV 1Q	FAV 1Q	FAV 1Q	FAV 2Q	FAV 2Q

GROUND: Throstle Nest, Newlands, Farsley, Leeds, LS28 5BE.
Capacity: 3,500 **Seats:** 1,750 **Covered:** 1,750
Nearest Railway Station New Pudsey - 1km
Bus Route Town St Slaters Rd - stop 340m away

ATHERSLEY RECREATION
Nickname: Penguins   **Club Colours:** Black and white   Founded 1979

Club Contact Details 07910 121 070   petegoodlad@yahoo.co.uk

Previous Names: Athersley North Juniors 1979-86.
Previous Leagues: Barnsley Junior. Barnsley Association. Sheffield & Hallamshire County Senior 1997-2012.
HONOURS
FA Comps: None
League: Barnsley Junior 1986-87. Barnsley Association 91-92, 92-93, 94-95, 95-96, 96-97. Sheffield & Hallamshire County Senior Division Two 1997-98, Premier Division 1999-2000, 03-04, 04-05, 06-07, 08-09, 11-12

10-11	11-12	12-13	13-14	14-15	15-16	16-17	17-18	18-19	19-20
SHSP 2	SHSP 1	NCE1 2	NCEP 10	NCEP 13	NCEP 18	NCEP 10	NCEP 17	NCEP 17	NCEP n&v
				FAC P	FAC EP	FAC EP	FAC EP	FAC EP	FAC EP
			FAV 2P	FAV 2Q	FAV 1P	FAV 1Q	FAV 1Q	FAV 1Q	FAV 1Q

GROUND: Sheerien Park, Ollerton Road, Athersley North, Barnsley, S71 3DP
Capacity: 2,000 **Seats:** 150   **Covered:** 420   **Shop:** Yes
Nearest Railway Station Barnsley - 3.4km
Bus Route Trowell Way - stop 80m away

BARTON TOWN
Nickname: Swans   **Club Colours:** Sky blue & navy blue   Founded 1995

Club Contact Details 01652 636 964   bartontown@gmail.com

Previous Names: Barton Town Old Boys >2017.

Previous Leagues: Lincolnshire 1995-2000, Humber (Founder member) 2000-01, Central Midlands 2001-07.

HONOURS

FA Comps: None

League: Lincolnshire 1996-97. Central Midlands Supreme Division 2005-06.

10-11		11-12		12-13		13-14		14-15		15-16		16-17		17-18		18-19		19-20	
NCE1	2	NCEP	11	NCEP	8	NCEP	3	NCEP	5	NCEP	10	NCEP	20	NCEP	12	NCEP	11	NCEP	n&v
FAC	P	FAC	Pr	FAC	P	FAC	P	FAC	P	FAC	P	FAC	EP	FAC	EP	FAC	EPr	FAC	P
FAV	2P	FAV	2P	FAV	1Q	FAV	2Q	FAV	2P	FAV	1Q	FAV	1Q	FAV	2Q	FAV	2P	FAV	2Q

GROUND: Marsh Lane, Barton-on-Humber DN18 5JD
Capacity: 3,000 **Seats:** 240 **Covered:** 540 **Shop:** No
Nearest Railway Station Barton-on-Humber - 0.5km
Bus Route Butts Road - stop 133m away

BOTTESFORD TOWN
Nickname: The Poachers   **Club Colours:** Blue & yellow   Founded 1974

Club Contact Details 01724 871 883   andrew.susworth@googlemail.com

Previous Names: None

Previous Leagues: Lincolnshire 1974-2000. Central Midlands 2000-07.

HONOURS

FA Comps: None

League: Lincolnshire 1989-90, 90-91, 91-92. Central Midlands Supreme Division 2006-07.

10-11		11-12		12-13		13-14		14-15		15-16		16-17		17-18		18-19		19-20	
NCE1	17	NCE1	16	NCE1	15	NCE1	3	NCE1	8	NCE1	3	NCEP	12	NCEP	8	NCEP	12	NCEP	n&v
FAC	1Q							FAC	EP	FAC	P	FAC	P	FAC	1Q	FAC	1Q	FAC	EP
FAV	1Q	FAV	2Q	FAV	2P	FAV	1Q	FAV	1Pr	FAV	2Q	FAV	3P	FAV	2Q	FAV	1Pr	FAV	2P

GROUND: Birkdale Park, Ontario Road, Bottesford, Scunthorpe DN17 2TQ
Capacity: 1,000 **Seats:** 90 **Covered:** 300
Nearest Railway Station Scunthorpe - 3.6km
Bus Route Maple Leaf - stop 149m away

BRIDLINGTON TOWN
Nickname: Seasiders   **Club Colours:** All red   Founded 1918

Club Contact Details 01262 606 879   dom@bridtownafc.com

Previous Names: Original Bridlington Town folded in 1994. Greyhound FC changed to Bridlington Town.

Previous Leagues: Yorkshire 1924-39, 59-82, NCEL 1982-90, 99-2003, Northern Premier 1990-94, 2003-08

HONOURS

FA Comps: FA Vase 1992-93

League: Yorkshire League 1974-75. Northern Counties East 1989-90, 2001-02, 09-10, NPL Division One 1992-93.

10-11		11-12		12-13		13-14		14-15		15-16		16-17		17-18		18-19		19-20	
NCEP	3	NCEP	2	NCEP	3	NCEP	12	NCEP	8	NCEP	5	NCEP	3	NCEP	9	NCEP	3	NCEP	n&v
FAC	P	FAC	P	FAC	EP	FAC	Pr	FAC	1Q	FAC	EP	FAC	2Qr	FAC	P	FAC	P	FAC	P
FAV	1Pr	FAV	3P	FAV	1P	FAV	3P	FAV	1Q	FAV	2Q	FAV	1P	FAV	1P	FAV	1P	FAV	3P

GROUND: Neil Hudgell Law Stadium, Queensgate, Bridlington YO16 7LN
Capacity: 3,000 **Seats:** 500 **Covered:** 500 **Shop:** Yes
Nearest Railway Station York
Bus Route 12 & 45

ECCLESHILL UNITED
Nickname: The Eagles   Club Colours: Blue & white   Founded 1948

Club Contact Details 01274 615 739

Previous Names: -
Previous Leagues: Bradford Amateur. West Riding County Amateur >1985
HONOURS
FA Comps: None
League: West Riding County Amateur 1976-77.
Northern Counties East Division One 1996-97.

	10-11	11-12	12-13	13-14	14-15	15-16	16-17	17-18	18-19	19-20
	NCE1 10	NCE1 6	NCE1 14	NCE1 4	NCE1 13	NCE1 13	NCE1 9	NCE1 4	NCEP 10	NCEP n&v
		FAC 1Q	FAC 1Q	FAC 1Q	FAC EP				FAC EP	FAC Pr
	FAV 2P	FAV 2P	FAV 1Q	FAV 1P	FAV 1Q	FAV EP	FAV 1Q	FAV 1Q	FAV 1Q	FAV 1Q

GROUND: Kingsway, Wrose, Bradford BD2 1PN
Capacity: 2,225   **Seats:** 225   **Covered:** 415
Nearest Railway Station Frizinghall - 1.7km
Bus Route Kingsway Plumpton Drive - stop 97m away

GARFORTH TOWN
Nickname: The Miners   Club Colours: Blue   Founded 1964

Club Contact Details   secretary@garforthtown.net

Previous Names: Garforth Miners 1964-85
Previous Leagues: Leeds Sunday Comb. 1972-76, West Yorkshire 1976-78, Yorkshire 1978-82, NCE 1982-2007. Northern Premier 2007-13.
HONOURS
FA Comps: None
League: Northern Counties East Division 1 1997-98

	10-11	11-12	12-13	13-14	14-15	15-16	16-17	17-18	18-19	19-20
	NP1N 13	NP1N 5	NP1N 22	NCEP 14	NCEP 14	NCEP 16	NCEP 15	NCEP 13	NCEP 14	NCEP n&v
	FAC P	FAC 1Q	FAC 1Q	FAC EP	FAC P	FAC EP	FAC EP	FAC EP	FAC 1Q	FAC P
	FAT 1Qr	FAT 1Q	FAT P	FAV 1P	FAV 2Q	FAV 2P	FAV 1Q	FAV 1P	FAV 1P	FAV 2Q

GROUND: Community Stadium, Cedar Ridge, Garforth, Leeds LS25 2PF
Capacity: 3,000   **Seats:** 278   **Covered:** 200
Nearest Railway Station East Garforth - 1km. Garforth - 1.2km.
Bus Route Aberford Road - stop 128m away

GOOLE AFC
Nickname: The Vikings   Club Colours: Red   Founded 1997

Club Contact Details 01405 762 794 (Match days)   jumbosmith96@icloud.com

Previous Names: Replacement for Goole Town which folded at the end of the 1995-96 season.
Previous Leagues: Central Midlands 1997-98. Northern Counties East 2000-04. Northern Premier 2004-18.
HONOURS
FA Comps: None
League: Central Midlands 1997-98.
Northern Counties East Division One 1999-2000, Premier Division 2003-04.

	10-11	11-12	12-13	13-14	14-15	15-16	16-17	17-18	18-19	19-20
	NP1S 13	NP1S 10	NP1N 21	NP1S 13	NP1S 16	NP1S 19	NP1N 21	NP1N 22	NCEP 18	NCEP n&v
	FAC P	FAC Pr	FAC P	FAC P	FAC Pr	FAC 1Qr	FAC P	FAC P	FAC EP	FAC Pr
	FAT Pr	FAT 1Q	FAT Pr	FAT P	FAT 2Q	FAT 1Q	FAT 1Qr	FAT P	FAV 1Q	FAV 1Q

GROUND: Victoria Pleasure Gardens, Marcus Road, Goole DN14 6SL
Capacity: 3,000   **Seats:** 300   **Covered:** 800   Yes
Nearest Railway Station Goole - 0.5km
Bus Route Goole Newport Street - stop 200m away

GRIMSBY BOROUGH
Nickname: The Wilderness Boys **Club Colours:** All red

Founded 2003

Club Contact Details 07890 318 054 nigelfanthorpe@hotmail.co.uk

Previous Names: None
Previous Leagues: Lincolnshire 2003-04. Central Midlands 2004-08.
HONOURS
FA Comps: None
League: None

	10-11	11-12	12-13	13-14	14-15	15-16	16-17	17-18	18-19	19-20
	NCE1 15	NCE1 18	NCE1 17	NCE1 16	NCE1 22	NCE1 19	NCE1 4	NCE1 3	NCE1 1	NCEP n&v
		FAC EP						FAC 1Q	FAC 1Q	FAC EP
	FAV 2Q	FAV 2Q	FAV 1Q	FAV 2Q	FAV 1Q		FAV 2Q	FAV 1Q	FAV 1Q	FAV 3P

GROUND: The Bradley Football Development Centre, Bradley Road, Grimsby, DN37 0AG
Capacity: 1,000 **Seats:** 180 **Covered:** 200 **Shop:** Yes
Nearest Railway Station Grimsby Town - 3km
Bus Route Crowland Avenue - stop 463m away

HANDSWORTH PARRAMORE
Nickname: Amber Parras **Club Colours:** Amber & black

Founded 1986

Club Contact Details 01909 479 955 johnbrunsmeer@hotmail.co.uk

Previous Names: Parramore Sports > 2010. Sheffield Parramore 2010-2011. Worksop Parramore 2011-14.
Previous Leagues: Sheffield & Hallam County Senior 1986-2008. Central Midlands 2008-11
HONOURS
FA Comps: None
League: Central Midland Supreme Division 2010-11.

	10-11	11-12	12-13	13-14	14-15	15-16	16-17	17-18	18-19	19-20
	CM Su 1	NCE1 3	NCEP 7	NCEP 4	NCEP 7	NCEP 2	NCEP 4	NCEP 4	NCEP 8	NCEP n&v
					FAC P	FAC P	FAC P	FAC 2Qr	FAC P	FAC P
					FAV 1P	FAV 3P	FAV 1P	FAV 1P	FAV 1P	FAV 2Q

GROUND: The Windsor Foodservice Stadium, Sandy Land, Worksop S80 1UJ
Capacity: 2,500 **Seats:** 200 **Covered:** 750
Nearest Railway Station Worksop - 0.5km
Bus Route Grafton Street - stop 114m away

HEMSWORTH M.W.
Nickname: Wells **Club Colours:** Dark blue

Founded 1981

Club Contact Details 01977 614 997
Previous Names: None
Previous Leagues: Doncaster Senior. West Riding County Amateur 1995-2008.
HONOURS
FA Comps: None
League: West Riding County Amateur Division One 1996-97.
Northern Counties East Division One 2015-16.

	10-11	11-12	12-13	13-14	14-15	15-16	16-17	17-18	18-19	19-20
	NCE1 16	NCE1 8	NCE1 13	NCE1 17	NCE1 3	NCE1 1	NCEP 9	NCEP 6	NCEP 4	NCEP n&v
	FAC Pr	FAC EP	FAC P			FAC EP	FAC P	FAC EP	FAC EPr	FAC P
	FAV 1Q	FAV 2Q	FAV 1Q	FAV 2Q	FAV 2Q	FAV 2P	FAV 2P	FAV 2Q	FAV 2P	FAV 1P

GROUND: Wakefield Road, Fitzwilliam, Pontefract WF9 5AJ
Capacity: 2,000 **Seats:** 100 **Covered:** 100 **Shop:** Yes
Nearest Railway Station Fitzwilliam - 0.4km
Bus Route Wakefield Road - stop 22m away

KNARESBOROUGH TOWN
Nickname: The Boro   Club Colours: Red and black

Founded 1902

Club Contact Details 01423 548 896   knaresboroughtownafc@gmail.com

Previous Names: -
Previous Leagues: York. Harrogate & District. West Yorkshire.
HONOURS
FA Comps: None
League: York 1902-03, 03-04, 04-05, 08-09, 24-25, 25-26, 28-29, 33-34, 34-35, Div.2 51-52, Div.1 52-53. Harrogate & District 64-65, 65-66, 66-67. West Yorkshire Prem 2008-09. Northern Counties East Division One 2017-18.

10-11		11-12		12-13		13-14		14-15		15-16		16-17		17-18		18-19		19-20	
WYkP	2	WYkP	3	NCE1	8	NCE1	6	NCE1	12	NCE1	8	NCE1	7	NCE1	1	NCEP	9	NCEP	n&v
								FAC	P							FAC	2Q	FAC	EP
						FAV	2Q	FAV	1Q	FAV	1Q	FAV	1Q	FAV	2P	FAV	1Q	FAV	1P

GROUND: Manse Lane, Knaresborough, HG5 8LF
Capacity: 1,000 **Seats:** 73 **Covered:** 173
Nearest Railway Station Knaresborough - 1.5km
Bus Route Aspin Park School - stop 168 away

LIVERSEDGE
Nickname: Sedge   Club Colours: Sky blue

Founded 1910

Club Contact Details 01274 862 108   simonturfrey@aol.com

Previous Names: None
Previous Leagues: Bradford 1919-22. West Riding Co. Amateur 1922-27, 49-72. Spen Valley 1947-49. Yorkshire 1972-82.
HONOURS
FA Comps: None
League: West Riding County Amateur 1923-24, 25-26, 26-27, 64-65, 65-66, 68-69. Spen Valley 1948-49.

10-11		11-12		12-13		13-14		14-15		15-16		16-17		17-18		18-19		19-20	
NCEP	17	NCEP	14	NCEP	15	NCEP	20	NCEP	18	NCEP	14	NCEP	11	NCEP	11	NCEP	13	NCEP	n&v
FAC	EP	FAC	EP	FAC	Pr	FAC	EP	FAC	EP	FAC	EP	FAC	EP	FAC	1Qr	FAC	P	FAC	1Q
FAV	2Qr	FAV	2Q	FAV	2Q	FAV	1P	FAV	2Q	FAV	1Q	FAV	2Q	FAV	1P	FAV	1Q	FAV	2Q

GROUND: Clayborn Ground, Quaker Lane, Hightown Road, Cleckheaton WF15 8DF
Capacity: 2,000 **Seats:** 250 **Covered:** 750 **Shop:** Yes
Nearest Railway Station Low Moor - 4.5km
Bus Route Hightown Road - stop 142m away

MALTBY MAIN
Nickname: Miners   Club Colours: Red and black

Founded 1916

Club Contact Details 07795 693 683   john_mills_@hotmail.co.uk

Previous Names: Maltby Miners Welfare 1970-96
Previous Leagues: Sheffield Association 1919-29, 39-41, 45-49, 65-70, 72-73. Rotherham Minor 1929-36. Sheffield Amateur 1936-39. Rotherham Association 1942-45, 55-58. Yorkshire League 1949-55, 73-82. Doncaster & District 1958-65.
HONOURS
FA Comps: None
League: Sheffield Association 1925-26, 26-27.

10-11		11-12		12-13		13-14		14-15		15-16		16-17		17-18		18-19		19-20	
NCEP	11	NCEP	18	NCEP	14	NCEP	15	NCEP	19	NCEP	7	NCEP	14	NCEP	5	NCEP	6	NCEP	n&v
FAC	P	FAC	EP	FAC	1Q	FAC	EP	FAC	P	FAC	1Q	FAC	EP	FAC	EP	FAC	1Q	FAC	1Q
FAV	1Qr	FAV	1Q	FAV	2Q	FAV	1Q	FAV	2Qr	FAV	2P	FAV	1Q	FAV	2Q	FAV	2Q	FAV	1Q

GROUND: Muglet Lane, Maltby, Rotherham S66 7JQ
Capacity: 2,000 **Seats:** 150 **Covered:** 300 **Shop:** No
Nearest Railway Station Rotherham Central - 8 miles
Bus Route Duke Avenue - stop 78m away

PENISTONE CHURCH

Nickname: None **Club Colours:** Black & white **Founded** 1906

Club Contact Details penistonechurchfc@gmail.com

Previous Names: Formed after the merger of Penistone Choirboys and Penistone Juniors.
Previous Leagues: Sheffield Junior 1906-07. Sheffield Amateur 1907-48. Hatchard League/Sheffield Association 1948-83. Sheffield & Hallamshire County Senior (Founder Members) 1983-14.
HONOURS
FA Comps: None
League: Sheffield & Hallamshire County Senior Division One 1993-94, 2000-01.

	10-11	11-12	12-13	13-14	14-15	15-16	16-17	17-18	18-19	19-20
	Sh&HP 3	Sh&HP 4	Sh&HP 3	Sh&HP 4	NCE1 9	NCE1 5	NCE1 6	NCEP 7	NCEP 2	NCEP n&v
FAC						EP	EP	2Q	P	EPr
FAV				1Q	1Q	2Q	1P	1Q	1Q	1P

GROUND: Church View Road, Penistone, Sheffield S36 6AT
Capacity: 1,000 **Seats:** 100 **Covered:** 150 **Shop:** Yes
Nearest Railway Station Penistone - 0.2km
Bus Route Church View Road - stop 149m away

SILSDEN

Nickname: The Cobbydalers **Club Colours:** Red and black **Founded** 1904

Club Contact Details 01535 958 850 john.silsdenfc@hotmail.co.uk

Previous Names: Reformed in 1980.
Previous Leagues: Craven & District. West Riding County Amateur. North West Counties >2019.
HONOURS
FA Comps: None
League: Craven Premier Division 1998-99. West Riding County Am. Division Two 99-2000, Division One 2000-01, Premier Division 2002-03. North West Counties Division One 2017-18.

	10-11	11-12	12-13	13-14	14-15	15-16	16-17	17-18	18-19	19-20
	NWCP 16	NWCP 12	NWCP 18	NWCP 15	NWCP 10	NWCP 21	NWC1 11	NWC1 1	NWCP 9	NCEP n&v
FAC	EPr	Pr	EP		EP	P	EPr		EP	EPr
FAV	1Q	1Q		2Q	1P	1P	2Q	2Q	3P	1Q

GROUND: Keighley Road, Keighley Road, Silsden BD20 0EH
Capacity: **Seats:** Yes **Covered:** Yes
Nearest Railway Station Steeton & Silsden - 1.1km
Bus Route Keighley Road stop - 55m away

STAVELEY MINERS WELFARE

Nickname: The Welfare **Club Colours:** Blue & white **Founded** 1989

Club Contact Details 01246 471 441 staveleyed@hotmail.co.uk

Previous Names: None
Previous Leagues: Chesterfield & District Amateur 1989-91. Sheffield & Hallamshire County Senior 1991-93.
HONOURS
FA Comps: None
League: Sheffield & Hallamshire County Senior Division Three 1991-92, Division Two 1992-93. Northern Counties East Division One 2010-11.

	10-11	11-12	12-13	13-14	14-15	15-16	16-17	17-18	18-19	19-20
	NCE1 1	NCEP 5	NCEP 13	NCEP 17	NCEP 9	NCEP 8	NCEP 6	NCEP 16	NCEP 7	NCEP n&v
FAC	P	2Q	Pr	P	1Q	EP	EP	P	2Q	1Q
FAV	4P	SF	2P	3P	1Q	1Q	3P	1P	1Pr	1Q

GROUND: Inkersall Road, Staveley, Chesterfield, S43 3JL
Capacity: 5,000 **Seats:** 220 **Covered:** 400 **Shop:** Yes
Nearest Railway Station Chesterfield - 5,4km
Bus Route Market Street - stop 156m away

NORTHERN COUNTIES EAST LEAGUE

THACKLEY

Nickname: Dennyboys **Club Colours:** Red and white **Founded** 1930

Club Contact Details 01274 615 571 mick.lodge@btinternet.com

Previous Names: Thackley Wesleyians 1930-39
Previous Leagues: Bradford Amateur, West Riding County Amateur, West Yorkshire, Yorkshire 1967-82
HONOURS
FA Comps: None
League: West Riding County Amateur x5. West Yorkshire 1965-66, 66-67. Yorkshire Division Two 1973-74.

	10-11	11-12	12-13	13-14	14-15	15-16	16-17	17-18	18-19	19-20
NCEP	8	10	10	13	12	12	5	15	15	n&v
FAC	2Q	P	EP	EP	EP	1Qr	EP	EP	EP	EP
FAV	2P	1P	1P	3P	3P	1Qr	1Q	2Q	2P	2Q

GROUND: Dennyfield, Ainsbury Avenue, Thackley, Bradford BD10 0TL
Capacity: 3000 **Seats:** 300 **Covered:** 600
Nearest Railway Station Baildon - 1.4km
Bus Route Thackley Road - stop 200m away

YORKSHIRE AMATEUR

Nickname: Ammers **Club Colours:** White and red **Founded** 1918

Club Contact Details 0113 289 2886

Previous Names: None
Previous Leagues: Yorkshire 1920-24, 30-82.
HONOURS
FA Comps: None
League: Yorkshire 1931-32, Division Two 1958-59, Division Three 1977-78.

	10-11	11-12	12-13	13-14	14-15	15-16	16-17	17-18	18-19	19-20
NCE1	3	19	21	19	10	11	13	2		
NCEP									5	n&v
FAC		EP				EP				EP
FAV	2Q	1P	2Q	1Q	1P	2Q	1Q		1Q	3P

GROUND: Bracken Edge, Roxholme Road, Leeds, LS8 4DZ (Sat. Nav. LS7 4JG)
Capacity: 1,550 **Seats:** 200 **Covered:** 160 **Shop:** Yes
Nearest Railway Station Leeds - 3.5km
Bus Route Harehills Ln Roxholme Ave - stop 168m away

DIVISION ONE

ARMTHORPE WELFARE
Nickname: Wellie   **Club Colours:** All blue

Founded 1926

Club Contact Details   armthorpe.welfare@hotmail.co.uk

HONOURS
FA Comps: None
League: Doncaster & District Senior 1952-53, 53-54, 54-55, 56-57, 57-58, 60-61, 61-62, 64-65, 82-83, Div.3 77-78, Div.2 78-79, Div.1 81-82. NCE
Div.1 Central 1984-85.

10-11		11-12		12-13		13-14		14-15		15-16		16-17		17-18		18-19		19-20	
NCEP	13	NCEP	13	NCEP	20	NCEP	18	NCEP	17	NCEP	19	NCEP	21	NCE1	16	NCE1	17	NCE1	n&v
FAC	P	FAC	1Qr	FAC	EP	FAC	EP	FAC	P	FAC	2Q	FAC	EP	FAC	EPr				
FAV	2Pr	FAV	3P	FAV	2P	FAV	2P	FAV	2Q	FAV	1P	FAV	1Q	FAV	2Q	FAV	1Q	FAV	1Q

GROUND: Welfare Ground, Church Street, Armthorpe, Doncaster DN3 3AG
Nearest Railway Station Kirk Sandall - 3.4km
Bus Route Beech Road - stop 13m away

BRIGG TOWN
Nickname: Zebras   **Club Colours:** Black and white

Founded 1864

Club Contact Details   gavinduncanbriggtownfc@gmail.com

HONOURS
FA Comps: FAV 1995-96, 2002-03
League: Midland Counties 1977-78. Northern Counties East Premier 2000-01. Lincolnshire League x8,

10-11		11-12		12-13		13-14		14-15		15-16		16-17		17-18		18-19		19-20	
NP1S	4	NP1S	17	NP1S	13	NP1S	18	NP1S	22	NCEP	21	NCE1	14	NCE1	21	Lincs	2	NCE1	n&v
FAC	2Qr	FAC	P	FAC	P	FAC	1Qr	FAC	P	FAC	EP	FAC	1Q						
FAT	P	FAT	1Q	FAT	P	FAT	2Q	FAT	Pr	FAV	1Q	FAV	1Q					FAV	2Q

GROUND: The Hawthorns, Hawthorn Avenue, Brigg DN20 8PG
Nearest Railway Station Brigg - 0.9km
Bus Route Vale of Ancholme School - stop 189m away

CAMPION
Nickname: **Club Colours:** Red & black

Founded 1963

Club Contact Details 01274 491 919   campionsecretary@gmail.com

HONOURS
FA Comps: None
League: West Riding Amateur Division Two 1989-90, Division One 92-93.

10-11		11-12		12-13		13-14		14-15		15-16		16-17		17-18		18-19		19-20	
WRCP	3	WRCP	9	WRCP	12	WRCP	3	WRCP	3	WRCP	3	NCE1	8	NCE1	9	NCE1	2	NCE1	n&v
																		FAC	EP
														FAV	1Q	FAV	1Q	FAV	1Q

GROUND: Scotchman Road, Bradford BD9 5AT.
Nearest Railway Station Frizinghall - 1.9km
Bus Route Toller Lane Masham Place - 109m away

DRONFIELD TOWN
Nickname: None   **Club Colours:** Red & black

Founded 1998

Club Contact Details   secretary@dronfieldtownfc.com

HONOURS
FA Comps: None
League: Hope Valley B Div 2001-02, A Div 2002-03, Prem 2003-04. Midland Regional Alliance Division One 2005-06, Premier 2007-08. Central
Midlands North 2012-13.

10-11		11-12		12-13		13-14		14-15		15-16		16-17		17-18		18-19		19-20	
CM Su	7	CMN	3	CMN	1	NCE1	14	NCE1	19	NCE1	15	NCE1	19	NCE1	14	NCE1	6	NCE1	n&v
								FAV	1P	FAV	1P	FAV	1Q	FAV	1P	FAV	2P	FAV	2Q

GROUND: Stonelow Playing Fields, Stonelow Road, Dronfield, S18 2EU
Nearest Railway Station Dronfield - 0.9km
Bus Route Oakhill Road Bottom - stop 270m away

EAST HULL
Nickname: Carnegie, EYC Club Colours: Black & white Founded

Club Contact Details

HONOURS
FA Comps: None
League: East Riding County Division One 2009-10, Premier Division 2013-14.
Humber Premier Division One 2014-15

10-11	11-12	12-13	13-14	14-15	15-16	16-17	17-18	18-19	19-20
ERCP 7	ERCP 5	ERCP 4	ERCP 1	Humb1 1	HumbP 14	HumbP 5	NCE1 18	NCE1 13	NCE1 n&v

GROUND: Dunswell Park, Dunswell HU6 0AA
Nearest Railway Station Hull (4 miles)

EMLEY AFC
Nickname: Pewits Club Colours: Maroon and sky blue Founded 2005

Club Contact Details 01924 849 392

HONOURS
FA Comps: None
League: None

	10-11	11-12	12-13	13-14	14-15	15-16	16-17	17-18	18-19	19-20
	NCE1 8	NCE1 10	NCE1 7	NCE1 8	NCE1 5	NCE1 4	NCE1 3	NCE1 12	NCE1 12	NWC1N n&v
FAC	P	EP	EP	P	P	P	P	EP		
FAV	2P	1P	4P	1P	1P	2Q	2P	1P	1Q	2Q

GROUND: The Welfare Ground, Off Upper Lane, Emley, nr Huddersfield HD8 9RE.
Nearest Railway Station Denby Dale - 5km
Bus Route Upper Lane Church Street - stop 61m away

GLASSHOUGHTON WELFARE
Nickname: Welfare or Blues Club Colours: Royal blue & white Founded 1964

Club Contact Details 01977 511 234   frankmaclachlan499@gmail.com

HONOURS
FA Comps: None
League: None

	10-11	11-12	12-13	13-14	14-15	15-16	16-17	17-18	18-19	19-20
	NCE1 7	NCE1 2	NCEP 16	NCEP 16	NCEP 21	NCE1 16	NCE1 11	NCE1 6	NCE1 11	NCE1 n&v
FAC		Pr	EP	EP	EP	EPr			EP	
FAV	1Q	2P	2Q	2Q	1Q	1Q	2Qr	2Q	1P	1P

GROUND: Glasshoughton Centre, Leeds Road, Glasshoughton, Castleford WF10 4PF
Nearest Railway Station Glasshoughton - 0.8km
Bus Route Leeds Road Carr Lane - stop 83m away

HALL ROAD RANGERS
Nickname: Rangers Club Colours: Blue & white Founded 1959

Club Contact Details   hallroadrangers@live.co.uk

HONOURS
FA Comps: None
League: Yorkshire Division Three 1972-73, 79-80. Northern Counties East Division One 2016-17.

	10-11	11-12	12-13	13-14	14-15	15-16	16-17	17-18	18-19	19-20
	NCEP 14	NCEP 16	NCEP 22	NCE1 11	NCE1 17	NCE1 17	NCE1 1	NCEP 19	NCEP 20	NCE1 n&v
FAC	EPr	Pr	EP	EP				EP		EP
FAV	1Q	2Q	1P	1Q	2Q	2Q	2P	2P		2Q

GROUND: Hawroth Park, Dawson Drive, Hull HU6 7DY
Nearest Railway Station Cottingham - 3.5km
Bus Route Larard Avenue - stop 158m away

HALLAM
Nickname: Countrymen — Club Colours: Blue and white — Founded 1860

Club Contact Details 0114 230 9484 — theclub@hallamfc.co.uk

HONOURS
FA Comps: None
League: Hatchard 1902-03, 48-49. Sheffield Amateur 1922-23, 26-27.
Sheffield Association 1949-50. Yorkshire Division Two 1960-61.

	10-11	11-12	12-13	13-14	14-15	15-16	16-17	17-18	18-19	19-20
	NCEP 19	NCE1 14	NCE1 12	NCE1 20	NCE1 14	NCE1 6	NCE1 5	NCE1 8	NCE1 3	NCE1 n&v
FAC	EP	EP	EP				EP	P	EP	
FAV	1P	1Q	1Q	1Q	2Q	2P	2P	2Q	2P	1Q

GROUND: Sandygate Road, Crosspool, Sheffield S10 5SE
Nearest Railway Station Sheffield - 4.5km
Bus Route Ringstead Crescent - stop 19m away

HARROGATE RAILWAY ATH.
Nickname: The Rail — Club Colours: Red and green — Founded 1935

Club Contact Details 01423 883 104 — shep@therailfc.com

HONOURS
FA Comps: None
League: West Yorkshire 1953-54.
Northern Counties East Division Two North 1983-84, Division one 1989-99.

	10-11	11-12	12-13	13-14	14-15	15-16	16-17	17-18	18-19	19-20
	NP1N 20	NP1N 21	NP1N 18	NP1N 13	NP1N 8	NP1N 21	NCEP 19	NCEP 20	NCEP 19	NCE1 n&v
FAC	P	1Q	Pr	Pr	2Q	Pr	1Q	Pr	EP	EP
	FAT 3Q	FAT 1Q	FAT 1Q	FAT P	FAT P	FAT P	FAV 2Q	FAV 1P	FAV 1Q	FAV 1Q

GROUND: Station View, Starbeck, Harrogate, North Yorkshire HG2 7JA
Nearest Railway Station Starbeck - 0.1km
Bus Route Henry Peacock - stop 134m away

NORTH FERRIBY
Nickname: The Villagers — Club Colours: Green and white — Founded 2019

Club Contact Details 01482 634 601 — info@northferriby.co.uk

HONOURS
FA Comps: None
League: None

10-11	11-12	12-13	13-14	14-15	15-16	16-17	17-18	18-19	19-20
									NCE1 n&v

GROUND: The Dransfield Stadium, Grange Lane, Church Road, North Ferriby HU14 3AB
Nearest Railway Station Ferriby - 5 min walk from the ground.

NOSTELL MINERS WELFARE
Nickname: The Welfare — Club Colours: Yellow and black — Founded 1928

Club Contact Details 01924 866 010 — nostwellmwfc@hotmail.com

HONOURS
FA Comps: None
League: West Yorkshire Premier Division 2004-05

	10-11	11-12	12-13	13-14	14-15	15-16	16-17	17-18	18-19	19-20
	NCEP 9	NCEP 17	NCEP 18	NCEP 21	NCEP 15	NCEP 22	NCE1 22	NCE1 17	NCE1 5	NCE1 n&v
FAC	EPr	EP	EP	EP	EP	EPr	EPr			EPr
FAV	1Q	2Qr	1P	1Q	2Q	1Q	2Q	2Q	1Q	1P

GROUND: The Welfare Ground, Crofton Co. Centre, Middle Lane, New Crofton WF4 1LB
Nearest Railway Station Streethouse - 2.9km
Bus Route The Slipper Pub - stop 372m away

PARKGATE

Nickname: The Steelmen **Club Colours:** Red & black

Founded 1969

Club Contact Details 01709 826 600   brucebickerdike@hotmail.co.uk

HONOURS
FA Comps: None
League: Northern Counties East Division One 2006-07.

	10-11	11-12	12-13	13-14	14-15	15-16	16-17	17-18	18-19	19-20
NCEP/NCE1	NCEP 2	NCEP 7	NCEP 9	NCEP 19	NCEP 16	NCEP 17	NCEP 17	NCEP 21	NCE1 8	NCE1 n&v
FAC	1Q	1Q	EP	EP	EP	EP	P	P	1Qr	
FAV	2Q	3P	3P	2P	1Q	1Q	1Q	2Q	2Q	1Q

GROUND: Roundwood Sports Complex, Green Lane, Rawmarsh S62 6LA
Nearest Railway Station Swinton - 3.4km
Bus Route Roundwood Grove - stop 57m away

RETFORD

Nickname: The Choughs **Club Colours:** All blue

Founded 2015

Club Contact Details 07766 700 536   kevswarfc@gmail.com

HONOURS
FA Comps: None
League: Central Midlands North Division 2018-19

	10-11	11-12	12-13	13-14	14-15	15-16	16-17	17-18	18-19	19-20
CMN/NCE1						CMN 7	CMN 6	CMN 5	CMN 1	NCE1 n&v
FAV							FAV 2Q			FAV 1Q

GROUND: Babworth Road, Retford DN22 6NJ
Nearest Railway Station Retford - 0.8 miles from the ground.

ROSSINGTON MAIN

Nickname: The Colliery **Club Colours:** All blue

Founded 1919

Club Contact Details 01302 864 870 (MD)   g-parsons2@sky.com

HONOURS
FA Comps: None
League: Doncaster & District Senior 1944-45.
Central Midlands Premier Division 1984-85.

	10-11	11-12	12-13	13-14	14-15	15-16	16-17	17-18	18-19	19-20
NCE1	NCE1 14	NCE1 7	NCE1 18	NCE1 13	NCE1 15	NCE1 20	NCE1 15	NCE1 13	NCE1 14	NCE1 n&v
FAC	EP	EPr	EP							
FAV	1Q	2Q	1Q	2Q	2Q	2Q	2Q	1P	2Q	2Q

GROUND: Welfare Ground, Oxford Street, Rossington, Doncaster DN11 0TE
Nearest Railway Station Doncaster - 6.4km
Bus Route Grantham Street - stop 149m away

SELBY TOWN

Nickname: The Robins **Club Colours:** All red

Founded 1919

Club Contact Details 01757 210 900   toonarkley@yahoo.co.uk

HONOURS
FA Comps: None
League: Yorkshire 1932-33, 34-35, 35-36, 52-53, 53-54.
Northern Counties East Division One 1995-96.

	10-11	11-12	12-13	13-14	14-15	15-16	16-17	17-18	18-19	19-20
NCEP/NCE1	NCEP 15	NCEP 20	NCE1 16	NCE1 12	NCE1 11	NCE1 10	NCE1 10	NCE1 7	NCE1 9	NCE1 n&v
FAC	P	EP	EP						Pr	
FAV	2Qr	1P	2Q	1Q	1P	1P	1Q	1Q	1Q	2P

GROUND: Richard Street, Scott Road, Selby YO8 4BN
Nearest Railway Station Selby - 0.8km
Bus Route Leisure Centre - stop 73m away

SKEGNESS TOWN
Nickname: Lilywhites **Club Colours:** White & red
Founded 1947

Club Contact Details 07960 756 351   thegrays23@hotmail.com

HONOURS
FA Comps: None
League: Lincolnshire 1951-52, 55-56, 2006-07, 07-08, 13-14, 15-16, 16-17.

10-11	11-12	12-13	13-14	14-15	15-16	16-17	17-18	18-19	19-20
Lincs 5	Lincs 12	Lincs 8	Lincs 1	Lincs 2	Lincs 1	Lincs 1	Lincs 2	NCE1 15	NCE1 n&v
							FAV 2Q	FAV 2Q	FAV 2Q

GROUND: Wainfleet Road, Skegness, Lincolnshire PE25 2EL
Nearest Railway Station Skegness ½ mile

SWALLOWNEST
Nickname: None **Club Colours:** All royal blue
Founded 2006

Club Contact Details 0114 287 2510   kent97@btinternet.com

HONOURS
FA Comps: None
League: South Yorkshire Amateur Premier Division 2007-08.
Sheffield & Hallamshire County Senior Div.2 2008-09, Prem 10-11, 16-17.

10-11	11-12	12-13	13-14	14-15	15-16	16-17	17-18	18-19	19-20
Sh&HP 1	Sh&HP 3	Sh&HP 6	Sh&HP 5	Sh&HP 3	Sh&HP 7	Sh&HP 1	NCE1 11	NCE1 10	NCE1 n&v
								FAV 1P	FAV 1Q

GROUND: Rotherham Road, Sheffield S26 4UR.
Nearest Railway Station Woodhouse - 2.2km
Bus Route Park Street - stop 61m away

WINTERTON RANGERS
Nickname: Rangers **Club Colours:** All blue
Founded 1930

Club Contact Details 01724 732 628   wintertonrangers2018@mail.com

HONOURS
FA Comps: None
League: Yprkshire Division One 1971-72, 76-77, 78-79.
Northern Counties East Division One 1989-90, Premier 2007-08.

10-11	11-12	12-13	13-14	14-15	15-16	16-17	17-18	18-19	19-20
NCEP 5	NCEP 6	NCEP 19	NCEP 22	NCE1 18	NCE1 8	NCE1 12	NCE1 10	NCE1 4	NCE1 n&v
FAC 1Qr	FAC EP	FAC EP	FAC EP	FAC P					FAC P
FAV 2P	FAV 2Q	FAV 2Q	FAV 2Q	FAV 1P	FAV 1Q	FAV 1Q	FAV 1Q	FAV 3P	FAV 1P

GROUND: West Street, Winterton, Scunthorpe DN15 9QF.
Nearest Railway Station Scunthorpe - 6¼ miles
Bus Route Post Office - stop 150m away

WORSBROUGH BRIDGE ATHLETIC
Nickname: The Briggers **Club Colours:** All red
Founded 1923

Club Contact Details 01226 284 452   mrsmooth705@gmail.com

HONOURS
FA Comps: None
League: Barnsley Division One 1952-53, 58-59, 59-60.
Sheffield Association Division One 1965-66, 69-70.

10-11	11-12	12-13	13-14	14-15	15-16	16-17	17-18	18-19	19-20
NCE1 12	NCE1 11	NCE1 9	NCE1 10	NCE1 16	NCE1 21	NCE1 20	NCE1 19	NCE1 7	NCE1 n&v
FAV 2Q	FAV 2Q	FAV 1Q	FAV 2Q	FAV 2Q	FAV 1Q		FAV 1Q	FAV 2Q	FAV 1Q

GROUND: Park Road, Worsbrough Bridge, Barnsley S70 5LJ
Nearest Railway Station Barnsley - 3.1km
Bus Route West Street - stop 29m away

ASHINGTON

Nickname: The Colliers **Club Colours:** Black & White

Founded 1883

Club Contact Details 01670 811 991

Previous Names: None

Previous Leagues: East Northumberland. Northern Alliance 1892-93, 1902-14, 69-70. North Eastern 1914-21, 29-58, 62-64. Football League 1921-29. Midland 1958-60. Northern Counties 1960-62. Wearside 1964-65. North Regional 1965-68. N.P.L. 1968-69.

HONOURS

FA Comps: None

League: East Northumberland 1897-98. Northern Alliance 1913-14. Northern Division Two 2000-01, 03-04.

	10-11		11-12		12-13		13-14		14-15		15-16		16-17		17-18		18-19		19-20	
NL 1	8	NL 1	5	NL 1	7	NL 1	6	NL 1	13	NL 1	12	NL 1	16	NL 1	12	NL 1	16	NL 1	n&v
FAC	3Q	FAC	4Q	FAC	1Q	FAC	P	FAC	1Qr	FAC	P	FAC	EP	FAC	P	FAC	EP	FAC	P
FAV	4P	FAV	5P	FAV	4P	FAV	4P	FAV	2P	FAV	2P	FAV	2Q	FAV	1P	FAV	2P	FAV	1Q

GROUND: Woodhorn Lane, Ashington NE63 9FW

Capacity: 2,000 **Seats:** 400 **Covered:** 900 **Shop:** Yes

Bus Route No.1 - alight at Wansbeck Hospital - 71m away

BILLINGHAM TOWN

Nickname: Billy Town **Club Colours:** All blue

Founded 1967

Club Contact Details 01642 560 800

Previous Names: Billingham Social Club

Previous Leagues: Stockton & District 1968-74 Teesside 1974-82

HONOURS

FA Comps: None

League: Stockton & District Division Two 1968-69. Teesside 1978-79, 81-82. Northern Division Two 2018-19.

	10-11		11-12		12-13		13-14		14-15		15-16		16-17		17-18		18-19		19-20	
NL 1	15	NL 1	17	NL 1	20	NL 1	23	NL 2	18	NL 2	11	NL 2	5	NL 2	9	NL 2	1	NL 1	n&v
FAC	EP	FAC	P	FAC	P	FAC	P	FAC	EP					FAC	EP			FAC	P
FAV	1P	FAV	2P	FAV	1Q	FAV	2Qr	FAV	2Q	FAV	1Q	FAV	4P	FAV	2P	FAV	1P	FAV	1P

GROUND: Bedford Terrace, Billingham, Cleveland TS23 4AE

Capacity: 3,000 **Seats:** 176 **Covered:** 600 **Shop:** No

Nearest Railway Station Billingham - 0.4km

Bus Route Warwick Crescent - stop 136m away

BISHOP AUCKLAND

Nickname: Two Blues **Club Colours:** Light & dark blue

Founded 1886

Club Contact Details 01388 604 605

Previous Names: Auckland Town 1889-1893

Previous Leagues: Northern Alliance 1890-91, Northern League 1893-1988, Northern Premier 1988-2006

HONOURS

FA Comps: FA Amateur Cup 1895-96, 1899-1900, 1913-14, 20-21, 21-22, 34-35, 38-39, 54-55, 55-56, 56-57.

League: Northern League 1898-99, 1900-01, 01-02, 08-09, 09-10, 11-12, 20-21, 30-31, 38-39, 46-47, 49-50, 50-51, 51-52, 53-54, 54-55, 55-56, 66-67, 84-85, 85-86.

	10-11		11-12		12-13		13-14		14-15		15-16		16-17		17-18		18-19		19-20	
NL 1	14	NL 1	8	NL 1	6	NL 1	8	NL 1	11	NL 1	8	NL 1	8	NL 1	19	NL 1	3	NL 1	n&v
FAC	Pr	FAC	EP	FAC	2Q	FAC	1Qr	FAC	1Q	FAC	P	FAC	4Q	FAC	EPr	FAC	EP	FAC	EP
FAV	1P	FAV	2Q	FAV	1P	FAV	2Q	FAV	2P	FAV	1P	FAV	2Q	FAV	2Q	FAV	1P	FAV	2P

GROUND: Heritage Park, Stadium Way, Bishop Auckland, Co. Durham DL14 9AE

Capacity: 2,004 **Seats:** 250 **Covered:** 722

Nearest Railway Station Bishop Auckland - 2.2km

Bus Route Bus stops right outside the ground.

CONSETT
Nickname: Steelman   **Club Colours:** All white   Founded 1899

Club Contact Details 01207 588 886

Previous Names: Consett Celtic 1899-1922.

Previous Leagues: Northern Alliance 1919-26, 35-37, North Eastern 1926-35, 37-58, 62-64, Midland 1958-60, Northern Counties 1960-62, Wearside 1964-70.

HONOURS

FA Comps: None

League: North Eastern 1939-40, Division Two 26-27. Northern Counties 1961-62. Northern Division Two 1988-89, 05-06.

10-11	11-12	12-13	13-14	14-15	15-16	16-17	17-18	18-19	19-20
NL 1 2	NL 1 15	NL 1 9	NL 1 11	NL 1 9	NL 1 7	NL 1 7	NL 1 9	NL 1 4	NL 1 n&v
FAC EPr	FAC EP	FAC EPr	FAC EP	FAC 1Q	FAC 2Q	FAC 2Qr	FAC 1Q	FAC 2Qr	FAC EPr
FAV 2Q	FAV 3P	FAV 2P	FAV 2Q	FAV 4P	FAV 2P	FAV 2Q	FAV 2Q	FAV 2Q	FAV

GROUND: Belle View Stadium, Deleves Lane, Consett DH8 7BF

Capacity: 2,950   **Seats:** 200   **Covered:** 200   **Shop:** No

Bus Route Mortons Garage - stop 174m away

GUISBOROUGH TOWN
Nickname: Priorymen   **Club Colours:** Red & white   Founded 1973

Club Contact Details 01287 636 925

Previous Names: None

Previous Leagues: Middlesbrough & District 1973-77. Northern Alliance 1977-80. Midland 1980-82. Northern Counties East 1982-85.

HONOURS

FA Comps: None

League: Northern Alliance 1979-80.

10-11	11-12	12-13	13-14	14-15	15-16	16-17	17-18	18-19	19-20
NL 2 2	NL 1 16	NL 1 11	NL 1 4	NL 1 3	NL 1 3	NL 1 20	NL 1 15	NL 1 15	NL 1 n&v
FAC EP	FAC P	FAC Pr	FAC 3Q	FAC EPr	FAC 1Qr	FAC P	FAC P	FAC 1Q	FAC P
FAV 2Q	FAV 1Pr	FAV 1P	FAV 1P	FAV 2P	FAV 2P	FAV 1P	FAV 1Q	FAV 1Pr	FAV 2P

GROUND: King George V Ground, Howlbeck Road, Guisborough TS14 6LE

Capacity: **Seats:** Yes   **Covered:** Yes

Bus Route Howlbeck Road - stop 49m away

HEBBURN TOWN
Nickname: Hornets   **Club Colours:** Yellow & black   Founded 1912

Club Contact Details 0191 483 5101

Previous Names: Reyrolles, Hebburn Reyrolles > 1988, Hebburn 1988-2000.

Previous Leagues: Tyneside. Northern Combination. Wearside 1960-89.

HONOURS

FA Comps: None

League: Tyneside 1938-39. Northern Combination 1943-44. Wearside 1966-67.

10-11	11-12	12-13	13-14	14-15	15-16	16-17	17-18	18-19	19-20
NL 2 10	NL 2 3	NL 1 18	NL 1 22	NL 2 5	NL 2 10	NL 2 11	NL 2 2	NL 1 2	NL 1 n&v
FAC EPr	FAC 4Q	FAC P	FAC P	FAC EPr	FAC EP			FAC EP	FAC Pr
FAV 2P	FAV 1P	FAV 2Q	FAV 1Q	FAV 1Q	FAV 1P	FAV 1Q	FAV 2Q	FAV 5P	FAV

GROUND: Hebburn Sports & Social, Victoria Rd West, Hebburn, Tyne & Wear NE31 1UN

Capacity: **Seats:** Yes   **Covered:** Yes

Nearest Railway Station Hebburn - 1km

Bus Route Victoria Road West - stop 74m away

NEWCASTLE BENFIELD
Nickname: The Lions **Club Colours:** Blue & white **Founded** 1988

Club Contact Details 07525 275 641

Previous Names: Heaton Corner House. Newcastle Benfield Saints.
Previous Leagues: Northern Alliance 1988-2003
HONOURS
FA Comps: None
League: Northern Alliance Division Two 1989-90, Division One 1994-95, 2002-03.
Northern Division One 2008-09.

	10-11	11-12	12-13	13-14	14-15	15-16	16-17	17-18	18-19	19-20
	NL 1 4	NL 1 12	NL 1 21	NL 1 14	NL 1 10	NL 1 18	NL 1 10	NL 1 7	NL 1 10	NL 1 n&v
FAC	2Q	1Q	EP	EP	2Q	P	1Q	3Q	1Qr	1Q
FAV	2Q	4P	2P	QF	3P	1P	2P	4P	4P	3P

GROUND: Sam Smiths Park, Benfield Road, Walkergate NE6 4NU
Capacity: 2,000 **Seats:** 150 **Covered:** 250
Nearest Railway Station Walkergate - 492m
Bus Route Benfield Comprehensive School - 96m away

NEWTON AYCLIFFE
Nickname: Aycliffe **Club Colours:** Blue **Founded** 1965

Club Contact Details 01325 312 768

Previous Names: None
Previous Leagues: Wearside 1984-94, 2008-09. Darlington & District. Durham Alliance > 2008.
HONOURS
FA Comps: None
League: Darlington & District Division 'A' 2004-05. Durham Alliance 2007-08. Wearside 2008-09.
Northern Division Two 2010-11.

	10-11	11-12	12-13	13-14	14-15	15-16	16-17	17-18	18-19	19-20
	NL 2 1	NL 1 9	NL 1 17	NL 1 18	NL 1 18	NL 1 6	NL 1 9	NL 1 14	NL 1 12	NL 1 n&v
FAC		EP	EP	EPr	Pr	2Qr	EPr	P	EPr	EP
FAV	1Q	1Qr	1P	1Q	1Q	FAT 5P	3P	1Q	1Qr	2Q

GROUND: Moore Lane Park, Moore Lane, Newton Aycliffe, Co. Durham DL5 5AG
Capacity: **Seats:** Yes **Covered:** Yes
Nearest Railway Station Newton Aycliffe - 2km
Bus Route Shafto Way - stop 271m away

NORTH SHIELDS
Nickname: Robins **Club Colours:** All red **Founded** 1896

Club Contact Details 07929 336 645

Previous Names: North Shields Athletic 1896-15, Preston Colliery 1919-1928, North Shields FC 1928-92. North Shields Athletic 1995-99.
Previous Leagues: Northern Combination. Northern Alliance. North Eastern. Midland. Northern Counties/North Eastern 1960-64.
Northern 1964-89. Northern Counties East 1989-92. Wearside 1992-2004.
HONOURS
FA Comps: FA Amateur Cup 1968-69. FA Vase 2014-15.
League: Northern Alliance 1906-07, 07-08. North Eastern Div.2 28-29, Div.1 49-50. Northern Counties 60-61.
Northern Div.1 68-69, Div.2 2013-14. Northern Counties East Prem 91-92. Wearside 98-99, 01-02, 03-04.

	10-11	11-12	12-13	13-14	14-15	15-16	16-17	17-18	18-19	19-20
	NL 2 4	NL 2 8	NL 2 8	NL 2 1	NL 1 4	NL 1 5	NL 1 3	NL 1 8	NL 1 9	NL 1 n&v
FAC	Pr	EPr	EPr	EP	Pr	Pr	P	EPr	EP	EPr
FAV	1Q	1Q	1Q	1Pr	F	4P	3P	3P	1Q	1Q

GROUND: Daren Persson Staduim, West Percy Road, Chirton, North Shields NE29 6UA
Capacity: 1,500 **Seats:** Yes **Covered:** Yes
Nearest Railway Station Meadow Well - 392m
Bus Route Waterville Road - stop 29m away

NORTHALLERTON TOWN
Nickname: Town **Club Colours:** Black & white Founded 1994

Club Contact Details 01609 778 337

Previous Names: Northallerton FC 1994.
Previous Leagues: Harrogate & District.
HONOURS
FA Comps: None
League: Northern Division Two 1996-97.

	10-11	11-12	12-13	13-14	14-15	15-16	16-17	17-18	18-19	19-20
	NL 2 9	NL 2 9	NL 2 6	NL 2 7	NL 2 10	NL 2 8	NL 2 9	NL 2 4	NL 2 3	NL 1 n&v
FAC	1Q	P	EP	EP	P		P	P	EP	P
FAV	1P	2Q	1Pr	1Q	1Q	1Q	2Q	2Q	2Q	2Q

GROUND: The Calvert Stadium, Ainderby Road, Northallerton DL7 8HJ
Capacity:　　**Seats:** 200　**Covered:** 400
Nearest Railway Station Northallerton - 0.3km
Bus Route Chantry Road - stop 81m away

PENRITH
Nickname: Blues **Club Colours:** All blue Founded 1894

Club Contact Details 01768 865 990　　　　ianwhite77@hotmail.com

Previous Names: Penrith 1894-2007. Penrith Town 2007-08. Back to Penrith after a merger with Penrith United.
Previous Leagues: North Eastern. Northern 1947-82. North West Counties 1982-87, 90-97. Northern Premier League 1987-90.
HONOURS
FA Comps: None
League: Northern Division Two 2002-03, 07-08.

	10-11	11-12	12-13	13-14	14-15	15-16	16-17	17-18	18-19	19-20
	NL 1 17	NL 1 19	NL 1 13	NL 1 13	NL 1 14	NL 1 14	NL 1 12	NL 1 17	NL 1 18	NL 1 n&v
FAC	EP	1Q	EP	3Q	EP	EP	Pr	Pr	EP	EP
FAV	2Q	2Q	1P	1P	1Q	1Q	3P	2Q	2Q	1Q

GROUND: The Frenchfield Stadium, Carleton, Frenchfield, Penrith CA11 8UA
Capacity: 1,500　**Seats:** 200　**Covered:** 1,000　**Shop:** No
Nearest Railway Station Penrith North Lakes - 2.3km
Bus Route Oak Road - stop 727m away

RYHOPE COLLIERY WELFARE
Nickname: Colliery Welfare **Club Colours:** Red & white Founded 1892

Club Contact Details 07961 767 957

Previous Names: Vaux Ryhope 1988-92 (After merging with Sporting Club Vaux - previously South Hetton).
Previous Leagues: Wearside >2012, 2013-14. Northern 2012-13.
HONOURS
FA Comps: None
League: Wearside 1927-28, 61-62, 62-63, 63-64, 65-66, 2010-11, 11-12.

	10-11	11-12	12-13	13-14	14-15	15-16	16-17	17-18	18-19	19-20
	Wear 1	Wear 1	NL 2 2	Wear 2	NL 2 6	NL 2 2	NL 1 17	NL 1 11	NL 1 11	NL 1 n&v
FAC						EPr	EPr	EP	EP	EPr
FAV					2P	1Q	2P	2P	2Q	2P

GROUND: Ryhope Recreation Park, Ryhope Street, Ryhope, Sunderland SR2 0AB
Capacity:　　**Seats:** Yes　**Covered:** Yes
Nearest Railway Station Sunderland - 3.8km
Bus Route Ryhope Street-post office - stop 79m away

SEAHAM RED STAR
Nickname: The Star   **Club Colours:** Red & white   Founded 1973

Club Contact Details 07834 473 001

Previous Names: Seaham Colliery Welfare Red Star 1978-87.
Previous Leagues: Houghton & District 1973-74. Northern Alliance 1974-79. Wearside 1979-83.
HONOURS
FA Comps: None
League: Wearside 1981-82.
Northern League Division Two 2014-15.

10-11	11-12	12-13	13-14	14-15	15-16	16-17	17-18	18-19	19-20
NL 2 17	NL 2 20	NL 2 10	NL 2 4	NL 2 1	NL 1 9	NL 1 14	NL 1 18	NL 1 14	NL 1 n&v
FAC EP			FAC EP	FAC P	FAC EPr	FAC EP	FAC EP	FAC P	FAC 1Q
FAV 1Q	FAV 1Q	FAV 1Q	FAV 1Q	FAV 3P	FAV 3P	FAV 1Q	FAV 2Q	FAV 1P	FAV 1P

GROUND: Seaham Town Park, Stockton Road, Seaham, Co.Durham SR7 0HP
Capacity: 500   **Seats:** Yes   **Covered:** Yes
Nearest Railway Station Seaham - 1.5km
Bus Route Mill Inn (Stockton Rd) - stop 201m away

SHILDON
Nickname: Railwaymen   **Club Colours:** Red   Founded 1890

Club Contact Details 01388 773 877

Previous Names: Shildon Athletic > 1923.
Previous Leagues: Auckland & Dist 1892-86, Wear Valley 1896-97, Northern 1903-07, North Eastern 1907-32
HONOURS
FA Comps: None
League: Northern 1933-34, 34-35, 35-36,36-37, 39-40, 2015-16, Division Two 2001-02.

10-11	11-12	12-13	13-14	14-15	15-16	16-17	17-18	18-19	19-20
NL 1 5	NL 1 10	NL 1 8	NL 1 3	NL 1 2	NL 1 1	NL 1 4	NL 1 3	NL 1 6	NL 1 n&v
FAC 3Q	FAC 1Qr	FAC 2Q	FAC P	FAC 4Qr	FAC EPr	FAC 2Q	FAC 4Q	FAC P	FAC EP
FAV 3P	FAV 1P	FAV SF	FAV 2P	FAV 3P	FAV 1P	FAV 4P	FAV 2P	FAV 3P	FAV 2P

GROUND: Dean Street, Shildon, Co. Durham DL4 1HA
Capacity: 4,000   **Seats:** 480   **Covered:** 1000
Nearest Railway Station Shildon - 1.2km
Bus Route St. Johns Church - stop 149m away

STOCKTON TOWN
Nickname: **Club Colours:** Yellow and blue   Founded 1979

Club Contact Details 01642 604 915

Previous Names: Hartburn Juniors 1979-2003.
Previous Leagues: Teeside 2009-10. Wearside 2010-2016.
HONOURS
FA Comps: None
League: Wearside 2012-13, 13-14, 14-15,15-16. Northern Division Two 2016-17.

10-11	11-12	12-13	13-14	14-15	15-16	16-17	17-18	18-19	19-20
Wear 10	Wear 3	Wear 1	Wear 1	Wear 1	Wear 1	NL 2 1	NL 1 6	NL 1 7	NL 1 n&v
							FAC EP	FAC EPr	FAC 2Q
						FAV 2P	FAV F	FAV 3P	FAV 4P

GROUND: Bishopton Road West, Stockton-on-Tees TS19 0QD
Capacity: **Seats:** Yes   **Covered:** Yes
Nearest Railway Station Stockton - 1.4km
Bus Route Whitehouse Drive - stop 101m away

SUNDERLAND RYHOPE C.A.
Nickname: The CA   Club Colours: Red & white

Founded 1961

Club Contact Details
Previous Names: Ryhope Youth Club 1961-71. Ryhope Community Association 1971-99. Kennek Ryhope CA 1999-2007.
Previous Leagues: Seham & District. Houghton & District. Northern Alliance 1978-82.
HONOURS
FA Comps: None
League: None

	10-11	11-12	12-13	13-14	14-15	15-16	16-17	17-18	18-19	19-20
NL	NL 1 13	NL 1 4	NL 1 22	NL 1 19	NL 1 16	NL 1 13	NL 1 11	NL 1 4	NL 1 5	NL 1 n&v
FAC	FAC EP	FAC P	FAC EPr	FAC EP	FAC EPr	FAC EPr	FAC EP	FAC 2Q	FAC Pr	FAC 1Qr
FAV	FAV 1Q	FAV 1P	FAV 2P	FAV 1P	FAV 2P	FAV 5P	FAV 5P	FAV 2Pr	FAV 4P	FAV 2P

GROUND: Meadow Park, Beachbrooke, Stockton Road, Ryhope, Sunderland SR2 0NZ
Capacity: 1,500   **Seats:** 150   **Covered:** 200
Nearest Railway Station Seaham - 3.3km
Bus Route Ryhope Hospital - 94m away

THORNABY
Nickname: The Blues   Club Colours: All blue

Founded 1980

Club Contact Details 01642 672 896
Previous Names: Stockton Cricket Club 1965-1980, Stockton 1980-99 and Thornaby-on-Tees 1999-2000
Previous Leagues: Wearside 1980-85.
HONOURS
FA Comps: None
League: Northern Division Two 1987-88, 91-92.

	10-11	11-12	12-13	13-14	14-15	15-16	16-17	17-18	18-19	19-20
NL	NL 2 14	NL 2 19	NL 2 19	NL 2 14	NL 2 7	NL 2 7	NL 2 16	NL 2 6	NL 2 2	NL 1 n&v
FAC						FAC EP	FAC EP			FAC 1Qr
FAV	FAV 1Q	FAV 1Q	FAV 1Q	FAV 1Q	FAV 1Q	FAV 1Q	FAV 1Q	FAV 2P	FAV 1Q	FAV 2P

GROUND: Teesdale Park, Acklam Road, Thornaby, Cleveland TS17 7JU
Capacity: **Seats:**   **Covered:**
Nearest Railway Station Thornaby - 1.2km
Bus Route Millfield Close - stop 143m away

WEST AUCKLAND TOWN
Nickname: West   Club Colours: Yellow and black

Founded 1893

Club Contact Details
Previous Names: West Auckland 1893-1914.
Previous Leagues: Wear Valley 1896-1900. South Durham Alliance 1900-05. Mid Durham 1905-08.
HONOURS
FA Comps: None
League: Northern 1959-60, 60-61, Division Two 1990-91.

	10-11	11-12	12-13	13-14	14-15	15-16	16-17	17-18	18-19	19-20
NL	NL 1 6	NL 1 2	NL 1 4	NL 1 5	NL 1 5	NL 1 17	NL 1 18	NL 1 5	NL 1 8	NL 1 n&v
FAC	FAC 2Q	FAC EPr	FAC 2Qr	FAC 3Qr	FAC Pr	FAC P	FAC P	FAC EP	FAC P	FAC EP
FAV	FAV 2P	FAV F	FAV F	FAV F	FAV 2P	FAV 1P	FAV 2Q	FAV 4P	FAV QF	FAV 5P

GROUND: Darlington Road, West Auckland, Co. Durham DL14 9AQ
Capacity: 2,000   **Seats:** 250   **Covered:** 250
Nearest Railway Station Bishop Auckland - 4.1km
Bus Route Oakley Grange Farm - stop 128m away

WHICKHAM
Nickname: The Home Guard   **Club Colours:** Black & white

Founded 1944

Club Contact Details 0191 420 0186

Previous Names: Founded as Axwell Park Colliery Welfare.
Previous Leagues: Derwent Valley. Northern Combination. Wearside 1974-88.
HONOURS
FA Comps: FA Vase 1980-81.
League: Northern Combination 1969-70, 72-73, 73-74.
Wearside 1977-78, 87-88. Northern Division Two 1994-95.

	10-11		11-12		12-13		13-14		14-15		15-16		16-17		17-18		18-19		19-20	
NL	2	6	2	15	2	16	2	8	2	8	2	12	2	6	2	3	1	17	1	n&v
FAC			EP						P		EP						EP		P	
FAV		1Q		1Q				4P		2P		2Q		1Q		1P		1P		1Q

GROUND: Glebe Sports Club, Rectory Lane, Whickham NE16 4PF
Capacity: 4,000 **Seats:** Yes **Covered:** Yes
Nearest Railway Station Metrocentre - 2.1km
Bus Route Whaggs Lane-south - stop 105m away

WHITLEY BAY
Nickname: The Seahorses   **Club Colours:** Blue & white

Founded 1897

Club Contact Details 0191 291 3637

Previous Names: Whitley Bay Athletic 1950-58
Previous Leagues: Tyneside 1909-10, Northern Alliance 1950-55, North Eastern 1955-58, Northern 1958-88. Northern Premier League 1988-00.
HONOURS
FA Comps: FA Vase 2001-02, 08-09, 09-10, 10-11.
League: Northern Alliance 1952-53, 53-54. Northern 1964-65, 65-66, 06-07.
Northern Premier League Division One 1990-91.

	10-11		11-12		12-13		13-14		14-15		15-16		16-17		17-18		18-19		19-20	
NL	1	3	1	6	1	3	1	10	1	15	1	16	1	6	1	16	1	13	1	n&v
FAC				3Q		P		EP		EPr		3Q		EPr		1Q		2Q		EP
FAV		F		5P		4P		3P		3P		2P		2Q		3P		2Q		1Q

GROUND: Hillheads Park, Rink Way, Whitley Bay NE25 8HR
Capacity: 4,500 **Seats:** 450 **Covered:** 650 **Shop:** Yes
Nearest Railway Station Monkseaton - 768m
Bus Route Whitley Bay Ice Rink - stop 149m away

DIVISION TWO

BEDLINGTON TERRIERS
Nickname: Terriers   Club Colours: All red.

Founded 1949

Club Contact Details 07935 840 277

HONOURS
FA Comps: None
League: Northern Combination 1954-55. Northern Alliance 1966-67.
Northern DivisioN Two 1993-94, Division One 97-98, 98-99, 99-00, 2000-01, 01-02.

10-11		11-12		12-13		13-14		14-15		15-16		16-17		17-18		18-19		19-20	
NL 1	9	NL 1	7	NL 1	15	NL 1	20	NL 1	17	NL 1	22	NL 2	12	NL 2	16	NL 2	14	NL 2	n&v
FAC	EP	FAC	2Q	FAC	1Q					FAC	EPr	FAC	EP						
FAV	1P	FAV	2P	FAV	2P					FAV	2Q	FAV	1Q	FAV	2P	FAV	2P	FAV	1Q

GROUND: Doctor Pitt Welfare Park, Park Road, Bedlington NE22 5DP
Nearest Railway Station Cramlington - 5km
Bus Route Allgood Terrace - stop 216m away

BILLINGHAM SYNTHONIA
Nickname: Synners   Club Colours: Green & white

Founded 1923

Club Contact Details 01642 530 203

HONOURS
FA Comps: None
League: Teeside 1936-37.
Northern 1956-57, 88-89, 89-90, 95-96. Division Two 86-87.

10-11		11-12		12-13		13-14		14-15		15-16		16-17		17-18		18-19		19-20	
NL 1	12	NL 1	11	NL 1	12	NL 1	20	NL 1	20	NL 2	5	NL 2	3	NL 1	22	NL 2	10	NL 2	n&v
FAC	P	FAC	P	FAC	EP	FAC	Pr	FAC	EP	FAC	EPr	FAC	1Qr	FAC	EP	FAC	EPr		
FAV	5P	FAV	5Pr	FAV	3P	FAV	3P	FAV	1P	FAV	2Q	FAV	1P	FAV	2Qr	FAV	2Q	FAV	2Q

GROUND: Norton (Teesside) Sports Complex, Station Road, Norton TS20 1PE
Nearest Railway Station Billingham - 2.7km
Bus Route Jameson Road - stop 400m away

BIRTLEY TOWN
Nickname: The Hoops   Club Colours: Green & white

Founded 1993

Club Contact Details

HONOURS
FA Comps: None
League: Wearside Division Two 1994-95, Division One 2002-03, 06-07.

10-11		11-12		12-13		13-14		14-15		15-16		16-17		17-18		18-19		19-20	
NL 2	13	NL 2	6	NL 2	17	NL 2	13	NL 2	17	NL 2	21	NAI P	8	NAI P	2	NL 2	13	NL 2	n&v
		FAC	EP	FAC	P														
FAV	1P	FAV	2Q	FAV	1Q	FAV	2Q	FAV	2Q	FAV	1Q	FAV	2Q			FAV	2Q	FAV	1Q

GROUND: Birtley Sports Complex, Durham Road, Birtley DH3 2TB
Nearest Railway Station Chester-Le-Street
Bus Route Numbers 21 & 81 stop near the ground

BRANDON UNITED
Nickname: United   Club Colours: All red

Founded 1968

Club Contact Details 07555 586 305

HONOURS
FA Comps: None
League: Durham & District Sunday Div.2 1969-70, Div.1 73-74, 74-75, 75-76, 76-77.
Northern Alliance Div.2 77-78, 78-79. Northern 2002-03, Div.2 84-85, 99-2000.

10-11		11-12		12-13		13-14		14-15		15-16		16-17		17-18		18-19		19-20	
NL 2	19	NL 2	17	NL 2	18	NL 2	19	NL 2	22	NL 2	15	NL 2	14	NL 2	19	NL 2	19	NL 2	n&v
FAC	EP																		
FAV	2Q	FAV	2Q	FAV	1Q			FAV	1Q	FAV	1Q	FAV	1Q	FAV	1Q	FAV	1P	FAV	1Q

GROUND: Welfare Park, Rear Commercial Street, Brandon DH7 8PL
Nearest Railway Station Durham - 4.4km
Bus Route S Lukes Church - stop 52m away

CARLISLE CITY
Nickname: Sky Blues Club Colours: All sky blue Founded 1975

Club Contact Details 01228 523 777

HONOURS
FA Comps: None
League: Northern Alliance Division One 1991-92.

10-11	11-12	12-13	13-14	14-15	15-16	16-17	17-18	18-19	19-20
NAI P 6	NAI P 5	NAI P 3	NAI P 2	NAI P 2	NAI P 3	NWC1 14	NWC1 11	NWC1N 6	NL 2 n&v
						FAV 1Q	FAV 2Q	FAV 2Q	FAV 1Q

GROUND: Petteril Bank Road, Carlisle CA1 3AF
Nearest Railway Station Carlisle - 1.9km
Bus Route Ridgemount Road stop - 321m away

CHESTER-LE-STREET TOWN
Nickname: Cestrians Club Colours: Blue & white Founded 1972

Club Contact Details 0191 388 7283

HONOURS
FA Comps: None
League: Washington 1975-76. Wearside 1980-81.
Northern Division Two 1983-84, 97-98.

10-11	11-12	12-13	13-14	14-15	15-16	16-17	17-18	18-19	19-20
NL 2 8	NL 2 12	NL 2 13	NL 2 11	NL 2 13	NL 2 3	NL 2 21	NL 2 14	NL 2 5	NL 2 n&v
FAC 1Q	FAC EPr	FAC EPr				FAC P	FAC EP		
FAV 2Q	FAV 1Q	FAV 2Q	FAV 1Q	FAV 2Q	FAV 1P	FAV 2P	FAV 1Q	FAV 1Q	FAV 1Q

GROUND: Moor Park, Chester Moor, Chester-le-Street, Co.Durham DH2 3RW
Nearest Railway Station Chester-le-Street - 2.2km
Bus Route Inn (A167) - stop 69m away

CROOK TOWN
Nickname: Black & Ambers Club Colours: Amber and black Founded 1889

Club Contact Details 01388 762 959

HONOURS
FA Comps: FA Am C 00-01,53-54, 58-59, 61-62, 63-64.
League: Northern 1914-15, 26-27, 52-53, 58-59, 62-63, Division Two 2012-13.

10-11	11-12	12-13	13-14	14-15	15-16	16-17	17-18	18-19	19-20
NL 2 12	NL 2 10	NL 2 1	NL 1 15	NL 1 22	NL 2 18	NL 2 17	NL 2 18	NL 2 9	NL 2 n&v
FAC P	FAC EP	FAC Pr	FAC 1Q	FAC EP	FAC EP				
FAV 2Q	FAV 2P	FAV 1Q	FAV 2P	FAV 2Q	FAV 1Q	FAV 1Q	FAV 2Q	FAV 2Q	FAV 1P

GROUND: The Sir Tom Cowie Millfield, West Road, Crook, Co.Durham DL15 9PW

Bus Route Bus stops right outside the ground

DURHAM CITY
Nickname: City Club Colours: Yellow/blue/yellow Founded 1949

Club Contact Details 01388 745 912

HONOURS
FA Comps: None
League: Northern 1994-95, 2007-08, Division Two 98-99.
Northern Premier Division One North 2008-09.

10-11	11-12	12-13	13-14	14-15	15-16	16-17	17-18	18-19	19-20
NP1N 17	NP1N 9	NL 1 14	NL 1 9	NL 1 12	NL 1 20	NL 2 10	NL 2 11	NL 2 20	NL 2 n&v
FAC 1Q	FAC P	FAC 1Q	FAC Pr	FAC P	FAC EP	FAC EP			
FAT 1Q	FAT 2Qr	FAV 1P	FAV 2Q	FAV 2Q	FAV 1P	FAV 1Q	FAV 2Q	FAV 1Q	FAV 2Q

GROUND: Hall Lane, Willington, County Durham DL15 0QG
Nearest Railway Station Durham
Bus Route Mortons Garage - stop 174m away

EASINGTON COLLIERY
Nickname: The Colliery   **Club Colours:** All green   Founded 1913

Club Contact Details

HONOURS

FA Comps: None

League: Wearside 1929-30, 31-32, 32-33, 47-48, 48-49.

	10-11	11-12	12-13	13-14	14-15	15-16	16-17	17-18	18-19	19-20
	Wear 2	NL 2 22	Wear 21	Wear 6	Wear 2	NL 2 6	NL 2 7	NL 2 10	NL 2 16	NL 2 n&v
FAC							FAC EP			
FAV	FAV 1P	FAV 2Q				FAV 2Q	FAV 1P	FAV 1Q		FAV 2Q

GROUND: Memorial Avenue, Seaside Lane, Easington Colliery SR8 3PL

Bus Route Black Diamond - stop 43m away

ESH WINNING
Nickname: Stags   **Club Colours:** Yellow and green   Founded 1885

Club Contact Details 07432 648 072

HONOURS

FA Comps: None

League: Northern 1912-13.
Durham & District Sunday 1978-79, 79-80, Division Two 72-73.

	10-11	11-12	12-13	13-14	14-15	15-16	16-17	17-18	18-19	19-20
	NL 1 21	NL 2 11	NL 2 20	NL 2 22	NL 2 20	NL 2 20	NL 2 21	NL 2 13	NL 2 17	NL 2 n&v
FAC	FAC EP	FAC EP	FAC P							
FAV	FAV 2Qr	FAV 2Q	FAV 2P	FAV 1Q	FAV 2Q	FAV 1Q	FAV 2Q	FAV 1Q	FAV 1Q	FAV 2Q

GROUND: West Terrace, Waterhouse, Durham DH7 9BQ

Bus Route Church (Russell St) - stop 158m away

HEATON STANNINGTON
Nickname: The Stan   **Club Colours:** Black & white stripes   Founded 1910

Club Contact Details 0191 281 9230

HONOURS

FA Comps: None

League: Northern Amateur 1936-37, 85-86. Tyneside Amateur 1983-84.
Northern Alliance Premier Division 2011-12, 12-13.

	10-11	11-12	12-13	13-14	14-15	15-16	16-17	17-18	18-19	19-20
	NAI P 5	NAI P 1	NAI P 1	NL 2 5	NL 2 9	NL 2 9	NL 2 4	NL 2 5	NL 2 4	NL 2 n&v
FAC						FAC P	FAC EP	FAC P	FAC EPr	
FAV					FAV 2Q	FAV 2Q	FAV 2Q	FAV 1Q	FAV 1Q	FAV 1Q

GROUND: Grounsell Park, Newton Road, Newcastle upon Tyne NE7 7HP

Nearest Railway Station Longbenton - 1.2km

Bus Route No.38 stops at the ground

JARROW
Nickname: **Club Colours:** Royal blue & white   Founded 1894

Club Contact Details 0191 489 3743

HONOURS

FA Comps: None

League: Northern Alliance 1898-99. Wearside 2016-17.

	10-11	11-12	12-13	13-14	14-15	15-16	16-17	17-18	18-19	19-20
	Wear 5	Wear 6	Wear 9	Wear 10	Wear 12	Wear 8	Wear 1	NL 2 12	NL 2 11	NL 2 n&v
FAV									FAV 1Q	FAV 1P

GROUND: Perth Green Community Assoc., Inverness Road, Jarrow NE32 4AQ

Nearest Railway Station Brockley Whins - 530m

Bus Route Inverness Road-youth club - stop 75m away

NEWCASTLE UNIVERSITY

Nickname: Club Colours: Blue   Founded

Club Contact Details 07971 852 468

HONOURS
FA Comps: None
League: Northern Alliance Premier Division 2017-18.

10-11	11-12	12-13	13-14	14-15	15-16	16-17	17-18	18-19	19-20
NAI 1 4	NAI 1 8	NAI 1 13	NAI 1 7	NAI 1 8	NAI 1 2	NAI P 2	NAI P 1	NAI P 2	NL 2 n&v
									FAV 1Q

GROUND: Kimberley Park, Broomhouse Road NE42 5EH
Nearest Railway Station Newcastle
Bus Route No.686 stops 50 metres to the East on Broomhouse Road.

REDCAR ATHLETIC

Nickname: Club Colours: Red and navy   Founded 1993

Club Contact Details 01642 470 963

HONOURS
FA Comps: None
League: Wearside 2017-18.

10-11	11-12	12-13	13-14	14-15	15-16	16-17	17-18	18-19	19-20
Wear 4	Wear 2	Wear 5	Wear 3	Wear 4	Wear 2	Wear 2	Wear 1	NL 2 7	NL 2 n&v
								FAV 2Q	FAV 1Q

GROUND: Green Lane, Redcar TS10 3RW
Nearest Railway Station Redcar
Bus Route X3 & X4

RYTON & CRAWCROOK ALBION

Nickname: The Albion   Club Colours: Black & royal blue   Founded 1970

Club Contact Details 0191 413 4448

HONOURS
FA Comps: None
League: Northern Alliance Division One 1996-97.

10-11	11-12	12-13	13-14	14-15	15-16	16-17	17-18	18-19	19-20
NL 1 22	NL 2 18	NL 2 14	NL 2 21	NL 2 12	NL 2 16	NL 2 20	NL 2 17	NL 2 12	NL 2 n&v
FAC EP	FAC EP								
FAV 2Q	FAV 2Q	FAV 2Q	FAV 2Q	FAV 1Qr	FAV 1Q	FAV 2Q	FAV 1Q	FAV 2Q	FAV 2Q

GROUND: Kingsley Park, Stannerford Road, Crawcrook NE40 3SN
Nearest Railway Station Wylam - 1.5km
Bus Route Stannerford Road - stop 121m away

SUNDERLAND WEST END

Nickname: Club Colours: Red & white   Founded

Club Contact Details

HONOURS
FA Comps: None
League: None

10-11	11-12	12-13	13-14	14-15	15-16	16-17	17-18	18-19	19-20
Wear 19	Wear 4	Wear 8	Wear 9	Wear 8	Wear 3	Wear 10	Wear 3	Wear 2	NL 2 n&v
									FAV 2Q

GROUND: Washington Road, Sunderland, Tyne & Wear SR5 3NS

TOW LAW TOWN
Nickname: Lawyers **Club Colours:** Black & white **Founded** 1890

Club Contact Details 01388 731 443

HONOURS
FA Comps: None
League: Northern 1923-24, 24-25, 94-95.

10-11	11-12	12-13	13-14	14-15	15-16	16-17	17-18	18-19	19-20
NL 1 18	NL 1 21	NL 2 11	NL 2 10	NL 2 21	NL 2 14	NL 2 13	NL 2 8	NL 2 15	NL 2 n&v
FAC EP	FAC EP	FAC EP	FAC EP						
FAV 1P	FAV 2Q	FAV 1Q	FAV 1Q	FAV 1Q	FAV 2Q	FAV 1Q	FAV 2P	FAV 2Q	FAV 1Q

GROUND: Ironworks Ground, Tow Law, Bishop Auckland DL13 4EQ
Nearest Railway Station Wolsingham - 4.8km
Bus Route Mart (Castle Bank) - stop 241m away

WASHINGTON
Nickname: Mechanics **Club Colours:** All red **Founded** 1947

Club Contact Details

HONOURS
FA Comps: None
League: North Eastern Division Two 1927-28. Washington Amateur 1955-56, 56-57,57-58, 58-59, 59-60, 61-62,62-63.

10-11	11-12	12-13	13-14	14-15	15-16	16-17	17-18	18-19	19-20
NL 2 16	NL 2 14	NL 2 12	NL 2 9	NL 2 2	NL 1 10	NL 1 19	NL 1 21	NL 2 18	NL 2 n&v
		FAC EP		FAC P	FAC 2Qr	FAC 1Q	FAC EP	FAC EP	
FAV 1P	FAV 1Q	FAV 2Q	FAV 2Q	FAV 2Q	FAV 2Q	FAV 1Q	FAV 2Q	FAV 2Q	FAV 1Q

GROUND: New Ferens Park, Belmont, Durham DH1 1GG

WEST ALLOTMENT CELTIC
Nickname: Celtic **Club Colours:** Green & white **Founded** 1928

Club Contact Details 0191 250 7008

HONOURS
FA Comps: None
League: Northern Am. 1956-57, 57-58, 58-59, 59-60, 81-82, 82-83, Div 2: 38-39.
Northern All. 1986-87, 90-91, 91-92, 97-98, 98-99, 99-2000, 01-02, 03-04. Northern Div 2 2004-05

10-11	11-12	12-13	13-14	14-15	15-16	16-17	17-18	18-19	19-20
NL 1 20	NL 2 7	NL 2 7	NL 2 2	NL 1 19	NL 1 19	NL 1 22	NL 2 15	NL 2 6	NL 2 n&v
FAC EP	FAC EPr	FAC P	FAC EP	FAC 1Q	FAC EP	FAC EP	FAC EP		
FAV 2Q	FAV 1Q	FAV 1Q	FAV 2Q	FAV 1P	FAV 2Q	FAV 1Q	FAV 1Q	FAV 2Q	FAV 1P

GROUND: Druid Park, Callerton Lane, Woolsington NE13 8DF
Nearest Railway Station Callerton Parkway - 116m
Bus Route Bus stops 70m from the ground.

WILLINGTON
Nickname: The Blue & Whites **Club Colours:** Blue & white **Founded** 1906

Club Contact Details 01388 745 912

HONOURS
FA Comps: FA Amateur Cup 1949-50.
League: Northern 1913-14, 25-26, 29-30.

10-11	11-12	12-13	13-14	14-15	15-16	16-17	17-18	18-19	19-20
Wear 14	Wear 5	Wear 2	NL 2 15	NL 2 11	NL 2 19	NL 2 18	NL 2 7	NL 2 8	NL 2 n&v
FAV 1Q	FAV 2Q	FAV 2Q	FAV 2Q	FAV 1Q	FAV 1Q	FAV 1Q	FAV 2Q	FAV 1Qr	FAV 1Q

GROUND: Hall Lane, Willington, Co. Durham DL15 0QG

Bus Route Police House - stop 129m away

AXMINSTER TOWN

Nickname: The Tigers   Club Colours: Amber and black

Founded 1903

Club Contact Details martinkeightly@gmail.com

HONOURS
FA Comps: None
League: None

10-11	11-12	12-13	13-14	14-15	15-16	16-17	17-18	18-19	19-20
SW1E 16	SW1E 16	SW1E 11	SW1E 12	SW1E 18	SW1E 8	SW1E 6	SW1E 10	SW1E 6	SWPE n&v
							FAV 1Q	FAV 2Q	FAV 2Q

GROUND: Tiger Way EX13 5HN
Nearest Railway Station Axminster
Bus Route 885 & 30

BOVEY TRACEY

Nickname: Moorlanders   Club Colours: Red and black

Founded 1950

Club Contact Details boveytraceyafc@aol.com

HONOURS
FA Comps: None
League: None

10-11	11-12	12-13	13-14	14-15	15-16	16-17	17-18	18-19	19-20
SWPP 17	SWPP 16	SWPP 15	SWPP 15	SWPP 19	SW1E 16	SW1E 13	SW1E 3	SW1E 2	SWPE n&v
									FAV 1P

GROUND: Mill Marsh Park, Ashburton Rd, Bovey TQ13 9FF
Nearest Railway Station Newton Abbot
Bus Route 178 & 39

BRIXHAM AFC

Nickname: The Blues   Club Colours: All blue

Founded 2012

Club Contact Details jwharris@talktalk.net

HONOURS
FA Comps: None
League: None

10-11	11-12	12-13	13-14	14-15	15-16	16-17	17-18	18-19	19-20
		SDevP 4	SDevP 2	SW1E 9	SW1E 9	SW1E 5	SW1E 13	SW1E 3	SWPE n&v

GROUND: Wall Park Road TQ5 9UE
Nearest Railway Station Paignton
Bus Route 92

CREDITON UNITED

Nickname: The Kirton   Club Colours: All yellow

Founded 1910

Club Contact Details 01363 774 671

HONOURS
FA Comps: None
League: None

10-11	11-12	12-13	13-14	14-15	15-16	16-17	17-18	18-19	19-20
SW1E 15	SW1E 4	SW1E 16	SW1E 6	SW1E 11	SW1E 14	SW1E 8	SW1E 6	SW1E 10	SWPE n&v
FAV 1Qr	FAV 2Q	FAV 1Q		FAV 1P	FAV 2Q	FAV 1Q	FAV 1P	FAV 1Q	FAV 1Q

GROUND: Lords Meadow, Commercial Road, Crediton EX17 1ER
Nearest Railway Station Crediton
Bus Route 5 & 5B

CULLOMPTON RANGERS
Nickname: The Cully Club Colours: Red & black

Founded 1945

Club Contact Details 01884 33090 alanslark1@gmail.com

HONOURS
FA Comps: None
League: East Devon Senior Division One 1950-51, 78-79.
Devon & Exeter Premier Division 1961-62, 63-64.

10-11		11-12		12-13		13-14		14-15		15-16		16-17		17-18		18-19		19-20	
SWPP	16	SWPP	15	SWPP	17	SWPP	18	SWPP	12	SWPP	13	SWPP	9	SWPP	13	SWPP	8	SWPE	n&v
FAV	2Q	FAV	2P	FAV	2Q	FAV	2Q	FAV	1Q	FAV	1Q	FAV	2Pr	FAV	2P	FAV	2Q	FAV	1P

GROUND: Speeds Meadow, Cullompton EX15 1DW
Nearest Railway Station Tiverton Parkway
Bus Route Falcon - alight at The Weary Traveller, 20min walk from there.

DARTMOUTH AFC
Nickname: The Darts Club Colours: Red & white

Founded 1999

Club Contact Details 01803 832 902

HONOURS
FA Comps: None
League: Devon 2001-02, 02-03, 06-07. South Devon Division One 2013-14.

10-11		11-12		12-13		13-14		14-15		15-16		16-17		17-18		18-19		19-20	
SWPP	18	SWPP	14	SDev1	4	SDev1	1	SDevP	3	SDevP	2	SDevP	5	SDevP	6	SDevP	3	SWPE	n&v

GROUND: Longcross, Dartmouth TQ5 9LW
Nearest Railway Station Totnes
Bus Route 3, 120

ELBURTON VILLA
Nickname: The Villa Club Colours: Red & white stripes

Founded 1982

Club Contact Details 01752 480 025 pope.n@sky.com

HONOURS
FA Comps: None
League: Plymouth & District Division One 1990-91.

10-11		11-12		12-13		13-14		14-15		15-16		16-17		17-18		18-19		19-20	
SWPP	19	SWPP	11	SWPP	3	SWPP	12	SWPP	18	SWPP	20	SW1W	2	SW1W	3	SWPP	15	SWPE	n&v
								FAV	1Q	FAV	1Q	FAV	1Q	FAV	1Q	FAV	1P	FAV	1Q

GROUND: Haye Road, Elburton, Plymouth PL9 8HS
Nearest Railway Station Plymouth

ELMORE
Nickname: Eagles Club Colours: All green

Founded 1947

Club Contact Details 01884 252 341

HONOURS
FA Comps: None
League: Devon & Exeter Premier Division 2017-18.

10-11		11-12		12-13		13-14		14-15		15-16		16-17		17-18		18-19		19-20	
West1	19	West1	14	West1	12	SWPP	17	SWPP	Exp	D&EP	5	D&EP	3	D&EP	1	SW1E	5	SWPE	n&v
FAC	EP			FAC	EP														
FAV	1Q	FAV	2Q	FAV	1Q	FAV	1Qr	FAV	1Q										

GROUND: Horsdon Park, Heathcoat Way, Tiverton, Devon EX16 6DB
Nearest Railway Station Tiverton Parkway

HOLSWORTHY AFC

Nickname: The Magpies   **Club Colours:** Black & white   **Founded** 1891

Club Contact Details 01409 254 295

HONOURS
FA Comps: None
League: None

10-11	11-12	12-13	13-14	14-15	15-16	16-17	17-18	18-19	19-20
SW1W 10	SW1W 15	SW1W 13	SW1W 15	SW1W 13	SW1W 11	SW1W 15	SW1W 11	SW1E 8	SWPE n&v

GROUND: Upcott Field, North Road, Holsworthy EX22 6HF

Bus Route 85

HONITON TOWN

Nickname: The Hippos   **Club Colours:** Red & black   **Founded**

Club Contact Details 01404 42379   alanmackay2009@hotmail.com

HONOURS
FA Comps: None
League: Devon & Exeter Division One 2014-15, Premier Division 16-17.

10-11	11-12	12-13	13-14	14-15	15-16	16-17	17-18	18-19	19-20
D&E1 13	D&E2 8	D&E2 5	D&E1 2	D&E1 1	D&EP 3	D&EP 1	SW1E 14	SW1E 14	SWPE n&v

GROUND: Moutbatten Park, Ottery Moor Lane, Honiton EX14 1AW
Nearest Railway Station Honiton

ILFRACOMBE TOWN

Nickname: Bluebirds   **Club Colours:** All blue   **Founded** 1902

Club Contact Details 01271 865 939   afalcock@aol.com

HONOURS
FA Comps:
League: North Devon Premier Division 2016-17.

10-11	11-12	12-13	13-14	14-15	15-16	16-17	17-18	18-19	19-20
WestP 3	WestP 11	WestP 16	WestP 18	NDevP 6	NDevP 6	NDevP 1	SW1E 7	SW1E 8	SWPE n&v
FAC P	FAC EP	FAC EP	FAC P						
FAV 1P	FAV 3Pr	FAV 1Q	FAV 1Q	FAV 2Q				FAV 1Q	FAV 1Q

GROUND: Marlborough Park, Ilfracombe, Devon EX34 8PD
Nearest Railway Station Barnstaple

IVYBRIDGE TOWN

Nickname: The Ivys   **Club Colours:** Green & black   **Founded** 1925

Club Contact Details 01752 896 686   secretary@ivybridgefc.com

HONOURS
FA Comps: None
League: Devon County 2005-06.

10-11	11-12	12-13	13-14	14-15	15-16	16-17	17-18	18-19	19-20
SWPP 7	SWPP 19	SWPP 13	SWPP 4	SWPP 4	SWPP 9	SWPP 17	SWPP 18	SWPP 12	SWPE n&v
					FAV 2Q	FAV 1Q	FAV 1P	FAV 2P	FAV 2Q

GROUND: Erme Valley, Ermington Road, Ivybridge PL21 9ES
Nearest Railway Station Ivybridge - 1.8km
Bus Route Community Centre - stop 251m away

MILLBROOK AFC
Nickname: Magpies / Brook   **Club Colours:** Black & white

Founded 1888

Club Contact Details 01752 822 113

HONOURS
FA Comps: None
League: South West Peninsula Division One West 2017-18.

10-11	11-12	12-13	13-14	14-15	15-16	16-17	17-18	18-19	19-20
EC1 5	EC1 2	ECP 6	ECP 3	SW1W 15	SW1W 13	SW1W 4	SW1W 1	SWPP 10	SWPE n&v
									FAV 1Q

GROUND: Jenkins Park PL10 1EN

NEWTON ABBOT SPURS
Nickname: The Spurs   **Club Colours:**

Founded 1938

Club Contact Details 01626 365 343

HONOURS
FA Comps: None
League: None

10-11	11-12	12-13	13-14	14-15	15-16	16-17	17-18	18-19	19-20
SW1E 14	SW1E 9	SW1E 4	SW1E 11	SW1E 17	SW1E 7	SW1E 4	SW1E 2	SW1E 12	SWPE n&v
								FAV 2Q	FAV 1P

GROUND: Recreation Ground, Marsh Road, Newton Abbot TQ12 2AR
Nearest Railway Station Newton Abbot

PLYMOUTH MAJON
Nickname: The Johnies   **Club Colours:** Blue and black

Founded

Club Contact Details

HONOURS
FA Comps: None
League: Plymouth & West Devon Premier Division 2015-16.

10-11	11-12	12-13	13-14	14-15	15-16	16-17	17-18	18-19	19-20
	PWDevP 6	PWDevP 4	PWDevP 8	PWDevP	PWDevP 1	SW1W 10	SW1W 12	SW1W 9	SWPE n&v

GROUND: University of Mark & St Johns, Derriford Road PL6 8BH
Nearest Railway Station Plymouth

SIDMOUTH TOWN
Nickname: The Vikings   **Club Colours:** Green and black

Founded 1895

Club Contact Details 01395 577 087

HONOURS
FA Comps: None
League: Devon & Exeter Premier Division 2010-11

10-11	11-12	12-13	13-14	14-15	15-16	16-17	17-18	18-19	19-20
D&EP 1	SW1E 14	SW1E 15	SW1E 13	SW1E 10	SW1E 12	SW1E 11	SW1E 11	SW1E 9	SWPE n&v
								FAV 1P	FAV 2Q

GROUND: Manstone Recreation Ground, Manstone Lane, Sidmouth EX10 9TF
Nearest Railway Station Sidmouth

STOKE GABRIEL

Nickname: The Railwaymen   **Club Colours:** Maroon & blue

Founded 1905

Club Contact Details 01803 782 913

HONOURS
FA Comps: None
League: Devon County 1994-95, 96-97.
South West Peninsula Division One East 2013-14, 16-17, 18-19.

10-11	11-12	12-13	13-14	14-15	15-16	16-17	17-18	18-19	19-20
SW1E 3	SW1E 2	SW1E 2	SW1E 1	SWPP 14	SWPP 19	SW1E 1	SWPP 12	SW1E 1	SWPE n&v

GROUND: G J Churchward Memorial TQ9 6RR
Nearest Railway Station Paignton - 4.3km
Bus Route Ramslade Touring Park - stop 344m away

TORPOINT ATHLETIC

Nickname: The Point   **Club Colours:** Yellow & black

Founded 1887

Club Contact Details 01752 812 889   robbietafc81@live.co.uk

HONOURS
FA Comps: None
League: South Western 1964-65, 66-67.

10-11	11-12	12-13	13-14	14-15	15-16	16-17	17-18	18-19	19-20
SWPP 4	SWPP 12	SWPP 14	SWPP 10	SWPP 13	SWPP 8	SWPP 12	SWPP 11	SWPP 7	SWPE n&v
FAC 1Q	FAC P	FAC EP		FAC EP					
FAV QF	FAV 2P		FAV 1Q	FAV 2Q	FAV 2P	FAV 3P	FAV 1Q	FAV 1P	FAV 1P

GROUND: The Mill, Mill Lane, Carbeile Road, Torpoint PL11 2RE
Nearest Railway Station Dockyard (plymouth) - 2.5km
Bus Route Carbeile Inn - stop 338m away

TORRIDGESIDE

Nickname: T-Side   **Club Colours:** Claret and blue

Founded 1989

Club Contact Details andreasussex@btinternet.com

HONOURS
FA Comps: None
League: North Devon Premier Division 2012-13.

10-11	11-12	12-13	13-14	14-15	15-16	16-17	17-18	18-19	19-20
NDevP 6	NDevP 5	NDevP 1	NDevP 8	NDevP 3	NDevP 2	SW1E 7	SW1E 8	SW1E 4	SWPE n&v

GROUND: Donnacroft, Torrington EX38 7HT

TORRINGTON

Nickname: The Super Greens   **Club Colours:** All green

Founded 1908

Club Contact Details cm@torringtonafc.co.uk

HONOURS
FA Comps: None
League: Western Division One 2002-03. North Devon Senior Division 2008-09.

10-11	11-12	12-13	13-14	14-15	15-16	16-17	17-18	18-19	19-20
NDevP 8	NDevP 15	NDevP 2	NDevP 3	NDevP 10	NDevP 4	NDevP 7	NDevP 7	NDevP 5	SWPE n&v

GROUND: Vicarage Field, Torrington EX38 7AJ

PREMIER WEST

BODMIN TOWN
Nickname: Black & Ambers   **Club Colours:** Yellow & black

Founded 1889

Club Contact Details 01208 78165   nickgiles@live.co.uk

HONOURS
FA Comps: None
League: Bodmin & District 1922-23, 26-27. South Western 1990-91, 93-94, 2005-06.
South West Peninsula Premier Division 2007-08, 08-09, 11-12, 12-13, 15-16.

10-11		11-12		12-13		13-14		14-15		15-16		16-17		17-18		18-19		19-20	
SWPP	2	SWPP	1	SWPP	1	SWPP	7	SWPP	2	SWPP	1	SWPP	3	SWPP	5	SWPP	9	SWPW	n&v
FAC	1Q	FAC	3Qr	FAC	1Qr	FAC	P	FAC	1Qr	FAC	2Q	FAC	Pr	FAC	2Qr	FAC	Pr		
FAV	4P	FAV	2Pr	FAV	5P	FAV	4P	FAV	4P	FAV	4P	FAV	3P	FAV	2P	FAV	3P	FAV	2Q

GROUND: Priory Park, Bodmin, Cornwall PL31 2AE
Nearest Railway Station Bodmin General - 587m

CALLINGTON TOWN
Nickname: The Pasty Men   **Club Colours:** Red & black

Founded 1989

Club Contact Details 01579 382 647

HONOURS
FA Comps: None
League: East Cornwall Combination 1997-98, 98-99.
South West Peninsula Division One West 2013-14.

10-11		11-12		12-13		13-14		14-15		15-16		16-17		17-18		18-19		19-20	
SW1W	3	SW1W	6	SW1W	5	SW1W	1	SWPP	11	SWPP	16	SWPP	15	SWPP	19	SWPP	17	SWPW	n&v
																FAV	1Q	FAV	1Q

GROUND: Ginsters Marshfield Parc PL17 7BT
Nearest Railway Station Gunnislake

CAMELFORD
Nickname: Camels   **Club Colours:** Blue and white

Founded 1893

Club Contact Details   hilarykent35@gmail.com

HONOURS
FA Comps: None
League: South West Peninsula Division One West 2010-11.

10-11		11-12		12-13		13-14		14-15		15-16		16-17		17-18		18-19		19-20	
SW1W	1	SWPP	9	SWPP	9	SW1W	14	SWPP	17	SWPP	15	SWPP	14	SWPP	10	SWPP	18	SWPW	n&v
						FAV	2Q	FAV	1Qr	FAV	1P	FAV	1Q	FAV	2Q	FAV	2Qr	FAV	1P

GROUND: Trefew Park, PL32 9TS

DOBWALLS
Nickname: The Reds   **Club Colours:** Red and black

Founded 1922

Club Contact Details dodwallsfootball@gmail.com

HONOURS
FA Comps: None
League: None

10-11		11-12		12-13		13-14		14-15		15-16		16-17		17-18		18-19		19-20	
SW1W	11	SW1W	10	SW1W	8	SW1W	8	SW1W	12	SW1W	15	SW1W	11	SW1W	14	SW1W	10	SWPW	n&v

GROUND: Lantoom Park, Duloe Road, Dobwalls PL14 4LR
Nearest Railway Station Liskeard

FALMOUTH TOWN
Nickname: The Ambers   **Club Colours:** Amber & black   Founded 1949

Club Contact Details 01326 375 156   pascoerichard@hotmail.com

HONOURS
FA Comps: None
League: South Western 1961-62, 65-66, 67-68, 70-71, 71-72, 72-73, 73-74, 85-86, 86-87, 88-89, 89-90, 91-92, 96-97, 99-2000. Western 74-75, 75-76, 76-77, 77-78. Cornwall Comb 83-84.

	10-11	11-12	12-13	13-14	14-15	15-16	16-17	17-18	18-19	19-20
SWPP	5	3	16	16	16	11	10	3	6	
SWPW										n&v
FAC	EPr	EP								
FAV	1Qr	3P			1P	1Q			2P	3P

GROUND: Bickland Park, Bickland Water Road, Falmouth TR11 4PB
Nearest Railway Station Penmere - 1.3km
Bus Route Conway Road - stop 54m away

GODOLPHIN ATLANTIC (NEWQUAY)
Nickname: G Army   **Club Colours:** Sky blue & white   Founded 1980

Club Contact Details   godolphin.arms@btconnect.com

HONOURS
FA Comps: None
League: South West Peninsula Division One West 2012-13.

	10-11	11-12	12-13	13-14	14-15	15-16	16-17	17-18	18-19	19-20
SW1W	2	4	1							
SWPP				5	7	5	13	17	14	
SWPW										n&v
FAV								1Q	2Q	1Q

GROUND: Godolphin Way, Newquay TR7 3BU
Nearest Railway Station Newquay - 1.2km
Bus Route Brook House Inn - stop 136m away

HELSTON ATHLETIC
Nickname: The Blues   **Club Colours:** All blue & white   Founded 1896

Club Contact Details 01326 573742 (Clubhouse)   paul.m.hendy@btinternet.com

HONOURS
FA Comps: None
League: Cornwall Senior 1936-37, 37-38, 39-40. Cornwall Comb. 87-88, 2000-01, 10-11. South West Peninsula Division One West 2014-15.

	10-11	11-12	12-13	13-14	14-15	15-16	16-17	17-18	18-19	19-20
CornC	1									
SW1W		2	2	3	1					
SWPP						10	16	9	11	
SWPW										n&v
FAV							1P	1Q	1Q	1P

GROUND: Kellaway Park, Helston TR13 8PJ

Bus Route Tesco - stop 101m away

LAUNCESTON
Nickname: The Clarets   **Club Colours:** All claret   Founded 1891

Club Contact Details 01566 773 279   launcestonfc@aol.com

HONOURS
FA Comps: None
League: South Western 1994-95.

	10-11	11-12	12-13	13-14	14-15	15-16	16-17	17-18	18-19	19-20
SWPP	11	5	5	8	10	14	11	7	16	
SWPW										n&v
FAC	EP									
FAV	2Q								2Q	1Q

GROUND: Pennygillam Ind. Est., Launceston PL15 7ED

LISKEARD ATHLETIC
Nickname: The Blues **Club Colours:** All blue

Founded 1946

Club Contact Details 01579 342 665

HONOURS
FA Comps: None
League: South Western 1976-77, 78-79. Western Premier Division 1987-88.
South West Peninsula Division One West 2018-19.

	10-11	11-12	12-13	13-14	14-15	15-16	16-17	17-18	18-19	19-20
	SWPP 12	SWPP 7	SWPP 18	SWPP 20	SW1W 6	SW1W 7	SW1W 8	SW1W 5	SW1W 1	SWPP n&v
	FAV 2Q	FAV 1P					FAV 1Q		FAV 1Q	FAV 1Q

GROUND: Lux Park PL14 3HZ
Nearest Railway Station Liskeard

MOUSEHOLE
Nickname: The Seagulls **Club Colours:** White and green

Founded 1923

Club Contact Details 01736 731 518

HONOURS
FA Comps: None
League: South West Peninsula League Division One West 2015-16.

10-11	11-12	12-13	13-14	14-15	15-16	16-17	17-18	18-19	19-20
SW1W 14	SW1W 17	SW1W 15	SW1W 2	SW1W 7	SW1W 1	SW1W 6	SW1W 4	SW1W 2	SWPW n&v

GROUND: Trungle Parc, Paul, Penzance TR19 6UG

NEWQUAY
Nickname: The Peppermints **Club Colours:** Red & white

Founded 1890

Club Contact Details 01637 872 935

HONOURS
FA Comps: None
League: South Western 1958-59, 59-60, 77-78, 79-80, 81-82, 83-84, 87-88.
South West Peninsula Division One West 2011-12.

	10-11	11-12	12-13	13-14	14-15	15-16	16-17	17-18	18-19	19-20
	SW1W 9	SW1W 1	SWPP 12	SWPP 11	SWPP 15	SWPP 18	SWPP 19	SWPP 14	SWPP 13	SWPW n&v
	FAV 1P			FAV EP	FAV 1P	FAV 2Q			FAV 1P	FAV 1Q

GROUND: Mount Wise TR7 2BU
Nearest Railway Station Newquay - 0.8km
Bus Route Windsor Court - stop 117m away

PENZANCE
Nickname: The Magpies **Club Colours:** White and black

Founded 1888

Club Contact Details 01736 361 964

HONOURS
FA Comps: None
League: South Western 1955-56, 56-57, 74-75. South West Peninsula League Division One West 2008-09.

	10-11	11-12	12-13	13-14	14-15	15-16	16-17	17-18	18-19	19-20
	SWPP 9	SWPP 17	SWPP 19	SW1W 14	SW1W 14	SW1W 10	SW1W 17	SW1W 10	SW1W 12	SWPW n&v
	FAV 2Q	FAV 2Q								

GROUND: Penlee Park, Alexandra Place, Penzance TR18 4NE
Nearest Railway Station Penzance

PORTHLEVEN

Nickname: The Fisher Men   **Club Colours:** Yellow and black

Founded 1898

Club Contact Details 01326 569 655

HONOURS
FA Comps: None
League: None

10-11	11-12	12-13	13-14	14-15	15-16	16-17	17-18	18-19	19-20
SW1W 6	SW1W 12	SW1W 11	SW1W 11	SW1W 11	SW1W 16	SW1W 12	SW1W 6	SW1W 3	SWPW n&v
FAV 2Q	FAV 1Q	FAV 2Q		FAV 1Q	FAV 1Q			FAV 2Q	FAV 2Q

GROUND: Gala Parc, Mill Lane, Porthleven TR13 9LQ

SALTASH UNITED

Nickname: The Ashes   **Club Colours:** Red & white

Founded 1945

Club Contact Details 01752 845 746

HONOURS
FA Comps: None
League: South Western 1953-54, 75-76. Western Division One 1976-77, Premier 1984-85, 86-87, 88-89.

10-11	11-12	12-13	13-14	14-15	15-16	16-17	17-18	18-19	19-20
SWPP 6	SWPP 4	SWPP 6	SWPP 3	SWPP 3	SWPP 6	SWPP 2	SWPP 4	SWPP 4	SWPW n&v
FAC EPr	FAC EP	FAC EP	FAC EP	FAC 1Q	FAC EP			FAC P	FAC EP
FAV 2P	FAV 2P	FAV 1P	FAV 3P	FAV 1P	FAV 1Q		FAV 2Q	FAV 3P	FAV 2P

GROUND: Kimberley Stadium, Callington Road, Saltash PL12 6DX
Nearest Railway Station Saltash - 0.9km
Bus Route Callington Road St Annes - stop 40m away

ST. AUSTELL

Nickname: The Lillywhites   **Club Colours:** White and black

Founded 1890

hotspurs403@gmail.com

Club Contact Details 01726 66099

HONOURS
FA Comps: None
League: South Western 1968-69. South West Peninsula Premier 2014-15.

10-11	11-12	12-13	13-14	14-15	15-16	16-17	17-18	18-19	19-20
SWPP 10	SWPP 8	SWPP 4	SWPP 9	SWPP 1	SWPP 2	SWPP 4	SWPP 6	SWPP 5	SWPW n&v
			FAC EP	FAC P	FAC P	FAC EPr	FAC EPr		FAC EP
		FAV 2P	FAV 1Q	FAV SF	FAV 2P	FAV 2Q	FAV 2Q	FAV 4P	FAV 2P

GROUND: Poltair Park, Trevarthian Road, St Austell PL25 4LR
Nearest Railway Station St Austell - 0.3km
Bus Route Poltair Road - stop 33m away

ST. BLAZEY

Nickname: The Green & Blacks   **Club Colours:** Green & black

Founded 1896

geoallen.spurs1@btinternet.com

Club Contact Details 01725 814 110

HONOURS
FA Comps: None
League: South Western 1954-55, 57-58, 62-63, 63-64, 80-81, 82-83, 98-99, 2000-01, 01-02, 02-03, 03-04, 04-05, 06-07.

10-11	11-12	12-13	13-14	14-15	15-16	16-17	17-18	18-19	19-20
SWPP 8	SWPP 18	SWPP 8	SWPP 13	SWPP 9	SWPP 17	SWPP 20	SW1W 7	SW1W 11	SWPW n&v
FAC EPr	FAC P		FAC P						
FAV 3P	FAV 2Q	FAV 3P	FAV 2Q	FAV 2P	FAV 2Q		FAV 1Q		FAV 2Q

GROUND: Blaise Park, Station Road, St Blazey PL24 2ND

ST. DENNIS

Nickname: The Saints   **Club Colours:** Light blue

Founded 1902

Club Contact Details 01726 822 635

HONOURS
FA Comps: None
League: Cornwall Combination 1975-76. East Cornwall Premier 1991-92, 99-00, 10-11, Division One 09-10.

10-11	11-12	12-13	13-14	14-15	15-16	16-17	17-18	18-19	19-20
ECorP 1	SW1W 9	SW1W 6	SW1W 9	SW1W 4	SW1W 6	SW1W 7	SW1W 8	SW1W 5	SWPW n&v

GROUND: Boscawen Park, St Dennis PL26 8DW

STICKER

Nickname: The Sticky   **Club Colours:** Yellow and blue

Founded 1911

Club Contact Details 01726 71003   chrisjohnosborne@aol.com

HONOURS
FA Comps: None
League: South West Peninsula Division One West 2016-17.

10-11	11-12	12-13	13-14	14-15	15-16	16-17	17-18	18-19	19-20
ECP 3	ECP 2	SW1W 4	SW1W 4	SW1W 5	SW1W 3	SW1W 1	SWPP 15	SWPP 19	SWPW n&v

GROUND: Burngullow Park PL26 7EN
Nearest Railway Station St Austell - 4.4km
Bus Route Hewas Inn (Fore St) - stop 1.1km away

WADEBRIDGE TOWN

Nickname: The Bridgers   **Club Colours:** All red

Founded 1894

Club Contact Details 01208 812 537

HONOURS
FA Comps: None
League: South West Peninsula League Division One West 2007-08.

10-11	11-12	12-13	13-14	14-15	15-16	16-17	17-18	18-19	19-20
SWPP 20	SW1W 11	SW1W 3	SW1W 7	SW1W 10	SW1W 14	SW1W 14	SW1W 9	SW1W 4	SWPW n&v
FAV 2Q	FAV 2Q	FAV 1Q	FAV 2Q	FAV 2Q	FAV 2Q				

GROUND: Bodieve Park, Bodieve Road, Wadebridge PL27 6EA

WENDRON UNITED

Nickname: The Dron   **Club Colours:** Maroon and blue

Founded 1986

Club Contact Details 01209 860 946

HONOURS
FA Comps: None
League: None

10-11	11-12	12-13	13-14	14-15	15-16	16-17	17-18	18-19	19-20
CornC 10	CornC 11	CornC 12	CornC 2	CornC 2	SW1W 9	SW1W 13	SW1W 13	SW1W 6	SWPW n&v

GROUND: Underlane TR13 0EH

AFC UCKFIELD TOWN
Nickname: The Oakmen **Club Colours:** Red & black
Founded 1988

Club Contact Details 01825 890 905   grahamsullivan27@gmail.com

Previous Names: Wealden 1988-2010. AFC Uckfield & Uckfield Town merged in 2014.
Previous Leagues: None
HONOURS
FA Comps: None
League: Sussex County Division Two 2010-11.

10-11		11-12		12-13		13-14		14-15		15-16		16-17		17-18		18-19		19-20	
SxC2	1	SxC1	8	SxC1	21	SxC1	10	SxC2	2	SCP	15	SCP	18	SCP	14	SCP	7	SCP	n&v
												FAC	EP	FAC	EPr	FAC	2Q	FAC	Pr
										FAV	1Q	FAV	2Q	FAV	2Q	FAV	4P	FAV	3P

GROUND: The Oaks, Old Eastbourne Road, Uckfield TN22 5QL
Capacity: **Seats:** Yes   **Covered:** Yes
Nearest Railway Station Uckfield - 2.1km

ALFOLD
Nickname: Fold **Club Colours:** Maroon
Founded 1928

Club Contact Details wayne.mouring@btopenworld.com

Previous Names: Formed after the split of Loxwood and Alfold FC (Established 1920) in 1928.
Previous Leagues: Cranleigh & District. Horsham & District. West Sussex > 2016.
HONOURS
FA Comps: None
League: Horsham & District 1953-54. West Sussex Division Two North 1980-81, 93-94, Premier 2002-03. Southern Combination Division One 2018-19.

10-11		11-12		12-13		13-14		14-15		15-16		16-17		17-18		18-19		19-20	
				WSux2	2	WSux1	9	WSux1	6	SC2	13	SC2	14	SC2	4	SC1	1	SCP	n&v
																		FAV	1Q

GROUND: Recreation Ground, Dunsfold Road, Alfold, Surrey GU6 8JB
Capacity: **Seats:** 50   **Covered:** Yes

Bus Route 42

BROADBRIDGE HEATH
Nickname: The Bears **Club Colours:** All royal blue
Founded 1919

Club Contact Details 01403 211 311   crispandy@hotmail.com

Previous Names: None
Previous Leagues: Horsham & District >1971. West Sussex 1971-79. Southern Counties Combination 1979-83.
HONOURS
FA Comps: None
League: West Sussex Division One 1975-76.

10-11		11-12		12-13		13-14		14-15		15-16		16-17		17-18		18-19		19-20	
SxC2	6	SxC2	5	SxC2	6	SxC2	2	SxC1	9	SCP	9	SCP	8	SCP	15	SCP	6	SCP	n&v
														FAC	EP	FAC	EP	FAC	P
								FAV	2Q	FAV	2Q	FAV	1Q	FAV	2P	FAV	2Q	FAV	1Q

GROUND: Countryside Stadium, High Wood Hill Sports Ground, Broadbridge Heath RH12 3YS
Capacity: **Seats:** 100   **Covered:** 50
Nearest Railway Station Dorking - 93 towards Horsham, alight at Shelley Arms, 20min walk from there.
Bus Route 63, 68 & 93

CRAWLEY DOWN GATWICK
Nickname: The Anvils   Club Colours: All Red   Founded 1993

Club Contact Details 01342 717 140   martinmd@btinternet.com

Previous Names: Crawley Down United > 1993. Crawley Down Village > 1999. Crawley Down > 2012.
Previous Leagues: Mid Sussex, Sussex County > 2011. Isthmian 2011-14.
HONOURS
FA Comps: None
League: Mid-Sussex Premier Division 1994-95. Sussex County Division One 2010-11.

	10-11	11-12	12-13	13-14	14-15	15-16	16-17	17-18	18-19	19-20
	SxC1 1	Isth1S 16	Isth1S 13	Isth1S 23	SxC1 19	SC1 2	SCP 11	SCP 12	SCP 9	SCP n&v
FAC	EP	1Q	P	P	EPr	EP	P	EP	EP	EP
FAV/FAT	FAV 1P	FAT P	FAT 1Q	FAT 1Q	FAV 2P	FAV 1Q	FAV 1Q	FAV 2Q	FAV 1Q	FAV 2Q

GROUND: The Haven Centre, Hophurst Lane, Crawley Down RH10 4LJ
Capacity: 1,000 **Seats:** Yes **Covered:** 50
Nearest Railway Station Three Bridges - 291 towards Tunbridge Wells, alight at the War Memorial, 4min walk from there.
Bus Route 291

EAST PRESTON
Nickname: EP   Club Colours: Black and white   Founded 1966

Club Contact Details 01903 776 026   keweia@btinternet.com

Previous Names: None
Previous Leagues: Worthing & District 1966-68. West Sussex 1968-83.
HONOURS
FA Comps: None
League: West Sussex Premier Division 1977-78, 80-81, 81-82, 82-83.
Sussex County Division Three 1983-84, Division Two 1997-98, 2011-12, Division One 2013-14.

	10-11	11-12	12-13	13-14	14-15	15-16	16-17	17-18	18-19	19-20
	SxC2 14	SxC2 1	SxC1 3	SxC1 1	SxC1 11	SCP 19	SC1 3	SCP 13	SCP 14	SCP n&v
FAC	EP		P	1Q	2Q	EP	1Q	P	EP	EP
FAV	2Q	1P	2Q	5P	2P	1Q	2Q	1Qr	1P	1Q

GROUND: Roundstone Recreation Ground, Lashmar Road, East Preston BN16 1ES
Capacity: **Seats:** Yes **Covered:** Yes
Nearest Railway Station Angmering - 0.8km
Bus Route Windlesham Gardens - stop 209m away

EASTBOURNE TOWN
Nickname: Town   Club Colours: Yellow and blue   Founded 1881

Club Contact Details 01323 724 328   rb.marsh@talk21.com

Previous Names: Devonshire Park 1881-89
Previous Leagues: Southern Amateur 1907-46, Corinthian 1960-63, Athenian 1963-76, Sussex County 1976-2007. Isthmian 2007-14.
HONOURS
FA Comps: None
League: Sussex County 1976-77, 2006-07.

	10-11	11-12	12-13	13-14	14-15	15-16	16-17	17-18	18-19	19-20
	Isth1S 18	Isth1S 14	Isth1S 11	Isth1S 24	SxC1 4	SCP 2	SCP 5	SCP 5	SCP 3	SCP n&v
FAC	1Q	1Q	2Q	P	P	3Q	1Q	1Q	EP	P
FAT/FAV	FAT P	FAT 1Q	FAT 1Q	FAT 1Qr	FAV 1P	FAV 3P	FAV 4P	FAV 4P	FAV 3P	FAV 3P

GROUND: The Saffrons, Compton Place Road, Eastbourne BN21 1EA
Capacity: 3,000 **Seats:** 200 **Covered:** Yes
Nearest Railway Station Eastbourne - 0.4km
Bus Route Saffrons Road Cricket Club - stop 100m away

EASTBOURNE UNITED

Nickname: The U's   **Club Colours:** Red and blue   Founded 1894

Club Contact Details 01323 726 989   secretary@eastbourneunitedafc.com

Previous Names: 1st Sussex Royal Engineers. Eastbourne Old Comrades 1922. Eastbourne United (merged with Shinewater Assoc in 2000)

Previous Leagues: Sussex County 1921-28, 32-56. Spartan 1928-32. Metropolitan 1956-64. Athenian 1964-77. Isthmian 1977-92.

HONOURS

FA Comps: None

League: Athenian Division Two 1966-67, Division One 68-69. Sussex County Division One 1954-55, 55-56, 2008-09, Division Two 2013-14.

	10-11		11-12		12-13		13-14		14-15		15-16		16-17		17-18		18-19		19-20	
	SxC1	20	SxC2	6	SxC2	4	SxC2	1	SxC1	12	SCP	10	SCP	7	SCP	16	SCP	18	SCP	n&v
FAC	EP						FAC	1Q	FAC	P	FAC	1Q	FAC	1Q	FAC	P	FAC	EP	FAC	EP
FAV	2Q				FAV	1Q	FAV	SF	FAV	2P	FAV	2Q	FAV	2P	FAV	1Q	FAV	1Q	FAV	1Q

GROUND: The Oval, Channel View Road, Eastbourne, BN22 7LN

Capacity: 3,000   **Seats:** 160   **Covered:** 160   **Shop:** Yes

Nearest Railway Station Eastbourne - 2km

Bus Route Desmond Road - stop 240m away

HASSOCKS

Nickname: The Robins   **Club Colours:** Red and black   Founded 1902

Club Contact Details 01273 846 040   sarahajohn@btinternet.com

Previous Names: None

Previous Leagues: Mid Sussex, Brighton & Hove & District >1981.

HONOURS

FA Comps: None

League: Brighton, Hove & District Division Two 1965-66, Division One 71-72. Sussex County Division Three 1991-92.

	10-11		11-12		12-13		13-14		14-15		15-16		16-17		17-18		18-19		19-20	
	SxC1	6	SxC1	4	SxC1	7	SxC1	6	SxC1	15	SCP	13	SCP	13	SCP	18	SCP	12	SCP	n&v
FAC	1Q	FAC	EP	FAC	EP	FAC	1Q	FAC	EP					FAC	EP	FAC	EP	FAC	Pr
FAV	1Q	FAV	2Qr	FAV	1P	FAV	1P	FAV	2P			FAV	1Q	FAV	2Q	FAV	1Q	FAV	2Q

GROUND: The Beacon, Brighton Road, Hassocks BN6 9LU

Capacity: 1,800   **Seats:** 270   **Covered:** 100

Nearest Railway Station Hassocks - 1.2km

Bus Route Friars Oak Cottages - stop 211m away

HORLEY TOWN

Nickname: The Clarets   **Club Colours:** Claret & blue   Founded 1896

Club Contact Details 01293 822 000   mark@avocettm.co.uk

Previous Names: Horley >1975

Previous Leagues: Surrey Intermediate 1925-51, 55- Surrey Senior 1951-55, 71-78, London Spartan 1978-81, Athenian 1981-84, Combined Counties 1984-96, 03-19. Surrey County Senior 2002-03.

HONOURS

FA Comps: None

League: Surrey Intermediate 1926-27, Eastern Section 1950-51. Surrey Senior 1976-77.

	10-11		11-12		12-13		13-14		14-15		15-16		16-17		17-18		18-19		19-20	
	CCP	16	CCP	7	CCP	12	CCP	19	CCP	12	CCP	6	CCP	7	CCP	14	CCP	10	SCP	n&v
FAC	P	FAC	1Q	FAC	Pr	FAC	1Q	FAC	EP	FAC	Pr	FAC	EP	FAC	P	FAC	P	FAC	1Q
FAV	1P	FAV	2Q	FAV	1P	FAV	1Q	FAV	3P	FAV	1Q	FAV	1P	FAV	4P	FAV	2P	FAV	1P

GROUND: The New Defence, Court Lodge Road, Horley RH6 8SP

Capacity: 1800   **Seats:** 150   **Covered:** 100   **Shop:** Yes

Nearest Railway Station Horley

Bus Route Metrobus 100, 526

HORSHAM YMCA
Nickname: YM's   **Club Colours:** White and black

Founded 1898

Club Contact Details 01403 252 689   alan.maguire@hotmail.co.uk

Previous Names: None
Previous Leagues: Horsham & District, Brighton & Hove, Mid Sussex, Sussex County 1959-2006, 08-09. Isthmian 2006-08, 09-11.
HONOURS
FA Comps: None
League: Sussex County 2004-05, 05-06.

10-11		11-12		12-13		13-14		14-15		15-16		16-17		17-18		18-19		19-20	
Isth1S	22	SxC1	16	SxC1	10	SxC1	4	SxC1	5	SCP	7	SCP	10	SCP	4	SCP	2	SCP	n&v
FAC	P	FAC	EPr	FAC	EP	FAC	EP	FAC	Pr	FAC	2Qr	FAC	EP	FAC	EP	FAC	1Q	FAC	1Q
FAT	P	FAV	1P	FAV	2P	FAV	1Q	FAV	2P	FAV	2Q	FAV	3P	FAV	1P	FAV	1P	FAV	1P

GROUND: Gorings Mead, Horsham, West Sussex RH13 5BP
Capacity: 1,575 **Seats:** 150 **Covered:** 200
Nearest Railway Station Horsham - 0.9km
Bus Route Brighton Road - stop 205m away

LANCING
Nickname: The Lancers   **Club Colours:** Yellow and blue

Founded 1941

Club Contact Details 01903 767 285   daniel@fuller-smith.co.uk

Previous Names: Lancing Athletic 1941-57
Previous Leagues: Brighton & Hove & District 1946-48.
HONOURS
FA Comps: None
League: Brighton 1946-47, 47-48. Sussex County Division Two 1957-58, 69-70.

10-11		11-12		12-13		13-14		14-15		15-16		16-17		17-18		18-19		19-20	
SxC2	2	SxC1	2	SxC1	13	SxC1	18	SxC1	8	SCP	4	SCP	12	SCP	10	SCP	13	SCP	n&v
FAC	P	FAC	P	FAC	P	FAC	EPr	FAC	EP	FAC	EP	FAC	EPr	FAC	EPr	FAC	2Q	FAC	EPr
FAV	4P	FAV	3P	FAV	1P	FAV	2Q	FAV	2Q	FAV	1P	FAV	2P	FAV	2Q	FAV	1Q	FAV	3Pr

GROUND: Culver Road, Lancing, West Sussex BN15 9AX
Capacity: 2,000 **Seats:**   **Covered:**
Nearest Railway Station Lancing - 0.2km
Bus Route North Road Post Office - stop 123m away

LANGNEY WANDERERS
Nickname: **Club Colours:** White and red

Founded 2010

Club Contact Details 01323 766 265   saunderstracey@sky.com

Previous Names: None
Previous Leagues: East Sussex.
HONOURS
FA Comps: None
League: East Sussex Premier 2012-13. Sussex County Division Three 2013-14.

10-11	11-12	12-13		13-14		14-15		15-16		16-17		17-18		18-19		19-20	
		EsSuP	1	SxC3	1	SxC3	3	SC1	9	SC1	8	SC1	2	SCP	15	SCP	n&v
														FAC	EP	FAC	EP
										FAV	1Qr	FAV	2Q	FAV	1Q	FAV	1Q

GROUND: Langney Sports Club, Priory Lane, Eastbourne BN23 7QH
Capacity: 4,151 **Seats:** 542 **Covered:** 2,500   Yes
Nearest Railway Station Pevensey & Westham - 15-20 mins walk.
Bus Route The LOOP Bus from the town centre.

LINGFIELD

Nickname: The Lingers   **Club Colours:** Red & Yellow   Founded 1893

Club Contact Details 01342 834 269   toveyj@yahoo.co.uk

Previous Names: None.
Previous Leagues: Redhill. Surrey Intermediate. Combined Counties. Mid Sussex. Sussex County > 2014. Southern Counties East 2014-15.
HONOURS
FA Comps: None
League: POST WAR: Edenbridge & Caterham 1952-53. Surrey Intermediate Prem B 76-77,
Prem A 77-78, 78-79. Mid Sussex Prem 92-93. Sussex County Division Three 97-98.

10-11		11-12		12-13		13-14		14-15		15-16		16-17		17-18		18-19		19-20	
SxC1	11	SxC1	7	SxC1	6	SxC1	15	SCE	17	SC1	8	SC1	5	SC1	3	SCP	8	SCP	n&v
FAC	P	FAC	1Qr	FAC	1Q	FAC	EP	FAC	EP	FAC	EP			FAC	EP	FAC	EP	FAC	EP
FAV	1Q	FAV	1Q	FAV	1P	FAV	1P	FAV	3P	FAV	2Q	FAV	1P	FAV	1Q	FAV	2Q	FAV	1Q

GROUND: Sports Pavillion, Godstone Road, Lingfield, Surrey RH7 6BT
Capacity: 2,000   **Seats:** Yes   **Covered:** Yes   **Shop:** No
Nearest Railway Station Lingfield - 1.2km
Bus Route Godstone Road - stop 391m away

LITTLE COMMON

Nickname: The Green Lane Boys   **Club Colours:** Claret & blue   Founded 1966

Club Contact Details 01424 845 861   danieleldridge11@btinternet.com

Previous Names: Albion United 1966-86
Previous Leagues: East Sussex. Sussex County
HONOURS
FA Comps: None
League: East Sussex 1975-76, 76-77, 2004-05. Southern Combination Division One 2017-18.

10-11		11-12		12-13		13-14		14-15		15-16		16-17		17-18		18-19		19-20	
SxC2	13	SxC2	16	SxC2	3	SxC2	4	SxC2	7	SC1	7	SC1	2	SC1	1	SCP	16	SCP	n&v
														FAC	EP	FAC	EPr	FAC	1Q
										FAV	1Q	FAV	2Q	FAV	1Q	FAV	2Q	FAV	1Q

GROUND: The Oval, Channel View Road, Eastbourne BN22 7LN
Capacity: 3,000   **Seats:** 160   **Covered:** 160
Nearest Railway Station Eastbourne - 25min walk
Bus Route Desmond Road - stop 240m away

LOXWOOD

Nickname: Magpies   **Club Colours:** White and black   Founded 1920

Club Contact Details 07791 766 857   secretary@loxwoodfc.co.uk

Previous Names: None
Previous Leagues: West Sussex 1995-2006.
HONOURS
FA Comps: None
League: West Sussex Division Two North 1998-99, 2001-02.
Sussex County Division Three 2007-08.

10-11		11-12		12-13		13-14		14-15		15-16		16-17		17-18		18-19		19-20	
SxC2	6	SxC2	5	SxC2	9	SxC2	3	SxC1	6	SCP	8	SCP	6	SCP	11	SCP	17	SCP	n&v
										FAC	EP	FAC	P	FAC	P	FAC	Pr	FAC	EPr
								FAV	2P	FAV	2P	FAV	1Q	FAV	1Q	FAV	1Q	FAV	2Q

GROUND: Loxwood Sports Ass., Plaistow Road, Loxwood RH14 0SX
Capacity: **Seats:** 100   **Covered:** Yes

Bus Route Plaistow Road - stop 28m away

NEWHAVEN
Nickname: The Dockers — **Club Colours:** Red & yellow

Founded 1887

Club Contact Details 01273 513 940 — martin.garry@premierfoods.co.uk

Previous Names: None
Previous Leagues: Brighton, Hove & District 1887-1920.
HONOURS
FA Comps: None
League: Sussex County Division One 1953-54, 73-74, Division Two 1971-72, 90-91, Division Three 2011-12.

10-11		11-12		12-13		13-14		14-15		15-16		16-17		17-18		18-19		19-20	
SxC3	7	SxC3	1	SxC2	2	SxC1	13	SxC1	7	SCP	3	SCP	9	SCP	9	SCP	4	SCP	n&v
												FAC	EPr	FAC	Pr	FAC	P	FAC	P
FAV	1Q	FAV	2Q	FAV	1Q	FAV	1Pr	FAV	1Q	FAV	2P	FAV	3P	FAV	2Q	FAV	2P	FAV	3P

GROUND: The Trafalgar Ground, Fort Road Newhaven East Sussex BN9 9DA
Capacity: Yes **Seats:** Yes **Covered:** Yes
Nearest Railway Station Newhaven Harbour - 0.4km
Bus Route Court Farm Road - stop 20m away

PAGHAM
Nickname: The Lions — **Club Colours:** White and black

Founded 1903

Club Contact Details 01243 266 112 — paghamfootballclub@outlook.com

Previous Names: None
Previous Leagues: Bognor & Chichester 1903-50, West Sussex 50-69
HONOURS
FA Comps: None
League: West Sussex Division One South 1962-63, Prmeier 65-66, 68-69, 69-70.
Sussex County Division Two 1978-79, 86-87, 2006-07, Division One 80-81, 87-88, 88-89.

10-11		11-12		12-13		13-14		14-15		15-16		16-17		17-18		18-19		19-20	
SxC1	4	SxC1	6	SxC1	5	SxC1	7	SxC1	3	SCP	6	SCP	4	SCP	3	SCP	11	SCP	n&v
FAC	P	FAC	EP	FAC	1Qr	FAC	EP	FAC	1Q	FAC	1Q	FAC	1Q	FAC	1Q	FAC	1Q	FAC	EPr
FAV	2Q	FAV	2P	FAV	1Pr	FAV	2Q	FAV	2P	FAV	2P	FAV	2Q	FAV	1P	FAV	3P	FAV	1Q

GROUND: Nyetimber Lane, Pagham, West Sussex PO21 3JY
Capacity: 1,500 **Seats:** 200 **Covered:** 200
Nearest Railway Station Bognor Regis - 4.3km
Bus Route The Bear Inn - stop 119m away

PEACEHAVEN & TELSCOMBE
Nickname: The Tye — **Club Colours:** Black and white

Founded 1923

Club Contact Details 01273 582 471 — peacehavenfc@hotmail.com

Previous Names: Formed when Peacehaven Rangers and Telscombe Tye merged.
Previous Leagues: Sussex County 1969-2013. Isthmian 2013-16.
HONOURS
FA Comps: None
League: Brighton, H&D Junior 1951-52, Intermediate 63-64, Senior 68-69. Sussex County Division One 1978-79, 81-82, 82-83, 91-92, 92-93, 94 -95, 95-96, 2012-13, Division Three 2005-06, Division Two 2008-09. Isthmian Division One South 2013-14.

10-11		11-12		12-13		13-14		14-15		15-16		16-17		17-18		18-19		19-20	
SxC1	3	SxC1	5	SxC1	1	Isth1S	1	Isth P	21	Isth1S	24	SCP	14	SCP	7	SCP	10	SCP	n&v
FAC	P	FAC	P	FAC	P	FAC	1Q	FAC	1Qr	FAC	P	FAC	1Q	FAC	EPr	FAC	EP	FAC	EPr
FAV	2P	FAV	3P	FAV	4P	FAT	1Q	FAT	3Q	FAT	1Q	FAV	2Q	FAV	1Q	FAV	2P	FAV	1P

GROUND: The Sports Park, Piddinghoe Ave, Peacehaven, BN10 8RJ
Capacity: 3,000 **Seats:** 350 **Covered:** Yes
Nearest Railway Station Newhaven - 3.2km
Bus Route Slindon Avenue - stop 140m away

SALTDEAN UNITED
Nickname: The Tigers   **Club Colours:** Red & black

Founded 1966

Club Contact Details 01273 309 898   secretary@saltdeanunitedfc.co.uk

Previous Names: None
Previous Leagues: None
HONOURS
FA Comps: None
League: Sussex County/Southern Combination Division Three 1988-89, Division Two 95-96 / Division One 2016-17.

10-11	11-12	12-13	13-14	14-15	15-16	16-17	17-18	18-19	19-20
SxC3 5	SxC3 2	SxC2 18	SxC2 13	SxC2 13	SC1 17	SC1 1	SCP 8	SCP 5	SCP n&v
							FAC EP	FAC Pr	FAC P
FAV 2Q	FAV 1Q	FAV 1Q	FAV 1Q	FAV 1Q		FAV 1Q	FAV 1P	FAV 1P	FAV 1Q

GROUND: Hill Park, Coombe Vale Saltdean Brighton East Sussex BN2 8HJ
Capacity: **Seats:** Yes   **Covered:** Yes
Nearest Railway Station Southease - 5km
Bus Route Saltdean Vale Shops - stop 175m away

STEYNING TOWN
Nickname: The Barrowmen   **Club Colours:** Red & white

Founded 1892

Club Contact Details 01903 814 601   secretary.sfcfc@gmail.com

Previous Names: Steyning FC 1892-1979.
Previous Leagues: West Sussex (FM) 1896-1919. Brighton, Hove & District 1919-64. Sussex County 1964-86. Wessex (FM) 1986-88. Combined
HONOURS Counties 1988-93.
FA Comps: None
League: Brighton, H&D Division Two 1933-34, 38-39.
    Sussex County Division Two 1977-78, Division One 1984-85, 85-86.

10-11	11-12	12-13	13-14	14-15	15-16	16-17	17-18	18-19	19-20
SxC2 16	SxC2 13	SxC2 10	SxC2 11	SxC2 10	SC1 10	SC1 6	SC1 11	SC1 2	SCP n&v
							FAC P		FAC P
	FAV 1Q	FAV 1Q	FAV 1Q	FAV 2Q	FAV 2P	FAV 1Q	FAV 2Q	FAV 3P	FAV 1Qr

GROUND: The Shooting Field, Steyning, West Sussex BN44 3RQ
Capacity: **Seats:** Yes   **Covered:** Yes

Bus Route Middle Mead - stop 52m away

AFC VARNDEANIANS

Nickname: Club Colours: Red & black

Founded 1929

Club Contact Details   stevematthews@utilitymatters.com

HONOURS
FA Comps: None
League: Brighton & HD Division One 1973-74, 99-2000, 00-01, 02-03.
Mid Sussex Premier 03-04, 06-07, 08-09. Southern Combination Division Two 15-16.

10-11	11-12	12-13	13-14	14-15	15-16	16-17	17-18	18-19	19-20
MSuxP 9	MSuxP 5	MSuxP 7	MSuxP 2	MSuxP 7	SC2 1	SC1 18	SC1 14	SC1 3	SC1 n&v
									FAC 1Q
								FAV 2Q	FAV 1Q

GROUND: Withdean Stadium, Tongdean Lane, Brighton BN1 5JD
Nearest Railway Station Preston Park - 0.9km
Bus Route Bottom of Valley Drive - stop 91m away

ARUNDEL

Nickname: Mulletts   Club Colours: Red and white

Founded 1889

Club Contact Details 01903 882 548   mullets@btinternet.com

HONOURS
FA Comps: None
League: Sussex County Division One 1957-58, 58-59, 86-87.

10-11	11-12	12-13	13-14	14-15	15-16	16-17	17-18	18-19	19-20
SxC1 9	SxC1 17	SxC1 14	SxC1 12	SxC1 10	SCP 12	SCP 15	SCP 17	SCP 19	SC1 n&v
FAC P	FAC P	FAC EP	FAC EPr	FAC EP	FAC EP	FAC Pr	FAC 1Q	FAC EP	FAC 1Qr
FAV 2Q	FAV 2Q	FAV 2Q	FAV 2Q	FAV 1P	FAV 2Q	FAV 1Q	FAV 1Q	FAV 1Q	FAV 2Q

GROUND: Mill Road, Arundel, W. Sussex BN18 9PA
Nearest Railway Station Arundel - 1.6km

BEXHILL UNITED

Nickname: The Pirates   Club Colours: White and black

Founded 2002

Club Contact Details 07791 368 049   simon_dunne@hotmail.co.uk

HONOURS
FA Comps: None
League: Sussex County 1956-57, 65-66, 66-67.

10-11	11-12	12-13	13-14	14-15	15-16	16-17	17-18	18-19	19-20
SxC2 4	SxC2 7	SxC2 11	SxC2 8	SxC2 6	SC1 14	SC1 10	SC1 7	SC1 4	SC1 n&v
					FAC P				FAC EP
				FAV 2Q	FAV 1Q	FAV 1Q	FAV 2Q	FAV 1Q	FAV 2Q

GROUND: The Polegrove, Brockley Road, Bexhill on Sea TN39 3EX
Nearest Railway Station Collington - 0.3km
Bus Route Polegrove - stop 91m away

BILLINGSHURST

Nickname: Hurst   Club Colours: Red & black

Founded 1891

Club Contact Details 01403 786 445   kevtilley@btinternet.com

HONOURS
FA Comps: None
League: West Sussex Premier Division 2011-12.

10-11	11-12	12-13	13-14	14-15	15-16	16-17	17-18	18-19	19-20
	WSuxP 1	SxC3 4	SxC3 11	SxC3 6	SC2 5	SC1 15	SC1 16	SC1 12	SC1 n&v
							FAV 2Q	FAV 1Q	

GROUND: Jubilee Fields, Newbridge Road, Billingshurst, West Sussex RH14 9HZ
Nearest Railway Station Billingshurst - 1.7km
Bus Route Hole Farm - stop 126m away

HAILSHAM TOWN
Nickname: The Stringers   **Club Colours:** Yellow & green

Founded 1885

Club Contact Details 01323 840 446   robvsquires@yahoo.co.uk

HONOURS
FA Comps: None
League: Southern Counties Combination 1975-76.

10-11		11-12		12-13		13-14		14-15		15-16		16-17		17-18		18-19		19-20	
SxC1	16	SxC1	2	SxC1	12	SxC1	16	SxC1	17	SCP	18	SCP	20	SC1	8	SC1	8	SC1	n&v
FAC	EP	FAC	EP	FAC	EP	FAC	EP	FAC	EP	FAC	EP	FAC	EP	FAC	EP				
FAV	1Q	FAV	1Q	FAV	1Q	FAV	1Q	FAV	1P	FAV	2P	FAV	1Q	FAV	1Q	FAV	2Q	FAV	1Q

GROUND: The Beaconfield, Western Road, Hailsham BN27 3DN
Nearest Railway Station Polegate - 4.4km
Bus Route Bramble Drive - stop 190m away

LITTLEHAMPTON TOWN
Nickname: Marigolds   **Club Colours:** Gold and black

Founded 1896

Club Contact Details 01903 716 390   paulcox280458@yahoo.co.uk

HONOURS
FA Comps: None
League: Sussex County Division Two 1996-97, 2003-04, 12-13, Division One 1990-91, 2014-15.

10-11		11-12		12-13		13-14		14-15		15-16		16-17		17-18		18-19		19-20	
SxC2	11	SxC2	4	SxC2	1	SxC1	3	SxC1	1	SCP	11	SCP	16	SCP	20	SC1	6	SC1	n&v
FAC	EPr	FAC	EP	FAC	1Q	FAC	1Q	FAC	1Q	FAC	P	FAC	EP	FAC	1Qr	FAC	EPr		
FAV	1Q	FAV	2P	FAV	2Pr	FAV	2P	FAV	3Pr	FAV	1P	FAV	2Qr	FAV	1Q	FAV	2Q	FAV	1Q

GROUND: St Flora Sportsfield, St Flora's Road, Littlehampton BN17 6BD
Nearest Railway Station Littlehampton - 1km
Bus Route Parkside Avenue - stop 79m away

MIDHURST & EASEBOURNE
Nickname: The Stags   **Club Colours:** All blue

Founded 1946

Club Contact Details 01730 816 557   midhurstfc@gmail.com

HONOURS
FA Comps: None
League: West Sussex 1955-56, 62-63, 64-65, Premier 67-68.
Sussex County Division Three 94-95, 2002-03.

10-11		11-12		12-13		13-14		14-15		15-16		16-17		17-18		18-19		19-20	
SxC2	15	SxC2	15	SxC2	8	SxC2	14	SxC2	8	SC1	15	SC1	9	SC1	13	SC1	16	SC1	n&v
														FAV	2Q	FAV	1Q	FAV	2Q

GROUND: Rotherfield, Dodsley Lane, Easebourne, Midhurst GU29 9BE

Bus Route Dodsley Grove - Stop 125m away

MILE OAK
Nickname: The Oak   **Club Colours:** Tangerine and black

Founded 1960

Club Contact Details 01273 423 854   tewey62@virginmedia.com

HONOURS
FA Comps: None
League: Brighton & Hove District Div.8 1960-61, Div.4 65-66, Div.2 72-73,
Div.1 73-74, Prem 1980-81. Sussex County Division Two 94-95.

10-11		11-12		12-13		13-14		14-15		15-16		16-17		17-18		18-19		19-20	
SxC2	7	SxC2	10	SxC2	7	SxC2	7	SxC2	5	SC1	6	SC1	4	SC1	6	SC1	7	SC1	n&v
FAC	EP	FAC	EPr							FAC	EP	FAC	EP	FAC	EP				
FAV	2Q	FAV	2Q			FAV	1Qr	FAV	2Q	FAV	2Q	FAV	2Q	FAV	2Q	FAV	1Qr	FAV	1P

GROUND: Mile Oak Recreation Ground, Chalky Road, Portslade BN41 2WF
Nearest Railway Station Fishersgate - 2.1km
Bus Route New England Rise - stop 11m away

OAKWOOD

Nickname: The Oaks   **Club Colours:** Red & black

Founded 1962

Club Contact Details 01293 515 742   sarah.daly13@hotmail.co.uk

HONOURS

FA Comps: None

League: Crawley Division One 1973-74. Sussex County Division Three 1984-85, Division Two 2005-06.

10-11		11-12		12-13		13-14		14-15		15-16		16-17		17-18		18-19		19-20	
SxC2	17	SxC2	18	SxC2	15	SxC2	12	SxC2	4	SC1	3	SC1	14	SC1	17	SC1	15	SC1	n&v
FAC	EP											FAC	EP						
FAV	1Q	FAV	1Q	FAV	1Q	FAV	1Q	FAV	1Q	FAV	2Q	FAV	2Q	FAV	1Q	FAV	1Q	FAV	2Q

GROUND: Tinsley Lane, Three Bridges, Crawley RH10 8AT

Nearest Railway Station Three Bridges - 1.3km

Bus Route Maxwell Way - Stop 98m away

ROFFEY

Nickname: **Club Colours:** Blue and white

Founded 1901

Club Contact Details afchantrill@gmail.com

HONOURS

FA Comps: None

League: Mid Sussex Division One 2009-10.

10-11		11-12		12-13		13-14		14-15		15-16		16-17		17-18		18-19		19-20	
MSuxP	2	SxC3	16	SxC3	8	SxC3	3	SxC3	8	SC2	2	SC2	7	SC2	6	SC2	3	SC1	n&v

GROUND: Chennells, Bartholomew Way, Horsham RH12 5JL

SEAFORD TOWN

Nickname: The Badgers   **Club Colours:** All red

Founded 1888

Club Contact Details 01323 892 221   secretary@seafordtownfc.com

HONOURS

FA Comps: None

League: Lewes 1907-08.
Sussex County Division Three 1985-86, Division Two 1988-89, 2005-06.

10-11		11-12		12-13		13-14		14-15		15-16		16-17		17-18		18-19		19-20	
SxC2	5	SxC2	17	SxC2	12	SxC2	17	SxC2	15	SC1	16	SC1	13	SC1	12	SC1	11	SC1	n&v
		FAV	1P	FAV	2Q	FAV	2Q	FAV	2Q	FAV	1Q	FAV	2Q	FAV	1Q	FAV	2Q	FAV	2P

GROUND: The Crouch, Bramber Road, Seaford BN25 1AF

Nearest Railway Station Seaford - 0.6km

Bus Route Seaford Head Lower School - stop 168m away

SELSEY

Nickname: Blues   **Club Colours:** All blue

Founded 1903

Club Contact Details 01243 603 420   selseyfootballclub@yahoo.com

HONOURS

FA Comps: None

League: West Sussex Division One 1938-39, 54-55, 56-57, 57-58, 58-59, 60-61.
Sussex County Division Two 1963-64, 75-76.

10-11		11-12		12-13		13-14		14-15		15-16		16-17		17-18		18-19		19-20	
SxC1	17	SxC1	12	SxC1	18	SxC1	17	SxC1	20	SC1	13	SC1	7	SC1	9	SC1	5	SC1	n&v
FAC	EP	FAC	P	FAC	EP	FAC	EP	FAC	EP	FAC	EP							FAC	EP
FAV	1Q	FAV	1Q	FAV	1Q	FAV	1Q	FAV	1Q	FAV	2Q	FAV	2Q	FAV	2Q	FAV	2Q	FAV	1Q

GROUND: The Bunn Leisure Stadium, High Street, Selsey, Chichester, PO20 0QG

Bus Route Medical Centre - stop 92m away

SHOREHAM
Nickname: Musselmen   **Club Colours:** All blue

Founded 1892

Club Contact Details 01273 454 261   stuart.slaney@gmail.com

HONOURS
FA Comps: None
League: West Sussex Junior Division 1897-98, Senior Division 1902-03, 04-05, 05-06. Sussex County Division One 1951-52, 52-53, 77-78, Division Two 1961-62, 76-77, 84-85, 93-94. Southern Combination Premier Division 2016-17.

10-11		11-12		12-13		13-14		14-15		15-16		16-17		17-18		18-19		19-20	
SxC1	18	SxC1	18	SxC1	17	SxC1	14	SxC1	16	SCP	17	SCP	1	Isth1S	24	SCP	20	SC1	n&v
FAC	EP	FAC	1Q	FAC	EPr	FAC	1Q	FAC	P	FAC	1Q	FAC	P	FAC	1Q	FAC	P	FAC	P
FAV	1P	FAV	2Q	FAV	1Q	FAV	2Q	FAV	2Q	FAV	1Q	FAV	1P	FAT	P	FAV	2Q	FAV	1Q

GROUND: Middle Road, Shoreham-by-Sea, West Sussex, BN43 6GA
Nearest Railway Station Shoreham-by-Sea - 1.1km
Bus Route Hammy Lane - stop 150m away

SOUTHWICK
Nickname: The Wickers   **Club Colours:** Red & black

Founded 1882

Club Contact Details 01273 701 010   clive.harman1966@btinternet.com

HONOURS
FA Comps: None
League: West Sussex Senior 1896-97, 97-98. Sussex County Div.1 25-26, 27-28, 29-30, 47-48, 68-69, 74-75, Div.2 2000-01, Div.3 14-15. Isthmian D2S 1985-86.

10-11		11-12		12-13		13-14		14-15		15-16		16-17		17-18		18-19		19-20	
SxC2	12	SxC2	8	SxC2	14	SxC3	9	SxC3	1	SC1	5	SC1	11	SC1	18	SC1	13	SC1	n&v
FAC	EP																		
FAV	2Q			FAV	1Q	FAV	2Q	FAV	2Q	FAV	1Q	FAV	1Q	FAV	1Q	FAV	2Q	FAV	1Q

GROUND: Old Barn Way, Southwick BN42 4NT
Nearest Railway Station Fishersgate - 0.4km
Bus Route Old Barn Way - stop 151m away

STORRINGTON COMMUNITY
Nickname: The Swans   **Club Colours:** All blue

Founded 1920

Club Contact Details 01903 745 860   keithdalmon@btinternet.com

HONOURS
FA Comps: None
League: Sussex County Division Three 2004-05.

10-11		11-12		12-13		13-14		14-15		15-16		16-17		17-18		18-19		19-20	
SxC2	8	SxC2	9	SxC2	10	SxC2	15	SxC2	14	SC1	4	SC1	12	SC1	15	SC1	14	SC1	n&v
																		FAV	1Q

GROUND: Recreation Ground, Pulborough Road, Storrington RH20 4HJ
Nearest Railway Station Pulborough - 5.6km
Bus Route Brow Close - stop 238m away

WICK
Nickname: The Wickers   **Club Colours:** Red & black

Founded 1892

Club Contact Details 01903 713 535   wickfootballclub@outlook.com

HONOURS
FA Comps: None
League: Sussex County Division Two 1981-82, 85-86, 89-90, 93-94.

10-11		11-12		12-13		13-14		14-15		15-16		16-17		17-18		18-19		19-20	
SxC1	15	SxC1	14	SxC1	16	SxC2	6	SxC2	3	SCP	16	SCP	19	SC1	5	SC1	9	SC1	n&v
FAC	EP	FAC	EP									FAC	EP	FAC	EP	FAC	EP		
FAV	1P	FAV	1Q	FAV	2Q							FAV	1P	FAV	1Q	FAV	1P	FAV	1Q

GROUND: Crabtree Park, Coomes Way, Wick, Littlehampton, W Sussex BN17 7LS
Nearest Railway Station Littlehampton - 1.7km
Bus Route Seaton Road - stop 250 m away

WORTHING UNITED
Nickname: Mavericks   **Club Colours:** Sky blue & white

Founded 1952

Club Contact Details 01903 234 466   secretary@worthingunitedfc.co.uk

HONOURS
FA Comps: None
League: Sussex County Division Two 1973-74, 2014-15, Division Three 1989-90.

10-11		11-12		12-13		13-14		14-15		15-16		16-17		17-18		18-19		19-20	
SxC2	3	SxC1	14	SxC1	22	SxC1	20	SxC2	1	SCP	14	SCP	17	SCP	19	SC1	17	SC1	n&v
FAC	P					FAC	EPr	FAC	EP	FAC	EPr	FAC	EP	FAC	EP	FAC	P		
FAV	2Q			FAV	1Qr	FAV	2Q	FAV	2Q	FAV	1P	FAV	1Q	FAV	1Q	FAV	1Q	FAV	2Q

GROUND: The Robert Albon Memorial Ground, Lyons Way BN14 9JF
Nearest Railway Station East Worthing - 1.9km
Bus Route Lyons Farm Sainsbury's - stop 203m away

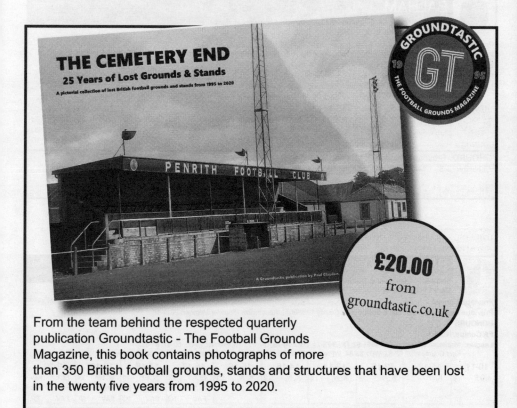

From the team behind the respected quarterly
publication Groundtastic - The Football Grounds
Magazine, this book contains photographs of more
than 350 British football grounds, stands and structures that have been lost
in the twenty five years from 1995 to 2020.

It is a seminal work and promises to be a key point of reference for many years
to come.

SOUTHERN COUNTIES EAST LEAGUE   IN: Balham (LM - CCP). Tower Hamlets (LM - ES)

AFC CROYDON ATHLETIC
Nickname: The Rams   Club Colours: All maroon   Founded 2012

Club Contact Details 020 8689 5322   secretary@afccroydonathletic.co.uk

Previous Names: None
Previous Leagues: Combined Counties 2012-15.
HONOURS
FA Comps: None
League: None

10-11	11-12	12-13	13-14	14-15	15-16	16-17	17-18	18-19	19-20
		CC1 8	CC1 7	CC1 2	SCE 11	SCEP 7	SCEP 13	SCEP 15	SCEP n&v
			FAC EP	FAC EP	FAC EP	FAC EP	FAC P	FAC 1Q	FAC Pr
		FAV 1P	FAV 1P	FAV 2Q	FAV 1Pr	FAV 2Q	FAV 2Q	FAV 2P	FAV 1Q

GROUND: Mayfield Stadium, off Mayfield Road, Thornton Heath CR7 6DN
Capacity: 3,000 **Seats:** 301 **Covered:** 660 **Shop:** Yes
Nearest Railway Station Croydon

BALHAM
Nickname: Club Colours: Red and white   Founded 2011

Club Contact Details 020 8942 8062

Previous Names: None
Previous Leagues: Surrey South Eastern Combination 2011-15. Surrey Elite Intermediate 2015-2016. Combined Counties 2016-20.
HONOURS
FA Comps: None
League: Surrey South Eastern Combination Intermediate Division One 2013-14.

10-11	11-12	12-13	13-14	14-15	15-16	16-17	17-18	18-19	19-20
	SSECJ1 4	SSECI2 3	SSECI1 1	SuEI 3	SuEI 2	CC1 3	CCP 5	CCP 18	CCP n&v
								FAC P	FAC 2Q
							FAV 1P	FAV 1Q	FAV 1Q

GROUND: Croydon Athletic FC, Mayfield Stadium, off Mayfield Road, Thornton Heath CR7 6DN
Capacity: 3,00 **Seats:** 301 **Covered:** 660

BEARSTED
Nickname: The Bears   Club Colours: White and blue   Founded 1895

Club Contact Details 07849 089 875   benton951@aol.com

Previous Names: None
Previous Leagues: Maidstone & District. Kent County 1982-2011. Kent Invicta (Founder Member) 2011-16.
HONOURS
FA Comps: None
League: Maidstone & District Div.6 1961-62, Div.3 73-74, Div.2 74-75, Div.1 77-78, Premier 79-80, 80-81, 81-82.
Kent County WD2 82-83, WD1 83-84, WPrem 87-87, WSen 87-88, D1W 96-97, Prem 2000-01, 01-02. Kent Invicta 2015-16.

10-11	11-12	12-13	13-14	14-15	15-16	16-17	17-18	18-19	19-20
KC P 8	K_Iv 7	K_Iv 4	K_Iv 6	K_Iv 2	K_Iv 1	SCEP 12	SCEP 14	SCEP 14	SCEP n&v
							FAC EP	FAC P	FAC EPr
						FAV 1Q	FAV 1Q	FAV 4P	FAV 2P

GROUND: Otham Sports Ground, White Horse Lane, Otham ME15 8RG
Capacity: **Seats:** Yes **Covered:** Yes
Nearest Railway Station Bearsted - 3.2km
Bus Route Arriva No.13

PREMIER DIVISION

BECKENHAM TOWN
Nickname: Reds   **Club Colours:** All red   Founded 1887

Club Contact Details 07774 728 758   peterpalmer3@sky.com

Previous Names: Original club folded in 1969 and reformed based on the Stanhope Rovers Junior team in 1971.

Previous Leagues: London 1923-35, 51-61. Kent County Amateur 1935-51. Aetolian 1961-64. Greater London 1964-69. South East London Amateur 1971-75. London Spartan 1975-82.

HONOURS

FA Comps: None

League: London Division One 1927-28.

10-11		11-12		12-13		13-14		14-15		15-16		16-17		17-18		18-19		19-20	
Kent P	10	Kent P	6	Kent P	11	SCE	8	SCE	9	SCE	12	SCEP	18	SCEP	4	SCEP	5	SCEP	n&v
FAC	2Q	FAC	2Qr	FAC	1Q	FAC	EP	FAC	EP	FAC	P	FAC	P	FAC	EP	FAC	1Qr	FAC	P
FAV	3P	FAV	1P	FAV	1P	FAV	3P	FAV	2Q	FAV	2P	FAV	1P	FAV	3P	FAV	1P	FAV	1Pr

GROUND: Eden Park Avenue, Beckenham Kent BR3 3JL

Capacity: 4,000 **Seats:** 120 **Covered:** 120 **Shop:** Yes

Nearest Railway Station Eden Park - 0.3km

CANTERBURY CITY
Nickname: **Club Colours:** Burgundy and white   Founded 1904

Club Contact Details 01795 591 900   secretary@cantcityfc.net

Previous Names: None

Previous Leagues: Kent 1947-59, 94-01, Metropolitan 1959-60, Southern 1960-94, Kent County 2007-11.

HONOURS

FA Comps: None

League: Kent County Division Two East 2007-08, One East 08-09.

10-11		11-12		12-13		13-14		14-15		15-16		16-17		17-18		18-19		19-20	
KC P	2	Kent P	9	Kent P	9	SCE	12	SCE	12	SCE	8	SCEP	9	SCEP	10	SCEP	9	SCEP	n&v
						FAC	EP	FAC	P	FAC	P	FAC	Pr	FAC	EP	FAC	EP	FAC	P
				FAV	1P	FAV	1Q	FAV	1Q	FAV	3P	FAV	2P	FAV	2P	FAV	SF	FAV	2P

GROUND: Shepherd Neame Stadium, Salters Lane, Faversham ME13 8ND

Capacity: 2,500 **Seats:** 180 **Covered:** 180 **Shop:** Yes

---

CHATHAM TOWN
Nickname: Chats   **Club Colours:** All red & black   Founded 1882

Club Contact Details 01634 401 130   secretary@chathamtownfc.com

Previous Names: Chatham FC 1882-1974, Medway FC 1974-79

Previous Leagues: Southern 1894-1900, 1920-21, 27-29, 83-88, 2001-06, Kent 1894-96, 1901-1905, 29-59, 68-83, 88-2001, Aetolian 1959-64, Metropolitan 1964-68, Isthmian 2006-17.

HONOURS

FA Comps: None

League: Kent 1894-95, 1903-04, 04-05, 71-72, 73-74, 75-76, 76-77, 79-80, 2000-01. Aetolian 1963-64.

10-11		11-12		12-13		13-14		14-15		15-16		16-17		17-18		18-19		19-20	
Isth1S	21	Isth1N	15	Isth1N	13	Isth1N	12	Isth1N	21	Isth1S	19	Isth1S	22	SCEP	16	SCEP	4	SCEP	n&v
FAC	P	FAC	1Q	FAC	P	FAC	4Q	FAC	P	FAC	2Q	FAC	Pr	FAC	EPr	FAC	P	FAC	EP
FAT	P	FAT	P	FAT	1Q	FAT	2Q	FAT	1Qr	FAT	1Q	FAT	P	FAV	2Q	FAV	2P	FAV	4P

GROUND: Maidstone Road, Chatham ME4 6LR

Capacity: 2,000 **Seats:** 600 **Covered:** 600 **Shop:** Yes

Nearest Railway Station Chatham - 1.4km

Bus Route Bus stops outside the ground.

CORINTHIAN

Nickname: The Hoops   Club Colours: Green & white hoops

Founded 1972

Club Contact Details 01474 573 116   corinthians@billingsgroup.com

Previous Names: Welling United Reserves > 2009.
Previous Leagues: Southern 1985-91.
HONOURS
FA Comps: None
League: Southern Counties East 2003-04.

	10-11	11-12	12-13	13-14	14-15	15-16	16-17	17-18	18-19	19-20
	Kent P 12	Kent P 7	Kent P 4	SCE 5	SCE 6	SCE 6	SCEP 10	SCEP 9	SCEP 2	SCEP n&v
FAC		P	P	P	EP	P	EP	EPr	1Qr	EP
FAV	1P	2Q	1Q	1P	1P	1P	4P	2P	2P	

GROUND: Gay Dawn Farm, Valley Road, Longfield DA3 8LY
Capacity: **Seats:** Yes   **Covered:** Yes
Nearest Railway Station Longfield - 1.5 miles away

CROWBOROUGH ATHLETIC

Nickname: The Crows   Club Colours: Navy blue and sky blue

Founded 1894

Club Contact Details 07557 107 445   cafcsec@outlook.com

Previous Names: -
Previous Leagues: Sussex County 1974-2008. Isthmian 2008-09. Sussex County 2009-14.
HONOURS
FA Comps: None
League: Sussex County Division Two 1992-93, 2004-05, Division Three 2003-04, Division One 2007-08.

	10-11	11-12	12-13	13-14	14-15	15-16	16-17	17-18	18-19	19-20
	SxC1 12	SxC1 13	SxC1 15	SxC1 5	SCE 10	SCE 7	SCEP 2	SCEP 3	SCEP 13	SCEP n&v
FAC	EP	EP	P	EPr	EPr	EPr	EP	2Q	EPr	EP
FAV	1Q	1Q	1Q	1Q	2P	1Q	5P	4P	2P	1P

GROUND: Crowborough Co. Stadium, Alderbrook Rec, Fermor Road, TN6 3AN
Capacity: 2,000   **Seats:** 150   **Covered:** 150

DEAL TOWN

Nickname: The Hoops   Club Colours: Black & white

Founded 1908

Club Contact Details 01304 375 623   secretary@dealtownfc.co.uk

Previous Names: Deal Cinque Ports FC > 1920
Previous Leagues: Thanet. East Kent. Kent 1894-96, 1900-27, 32-39, 45-59, 72-84, Southern 1894-1901 & 84-90, Aetolian 1959-64, Greater London 1964-65, Metropolitan 1965-71, Metropolitan London 1971-72
HONOURS
FA Comps: FA Vase 1999-2000
League: Kent 1953-54. Southern Counties East 1999-2000.

	10-11	11-12	12-13	13-14	14-15	15-16	16-17	17-18	18-19	19-20
	Kent P 11	Kent P 15	Kent P 12	SCE 13	SCE 13	SCE 9	SCEP 13	SCEP 7	SCEP 11	SCEP n&v
FAC	P	P	P	P	Pr	2Q	EP	P	EPr	EP
FAV	1Q	2P	2P	1Q	1Q	2P	2Qr	1P	1P	5P

GROUND: Charles Sports Ground, St Leonards Road, Deal CT14 9AU
Capacity: 2,500   **Seats:** 180   **Covered:** 180   **Shop:** Yes
Nearest Railway Station Deal - 3/4 mile away

ERITH & BELVEDERE
Nickname: Deres   **Club Colours:** Blue & white   Founded 1922

Club Contact Details 07729 358 033   deres.secretary@hotmail.com

Previous Names: Belvedere & District FC (Formed 1918 restructured 1922)
Previous Leagues: Kent 1922-29, 31-39, 78-82. London. Corinthian 1945-63. Athenian 1963-78. Southern. Kent League 2005-13. Isthmian 2013-14.
HONOURS
FA Comps: None
League: Kent Division One / Premier 1981-82 / 2012-13.

	10-11	11-12	12-13	13-14	14-15	15-16	16-17	17-18	18-19	19-20
	Kent P 5	Kent P 2	Kent P 1	Isth1N 24	SCEP 3	SCEP 16	SCEP 20	SCE1 4	SCE1 2	SCEP n&v
FAC	2Q	1Q	EP	P	Pr	P	EP	P	EPr	P
FAV	2P	1Q	3P	FAT QF	2P	2P	1Q	1Pr	1Q	1P

GROUND: Park View Road, Welling DA16 1SY
Capacity: 4,000   **Seats:** 1,070   **Covered:** 1,000   **Shop:** Yes
Nearest Railway Station Welling - 1.1km

ERITH TOWN
Nickname: The Dockers   **Club Colours:** Red & black stripes   Founded 1956

Club Contact Details 07877 766 794   secretary@erithtown.co.uk

Previous Names: Woolwich Town 1959-89 and 1990-97.
Previous Leagues: London Metropolitan Sunday. London Spartan.
HONOURS
FA Comps: None
League: London Metropolitan Sunday Senior Section 1965-66, 70-71, 74-75.

	10-11	11-12	12-13	13-14	14-15	15-16	16-17	17-18	18-19	19-20
	Kent P 8	Kent P 4	Kent P 3	SCE 3	SCE 19	SCE 13	SCEP 17	SCEP 17	SCEP 6	SCEP n&v
FAC	2Q	2Q	EP	P	EP	P	P	1Q	2Q	EP
FAV	2Q	2P	2P	3P	2P	2Q	1Q	2P	3P	1Qr

GROUND: Erith Stadium, Avenue Road, Erith DA8 3AT
Capacity: **Seats:** Yes   **Covered:** Yes
Nearest Railway Station Erith

FISHER
Nickname: The Fish   **Club Colours:** Black & white stripes   Founded 1908

Club Contact Details 07854 172 490   secretary.fisherfc@yahoo.com

Previous Names: Fisher Athletic. Reformed as Fisher F.C. in 2009.
Previous Leagues: Parthenon, Kent Amateur, London Spartan, Southern, Isthmian, Conference.
HONOURS
FA Comps: None
League: Southern Southern Division 1982-83, Premier 86-87, Eastern 2004-05.

	10-11	11-12	12-13	13-14	14-15	15-16	16-17	17-18	18-19	19-20
	Kent P 16	Kent P 10	Kent P 14	SCEP 14	SCEP 16	SCEP 17	SCEP 19	SCE1 3	SCEP 3	SCEP n&v
FAC		P	EPr	EP	P	EP			EP	EP
FAV	1P	2Q	2Q	2Q	1Pr	2P		1P	1Qr	2P

GROUND: St Pauls Sports Ground, Salter Road, Rotherhithe, London SE16 5EF
Capacity: **Seats:** Yes   **Covered:** Yes
Nearest Railway Station Rotherhithe, on the London Overground (1 km)

GLEBE
Founded 2013

Nickname: **Club Colours:** Red & black

Club Contact Details 07432 291 838   lukejefferies@virginmedia.com

Previous Names: Glebe Wickham Youth Team founded in 1995 with an adult side formed in 2013.
Previous Leagues: Kent Invicta 2013-16.
HONOURS
FA Comps: None
League: Southern Counties east Division One 2016-17.

10-11	11-12	12-13	13-14	14-15	15-16	16-17	17-18	18-19	19-20
			K_lv 10	K_lv 7	K_lv 3	SCE1 1	SCEP 12	SCEP 8	SCEP n&v
					FAC EP	FAC EP	FAC 2Qr	FAC EP	FAC P
			FAV 2Q	FAV 1Q	FAV 1Q	FAV 3P	FAV 1Qr	FAV 2Q	FAV 4P

GROUND: Foxbury Avenue, Chislehurst, Bromley BR7 6SD
Capacity: 1,200 **Seats:** Yes **Covered:** Yes
Nearest Railway Station Sidcup - 1.9km
Bus Route Nos. 269 & 260.

HOLLANDS & BLAIR
Founded 1967

Nickname: Blair **Club Colours:** All red

Club Contact Details 01634 573 839   laurence.plummer@btinternet.com

Previous Names: Hollands & Blair United 1970-74
Previous Leagues: Rochester & District 1970-2004. Kent County 2004-11
HONOURS
FA Comps: None
League: Rochester & District Premier 1989-90, 93-94, 2002-03, 03-04. Kent County Division Two Easy 2004-05, Division One East 05-06, Premier 08-9, 10-11. Kent Invicta 2013-14, 14-15.

10-11	11-12	12-13	13-14	14-15	15-16	16-17	17-18	18-19	19-20
KC P 1	K_lv 3	K_lv 2	K_lv 1	K_lv 1	SCE 2	SCEP 8	SCEP 18	SCEP 18	SCEP n&v
						FAC Pr	FAC P	FAC EP	FAC EP
					FAV 2Q	FAV 1P	FAV 1P	FAV 1Q	FAV 2Q

GROUND: Star Meadow Sports Club, Darland Avenue, Gillingham, Kent ME7 3AN
Capacity: **Seats:** Yes **Covered:** Yes

K SPORTS
Founded 1919

Nickname: The Paperboys **Club Colours:** Black & white

Club Contact Details 07725 941 711   tonyhighsted@yahoo.co.uk

Previous Names: Reeds International. APM. APM Contrast.
Previous Leagues: Kent County >2015.
HONOURS
FA Comps: None
League: Kent Division Two 1929-30, 30-31, 31-32, 46-47.
Kent County Senior Division West 1959-60, 63-64, Premier West 1990-91.

10-11	11-12	12-13	13-14	14-15	15-16	16-17	17-18	18-19	19-20
KC1E 2	KC P 6	KC P 6	KC P 3	KC P 4	K_lv 6	SCE1 5	SCE1 2	SCEP 12	SCEP n&v
								FAC EPr	FAC EP
							FAV 1P	FAV 2Q	FAV 2Q

GROUND: Cobdown Sports & Social Club, Station Road, Ditton, Aylesford, Kent ME20 6AU
Capacity: **Seats:** **Covered:**
Nearest Railway Station Aylesford

LORDSWOOD
Nickname: Lords   **Club Colours:** Orange   Founded 1968

Club Contact Details 01634 669 138   slew1953@hotmail.co.uk

Previous Names: None.
Previous Leagues: Rochester & Dist. Kent County.
HONOURS
FA Comps: None
League: None

10-11	11-12	12-13	13-14	14-15	15-16	16-17	17-18	18-19	19-20
Kent P 13	Kent P 12	Kent P 5	SCE 11	SCE 15	SCE 4	SCEP 16	SCEP 8	SCEP 10	SCEP n&v
FAC EP	FAC P	FAC Pr	FAC EP	FAC Pr	FAC EP	FAC EPr	FAC EP	FAC EP	FAC EP
FAV 1P	FAV 1P	FAV 4P	FAV 3P	FAV 1P	FAV 3P	FAV 1P	FAV 3P	FAV 2P	FAV 2Q

GROUND: Martyn Grove, Northdane Way, Walderslade, ME5 8YE
Capacity: 600   **Seats:** 123   **Covered:** 123
Nearest Railway Station Chatham - 4.8km
Bus Route Lords Wood Leisure Centre - stop 30m away

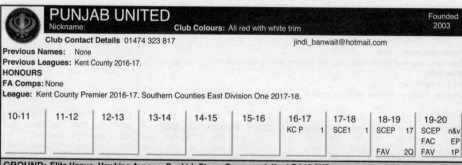

PUNJAB UNITED
Nickname: **Club Colours:** All red with white trim   Founded 2003

Club Contact Details 01474 323 817   jindi_banwait@hotmail.com

Previous Names: None
Previous Leagues: Kent County 2016-17.
HONOURS
FA Comps: None
League: Kent County Premier 2016-17. Southern Counties East Division One 2017-18.

10-11	11-12	12-13	13-14	14-15	15-16	16-17	17-18	18-19	19-20
						KC P 1	SCE1 1	SCEP 17	SCEP n&v
									FAC EP
								FAV 2Q	FAV 1P

GROUND: Elite Venue, Hawkins Avenue, Dunkirk Close, Gravesend, Kent DA12 5ND
Capacity: **Seats:**   **Covered:**
Nearest Railway Station Gravesend - 2.7km

SHEPPEY UNITED
Nickname: **Club Colours:** Red & white stripes   Founded 1890

Club Contact Details 01795 669 547   jon.longhurst@bond-group.co.uk

Previous Names: AFC Sheppy 2007-2010. Sheppey & Sheerness United after merger 2013-14.
Previous Leagues: Kent County > 2014.
HONOURS
FA Comps: None
League: Kent 1905-06, 06-07, 72-73, 74-75, 78-79, 94-95. Greater London Section B 1964-65.

10-11	11-12	12-13	13-14	14-15	15-16	16-17	17-18	18-19	19-20
KC1E 11	KC1E 4	KC P Exp	KC P 2	K_lv 5	K_lv 2	SCEP 6	SCEP 11	SCEP 7	SCEP n&v
						FAC EP	FAC P	FAC EP	FAC 1Q
		FAV 2Q			FAV 2Q	FAV 2Q	FAV 2P	FAV 3P	FAV 1P

GROUND: Havill Stadium, Holm Park, Queenborough Road ME12 3DB
Capacity: 1,450 **Seats:** 170 **Covered:** 470

TOWER HAMLETS

Nickname: Green Army   **Club Colours:** Orange & black

Founded 2000

Club Contact Details 020 8980 1885
Previous Names: Bethnal Green United 2000-2013.
Previous Leagues: Canery Wharf Summer League. Inner London. London Intermediate. Middlesex County >2009. Essex Senior 2009-20.
HONOURS
FA Comps: None
League: Middlesex County Premier Division 2008-09.

10-11	11-12	12-13	13-14	14-15	15-16	16-17	17-18	18-19	19-20
ESen 4	ESen 9	ESen 12	ESen 4	ESen 17	ESen 17	ESen 20	ESen 11	ESen 16	ESen n&v
			FAC P	FAC EP	FAC Pr	FAC P	FAC P	FAC EP	FAC P
			FAV 1P	FAV 1P	FAV 1Q	FAV 1Q	FAV 2P	FAV 1Q	FAV 2Q

GROUND: Phoenix FC, Mayplace Ground, Mayplace Road East, Barnehurst, Kent DA7 6JT
Capacity: 2,000   **Seats:** 439   **Covered:** Yes
Nearest Railway Station Barnehurst - 1.1km
Bus Route 492 stops at the ground

TUNBRIDGE WELLS

Nickname: The Wells   **Club Colours:** All red

Founded 1886

Club Contact Details 07912 060 857   secretary@twfcexec.com
Previous Names: None.
Previous Leagues: South Eastern. Southern Amateur 1908-11. Isthminan 1911-13. Spartan 1913-14. Kent.
HONOURS
FA Comps: None
League: Southern Amateur Section B 1909-10. Kent Division One 1984-85.

10-11	11-12	12-13	13-14	14-15	15-16	16-17	17-18	18-19	19-20
Kent P 6	Kent P 5	Kent P 7	SCE 4	SCE 5	SCE 14	SCEP 15	SCEP 15	SCEP 16	SCEP n&v
FAC 1Q	FAC P	FAC EP	FAC 1Q	FAC EP	FAC Pr	FAC EPr	FAC 2Q	FAC EPr	FAC P
FAV 3P	FAV 4P	FAV F	FAV 3P	FAV 4Pr	FAV 2P	FAV 1P	FAV 2Qr	FAV 1P	FAV 1Pr

GROUND: Culverden Stadium, Culverden Down, Tunbridge Wells TN4 9SG
Capacity: 3,750   **Seats:** 250   **Covered:** 1,000
Nearest Railway Station Tunbridge Wells 1.5km. High Brooms - 1.8km

WELLING TOWN

Nickname: The Boots   **Club Colours:** Green and black

Founded 2014

Club Contact Details 07891 431 735   info@wellingtontown.co.uk
Previous Names: None
Previous Leagues: Kent County 2016-18.
HONOURS
FA Comps: None
League: Kent County Division Two West 2017-18. Southern Counties East Division One 2018-19.

10-11	11-12	12-13	13-14	14-15	15-16	16-17	17-18	18-19	19-20
						KC3W 2	KC2W 1	SCE1 1	SCEP n&v
									FAC EP
									FAV 3P

GROUND: Bayliss Avenue, Thamesmead, London SE28 8NJ
Capacity: **Seats:**   **Covered:**
Nearest Railway Station Abbey Wood - 2 miles
Bus Route 177, 229 401, 472

DIVISION ONE

BRIDON ROPES
Nickname: The Ropes **Club Colours:** Blue and red

Founded 1935

Club Contact Details 0208 856 1923 cburtonsmith@gmail.com

HONOURS
FA Comps: None
League: Spartan Division Two 1991-92. Kent County Division One West 2009-10.

10-11	11-12	12-13	13-14	14-15	15-16	16-17	17-18	18-19	19-20
KC P 4	K_lv 4	K_lv 7	K_lv 8	K_lv 10	K_lv 5	SCE1 7	SCE1 5	SCE1 4	SCE1 n&v
						FAC EP			FAC P
					FAV 1P	FAV 1P	FAV 2Q	FAV 2Qr	FAV 2Q

GROUND: Charlton Park Lane, Charlton, London SE7 8QS
Nearest Railway Station Charlton - 1.3km

CROYDON
Nickname: The Trams **Club Colours:** Sky & navy blue

Founded 1953

Club Contact Details 02086 545524 (CH-0208 6548555) judy@kinetic-foundation.org.uk

HONOURS
FA Comps: None
League: Spartan 1963-64. Athenian Division Two 1965-66. Isthmian Division One 1999-00.

10-11	11-12	12-13	13-14	14-15	15-16	16-17	17-18	18-19	19-20
CCP 20	CCP 16	CCP 14	CCP 13	SCE 18	SCE 18	SCEP 11	SCEP 5	SCEP 20	SCE1 n&v
FAC P	FAC EP	FAC EP	FAC P	FAC 1Q	FAC 2Q	FAC Pr	FAC Pr	FAC P	FAC EP
FAV 1P	FAV 1Q	FAV 3P	FAV 2Q	FAV 1Qr	FAV 1P	FAV 4P	FAV 2P	FAV 1Q	FAV 2Q

GROUND: Croydon Sports Arena, Albert Road, South Norwood SE25 4QL
Nearest Railway Station Croydon Tramlink - 1/4 mile
Bus Route No.312

FC ELMSTEAD
Nickname: The Cocks **Club Colours:** Sky blue & red

Founded 1958

Club Contact Details 07711 287295 stewartmurphy1001@gmail.com

HONOURS
FA Comps: None
League: None

10-11	11-12	12-13	13-14	14-15	15-16	16-17	17-18	18-19	19-20
			KC3W 2	KC2W 2	K_lv 11	SCE1 11	SCE1 8	SCE1 13	SCE1 n&v
					FAV 1Q	FAV 1P	FAV 1Q	FAV 1Q	FAV 1Q

GROUND: Sutton Athletic FC, Lower Road, Hextable, Kent BR8 7RZ
Nearest Railway Station Swanley - 2.4km

FOREST HILL PARK
Nickname: **Club Colours:** All blue

Founded 1992

Club Contact Details 07774 294 236 info@fhpfc.co.uk

HONOURS
FA Comps: None
League: South London Alliance Division One 2005-06. Kent County Division Two West 2009-10.

10-11	11-12	12-13	13-14	14-15	15-16	16-17	17-18	18-19	19-20
KC1W 9	KC P 6	KC P 7	KC1W 10	KC1W 5	K_lv 13	SCE1 12	SCE1 16	SCE1 7	SCE1 n&v
							FAV 2Q	FAV 2Q	FAV 1Q

GROUND: Ladywell Arena, Silvermere Road, Catford, London SE6 4QX
Nearest Railway Station Ladywell and Catford Bridge.
Bus Route 47, 54, 75, 136, 181, 185, 199, 208

GREENWAYS
Nickname:
Club Colours: Green and black
Founded 1965

Club Contact Details 07889 313 935
greenwaysfc@hotmail.com

HONOURS
FA Comps: None
League: Gravesend Premier x7. Kent County Premier 1988-89.

10-11	11-12	12-13	13-14	14-15	15-16	16-17	17-18	18-19	19-20
KC1W 5	KC P 8	KC P 7	KC P 5	KC P 7	KC P 8	KC P 2	KC P 2	SCE1 10	SCE1 n&v
									FAV 1Q

GROUND: K Sports, Cobdown, Station Road, Ditton, Aylesford, Kent ME20 6AU

HOLMESDALE
Nickname: The Dalers
Club Colours: Green & yellow
Founded 1956

Club Contact Details 07875 730 862
mitchell1982@sky.com

HONOURS
FA Comps: None
League: Thorton Heath & District Division Six 1956-57, Two 61-62, One 71-72, Premier 86-87. Surrey South Eastern Comb. Prem 92-93. Kent County Div.1W 2005-06, Prem 06-07.

10-11	11-12	12-13	13-14	14-15	15-16	16-17	17-18	18-19	19-20
Kent P 14	Kent P 13	Kent P 16	SCE 10	SCE 14	SCE 19	SCE1 6	SCE1 7	SCE1 6	SCE1 n&v
FAC EP	FAC EP	FAC EP	FAC P	FAC P	FAC P	FAC EP	FAC EP		
FAV 1Q	FAV 1Q	FAV 2Q	FAV 2Q	FAV 1Q	FAV 1Qr	FAV 2Q	FAV 1Q	FAV 1Q	FAV 2Q

GROUND: Holmesdale Sp.& Soc.Club, 68 Oakley Rd, Bromley BR2 8HG
Nearest Railway Station Hayes - 2.1km

KENNINGTON
Nickname:
Club Colours: Amber & black
Founded 1888

Club Contact Details 01233 611 838
kevin@lab-services.co.uk

HONOURS
FA Comps: None
League: Kent County Premier 2017-18.

10-11	11-12	12-13	13-14	14-15	15-16	16-17	17-18	18-19	19-20
KC1E 10	KC1E 11	KC1E 4	KC1E 4	KC1E 2	KC P 2	KC P 4	KC P 1	SCE1 3	SCE1 n&v

GROUND: Homelands Stadium, Ashford Road, Kingsnorth, Ashford TN26 1NJ

KENT FOOTBALL UNITED
Nickname:
Club Colours: All blue
Founded 2010

Club Contact Details 07875 488 856
m.bolton.kfu@gmail.com

HONOURS
FA Comps: None
League: None

10-11	11-12	12-13	13-14	14-15	15-16	16-17	17-18	18-19	19-20
	K_lv 13	K_lv 11	K_lv 11	K_lv 15	K_lv 17	SCE1 4	SCE1 9	SCE1 14	SCE1 n&v
	FAV 2Q	FAV 1Q	FAV 1Q					FAV 1Q	FAV 1Q

GROUND: Glentworth Club, Lowfield Street, Dartford DA1 1JB
Nearest Railway Station Dartford - 0.8 km

LEWISHAM BOROUGH
Nickname: The Boro **Club Colours:** Blue
Founded 2003

Club Contact Details 07712 149980 — eno.mwamba@lbcfc.co.uk

HONOURS
FA Comps: None
League: Kent County Division One West 2003-04, Premier 2005-06.

10-11	11-12	12-13	13-14	14-15	15-16	16-17	17-18	18-19	19-20
KC P 6	K_lv 8	K_lv 16	K_lv 13	K_lv 16	K_lv 20	SCE1 19	SCE1 18	SCE1 11	SCE1 n&v
							FAV 1Q	FAV 1Q	

GROUND: Ladywell Arena, Silvermere Road, Catford, London SE6 4QX
Nearest Railway Station Ladywell and Catford Bridge.
Bus Route 47, 54, 75, 136, 181, 185, 199, 208

LYDD TOWN
Nickname: The Lydders **Club Colours:** Red and green
Founded 1885

Club Contact Details 01797 321 904 — brucemarchant@hotmail.com

HONOURS
FA Comps: None
League: Kent County Premier East 1969-70, 70-71, Senior East 1989-90, 90-91, 91-92, Division One East 92-93, 93-94.

10-11	11-12	12-13	13-14	14-15	15-16	16-17	17-18	18-19	19-20
KC2E 20	K_lv 12	K_lv 6	K_lv 2	K_lv 3	K_lv 8	SCE1 9	SCE1 10	SCE1 12	SCE1
							FAV 1Q	FAV 1Q	FAV 1Qr

GROUND: The Lindsey Field, Dengemarsh Road, Lydd, Kent TN29 9JH

MERIDIAN VP
Nickname: **Club Colours:** All sky blue
Founded 1995

Club Contact Details 07977 274 179 — dtamna@globalnet.co.uk

HONOURS
FA Comps: None
League: None

10-11	11-12	12-13	13-14	14-15	15-16	16-17	17-18	18-19	19-20
KC2W 12	K_lv 15	K_lv 15	K_lv 14	K_lv 12	K_lv 12	SCE1 17	SCE1 15	SCE1 18	SCE1 n&v
					FAV 1P	FAV 1Q	FAV 2P	FAV 1Q	FAV 1Q

GROUND: Meridian Sports & Social Club, Charlton Park Lane, London SE7 8QS
Nearest Railway Station Charlton - 1.3km

ROCHESTER UNITED
Nickname: **Club Colours:** Red and black
Founded 1982

Club Contact Details 07775 735 543 — toniwalker709@gmail.com

HONOURS
FA Comps: None
League: Rochester & District Division One 1997-98. Kent County Division One West 2007-08. Kent Invicta 2011-12.

10-11	11-12	12-13	13-14	14-15	15-16	16-17	17-18	18-19	19-20
KC P 15	K_lv 1	Kent P 13	SCE 15	SCE 20	SCE 15	SCEP 14	SCEP 20	SCE1 17	SCE1 n&v
					FAC 1Q	FAC Pr	FAC EPr	FAC EP	
				FAV 1P	FAV 2Q	FAV 2Q	FAV 1Q	FAV 1Q	FAV 1Q

GROUND: Rochester United Sports Ground, Rede Court Road, Strood ME2 3TU
Nearest Railway Station Strood - 2.1km

RUSTHALL
Nickname: The Rustics   **Club Colours:** Green & white stripes   Founded 1899

Club Contact Details 07976 386 527   deanjacquin@icloud.com

HONOURS
FA Comps: None
League: Tunbridge Wells 1904-05, 22-23, 23-24, 24-25, 25-26, 29-30, 30-31, 34-35, 37-38, 38-39, 51-52.
Kent county Division Two West 1983-84, Division One West 1984-85, 2004-05.

10-11	11-12	12-13	13-14	14-15	15-16	16-17	17-18	18-19	19-20
KC P 14	K_lv 11	K_lv 12	K_lv 7	K_lv 13	K_lv 19	SCE1 2	SCEP 19	SCEP 19	SCE1 n&v
							FAC EPr	FAC Pr	FAC EP
						FAV 2Q	FAV 1P	FAV 1P	FAV 1P

GROUND: Jockey Farm, Nellington Road, Rusthall, Tunbridge Wells TN4 8SH
Nearest Railway Station High Rocks - 1.5km

SNODLAND TOWN
Nickname: **Club Colours:** Royal blue & yellow   Founded 2012

Club Contact Details 07999 457 864   terry.reeves55@virginmedia.com

HONOURS
FA Comps: None
League: None

10-11	11-12	12-13	13-14	14-15	15-16	16-17	17-18	18-19	19-20
		KC P 11	KC P 4	KC P 9	KC1E 3	SCE1 8	SCE1 6	SCE1 15	SCE1 n&v
							FAV 1Q	FAV 1Q	FAV 1P

GROUND: Potyns Field, Paddlesworth Road, Snodland ME6 5DP
Nearest Railway Station Snodland - 1.3km

SPORTING CLUB THAMESMEAD
Nickname: The Acre   **Club Colours:** Red & black   Founded 1900

Club Contact Details 0208 320 4488   montyleach@hotmail.co.uk

HONOURS
FA Comps: None
League: South London Alliance Division One 2008-09.

10-11	11-12	12-13	13-14	14-15	15-16	16-17	17-18	18-19	19-20
KC2W 4	K_lv 10	K_lv 5	K_lv 9	K_lv 6	K_lv 9	SCE1 10	SCE1 12	SCE1 9	SCE1 n&v
					FAC P	FAC EP			
				FAV 1Q	FAV 1Qr	FAV 2P	FAV 2Q	FAV 2Q	FAV 1P

GROUND: Sporting Club Thamesmead, Bayliss Avenue, Thamesmead SE28 8NJ
Nearest Railway Station Abbey Wood - 1.8km

STANSFELD
Nickname: Palace   **Club Colours:** Yellow & blue stripes   Founded 1961

Club Contact Details 07861 885 590   stansfeldfc@hotmail.com

HONOURS
FA Comps: None
League: Kent County Division Two (Western) 1958-59, Premier (Western) 62-63, 63-64, 77-78, Senior (Western) 84-85, 86-87, 88-89, 89-90, Premier 94-95, 2009-10.

10-11	11-12	12-13	13-14	14-15	15-16	16-17	17-18	18-19	19-20
KC P 13	KC P 2	KC P 9	KC P 6	KC P 2	KC P 4	KC P 9	SCE1 13	SCE1 8	SCE1 n&v
							FAV 2Q	FAV 1Q	FAV 1Q

GROUND: Glebe FC, Foxbury Avenue, Chislehurst, Bromley BR7 6HA
Nearest Railway Station Sidcup - 1.9km

SUTTON ATHLETIC

Nickname: **Club Colours:** Green & white

Founded 1898

Club Contact Details 07778 053 433   guy.eldridge@btconnect.com

HONOURS

FA Comps: None

League: Dartford 1952-53, 53-54, 54-55, 56-57, 58-59, 59-60, 60-61, 61-62, 62-63, 63-64, 64-65.
Kent County D2W 68-69, D1W 69-70, PremW 70-71, SeniorW 76-77.

10-11		11-12		12-13		13-14		14-15		15-16		16-17		17-18		18-19		19-20	
KC P	11	K_lv	6	K_lv	8	K_lv	3	K_lv	4	K_lv	4	SCE1	3	SCE1	11	SCE1	5	SCE1	n&v
																		FAC	1Q
																FAV	1Q	FAV	1Q

GROUND: London Hire Stadium, Lower Road, Hextable, Kent BR8 7RZ

Nearest Railway Station Swanley - 2.4km

ARLESEY TOWN
Nickname: The Blues   **Club Colours:** Light & dark blue   Founded 1891

Club Contact Details 01462 734 504

Previous Names: None

Previous Leagues: Biggleswade & Dist., Bedfordshire Co. (South Midlands) 1922-26, 27-28, Parthenon, London 1958-60, United Co. 1933-36, 82-92, Spartan South Mid. 1992-2000, Isthmian 2000-04, 06-08, Southern 2004-07, 08-18.

HONOURS

FA Comps: FA Vase 1994-95.

League: South Midlands Premier 1951-52, 52-53, 94-95, 95-96. Spartan South Midlands Premier 1999-2000. United Counties Premier Division 1984-85. Isthmian Division Three 2000-01. Southern Division One Central 2010-11.

10-11		11-12		12-13		13-14		14-15		15-16		16-17		17-18		18-19		19-20	
SthC	1	SthP	18	SthP	6	SthP	15	SthP	22	SthC	16	SthC	15	SthC	22	SSM P	8	SSM P	n&v
FAC	1Q	FAC	1P	FAC	1P	FAC	3Q	FAC	1Q	FAC	1Q	FAC	Pr	FAC	1Q	FAC	EP	FAC	1Q
FAT	2Qr	FAT	2Q	FAT	2Qr	FAT	1P	FAT	2Qr	FAT	Pr	FAT	Pr	FAT	1Q	FAV	2Q	FAV	1Q

GROUND: New Lamb Meadow, Hitchin Road, Arlesey SG15 6RS

Capacity: 2,920 **Seats:** 150 **Covered:** 600   Yes

Nearest Railway Station Arlesey - 2.6km

Bus Route Prince of Wales - stop 100m away

AYLESBURY VALE DYNAMOES
Nickname: The Moles   **Club Colours:** Red & black   Founded 1930

Club Contact Details 01296 431 655

Previous Names: Negretti & Zambra FC 1930-54, Stocklake 1954-2000, Haywood United 00, Haywood FC 00-06, Aylesbury Vale 06-09, Aylesbury 09-19

Previous Leagues: Aylesbury District. Wycombe & District. Chiltern, Spartan South Midlands >2010. Southern 2010-19.

HONOURS

FA Comps: None

League: Spartan South Midlands Division One 2003-04, Premier Division 2009-10.

10-11		11-12		12-13		13-14		14-15		15-16		16-17		17-18		18-19		19-20	
SthC	8	SthC	20	SthC	12	SthC	16	SthC	3	SthC	8	SthC	19	Sth1E	21	SthC	19	SSM P	n&v
FAC	Pr	FAC	P	FAC	P	FAC	1Q	FAC	1Q	FAC	1Qr	FAC	P	FAC	1Q	FAC	Pr	FAC	P
FAT	1Qr	FAT	1Qr	FAT	P	FAT	1Q	FAT	1Q	FAT	1Qr	FAT	P	FAT	1Qr	FAT	P	FAV	1P

GROUND: SRD Stadium, Haywood Way, Aylesbury, Bucks. HP19 9WZ

Capacity: **Seats:** Yes   **Covered:** Yes   No

Nearest Railway Station Aylesbury Vale Parkway - 1.2km

Bus Route O'grady Way - stop 200m away

BALDOCK TOWN
Nickname: The Reds   **Club Colours:** All red   Founded 1905

Club Contact Details 07968 215 395

Previous Names: Baldock 1905-21. Folded in 2001 reformed as Baldock 2003-06. Baldock Town 2006-08. Baldock Town Letchworth 2008-11.

Previous Leagues: Herts County 1905-25, 46-47, 2007-13. Beds & Dist/South Midlands 1925-39, 47-54, 64-83. Parthenon 1954-59. London 1959-64. United Counties 1983-87. Southern 1987-2001. North Herts 2003-06. North & Mid Herts (FM) 2006-07.

HONOURS

FA Comps: None

League: Herts Senior County Northern Div. 1920-21, Div.1 2007-08, Premier 11-12. South Midlands Div.2 47-38, Div.1 49-50, Premier 27-28, 65-66, 67-68, 69-70.

10-11		11-12		12-13		13-14		14-15		15-16		16-17		17-18		18-19		19-20	
HertP	4	HertP	1	HertP	2	SSM1	7	SSM1	10	SSM1	3	SSM1	3	SSM1	2	SSM P	5	SSM P	n&v
								FAC	P	FAC	EP	FAC	EP	FAC	2Q	FAC	P	FAC	EP
FAV	1P					FAV	1P	FAV	1P	FAV	2Q	FAV	1P	FAV	1P	FAV	2P	FAV	1P

GROUND: Arlesey Town FC, Armadillo Stadium, Hitchin Road, Arlesey SG15 6RS

Capacity: 2,920 **Seats:** 150 **Covered:** 600

Nearest Railway Station Arlesey - 2.6km

Bus Route Prince of Wales - stop 100m away

BIGGLESWADE UNITED
Nickname: United   **Club Colours:** Red and navy   Founded 1959

Club Contact Details 07714 661 827   info@biggleswadeunited.com

Previous Names: None

Previous Leagues: North Hertfordshire 1959-69. Midlands 1969-84. Hertfordshire Senior County 1984-86. Bedford & District 1986-96. South Midlands 1996-97.

HONOURS

FA Comps: None

League: Bedford & District Division Two 1990-91, Division One 91-92, Premier 94-95, 95-96. South Midlands Division One 1996-97.

	10-11	11-12	12-13	13-14	14-15	15-16	16-17	17-18	18-19	19-20
SSM P	20	19	18	17	13	10	9	8	4	n&v
FAC	EP	P	P	1Q	1Q	1Q	1Q	EPr	EPr	P
FAV	2Q	1P	2Q	1Q	2Q	2P	2Pr	1P	1P	1Pr

GROUND: Second Meadow, Fairfield Rd, Biggleswade, Beds SG18 0BS
Capacity: 2,000 **Seats:** 260 **Covered:** 130
Nearest Railway Station Biggleswade - 0.9km
Bus Route Fairfield Road - stop 85m away

BROADFIELDS UNITED
Nickname: The Fighting Cocks   **Club Colours:** Blue and white   Founded 1993

Club Contact Details 01895 823 474   websterlocke@aol.com

Previous Names: None

Previous Leagues: Middlesex >2015

HONOURS

FA Comps: None

League: Southern Olympian Division Four 1994-95. Middlesex County Senior Division 1996-97.

	10-11	11-12	12-13	13-14	14-15	15-16	16-17	17-18	18-19	19-20
MidxP	5	8	5	15	4					
SSM1						11	11	4	2	
SSM P										n&v
FAC									P	EP
FAV				2Q	1Q	1Q	2P	1P	1P	1P

GROUND: Harefield United FC, Breakspear Road North, Harefield, Middlesex UB9 6PE
Capacity: 1,200 **Seats:** 150 **Covered:** Yes
Nearest Railway Station Denham - 3km
Bus Route Wickham Close - stop 150m away

COLNEY HEATH
Nickname: Magpies   **Club Colours:** Black & white stripes   Founded 1907

Club Contact Details 01727 824 325

Previous Names: None

Previous Leagues: Herts Senior County League 1953-2000

HONOURS

FA Comps: None

League: Herts County Division Two 1953-54 Division One A 55-56, Prem 58-99, 99-00, Division One 88-89, Spartan South Midlands Division One 2005-06.

	10-11	11-12	12-13	13-14	14-15	15-16	16-17	17-18	18-19	19-20
SSM P	5	8	13	3	14	20	18	11	6	n&v
FAC	1Q	P	EP	EP	P			2Qr	P	1Q
FAV	1P	1Q	2P	3Pr	1P		1P	1P	1Pr	2P

GROUND: The Recreation Ground, High St, Colney Heath, St Albans AL4 0NP
Capacity: **Seats:** Yes **Covered:** Yes
Nearest Railway Station Welham Green - 3.6km
Bus Route Crooked Billet Ph - stop 50m away

CRAWLEY GREEN

Founded 1992

Nickname: **Club Colours:** All maroon

Club Contact Details

Previous Names: None
Previous Leagues: None
HONOURS
FA Comps: None
League: Spartan South Midlands Division Two 2004-05.

10-11		11-12		12-13		13-14		14-15		15-16		16-17		17-18		18-19		19-20	
SSM1	4	SSM1	6	SSM1	4	SSM1	5	SSM1	7	SSM1	2	SSM P	11	SSM P	18	SSM P	10	SSM P	n&v
FAC	1Qr	FAC	EP	FAC	EP	FAC	P	FAC	EP	FAC	EP	FAC	P	FAC	P	FAC	P	FAC	EP
FAV	1Q	FAV	2Q	FAV	2Qr	FAV	1Q	FAV	2Q	FAV	2Q	FAV	1P	FAV	2P	FAV	1P	FAV	1P

GROUND: The Stadium at The Brache, Park Street, Luton LU1 3HH
Capacity: 4,000 **Seats:** 160 **Covered:** Yes

DUNSTABLE TOWN

Founded 1883

Nickname: The Duns / The Blues **Club Colours:** Blue & white

Club Contact Details 01582 891 433

Previous Names: Dunstable Town 1883-1976. Dunstable FC 1976-98.
Previous Leagues: Metropolitan & District 1950-61, 64-65. United Counties 1961-63. Southern 1965-76, 2004-09, 13-19.
HONOURS Spartan South Midlands 1998-2003, 09-13. Isthmian 2003-04.
FA Comps: None
League: Spartan South Midlands Division One 1999-00, Premier 2002-03, 12-13. Southern Division One Central 2013-14.

10-11		11-12		12-13		13-14		14-15		15-16		16-17		17-18		18-19		19-20	
SSM P	7	SSM P	2	SSM P	1	SthC	1	SthP	14	SthP	11	SthP	16	SthP	24	SthC	20	SSM P	n&v
FAC	EP	FAC	3Q	FAC	1Qr	FAC	2Q	FAC	2Q	FAC	3Q	FAC	1Q	FAC	1Q	FAC	Pr	FAC	1Q
FAV	5P	FAV	2P	FAV	3P	FAT	2Q	FAT	1Q	FAT	1Q	FAT	2Q	FAT	1Q	FAT	1Q	FAV	1Q

GROUND: Creasey Park Stadium, Brewers Hill Rd, Dunstable LU6 1BB
Capacity: 3,500 **Seats:** 350 **Covered:** 1000 **Shop:** Yes

Bus Route Langridge Court - stop 100m away

EDGWARE TOWN

Founded 1939

Nickname: The Wares **Club Colours:** Green and white

Club Contact Details 0208 205 1645

Previous Names: Edgware 1972-87. Original Edgware Town folded in 2008 and re-formed in 2014.
Previous Leagues: Corinthian 1946-63. Athenian 1963-84. Spartan 1984-90, 2006-07. Isthmian 1990-2006, 2007-08.
HONOURS
FA Comps: None
League: Middlesex Senior 1939-40, 43-44, 44-45 (shared). London Western Section 1945-46. London Spartan Premier 1987-88, 89-90. Isthmian Division Three 1991-92. Spartan South Midlands Premier 2006-07, Division One 2015-16.

10-11	11-12	12-13	13-14	14-15		15-16		16-17		17-18		18-19		19-20	
				SSM1	9	SSM1	1	SSM P	17	SSM P	10	SSM P	13	SSM P	n&v
								FAC	P	FAC	EPr	FAC	EP	FAC	EP
						FAV	3P	FAV	2Q	FAV	1P	FAV	2Q	FAV	2Q

GROUND: Silver Jubilee Park, Townsend Lane, London NW9 7NE
Capacity: 1,990 **Seats:** 298 **Covered:**
Nearest Railway Station Hendon - 1.1km
Bus Route Queensbury Road - stop 660m away

EYNESBURY ROVERS
Nickname: Rovers **Club Colours:** Royal blue & white Founded 1897

Club Contact Details

Previous Names: None
Previous Leagues: Biggleswade & District. St Neots Junior. Bed & District. South Midlands 1934-39. United Counties 1946-52, 63-2019. Eastern Counties 1952-63.
HONOURS
FA Comps: None
League: St Neots Junior 1910-11. Bedford & District Division Two 1926-27, 30-31, 31-32. United Counties Division 1 1976-77.

	10-11	11-12	12-13	13-14	14-15	15-16	16-17	17-18	18-19	19-20
	UCL 1 6	UCL 1 6	UCL 1 3	UCL 1 2	UCL P 11	UCL P 6	UCL P 5	UCL P 7	UCL P 6	SSM P n&v
				FAC EP		FAC EP	FAC 1Q	FAC P	FAC Pr	FAC EPr
	FAV 2Q	FAV 1Q	FAV 1Q	FAV 2P	FAV 1Qr	FAV 1P	FAV 1Q	FAV 1P	FAV 1Q	FAV 4P

GROUND: Alfred Hall Memorial Ground, Hall Road, Eynesbury, St Neots PE19 2SF
Capacity: **Seats:** Yes   **Covered:** Yes
Nearest Railway Station St Neots - 2.1km
Bus Route Ernulf Academy Forecourt - stop 150m away

HAREFIELD UNITED
Nickname: Hares **Club Colours:** Red & black Founded 1868

Club Contact Details 01895 823 474

Previous Names: None
Previous Leagues: Uxbridge & District, Great Western Comb, Panthernon, Middlesex, Athenian & Isthmian.
HONOURS
FA Comps: None
League: Great Western Comb. Division Two 1947-48, Division One 50-51. Parthenon 1964-65. Spartan South Midlands Division One 2018-19.

	10-11	11-12	12-13	13-14	14-15	15-16	16-17	17-18	18-19	19-20
	SSM P 21	SSM P 18	SSM P 10	SSM P 14	SSM P 4	SSM P 21	SSM1 8	SSM1 9	SSM1 1	SSM P n&v
	FAC P	FAC Pr	FAC 2Qr	FAC P	FAC P	FAC EPr	FAC 1Q			FAC P
	FAV 2Q	FAV 1Q	FAV 1Q	FAV 1Q	FAV 1P	FAV 1P	FAV 2Q	FAV 1Q	FAV 1P	FAV 2Q

GROUND: Preston Park, Breakespeare Road North, Harefield, UB9 6NE
Capacity: 1,200 **Seats:** 150 **Covered:** Yes **Shop:** No
Nearest Railway Station Denham - 3km
Bus Route Wickham Close - stop 150m away

HARPENDEN TOWN
Nickname: The Harps **Club Colours:** Yellow & blue Founded 1891

Club Contact Details

Previous Names: Harpenden FC 1891-1908.
Previous Leagues: Herts Senior County (founder member) 1898-1900, 1908-22, 48-57. Mid-Herts 1900-08. South Midlands 1957-97.
HONOURS
FA Comps: None
League: Herts Senior County Western Division 1910-11, 11-12, 20-21, Premier 50-51, 52-53, 54-55. South Midlands Division One 1989-90, Premier 61-62, 64-65.

	10-11	11-12	12-13	13-14	14-15	15-16	16-17	17-18	18-19	19-20
	SSM1 7	SSM1 5	SSM1 7	SSM1 8	SSM1 6	SSM1 4	SSM1 2	SSM P 3	SSM P 14	SSM P n&v
							FAC P	FAC EP	FAC P	FAC EP
						FAV 2Q	FAV 1Q	FAV 1P	FAV 1P	FAV 1Q

GROUND: Rothamstead Park, Amenbury Lane, Harpenden AL5 2EF
Capacity: **Seats:** Yes   **Covered:** Yes
Nearest Railway Station Harpenden - 0.6km
Bus Route Amenbury Lane - stop 250m away

LEIGHTON TOWN
Nickname: Reds   **Club Colours:** Red & white   Founded 1885

Club Contact Details 01525 373 311

Previous Names: Leighton United 1922-63

Previous Leagues: Leighton & District. South Midlands 1922-24, 26-29, 46-54, 55-56, 76-92. Spartan 1922-53, 67-74. Isthmian 1992-2004. Southern 2004-16.

HONOURS

FA Comps: None

League: South Midlands 1966-67, 91-92. Isthmian Division Two 2003-04.

	10-11		11-12		12-13		13-14		14-15		15-16		16-17		17-18		18-19		19-20
SthC	7	SthC	13	SthC	21	SthC	19	SthC	18	SthC	21	SSM P	16	SSM P	4	SSM P	11	SSM P	n&v
FAC	1Q	FAC	3Q	FAC	Pr	FAC	P	FAC	P	FAC	1Q	FAC	EP	FAC	P	FAC	EP	FAC	1Q
FAT	P	FAT	1Q	FAT	P	FAT	P	FAT	1Qr	FAT	1Q	FAV	2Q	FAV	QF	FAV	3P	FAV	QF

GROUND: Lake Street, Leighton Buzzard, Beds LU7 1RX
Capacity: 2,800 **Seats:** 400 **Covered:** 300
Nearest Railway Station Leighton Buzzard - 1.3km
Bus Route Morrisons (Lake St) - stop 60m away

LEVERSTOCK GREEN
Nickname: The Green / The Trees   **Club Colours:** White and green   Founded 1895

Club Contact Details 01442 246 280

Previous Names: None

Previous Leagues: West Herts (pre 1954) & Herts Senior County 1954-91. South Midlands 1991-97.

HONOURS

FA Comps: None

League: Herts Senior County Division One 1978-79. South Midlands Senior Division 1996-97.

	10-11		11-12		12-13		13-14		14-15		15-16		16-17		17-18		18-19		19-20
SSM P	4	SSM P	11	SSM P	15	SSM P	20	SSM P	15	SSM P	18	SSM P	12	SSM P	7	SSM P	17	SSM P	n&v
FAC	EP	FAC	EP	FAC	EP	FAC	EP	FAC	2Q	FAC	EP	FAC	EP	FAC	Pr	FAC	2Q	FAC	EPr
FAV	5P	FAV	2Pr	FAV	1Q	FAV	1Q	FAV	2Q	FAV	2Q	FAV	2P	FAV	2Q	FAV	3P	FAV	1Qr

GROUND: Pancake Lane, Leverstock Green, Hemel Hempstead, Herts HP2 4NQ
Capacity: 1,500 **Seats:** 50 **Covered:** 100
Nearest Railway Station Apsley - 3.2km
Bus Route Pancake Lane - stop 300m away

LONDON COLNEY
Nickname: Blueboys   **Club Colours:** Royal blue and white   Founded 1907

Club Contact Details 01727 822 132

Previous Names: None

Previous Leagues: Herts Senior 1955-93.

HONOURS

FA Comps: None

League: Herts Senior County 1956-57, 59-60, 86-87, 88-89. 89-90. South Midlands Senior Division 1994-95. Spartan South Midlands Premier Division 2001-02, 16-17, Division One 2011-12.

	10-11		11-12		12-13		13-14		14-15		15-16		16-17		17-18		18-19		19-20
SSM1	5	SSM1	1	SSM P	7	SSM P	7	SSM P	2	SSM P	2	SSM P	1	SSM P	13	SSM P	15	SSM P	n&v
FAC	1Q	FAC	EP	FAC	P	FAC	EPr	FAC	1Q	FAC	P	FAC	1Q	FAC	EPr	FAC	EP	FAC	1Q
FAV	1Q	FAV	1Q	FAV	2Q	FAV	1Q	FAV	3P	FAV	3P	FAV	1Pr	FAV	1P	FAV	1P	FAV	2Q

GROUND: Cotlandswick Playing Fields, London Colney, Herts AL2 1DW
Capacity: 1,000 **Seats:** Yes **Covered:** Yes
Nearest Railway Station Park Street - 2.3km
Bus Route Leisure Centre - stop 430m away

NEWPORT PAGNELL TOWN
Nickname: Swans   **Club Colours:** White & green
Founded 1963

Club Contact Details 01908 611 993
Previous Names: Newport Pagnell Wanderers > 1972.
Previous Leagues: North Bucks 1963-71. South Midlands 1971-73. United Counties 1973-2019.
HONOURS
FA Comps: None
League: United Counties Division One 1981-82, 2001-02.

	10-11	11-12	12-13	13-14	14-15	15-16	16-17	17-18	18-19	19-20
League	UCL P 3	UCL P 5	UCL P 6	UCL P 16	UCL P 10	UCL P 3	UCL P 10	UCL P 3	UCL P 8	SSM P n&v
FAC	1Q	Pr	1Q	P	EP	Pr	EP	Pr	EP	P
FAV	1P	4P	2P	2Q	2Q	1Q	QF	2P	4P	3P

GROUND: Willen Road, Newport Pagnell MK16 0DF
Capacity: 2,000 **Seats:** 100 **Covered:** 100

Bus Route Green Park Drive - stop 160m away

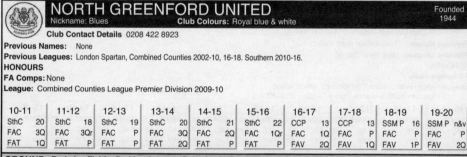

NORTH GREENFORD UNITED
Nickname: Blues   **Club Colours:** Royal blue & white
Founded 1944

Club Contact Details 0208 422 8923
Previous Names: None
Previous Leagues: London Spartan, Combined Counties 2002-10, 16-18. Southern 2010-16.
HONOURS
FA Comps: None
League: Combined Counties League Premier Division 2009-10

	10-11	11-12	12-13	13-14	14-15	15-16	16-17	17-18	18-19	19-20
League	SthC 20	SthC 18	SthC 19	SthC 20	SthC 21	SthC 22	CCP 13	CCP 13	SSM P 16	SSM P n&v
FAC	3Q	3Qr	P	3Q	2Q	1Qr	1Q	P	P	P
	FAT 1Q	FAT P	FAT P	FAT 2Q	FAT P	FAT P	FAV 2Q	FAV 1Q	FAV 1P	FAV 2Q

GROUND: Berkeley Fields, Berkley Avenue, Greenford UB6 0NX
Capacity: 2,000 **Seats:** 150 **Covered:** 100
Nearest Railway Station Greenford or Sudbury Hill (Piccadilly Line).
Bus Route No.92

OXHEY JETS
Nickname: Jets   **Club Colours:** Blue and white
Founded 1972

Club Contact Details 020 8421 6277
Previous Names: None
Previous Leagues: Youth Leagues > 1981. Herts Senior County 1981-2004.
HONOURS
FA Comps: None
League: Herts Senior County Premier 2000-01, 01-02, 02-03. Spartan South Midladns Division One 2004-2005.

	10-11	11-12	12-13	13-14	14-15	15-16	16-17	17-18	18-19	19-20
League	SSM P 19	SSM P 17	SSM P 3	SSM P 18	SSM P 12	SSM P 17	SSM P 15	SSM P 19	SSM P 9	SSM P n&v
FAC	1Q	2Q	P	EPr	EP	EPr	P	EP	EP	EP
FAV	2Q	1P	3P	2P	2P	2Q	1P	1P	2Q	2P

GROUND: Boundary Stadium, Altham Way, South Oxhey, Watford WD19 6FW
Capacity: 2,000 **Seats:** 150 **Covered:** 100 **Shop:** No
Nearest Railway Station Carpenders Park - 1km
Bus Route Lytham Avenue - stop 75m away

SPARTAN SOUTH MIDLANDS LEAGUE

POTTON UNITED
Nickname: Royals   Club Colours: All blue   Founded 1943

Club Contact Details 01767 261 100
Previous Names: None
Previous Leagues: South Midlands 1946-55. United Counties 1961-2018.
HONOURS
FA Comps: None
League: United Counties 1986-87, 88-89, Division One 2003-04.

	10-11	11-12	12-13	13-14	14-15	15-16	16-17	17-18	18-19	19-20
	UCL 1 15	UCL 1 15	UCL 1 16	UCL 1 10	UCL 1 3	UCL 1 7	UCL 1 6	UCL 1 2	SSM P 7	SSM P n&v
FAC	EP					EP		1Q	EP	EP
FAV	1Q	2Q	2Q	1Q	2Q	2Q	1Q	2Q	2Q	1Q

GROUND: The Hutchinson Hollow, Bigglewade Road, Potton, Beds SG19 2LX
Capacity: 2,000   Seats: Covered:
Nearest Railway Station Sandy - 4.4km
Bus Route The Ridgewy - stop 11m away

TRING ATHLETIC
Nickname: Athletic   Club Colours: Red and black   Founded 1958

Club Contact Details 01442 891 144 (MD)
Previous Names: Tring Athletic Youth 1958-71.
Previous Leagues: West Herts 1958-88.
HONOURS
FA Comps: None
League: West Herts Division One 1961-62, 64-65, 65-66.
Spartan South Midlands Senior Division 1999-2000.

	10-11	11-12	12-13	13-14	14-15	15-16	16-17	17-18	18-19	19-20
	SSM P 2	SSM P 6	SSM P 22	SSM P 10	SSM P 10	SSM P 12	SSM P 5	SSM P 17	SSM P 2	SSM P n&v
FAC	1Q	P	Pr	P	EP	P	EP	EP	EP	EP
FAV	3P	2P	1Q	3P	3P	1P	4P	5P	3Pr	1P

GROUND: Grass Roots Stadium, Pendley Sports Centre, Cow Lane, Tring HP23 5NS
Capacity: 2,000   Seats: 125   Covered: 100+   Shop: Yes
Nearest Railway Station Tring - 1.5km
Bus Route Bus stops at the ground.

WEMBLEY

Nickname: The Lions   Club Colours: Red   Founded 1946

Club Contact Details 0208 904 8169
Previous Names: None
Previous Leagues: Middlesex Senior. Spartan 1949-51. Delphian 1951-56. Corinthian 1956-63. Athenian 1963-75. Isthmian 1975-2006. Combined Counties 2006-14.
HONOURS
FA Comps: None
League: Middlesex Senior 1947-48. Spartan Division One Western 1950-51.

	10-11	11-12	12-13	13-14	14-15	15-16	16-17	17-18	18-19	19-20
	CCP 14	CCP 10	CCP 15	CCP 9	SSM P 7	SSM P 11	SSM P 4	SSM P 9	SSM P 12	SSM P n&v
FAC	EP	1Q	Pr	Pr	EPr	Pr	Pr	P	EP	P
FAV	2Q	2Qr	1P	1P	2P	1Q	3P	2P	2Q	2Q

GROUND: Vale Farm, Watford Road, Sudbury, Wembley HA0 3HG.
Capacity: 2450   Seats: 350   Covered: 950   Shop: No
Nearest Railway Station Sudbury Town Underground - 1km Sudbury & Harrow Road
Bus Route Butlers Green - stop 150m away

IN: Hackney Wicks (LM - ECS).
OUT: FC Broxbourne Borough (WD), Brimsdown (LM - ECS).

SPARTAN SOUTH MIDLANDS LEAGUE

DIVISION ONE

AMERSHAM TOWN
Nickname: The Magpies **Club Colours:** Black & white stripes

Founded 1890

Club Contact Details

HONOURS
FA Comps: None
League: Wycombe & District Combination 1902-03, 19-20, 20.21.
Hellenic Division One 1962-63, Premier 63-64.

10-11	11-12	12-13	13-14	14-15	15-16	16-17	17-18	18-19	19-20
SSM1 20	SSM1 20	SSM1 20	SSM1 16	SSM1 21	SSM2 12	SSM2 16	SSM2 6	SSM1 17	SSM1 n&v
	FAV 2Q	FAV 2P				FAV 1Q	FAV 1Q	FAV 2Q	FAV 2Q

GROUND: Spratleys Meadow, School Lane, Amersham, Bucks HP7 0EL

AMPTHILL TOWN
Nickname: The Amps **Club Colours:** Amber and black

Founded 1881

Club Contact Details 01525 404 440

HONOURS
FA Comps: None
League: South Midlands Premier Division 1959-60.

10-11	11-12	12-13	13-14	14-15	15-16	16-17	17-18	18-19	19-20
SSM1 16	SSM1 2	SSM P 5	SSM P 2	SSM P 21	SSM1 14	SSM1 14	SSM1 14	SSM1 10	SSM1 n&v
FAC EP									
FAV 2Q	FAV 4P	FAV 5P	FAV QF	FAV 2P	FAV 1Q	FAV 1Q	FAV 1P	FAV 1Q	FAV 1Q

GROUND: Ampthill Park, Woburn Street, Ampthill MK45 2HX
Nearest Railway Station Flitwick - 3.1km. Millbrook - 3.4km
Bus Route Alameda Road - stop 117m away

BEDFORD
Nickname: The B's **Club Colours:** Black & white

Founded 1957

Club Contact Details

HONOURS
FA Comps: None
League: None

10-11	11-12	12-13	13-14	14-15	15-16	16-17	17-18	18-19	19-20
SSM1 13	SSM1 12	SSM1 5	SSM1 3	SSM1 3	SSM P 22	SSM1 19	SSM1 12	SSM1 5	SSM1 n&v
FAC EP	FAC EP			FAC EP	FAC EP	FAC EP			
FAV 2Q	FAV 2Q		FAV 1Q	FAV 2Q	FAV 1Q	FAV 1Q	FAV 1Qr	FAV 1Q	FAV 2Q

GROUND: McMullen Park, Meadow Lane, Cardington, Bedford, MK44 3SB
Nearest Railway Station Bedford St Johns - 3.8km
Bus Route Meadow Lane - stop 141m away

BUCKINGHAM ATHELTIC
Nickname: The Ath **Club Colours:** Sky blue & navy blue

Founded 1933

Club Contact Details 01280 816 945 (MD)

HONOURS
FA Comps: None
League: North Bucks Premier Division 1984-85. South Midlands Division One 1985-86, 90-91, Spartan South Midlands Division Two 2002-03.

10-11	11-12	12-13	13-14	14-15	15-16	16-17	17-18	18-19	19-20
SSM1 18	SSM1 18	SSM1 11	SSM1 13	SSM1 15	SSM1 8	SSM1 10	SSM1 7	SSM1 4	SSM1 n&v
FAV 1Qr	FAV 1Q	FAV 2Q	FAV 2Q	FAV 1Qr	FAV 2Q	FAV 1Q	FAV 1P	FAV 1Pr	FAV 1P

GROUND: Stratford Fields, Stratford Road, Buckingham MK18 1NY

Bus Route High Street - stop 206m away

ENFIELD BOROUGH
Nickname: Panthers   **Club Colours:** Red & black

Founded 2016

Club Contact Details 07493 377 484

HONOURS
FA Comps: None
League: None

10-11	11-12	12-13	13-14	14-15	15-16	16-17	17-18	18-19	19-20
						SSM2 3	SSM1 10	SSM1 9	SSM1 n&v
							FAV 2P	FAV 1P	FAV 2Q

GROUND: Wingate & Finchley FC, Maurice Rebak Stadium, Summers Lane, N12 0PD
Nearest Railway Station New Southgate - 2.3km

HACKNEY WICK
Nickname: The Wickers   **Club Colours:** Yellow & black

Founded 1995

Club Contact Details 07388 372 989 (Secretary)

HONOURS
FA Comps: None
League: Essex Sunday Corinthian 2011-12.

10-11	11-12	12-13	13-14	14-15	15-16	16-17	17-18	18-19	19-20
	EsxSC 1	ESen 10	ESen 20	ESen 15	ESen 8	ESen 17	ESen 21	EC1S 6	EC1S n&v
					FAC EP	FAC EP	FAC EP	FAC P	FAC EP
				FAV 2Q	FAV 1Q	FAV 1P	FAV 1Q	FAV 2Q	FAV 1P

GROUND: Witham Town FC, Spa Road, Witham CM8 1UN
Nearest Railway Station Witham - 1.1km
Bus Route Cuppers Close - stop 200m away

HILLINGDON BOROUGH
Nickname: The Hillmen, Boro   **Club Colours:** White & royal blue

Founded 1990

Club Contact Details 01895 639 544   accounts@middlesexstadium.com

HONOURS
FA Comps: None
League: None

10-11	11-12	12-13	13-14	14-15	15-16	16-17	17-18	18-19	19-20
SSM P 16	SSM P 10	SSM P 19	SSM P 11	SSM P 22	SSM1 16	SSM1 9	SSM1 16	SSM1 16	SSM1 n&v
FAC EP	FAC EP	FAC EP	FAC P	FAC EP	FAC EPr				
FAV 1P	FAV 1P	FAV 2Q	FAV 1P	FAV 2Q	FAV 1Q	FAV 2Q	FAV 2Q		FAV 2Q

GROUND: Middlesex Stadium, Breakspear Rd, Ruislip HA4 7SB
Nearest Railway Station Willow Lawn - 737m
Bus Route Howletts Lane - stop 98m away

LANGFORD
Nickname: Reds   **Club Colours:** Red & white

Founded 1908

Club Contact Details 01462 816 106

HONOURS
FA Comps: None
League: Bedford & District 1931-32, 49-50. South Midlands Premier Division 1988-89.

10-11	11-12	12-13	13-14	14-15	15-16	16-17	17-18	18-19	19-20
SSM P 23	SSM1 10	SSM1 16	SSM1 19	SSM1 13	SSM1 18	SSM1 4	SSM1 17	SSM1 11	SSM1 n&v
FAC EP	FAC EP						FAC EP		
FAV 1P	FAV 1Q	FAV 2Q	FAV 1Q	FAV 1Qr	FAV 1Q	FAV 1Q	FAV 2Q	FAV 2Q	FAV 2Qr

GROUND: Forde Park, Langford Road, Henlow, Beds SG16 6AF
Nearest Railway Station Arlesey - 1.9km
Bus Route Newtown (Langford Rd) - stop 24m away

LONDON LIONS
Nickname: Lions **Club Colours:** All blue
Founded 1995

Club Contact Details 0208 441 6051

HONOURS
FA Comps: None
League: Hertfordshire Senior County Division One 1999-2000, Premier 09-10, 16-17. Spartan South Midlands Division One 2012-13.

10-11	11-12	12-13	13-14	14-15	15-16	16-17	17-18	18-19	19-20
SSM1 8	SSM1 7	SSM1 1	SSM P 22	SSM1 17	HertP 5	HertP 1	SSM1 6	SSM1 6	SSM1 n&v
		FAC 1Q	FAC EPr					FAC P	
	FAV 1Q	FAV 2P	FAV 2Q			FAV 1Q	FAV 2P	FAV 2Q	FAV 1Q

GROUND: Rowley Lane Sports Ground, Rowley Lane, Barnet EN5 3HW
Nearest Railway Station Elstree & Borehamwood - 2.4km
Bus Route Buses stop on Rowley Lane.

LONDON TIGERS
Nickname: Tigers **Club Colours:** Amber and black
Founded 1986

Club Contact Details 020 7289 3395 (10am-6pm)   info@londontigers.org

HONOURS
FA Comps: None
League: None

10-11	11-12	12-13	13-14	14-15	15-16	16-17	17-18	18-19	19-20
SSM P 12	SSM P 14	SSM P 20	SSM P 15	SSM P 17	SSM P 13	SSM P 21	SSM P 15	SSM P 20	SSM1 n&v
FAC EP			FAC P	FAC 2Q	FAC EPr	FAC EPr			FAC EP
FAV 1Q		FAV 2Q	FAV 1Q	FAV 1Q	FAV 1P	FAV 2Q		FAV 1Q	FAV 2Q

GROUND: Northwood Park, Cheshunt Avenue, Northwood HA6 1HR

MILTON KEYNES ROBINS
Nickname: Robins **Club Colours:** All red
Founded 1883

Club Contact Details 01908 375 978

HONOURS
FA Comps: None
League: Aylesbury & Dist. 1902-03, 67-68. North Bucks 24-25, 28-29, 33-34, 35-36, 36-37, 38-39, 48-49, 49-50. Southern Southern Division 90 -91. United Counties 83-84, 85-86.

10-11	11-12	12-13	13-14	14-15	15-16	16-17	17-18	18-19	19-20
UCL 1 16	UCL 1 11	UCL 1 15	UCL 1 11	UCL 1 16	UCL 1 17	UCL 1 5	UCL 1 7	SSM1 14	SSM1 n&v
							FAC EP		
FAV 1Q	FAV 2P		FAV 2Q		FAV 1Q	FAV 1P	FAV 1Q		FAV 2P

GROUND: Irish Centre, Manor Fields, Bletchley, Milton Keynes MK2 2HX
Nearest Railway Station Fenny Stratford - 0.6km
Bus Route Wharfside - stop 300m away

NEW SALAMIS
Nickname: **Club Colours:** Red & white
Founded 1971

Club Contact Details

HONOURS
FA Comps: Sunday Cup 2015-16.
League: KOPA 1984-85, 93-94, 99-00, 00-01, 08-09, 10-11, 11-12, 12-13, 14-15, 15-16, 16-17, 17-18

10-11	11-12	12-13	13-14	14-15	15-16	16-17	17-18	18-19	19-20
KOPA 1	KOPA 1	KOPA 1		KOPA 1	KOPA 1	KOPA 1	KOPA 1	HertP 2	SSM1 n&v
									FAV 1P

GROUND: Haringey Boro FC, Coles Park, White Hart Lane, Tottenham N17 7JP
Nearest Railway Station White Hart Lane - 1.5km. Wood Green (UG) - 1.5km
Bus Route W3 stops outside the ground (see directions).

PARK VIEW

Founded

Nickname: **Club Colours:** White

Club Contact Details

HONOURS

FA Comps:

League: Middlesex County Division One C&E 2007-08. Amateur Combination Intermediate Division One North 2014-15, Senior Division Two North 15-15, Senior Division One 16-17.

10-11	11-12	12-13	13-14	14-15	15-16	16-17	17-18	18-19	19-20
		LonCom	LonCom 2	AMCl1N 1	AmC2N 1	AmC1 1	SSM2 1	SSM1 13	SSM1 n&v
									FAV 1Q

GROUND: New River Stadium, White Hart Lane, Wood Green N22 5QW

RAYNERS LANE

Founded 1933

Nickname: The Lane   **Club Colours:** Yellow and green

Club Contact Details 0208 868 8724

HONOURS

FA Comps: None

League: Hellenic Division One 1982-83, Division One East 2012-13.

10-11	11-12	12-13	13-14	14-15	15-16	16-17	17-18	18-19	19-20
Hel1E 7	Hel1E 3	Hel1E 1	Hel1E 9	Hel1E 7	Hel1E 5	Hel1E 11	SSM1 13	SSM1 12	SSM1 n&v
					FAV 2Q	FAV 2Q	FAV 2Q	FAV 1P	FAV 1Q

GROUND: Tithe Farm Social Club, Rayners Lane, South Harrow HA2 0XH

Nearest Railway Station Rayners Lane underground - 680m

Bus Route Clitheroe Avenue - stop 64m away

SHEFFORD TOWN & CAMPTON

Founded 2010

Nickname: **Club Colours:** Red & white

Club Contact Details

HONOURS

FA Comps: None

League: Bedfordshire County Premier Division 2011-12, 17-18, 18-19.

10-11	11-12	12-13	13-14	14-15	15-16	16-17	17-18	18-19	19-20
BedCP 2	BedCP 1	BedCP 7	BedCP 11	BedCP 5	BedCP 9	BedCP 7	BedCP 1	BedCP 1	SSM1 n&v

GROUND: Shefford Sports Club, Hitchin Road, Shefford SG17 5JD

ST PANTELEIMON

Founded 2015

Nickname: The Saints   **Club Colours:** Yellow & blue

Club Contact Details

HONOURS

FA Comps: None

League: Middlesex County Division One (Central & East) 2018-19.

10-11	11-12	12-13	13-14	14-15	15-16	16-17	17-18	18-19	19-20
					KOPA	KOPA	KOPA	Midx1SE 1	SSM1 n&v
								FAV 1P	FAV 1Q

GROUND: North Greenford United, Berkeley Fields

Nearest Railway Station Greenford or Sudbury Hill (Piccadilly Line).

Bus Route No.92

STOTFOLD
Nickname: The Eagles   **Club Colours:** Amber and black

Founded 1904

Club Contact Details 01462 730 765

HONOURS
FA Comps: None
League: South Midlands 1980-81. United Counties Premier 2007-08.

	10-11		11-12		12-13		13-14		14-15		15-16		16-17		17-18		18-19		19-20	
SSM P	13	SSM P	9	SSM P	14	SSM P	19	SSM P	16	SSM P	15	SSM P	13	SSM P	21	SSM P	19	SSM1	n&v
FAC	EP	FAC	1Q	FAC	Pr	FAC	P	FAC	EP	FAC	EP	FAC	1Q	FAC	EP	FAC	EP	FAC	P
FAV	3P	FAV	1Q	FAV	1Q	FAV	1P	FAV	2Q	FAV	2P	FAV	1Qr	FAV	1Q	FAV	2Q	FAV	1Q

GROUND: Roker Park, The Green, Stotfold, Hitchin, Herts SG5 4AN
Nearest Railway Station Arlesey - 2.9km
Bus Route The Green - stop 80m away

WINSLOW UNITED
Nickname: The Ploughmen   **Club Colours:** Yellow and blue

Founded 1891

Club Contact Details 01296 713 057

HONOURS
FA Comps: None
League: South Midlands Division One 1974-75.

	10-11		11-12		12-13		13-14		14-15		15-16		16-17		17-18		18-19		19-20	
SSM2	4	SSM2	7	SSM1	14	SSM1	9	SSM1	14	SSM1	19	SSM1	16	SSM1	3	SSM1	3	SSM1	n&v
																FAC	EP	FAC	EP
		FAV	1P	FAV	2Q	FAV	2Q	FAV	1Qr	FAV	2Q	FAV	2Q	FAV	1Q	FAV	2Q	FAV	2Q

GROUND: The Recreation Ground, Elmfields Gate, Winslow, Bucks MK18 3JG

Bus Route Elmside - stop 210m away

ANSTEY NOMADS
Nickname: Nomads **Club Colours:** Red & white

Founded 1947

Club Contact Details 07946 856 430

Previous Names: -
Previous Leagues: Leicestershire Senior. East Midlands Counties 2009-18.
HONOURS
FA Comps: None
League: Leicestershire Senior 1951-52, 53-54, 81-82, 82-83, 2008-09, Division Two 1973-74.

10-11		11-12		12-13		13-14		14-15		15-16		16-17		17-18		18-19		19-20	
EMC	12	EMC	9	EMC	14	EMC	17	EMC	14	EMC	4	EMC	17	EMC	2	UCL 1	2	UCL P	n&v
		FAC	EP	FAC	EP							FAC	EP			FAC	2Q	FAC	EP
FAV	1P	FAV	2Q	FAV	2Q	FAV	1Q	FAV	1Q	FAV	1P	FAV	2Q	FAV	1Q	FAV	1Q	FAV	2Q

GROUND: Davidson Homes Park, Cropston Road, Anstey, Leicester LE7 7BP
Capacity: 1000 **Seats:** 100 **Covered:** Yes
Nearest Railway Station Leicester - 6.2km

BOSTON TOWN
Nickname: Poachers **Club Colours:** All blue

Founded 1964

Club Contact Details 01205 365 470 btfcsec@hotmail.co.uk

Previous Names: Boston 1964-1994
Previous Leagues: Lincolnshire. Central Alliance 1965-66. Eastern Counties 1966-68. Midland 1968-82. Northern Counties East 1982-87. Central
HONOURS Midlands 1987-91.
FA Comps: None
League: Lincolnshire 1964-65. Central Alliance 1965-65. Midland 1974-75, 78-79, 80-81.
Central Midlands Supreme 1988-89. United Counties League 1994-95, 2000-01.

10-11		11-12		12-13		13-14		14-15		15-16		16-17		17-18		18-19		19-20	
UCL P	7	UCL P	14	UCL P	10	UCL P	14	UCL P	12	UCL P	16	UCL P	20	UCL P	13	UCL P	17	UCL P	n&v
FAC	Pr	FAC	P	FAC	EP	FAC	P	FAC	1Q	FAC	EP	FAC	EP	FAC	3Q	FAC	EP	FAC	2Q
FAV	2Q	FAV	2P	FAV	3P	FAV	1P	FAV	2Q	FAV	1Q	FAV	2Q	FAV	2Q	FAV	1Q	FAV	1Q

GROUND: DWB Stadium, Tattershall Road, Boston, Lincs PE21 9LR
Capacity: 6,000 **Seats:** 450 **Covered:** 950
Nearest Railway Station Boston - 1.6km
Bus Route Bus stops outside the ground

COGENHOE UNITED
Nickname: Cooks **Club Colours:** All blue

Founded 1967

Club Contact Details 01604 890 521 cogenhoeunited@outlook.com

Previous Names: None
Previous Leagues: Central Northants Combination 1967-85.
HONOURS
FA Comps: None
League: Central Northants Combination Division Two 1951-52, Premier 80-81, 82-83, 83-84. United Counties 2004-05.

10-11		11-12		12-13		13-14		14-15		15-16		16-17		17-18		18-19		19-20	
UCL P	15	UCL P	12	UCL P	8	UCL P	5	UCL P	5	UCL P	5	UCL P	13	UCL P	8	UCL P	7	UCL P	n&v
FAC	P	FAC	P	FAC	EP	FAC	EPr	FAC	P	FAC	2Q	FAC	P	FAC	P	FAC	EP		
FAV	1P	FAV	2P	FAV	2Q	FAV	1Q	FAV	1Q	FAV	1P	FAV	1Q	FAV	4P	FAV	2P		

GROUND: Compton Park, Brafield Road, Cogenhoe NN7 1ND
Capacity: 5,000 **Seats:** 100 **Covered:** 200

Bus Route Orchard Way - stop 190m away

DEEPING RANGERS
Nickname: Rangers   **Club Colours:** Claret and blue   Founded 1964

Club Contact Details 01778 344 701   secretary@deepingrangersfc.co.uk

Previous Names: None
Previous Leagues: Peterborough & District 1966 - 1999.
HONOURS
FA Comps: None
League: United Counties Premier Division 2006-07.

	10-11	11-12	12-13	13-14	14-15	15-16	16-17	17-18	18-19	19-20
UCL P	14	4	5	4	9	10	2	5	2	n&v
FAC	EP	2Q	EP	EP	EP	2Q	1Q	2Q	Pr	2Q
FAV	1P	3P	2P	2Q	3P	2Q	1Qr	3P	5P	2P

GROUND: The Haydon Whitham Stadium, Outgang Road, Market Deeping PE6 8LQ
Capacity: 2,000 **Seats:** 164 **Covered:** 250

Bus Route Buttercup Court - stop 720m away

DESBOROUGH TOWN
Nickname: Ar Tam   **Club Colours:** All royal blue   Founded 1896

Club Contact Details 01536 761 350

Previous Names: None
Previous Leagues: Northamptonshire change name to United Counties in 1934.
HONOURS
FA Comps: None
League: Northamptonshire/United Counties 1900-01, 01-02, 06-07, 20-21, 23-24, 24-25, 27-28 / 48-49, 66-67.

	10-11	11-12	12-13	13-14	14-15	15-16	16-17	17-18	18-19	19-20
UCL P	19	16	11	4	14	15	4	9	9	n&v
FAC	1Q	EPr	EPr	P	EP	EP	P	P	P	EP
FAV	2Q	1P	2P	2P	2Q	1Q	1P	4P	3P	1Q

GROUND: Waterworks Field, Braybrooke Road, Desborough NN14 2LJ
Capacity: 8,000 **Seats:** 250 **Covered:** 500

Bus Route Bus stops outside the ground.

HARBOROUGH TOWN
Nickname: The Bees   **Club Colours:** Yellow and black   Founded 1976

Club Contact Details 01858 467 339

Previous Names: Harborough Town Juniors 1976-2008. Juniors merged with adult team Spencer United to form today's club.
Previous Leagues: Northants Combination.
HONOURS
FA Comps: None
League: Northants Combination Premier Division 2009-10.

	10-11	11-12	12-13	13-14	14-15	15-16	16-17	17-18	18-19	19-20
	UCL 1 17	UCL 1 2	UCL P 19	UCL P 17	UCL P 20	UCL P 11	UCL P 11	UCL P 11	UCL P 11	UCL P n&v
FAC					P	P	P	P	P	EP
FAV		1Pr	2Q	1P	1Q	1Q	1P	1Q	2Q	2P

GROUND: Bowden's Park, Northampton Road, Market Harborough, Leics. LE16 9HF
Capacity: **Seats:** Yes **Covered:** Yes
Nearest Railway Station Market Harborough - 1.5km
Bus Route Leisure Centre - stop 200m away

HOLBEACH UNITED

Nickname: Tigers **Club Colours:** Gold & black

Founded 1929

Club Contact Details 01406 424 761

Previous Names: None
Previous Leagues: King's Lynn. Peterborough & District 1936-46. United Counties 1946-55, Eastern 1955-62, Midland Counties 1962-63.
HONOURS
FA Comps: None
League: United Counties 1989-90, 02-03, 12-13.

	10-11	11-12	12-13	13-14	14-15	15-16	16-17	17-18	18-19	19-20
UCL P	17	6	1	11	6	4	7	4	5	n&v
FAC	EP	Pr	1Q	P	P	2Qr	1Q	1Q	EP	P
FAV	2Q	1P	2Q	1P	5P	2P	2P	2P	3P	1P

GROUND: Carters Park, Park Road, Holbeach, Lincs PE12 7EE
Capacity: 4,000 **Seats:** 200 **Covered:** 450 **Shop:** No

Bus Route Carter's Park - stop 70m away

LEICESTER NIRVANA

Nickname: **Club Colours:** Red and black

Founded 2008

Club Contact Details 01162 660 009 nirvanafc@hotmail.co.uk

Previous Names: Thurnby Rangers and Leicester Nirvana merged to form today's club in.2008. Thurnby Nirvana 2008-15.
Previous Leagues: Leicestershire Senior >2010 East Midland Counties 2010-14
HONOURS
FA Comps: None
League: Leicestershire Senior Division One 1997-98, 2000-01, Premier Division 04-05. East Midland Counties 2013-14.

	10-11	11-12	12-13	13-14	14-15	15-16	16-17	17-18	18-19	19-20
EMC / UCL P	9	7	3	1	2	2	17	6	12	n&v
FAC		1Qr	1Qr	EPr	P	P	EP	EP	EP	Pr
FAV	1P	1Q	1Q	2Q	4P	4P	2Q	2P	5P	2P

GROUND: Hamilton Park, Sandhills Avenue, Leicester LE5 1LU
Capacity: **Seats:** Yes **Covered:** Yes
Nearest Railway Station Syston - 3.9km
Bus Route Lakeview Chase - stop 70m away

LOUGHBOROUGH UNIVERSITY

Nickname: The Scholars **Club Colours:** Purple

Founded 1920

Club Contact Details 07561 468 745 footballsecretary@lboro.ac.uk

Previous Names: Loughborough College
Previous Leagues: Leicestershire Senior. Midland Combination. Midland Alliance 2009-14. Midland 2014-19.
HONOURS
FA Comps: None
League: Midland Combination 2008-09.

	10-11	11-12	12-13	13-14	14-15	15-16	16-17	17-18	18-19	19-20
MidAl / MFLP / UCL P	4	5	4	14	20	14	18	18	18	n&v
FAC	EP	1Q	P	1Q	P	P	P	1Q	Pr	P
FAV	2Q	1P	1Q	2P	1Q	1Pr	2Q	2Q	1P	2P

GROUND: Loughborough Uni Stadium, Holywell Sports Complex, Holywell Park LE11 3QF
Capacity: 3,300 **Seats:** Yes **Covered:** Yes
Nearest Railway Station Loughborough - 4km
Bus Route Wheatsheaf stop - 172m away

LUTTERWORTH TOWN

Nickname: The Swifts   **Club Colours:** Orange and black

Founded 1955

Club Contact Details 07927 744 247   lutterworthtownfc@hotmail.com

Previous Names: -
Previous Leagues: Leicestershrie Senior >2017
HONOURS
FA Comps: None
League: Leicestershire Senior Division Two 1980-81, Premier 90-91, 2016-17.
United Counties Division One 2018-19.

10-11	11-12	12-13	13-14	14-15	15-16	16-17	17-18	18-19	19-20
LeicS1 15	LeicS1 14	LeicS1 6	LeicS1 6	LeicS1 7	LeicS1 3	LeicSP 1	UCL 1 3	UCL 1 1	UCL P n&v
								FAC EP	FAC 1Q
							FAV 1P	FAV 1Q	FAV 4P

GROUND: Dunley Way, Lutterworth, Leicestershire, LE17 4NP
Capacity: **Seats:** Yes   **Covered:** Yes

Bus Route Elizabethan Way - stop 300m away

NORTHAMPTON O.N.C.

Nickname: The Chens   **Club Colours:** White and navy

Founded 1946

Club Contact Details 01604 634 045

Previous Names: Chenecks FC 1946-60. ON (Old Northamptonians) Chenecks 1960-
Previous Leagues: Northampton Minor 1946-50. Northampton Town 1950-69.
HONOURS
FA Comps: None
League: United Counties Division One 1977-78, 79-80.

10-11	11-12	12-13	13-14	14-15	15-16	16-17	17-18	18-19	19-20
UCL 1 14	UCL 1 12	UCL 1 11	UCL 1 6	UCL 1 6	UCL 1 2	UCL P 12	UCL P 17	UCL P 15	UCL P n&v
						FAC EPr	FAC P	FAC EP	FAC EP
					FAV 2Q	FAV 1P	FAV 1P	FAV 1Q	FAV 1P

GROUND: Old Northamptonians Sports Ground, Billing Road NN1 5RT
Capacity: 1,000 **Seats:** Yes **Covered:** Yes
Nearest Railway Station Northampton - 2.7km
Bus Route School for Boys - stop 80m away

OADBY TOWN

Nickname: The Poachers   **Club Colours:** All red

Founded 1937

Club Contact Details 01162 715 728

Previous Names: Oadby Imperial > 1951.
Previous Leagues: Leicestershire Senior. Midland Alliance > 2011. East Midlands Counties 2011-12.
HONOURS
FA Comps: None
League: Leicestershire Senior Division Two 1951-52, Premier 63-64, 67-68, 68-69, 72-73, 94-95, 96-97, 97-98, 98-99. Midland
Alliance 99-00. United Counties Division One 2013-14.

10-11	11-12	12-13	13-14	14-15	15-16	16-17	17-18	18-19	19-20
MidAl 22	EMC 3	UCL 1 4	UCL 1 1	UCL P 13	UCL P 21	UCL P 19	UCL P 19	UCL P 10	UCL P n&v
FAC 2Q	FAC Pr	FAC P	FAC EP	FAC EP	FAC 2Q	FAC EP	FAC EP	FAC EP	FAC EP
FAV 1Q	FAV 5P	FAV 2P	FAV 2P	FAV 1P	FAV 2Q	FAV 1Q	FAV 1Q	FAV 1Q	FAV 1Q

GROUND: Freeway Park, Wigston Road, Oadby LE2 5QG
Capacity: 5,000 **Seats:** 224 **Covered:** 224 **Shop:** Yes
Nearest Railway Station South Wigston - 3.6km
Bus Route Brabazon Road - stop 35m away

PETERBOROUGH NORTHERN STAR

Nickname: Star   **Club Colours:** Black & white   Founded 1900

Club Contact Details 01733 552 416   clubsecretary@pnsfc.co.uk

Previous Names: Eye United 1900-31. Northam Star SC 1931-51. Eye United 1951-2005.
Previous Leagues: Peterborough Lge >2003
HONOURS
FA Comps: None
League: Peterborough 2002-03. United Counties League Division One 2008-09.

10-11		11-12		12-13		13-14		14-15		15-16		16-17		17-18		18-19		19-20	
UCL P	6	UCL P	7	UCL P	13	UCL P	9	UCL P	7	UCL P	17	UCL P	15	UCL P	16	UCL P	16	UCL P	n&v
				FAC	1Q	FAC	P	FAC	P	FAC	EP	FAC	EP	FAC	EP	FAC	EP	FAC	P
		FAV	QF	FAV	2P	FAV	2Q	FAV	3P	FAV	2Q	FAV	1P	FAV	2P	FAV	2P	FAV	1P

GROUND: Chestnut Avenue, Peterborough, Cambs PE1 4PE
Capacity: 1,500 **Seats:** Yes **Covered:** yes
Nearest Railway Station Peterborough - 2.6km
Bus Route Hawthorn Road - stop 35m away

PINCHBECK UNITED

Nickname: **Club Colours:** Red and black   Founded 1935

Club Contact Details 07786 984 987

Previous Names: -
Previous Leagues: Peterborough & Distroct >2017
HONOURS
FA Comps: None
League: Peterborough & District Premier Division 1989-90, 90-91, 2011-12.
United Counties Division One 2017-18.

10-11		11-12		12-13		13-14		14-15		15-16		16-17		17-18		18-19		19-20	
		P&D P	1	P&D P	15	P&D P	15	P&D P	7	P&D P	3	P&D P	2	UCL 1	1	UCL P	4	UCL P	n&v
																FAC	EP	FAC	EP
														FAV	1Q	FAV	2Q	FAV	1P

GROUND: Sir Harley Stewart Field, Winfrey Avenue, Spalding PE11 1DA
Capacity: **Seats:** Yes **Covered:** Yes
Nearest Railway Station Spalding - 0.2km
Bus Route Broad Street - stop 100m away

QUORN

Nickname: Reds   **Club Colours:** All red   Founded 1924

Club Contact Details 07891 512 346

Previous Names: Quorn Methodists >1952
Previous Leagues: Leicestershire Senior, Midland Alliance > 2007. NPL 2007-2012. United Counties 2012-13. Midland Alliance 2013-14.
Midland 2014-19.
HONOURS
FA Comps: None
League: Leicestershire Senior 2000-01

10-11		11-12		12-13		13-14		14-15		15-16		16-17		17-18		18-19		19-20	
NP1S	15	NP1S	21	UCL P	7	MidAl	5	MFLP	11	MFLP	17	MFLP	11	MFLP	11	MFLP	6	UCL P	n&v
FAC	P	FAC	2Q	FAC	1Q	FAC	Pr	FAC	P	FAC	EP	FAC	EP	FAC	P	FAC	1Q	FAC	EP
FAT	1Q	FAT	P	FAV	1P	FAV	1Q	FAV	2Q	FAV	2P	FAV	3P	FAV	2P	FAV	2P	FAV	2P

GROUND: Farley Way Stadium, Farley Way, Quorn, Leicestershire LE12 8RB
Capacity: 1,550 **Seats:** 350 **Covered:** 250
Nearest Railway Station Quorn & Woodhouse - 1.5km
Bus Route Alexander Road stop - 189m away

ROTHWELL CORINTHIANS
Nickname: Corinthians **Club Colours:** Red and white

Founded 1934

Club Contact Details 01536 711 706

Previous Names: None
Previous Leagues: Kettering & District Amateur/East Midlands Alliance 1934-95.
HONOURS
FA Comps: None
League: None

10-11	11-12	12-13	13-14	14-15	15-16	16-17	17-18	18-19	19-20
UCL P 21	UCL 1 8	UCL 1 17	UCL 1 15	UCL 1 2	UCL P 14	UCL P 16	UCL P 15	UCL P 18	UCL P n&v
FAC EP	FAC P	FAC EP			FAC EP	FAC EP	FAC EP	FAC P	FAC 1Q
FAV 1Qr	FAV 1Q	FAV 1Q	FAV 1Q	FAV 2Q	FAV 2Qr	FAV 2P	FAV 1Qr	FAV 1Q	FAT 2P

GROUND: Sergeants Lawn, Desborough Road, Rothwell NN14 6JQ
Capacity: **Seats:** 50   **Covered:** 200
Nearest Railway Station Kettering - 5.6km

RUGBY TOWN
Nickname: The Valley **Club Colours:** Sky blue

Founded 1956

Club Contact Details 01788 844 806

Previous Names: Valley Sports 1956-71, Valley Sport Rugby 1971-73, VS Rugby 1973-2000, Rugby United 2000-05
Previous Leagues: Rugby & District 1956-62, Coventry & Partnership, North Warwickshire 1963-69, United Counties 1969-75 West Midlands 1975-83. Southern 1983-2015. Northern Premier 2015-17. Midland Football 2017-18.
HONOURS
FA Comps: FA Vase 1982-83.
League: Southern Midland Division 1986-87. Midland Combination Division 1 2001-02.

10-11	11-12	12-13	13-14	14-15	15-16	16-17	17-18	18-19	19-20
SthC 6	SthC 6	SthC 2	SthC 2	SthC 6	NP1S 9	NP1S 21	MFLP 6	UCL P 3	UCL P n&v
FAC 1Q	FAC Pr	FAC 1Qr	FAC 3Qr	FAC 2Q	FAC 3Qr	FAC 2Q	FAC P	FAC EP	FAC EP
FAT 2Q	FAT Pr	FAT 1Qr	FAT 1Qr	FAT P	FAT P	FAT Pr	FAV 2Pr	FAV 1P	FAV 2P

GROUND: Butlin Road, Rugby, Warwicks CV21 3SD
Capacity: 6,000 **Seats:** 750 **Covered:** 1,000 **Shop:** Yes
Nearest Railway Station Rugby - 1km
Bus Route Jolly Brewers stop - 127m away

SHEPSHED DYNAMO
Nickname: Dynamo **Club Colours:** Black & white

Founded 1994

Club Contact Details 07866 500 187   dannypole@aol.com

Previous Names: Shepshed Albion/Charterhouse > 1994
Previous Leagues: Leics Sen 1907-16,19-27, 46-50, 51-81, Mid Co 81-82,N.C.E. 82-83, Sth 83-88, 96-04, N.P.L.88-93, 04-12, Mid Com 93-94, Mid All 94-95,13-14. UCL 12-13. Midland 2014-19.
HONOURS
FA Comps: Leicestershire Senior Cup x7
League: Midland Counties 1981-82. Northern Counties East 1982-83. Midland Alliance 1995-96.

10-11	11-12	12-13	13-14	14-15	15-16	16-17	17-18	18-19	19-20
NP1S 21	NP1S 22	UCL P 9	MidAl 16	MFLP 16	MFLP 4	MFLP 15	MFLP 7	MFLP 7	UCL P n&v
FAC Pr	FAC Pr	FAC EP	FAC P	FAC 1Q	FAC 1Qr	FAC EP	FAC 2Q	FAC EPr	FAC EP
FAT 1Q	FAT P	FAV 2P	FAV 2Q	FAV 2P	FAV 1Q	FAV 4P	FAV 3P	FAV 4P	FAV 3P

GROUND: The Dovecote, Butt Hole Lane, Shepshed, Leicestershire LE12 9BN
Capacity: 2,050 **Seats:** 570 **Covered:** 400 **Shop:** Yes

Bus Route Market Place stop - 229m away

SLEAFORD TOWN

Nickname: Town   **Club Colours:** Green and black

Founded 1968

Club Contact Details 01529 415 951

Previous Names: None
Previous Leagues: Lincolnshire 1968-2003.
HONOURS
FA Comps: None
League: United Counties Division One 2005-06.

10-11	11-12	12-13	13-14	14-15	15-16	16-17	17-18	18-19	19-20
UCL P 18	UCL P 19	UCL P 18	UCL P 13	UCL P 19	UCL P 7	UCL P 14	UCL P 18	UCL P 13	UCL P n&v
FAC EP	FAC EP	FAC P	FAC 1Q	FAC EP	FAC EP	FAC P	FAC EP	FAC EP	FAC EP
FAV 1Q	FAV 2Q	FAV 1P	FAV 2Q	FAV 2Q	FAV 4P	FAV 3Pr	FAV 1Q	FAV 1Pr	FAV 1Q

GROUND: Eslaforde Park, Boston Road, Sleaford, Lincs NG34 9GH
Capacity: 1,000   **Seats:** 88   **Covered:** 88
Nearest Railway Station Sleaford - 1.4km
Bus Route Eslaforde Park - stop 90m away

WELLINGBOROUGH TOWN

Nickname: Doughboys   **Club Colours:** Yellow & blue

Founded 1867

Club Contact Details 01933 441 388

Previous Names: Original team (Formed 1867) folded in 2002 reforming in 2004
Previous Leagues: Metropolitan. Southern.
HONOURS
FA Comps: None
League: United Counties 1964-65.

10-11	11-12	12-13	13-14	14-15	15-16	16-17	17-18	18-19	19-20
UCL P 5	UCL P 8	UCL P 15	UCL P 8	UCL P 15	UCL P 20	UCL P 9	UCL P 14	UCL P 14	UCL P n&v
FAC 1Q	FAC EP	FAC P	FAC EPr	FAC EP	FAC EP	FAC EP	FAC P	FAC P	FAC P
FAV 1P	FAV 1Q	FAV 1Q	FAV 2Q	FAV 2Q	FAV 2Q	FAV 2Q	FAV 1Q	FAV 2P	FAV 3P

GROUND: Dog and Duck, London Road, Wellingborough NN8 2DP
Capacity: 2,500   **Seats:** Yes   **Covered:** Yes
Nearest Railway Station Wellingborough - 1.2km
Bus Route The Dog & Duck Pub - stop 50m away

DIVISION ONE

AYLESTONE PARK
Nickname: Club Colours: Red Founded 1967

Club Contact Details 0116 278 5485

HONOURS
FA Comps: None
League: None

10-11	11-12	12-13	13-14	14-15	15-16	16-17	17-18	18-19	19-20
LeicSP 8	LeicSP 3	EMC 7	EMC 18	EMC 19	EMC 5	EMC 4	EMC 9	UCL 1 8	UCL 1 n&v
						FAC EP	FAC P		
	FAV 2Q		FAV 2Q	FAV 1Q	FAV 2Q	FAV 1Q	FAV 1Q	FAV 1P	FAV 1Q

GROUND: Mary Linwood Recreation Ground, Saffron Lane, Leicester LE2 6TG
Nearest Railway Station South Wigston - 1.1km

BIRSTALL UNITED SOCIAL
Nickname: Club Colours: White and navy Founded 1961

Club Contact Details 0116 267 1230

HONOURS
FA Comps: None
League: Leicester Mutual Division One 1972-73, 73-74, 75-76.
Leicestershire Senior Division Two 1976-77, Premier 2015-16.

10-11	11-12	12-13	13-14	14-15	15-16	16-17	17-18	18-19	19-20
LeicSP 9	LeicSP 6	LeicSP 11	LeicSP 4	LeicSP 4	LeicSP 1	EMC 3	EMC 8	UCL 1 17	UCL 1 n&v
							FAC P		
	FAV 2Q	FAV 1Q				FAV 2Qr	FAV 1Q	FAV 2Q	FAV 2Q

GROUND: Meadow Lane, Birstall LE4 4FN
Nearest Railway Station Syston

BLACKSTONES
Nickname: Stones Club Colours: Green and white Founded 1920

Club Contact Details 01780 757 835 imacgilli@outlook.com

HONOURS
FA Comps: None
League: Peterborough & District 1918-19, Division Two 1961-62, Division One 75-76.

10-11	11-12	12-13	13-14	14-15	15-16	16-17	17-18	18-19	19-20
UCL P 9	UCL P 11	UCL P 20	UCL 1 20	UCL 1 17	UCL 1 10	UCL 1 14	UCL 1 8	UCL 1 5	UCL 1 n&v
FAC EPr	FAC EP	FAC P	FAC EP						
FAV 2Qr	FAV 1Q	FAV 2Q	FAV 2Q	FAV 2Q	FAV 1P	FAV 2Q	FAV 1Q	FAV 1Q	FAV 2Q

GROUND: Lincoln Road, Stamford, Lincs PE9 1SH
Nearest Railway Station Stamford - 1.5km
Bus Route Junction with Kesteven Rd - stop 75m away

BOURNE TOWN
Nickname: Wakes Club Colours: Claret & sky blue Founded 1883

Club Contact Details 07709 785 273

HONOURS
FA Comps: None
League: Peterborough & District 1933-34, 39-40, 45-46, 46-47. Central Alliance Division One South 59-60. United Counties Premier 65-66, 68-69, 69-70, 71-72, 90-91.

10-11	11-12	12-13	13-14	14-15	15-16	16-17	17-18	18-19	19-20
UCL 1 12	UCL 1 14	UCL 1 10	UCL 1 21	UCL 1 10	UCL 1 5	UCL 1 15	UCL 1 10	UCL 1 13	UCL 1 n&v
					FAV 2Q	FAV 1Q	FAV 2Q	FAV 1Q	FAV 2Q

GROUND: Abbey Lawn, Abbey Road, Bourne, Lincs PE10 9EN

Bus Route Nowells Lane - stop 105m away

BUGBROOKE ST MICHAELS
Nickname: Badgers · Club Colours: White and black · Founded 1929

Club Contact Details 01604 830 707 · graybags05@btinternet.com

HONOURS
FA Comps: None
League: Central Northants Combination 1968-69, 69-70, 71-72, 76-77, 85-86.
United Counties Division One 1998-99.

10-11	11-12	12-13	13-14	14-15	15-16	16-17	17-18	18-19	19-20
UCL 1 3	UCL 1 3	UCL 1 7	UCL 1 18	UCL 1 11	UCL 1 18	UCL 1 3	UCL 1 18	UCL 1 4	UCL 1 n&v
	FAC P	FAC 1Q	FAC EP						FAC P
FAV 2Q	FAV 1P	FAV 2Q	FAV 2Q	FAV 1Q	FAV 1Q			FAV 2Qr	FAV 1Q

GROUND: Birds Close, Gayton Road, Bugbrooke NN7 3PH

Bus Route Bakers Arms Pub - stop 500m away

BURTON PARK WANDERERS
Nickname: The Wanderers · Club Colours: Blue & black · Founded 1961

Club Contact Details 07794 959 915

HONOURS
FA Comps: None
League: None

10-11	11-12	12-13	13-14	14-15	15-16	16-17	17-18	18-19	19-20
UCL 1 8	UCL 1 9	UCL 1 19	UCL 1 8	UCL 1 18	UCL 1 19	UCL 1 19	UCL 1	UCL 1 12	UCL 1 n&v
				FAV 2Q	FAV 1Qr	FAV 1Q	FAV 2Q	FAV 2Q	FAV 1Q

GROUND: Latimer Park, Polwell Lane, Burton Latimer, Northants NN15 5PS
Nearest Railway Station Kettering - 4.1km
Bus Route Station Road - stop 120m away

HARROWBY UNITED
Nickname: The Arrows · Club Colours: Blue · Founded 1949

Club Contact Details 01476 401 201

HONOURS
FA Comps: None
League: Midlands Regional Alliance Premier Division 1989-90.
United Counties Division One 1991-92.

10-11	11-12	12-13	13-14	14-15	15-16	16-17	17-18	18-19	19-20
		UCL 1 6	UCL 1 3	UCL P 17	UCL P 18	UCL P 21	UCL 1 5	UCL 1 7	UCL 1 n&v
				FAC EP	FAC EP	FAC P	FAC EP		
			FAV 1P	FAV 2Q	FAV 1P	FAV 1Q	FAV 1P	FAV 2Q	FAV 2Q

GROUND: Harrowby Stadium, Dickens Road, Grantham NG31 9QY
Nearest Railway Station Grantham - 2.6km
Bus Route St Wulframs School - stop 100m away

HOLWELL SPORTS
Nickname: · Club Colours: Yellow and green · Founded 1902

Club Contact Details 01664 812 080

HONOURS
FA Comps: None
League: Leic Senior Premier 1911-12, 87-88, 91-92, 92-93, Division One 1984-85.
Leicester & District 1907-08, 08-09. Melton Mowbray & Dist Am 1933-34.

10-11	11-12	12-13	13-14	14-15	15-16	16-17	17-18	18-19	19-20
EMC 13	EMC 11	EMC 5	EMC 9	EMC 8	EMC 16	EMC 16	EMC 18	UCL 1 14	UCL 1 n&v
FAC EPr		FAC EP	FAC EP	FAC 1Q	FAC 1Qr				
FAV 2P	FAV 1P	FAV 1Q	FAV 3P	FAV 2Q	FAV 2Q	FAV 1P	FAV 2Q	FAV 1Q	FAV 1Q

GROUND: Welby Road, Asfordby Hill, Melton Mowbray, Leicestershire LE14 3RD
Nearest Railway Station Melton Mowbray - 2.8km

HUNTINGDON TOWN
Nickname: The Hunters   **Club Colours:** Red & black   Founded 1995

Club Contact Details 07974 664 818

HONOURS
FA Comps: None
League: Cambridgeshire Division 1B 1999-2000.
United Counties Division One 2011-12.

10-11	11-12	12-13	13-14	14-15	15-16	16-17	17-18	18-19	19-20
UCL 1 5	UCL 1 1	UCL P 4	UCL P 2	UCL P 16	UCL P 22	UCL P 22	UCL 1 12	UCL 1 18	UCL 1 n&v
	FAC 1Q	FAC 1Q	FAC 1Q	FAC EP	FAC EPr	FAC EP	FAC EP		
FAV 2Q	FAV 2Q	FAV 1Q	FAV 3P	FAV 2P	FAV 1Q	FAV 2Q	FAV 2Q	FAV 1Q	FAV 1P

GROUND: Jubilee Park, Kings Ripton Road,, Huntingdon, Cambridgeshire PE28 2NR
Nearest Railway Station Huntingdon - 3.4km
Bus Route Newnham Close - stop 1km away

IRCHESTER UNITED
Nickname: The Romans   **Club Colours:** Red and black   Founded 1885

Club Contact Details 01933 312 877

HONOURS
FA Comps: None
League: Rushden & District 1928-29, 29-30, 36-37. Northants / United Counties Division Two 1930-31, 31-32 / United Counties Division One 2009-10.

10-11	11-12	12-13	13-14	14-15	15-16	16-17	17-18	18-19	19-20
UCL P 10	UCL P 20	UCL P 21	UCL 1 19	UCL 1 15	UCL 1 16	UCL 1 8	UCL 1 13	UCL 1 10	UCL 1 n&v
	FAC EP	FAC EP	FAC EP						
FAV 1Q	FAV 2Q	FAV 2Q	FAV 2Q	FAV 1P	FAV 1Q	FAV 2Q	FAV 2Q	FAV 2P	FAV 1Q

GROUND: Alfred Street, Irchester NN29 7DR
Nearest Railway Station Wellingborough - 3.1km
Bus Route Alfred Street - stop 100m away

LONG BUCKBY AFC
Nickname: Bucks   **Club Colours:** All claret   Founded 1937

Club Contact Details 07749 393 045   lbafc.dja@gmail.com

HONOURS
FA Comps: None
League: United Counties Division Three 1969-70, Division Two 70-71, 71-72, Premier Division 2011-12.

10-11	11-12	12-13	13-14	14-15	15-16	16-17	17-18	18-19	19-20
UCL P 4	UCL P 1	UCL P 16	UCL P 18	UCL P 21	UCL 1 6	UCL 1 13	UCL 1 17	UCL 1 15	UCL 1 n&v
FAC EP	FAC 3Q	FAC EP	FAC EP	FAC EPr	FAC 1Q				
FAV 5P	FAV 3P	FAV 1Pr	FAV 1Q	FAV 2Q	FAV 2Q	FAV 1Q	FAV 1Q	FAV 2Q	FAV 2P

GROUND: Station Road, Long Buckby NN6 7PL
Nearest Railway Station Long Buckby - 0.3km
Bus Route Watson Road - stop 70m away

LUTTERWORTH ATHLETIC
Nickname: The Athletic   **Club Colours:** Green & white   Founded 1983

Club Contact Details 01455 554 046   djones20335783@aol.com

HONOURS
FA Comps: None
League: Leicester & District Division Two 1994-95, Premier 2004-05.

10-11	11-12	12-13	13-14	14-15	15-16	16-17	17-18	18-19	19-20
LeicSP 6	LeicSP 2	EMC 13	UCL 1 5	UCL 1 4	UCL 1 11	UCL 1 12	UCL 1 11	UCL 1 6	UCL 1 n&v
FAV 1Q	FAV 1P	FAV 2Q	FAV 1Q		FAV 1Q	FAV 1Q	FAV 1Q	FAV 1Q	FAV 1Q

GROUND: Weston Arena, Hall Park, Hall Lane, Bitteswell, Lutterworth LE17 4LN

Bus Route Manor Farm - stop 1.5km away

MELTON TOWN
Nickname: **Club Colours:** Red   **Founded** 2004

Club Contact Details 01664 480 576   secretarymeltonmowbrayfc@hotmail.com

HONOURS
FA Comps: None
League: None

10-11	11-12	12-13	13-14	14-15	15-16	16-17	17-18	18-19	19-20
LeicS1 12	LeicS1 6	LeicS1 2	LeicSP 2	LeicSP 2	LeicSP 3	UCL 1 9	UCL1 16	UCL 1 3	UCL1 n&v
									FAC P
							FAV 2Q	FAV 1Qr	FAV 1Q

GROUND: Melton Sports Village, Burton Road, Melton Mowbray LE13 1DR

NORTHAMPTON SILEBY RANGERS
Nickname: Rangers   **Club Colours:** Red and black   **Founded** 1968

Club Contact Details 01604 670 366

HONOURS
FA Comps: None
League: Northampton Town 1988-89 89-90. United Counties Division One 1993-94, 2002-03, 04-05, 12-13.

10-11	11-12	12-13	13-14	14-15	15-16	16-17	17-18	18-19	19-20
UCL 1 9	UCL 1 16	UCL 1 1	UCL P 15	UCL P 18	UCL P 19	UCL P 8	UCL P 22	UCL 1 9	UCL 1 n&v
				FAC 1Q	FAC P	FAC P	FAC EP	FAC Pr	
			FAV 1P	FAV 1Q	FAV 2P	FAV 2P	FAV 2Q	FAV 2Q	FAV 2Q

GROUND: Fernie Fields Sports Ground, Moulton, Northampton NN3 6BD
Nearest Railway Station Northampton - 5.5km
Bus Route Booth Rise - stop 205m away

RAUNDS TOWN
Nickname: Shopmates   **Club Colours:** Red & black   **Founded** 1946

Club Contact Details 01933 623 351

HONOURS
FA Comps: None
League: United Counties Division One 1982-83.

10-11	11-12	12-13	13-14	14-15	15-16	16-17	17-18	18-19	19-20
UCL P 20	UCL 1 13	UCL 1 14	UCL 1 12	UCL 1 9	UCL 1 8	UCL 1 7	UCL 1 4	UCL 1 19	UCL 1 n&v
FAC EP	FAC EP				FAC P	FAC EP	FAC EPr	FAC EP	
FAV 2Q	FAV 2Q	FAV 2Q		FAV 1Q	FAV 1P	FAV 1Q	FAV 2Q	FAV 2Q	FAV 2Q

GROUND: Kiln Park, London Road, Raunds, Northants NN9 6EQ

Bus Route Bus stops outside the ground.

RUSHDEN & HIGHAM UNITED
Nickname: The Lankies   **Club Colours:** Red and black   **Founded** Formed:

Club Contact Details 01933 410 036   rhufcsec@yahoo.co.uk

HONOURS
FA Comps: None
League: None

10-11	11-12	12-13	13-14	14-15	15-16	16-17	17-18	18-19	19-20
UCL1 10	UCL1 5	UCL1 8	UCL1 14	UCL1 13	UCL1 13	UCL1 16	UCL1 9	UCL1 11	UCL1 n&v
	FAC EP	FAC EP	FAC EP						
FAV 1Q	FAV 2Q	FAV 2Q	FAV 1Q		FAV 1Q	FAV 1Q	FAV 1P	FAV 1Q	FAV 1Q

GROUND: Hayden Road, Rushden, Northants NN10 9LA

Bus Route Ashwell Road - stop 60m away

818   www.nonleagueclubdirectory.co.uk

SAFFRON DYNAMO
Nickname: Club Colours: Red and black   Founded 1963

Club Contact Details 07957 151 630

HONOURS
FA Comps: None
League: None

10-11	11-12	12-13	13-14	14-15	15-16	16-17	17-18	18-19	19-20
LeicSP 11	LeicSP 13	LeicSP 13	LeicSP 13	LeicSP 3	LeicSP 7	LeicSP 2	LeicSP 5	LeicSP 2	UCL 1 n&v
	FAV 1Q							FAV 2P	FAV 1Q

GROUND: King's Park, Cambridge Road, Whetstone LE9 1SJ

ST. ANDREWS
Nickname: The Saints   Club Colours: Black & white   Founded 1973

Club Contact Details 0116 283 9298

HONOURS
FA Comps: None
League: Leicestershire City Premier x4. Leicestershire Senior 1989-90, 93-94, 95-96. East Midlands Counties 2015-16.

10-11	11-12	12-13	13-14	14-15	15-16	16-17	17-18	18-19	19-20
EMC 17	EMC 4	EMC 16	EMC 7	EMC 2	EMC 1	MFLP 9	UCL P 21	UCL 1 16	UCL 1 n&v
FAC EP		FAC EP		FAC EPr	FAC EP	FAC EP	FAC EPr	FAC EP	
FAV 2Q	FAV 2P	FAV EP	FAV SF	FAV 2P	FAV 3P	FAV 1P	FAV 2Q	FAV 1Q	FAV 2Q

GROUND: Canal Street, Aylestone, Leicester LE2 8DR
Nearest Railway Station South Wigston - 3km

WELLINGBOROUGH WHITWORTH
Nickname: Flourmen   Club Colours: Red & black   Founded 1973

Club Contact Details 07776 160 169

HONOURS
FA Comps: None
League: Rushden & District 1975-76, 76-77. United Counties Division One 2006-07.

10-11	11-12	12-13	13-14	14-15	15-16	16-17	17-18	18-19	19-20
UCL 1 13	UCL 1 4	UCL 1 13	UCL 1 17	UCL 1 7	UCL 1 15	UCL 1 2	UCL P 20	UCL P 20	UCL 1 n&v
		FAC EP			FAC EP	FAC EP	FAC EP	FAC EP	FAC EP
	FAV 1Q	FAV 2Q	FAV 2Q	FAV 1Q	FAV 1Q	FAV 2Q	FAV 2Q	FAV 1Q	FAV 1Q

GROUND: Victoria Mill Ground, London Road, Wellingborough NN8 2DP
Nearest Railway Station Wellingborough - 1.2km
Bus Route The Dog & Duck Pub - stop 50m away

WHITTLESEY ATHLETIC
Nickname: Club Colours: Navy and white   Founded 2014

Club Contact Details 07941 631 681

HONOURS
FA Comps: None
League: None

10-11	11-12	12-13	13-14	14-15	15-16	16-17	17-18	18-19	19-20
					P&D P 2	UCL 1 Exp	P&D P 3	P&D P 5	UCL 1 n&v

GROUND: Feldale Field, Drybread Road, Whittlesey, PE7 1YP

IN: Blackfield & Langley (VR - SLP). **OUT:** Solent University (WD).

AFC PORTCHESTER
Nickname: Portchy/Royals   **Club Colours:** Tangerine and black   Founded 1971

Club Contact Details 01329 233 833 (Clubhouse)   secretary@afcportchester.co.uk

Previous Names: Loyds Sports 1971-73. Colourvison Rangers 1973-76. Wilcor Mill 1976-2003.
Previous Leagues: City of Portsmouth Sunday. Portsmouth & District >1998. Hampshire 1998-2004.
HONOURS
FA Comps: None
League: Portsmouth & Football 1997-98. Hampshire Division One 2001-02.

10-11		11-12		12-13		13-14		14-15		15-16		16-17		17-18		18-19		19-20	
Wex1	3	Wex1	2	WexP	15	WexP	8	WexP	3	WexP	6	WexP	8	WexP	6	WexP	13	WexP	n&v
		FAC	Pr	FAC	EP	FAC	2Q	FAC	P	FAC	2Q	FAC	2Q	FAC	2Q	FAC	EPr	FAC	EPr
FAV	2Q	FAV	2Q	FAV	2Q	FAV	3P	FAV	3P	FAV	1P	FAV	2Q	FAV	1P	FAV	1Q	FAV	2P

GROUND: The Crest Finance Stadium, Cranleigh Road, Portchester, Hampshire PO16 9DP
Capacity: **Seats:** Yes   **Covered:** Yes
Nearest Railway Station Porchester - 15.km
Bus Route Sandport Grove stop

AFC STONEHAM
Nickname: The Purples   **Club Colours:** All purple   Founded 1919

Club Contact Details 07933 111 381   secretary@afcstoneham.co.uk

Previous Names: Ordnance Survey > 2006. Stoneham 2006-07.
Previous Leagues: Hampshire Premier League >2015
HONOURS
FA Comps: None
League: Southampton Senior 1982-83, 92-93, 96-97. Hampshire Premier 2007-08. Wessex Division One 2018-19.

10-11		11-12		12-13		13-14		14-15		15-16		16-17		17-18		18-19		19-20	
HantP	8	HantP	4	HantP	2	HantP	12	HantP	4	Wex1	8	Wex1	8	Wex1	5	Wex1	1	WexP	n&v
																FAC	1Q	FAC	Pr
												FAV	1P	FAV	1Q	FAV	1P	FAV	1Q

GROUND: The HP Arena, Jubilee Park, Chestnut Avenue, Eastleigh SO50 9PF
Capacity: **Seats:** Yes   **Covered:** Yes
Nearest Railway Station Southampton Airport Parkway - 1.6km
Bus Route Golf Driving Range stop

ALRESFORD TOWN
Nickname: The Magpies   **Club Colours:** White and black   Founded 1898

Club Contact Details 07703 346 672   secretary.alresfordtownfc@gmail.com

Previous Names: None
Previous Leagues: Winchester League, North Hants league, Hampshire League
HONOURS
FA Comps: None
League: North Hampshire 1999-2000.

10-11		11-12		12-13		13-14		14-15		15-16		16-17		17-18		18-19		19-20	
WexP	15	WexP	15	WexP	2	WexP	2	WexP	16	WexP	20	WexP	5	WexP	7	WexP	12	WexP	n&v
FAC	Pr	FAC	P	FAC	P	FAC	EP	FAC	Pr	FAC	EP	FAC	2Q	FAC	P	FAC	EPr	FAC	EPr
FAV	1Q	FAV	1P	FAV	2Q	FAV	4P	FAV	3P	FAV	1Q	FAV	2P	FAV	2Q	FAV	2P	FAV	2Q

GROUND: Arlebury Park, The Avenue, Alresford, Hants SO24 9EP
Capacity: **Seats:** Yes   **Covered:** Yes
Nearest Railway Station Alresford - 620m
Bus Route Bridge Road stop

AMESBURY TOWN
Nickname: Blues   **Club Colours:** Royal blue & white   Founded 1904

Club Contact Details 01980 623 489   amesburytownfc@gmail.com

Previous Names: Amesbury FC 1904-1984.

Previous Leagues: Salisbury & District Junior 1904-06. Salisbury & District 1906-56, 97-98. Wiltshire 1956-71. Wiltshire Combination/County 71-. Western 1994-97. Hampshire 1998-2004.

HONOURS

FA Comps: None

League: Salisbury & District Division Two 1954-55, Division One 55-56. Wiltshire Division One 1959-60. Wiltshire Combination/County 1974-75, 79-80 / Division One 90-91, 91-92. Hampshire Premier 1999-2000.

	10-11	11-12	12-13	13-14	14-15	15-16	16-17	17-18	18-19	19-20
League	Wex1 13	Wex1 14	Wex1 14	Wex1 10	Wex1 4	Wex1 2	WexP 19	WexP 20	Wex1 2	WexP n&v
FAC	EP					EP	P	P	EP	EP
FAV	1Q	1Q	1Q	1Q	2Q	1Q	1P	2Q	1Q	1Q

GROUND: Bonnymead Park Recreation Road Amesbury SP4 7BB
Capacity: **Seats:** Yes   **Covered:** Yes

Bus Route Mandalay Guest House - stop 600m away

BAFFINS MILTON ROVERS
Nickname: None   **Club Colours:** All royal blue   Founded 2011

Club Contact Details 07980 403 336

Previous Names: Formed when Sunday league teams Baffins Milton and Milton Rovers merged.

Previous Leagues: Hampshire Premier >2016

HONOURS

FA Comps: None

League: Portsmouth Saturday Premier Division 2011-12. Hampshire Premier Senior Division , 2013-14, 15-16.

	10-11	11-12	12-13	13-14	14-15	15-16	16-17	17-18	18-19	19-20
League		PorS P 1	PorS P 2	HantP 1	HantP 2	HantP 1	Wex1 2	WexP 9	WexP 5	WexP n&v
FAC									P	P
FAV								3P	4P	2P

GROUND: Kendall Wharf, Eastern Road, Portsmouth PO3 5LY
Capacity: **Seats:** 120   **Covered:** Yes
Nearest Railway Station Hilsea - 1.3km
Bus Route Robinson Way - stop 420m away

BASHLEY
Nickname: The Bash   **Club Colours:** Gold and black   Founded 1947

Club Contact Details 01425 620 280   footballsecretary@bashleyfc.org.uk

Previous Names: None

Previous Leagues: Bournemouth 1953-83, Hampshire 1983-86, Wessex 1986-89, Southern 1989-2004, 06-16. Isthmian 2004-06

HONOURS

FA Comps: None

League: Hampshire Division Three 1984-85. Wessex 1986-87, 87-88, 88-89. Southern Southern Division 1989-90, Division One South & West 2006-07.

	10-11	11-12	12-13	13-14	14-15	15-16	16-17	17-18	18-19	19-20
League	SthP 11	SthP 13	SthP 17	SthP 23	Sthsw 22	Sthsw 22	WexP 14	WexP 14	WexP 9	WexP n&v
FAC	3Q	1Q	1Qr	2Q	P	P	EP	EP	EP	EP
FAT	1Q	1Qr	1Qr	1Q	P	1Q	2Q	1P	1P	2Q

GROUND: Bashley Road Ground, Bashley Road, New Milton, Hampshire BH25 5RY
Capacity: 4,250 **Seats:** 250 **Covered:** 1,200 **Shop:** Yes
Nearest Railway Station New Milton - 1.9km
Bus Route Village Store & PO - stop 230m away

BLACKFIELD & LANGLEY

Nickname: Watersiders **Club Colours:** Green

Founded 1935

Club Contact Details 02380 893 603   d-sangster@sky.com

Previous Names: None
Previous Leagues: Southampton Junior. Southampton Senior. Hampshire 1950-2000. Wessex 2000-18. Southern 2018-20 (Took voluntary relegation).
HONOURS
FA Comps: None
League: Southampton Junior Division One 1945-46. Southampton West Division 1946-47. Hampshire Division Three West 1951-52, Division Two 1984-85, Premier Division 97-98. Wessex Premier Division 2012-13, 17-18. Southern D1S 2018-19.

10-11		11-12		12-13		13-14		14-15		15-16		16-17		17-18		18-19		19-20	
WexP	14	WexP	16	WexP	1	WexP	6	WexP	5	WexP	3	WexP	4	WexP	1	SthS	1	SthPS	n&v
FAC	P	FAC	1Q	FAC	4Q	FAC	EP	FAC	2Qr	FAC	3Q	FAC	P	FAC	EPr	FAC	P	FAC	3Q
FAV	1P	FAV	2P	FAV	4P	FAV	4P	FAV	3P	FAV	1P	FAV	3P	FAV	4Pr	FAT	P	FAT	2Q

GROUND: Gang Warily Rec., Newlands Rd, Southampton SO45 1GA
Capacity: 2,000 **Seats:** 180 **Covered:** Yes
Nearest Railway Station Beaulieu Road - 7.2 miles
Bus Route Gang Warily Leisure Centre - stop 50m away

BOURNEMOUTH

Nickname: Poppies **Club Colours:** Red and white

Founded 1875

Club Contact Details 01202 515 123   bournemouthwessex@gmail.com

Previous Names: Bournemouth Rovers, Bournemouth Wanderers, Bournemouth Dean Park.
Previous Leagues: Hampshire 1896-98, 1903-39 & 46-86.
HONOURS
FA Comps: None
League: None

10-11		11-12		12-13		13-14		14-15		15-16		16-17		17-18		18-19		19-20	
WexP	5	WexP	9	WexP	13	WexP	15	WexP	18	WexP	18	WexP	17	WexP	18	WexP	3	WexP	n&v
FAC	P	FAC	2Qr	FAC	EP	FAC	P	FAC	Pr	FAC	EP	FAC	EP	FAC	EP	FAC	P	FAC	P
FAV	3P	FAV	QF	FAV	2P	FAV	1Q	FAV	2Q	FAV	2Q	FAV	1P	FAV	2Q	FAV	2P	FAV	1P

GROUND: Victoria Park, Namu Road, Winton, Bournemouth BH9 2RA
Capacity: 3,000 **Seats:** 205 **Covered:** 205 **Shop:** Yes

BROCKENHURST

Nickname: The Badgers **Club Colours:** Blue and white

Founded 1898

Club Contact Details 01590 623 544   brockenhurstfcsec@gmail.com

Previous Names: None
Previous Leagues: Hampshire 1924-26, 35-37, 47-86.
HONOURS
FA Comps: None
League: Hampshire Division Three 1959-60, Division Two 70-71, Division One 75-76. Wessex Division One 2012-13.

10-11		11-12		12-13		13-14		14-15		15-16		16-17		17-18		18-19		19-20	
WexP	22	Wex1	5	Wex1	1	WexP	11	WexP	14	WexP	14	WexP	10	WexP	13	WexP	15	WexP	n&v
FAC	EP	FAC	1Q	FAC	EP	FAC	1Q	FAC	EP	FAC	3Q	FAC	P	FAC	P	FAC	P	FAC	EP
FAV	2Q	FAV	1P	FAV	1Q	FAV	2Q	FAV	1Q	FAV	1Q	FAV	2Q	FAV	2P	FAV	2P	FAV	2P

GROUND: Grigg Lane, Brockenhurst, Hants SO42 7RE
Capacity: 2,000 **Seats:** 200 **Covered:** 300
Nearest Railway Station Brockenhurst - 0.5km
Bus Route Brockenhurst College - stop 260m away

CHRISTCHURCH
Nickname: The Church   **Club Colours:** All Blue

Founded 1885

Club Contact Details 01202 473 792   secretary@christchurchfc.co.uk

Previous Names: None
Previous Leagues: Hampshire
HONOURS
FA Comps: None
League: Hampshire Division Two 1937-38, 47-48, 85-86, Division Three 52-53.
Wessex Division One 2017-18.

	10-11		11-12		12-13		13-14		14-15		15-16		16-17		17-18		18-19		19-20	
WexP	6	WexP	3	WexP	3	WexP	16	WexP	21	Wex1	6	Wex1	4	Wex1	1	WexP	16	WexP	n&v
FAC	EP	FAC	EP	FAC	1Q	FAC	EP	FAC	EPr	FAC	P	FAC	EP	FAC	EP	FAC	EPr	FAC	P
FAV	1Pr	FAV	3P	FAV	1P	FAV	1Pr	FAV	2Q	FAV	1Q	FAV	2Q	FAV	3P	FAV	2Q	FAV	4P

GROUND: Hurn Bridge Sports Ground, Avon Causeway, Christchurch BH23 6DY
Capacity: 1,200 **Seats:** 215 **Covered:** 265
Nearest Railway Station Christchurch - 4.6km
Bus Route Post Office - stop 100m away

COWES SPORTS
Nickname: Yachtsmen   **Club Colours:** Blue & White

Founded 1881

Club Contact Details 01983 718 277   secretary.cowessportsfc@outlook.com

Previous Names: Cowes
Previous Leagues: Hampshire (FM) 1896-98, 1903-94. Southern 1898-99.
HONOURS
FA Comps: None
League: Hampshire Division One 1896-97, 1908-09 (jt), 26-27, 27-28, 30-31, 36-37, 55-56, 93-94, Division Two 1974-75.
Southern Division Two South West 1898-99.

	10-11		11-12		12-13		13-14		14-15		15-16		16-17		17-18		18-19		19-20	
Wex1	8	Wex1	6	Wex1	4	Wex1	3	Wex1	2	WexP	11	WexP	18	WexP	19	WexP	18	WexP	n&v
FAC	EP	FAC	EP	FAC	EP	FAC	P	FAC	P	FAC	P	FAC	EP	FAC	EP	FAC	EP	FAC	EP
FAV	2Q	FAV	3P	FAV	2Q	FAV	2Q	FAV	1P	FAV	2Q	FAV	2Q	FAV	1Q	FAV	1Q	FAV	1P

GROUND: Westwood Park Reynolds Close off Park Rd Cowes Isle of Wight PO31 7NT
Capacity: **Seats:** Yes **Covered:** Yes

Bus Route Parklands Avenue - stop 100m away

FAREHAM TOWN
Nickname: Creeksiders   **Club Colours:** Red & black stripes

Founded 1947

Club Contact Details 07889 491 903   farehamtnfc@gmail.com

Previous Names: Formed when Fareham FC, Fareham Brotherhood and Fareham Youth Centre merged.
Previous Leagues: Portsmouth 1946-49. Hampshire 1949-79. Southern 1979-98.
HONOURS
FA Comps: None
League: Hampshire League Division 3 East 1949-50, Premier 1959-60, 62-63, 63-64, 64-65, 65-66, 66-67, 72-73, 74-75.

	10-11		11-12		12-13		13-14		14-15		15-16		16-17		17-18		18-19		19-20	
WexP	8	WexP	12	WexP	9	WexP	10	WexP	19	WexP	12	WexP	12	WexP	16	WexP	17	WexP	n&v
FAC	P	FAC	EP	FAC	2Q	FAC	1Q	FAC	P	FAC	EP	FAC	1Qr	FAC	P	FAC	P	FAC	1Q
FAV	2Q	FAV	1P	FAV	2Q	FAV	2P	FAV	1P	FAV	1Q	FAV	2Q	FAV	2P	FAV	1P	FAV	2Q

GROUND: Cams Alders, Palmerston Drive, Fareham, Hants PO14 1BJ
Capacity: 2,000 **Seats:** 450 **Covered:** 500 **Shop:** Yes
Nearest Railway Station Fareham - 0.9km
Bus Route Fairfield Avenue - stop 250m away

FLEET TOWN

Nickname: The Blues   **Club Colours:** Blue & white

Founded 1890

Club Contact Details 01252 623 804 Match day only   secretary@fleettownfc.co.uk

Previous Names: Fleet FC 1890-1963

Previous Leagues: Hampshire 1961-77, Athenian, Combined Counties, Chiltonian, Wessex 1989-95, 2000-02, Southern 1995-2000, 02-04, 07-08, 11-19. Isthmian 2004-07, 2008-11.

HONOURS

FA Comps: None

League: Wessex 1994-95.

10-11		11-12		12-13		13-14		14-15		15-16		16-17		17-18		18-19		19-20	
Isth1S	13	SthC	21	SthC	18	Sthsw	21	Sthsw	19	SthC	17	SthC	14	Sth1E	19	SthS	20	WexP	n&v
FAC	2Qr	FAC	1Q	FAC	P	FAC	P	FAC	2Q	FAC	1Qr	FAC	1Qr	FAC	Pr	FAC	1Q	FAC	1Q
FAT	1Q	FAT	1Q	FAT	Pr	FAT	P	FAT	1Q	FAT	P	FAT	1Q	FAT	Pr	FAT	1Q	FAV	1Qr

GROUND: Calthorpe Park, Crookham Road, Fleet, Hants GU51 5FA
Capacity: 2,000   **Seats:** 250   **Covered:** 250   **Shop:** Yes
Nearest Railway Station Fllet - 2.1km
Bus Route Leawood Road - stop 150m away

HAMBLE CLUB

Nickname: The Monks   **Club Colours:** All yellow

Founded 1969

Club Contact Details 07977 324 923   secretary.hambleclubfc@gmail.com

Previous Names: None

Previous Leagues: Hampshire Premier 1993-2016.

HONOURS

FA Comps: None

League: Hampshire Premier 2014-15. Wessex Division One 2016-17.

10-11		11-12		12-13		13-14		14-15		15-16		16-17		17-18		18-19		19-20	
HantP	16	HantP	15	HantP	Exp	Hant1	2	HantP	1	HantP	3	Wex1	1	WexP	10	WexP	7	WexP	n&v
																FAC	P	FAC	P
														FAV	5P	FAV	3Pr	FAV	2Q

GROUND: Hamble Community Facility, Hamble Lane SO31 4JW
Capacity: **Seats:** Yes   **Covered:** Yes
Nearest Railway Station Hamble - 0.4km
Bus Route Hamble Lane School - stop 500m away

HAMWORTHY UNITED

Nickname: The Hammers   **Club Colours:** Maroon & sky blue

Founded 1926

Club Contact Details 01202 674 974   hamworthyutdsecretary@gmail.com

Previous Names: Hamworthy St. Michael merged with Trinidad Old Boys 1926

Previous Leagues: Dorset Combination (Founder Member) / Dorset Premier 1957-2004.

HONOURS

FA Comps: None

League: Dorset Premier 2002-03, 03-04.

10-11		11-12		12-13		13-14		14-15		15-16		16-17		17-18		18-19		19-20	
WexP	9	WexP	7	WexP	10	WexP	12	WexP	10	WexP	16	WexP	16	WexP	5	WexP	6	WexP	n&v
FAC	Pr	FAC	EP	FAC	P	FAC	2Q	FAC	EP	FAC	1Q	FAC	1Q	FAC	1Q	FAC	1Qr	FAC	P
FAV	2Q	FAV	1Q	FAV	2Q	FAV	1P	FAV	2Q	FAV	1Q	FAV	1Q	FAV	2Q	FAV	4P	FAV	3P

GROUND: The County Ground, Blandford Close, Hamworthy, Poole BH15 4BF
Capacity: 2,000   **Seats:**   **Covered:** Yes   **Shop:** No
Nearest Railway Station Poole - 1.4km
Bus Route Carter School - stop 100m away

HORNDEAN
Nickname: Deans   **Club Colours:** All red (All yellow)   Founded 1887

Club Contact Details 02392 591 363   horndeanfc1887@gmail.com

Previous Names: None
Previous Leagues: Waterlooville & District. Portsmouth. Hampshire 1972-86, 1995-2004. Wessex 1986-95
HONOURS
FA Comps: None
League: Waterlooville & District 1926-27, 29-30, 30-31, 31-32. Portsmouth Division Two 1953-54, Premier 68-69, 69-70, 70-71. Hampshire Division Four 1974-75, Division Three 75-76, Division Two 79-80.

10-11		11-12		12-13		13-14		14-15		15-16		16-17		17-18		18-19		19-20	
Wex1	2	WexP	17	WexP	11	WexP	17	WexP	11	WexP	5	WexP	6	WexP	4	WexP	2	WexP	n&v
		FAC	1Q	FAC	1Q	FAC	1Q	FAC	1Q	FAC	EP	FAC	EP	FAC	1Q	FAC	1Q	FAC	P
FAV	1Q	FAV	2Q	FAV	3P	FAV	2Q	FAV	2P	FAV	1P	FAV	1P	FAV	3P	FAV	2P	FAV	1Pr

GROUND: Five Heads Park Five Heads Road Horndean Hampshire PO8 9NZ
Capacity: **Seats:** Yes   **Covered:** Yes
Nearest Railway Station Rowlands Castle - 4.5km
Bus Route Horndean Com. School - stop 560m away

LYMINGTON TOWN
Nickname: Town   **Club Colours:** Red and white   Founded 1998

Club Contact Details 01590 671 305   secretary.lymingtontownfc@yahoo.com

Previous Names: None
Previous Leagues: Hampshire 1998-2004.
HONOURS
FA Comps: None
League: Wessex Division Two 2004-05.

10-11		11-12		12-13		13-14		14-15		15-16		16-17		17-18		18-19		19-20	
WexP	11	WexP	14	WexP	19	WexP	14	WexP	9	WexP	13	WexP	9	WexP	8	WexP	10	WexP	n&v
FAC	EP	FAC	Pr	FAC	EP	FAC	P	FAC	EP	FAC	EP	FAC	EPr	FAC	EP	FAC	2Q	FAC	P
FAV	1P	FAV	1Q	FAV	2Q	FAV	1P	FAV	2Qr	FAV	2P	FAV	1Q	FAV	1P	FAV	2Q	FAV	1P

GROUND: The Sports Ground, Southampton Road, Lymington SO41 9ZG
Capacity: 3,000 **Seats:** 200   **Covered:** 300
Nearest Railway Station Lymington Town - 0.6km
Bus Route Town Hall - Stop 110m away

PORTLAND UNITED
Nickname: Blues   **Club Colours:** All royal blue   Founded 1921

Club Contact Details 01305 861 489   secretary.portlandutdfc@aol.com

Previous Names: None
Previous Leagues: Western 1925-70. Dorset Combination 1970-76, 77-2001, Dorset Premier 2006-07. Wessex 2001-02.
HONOURS
FA Comps: None
League: Western Division Two 1930-31, 31-32. Dorset Combination 1998-99, 99-2000, Dorset Premier 2007-08, 08-09, 12-13, 13-14. Wessex Division One 2015-16, Premier 2016-17.

10-11		11-12		12-13		13-14		14-15		15-16		16-17		17-18		18-19		19-20	
Dor P	4	Dor P	3	Dor P	1	Dor P	1	Dor P	2	Wex1	1	WexP	1	WexP	15	WexP	4	WexP	n&v
														FAC	P	FAC	P	FAC	2Q
														FAV	2Q	FAV	1Q	FAV	1P

GROUND: New Grove Corner, Grove Road, Portland DT5 1DP
Capacity: 2,000 **Seats:** Yes   **Covered:** Yes

Bus Route Clifton Hotel - stop 280m away

SHAFTESBURY

Nickname: The Rockies   **Club Colours:** Red & white

Founded 1888

Club Contact Details 07769 114 362

Previous Names: Shaftesbury Town.
Previous Leagues: Dorset Junior. Dorset Senior 1931-57. Dorset Combination 1957-62, 76-2004. Wessex 2004-11. Dorset Premier 2011-16.

HONOURS

FA Comps: None
League: Dorset Junior 1905-06, 62-63. Dorset Senior 1932-33. Dorset Combination 1988-89, 96-97.
Dorset Premier 2015-16. Wessex Division One 2016-17.

10-11		11-12		12-13		13-14		14-15		15-16		16-17		17-18		18-19		19-20	
Wex1	19	Dor P	18	Dor P	11	Dor P	14	Dor P	4	Dor P	1	Wex1	3	WexP	12	WexP	14	WexP	n&v
														FAC	P	FAC	1Q	FAC	EP
FAV	2Q									FAV	2Q	FAV	2P	FAV	1Q	FAV	1P	FAV	1Q

GROUND: Cockrams, Coppice Street, Shaftesbury SP7 8PD
Capacity: **Seats:** Yes   **Covered:** Yes

Bus Route Linden Park - stop 100m away

TADLEY CALLEVA

Nickname: The Tadders   **Club Colours:** All yellow

Founded 1989

Club Contact Details 07926 830 806   secretarytcfc@gmail.com

Previous Names: Tadley FC 1989-99. Tadley Town 1999-2004.
Previous Leagues: Hampshire 1994-2004

HONOURS

FA Comps: None
League: Wessex Division One 2007-08.

10-11		11-12		12-13		13-14		14-15		15-16		16-17		17-18		18-19		19-20	
Wex1	16	Wex1	17	Wex1	7	Wex1	5	Wex1	3	Wex1	3	Wex1	7	Wex1	3	WexP	8	WexP	n&v
						FAC	P	FAC	EPr	FAC	EP	FAC	EP			FAC	EP	FAC	EP
				FAV	1Q	FAV	2Q	FAV	2Q	FAV	3Pr	FAV	1Q	FAV	2Q	FAV	2Q	FAV	1P

GROUND: Barlows Park Silchester Road Tadley Hampshire RG26 3PX
Capacity: 1,000 **Seats:**   **Covered:**
Nearest Railway Station Midgham - 5.1km
Bus Route Tadley Common Road - stop 60m away

DIVISION ONE

ALTON

Nickname: The Brewers   **Club Colours:** White and black   Founded 1990

Club Contact Details 07709 715 322   secretary@altonfc

HONOURS
FA Comps: None
League: Hampshire Division One 1998-99, Premier 2001-02.

	10-11	11-12	12-13	13-14	14-15	15-16	16-17	17-18	18-19	19-20
	WexP 13	WexP 10	WexP 18	CCP 21	CC1 13	Wex1 7	Wex1 12	Wex1 8	Wex1 13	Wex1 n&v
FAC	2Qr	P	P	P	1Q	EP				
FAV	2Q	2Pr	1P	1Q	1Q	1P	1P	1P	2Q	2Q

GROUND: Anstey Park Enclosure, Anstey Road, Alton, Hants GU34 2NB
Nearest Railway Station Alton - 0.6km
Bus Route Anstey Lane - stop 32m away

ANDOVER NEW STREET

Nickname: The Street   **Club Colours:** Green & black   Founded 1895

Club Contact Details 01264 358 358 (Wkends from 12)   andovernewstreetfc@hotmail.co.uk

HONOURS
FA Comps: None
League: None

	10-11	11-12	12-13	13-14	14-15	15-16	16-17	17-18	18-19	19-20
	Wex1 17	Wex1 10	Wex1 15	Wex1 15	Wex1 13	Wex1 16	Wex1 19	Wex1 2	WexP 20	Wex1 n&v
FAC									P	P
FAV	1P	2Q	1Q			1Q	1Q	1Q	2Q	1Q

GROUND: Foxcotte Park Charlton Andover Hampshire SP11 0TA
Nearest Railway Station Andover - 2.4km
Bus Route Charlton Cemetery - stop 120m away

ANDOVER TOWN

Nickname: **Club Colours:** All blue   Founded 2013

Club Contact Details 07730 590 183

HONOURS
FA Comps: None
League: None

	10-11	11-12	12-13	13-14	14-15	15-16	16-17	17-18	18-19	19-20
					WexP 12	WexP 4	WexP 13	WexP 2	Wex1 18	Wex1 n&v
FAC						Pr	1Q	1Q	EP	
FAV					2Q	1P	2P	1Q	1P	1Q

GROUND: Portway Stadium, West Portway Industrial Estate, Andover SP10 3LF
Nearest Railway Station Andover - 1.8km
Bus Route Arkwright Gate - stop 130m away

BEMERTON HEATH HARLEQUINS

Nickname: Quins   **Club Colours:** Black & white   Founded 1989

Club Contact Details 01722 331 925   bhhfc@gmail.co.uk

HONOURS
FA Comps: None
League: None

	10-11	11-12	12-13	13-14	14-15	15-16	16-17	17-18	18-19	19-20
	WexP 2	WexP 2	WexP 5	WexP 7	WexP 13	WexP 9	WexP 11	WexP 11	WexP 19	Wex1 n&v
FAC	EP	EP	EP	EP	1Q	1Q	1Q	EP	1Q	EPr
FAV	4P	3P	5P	2P	2P	2Q	3P	1Q	2Q	1Q

GROUND: Moon Park, Western Way, Bemerton Heath Salisbury SP2 9DR
Nearest Railway Station Salisbury - 2.1km
Bus Route Winding Way - stop 75m away

DOWNTON
Nickname: The Robins **Club Colours:** Red
Founded 1905

Club Contact Details 01725 512 162 secretary@downtonfc.com

HONOURS
FA Comps: None
League: Bournemouth League Division One x5, Senior Division One x7. Wessex League Division One 2010-11.

10-11		11-12		12-13		13-14		14-15		15-16		16-17		17-18		18-19		19-20	
Wex1	1	WexP	6	WexP	8	WexP	21	Wex1	12	Wex1	10	Wex1	11	Wex1	12	Wex1	7	Wex1	n&v
FAC	EP	FAC	EPr	FAC	EP	FAC	EP	FAC	EP										
FAV	2P	FAV	2P	FAV	3P	FAV	2Q			FAV	1Q	FAV	1Q	FAV	1P	FAV	1Q	FAV	1P

GROUND: Brian Whitehead Sports Ground Wick Lane Downton Wiltshire SP5 3NF

Bus Route The Bull - stop 180m away

EAST COWES VICTORIA ATHLETIC
Nickname: The Vics **Club Colours:** Red & white
Founded 1885

Club Contact Details 01983 297 165 ecvics@gmail.com

HONOURS
FA Comps: None
League: Hampshire Division Two 1947-48, 63-64, 71-72, Division One 85-86, 86-87.

10-11		11-12		12-13		13-14		14-15		15-16		16-17		17-18		18-19		19-20	
Wex1	15	Wex1	4	Wex1	8	Wex1	16	Wex1	15	Wex1	18	Wex1	20	Wex1	16	Wex1	10	Wex1	n&v
				FAC	P	FAC	EP												
FAV	2Q	FAV	1Q	FAV	1Q	FAV	2Q	FAV	2Q	FAV	1Q	FAV	2Q	FAV	1Q	FAV	2Q	FAV	1P

GROUND: Beatrice Avenue, East Cowes, Isle of Wight PO32 6PA

Bus Route Osborne House - stop 400m away

FAWLEY
Nickname: Oilers **Club Colours:** Sky and navy blue
Founded 1923

Club Contact Details 02380 893 750 (Club) fmahawleyafc@aol.com

HONOURS
FA Comps: None
League: Hampshire Division Three 1994-95.

10-11		11-12		12-13		13-14		14-15		15-16		16-17		17-18		18-19		19-20	
WexP	20	WexP	19	WexP	17	WexP	20	WexP	17	WexP	19	WexP	20	Wex1	9	Wex1	11	Wex1	n&v
				FAC	EP	FAC	EP	FAC	EP	FAC	EP	FAC	EP	FAC	EP				
		FAV	2P	FAV	1P	FAV	2Q	FAV	1Q	FAV	1Q	FAV	1Q	FAV	2Q	FAV	2Q	FAV	1Q

GROUND: Waterside Spts & Soc. club, 179 Long Lane, Holbury, Soto, SO45 2PA
Nearest Railway Station Netley - 5.3km
Bus Route New Forest Academy - stop 100m away

FOLLAND SPORTS
Nickname: Planemakers **Club Colours:** All red
Founded 1938

Club Contact Details 02380 452 173 follandsportsfc@hotmail.co.uk

HONOURS
FA Comps: None
League: Hampshire 1941-42, Division Four 79-80, Division Three 80-81. Southampton Senior 1961-62, 67-68. Wessex Division One 2009-10.

10-11		11-12		12-13		13-14		14-15		15-16		16-17		17-18		18-19		19-20	
WexP	12	WexP	5	WexP	7	WexP	3	WexP	8	WexP	21	Wex1	17	Wex1	18	Wex1	16	Wex1	n&v
FAC	3Q	FAC	EP	FAC	P	FAC	P	FAC	2Qr	FAC	EP	FAC	EP						
FAV	1P	FAV	2Q	FAV	3P	FAV	2P	FAV	2P	FAV	2Q	FAV	1Q	FAV	1Q	FAV	1Q	FAV	1Q

GROUND: Folland Park, Kings Ave, Hamble, Southampton SO31 4NF
Nearest Railway Station Hamble - 1km
Bus Route Verdon Avenue - stop 300m away

HYTHE & DIBDEN
Nickname: The Boatmen **Club Colours:** Green and white

Founded 1902

FOOTBALL CLUB **Club Contact Details** -7789 266 473   hythedibdenfc@aol.com

HONOURS
FA Comps: None
League: Hampshire Division Three West 1949-50.
Southampton Division Two 1970-71, 75-76.

	10-11	11-12	12-13	13-14	14-15	15-16	16-17	17-18	18-19	19-20
Wex1	14	18	16	4	7	11	18	15	3	n&v
FAC						EP				1Q
FAV	2Q		1Q	1P	1Q	2Q	1Q	2Q	1Q	2Q

GROUND: Clayfields, Claypit Lane, Dibden SO45 5TN
Nearest Railway Station Southampton Town Quay - 3.5km
Bus Route Drapers Copse - stop 200m away

LAVERSTOCK & FORD
Nickname: The Stock **Club Colours:** Green & white hoops

Founded 1956

Club Contact Details 01722 327 401   sec.laverstockandfordfc@gmail.com

HONOURS
FA Comps: None
League: Hampshire Division Two 2002-03.

	10-11	11-12	12-13	13-14	14-15	15-16	16-17	17-18	18-19	19-20
WexP/Wex1	WexP 17	WexP 22	Wex1 13	Wex1 9	Wex1 8	Wex1 5	Wex1 6	Wex1 7	Wex1 9	Wex1 n&v
FAC	P						EP	P		
FAV	1P		1Q	1P	2Q	1P	1Q	1Q	1Q	2Q

GROUND: The Dell, Church Road, Laverstock, Salisbury, Wilts SP1 1QX
Nearest Railway Station Salisbury - 2.5km
Bus Route St Andrews School - stop 40m away

NEW MILTON TOWN
Nickname: The Linnets **Club Colours:** Navy and red

Founded 1998

Club Contact Details 01425 628 191   secretry@newmiltontownfc.co.uk

HONOURS
FA Comps: None
League: Wessex 1998-99, 2004-05.

	10-11	11-12	12-13	13-14	14-15	15-16	16-17	17-18	18-19	19-20
WexP/Wex1	WexP 19	WexP 20	WexP 21	Wex1 11	Wex1 6	Wex1 14	Wex1 14	Wex1 10	Wex1 17	Wex1 n&v
FAC	EPr	EPr	EP			EP				
FAV	1Q	2Q	2P		2Q	1P	1Q	2Q	2Q	1Q

GROUND: Fawcetts Fields, Christchurch Road, New Milton BH25 6QF
Nearest Railway Station New Milton - 1.1km
Bus Route Old Milton Green - stop 150m away

NEWPORT (I.O.W.)
Nickname: The Port **Club Colours:** Yellow and blue

Founded 1888

Club Contact Details 01983 525 027   secretary@niowfc.com

HONOURS
FA Comps: None
League: Isle of Wight 1907-08, 08-09, 09-10, 23-24. Hampshire 1929-30, 32-33, 38-39, 47-48, 49-50, 52-53, 53-54, 56-57, 79-79, 79-80, 80-81. Southern Eastern Division 2000-01.

	10-11	11-12	12-13	13-14	14-15	15-16	16-17	17-18	18-19	19-20
WexP/Wex1	WexP 10	WexP 13	WexP 6	WexP 4	WexP 7	WexP 10	WexP 15	WexP 21	Wex1 6	Wex1 n&v
FAC	1Q	1Q	2Q	P	2Qr	1Q	EP	EP	P	
FAV	3P	1Q	1Q	5Pr	2P	3P	2P	4P	2P	1P

GROUND: East Cowes Vics FC, Beatrice Avenue, Isle of Wight PO32 6PA

Bus Route Osborne House - stop 400m away

PETERSFIELD TOWN

Nickname: Rams   **Club Colours:** Red & black   Founded 1993

Club Contact Details 01730 233 416   secretary.petersfieldtownfc@outlook.com

HONOURS
FA Comps: None
League: Wessex Division One 2013-14, Premier Division 2014-15.

	10-11		11-12		12-13		13-14		14-15		15-16		16-17		17-18		18-19		19-20	
	Wex1	11	Wex1	12	Wex1	6	Wex1	1	WexP	1	SthC	13	SthC	22	WexP	22	Wex1	15	Wex1	n&v
FAC	EP		FAC	EP	FAC	EPr	FAC	P	FAC	EP	FAC	3Q	FAC	P	FAC	EP	FAC	P		
FAV	1Q		FAV	2Q	FAV	1P	FAV	1P	FAV	2Q	FAT	P	FAT	Pr	FAV	2Q	FAV	2Q	FAV	2P

GROUND: Love Lane, Petersfield, Hampshire GU31 4BW
Nearest Railway Station Petersfield - 0.8km
Bus Route Madeline Road - stop 140m away

RINGWOOD TOWN

Nickname: The Peckers   **Club Colours:** Red and white   Founded 1879

Club Contact Details 01425 473 448   ringwoodtownfc@live.co.uk

HONOURS
FA Comps: None
League: Hampshire Division three 1995-96.

	10-11		11-12		12-13		13-14		14-15		15-16		16-17		17-18		18-19		19-20	
	Wex1	6	Wex1	9	Wex1	9	Wex1	13	Wex1	11	Wex1	13	Wex1	5	Wex1	11	Wex1	12	Wex1	n&v
FAC	1Q		FAC	EP	FAC	EP									FAC	EP				
FAV	1Q		FAV	2Q	FAV	1Q	FAV	1Q	FAV	1P	FAV	2Q	FAV	1Q	FAV	2Q	FAV	1Q	FAV	1Q

GROUND: Long Lane, Ringwood, Hampshire BH24 3BX

Bus Route Crow Crossroads - stop 100m away

ROMSEY TOWN
Nickname: Town   **Club Colours:** Red & black   Founded 1886

Club Contact Details 01794 516 691   romseytownfc@gmail.com

HONOURS
FA Comps: None
League: Post War: Southampton West 1951-52, Senior Div.2 72-73, Senior Div.1 73-74, 76-77, Prem 80-81, 83-84. Hampshire Div.4 75-76, Div.2 78-79. Wessex 89-90.

	10-11		11-12		12-13		13-14		14-15		15-16		16-17		17-18		18-19		19-20	
	WexP	16	WexP	8	WexP	20	WexP	22	Wex1	14	Wex1	9	Wex1	13	Wex1	6	Wex1	4	Wex1	n&v
FAC	EPr		FAC	EP	FAC	P	FAC	EP	FAC	EP							FAC	EP	FAC	EP
FAV	2Q		FAV	2Q	FAV	2Q	FAV	2Q	FAV	1Q	FAV	2Q	FAV	1P	FAV	1P	FAV	1Qr	FAV	1P

GROUND: The By-Pass Ground, South Front, Romsey SO51 8GJ
Nearest Railway Station Romsey - 0.5km
Bus Route Linden Road - stop 100m away

TOTTON & ELING
Totton & Eling Football Club   Nickname: The Millers   **Club Colours:** Red & black   Founded 1925

Club Contact Details 07876 776 985   tefcsecretary@gmail.com

HONOURS
FA Comps: None
League: Hampshire Division three 1974-75, Division One 1987-88, 88-89. Wessex Division One 2008-09.

	10-11		11-12		12-13		13-14		14-15		15-16		16-17		17-18		18-19		19-20	
	WexP	18	WexP	11	WexP	12	WexP	8	WexP	20	Wex1	15	Wex1	15	Wex1	14	Wex1	19	Wex1	n&v
FAC	1Q		FAC	P	FAC	1Qr	FAC	Pr	FAC	EP										
FAV	1Q		FAV	1Q	FAV	1Q	FAV	1Q	FAV	1Q							FAV	1P	FAV	1Q

GROUND: Millers Park, Salisbury Road, Totton SO40 2RW
Nearest Railway Station Totton - 2.9km
Bus Route Cooks Lane - stop 280m away

UNITED SERVICES PORTSMOUTH
Nickname: The Navy   **Club Colours:** Royal blue & red

Founded 1962

Club Contact Details 07887 541 782   usportsmouthfc@hotmail.co.uk

HONOURS
FA Comps: None
League: Hampshire Division Two 1967-68, 77-78, 80-81.

	10-11	11-12	12-13	13-14	14-15	15-16	16-17	17-18	18-19	19-20
Wex1	5	13	12	7	5	4	9	4	5	n&v
FAC						EP	P		P	EP
FAV	1Q	2Q	2Q	2Q	2P	2Qr	1Q	1P	2Q	1Q

GROUND: Victory Stadium, HMS Temeraire, Burnaby Road, Portsmouth PO1 2HB
Nearest Railway Station Portsmouth Harbour - 0.7km
Bus Route University - stop 120m away

VERWOOD TOWN
Nickname: The Potters   **Club Colours:** Red & black

Founded 1920

Club Contact Details 01202 814 007   secretary@vtfc.co.uk

HONOURS
FA Comps: None
League: Wessex Division One 2011-12.

	10-11	11-12	12-13	13-14	14-15	15-16	16-17	17-18	18-19	19-20
Wex	9	1	P 14	P 19	P 15	P 17	P 22	1 17	1 8	1 n&v
FAC	EPr	EP	EP	EP	EP	P	Pr	EPr		
FAV	3P	1Q	1Qr	2P	3P	2Q	1Q	1Q	2Qr	2Q

GROUND: Potterne Park Potterne Way Verwood Dorset BH21 6RS

Bus Route Potterne Bridge - stop 280m away

WHITCHURCH UNITED
Nickname: Jam Boys   **Club Colours:** Red & white stripes

Founded 1903

Club Contact Details 01256 892 493   secretary.wufc@gmail.com

HONOURS
FA Comps: None
League: Hampshire Division Two 1989-90.

	10-11	11-12	12-13	13-14	14-15	15-16	16-17	17-18	18-19	19-20
Wex	1 7	1 8	1 2	P 13	P 6	P 15	P 21	1 13	1 14	1 n&v
FAC		2Q	EP	EPr	EPr	EPr	P	EP		
FAV	1Q	2Q	2Q	1Q	2Q	1Pr	2Q	2Q	1Q	1Q

GROUND: Longmeadow, Winchester Road, Whitchurch, Hampshire RG28 7RB
Nearest Railway Station Whitchurch - 1.7km
Bus Route Charcot Close - stop 100m away

AFC BRIDGNORTH
Nickname: Meadow Men   **Club Colours:** Blue & white
Founded 2013

Club Contact Details

HONOURS
FA Comps: None
League: West Midlands (Reg) Division One 2013-14.

10-11	11-12	12-13	13-14	14-15	15-16	16-17	17-18	18-19	19-20
			WM1 1	WMP 2	WMP 2 FAC P	WMP 8 FAC EP	WMP 18	WMP 12	WMP n&v
				FAV 1P	FAV 2P	FAV 1Q	FAV 1Q	FAV 1Q	FAV 1Q

GROUND: Crown Meadow, Innage Lane, Bridgnorth WV16 4HS

Bus Route Bus stops outside the ground.

BEWDLEY TOWN
Nickname: None   **Club Colours:** Royal blue & yellow
Founded 1978

Club Contact Details 07739 626 169

HONOURS
FA Comps: None
League: West Midlands (Reg) Division One South 2002-03, Division One 2004-05.

10-11	11-12	12-13	13-14	14-15	15-16	16-17	17-18	18-19	19-20
WMP 6	WMP 4	WMP 8	WMP 7	WMP 17	WMP 16	WMP 6	WMP 7	WMP 6	WMP n&v
FAC P	FAC 1Q	FAC 1Q	FAC EP	FAC EP			FAC EP		
FAV 2Q	FAV 1Q	FAV 1P	FAV 1Q	FAV 1Q	FAV 1Q	FAV 2Q	FAV 1Q	FAV 1P	FAV 1Q

GROUND: Ribbesford Meadows, Ribbesford, Bewdley, Worcs DY12 2TJ

Bus Route Burlish Farm - stop 1km away

BILSTON TOWN COMMUNITY
Nickname: The Steelmen   **Club Colours:** Orange & black
Founded 1894

Club Contact Details

HONOURS
FA Comps: None
League: Walsall & District 1895-96, 1900-01, 01-02, 32-33, 35-36, 47-48. Birmingham & District/West Mids (Reg) Division One 1956
-57, Premier 60-61, 72-73.

10-11	11-12	12-13	13-14	14-15	15-16	16-17	17-18	18-19	19-20
WM1 9	WM1 9	WM1 2	WMP 16	WMP 13	WMP 20	WMP 15	WMP 11	WMP 13	WMP n&v
		FAV 1P	FAV 2Q	FAV 1Q	FAV 2Q	FAV 2Q	FAV 2Q		FAV 1Q

GROUND: Queen Street Stadium, Queen Street, Bilston WV14 7EX
Nearest Railway Station Bilston Central - 550m
Bus Route Bus stops outside the ground

BLACK COUNTRY RANGERS
Nickname: **Club Colours:** Red
Founded 1996

Club Contact Details 0121 559 5564

HONOURS
FA Comps: None
League: West Midlands (Reg) Division Two 2009-10, Division One 10-11.

10-11	11-12	12-13	13-14	14-15	15-16	16-17	17-18	18-19	19-20
WM1 1	WMP 2	WMP 5	WMP 5 FAC P	WMP 10 FAC EP	WMP 15	WMP 13	WMP 4	WMP 8	WMP n&v
	FAV 2P	FAV 2P	FAV 1Q	FAV 1Q	FAV 1Pr	FAV 2Q		FAV 1P	FAV 2Q

GROUND: York Road Stadium, York Road, Oldbury B65 0RR
Nearest Railway Station Old Hill - 1.8km
Bus Route Cranmoor Crescent - stop 50m away

CRADLEY TOWN

Nickname: The Lukes or Hammers **Club Colours:** Red and black

Founded 1948

Club Contact Details

HONOURS
FA Comps: None
League: West Midlands (Reg) Division One 1990-91.

	10-11	11-12	12-13	13-14	14-15	15-16	16-17	17-18	18-19	19-20
WMP	8	8	10	10	15	8	10	8	11	n&v
FAC	EP	EPr	Pr	EP			EPr			
FAV	1Q	1Q	2Q	1P	2Q	1P	1Q	2Q	2Q	1Q

GROUND: The Beeches, Beeches View Avenue, Cradley, Halesowen B63 2HB
Nearest Railway Station Cradley Heath - 2km
Bus Route Hedgefield Grove - stop 200m away

DARLASTON TOWN (1874)

Nickname: **Club Colours:** Blue and white

Founded 1874

Club Contact Details 01922 616 165

HONOURS
FA Comps: None
League: West Midlands (Regional) Division One 2006-07.

	10-11	11-12	12-13	13-14	14-15	15-16	16-17	17-18	18-19	19-20
WMP	16	22	21		WM2 3	WM1 5	WM1 7	WM1 6	WM1 2	WMP n&v
FAV	2Q									

GROUND: Bentley Leisure Pavilion, Bentley Road North, Bentley WS2 0EA

DUDLEY SPORTS

Nickname: The Piemen **Club Colours:** Green & white

Founded 1925

Club Contact Details 01384 826 420

HONOURS
FA Comps: None
League: None

	10-11	11-12	12-13	13-14	14-15	15-16	16-17	17-18	18-19	19-20
WMP	14	12	17	17	12	6	17	16	15	n&v
FAC			EPr				P			
FAV	1Q	2Q	1Q	2Q	1Q	2Q	2Q	2Q	2Q	1Q

GROUND: Hillcrest Avenue, Brierley Hill, West Mids DY5 3QH
Nearest Railway Station Lye - 2.1km Stourbridge - 2.5km Cradley Heath - 2.8km
Bus Route Lancaster Road - stop 60m away

DUDLEY TOWN

Nickname: The Duds or Robins **Club Colours:** Red & black

Founded 1888

Club Contact Details

HONOURS
FA Comps: None
League: Birmingham Combination 1933-34. Southern Midland Division 1984-85.

	10-11	11-12	12-13	13-14	14-15	15-16	16-17	17-18	18-19	19-20
WMP	13	7	6	9	14	13	18	17	10	n&v
FAC	P		1Q	EPr	P					
FAV	2Qr	2Q	1Q	2P	2Q	1Q	1Q	2Q	2Q	2P

GROUND: Sporting Khalsa FC, Asprey Arena, Noose Lane, Willenhall WV13 3BB

LITTLETON
Nickname: The Ton **Club Colours:** Red/red/white
Founded 1890

Club Contact Details 01905 909 125

HONOURS
FA Comps: None
League: Midland Combination Division Three 2001-02.

10-11	11-12	12-13	13-14	14-15	15-16	16-17	17-18	18-19	19-20
MCm1 5	MCm1 2	MCmP 2	MCmP 11	MFL1 9	MFL1 9	MFL1 9	MFL1 8	MFL1 17	WMP n&v
					FAV 2Q	FAV 2Q	FAV 2Q	FAV 2Q	FAV 1Q

GROUND: 5 Acres, Pebworth Road, North Littleton, Evesham, Worcs, WR11 8QL
Nearest Railway Station Honeybourne - 3.1km
Bus Route The Ivy Inn stop - 1.2km away

PERSHORE TOWN
Nickname: Town **Club Colours:** Blue & white
Founded 1988

Club Contact Details

HONOURS
FA Comps: None
League: Midland Combination Division Two 1989-90, Premier 1993-94.

10-11	11-12	12-13	13-14	14-15	15-16	16-17	17-18	18-19	19-20
MCmP 13	MCmP 16	MCmP 13	MCmP 15	MFL1 11	MFL1 14	MFL1 18	MFL1 18	WMP 14	WMP n&v
FAV 2Q	FAV 2Q	FAV 2Q	FAV 2Q	FAV 2Q	FAV 1Q	FAV 1Q	FAV 2Q	FAV 1Q	FAV 1Qr

GROUND: King George V Playing Field, King George's Way, Pershore WR10 1QU
Nearest Railway Station Pershore - 2.1km
Bus Route Abbey Tea Rooms stop - 167m away

SHAWBURY UNITED
Nickname: **Club Colours:** Black & white
Founded 1992

Club Contact Details 01939 233 287   daibando161274@aol.com

HONOURS
FA Comps: None
League: West Midlands (Regional) Premier Division 2015-16.

10-11	11-12	12-13	13-14	14-15	15-16	16-17	17-18	18-19	19-20
WMP 17	WMP 10	WMP 4	WMP 4	WMP 7	WMP 1	MFLP 19	MFLP 21	WMP 6	WMP n&v
						FAC EPr	FAC EP	FAC EP	
FAV 1Q	FAV 2Q	FAV 2P	FAV 1P	FAV 2Q	FAV 1Q	FAV 1P	FAV 1Q	FAV 1Q	FAV 1Pr

GROUND: Ludlow FC, Bromfield Road, Ludlow SY8 2BN

SHIFNAL TOWN
Nickname: The Town or Reds **Club Colours:** Red & white
Founded 1964

Club Contact Details 07986 563 156

HONOURS
FA Comps: None
League: West Midlands (Regional) Division One 1978-79, 2015-16, Premier Division 2006-07.

10-11	11-12	12-13	13-14	14-15	15-16	16-17	17-18	18-19	19-20
WMP 9	WMP 16	WMP 19	WMP 19	WMP 21	WM1 1	WMP 11	WMP 15	WMP 19	WMP n&v
FAC EPr	FAC EPr	FAC EP							
FAV 2Pr	FAV 1Q	FAV 1Q	FAV 1Q	FAV 2Q	FAV 1Q	FAV 1P	FAV 1P	FAV 1Q	FAV 2Q

GROUND: Coppice Green Lane, Shifnal, Shrops TF11 8PD
Nearest Railway Station Shifnal - 0.8km
Bus Route Green (Barn Rd) - stop 100m away

SMETHWICK

Nickname: **Club Colours:** Blue & yellow

Founded 1977

Club Contact Details 01384 826 420

HONOURS

FA Comps: None

League: Midland Combination Division Three 2007-08.
West Midlands Division One 2012-13.

10-11		11-12		12-13		13-14		14-15		15-16		16-17		17-18		18-19		19-20	
WM2	4	WM1	4	WM1	1	WMP	12	WMP	19	WMP	12	WMP	16	WMP	14	WMP	14	WMP	n&v
												FAV	1Q	FAV	2Q	FAV	1P	FAV	2Q

GROUND: The Beeches, Packwood Road, Tividale B69 1UL

WEDNESFIELD

Nickname: The Cottagers   **Club Colours:** Red & white

Founded 1961

Club Contact Details

HONOURS

FA Comps: None

League: West Midlands Division One A 1976-77, Division One 77-78, Premier 95-96, 96-97.

10-11		11-12		12-13		13-14		14-15		15-16		16-17		17-18		18-19		19-20	
WMP	4	WMP	6	WMP	18	WMP	15	WMP	22	WM1	4	WM1	2	WMP	5	WMP	5	WMP	n&v
FAC	2Q															FAC	Pr	FAC	EP
FAV	2P			FAV	1Q	FAV	1Q	FAV	1Q	FAV	1Q	FAV	1Q	FAV	1P	FAV	1P	FAV	1Q

GROUND: Cottage Ground, Amos Lane, Wednesfield WV11 1ND

Nearest Railway Station Wolverhampton - 3km

Bus Route Cottages Homes - stop 20m away

WEM TOWN

Nickname: Town   **Club Colours:** Red

Founded 1883

Club Contact Details

HONOURS

FA Comps: None

League: Shropshire County 2008-09. West Midlands (Reg) Division One 2017-18.

10-11		11-12		12-13		13-14		14-15		15-16		16-17		17-18		18-19		19-20	
WM1	4	WM1	12	WM1	3	WM1	4	WM1	7	WM1	9	WM1	9	WM1	1	WMP	18	WMP	n&v
																FAV	2Q	FAV	1Q

GROUND: Butler Sports Centre, Bowens Field, Wem SY4 5AP

WOLVERHAMPTON CASUALS

Nickname: The Cassies   **Club Colours:** Green

Founded 1899

Club Contact Details 01902 783 214

HONOURS

FA Comps: None

League: West Midlands (Reg) Division One 1994-95.

10-11		11-12		12-13		13-14		14-15		15-16		16-17		17-18		18-19		19-20	
WMP	12	WMP	3	WMP	3	WMP	3	WMP	6	WMP	7	WMP	2	WMP	9	WMP	3	WMP	n&v
		FAC	EP	FAC	1Qr	FAC	P	FAC	EP	FAC	EP	FAC	EPr	FAC	P			FAC	EPr
FAV	1P	FAV	1Q	FAV	1Q	FAV	2Q	FAV	1Q	FAV	2Q	FAV	2P	FAV	1Q	FAV	2Q	FAV	2Q

GROUND: Brinsford Stadium, Brinsford Lane, Wolverhampton WV10 7PR

Nearest Railway Station Billbrook - 4.8km

Bus Route Old Heath House - stop 350m away

WOLVERHAMPTON SPORTING C
Nickname: Wolves Sporting   **Club Colours:** Black & orange   Founded 2001

Club Contact Details

HONOURS
FA Comps: None
League: West Midlands (Reg) Division Two 2006-07, Premier 2017-18.

10-11	11-12	12-13	13-14	14-15	15-16	16-17	17-18	18-19	19-20
WMP 18	WMP 19	WMP 10	WMP 18	WMP 16	WMP 4	WMP 3	WMP 1	MFLP 20	WMP n&v
						FAC EP	FAC EP	FAC EP	FAC EP
FAV 1P	FAV 2Q	FAV 2Q	FAV 1Q	FAV 1Q	FAV 1Q	FAV 1P	FAV 5P	FAV 2P	FAV 2Q

GROUND: Pride Park, Hazel Lane, Great Wyrley, Staffs WS6 6AA
Nearest Railway Station Ladywood - 1km
Bus Route Hazel Lane - stop 270m away

WORCESTER RAIDERS
Nickname: Raiders   **Club Colours:** Red and black   Founded 2001

Club Contact Details 07532 266 897

HONOURS
FA Comps: None
League: West Mildlands (Regional) Division One 2018-19.

10-11	11-12	12-13	13-14	14-15	15-16	16-17	17-18	18-19	19-20
			WM2 3	WM1 14	WM1 12	WM1 3	WM1 7	WM1 1	WMP n&v

GROUND: Claines Lane, Worcester, Worcestershire WR3 7SS
Nearest Railway Station Worcester Foregate Street
Bus Route 303 from Foregate Street Station to Bevere Lane (10min journey), ground 14min walk from there.

PREMIER DIVISION

BITTON

Nickname: The Ton   **Club Colours:** Red & white   Founded 1892

Club Contact Details 01179 323 222   jaynelangdon@btconnect.com

Previous Names: None
Previous Leagues: Avon Premier Combination, Gloucestershire County 1995-97.
HONOURS
FA Comps: None
League: Western League Premier Division 2008-09.

	10-11	11-12	12-13	13-14	14-15	15-16	16-17	17-18	18-19	19-20
WestP	2	2	7	6	7	14	19	10	3	n&v
FAC	1Q	EPr	P	P	EP	P	P	EPr	2Q	P
FAV	4P	4P	4P	3P	1Q	2Q	2Q	1Q	1P	

GROUND: Bath Road, Bitton, Bristol BS30 6HX
Capacity: 1,000 **Seats:** 48 **Covered:** 200
Nearest Railway Station Bitton - 500m
Bus Route Cherry Garden Road - stop 50m away

BRADFORD TOWN

Nickname: Bobcats   **Club Colours:** All royal blue   Founded 1992

Club Contact Details 07912 184 104   secretary@bradfordtownfc.com

Previous Names: None
Previous Leagues: Wiltshire County 1992-2005.
HONOURS
FA Comps: None
League: Western Division One 2013-14.

	10-11	11-12	12-13	13-14	14-15	15-16	16-17	17-18	18-19	19-20
West1/WestP	West1 6	West1 5	West1 3	West1 1	WestP 8	WestP 8	WestP 5	WestP 4	WestP 7	WestP n&v
FAC	EPr	EP	EP	EP	1Q	2Q	EP	EP	EP	1Q
FAV	2Q	1P	2Q	1P	5P	4P	4P	5P	3P	5P

GROUND: Bradford Sports & Social Club, Trowbridge Rd, Bradford on Avon BA15 1EE
Capacity: **Seats:** Yes **Covered:** Yes
Nearest Railway Station Bradford-upon-Avon - 0.3km
Bus Route Junction Road _ stop 30m away

BRIDGWATER TOWN

Nickname: The Robins   **Club Colours:** Red & white   Founded 1984

Club Contact Details 01278 446 899   ianbarber4@gmail.com

Previous Names: Bridgwater Town
Previous Leagues: Somerset Senior 1984-94. Western 1994-2007. Southern 2007-2017.
HONOURS
FA Comps: None
League: Somerset Senior Division One 1986-87, Premier 89-90, 90-91, 91-92. Western Division One 1995-96.

	10-11	11-12	12-13	13-14	14-15	15-16	16-17	17-18	18-19	19-20
Sthsw/WestP	Sthsw 18	Sthsw 15	Sthsw 19	Sthsw 14	Sthsw 12	Sthsw 19	Sthsw 22	WestP 8	WestP 4	WestP n&v
FAC	1Q	1Q	P	3Q	2Q	P	P	1Q	EP	1Q
FAT/FAV	FAT 1Q	FAT P	FAT 2Q	FAT 1Q	FAT P	FAT Pr	FAT Pr	FAV 3Pr	FAV 2Q	FAV 3P

GROUND: Fairfax Park, College Way, Bath Road, Bridgwater, Somerset TA6 4TZ
Capacity: 2,500 **Seats:** 128 **Covered:** 500 **Shop:** Yes
Nearest Railway Station Bridgwater - 0.7km

BRIDPORT
Nickname: Bees   **Club Colours:** Red and black   Founded 1885

Club Contact Details 01308 423 834   sevie@tiscali.co.uk

Previous Names: None
Previous Leagues: Dorset. South Dorset. West Dorset. Perry Street. Dorset Combination (Founding Memeber) 1957-61, 84-88. Western 1961-84.
HONOURS
FA Comps: None
League: Dorset Combination 1985-86, 86-87, 87-88.

	10-11	11-12	12-13	13-14	14-15	15-16	16-17	17-18	18-19	19-20
	West1 3	WestP 14	WestP 14	WestP 12	WestP 14	WestP 16	WestP 16	WestP 7	WestP 13	WestP n&v
FAC	P	P	EP	P	EP	1Q	EP	3Q	1Q	EP
FAV	1P	1P	2Q	1Q	2P	1P	1Q	1Q	1P	1Q

GROUND: St Mary's Field, Bridport, Dorset DT6 5LN
Capacity: 2,000 **Seats:** 150 **Covered:** Yes

Bus Route Leisure Centre - stop 20m away

BRISLINGTON
Nickname: Bris   **Club Colours:** Red & black   Founded 1956

Club Contact Details 01179 774 030   kevinhazell@me.com

Previous Names: Formed as an U16 team.
Previous Leagues: Bristol Church of England. Bristol & Suburban. Somerset Senior until 1991.
HONOURS
FA Comps: None
League: Somerset Senior 1988-89. Western Division One 1994-95.

	10-11	11-12	12-13	13-14	14-15	15-16	16-17	17-18	18-19	19-20
	WestP 15	WestP 7	WestP 2	WestP 10	WestP 10	WestP 11	WestP 10	WestP 16	WestP 18	WestP n&v
FAC	EP	1Q	EP	4Q	P	EP	2Q	P	EP	P
FAV	1P	1Q	1P	2P	1P	1Q	2Q	2Q	1Q	1Q

GROUND: Ironmould Lane, Brislington, Bristol BS4 4TZ
Capacity: 2,000 **Seats:** 144 **Covered:** 1,500
Nearest Railway Station Keynsham - 3km
Bus Route Ironmould Lane - stop 100m away

BUCKLAND ATHLETIC
Nickname: The Bucks   **Club Colours:** Yellow with black trim   Founded 1977

Club Contact Details 01626 361 020   phardingham@virginmedia.com

Previous Names: None
Previous Leagues: Torbay Pioneer 1977-87. Devon & Exeter 1987-2000. Devon County 2000-07. South West Peninsula 2007-12.
HONOURS
FA Comps: None
League: Devon & Exeter Senior Third Division 1987-88, Premier 94-95, 99-00.
South West Peninsula Premier 2009-10, 10-11.

	10-11	11-12	12-13	13-14	14-15	15-16	16-17	17-18	18-19	19-20
	SWPP 1	SWPP 2	WestP 10	WestP 11	WestP 2	WestP 4	WestP 4	WestP 5	WestP 9	WestP n&v
FAC	EPr	Pr	2Q	EP	EP	P	EP	EP	1Q	EP
FAV	2Q	1P	2P	2P	3P	3P	QF	2P	2Q	4P

GROUND: Homers Heath, South Quarry, Kingskerswell Road, Newton Abbot TQ12 5JU
Capacity: 1,000 **Seats:** Yes **Covered:** Yes
Nearest Railway Station Newton Abbot approx 2 miles from the ground.

CADBURY HEATH
Nickname: The Heathens   **Club Colours:** Red & white   Founded 1894

Club Contact Details 07971 399 268   martinbristol1955@hotmail.com

Previous Names: None
Previous Leagues: Bristol & District. Bristol Premier Combination. Gloucestershire County 1968-75, 80-2000. Midland Combination 1975-77.
HONOURS
FA Comps: None
League: Gloucestershire County 1970-71, 71-72, 72-73, 73-74, 93-94, 97-98, 98-99.
Western League Division One 2011-12.

10-11		11-12		12-13		13-14		14-15		15-16		16-17		17-18		18-19		19-20	
West1	4	West1	1	WestP	4	WestP	13	WestP	11	WestP	12	WestP	11	WestP	18	WestP	14	WestP	n&v
		FAC	2Q	FAC	P	FAC	EP	FAC	EP	FAC	EP	FAC	3Q	FAC	2Qr	FAC	1Q	FAC	EP
FAV	4P	FAV	2P	FAV	2P	FAV	1P	FAV	2Q	FAV	2P	FAV	2Q	FAV	1P	FAV	3P	FAV	2Q

GROUND: Springfield, Cadbury Heath Road, Bristol BS30 8BX
Capacity: 2,000 **Seats:** Yes   **Covered:** Yes
Nearest Railway Station Oldland - 1.2km
Bus Route The King William IV - stop 100m away

CHIPPING SODBURY TOWN
Nickname: The Sods   **Club Colours:** Black & white   Founded 1885

Club Contact Details 07778 678 823   g.endicott@btopenworld.com

Previous Names: None
Previous Leagues: Gloucester County 2008-2015.
HONOURS
FA Comps: None
League: Western Division One 2015-16.

10-11		11-12		12-13		13-14		14-15		15-16		16-17		17-18		18-19		19-20	
GlCo	3	GlCo	18	GlCo	15	GlCo	11	GlCo	3	West1	1	WestP	13	WestP	13	WestP	10	WestP	n&v
														FAC	P	FAC	1Q	FAC	EP
												FAV	1Q	FAV	1Q	FAV	2Q	FAV	1Q

GROUND: The Ridings, Wickwar Road, Chipping Sodbury, Bristol BS37 6GA
Capacity: **Seats:** Yes   **Covered:** Yes
Nearest Railway Station Yate - 2.7km
Bus Route Wickwar Road - stop 50m away

CLEVEDON TOWN
Nickname: Seasiders   **Club Colours:** Blue with white   Founded 1880

Club Contact Details 01275 871 600   erichowe@hotmail.co.uk

Previous Names: Clevedon FC and Ashtonians merged in 1974
Previous Leagues: Western (Founder Members 1892), 1945-58, 73-93. Bristol & District. Bristol Suburban. Somerset Senior. Southern 1993-2015.
HONOURS
FA Comps: None
League: Bristol & Suburban 1925-26, 27-28, 28-29. Somerset Senior 36-37. Bristol Charity 37-38, 40-41. Western 92-93. Southern Midland Division 98-99, Divions 1W 2005-06.

10-11		11-12		12-13		13-14		14-15		15-16		16-17		17-18		18-19		19-20	
Sthsw	20	Sthsw	20	Sthsw	15	Sthsw	17	Sthsw	18	WestP	19	WestP	14	WestP	12	WestP	6	WestP	n&v
FAC	3Q	FAC	2Q	FAC	2Q	FAC	3Qr	FAC	P	FAC	3Q	FAC	P	FAC	P	FAC	EP	FAC	P
FAT	P	FAT	P	FAT	Pr	FAT	2Q	FAT	P	FAV	1Q	FAV	2P	FAV	2Q	FAV	2Q	FAV	1Q

GROUND: Everyone Active Stadium, Davis Lane, Clevedon BS21 6TG
Capacity: 3,500 **Seats:** 300   **Covered:** 1,600   **Shop:** Yes
Nearest Railway Station Yatton - 4km
Bus Route Sercombe Park - stop 400m away

CRIBBS

Nickname: Cribbs — Club Colours: Blue — Founded 1976

Club Contact Details 0117 950 2303 — welshwizard1973@aol.com

Previous Names: Sun Life Assurance 1976. AXA>2011. Cribbs Friends Life 2011-13
Previous Leagues: Bristol & Avon. Avon Premier Combination. Gloucestershire County > 2012.
HONOURS
FA Comps: None
League: Gloucester County 2011-12.

	10-11	11-12	12-13	13-14	14-15	15-16	16-17	17-18	18-19	19-20
League	GlCo 2	GlCo 1	West1 8	West1 5	West1 3	WestP 5	WestP 8	WestP 11	WestP 8	WestP n&v
FAC					FAC P	FAC EP	FAC EPr	FAC EP	FAC EP	FAC P
FAV				FAV 2Q	FAV 1Q	FAV 1Q	FAV 1Q	FAV 2Q	FAV 4P	FAV 3P

GROUND: The Lawns, Station Road, Henbury, Bristol BS10 7TB
Capacity: 1,000 Seats: 100 Covered: Yes
Nearest Railway Station Pilning - 4.3km. Sea Mills - 4.5km. Patchway - 4.5km
Bus Route Rugby Club - stop 400m away

EXMOUTH TOWN

Nickname: The Town — Club Colours: All royal blue — Founded 1933

Club Contact Details 01395 263 348 — chardtapp1@hotmail.co.uk

Previous Names: None
Previous Leagues: Western 1973-2006. South West Peninsula (FM) 2007-19.
HONOURS
FA Comps: None
League: Western 1983-84, 85-86.
South West Peninsula Division One East 2012-13.

	10-11	11-12	12-13	13-14	14-15	15-16	16-17	17-18	18-19	19-20
League	SW1E 11	SW1E 5	SW1E 1	SWPP 2	SWPP 8	SWPP 12	SWPP 5	SWPP 16	SWPP 2	WestP n&v
FAC								FAC EP		FAC 1Q
FAV			FAV 1P	FAV 2Q		FAV 2Q	FAV 5P	FAV 2P	FAV 2P	FAV 2P

GROUND: King George V, Exmouth EX8 3EE
Capacity: Seats: 50 Covered: Yes
Nearest Railway Station Exmouth - 0.6km
Bus Route Exeter Road - stop 143m away

HALLEN

Nickname: The Armadillos — Club Colours: Blue — Founded 1949

Club Contact Details 01179 505 559 — sinbad88@hotmail.co.uk

Previous Names: Lawrence Weston Athletic, Lawrence Weston Hallen
Previous Leagues: Bristol & District. Bristol Premier. Gloucestershire County 1987-92. Hellenic 1992-2000.
HONOURS
FA Comps: None
League: Gloucestershire County 1988-89, 92-93. Hellenic Division One 1996-97. Western Division One 2003-04.

	10-11	11-12	12-13	13-14	14-15	15-16	16-17	17-18	18-19	19-20
League	WestP 16	WestP 4	WestP 9	WestP 15	WestP 17	WestP 17	WestP 18	WestP 17	WestP 12	WestP n&v
FAC	FAC P	FAC 1Qr	FAC P	FAC 1Q	FAC P	FAC EPr	FAC EP	FAC EPr	FAC P	FAC EP
FAV	FAV 2Qr	FAV 2Q	FAV 1P	FAV 5P	FAV 2P	FAV 2P	FAV 2Q	FAV 1Q	FAV 1Q	FAV 1Q

GROUND: Hallen Centre, Moorhouse Lane, Hallen Bristol BS10 7RU
Capacity: 2,000 Seats: 200 Covered: 200
Nearest Railway Station St Andrews Road - 2.7km
Bus Route Moorhouse Park - stop 250m away

KEYNSHAM TOWN

Nickname: K's   **Club Colours:** Amber and black

Founded 1895

Club Contact Details   jules1233@live.com

Previous Names: None

Previous Leagues: East Bristol & District >late 1950s. Bristol Premier Combination >1967. Somerset County 1967-73.

HONOURS

FA Comps: None

League: Bristol & District Division Three 1898-99, Division Two 1948-49. Western Division One 1977-78, 2018-19.

10-11		11-12		12-13		13-14		14-15		15-16		16-17		17-18		18-19		19-20	
West1	16	West1	13	West1	13	West1	19	West1	17	West1	9	West1	4	West1	3	West1	1	WestP	n&v
FAC	EP											FAC	EP	FAC	EP	FAC	EPr	FAC	EP
FAV	2P	FAV	2Q	FAV	1Q	FAV	2Q	FAV	2Q	FAV	2Qr	FAV	2Q	FAV	1Q	FAV	1Q	FAV	1Q

GROUND: AJN Stadium, Bristol Road, Keynsham BS31 2BE
Capacity: 3,000   **Seats:**   **Covered:**
Nearest Railway Station Keynsham - 0.7km
Bus Route Rugby Club - stop 50m away

ODD DOWN

Nickname: The Down   **Club Colours:** All blue

Founded 1901

Club Contact Details 01225 832 491   lorainebrown@btinternet.com

Previous Names: None

Previous Leagues: Bath & District. Wiltshire. Somerset Senior. Mid-Somerset.

HONOURS

FA Comps: None

League: Western Division One 1992-93, Premier Division 2015-16.

10-11		11-12		12-13		13-14		14-15		15-16		16-17		17-18		18-19		19-20	
WestP	8	WestP	9	WestP	8	WestP	4	WestP	5	WestP	1	WestP	7	WestP	14	WestP	15	WestP	n&v
FAC	Pr	FAC	P	FAC	P	FAC	EPr	FAC	P	FAC	P	FAC	P	FAC	1Q	FAC	EP	FAC	EP
FAV	2P	FAV	2Q	FAV	2P	FAV	2P	FAV	3P	FAV	2P	FAV	2P	FAV	1P	FAV	1P	FAV	1Q

GROUND: Lew Hill Memorial Ground, Combe Hay Lane, Odd Down BA2 8PA
Capacity: 1,000   **Seats:** 160   **Covered:** 250
Nearest Railway Station Oldfield Park - 2.9km
Bus Route St Gregory's School - stop 50m away

PLYMOUTH PARKWAY AFC

Nickname: The Parkway   **Club Colours:** All Yellow

Founded 1988

Club Contact Details 07786 571 308   gennyt@sky.com

Previous Names: None

Previous Leagues: Plymouth & District. South West Peninsula 2007-18.

HONOURS

FA Comps: None

League: Plymouth & District Division Two 1990-91.
South West Peninsula Premier Division 2013-14, 17-18.

10-11		11-12		12-13		13-14		14-15		15-16		16-17		17-18		18-19		19-20	
SWPP	3	SWPP	6	SWPP	2	SWPP	1	SWPP	5	SWPP	4	SWPP	7	SWPP	1	WestP	2	WestP	n&v
				FAC	1Qr	FAC	1Q	FAC	P	FAC	1Q	FAC	1Q	FAC	EP	FAC	2Q	FAC	1Q
FAV	3P	FAV	1P	FAV	1Q	FAV	3P	FAV	2P	FAV	2P	FAV	1Pr	FAV	3P	FAV	1P	FAV	QF

GROUND: Bolitho Park, St Peters Road, Manadon, Plymouth PL5 3JG
Capacity: **Seats:** Yes   **Covered:** Yes
Nearest Railway Station St Budeaux Road - 2.8km
Bus Route St Peters Road - stop 10m away

ROMAN GLASS ST GEORGE
Nickname: The Glass   Club Colours: White and black   Founded 1872

Club Contact Details 07770 331 491   adamwolves2@hotmail.com

Previous Names: St George. Bristol St George. Merged with Roman Glass in 1995 to form today's club.

Previous Leagues: Bristol & District/Western (Founder Members) 1892-1903, 1928-35. Bristol & District 1935-57. Bristol Premier Combination (FM) 1957-68. Gloucestershire County (FM) 1968-87, 99-2007. County of Avon Premier Comb 1987-95.

HONOURS

FA Comps: None

League: Bristol & District Div.1 1949-50. Bristol Premier Com. Div.1 1963-64, 64-65, 65-66, 66-67, 67-68, 88-89, Prem 92-93. .Gloucestershire County 1969-70, 2001-02, 06-07.

10-11		11-12		12-13		13-14		14-15		15-16		16-17		17-18		18-19		19-20	
West1	15	West1	8	West1	17	West1	12	West1	20	West1	18	West1	15	West1	2	WestP	17	WestP	n&v
																FAC	EP	FAC	P
				FAV	2Q	FAV	2Q	FAV	2Q	FAV	1Qr	FAV	2Q	FAV	2Q	FAV	1P	FAV	3P

GROUND: Oaklands Park, Gloucester Road, Almondsbury BS32 4AG

Capacity: 2,000 **Seats:** **Covered:**

Nearest Railway Station Patchway - 2.6km

Bus Route Alondsbury Depot - stop 100m away

SHEPTON MALLET
Nickname: The Mallet   Club Colours: Black & white   Founded 1986

Club Contact Details 01749 344 609   gkrkb@tiscali.co.uk

Previous Names: None

Previous Leagues: Somerset Senior.

HONOURS

FA Comps: None

League: Somerset Senior League 2000-01.

10-11		11-12		12-13		13-14		14-15		15-16		16-17		17-18		18-19		19-20	
West1	14	West1	16	West1	7	West1	2	WestP	9	WestP	10	WestP	12	WestP	6	WestP	11	WestP	n&v
						FAC	EPr	FAC	Pr	FAC	EP	FAC	P	FAC	EP	FAC	EPr	FAC	1Qr
FAV	2Q	FAV	1Q	FAV	1Q	FAV	2P	FAV	3P	FAV	2Q	FAV	1Q	FAV	2Q	FAV	1Q	FAV	1P

GROUND: Playing Fields, Old Wells Road, West Shepton, Shepton Mallet BA4 5XN

Capacity: 2,500 **Seats:** 120 **Covered:** Yes

Bus Route West Lodge - stop 180m away

STREET
Nickname: The Cobblers   Club Colours: All green   Founded 1880

Club Contact Details 01458 445 987   streetfootballclub@outlook.com

Previous Names: None

Previous Leagues: Somerset Senior 1880-1911, 22-30, 60-98. Western 1911-22, 30-39, 46-60, 98-2018. Southern 2018-19.

HONOURS

FA Comps: None

League: Somerset Senior 1892-93, 95-96, 97-98, 98-99, 1909-10, 63-64, 65-66, 1996-97, Division Three 93-94. Western Premier 2017-18.

10-11		11-12		12-13		13-14		14-15		15-16		16-17		17-18		18-19		19-20	
WestP	13	WestP	10	WestP	6	WestP	5	WestP	13	WestP	7	WestP	2	WestP	1	SthS	8	WestP	n&v
FAC	P	FAC	EP	FAC	EP	FAC	1Q	FAC	EPr	FAC	P	FAC	1Q	FAC	P	FAC	1Qr	FAC	P
FAV	2Q	FAV	1Q	FAV	1P	FAV	2Q	FAV	2Q	FAV	1Q	FAV	1P	FAV	1P	FAT	2Qr	FAV	2Q

GROUND: The Tannery Ground, Middlebrooks, Street BA16 0TA

Capacity: 1,000 **Seats:** 150 **Covered:** 25

Bus Route Green Lane Ave - stop 220m away

TAVISTOCK

Nickname: The Lambs   **Club Colours:** Red & black

Founded 1888

Club Contact Details 01822 614 447   secretary@tavistockfc.com

Previous Names:
Previous Leagues: South Western 1952-61, 68-2007. South West Peninsula 2007-19.
HONOURS
FA Comps: None
League: Devon 1900-01. Plymouth Combination Division One 1950-51.
South West Peninsula League Division One East 2014-15, Premier 16-17, 18-19.

10-11		11-12		12-13		13-14		14-15		15-16		16-17		17-18		18-19		19-20	
SWPP	13	SWPP	10	SWPP	10	SWPP	19	SW1E	1	SWPP	3	SWPP	1	SWPP	2	SWPP	1	WestP	n&v
FAC	P	FAC	1Q	FAC	EP	FAC	EP							FAC	2Q	FAC	EP	FAC	3Q
FAV	1P	FAV	1P	FAV	1Q	FAV	2P	FAV	1Q			FAV	1P	FAV	2P	FAV	2P	FAV	3P

GROUND: Langsford Park, Red & Black Club, Crowndale Road, Tavistock PL19 8JR
Capacity: **Seats:** Yes   **Covered:** Yes
Nearest Railway Station Gunnislake - 4.9km
Bus Route Canons Way - stop 694m away

WELLINGTON

Nickname: Wellie   **Club Colours:** Orange and black

Founded 1892

Club Contact Details 01823 664 810   jeffandjane@talktalk.net

Previous Names: None
Previous Leagues: Taunton Saturday, Somerset Senior.
HONOURS
FA Comps: None
League: Western Division One 2007-08, 16-17.

10-11		11-12		12-13		13-14		14-15		15-16		16-17		17-18		18-19		19-20	
WestP	18	West1	18	West1	18	West1	8	West1	6	West1	12	West1	1	WestP	15	WestP	16	WestP	n&v
FAC	P	FAC	EP											FAC	EP	FAC	EPr	FAC	EP
FAV	2P	FAV	2Q	FAT	2Q			FAV	2Q			FAV	1Q	FAV	2P	FAV	1Q	FAV	1Q

GROUND: Wellington Playing Field, North Street, Wellington TA21 8NE
Capacity: 1,500 **Seats:** 200   **Covered:** 200

Bus Route Nth St Police Station - stop 150m away

WESTBURY UNITED

Nickname: White Horse Men   **Club Colours:** Green and black

Founded 1920

Club Contact Details 01373 764 197   secretary@westburyunited.co.uk

Previous Names: Formed after the merger of Westbury Old Comrades FC and Westbury Great Western Railway XI
Previous Leagues: Wiltshire County 1920-1984.
HONOURS
FA Comps: None
League: Wiltshire 1934-35, 37-38, 38-39, 49-50, 50-51, 55-56.
Western Division One 1991-92, 2017-18.

10-11		11-12		12-13		13-14		14-15		15-16		16-17		17-18		18-19		19-20	
West1	17	West1	17	West1	19	West1	20	West1	22	West1	22	West1	12	West1	1	WestP	5	WestP	n&v
FAC	P															FAC	1Q	FAC	EP
FAV	1Q	FAV	1Q	FAV	1P	FAV	1Q	FAV	1Q	FAV	1Q	FAV	2Q	FAV	2Q	FAV	1P	FAV	1P

GROUND: Meadow Lane, Westbury, Wiltshire BA13 3AF
Capacity: **Seats:** Yes   **Covered:** Yes
Nearest Railway Station Westbury - 1.1km
Bus Route Springfield Road - stop 200m away

ALMONDSBURY
Nickname: The Almonds   **Club Colours:** Green & white   **Founded** 1969

Club Contact Details 01454 612 240   doug2004.coles@blueyonder.co.uk

HONOURS
FA Comps: None
League: Bristol Suburban Premier Division 1990-91. Gloucestershire County 2003-04.

10-11		11-12		12-13		13-14		14-15		15-16		16-17		17-18		18-19		19-20	
West1	12	West1	9	West1	10	West1	9	West1	5	West1	11	West1	22	West1	13	Hel1W	7	West1	n&v
FAC	P	FAC	EP	FAC	1Q			FAC	EP	FAC	1Q								
FAV	2Q	FAV	1Q	FAV	1Q	FAV	1P	FAV	1Q	FAV	2Q	FAV	2Q	FAV	1Q	FAV	2P	FAV	1Q

GROUND: The Field, Gloucester Road, Almondsbury, Bristol BS32 4AA
Nearest Railway Station Patchway - 2.9km
Bus Route Over Lane - stop 70m away

ASHTON & BACKWELL UNITED
Nickname: The Stags   **Club Colours:** Maroon & blue   **Founded** 2010

Club Contact Details ashtonbackwellsecretary@gmail.com

HONOURS
FA Comps: None
League: None

10-11		11-12		12-13		13-14		14-15		15-16		16-17		17-18		18-19		19-20	
SomP	7	SomP	3	SomP	3	West1	14	West1	8	West1	8	West1	7	West1	18	West1	4	West1	n&v
										FAC	EP	FAC	EP						
		FAV	2Q	FAV	2Q	FAV	1P	FAV	2Q	FAV	2Q	FAV	2Q	FAV	2Q	FAV	2Q	FAV	2Q

GROUND: The Lancer Scott Stadium, West Town Road, Backwell. BS48 3HQ
Nearest Railway Station Nailsea & Backwell - 0.9km
Bus Route Spar (Rodney Rd) - stop 150m away

BISHOP SUTTON
Nickname: Bishops   **Club Colours:** All blue   **Founded** 1977

Club Contact Details 01275 332 855   bishopsuttonafcsecretary@hotmail.co.uk

HONOURS
FA Comps: None
League: Western Division One 1997-98, Premier Division 2012-13.

10-11		11-12		12-13		13-14		14-15		15-16		16-17		17-18		18-19		19-20	
WestP	5	WestP	6	WestP	1	WestP	9	WestP	19	West1	21	West1	16	West1	12	West1	17	West1	n&v
FAC	P	FAC	1Q	FAC	Pr	FAC	P	FAC	EP	FAC	EP								
FAV	1Pr	FAV	2P	FAV	2Q	FAV	1P	FAV	1Q	FAV	1P	FAV	2Q	FAV	2Q	FAV	1Q	FAV	1Q

GROUND: Lakeview, Wick Road, Bishops Sutton, Bristol BS39 5XN.

Bus Route Butchers Arms Pub - stop 50m away

BISHOPS LYDEARD
Nickname: **Club Colours:** Red & black stripes/   **Founded** 1912

Club Contact Details itspeebee@gmail.com

HONOURS
FA Comps: None
League: Somerset County Division One 2004-05, Premier Division 15-16.

10-11		11-12		12-13		13-14		14-15		15-16		16-17		17-18		18-19		19-20	
SomP	12	SomP	11	SomP	13	SomP	10	SthP	6	SomP	1	West1	6	West1	14	West1	12	West1	n&v
																FAV	2Q	FAV	1Q

GROUND: Cottlestone Road, Bishops Lydeard, Taunton, TA4 3BA
Nearest Railway Station Bishops Lydeard - 1.5km
Bus Route Darby Way - 80m away

BRISTOL TELEPHONES
Nickname: The Phones   **Club Colours:** All pale blue

Founded 1948

Club Contact Details 01275 891 776   steve.watkins56@talktalk.net

HONOURS
FA Comps: None
League: Bristol & Suburban Premier Division 2010-11, 12-13.
Gloucestershire County 2016-17.

10-11	11-12	12-13	13-14	14-15	15-16	16-17	17-18	18-19	19-20
Br&SuP1 1	Br&SuP1 3	Br&SuP1 1	GlCo 3	GlCo 8	GlCo 10	GlCo 1	West1 16	West1 20	West1 n&v
								FAV 1Q	FAV 1Q

GROUND: BTRA Sports Ground, Stockwood Lane, Stockwood, Bristol BS14 8SJ
Nearest Railway Station Keynsham - 3.6km
Bus Route Battson Road - stop 50m away

CALNE TOWN
Nickname: Lilywhites   **Club Colours:** White and black

Founded 1886

The Lilywhites **Club Contact Details** 07795 833 702   wmm498@msn.com

HONOURS
FA Comps: None
League: None

10-11	11-12	12-13	13-14	14-15	15-16	16-17	17-18	18-19	19-20
West1 11	West1 4	West1 9	West1 13	West1 15	West1 15	West1 21	West1 17	West1 8	West1 n&v
FAC EP	FAC EP	FAC EP	FAC EP						
FAV 1P	FAV 2Q	FAV 1P	FAV 1Q	FAV 2Q	FAV 1P	FAV 1P	FAV 2Q	FAV 1Q	FAV 1Q

GROUND: Bremhill View, Calne, Wiltshire SN11 9EE

Bus Route Northend - stop 80m away

CHEDDAR
Nickname: The Cheesemen   **Club Colours:** Yellow and black

Founded 1892

Club Contact Details 01934 707 271   secretarycheddarfc@gmail.com

HONOURS
FA Comps: None
League: Cheddar Valley 1910-11.
Somerset Senior Division One 2003-04.

10-11	11-12	12-13	13-14	14-15	15-16	16-17	17-18	18-19	19-20
SomP 4	SomP 2	West1 11	West1 17	West1 10	WestP 5	West1 3	West1 4	West1 2	West1 n&v
						FAC EPr	FAC EP	FAC P	FAC EP
			FAV 1Q	FAV 1Q	FAV 1Q	FAV 2Q	FAV 1Q	FAV 2P	FAV 2Q

GROUND: Bowdens Park, Draycott Road, Cheddar BS27 3RL

Bus Route Church Street - stop 400m away

CORSHAM TOWN
Nickname: The Peacocks   **Club Colours:** Red & white

Founded 1883

Club Contact Details   les.bateman63@btinternet.com

HONOURS
FA Comps: None
League: Wiltshire Division Two 1960-61, Division One 97-98.
Western Premier Division 2006-07.

10-11	11-12	12-13	13-14	14-15	15-16	16-17	17-18	18-19	19-20
WestP 10	WestP 18	West1 4	West1 7	West1 9	West1 10	West1 19	West1 20	West1 3	West1 n&v
FAC P	FAC EP	FAC EP	FAC 1Qr	FAC EP					
FAV 2Q	FAV 1Qr	FAV 1Q	FAV 2Q	FAV 2Q	FAV 1P	FAV 2Q	FAV 1Q	FAV 2Q	FAV 2Q

GROUND: Southbank Ground, Lacock Road, Corsham SN13 9HS
Nearest Railway Station Chippenham - 5.8km
Bus Route St Patrick's School - stop 50m away

DEVIZES TOWN
Founded 1885

Nickname: The Town **Club Colours:** Red & white stripes

Club Contact Details 01380 722 817   neil@hallmarkflooringltd.co.uk

HONOURS
FA Comps: None
League: Wiltshire Senior 1895-96, 89-99, 35-36, 48-49, 51-52, 53-54, Premier 61-62, 63-64. Western Premier Division 1972-73, Division One 99-2000.

10-11	11-12	12-13	13-14	14-15	15-16	16-17	17-18	18-19	19-20
West1 5	West1 19	West1 21	West1 11	West1 18	West1 19	West1 11	West1 5	West1 11	West1 n&v
	FAC EP								
FAV 2Q	FAV 1P	FAV 1Q	FAV 1Q	FAV 1Q	FAV 1Q	FAV 1P	FAV 1Q	FAV 1Q	FAV 2Q

GROUND: Nursteed Road, Devizes, Wiltshire SN10 3DX

Bus Route Eastleigh Road - stop 80m away

HENGROVE ATHLETIC
Founded 1948

Nickname: The Grove **Club Colours:** Green & white

Club Contact Details 07884 492 217   secretary@hengroveathletic.com

HONOURS
FA Comps: None
League: Somerset County Premier Division 2005-06.

10-11	11-12	12-13	13-14	14-15	15-16	16-17	17-18	18-19	19-20
West1 10	West1 10	West1 2	WestP 21	West1 12	West1 7	West1 2	WestP 9	WestP 19	West1 n&v
	FAC EP	FAC P	FAC EP	FAC EP		FAC EPr	FAC P	FAC EP	FAC' EP
FAV 2Pr	FAV 2Q	FAV 2Q	FAV 2Q	FAV 2Q	FAV 3P	FAV 1P	FAV 2P	FAV 1Q	FAV 1Q

GROUND: Norton Lane, Whitchurch, Bristol BS14 0BT
Nearest Railway Station Bedminster - 2.5km
Bus Route Wooton Park - stop 100m away

LEBEQ UNITED
Founded 2008

Nickname: **Club Colours:** Red

Club Contact Details Lebequnited@hotmail.com

HONOURS
FA Comps: None
League: Bristol & Suburban Division Three 2009-10, Division Two 11-12, Premier Division One 15-16. Gloucestershire County 2018-19.

10-11	11-12	12-13	13-14	14-15	15-16	16-17	17-18	18-19	19-20
Br&Su2 7	Br&Su2 1	Br&Su1 4	Br&SuP2 3	Br&SuP1 8	Br&SuP1 1	GlCo 10	GlCo 2	GlCo 1	West1 n&v

GROUND: Oaklands Park, Almondsbury, Bristol BS32 4AG

LONGWELL GREEN SPORTS
Founded 1966

Nickname: The Green **Club Colours:** Blue & white

Club Contact Details daunceyt@blueyonder.co.uk

HONOURS
FA Comps: None
League: Bristol & District Division Four 1982-83.

10-11	11-12	12-13	13-14	14-15	15-16	16-17	17-18	18-19	19-20
WestP 17	WestP 13	WestP 15	WestP 14	WestP 16	WestP 18	WestP 17	WestP 19	West1 5	West1 n&v
FAC P	FAC P	FAC EPr	FAC Pr	FAC 1Q	FAC P	FAC EP	FAC EP	FAC EPr	
FAV 2Q	FAV 1Qr	FAV 2Pr	FAV 1P	FAV 1P	FAV 2Qr	FAV 2Q	FAV 2Q	FAV 1P	FAV 1Q

GROUND: Longwell Green Com. Centre, Shellards Road BS30 9DU
Nearest Railway Station Bitton - 1.4km
Bus Route Sally Barn Close - stop 500m away

OLDLAND ABBOTONIANS
Nickname: The O's   **Club Colours:** Blue & white

Founded 1910

Club Contact Details 01179 328 263   secretary@oldlandfootball.com

HONOURS
FA Comps: None
League: Somerset County Division One 2004-05.

	10-11	11-12	12-13	13-14	14-15	15-16	16-17	17-18	18-19	19-20
West1	2	11	5	21	14	4	17	7	18	n&v
FAC				EP			P			
FAV			1Q	1Q	1Q	2Q	2Q	2Q	1Q	

GROUND: Aitchison Playing Field, Castle Road, Oldland Common, Bristol BS30 9SZ
Nearest Railway Station Oldland - 400m
Bus Route The Clamp - stop 130m away

PORTISHEAD TOWN
Nickname: Posset   **Club Colours:** White and black

Founded 1912

Club Contact Details 01275 817 600   andy.carling@yahoo.co.uk

HONOURS
FA Comps: None
League: Somerset County 1993-94, 94-95, 95-96, 97-98.

	10-11	11-12	12-13	13-14	14-15	15-16	16-17	17-18	18-19	19-20
West1	18	12	14	22	21	6	14	21	16	n&v
FAC	EP						1Q			
FAV	2Q	1Q	1Q	1Q	2Q	1P	2Q	2Q	1Q	2Q

GROUND: Bristol Road, Portishead, Bristol BS20 6QG
Nearest Railway Station Avonmouth - 5.1km
Bus Route Glebe Road - stop 50m away

RADSTOCK TOWN
Nickname: The Miners   **Club Colours:** Red and black

Founded 1895

Club Contact Details 01761 435 004   ianlanning9@gmail.com

HONOURS
FA Comps: None
League: Somerset Senior Division One 1996-97.

	10-11	11-12	12-13	13-14	14-15	15-16	16-17	17-18	18-19	19-20
West	P 12	P 16	P 17	P 1	1 13	1 13	1 5	1 6	1 15	1 n&v
FAC	P	P	EP	EP	EP					
FAV	1P	1Q	2Q	2Q	1P	2Q	1Q	1P	2Q	2Q

GROUND: Southfields Recreation Ground, Southfields, Radstock BA3 3NZ

Bus Route Withies Park - stop 80m away

SHERBORNE TOWN
Nickname: **Club Colours:** Black & white

Founded 1894

Club Contact Details 01935 816 110   michellethurgood@sky.com

HONOURS
FA Comps: None
League: Dorset Premier 1981-82. Western Division One 2012-13.

	10-11	11-12	12-13	13-14	14-15	15-16	16-17	17-18	18-19	19-20
West	P 14	P 17	1 1	P 9	P 12	P 13	P 20	P 19	1 13	1 n&v
FAC	2Q	EP	1Q	P	1Q	Pr	EP	EP		
FAV	1Pr	2Q	2P	2Q	1P	1Q	1P	1Q	2Q	2Qr

GROUND: Raleigh Grove, Terrace Playing Field, Sherborne DT9 5NS
Nearest Railway Station Sherborne - 0.5km
Bus Route Sherborne Station - stop 0.5km away

WARMINSTER TOWN
Nickname: The Red & Blacks   **Club Colours:** Red & black stripes   Founded 1878

Club Contact Details 01985 217 828   chrisjrobbins58@gmail.com

HONOURS
FA Comps: None
League: None

	10-11	11-12	12-13	13-14	14-15	15-16	16-17	17-18	18-19	19-20
	Wex1 12	Wex1 16	West1 15	West1 18	West1 16	West1 17	West1 18	West1 22	West1 6	West1 n&v
FAC	EP									
FAV	2Q		2Q	1P	1Q	2Q	1Q	2Q	2Q	4P

GROUND: Weymouth Street, Warminster BA12 9NS
Nearest Railway Station Warminster - 0.9km
Bus Route Glebe Field - stop 80m away

WELLS CITY
Nickname: **Club Colours:** All blue   Founded 1890

Club Contact Details 01749 679 971   daveg55@hotmail.co.uk

HONOURS
FA Comps: None
League: Western Division One 1949-50, 2009-10.

	10-11	11-12	12-13	13-14	14-15	15-16	16-17	17-18	18-19	19-20
	WestP 9	WestP 12	WestP 19	West1 6	West1 19	West1 2	WestP 15	WestP 20	West1 10	West1 n&v
FAC		2Q	P	1Q			FAC EPr	P	EP	
FAV	1Q	1P	2Q	1Q	1Q	1P	2Q	1Q	2Q	2Q

GROUND: Athletic Ground, Rowdens Road, Wells, Somerset BA5 1TU

Bus Route The Police Station - stop 20m away

WELTON ROVERS
Nickname: Rovers   **Club Colours:** Green & white   Founded 1887

Club Contact Details 07970 791 644   garethpaisey@outlook.com

HONOURS
FA Comps: None
League: Western 1911-12, 64-65, 65-66, 66-67, 73-74, Division One 59-60, 87-88.

	10-11	11-12	12-13	13-14	14-15	15-16	16-17	17-18	18-19	19-20
	WestP 19	West1 7	West1 16	West1 6	West1 2	WestP 20	West1 20	West1 8	West1 9	West1 n&v
FAC	EP	EP	EP		EP	EP	EP			
FAV	1Q	1Q	2Q	1Q	2P	3P	1Q	1Q	2Q	1Q

GROUND: West Clewes, North Road, Midsomer Norton, Bath BA3 2QD

Bus Route Elm View - 50m away

WINCANTON TOWN
Nickname: Winky   **Club Colours:** Yellow & black   Founded 1890

Club Contact Details 01963 31815   cmartin10101981@gmail.com

HONOURS
FA Comps: None
League: Yeovil & District Division Two 1988-89, Division One 89-90, Premier 90-91.
Dorset Senior Division 2006-07.

	10-11	11-12	12-13	13-14	14-15	15-16	16-17	17-18	18-19	19-20
	Dor P 7	Dor P 4	Dor P 2	West1 4	West1 4	West1 16	West1 13	West1 10	West1 14	West1 n&v
FAC						P				
FAV				1Q	EP	1Q	1Q	2Q	1Q	2Q

GROUND: Wincanton Sports Ground, Moor Lane, Wincanton. BA9 9EJ
Nearest Railway Station Templecombe - 4.9km
Bus Route Balsam Lane - stop 1.2km away

CLUB INDEX

The National League System Clubs as they line up for the 2020-21 season

1874 NORTHWICH	NORTH WEST COUNTIES PREMIER	721
ABBEY HEY	NORTH WEST COUNTIES DIVISION 1S	733
ABBEY HULTON UNITED	NORTH WEST COUNTIES DIVISION 1S	733
ABBEY RANGERS	COMBINED COUNTIES PREMIER	654
ABINGDON TOWN	HELLENIC DIVISION ONE EAST	701
ABINGDON UNITED	HELLENIC DIVISION ONE EAST	701
AFC ALDERMASTON	HELLENIC DIVISION ONE EAST	701
AFC BLACKPOOL	NORTH WEST COUNTIES DIVISION 1N	728
AFC BRIDGNORTH	WEST MIDLANDS (REGIONAL) PREMIER	832
AFC CROYDON ATHLETIC	SOUTHERN COUNTIES EAST PREMIER	784
AFC DARWEN	NORTH WEST COUNTIES DIVISION 1N	728
AFC DUNSTABLE	SOUTHERN LEAGUE D1 CENTRAL	634
AFC FYLDE	NATIONAL NORTH	514
AFC HAYES	COMBINED COUNTIES DIVISION ONE	661
AFC LIVERPOOL	NORTH WEST COUNTIES DIVISION 1N	728
AFC MANSFIELD	NORTHERN COUNTIES EAST PREMIER	738
AFC PORTCHESTER	WESSEX PREMIER	820
AFC RUSHDEN & DIAMONDS	SOUTHERN LEAGUE PREMIER CENTRAL	610
AFC STONEHAM	WESSEX PREMIER	820
AFC SUDBURY	ISTHMIAN NORTH	547
AFC SUDBURY RESERVES	EASTERN COUNTIES DIVISION ONE NORTH	679
AFC TELFORD UNITED	NATIONAL NORTH	514
AFC TOTTON	SOUTHERN LEAGUE D1 SOUTH	644
AFC UCKFIELD TOWN	SOUTHERN COMBINATION PREMIER	772
AFC VARNDEANIANS	SOUTHERN COMBINATION DIVISION ONE	779
AFC WULFRUNIANS	MIDLAND FOOTBALL LEAGUE PREMIER	709
ALBION SPORTS	NORTHERN COUNTIES EAST PREMIER	738
ALDERSHOT TOWN	NATIONAL LEAGUE	502
ALFOLD	SOUTHERN COMBINATION PREMIER	772
ALFRETON TOWN	NATIONAL NORTH	514
ALMONDSBURY	WESTERN LEAGUE DIVISION ONE	844
ALRESFORD TOWN	WESSEX PREMIER	820
ALSAGER TOWN	NORTH WEST COUNTIES DIVISION 1S	733
ALTON	WESSEX DIVISION ONE	827
ALTRINCHAM	NATIONAL LEAGUE	502
ALVECHURCH	SOUTHERN LEAGUE PREMIER CENTRAL	610
AMERSHAM TOWN	SPARTAN SOUTH MIDLANDS DIVISION ONE	803
AMESBURY TOWN	WESSEX PREMIER	820
AMPTHILL TOWN	SPARTAN SOUTH MIDLANDS DIVISION ONE	803
ANDOVER NEW STREET	WESSEX DIVISION ONE	827
ANDOVER TOWN	WESSEX DIVISION ONE	827
ANSTEY NOMADS	UNITED COUNTIES PREMIER	808
ARDLEY UNITED	HELLENIC PREMIER	695
ARLESEY TOWN	SPARTAN SOUTH MIDLANDS PREMIER	796
ARMTHORPE WELFARE	NORTHERN COUNTIES EAST DIVISION ONE	745

GROUNDS OF GREAT BRITAIN
A small selection of some of the grounds our photographers have visited

Corintian Casuals going places. Photo Keith Clayton.

Hemsworth Miners Welfare. Photo Bill Wheatcroft.

Main Stand Avro.

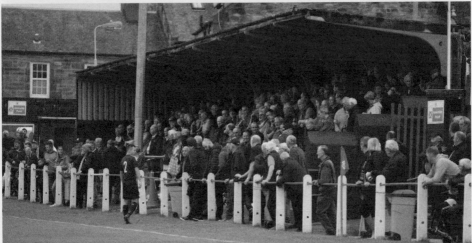

Main Stand Bonnyrigg. Photos Keith Clayton.

Main Stand Charnock Richard.

York City. (At the time of going to press there was some uncertainty that the club would be moving in to their new home for 2020-21)

Burscough 1998/99.

Boston United. Photos Bill Wheatcroft.   Three grounds we say good bye to in 2020.

Main Stand Runcorn Town. Photo Keith Clayton.

Main Stand Squires Gate. Photo Keith Clayton.

Main Stand Penybont. Photos Keith Clayton.

Main Stand Staveley Miners Welfare.

Willand Rovers Main Stand. Photos Keith Clayton.

Alfreton Town.

Eastwood Town.

Evesham United. Photos Bill Wheatcroft.

Bangor City.

Belper Town.

Birstall United Social. Photos Bill Wheatcroft.

Hendon. Photos Bill Wheatcroft.

Holwell Sports.

Ilkeston Town.

Kettering Town. Photos Bill Wheatcroft.

Kings Lynn Town. Photo Bill Wheatcroft.

Kimberley MW 2019. Photo Bill Wheatcroft.

The Central Midlands League hired Peel Croft, the home of Burton Rugby Club and former Football League venue, for a couple of games at the start of the season, the Chairman's Cup and Invitational Cup Final.

Coleshill Town. Photos Bill Wheatcroft.

Lichfield City FC.

Holbrook St Michaels. Photos Bill Wheatcroft.

CLUB INDEX

CLUB INDEX

CLUB INDEX

CLUB INDEX

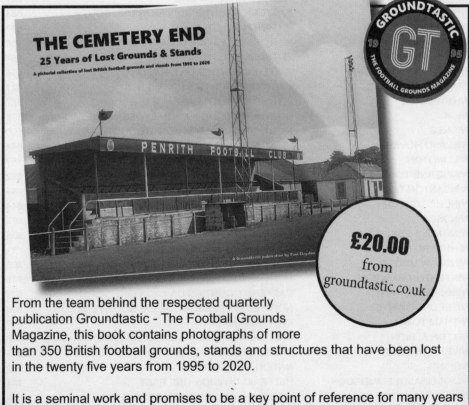